18. $\displaystyle \int \frac{u^2\,du}{\sqrt{a+bu}} = \frac{2}{15b^3}(3b^2u^2 - 4abu + 8a^2)\sqrt{a+bu} + C$

19. $\displaystyle \int \frac{u^n\,du}{\sqrt{a+bu}} = \frac{2u^n\sqrt{a+bu}}{b(2n+1)} - \frac{2an}{b(2n+1)}\int \frac{u^{n-1}\,du}{\sqrt{a+bu}}$

20. $\displaystyle \int \frac{du}{u\sqrt{a+bu}} = \begin{cases} \dfrac{1}{\sqrt{a}}\ln\left|\dfrac{\sqrt{a+bu}-\sqrt{a}}{\sqrt{a+bu}+\sqrt{a}}\right| + C & \text{if } a>0 \\[3mm] \dfrac{2}{\sqrt{-a}}\tan^{-1}\sqrt{\dfrac{a+bu}{-a}} + C & \text{if } a<0 \end{cases}$

21. $\displaystyle \int \frac{du}{u^n\sqrt{a+bu}}$

22. $\displaystyle \int \frac{\sqrt{a+bu}\,du}{u} = 2\sqrt{a+bu} + a\int \frac{du}{u\sqrt{a+bu}}$

23. $\displaystyle \int \frac{\sqrt{a+bu}\,du}{u^n} = -\frac{(a+bu)^{3/2}}{a(n-1)u^{n-1}} - \frac{b(2n-5)}{2a(n-1)}\int \frac{\sqrt{a+bu}\,du}{u^{n-1}}$

Forms Containing $a^2 \pm u^2$

24. $\displaystyle \int \frac{du}{a^2+u^2} = \frac{1}{a}\tan^{-1}\frac{u}{a} + C$

25. $\displaystyle \int \frac{du}{a^2-u^2} = \frac{1}{2a}\ln\left|\frac{u+a}{u-a}\right| + C = \begin{cases} \dfrac{1}{a}\tanh^{-1}\dfrac{u}{a} + C & \text{if } |u|<a \\[3mm] \dfrac{1}{a}\coth^{-1}\dfrac{u}{a} + C & \text{if } |u|>a \end{cases}$

26. $\displaystyle \int \frac{du}{u^2-a^2} = \frac{1}{2a}\ln\left|\frac{u-a}{u+a}\right| + C = \begin{cases} -\dfrac{1}{a}\tanh^{-1}\dfrac{u}{a} + C & \text{if } |u|<a \\[3mm] -\dfrac{1}{a}\coth^{-1}\dfrac{u}{a} + C & \text{if } |u|>a \end{cases}$

Forms Containing $\sqrt{u^2 \pm a^2}$

In formulas 27 through 38, we may replace

$$\ln(u + \sqrt{u^2+a^2}) \quad \text{by} \quad \sinh^{-1}\frac{u}{a}$$

$$\ln|u + \sqrt{u^2-a^2}| \quad \text{by} \quad \cosh^{-1}\frac{u}{a}$$

$$\ln\left|\frac{a + \sqrt{u^2+a^2}}{u}\right| \quad \text{by} \quad \sinh^{-1}\frac{a}{u}$$

27. $\displaystyle \int \frac{du}{\sqrt{u^2\pm a^2}} = \ln|u + \sqrt{u^2\pm a^2}| + C$

28. $\displaystyle \int \sqrt{u^2\pm a^2}\,du = \frac{u}{2}\sqrt{u^2\pm a^2} \pm \frac{a^2}{2}\ln|u + \sqrt{u^2\pm a^2}| + C$

29. $\displaystyle \int u^2\sqrt{u^2\pm a^2}\,du = \frac{u}{8}(2u^2\pm a^2)\sqrt{u^2\pm a^2}$
$$- \frac{a^4}{8}\ln|u + \sqrt{u^2\pm a^2}| + C$$

30. $\displaystyle \int \frac{\sqrt{u^2+a^2}\,du}{u} = \sqrt{u^2+a^2} - a\ln\left|\frac{a + \sqrt{u^2+a^2}}{u}\right| + C$

31. $\displaystyle \int \frac{\sqrt{u^2-a^2}\,du}{u} = \sqrt{u^2-a^2} - a\sec^{-1}\frac{u}{a} + C$

32. $\displaystyle \int \frac{\sqrt{u^2\pm a^2}\,du}{u^2} = -\frac{\sqrt{u^2\pm a^2}}{u} + \ln|u + \sqrt{u^2\pm a^2}| + C$

33. $\displaystyle \int \frac{u^2\,du}{\sqrt{u^2\pm a^2}} = \frac{u}{2}\sqrt{u^2\pm a^2} - \frac{\pm a^2}{2}\ln|u + \sqrt{u^2\pm a^2}| + C$

34. $\displaystyle \int \frac{du}{u\sqrt{u^2+a^2}} = -\frac{1}{a}\ln\left|\frac{a + \sqrt{u^2+a^2}}{u}\right| + C$

35. $\displaystyle \int \frac{du}{u\sqrt{u^2-a^2}} = \frac{1}{a}\sec^{-1}\frac{u}{a} + C$

36. $\displaystyle \int \frac{du}{u^2\sqrt{u^2\pm a^2}} = -\frac{\sqrt{u^2\pm a^2}}{\pm a^2 u} + C$

37. $\displaystyle \int (u^2\pm a^2)^{3/2}\,du = \frac{u}{8}(2u^2\pm 5a^2)\sqrt{u^2\pm a^2}$
$$+ \frac{3a^4}{8}\ln|u + \sqrt{u^2\pm a^2}| + C$$

38. $\displaystyle \int \frac{du}{(u^2\pm a^2)^{3/2}} = \frac{u}{\pm a^2\sqrt{u^2\pm a^2}} + C$

Forms Containing $\sqrt{a^2 - u^2}$

39. $\displaystyle \int \frac{du}{\sqrt{a^2-u^2}} = \sin^{-1}\frac{u}{a} + C$

40. $\displaystyle \int \sqrt{a^2-u^2}\,du = \frac{u}{2}\sqrt{a^2-u^2} + \frac{a^2}{2}\sin^{-1}\frac{u}{a} + C$

41. $\displaystyle \int u^2\sqrt{a^2-u^2}\,du = \frac{u}{8}(2u^2-a^2)\sqrt{a^2-u^2} + \frac{a^4}{8}\sin^{-1}\frac{u}{a} + C$

42. $\displaystyle \int \frac{\sqrt{a^2-u^2}\,du}{u} = \sqrt{a^2-u^2} - a\ln\left|\frac{a + \sqrt{a^2-u^2}}{u}\right| + C$
$$= \sqrt{a^2-u^2} - a\cosh^{-1}\frac{a}{u} + C$$

43. $\displaystyle \int \frac{\sqrt{a^2-u^2}\,du}{u^2} = -\frac{\sqrt{a^2-u^2}}{u} - \sin^{-1}\frac{u}{a} + C$

(This table is continued on the back endpapers.)

OTHER TEXTBOOKS OF INTEREST TO CALCULUS STUDENTS AND INSTRUCTORS FROM HARPERCOLLINS COLLEGE PUBLISHERS

BEFORE CALCULUS, *Functions, Graphs, and Analytic Geometry,* Third Edition by Louis Leithold
In the third edition of *Before Calculus* (*BC3*), Leithold utilizes modern technology in the form of the hand-held graphics calculator in discussions, examples, illustrations, and exercises. The calculus oriented coverage that previews topics in calculus makes *BC3* a solid stepping stone to the study of THE CALCULUS 7 (*TC7*). The precalculus sections in the appendix of *TC7* are adapted from the corresponding sections in *BC3*.

GRAPHING CALCULATOR CALCULUS WORKBOOK, An Exploratory Approach by Al Shenk
This textbook-independent manual includes worksheets and assignments that cover basic calculus techniques, facts, and technology tips for solving problems and supporting results.

AN HP 48G CALCULUS COMPANION by Jerold Mathews and Jack Eidswick
This versatile textbook-independent manual utilizes the graphical, symbolic, and numerical power of the HP 48G graphics calculator to enhance the teaching and learning of calculus.

THE DERIVE CALCULUS WORKBOOK by Lisa Townsley Kulich and Barbara Victor
This laboratory manual, intended as a supplement to any calculus text, encourages students to explore the concepts of calculus, while developing their skills using *Derive,* and to improve their ability to communicate mathematics.

CALCULUS LABS USING MATHEMATICA and CALCULUS LABS USING MAPLE by Arthur Sparks, John Davenport, and James Braselton
These textbook-independent manuals are designed to enrich the traditional calculus course and to serve as ideal supplements for learning how to use *Mathematica* and *Maple.*

LABORATORY EXPLORATIONS IN CALCULUS WITH APPLICATIONS TO PHYSICS by Joan Hundhausen and F. Richard Yeatts
This laboratory manual consists of more than thirty self-contained textbook-independent projects whose topics vary from "Dimensions and Scaling" to "The Slingshot."

THE CALCULUS 7

Louis Leithold

HarperCollins*CollegePublishers*

Sponsoring Editor: Kevin Connors
Developmental Editor: Robin Geller
Project Editor: Dee Netzel
Design Administrator: Jess Schaal
Art Development Editor: Vita Jay
Text and Cover Design: Lesiak/Crampton Design Inc: Lucy Lesiak
Cover Artist: Dan Douke
Figures: Precision Graphics
Production Administrator: Randee Wire
Project Coordination: Elm Street Publishing Services, Inc.
Compositor: Interactive Composition Corporation
Printer and Binder: R.R. Donnelley & Sons Company
Cover Printer: Phoenix Color Corp.

The Calculus 7

HarperCollins® and ■® are registered trademarks of HarperCollins Publishers Inc.

Library of Congress Cataloging-in-Publication Data

Leithold, Louis.
        The calculus 7 / Louis Leithold.
            p.   cm.
        Rev. ed. of: Calculus with analytic geometry.   6th ed. c1990.
        Includes index.
        ISBN 0-673-46913-1
        1. Calculus.   I. Leithold, Louis.   Calculus with analytic
    geometry.   6th ed.   II. Title.
    QA303.L428   1995
    515'.15—dc20   95-24799

97 98 99 9 8 7 6 5 4 3

*To my son Gordon Marc;
his sons Justin and Matthew;
and their godfather David*

COVER ARTIST

Dan Douke, a painter working in Southern California and currently professor of art at California State University at Los Angeles, exhibits his work regularly at Tortue Gallery in Santa Monica and O.K. Harris Works of Art in New York. Professor Douke prepared the following statement regarding the painting reproduced on the front cover:

> The enormous advance of technology in the final decade of the twentieth century, fueled by Western society's utopian belief in an electronic information paradise, motivated this painting, specially commissioned for *TC*7, and which stems directly from my recent work of futuristic objects. In this painting I seek to visualize an encounter with image and imagination to edge the elusive idea toward a tactile form. I desire that the work seem oddly familiar, perhaps like a part of something bigger, more powerful and futuristic, yet appear used. The painting is in fact a metaphor for an individual's desire to seek and experience the acquisition of knowledge.

CONTENTS

5   LOGARITHMIC, EXPONENTIAL, INVERSE TRIGONOMETRIC, AND HYPERBOLIC FUNCTIONS   **423**

6   ADDITIONAL APPLICATIONS OF THE DEFINITE INTEGRAL   **533**

7   TECHNIQUES OF INTEGRATION, INDETERMINATE FORMS, AND IMPROPER INTEGRALS   **573**

PREFACE

"Everything should be made as simple as possible, but not simpler."

Albert Einstein

The Calculus 7 (hereafter abbreviated as *TC7*) is designed both for prospective mathematics majors and for students whose primary interest is in engineering, the physical and social sciences, or nontechnical fields. The presentation is still geared to a beginner's experience and maturity. The step-by-step explanations, abundant worked examples, and wide variety of exercises continue to be distinctive features of the text.

At no time between successive editions have more changes occurred in the teaching of calculus than in the period between the sixth and seventh editions of this text. Many of these changes are the result of the availability of modern technology in the form of the hand-held graphics calculator. Some other changes have come about because of the so-called *calculus reform* movement. I have addressed this movement by observing the principle: REFORM WITH REASON. To adhere to this principle, I have applied the following guidelines:

1. Technology should be incorporated to enhance the teaching and learning of calculus, *not* to replace the mathematics or de-emphasize the theoretical topics.
2. Definitions and theorems should be stated formally, *not* informally.
3. Students should be aware that proofs of theorems are necessary.
4. When a proof is given, it should be well motivated and carefully explained, so that it is understandable to anyone who has achieved an average mastery of the preceding sections of the book.
5. When a theorem is stated without proof, the discussion should be augmented by both figures and examples; in such cases, stress the fact that what is presented is an illustration of the statement of the theorem and is *not* a proof.
6. Mathematical modeling of real-life applications should be emphasized.
7. Writing in mathematics should be stressed.

The fourteen chapters in *TC7* can be classified into two segments: Chapters 1–9, functions of a single variable including infinite series; and Chapters 10–14, vectors and functions of more than one variable. *TC7* incorporates changes in both segments. In all alterations, I maintain a healthy balance between a rigorous approach and an intuitive point of view.

To achieve my objectives, I have incorporated the following features:

GRAPHICS CALCULATOR "ACTIVE"

Throughout the presentation, *TC7* uses the hand-held graphics calculator—not only powerful and fascinating as a learning device, but also vital as a problem-solving tool. The graphics calculator is integrated directly into the exposition according to the philosophy I learned at my three summer institutes with TICAP (Technology Intensive Calculus for Advanced Placement) and summarized as follows:

1. Do *analytically* (with paper and pencil), then SUPPORT *numerically and graphically* (with a graphics calculator).
2. Do *numerically and graphically*, then CONFIRM *analytically*.
3. Do *numerically and graphically* because other methods are *impractical or impossible*.

MATHEMATICAL MODELING AND WORD PROBLEMS

Mathematical modeling of practical situations stated as word problems appear in such diverse fields as physics, chemistry, engineering, business, economics, psychology, sociology, biology, and medicine. Functions as mathematical models are first introduced in Section 1.3 and appear prominently throughout the rest of the text. Section 1.3 contains step-by-step suggestions for obtaining a function as a mathematical model.

WRITING IN MATHEMATICS

To complete the solution of each word-problem example, a *conclusion* that answers the questions of the problem is stated. The student must write a similar conclusion consisting of one or more complete sentences for each word-problem exercise. Included at the end of nearly every exercise set is a writing exercise that might ask a question pertaining to *how* or *why* a specific procedure works, or that might require the student to *describe*, *explain*, or *justify* a particular process.

EXERCISES

Revised from previous editions and graded in difficulty, the exercises provide a wide variety of problem types, ranging from computational to applied and theoretical problems to the calculator-active and writing exercises as described above. They occur at the end of sections and as miscellaneous exercises at the end of each chapter.

EXAMPLES AND ILLUSTRATIONS

Examples, carefully chosen to prepare students for the exercises, are models for the exercise solutions. An illustration demonstrates a particular concept, definition, or theorem; it is a prototype of the idea being presented.

VISUAL ART PROGRAM

Four colors are used throughout the text and for many of the more complicated figures. All of the artwork has been redrawn for *TC7*. Graphs plotted on a graphics calculator are shown on a calculator screen surrounded by a color border. Graphs sketched by hand are purposely shown in the same color as the axes to avoid the possibility of reproduction errors caused by improper registration during the printing process. All the three-dimensional figures are computer generated to ensure mathematical accuracy. These figures, which are more vivid than the styles of previous editions, were created with the assistance of Mathematica® and Adobe Illustrator®.

PEDAGOGICAL DEVICES

Each chapter begins with an introduction entitled "Looking Ahead." A list of suggestions for review appears at the end of the chapter. Together, these features serve as an overall survey of the chapter when a student studies for a test.

CHAPTER-BY-CHAPTER COVERAGE

Chapter 1   Functions, Limits, and Continuity

The three topics in the title of this chapter are at the heart of any first course in calculus. All the limit theorems are stated, and some proofs are presented in the text, while other proofs are outlined in the exercises. Section 1.3, new to this edition, involves obtaining functions as mathematical models in anticipation of their use later in applications. These models then provide the student with an early peek at how calculus is applied in real-world situations. Section 1.4, also new, utilizes the graphics calculator to introduce the concept of the limit of a function.

Chapter 2   The Derivative and Differentiation

In Section 2.1, the tangent line to the graph of a function is defined before the derivative to demonstrate in advance the derivative's geometrical interpretation. Physical applications of the derivative in rectilinear motion are presented only after theorems on differentiation are proved so that these theorems can be applied to these applications. The derivatives of all six trigonometric functions appear in Section 2.7, and they are then available as examples for the initial presentation of the chain rule in the next section. The numerical derivative, a new topic in this edition and introduced in Section 2.3, is employed on a graphics calculator to approximate derivatives and to plot their graphs. In Section 2.4, particle motion on a line is simulated on a graphics calculator.

Chapter 3   Behavior of Functions and Their Graphs, Extreme Function Values, and Approximations

The traditional applications of the derivative to problems involving maxima and minima as well as to curve sketching are presented in this chapter. Limits at infinity and their applications to find horizontal asymptotes have been moved to this chapter where they are applied to sketching graphs. The graphics calculator is utilized extensively both to support results obtained analytically and to conjecture properties that are then confirmed analytically. A new feature of this edition pertains to exercises where the student is asked to sketch the graph of a function from the graph of its derivative and vice versa. The tangent line approximation is presented along with Newton's method and differentials in the chapter's final section.

Chapter 4   The Definite Integral and Integration

The first two sections involve antidifferentiation. I use the term "antidifferentiation" instead of "indefinite integration," but the standard notation $\int f(x)\,dx$ is retained. This notation will suggest that some relation must exist between definite integrals and antiderivatives, but I see no harm in this as long as the presentation gives the theoretically proper view of the definite integral as the limit of sums. Such a limit is applied to define the area of a plane region prior to its use in the definition of the definite integral. The capability of a graphics calculator to approximate the value of a definite integral is introduced early prior to the proof of the second fundamental theorem of the calculus used to compute values analytically. This capability enables us to demonstrate properties of the definite integral on a calculator as they are developed. Section 4.3 on separable differential equations offers applications to rectilinear motion where motion is again simulated on a graphics calculator. Other applications in this chapter include the complete discussion of area of a plane region as well as volumes of solids, moved forward from the previous edition. Section 4.9 begins with volumes by slicing, and then volumes of solids of revolution by disks and washers are considered as special cases of volumes by slicing. Volumes of solids of revolution by cylindrical shells are discussed in Section 4.10.

Chapter 5   Logarithmic, Exponential, Inverse Trigonometric, and Hyperbolic Functions

Inverse functions are covered in the first section, and the next five sections are devoted to logarithmic and exponential functions. The natural logarithmic function is defined first, and then the natural exponential function is defined as its inverse. This procedure allows us to give a precise meaning to an irrational exponent of a positive number. The exponential function to the base a, where a is positive, is then defined; the logarithmic function to the base a is the inverse of this function. Applications of these functions include the laws of growth and decay, bounded growth involving the learning curve, and the standardized normal probability density function. The final three sections are devoted to the remaining transcendental (non-algebraic) functions: the inverse trigonometric and hyperbolic functions.

Chapter 6   Additional Applications of the Definite Integral

In this chapter, applications of the definite integral highlight not only the manipulative techniques but also the fundamental principles involved. Length of arc, a geometric application, is treated in Section 6.1. The other four sections are devoted to physical applications, including centers of mass of rods and plane regions, work, and force due to fluid pressure. In each application, the definitions of the new terms are intuitively motivated and explained. All of the sections have been rewritten with extra worked-out examples, some of them utilizing the graphics calculator to approximate the value of the definite integral.

Chapter 7   Techniques of Integration, Indeterminate Forms, and Improper Integrals

Techniques of integration involve an important computational aspect of calculus. They are discussed in the first five sections, shortened from eight in previous editions. I have explained the theoretical backgrounds of each different method after an introductory motivation. The mastery of integration techniques depends upon the examples, and I have used as illustrations problems that the student will certainly meet in practice. Two more applications of integration are introduced in Section 7.4: logistic growth, occurring in economics, biology, and sociology; and the law of mass action from chemistry. Two numerical methods for approximating definite integrals are given in Section 7.6. These procedures are important because of their suitability to computers and graphics calculators. The material on the approximation of definite integrals includes the statement of theorems on the bounds of the error involved in these approximations. The remaining four sections on indeterminate forms and improper integrals have been repositioned in this edition; they immediately precede the material on infinite series, where many of the results are applied. Applications of improper integrals include the probability density function as well as some in geometry and economics.

Chapter 8   Polynomial Approximations, Sequences, and Infinite Series

The material on sequences and series has been condensed to one chapter from two in previous editions. All of the topics are still included, but some of the discussions have been shortened without sacrificing any mathematical integrity. This chapter is self-contained and can be covered anytime after the completion of the first seven chapters. The first section pertains to polynomial approximations by Taylor's formula. This formula is generalized to Taylor's series in Section 8.9. Sections 8.2–8.6 are devoted to sequences and infinite series of constant terms, with Section 8.6 giving a summary of tests for convergence of an infinite series. Sections 8.7–8.10 are concerned with infinite series of variable terms called power series. The topics in this chapter lend themselves to the incorporation of the graphics calculator not only to enhance the treatment but also to allow students to examine and investigate convergence and divergence of infinite series and polynomial approximations.

Chapter 9   Parametric Equations, Plane Curves, and Polar Graphs

The three topics of this chapter have been grouped together to complete the treatment of the calculus of a single variable. The first two sections, pertaining to parametric equations and plane curves, are prerequisite to the study of vectors. The next two sections cover polar graphs, and the final section presents a unified treatment of conic sections and polar equations of conics. The discussion of conic sections in rectangular coordinates, now usually taught in a precalculus course, has been relegated to the Appendix in this edition.

Chapter 10   Vectors and Planes, Lines, and Surfaces in Space

Vectors in both the plane and three-dimensional space are now treated in the same chapter rather than separately as in earlier editions. Vectors in the plane are defined in Section 10.1. In Section 10.2, prior to defining a three-dimensional vector, the three-dimensional number space, denoted by R^3, is introduced. The chapter also provides a vector approach to solid analytic geometry with the study of planes and lines in R^3 in Section 10.4 and surfaces in Section 10.6.

Chapter 11   Vector-Valued Functions

As with vectors in Chapter 10, vector-valued functions in both the plane and three dimensions are discussed simultaneously in this chapter. Curves in both spaces, defined by either a vector-valued function or a set of parametric equations, as well as their properties are also treated concurrently. The applications are to geometry, physics, and engineering. In Section 11.5 on curvilinear motion, the graphics calculator is applied to simulate the motion of a projectile in a plane.

Chapter 12   Differential Calculus of Functions of More Than One Variable

The topics contained in this chapter have been condensed from two chapters in previous editions, again without sacrificing any mathematical integrity. Limits, continuity, partial derivatives, differentiability, and the chain rule for functions of more than one variable are discussed in the first five sections. Applications in these sections include finding rates of change and computing approximations. Section 12.6 on directional derivatives and gradients is followed by a section that shows the application of the gradient to find tangent planes and normals to surfaces. Additional applications of partial derivatives that appear in the last two sections are the solution of extrema problems and Lagrange multipliers.

Chapter 13   Multiple Integration

The integral calculus of functions of more than one variable contained in Sections 13.2–13.6 is preceded by a section on cyclindrical and spherical coordinates repositioned in this edition to appear closer to their application in later sections. Double integrals of functions of two variables are introduced in Section 13.2 and applied in physics, engineering, and geometry in the following two sections. The remaining two sections of the chapter pertain to triple integrals of functions of two variables and some of their applications.

Chapter 14   Introduction to the Calculus of Vector Fields

An expanded treatment of vector calculus is presented in the six sections of this final chapter. The coverage includes vector fields, line integrals, Green's theorem, Gauss's divergence theorem, and Stokes's theorem. The approach in this chapter is intuitive and the applications are to physics and engineering.

APPENDIX

Topics in algebra, trigonometry, and analytic geometry, usually taught in a precalculus course, now appear in an Appendix, thus freeing the main body of the text for strictly calculus topics. This modification accounts for the deletion of the words *with Analytic Geometry* from the title of this edition. Dependent upon the preparation of the students in a particular class, the Appendix sections may be covered in detail, treated as a review, or omitted.

SUPPLEMENTARY SECTIONS

Supplementary sections follow the Appendix; these sections include subject matter that can be covered or omitted without affecting the understanding of subsequent text material. These sections, designated by the number of the section in the main body of the text, contain theoretical discussions and some of the more difficult proofs.

Louis Leithold

ACKNOWLEDGMENTS

REVIEWERS

Benita Albert, Oak Ridge High School

Daniel D. Anderson, University of Iowa

Richard Armstrong, Saint Louis Community College at Florissant Valley

Carole A. Bauer, Triton College

Jack Berman, Northwestern Michigan College

Michael L. Berry, West Virginia Wesleyan College

James F. Brown, Midland College

Phillip Clarke, Los Angeles Valley College

Charles Coppin, University of Dallas

Larry S. Dilley, Central Missouri State University

Peter Embalabala, Lincoln Land Community College

Leon Gerber, Saint John's University

Ronald E. Goetz, Saint Louis Community College at Meramac

William L. Grimes, Central Missouri State University

Kay Hodge, Midland College

Charles S. Johnson, Los Angeles Valley College

John E. Kinikin, Arcadia High School

Stephen Kokoska, Bloomsburg University of Pennsylvania

Ron Lancaster

Benny Lo, Ohlone College

Miriam Long, Madonna University

Robert McCarthy, Community College of Allegheny County

Lawrence P. Merbach, North Dakota State College of Science

Janet Mills, Seattle University

James M. Parks, State University of New York College at Potsdam

Terry Reeves, Red Rock Community College

William H. Richardson, Wichita State University

Ricardo A. Salinas, San Antonio College

Lillian Seese, Saint Louis Community College at Meramac

Luzviminda Villar Shin, Los Angeles Valley College

Laurence Small, Los Angeles Pierce College

James Smolko, Lakeland Community College

Armond E. Spencer, State University of New York College at Potsdam
Anthony E. Vance, Austin Community College
Jan Vandever, South Dakota State University
Gerald L. White, Western Illinois University
Douglas Wilberscheid, Indian River Community College
Don Williams, Brazosport College
Andre L. Yandl, Seattle University

PREPARATION OF SOLUTIONS AND ANSWERS FOR EXERCISES

Leon Gerber, Saint John's University, assisted by Shmuel Gerber

CHECKERS OF ANSWERS FOR EXERCISES

Ronald E. Goetz, Saint Louis Community College at Meramac
Charles S. Johnson, Los Angeles Valley College
Robert McCarthy, Community College of Allegheny County
Lawrence P. Merbach, North Dakota State College of Science
Luzviminda Villar Shin, Los Angeles Valley College
Armond E. Spencer, State University of New York College at Potsdam

COVER ARTIST

Dan Douke, courtesy of Tortue Gallery, Santa Monica

To these people, to the staff at HarperCollins College Publishers, and to all the users of the first six editions of this text, I express my deep appreciation. I wish to single out special thanks to Leon Gerber, Saint John's University, and Laurence Small, Los Angeles Pierce College, for their diligent efforts reviewing the manuscript in its various prepublication versions as well as for their significant contributions to the new exercises in this edition. I also thank my editor, Kevin Connors, HarperCollins College Publishers, for his unfaltering dedication, encouragement, and support of this project.

L. L.

SUPPLEMENTS TO ACCOMPANY *THE CALCULUS 7*

For Students

An Outline for the Study of Calculus by Leon Gerber, Saint John's University, and the late John Minnick, DeAnza College.

To assist students in their study of *TC7*, this three-volume outline contains detailed step-by-step solutions for half the even-numbered exercises (those having numbers divisible by 4). The manuals also include statements of all the important theorems and definitions, as well as sample tests with solutions for each chapter.

For Instructors

Instructor's Solutions Manual for THE CALCULUS 7 by Leon Gerber, Saint John's University.

In two volumes, these manuals contain worked-out solutions for all the exercises in *TC7*.

Test Generator/Editor with Quizmaster

This computerized test bank is available in both DOS and Macintosh versions. Both the *Test Generator* and *Editor* are fully networkable. The *Test Generator*, written for *TC7*, can be used to select objective problems and questions for ready-made tests. The *Editor* enables instructors to edit any preexisting data or to create their own questions. *QuizMaster* permits instructors to create tests and quizzes from the *Test Generator/Editor* and to save them on disks so that they can be used by students on a stand-alone desktop computer or a network.

Also available is a printed test bank that includes three different but equivalent tests for each chapter, generated using questions in the computerized test bank.

Additional Ancillaries of Interest to Calculus Students and Instructors from HarperCollins College Publishers

These materials are listed following the front cover endsheets.

HISTORICAL BACKGROUND OF THE CALCULUS

Some of the ideas of calculus can be found in the works of the ancient Greek mathematicians at the time of Archimedes (287–212 B.C.) and in works of the early seventeenth century by René Descartes (1596–1650), Pierre de Fermat (1601–1665), John Wallis (1616–1703), and Isaac Barrow (1630–1677). However, the invention of calculus is often attributed to Sir Isaac Newton (1642–1727) and Gottfried Wilhelm Leibniz (1646–1716) because they began the generalization and unification of the subject. There were other mathematicians of the seventeenth and eighteenth century who joined in the development of the calculus; some of them were Jakob Bernoulli (1654–1705), Johann Bernoulli (1667–1748), Leonhard Euler (1707–1783), and Joseph L. Lagrange (1736–1813). However, it wasn't until the nineteenth century that the processes of calculus were given a sound foundation by such mathematicians as Bernhard Bolzano (1781–1848), Augustin L. Cauchy (1789–1857), Karl Weierstrass (1815–1897), and Richard Dedekind (1831–1916).

PREPARATION FOR YOUR STUDY OF CALCULUS

Learning calculus can be one of your most stimulating and exciting educational experiences. For this to happen you must enter into your calculus course with a knowledge of certain mathematical subject matter from courses in algebra, geometry, and precalculus.

Precalculus topics of special importance appear in the Appendix sections A.1–A.11 in the back of the book. Specific facts about the real numbers as well as some basic notations are presented in Section A.1. You should be familiar with this content before you begin Chapter 1. Refer to Sections A.2–A.8 and A.10 for a review of topics in analytic geometry. Section A.9 reviews the trigonometric functions. You may need to study Section A.11 pertaining to partial fractions prior to Section 7.4 on integration of rational functions.

Visualization by means of graphs plays an important part in your study of calculus. We shall obtain these graphs in two ways: by hand and by high-speed automatic graphing devices such as graphics calculators and computers with appropriate software. These devices operate in a similar manner, but for student use a hand-held graphics calculator is obviously more practical than a desktop computer. In single-variable calculus, we shall, therefore, apply a graphics calculator. For multivariable calculus, three-dimensional graphs will be generated by a computer with graphing software.

When we obtain a graph by hand we use the terminology *sketch the graph*. When an electronic device is used, we state *plot the graph*. Graphs plotted on a graphics calculator are represented by figures showing a calculator screen with the window and equations of the displayed graphs indicated below the screen. Graphics calculators are not strictly automatic since they require a human operator to press specific keys, but because these keys depend on the manufacturer and model of the calculator, you should consult your calculator owner's manual for information on how to perform specific operations.

With the basic preliminaries out of the way, you are now ready to begin your course in calculus, the foundation for much of mathematics and for many of the greatest accomplishments of the modern world.

FUNCTIONS, LIMITS, AND CONTINUITY

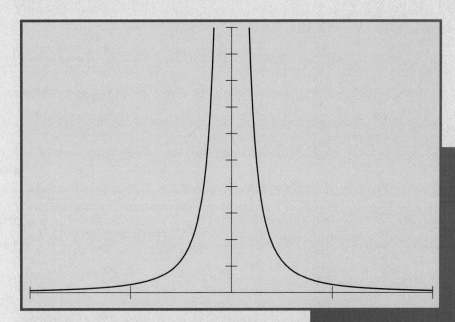

You have undoubtedly encountered *functions* in previous mathematics courses, but because they are fundamental in calculus and serve as a unifying concept throughout the text, we devote the first two sections to a review of them. Section 1.3 is designed to give you practice in obtaining functions as mathematical models of realworld situations as well as to preview some applications of calculus.

The two underlying mathematical operations in calculus are *differentiation* and *integration*. These operations involve computation of the *derivative* and the *definite integral*, each based on the notion of *limit*, probably the single most important topic in calculus. We begin our treatment of limits in Section 1.4 with a graphical introduction to limits of functions. The notion of a limit is first given a step-by-step foundation, which begins with computing the value of a function near a number and ends with developing an intuitive idea of the limiting process. The formal definition of a limit and limit theorems are introduced in Section 1.5 to simplify computation of limits of elementary algebraic functions. In Sections 1.6 and 1.7, the concept of limit is extended to include additional types of functions and infinite limits.

Probably the most important class of functions studied in calculus are *continuous functions*. Continuity of a function at a number is defined in Section 1.8 while continuity of a composite function, continuity on an interval, and the intermediate-value theorem are topics of Section 1.9. The *squeeze theorem*, a key theorem in calculus, is presented in Section 1.10 and applied there to establish the limit of the ratio of sin *t* to *t* as *t* approaches zero. This result is important in the discussion of the continuity of the trigonometric functions in the same section.

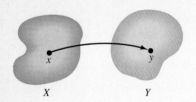

FIGURE 1

Table 1

x	$y = x^2$
1	1
$\frac{3}{2}$	$\frac{9}{4}$
4	16
0	0
-1	1
$-\frac{3}{2}$	$\frac{9}{4}$
-4	16

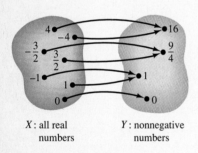

X: all real numbers Y: nonnegative numbers

FIGURE 2

1.1 FUNCTIONS AND THEIR GRAPHS

Often in practical applications the value of one quantity depends on the value of another. A person's salary may depend on the number of hours worked; the total production at a factory may depend on the number of machines used; the distance traveled by an object may depend on the time elapsed since it left a specific point; the volume of space occupied by a gas having a constant pressure depends on the temperature of the gas; the resistance of an electrical cable of fixed length depends on its diameter; and so forth. A relationship between such quantities is often given by means of a *function*. In calculus, the quantities in the relationship are real numbers.

> A function can be thought of as a correspondence from a set X of real numbers x to a set Y of real numbers y, where the number y is unique for a specific value of x.

A visualization of such a correspondence appears in Figure 1. Stating the concept of a function another way, we intuitively consider the real number y in set Y to be a *function* of the real number x in set X if there is some rule by which a unique value of y is assigned to a value of x. This rule is often given by an equation. For example, the equation

$$y = x^2$$

defines a function for which X is the set of all real numbers and Y is the set of nonnegative numbers. The value of y assigned to the value of x is obtained by multiplying x by itself. Table 1 gives some of these values and Figure 2 illustrates the correspondence of the numbers in the table.

Symbols such as f, g, and h are used to denote functions. The set X of real numbers described above is the *domain* of the function and the set Y of real numbers assigned to the values of x in X is the range of the function. The domain and range are often written with the interval notation described in Appendix Section A.1.

▷ **ILLUSTRATION 1**   With interval notation, the domain of the function defined by the equation

$$y = x^2$$

is $(-\infty, +\infty)$ and the range is $[0, +\infty)$.   ◄

▷ **ILLUSTRATION 2**   Let f be the function defined by the equation

$$y = \sqrt{x - 2}$$

Because the numbers are confined to real numbers, y is a function of x only for $x - 2 \geq 0$ because for any x satisfying this inequality, a unique value of y is determined. However, if $x < 2$, a square root of a negative number is obtained, and hence no real number y exists. Therefore we must restrict x so that $x \geq 2$. Thus the domain of f is the interval $[2, +\infty)$, and the range is $[0, +\infty)$.   ◄

▷ **ILLUSTRATION 3**   Let g be the function defined by the equation

$$y = \sqrt{x^2 - 9}$$

We observe that y is a function of x only for $x \geq 3$ or $x \leq -3$ (or simply $|x| \geq 3$); for any x satisfying either of these inequalities, a unique value of y is determined. No real value of y is determined if x is in the open interval $(-3, 3)$, because for these values of x a square root of a negative number is obtained. Hence the domain of g is $(-\infty, -3] \cup [3, +\infty)$, and the range is $[0, +\infty)$.   ◀

We can consider a function as a set of *ordered pairs*. For instance, the function defined by the equation $y = x^2$ consists of all the ordered pairs (x, y) satisfying the equation. The ordered pairs in this function given by Table 1 are $(1, 1)$, $(\frac{3}{2}, \frac{9}{4})$, $(4, 16)$, $(0, 0)$, $(-1, 1)$, $(-\frac{3}{2}, \frac{9}{4})$, and $(-4, 16)$. Of course, there is an unlimited number of ordered pairs in the function. Some others are $(2, 4)$, $(-2, 4)$, $(5, 25)$, $(-5, 25)$, $(\sqrt{3}, 3)$, and so on.

▷ **ILLUSTRATION 4**   The function f of Illustration 2 is the set of ordered pairs (x, y) for which $y = \sqrt{x - 2}$. With symbols we write

$$f = \{(x, y) \mid y = \sqrt{x - 2}\}$$

Some of the ordered pairs in f are $(2, 0)$, $(\frac{9}{4}, \frac{1}{2})$, $(3, 1)$, $(4, \sqrt{2})$, $(5, \sqrt{3})$, $(6, 2)$, $(11, 3)$.   ◀

▷ **ILLUSTRATION 5**   The function g of Illustration 3 is the set of ordered pairs (x, y) for which $y = \sqrt{x^2 - 9}$; that is,

$$g = \{(x, y) \mid y = \sqrt{x^2 - 9}\}$$

Some of the ordered pairs in g are $(3, 0)$, $(4, \sqrt{7})$, $(5, 4)$, $(-3, 0)$, $(-\sqrt{13}, 2)$.   ◀

We now state formally that a function is a set of ordered pairs. Defining a function this way, rather than as a rule or correspondence, makes its meaning precise.

1.1.1 Definition of a Function

A **function** is a set of ordered pairs of numbers (x, y) in which no two distinct ordered pairs have the same first number. The set of all admissible values of x is called the *domain* of the function, and the set of all resulting values of y is called the *range* of the function.

In this definition, the restriction that no two distinct ordered pairs can have the same first number ensures that y is unique for a specific value of x. The symbols x and y denote *variables*. Because the value of y is dependent on the choice of x, x denotes the **independent variable** and y denotes the **dependent variable.**

If f is the function having domain variable x and range variable y, the symbol $f(x)$ (read "f of x") denotes the particular value of y that corresponds to the value of x. The notation $f(x)$, called a **function value,** is due to the Swiss mathematician and physicist Leonhard Euler (1707–1783).

▷ **ILLUSTRATION 6** In Illustration 2, $f = \{(x, y) \mid y = \sqrt{x - 2}\}$. Thus

$$f(x) = \sqrt{x - 2}$$

We compute $f(x)$ for some specific values of x.

$$f(3) = \sqrt{3 - 2} \qquad f(5) = \sqrt{5 - 2}$$
$$= 1 \qquad\qquad = \sqrt{3}$$
$$f(6) = \sqrt{6 - 2} \qquad f(9) = \sqrt{9 - 2}$$
$$= 2 \qquad\qquad = \sqrt{7} \qquad\qquad ◀$$

When defining a function, the domain must be given either implicitly or explicitly. For instance, if f is defined by

$$f(x) = 3x^2 - 5x + 2$$

the function has a value if x is any real number; the domain is, therefore, the set of all real numbers. However, if f is defined by

$$f(x) = 3x^2 - 5x + 2 \qquad 1 \le x \le 10$$

then the domain of f consists of all real numbers between and including 1 and 10.

Similarly, if g is defined by the equation

$$g(x) = \frac{5x - 2}{x + 4}$$

it is implied that $x \ne -4$, because the quotient is undefined for $x = -4$; hence, the domain of g is the set of all real numbers except -4.

If h is defined by the equation

$$h(x) = \sqrt{4 - x^2}$$

the domain of h is the closed interval $[-2, 2]$ because $\sqrt{4 - x^2}$ is not a real number for $x > 2$ or $x < -2$. The range of h is $[0, 2]$.

▶ **EXAMPLE 1** Given that f is the function defined by

$$f(x) = x^2 + 3x - 4$$

find: **(a)** $f(0)$; **(b)** $f(2)$; **(c)** $f(h)$; **(d)** $f(2h)$; **(e)** $f(2x)$; **(f)** $f(x + h)$; **(g)** $f(x) + f(h)$.

Solution

(a) $f(0) = 0^2 + 3 \cdot 0 - 4$ **(b)** $f(2) = 2^2 + 3 \cdot 2 - 4$
$\qquad\qquad = -4$ $\qquad\qquad = 6$

(c) $f(h) = h^2 + 3h - 4$ **(d)** $f(2h) = (2h)^2 + 3(2h) - 4$
$\qquad\qquad\qquad\qquad\qquad\qquad\qquad\qquad = 4h^2 + 6h - 4$

(e) $f(2x) = (2x)^2 + 3(2x) - 4$
$\qquad\qquad = 4x^2 + 6x - 4$

(f) $f(x + h) = (x + h)^2 + 3(x + h) - 4$
$$= x^2 + 2hx + h^2 + 3x + 3h - 4$$
$$= x^2 + (2h + 3)x + (h^2 + 3h - 4)$$

(g) $f(x) + f(h) = (x^2 + 3x - 4) + (h^2 + 3h - 4)$
$$= x^2 + 3x + (h^2 + 3h - 8) \quad \blacktriangleleft$$

Compare the computations in parts (f) and (g) of Example 1. In part (f) the computation is for $f(x + h)$, which is the function value at the sum of x and h. In part (g), where $f(x) + f(h)$ is computed, we obtain the sum of the two function values $f(x)$ and $f(h)$.

In Chapter 2 we need to compute quotients of the form

$$\frac{f(x + h) - f(x)}{h} \quad h \neq 0$$

This quotient arises as the slope of the line through the points $(x, f(x))$ and $(x + h, f(x + h))$ on the graph of the function defined by $y = f(x)$. See Figure 3. If, in the computation, the difference of two radicals appears in the numerator, we rationalize the numerator, as in part (b) of the following example.

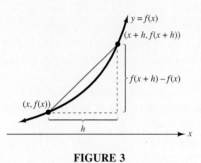

FIGURE 3

▶ **EXAMPLE 2**   Find

$$\frac{f(x + h) - f(x)}{h}$$

where $h \neq 0$, if **(a)** $f(x) = 4x^2 - 5x + 7$; **(b)** $f(x) = \sqrt{x}$.

Solution

(a) $\dfrac{f(x + h) - f(x)}{h} = \dfrac{4(x + h)^2 - 5(x + h) + 7 - (4x^2 - 5x + 7)}{h}$

$$= \frac{4x^2 + 8hx + 4h^2 - 5x - 5h + 7 - 4x^2 + 5x - 7}{h}$$

$$= \frac{8hx - 5h + 4h^2}{h}$$

$$= 8x - 5 + 4h$$

(b) $\dfrac{f(x + h) - f(x)}{h} = \dfrac{\sqrt{x + h} - \sqrt{x}}{h}$

$$= \frac{(\sqrt{x + h} - \sqrt{x})(\sqrt{x + h} + \sqrt{x})}{h(\sqrt{x + h} + \sqrt{x})}$$

$$= \frac{(x + h) - x}{h(\sqrt{x + h} + \sqrt{x})}$$

$$= \frac{h}{h(\sqrt{x + h} + \sqrt{x})}$$

$$= \frac{1}{\sqrt{x + h} + \sqrt{x}}$$

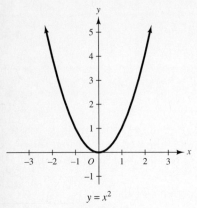

$y = x^2$

FIGURE 4

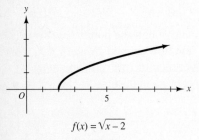

$f(x) = \sqrt{x-2}$

FIGURE 5

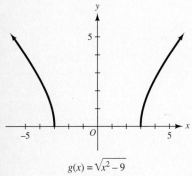

$g(x) = \sqrt{x^2 - 9}$

FIGURE 6

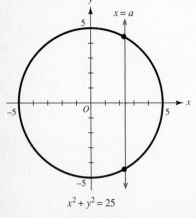

$x^2 + y^2 = 25$

FIGURE 7

In the second step of part (b) of this solution the numerator and denominator are multiplied by the conjugate of the numerator in order to rationalize the numerator, and this gives a common factor of h in the numerator and denominator.   ◀

The concept of a function as a set of ordered pairs leads to the following definition of the *graph of a function*.

> **1.1.2 Definition of the Graph of a Function**
>
> If f is a function, then the **graph of f** is the set of all points (x, y) in the plane R^2 for which (x, y) is an ordered pair in f.

From this definition, the graph of a function f is the same as the graph of the equation $y = f(x)$.

The graph of the function of Illustration 1 is the parabola sketched in Figure 4. The graph of function f of Illustrations 2 and 4 and sketched in Figure 5 is the top half of a parabola. The graph of function g of Illustrations 3 and 5 is sketched in Figure 6; this graph is the top half of a hyperbola.

Recall that for a function a unique value of the dependent variable exists for each value of the independent variable in the domain of the function. In geometric terms, this means:

> A vertical line intersects the graph of a function in at most one point.

Observe that in Figures 4, 5, and 6, a vertical line intersects each graph in at most one point.

▷   **ILLUSTRATION 7**   Consider the set $\{(x, y) \mid x^2 + y^2 = 25\}$, whose graph is the circle, of radius 5 with center at the origin, sketched in Figure 7. This set of ordered pairs is not a function because for any x in the interval $(-5, 5)$ two ordered pairs have x as the first number. For example, both $(3, 4)$ and $(3, -4)$ are ordered pairs in the given set. Furthermore, observe that a vertical line having the equation $x = a$, where $-5 < a < 5$, intersects the circle in two points.   ◀

▶   **EXAMPLE 3**   Determine the domain of the function g defined by

$$g(x) = \sqrt{x(x-2)}$$

Support the answer by plotting the graph on a graphics calculator.

Solution   Because $\sqrt{x(x-2)}$ is not a real number when $x(x-2) < 0$, the domain of g consists of the values of x for which $x(x-2) \geq 0$. This inequality will be satisfied when one of the following two cases holds: $x \geq 0$ and $x - 2 \geq 0$; or $x \leq 0$ and $x - 2 \leq 0$.

Case 1: $x \geq 0$ and $x - 2 \geq 0$. That is,

$$x \geq 0 \quad \text{and} \quad x \geq 2$$

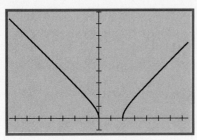

[-7.5, 7.5] by [-1, 9]

$g(x) = \sqrt{x(x-2)}$

FIGURE 8

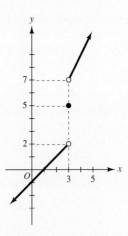

$f(x) = \begin{cases} x-1 & \text{if } x < 3 \\ 5 & \text{if } x = 3 \\ 2x+1 & \text{if } 3 < x \end{cases}$

FIGURE 9

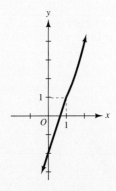

$g(x) = \begin{cases} 3x-2 & \text{if } x < 1 \\ x^2 & \text{if } 1 \le x \end{cases}$

FIGURE 10

Both inequalities hold if $x \ge 2$, which is the interval $[2, +\infty)$.

Case 2: $x \le 0$ and $x - 2 \le 0$. That is,

$$x \le 0 \quad \text{and} \quad x \le 2$$

Both inequalities hold if $x \le 0$, which is the interval $(-\infty, 0]$.

The solutions for the two cases are combined to obtain the domain of g. It is $(-\infty, 0] \cup [2, +\infty)$.

The graph of g is plotted in Figure 8. The graph comes down from the left to $x = 0$, goes up to the right from $x = 2$ and contains no points when x is in the open interval $(0, 2)$. The graph, therefore, supports our answer ◀

You have seen that the domain of a function can usually be determined by the function's definition. Often the range can be determined by the graph of the function as in the next example involving a *piecewise-defined function,* one that is defined by using more than one expression.

▶ **EXAMPLE 4**   Let f be the function defined by

$$f(x) = \begin{cases} x - 1 & \text{if } x < 3 \\ 5 & \text{if } x = 3 \\ 2x + 1 & \text{if } 3 < x \end{cases}$$

Determine the domain and range of f, and sketch its graph.

Solution   The domain of f is $(-\infty, +\infty)$. Figure 9 shows the graph of f; it consists of the portion of the line $y = x - 1$ for which $x < 3$, the point $(3, 5)$, and the portion of the line $y = 2x + 1$ for which $3 < x$. The function values are either numbers less than 2, the number 5, or numbers greater than 7. Therefore the range of f is the number 5 and those numbers in $(-\infty, 2) \cup (7, +\infty)$. ◀

Piecewise-defined functions will be useful to us in our study of limits, continuity, and the derivative as examples and counterexamples of functions having certain properties. For instance, the graph of the function in Example 4 has a break at the point where $x = 3$ which, as you will learn in Section 1.8, indicates that the function is *discontinuous* for that value of x. In the following example, we have a piecewise-defined function whose graph has no break at the value of x at which the defining expressions change, in this case at $x = 1$.

▶ **EXAMPLE 5**   Let g be the function defined by

$$g(x) = \begin{cases} 3x - 2 & \text{if } x < 1 \\ x^2 & \text{if } 1 \le x \end{cases}$$

Determine the domain and range of g, and sketch its graph.

Solution   The domain of g is $(-\infty, +\infty)$. The graph contains the portion of the line $y = 3x - 2$ for which $x < 1$ and the portion of the parabola $y = x^2$ for which $1 \le x$. The graph is sketched in Figure 10. The range is $(-\infty, +\infty)$. ◀

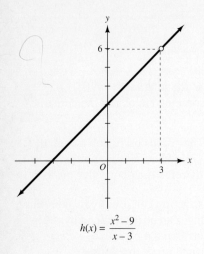

$$h(x) = \frac{x^2 - 9}{x - 3}$$

FIGURE 11

▶ **EXAMPLE 6**   The function h is defined by

$$h(x) = \frac{x^2 - 9}{x - 3}$$

Determine the domain and range of h, and sketch its graph.

Solution   Because $h(x)$ is defined for all x except 3, the domain of h is the set of all real numbers except 3. When $x = 3$, both the numerator and denominator are zero, and $0/0$ is undefined.

Factoring the numerator into $(x - 3)(x + 3)$ we obtain

$$h(x) = \frac{(x - 3)(x + 3)}{x - 3}$$

or $h(x) = x + 3$, provided that $x \neq 3$. In other words, the function h can be defined by

$$h(x) = x + 3 \qquad \text{if } x \neq 3$$

The graph of h consists of all points on the line $y = x + 3$ except the point $(3, 6)$, and it appears in Figure 11. The range of h is the set of all real numbers except 6.   ◀

In Example 6, the graph has a "hole," or "deleted point," at $x = 3$ where $h(3)$ is not defined. In the next example, the graph also has a hole at $x = 3$, but the function value at 3 is defined.

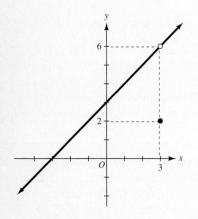

$$H(x) = \begin{cases} x + 3 & \text{if } x \neq 3 \\ 2 & \text{if } x = 3 \end{cases}$$

FIGURE 12

▶ **EXAMPLE 7**   Let H be the function defined by

$$H(x) = \begin{cases} x + 3 & \text{if } x \neq 3 \\ 2 & \text{if } x = 3 \end{cases}$$

Determine the domain and range of H and sketch its graph.

Solution   Because H is defined for all x, its domain is $(-\infty, +\infty)$. The graph of H is sketched in Figure 12. The range is the set of all real numbers except 6.   ◀

▶ **EXAMPLE 8**   The function f is defined by

$$f(x) = \begin{cases} x^2 & \text{if } x \neq 2 \\ 7 & \text{if } x = 2 \end{cases}$$

Determine the domain and range of f and sketch its graph.

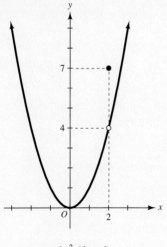

$$f(x) = \begin{cases} x^2 & \text{if } x \neq 2 \\ 7 & \text{if } x = 2 \end{cases}$$

FIGURE 13

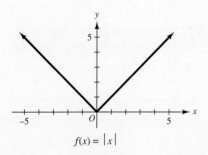

$f(x) = |x|$

FIGURE 14

Solution Because f is defined for all x, the domain is $(-\infty, +\infty)$. The graph, appearing in Figure 13, consists of the point $(2, 7)$ and all points on the parabola $y = x^2$ except $(2, 4)$. The range is $[0, +\infty)$. ◄

The function in the next example is called the **absolute value function.**

► **EXAMPLE 9** Determine the domain and range of the function f for which

$$f(x) = |x|$$

and sketch its graph.

Solution From the definition of $|x|$,

$$f(x) = \begin{cases} x & \text{if } x \geq 0 \\ -x & \text{if } x < 0 \end{cases}$$

The domain is $(-\infty, +\infty)$. The graph of f consists of two half lines through the origin and above the x axis; one has slope 1 and the other has slope -1. See Figure 14. The range is $[0, +\infty)$. ◄

The absolute value function is *built-in* on graphics calculators and is usually denoted by *ABS*. Another function built-in on graphics calculators is the **greatest integer function** whose function values are denoted by $[\![x]\!]$ defined by

$$[\![x]\!] = n \qquad \text{if } n \leq x < n + 1, \text{ where } n \text{ is an integer}$$

That is, $[\![x]\!]$ is the greatest integer less than or equal to x. In particular, $[\![1]\!] = 1$, $[\![1.3]\!] = 1$, $[\![0.5]\!] = 0$, $[\![-4.2]\!] = -5$, and $[\![-8]\!] = -8$.

The graph of the greatest integer function is sketched in Figure 15. Its domain is the set of all real numbers and its range consists of all the integers. On many graphics calculators the greatest integer function is denoted by *INT*.

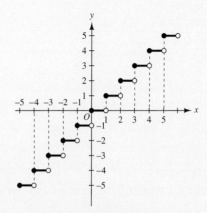

greatest integer function

FIGURE 15

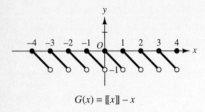

$G(x) = [\![x]\!] - x$

FIGURE 16

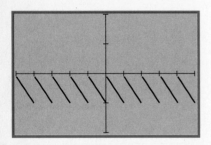

[–5, 5] by [–2, 2]

$G(x) = INT(x) - x$

FIGURE 17

▶ **EXAMPLE 10**   Sketch the graph of the function G defined by

$$G(x) = [\![x]\!] - x$$

and determine its domain and range. Support the answer by plotting the graph on a graphics calculator.

Solution   Because G is defined for all values of x, its domain is $(-\infty, +\infty)$. From the definition of $[\![x]\!]$, we have the following:

If $-2 \le x < -1$, $[\![x]\!] = -2$; therefore $G(x) = -2 - x$
If $-1 \le x < 0$, $[\![x]\!] = -1$; therefore $G(x) = -1 - x$
If $0 \le x < 1$, $[\![x]\!] = 0$; therefore $G(x) = -x$
If $1 \le x < 2$, $[\![x]\!] = 1$; therefore $G(x) = 1 - x$
If $2 \le x < 3$, $[\![x]\!] = 2$; therefore $G(x) = 2 - x$

and so on. More generally, if n is any integer, then

If $n \le x < n + 1$, $[\![x]\!] = n$; therefore $G(x) = n - x$

With these function values we sketch the graph of G appearing in Figure 16. From the graph we observe that the range is $(-1, 0]$. We plot the graph of $G(x) = INT(x) - x$ and obtain Figure 17, which supports our answer. ◀

EXERCISES 1.1

In Exercises 1 through 4, determine if the set is a function. If it is a function state its domain.

1. (a) $\{(x, y) \mid y = \sqrt{x - 4}\}$
   (b) $\{(x, y) \mid y = \sqrt{x^2 - 4}\}$
   (c) $\{(x, y) \mid y = \sqrt{4 - x^2}\}$
   (d) $\{(x, y) \mid x^2 + y^2 = 4\}$

2. (a) $\{(x, y) \mid y = \sqrt{x + 1}\}$
   (b) $\{(x, y) \mid y = \sqrt{x^2 - 1}\}$
   (c) $\{(x, y) \mid y = \sqrt{1 - x^2}\}$
   (d) $\{(x, y) \mid x^2 + y^2 = 1\}$

3. (a) $\{(x, y) \mid y = x^2\}$ **(b)** $\{(x, y) \mid x = y^2\}$
   (c) $\{(x, y) \mid y = x^3\}$ **(d)** $\{(x, y) \mid x = y^3\}$

4. (a) $\{(x, y) \mid y = (x - 1)^2 + 2\}$
   (b) $\{(x, y) \mid x = (y - 2)^2 + 1\}$
   (c) $\{(x, y) \mid y = (x + 2)^3 - 1\}$
   (d) $\{(x, y) \mid x = (y + 1)^3 - 2\}$

5. Given $f(x) = 2x - 1$, find
   (a) $f(3)$; **(b)** $f(-2)$; **(c)** $f(0)$; **(d)** $f(a + 1)$;
   (e) $f(x + 1)$; **(f)** $f(2x)$; **(g)** $2f(x)$; **(h)** $f(x + h)$;
   (i) $f(x) + f(h)$; **(j)** $\dfrac{f(x + h) - f(x)}{h}, h \ne 0.$

6. Given $f(x) = \dfrac{3}{x}$, find

   (a) $f(1)$; **(b)** $f(-3)$; **(c)** $f(6)$; **(d)** $f(\frac{1}{3})$; **(e)** $f\left(\dfrac{3}{a}\right)$;

   (f) $f\left(\dfrac{3}{x}\right)$; **(g)** $\dfrac{f(3)}{f(x)}$; **(h)** $f(x - 3)$; **(i)** $f(x) - f(3)$;

   (j) $\dfrac{f(x + h) - f(x)}{h}, h \ne 0.$

7. Given $f(x) = 2x^2 + 5x - 3$, find
   (a) $f(-2)$; **(b)** $f(-1)$; **(c)** $f(0)$; **(d)** $f(3)$;
   (e) $f(h + 1)$; **(f)** $f(2x^2)$; **(g)** $f(x^2 - 3)$;
   (h) $f(x + h)$; **(i)** $f(x) + f(h)$;
   (j) $\dfrac{f(x + h) - f(x)}{h}, h \ne 0.$

8. Given $g(x) = 3x^2 - 4$, find
   (a) $g(-4)$; **(b)** $g(\frac{1}{2})$; **(c)** $g(x^2)$; **(d)** $g(3x^2 - 4)$;
   (e) $g(x - h)$; **(f)** $g(x) - g(h)$;
   (g) $\dfrac{g(x + h) - g(x)}{h}, h \ne 0.$

9. Given $F(x) = \sqrt{x + 9}$, find
   (a) $F(x + 9)$; **(b)** $F(x^2 - 9)$; **(c)** $F(x^4 - 9)$;
   (d) $F(x^2 + 6x)$; **(e)** $F(x^4 - 6x^2)$;
   (f) $\dfrac{F(x + h) - F(x)}{h}, h \ne 0.$

10. Given $G(x) = \sqrt{4 - x}$, find

(a) $G(4 - x)$; (b) $G(4 - x^2)$; (c) $G(4 - x^4)$;

(d) $G(4x - x^2)$; (e) $G(-x^4 - 4x^2)$;

(f) $\dfrac{G(x + h) - G(h)}{h}$, $h \neq 0$.

In Exercises 11 through 46, sketch by hand the graph of the function and determine its domain and range.

11. $f(x) = 3x - 1$

12. $g(x) = 4 - x$

13. $F(x) = 2x^2$

14. $G(x) = x^2 + 2$

15. $g(x) = 5 - x^2$

16. $f(x) = (x - 1)^2$

17. $G(x) = \sqrt{x - 1}$

18. $F(x) = \sqrt{9 - x}$

19. $f(x) = \sqrt{x^2 - 4}$

20. $g(x) = \sqrt{4 - x^2}$

21. $g(x) = \sqrt{9 - x^2}$

22. $f(x) = \sqrt{x^2 - 1}$

23. $h(x) = |x - 3|$

24. $H(x) = |5 - x|$

25. $F(x) = |3x + 2|$

26. $G(x) = \dfrac{x^2 - 4}{x - 2}$

27. $H(x) = \dfrac{x^2 - 25}{x + 5}$

28. $f(x) = \dfrac{2x^2 + 7x + 3}{x + 3}$

29. $f(x) = \dfrac{x^2 - 4x + 3}{x - 1}$

30. $g(x) = \dfrac{(x^2 - 4)(x - 3)}{x^2 - x - 6}$

31. $f(x) = \begin{cases} -2 & \text{if } x \leq 3 \\ 2 & \text{if } 3 < x \end{cases}$

32. $g(x) = \begin{cases} -4 & \text{if } x < -2 \\ -1 & \text{if } -2 \leq x \leq 2 \\ 3 & \text{if } 2 < x \end{cases}$

33. $g(x) = \begin{cases} 2x - 1 & \text{if } x \neq 2 \\ 0 & \text{if } x = 2 \end{cases}$

34. $f(x) = \begin{cases} 3x + 2 & \text{if } x \neq 1 \\ 8 & \text{if } x = 1 \end{cases}$

35. $F(x) = \begin{cases} x^2 - 4 & \text{if } x \neq 3 \\ -2 & \text{if } x = 3 \end{cases}$

36. $G(x) = \begin{cases} 9 - x^2 & \text{if } x \neq -3 \\ 4 & \text{if } x = -3 \end{cases}$

37. $G(x) = \begin{cases} 1 - x^2 & \text{if } x < 0 \\ 3x + 1 & \text{if } 0 \leq x \end{cases}$

38. $F(x) = \begin{cases} x^2 - 4 & \text{if } x < 3 \\ 2x - 1 & \text{if } 3 \leq x \end{cases}$

39. $g(x) = \begin{cases} 6x + 7 & \text{if } x \leq -2 \\ 4 - x & \text{if } -2 < x \end{cases}$

40. $f(x) = \begin{cases} x - 2 & \text{if } x \leq 0 \\ x^2 + 1 & \text{if } 0 < x \end{cases}$

41. $h(x) = \begin{cases} x + 3 & \text{if } x < -5 \\ \sqrt{25 - x^2} & \text{if } -5 \leq x \leq 5 \\ 3 - x & \text{if } 5 < x \end{cases}$

42. $H(x) = \begin{cases} x + 2 & \text{if } x \leq -4 \\ \sqrt{16 - x^2} & \text{if } -4 < x < 4 \\ 2 - x & \text{if } 4 \leq x \end{cases}$

43. $F(x) = \dfrac{x^3 - 2x^2}{x - 2}$

44. $G(x) = \dfrac{x^3 + 3x^2}{x + 3}$

45. $f(x) = [\![x - 4]\!]$

46. $g(x) = [\![x + 2]\!]$

47. (a) Sketch the graph of the *unit step function,* denoted by U and defined by

$$U(x) = \begin{cases} 0 & \text{if } x < 0 \\ 1 & \text{if } 0 \leq x \end{cases}$$

Define each of the following functions piecewise and sketch their graphs: (b) $U(x - 1)$; (c) $U(x) - 1$; (d) $U(x) - U(x - 1)$.

48. Define each of the following functions piecewise and sketch their graphs where U is the unit step function defined in Exercise 47:

(a) $x \cdot U(x)$; (b) $(x + 1) \cdot U(x + 1)$;

(c) $(x + 1) \cdot U(x + 1) - x \cdot U(x)$.

49. (a) Sketch the graph of the *signum function* (or *sign function*), denoted by sgn and defined by

$$\text{sgn } x = \begin{cases} -1 & \text{if } x < 0 \\ 0 & \text{if } x = 0 \\ 1 & \text{if } 0 < x \end{cases}$$

sgn x is read "signum of x." Define each of the following functions piecewise and sketch their graphs:

(b) $x \cdot \text{sgn}(x)$; (c) $2 - x \cdot x \text{ sgn}(x)$; (d) $x - 2 \text{ sgn}(x)$.

50. Define each of the following functions piecewise where sgn is the signum function defined in Exercise 49: (a) $\text{sgn}(x + 1)$; (b) $\text{sgn}(x - 1)$;

(c) $\text{sgn}(x + 1) - \text{sgn}(x - 1)$.

51. The graph of the function f in the figure resembles the letter W. Define $f(x)$ piecewise.

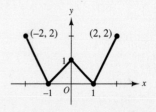

52. The graph of the function f in the figure resembles the letter M. Define $f(x)$ piecewise.

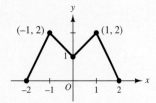

53. In the figure, the graph resembling the letter X is the union of the graphs of two functions f_1 and f_2 plotted in the $[-1, 1]$ by $[-1, 1]$ window. Define $f_1(x)$ and $f_2(x)$.

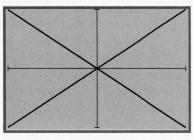

$[-1, 1]$ by $[-1, 1]$

54. There are three functions $f_1, f_2,$ and f_3, the union of whose graphs plotted in the $[-1, 1]$ by $[-1, 1]$ window resembles the letter Z. Define $f_1(x), f_2(x),$ and $f_3(x)$.

In Exercises 55 through 58, do the following: (a) Define the function piecewise without absolute value bars; (b) Sketch the graph of the function for your definition in part (a); (c) Support your answers in parts (a) and (b) by plotting the graph of the function.

55. $f(x) = |x^2 - 1|$ **56.** $g(x) = |4 - x^2|$

57. $g(x) = |x| \cdot |5 - x|$ **58.** $f(x) = |x| \cdot |x - 3|$

In Exercises 59 and 60, sketch the graph of the function and determine its domain and range. Support your answer by plotting the graph of the function.

59. $h(x) = x - [\![x]\!]$ **60.** $F(x) = x + [\![x]\!]$

61. Graphs of the functions in Exercises 51 and 52 resemble letters of the alphabet. Define two other functions whose graphs resemble two different letters of the alphabet and sketch their graphs.

62. In this section we used the symbolisms f, $f(x)$, and $y = f(x)$ pertaining to a particular function and having different meanings. Explain what each notation means, and in your explanation make up a function and use that function to distinguish the three symbolisms.

63. Explain why the definition of the graph of a function is consistent with the definition of a function as a set of ordered pairs. In your explanation use a specific example.

1.2 OPERATIONS ON FUNCTIONS AND TYPES OF FUNCTIONS

New functions may be formed from given functions by adding, subtracting, multiplying, and dividing function values. Accordingly, these new functions are known as the *sum, difference, product,* and *quotient* of the original functions.

1.2.1 Definitions of the Sum, Difference, Product, and Quotient of Two Functions

Given the two functions f and g:

(i) their **sum,** denoted by $f + g$, is the function defined by

$$(f + g)(x) = f(x) + g(x)$$

(ii) their **difference,** denoted by $f - g$, is the function defined by

$$(f - g)(x) = f(x) - g(x)$$

(iii) their **product,** denoted by $f \cdot g$, is the function defined by

$$(f \cdot g)(x) = f(x) \cdot g(x)$$

(iv) their **quotient,** denoted by f/g, is the function defined by

$$(f/g)(x) = f(x)/g(x) \qquad g(x) \neq 0$$

In each case the *domain* of the resulting function consists of those values of x common to the domains of f and g, with the additional requirement in case (iv) that the values of x for which $g(x) = 0$ are excluded.

▶ **EXAMPLE 1**   Given that f and g are the functions defined by

$$f(x) = \sqrt{x + 1} \quad \text{and} \quad g(x) = \sqrt{x - 4}$$

define the following functions and determine the domain of the resulting function: **(a)** $f + g$; **(b)** $f - g$; **(c)** $f \cdot g$; **(d)** f/g.

Solution

(a) $(f + g)(x) = \sqrt{x + 1} + \sqrt{x - 4}$

(b) $(f - g)(x) = \sqrt{x + 1} - \sqrt{x - 4}$

(c) $(f \cdot g) = \sqrt{x + 1} \cdot \sqrt{x - 4}$

(d) $(f/g)(x) = \dfrac{\sqrt{x + 1}}{\sqrt{x - 4}}$

The domain of f is $[-1, +\infty)$, and the domain of g is $[4, +\infty)$. So in parts (a), (b), and (c) the domain of the resulting function is $[4, +\infty)$. In part (d) the denominator is zero when $x = 4$; thus 4 is excluded from the domain, and the domain is therefore $(4, +\infty)$. ◀

Obtaining the *composite function* of two given functions is another operation on functions.

1.2.2 Definition of a Composite Function

Given the two functions f and g, the **composite function,** denoted by $f \circ g$, is defined by

$$(f \circ g)(x) = f(g(x))$$

and the domain of $f \circ g$ is the set of all numbers x in the domain of g such that $g(x)$ is in the domain of f.

The definition indicates that when computing $(f \circ g)(x)$, we first apply function g to x and then function f to $g(x)$. To visualize this computation see Figure 1. Function g assigns the value $g(x)$ to the number x in the domain of g. Then function f assigns the value $f(g(x))$ to the number $g(x)$ in the domain of f. Observe in Figure 1 that the range of g is a subset of the domain of f and the range of $f \circ g$ is a subset of the range of f.

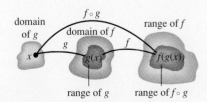

FIGURE 1

▷ **ILLUSTRATION 1**   If f and g are defined by

$$f(x) = \sqrt{x} \quad \text{and} \quad g(x) = 2x - 3$$

$$
\begin{aligned}
(f \circ g)(x) &= f(g(x)) \\
&= f(2x - 3) \\
&= \sqrt{2x - 3}
\end{aligned}
$$

The domain of g is $(-\infty, +\infty)$, and the domain of f is $[0, +\infty)$. The domain of $f \circ g$ is, therefore, the set of real numbers x for which $2x - 3 \geq 0$ or, equivalently, $[\frac{3}{2}, +\infty)$.   ◀

▶ **EXAMPLE 2**   Given

$$f(x) = \frac{5}{x - 2} \quad \text{and} \quad g(x) = 2x + 1$$

Compute $(f \circ g)(3)$ by two methods: **(a)** Find $g(3)$ and use that number to find $f(g(3))$; **(b)** Compute $(f \circ g)(x)$ and use that value to find $(f \circ g)(3)$.

Solution

(a)
$$
\begin{aligned}
g(3) &= 2(3) + 1 \\
&= 7
\end{aligned}
$$

Thus

$$
\begin{aligned}
f(g(3)) &= f(7) \\
&= \frac{5}{7 - 2} \\
&= 1
\end{aligned}
$$

(b)
$$
\begin{aligned}
(f \circ g)(x) &= f(g(x)) \\
&= f(2x + 1) \\
&= \frac{5}{(2x + 1) - 2} \\
&= \frac{5}{2x - 1}
\end{aligned}
$$

Therefore

$$
\begin{aligned}
(f \circ g)(3) &= \frac{5}{2(3) - 1} \\
&= 1
\end{aligned}
$$
◀

▶ **EXAMPLE 3**   Given that f and g are defined by

$$f(x) = \sqrt{x} \quad \text{and} \quad g(x) = x^2 - 1$$

find: **(a)** $f \circ f$; **(b)** $g \circ g$; **(c)** $f \circ g$; **(d)** $g \circ f$. Also determine the domain of the composite function in each part.

Solution   The domain of f is $[0, +\infty)$ and the domain of g is $(-\infty, +\infty)$.

(a)
$$
\begin{aligned}
(f \circ f)(x) &= f(f(x)) \\
&= f(\sqrt{x}) \\
&= \sqrt{\sqrt{x}} \\
&= \sqrt[4]{x}
\end{aligned}
$$

The domain is $[0, +\infty)$.

(b)
$$
\begin{aligned}
(g \circ g)(x) &= g(g(x)) \\
&= g(x^2 - 1) \\
&= (x^2 - 1)^2 - 1 \\
&= x^4 - 2x^2
\end{aligned}
$$

The domain is $(-\infty, +\infty)$.

(c) $(f \circ g)(x) = f(g(x))$
$\qquad\qquad = f(x^2 - 1)$
$\qquad\qquad = \sqrt{x^2 - 1}$

The domain is

$(-\infty, -1] \cup [1, +\infty).$

(d) $(g \circ f)(x) = g(f(x))$
$\qquad\qquad = g(\sqrt{x})$
$\qquad\qquad = (\sqrt{x})^2 - 1$
$\qquad\qquad = x - 1$

The domain is $[0, +\infty)$.

In part (d) note that even though $x - 1$ is defined for all values of x, the domain of $g \circ f$, by the definition of a composite function, is the set of all numbers x in the domain of f such that $f(x)$ is in the domain of g. Thus the domain of $g \circ f$ must be a subset of the domain of f. ◀

Observe from the results of parts (c) and (d) of Example 3 that $(f \circ g)(x)$ and $(g \circ f)(x)$ are not necessarily equal.

An important theorem in calculus, called the *chain rule,* discussed in Section 2.8, involves composite functions. When applying the chain rule it is necessary to think of a function as the composition of two other functions, as shown in the following illustration.

▷ **ILLUSTRATION 2**　　If $h(x) = (4x^2 + 1)^3$, we can express h as the composition of the two functions f and g for which

$\qquad f(x) = x^3 \qquad \text{and} \qquad g(x) = 4x^2 + 1$

because

$\qquad (f \circ g)(x) = f(g(x))$
$\qquad\qquad\quad = f(4x^2 + 1)$
$\qquad\qquad\quad = (4x^2 + 1)^3$ ◀

The function h in Illustration 2 can be expressed as the composition of other pairs of functions. For example, if

$\qquad F(x) = (4x + 1)^3 \qquad \text{and} \qquad G(x) = x^2$

then

$\qquad (F \circ G)(x) = F(G(x))$
$\qquad\qquad\quad = F(x^2)$
$\qquad\qquad\quad = (4x^2 + 1)^3$

▶ **EXAMPLE 4**　　Given

$\qquad h(x) = \dfrac{1}{\sqrt{x^2 + 3}}$

express h as the composition of two functions f and g in two ways: **(a)** the function f contains the radical; **(b)** the function g contains the radical.

Solution

(a) $f(x) = \dfrac{1}{\sqrt{x + 3}}$ (b) $f(x) = \dfrac{1}{x}$

$g(x) = x^2$ $g(x) = \sqrt{x^2 + 3}$

Then   Then

$$(f \circ g)(x) = f(g(x))$$ $$(f \circ g)(x) = f(g(x))$$
$$= f(x^2)$$ $$= f(\sqrt{x^2 + 3})$$
$$= \frac{1}{\sqrt{x^2 + 3}}$$ $$= \frac{1}{\sqrt{x^2 + 3}}$$ ◄

A function whose range consists of only one number is called a **constant function**. Thus if $f(x) = c$, and if c is any real number, then f is a constant function, and its graph is a horizontal line at a directed distance of c units from the x axis.

▷   **ILLUSTRATION 3**

(a) The function defined by $f(x) = 5$ is a constant function, and its graph, sketched in Figure 2, is a horizontal line 5 units above the x axis.
(b) The function defined by $g(x) = -4$ is a constant function whose graph is a horizontal line 4 units below the x axis. See Figure 3.   ◄

A **linear function** is defined by

$$f(x) = mx + b$$

where m and b are constants and $m \neq 0$. Its graph is a line having slope m and y intercept b.

▷   **ILLUSTRATION 4**   The function defined by

$$f(x) = 2x - 6$$

is linear. Its graph is the line shown in Figure 4.   ◄

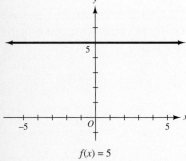

$f(x) = 5$

FIGURE 2

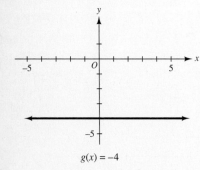

$g(x) = -4$

FIGURE 3

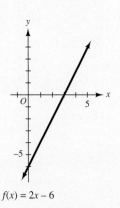

$f(x) = 2x - 6$

FIGURE 4

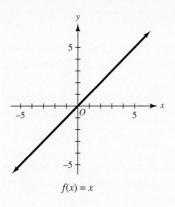

$f(x) = x$

FIGURE 5

The particular linear function defined by

$$f(x) = x$$

is called the **identity function.** Its graph, sketched in Figure 5, is the line bisecting the first and third quadrants.

If a function f is defined by

$$f(x) = a_n x^n + a_{n-1}x^{n-1} + a_{n-2}x^{n-2} + \ldots + a_1 x + a_0$$

where $a_0, a_1, \ldots, a_n$ are real numbers ($a_n \neq 0$) and n is a nonnegative integer, then f is called a **polynomial function** of degree n. Thus the function defined by

$$f(x) = 3x^5 - x^2 + 7x - 1$$

is a polynomial function of degree 5.

A linear function is a polynomial function of degree 1. If the degree of a polynomial function is 2, it is called a **quadratic function,** and if the degree is 3, it is called a **cubic function.**

If a function can be expressed as the quotient of two polynomial functions, it is called a **rational function.**

An **algebraic function** is one formed by a finite number of algebraic operations on the identity function and a constant function. These algebraic operations include addition, subtraction, multiplication, division, raising to powers, and extracting roots. Polynomial and rational functions are particular kinds of algebraic functions. A complicated example of an algebraic function is the one defined by

$$f(x) = \frac{(x^2 - 3x + 1)^3}{\sqrt{x^4 + 1}}$$

In addition to algebraic functions, we shall consider transcendental functions, examples of which are the trigonometric functions discussed in Appendix Section A.9 and logarithmic and exponential functions introduced in Chapter 5.

An *even function* is one whose graph is symmetric with respect to the y axis, and an *odd function* is one whose graph is symmetric with respect to the origin. Following are the formal definitions.

1.2.3 Definition of an Even and an Odd Function

(i) A function f is an **even function** if for every x in the domain of f, $f(-x) = f(x)$.

(ii) A function f is an **odd function** if for every x in the domain of $f, f(-x) = -f(x)$.

In both parts (i) and (ii) it is understood that $-x$ is in the domain of f whenever x is.

The symmetry properties of even and odd functions follow from the symmetry tests given in Appendix Section A.2.

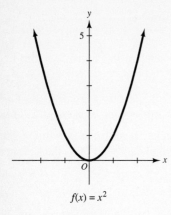

$f(x) = x^2$

FIGURE 6

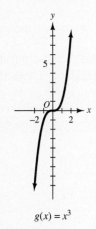

$g(x) = x^3$

FIGURE 7

▷ **ILLUSTRATION 5**

(a) If $f(x) = x^2$, $f(-x) = (-x)^2$. Therefore $f(-x) = f(x)$, and f is an even function. Its graph is a parabola symmetric with respect to the y axis. See Figure 6.

(b) If $g(x) = x^3$, $g(-x) = (-x)^3$. Because $g(-x) = -g(x)$, g is an odd function. The graph of g, shown in Figure 7, is symmetric with respect to the origin. ◀

▶ **EXAMPLE 5**   Plot the graph of the given function and from the graph conjecture whether the function is even, odd, or neither; then confirm the conjecture analytically:

(a) $f(x) = 3x^4 - 2x^2 + 7$

(b) $g(x) = 3x^5 - 4x^3 - 9x$

(c) $h(x) = 2x^4 + 7x^3 - x^2 + 9$

Solution

(a) The graph of f, plotted in Figure 8, appears symmetric with respect to the y axis. We, therefore, suspect the function is even. To prove this fact analytically, we compute $f(-x)$:

$$f(-x) = 3(-x)^4 - 2(-x)^2 + 7$$
$$= 3x^4 - 2x^2 + 7$$
$$= f(x)$$

Because $f(-x) = f(x)$, f is even.

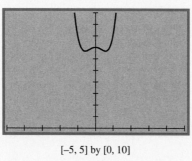

[−5, 5] by [0, 10]

$f(x) = 3x^4 - 2x^2 + 7$

FIGURE 8

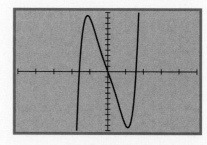

[−5, 5] by [−11, 11]

$g(x) = 3x^5 - 4x^3 - 9x$

FIGURE 9

(b) Figure 9 shows the graph of g apparently symmetric with respect to the origin. We suspect, therefore, that the function is odd. We compute $g(-x)$:

$$g(-x) = 3(-x)^5 - 4(-x)^3 - 9(-x)$$
$$= -3x^5 + 4x^3 + 9x$$
$$= -(3x^5 - 4x^3 - 9x)$$
$$= -g(x)$$

Because $g(-x) = -g(x)$, we have proved analytically that g is odd.

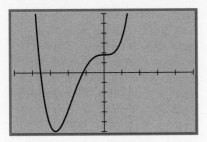

[−5, 5] by [−30, 30]

$h(x) = 2x^4 + 7x^3 - x^2 + 9$

FIGURE 10

(c) Because the graph of h, appearing in Figure 10, is not symmetric with respect to either the y axis or the origin, the function is neither even nor odd. We compute $h(-x)$:

$$h(-x) = 2(-x)^4 + 7(-x)^3 - (-x)^2 + 9$$
$$= 2x^4 - 7x^3 - x^2 + 9$$

Because $h(-x) \neq h(x)$ and $h(-x) \neq -h(x)$, we have confirmed that h is neither even nor odd. ◀

▶ **EXAMPLE 6**   Given

$$F(x) = |x + 3| - |x - 3|$$

(a) Define $F(x)$, without absolute value bars, piecewise in the following intervals: $(-\infty, -3)$; $[-3, 3)$; $[3, +\infty)$. **(b)** Support the answer in part (a) graphically by plotting the graph of F from the given equation. **(c)** From the graph in part (b) state whether F is even, odd, or neither. **(d)** Confirm the answer in part (c) analytically from the given equation.

Solution

(a) From the definition of the absolute value of a number

$$|x + 3| = \begin{cases} x + 3 & \text{if } x + 3 \geq 0 \\ -(x + 3) & \text{if } x + 3 < 0 \end{cases}$$

and

$$|x - 3| = \begin{cases} x - 3 & \text{if } x - 3 \geq 0 \\ -(x - 3) & \text{if } x - 3 < 0 \end{cases}$$

That is,

$$|x + 3| = \begin{cases} x + 3 & \text{if } x \geq -3 \\ -x - 3 & \text{if } x < -3 \end{cases}$$

and

$$|x - 3| = \begin{cases} x - 3 & \text{if } x \geq 3 \\ -x + 3 & \text{if } x < 3 \end{cases}$$

If $x \in (-\infty, -3)$, $|x + 3| = -x - 3$ and $|x - 3| = -x + 3$. Hence

$$|x + 3| - |x - 3| = -x - 3 - (-x + 3)$$
$$= -6$$

If $x \in [-3, 3)$, $|x + 3| = x + 3$ and $|x - 3| = -x + 3$. Thus

$$|x + 3| - |x - 3| = x + 3 - (-x + 3)$$
$$= 2x$$

If $x \in [3, +\infty)$, $|x + 3| = x + 3$ and $|x - 3| = x - 3$. Therefore

$$|x + 3| - |x - 3| = x + 3 - (x - 3)$$
$$= 6$$

With these results, we define $F(x)$ piecewise as follows:

$$F(x) = \begin{cases} -6 & \text{if } x < -3 \\ 2x & \text{if } -3 \leq x < 3 \\ 6 & \text{if } 3 \leq x \end{cases}$$

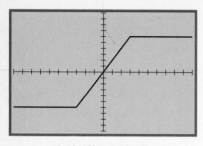

[−10, 10] by [−10, 10]

$F(x) = |x + 3| - |x - 3|$

FIGURE 11

(b) Figure 11 shows the graph of F plotted from the given equation. The graph supports our answer in part (a).

(c) Because the graph in Figure 11 is symmetric with respect to the origin, function F is odd.

(d) We confirm our answer in part (c) by computing $F(-x)$ from the given equation:

$$F(-x) = |-x + 3| - |-x - 3|$$
$$= |-(x - 3)| - |-(x + 3)|$$
$$= |x - 3| - |x + 3|$$
$$= -F(x)$$

We have, therefore, proved analytically that F is odd. ◀

EXERCISES 1.2

In Exercises 1 through 10, define the following functions and determine the domain of the resulting function:
(a) $f + g$; (b) $f - g$; (c) $f \cdot g$; (d) f/g; (e) g/f.

1. $f(x) = x - 5$; $g(x) = x^2 - 1$

2. $f(x) = \sqrt{x}$; $g(x) = x^2 + 1$

3. $f(x) = \dfrac{x + 1}{x - 1}$; $g(x) = \dfrac{1}{x}$

4. $f(x) = \sqrt{x}$; $g(x) = 4 - x^2$

5. $f(x) = \sqrt{x}$; $g(x) = x^2 - 1$

6. $f(x) = |x|$; $g(x) = |x - 3|$

7. $f(x) = x^2 + 1$; $g(x) = 3x - 2$

8. $f(x) = \sqrt{x + 4}$; $g(x) = x^2 - 4$

9. $f(x) = \dfrac{1}{x + 1}$; $g(x) = \dfrac{x}{x - 2}$

10. $f(x) = x^2$; $g(x) = \dfrac{1}{\sqrt{x}}$

In Exercises 11 through 14, for the functions f and g and the number c, compute $(f \circ g)(c)$ by two methods; (a) Find $g(c)$ and use that number to find $f(g(c))$; (b) Compute $(f \circ g)(x)$ and use that value to find $(f \circ g)(c)$.

11. $f(x) = 3x^2 - 4x$; $g(x) = 2x - 5$; $c = 4$

12. $f(x) = \sqrt{x^2 - 36}$; $g(x) = x^2 - 3x$; $c = 5$

13. $f(x) = \dfrac{1}{x - 1}$; $g(x) = \dfrac{2}{x^2 + 1}$; $c = \dfrac{1}{2}$

14. $f(x) = \dfrac{2\sqrt{x + 3}}{x}$; $g(x) = \dfrac{2x + 5}{x^4}$; $c = -2$

In Exercises 15 through 24, define the following functions and determine the domain of the composite function:
(a) $f \circ g$; (b) $g \circ f$; (c) $f \circ f$; (d) $g \circ g$.

15. $f(x) = x - 2$; $g(x) = x + 7$

16. $f(x) = 3 - 2x$; $g(x) = 6 - 3x$

17. The functions of Exercise 1

18. The functions of Exercise 2

19. $f(x) = \sqrt{x - 2}$; $g(x) = x^2 - 2$

20. $f(x) = x^2 - 1$; $g(x) = \dfrac{1}{x}$

21. $f(x) = \dfrac{1}{x}$; $g(x) = \sqrt{x}$

22. $f(x) = \sqrt{x}$; $g(x) = -\dfrac{1}{x}$

23. $f(x) = |x|$; $g(x) = |x + 2|$

24. $f(x) = \sqrt{x^2 - 1}$; $g(x) = \sqrt{x - 1}$

In Exercises 25 and 26, define the following functions and determine the domain of the resulting function:
(a) $f(x^2)$; (b) $[f(x)]^2$; (c) $(f \circ f)(x)$; (d) $(f \circ f)(-x)$.

25. $f(x) = \sqrt{x}$

26. $f(x) = \dfrac{1}{x - 1}$

In Exercises 27 through 32, express h as the composition of two functions f and g in two ways.

27. $h(x) = \sqrt{x^2 - 4}$

28. $h(x) = (9 + x^2)^{-2}$

29. $h(x) = \left(\dfrac{1}{x - 2}\right)^3$

30. $h(x) = \dfrac{4}{\sqrt[3]{x^3 + 3}}$

31. $h(x) = (x^2 + 4x - 5)^4$

32. $h(x) = \sqrt{|x| + 4}$

In Exercises 33 through 38, plot on your graphics calculator the graph of the function and from the graph conjecture whether the function is even, odd, or neither. Then confirm your conjecture analytically.

33. **(a)** $f(x) = 2x^4 - 3x^2 + 1$ **(b)** $g(x) = 5x^5 + 1$

34. **(a)** $f(x) = x^2 + 2x + 2$ **(b)** $g(x) = x^6 - 1$

35. **(a)** $f(x) = 5x^3 - 7x$ **(b)** $g(x) = |x|$

36. **(a)** $f(x) = 4x^5 + 3x^3$ **(b)** $g(x) = x^3 + 1$

37. **(a)** $f(x) = \sqrt[3]{x}$ **(b)** $g(x) = 5x^4 - 4$

38. **(a)** $f(x) = \dfrac{|x|}{x}$ **(b)** $g(x) = 2|x| + 3$

In Exercises 39 and 40, determine analytically whether the function is even, odd, or neither.

39. (a) $f(y) = \dfrac{y^3 - y}{y^2 + 1}$ **(b)** $g(r) = \dfrac{r^2 - 1}{r^2 + 1}$

    (c) $f(x) = \dfrac{|x|}{x^2 + 1}$

40. (a) $h(x) = \dfrac{x^2 - 5}{2x^3 + x}$ **(b)** $g(z) = \dfrac{z - 1}{z + 1}$

    (c) $f(x) = \begin{cases} -1 & \text{if } x < 0 \\ 1 & \text{if } 0 \le r \end{cases}$

In Exercises 41 through 44, do the following: (a) Define $f(x)$, without absolute value bars, in the indicated intervals. (b) Support your answer in part (a) graphically by plotting on your graphics calculator the graph of f from the given equation. (c) From the graph in part (b) state whether f is even, odd, or neither. (d) Confirm your answer in part (c) analytically from the given equation.

41. $f(x) = \dfrac{|x|}{x}$; $(-\infty, 0)$, $(0, +\infty)$

42. $f(x) = x|x|$; $(-\infty, 0)$, $[0, +\infty)$

43. $f(x) = |x - 2| - |x + 2|$; $(-\infty, -2)$, $[-2, 2)$, $[2, +\infty)$

44. $f(x) = \dfrac{|x + 1| - |x - 1|}{x}$; $(-\infty, -1)$, $[-1, 0)$, $(0, 1]$, $(1, +\infty)$

45. Is the composition of two functions commutative; that is, if f and g are any two functions, are $(f \circ g)(x)$ and $(g \circ f)(x)$ equal? Justify your answer by giving an example.

If f and g are two functions such that $(f \circ g)(x) = x$ and $(g \circ f)(x) = x$, then f and g are inverses of each other. In Exercises 46 through 50, show that f and g are inverses of each other.

46. $f(x) = 2x - 3$ and $g(x) = \dfrac{x + 3}{2}$

47. $f(x) = \dfrac{1}{x + 1}$ and $g(x) = \dfrac{1 - x}{x}$

48. $f(x) = x^2$, $x \ge 0$, and $g(x) = \sqrt{x}$

49. $f(x) = x^2$, $x \le 0$, and $g(x) = -\sqrt{x}$

50. $f(x) = (x - 1)^3$ and $g(x) = 1 + \sqrt[3]{x}$

51. The unit step function U and the signum function sgn were defined in Exercises 47 and 49, respectively, of

Exercises 1.1. **(a)** Define sgn $(U(x))$ and sketch the graph. **(b)** Define $U(\text{sgn }(x))$ and sketch the graph.

52. Prove that if f and g are both odd functions, then $(f + g)$ and $(f - g)$ are also odd functions, and $f \cdot g$ and f/g are both even functions.

53. Determine whether the composite function $f \circ g$ is odd or even in each of the following cases: **(a)** f and g are both odd; **(b)** f is even and g is odd: **(c)** g is even.

54. Find formulas for $(f \circ g)(x)$ if

$$f(x) = \begin{cases} 0 & \text{if } x < 0 \\ 2x & \text{if } 0 \le x \le 1 \\ 0 & \text{if } 1 < x \end{cases}$$

and

$$g(x) = \begin{cases} 1 & \text{if } x < 0 \\ \frac{1}{2}x & \text{if } 0 \le x \le 1 \\ 1 & \text{if } 1 < x \end{cases}$$

Sketch the graphs of f, g, and $f \circ g$.

55. Find formulas for $(g \circ f)(x)$ for the functions of Exercise 54. Sketch the graph of $g \circ f$.

56. If $f(x) = x^2 + 2x + 2$, find two functions g for which $(f \circ g)(x) = x^2 - 4x + 5$.

57. If $f(x) = x^2$, find two functions g for which $(f \circ g)(x) = 4x^2 - 12x + 9$.

58. Prove that if f and g are both linear functions, then $f \circ g$ is a linear function.

59. There is one function whose domain is the set of all real numbers that is both even and odd. What is that function? Prove it is the only such function.

60. Suppose $f(x) = \dfrac{1}{x}$, $g(x) = -\dfrac{1}{x}$, and $h(x) = -x$. Show that $(f \circ g)(x) = (g \circ f)(x)$ and explain why neither $f \circ g$ nor $g \circ f$ is the same as h.

61. Plot on your graphics calculator the graphs of the two functions F and G defined by

$$F(x) = \frac{\sqrt{x + 1}}{\sqrt{x - 4}} \quad \text{and} \quad G(x) = \sqrt{\frac{x + 1}{x - 4}}$$

[Note that F is the same function as f/g in Example 1(d)]. Explain why the graphs of F and G are not the same and, consequently, why the two functions are not equal.

1.3 FUNCTIONS AS MATHEMATICAL MODELS

In applications of calculus, we need to express a real-world situation in terms of a functional relationship, called a **mathematical model** of the situation. This section is designed to give you practice in obtaining functions as mathematical models and at the same time we will preview some of the applications you will encounter later.

Although no one specific method is always used to obtain a mathematical model, here are some steps that give a possible procedure for you to follow. As you read through the examples, refer to these steps to see how they are applied.

> **Suggestions for Solving Problems Involving a Function as a Mathematical Model**
>
> 1. Read the problem carefully so that you understand it. To gain understanding, it is often helpful to make up a specific example that involves a similar situation in which all the quantities are known. Another aid is to draw a picture if feasible, as shown in Examples 4 and 5.
> 2. Determine the known and unknown quantities. Use a symbol, say x, for the independent variable, and a symbol, say f, for the function you will obtain; then $f(x)$ symbolizes the function value. Because x and $f(x)$ are symbols for numbers their definitions should indicate this fact. For example, if the independent variable represents length and length is measured in feet, then if x is the symbol for the variable, x should be defined as the number of feet in the length or, equivalently, x feet is the length.
> 3. Write down any numerical facts known about the variable and the function value.
> 4. From the information in step 3, determine two algebraic expressions for the same number, one in terms of the variable and one in terms of the function value. From these two expressions form an equation that defines the function. You now have a function as a mathematical model of the problem.
> 5. To complete the problem once you have applied the mathematical model to solve for the unknown quantities, *write a conclusion*, consisting of one or more sentences, that answers the questions of the problem. Be sure your conclusion contains the correct units of measurement.

▶ **EXAMPLE 1**   The volume of a gas having a constant pressure is directly proportional to the absolute temperature, and at a temperature of 175° the gas occupies 100 m³. **(a)** Find a mathematical model expressing volume as a function of temperature. **(b)** What is the volume of the gas at a temperature of 140°?

Solution

(a) Let $f(x)$ cubic meters be the volume of a gas whose temperature is x degrees. Then by the definition of directly proportional

$$f(x) = kx \tag{1}$$

where k is a constant. Because the volume of the gas is 100 m³ at a temperature of 175°, we replace x by 175 and $f(x)$ by 100 in (1) and obtain

$$100 = k(175)$$
$$k = \tfrac{4}{7}$$

Substituting this value of k in (1), we have

$$f(x) = \tfrac{4}{7}x$$

(b) From the above expression for $f(x)$, we get

$$f(140) = \tfrac{4}{7}(140)$$
$$= 80$$

<u>Conclusion:</u>   At a temperature of $140°$ the volume of the gas is 80 m³.   ◄

▶   **EXAMPLE 2**   A wholesaler sells a product by the pound (or fraction of a pound); if not more than 10 pounds are ordered, the wholesaler charges $2 per pound. However, to invite large orders the wholesaler charges only $1.80 per pound if more than 10 pounds are ordered. **(a)** Find a mathematical model expressing the total cost of the order as a function of the amount of the product ordered. **(b)** Sketch the graph of the function in part (a). **(c)** Determine the total cost of an order of 9.5 1b and of an order of 10.5 1b.

Solution

(a) Let $C(x)$ dollars be the total cost of an order of x pounds of the product. Then

$$C(x) = \begin{cases} 2x & \text{if } 0 \leq x \leq 10 \\ 1.8x & \text{if } 10 < x \end{cases}$$

(b) The graph of function C appears in Figure 1.
(c) $C(x)$ is obtained from the equation $C(x) = 2x$ when $0 \leq x \leq 10$ and from the equation $C(x) = 1.8x$ when $10 < x$. Therefore,

$$C(9.5) = 2(9.5) \qquad C(10.5) = (1.8)(10.5)$$
$$= 19 \qquad\qquad\qquad = 18.90$$

<u>Conclusion:</u>   The total cost of 9.5 1b is $19 and the total cost of 10.5 lb is $18.90.   ◄

Observe from part (b) of Example 2 that the graph of C has a break at the point where $x = 10$, which indicates that function C is *discontinuous* at $x = 10$. We will elaborate on this property in Section 1.8. For now, notice that because of this discontinuity of C, it would be advantageous to increase the size of some orders to take advantage of a lower total cost. In particular, it would be unwise to purchase 9.5 1b for $19 when 10.5 1b can be bought for $18.90.

In the next example, we have a composite function as a mathematical model.

▶   **EXAMPLE 3**   In a forest a predator feeds on prey, and for the first fifteen weeks since the end of the hunting season the predator population is a function f of x, the number of prey in the forest, which in turn is a function g of t, the number of weeks that have elapsed since the end of the hunting season. If

$$f(x) = \tfrac{1}{48}x^2 - 2x + 50 \quad \text{and} \quad g(t) = 4t + 52$$

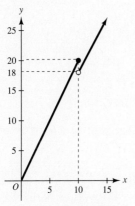

$$C(x) = \begin{cases} 2x & \text{if } 0 \leq x \leq 10 \\ 1.8x & \text{if } 10 < x \end{cases}$$

FIGURE 1

where $0 \leq t \leq 15$, do the following: **(a)** Find a mathematical model expressing the predator population as a function of the number of weeks since the end of the hunting season. **(b)** Find the predator population 11 weeks after the close of the hunting season.

Solution

(a) The predator population t weeks after the close of the hunting season is given by $(f \circ g)(t)$, where $0 \leq t \leq 15$.

$$(f \circ g)(t) = f(g(t))$$
$$= f(4t + 52)$$
$$= \tfrac{1}{48}(4t + 52)^2 - 2(4t + 52) + 50$$

(b) When $t = 11$, we have

$$(f \circ g)(11) = \tfrac{1}{48}(96)^2 - 2(96) + 50$$
$$= 50$$

<u>Conclusion:</u>   Eleven weeks after the close of the hunting season the predator population is 50.   ◄

In Section 2.8 we will return to the situation in Example 3 and determine the rate at which the predator population is growing 11 weeks after the close of the hunting season.

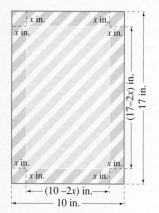

FIGURE 2

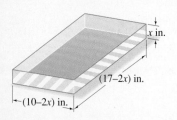

FIGURE 3

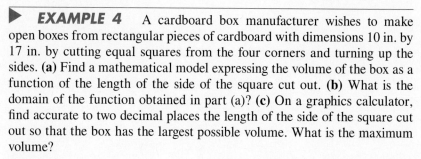

[0, 5] by [0, 200]

$V(x) = 170x - 54x^2 + 4x^3$

FIGURE 4

▶   ***EXAMPLE 4***   A cardboard box manufacturer wishes to make open boxes from rectangular pieces of cardboard with dimensions 10 in. by 17 in. by cutting equal squares from the four corners and turning up the sides. **(a)** Find a mathematical model expressing the volume of the box as a function of the length of the side of the square cut out. **(b)** What is the domain of the function obtained in part (a)? **(c)** On a graphics calculator, find accurate to two decimal places the length of the side of the square cut out so that the box has the largest possible volume. What is the maximum volume?

Solution

(a) Let x inches be the length of the side of the square cut out and $V(x)$ cubic inches be the volume of the box. Figure 2 represents a given piece of cardboard and Figure 3 represents the box obtained from the cardboard. The number of inches in the dimensions of the box are x, $10 - 2x$, and $17 - 2x$. Therefore,

$$V(x) = x(10 - 2x)(17 - 2x)$$
$$= 170x - 54x^2 + 4x^3$$

(b) From the expression for $V(x)$ in part (a), we observe that $V(0) = 0$ and $V(5) = 0$. From conditions of the problem we know that x can be neither negative nor greater than 5. Thus the domain of V is the closed interval $[0, 5]$.

(c) The graph of function V plotted in the $[0, 5]$ by $[0, 200]$ window appears in Figure 4. We observe that V has a maximum value on its domain. The x coordinate of the highest point on the graph gives the length of the side of the square to be cut out for maximum volume and the y coordinate gives the maximum volume. On our graphics calculator, we determine the highest point is (2.03, 156.03).

<u>Conclusion:</u>   The length of the side of the square cut out should be 2.03 in. to give the box a maximum volume of 156.03 in.^{3} ◀

In Section 3.2, we will apply calculus to confirm analytically the answer in Example 4(c).

▶ **EXAMPLE 5**   A closed tin can of volume 60 in.^{3} is to be in the form of a right-circular cylinder. **(a)** Find a mathematical model expressing the total surface area of the can as a function of the base radius. **(b)** What is the domain of the function in part (a)? **(c)** On a graphics calculator, find accurate to two decimal places the base radius of the can if the least amount of tin is to be used in its manufacture.

Solution

h in.

FIGURE 5

(a) See Figure 5 showing the cylindrical can where r inches is the base radius and h inches is the height. The least amount of tin will be required when the total surface area is a minimum. The lateral surface area is $2\pi rh$ square inches, and the area of both the top and bottom is πr^2 square inches. If S square inches is the total surface area,

$$S = 2\pi rh + 2\pi r^2 \qquad (2)$$

Because $\pi r^2 h$ cubic inches is the volume of a right-circular cylinder and the volume of the can is to be 60 in.^{3}, we have

$$\pi r^2 h = 60$$

Solving this equation for h and substituting into (2), we obtain S as a function of r:

$$S(r) = 2\pi r\left(\frac{60}{\pi r^2}\right) + 2\pi r^2$$

$$S(r) = \frac{120}{r} + 2\pi r^2$$

(b) To obtain the domain of S, we observe from the equation defining $S(r)$ that r cannot be 0. Theoretically, however, r may be any positive number. Therefore, the domain of S is $(0, +\infty)$.

(c) Figure 6 shows the graph of function S plotted in the $[0, 10]$ by $[0, 200]$ window. The r coordinate of the lowest point on the graph gives the radius for the minimum total surface area. On our graphics calculator we determine that the lowest point is (2.12, 84.84).

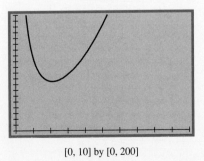

[0, 10] by [0, 200]

$$S(r) = \frac{120}{r} + 2\pi r^2$$

FIGURE 6

<u>Conclusion:</u>   The least amount of tin will be used in the manufacture of the can when the base radius is 2.12 in.   ◀

We will confirm analytically the answer in Example 5(c) as an application of calculus in Section 3.9.

▶ **EXAMPLE 6**   In a community of 8000 people, the rate at which a rumor spreads is jointly proportional to the number of people who have heard the rumor and the number of people who have not heard it. When 20 people have heard the rumor, it is being spread at the rate of 200 people per hour. **(a)** Find a mathematical model expressing the rate at which the rumor is spreading as a function of the number of people who have heard it. **(b)** How fast is the rumor spreading when 500 people have heard it? **(c)** On a graphics calculator, estimate how many people have heard the rumor when the rumor is being spread at the greatest rate.

Solution

(a) Let $f(x)$ people per hour be the rate at which the rumor is spreading when x people have heard it. Then by the definition of directly proportional

$$f(x) = kx(8000 - x) \tag{3}$$

where k is a constant. Because the rumor is being spread at the rate of 200 people per hour when 20 people have heard it, we replace x by 20 and $f(x)$ by 200 in (3) and we have

$$200 = k(20)(8000 - 20)$$

$$k = \frac{1}{798}$$

Replacing k in (3) by this value, we obtain

$$f(x) = \frac{x(8000 - x)}{798}$$

(b) From the preceding expression for $f(x)$, we have

$$f(500) = \frac{500(8000 - 500)}{798}$$

$$= 4699.25$$

<u>Conclusion:</u>   The rumor is being spread at the rate of 4699 people per hour when 500 people have heard it.

(c) Figure 7 shows the graph of f plotted in the [0, 8000] by [0, 25,000] window. We determine that the highest point on the graph occurs when $x = 4000$.

<u>Conclusion:</u>   The rumor is being spread at the greatest rate when 4000 people, half of the population, have heard the rumor.   ◀

We will return to the situation in Example 6 in Sections 3.2 and 7.4 to illustrate two different applications of calculus. In Section 3.2, we will confirm analytically the answer in part (c). Then in Section 7.4, we will obtain a model expressing the number of people who have heard the rumor as a function of the length of time the rumor has been spreading, so that we can determine how many people have heard the rumor at any particular time. You will learn that the graph of this model is called a curve of *logistic growth*. We will also prove in Section 7.4 that the entire population will eventually hear the rumor.

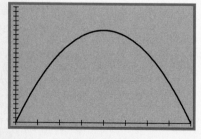

[0, 8000] by [0, 25,000]

$$f(x) = \frac{x(8000 - x)}{798}$$

FIGURE 7

EXERCISES 1.3

In each exercise, you are to obtain a function as a mathematical model of a particular situation. Many of these models will appear again later in the text when we apply calculus to the situation. Define the independent variable and the function value as numbers and indicate the units of measurement. In some of the exercises, the independent variable, by definition, may represent a nonnegative integer. For instance, in Exercise 1 if x represents the number of workers, then x must be a nonnegative integer. In such exercises, to have the continuity requirements (no break in the graph) necessary to apply calculus later, allow the independent variable to represent a nonnegative real number. Be sure you complete the exercise by writing a conclusion.

1. The daily payroll for a work crew is directly proportional to the number of workers, and a crew of 12 workers earns a payroll of $810. **(a)** Find a mathematical model expressing the daily payroll as a function of the number of workers. **(b)** What is the daily payroll for a crew of 15 workers?

2. A person's approximate brain weight is directly proportional to his or her body weight, and a person weighing 150 1b has an approximate brain weight of 4 1b. **(a)** Find a mathematical model expressing the approximate brain weight of a person as a function of the person's body weight. **(b)** Find the approximate brain weight of a person whose body weight is 176 lb.

3. The period (the time for one complete oscillation) of a pendulum is directly proportional to the square root of the length of the pendulum, and a pendulum of length 8 ft has a period of 2 sec. **(a)** Find a mathematical model expressing the period of a pendulum as a function of its length. **(b)** Find the period of a pendulum of length 2 ft.

4. For a vibrating string, the rate of vibrations is directly proportional to the square root of the tension on the string, and a particular string vibrates 864 times per second under a tension of 24 kg. **(a)** Find a mathematical model expressing the number of vibrations as a function of the tension. **(b)** Find the number of vibrations per second under a tension of 6 kg.

5. Shipping charges are often based on a formula that offers a lower charge per pound as the size of the shipment is increased. Suppose shipping charges are as follows: $2.20 per pound if the weight does not exceed 50 1b; $2.10 per pound if the weight is more than 50 1b but does not exceed 200 1b; $2.05 per pound if the weight is more than 200 1b. **(a)** Find a mathematical model expressing the total cost of a shipment as a function of its weight. **(b)** Sketch the graph of your function in part (a). **(c)** Determine the total cost of a shipment of 50 1b, 51 1b, 52 1b, 53 1b, 200 1b, 202 1b, 204 lb, and 206 1b.

6. In 1995, the postage of a domestic first-class letter was computed as follows: 32 cents for the first ounce or less, then 23 cents for each ounce (or fractional part of an ounce) for the next 10 oz. **(a)** Find a mathematical model expressing the postage of a first-class letter, weighing not more than 11 oz, as a function of its weight. **(b)** Sketch the graph of your function in part (a). **(c)** Determine the postage of a first-class letter weighing 1.6 oz, 2 oz, 2.1 oz, 8.4 oz, and 11 oz.

7. The cost of a telephone call from Mendocino to San Francisco during business hours is 40 cents for the first minute and 30 cents for each additional minute or fractional part thereof. **(a)** Find a mathematical model expressing the cost of a telephone call, lasting not more than 5 min, as a function of the duration of the call. **(b)** Sketch the graph of your function in part (a). **(c)** Determine the cost of a conversation lasting 0.5 min, 2 min, 2.5 min, 3 min, 3.5 min, and 5 min.

8. The regular adult admission price to an evening performance at the Coast Cinema is $7, while the price for children under 12 years of age is $4 and the price for seniors at least 60 years of age is $5. **(a)** Find a mathematical model expressing the admission price as a function of the person's age. **(b)** Sketch the graph of your function in part (a).

9. The consumer demand for a particular toy in a certain marketplace is a function f of p, the number of dollars in its price, which in turn is a function g of t. the number of months since the toy reached the marketplace. If

$$f(p) = \frac{5000}{p^2} \quad \text{and} \quad g(t) = \frac{1}{20}t^2 + \frac{7}{20}t + 5$$

do the following: **(a)** Find a mathematical model expressing the consumer demand as a function of the number of months since the toy reached the marketplace. **(b)** Find the consumer demand 5 months after the toy reached the marketplace.

10. In a lake a large fish feeds on a medium-size fish, and the population of the large fish is a function f of x, the number of medium-size fish in the lake. In turn the medium-size fish feed on small fish, and the population of the medium-size fish is a function of w, the number of small fish in the lake. If

$$f(x) = \sqrt{20x} + 150 \quad \text{and} \quad g(w) = \sqrt{w} + 5000$$

do the following: **(a)** Find a mathematical model expressing the population of the large fish as a function of the number of small fish in the lake. **(b)** Find the number of large fish when the lake contains 9 million small fish.

11. The surface area of a sphere is a function of its radius. If r centimeters is the radius of a sphere and $A(r)$ square centimeters is the surface area, then $A(r) = 4\pi r^2$. Suppose a balloon maintains the shape of a sphere as it is being inflated so that the radius is changing at a constant rate of 3 centimeters per second. If $f(t)$ centimeters is the radius of the balloon after t seconds, do the following: **(a)** Compute $(A \circ f)(t)$ and interpret your result. **(b)** Find the surface area of the balloon after 4 seconds.

12. The volume of a sphere is a function of its radius. If r feet is the radius of a sphere and $V(r)$ cubic feet is the volume, then $V(r) = \frac{4}{3}\pi r^3$. Suppose a spherical snowball with a radius of 2 ft started to melt so that its radius is changing at a constant rate of 4.5 inches per minute. If $f(t)$ feet is the radius of the snowball after t minutes, do the following: **(a)** Compute $(V \circ f)(t)$ and interpret your result. **(b)** Find the volume of the snowball after 3 minutes.

13. A rectangular field is to be enclosed with 240 m of fence. **(a)** Find a mathematical model expressing the area of the field as a function of its length. **(b)** What is the domain of your function in part (a)? **(c)** By plotting on your graphics calculator the graph of your function in part (a), estimate to the nearest meter the dimensions of the largest rectangular field that can be enclosed with the 240 m of fence.

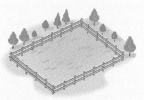

14. A rectangular garden is to be fenced off with 100 ft of fencing material. **(a)** Find a mathematical model expressing the area of the garden as a function of its length. **(b)** What is the domain of your function in part (a)? **(c)** By plotting on your graphics calculator the graph of your function in part (a), estimate to the nearest foot the dimensions of the largest rectangular garden that can be fenced off with the 100 ft of material.

15. Do Exercise 13 if one side of the field is to have a river as a natural boundary and the fencing material is to be used for the other three sides.

16. Do Exercise 14 if the garden is to be placed so that a side of a house serves as a boundary and the fencing material is to be used for the other three sides.

17. A manufacturer of open tin boxes wishes to use pieces of tin with dimensions 8 in. by 15 in. by cutting equal squares from the four corners and turning up the sides. **(a)** Find a mathematical model expressing the volume of the box as a function of the length of the side of the square cut out. **(b)** What is the domain of your function in part (a)? **(c)** On your graphics calculator, find accurate to the nearest tenth of an inch the length of the side of the square to be cut out so that the box has the largest possible volume. What is the maximum volume to the nearest cubic inch?

18. A carboard box manufacturer makes open boxes from square pieces of cardboard of side 12 cm by cutting equal squares from the four corners and turning up the sides. **(a)** Find a mathematical model expressing the volume of the box as a function of the length of the side of the square cut out. **(b)** What is the domain of your function in part (a)? **(c)** On your graphics calculator, find accurate to the nearest centimeter the length of the side of the square to be cut out so that the volume of the box is a maximum. What is the maximum volume to the nearest cubic centimeter?

19. Do Exercise 17 if the manufacturer makes the open boxes from rectangular pieces of tin with dimensions 12 in. by 15 in. In part (c) find the length of the side of the square to be cut out and the volume accurate to two decimal places.

20. Do Exercise 18 if the manufacturer makes the open boxes from rectangular pieces of cardboard with dimensions 40 cm by 50 cm. In part (c) find the length of the side of the square to be cut and the volume accurate to two decimal places.

21. For the tin can of Example 5, suppose that the cost of material for the top and bottom is twice as much as it is for the sides. **(a)** Find a mathematical model expressing the total cost of material as a function of the base radius of the can. **(b)** What is the domain of your function in part (a)? **(c)** On your graphics calculator, find accurate to two decimal places the base radius for the total cost of material to be the least.

22. Do Example 5 if the tin can is open instead of closed.

23. A page of print is to contain 24 in.^{2} of printed region, a margin of 1.5 in. at the top and bottom, and a margin of 1 in. at the sides. **(a)** Find a mathematical model expressing the total area of the page as a function of the width of the printed portion. **(b)** What is the domain of your function in part (a)? **(c)** On your graphics calculator, determine accurate to the nearest one-hundredth of an inch the dimensions of the smallest page that satisfies these requirements.

1.5 in.

1 in.

24. A one-story building having a rectangular floor space of 13,200 ft^2 is to be constructed where a walkway 22 ft wide is required in the front and back and a walkway 15 ft wide is required on each side. **(a)** Find a mathematical model expressing the total area of the lot on which the building and walkways will be located as a function of the length of the front and back of the building. **(b)** What is the domain of your function in part (a)? **(c)** On your graphics calculator, determine accurate to the nearest one-hundredth of a foot the dimensions of the lot having the least area on which this building can be located.

22 ft   15 ft

25. You wish to use a particular mailing service to ship a package in the shape of a rectangular box with a square cross section such that the sum of its length and girth (the perimeter of a cross section) is 100 in., the maximum allowable by the service. **(a)** Find a mathematical model expressing the volume of the box as a function of its length. **(b)** What is the domain of your function in part (a)? **(c)** On your graphics calculator, find accurate to the nearest inch the dimensions of the package having the greatest possible volume that can be mailed by this service.

x in.

26. In a limited environment where A is the optimum number of bacteria supportable by the environment, the rate of bacterial growth is jointly proportional to the number present and the difference between A and the number present. Suppose 1 million bacteria is the optimum number supportable by a particular environment, and the rate of growth is 60 bacteria per minute when 1000 bacteria are present. **(a)** Find a mathematical model expressing the rate of bacterial growth as a function of the number of bacteria present. **(b)** What is the rate of growth when 100,000 bacteria are present? **(c)** On your graphics calculator, determine to the nearest one thousand how many bacteria are present when the rate of growth is a maximum.

27. Fort Bragg in northern California is a small town of population 5000. Suppose the rate of growth of an epidemic (the rate of change of the number of infected persons) in Fort Bragg is jointly proportional to the number of people infected and the number of people not infected. When 100 people are infected, the epidemic is growing at the rate of 9 people per day. **(a)** Find a mathematical model expressing the rate of growth of the epidemic as a function of the number of people infected. **(b)** How fast is the epidemic growing when 200 people are infected? **(c)** On your graphics calculator, determine how many people are infected when the rate of growth of the epidemic is a maximum.

28. A tent in the shape of a pyramid with a square base is to be constructed from a square piece of material of side 5 m. In the base of the pyramid, let x meters be the distance from the center to a side. See the figure. **(a)** Find a mathematical model expressing the volume of the tent as a function of x. *Hint:* The formula for the volume of a pyramid is $V = \frac{1}{3}Bh$, where V, B, and h are, respectively, the measures of the volume, area of the base, and altitude. **(b)** Find the volume of the pyramid when $x = 0.8$. **(c)** On your graphics calculator, find accurate to the nearest one-hundredth of a meter the value of x for which the volume of the pyramid is a maximum.

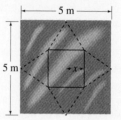

1.4 GRAPHICAL INTRODUCTION TO LIMITS OF FUNCTIONS

Our first encounter with limits pertains to *limits of functions.* To give you an intuitive feeling of the limit of a function we concentrate in this section on a graphical interpretation, the results of which we confirm analytically using inequalities. Our discussion here paves the way for the formal definition stated in Section 1.5.

We begin with a particular function:

$$f(x) = \frac{2x^2 + x - 3}{x - 1} \tag{1}$$

Observe that when $x = 1$, this function is not defined; that is, $f(1)$ does not exist. The function is defined, however, when x is any other real number. We shall investigate the function values when x is close to 1 but not equal to 1. You may ask why we would wish to consider such function values. The following illustration addresses that question.

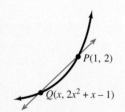

FIGURE 1

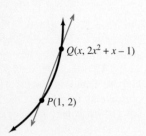

FIGURE 2

▷ **ILLUSTRATION 1**   The point $P(1, 2)$ is on the curve having the equation

$$y = 2x^2 + x - 1$$

Let $Q(x, 2x^2 + x - 1)$ be another point on this curve, distinct from P. Figures 1 and 2 each show a portion of the graph of the equation and the secant line through Q and P where Q is near P. In Figure 1 the x coordinate of Q is less than 1, and in Figure 2 it is greater than 1. Suppose $f(x)$ is the slope of the line PQ. Then

$$f(x) = \frac{(2x^2 + x - 1) - 2}{x - 1}$$

$$f(x) = \frac{2x^2 + x - 3}{x - 1}$$

which is Equation (1). Furthermore, $x \neq 1$ because P and Q are distinct points. As x gets closer and closer to 1, the values of $f(x)$ get closer and closer to the number that we shall define in Section 2.1 as the slope of the tangent line to the curve at the point P. ◄

Returning now to function f defined by Equation (1), let us compute function values $f(x)$ when x takes on the numbers 0, 0.25, 0.50, 0.75, 0.9, 0.99, 0.999, 0.9999, 0.99999, and so on. We are taking x closer and closer to 1 but less than 1; in other words, the variable x is approaching 1 through numbers that are less than 1. Table 1 gives the function values of these numbers.

Now let the variable x approach 1 through numbers that are greater than 1; that is, let x take on the numbers 2, 1.75, 1.5, 1.25, 1.1, 1.01, 1.001, 1.0001, 1.00001, and so on. The function values of these numbers appear in Table 2.

Observe from both tables that as x gets closer and closer to 1, $f(x)$ gets closer and closer to 5; and the closer x is to 1, the closer $f(x)$ is to 5. For instance, from Table 1, when $x = 0.9, f(x) = 4.8$; that is, when x is 0.1 less than 1, $f(x)$ is 0.2 less than 5. When $x = 0.999, f(x) = 4.998$; that is, when x is 0.001 less than 1, $f(x)$ is 0.002 less than 5. Furthermore, when $x = 0.9999, f(x) = 0.49998$; that is, when x is 0.0001 less than 1, $f(x)$ is 0.0002 less than 5.

Table 2 shows that when $x = 1.1, f(x) = 5.2$; that is, when x is 0.1 greater than 1, $f(x)$ is 0.2 greater than 5. When $x = 1.001, f(x) = 5.002$; that is, when x is 0.001 greater than 1, $f(x)$ is 0.002 greater than 5. When $x = 1.0001, f(x) = 5.0002$; that is, when x is 0.0001 greater than 1, $f(x)$ is 0.0002 greater than 5.

Therefore, from the two tables we see that when x differs from 1 by ± 0.001, (i.e, $x = 0.999$ or $x = 1.001$), $f(x)$ differs from 5 by ± 0.002 (i.e., $f(x) = 4.998$ or $f(x) = 5.002$). And when x differs from 1 by ± 0.0001, $f(x)$ differs from 5 by ± 0.0002.

Now, looking at the situation another way, we consider the values of $f(x)$ first. We see that we can make the value of $f(x)$ as close to 5 as we please by taking x close enough to 1; that is, $|f(x) - 5|$ can be made as small as we please by making $|x - 1|$ small enough. But bear in mind that x never takes on the value 1.

This condition can be denoted more precisely by using two symbols for the small differences. The symbols usually used are the Greek letters ϵ (epsilon) and δ (delta). So we state that for any given positive number ϵ there is an appropriately chosen positive number δ such that, if $|x - 1|$ is less than δ and $|x - 1| \neq 0$ (i.e., $x \neq 1$), then $|f(x) - 5|$ will be less than ϵ. It is important to realize that ϵ is chosen first and that the size of δ depends

Table 1

x	$f(x) = \dfrac{2x^2 + x - 3}{x - 1}$
0	3
0.25	3.5
0.5	4
0.75	4.5
0.9	4.8
0.99	4.98
0.999	4.998
0.9999	4.9998
0.99999	4.99998

Table 2

x	$f(x) = \dfrac{2x^2 + x - 3}{x - 1}$
2	7
1.75	6.5
1.5	6.0
1.25	5.5
1.1	5.2
1.01	5.02
1.001	5.002
1.0001	5.0002
1.00001	5.00002

on the size of ϵ. Still another way of phrasing this is: Given any positive number ϵ, we can make $|f(x) - 5| < \epsilon$ by taking $|x - 1|$ small enough; that is, there is some sufficiently small positive number δ such that

$$\text{if} \quad 0 < |x - 1| < \delta \quad \text{then} \quad |f(x) - 5| < \epsilon \tag{2}$$

Observe that the numerator of the fraction in (1) can be factored so that

$$f(x) = \frac{(2x + 3)(x - 1)}{x - 1}$$

If $x \neq 1$, the numerator and denominator can be divided by $x - 1$ to obtain

$$f(x) = 2x + 3 \qquad x \neq 1 \tag{3}$$

Equation (3) with the stipulation that $x \neq 1$ is just as suitable as (1) for a definition of $f(x)$.

Let us see what all this means graphically for this particular function defined by either (1) or (3). Figure 3 illustrates the geometric significance of ϵ and δ. Observe that if x on the horizontal axis lies between $1 - \delta$ and $1 + \delta$, then $f(x)$ on the vertical axis will lie between $5 - \epsilon$ and $5 + \epsilon$; or, equivalently,

$$\text{if} \quad 0 < |x - 1| < \delta \quad \text{then} \quad |f(x) - 5| < \epsilon$$

Another way of stating this is as follows: $f(x)$ on the vertical axis can be restricted to lie between $5 - \epsilon$ and $5 + \epsilon$ by restricting x on the horizontal axis to lie between $1 - \delta$ and $1 + \delta$.

We shall now demonstrate graphically how to choose a suitable δ for a given ϵ. Figure 4 shows the graph of our function f plotted in the $[0, 4.7]$ by $[4, 6]$ window. The graph has a "hole" at the point $(1, 5)$, which may or may not show up on your calculator, dependent on the model and window.

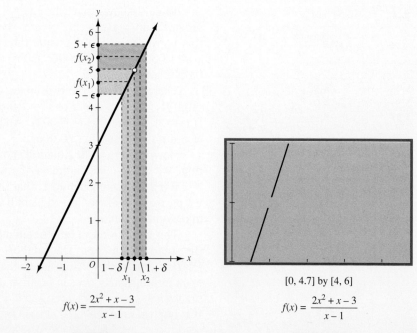

$$f(x) = \frac{2x^2 + x - 3}{x - 1}$$

$$[0, 4.7] \text{ by } [4, 6]$$

$$f(x) = \frac{2x^2 + x - 3}{x - 1}$$

FIGURE 3   **FIGURE 4**

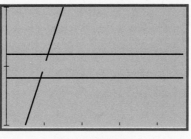

[0, 4.7] by [4, 6]

$$f(x) = \frac{2x^2 + x - 3}{x - 1}$$

$y = 4.8$ and $y = 5.2$

FIGURE 5

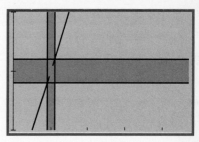

[0, 4.7] by [4, 6]

$$f(x) = \frac{2x^2 + x - 3}{x - 1}$$

$y = 4.8$ and $y = 5.2$

$x = 0.9$ and $x = 1.1$

FIGURE 6

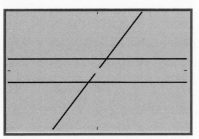

[0.9, 1.1] by [4.9, 5.1]

$$f(x) = \frac{2x^2 + x - 3}{x - 1}$$

$y = 4.98$ and $y = 5.02$

FIGURE 7

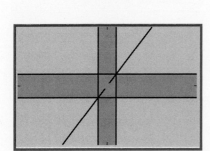

[0.9, 1.1] by [4.9, 5.1]

$$f(x) = \frac{2x^2 + x - 3}{x - 1}$$

$y = 4.98$ and $y = 5.02$

$x = 0.99$ and $x = 1.01$

FIGURE 8

Suppose $\epsilon = 0.2$; that is, we wish to restrict $f(x)$ on the vertical axis to be between $5 - 0.2$ and $5 + 0.2$ or, equivalently, between 4.8 and 5.2. We plot the lines $y = 4.8$ and $y = 5.2$ in the same window as the graph of f as shown in Figure 5, and we observe that the lines intersect the graph of f at the points where $x = 0.9$ and $x = 1.1$, respectively. Thus for $\epsilon = 0.2$, we take $\delta = 0.1$ and state that

$$\text{if} \quad 0 < |x - 1| < 0.1 \quad \text{then} \quad |f(x) - 5| < 0.2$$

This is statement (2) with $\epsilon = 0.2$ and $\delta = 0.1$, which agrees with what we find in Tables 1 and 2. If your calculator has the *shade* feature, you can get further graphical support by plotting the graph of f, the shaded horizontal rectangle between the lines $y = 4.8$ and $y = 5.2$, and the shaded vertical rectangle between the lines $x = 0.9$ and $x = 1.1$ in the [0, 4.7] by [4, 6] window as shown in Figure 6.

Suppose we now let $\epsilon = 0.02$ and plot the graph of f and the lines $y = 4.98$ and $y = 5.02$ in the [0.9, 1.1] by [4.9, 5.1] window as shown in Figure 7. We observe that the lines intersect the graph of f at the points where $x = 0.99$ and $x = 1.01$, respectively. For $\epsilon = 0.02$ we, therefore, take $\delta = 0.01$ and state that

$$\text{if} \quad 0 < |x - 1| < 0.01 \quad \text{then} \quad |f(x) - 5| < 0.02$$

This is statement (2) with $\epsilon = 0.02$ and $\delta = 0.01$, which also agrees with the information in Tables 1 and 2. Again we obtain additional graphic support from Figure 8 showing the shaded horizontal rectangle between the lines $y = 4.98$ and $y = 5.02$, the shaded vertical rectangle between the lines $x = 0.99$ and $x = 1.01$, and the graph of f in the [0.9, 1.1] by [4.9, 5.1] window.

We could give ϵ any small positive value and find a suitable value for δ such that if $|x - 1| < \delta$ and $x \neq 1$ (that is, $0 < |x - 1| < \delta$), then $|f(x) - 5|$ will be less than ϵ. Note that the values of ϵ are chosen arbitrarily and can be as small as desired, and that the value of δ is dependent on the ϵ chosen. We should also point out that the smaller the value of ϵ, the smaller will be the corresponding value of δ. Because for any $\epsilon > 0$ we can find a $\delta > 0$ such that statement (2) holds, we state that the limit of $f(x)$ as x approaches 1 is equal to 5, or, expressed with symbols,

$$\lim_{x \to 1} f(x) = 5$$

Observe that in this equation we have a new use of the "equals" symbol. Here for no value of x does $f(x)$ have the value 5. The "equals" symbol is appropriate because the left side is written as $\lim_{x \to 1} f(x)$.

From (3) it is apparent that $f(x)$ can be made as close to 5 as we please by taking x sufficiently close to 1, and this property of the function f does not depend on f being defined when $x = 1$. This fact gives the distinction between $\lim_{x \to 1} f(x)$ and the function value at 1; that is, $\lim_{x \to 1} f(x) = 5$, *but $f(1)$ does not exist.* Consequently, in statement (2), we write $0 < |x - 1|$ because we are concerned only with values of $f(x)$ for x close to 1, but not for $x = 1$.

▷   **ILLUSTRATION 2**   Let g be the function defined by

$$g(x) = \begin{cases} 2x + 3 & \text{if } x \neq 1 \\ 7 & \text{if } x = 1 \end{cases}$$

The graph of g is sketched in Figure 9. Except at $x = 1$, this function g has the same values as our function f defined by Equation (1). Consequently, because the fact that $\lim_{x \to 1} f(x) = 5$ has nothing whatsoever to do with what happens at $x = 1$, we can apply the above argument to function g and conclude that for any $\epsilon > 0$ there exists a $\delta > 0$ such that

$$\text{if} \quad 0 < |x - 1| < \delta \quad \text{then} \quad |g(x) - 5| < \epsilon$$

so that $\lim_{x \to 1} g(x) = 5$. Note that $g(1) = 7$; thus for this function both the limit of the function and the function values exist for $x = 1$ but they are not equal.   ◀

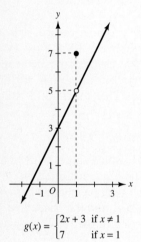

$$g(x) = \begin{cases} 2x + 3 & \text{if } x \neq 1 \\ 7 & \text{if } x = 1 \end{cases}$$

FIGURE 9

▷   **ILLUSTRATION 3**   Let h be the function defined by

$$h(x) = 2x + 3$$

The graph of h consists of all points on the line $y = 2x + 3$, shown in Figure 10. Again, except at $x = 1$, we have a function with the same values as our function f of Equation (1) as well as our function g of Illustration 2. So once more we can apply the same argument and conclude that for any $\epsilon > 0$ there exists a $\delta > 0$ such that

$$\text{if} \quad 0 < |x - 1| < \delta \quad \text{then} \quad |h(x) - 5| < \epsilon$$

so that $\lim_{x \to 1} h(x) = 5$. This time, however, the function value and the limit both exist and are equal for $x = 1$. A consequence of this fact, as you will learn in Section 1.8, is that function h is *continuous* at $x = 1$. Observe that the graph of h in Figure 10 does not have a hole at $x = 1$ whereas the graphs of f and g in Figures 3 and 9, respectively, do have a hole there. You will learn in Section 1.8 that functions f and g are *discontinuous* at $x = 1$.   ◀

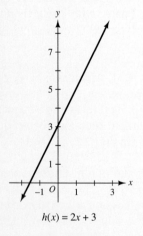

$h(x) = 2x + 3$

FIGURE 10

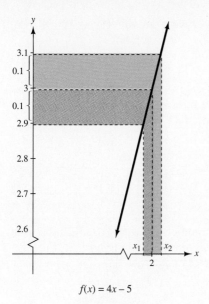

$f(x) = 4x - 5$

FIGURE 11

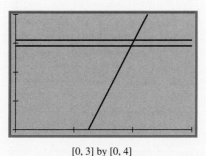

[0, 3] by [0, 4]

$f(x) = 4x - 5$

$y = 2.9$ and $y = 3.1$

FIGURE 12

▶ **EXAMPLE 1**   Let function f be defined by

$$f(x) = 4x - 5$$

(a) Use a figure similar to Figure 3 for $\epsilon = 0.1$ to determine a $\delta > 0$ such that

$$\text{if}\quad 0 < |x - 2| < \delta \quad \text{then}\quad |f(x) - 3| < 0.1$$

(b) Support the choice of δ in part (a) on a graphics calculator.

Solution

(a) Refer to Figure 11 and observe that the function values increase as x increases. Thus the figure indicates that we need a value of x_1 such that $f(x_1) = 2.9$ and a value of x_2 such that $f(x_2) = 3.1$; that is, we need an x_1 and an x_2 such that

$$4x_1 - 5 = 2.9 \qquad\qquad 4x_2 - 5 = 3.1$$
$$x_1 = \frac{7.9}{4} \qquad\qquad x_2 = \frac{8.1}{4}$$
$$x_1 = 1.975 \qquad\qquad x_2 = 2.025$$

Because $2 - 1.975 = 0.025$ and $2.025 - 2 = 0.025$, we choose $\delta = 0.025$ so that we have the statement

$$\text{if}\quad 0 < |x - 2| < 0.025 \quad \text{then}\quad |f(x) - 3| < 0.1$$

(b) On our graphics calculator we plot the graph of f and the lines $y = 2.9$ and $y = 3.1$ in the $[0, 3]$ by $[0, 4]$ window as shown in Figure 12. With the *intersection* (or *trace* and *zoom*) capability of our calculator, we determine that the line $y = 2.9$ intersects the graph of f at $x = 1.975$ and the line $y = 3.1$ intersects the graph of f at $x = 2.025$, which supports our choice of δ in part (a).   ◀

In the next example we use the symbol $\Rightarrow$ for the first time. The arrow $\Rightarrow$ means *implies*. We also use the double arrow $\Leftrightarrow$, which means the statement preceding it and the statement following it are *equivalent*.

▶ **EXAMPLE 2**   Confirm analytically the choice of δ in Example 1 by using properties of inequalities.

Solution   We wish to determine a $\delta > 0$ such that

$$\text{if}\quad 0 < |x - 2| < \delta \quad \text{then}\quad |f(x) - 3| < 0.1$$
$$\Leftrightarrow\quad \text{if}\quad 0 < |x - 2| < \delta \quad \text{then}\quad |(4x - 5) - 3| < 0.1$$
$$\Leftrightarrow\quad \text{if}\quad 0 < |x - 2| < \delta \quad \text{then}\quad 4|x - 2| < 0.1$$
$$\Leftrightarrow\quad \text{if}\quad 0 < |x - 2| < \delta \quad \text{then}\quad |x - 2| < 0.025$$

This statement indicates that a suitable choice for δ is 0.025. Then we have the following argument:

$$0 < |x - 2| < 0.025$$
$$\Rightarrow \quad 4|x - 2| < 4(0.025)$$
$$\Rightarrow \quad |4x - 8| < 0.1$$
$$\Rightarrow \quad |(4x - 5) - 3| < 0.1$$
$$\Rightarrow \quad |f(x) - 3| < 0.1$$

We have confirmed analytically that

$$\text{if} \quad 0 < |x - 2| < 0.025 \quad \text{then} \quad |f(x) - 3| < 0.1 \qquad (4)$$

◀

In Examples 1 and 2 any positive number less than 0.025 can be used in place of 0.025 as the required δ. Observe this fact in Figure 11. Furthermore, if $0 < \gamma < 0.025$ and statement (4) holds, we have

$$\text{if} \quad 0 < |x - 2| < \gamma \quad \text{then} \quad |f(x) - 3| < 0.1$$

because every number x satisfying the inequality $0 < |x - 2| < \gamma$ also satisfies the inequality $0 < |x - 2| < 0.025$.

The solutions of Examples 1 and 2 consisted of finding a δ for a specific ε. You will learn in Section 1.5 that if for any ε > 0 we can find a δ > 0 such that

$$\text{if} \quad 0 < |x - 2| < \delta \quad \text{then} \quad |(4x - 5) - 3| < \epsilon$$

we shall have established that $\lim_{x \to 2} (4x - 5) = 3$. We do this in Example 1 of Section 1.5.

▶ **EXAMPLE 3**   Let function f be defined by

$$f(x) = x^2$$

(a) Use a figure with ε = 0.3 to determine a δ > 0 such that

$$\text{if} \quad 0 < |x - 2| < \delta \quad \text{then} \quad |f(x) - 4| < 0.3$$

(b) Support the choice of δ in part (a) on a graphics calculator.

Solution

(a) Figure 13 shows a piece of the graph of f in the neighborhood of the point (2, 4). If x > 0, the function values increase as the values of x increase. The figure, therefore, indicates that we need a positive value of x_1 such that $f(x_1) = 3.7$ and a positive value of x_2 such that $f(x_2) = 4.3$; that is, we need an $x_1 > 0$ and an $x_2 > 0$ such that

$$x_1^2 = 3.7 \qquad x_2^2 = 4.3$$
$$x_1 = \sqrt{3.7} \qquad x_2 = \sqrt{4.3}$$
$$x_1 \approx 1.92 \qquad x_2 \approx 2.07$$

Then $2 - 1.92 = 0.08$ and $2.07 - 2 = 0.07$. Because $0.07 < 0.08$, we choose δ = 0.07 so that we have the statement

$$\text{if} \quad 0 < |x - 2| < 0.07 \quad \text{then} \quad |f(x) - 4| < 0.3$$

Any positive number less than 0.07 can be selected as the required δ.

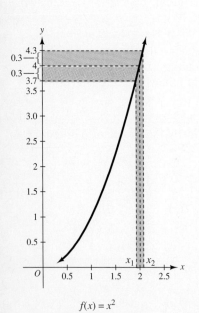

$f(x) = x^2$

FIGURE 13

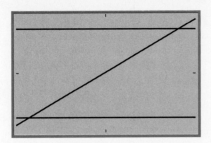

[1.91, 2.09] by [3.6, 4.4]

$f(x) = x^2$

$y = 3.7$ and $y = 4.3$

FIGURE 14

(b) Figure 14 shows the graph of f and the lines $y = 3.7$ and $y = 4.3$ plotted in the $[1.91, 2.09]$ by $[3.6, 4.4]$ window. On our calculator we determine that the line $y = 3.7$ intersects the graph of f at $x = 1.92$ and the line $y = 4.3$ intersects the graph of f at $x = 2.07$, which supports our choice of δ in part (a). ◀

▶ **EXAMPLE 4** Confirm analytically the choice of δ in Example 3 by using properties of inequalities.

Solution

(a) We wish to determine a $\delta > 0$ such that

$$\text{if} \quad 0 < |x - 2| < \delta \quad \text{then} \quad |f(x) - 4| < 0.3$$
$$\Leftrightarrow \quad \text{if} \quad 0 < |x - 2| < \delta \quad \text{then} \quad |x^2 - 4| < 0.3 \qquad \textbf{(5)}$$
$$\Leftrightarrow \quad \text{if} \quad 0 < |x - 2| < \delta \quad \text{then} \quad |x - 2||x + 2| < 0.3$$

Notice on the right-hand side of this statement that in addition to the factor $|x - 2|$, we have the factor $|x + 2|$. We need to obtain, therefore, an inequality involving $|x + 2|$. We do this by putting a restriction on the δ we are seeking. Let us restrict our δ to be less than or equal to 0.1, which seems reasonable. Then

$$0 < |x - 2| < \delta \quad \text{and} \quad \delta \le 0.1$$
$$\Rightarrow \quad 0 < |x - 2| < 0.1$$
$$\Rightarrow \quad -0.1 < x - 2 < 0.1$$
$$\Rightarrow \quad 3.9 < x + 2 < 4.1$$
$$\Rightarrow \quad |x + 2| < 4.1$$

Thus

$$0 < |x - 2| < \delta \quad \text{and} \quad \delta \le 0.1$$
$$\Rightarrow \quad 0 < |x - 2| < \delta \quad \text{and} \quad |x + 2| < 4.1$$
$$\Rightarrow \quad |x - 2||x + 2| < \delta(4.1)$$

Remember statement (5) is our goal. Thus we should require

$$\delta(4.1) \le 0.3 \quad \Leftrightarrow \quad \delta \le \tfrac{3}{41}$$

We have now put two restrictions on δ: $\delta \le 0.1$ and $\delta \le \tfrac{3}{41}$. So that both restrictions hold, we take $\delta = \tfrac{3}{41}$, the smaller of the two numbers. Using this δ, we have the following argument:

$$0 < |x - 2| < \tfrac{3}{41}$$
$$\Rightarrow \quad |x - 2| < \tfrac{3}{41} \quad \text{and} \quad |x + 2| < 4.1$$
$$\Rightarrow \quad |x - 2||x + 2| < \tfrac{3}{41}(4.1)$$
$$\Rightarrow \quad |x^2 - 4| < 0.3$$

We have, therefore, determined a δ so that statement (5) holds. Because $\tfrac{3}{41} \approx 0.07$ we have confirmed our choice of δ in Example 3. ◀

We now apply the above concepts to determine how accurately one quantity should be measured to insure a specific accuracy of the measurement of a second quantity dependent upon the first quantity.

▶ **EXAMPLE 5**   For the situation in Example 1 of Section 1.3, what should be the temperature of the gas if the gas is to occupy between 79.5 m³ and 80.5 m³?

Solution   In Example 1 of Section 1.3 we obtained the following mathematical model of the situation:

$$f(x) = \tfrac{4}{7}x$$

where $f(x)$ cubic meters is the volume of a gas whose temperature is x degrees. Because $f(140) = 80$, the gas occupies 80 m³ at a temperature of 140°. We wish to determine how close x must be to 140 in order for $f(x)$ to be within 0.5 of 80; that is, for $\epsilon = 0.5$, we wish to determine a $\delta > 0$ such that

$$\text{if }\quad 0 < |x - 140| < \delta \quad\text{then}\quad |f(x) - 80| < 0.5$$
$$\Leftrightarrow\quad \text{if }\quad 0 < |x - 140| < \delta \quad\text{then}\quad |\tfrac{4}{7}x - 80| < 0.5$$
$$\Leftrightarrow\quad \text{if }\quad 0 < |x - 140| < \delta \quad\text{then}\quad \tfrac{7}{4}|\tfrac{4}{7}x - 80| < \tfrac{7}{4}(0.5)$$
$$\Leftrightarrow\quad \text{if }\quad 0 < |x - 140| < \delta \quad\text{then}\quad |x - 140| < 0.875$$

Therefore, we take $\delta = 0.875$, and we have the following argument:

$$0 < |x - 140| < 0.875$$
$$\Rightarrow\qquad \tfrac{4}{7}|x - 140| < \tfrac{4}{7}(0.875)$$
$$\Rightarrow\qquad |\tfrac{4}{7}x - 80| < 0.5$$

Hence

$$\text{if }\quad 0 < |x - 140| < 0.875 \quad\text{then}\quad |f(x) - 80| < 0.5$$

<u>Conclusion:</u>   For the volume to occupy between 79.5 m³ and 80.5 m³ the temperature of the gas should be between 139.125° and 140.875°.   ◀

▶ **EXAMPLE 6**   The circular top of a coffee table is to have an area differing from 225π in.² by less than 4 in.² How accurately must the radius of the top be measured?

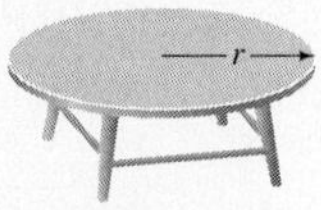

Solution   See Figure 15. If r inches is the radius of the circular top and $A(r)$ square inches is the area, then

$$A(r) = \pi r^2$$

$A(r) = \pi r^2$

FIGURE 15

The area is 225π in.² when the radius is 15 in. We wish to determine how close r must be to 15 in order for $A(r)$ to be within 4 of 225π. That is, if $\epsilon = 4$, we wish to find a $\delta > 0$ such that

$$\text{if }\quad 0 < |r - 15| < \delta \quad\text{then}\quad |A(r) - 225\pi| < 4$$
$$\Leftrightarrow\quad \text{if }\quad 0 < |r - 15| < \delta \quad\text{then}\quad |\pi r^2 - 225\pi| < 4$$
$$\Leftrightarrow\quad \text{if }\quad 0 < |r - 15| < \delta \quad\text{then}\quad |r - 15||r + 15| < \frac{4}{\pi} \qquad\textbf{(6)}$$

Because we have the factor $|r + 15|$ on the right-hand side of statement (6) we need an inequality involving this factor. To obtain such an inequality we restrict our δ so that $\delta \le 1$. Then

$$0 < |r - 15| < \delta \quad\text{and}\quad \delta \le 1 \ \Rightarrow\ 0 < |r - 15| < 1$$
$$\Rightarrow\qquad -1 < r - 15 < 1 \quad\Rightarrow\quad 14 < r < 16$$
$$\Rightarrow\qquad 29 < r + 15 < 31 \quad\Rightarrow\quad |r + 15| < 31$$

Therefore

if $0 < |r - 15| < \delta$ and $\delta \le 1$ then $|r - 15||r + 15| < \delta(31)$

Because we want statement (6) to hold, we will require that

$$\delta(31) \le \frac{4}{\pi} \quad \Leftrightarrow \quad \delta \le \frac{4}{31\pi}$$

We now have two restrictions on δ: $\delta \le 1$ and $\delta \le \frac{4}{31\pi}$. We choose δ as $\frac{4}{31\pi}$, the smaller of these two numbers. With this δ we have the following argument:

$$0 < |r - 15| < \frac{4}{31\pi}$$

$$\Rightarrow \quad |r - 15| < \frac{4}{31\pi} \text{ and } |r + 15| < 31$$

$$\Rightarrow \quad |r - 15||r + 15| < \frac{4}{31\pi}(31)$$

$$\Rightarrow \quad \pi|r^2 - 225| < 4$$

Therefore

$$\text{if} \quad 0 < |r - 15| < \frac{4}{31\pi} \quad \text{then} \quad |A(r) - 225\pi| < 4$$

Because $\frac{4}{31\pi} \approx 0.041$, we make the following conclusion.

<u>Conclusion:</u> The radius of the top should be between 14.959 in. and 15.041 in. in order for the circular top to have an area differing from 225π in.² by less than 4 in.² ◀

EXERCISES 1.4

In Exercises 1 and 2, you are given $f(x)$, a, L, ϵ, and a figure. From the figure determine a $\delta > 0$ such that

if $0 < |x - a| < \delta$ then $|f(x) - L| < \epsilon$

1. $f(x) = 2x - 5$; $a = 3$; $L = 1$; $\epsilon = 0.2$

2. $f(x) = 2 - 3x$; $a = -1$; $L = 5$; $\epsilon = 0.6$

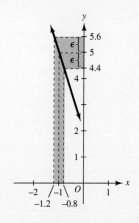

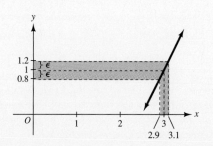

*In Exercises 3 through 14, you are given $f(x)$, a, L, and ϵ.
(a) Use a figure similar to those in Exercises 1 and 2 and in Example 1 and arguments similar to those in Example 1 to determine a $\delta > 0$ such that*

$$\text{if }\quad 0 < |x - a| < \delta \quad \text{ then }\quad |f(x) - L| < \epsilon$$

(b) Support your choice of δ in part (a) on your graphics calculator.

3. $f(x) = x - 1$; $a = 4$; $L = 3$; $\epsilon = 0.03$
4. $f(x) = x + 2$; $a = 3$; $L = 5$; $\epsilon = 0.02$
5. $f(x) = 2x + 4$; $a = 3$; $L = 10$; $\epsilon = 0.01$
6. $f(x) = 3x - 1$; $a = 2$; $L = 5$; $\epsilon = 0.1$
7. $f(x) = 5x - 3$; $a = 1$; $L = 2$; $\epsilon = 0.05$
8. $f(x) = 4x - 5$; $a = 2$; $L = 3$; $\epsilon = 0.001$
9. $f(x) = 3 - 4x$; $a = -1$; $L = 7$; $\epsilon = 0.02$
10. $f(x) = 2 + 5x$; $a = -2$; $L = -8$; $\epsilon = 0.002$
11. $f(x) = \dfrac{x^2 - 4}{x + 2}$; $a = -2$; $L = -4$; $\epsilon = 0.01$
12. $f(x) = \dfrac{9x^2 - 1}{3x - 1}$; $a = \dfrac{1}{3}$; $L = 2$; $\epsilon = 0.01$
13. $f(x) = \dfrac{4x^2 - 4x - 3}{2x + 1}$; $a = -\dfrac{1}{2}$; $L = -4$; $\epsilon = 0.03$
14. $f(x) = \dfrac{3x^2 - 8x - 3}{x - 3}$; $a = 3$; $L = 10$; $\epsilon = 0.05$

For Exercises 15 and 16, follow the same instructions as for Exercises 1 and 2.
15. $f(x) = x^2 + 1$; $a = -2$; $L = 5$; $\epsilon = 1$

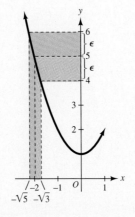

16. $f(x) = 8 - x^2$; $a = 2$; $L = 4$; $\epsilon = 0.5$

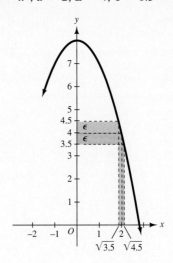

In Exercises 17 through 24, you are given $f(x)$, a, L, and ϵ. (a) Use a figure similar to those in Exercises 15 and 16 and in Example 3 and arguments similar to those in Example 3 to determine a $\delta > 0$ such that

$$\text{if }\quad 0 < |x - a| < \delta \quad \text{ then }\quad |f(x) - L| < \epsilon$$

17. $f(x) = x^2$; $a = 3$; $L = 9$; $\epsilon = 0.5$
18. $f(x) = x^2$; $a = 0.5$; $L = 0.25$; $\epsilon = 0.1$
19. $f(x) = x^2$; $a = -1$; $L = 1$; $\epsilon = 0.2$
20. $f(x) = x^2 - 5$; $a = 1$; $L = -4$; $\epsilon = 0.15$
21. $f(x) = x^2 - 2x + 1$; $a = 2$; $L = 1$; $\epsilon = 0.4$
22. $f(x) = x^2 + 4x + 4$; $a = -1$; $L = 1$; $\epsilon = 0.08$
23. $f(x) = 2x^2 + 5x + 3$; $a = -3$; $L = 6$; $\epsilon = 0.6$
24. $f(x) = 3x^2 - 7x + 2$; $a = 1$; $L = -2$; $\epsilon = 0.3$

In Exercises 25 through 36, confirm analytically (by using properties of inequalities) your choice of δ in the indicated exercise.

25. Exercise 3   **26.** Exercise 4
27. Exercise 7   **28.** Exercise 8
29. Exercise 13   **30.** Exercise 14
31. Exercise 17   **32.** Exercise 18
33. Exercise 21   **34.** Exercise 22
35. Exercise 23   **36.** Exercise 24

In Exercises 37 through 44, first obtain a function as a mathematical model of the situation. Define the independent variable and the function value as numbers and indicate the units of measurement. Be sure you complete the exercise by writing a conclusion.

37. A person earning \$15 per hour is paid only for the actual time on the job. How close to 8 hours must a person work in order to earn within 25 cents of \$120?

38. For the situation in Example 1 of Section 1.3 what should be the temperature of the gas if the gas is to occupy between 79.95 m³ and 80.05 m³?

39. A fence is to be built around a square flower garden. How close to 10 ft must the length of each side of the garden be in order for the total length of fencing material to be between 39.96 ft and 40.04 ft?

40. A circular sign is to be constructed so that its circumference is within 0.1 ft of 6π ft. How close to 3 ft must the radius of the sign be?

41. For the flower garden of Exercise 39, how close to 10 ft must each side of the garden be in order for the area of the garden to be within 0.5 ft² of 100 ft²?

42. For the sign of Exercise 40, how close to 3 ft must the radius of the sign be in order for the area of the sign to be within 0.2 ft² of 9π ft²?

43. The number of feet a body falls from rest in t seconds varies directly as the square of t, and a body falls from rest 64 ft in 2 sec. How close to 5 sec will it take a body to fall between 398 ft and 402 ft?

44. The number of pounds per square foot in the force of the wind on a plane surface when the wind's velocity is v miles per hour varies directly as the square of v. Suppose the force is 2 lb/ft² when the wind's velocity is 20 mi/hr. How close to 30 mi/hr will the wind's velocity be when the force of the wind on a plane surface is between 4.45 lb/ft² and 4.55 lb/ft²?

1.5 DEFINITION OF THE LIMIT OF A FUNCTION AND LIMIT THEOREMS

We are now ready to state the formal definition of the limit of a function. The definition contains the statement involving the inequalities with the ϵ and δ notation you encountered frequently in Section 1.4.

> ### 1.5.1 Definition of the Limit of a Function
>
> Let f be a function defined at every number in some open interval containing a, except possibly at the number a itself. The **limit of $f(x)$ as x approaches a is L,** written as
>
> $$\lim_{x \to a} f(x) = L$$
>
> if the following statement is true:
> Given any $\epsilon > 0$, however small, there exists a $\delta > 0$ such that
>
> $$\text{if} \quad 0 < |x - a| < \delta \quad \text{then} \quad |f(x) - L| < \epsilon \qquad \textbf{(1)}$$

In words, this definition states that the function values $f(x)$ approach a limit L as x approaches a number a if the absolute value of the difference between $f(x)$ and L can be made as small as we please by taking x sufficiently near a but not equal to a.

Note that in the definition nothing is mentioned about the function value when $x = a$. Remember, as we pointed out in Section 1.4, the function f need not be defined at a in order for $\lim_{x \to a} f(x)$ to exist. Moreover, even if f is defined at a, $\lim_{x \to a} f(x)$ may exist without having the same value as $f(a)$ as was the case for the function of Illustration 2 in Section 1.4.

A geometric interpretation of the definition of the limit of a function f appears in Figure 1 showing a portion of the graph of f near the point where $x = a$. Because f is not necessarily defined at a, there need be no point on

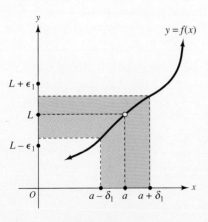

FIGURE 1

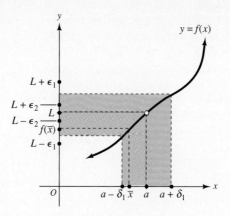

FIGURE 2

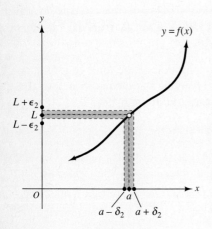

FIGURE 3

the graph with abscissa a. Observe that if x on the horizontal axis lies between $a - \delta_1$ and $a + \delta_1$, then $f(x)$ on the vertical axis will lie between $L - \epsilon_1$ and $L + \epsilon_1$. Stated another way, by restricting x on the horizontal axis to lie between $a - \delta_1$ and $a + \delta_1$, then $f(x)$ on the vertical axis can be restricted to lie between $L - \epsilon_1$ and $L + \epsilon_1$. Thus

$$\text{if} \quad 0 < |x - a| < \delta_1 \quad \text{then} \quad |f(x) - L| < \epsilon_1$$

Figure 2 shows how a smaller value of ϵ can require a different choice for δ. In the figure it is seen that for $\epsilon_2 < \epsilon_1$, the δ_1 value is too large; that is, there are values of x for which $0 < |x - a| < \delta_1$, but $|f(x) - L|$ is not less than ϵ_2. For instance, $0 < |\bar{x} - a| < \delta_1$ but $|f(\bar{x}) - L| > \epsilon_2$. So we must choose a smaller value δ_2 shown in Figure 3 such that

$$\text{if} \quad 0 < |x - a| < \delta_2 \quad \text{then} \quad |f(x) - L| < \epsilon_2$$

However, for any choice of $\epsilon > 0$, no matter how small, there exists a $\delta > 0$ such that statement (1) holds. Therefore $\lim\limits_{x \to a} f(x) = L$.

In our first example of this section, we return to the function of Examples 1 and 2 in Section 1.4.

▶ **EXAMPLE 1**   Use the definition of a limit to prove

$$\lim_{x \to 2} (4x - 5) = 3$$

Solution   The first requirement of Definition 1.5.1 is that $4x - 5$ be defined at every number in some open interval containing 2 except possibly at 2. Because $4x - 5$ is defined for all real numbers, any open interval containing 2 will satisfy this requirement. Now we must show that for any $\epsilon > 0$, there exists a $\delta > 0$ such that

$$\text{if} \quad 0 < |x - 2| < \delta \quad \text{then} \quad |(4x - 5) - 3| < \epsilon \tag{2}$$

$$\Leftrightarrow \quad \text{if} \quad 0 < |x - 2| < \delta \quad \text{then} \quad 4|x - 2| < \epsilon$$

$$\Leftrightarrow \quad \text{if} \quad 0 < |x - 2| < \delta \quad \text{then} \quad |x - 2| < \tfrac{1}{4}\epsilon$$

This statement indicates that $\frac{1}{4}\epsilon$ is a satisfactory δ. With this choice of δ we have the following argument:

$$0 < |x - 2| < \delta$$
$$\Rightarrow \qquad 4|x - 2| < 4\delta$$
$$\Rightarrow \qquad |4x - 8| < 4\delta$$
$$\Rightarrow \quad |(4x - 5) - 3| < 4\delta$$
$$\Rightarrow \quad |(4x - 5) - 3| < \epsilon \qquad (\text{because } \delta = \tfrac{1}{4}\epsilon)$$

We have, therefore, established that if $\delta = \frac{1}{4}\epsilon$, statement (2) holds. This proves that $\lim\limits_{x \to 2} (4x - 5) = 3$.

In particular, if $\epsilon = 0.1$, then we take $\delta = \frac{1}{4}(0.1)$, that is, $\delta = 0.025$. This value of δ corresponds to the one found in Examples 1 and 2 of Section 1.4.

Any positive number less than $\frac{1}{4}\epsilon$ can also be used as the required δ.
◄

In the supplement of this section, we give an example showing how to apply Definition 1.5.1 to prove that $\lim\limits_{x \to 2} x^2 = 4$.

To compute limits by methods easier than using the definition, we employ theorems whose proofs are based on the definition. These theorems, as well as others on limits of functions that appear in later sections of this chapter, are labeled *limit theorems*.

1.5.2 Limit Theorem 1   Limit of a Linear Function

If m and b are any constants,

$$\lim_{x \to a} (mx + b) = ma + b$$

Proof   From the definition of the limit of a function, we must show that for any $\epsilon > 0$ there exists a $\delta > 0$ such that

$$\text{if} \quad 0 < |x - a| < \delta \quad \text{then} \quad |(mx + b) - (ma + b)| < \epsilon \qquad \textbf{(3)}$$

Case 1: $m \neq 0$.

Because $|(mx + b) - (ma + b)| = |m| \cdot |x - a|$, we want to find a $\delta > 0$ for any $\epsilon > 0$ such that

$$\text{if} \quad 0 < |x - a| < \delta \quad \text{then} \quad |m| \cdot |x - a| < \epsilon$$

or, because $m \neq 0$,

$$\text{if} \quad 0 < |x - a| < \delta \quad \text{then} \quad |x - a| < \frac{\epsilon}{|m|}$$

This statement will hold if $\delta = \epsilon/|m|$; so we conclude that

$$\text{if } 0 < |x - a| < \delta \text{ and } \delta = \frac{\epsilon}{|m|} \text{ then } |(mx + b) - (ma + b)| < \epsilon$$

This proves the theorem for Case 1.

Case 2: $m = 0$

If $m = 0$, then $|(mx + b) - (ma + b)| = 0$ for all values of x. So take δ to be any positive number, and statement (3) holds. This proves the theorem for Case 2.
■

▷ **ILLUSTRATION 1**   From Limit Theorem 1,

$$\lim_{x \to 2} (3x + 5) = 3 \cdot 2 + 5$$
$$= 11$$ ◀

1.5.3 Limit Theorem 2   Limit of a Constant

If c is a constant, then for any number a

$$\lim_{x \to a} c = c$$

This theorem follows immediately from Limit Theorem 1 by taking $m = 0$ and $b = c$.

1.5.4 Limit Theorem 3   Limit of the Identity Function

$$\lim_{x \to a} x = a$$

This theorem also follows immediately from Limit Theorem 1 by taking $m = 1$ and $b = 0$.

▷ **ILLUSTRATION 2**   From Limit Theorem 2,

$$\lim_{x \to 5} 7 = 7$$

and from Limit Theorem 3,

$$\lim_{x \to -6} x = -6$$ ◀

1.5.5 Limit Theorem 4   Limit of the Sum and Difference of Two Functions

If $\lim_{x \to a} f(x) = L$ and $\lim_{x \to a} g(x) = M$, then

$$\lim_{x \to a} [f(x) \pm g(x)] = L \pm M$$

The proof of Limit Theorem 4 appears in the supplement of this section. In the statement of the theorem the fact that $\lim_{x \to a} f(x) = L$ and $\lim_{x \to a} = M$ indicates that these limits exist. In other words you can't simply say that the limit of the sum of two functions is the sum of their limits. You must add the qualification: *provided the limits exist.* See Exercise 44 in Exercises 1.6 and Exercise 50 in Exercises 1.7.

The next limit theorem is an extension of Limit Theorem 4 to any finite number of functions. You are asked to supply the proof by mathematical induction in Supplementary Exercise 10.

1.5.6 Limit Theorem 5   Limit of the Sum and Difference of n Functions

If $\lim_{x \to a} f_1(x) = L_1$, $\lim_{x \to a} f_2(x) = L_2$, . . . , and $\lim_{x \to a} f_n(x) = L_n$, then

$$\lim_{x \to a} [f_1(x) \pm f_2(x) \pm \ldots \pm f_n(x)] = L_1 \pm L_2 \pm \ldots \pm L_n$$

The limit of the product of two functions is given by the next limit theorem. Again notice that the theorem states that the limit of the product of two functions is the product of their limits if the limits exist. For the proof, refer to the supplement of this section.

1.5.7 Limit Theorem 6   Limit of the Product of Two Functions

If $\lim\limits_{x \to a} f(x) = L$ and $\lim\limits_{x \to a} g(x) = M$, then

$$\lim\limits_{x \to a} [f(x) \cdot g(x)] = L \cdot M$$

▷ **ILLUSTRATION 3**   From Limit Theorem 3, $\lim\limits_{x \to 4} x = 4$, and from Limit Theorem 1, $\lim\limits_{x \to 4} (2x + 1) = 9$. Thus from Limit Theorem 6

$$\begin{aligned} \lim\limits_{x \to 4} [x(2x + 1)] &= \lim\limits_{x \to 4} x \cdot \lim\limits_{x \to 4} (2x + 1) \\ &= 4 \cdot 9 \\ &= 36 \end{aligned}$$ ◀

Limit Theorem 6 also can be extended to any finite number of functions by applying mathematical induction, as you are asked to do in Supplementary Exercise 13.

1.5.8 Limit Theorem 7   Limit of the Product of n Functions

If $\lim\limits_{x \to a} f_1(x) = L_1$, $\lim\limits_{x \to a} f_2(x) = L_2, \ldots,$ and $\lim\limits_{x \to a} f_n(x) = L_n$, then

$$\lim\limits_{x \to a} [f_1(x) f_2(x) \ldots f_n(x)] = L_1 L_2 \ldots L_n$$

1.5.9 Limit Theorem 8   Limit of the nth Power of a Function

If $\lim\limits_{x \to a} f(x) = L$ and n is any positive integer, then

$$\lim\limits_{x \to a} [f(x)]^n = L^n$$

The proof follows immediately from Limit Theorem 7 by taking $f_1(x)$, $f_2(x), \ldots, f_n(x)$ all equal to $f(x)$ and $L_1, L_2, \ldots, L_n$ all equal to L.

▷ **ILLUSTRATION 4**   From Limit Theorem 1, $\lim\limits_{x \to -2} (5x + 7) = -3$. Therefore, from Limit Theorem 8

$$\begin{aligned} \lim\limits_{x \to -2} (5x + 7)^4 &= \left[\lim\limits_{x \to -2} (5x + 7) \right]^4 \\ &= (-3)^4 \\ &= 81 \end{aligned}$$ ◀

The next limit theorem, regarding the limit of the quotient of two functions, not only requires the existence of the limits of the two functions, but also requires that the limit of the function in the denominator is not zero.

1.5.10 Limit Theorem 9   Limit of the Quotient of Two Functions

If $\lim\limits_{x \to a} f(x) = L$ and $\lim\limits_{x \to a} g(x) = M$, then

$$\lim_{x \to a} \frac{f(x)}{g(x)} = \frac{L}{M} \qquad \text{if } M \neq 0$$

The proof of this theorem appears in Section 1.9.

▷ **ILLUSTRATION 5**   From Limit Theorem 3, $\lim\limits_{x \to 4} x = 4$, and from Limit Theorem 1, $\lim\limits_{x \to 4} (-7x + 1) = -27$. Therefore from Limit Theorem 9,

$$\lim_{x \to 4} \frac{x}{-7x + 1} = \frac{\lim\limits_{x \to 4} x}{\lim\limits_{x \to 4} (-7x + 1)}$$
$$= \frac{4}{-27}$$
$$= -\frac{4}{27}$$

◀

1.5.11 Limit Theorem 10   Limit of the nth Root of a Function

If n is a positive integer and $\lim\limits_{x \to a} f(x) = L$, then

$$\lim_{x \to a} \sqrt[n]{f(x)} = \sqrt[n]{L}$$

with the restriction that if n is even, $L > 0$

The proof of this theorem also appears in Section 1.9.

▷ **ILLUSTRATION 6**   From Illustration 5 and Limit Theorem 10,

$$\lim_{x \to 4} \sqrt[3]{\frac{x}{-7x + 1}} = \sqrt[3]{\lim_{x \to 4} \frac{x}{-7x + 1}}$$
$$= \sqrt[3]{-\frac{4}{27}}$$
$$= -\frac{\sqrt[3]{4}}{3}$$

◀

We now state two theorems, which are special cases of Limit Theorems 9 and 10, respectively. Each of these theorems is used in Section 1.9 for the proof of the corresponding limit theorem.

1.5.12 Theorem

If a is any real number except zero

$$\lim_{x \to a} \frac{1}{x} = \frac{1}{a}$$

1.5.13 Theorem

If $a > 0$ and n is a positive integer, or if $a \leq 0$ and n is an odd positive integer, then

$$\lim_{x \to a} \sqrt[n]{x} = \sqrt[n]{a}$$

The proofs of Theorems 1.5.12 and 1.5.13 are given in the supplement of this section.

In the following examples, we apply the above theorems to compute limits. To indicate the limit theorem being applied we write the abbreviation "L.T." followed by the theorem number; for instance, "L.T. 2" refers to Limit Theorem 2.

▶ **EXAMPLE 2**   Find $\lim_{x \to 3} (x^2 + 7x - 5)$ and, when appropriate, indicate the limit theorems being applied.

Solution

$$\begin{aligned}
\lim_{x \to 3} (x^2 + 7x - 5) &= \lim_{x \to 3} x^2 + \lim_{x \to 3} 7x - \lim_{x \to 3} 5 && \textbf{(L.T. 5)} \\
&= \lim_{x \to 3} x \cdot \lim_{x \to 3} x + \lim_{x \to 3} 7 \cdot \lim_{x \to 3} x - \lim_{x \to 3} 5 && \textbf{(L.T. 6)} \\
&= 3 \cdot 3 + 7 \cdot 3 - 5 && \textbf{(L.T. 3 and L.T. 2)} \\
&= 9 + 21 - 5 \\
&= 25 && ◀
\end{aligned}$$

You should realize that the limit in Example 2 was evaluated solely by direct application of limit theorems. Note that for function f in the example not only is $\lim_{x \to 3} f(x)$ equal to 25 but $f(3)$ also equals 25. But remember, $\lim_{x \to a} f(x)$ and $f(a)$ are not always equal.

▶ **EXAMPLE 3**   Find the following limit and, when appropriate, indicate the limit theorems being applied:

$$\lim_{x \to 2} \sqrt{\frac{x^3 + 2x + 3}{x^2 + 5}}$$

Solution

$$\lim_{x \to 2} \sqrt{\frac{x^3 + 2x + 3}{x^2 + 5}} = \sqrt{\lim_{x \to 2} \frac{x^3 + 2x + 3}{x^2 + 5}} \qquad \textbf{(L.T. 10)}$$

$$= \sqrt{\frac{\lim_{x \to 2}(x^3 + 2x + 3)}{\lim_{x \to 2}(x^2 + 5)}} \qquad \textbf{(L.T. 9)}$$

$$= \sqrt{\frac{\lim_{x \to 2} x^3 + \lim_{x \to 2} 2x + \lim_{x \to 2} 3}{\lim_{x \to 2} x^2 + \lim_{x \to 2} 5}} \qquad \textbf{(L.T. 5)}$$

$$= \sqrt{\frac{(\lim_{x \to 2} x)^3 + \lim_{x \to 2} 2 \cdot \lim_{x \to 2} x + \lim_{x \to 2} 3}{(\lim_{x \to 2} x)^2 + \lim_{x \to 2} 5}} \qquad \textbf{(L.T. 6} \\ \textbf{and L.T. 8)}$$

$$= \sqrt{\frac{2^3 + 2 \cdot 2 + 3}{2^2 + 5}} \qquad \textbf{(L.T. 3 and L.T. 2)}$$

$$= \sqrt{\frac{8 + 4 + 3}{9}}$$

$$= \frac{\sqrt{15}}{3} \qquad \blacktriangleleft$$

▶ **EXAMPLE 4** Given

$$f(x) = \frac{x^2 - 25}{x - 5}$$

(a) Use a calculator to tabulate values of $f(x)$ when x is 4, 4.5, 4.9, 4.99, 4.999 and when x is 6, 5.5, 5.1, 5.01, 5.001. What does $f(x)$ appear to be approaching as x approaches 5?

(b) Confirm your answer in part (a) analytically by computing $\lim_{x \to 5} f(x)$.

Solution

(a) Tables 1 and 2 give the values of $f(x)$ for the specified values of x. From the tables, $f(x)$ appears to be approaching 10 as x approaches 5.

(b) Here we have a situation different than in the preceding examples. Limit Theorem 9 cannot be applied to the quotient $\dfrac{x^2 - 25}{x - 5}$ because $\lim_{x \to 5}(x - 5) = 0$. However, factoring the numerator we obtain

$$\frac{x^2 - 25}{x - 5} = \frac{(x - 5)(x + 5)}{x - 5}$$

If $x \neq 5$, the numerator and denominator can be divided by $x - 5$ to obtain $x + 5$. Remember that when computing the limit of a function as x approaches 5, we are considering values of x close to 5 but not equal

Table 1

x	$f(x) = \dfrac{x^2 - 25}{x - 5}$
4	9
4.5	9.5
4.9	9.9
4.99	9.99
4.999	9.999

Table 2

x	$f(x) = \dfrac{x^2 - 25}{x - 5}$
6	11
5.5	10.5
5.1	10.1
5.01	10.01
5.001	10.001

to 5. Therefore, it is possible to divide the numerator and denominator by $x - 5$. The solution takes the following form:

$$\lim_{x \to 5} \frac{x^2 - 25}{x - 5} = \lim_{x \to 5} \frac{(x - 5)(x + 5)}{x - 5}$$

$$= \lim_{x \to 5} (x + 5)$$

$$= 10 \qquad\qquad \text{(L.T. 1)} \qquad \blacktriangleleft$$

▶ **EXAMPLE 5**   Given

$$g(x) = \frac{\sqrt{x} - 2}{x - 4}$$

(a) Use a calculator to tabulate to four decimal places values of $g(x)$ when x is 3, 3.5, 3.9, 3.99, 3.999 and when x is 5, 4.5, 4.1, 4.01, 4.001. What does $g(x)$ appear to be approaching as x approaches 4?
(b) Support the answer in part (a) by plotting the graph of g in a convenient window.
(c) Confirm the answer in part (a) analytically by computing $\lim_{x \to 4} g(x)$ and, when appropriate, indicate the limit theorems being applied.

Solution

(a) Tables 3 and 4 give the values of $g(x)$ for the specified values of x. From the tables, $g(x)$ appears to be approaching 0.2500 as x approaches 4.
(b) Figure 4 shows the graph of g plotted in the $[1, 5.7]$ by $[0, 1]$ window. The graph has a hole at the point $(4, 0.25)$. Using the trace capability of our calculator, we observe that $g(x)$ is approaching 0.25 as x approaches 4, which supports our answer in part (a).
(c) As in Example 4, Limit Theorem 9 cannot be applied to the quotient $\dfrac{\sqrt{x} - 2}{x - 4}$ because $\lim_{x \to 4} (x - 4) = 0$. To simplify the quotient we rationalize the numerator by multiplying the numerator and denominator by $\sqrt{x} + 2$.

$$\frac{\sqrt{x} - 2}{x - 4} = \frac{(\sqrt{x} - 2)(\sqrt{x} + 2)}{(x - 4)(\sqrt{x} + 2)}$$

$$= \frac{x - 4}{(x - 4)(\sqrt{x} + 2)}$$

Because we are evaluating the limit as x approaches 4, we are considering values of x close to 4 but not equal to 4. Hence we can divide the numerator and denominator by $x - 4$. Therefore

$$\frac{\sqrt{x} - 2}{x - 4} = \frac{1}{\sqrt{x} + 2} \qquad \text{if } x \neq 4$$

Table 3

x	$g(x) = \dfrac{\sqrt{x} - 2}{x - 4}$
3	0.2679
3.5	0.2583
3.9	0.2516
3.99	0.2502
3.999	0.2500

Table 4

x	$g(x) = \dfrac{\sqrt{x} - 2}{x - 4}$
5	0.2361
4.5	0.2426
4.1	0.2485
4.01	0.2498
4.001	0.2500

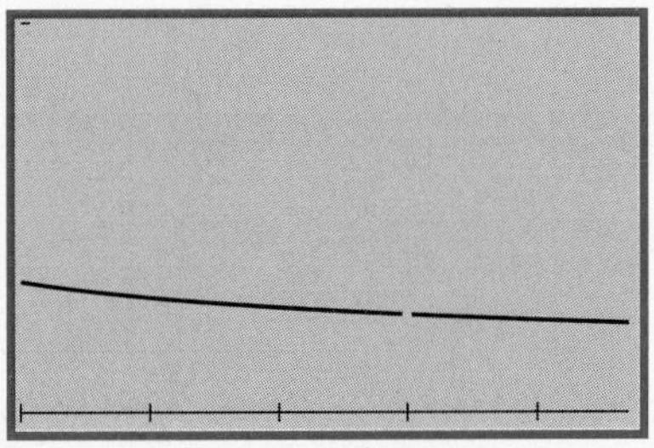

$[1, 5.7]$ by $[0, 1]$

$$g(x) = \frac{\sqrt{x} - 2}{x - 4}$$

FIGURE 4

The solution is as follows:

$$\lim_{x \to 4} \frac{\sqrt{x} - 2}{x - 4} = \lim_{x \to 4} \frac{(\sqrt{x} - 2)(\sqrt{x} + 2)}{(x - 4)(\sqrt{x} + 2)}$$

$$= \lim_{x \to 4} \frac{x - 4}{(x - 4)(\sqrt{x} + 2)}$$

$$= \lim_{x \to 4} \frac{1}{\sqrt{x} + 2}$$

$$= \frac{\displaystyle\lim_{x \to 4} 1}{\displaystyle\lim_{x \to 4} (\sqrt{x} + 2)} \qquad \text{(L.T. 9)}$$

$$= \frac{1}{\displaystyle\lim_{x \to 4} \sqrt{x} + \lim_{x \to 4} 2} \qquad \text{(L.T. 2 and L.T. 4)}$$

$$= \frac{1}{\sqrt{\displaystyle\lim_{x \to 4} x} + 2} \qquad \text{(L.T. 10 and L.T. 2)}$$

$$= \frac{1}{\sqrt{4} + 2} \qquad \text{(L.T. 3)}$$

$$= \frac{1}{4} \qquad \blacktriangleleft$$

From time to time we will need two other limit statements that are equivalent to

$$\lim_{x \to a} f(x) = L$$

These statements are given in the following two theorems whose proofs you are asked to supply in Exercises 63 and 64.

1.5.14 Theorem

$$\lim_{x \to a} f(x) = L \quad \text{if and only if} \quad \lim_{x \to a} [f(x) - L] = 0$$

1.5.15 Theorem

$$\lim_{x \to a} f(x) = L \quad \text{if and only if} \quad \lim_{t \to 0} f(t + a) = L$$

The following theorem states that a function cannot approach two different limits at the same time. It is called a *uniqueness theorem* because it guarantees that if the limit of a function exists, it is unique.

1.5.16 Theorem

If $\lim_{x \to a} f(x) = L_1$ and $\lim_{x \to a} f(x) = L_2$ then $L_1 = L_2$.

Because of this theorem we can state that if a function f has a limit L at the number a, then L is *the* limit of f at a. The proof of the theorem appears in the supplement of this section.

EXERCISES 1.5

In Exercises 1 through 10, prove the limit is the indicated number by applying Definition 1.5.1.

1. $\lim\limits_{x \to 2} 7 = 7$

2. $\lim\limits_{x \to 5} (-4) = -4$

3. $\lim\limits_{x \to 4} (2x + 1) = 9$

4. $\lim\limits_{x \to 1} (4x + 3) = 7$

5. $\lim\limits_{x \to 3} (7 - 3x) = -2$

6. $\lim\limits_{x \to -4} (2x + 7) = -1$

7. $\lim\limits_{x \to -2} (1 + 3x) = -5$

8. $\lim\limits_{x \to -2} (7 - 2x) = 11$

9. $\lim\limits_{x \to -1} \dfrac{x^2 - 1}{x + 1} = -2$

10. $\lim\limits_{x \to 3} \dfrac{x^2 - 9}{x - 3} = 6$

In Exercises 11 through 24, find the limit and, when appropriate, indicate the limit theorems being applied.

11. $\lim\limits_{x \to 5} (3x - 7)$

12. $\lim\limits_{x \to -4} (5x + 2)$

13. $\lim\limits_{x \to 2} (x^2 + 2x - 1)$

14. $\lim\limits_{x \to 3} (2x^2 - 4x + 5)$

15. $\lim\limits_{z \to -2} (z^3 + 8)$

16. $\lim\limits_{y \to -1} (y^3 - 2y^2 + 3y - 4)$

17. $\lim\limits_{x \to 3} \dfrac{4x - 5}{5x - 1}$

18. $\lim\limits_{x \to 2} \dfrac{3x + 4}{8x - 1}$

19. $\lim\limits_{t \to 2} \dfrac{t^2 - 5}{2t^3 + 6}$

20. $\lim\limits_{x \to -1} \dfrac{2x + 1}{x^2 - 3x + 4}$

21. $\lim\limits_{r \to 1} \sqrt{\dfrac{8r + 1}{r + 3}}$

22. $\lim\limits_{x \to 2} \sqrt{\dfrac{x^2 + 3x + 4}{x^3 + 1}}$

23. $\lim\limits_{x \to 4} \sqrt[3]{\dfrac{x^2 - 3x + 4}{2x^2 - x - 1}}$

24. $\lim\limits_{x \to -3} \sqrt[3]{\dfrac{5 + 2x}{5 - x}}$

In Exercises 25 through 30, do the following: (a) Use a calculator to tabulate to four decimal places values of $f(x)$ for the specified values of x. What does $f(x)$ appear to be approaching as x approaches c? (b) Support your answer in part (a) by plotting the graph of f in a convenient window. (c) Confirm your answer in part (a) analytically by computing $\lim\limits_{x \to c} f(x)$ and, when appropriate, indicate the limit theorems being applied.

25. $f(x) = \dfrac{x - 2}{x^2 - 4}$; x is 1, 1.5, 1.9, 1.99, 1.999 and x is 3, 2.5, 2.1, 2.01, 2.001; $c = 2$

26. $f(x) = \dfrac{2x^2 + 3x - 2}{x^2 - 6x - 16}$; x is -3, -2.5, -2.1, -2.01, -2.001 and x is -1, -1.5, -1.9, -1.99, -1.999; $c = -2$

27. $f(x) = \dfrac{x^2 + 5x + 6}{x^2 - x - 12}$; x is -4, -3.5, -3.1, -3.01, -3.001, -3.0001 and x is -2, -2.5, -2.9, -2.99, -2.999, -2.9999; $c = -3$

28. $f(x) = \dfrac{2x - 3}{4x^2 - 9}$; x is 1, 1.4, 1.49, 1.499, 1.4999 and x is 2, 1.6, 1.51, 1.501, 1.5001; $c = \frac{3}{2}$

29. $f(x) = \dfrac{3 - \sqrt{x}}{9 - x}$; x is 8, 8.5, 8.9, 8.99, 8.999 and x is 10, 9.5, 9.1, 9.01, 9.001; $c = 9$

30. $f(x) = \dfrac{2 - \sqrt{4 - x}}{x}$; x is -1, -0.5, -0.1, -0.01, -0.001 and x is 1, 0.5, 0.1, 0.01, 0.001; $c = 0$

In Exercises 31 through 46, find the limit and, when appropriate, indicate the limit theorems being applied.

31. $\lim\limits_{x \to 7} \dfrac{x^2 - 49}{x - 7}$

32. $\lim\limits_{z \to -5} \dfrac{z^2 - 25}{z + 5}$

33. $\lim\limits_{x \to -3/2} \dfrac{4x^2 - 9}{2x + 3}$

34. $\lim\limits_{x \to 1/3} \dfrac{3x - 1}{9x^2 - 1}$

35. $\lim\limits_{s \to 4} \dfrac{3s^2 - 8s - 16}{2s^2 - 9s + 4}$

36. $\lim\limits_{x \to 4} \dfrac{3x^2 - 17x + 20}{4x^2 - 25x + 36}$

37. $\lim\limits_{y \to -2} \dfrac{y^3 + 8}{y + 2}$

38. $\lim\limits_{s \to 1} \dfrac{s^3 - 1}{s - 1}$

39. $\lim\limits_{y \to -3} \sqrt{\dfrac{y^2 - 9}{2y^2 + 7y + 3}}$

40. $\lim\limits_{t \to 3/2} \sqrt{\dfrac{8t^3 - 27}{4t^2 - 9}}$

41. $\lim\limits_{x \to 1} \dfrac{\sqrt{x} - 1}{x - 1}$

42. $\lim\limits_{x \to -1} \dfrac{\sqrt{x + 5} - 2}{x + 1}$

43. $\lim\limits_{h \to 0} \dfrac{\sqrt{h + 2} - \sqrt{2}}{h}$

44. $\lim\limits_{x \to 1} \dfrac{\sqrt[3]{x} - 1}{x - 1}$

45. $\lim\limits_{x \to -1} \dfrac{2x^2 - x - 3}{x^3 + 2x^2 + 6x + 5}$

46. $\lim\limits_{x \to -2} \dfrac{x^3 - x^2 - x + 10}{x^2 + 3x + 2}$

47. If $f(x) = x^2 + 5x - 3$, show analytically that $\lim\limits_{x \to 2} f(x) = f(2)$. Support your answer graphically.

48. If $F(x) = 2x^3 + 7x - 1$, show analytically that $\lim\limits_{x \to -1} F(x) = F(-1)$. Support your answer graphically.

49. If $g(x) = \dfrac{x^2 - 1}{x - 1}$, why does $g(1)$ not exist? Show analytically that $\lim\limits_{x \to 1} g(x)$ does exist and find the limit. Support your answer graphically.

50. If $G(x) = \dfrac{x - 1}{x^2 - 1}$, why does $G(1)$ not exist? Show analytically that $\lim\limits_{x \to 1} G(x)$ does exist and find the limit. Support your answer graphically.

51. If $h(x) = \dfrac{\sqrt{x + 9} - 3}{x}$, why does $h(0)$ not exist?
Show analytically that $\lim\limits_{x \to 0} h(x)$ does exist and find the limit. Support your answer graphically.

52. If $H(x) = \dfrac{x}{\sqrt{x + 1} - 1}$, why does $H(0)$ not exist?
Show analytically that $\lim\limits_{x \to 0} H(x)$ does exist and find the limit. Support your answer graphically.

53. If
$$f(x) = \begin{cases} 2x - 1 & \text{if } x \neq 2 \\ 1 & \text{if } x = 2 \end{cases}$$
find $\lim\limits_{x \to 2} f(x)$ and show that $\lim\limits_{x \to 2} f(x) \neq f(2)$. Sketch the graph of f.

54. If
$$f(x) = \begin{cases} x^2 - 9 & \text{if } x \neq -3 \\ 4 & \text{if } x = -3 \end{cases}$$
find $\lim\limits_{x \to -3} f(x)$ and show that $\lim\limits_{x \to -3} f(x) \neq f(-3)$. Sketch the graph of f.

In Exercises 55 through 58, answer parts (a)–(c) from the graph of f sketched in the accompanying figure.

55. The domain of f is $(-\infty, +\infty)$. **(a)** Define $f(x)$ piecewise. **(b)** What are $f(-3), f(0)$, and $f(3)$? **(c)** What are $\lim\limits_{x \to -3} f(x), \lim\limits_{x \to 0} f(x)$ and $\lim\limits_{x \to 3} f(x)$?

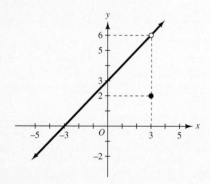

56. The domain of f is $(-\infty, +\infty)$. **(a)** Define $f(x)$ piecewise. **(b)** What are $f(-2), f(0)$ and $f(2)$? **(c)** What are $\lim\limits_{x \to -2} f(x), \lim\limits_{x \to 0} f(x)$, and $\lim\limits_{x \to 2} f(x)$?

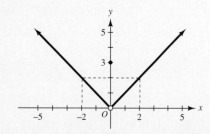

57. The domain of f is $[-5, 5]$. **(a)** Define $f(x)$ piecewise. **(b)** What are $f(-4), f(-3), f(3)$, and $f(4)$? **(c)** What are $\lim\limits_{x \to -4} f(x), \lim\limits_{x \to -3} f(x), \lim\limits_{x \to 3} f(x)$, and $\lim\limits_{x \to 4} f(x)$?

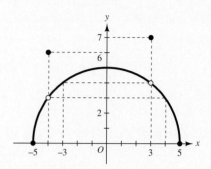

58. The domain of f is $(-\infty, 2]$. **(a)** Define $f(x)$ piecewise. **(b)** What are $f(-1), f(0), f(1)$, and $f(\sqrt{3})$? **(c)** What are $\lim\limits_{x \to -1} f(x), \lim\limits_{x \to 0} f(x), \lim\limits_{x \to 1} f(x)$, and $\lim\limits_{x \to \sqrt{3}} f(x)$?

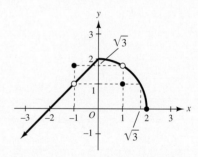

In Exercises 59 through 62, sketch a graph of some function f satisfying the given properties. In each exercise the domain of f is $(-\infty, +\infty)$.

59. $f(2) = 3$; $\lim\limits_{x \to 2} f(x) = 1$; $\lim\limits_{x \to a} f(x) = f(a)$ if $a \neq 2$; the range of f is the set of all real numbers.

60. $f(-3) = 4$; $f(3) = -5$; $\lim\limits_{x \to -3} f(x) = -5$; $\lim\limits_{x \to 3} f(x) = 4$; $\lim\limits_{x \to a} f(x) = f(a)$ if $a \neq \pm 3$; the range of f is the set of all real numbers.

61. $\lim\limits_{x \to -6} f(x) \neq f(-6)$; $\lim\limits_{x \to 6} f(x) \neq f(6)$; $\lim\limits_{x \to a} f(x) = f(a)$ if $a \neq \pm 6$; the range of f is the set of all nonnegative numbers.

62. $f(-2) \neq f(2)$; $\lim\limits_{x \to -2} f(x) \neq f(-2)$; $\lim\limits_{x \to 2} f(x) \neq f(2)$; $\lim\limits_{x \to a} f(x) = f(a)$ if $a \neq \pm 2$; the range of f is the closed interval $[-3, 3]$.

63. Prove Theorem 1.5.14. *Hint:* Because the theorem has an *if and only if* qualification, the proof requires two parts. To prove that $\lim_{x \to a} f(x) = L$ if $\lim_{x \to a} [f(x) - L] = 0$, start with $\lim_{x \to a} f(x)$, replace $f(x)$ by $[f(x) - L] + L$, and then apply Limit Theorem 4. To prove that $\lim_{x \to a} f(x) = L$ only if $\lim_{x \to a} [f(x) - L] = 0$ or, equivalently, $\lim_{x \to a} [f(x) - L] = 0$ if $\lim_{x \to a} f(x) = L$ apply Limit Theorem 4 to $\lim_{x \to a} [f(x) - L]$.

64. Prove Theorem 1.5.15. *Hint:* As in the proof of Theorem 1.5.14 the proof requires two parts. To prove that $\lim_{x \to a} f(x) = L$ if $\lim_{t \to 0} f(t + a) = L$, apply Definition 1.5.1 and then replace $t + a$ by x and t by $x - a$. To prove that $\lim_{x \to a} f(x) = L$ only if $\lim_{t \to 0} f(t + a) = L$ or, equivalently, $\lim_{t \to 0} f(t + a) = L$

if $\lim_{x \to a} f(x) = L$, apply Definition 1.5.1 and replace x by $t + a$ and $x - a$ by t.

65. If P is a polynomial function, why does $\lim_{x \to a} P(x)$ exist for all numbers a and why can this limit be determined by computing $P(a)$? If R is a rational function, why can't a similar statement be made regarding $\lim_{x \to a} R(x)$? How would you modify the statement for the limit of a rational function?

66. If $\lim_{x \to a} f(x)$ exists and $\lim_{x \to a} [f(x) + g(x)]$ does not exist, explain why you can conclude that $\lim_{x \to a} g(x)$ does not exist.

67. Without using the words *limit* or *approaches* and without using symbols such as ϵ and δ, state in words what the following symbolism means: $\lim_{x \to a} f(x) = L$.

1.6 ONE-SIDED LIMITS

So far in our discussion of the limit of a function as the independent variable x approaches a number a, we have been concerned with values of x close to a and either greater than a or less than a, that is, values of x in an open interval containing a but not at a itself. Suppose, however, that we have the function defined by

$$f(x) = \sqrt{x - 4}$$

Because $f(x)$ does not exist if $x < 4$, f is not defined on any open interval containing 4. Thus $\lim_{x \to 4} \sqrt{x - 4}$ has no meaning. If, however, x is restricted to numbers greater than 4, the value of $\sqrt{x - 4}$ can be made as close to 0 as we please by taking x sufficiently close to 4 but greater than 4. In such a case we let x approach 4 from the right and consider the **right-hand limit** (or the **one-sided limit from the right**), which we now define.

1.6.1 Definition of Right-Hand Limit

Let f be a function defined at every number in some open interval (a, c). Then the **limit of $f(x)$, as x approaches a from the right, is L**, written

$$\lim_{x \to a^+} f(x) = L$$

if for any $\epsilon > 0$, however small, there exists a $\delta > 0$ such that

$$\text{if} \quad 0 < x - a < \delta \quad \text{then} \quad |f(x) - L| < \epsilon$$

Note that in the last line of the definition, no absolute-value bars appear around $x - a$ because we are considering only values of x for which $x > a$.

Computing the limit of $\sqrt{x - 4}$, as x approaches 4 from the right, we have from the definition

$$\lim_{x \to 4^+} \sqrt{x - 4} = 0$$

If, when considering the limit of a function, the independent variable x is restricted to numbers less than a, we say that x approaches a from the left. The limit is called the **left-hand limit** (or the **one-sided limit from the left**).

1.6.2 Definition of Left-Hand Limit

Let f be a function defined at every number in some open interval (d, a). Then the **limit of $f(x)$, as x approaches a from the left, is L**, written

$$\lim_{x \to a^-} f(x) = L$$

if for any $\epsilon > 0$, however small, there exists a $\delta > 0$ such that

$$\text{if} \quad 0 < a - x < \delta \quad \text{then} \quad |f(x) - L| < \epsilon$$

We refer to $\lim_{x \to a} f(x)$ as the **two-sided limit** to distinguish it from the one-sided limits.

Limit Theorems 1–10 given in Section 1.5 remain valid when "$x \to a$" is replaced by either "$x \to a^+$" or "$x \to a^-$."

▷   **ILLUSTRATION 1**   Figure 1 shows the graph of the signum function defined in Exercise 49 of Exercises 1.1 by

$$\text{sgn } x = \begin{cases} -1 & \text{if } x < 0 \\ 0 & \text{if } x = 0 \\ 1 & \text{if } 0 < x \end{cases}$$

Because $\text{sgn } x = -1$ if $x < 0$ and $\text{sgn } x = 1$ if $0 < x$, we have

$$\lim_{x \to 0^-} \text{sgn } x = \lim_{x \to 0^-} (-1) \qquad \lim_{x \to 0^+} \text{sgn } x = \lim_{x \to 0^+} 1$$
$$= -1 \qquad\qquad\qquad = 1 \qquad ◀$$

In Illustration 1, because the left-hand limit and the right-hand limit are not equal, the two-sided limit $\lim_{x \to 0} \text{sgn } x$ does not exist. The concept of the two-sided limit failing to exist because the two one-sided limits are unequal is stated in the following theorem.

1.6.3 Theorem

$\lim_{x \to a} f(x)$ exists and is equal to L if and only if $\lim_{x \to a^-} f(x)$ and $\lim_{x \to a^+} f(x)$ both exist and both are equal to L.

The proof of this theorem is left as an exercise (see Exercise 34).

▷   **ILLUSTRATION 2**   In Example 2 of Section 1.3 we had the following function where $C(x)$ dollars is the total cost of an order of x pounds of a product:

$$C(x) = \begin{cases} 2x & \text{if } 0 \le x \le 10 \\ 1.8x & \text{if } 10 < x \end{cases}$$

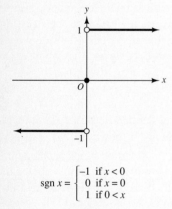

$$\text{sgn } x = \begin{cases} -1 & \text{if } x < 0 \\ 0 & \text{if } x = 0 \\ 1 & \text{if } 0 < x \end{cases}$$

FIGURE 1

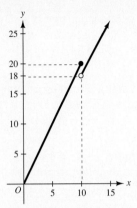

$$C(x) = \begin{cases} 2x & \text{if } 0 \le x \le 10 \\ 1.8x & \text{if } 10 < x \end{cases}$$

FIGURE 2

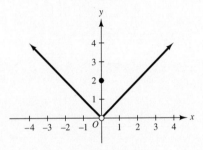

$$g(x) = \begin{cases} |x| & \text{if } x \ne 0 \\ 2 & \text{if } x = 0 \end{cases}$$

FIGURE 3

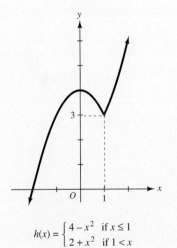

$$h(x) = \begin{cases} 4 - x^2 & \text{if } x \le 1 \\ 2 + x^2 & \text{if } 1 < x \end{cases}$$

FIGURE 4

The graph of C is sketched in Figure 2. Observe the break in the graph at $x = 10$. Let us examine $\lim\limits_{x \to 10} C(x)$. Because the definition of $C(x)$ when $x < 10$ is different from the definition when $x > 10$, we must distinguish between the left-hand limit at 10 and the right-hand limit at 10. We have

$$\lim_{x \to 10^-} C(x) = \lim_{x \to 10^-} 2x \qquad \lim_{x \to 10^+} C(x) = \lim_{x \to 10^+} 1.8x$$
$$= 20 \qquad\qquad\qquad = 18$$

Because $\lim\limits_{x \to 10^-} C(x) \ne \lim\limits_{x \to 10^+} C(x)$, we conclude from Theorem 1.6.3 that $\lim\limits_{x \to 10} C(x)$ does not exist. In Section 1.8, we return to this function as an example of a *discontinuous* function.   ◀

▶ **EXAMPLE 1**   Let g be defined by

$$g(x) = \begin{cases} |x| & \text{if } x \ne 0 \\ 2 & \text{if } x = 0 \end{cases}$$

(a) Sketch the graph of g. **(b)** Find $\lim\limits_{x \to 0} g(x)$ if it exists.

Solution

(a) The graph is sketched in Figure 3. Observe the break in the graph at the origin.

(b) $$\lim_{x \to 0^-} g(x) = \lim_{x \to 0^-} (-x) \qquad \lim_{x \to 0^+} g(x) = \lim_{x \to 0^+} x$$
$$= 0 \qquad\qquad\qquad\qquad = 0$$

Because $\lim\limits_{x \to 0^-} g(x) = \lim\limits_{x \to 0^+} g(x)$, we conclude from Theorem 1.6.3 that $\lim\limits_{x \to 0} g(x)$ exists and is equal to 0. Notice that $g(0) = 2$, which has no effect on $\lim\limits_{x \to 0} g(x)$.   ◀

▶ **EXAMPLE 2**   Let h be defined by

$$h(x) = \begin{cases} 4 - x^2 & \text{if } x \le 1 \\ 2 + x^2 & \text{if } 1 < x \end{cases}$$

(a) Sketch the graph of h. **(b)** Find each of the following limits if they exist: $\lim\limits_{x \to 1^-} h(x); \lim\limits_{x \to 1^+} h(x); \lim\limits_{x \to 1} h(x)$.

Solution

(a) The graph of h appears in Figure 4.

(b) $$\lim_{x \to 1^-} h(x) = \lim_{x \to 1^-} (4 - x^2) \qquad \lim_{x \to 1^+} h(x) = \lim_{x \to 1^+} (2 + x^2)$$
$$= 3 \qquad\qquad\qquad\qquad\qquad = 3$$

Because $\lim\limits_{x \to 1^-} h(x) = \lim\limits_{x \to 1^+} h(x)$ and both are equal to 3, then from Theorem 1.6.3, $\lim\limits_{x \to 1} h(x) = 3$.   ◀

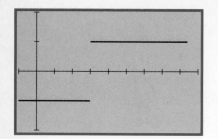

[−1, 8.4] by [−2, 2]

$$f(x) = \frac{|x-3|}{x-3}$$

FIGURE 5

▶ **EXAMPLE 3**   Let f be defined by

$$f(x) = \frac{|x-3|}{x-3}$$

(a) Plot the graph of f and from the graph make a conjecture regarding $\lim_{x\to 3} f(x)$. **(b)** Confirm analytically the conjecture in part (a).

Solution

(a) Figure 5 shows the graph of f plotted in the $[-1, 8.4]$ by $[-2, 2]$ window. Because of the break in the graph at the point where $x = 3$, we suspect $\lim_{x\to 3} f(x)$ does not exist.

(b) Because

$$|x-3| = \begin{cases} x-3 & \text{if } x \geq 3 \\ 3-x & \text{if } x < 3 \end{cases} \quad \text{then} \quad \frac{|x-3|}{x-3} = \begin{cases} 1 & \text{if } x \geq 3 \\ -1 & \text{if } x < 3 \end{cases}$$

We compute the one-sided limits at 3.

$$\lim_{x\to 3^-} f(x) = \lim_{x\to 3^-} \frac{|x-3|}{x-3} \qquad \lim_{x\to 3^+} f(x) = \lim_{x\to 3^+} \frac{|x-3|}{x-3}$$
$$= \lim_{x\to 3^-} (-1) \qquad\qquad\quad = \lim_{x\to 3^+} 1$$
$$= -1 \qquad\qquad\qquad\quad = 1$$

Because $\lim_{x\to 3^-} f(x) \neq \lim_{x\to 3^+} f(x)$, we have confirmed analytically that $\lim_{x\to 3} f(x)$ does not exist.   ◀

▶ **EXAMPLE 4**   Let f be defined by

$$f(x) = \begin{cases} x+5 & \text{if } x < -3 \\ \sqrt{9-x^2} & \text{if } -3 \leq x \leq 3 \\ 3-x & \text{if } 3 < x \end{cases}$$

(a) Sketch the graph of f. **(b)** Find, if they exist, each of the following limits: $\lim_{x\to -3^-} f(x)$, $\lim_{x\to -3^+} f(x)$, $\lim_{x\to -3} f(x)$, $\lim_{x\to 3^-} f(x)$, $\lim_{x\to 3^+} f(x)$, $\lim_{x\to 3} f(x)$.

Solution

(a) The graph of f is sketched in Figure 6.

(b)
$$\lim_{x\to -3^-} f(x) = \lim_{x\to -3^-} (x+5) \qquad \lim_{x\to -3^+} f(x) = \lim_{x\to -3^+} \sqrt{9-x^2}$$
$$= 2 \qquad\qquad\qquad\qquad\qquad = 0$$

Because $\lim_{x\to -3^-} f(x) \neq \lim_{x\to -3^+} f(x)$, then $\lim_{x\to -3} f(x)$ does not exist.

$$\lim_{x\to 3^-} f(x) = \lim_{x\to 3^-} \sqrt{9-x^2} \qquad \lim_{x\to 3^+} f(x) = \lim_{x\to 3^+} (3-x)$$
$$= 0 \qquad\qquad\qquad\qquad\qquad = 0$$

Because $\lim_{x\to 3^-} f(x) = \lim_{x\to 3^+} f(x)$, then $\lim_{x\to 3} f(x)$ exists and is 0.   ◀

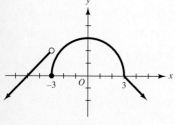

$$f(x) = \begin{cases} x+5 & \text{if } x < -3 \\ \sqrt{9-x^2} & \text{if } -3 \leq x \leq 3 \\ 3-x & \text{if } 3 < x \end{cases}$$

FIGURE 6

EXERCISES 1.6

In Exercises 1 through 22, sketch the graph of the function and find the indicated limit if it exists; if the limit does not exist, state the reason.

1. $f(x) = \begin{cases} 2 & \text{if } x < 1 \\ -1 & \text{if } x = 1 \\ -3 & \text{if } 1 < x \end{cases}$

(a) $\lim\limits_{x \to 1^+} f(x)$; (b) $\lim\limits_{x \to 1^-} f(x)$; (c) $\lim\limits_{x \to 1} f(x)$

2. $f(x) = \begin{cases} -2 & \text{if } x < 0 \\ 2 & \text{if } 0 \le x \end{cases}$

(a) $\lim\limits_{x \to 0^+} f(x)$; (b) $\lim\limits_{x \to 0^-} f(x)$; (c) $\lim\limits_{x \to 0} f(x)$

3. $f(t) = \begin{cases} t + 4 & \text{if } t \le -4 \\ 4 - t & \text{if } -4 < t \end{cases}$

(a) $\lim\limits_{t \to -4^+} f(t)$; (b) $\lim\limits_{t \to -4^-} f(t)$; (c) $\lim\limits_{t \to -4} f(t)$

4. $g(s) = \begin{cases} s + 3 & \text{if } s \le -2 \\ 3 - s & \text{if } -2 < s \end{cases}$

(a) $\lim\limits_{s \to -2^+} g(s)$; (b) $\lim\limits_{s \to -2^-} g(s)$; (c) $\lim\limits_{s \to -2} g(s)$

5. $F(x) = \begin{cases} x^2 & \text{if } x \le 2 \\ 8 - 2x & \text{if } 2 < x \end{cases}$

(a) $\lim\limits_{x \to 2^+} F(x)$; (b) $\lim\limits_{x \to 2^-} F(x)$; (c) $\lim\limits_{x \to 2} F(x)$

6. $h(x) = \begin{cases} 2x + 1 & \text{if } x < 3 \\ 10 - x & \text{if } 3 \le x \end{cases}$

(a) $\lim\limits_{x \to 3^+} h(x)$; (b) $\lim\limits_{x \to 3^-} h(x)$; (c) $\lim\limits_{x \to 3} h(x)$

7. $g(r) = \begin{cases} 2r + 3 & \text{if } r < 1 \\ 2 & \text{if } r = 1 \\ 7 - 2r & \text{if } 1 < r \end{cases}$

(a) $\lim\limits_{r \to 1^+} g(r)$; (b) $\lim\limits_{r \to 1^-} g(r)$; (c) $\lim\limits_{r \to 1} g(r)$

8. $g(t) = \begin{cases} 3 + t^2 & \text{if } t < -2 \\ 0 & \text{if } t = -2 \\ 11 - t^2 & \text{if } -2 < t \end{cases}$

(a) $\lim\limits_{t \to -2^+} g(t)$; (b) $\lim\limits_{t \to -2^-} g(t)$; (c) $\lim\limits_{t \to -2} g(t)$

9. $f(x) = \begin{cases} x^2 - 4 & \text{if } x < 2 \\ 4 & \text{if } x = 2 \\ 4 - x^2 & \text{if } 2 < x \end{cases}$

(a) $\lim\limits_{x \to 2^+} f(x)$; (b) $\lim\limits_{x \to 2^-} f(x)$; (c) $\lim\limits_{x \to 2} f(x)$

10. $f(x) = \begin{cases} 2x + 3 & \text{if } x < 1 \\ 4 & \text{if } x = 1 \\ x^2 + 2 & \text{if } 1 < x \end{cases}$

(a) $\lim\limits_{x \to 1^+} f(x)$; (b) $\lim\limits_{x \to 1^-} f(x)$; (c) $\lim\limits_{x \to 1} f(x)$

11. $F(x) = |x - 5|$

(a) $\lim\limits_{x \to 5^+} F(x)$; (b) $\lim\limits_{x \to 5^-} F(x)$; (c) $\lim\limits_{x \to 5} F(x)$

12. $f(x) = 3 + |2x - 4|$

(a) $\lim\limits_{x \to 2^+} f(x)$; (b) $\lim\limits_{x \to 2^-} f(x)$; (c) $\lim\limits_{x \to 2} f(x)$

13. $G(x) = |2x - 3| - 4$

(a) $\lim\limits_{x \to 3/2^+} G(x)$; (b) $\lim\limits_{x \to 3/2^-} G(x)$; (c) $\lim\limits_{x \to 3/2} G(x)$

14. $F(x) = \begin{cases} |x - 1| & \text{if } x < -1 \\ 0 & \text{if } x = -1 \\ |1 - x| & \text{if } -1 < x \end{cases}$

(a) $\lim\limits_{x \to -1^+} F(x)$; (b) $\lim\limits_{x \to -1^-} F(x)$; (c) $\lim\limits_{x \to -1} F(x)$

15. $f(x) = \dfrac{|x|}{x}$

(a) $\lim\limits_{x \to 0^+} f(x)$; (b) $\lim\limits_{x \to 0^-} f(x)$; (c) $\lim\limits_{x \to 0} f(x)$

16. $S(x) = |\operatorname{sgn} x|$ (sgn x is defined in Illustration 1)

(a) $\lim\limits_{x \to 0^+} S(x)$; (b) $\lim\limits_{x \to 0^-} S(x)$; (c) $\lim\limits_{x \to 0} S(x)$

17. $f(x) = \begin{cases} 2 & \text{if } x < -2 \\ \sqrt{4 - x^2} & \text{if } -2 \le x \le 2 \\ -2 & \text{if } 2 < x \end{cases}$

(a) $\lim\limits_{x \to -2^-} f(x)$; (b) $\lim\limits_{x \to -2^+} f(x)$; (c) $\lim\limits_{x \to -2} f(x)$;
(d) $\lim\limits_{x \to 2^-} f(x)$; (e) $\lim\limits_{x \to 2^+} f(x)$; (f) $\lim\limits_{x \to 2} f(x)$

18. $f(x) = \begin{cases} x + 1 & \text{if } x < -1 \\ x^2 & \text{if } -1 \le x \le 1 \\ 2 - x & \text{if } 1 < x \end{cases}$

(a) $\lim\limits_{x \to -1^-} f(x)$; (b) $\lim\limits_{x \to -1^+} f(x)$; (c) $\lim\limits_{x \to -1} f(x)$;
(d) $\lim\limits_{x \to 1^-} f(x)$; (e) $\lim\limits_{x \to 1^+} f(x)$; (f) $\lim\limits_{x \to 1} f(x)$

19. $f(t) = \begin{cases} \sqrt[3]{t} & \text{if } t < 0 \\ \sqrt{t} & \text{if } 0 \le t \end{cases}$

(a) $\lim\limits_{t \to 0^+} f(t)$; (b) $\lim\limits_{t \to 0^-} f(t)$; (c) $\lim\limits_{t \to 0} f(t)$

20. $g(x) = \begin{cases} \sqrt[3]{-x} & \text{if } x \le 0 \\ \sqrt[3]{x} & \text{if } 0 < x \end{cases}$

(a) $\lim\limits_{x \to 0^+} g(x)$; (b) $\lim\limits_{x \to 0^-} g(x)$; (c) $\lim\limits_{x \to 0} g(x)$

21. $F(x) = \begin{cases} \sqrt{x^2 - 9} & \text{if } x \le -3 \\ \sqrt{9 - x^2} & \text{if } -3 < x < 3 \\ \sqrt{x^2 - 9} & \text{if } 3 \le x \end{cases}$

(a) $\lim\limits_{x \to -3^-} F(x)$; (b) $\lim\limits_{x \to -3^+} F(x)$; (c) $\lim\limits_{x \to -3} F(x)$;
(d) $\lim\limits_{x \to 3^-} F(x)$; (e) $\lim\limits_{x \to 3^+} F(x)$; (f) $\lim\limits_{x \to 3} F(x)$

22. $G(t) = \begin{cases} \sqrt[3]{t+1} & \text{if } t \le -1 \\ \sqrt{1-t^2} & \text{if } -1 < t < 1 \\ \sqrt[3]{t-1} & \text{if } 1 \le t \end{cases}$

(a) $\lim\limits_{t \to -1^-} G(t)$; (b) $\lim\limits_{t \to -1^+} G(t)$; (c) $\lim\limits_{t \to -1} G(t)$;
(d) $\lim\limits_{t \to 1^-} G(t)$; (e) $\lim\limits_{t \to 1^+} G(t)$; (f) $\lim\limits_{t \to 1} G(t)$

23. $F(x) = x - 2 \, \text{sgn} \, x$, where sgn x is defined in Illustration 1. Find, if they exist: (a) $\lim\limits_{x \to 0^+} F(x)$;
(b) $\lim\limits_{x \to 0^-} F(x)$; (c) $\lim\limits_{x \to 0} F(x)$.

24. $h(x) = \text{sgn} \, x - U(x)$, where sgn x is defined in Illustration 1, and U is the unit step function defined by

$$U(x) = \begin{cases} 0 & \text{if } x < 0 \\ 1 & \text{if } 0 \le x \end{cases}$$

Find, if they exist: (a) $\lim\limits_{x \to 0^+} h(x)$; (b) $\lim\limits_{x \to 0^-} h(x)$;
(c) $\lim\limits_{x \to 0} h(x)$.

25. Find, if they exist: (a) $\lim\limits_{x \to 2^+} [\![x]\!]$; (b) $\lim\limits_{x \to 2^-} [\![x]\!]$;
(c) $\lim\limits_{x \to 2} [\![x]\!]$.

26. Find, if they exist: (a) $\lim\limits_{x \to 4^+} [\![x - 3]\!]$; (b) $\lim\limits_{x \to 4^-} [\![x - 3]\!]$;
(c) $\lim\limits_{x \to 4} [\![x - 3]\!]$.

27. Let $h(x) = (x - 1) \, \text{sgn} \, x$. Sketch the graph of h.
Find, if they exist: (a) $\lim\limits_{x \to 0^+} h(x)$; (b) $\lim\limits_{x \to 0^-} h(x)$;
(c) $\lim\limits_{x \to 0} h(x)$.

28. Let $G(x) = [\![x]\!] + [\![4 - x]\!]$. Sketch the graph of G.
Find, if they exist: (a) $\lim\limits_{x \to 3^+} G(x)$; (b) $\lim\limits_{x \to 3^-} G(x)$;
(c) $\lim\limits_{x \to 3} G(x)$.

29. Given $f(x) = \begin{cases} 3x + 2 & \text{if } x < 4 \\ 5x + k & \text{if } 4 \le x \end{cases}$. Find the value of
k such that $\lim\limits_{x \to 4} f(x)$ exists.

30. Given $f(x) = \begin{cases} kx - 3 & \text{if } x \le -1 \\ x^2 + k & \text{if } -1 < x \end{cases}$. Find the value
of k such that $\lim\limits_{x \to -1} f(x)$ exists.

31. Given $f(x) = \begin{cases} x^2 & \text{if } x \le -2 \\ ax + b & \text{if } -2 < x < 2 \\ 2x - 6 & \text{if } 2 \le x \end{cases}$. Find the
values of a and b such that $\lim\limits_{x \to -2} f(x)$ and $\lim\limits_{x \to 2} f(x)$
both exist.

32. Given $f(x) = \begin{cases} 2x - a & \text{if } x < -3 \\ ax + 2b & \text{if } -3 \le x \le 3 \\ b - 5x & \text{if } 3 < x \end{cases}$. Find the
values of a and b such that $\lim\limits_{x \to -3} f(x)$ and $\lim\limits_{x \to 3} f(x)$
both exist.

33. Let $f(x) = \begin{cases} -1 & \text{if } x < 0 \\ 1 & \text{if } 0 < x \end{cases}$. Show that $\lim\limits_{x \to 0} f(x)$ does
not exist but that $\lim\limits_{x \to 0} |f(x)|$ does exist.

34. Prove Theorem 1.6.3.

In Exercises 35 and 36, evaluate the limits if they exist in parts (a)–(k) from the graph of function f sketched in the accompanying figure.

35. The domain of f is $[-1, 5]$. (a) $\lim\limits_{x \to -1^+} f(x)$; (b) $\lim\limits_{x \to 0^-} f(x)$;
(c) $\lim\limits_{x \to 0^+} f(x)$; (d) $\lim\limits_{x \to 0} f(x)$; (e) $\lim\limits_{x \to 2^-} f(x)$; (f) $\lim\limits_{x \to 2^+} f(x)$;
(g) $\lim\limits_{x \to 2} f(x)$; (h) $\lim\limits_{x \to 3^-} f(x)$; (i) $\lim\limits_{x \to 3^+} f(x)$; (j) $\lim\limits_{x \to 3} f(x)$;
(k) $\lim\limits_{x \to 5^-} f(x)$.

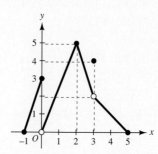

36. The domain of f is $[0, 5]$. (a) $\lim\limits_{x \to 0^+} f(x)$; (b) $\lim\limits_{x \to 1^-} f(x)$;
(c) $\lim\limits_{x \to 1^+} f(x)$; (d) $\lim\limits_{x \to 1} f(x)$; (e) $\lim\limits_{x \to 2^-} f(x)$; (f) $\lim\limits_{x \to 2^+} f(x)$;
(g) $\lim\limits_{x \to 2} f(x)$; (h) $\lim\limits_{x \to 4^-} f(x)$; (i) $\lim\limits_{x \to 4^+} f(x)$; (j) $\lim\limits_{x \to 4} f(x)$;
(k) $\lim\limits_{x \to 5^-} f(x)$.

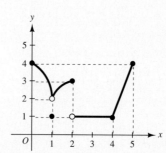

In Exercises 37 and 38, sketch a graph of some function f satisfying the given properties.

37. The domain of f is $[-1, 3]$. $f(-1) = -2$; $f(0) = 0$;
$f(1) = 2$; $f(2) = 4$; $f(3) = 1$; $\lim\limits_{x \to -1^+} f(x) = -2$;
$\lim\limits_{x \to 0^-} f(x) = 0$; $\lim\limits_{x \to 0^+} f(x) = 3$; $\lim\limits_{x \to 1} f(x) = 4$;
$\lim\limits_{x \to 2^-} f(x) = 4$; $\lim\limits_{x \to 2^+} f(x) = 0$; $\lim\limits_{x \to 3^-} f(x) = 5$.

38. The domain of f is $[-4, 4]$. $f(-4) = 3$; $f(-2) = -3$;
$f(0) = 1$; $f(2) = -1$; $f(4) = 0$; $\lim\limits_{x \to -4^+} f(x) = 0$;
$\lim\limits_{x \to -2} f(x) = 1$; $\lim\limits_{x \to 0^-} f(x) = 1$; $\lim\limits_{x \to 0^+} f(x) = 4$;
$\lim\limits_{x \to 2} f(x) = -1$; $\lim\limits_{x \to 4^-} f(x) = 0$.

39. In part (a) of Exercise 5 in Exercises 1.3 you were asked to find a mathematical model expressing the total cost of a shipment as a function of its weight. If f is that function and x is the independent variable, find each of the following: **(a)** $\lim\limits_{x \to 50^-} f(x)$;
(b) $\lim\limits_{x \to 50^+} f(x)$; **(c)** $\lim\limits_{x \to 200^-} f(x)$; **(d)** $\lim\limits_{x \to 200^+} f(x)$.

40. In part (a) of Exercise 6 in Exercises 1.3 you were asked to find a mathematical model expressing the postage in 1995 of a first-class letter weighing not more than 11 oz as a function of its weight. If F is that function and x is the independent variable, find each of the following: **(a)** $\lim\limits_{x \to 0^+} F(x)$; **(b)** $\lim\limits_{x \to 1^-} F(x)$;
(c) $\lim\limits_{x \to 1^+} F(x)$; **(d)** $\lim\limits_{x \to 2^-} F(x)$; **(e)** $\lim\limits_{x \to 10^-} F(x)$;
(f) $\lim\limits_{x \to 10^+} F(x)$; **(g)** $\lim\limits_{x \to 11^-} F(x)$.

41. In part (a) of Exercise 7 in Exercises 1.3 you were asked to find a mathematical model expressing the cost of a telephone call, lasting not more than 5 min, from Mendocino to San Francisco. If g is that function and x is the independent variable, find each of the following: **(a)** $\lim\limits_{x \to 1^-} g(x)$; **(b)** $\lim\limits_{x \to 1^+} g(x)$;
(c) $\lim\limits_{x \to 2^-} g(x)$; **(d)** $\lim\limits_{x \to 5^-} g(x)$.

42. In part (a) of Exercise 8 in Exercises 1.3 you were asked to find a mathematical model expressing the admission price at the Coast Cinema as a function of the person's age. If G is that function and x is the independent variable, find each of the following: **(a)** $\lim\limits_{x \to 12^-} G(x)$; **(b)** $\lim\limits_{x \to 12^+} G(x)$;
(c) $\lim\limits_{x \to 60^-} G(x)$; **(d)** $\lim\limits_{x \to 60^+} G(x)$.

43. Let functions f and g be defined as follows:
$$f(x) = \begin{cases} x^2 + 3 & \text{if } x \leq 1 \\ x + 1 & \text{if } 1 < x \end{cases}$$
$$g(x) = \begin{cases} x^2 & \text{if } x \leq 1 \\ 2 & \text{if } 1 < x \end{cases}$$

(a) Show that $\lim\limits_{x \to 1^-} f(x)$ and $\lim\limits_{x \to 1^+} f(x)$ both exist but are not equal, and hence $\lim\limits_{x \to 1} f(x)$ does not exist.

(b) Show that $\lim\limits_{x \to 1^-} g(x)$ and $\lim\limits_{x \to 1^+} g(x)$ both exist but are not equal, and hence $\lim\limits_{x \to 1} g(x)$ does not exist.

(c) Find formulas for $f(x) \cdot g(x)$.

(d) Prove that $\lim\limits_{x \to 1} [f(x) \cdot g(x)]$ exists by showing that $\lim\limits_{x \to 1^-} [f(x) \cdot g(x)] = \lim\limits_{x \to 1^+} [f(x) \cdot g(x)]$.

44. Let functions f and g be defined as follows:
$$f(x) = \begin{cases} x + 1 & \text{if } x < 1 \\ x - 1 & \text{if } 1 \leq x \end{cases}$$
$$g(x) = \begin{cases} 1 - x & \text{if } x < 1 \\ 1 + x & \text{if } 1 \leq x \end{cases}$$

(a) Show that neither $\lim\limits_{x \to 1} f(x)$ nor $\lim\limits_{x \to 1} g(x)$ exists.

(b) Define the function $f + g$.

(c) Show that $\lim\limits_{x \to 1} [f(x) + g(x)]$ exists.

(d) From the results of parts (a) and (c)
$$\lim\limits_{x \to 1} [f(x) + g(x)] \neq \lim\limits_{x \to 1} f(x) + \lim\limits_{x \to 1} g(x)$$
Does this fact contradict Limit Theorem 4 (1.5.5)? Why?

45. Without using the words *limit* or *approaches* and without using symbols such as ϵ and δ, state in words what each symbolism means: **(a)** $\lim\limits_{x \to a^-} f(x) = L$;
(b) $\lim\limits_{x \to a^+} f(x) = L$

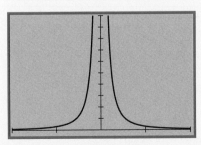

[−2, 2] by [0, 100]

$$f(x) = \frac{3}{x^2}$$

FIGURE 1

1.7 INFINITE LIMITS

In this section, we discuss functions whose values *increase or decrease without bound* as the independent variable gets closer and closer to a fixed number. We begin with the function defined by

$$f(x) = \frac{3}{x^2}$$

The domain of f is the set of all real numbers except 0 and the range is the set of all positive numbers. Figure 1 shows the graph of f plotted in the $[-2, 2]$ by $[0, 100]$ window. Observe that as the x coordinates of points on the graph approach zero from either the left or the right, the y coordinates, or $f(x)$, increase. Let us now compute some function values when x is close

Table 1

x	$f(x) = \dfrac{3}{x^2}$
1	3
0.5	12
0.25	48
0.1	300
0.01	30,000
0.001	3,000,000

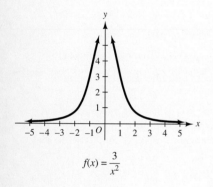

$$f(x) = \frac{3}{x^2}$$

FIGURE 2

to 0. Let x approach 0 from the right; that is, let x be 1, 0.5, 0.25, 0.1, 0.01 and 0.001 and determine the corresponding values of $f(x)$ shown in Table 1. Notice from this table that $f(x)$ increases as x gets closer and closer to 0, through values greater than 0. Actually, we can make $f(x)$ as large as we please for all values of x sufficiently close to 0 and x greater than 0. Because of this fact we say that $f(x)$ *increases without bound* as x approaches 0 through values greater than 0, and we write

$$\lim_{x \to 0^+} \frac{3}{x^2} = +\infty$$

Now let x approach 0 from the left; in particular, let x take on the values $-1, -0.5, -0.25, -0.1, -0.01,$ and -0.001. Because of symmetry with respect to the y axis, the function values are the same as the function values for the corresponding positive values of x. Thus again $f(x)$ *increases without bound* as x gets closer and closer to 0 through values less than 0, and we write

$$\lim_{x \to 0^-} \frac{3}{x^2} = +\infty$$

Therefore, as x approaches 0 from either the right or the left, $f(x)$ *increases without bound,* and we write

$$\lim_{x \to 0} \frac{3}{x^2} = +\infty$$

From the above information we sketch the graph of f shown in Figure 2, which of course corresponds to the graph plotted in Figure 1. Observe that both "branches" of the curve get closer and closer to the y axis as x approaches 0. For this graph, the y axis is a *vertical asymptote,* defined later in this section.

1.7.1 Definition of Function Values Increasing Without Bound

Let f be a function defined at every number in some open interval I containing a, except possibly at the number a itself. **As x approaches a, $f(x)$ increases without bound,** which is written

$$\lim_{x \to a} f(x) = +\infty \qquad\qquad (1)$$

if for any number $N > 0$ there exists a $\delta > 0$ such that

$$\text{if} \quad 0 < |x - a| < \delta \quad \text{then} \quad f(x) > N$$

This definition can be stated another way as follows: "The function values $f(x)$ increase without bound as x approaches a number a if $f(x)$ can be made as large as we please (that is, greater than any positive number N) for all values of x sufficiently close to a but not equal to a.

We stress again, as we did when discussing interval notation in Appendix Section A.1, that $+\infty$ is not a symbol for a real number; hence when we write $\lim_{x \to a} f(x) = +\infty$, it does not have the same meaning as $\lim_{x \to a} f(x) = L$, where L is a real number. Equation (1) can be read as "the

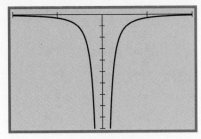

[−2, 2] by [−100, 0]

$$g(x) = \frac{-3}{x^2}$$

FIGURE 3

limit of $f(x)$ as x approaches a is positive infinity." In such a case the limit does not exist, but the symbol $+\infty$ indicates the behavior of the function values $f(x)$ as x gets closer and closer to a.

In an analogous manner we can indicate the behavior of a function whose function values *decrease without bound*. To lead up to this, consider the function g defined by the equation

$$g(x) = \frac{-3}{x^2}$$

Figure 3 shows the graph of this function plotted in the $[-2, 2]$ by $[-100, 0]$ window. The function values given by $g(x) = \dfrac{-3}{x^2}$ are the negatives of the function values given by $f(x) = \dfrac{3}{x^2}$. So for function g, as x approaches 0, either from the right or the left, $g(x)$ *decreases without bound,* and we write

$$\lim_{x \to 0} \frac{-3}{x^2} = -\infty$$

1.7.2 Definition of Function Values Decreasing Without Bound

Let f be a function defined at every number in some open interval I containing a, except possibly at the number a itself. **As x approaches a, $f(x)$ decreases without bound**, which is written

$$\lim_{x \to a} f(x) = -\infty \tag{2}$$

if for any number $N < 0$ there exists a $\delta > 0$ such that

$$\text{if} \quad 0 < |x - a| < \delta \quad \text{then} \quad f(x) < N$$

Note: Equation (2) can be read as "the limit of $f(x)$ as x approaches a is negative infinity," observing again that the limit does not exist and that the symbol $-\infty$ indicates only the behavior of the function values as x approaches a.

We can consider one-sided "infinite" limits. We state, $\lim\limits_{x \to a^+} f(x) = +\infty$ if f is defined at every number in some open interval (a, c) and if for any number $N > 0$ there exists a $\delta > 0$ such that

$$\text{if} \quad 0 < x - a < \delta, \quad \text{then} \quad f(x) > N$$

Similar definitions can be given if $\lim\limits_{x \to a^-} f(x) = +\infty$, $\lim\limits_{x \to a^+} f(x) = -\infty$, and $\lim\limits_{x \to a^-} f(x) = -\infty$. You are asked to write these definitions in Exercise 52.

Now suppose that h is the function defined by the equation

$$h(x) = \frac{2x}{x - 1} \tag{3}$$

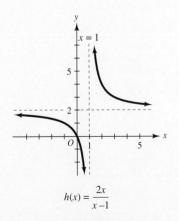

$$h(x) = \frac{2x}{x-1}$$

FIGURE 4

The graph of h is sketched in Figure 4 showing the line $x = 1$ as a dashed line (a *vertical asymptote* of the graph). By referring to Figures 1, 3, and 4, note the difference in behavior of the function of Figure 4 from the functions of the other two figures. Observe that

$$\lim_{x \to 1^-} \frac{2x}{x-1} = -\infty \tag{4}$$

$$\lim_{x \to 1^+} \frac{2x}{x-1} = +\infty \tag{5}$$

That is, for the function defined by (3), as x approaches 1 through values less than 1, the function values decrease without bound, and as x approaches 1 through values greater than 1, the function values increase without bound.

Before giving some examples, we need two limit theorems involving "infinite" limits.

1.7.3 Limit Theorem 11

If r is any positive integer, then

(i) $\lim_{x \to 0^+} \dfrac{1}{x^r} = +\infty$;

(ii) $\lim_{x \to 0^-} \dfrac{1}{x^r} = \begin{cases} -\infty & \text{if } r \text{ is odd} \\ +\infty & \text{if } r \text{ is even} \end{cases}$

Proof We prove part (i). The proof of part (ii) is analogous and is left as an exercise (see Supplementry Exercise 3). We must show that for any $N > 0$ there exists a $\delta > 0$ such that

if $0 < x < \delta$ then $\dfrac{1}{x^r} > N$

or, equivalently, because $x > 0$ and $N > 0$,

if $0 < x < \delta$ then $x^r < \dfrac{1}{N}$

or, equivalently, because $r > 0$,

if $0 < x < \delta$ then $x < \left(\dfrac{1}{N}\right)^{1/r}$

The above statement holds if $\delta = \left(\dfrac{1}{N}\right)^{1/r}$. Therefore when $\delta = \left(\dfrac{1}{N}\right)^{1/r}$

if $0 < x < \delta$ then $\dfrac{1}{x^r} > N$ ∎

▷ ILLUSTRATION 1   From Limit Theorem 11(i)

$$\lim_{x \to 0^+} \frac{1}{x^3} = +\infty \quad \text{and} \quad \lim_{x \to 0^+} \frac{1}{x^4} = +\infty$$

From Limit Theorem 11(ii)

$$\lim_{x \to 0^-} \frac{1}{x^3} = -\infty \quad \text{and} \quad \lim_{x \to 0^-} \frac{1}{x^4} = +\infty$$ ◀

Limit Theorem 12, which follows, involves the limit of a rational function for which the limit of the denominator is zero and the limit of the numerator is a nonzero constant. Such a situation occurs in (4) and (5).

1.7.4 Limit Theorem 12

If a is any real number and if $\lim_{x \to a} f(x) = 0$ and $\lim_{x \to a} g(x) = c$, where c is a constant not equal to 0, then

(i) if $c > 0$ and if $f(x) \to 0$ through positive values of $f(x)$,

$$\lim_{x \to a} \frac{g(x)}{f(x)} = +\infty$$

(ii) if $c > 0$ and if $f(x) \to 0$ through negative values of $f(x)$,

$$\lim_{x \to a} \frac{g(x)}{f(x)} = -\infty$$

(iii) if $c < 0$ and if $f(x) \to 0$ through positive values of $f(x)$,

$$\lim_{x \to a} \frac{g(x)}{f(x)} = -\infty$$

(iv) if $c < 0$ and if $f(x) \to 0$ through negative values of $f(x)$,

$$\lim_{x \to a} \frac{g(x)}{f(x)} = +\infty$$

The theorem is also valid if "$x \to a$" is replaced by "$x \to a^+$" or "$x \to a^-$."

The proof of part (i) appears in the supplement of this section. The proofs of the other parts are left as Supplementary Exercises 4–6.

When Limit Theorem 12 is applied, we can often get an indication of whether the result is $+\infty$ or $-\infty$ by taking a *suitable value* of x near a to ascertain if the quotient is positive or negative, as shown in the following illustration.

▷ **ILLUSTRATION 2**   In (4) we have

$$\lim_{x \to 1^-} \frac{2x}{x - 1}$$

Limit Theorem 12 is applicable because $\lim_{x \to 1^-} 2x = 2$ and $\lim_{x \to 1^-} (x - 1) = 0$. We wish to determine if we have $+\infty$ or $-\infty$. Because $x \to 1^-$, take a value of x near 1 and less than 1; for instance, take $x = 0.9$ and compute

$$\frac{2(0.9)}{0.9 - 1} = -18$$

The negative quotient leads us to suspect that

$$\lim_{x \to 1^-} \frac{2x}{x - 1} = -\infty$$

This result follows from part (ii) of Limit Theorem 12, because when $x \rightarrow 1^-$, $x - 1$ is approaching 0 through negative values.

For the limit in (5), because $x \rightarrow 1^+$, take $x = 1.1$ and compute

$$\frac{2(1.1)}{1.1 - 1} = 22$$

Because the quotient is positive we suspect that

$$\lim_{x \to 1^+} \frac{2x}{x - 1} = +\infty$$

This result follows from part (i) of Limit Theorem 12, because when $x \rightarrow 1^+$, $x - 1$ is approaching 0 through positive values. ◀

When using the procedure described in Illustration 2, be careful that the value of x selected is close enough to a to indicate the true behavior of the quotient. For instance, when computing $\lim\limits_{x \to 1^-} \dfrac{2x}{x - 1}$, the value of x selected must not only be less than 1 but also greater than 0.

▶ **EXAMPLE 1**   Let

$$F(x) = \frac{x^2 + x + 2}{x^2 - 2x - 3}$$

Find: **(a)** $\lim\limits_{x \to 3^+} F(x)$; **(b)** $\lim\limits_{x \to 3^-} F(x)$. **(c)** Support the answers in parts (a) and (b) by plotting the graph of F.

Solution

(a) $\lim\limits_{x \to 3^+} \dfrac{x^2 + x + 2}{x^2 - 2x - 3} = \lim\limits_{x \to 3^+} \dfrac{x^2 + x + 2}{(x - 3)(x + 1)}$

The limit of the numerator is 14, which can be verified easily.

$$\lim_{x \to 3^+} (x - 3)(x + 1) = \lim_{x \to 3^+} (x - 3) \cdot \lim_{x \to 3^+} (x + 1)$$
$$= 0 \cdot 4$$
$$= 0$$

The limit of the denominator is 0, and the denominator is approaching 0 through positive values. Then from Limit Theorem 12(i),

$$\lim_{x \to 3^+} \frac{x^2 + x + 2}{x^2 - 2x - 3} = +\infty$$

(b) $\lim\limits_{x \to 3^-} \dfrac{x^2 + x + 2}{x^2 - 2x - 3} = \lim\limits_{x \to 3^-} \dfrac{x^2 + x + 2}{(x - 3)(x + 1)}$

As in part (a), the limit of the numerator is 14.

$$\lim_{x \to 3^-} (x - 3)(x + 1) = \lim_{x \to 3^-} (x - 3) \cdot \lim_{x \to 3^-} (x + 1)$$
$$= 0 \cdot 4$$
$$= 0$$

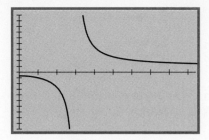

[0, 9.4] by [−10, 10]

$$f(x) = \frac{x^2 + x + 2}{x^2 - 2x - 3}$$

FIGURE 5

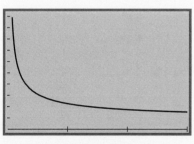

[2, 5] by [0, 10]

$$f(x) = \frac{\sqrt{x^2 - 4}}{x - 2}$$

FIGURE 6

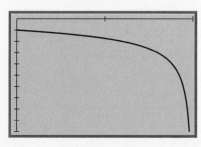

[0, 2] by [−10, 0]

$$g(x) = \frac{\sqrt{4 - x^2}}{x - 2}$$

FIGURE 7

In this case, the limit of the denominator is zero, but the denominator is approaching zero through negative values. From Limit Theorem 12(ii),

$$\lim_{x \to 3^-} \frac{x^2 + x + 2}{x^2 - 2x - 3} = -\infty$$

(c) Figure 5 shows the graph of F plotted in the [0, 9.4] by [−10, 10] window, which supports our answers in parts (a) and (b). ◀

▶ **EXAMPLE 2**   Let

$$f(x) = \frac{\sqrt{x^2 - 4}}{x - 2} \qquad g(x) = \frac{\sqrt{4 - x^2}}{x - 2}$$

Find: **(a)** $\lim_{x \to 2^+} f(x)$; **(b)** $\lim_{x \to 2^-} g(x)$. Support each answer by plotting the graph of the function.

Solution

(a) Because $x \to 2^+$, $x - 2 > 0$; so $x - 2 = \sqrt{(x - 2)^2}$. Thus

$$\lim_{x \to 2^+} \frac{\sqrt{x^2 - 4}}{x - 2} = \lim_{x \to 2^+} \frac{\sqrt{(x - 2)(x + 2)}}{\sqrt{(x - 2)^2}}$$

$$= \lim_{x \to 2^+} \frac{\sqrt{x - 2}\,\sqrt{x + 2}}{\sqrt{x - 2}\sqrt{x - 2}}$$

$$= \lim_{x \to 2^+} \frac{\sqrt{x + 2}}{\sqrt{x - 2}}$$

The limit of the numerator is 2. The limit of the denominator is 0, and the denominator is approaching 0 through positive values. Therefore, by Limit Theorem 12(i) it follows that

$$\lim_{x \to 2^+} \frac{\sqrt{x^2 - 4}}{x - 2} = +\infty$$

The graph of f plotted in the [2, 5] by [0, 10] window, shown in Figure 6, supports our answer.

(b) Because $x \to 2^-$, $x - 2 < 0$; so $x - 2 = -\sqrt{(2 - x)^2}$. Therefore

$$\lim_{x \to 2^-} \frac{\sqrt{4 - x^2}}{x - 2} = \lim_{x \to 2^-} \frac{\sqrt{2 - x}\,\sqrt{2 + x}}{-\sqrt{2 - x}\,\sqrt{2 - x}}$$

$$= \lim_{x \to 2^-} \frac{\sqrt{2 + x}}{-\sqrt{2 - x}}$$

The limit of the numerator is 2. The limit of the denominator is 0, and the denominator is approaching 0 through negative values. Hence by Limit Theorem 12(ii),

$$\lim_{x \to 2^-} \frac{\sqrt{4 - x^2}}{x - 2} = -\infty$$

Figure 7 shows the graph of g plotted in the [0, 2] by [−10, 0] window, which supports our answer. ◀

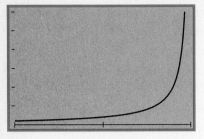

[3, 4] by [0, 30]

$$h(x) = \frac{[\![x]\!] - 4}{x - 4}$$

FIGURE 8

▶ **EXAMPLE 3** Given

$$h(x) = \frac{[\![x]\!] - 4}{x - 4}$$

(a) Plot the graph of h, and from the graph make a statement regarding the apparent behavior of $h(x)$ as x approaches 4 through values less than 4.
(b) Confirm the statement in part (a) analytically by finding $\lim\limits_{x \to 4^-} h(x)$.

Solution

(a) Figure 8 shows the graph of h plotted in the [3, 4] by [0, 30] window. From the graph, $h(x)$ appears to be increasing without bound as x approaches 4 through values less than 4.
(b) Because $\lim\limits_{x \to 4^-} [\![x]\!] = 3$, we have $\lim\limits_{x \to 4^-} ([\![x]\!] - 4) = -1$. Furthermore, $\lim\limits_{x \to 4^-} (x - 4) = 0$, and $x - 4$ is approaching 0 through negative values. Hence from Limit Theorem 12(iv),

$$\lim_{x \to 4^-} \frac{[\![x]\!] - 4}{x - 4} = +\infty$$

This result confirms our statement in part (a). ◀

Remember that because $+\infty$ and $-\infty$ are not symbols for real numbers, Limit Theorems 1–10 of Section 1.5 do not hold for "infinite" limits. Properties regarding such limits, however, are given by the following theorems, whose proofs are left as exercises (see Supplementary Exercises 7–9).

1.7.5 Theorem

    (i) If $\lim\limits_{x \to a} f(x) = +\infty$, and $\lim\limits_{x \to a} g(x) = c$, where c is any constant, then
$$\lim_{x \to a} [f(x) + g(x)] = +\infty$$
    (ii) If $\lim\limits_{x \to a} f(x) = -\infty$ and $\lim\limits_{x \to a} g(x) = c$, where c is any constant, then
$$\lim_{x \to a} [f(x) + g(x)] = -\infty$$
    The theorem holds if "$x \to a$" is replaced by "$x \to a^+$" or "$x \to a^-$."

▷ **ILLUSTRATION 3** Because

$$\lim_{x \to 2^+} \frac{1}{x - 2} = +\infty \quad \text{and} \quad \lim_{x \to 2^+} \frac{1}{x + 2} = \frac{1}{4}$$

it follows from Theorem 1.7.5(i) that $\lim\limits_{x \to 2^+} \left[\dfrac{1}{x - 2} + \dfrac{1}{x + 2} \right] = +\infty$ ◀

1.7.6 Theorem

If $\lim\limits_{x \to a} f(x) = +\infty$ and $\lim\limits_{x \to a} g(x) = c$, where c is any constant except 0, then

(i) if $c > 0$, $\lim\limits_{x \to a} f(x) \cdot g(x) = +\infty$;
(ii) if $c < 0$, $\lim\limits_{x \to a} f(x) \cdot g(x) = -\infty$.

The theorem holds if "$x \to a$" is replaced by "$x \to a^+$" or "$x \to a^-$."

▷ **ILLUSTRATION 4**

$$\lim_{x \to 3} \frac{5}{(x-3)^2} = +\infty \quad \text{and} \quad \lim_{x \to 3} \frac{x+4}{x-4} = -7$$

Therefore, from Theorem 1.7.6 (ii),

$$\lim_{x \to 3} \left[\frac{5}{(x-3)^2} \cdot \frac{x+4}{x-4} \right] = -\infty \qquad \blacktriangleleft$$

1.7.7 Theorem

If $\lim\limits_{x \to a} f(x) = -\infty$ and $\lim\limits_{x \to a} g(x) = c$, where c is any constant except 0, then

(i) if $c > 0$ $\lim\limits_{x \to a} f(x) \cdot g(x) = -\infty$;
(ii) if $c < 0$, $\lim\limits_{x \to a} f(x) \cdot g(x) = +\infty$.

The theorem holds if "$x \to a$" is replaced by "$x \to a^+$" or "$x \to a^-$."

▷ **ILLUSTRATION 5**   In Example 2(b) we showed

$$\lim_{x \to 2^-} \frac{\sqrt{4 - x^2}}{x - 2} = -\infty$$

Furthermore,

$$\lim_{x \to 2^-} \frac{x - 3}{x + 2} = -\frac{1}{4}$$

Thus, from Theorem 1.7.7(ii)

$$\lim_{x \to 2^-} \left[\frac{\sqrt{4 - x^2}}{x - 2} \cdot \frac{x - 3}{x + 2} \right] = +\infty \qquad \blacktriangleleft$$

We can apply infinite limits to find *vertical asymptotes* of a graph if there are any. Refer to Figure 9 showing the graph of the function defined by

$$f(x) = \frac{1}{(x - a)^2} \qquad \textbf{(6)}$$

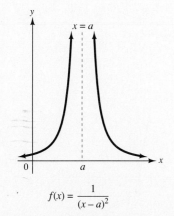

$$f(x) = \frac{1}{(x-a)^2}$$

FIGURE 9

Any line parallel to and above the x axis will intersect this graph in two points: one point to the left of the line $x = a$ and one point to the right of this line. Thus for any $k > 0$, no matter how large, the line $y = k$ will intersect the graph of f in two points; the distance of these two points from the line $x = a$ gets smaller and smaller as k gets larger and larger. The line $x = a$ is called a *vertical asymptote* of the graph of f.

1.7.8 Definition of a Vertical Asymptote

The line $x = a$ is a **vertical asymptote** of the graph of the function f if at least one of the following statements is true.

(i) $\lim\limits_{x \to a^+} f(x) = +\infty$

(ii) $\lim\limits_{x \to a^+} f(x) = -\infty$

(iii) $\lim\limits_{x \to a^-} f(x) = +\infty$

(iv) $\lim\limits_{x \to a^-} f(x) = -\infty$

▷ **ILLUSTRATION 6**   Each of Figures 10 through 13 shows a portion of the graph of a function for which the line $x = a$ is a vertical asymptote. In Figure 10, part (i) of Definition 1.7.8 applies; in Figure 11, part (ii) applies; and in Figures 12 and 13, parts (iii) and (iv), respectively, apply.

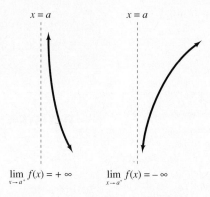

$$\lim_{x \to a^+} f(x) = +\infty \qquad \lim_{x \to a^+} f(x) = -\infty$$

FIGURE 10   **FIGURE 11**

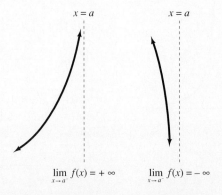

$$\lim_{x \to a^-} f(x) = +\infty \qquad \lim_{x \to a^-} f(x) = -\infty$$

FIGURE 12   **FIGURE 13**   ◀

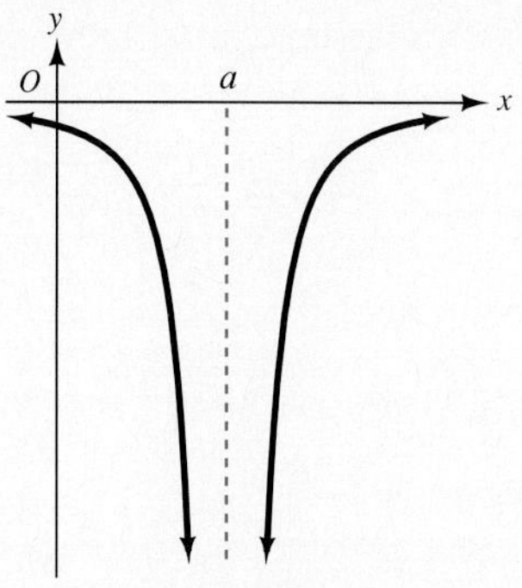

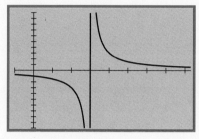

$$g(x) = -\frac{1}{(x-a)^2}$$

FIGURE 14

[-1, 8.4] by [-10, 10]

$$f(x) = \frac{3}{x-3}$$

FIGURE 15

For the function defined by (6), both parts (i) and (iii) of the above definition are true. See Figure 9. If g is the function defined by

$$g(x) = -\frac{1}{(x-a)^2}$$

then both parts (ii) and (iv) are true, and the line $x = a$ is a vertical asymptote of the graph of g. Figure 14 shows this situation.

▶ **EXAMPLE 4**   Find the vertical asymptote of the graph of function f defined by

$$f(x) = \frac{3}{x-3}$$

Support the answer by plotting the graph of f and the asymptote in the same window.

Solution   We investigate

$$\lim_{x \to 3^+} f(x) \quad \text{and} \quad \lim_{x \to 3^-} f(x)$$

because in both cases, the limit of the denominator is zero.

$$\lim_{x\to3^+} \frac{3}{x-3} = +\infty \qquad \lim_{x\to3^-} \frac{3}{x-3} = -\infty$$

From Definition 1.7.8 we conclude that the line $x = 3$ is a vertical asymptote of the graph of f.

The graph of f and the line $x = 3$ plotted in the $[-1, 8.4]$ by $[-10, 10]$ window, shown in Figure 15, supports our answer.   ◀

EXERCISES 1.7

In Exercises 1 through 12, do the following: (a) Use your calculator to tabulate values of $f(x)$ for the specified values of x, and from these values make a statement regarding the apparent behavior of $f(x)$. (b) Support your answer in part (a) by plotting the graph of f. (c) Confirm your answer in part (a) analytically by computing the indicated limit.

1. $f(x) = \dfrac{1}{x-5}$; x is 6, 5.5, 5.1, 5.01, 5.001, 5.0001;

$$\lim_{x\to5^+} \frac{1}{x-5}$$

2. $f(x) = \dfrac{1}{x-5}$; x is 4, 4.5, 4.9, 4.99, 4.999, 4.9999;

$$\lim_{x\to5^-} \frac{1}{x-5}$$

3. $f(x) = \dfrac{1}{(x-5)^2}$; x is 6, 5.5, 5.1, 5.01, 5.001, 5.0001 and x is 4, 4.5, 4.9, 4.99, 4.999, 4.9999;

$$\lim_{x\to5} \frac{1}{(x-5)^2}$$

4. $f(x) = \dfrac{x+2}{1-x}$; x is 0, 0.5, 0.9, 0.99, 0.999, 0.9999;

$$\lim_{x\to1^-} \frac{x+2}{1-x}$$

5. $f(x) = \dfrac{x+2}{1-x}$; x is 2, 1.5, 1.1, 1.01, 1.001, 1.0001;

$$\lim_{x\to1^+} \frac{x+2}{1-x}$$

6. $f(x) = \dfrac{x+2}{(x-1)^2}$; x is 0, 0.5, 0.9, 0.99, 0.999, 0.9999 and x is 2, 1.5, 1.1, 1.01, 1.001, 1.0001; $\lim\limits_{x\to1} \dfrac{x+2}{(x-1)^2}$

7. $f(x) = \dfrac{x-2}{x+1}$; x is 0, −0.5, −0.9, −0.99, −0.999, −0.9999; $\lim\limits_{x\to-1^+} \dfrac{x-2}{x+1}$

8. $f(x) = \dfrac{x - 2}{x + 1}$; x is $-2, -1.5, -1.1, -1.01, -1.001,$

-1.0001; $\lim\limits_{x \to -1^-} \dfrac{x - 2}{x + 1}$

9. $f(x) = \dfrac{x}{x + 4}$; x is $-5, -4.5, -4.1, -4.01, -4.001,$

-4.0001; $\lim\limits_{x \to -4^-} \dfrac{x}{x + 4}$

10. $f(x) = \dfrac{x}{x - 4}$; x is $5, 4.5, 4.1, 4.01, 4.001, 4.0001$;

$\lim\limits_{x \to 4^+} \dfrac{x}{x - 4}$

11. $f(x) = \dfrac{4x}{9 - x^2}$; x is $-4, -3.5, -3.1, -3.01,$

$-3.001, -3.0001$; $\lim\limits_{x \to -3^-} \dfrac{4x}{9 - x^2}$

12. $f(x) = \dfrac{4x^2}{9 - x^2}$; x is $4, 3.5, 3.1, 3.01, 3.001, 3.0001$;

$\lim\limits_{x \to 3^+} \dfrac{4x^2}{9 - x^2}$

In Exercises 13 through 32, find the limit analytically and support your answer by plotting the graph of the function on your graphics calculator.

13. $\lim\limits_{t \to 2^+} \dfrac{t + 2}{t^2 - 4}$

14. $\lim\limits_{t \to 2^-} \dfrac{-t + 2}{(t - 2)^2}$

15. $\lim\limits_{t \to 2^-} \dfrac{t + 2}{t^2 - 4}$

16. $\lim\limits_{x \to 0^+} \dfrac{\sqrt{3 + x^2}}{x}$

17. $\lim\limits_{x \to 0^-} \dfrac{\sqrt{3 + x^2}}{x}$

18. $\lim\limits_{x \to 0} \dfrac{\sqrt{3 + x^2}}{x^2}$

19. $\lim\limits_{x \to 3^+} \dfrac{\sqrt{x^2 - 9}}{x - 3}$

20. $\lim\limits_{x \to 4^-} \dfrac{\sqrt{16 - x^2}}{x - 4}$

21. $\lim\limits_{x \to 0^+} \left(\dfrac{1}{x} - \dfrac{1}{x^2} \right)$

22. $\lim\limits_{x \to 0^+} \dfrac{x^2 - 3}{x^3 + x^2}$

23. $\lim\limits_{x \to 0^-} \dfrac{2 - 4x^3}{5x^2 + 3x^3}$

24. $\lim\limits_{s \to 2^-} \left(\dfrac{1}{s - 2} - \dfrac{3}{s^2 - 4} \right)$

25. $\lim\limits_{t \to -4^-} \left(\dfrac{2}{t^2 + 3t - 4} - \dfrac{3}{t + 4} \right)$

26. $\lim\limits_{x \to 1^-} \dfrac{2x^3 - 5x^2}{x^2 - 1}$

27. $\lim\limits_{x \to 3^-} \dfrac{[\![x]\!] - x}{3 - x}$

28. $\lim\limits_{x \to 1^-} \dfrac{[\![x^2]\!] - 1}{x^2 - 1}$

29. $\lim\limits_{x \to 3^-} \dfrac{x^3 + 9x^2 + 20x}{x^2 + x - 12}$

30. $\lim\limits_{x \to -2^+} \dfrac{6x^2 + x - 2}{2x^2 + 3x - 2}$

31. $\lim\limits_{x \to 1^+} \dfrac{x - 1}{\sqrt{2x - x^2} - 1}$

32. $\lim\limits_{x \to 2^-} \dfrac{x - 2}{2 - \sqrt{4x - x^2}}$

33. Given

$$f(x) = \dfrac{x^2 + x - 6}{x^2 - 6x + 8}$$

(a) Plot the graph of f in the $[-1, 8.4]$ by $[-5, 5]$ window. From your graph make a conjecture about each of the following limits and then confirm your conjecture analytically: **(b)** $\lim\limits_{x \to 2^-} f(x)$; **(c)** $\lim\limits_{x \to 2^+} f(x)$; **(d)** $\lim\limits_{x \to 4^-} f(x)$; **(e)** $\lim\limits_{x \to 4^+} f(x)$.

34. Given

$$f(x) = \dfrac{x^2 + 2x - 3}{x^2 + x - 6}$$

(a) Plot the graph of f in the $[-4.7, 4.7]$ by $[-5, 5]$ window. From your graph make a conjecture about each of the following limits and then confirm your conjecture analytically: **(b)** $\lim\limits_{x \to -3^-} f(x)$; **(c)** $\lim\limits_{x \to -3^+} f(x)$; **(d)** $\lim\limits_{x \to 2^-} f(x)$; **(e)** $\lim\limits_{x \to 2^+} f(x)$.

In Exercises 35 and 36, find the vertical asymptote of the graph of the function and sketch the graph.

35. (a) $f(x) = \dfrac{1}{x}$ **(b)** $g(x) = \dfrac{1}{x^2}$

(c) $F(x) = \dfrac{1}{x^3}$ **(d)** $G(x) = \dfrac{1}{x^4}$

36. (a) $f(x) = -\dfrac{1}{x}$ **(b)** $g(x) = -\dfrac{1}{x^2}$

(c) $F(x) = -\dfrac{1}{x^3}$ **(d)** $G(x) = -\dfrac{1}{x^4}$

In Exercises 37 through 44, (a) find the vertical asymptote(s) of the graph of the function, and (b) apply your answer in part (a) to sketch the graph.

37. $f(x) = \dfrac{2}{x - 4}$

38. $f(x) = \dfrac{3}{x + 1}$

39. $f(x) = \dfrac{-2}{x + 3}$

40. $f(x) = \dfrac{-4}{x - 5}$

41. $f(x) = \dfrac{-2}{(x + 3)^2}$

42. $f(x) = \dfrac{4}{(x - 5)^2}$

43. $f(x) = \dfrac{5}{x^2 + 8x + 15}$

44. $f(x) = \dfrac{1}{x^2 + 5x - 6}$

In Exercises 45 and 46, evaluate the limits in parts (a)–(j) from the graph of function f sketched in the accompanying figure.

45. The domain of f is $[-2, 3]$. **(a)** $\lim\limits_{x\to-2^+} f(x)$;
(b) $\lim\limits_{x\to-1^-} f(x)$; **(c)** $\lim\limits_{x\to-1^+} f(x)$; **(d)** $\lim\limits_{x\to0} f(x)$;
(e) $\lim\limits_{x\to1^-} f(x)$; **(f)** $\lim\limits_{x\to1^+} f(x)$; **(g)** $\lim\limits_{x\to1} f(x)$; **(h)** $\lim\limits_{x\to2^-} f(x)$;
(i) $\lim\limits_{x\to2^+} f(x)$; **(j)** $\lim\limits_{x\to3^-} f(x)$.

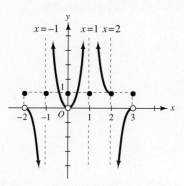

46. The domain of f is $[-4, 4]$. **(a)** $\lim\limits_{x\to-4^+} f(x)$;
(b) $\lim\limits_{x\to-2^-} f(x)$; **(c)** $\lim\limits_{x\to-2^+} f(x)$; **(d)** $\lim\limits_{x\to0} f(x)$;
(e) $\lim\limits_{x\to2^-} f(x)$; **(f)** $\lim\limits_{x\to2^+} f(x)$; **(g)** $\lim\limits_{x\to3^-} f(x)$; **(h)** $\lim\limits_{x\to3^+} f(x)$;
(i) $\lim\limits_{x\to3} f(x)$; **(j)** $\lim\limits_{x\to4^-} f(x)$.

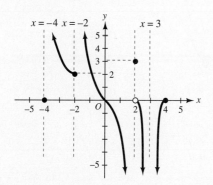

In Exercises 47 and 48, sketch a graph of some function f satisfying the given properties.

47. The domain of f is $[-5, 5]$. $f(-5) = 0$; $f(-3) = 2$; $f(-1) = 0$; $f(0) = 0$; $f(1) = 0$; $f(3) = -2$; $f(5) = -4$; $\lim\limits_{x\to-5^+} f(x) = +\infty$; $\lim\limits_{x\to-3} f(x) = 0$; $\lim\limits_{x\to-1^-} f(x) = +\infty$; $\lim\limits_{x\to-1^+} f(x) = -\infty$; $\lim\limits_{x\to0} f(x) = 0$; $\lim\limits_{x\to1} f(x) = +\infty$; $\lim\limits_{x\to3} f(x) = 0$; $\lim\limits_{x\to5^-} f(x) = -\infty$.

48. The domain of f is $[-2, 2]$. $f(-2) = 0$; $f(-1) = 0$; $f(0) = 5$; $f(1) = -5$; $f(2) = 3$; $\lim\limits_{x\to-2^+} f(x) = -\infty$; $\lim\limits_{x\to-1^-} f(x) = +\infty$; $\lim\limits_{x\to-1^+} f(x) = -\infty$; $\lim\limits_{x\to0^-} f(x) = 0$; $\lim\limits_{x\to0^+} f(x) = +\infty$; $\lim\limits_{x\to1} f(x) = -\infty$; $\lim\limits_{x\to2^-} f(x) = 3$.

49. If $C(t)$ dollars is the total cost per hour of lighting a factory with n fluorescent bulbs, each having an average life of t hours,

$$C(t) = n\left(\frac{r}{t} + \frac{epk}{1000}\right)$$

where r dollars is the renewal cost, e is the commercial efficiency constant, p watts is the power output of each bulb, and k dollars is the cost per hour of energy per 1000 watts. Find $\lim\limits_{t\to0^+} C(t)$.

50. Given

$$f(x) = \frac{1}{x - 2} \quad \text{and} \quad g(x) = \frac{1}{2 - x}$$

(a) Show that neither $\lim\limits_{x\to2} f(x)$ nor $\lim\limits_{x\to2} g(x)$ exists. **(b)** Define the function $f + g$. **(c)** Show that $\lim\limits_{x\to2} [f(x) + g(x)]$ exists. **(d)** From the results of parts (a) and (c)

$$\lim\limits_{x\to2} [f(x) + g(x)] \neq \lim\limits_{x\to2} f(x) + \lim\limits_{x\to2} g(x)$$

Does this fact contradict Limit Theorem 4 (1.5.5)?

51. According to Einstein's Special Theory of Relativity, no particle with positive mass can travel faster than the speed of light. The theory specifies that if $m(v)$ is the measure of the mass of a particle moving with a velocity of measure v, then

$$m(v) = \frac{m_0}{\sqrt{1 - \left(\dfrac{v}{c}\right)^2}}$$

where m_0 is the constant measure of the particle's rest mass relative to some reference frame, and c is the constant measure of the speed of light. Explain why none of the following limits exist: $\lim\limits_{v\to c^-} m(v)$; $\lim\limits_{v\to c^+} m(v)$; $\lim\limits_{v\to c} m(v)$. In your explanation indicate the behavior of $m(v)$ as v approaches c through values less than c.

52. Write a formal definition of each of the following one-sided infinite limits: **(a)** $\lim\limits_{x\to a^-} f(x) = +\infty$; **(b)** $\lim\limits_{x\to a^+} f(x) = -\infty$; **(c)** $\lim\limits_{x\to a^-} f(x) = -\infty$.

In Exercises 53 and 54, state in words what the indicated symbolism means without using the words limit, *approaches, infinity, increases without bound, or decreases without bound and without using symbols such as N and δ.*

53. $\lim\limits_{x \to a} f(x) = +\infty$ **54.** $\lim\limits_{x \to a} f(x) = -\infty$

55. If $P(x)$ is a polynomial and $Q(x) = x - a$, the graph of the function f defined by $f(x) = P(x)/Q(x)$ will have either the line $x = a$ as a vertical asymptote or a hole at the point where $x = a$. What is the connection between these two geometric concepts and $\lim\limits_{x \to a} f(x)$?

1.8 CONTINUITY OF A FUNCTION AT A NUMBER

In Example 2 of Section 1.3 and Illustration 2 of Section 1.6 we discussed the function C defined by

$$C(x) = \begin{cases} 2x & \text{if } 0 \le x \le 10 \\ 1.8x & \text{if } 10 < x \end{cases} \tag{1}$$

where $C(x)$ dollars is the total cost of x pounds of a product. We showed that $\lim\limits_{x \to 10} C(x)$ does not exist because $\lim\limits_{x \to 10^+} C(x) \ne \lim\limits_{x \to 10^-} C(x)$. The graph of C, sketched in Figure 1, has a break at the point where $x = 10$ because C is *discontinuous* at the number 10. This *discontinuity* is caused by the fact that $\lim\limits_{x \to 10} C(x)$ does not exist. We refer to this function again in Illustration 1.

In Section 1.4, we considered the function f defined by

$$f(x) = \frac{(2x + 3)(x - 1)}{x - 1} \tag{2}$$

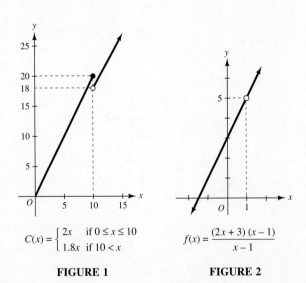

$$C(x) = \begin{cases} 2x & \text{if } 0 \le x \le 10 \\ 1.8x & \text{if } 10 < x \end{cases} \qquad f(x) = \frac{(2x+3)(x-1)}{x-1}$$

FIGURE 1   **FIGURE 2**

The graph of f consisting of all points on the line $y = 2x + 3$ except $(1, 5)$ appears in Figure 2. The graph has a break at the point $(1, 5)$ because this function is *discontinuous* at the number 1. This *discontinuity* occurs because $f(1)$ does not exist.

Suppose the function F has the same function values as the function f defined by (2) when $x \ne 1$ and suppose, for instance, $F(1) = 2$. Then F is defined for all values of x, but there is still a break in the graph (see

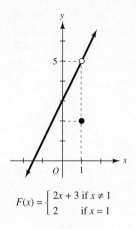

$$F(x) = \begin{cases} 2x + 3 & \text{if } x \neq 1 \\ 2 & \text{if } x = 1 \end{cases}$$

FIGURE 3

Figure 3), and the function is still *discontinuous* at 1. If, however, we define $F(1) = 5$, the graph has no break, and then the function F is said to be *continuous* at all values of x.

1.8.1 Definition of a Function Continuous at a Number

The function f is said to be **continuous** at the number a if and only if the following three conditions are satisfied:

(i) $f(a)$ exists;

(ii) $\lim\limits_{x \to a} f(x)$ exists;

(iii) $\lim\limits_{x \to a} f(x) = f(a)$.

If one or more of these three conditions fails to hold at a, the function f is said to be **discontinuous** at a.

▷ **ILLUSTRATION 1**   The graph of function C defined by (1) has the graph shown in Figure 1. Because the graph has a break at the point where $x = 10$, we will investigate the conditions of the above definition at the number 10.

(i) $C(10) = 10$

(ii) $\lim\limits_{x \to 10} C(x)$ does not exist.

Thus condition (i) is satisfied, but condition (ii) fails to hold at 10. We therefore conclude that C is discontinuous at 10.   ◄

The next illustration presents another situation in which the formula for computing the cost of more than 10 lb of a product is different from the formula for computing the cost of 10 lb or less. For this situation, however, the cost function is continuous at 10.

▷ **ILLUSTRATION 2**   A wholesaler who sells a product by the pound (or fraction of a pound) charges $2 per pound if 10 lb or less are ordered. If more than 10 lb are ordered, the wholesaler charges $20 plus $1.40 for each pound in excess of 10 lb. Therefore, if x pounds of the product are purchased at a total cost of $C(x)$ dollars, then $C(x) = 2x$ if $0 \leq x \leq 10$ and $C(x) = 20 + 1.4(x - 10)$ if $10 < x$; that is,

$$C(x) = \begin{cases} 2x & \text{if } 0 \leq x \leq 10 \\ 1.4x + 6 & \text{if } 10 < x \end{cases}$$

The graph of C is sketched in Figure 4. For this function, $C(10) = 20$ and

$$\lim_{x \to 10^-} C(x) = \lim_{x \to 10^-} 2x \qquad \lim_{x \to 10^+} C(x) = \lim_{x \to 10^+} (1.4x + 6)$$
$$= 20 \qquad\qquad\qquad = 20$$

Therefore, $\lim\limits_{x \to 10} C(x)$ exists and equals $C(10)$. Thus C is continuous at 10.   ◄

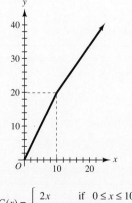

$$C(x) = \begin{cases} 2x & \text{if } 0 \leq x \leq 10 \\ 1.4x + 6 & \text{if } 10 < x \end{cases}$$

FIGURE 4

We now give some illustrations of discontinuous functions. In each illustration we sketch the graph of the given function, determine the points where the graph has a break, and show which of the three conditions in Definition 1.8.1 fails to hold at each discontinuity.

▷ **ILLUSTRATION 3**   Let f be defined by

$$f(x) = \begin{cases} 2x + 3 & \text{if } x \neq 1 \\ 2 & \text{if } x = 1 \end{cases}$$

The graph of this function, which appears in Figure 3, has a break at the point where $x = 1$. So we investigate there the conditions of Definition 1.8.1.

(i) $f(1) = 2$
(ii) $\lim_{x \to 1} f(x) = 5$
(iii) $\lim_{x \to 1} f(x) \neq f(1)$

Conditions (i) and (ii) are satisfied but condition (iii) is not satisfied. Function f is, therefore, discontinuous at 1.   ◀

Note that if in Illustration 3, $f(1)$ were defined to be 5, then $\lim_{x \to 1} f(x)$ and $f(1)$ would be equal and f would be continuous at 1. For this reason, the discontinuity in Illustration 3 is called a *removable discontinuity*.

In general, suppose that f is a function discontinuous at the number a but for which $\lim_{x \to a} f(x)$ exists. Then either $f(a)$ does not exist or else $f(a) \neq \lim_{x \to a} f(x)$. Such a discontinuity is a **removable discontinuity** because if f is redefined at a so that $f(a)$ is equal to $\lim_{x \to a} f(x)$, the new function becomes continuous at a. If the discontinuity is not removable, it is called an **essential discontinuity.**

▷ **ILLUSTRATION 4**   Let f be defined by

$$f(x) = \frac{1}{x - 2}$$

The graph of f, appearing in Figure 5, has a break at the point where $x = 2$; so we investigate there the conditions of Definition 1.8.1.

(i) $f(2)$ is not defined.

Because condition (i) is not satisfied, f is discontinuous at 2.
The discontinuity is essential because $\lim_{x \to 2} f(x)$ does not exist.   ◀

The discontinuity in Illustration 4 is called an **infinite discontinuity.**

▷ **ILLUSTRATION 5**   Let g be defined by

$$g(x) = \begin{cases} \dfrac{1}{x - 2} & \text{if } x \neq 2 \\ 3 & \text{if } x = 2 \end{cases}$$

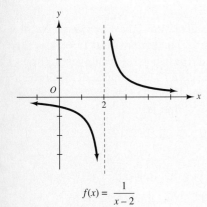

$$f(x) = \frac{1}{x - 2}$$

FIGURE 5

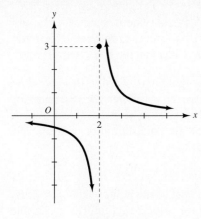

$$g(x) = \begin{cases} \dfrac{1}{x-2} & \text{if } x \neq 2 \\ 3 & \text{if } x = 2 \end{cases}$$

FIGURE 6

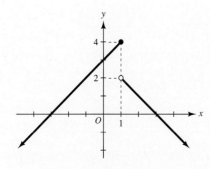

$$h(x) = \begin{cases} 3 + x & \text{if } x \leq 1 \\ 3 - x & \text{if } 1 < x \end{cases}$$

FIGURE 7

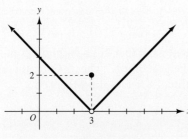

$$F(x) = \begin{cases} |x-3| & \text{if } x \neq 3 \\ 2 & \text{if } x = 3 \end{cases}$$

FIGURE 8

The graph of g appears in Figure 6. We check the three conditions of Definition 1.8.1 at 2.

(i) $g(2) = 3$

(ii) $\displaystyle\lim_{x \to 2^-} g(x) = \lim_{x \to 2^-} \frac{1}{x-2}$ $\displaystyle\lim_{x \to 2^+} g(x) = \lim_{x \to 2^+} \frac{1}{x-2}$

$\qquad\qquad = -\infty$ $\qquad\qquad\qquad = +\infty$

$\displaystyle\lim_{x \to 2} g(x)$ does not exist.

Because condition (ii) is not satisfied, g is discontinuous at 2.

The discontinuity is infinite and, of course, essential. ◀

▷ **ILLUSTRATION 6**   Let h be defined by

$$h(x) = \begin{cases} 3 + x & \text{if } x \leq 1 \\ 3 - x & \text{if } 1 < x \end{cases}$$

Figure 7 shows the graph of h. Because the graph has a break at the point where $x = 1$, we investigate the conditions of Definition 1.8.1 at 1.

(i) $h(1) = 4$

(ii) $\displaystyle\lim_{x \to 1^-} h(x) = \lim_{x \to 1^-} (3 + x)$ $\displaystyle\lim_{x \to 1^+} h(x) = \lim_{x \to 1^+} (3 - x)$

$\qquad\qquad = 4$ $\qquad\qquad\qquad = 2$

Because $\displaystyle\lim_{x \to 1^-} h(x) \neq \lim_{x \to 1^+} h(x)$, then $\displaystyle\lim_{x \to 1} h(x)$ does not exist.

Condition (ii) fails to hold at 1; so h is discontinuous at 1.

Because $\displaystyle\lim_{x \to 1} h(x)$ does not exist, the discontinuity is essential. ◀

The discontinuity in Illustration 6 is called a **jump discontinuity.**

▷ **ILLUSTRATION 7**   Let F be defined by

$$F(x) = \begin{cases} |x-3| & \text{if } x \neq 3 \\ 2 & \text{if } x = 3 \end{cases}$$

Figure 8 shows the graph of F. We check the three conditions of Definition 1.8.1 at 3.

(i) $F(3) = 2$

(ii) $\displaystyle\lim_{x \to 3^-} F(x) = \lim_{x \to 3^-} (3 - x)$ $\displaystyle\lim_{x \to 3^+} F(x) = \lim_{x \to 3^+} (x - 3)$

$\qquad\qquad = 0$ $\qquad\qquad\qquad = 0$

Therefore, $\displaystyle\lim_{x \to 3} F(x) = 0$

(iii) $\displaystyle\lim_{x \to 3} F(x) \neq F(3)$

Because condition (iii) is not satisfied, F is discontinuous at 3.

This discontinuity is removable because if $F(3)$ is redefined to be 0, then the new function is continuous at 3. ◀

▶ **EXAMPLE 1**   The function defined by

$$f(x) = \frac{\sqrt{x} - 2}{x - 4}$$

is discontinuous at 4. (a) Plot the graph of f in the $[0, 9.4]$ by $[0, 1]$ window. The graph has a break at the point where $x = 4$. Does the discontinuity appear to be removable or essential? If it appears to be removable speculate how $f(4)$ should be redefined so that the discontinuity is removed. (b) Confirm the answer in part (a) analytically.

Solution

(a) Figure 9 shows the graph of f with a hole at the point where $x = 4$. By using the trace key on our calculator we suspect that $\lim\limits_{x \to 4} f(x)$ exists and is 0.25. Thus the discontinuity appears to be removable if we redefine $f(4)$ as 0.25.

(b) We compute $\lim\limits_{x \to 4} f(x)$.

$$\begin{aligned} \lim_{x \to 4} f(x) &= \lim_{x \to 4} \frac{\sqrt{x} - 2}{x - 4} \\ &= \lim_{x \to 4} \frac{(\sqrt{x} - 2)(\sqrt{x} + 2)}{(x - 4)(\sqrt{x} + 2)} \\ &= \lim_{x \to 4} \frac{x - 4}{(x - 4)(\sqrt{x} + 2)} \\ &= \lim_{x \to 4} \frac{1}{\sqrt{x} + 2} \\ &= \frac{1}{4} \end{aligned}$$

We have confirmed our answer in part (a). We therefore redefine the function at 4, and we have the new function defined by

$$F(x) = \begin{cases} \dfrac{\sqrt{x} - 2}{x - 4} & \text{if } x \neq 4 \\ \dfrac{1}{4} & \text{if } x = 4 \end{cases}$$

This function is continuous at 4.   ◀

Theorems about functions continuous at a number are helpful for computing limits as well as for proving other theorems. The first of these theorems is obtained by applying Definition 1.8.1 and limit theorems.

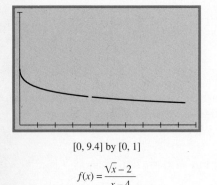

$[0, 9.4]$ by $[0, 1]$

$$f(x) = \frac{\sqrt{x} - 2}{x - 4}$$

FIGURE 9

1.8.2 Theorem

If f and g are two functions continuous at the number a, then

(i) $f + g$ is continuous at a;
(ii) $f - g$ is continuous at a;
(iii) $f \cdot g$ is continuous at a;
(iv) f/g is continuous at a, provided that $g(a) \neq 0$.

To illustrate the kind of proof required for each part of this theorem, we prove part (i).

Proof of (i)   Because f and g are continuous at a, from Definition 1.8.1

$$\lim_{x \to a} f(x) = f(a) \quad \text{and} \quad \lim_{x \to a} g(x) = g(a)$$

From these two limits and Limit Theorem 4,

$$\lim_{x \to a} [f(x) + g(x)] = f(a) + g(a)$$

which is the condition that $f + g$ is continuous at a.   ∎

The proofs of parts (ii), (iii), and (iv) are similar.

Consider the polynomial function f defined by

$$f(x) = b_0 x^n + b_1 x^{n-1} + b_2 x^{n-2} + \ldots + b_{n-1} x + b_n \qquad b_0 \neq 0$$

where n is a nonnegative integer and $b_0, b_1, \ldots, b_n$ are real numbers. By successive applications of limit theorems we can show that if a is any number,

$$\lim_{x \to a} f(x) = b_0 a^n + b_1 a^{n-1} + b_2 a^{n-2} + \ldots + b_{n-1} a + b_n$$
$$= f(a)$$

thus establishing the following theorem.

1.8.3 Theorem

A polynomial function is continuous at every number.

▷ **ILLUSTRATION 8**   If $f(x) = x^3 - 2x^2 + 5x + 1$, then f is a polynomial function and therefore, by Theorem 1.8.3, is continuous at every number. In particular, because f is continuous at 3, $\lim_{x \to 3} f(x) = f(3)$. Thus

$$\lim_{x \to 3} (x^3 - 2x^2 + 5x + 1) = 3^3 - 2(3)^2 + 5(3) + 1$$
$$= 27 - 18 + 15 + 1$$
$$= 25 \qquad ◄$$

1.8.4 Theorem

A rational function is continuous at every number in its domain.

Proof   If f is a rational function, it can be expressed as the quotient of two polynomial functions. So f can be defined by

$$f(x) = \frac{g(x)}{h(x)}$$

where g and h are two polynomial functions, and the domain of f consists of all numbers except those for which $h(x) = 0$.

If a is any number in the domain of f, then $h(a) \neq 0$; so by Limit Theorem 9,

$$\lim_{x \to a} f(x) = \frac{\lim\limits_{x \to a} g(x)}{\lim\limits_{x \to a} h(x)} \tag{3}$$

Because g and h are polynomial functions, by Theorem 1.8.3 they are continuous at a; so $\lim\limits_{x \to a} g(x) = g(a)$ and $\lim\limits_{x \to a} h(x) = h(a)$. Consequently, from (3),

$$\lim_{x \to a} f(x) = \frac{g(a)}{h(a)}$$

Therefore f is continuous at every number in its domain. ∎

▶ **EXAMPLE 2** Determine the numbers at which the following function is continuous:

$$f(x) = \frac{x^3 + 1}{x^2 - 9}$$

Solution The domain of f is the set R of real numbers except those for which $x^2 - 9 = 0$. Because $x^2 - 9 = 0$ when $x = \pm 3$, the domain of f is the set of all real numbers except 3 and -3.

Because f is a rational function, from Theorem 1.8.4 f is continuous at all real numbers except 3 and -3. ◀

▷ **ILLUSTRATION 9** Let f be the function of Example 2. Because 2 is in the domain of f, then by Theorem 1.8.4

$$\lim_{x \to 2} f(x) = f(2)$$
$$= \frac{2^3 + 1}{2^2 - 9}$$
$$= -\frac{9}{5}$$

◀

▶ **EXAMPLE 3** Determine the numbers at which the following function is continuous:

$$f(x) = \begin{cases} 2x - 3 & \text{if } x \leq 1 \\ x^2 & \text{if } 1 < x \end{cases}$$

Solution The functions having values $2x - 3$ and x^2 are polynomials and are therefore continuous everywhere. Thus the only number at which continuity is questionable is 1. We check the three conditions for continuity at 1.

(i) $f(1) = -1$. Thus condition (i) holds.

(ii) $\lim\limits_{x \to 1^-} f(x) = \lim\limits_{x \to 1^-} (2x - 3)$ $\qquad \lim\limits_{x \to 1^+} f(x) = \lim\limits_{x \to 1^+} x^2$
$$= -1 \qquad\qquad\qquad\qquad = 1$$

Because $\lim\limits_{x \to 1^-} f(x) \neq \lim\limits_{x \to 1^+} f(x)$, the two-sided limit $\lim\limits_{x \to 1} f(x)$ does not exist.

Thus f has a jump discontinuity at 1. Therefore, f is continuous at every real number except 1.   ◀

1.8.5 Theorem

If n is a positive integer and

$$f(x) = \sqrt[n]{x}$$

then

  (i) if n is odd, f is continuous at every number,
 (ii) if n is even, f is continuous at every positive number.

The proof of this theorem follows immediately from Theorem 1.5.13 which states that if $a > 0$ and n is a positive integer, or if $a \leq 0$ and n is an odd positive integer, then

$$\lim_{x \to a} \sqrt[n]{x} = \sqrt[n]{a}$$

▷ **ILLUSTRATION 10**

(a) If $f(x) = \sqrt[3]{x}$, then from Theorem 1.8.5 (i) f is continuous at every real number. Figure 10 shows the graph of f.
(b) If $g(x) = \sqrt{x}$, then from Theorem 1.8.5(ii), g is continuous at every positive number. The graph of g is sketched in Figure 11.   ◀

From time to time we need to apply a definition of continuity that uses ϵ and δ notation. To obtain this alternate definition we start with Definition 1.8.1, which states that the function f is continuous at the number a if

$$\lim_{x \to a} f(x) = f(a) \qquad (4)$$

Applying the definition of the limit of a function (1.5.1) where L is $f(a)$, (4) will hold if for any $\epsilon > 0$ there exists a $\delta > 0$ such that

$$\text{if} \quad 0 < |x - a| < \delta \quad \text{then} \quad |f(x) - f(a)| < \epsilon \qquad (5)$$

If f is to be continuous at a, $f(a)$ must exist; therefore in statement (5) the condition that $|x - a| > 0$ is not necessary, because when $x = a$, $|f(x) - f(a)|$ will be 0 and thus less than ϵ. We have, then, the following theorem, which serves as our desired alternate definition of continuity.

1.8.6 Theorem

The function f is continuous at the number a if f is defined on some open interval containing a and if for any $\epsilon > 0$ there exists a $\delta > 0$ such that

$$\text{if} \quad |x - a| < \delta \quad \text{then} \quad |f(x) - f(a)| < \epsilon$$

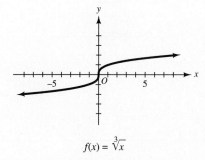

$$f(x) = \sqrt[3]{x}$$

FIGURE 10

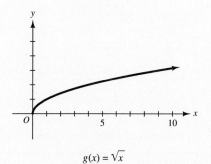

$$g(x) = \sqrt{x}$$

FIGURE 11

EXERCISES 1.8

In Exercises 1 through 14, sketch the graph of the function. By observing where there is a break in the graph, determine the number at which the function is discontinuous, and show why Definition 1.8.1 is not satisfied at this number.

1. $f(x) = \dfrac{x^2 + x - 6}{x + 3}$

2. $F(x) = \dfrac{x^2 - 3x - 4}{x - 4}$

3. $g(x) = \begin{cases} \dfrac{x^2 + x - 6}{x + 3} & \text{if } x \neq -3 \\ 1 & \text{if } x = -3 \end{cases}$

4. $G(x) = \begin{cases} \dfrac{x^2 - 3x - 4}{x - 4} & \text{if } x \neq 4 \\ 2 & \text{if } x = 4 \end{cases}$

5. $h(x) = \dfrac{5}{x - 4}$

6. $H(x) = \dfrac{1}{x + 2}$

7. $f(x) = \begin{cases} \dfrac{5}{x - 4} & \text{if } x \neq 4 \\ 2 & \text{if } x = 4 \end{cases}$

8. $g(x) = \begin{cases} \dfrac{1}{x + 2} & \text{if } x \neq -2 \\ 0 & \text{if } x = -2 \end{cases}$

9. $f(x) = \begin{cases} -1 & \text{if } x < 0 \\ 0 & \text{if } x = 0 \\ \sqrt{x} & \text{if } 0 < x \end{cases}$

10. $f(x) = \begin{cases} x - 1 & \text{if } x < 1 \\ 1 & \text{if } x = 1 \\ 1 - x & \text{if } 1 < x \end{cases}$

11. $g(t) = \begin{cases} t^2 - 4 & \text{if } t < 2 \\ 4 & \text{if } t = 2 \\ 4 - t^2 & \text{if } 2 < t \end{cases}$

12. $H(x) = \begin{cases} 6 + x & \text{if } x \leq -2 \\ 2 - x & \text{if } -2 < x \leq 2 \\ 2x - 1 & \text{if } 2 < x \end{cases}$

13. $f(x) = \dfrac{|x|}{x}$

14. $g(x) = \begin{cases} \dfrac{|x|}{x} & \text{if } x \neq 0 \\ 1 & \text{if } x = 0 \end{cases}$

In Exercises 15 through 28, the function is discontinuous at the number a. (a) Plot the graph of f in a convenient window and determine that the graph has a break at the point where x = a. Does the discontinuity appear to be removable or essential? If it appears to be removable speculate how f(a) should be redefined so that the discontinuity is removed. (b) Confirm your answer in part (a) analytically.

15. $f(x) = \dfrac{x^2 - 4}{x - 2}; a = 2$

16. $f(x) = \dfrac{x^2 + 4x + 3}{x + 3}; a = -3$

17. $f(x) = \dfrac{x - 9}{\sqrt{x} - 3}; a = 9$

18. $f(x) = \dfrac{x - 5}{\sqrt{x - 1} - 2}; a = 5$

19. $f(x) = \dfrac{\sqrt{x + 4} - 3}{x - 5}; a = 5$

20. $f(x) = \dfrac{\sqrt{x + 5} - \sqrt{5}}{x}; a = 0$

21. $f(x) = \dfrac{\sqrt{2} - \sqrt{x + 2}}{x}; a = 0$

22. $f(x) = \dfrac{2 - \sqrt{x + 1}}{x - 3}; a = 3$

23. $f(x) = \dfrac{\sqrt[3]{x} - 2}{x - 8}; a = 8$

24. $f(x) = \dfrac{\sqrt[3]{x + 1} - 1}{x}; a = 0$

25. $f(x) = \dfrac{x + 3}{3 - |x|}; a = -3$

26. $f(x) = \dfrac{x + 5}{|x + 1| - 4}; a = -5$

27. $f(x) = \dfrac{x + 3}{3 - |x|}; a = 3$

28. $f(x) = \dfrac{x + 5}{|x + 1| - 4}; a = 3$

In Exercises 29 through 40, determine the numbers at which the function is continuous and state the reason.

29. $f(x) = x^2(x + 3)^2$

30. $f(x) = (x - 5)^3(x^2 + 4)^5$

31. $g(x) = \dfrac{x}{x - 3}$

32. $h(x) = \dfrac{x + 1}{2x + 5}$

33. $F(x) = \dfrac{x^3 + 7}{x^2 - 4}$

34. $G(x) = \dfrac{x - 2}{x^2 + 2x - 8}$

35. $f(x) = \begin{cases} 3x - 1 & \text{if } x < 2 \\ 4 - x^2 & \text{if } 2 \leq x \end{cases}$

36. $f(x) = \begin{cases} (x + 2)^2 & \text{if } x \leq 0 \\ x^2 + 2 & \text{if } 0 < x \end{cases}$

37. $f(x) = \begin{cases} \dfrac{1}{x+1} & \text{if } x \le 1 \\ \dfrac{1}{3-x} & \text{if } 1 < x \end{cases}$

38. $f(x) = \begin{cases} \dfrac{1}{x} & \text{if } x < 3 \\ \dfrac{2}{9-x} & \text{if } 3 \le x \end{cases}$

39. $h(x) = \begin{cases} x + \sqrt[3]{x} & \text{if } x < 0 \\ x - \sqrt{x} & \text{if } 0 \le x \end{cases}$

40. $g(x) = \begin{cases} 2x - \sqrt[3]{x} & \text{if } x \le 1 \\ x\sqrt{x} & \text{if } 1 < x \end{cases}$

In Exercises 41 through 44, do the following: (a) Find the values of the constants c and k that make the function continuous at every number. (b) Sketch the graph of the resulting function.

41. $f(x) = \begin{cases} 3x + 7 & \text{if } x \le 4 \\ kx - 1 & \text{if } 4 < x \end{cases}$

42. $f(x) = \begin{cases} kx - 1 & \text{if } x \le 2 \\ kx^2 & \text{if } 2 \le x \end{cases}$

43. $f(x) = \begin{cases} x & \text{if } x \le 1 \\ cx + k & \text{if } 1 < x < 4 \\ -2x & \text{if } 4 \le x \end{cases}$

44. $f(x) = \begin{cases} x + 2c & \text{if } x < -2 \\ 3cx + k & \text{if } -2 \le x \le 1 \\ 3x - 2k & \text{if } 1 < x \end{cases}$

Exercises 45 and 46 pertain to the function f sketched in the accompanying figure. In parts (a)–(c) confirm analytically why f is discontinuous at the indicated number by showing why Definition 1.8.1 fails to hold.

45. **(a)** At $x = -3$; **(b)** at $x = 1$; **(c)** at $x = 3$. **(d)** Which of the discontinuities in parts (a)–(c) are essential? Why? **(e)** Which of the discontinuities in parts (a)–(c) are removable? How would you remove the discontinuity?

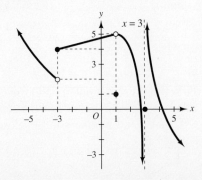

46. **(a)** At $x = 0$; **(b)** at $x = 2$; **(c)** at $x = 4$. **(d)** Which of the discontinuities in parts (a)–(c) are essential? Why? **(e)** Which of the discontinuities in parts (a)–(c) are removable? How would you remove the discontinuity?

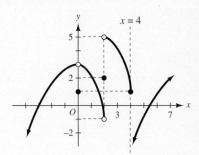

In Exercises 47 and 48, sketch a graph of some function f satisfying the given properties.

47. The domain of f is $(-4, 4)$. Function f is continuous at every number in the intervals $(-4, -2)$, $(-2, 2)$ and $(2, 4)$, and f is discontinuous at -2 and 2; $f(-2) = 0$ and $f(2) = 0$; $\lim\limits_{x \to -4^+} f(x) = +\infty$, $\lim\limits_{x \to -2^-} f(x) = 0$, $\lim\limits_{x \to 2^+} f(x) = 0$, and $\lim\limits_{x \to 4^-} f(x) = -\infty$.

48. Function f is continuous at every number in the intervals $(-\infty, -1)$, $(-1, 1)$, and $(1, +\infty)$; f is discontinuous at -1 and 1; $f(-1) = 0$ and $f(1) = 0$; $\lim\limits_{x \to -1^-} f(x)$ and $\lim\limits_{x \to -1^+} f(x)$ both exist but neither is 0; neither $\lim\limits_{x \to 1^-} f(x)$ nor $\lim\limits_{x \to 1^+} f(x)$ exists.

In Exercises 49 through 52, state the numbers at which the indicated function is discontinuous and show why Definition 1.8.1 is not satisfied at each discontinuity.

49. The function of Exercise 5 in Exercises 1.3 and Exercise 39 in Exercises 1.6, which is a mathematical model expressing the total cost of a shipment as a function of its weight.

50. The function of Exercise 6 in Exercises 1.3 and Exercise 40 in Exercises 1.6, which is a mathematical model expressing the postage in 1995 of a first-class letter weighing not more than 11 oz as a function of its weight.

51. The function of Exercise 7 in Exercises 1.3 and Exercise 41 in Exercises 1.6, which is a mathematical model expressing the cost of a telephone call, lasting not more than 5 min, from Mendocino to San Francisco as a function of the duration of the call.

52. The function of Exercise 8 in Exercises 1.3 and Exercise 42 in Exercises 1.6, which is a mathematical model expressing the admission price at the Coast Cinema as a function of the person's age.

53. Suppose at t minutes, $r(t)$ meters is the radius of a circular oil spill from a ruptured tanker and

$$r(t) = \begin{cases} 4t^2 + 20 & \text{if } 0 \le t \le 2 \\ 16t + 4 & \text{if } 2 < t \end{cases}$$

Prove that r is continuous at 2.

54. If $A(t)$ square meters is the area of the oil spill of Exercise 53 at t minutes, **(a)** define $A(t)$, and **(b)** prove that A is continuous at 2.

55. Prove that the function defined by

$$f(x) = \frac{x^n - 1}{x - 1}$$

where n is a positive integer, has a removable discontinuity at 1. *Hint:* To factor $x^n - 1$, use formula (12) in Supplementary Section 1.5.

56. The function f is defined by

$$f(x) = \lim_{n \to 0} \frac{2nx}{n^2 - nx}$$

Sketch the graph of f. At what values of x is f discontinuous?

57. If $f(x) = \begin{cases} -x & \text{if } x < 0 \\ 1 & \text{if } 0 \le x \end{cases}$ and $g(x) = \begin{cases} 1 & \text{if } x < 0 \\ x & \text{if } 0 \le x \end{cases}$

prove that f and g are both discontinuous at 0 but that the product $f \cdot g$ is continuous at 0.

58. Give an example to show that the product of two functions f and g may be continuous at a number a, where f is continuous at a but g is discontinuous at a.

59. Give an example of two functions that are both discontinuous at a number a but whose sum is continuous at a.

60. Explain why the definition of a function continuous at the number a guarantees that the graph of the function has no break at the point where $x = a$.

61. If function f is continuous at a and function g is discontinuous at a, why can we conclude that the sum of the two functions, $f + g$, is discontinuous at a?

62. If function f is discontinuous at a and function g is continuous at a, is it possible for the quotient of the two functions, f/g, to be continuous at a? Explain your answer.

1.9 CONTINUITY OF A COMPOSITE FUNCTION AND CONTINUITY ON AN INTERVAL

Recall the definition of a composite function (1.2.2): Given the functions f and g, the composite function, denoted by $f \circ g$, is defined by

$$(f \circ g)(x) = f(g(x))$$

and the domain of $f \circ g$ is the set of all numbers in the domain of g such that $g(x)$ is in the domain of f.

▷ **ILLUSTRATION 1**   If $f(x) = \sqrt{x}$ and $g(x) = 4 - x^2$, and if h is the composite function $f \circ g$, then

$$h(x) = f(g(x))$$
$$= f(4 - x^2)$$
$$= \sqrt{4 - x^2}$$

Because the domain of g is the set of all real numbers and the domain of f is the set of all nonnegative numbers, the domain of h is the set of all real numbers such that $4 - x^2 \ge 0$, that is, all numbers in the closed interval $[-2, 2]$. The graph of h is sketched in Figure 1.   ◀

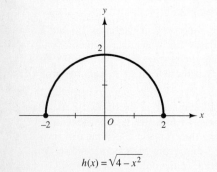

$h(x) = \sqrt{4 - x^2}$

FIGURE 1

From Figure 1, it appears that h is continuous at every number in the open interval $(-2, 2)$. Before proving this fact in Example 1, we need two more theorems, the first of which pertains to the limit of a composite function.

1.9.1 Theorem   Limit of a Composite Function

If $\lim\limits_{x \to a} g(x) = b$ and if the function f is continuous at b,
$$\lim_{x \to a} (f \circ g)(x) = f(b)$$
or, equivalently,
$$\lim_{x \to a} f(g(x)) = f(\lim_{x \to a} g(x))$$

Proof Because f is continuous at b, we have the following statement from Theorem 1.8.6. For any $\epsilon_1 > 0$ there exists a $\delta_1 > 0$ such that

$$\text{if} \quad |y - b| < \delta_1 \quad \text{then} \quad |f(y) - f(b)| < \epsilon_1 \tag{1}$$

Because $\lim\limits_{x \to a} g(x) = b$, for any $\delta_1 > 0$ there exists a $\delta_2 > 0$ such that

$$\text{if} \quad 0 < |x - a| < \delta_2 \quad \text{then} \quad |g(x) - b| < \delta_1 \tag{2}$$

If $0 < |x - a| < \delta_2$, we replace y in statement (1) by $g(x)$ and obtain the following: For any $\epsilon_1 > 0$ there exists a $\delta_1 > 0$ such that

$$\text{if} \quad |g(x) - b| < \delta_1 \quad \text{then} \quad |f(g(x)) - f(b)| < \epsilon_1 \tag{3}$$

From statements (3) and (2) we conclude that for any $\epsilon_1 > 0$ there exists a $\delta_2 > 0$ such that

$$\text{if} \quad 0 < |x - a| < \delta_2 \quad \text{then} \quad |f(g(x)) - f(b)| < \epsilon_1$$

from which it follows that

$$\lim_{x \to a} f(g(x)) = f(b)$$
$$\Leftrightarrow \quad \lim_{x \to a} f(g(x)) = f(\lim_{x \to a} g(x)) \qquad \blacksquare$$

Theorem 1.9.1 plays an important part in the proofs of Limit Theorems 9 and 10 at the end of this section. We now apply the theorem to prove the following theorem about the continuity of a composite function.

1.9.2 Theorem   Continuity of a Composite Function

If the function g is continuous at a and the function f is continuous at $g(a)$, then the composite function $f \circ g$ is continuous at a.

Proof Because g is continuous at a,

$$\lim_{x \to a} g(x) = g(a) \tag{4}$$

Now f is continuous at $g(a)$; thus we can apply Theorem 1.9.1 to the composite function $f \circ g$, thereby giving

$$\lim_{x \to a} (f \circ g)(x) = \lim_{x \to a} f(g(x))$$
$$= f(\lim_{x \to a} g(x))$$
$$= f(g(a)) \qquad \text{(by (4))}$$
$$= (f \circ g)(a)$$

which proves that $f \circ g$ is continuous at a. ∎

Theorem 1.9.2 states that *a continuous function of a continuous function is continuous.* The following example shows how it is used to determine the numbers for which a particular function is continuous.

▶ **EXAMPLE 1**   Determine the numbers at which the following function is continuous:

$$h(x) = \sqrt{4 - x^2}$$

Solution   The function h is the one obtained in Illustration 1 as the composite function $f \circ g$, where $f(x) = \sqrt{x}$ and $g(x) = 4 - x^2$. Because g is a polynomial function, it is continuous everywhere. Furthermore, f is continuous at every positive number by Theorem 1.8.5(ii). Therefore, by Theorem 1.9.2, h is continuous at every number x for which $g(x) > 0$, that is, when $4 - x^2 > 0$. Hence h is continuous at every number in the open interval $(-2, 2)$. ◀

Because the function h of Example 1 is continuous at every number in the open interval $(-2, 2)$, we say that h is *continuous on the open interval* $(-2, 2)$.

> **1.9.3 Definition of Continuity on an Open Interval**
>
> A function is said to be **continuous on an open interval** if and only if it is continuous at every number in the open interval.

We refer again to the function h of Example 1. Because h is not defined on any open interval containing either -2 or 2, we cannot consider $\lim_{x \to -2} h(x)$ or $\lim_{x \to 2} h(x)$. Therefore our definition (1.8.1) of continuity at a number does not permit h to be continuous at -2 and 2. Hence, to discuss the question of the continuity of h on the closed interval $[-2, 2]$, we must extend the concept of continuity to include continuity at an endpoint of a closed interval. This is done by first defining *right-hand continuity* and *left-hand continuity.*

1.9.4 Definition of Right-Hand Continuity

The function f is said to be **continuous from the right at the number a** if and only if the following three conditions are satisfied:

(i) $f(a)$ exists;

(ii) $\lim\limits_{x \to a^+} f(x)$ exists;

(iii) $\lim\limits_{x \to a^+} f(x) = f(a)$.

1.9.5 Definition of Left-Hand Continuity

The function f is said to be **continuous from the left at the number a** if and only if the following three conditions are satisfied:

(i) $f(a)$ exists;

(ii) $\lim\limits_{x \to a^-} f(x)$ exists;

(iii) $\lim\limits_{x \to a^-} f(x) = f(a)$.

1.9.6 Definition of Continuity on a Closed Interval

A function whose domain includes the closed interval $[a, b]$ is said to be **continuous on $[a, b]$** if and only if it is continuous on the open interval (a, b), as well as continuous from the right at a and continuous from the left at b.

▶ **EXAMPLE 2**   Prove that the function h of Example 1 is continuous on the closed interval $[-2, 2]$.

Solution   The function h is defined by

$$h(x) = \sqrt{4 - x^2}$$

and in Example 1 we showed that h is continuous on the open interval $(-2, 2)$. By applying Theorem 1.9.1 we compute $\lim\limits_{x \to -2^+} h(x)$ and $\lim\limits_{x \to 2^-} h(x)$.

$$\lim_{x \to -2^+} h(x) = \lim_{x \to -2^+} \sqrt{4 - x^2} \qquad \lim_{x \to 2^-} h(x) = \lim_{x \to 2^-} \sqrt{4 - x^2}$$
$$= 0 \qquad\qquad\qquad = 0$$
$$= h(-2) \qquad\qquad\qquad = h(2)$$

Thus h is continuous from the right at -2 and continuous from the left at 2. Hence by Definition 1.9.6, h is continuous on the closed interval $[-2, 2]$. The graph of h appears in Figure 1.   ◀

Observe the difference in terminology we used in Examples 1 and 2. In Example 1 we stated that *h is continuous at every number in the open interval* $(-2, 2)$, while in Example 2 we concluded that *h is continuous on the closed interval* $[-2, 2]$.

> **1.9.7 Definition of Continuity on a Half-Open Interval**
>
> **(i)** A function whose domain includes the interval half-open on the right $[a, b)$ is **continuous on $[a, b)$** if and only if it is continuous on the open interval (a, b) and continuous from the right at a.
>
> **(ii)** A function whose domain includes the interval half-open on the left $(a, b]$ is **continuous on $(a, b]$** if and only if it is continuous on the open interval (a, b) and continuous from the left at b.

Definitions similar to those in Definition 1.9.7 apply to continuity on the intervals $[a, +\infty)$ and $(-\infty, b]$.

▶ **EXAMPLE 3**   Determine the largest interval (or union of intervals) on which the following function is continuous:

$$f(x) = \frac{\sqrt{25 - x^2}}{x - 3}$$

Solution   We first determine the domain of f. The function is defined everywhere except when $x = 3$ or when $25 - x^2 < 0$ (that is, when $x > 5$ or $x < -5$). Therefore the domain of f is $[-5, 3) \cup (3, 5]$. Because

$$\lim_{x \to -5^+} f(x) = 0 \qquad \text{and} \qquad \lim_{x \to 5^-} f(x) = 0$$
$$= f(-5) \qquad\qquad\qquad\qquad = f(5)$$

f is continuous from the right at -5 and from the left at 5. Furthermore, f is continuous on the open intervals $(-5, 3)$ and $(3, 5)$. Therefore f is continuous on $[-5, 3) \cup (3, 5]$.   ◀

The importance of continuity of a function on a closed interval will become more and more apparent to you as you proceed through your study of calculus. This property is part of the hypothesis of many key theorems, such as the mean-value theorem, the fundamental theorems of the calculus, and the extreme-value theorem.

▷ **ILLUSTRATION 2**   In Example 4 of Section 1.3 we obtained as a mathematical model the function V defined by

$$V(x) = 170x - 54x^2 + 4x^3$$

and expressing the volume of a cardboard box as a function of the length of the side of a square cut from the four corners of a piece of cardboard. Because V is a polynomial function, it is continuous everywhere, and therefore continuous on its domain, the closed interval $[0, 5]$. This fact is necessary to apply the extreme-value theorem in Section 3.2 to find the value of x which makes $V(x)$ a maximum.   ◀

Another crucial theorem pertaining to a function continuous on a closed interval is the *intermediate-value theorem,* which we now discuss.

1.9.8 The Intermediate-Value Theorem

If the function f is continuous on the closed interval $[a, b]$, and if $f(a) \neq f(b)$, then for any number k between $f(a)$ and $f(b)$ there exists a number c between a and b such that $f(c) = k$.

The proof of the intermediate-value theorem, beyond the scope of this book, can be found in an advanced calculus text.

In terms of geometry, the intermediate-value theorem states that the graph of a function continuous on a closed interval must intersect every horizontal line $y = k$ between the lines $y = f(a)$ and $y = f(b)$ at least once. Refer to Figure 2, where $(0, k)$ is any point on the y axis between the points $(0, f(a))$ and $(0, f(b))$; the line $y = k$ intersects the graph of f at the point (c, k) where c lies between a and b.

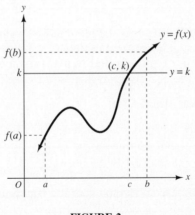

FIGURE 2

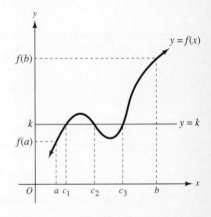

FIGURE 3

For some values of k, we may have more than one possible value for c. The theorem states that at least one value of c exists but such a value is not necessarily unique. Figure 3 shows three possible values of c (c_1, c_2, and c_3) for a particular k.

The intermediate-value theorem assures us that if the function f is continuous on the closed interval $[a, b]$, then $f(x)$ assumes every value between $f(a)$ and $f(b)$ as x assumes all values between a and b. The following two illustrations demonstrate the importance of the continuity of f on $[a, b]$ for this guarantee.

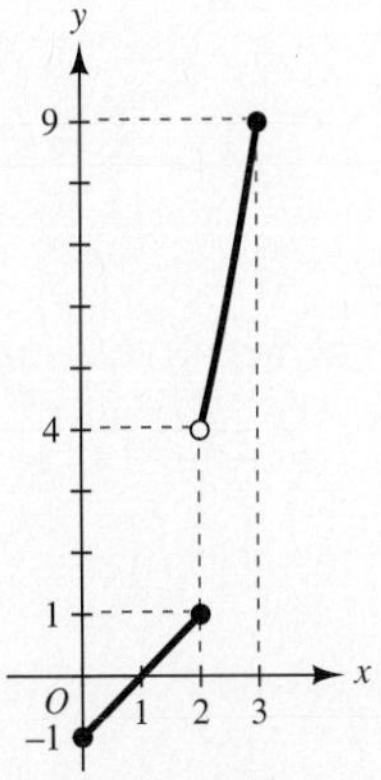

▷ **ILLUSTRATION 3**   Consider the function f defined by

$$f(x) = \begin{cases} x - 1 & \text{if } 0 \leq x \leq 2 \\ x^2 & \text{if } 2 < x \leq 3 \end{cases}$$

The graph of this function appears in Figure 4.

$$f(x) = \begin{cases} x - 1 \text{ if } 0 \leq x \leq 2 \\ x^2 \quad \text{if } 2 < x \leq 3 \end{cases}$$

FIGURE 4

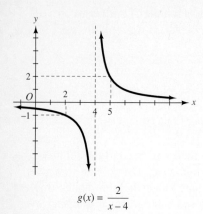

$$g(x) = \frac{2}{x-4}$$

FIGURE 5

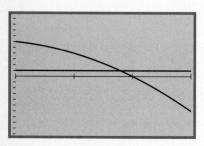

[2, 5] by [−10, 10]

$f(x) = 4 + 3x - x^2$

$y = 1$

FIGURE 6

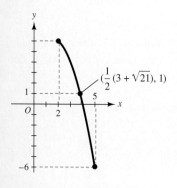

$f(x) = 4 + 3x - x^2, x \in [2, 5]$

FIGURE 7

The function f is discontinuous at 2, which is in the closed interval $[0, 3]$; $f(0) = -1$ and $f(3) = 9$. If k is any number between 1 and 4, there is no value of c such that $f(c) = k$ because there are no function values between 1 and 4.   ◀

▷ **ILLUSTRATION 4**   Let the function g be defined by

$$g(x) = \frac{2}{x-4}$$

The graph of this function is sketched in Figure 5.

The function g is discontinuous at 4, which is in the closed interval $[2, 5]$; $g(2) = -1$ and $g(5) = 2$. If k is any number between -1 and 2, there is no value of c between 2 and 5 such that $g(c) = k$. In particular, if $k = 1$, then $g(6) = 1$, but 6 is not in the interval $(2, 5)$.   ◀

▶ **EXAMPLE 4**   Given the function f defined by

$$f(x) = 4 + 3x - x^2 \qquad 2 \le x \le 5$$

(a) Verify that the intermediate-value theorem holds for $k = 1$ by plotting the graph of f and the line $y = 1$; estimate to four decimal places the number c in $(2, 5)$ such that $f(c) = 1$. **(b)** Confirm the estimate in part (a) analytically. **(c)** Sketch the graph of f on $[2, 5]$ and show the point $(c, 1)$.

Solution

(a) Because f is a polynomial function, it is continuous everywhere, and thus continuous on $[2, 5]$. Figure 6 shows the graph of f and the line $y = 1$ plotted in the $[2, 5]$ by $[-10, 10]$ window. On our calculator, we estimate c to be 3.7913.

(b) We solve the quadratic equation

$$4 + 3c - c^2 = 1$$
$$c^2 - 3c - 3 = 0$$
$$c = \frac{3 \pm \sqrt{9 + 12}}{2}$$
$$c = \frac{3 \pm \sqrt{21}}{2}$$

We reject $\frac{1}{2}(3 - \sqrt{21})$ because this number being negative is outside the interval $(2, 5)$. The number $\frac{1}{2}(3 + \sqrt{21})$ is in the interval $(2, 5)$, and

$$f\!\left(\frac{3 + \sqrt{21}}{2}\right) = 1$$

Because $(3 + \sqrt{21})/2 \approx 3.7913$, we have confirmed our estimate.

(c) The required graph appears in Figure 7.   ◀

The following theorem is a direct consequence, a corollary, of the intermediate-value theorem.

1.9.9 The Intermediate-Zero Theorem

If the function f is continuous on the closed interval $[a, b]$ and if $f(a)$ and $f(b)$ have opposite signs, then there exists a number c between a and b such that $f(c) = 0$; that is c is a zero of f.

Proof The hypothesis of the intermediate-value theorem is satisfied by function f, and because $f(a)$ and $f(b)$ have opposite signs, 0 qualifies as a number k between $f(a)$ and $f(b)$. Therefore, there is a number c between a and b such that $f(c) = 0$. ∎

In the following example we apply the intermediate-zero theorem to locate zeros of a function.

Table 1

x	−2	−1	0	1	2
$f(x)$	−15	1	1	−3	1

▶ **EXAMPLE 5**   **(a)** Apply the intermediate-zero theorem to show that the function defined by

$$f(x) = 2x^3 - 2x^2 - 4x + 1$$

has three zeros between −2 and 2. **(b)** Approximate these zeros to two decimal places on a graphics calculator.

Solution

(a) We compute values of $f(x)$ for integers from −2 to 2 as shown in Table 1. Because $f(-2)$ and $f(-1)$ have opposite signs, f has a zero between −2 and −1; f also has a zero between 0 and 1 and a zero between 1 and 2 for the same reason.

(b) The graph of f plotted in the $[-3, 3]$ by $[-5, 5]$ window appears in Figure 8. On our calculator we approximate the zeros as −1.14, 0.23, and 1.91. ◀

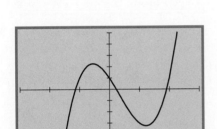

[−3, 3] by [−5, 5]

$f(x) = 2x^3 - 2x^2 - 4x + 1$

FIGURE 8

We now prove Limit Theorems 9 and 10 as we promised in Section 1.5. Notice the application of Theorem 1.9.1 (limit of a composite function).

Limit Theorem 9   Limit of the Quotient of Two Functions

If $\lim\limits_{x \to a} f(x) = L$ and if $\lim\limits_{x \to a} g(x) = M$, then

$$\lim_{x \to a} \frac{f(x)}{g(x)} = \frac{L}{M} \qquad \text{if } M \neq 0$$

Proof Let h be the function defined by $h(x) = 1/x$. Then the composite function $h \circ g$ is defined by $h(g(x)) = 1/g(x)$. The function h is continuous everywhere except at 0, which follows from Theorem 1.5.12. Hence

$$\lim_{x \to a} \frac{1}{g(x)} = \lim_{x \to a} h(g(x))$$
$$= h(\lim_{x \to a} g(x)) \qquad \text{(by Theorem 1.9.1)}$$
$$= h(M)$$
$$= \frac{1}{M}$$

From Limit Theorem 6 and the above result,

$$\lim_{x \to a} \frac{f(x)}{g(x)} = \lim_{x \to a} f(x) \cdot \lim_{x \to a} \frac{1}{g(x)}$$

$$= L \cdot \frac{1}{M}$$

$$= \frac{L}{M}$$

∎

> **Limit Theorem 10   Limit of the *n*th Root of a Function**
>
> If n is a positive integer and $\lim\limits_{x \to a} f(x) = L$, then
> $$\lim_{x \to a} \sqrt[n]{f(x)} = \sqrt[n]{L}$$
> with the restriction that if n is even, $L > 0$.

Proof   Let h be the function defined by $h(x) = \sqrt[n]{x}$. Then the composite function $h \circ f$ is defined by $h(f(x)) = \sqrt[n]{f(x)}$. From Theorem 1.8.5, h is continuous at L if n is odd, or if n is even and $L > 0$. Therefore

$$\lim_{x \to a} \sqrt[n]{f(x)} = \lim_{x \to a} h(f(x))$$

$$= h(\lim_{x \to a} f(x)) \qquad \text{(by Theorem 1.9.1)}$$

$$= h(L)$$

$$= \sqrt[n]{L}$$

∎

EXERCISES 1.9

In Exercises 1 through 6, define $f \circ g$ and determine the numbers at which $f \circ g$ is continuous.

1. (a) $f(x) = \sqrt{x}$; $g(x) = 9 - x^2$;
    (b) $f(x) = \sqrt{x}$; $g(x) = x^2 - 16$

2. (a) $f(x) = \sqrt{x}$; $g(x) = 16 - x^2$;
    (b) $f(x) = \sqrt{x}$; $g(x) = x^2 + 4$

3. (a) $f(x) = \sqrt{x}$; $g(x) = \dfrac{1}{x - 2}$;
    (b) $f(x) = \dfrac{1}{x - 2}$; $g(x) = \sqrt{x}$

4. (a) $f(x) = \sqrt[3]{x}$; $g(x) = \sqrt{x + 1}$;
    (b) $f(x) = \sqrt{x + 1}$; $g(x) = \sqrt[3]{x}$

5. $f(x) = \dfrac{\sqrt{4 - x^2}}{\sqrt{x - 1}}$; $g(x) = |x|$

6. $f(x) = \dfrac{\sqrt{x^2 - 1}}{\sqrt{4 - x}}$; $g(x) = |x|$

In Exercises 7 through 16, find the domain of the function, and then determine for each of the indicated intervals whether the function is continuous on that interval.

7. $f(x) = \dfrac{2}{x + 5}$; $(3, 7)$, $[-6, 4]$, $(-\infty, 0)$, $(-5, +\infty)$, $[-5, +\infty)$, $[-10, -5)$

8. $g(x) = \dfrac{x}{x - 2}$; $(-\infty, 0]$, $[0, +\infty)$, $(0, 2)$, $(0, 2]$, $[2, +\infty)$, $(2, +\infty)$

9. $f(t) = \dfrac{t}{t^2 - 1}$; $(0, 1)$, $(-1, 1)$, $[0, 1]$, $(-1, 0]$, $(-\infty, -1]$, $(1, +\infty)$

10. $f(r) = \dfrac{r + 3}{r^2 - 4}$; $(0, 4]$, $(-2, 2)$, $(-\infty, -2]$, $(2, +\infty)$, $[-4, 4]$, $(-2, 2]$

11. $g(x) = \sqrt{x^2 - 9}$; $(-\infty, -3)$, $(-\infty, -3]$, $(3, +\infty)$, $[3, +\infty)$, $(-3, 3)$

12. $f(x) = [\![x]\!]$; $(-\frac{1}{2}, \frac{1}{2})$, $(\frac{1}{4}, \frac{1}{2})$, $(1, 2)$, $[1, 2)$, $(1, 2]$

13. $f(t) = \dfrac{|t - 1|}{t - 1}$; $(-\infty, 1), (-\infty, 1], [-1, 1], (-1, +\infty),$
$(1, +\infty)$

14. $h(x) = \begin{cases} 2x - 3 & \text{if } x < -2 \\ x - 5 & \text{if } -2 \leq x \leq 1 \\ 3 - x & \text{if } 1 < x \end{cases}$;
$(-\infty, 1), (-2, +\infty), (-2, 1), [-2, 1), [-2, 1]$

15. $f(x) = \sqrt{4 - x^2}$; $(-2, 2), [-2, 2], [-2, 2), (-2, 2],$
$(-\infty, -2], (2, +\infty)$

16. $F(y) = \dfrac{1}{3 + 2y - y^2}$; $(-1, 3), [-1, 3], [-1, 3),$
$(-1, 3]$

In Exercises 17 through 22, determine the largest interval (or union of intervals) on which the function f ∘ g of the indicated exercise is continuous.

17. Exercise 1   18. Exercise 2   19. Exercise 3

20. Exercise 4   21. Exercise 5   22. Exercise 6

23. Determine the largest interval (or union of intervals) on which the function of Exercise 17 in Exercises 1.6 is continuous.

24. Determine the largest interval (or union of intervals) on which the function of Example 4 in Section 1.6 is continuous.

In Exercises 25 through 28, sketch the graph of a function f that satisfies the given properties.

25. *f* is continuous on $(-\infty, 2]$ and $(2, +\infty)$;
$\lim\limits_{x \to 0} f(x) = 4$; $\lim\limits_{x \to 2^-} f(x) = -3$; $\lim\limits_{x \to 2^+} f(x) = +\infty$;
$\lim\limits_{x \to 5} f(x) = 0$

26. *f* is continuous on $(-\infty, -2), [-2, 4],$ and $(4, +\infty)$;
$\lim\limits_{x \to -5} f(x) = 0$; $\lim\limits_{x \to -2^-} f(x) = -\infty$; $\lim\limits_{x \to -2^+} f(x) = -3$;
$\lim\limits_{x \to 0} f(x) = -1$; $\lim\limits_{x \to 4^-} f(x) = 2$; $\lim\limits_{x \to 4^+} f(x) = 5$;
$\lim\limits_{x \to 6} f(x) = 0$

27. *f* is continuous on $(-\infty, -3], (-3, 3),$ and $[3, +\infty)$;
$\lim\limits_{x \to -5} f(x) = 2$; $\lim\limits_{x \to -3^-} f(x) = 0$; $\lim\limits_{x \to -3^+} f(x) = 4$;
$\lim\limits_{x \to 0} f(x) = 1$; $\lim\limits_{x \to 3^-} f(x) = 0$; $\lim\limits_{x \to 3^+} f(x) = -5$;
$\lim\limits_{x \to 4} f(x) = 0$

28. *f* is continuous on $(-\infty, 0)$ and $[0, +\infty)$; $\lim\limits_{x \to -4} f(x) = 0$;
$\lim\limits_{x \to 0^-} f(x) = 3$; $\lim\limits_{x \to 0^+} f(x) = -3$; $\lim\limits_{x \to 4} f(x) = 2$

In Exercises 29 through 34, prove that the function obtained as a mathematical model in the indicated exercise of Exercises 1.3 is continuous on its domain.

29. (a) Exercise 13 (b) Exercise 15

30. (a) Exercise 14 (b) Exercise 16

31. (a) Exercise 17 (b) Exercise 19

32. (a) Exercise 18 (b) Exercise 20

33. (a) Exercise 21 (b) Exercise 23

34. (a) Exercise 22 (b) Exercise 24

In Exercises 35 through 42, determine if the intermediate-value theorem holds for the function f, the closed interval [a, b], and the given value of k. If the theorem does not hold, state the reason, and support your answer graphically. If the theorem holds, do the following: (a) Plot the graph of f and the line y = k on your graphics calculator and estimate to four decimal places the number c in (a, b) such that f(c) = k. (b) Confirm your estimate in part (a) analytically. (c) Sketch the graph of f on [a, b] and show the point (c, k).

35. $f(x) = 2 + x - x^2$; $[a, b] = [0, 3]$; $k = 1$

36. $f(x) = -\sqrt{100 - x^2}$; $[a, b] = [0, 8]$; $k = -8$

37. $f(x) = \sqrt{25 - x^2}$; $[a, b] = [-4.5, 3]$; $k = 3$

38. $f(x) = x^2 + 5x - 6$; $[a, b] = [-1, 2]$; $k = 4$

39. $f(x) = \dfrac{4}{x + 2}$; $[a, b] = [-3, 1]$; $k = \frac{1}{2}$

40. $f(x) = \dfrac{5}{2x - 1}$; $[a, b] = [0, 1]$; $k = 2$

41. $f(x) = \begin{cases} x^2 - 4 & \text{if } -2 \leq x < 1 \\ x^2 - 1 & \text{if } 1 \leq x \leq 3 \end{cases}$; $[a, b] = [-2, 3]$;
$k = -1$

42. $f(x) = \begin{cases} 1 + x & \text{if } -4 \leq x \leq -2 \\ 2 - x & \text{if } -2 < x \leq 1 \end{cases}$; $[a, b] = [-4, 1]$;
$k = \frac{1}{2}$

In Exercises 43 through 46, do the following: (a) Apply the intermediate-zero theorem to show that the function f has the indicated number of zeros between the numbers a and b. (b) Approximate these zeros to two decimal places on your graphics calculator.

43. $f(x) = x^3 - 6x + 3$; three zeros; $a = -5$; $b = 5$

44. $f(x) = x^4 + 7x^3 + x - 8$; two zeros; $a = -10$;
$b = 5$

45. $f(x) = 4x^4 - 3x^3 + 2x - 5$; two zeros; $a = -3$;
$b = 3$

46. $f(x) = 3x^4 - 21x^3 + 36x^2 + 2x - 8$; four zeros;
$a = -5$; $b = 5$

47. Show that the intermediate-zero theorem guarantees that the equation $x^3 - 4x^2 + x + 3 = 0$ has a root between 1 and 2 and use your graphics calculator to approximate the root to two decimal places.

48. Show that the intermediate-zero theorem guarantees that the equation $x^3 + x + 3 = 0$ has a root between -2 and 2, and use your graphics calculator to approximate the root to two decimal places.

49. From the equation defining $m(v)$, pertaining to Einstein's Special Theory of Relativity in Exercise 51 of Exercises 1.7, determine the largest interval on which m is continuous.

50. Prove that if the function f is continuous at a, then

$$\lim_{t \to 0} f(a - t) = f(a)$$

51. Prove that if $f(x)$ is nonnegative for all x in its domain and $\lim_{x \to a} [f(x)]^2$ exists and is positive, then

$$\lim_{x \to a} f(x) = \sqrt{\lim_{x \to a} [f(x)]^2}$$

52. Prove that if $\lim_{x \to a} f(x) = L$, then $\lim_{x \to a} |f(x)| = |L|$.

53. Suppose that f is a function for which

$$0 \le f(x) \le 1 \quad \text{if} \quad 0 \le x \le 1$$

Prove that if f is continuous on $[0, 1]$, there is at least one number c in $[0, 1]$ such that $f(c) = c$. *Hint:* If neither 0 nor 1 qualifies as c, then $f(0) > 0$ and $f(1) < 1$. Consider the function g for which $g(x) = f(x) - x$ and apply the intermediate-value theorem to g on $[0, 1]$.

54. Find the largest value of k for which the function defined by $f(x) = [\![x^2 - 2]\!]$ is continuous on the interval $[3, 3 + k)$.

55. Are the following two statements equivalent: (i) Function f is continuous on the closed interval $[a, b]$; (ii) Function f is continuous at every number in the closed interval $[a, b]$? Justify your answer.

1.10 CONTINUITY OF THE TRIGONOMETRIC FUNCTIONS AND THE SQUEEZE THEOREM

We assume you have studied trigonometry previously; however, because of the importance of the trigonometric functions in calculus, a brief review of them is presented in Appendix Section A.9.

In a trigonometry course, graphs of the trigonometric functions are sketched by intuitive considerations because two concepts of calculus, *continuity* and *differentiation,* are needed for a formal presentation of such graphs. In this section we discuss continuity of the trigonometric functions while Section 2.7, where we obtain the graphs, is devoted to differentiation of these functions.

In our treatment of continuity we apply the following limit:

$$\lim_{t \to 0} \frac{\sin t}{t} \tag{1}$$

Observe that the function defined by $f(t) = \dfrac{\sin t}{t}$ does not exist when $t = 0$ but does exist for all other values of t. To get an intuitive idea about the existence of the limit in (1) we first plot the graph of f in the $[-10, 10]$ by $[-1, 2]$ window, shown in Figure 1. Because $f(0)$ does not exist, the graph

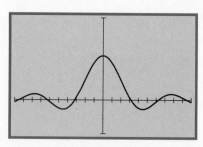

[–10, 10] by [–1, 2]

$$f(t) = \frac{\sin t}{t}$$

FIGURE 1

Table 1

t	$\dfrac{\sin t}{t}$
1.0	0.84147
0.9	0.87036
0.8	0.89670
0.7	0.92031
0.6	0.94107
0.5	0.95885
0.4	0.97355
0.3	0.98507
0.2	0.99335
0.1	0.99833
0.01	0.99998

Table 2

t	$\dfrac{\sin t}{t}$
−1.0	0.84147
−0.9	0.87036
−0.8	0.89670
−0.7	0.92031
−0.6	0.94107
−0.5	0.95885
−0.4	0.97355
−0.3	0.98507
−0.2	0.99335
−0.1	0.99833
−0.01	0.99998

has a hole on the y axis. From the figure, we suspect that probably the limit in (1) does exist and is equal to 1. To examine the limit further, we compute on our calculator the function values given by Table 1 and Table 2. From the two tables, we again suspect that if the limit in (1) exists, it may be equal to 1. That the limit does exist and does equal 1 is proved in Theorem 1.10.2, but in the proof of that theorem we need to use the following theorem, which we refer to as the *squeeze theorem*. The squeeze theorem not only is important in the proof of Theorem 1.10.2, but also is used to prove some major theorems in later sections.

> **1.10.1 The Squeeze Theorem**
>
> Suppose that the functions f, g, and h are defined on some open interval I containing a except possibly at a itself, and that $f(x) \le g(x) \le h(x)$ for all x in I for which $x \ne a$. Also suppose that $\lim_{x \to a} f(x)$ and $\lim_{x \to a} h(x)$ both exist and are equal to L. Then $\lim_{x \to a} g(x)$ exists and is equal to L.

We prove the squeeze theorem in the supplement of this section. Now, however, we interpret the theorem geometrically in the following illustration.

▷ **ILLUSTRATION 1** Let the functions f, g, and h be defined by

$$f(x) = -4(x - 2)^2 + 3$$

$$g(x) = \frac{(x - 2)(x^2 - 4x + 7)}{x - 2}$$

$$h(x) = 4(x - 2)^2 + 3$$

Graphs of these functions are plotted in the $[-1, 10]$ by $[-10, 10]$ window in Figure 2. The graphs of f and h are parabolas having their vertex at $(2, 3)$. The graph of g is a parabola with its vertex $(2, 3)$ deleted. Function g is not defined when $x = 2$; however, for all $x \ne 2$, $f(x) \le g(x) \le h(x)$. Furthermore, $\lim_{x \to 2} f(x) = 3$ and $\lim_{x \to 2} h(x) = 3$. The hypothesis of the squeeze theorem is therefore satisfied, from which it follows that $\lim_{x \to 2} g(x) = 3$. ◀

▶ **EXAMPLE 1** Given $|g(x) - 2| \le 3(x - 1)^2$ for all x. Use the squeeze theorem to find $\lim_{x \to 1} g(x)$.

Solution Because $|g(x) - 2| \le 3(x - 1)^2$ for all x, it follows that

$$-3(x - 1)^2 \le g(x) - 2 \le 3(x - 1)^2 \qquad \text{for all } x$$
$$\Leftrightarrow \quad -3(x - 1)^2 + 2 \le g(x) \le 3(x - 1)^2 + 2 \qquad \text{for all } x$$

Let $f(x) = -3(x - 1)^2 + 2$ and $h(x) = 3(x - 1)^2 + 2$. Then

$$\lim_{x \to 1} f(x) = 2 \quad \text{and} \quad \lim_{x \to 1} h(x) = 2 \tag{2}$$

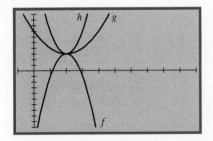

$[-1, 10]$ by $[-10, 10]$

$f(x) = -4(x - 2)^2 + 3$

$g(x) = \dfrac{(x - 2)(x^2 - 4x + 7)}{x - 2}$

$h(x) = 4(x - 2)^2 + 3$

FIGURE 2

Furthermore, for all x,

$$f(x) \le g(x) \le h(x) \qquad (3)$$

Thus from (2), (3), and the squeeze theorem

$$\lim_{x \to 1} g(x) = 2 \qquad \blacktriangleleft$$

▶ **EXAMPLE 2** Use the squeeze theorem to prove that

$$\lim_{x \to 0} \left| x \sin \frac{1}{x} \right| = 0$$

Support this fact graphically.

Solution Because $-1 \le \sin t \le 1$ for all t, then

$$0 \le \left| \sin \frac{1}{x} \right| \le 1 \qquad \text{if } x \ne 0$$

Therefore, if $x \ne 0$,

$$\left| x \sin \frac{1}{x} \right| = |x| \left| \sin \frac{1}{x} \right|$$
$$\le |x|$$

Hence

$$0 \le \left| x \sin \frac{1}{x} \right| \le |x| \qquad \text{if } x \ne 0 \qquad (4)$$

Because $\lim_{x \to 0} 0 = 0$ and $\lim_{x \to 0} |x| = 0$, it follows from inequality (4) and the squeeze theorem that

$$\lim_{x \to 0} \left| x \sin \frac{1}{x} \right| = 0$$

The graph of the function having values $\left| x \sin \dfrac{1}{x} \right|$, plotted in the $[-1, 1]$ by $[0, 1]$ window, appears in Figure 3. Observe the unusual oscillating behavior of the function when $-0.32 \le x \le 0.32$. The graph supports the fact that the limit is 0. ◀

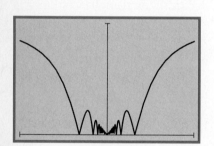

[–1, 1] by [0, 1]

$$f(x) = \left| x \sin \frac{1}{x} \right|$$

FIGURE 3

1.10.2 Theorem

$$\lim_{x \to 0} \frac{\sin t}{t} = 1$$

Proof First assume that $0 < t < \frac{1}{2} \pi$. Refer to Figure 4, which shows the unit circle $x^2 + y^2 = 1$ and the shaded sector BOP, where B is the point $(1, 0)$ and P is the point $(\cos t, \sin t)$. The area of a circular sector of radius r and central angle of radian measure t is determined by $\frac{1}{2} r^2 t$; so if S square units is the area of sector BOP,

$$S = \frac{1}{2} t \qquad (5)$$

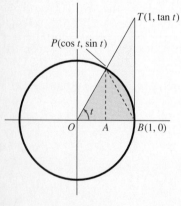

FIGURE 4

Consider now the triangle BOP, and let K_1 square units be the area of this triangle. Because $K_1 = \frac{1}{2}|\overline{AP}| \cdot |\overline{OB}|$, $|\overline{AP}| = \sin t$ and $|\overline{OB}| = 1$, we have

$$K_1 = \tfrac{1}{2}\sin t \tag{6}$$

If K_2 square units is the area of right triangle BOT, where T is the point $(1, \tan t)$, then $K_2 = \frac{1}{2}|\overline{BT}| \cdot |\overline{OB}|$. Because $\overline{BT} = \tan t$ and $\overline{OB} = 1$, we have

$$K_2 = \tfrac{1}{2}\tan t \tag{7}$$

From Figure 4 observe that

$$K_1 < S < K_2$$

Substituting from (5), (6), and (7) into this inequality

$$\tfrac{1}{2}\sin t < \tfrac{1}{2}t < \tfrac{1}{2}\tan t$$

Multiplying each member of this inequality by $2/\sin t$, which is positive because $0 < t < \frac{1}{2}\pi$, we have

$$1 < \frac{t}{\sin t} < \frac{1}{\cos t} \qquad \left(\text{because } \frac{\tan t}{\sin t} = \frac{1}{\cos t}\right)$$

Taking the reciprocal of each member of this inequality (which reverses the direction of the inequality signs),

$$\cos t < \frac{\sin t}{t} < 1 \tag{8}$$

From the right-hand inequality in the above,

$$\sin t < t \tag{9}$$

and from a half-measure identity in trigonometry,

$$\frac{1 - \cos t}{2} = \sin^2 \frac{1}{2}t \tag{10}$$

Replacing t by $\frac{1}{2}t$ in inequality (9) and squaring,

$$\sin^2 \tfrac{1}{2}t < \tfrac{1}{4}t^2 \tag{11}$$

Thus from (10) and (11),

$$\frac{1 - \cos t}{2} < \frac{t^2}{4}$$

$$\Leftrightarrow \qquad 1 - \tfrac{1}{2}t^2 < \cos t \tag{12}$$

From (8) and (12) and because $0 < t < \frac{1}{2}\pi$,

$$1 - \frac{1}{2}t^2 < \frac{\sin t}{t} < 1 \qquad \text{if } 0 < t < \tfrac{1}{2}\pi \tag{13}$$

If $-\frac{1}{2}\pi < t < 0$, then $0 < -t < \frac{1}{2}\pi$; so from (13),

$$1 - \frac{1}{2}(-t)^2 < \frac{\sin(-t)}{-t} < 1 \qquad \text{if } -\tfrac{1}{2}\pi < t < 0$$

But $\sin(-t) = -\sin t$; thus the above can be written as

$$1 - \frac{1}{2}t^2 < \frac{\sin t}{t} < 1 \qquad \text{if } -\tfrac{1}{2}\pi < t < 0 \qquad\qquad \textbf{(14)}$$

From (13) and (14) we conclude that

$$1 - \frac{1}{2}t^2 < \frac{\sin t}{t} < 1 \qquad \text{if } -\tfrac{1}{2}\pi < t < \tfrac{1}{2}\pi \quad \text{and} \quad t \neq 0 \qquad \textbf{(15)}$$

Because $\lim\limits_{t \to 0} (1 - \tfrac{1}{2}t^2) = 1$ and $\lim\limits_{t \to 0} 1 = 1$, it follows from (15) and the squeeze theorem that

$$\lim_{t \to 0} \frac{\sin t}{t} = 1 \qquad\qquad\qquad\qquad\qquad\qquad \blacksquare$$

▶ **EXAMPLE 3**   Given

$$f(x) = \frac{\sin 3x}{\sin 5x}$$

(a) Plot the graph of f in the $[-2, 2]$ by $[-5, 5]$ window. What does $f(x)$ appear to be approaching as x approaches 0? **(b)** Confirm the answer in part (a) analytically by finding $\lim\limits_{x \to 0} f(x)$.

Solution

(a) Figure 5 shows the graph of f plotted in the $[-0.6, 0.6]$ by $[-5, 5]$ window. Because $f(0)$ does not exist, the graph has a hole at the point where $x = 0$. On our calculator, $f(x)$ appears to be approaching 0.6 as x approaches 0.

(b) To find $\lim\limits_{x \to 0} f(x)$ we wish to write the quotient $\sin 3x / \sin 5x$ in such a way that Theorem 1.10.2 can be applied. If $x \neq 0$,

$$\frac{\sin 3x}{\sin 5x} = \frac{3\left(\dfrac{\sin 3x}{3x}\right)}{5\left(\dfrac{\sin 5x}{5x}\right)}$$

As x approaches zero, so do $3x$ and $5x$. Hence

$$\lim_{x \to 0} \frac{\sin 3x}{3x} = \lim_{3x \to 0} \frac{\sin 3x}{3x} \qquad\qquad \lim_{x \to 0} \frac{\sin 5x}{5x} = \lim_{5x \to 0} \frac{\sin 5x}{5x}$$
$$= 1 \qquad\qquad\qquad\qquad\qquad = 1$$

Therefore

$$\lim_{x \to 0} \frac{\sin 3x}{\sin 5x} = \frac{3 \lim\limits_{x \to 0}\left(\dfrac{\sin 3x}{3x}\right)}{5 \lim\limits_{x \to 0}\left(\dfrac{\sin 5x}{5x}\right)}$$

$$= \frac{3 \cdot 1}{5 \cdot 1}$$

$$= \frac{3}{5}$$

This result confirms our answer in part (a).   ◀

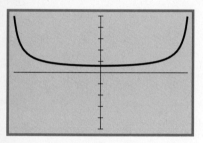

$[-0.6, 0.6]$ by $[-5, 5]$

$$f(x) = \frac{\sin 3x}{\sin 5x}$$

FIGURE 5

From Theorem 1.10.2 we can prove that the sine and cosine functions are continuous at 0.

1.10.3 Theorem

The sine function is continuous at 0.

Proof   We show that the three conditions necessary for continuity at a number are satisfied.

(i) $\sin 0 = 0$

(ii) $\lim\limits_{t \to 0} \sin t = \lim\limits_{t \to 0} \dfrac{\sin t}{t} \cdot t$

$$= \lim_{t \to 0} \frac{\sin t}{t} \cdot \lim_{t \to 0} t$$

$$= 1 \cdot 0$$

$$= 0$$

(iii) $\lim\limits_{t \to 0} \sin t = \sin 0$

Therefore the sine function is continuous at 0.   ∎

1.10.4 Theorem

The cosine function is continuous at 0.

Proof   We check the three conditions necessary for continuity at a number. In checking condition (ii) we use the fact that the sine function is continuous at 0, and we replace $\cos t$ by $\sqrt{1 - \sin^2 t}$ because $\cos t > 0$ when $-\frac{1}{2}\pi < t < \frac{1}{2}\pi$.

(i) $\cos 0 = 1$

(ii) $\lim\limits_{t \to 0} \cos t = \lim\limits_{t \to 0} \sqrt{1 - \sin^2 t}$

$$= \sqrt{\lim_{t \to 0} (1 - \sin^2 t)}$$

$$= \sqrt{1 - 0}$$

$$= 1$$

(iii) $\lim\limits_{t \to 0} \cos t = \cos 0$

Thus the cosine function is continuous at 0.   ∎

The limit in the statement of the following theorem, which we need to apply later, is obtained from the previous three theorems and limit theorems.

1.10.5 Theorem

$$\lim_{t \to 0} \frac{1 - \cos t}{t} = 0$$

Proof

$$\lim_{t \to 0} \frac{1 - \cos t}{t} = \lim_{t \to 0} \frac{(1 - \cos t)(1 + \cos t)}{t(1 + \cos t)}$$

$$= \lim_{t \to 0} \frac{1 - \cos^2 t}{t(1 + \cos t)}$$

$$= \lim_{t \to 0} \frac{\sin^2 t}{t(1 + \cos t)}$$

$$= \lim_{t \to 0} \frac{\sin t}{t} \cdot \lim_{t \to 0} \frac{\sin t}{1 + \cos t}$$

By Theorem 1.10.2

$$\lim_{t \to 0} \frac{\sin t}{t} = 1$$

and because the sine and cosine functions are continuous at 0 it follows that

$$\lim_{t \to 0} \frac{\sin t}{1 + \cos t} = \frac{0}{1 + 1}$$

$$= 0$$

Therefore

$$\lim_{t \to 0} \frac{1 - \cos t}{t} = 1 \cdot 0$$

$$= 0 \qquad \blacksquare$$

▶ **EXAMPLE 4**   Given

$$g(x) = \frac{1 - \cos x}{\sin x}$$

(a) Plot the graph of g in a convenient window. What does $g(x)$ appear to be approaching as x approaches 0? **(b)** Confirm the answer in part (a) analytically by finding $\lim_{x \to 0} g(x)$.

Solution

(a) Let us choose $[-3, 3]$ by $[-5, 5]$ as our window and plot the graph to obtain Figure 6. The graph has a hole at $x = 0$ because $g(0)$ does not exist. From the graph, $g(x)$ appears to be approaching 0 as x approaches 0.

(b) Because $\lim_{x \to 0} (1 - \cos x) = 0$ and $\lim_{x \to 0} \sin x = 0$, the limit theorems cannot be applied to the quotient $(1 - \cos x)/\sin x$. However, if the numerator and denominator are divided by x, which is permissible

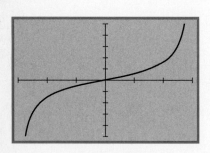

[−3, 3] by [−5, 5]

$$g(x) = \frac{1 - \cos x}{\sin x}$$

FIGURE 6

because $x \neq 0$, we are able to apply Theorems 1.10.2 and 1.10.5. Thus

$$\lim_{x \to 0} \frac{1 - \cos x}{\sin x} = \lim_{x \to 0} \frac{\dfrac{1 - \cos x}{x}}{\dfrac{\sin x}{x}}$$

$$= \frac{\displaystyle\lim_{x \to 0} \frac{1 - \cos x}{x}}{\displaystyle\lim_{x \to 0} \frac{\sin x}{x}}$$

$$= \frac{0}{1}$$

$$= 0$$

We have confirmed our answer in part (a).   ◀

▶ **EXAMPLE 5**   Given

$$h(x) = \frac{2 \tan^2 x}{x^2}$$

(a) Plot the graph of h in a convenient window. What does $h(x)$ appear to be approaching as x approaches 0? **(b)** Confirm the answer in part (a) analytically by finding $\lim\limits_{x \to 0} h(x)$.

Solution

(a) We plot the graph of h in the $\left[-\frac{1}{2}\pi, \frac{1}{2}\pi\right]$ by $[0, 10]$ window to obtain Figure 7. The graph has a hole at $x = 0$ because $h(0)$ does not exist. From the graph, $h(x)$ appears to be approaching 2 as x approaches 0.

(b) We apply the trigonometric identity

$$\tan x = \frac{\sin x}{\cos x}$$

and we have

$$\lim_{x \to 0} \frac{2 \tan^2 x}{x^2} = 2 \lim_{x \to 0} \frac{\sin^2 x}{x^2 \cdot \cos^2 x}$$

$$= 2 \lim_{x \to 0} \frac{\sin x}{x} \cdot \lim_{x \to 0} \frac{\sin x}{x} \cdot \lim_{x \to 0} \frac{1}{\cos^2 x}$$

$$= 2 \cdot 1 \cdot 1 \cdot 1$$

$$= 2$$

This result confirms our answer in part (a).   ◀

From Theorem 1.5.15 and the facts that the sine and cosine functions are continuous at 0, we can prove that the sine and cosine are continuous everywhere as stated in the following theorem.

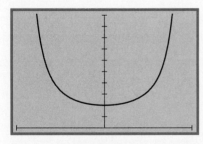

$\left[-\frac{1}{2}\pi, \frac{1}{2}\pi\right]$ by $[0, 10]$

$h(x) = \dfrac{2 \tan^2 x}{x^2}$

FIGURE 7

1.10.6 Theorem

The sine and cosine functions are continuous at every real number.

Proof   The set of all real numbers is the domain of both the sine and cosine functions. Therefore we must show that if a is any real number,

$$\lim_{x \to a} \sin x = \sin a \quad \text{and} \quad \lim_{x \to a} \cos x = \cos a$$

or, equivalently, from Theorem 1.5.15,

$$\lim_{t \to 0} \sin(t + a) = \sin a \quad \text{and} \quad \lim_{t \to 0} \cos(t + a) = \cos a \tag{16}$$

We use the identities

$$\sin(t + a) = \sin t \cos a + \cos t \sin a \tag{17}$$

$$\cos(t + a) = \cos t \cos a - \sin t \sin a \tag{18}$$

From (17),

$$\lim_{t \to 0} \sin(t + a) = \lim_{t \to 0} (\sin t \cos a + \cos t \sin a)$$

$$= \lim_{t \to 0} \sin t \cdot \lim_{t \to 0} \cos a + \lim_{t \to 0} \cos t \cdot \lim_{t \to 0} \sin a$$

$$= 0 \cdot \cos a + 1 \cdot \sin a$$

$$= \sin a$$

Therefore the first equation in (16) holds; so the sine function is continuous at every real number. From (18),

$$\lim_{t \to 0} \cos(t + a) = \lim_{t \to 0} (\cos t \cos a - \sin t \sin a)$$

$$= \lim_{t \to 0} \cos t \cdot \lim_{t \to 0} \cos a - \lim_{t \to 0} \sin t \cdot \lim_{t \to 0} \sin a$$

$$= 1 \cdot \cos a - 0 \cdot \sin a$$

$$= \cos a$$

Thus the second equation in (16) holds; so the cosine function is continuous at every real number. ∎

By using trigonometric identities, Theorem 1.8.4 about the continuity of a rational function, and Theorem 1.10.6 we can prove that the other four trigonometric functions are continuous on their domains.

1.10.7 Theorem

The tangent, cotangent, secant, and cosecant functions are continuous on their domains.

The proof of Theorem 1.10.7 is left as exercises (see Exercises 37 through 40).

EXERCISES 1.10

In Exercises 1 through 20, do the following: (a) Plot the graph of f in a convenient window. What does $f(x)$ appear to be approaching as x approaches 0? (b) Confirm your answer in part (a) analytically by finding $\lim\limits_{x \to 0} f(x)$.

1. $f(x) = \dfrac{\sin 4x}{x}$

2. $f(x) = \dfrac{2x}{\sin 3x}$

3. $f(x) = \dfrac{\sin 9x}{\sin 7x}$

4. $f(x) = \dfrac{\sin 3x}{\sin 6x}$

5. $f(x) = \dfrac{3x}{\sin 5x}$

6. $f(x) = \dfrac{\sin^3 x}{x^2}$

7. $f(x) = \dfrac{x^2}{\sin^2 3x}$

8. $f(x) = \dfrac{\sin^5 2x}{4x^5}$

9. $f(x) = \dfrac{x}{\cos x}$

10. $f(x) = \dfrac{1 - \cos x}{1 + \sin x}$

11. $f(x) = \dfrac{1 - \cos 4x}{x}$

12. $f(x) = \dfrac{1 - \cos 2x}{4x}$

13. $f(x) = \dfrac{3x^2}{1 - \cos^2 \frac{1}{2}x}$

14. $f(x) = \dfrac{1 - \cos^2 x}{2x^2}$

15. $f(x) = \dfrac{\tan x}{2x}$

16. $f(x) = \dfrac{\tan^4 2x}{4x^4}$

17. $f(x) = \dfrac{1 - \cos 2x}{\sin 3x}$

18. $f(x) = \dfrac{1 - \cos x}{x^2}$

19. $f(x) = \dfrac{x^2 + 3x}{\sin x}$

20. $f(x) = \dfrac{\sin x}{3x^2 + 2x}$

In Exercises 21 and 22, do the following: (a) Plot the graph of g in a convenient window. What appears to be the behavior of $g(t)$ as t approaches 0 through values greater than 0? (b) Confirm your answer in part (a) by finding $\lim\limits_{t \to 0^+} g(t)$.

21. $g(t) = \dfrac{\sin t}{t^2}$

22. $g(t) = \dfrac{\sin 4t}{\cos 3t - 1}$

In Exercises 23 and 24, do the following: (a) Plot the graph of h in a convenient window. What does $h(t)$ appear to be approaching as t approaches $\pi/2$? (b) Confirm your answer in part (a) analytically by finding $\lim\limits_{t \to \pi/2} h(t)$. Hint: Let $x = \frac{1}{2}\pi - t$.

23. $h(t) = \dfrac{1 - \sin t}{\frac{1}{2}\pi - t}$

24. $h(t) = \dfrac{\frac{1}{2}\pi - t}{\cos t}$

In Exercises 25 and 26, do the following: (a) Plot the graph of f in a convenient window. What does $f(x)$ appear to be approaching as x approaches π through values greater than π? (b) Confirm your answer in part (a) analytically by computing $\lim\limits_{x \to \pi^+} f(x)$. Hint: Let $t = x - \pi$.

25. $f(x) = \dfrac{\sin x}{x - \pi}$

26. $f(x) = \dfrac{\tan x}{x - \pi}$

27. If $R(\theta)$ feet is the range of a projectile, then

$$R(\theta) = \frac{{v_0}^2 \sin 2\theta}{g} \qquad 0 \le \theta \le \tfrac{1}{2}\pi$$

where v_0 ft/sec is the initial velocity, g ft/sec^2 is the constant acceleration due to gravity, and θ is the radian measure of the angle that the gun makes with the horizontal. Prove that R is continuous on its domain.

28. If a body of weight W pounds is dragged along a horizontal floor at constant velocity by means of a force of magnitude F pounds and directed at an angle of θ radians with the plane of the floor, then

$$F(\theta) = \frac{kW}{k \sin \theta + \cos \theta}$$

where k is a constant called the coefficient of friction and $0 < k < 1$. Prove that F is continuous on $[0, \frac{1}{2}\pi]$.

In Exercises 29 through 32, use the squeeze theorem to find the limit. In Exercises 29 and 30, support your answer graphically.

29. $\lim\limits_{x \to 0} x \cos \dfrac{1}{x}$

30. $\lim\limits_{x \to 0} x^2 \sin \dfrac{1}{\sqrt[3]{x}}$

31. $\lim\limits_{x \to 3} g(x)$, if $|g(x) + 4| < 2(3 - x)^4$ for all x

32. $\lim\limits_{x \to -2} g(x)$, if $|g(x) - 3| < 5(x + 2)^2$ for all x

In Exercises 33 and 34, find the limit if it exists and support your answer graphically.

33. $\lim\limits_{x \to 0} \dfrac{\sin(\sin x)}{x}$

34. $\lim\limits_{x \to 0} \sin x \sin \dfrac{1}{x}$

35. Given: $1 - \cos^2 x \le f(x) \le x^2$ for all x in the open interval $(-\frac{1}{2}\pi, \frac{1}{2}\pi)$. Find $\lim\limits_{x \to 0} f(x)$.

36. Given: $-\sin x \le f(x) \le 2 + \sin x$ for all x in the open interval $(-\pi, 0)$. Find $\lim\limits_{x \to -\pi/2} f(x)$.

In Exercises 37 through 40, prove that the function is continuous on its domain.

37. the tangent function

38. the cotangent function

39. the secant function

40. the cosecant function

41. If $|f(x)| \le M$ for all x and M is a constant, use the squeeze theorem to prove that $\lim\limits_{x \to 0} x^2 f(x) = 0$.

42. Suppose that $|f(x)| \le M$ for all x, where M is a constant. Furthermore, suppose that $\lim\limits_{x \to a} |g(x)| = 0$. Use the squeeze theorem to prove that $\lim\limits_{x \to a} f(x)g(x) = 0$.

43. If $|f(x)| \leq k|x - a|$ for all $x \neq a$, where k is a constant, prove that $\lim_{x \to a} f(x) = 0$.

44. Given $f(x) = \sin(1/x)$. Plot the graph of f in each of the following windows: **(a)** $[-2, 2]$ by $[-2, 2]$; **(b)** $[-1, 1]$ by $[-2, 2]$; **(c)** $[-0.5, 0.5]$ by $[-2, 2]$; **(d)** $[-0.25, 0.25]$ by $[-2, 2]$; **(e)** $[-0.1, 0.1]$ by $[-2, 2]$; **(f)** $[-0.01, 0.01]$ by $[-2, 2]$. **(g)** Do you suspect that $\lim_{x \to 0} f(x)$ exists and, if you do, what do

you suspect it is and why? Or, do you suspect that $\lim_{x \to 0} f(x)$ does not exist, and if so, why?

45. Do Exercise 44 if $f(x) = \cos \dfrac{1}{x}$.

46. Do Exercise 44 if $f(x) = \tan \dfrac{1}{x}$.

CHAPTER 1 REVIEW

▶ *SUGGESTIONS FOR REVIEW OF CHAPTER 1*

1. Define a *function* and include in your definition the meaning of *domain* and *range*.

2. Make up an example of a function having the indicated property:
   (a) The domain is the set of all real numbers.
   (b) The domain is the set of all nonnegative numbers.
   (c) The domain is the set of all negative numbers.
   (d) The domain is the set of all real numbers except 0.
   (e) The range is the set of all integers.

3. What do we mean by the *graph of a function?*

4. Make up an example of a function f having the indicated property:
   (a) The graph of f has a "hole" at $x = 4$, where $f(4)$ is not defined.
   (b) The graph of f has a "hole" at $x = 4$, where $f(4)$ is defined.
   (c) Function f is defined piecewise for $x < 2$ and $2 \leq x$, where the graph of f has a break at $x = 2$.
   (d) Function f is defined piecewise for $x < 2$ and $2 \leq x$, where the graph of f does not have a break at $x = 2$.

5. Define the *sum, difference, product,* and *quotient* of two functions f and g, and state how the domain of the resulting function is related to the domains of f and g.

6. Make up an example of two functions f and g, at least one of which is not a polynomial function, and define $(f + g)(x), (f - g)(x), (f \cdot g)(x)$, and $(f/g)(x)$. State the domains of f and g and the domains of the resulting functions.

7. Define the *composite function* of two functions f and g, and state how the domain of the composite function is related to the domains of f and g.

8. Make up an example of two functions f and g, at least one of which is not a polynomial function, and define $(f \circ g)(x)$ and $(g \circ f)(x)$. State the domains of f and g and the domains of $f \circ g$ and $g \circ f$.

9. What do we mean by: **(a)** an *even* function; **(b)** an *odd* function? Describe the symmetry of the graph of each kind of function.

10. Make up an example of a function, other than a polynomial, that is **(a)** even, **(b)** odd, and **(c)** neither even nor odd.

11. Define precisely using ϵ and δ notation what we mean by: *The limit of $f(x)$ as x approaches a is equal to L.* Now state in words what this definition means without using ϵ and δ notation and without using the words *limit* and *approaches*.

12. How is the definition of the limit of a function used to prove that $\lim_{x \to a} f(x) = L$?

13. Describe in geometric terms the relationship between ϵ and δ in the definition of the limit of a function.

14. Make up an example of a function f for which:
    (a) $f(a)$ does not exist but $\lim_{x \to a} f(x)$ does exist;
    (b) $f(a)$ exists but $\lim_{x \to a} f(x)$ does not exist;
    (c) both $f(a)$ and $\lim_{x \to a} f(x)$ exist but are not equal.

15. What do we mean when we say *the limit of a function, when it exists, is unique?* State the theorem that guarantees this fact.

16. How are limit theorems used to compute the limit of a function?

17. State the theorems regarding the limit of the sum, difference, product, and quotient of two functions.

18. Why is the following statement not precise: *the limit of the sum of two functions is the sum of their limits?* Make up an example of two functions for which the statement is incorrect.

19. Make up an example of two functions f and g, at least one of which is not a polynomial, and show how the theorems in Suggestion 17 are applied.

20. Define precisely using ϵ and δ notation each of the following: **(a)** $\lim_{x \to a^+} f(x) = L$; **(b)** $\lim_{x \to a^-} f(x) = L$.

Now state in words what each of these definitions means without using ϵ and δ notation and without using the words *limit* and *approaches*.

21. How are one-sided limits and two-sided limits connected?

22. When is it necessary to use one-sided limits to compute a two-sided limit? Make up an example to illustrate your answer.

23. When can one-sided limits be used to prove that a two-sided limit does not exist? Make up an example to illustrate your answer.

24. Define precisely using δ and N notation each of the following: **(a)** as x approaches a, $f(x)$ increases without bound; **(b)** as x approaches a, $f(x)$ decreases without bound. Now state in words what each of these definitions means without using δ and N notation and without using the words *limit, approaches, infinity, increases without bound,* or *decreases without bound.*

25. How do you evaluate the limit of a rational function for which the limit of the denominator is zero and the limit of the numerator is a nonzero constant?

26. What is a vertical asymptote of the graph of a function?

27. How can you find any vertical asymptotes for the graph of a function?

28. Make up examples of two rational functions, one whose graph has a hole at the point where $x = 3$ and the other whose graph has the line $x = 3$ as a vertical asymptote.

29. Define: function f is continuous at the number a.

30. Make up an example of a function discontinuous at the number 1 because of the indicated conditions: **(a)** $f(1)$ does not exist but $\lim_{x \to 1} f(x)$ does exist; **(b)** $f(1)$ exists but $\lim_{x \to 1} f(x)$ does not exist; **(c)** both $f(1)$ and $\lim_{x \to 1} f(x)$ exist; but are not equal.

31. What is the difference between an essential discontinuity and a removable discontinuity?

32. Make up an example of a function having an essential discontinuity at $x = 2$. Then make up an example of a function having a removable discontinuity at $x = 2$ and show how the discontinuity can be removed.

33. State the theorems pertaining to continuity of polynomial and rational functions. How are these theorems applied to find limits of these functions?

34. What conditions regarding continuity of functions f and g are necessary for the composite function $f \circ g$ to be continuous at the number a?

35. Make up an example of two functions f and g such that the composite function $f \circ g$ is continuous at every number in the open interval $(-3, 3)$. Show that your functions f and g satisfy the conditions in your answer for Suggestion 34.

36. Make up an example of a function that is discontinuous at a number c even though it is continuous from the right at c. Show that your function satisfies the requirements.

37. Define: the function f is continuous on the closed interval $[a, b]$.

38. State the intermediate-value theorem.

39. Make up an example of a function illustrating the intermediate-value theorem. Show that the hypothesis and conclusion of the theorem are satisfied by your function.

40. State the squeeze theorem. Make up an example of three functions f, g, and h satisfying the hypothesis of the squeeze theorem, and show that the conclusion holds.

41. Make up an example of three functions f, g, and h showing how the squeeze theorem is used to evaluate the limit of $g(x)$ when the limits of $f(x)$ and $h(x)$ are known.

42. What is $\lim_{t \to 0} \dfrac{\sin t}{t}$ and how is its value used to prove that the sine function is continuous at 0?

43. How is continuity of the sine function at 0 used to prove that the cosine function is continuous at 0?

44. How is the fact that the sine and cosine functions are continuous at 0 used to prove that the sine and cosine are continuous at every real number?

45. How is continuity of the other four trigonometric functions proved from the continuity of the sine and cosine functions?

▶ MISCELLANEOUS EXERCISES FOR CHAPTER 1

1. Given $f(x) = 4 - x^2$, find: **(a)** $f(1)$; **(b)** $f(-2)$; **(c)** $f(3)$; **(d)** $f(x - 1)$; **(e)** $f(x^2)$; **(f)** $\dfrac{f(x + h) - f(x)}{h}$, $h \neq 0$.

2. Given $g(x) = \sqrt{1 - x}$, find: **(a)** $g(1)$; **(b)** $g(-3)$; **(c)** $g(x + 1)$; **(d)** $g(1 - x^2)$; **(e)** $\dfrac{g(x + h) - g(x)}{h}$, $h \neq 0$.

In Exercises 3 through 6, define the following functions and determine the domain of the resulting function:
(a) $f + g$; (b) $f - g$; (c) $f \cdot g$; (d) f/g; (e) g/f; (f) $f \circ g$; (g) $g \circ f$.

3. $f(x) = \sqrt{x + 2}$; $g(x) = x^2 - 4$

4. $f(x) = x^2 - 9$; $g(x) = \sqrt{x + 5}$

5. $f(x) = \dfrac{1}{x^2}$; $g(x) = \sqrt{x}$

6. $f(x) = \dfrac{x}{x-1}$; $g(x) = \dfrac{1}{x+2}$

In Exercises 7 and 8, plot the graph of the function and from the graph conjecture whether the function is even, odd, or neither. Then confirm your conjecture analytically.

7. (a) $f(x) = 2x^3 - 3x$ (b) $g(x) = 5x^4 + 2x^2 - 1$
(c) $h(x) = 3x^5 - 2x^3 + x^2 - x$

(d) $F(x) = \dfrac{x^2 + 1}{x^3 - x}$

8. (a) $f(x) = \dfrac{x^3 - 2x}{x^2 - 1}$ (b) $g(x) = \dfrac{x}{|x|}$

(c) $h(x) = \dfrac{\sqrt[3]{x}}{x}$ (d) $F(x) = x^2[\![x]\!]$

In Exercises 9 and 10, plot the graph of the function and determine its domain and range.

9. (a) $f(x) = 4 - 2x$ (b) $g(x) = x^2 - 4$
(c) $h(x) = \sqrt{x^2 - 16}$ (d) $F(x) = \sqrt{16 - x^2}$
(e) $f(x) = |5 - x|$ (f) $g(x) = 5 - |x|$

10. (a) $g(x) = 3x + 2$ (b) $f(x) = 9 - x^2$
(c) $H(x) = \sqrt{1 - x^2}$ (d) $G(x) = \sqrt{x^2 - 1}$
(e) $g(x) = |x + 4|$ (f) $f(x) = |x| + 4$

In Exercises 11 through 14, sketch the graph of the function and determine its domain and range.

11. (a) $g(x) = \dfrac{x^2 - 16}{x + 4}$

(b) $G(x) = \begin{cases} x - 4 & \text{if } x \neq -4 \\ 3 & \text{if } x = -4 \end{cases}$

12. (a) $f(x) = \dfrac{x^2 + x - 6}{x - 2}$

(b) $F(x) = \begin{cases} x + 3 & \text{if } x \neq 2 \\ 1 & \text{if } x = 2 \end{cases}$

13. (a) $F(x) = \begin{cases} 3 - x & \text{if } x < 0 \\ 3 + 2x & \text{if } 0 \leq x \end{cases}$

(b) $h(x) = \begin{cases} x^2 - 1 & \text{if } x \leq 0 \\ x - 1 & \text{if } 0 < x \end{cases}$

14. (a) $G(x) = \begin{cases} 3x + 2 & \text{if } x \leq 0 \\ 4 - 2x & \text{if } x < 0 \end{cases}$

(b) $H(x) = \begin{cases} x^2 & \text{if } x < -1 \\ (x + 2)^2 & \text{if } -1 \leq x \end{cases}$

In Exercises 15 through 20, you are given $f(x)$, a, L, and ϵ. (a) Use a figure and arguments similar to those in Examples 1 and 3 of Section 1.4 to determine a $\delta > 0$ such that

$$\text{if } 0 < |x - a| < \delta \text{ then } |f(x) - L| < \epsilon$$

(b) Support your choice of δ in part (a) on your graphics calculator. (c) Confirm analytically by using properties of inequalities your choice of δ in part (a).

15. $f(x) = 2x - 5$; $a = 3$; $L = 1$; $\epsilon = 0.05$

16. $f(x) = 3x + 2$; $a = 1$; $L = 5$; $\epsilon = 0.2$

17. $f(x) = \dfrac{x^2 - 25}{x - 5}$; $a = 5$; $L = 10$; $\epsilon = 0.1$

18. $f(x) = \dfrac{2x^2 + 9x + 10}{x + 2}$; $a = -2$; $L = 1$; $\epsilon = 0.03$

19. $f(x) = x^2 + 4$; $a = 2$; $L = 8$; $\epsilon = 0.3$

20. $f(x) = x^2 - 3x$; $a = 3$; $L = 0$; $\epsilon = 0.08$

In Exercises 21 through 26, prove the limit is the indicated number by applying Definition 1.5.1; that is, for any $\epsilon > 0$, find a $\delta > 0$ such that

$$\text{if } 0 < |x - a| < \delta \text{ then } |f(x) - L| < \epsilon$$

21. $\displaystyle\lim_{x \to 3} (2x - 5) = 1$ **22.** $\displaystyle\lim_{x \to -2} (8 - 3x) = 14$

23. $\displaystyle\lim_{x \to -1} (3x + 8) = 5$ **24.** $\displaystyle\lim_{x \to 5} (4x - 11) = 9$

25. $\displaystyle\lim_{x \to -3/4} \dfrac{16x^2 - 9}{4x + 3} = -6$ **26.** $\displaystyle\lim_{x \to 1/3} \dfrac{1 - 9x^2}{1 - 3x} = 2$

In Exercises 27 through 34, find the limit and, when appropriate, indicate the limit theorems used.

27. $\displaystyle\lim_{x \to 2} (3x^2 - 4x + 5)$ **28.** $\displaystyle\lim_{x \to -2} \dfrac{x^2 - x - 6}{x^2 - 5x - 14}$

29. $\displaystyle\lim_{z \to -3} \dfrac{z^2 - 9}{z + 3}$ **30.** $\displaystyle\lim_{h \to 1} \dfrac{h^2 - 4}{3h^3 + 6}$

31. $\displaystyle\lim_{x \to 1/2} \sqrt[3]{\dfrac{4x^2 + 4x - 3}{4x^2 - 1}}$ **32.** $\displaystyle\lim_{t \to 0} \dfrac{1 - \sqrt{1 + t}}{t}$

33. $\displaystyle\lim_{t \to 0} \dfrac{\sqrt{9 - t} - 3}{t}$ **34.** $\displaystyle\lim_{y \to -4} \sqrt{\dfrac{5y + 4}{y - 5}}$

In Exercises 35 through 42, find the limit if it exists, and support your answer by plotting the graph of the function in a convenient window.

35. $\displaystyle\lim_{x \to -1} \dfrac{2x^2 - x - 3}{3x^2 + 8x + 5}$ **36.** $\displaystyle\lim_{y \to 3} \sqrt{\dfrac{y - 3}{y^3 - 27}}$

37. $\displaystyle\lim_{x \to 9} \dfrac{2\sqrt{x} - 6}{x - 9}$ **38.** $\displaystyle\lim_{y \to 5^-} \dfrac{\sqrt{25 - y^2}}{y - 5}$

39. $\lim\limits_{s \to 7} \dfrac{5 - \sqrt{4 + 3s}}{7 - s}$

40. $\lim\limits_{x \to 0^-} \dfrac{x^2 - 5}{2x^3 - 3x^2}$

41. $\lim\limits_{x \to 2^+} \dfrac{[\![x]\!] - 1}{[\![x]\!] - x}$

42. $\lim\limits_{x \to 5} \dfrac{\sqrt{x - 1} - 2}{x - 5}$

In Exercises 43 through 48, sketch the graph of the function and find the indicated limit if it exists; if the limit does not exist, state the reason.

43. $f(x) = \begin{cases} x^2 - 1 & \text{if } x < 3 \\ x + 5 & \text{if } 3 \le x \end{cases}$

    (a) $\lim\limits_{x \to 3^-} f(x)$; **(b)** $\lim\limits_{x \to 3^+} f(x)$; **(c)** $\lim\limits_{x \to 3} f(x)$.

44. $g(x) = \begin{cases} x - 2 & \text{if } x \le 0 \\ x^2 - 1 & \text{if } 0 < x \end{cases}$

    (a) $\lim\limits_{x \to 0^-} g(x)$; **(b)** $\lim\limits_{x \to 0^+} g(x)$; **(c)** $\lim\limits_{x \to 0} g(x)$.

45. $h(t) = \dfrac{|t - 1|}{t - 1}$

    (a) $\lim\limits_{t \to 1^-} h(t)$; **(b)** $\lim\limits_{t \to 1^+} h(t)$; **(c)** $\lim\limits_{t \to 1} h(t)$.

46. $f(r) = \begin{cases} |r - 2| & \text{if } r \ne 2 \\ 3 & \text{if } r = 2 \end{cases}$

    (a) $\lim\limits_{r \to 2^-} f(r)$; **(b)** $\lim\limits_{r \to 2^+} f(r)$; **(c)** $\lim\limits_{r \to 2} f(r)$.

47. $g(x) = \begin{cases} x - 4 & \text{if } x < -4 \\ \sqrt{16 - x^2} & \text{if } -4 \le x \le 4 \\ 4 - x & \text{if } 4 < x \end{cases}$

    (a) $\lim\limits_{x \to -4^-} g(x)$; **(b)** $\lim\limits_{x \to -4^+} g(x)$; **(c)** $\lim\limits_{x \to -4} g(x)$;

    (d) $\lim\limits_{x \to 4^-} g(x)$; **(e)** $\lim\limits_{x \to 4^+} g(x)$; **(f)** $\lim\limits_{x \to 4} g(x)$.

48. $h(x) = \begin{cases} x^2 - 4 & \text{if } x \le 2 \\ 2 - x & \text{if } 2 < x \le 4 \\ x - 2 & \text{if } 4 < x \end{cases}$

    (a) $\lim\limits_{x \to 2^-} h(x)$; **(b)** $\lim\limits_{x \to 2^+} h(x)$; **(c)** $\lim\limits_{x \to 2} h(x)$;

    (d) $\lim\limits_{x \to 4^-} h(x)$; **(e)** $\lim\limits_{x \to 4^+} h(x)$; **(f)** $\lim\limits_{x \to 4} h(x)$.

In Exercises 49 through 54, find the limit and support your answer graphically.

49. (a) $\lim\limits_{x \to -4^-} \dfrac{2x}{16 - x^2}$ **(b)** $\lim\limits_{x \to -4^+} \dfrac{2x}{16 - x^2}$

50. (a) $\lim\limits_{x \to -2^-} \dfrac{x - 1}{x^2 - 4}$ **(b)** $\lim\limits_{x \to -2^+} \dfrac{x - 1}{x^2 - 4}$

51. (a) $\lim\limits_{x \to 4^-} \dfrac{2x}{16 - x^2}$ **(b)** $\lim\limits_{x \to 4^+} \dfrac{2x}{16 - x^2}$

52. (a) $\lim\limits_{x \to 2^-} \dfrac{x - 1}{x^2 - 4}$ **(b)** $\lim\limits_{x \to 2^+} \dfrac{x - 1}{x^2 - 4}$

53. (a) $\lim\limits_{t \to 5} \dfrac{\sqrt{t} - 4}{(t - 5)^2}$ **(b)** $\lim\limits_{t \to 5^+} \dfrac{4 - t}{\sqrt{t} - 5}$

54. (a) $\lim\limits_{x \to -2} \dfrac{\sqrt{3 - x}}{(x + 2)^2}$ **(b)** $\lim\limits_{x \to -2^+} \dfrac{x - 3}{\sqrt{x + 2}}$

In Exercises 55 through 62, do the following: (a) Plot the graph of f in a convenient window. What does $f(x)$ appear to be approaching as x approaches 0? (b) Confirm your answer in part (a) analytically by computing $\lim\limits_{x \to 0} f(x)$.

55. $f(x) = \dfrac{x}{\sin 3x}$

56. $f(x) = \dfrac{x^2}{1 - \cos x}$

57. $f(x) = \dfrac{\sin 5x}{\sin 2x}$

58. $f(x) = \dfrac{1 - \cos 3x}{\sin 3x}$

59. $f(x) = \dfrac{1 - \cos^2 x}{x}$

60. $f(x) = \dfrac{4x}{\tan x}$

61. $f(x) = \dfrac{\csc 3x}{\cot x}$

62. $f(x) = \dfrac{2x^2 - 3x}{2 \sin x}$

In Exercises 63 through 68, find the vertical asymptotes of the graph of the function and use them to sketch the graph.

63. $f(x) = \dfrac{x + 8}{x - 4}$

64. $f(x) = \dfrac{3x - 2}{x - 2}$

65. $g(x) = 1 - \dfrac{1}{x^2}$

66. $f(x) = \dfrac{-2}{x^2 - x - 6}$

67. $f(x) = \dfrac{5x^2}{x^2 - 4}$

68. $h(x) = \dfrac{2x^2}{x^2 - 1}$

In Exercises 69 through 74, sketch the graph of the function; then by observing where there are breaks in the graph, determine the values of x at which the function is discontinuous, and show why Definition 1.8.1 is not satisfied at each discontinuity.

69. $f(x) = \dfrac{x + 2}{x^2 + x - 2}$

70. $g(x) = \dfrac{x^4 - 1}{x^2 - 1}$

71. $g(x) = \begin{cases} 2x + 1 & \text{if } x \le -2 \\ x - 2 & \text{if } -2 < x \le 2 \\ 2 - x & \text{if } 2 < x \end{cases}$

72. $F(x) = \begin{cases} |4 - x| & \text{if } x \ne 4 \\ -2 & \text{if } x = 4 \end{cases}$

73. $h(x) = \begin{cases} \dfrac{1}{x} & \text{if } x \le 1 \\ x^2 - 1 & \text{if } 1 < x \end{cases}$

74. $f(x) = \begin{cases} x^2 - 9 & \text{if } x < 3 \\ 5 & \text{if } x = 3 \\ 9 - x^2 & \text{if } 3 < x \end{cases}$

In Exercises 75 through 78, prove that the function is discontinuous at the number a. Then determine if the discontinuity is removable or essential. If the discontinuity is removable, redefine $f(a)$ so that the discontinuity is removed.

75. $f(x) = \dfrac{x^2 + 2x - 8}{x^2 + 3x - 4}; \ a = -4$

76. $f(x) = \begin{cases} 4 - x^2 & \text{if } x < 1 \\ 2x + 3 & \text{if } 1 \le x \end{cases}; \ a = 1$

77. $f(x) = \begin{cases} \dfrac{1}{x - 2} & \text{if } x \ne 2 \\ 3 & \text{if } x = 2 \end{cases}; \ a = 2$

78. $f(x) = \dfrac{|2x - 6|}{2x - 6}; \ a = 3$

In Exercises 79 through 82, the function is discontinuous at the number a. (a) Plot the graph of f which has a break at the point where $x = a$. Does the discontinuity appear to be removable or essential? If it appears to be removable speculate how $f(a)$ should be redefined so that the discontinuity is removed. (b) Confirm your answer in part (a) analytically.

79. $f(x) = \dfrac{|4 - x| - 3}{x - 1}; \ a = 1$

80. $f(x) = \dfrac{2 - \sqrt{x + 4}}{x}; \ a = 0$

81. $f(x) = \dfrac{x}{\sqrt{x + 9} - 3}; \ a = 0$

82. $f(x) = \dfrac{x - 1}{\sqrt[3]{x} - 1}; \ a = 1$

In Exercises 83 and 84, (a) define $f \circ g$, and (b) determine the numbers at which $f \circ g$ is continuous and state the reason.

83. **(a)** $f(x) = \sqrt{x}$ and $g(x) = 25 - x^2$

   (b) $f(x) = \dfrac{\sqrt{x^2 - 4}}{\sqrt{3 - x}}$ and $g(x) = |x|$

   (c) $f(x) = \operatorname{sgn} x$ and $g(x) = x^2 - 1$

84. **(a)** $f(x) = \sqrt{x}$ and $g(x) = x^2 - 25$

   (b) $f(x) = \sqrt{x + 1}$ and $g(x) = \dfrac{1}{x - 3}$

   (c) $f(x) = \operatorname{sgn} x$ and $g(x) = x^2 - x$

In Exercises 85 and 86 find the values of the constants a and b that make the function continuous at every number and sketch the graph of the resulting function.

85. $f(x) = \begin{cases} 2x + 1 & \text{if } x \le 3 \\ ax + b & \text{if } 3 < x < 5 \\ x^2 + 2 & \text{if } 5 \le x \end{cases}$

86. $f(x) = \begin{cases} 3x + 6a & \text{if } x < -3 \\ 3ax - 7b & \text{if } -3 \le x \le 3 \\ x - 12b & \text{if } 3 < x \end{cases}$

87. Let f be the function defined by

$$f(x) = \begin{cases} 1 & \text{if } x \text{ is an integer} \\ 0 & \text{if } x \text{ is not an integer} \end{cases}$$

   (a) Sketch the graph of f. **(b)** For what values of a does $\lim\limits_{x \to a} f(x)$ exist? **(c)** At what real numbers is f continuous?

88. Give an example of a function for which $\lim\limits_{x \to 0} |f(x)|$ exists but $\lim\limits_{x \to 0} f(x)$ does not exist.

In Exercises 89 through 92, determine the largest interval (or union of intervals) on which the function is continuous. Support your answer on your graphics calculator.

89. **(a)** $f(x) = \sqrt{25 - x^2}$ **(b)** $g(x) = \sqrt{x^2 - 25}$

90. **(a)** $f(x) = \dfrac{|x| + 1}{|x| - 1}$ **(b)** $g(x) = \dfrac{\sqrt{9 - x^2}}{x - 2}$

91. **(a)** $f(x) = \dfrac{|x - 2|}{x - 2}$ **(b)** $g(x) = \dfrac{x}{x^2 - 4}$

92. $F(x) = \begin{cases} x + 4 & \text{if } x < -4 \\ \sqrt{16 - x^2} & \text{if } -4 \le x \le 4 \\ 2 - x & \text{if } 4 < x \end{cases}$

In Exercises 93 through 96, do the following: (a) Verify that the intermediate-value theorem holds for the function f, the closed interval $[a, b]$ and the given value of k; (b) Plot the graph of f and the line $y = k$ on your graphics calculator and estimate to four decimal places the number c in (a, b) such that $f(c) = k$; (c) Confirm your estimate in part (b) analytically; (d) Sketch the graph of f on $[a, b]$ and show the point (c, k).

93. $f(x) = x^2 - 4x + 1; \ [a, b] = [-10, 0]; \ k = 10$

94. $f(x) = x^2 - 4x + 1; \ [a, b] = [0, 10]; \ k = 10$

95. $f(x) = x - \sqrt{16 - x^2}; \ [a, b] = [0, 4]; \ k = -2$

96. $f(x) = x - \sqrt{16 - x^2}; \ [a, b] = [-4, 0]; \ k = -2$

In Exercises 97 and 98, answer the questions from the graph of the function f sketched in the accompanying figure.

97. What is **(a)** $\lim\limits_{x \to -3} f(x)$; **(b)** $\lim\limits_{x \to -2} f(x)$; **(c)** $\lim\limits_{x \to 0} f(x)$;
(d) $\lim\limits_{x \to 2^-} f(x)$; **(e)** $\lim\limits_{x \to 2^+} f(x)$; **(f)** $\lim\limits_{x \to 3^-} f(x)$;
(g) $\lim\limits_{x \to 3^+} f(x)$? **(h)** At what numbers is f discontinuous? **(i)** Which discontinuities in part (h) are essential? **(j)** Which discontinuties in part (h) are removable? How would you redefine the function to remove these discontinuities?

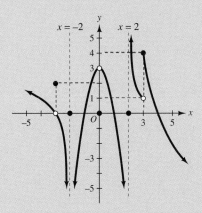

98. What is **(a)** $\lim\limits_{x \to -2^-} f(x)$; **(b)** $\lim\limits_{x \to -2^+} f(x)$; **(c)** $\lim\limits_{x \to -1} f(x)$;
(d) $\lim\limits_{x \to 0} f(x)$; **(e)** $\lim\limits_{x \to 1^-} f(x)$; **(f)** $\lim\limits_{x \to 1^+} f(x)$;
(g) $\lim\limits_{x \to 2} f(x)$? **(h)** At what numbers is f discontinuous? **(i)** Which discontinuities in part (h) are essential? **(j)** Which discontinuities in part (h) are removable? How would you redefine the function to remove these discontinuities?

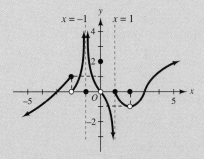

In Exercises 99 through 102, sketch the graph of a function f satisfying the given conditions.

99. $-5, -3, -2, -1, 0,$ and 2 are the only zeros of f;
$\lim\limits_{x \to -3} f(x) = 4$; $\lim\limits_{x \to -1^-} f(x) = -\infty$; $\lim\limits_{x \to -1^+} f(x) = 0$;
$\lim\limits_{x \to 0} f(x) = +\infty$; f is continuous at all numbers in the open intervals $(-\infty, -3)$, $(-3, -1)$, $(-1, 0)$, $(0, +\infty)$.

100. f is continuous on $(-\infty, -2)$, $[-2, 1)$, $[1, 3]$, and $(3, +\infty)$; $\lim\limits_{x \to -4} f(x) = 0$; $\lim\limits_{x \to -2^-} f(x) = +\infty$;
$\lim\limits_{x \to -2^+} f(x) = 0$; $\lim\limits_{x \to 0} f(x) = -3$; $\lim\limits_{x \to 1^-} f(x) = -\infty$;
$\lim\limits_{x \to 1^+} f(x) = 2$; $\lim\limits_{x \to 3^-} f(x) = 4$; $\lim\limits_{x \to 3^+} f(x) = -1$;
$\lim\limits_{x \to 5} f(x) = 0$.

101. The domain of f is $(-\infty, +\infty)$; $f(-4) = 2$; $-2, 0, 2,$ 4, and 6 are the only zeros of f; $\lim\limits_{x \to -4} f(x) = 0$;
$\lim\limits_{x \to -2^-} f(x) = -\infty$; $\lim\limits_{x \to -2^+} f(x) = +\infty$; $\lim\limits_{x \to 0^-} f(x) = 0$;
$\lim\limits_{x \to 0^+} f(x) = -3$; $\lim\limits_{x \to 4} f(x) = 5$; f is continuous at all numbers except $-4, -2, 0,$ and 4.

102. f is continuous on $(-\infty, -4]$, $(-4, 4)$, and $[4, +\infty)$;
$\lim\limits_{x \to -6} f(x) = 0$; $\lim\limits_{x \to -4^-} f(x) = 2$; $\lim\limits_{x \to -4^+} f(x) = +\infty$;
$\lim\limits_{x \to -2} f(x) = 0$; $\lim\limits_{x \to 0} f(x) = -3$; $\lim\limits_{x \to 2} f(x) = 0$;
$\lim\limits_{x \to 4^-} f(x) = 1$; $\lim\limits_{x \to 4^+} f(x) = -2$; $\lim\limits_{x \to 5} f(x) = 0$.

In Exercises 103 through 106, you are to obtain a function as a mathematical model of a particular situation. These models will appear again later in the text when we apply calculus to the situation. Define the independent variable and the function value as numbers and indicate the units of measurement. Be sure you complete the exercise by writing a conclusion.

103. An open metal pan is to be made by cutting out squares of the same size from the corners of a rectangular piece of metal 14 in. by 18 in. and turning up the sides.
   (a) Find a mathematical model expressing the volume of the pan as a function of the length of the side of the square cut out.
   (b) What is the domain of your function in part (a)?
   (c) Prove that the function is continuous on its domain.
   (d) On your graphics calculator find accurate to the nearest one-hundredth of an inch the length of the side of the square to be cut out so that the volume of the pan is a maximum. What is the maximum volume to the nearest cubic inch?

104. An open box having a square base is to have a volume of 4000 in.^{3}
   (a) Find a mathematical model expressing the total surface area of the box as a function of the length of a side of the square base.
   (b) What is the domain of your function in part (a)?

(c) Prove that the function is continuous on its domain.

(d) On your graphics calculator, determine to the nearest inch the dimensions of the box that can be constructed with the least amount of material.

105. A sign containing 50 m² of printed material is required to have margins of 4 m at the top and bottom and 2 m on each side.

(a) Find a mathematical model expressing the total area of the sign as a function of the horizontal dimension of the region covered by the printed material.

(b) What is the domain of your function in part (a)?

(c) Prove that the function is continuous on its domain.

(d) On your graphics calculator, determine to the nearest meter the dimensions of the smallest sign that will meet these specifications.

106. If a pond can support up to 10,000 fish, the rate of growth of the fish population is jointly proportional to the number of fish present and the difference between 10,000 and the number present. The rate of growth is 90 fish per week when 1000 fish are present.

(a) Find a mathematical model expressing the rate of population growth as a function of the number present.

(b) What is the domain of your function in part (a)?

(c) Prove that the function is continuous on its domain.

(d) On your graphics calculator, estimate the size of the fish population for the growth rate to be a maximum.

107. U and sgn are the unit step function and the signum function defined in Exercises 47 and 49, respectively, of Exercises 1.1. Find formulas for the function F defined by

$$F(x) = (\operatorname{sgn} x) \cdot U(x + 1)$$

and sketch its graph. At what number is F discontinuous and why?

In Exercises 108 and 109, use the squeeze theorem to find the limit.

108. $\lim\limits_{x \to 4} g(x)$ if $|g(x) + 5| < 3(4 - x)^2$ for all x

109. $\lim\limits_{x \to 1} \left[(x - 1)^2 \sin \dfrac{1}{\sqrt[3]{x - 1}} \right]$

110. Sketch the graph of f if $f(x) = [\![1 - x^2]\!]$ and $-2 \le x \le 2$. **(a)** Does $\lim\limits_{x \to 0} f(x)$ exist? **(b)** Is f continuous at 0?

111. Sketch the graph of g if $g(x) = (x - 1)[\![x]\!]$ and $0 \le x \le 2$. **(a)** Does $\lim\limits_{x \to 1} g(x)$ exist? **(b)** Is g continuous at 1?

112. (a) Prove that if $f(x) = g(x)$ for all values of x except a, then $\lim\limits_{x \to a} f(x) = \lim\limits_{x \to a} g(x)$ if the limits exist. **(b)** Prove that if $f(x) = g(x)$ for all values of x except a, then if $\lim\limits_{x \to a} g(x)$ does not exist, $\lim\limits_{x \to a} f(x)$ does not exist. *Hint:* Show that the assumption that $\lim\limits_{x \to a} f(x)$ does exist leads to a contradiction.

113. (a) Prove that if $\lim\limits_{h \to 0} f(x + h) = f(x)$, then
$$\lim\limits_{h \to 0} f(x + h) = \lim\limits_{h \to 0} f(x - h)$$
(b) Show that the converse of the theorem in (a) is not true by giving an example of a function for which $\lim\limits_{h \to 0} f(x + h) = \lim\limits_{h \to 0} f(x - h)$ but $\lim\limits_{h \to 0} f(x + h) \ne f(x)$.

114. If the domain of f is the set of all real numbers and f is continuous at 0, prove that if
$$f(a + b) = f(a) + f(b)$$
for all a and b, then f is continuous at every number.

115. If the domain of f is the set of all real numbers and f is continuous at 0, prove that if $f(a + b) = f(a) \cdot f(b)$ for all a and b, then f is continuous at every number.

116. Suppose the function f is defined on the open interval $(0, 1)$ and
$$f(x) = \frac{\sin \pi x}{x(x - 1)}$$
Define f at 0 and 1 so that f is continuous on the closed interval $[0, 1]$.

THE DERIVATIVE AND DIFFERENTIATION

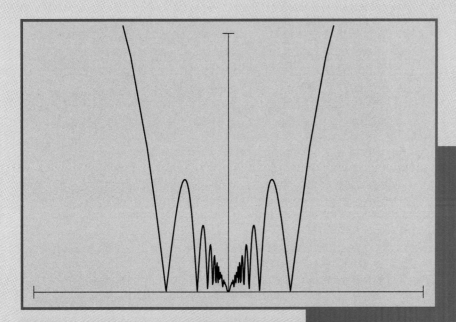

We introduce the *derivative* in Section 2.1 by first considering its geometric interpretation as the slope of the tangent line to the graph of a function. A function that has a derivative is said to be *differentiable*, and in Section 2.2 we discuss the relationship between differentiability and continuity. The *numerical derivative* is applied in Section 2.3 to approx-imate the derivative of a function on a graphics calculator and in later sections to support graphically computations of derivatives.

A derivative is computed by the operation of *differentiation*. Theorems that help perform this computation on algebraic functions are stated and proved in Section 2.4, which also introduces higher-order derivatives.

The interpretation of the derivative as a rate of change begins in Section 2.5 with applications to rectilinear motion. In Section 2.6, we extend the applications to other disciplines. For instance, the rate of growth of bacteria gives an application of the derivative in biology. The rate of change of a chemical reaction is of interest to a chemist. Economists are concerned with marginal concepts such as marginal revenue, marginal cost, and marginal profit, all of which are rates of change.

Differentiation of trigonometric functions is discussed in Section 2.7, and in Section 2.8 we state and prove the *chain rule*, a powerful tool used to differentiate composite functions. We apply the chain rule in Section 2.9 to obtain the formula giving the derivative of the power function for rational exponents and to differentiate functions defined implicitly. Problems involving related rates, treated in Section 2.10, provide another important application of the derivative.

FIGURE 1

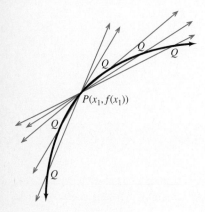

FIGURE 2

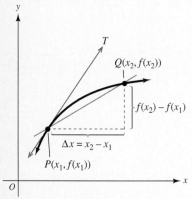

FIGURE 3

2.1 THE TANGENT LINE AND THE DERIVATIVE

Many important problems in calculus depend on determining the *tangent line* to the graph of a function at a specific point on the graph. We begin this section by defining what is meant by such a tangent line.

Recall from your plane geometry course that the tangent line at a point on a circle was defined as the line intersecting the circle at only that point. Such a definition does not suffice for a curve in general. For example, in Figure 1 the line that we wish to be the tangent line to the curve at point P intersects the curve at another point Q. To arrive at a suitable definition of the tangent line to the graph of a function at a point, we proceed by using a limiting process to define the *slope of the tangent line* at the point. Then the tangent line is determined by its slope and the point of tangency.

Consider the function f continuous at x_1. We wish to define the slope of the tangent line to the graph of f at $P(x_1, f(x_1))$. Let I be an open interval that contains x_1 and on which f is defined. Let $Q(x_2, f(x_2))$ be another point on the graph of f such that x_2 is also in I. Draw a line through P and Q. Any line through two points on a curve is called a **secant line;** therefore the line through P and Q is a secant line. In Figure 2 the secant line is shown for various values of x_2. Figure 3 shows one particular secant line. In this figure Q is to the right of P. However, Q may be on either the right or the left side of P, as seen in Figure 2.

The difference of the abscissas (the x coordinates) of Q and P is denoted by Δx (read "delta x") so that

$$\Delta x = x_2 - x_1$$

Observe that Δx represents the change in the value of x from x_1 to x_2 and may be either positive or negative. This change is called an **increment of x.** Be careful to note that the symbol Δx for an increment of x does not mean "delta multiplied by x."

Refer back to the secant line PQ in Figure 3; its slope is given by

$$m_{PQ} = \frac{f(x_2) - f(x_1)}{\Delta x}$$

Because $x_2 = x_1 + \Delta x$, the above equation can be written as

$$m_{PQ} = \frac{f(x_1 + \Delta x) - f(x_1)}{\Delta x}$$

Now think of point P as being fixed, and move point Q along the curve toward P; that is, Q approaches P. This is equivalent to stating that Δx approaches zero. As this occurs, the secant line turns about the fixed point P. If this secant line has a limiting position, it is this limiting position that we wish to be the tangent line to the graph at P. So we want the slope of the tangent line to the graph at P to be the limit of m_{PQ} as Δx approaches zero, if this limit exists. If $\lim_{\Delta x \to 0} m_{PQ}$ is $+\infty$ or $-\infty$, then as Δx approaches zero, the line PQ approaches the line through P parallel to the y axis. In this case we would want the tangent line to be the line $x = x_1$. Our discussion leads to the following definition.

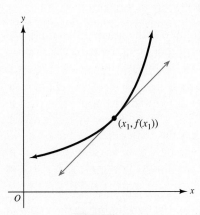

FIGURE 4

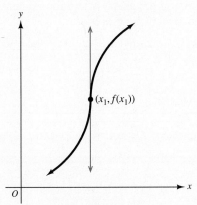

FIGURE 5

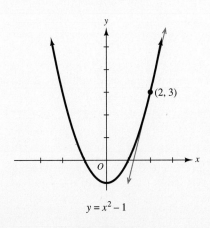

$y = x^2 - 1$

FIGURE 6

2.1.1 Definition of the Tangent Line to the Graph of a Function

Suppose the function f is continuous at x_1. The **tangent line** to the graph of f at the point $P(x_1, f(x_1))$ is

(i) the line through P having slope $m(x_1)$, given by

$$m(x_1) = \lim_{\Delta x \to 0} \frac{f(x_1 + \Delta x) - f(x_1)}{\Delta x} \tag{1}$$

if this limit exists;

(ii) the line $x = x_1$ if

$$\lim_{\Delta x \to 0^+} \frac{f(x_1 + \Delta x) - f(x_1)}{\Delta x} \text{ is } +\infty \text{ or } -\infty$$

and

$$\lim_{\Delta x \to 0^-} \frac{f(x_1 + \Delta x) - f(x_1)}{\Delta x} \text{ is } +\infty \text{ or } -\infty$$

Figure 4 shows the graph of a function f and its tangent line when $m(x_1)$ exists. Figure 5 shows the graph of a function f with a vertical tangent line at the point $(x_1, f(x_1))$.

If neither (i) nor (ii) of Definition 2.1.1 holds, there is no tangent line to the graph of f at the point $P(x_1, f(x_1))$.

The slope of the tangent line to the graph of a function at a point is also called the **slope of the graph** at the point.

▶ **EXAMPLE 1**   Find an equation of the tangent line to the parabola $y = x^2 - 1$ at the point $(2, 3)$. Sketch the parabola and show a segment of the tangent line at $(2, 3)$.

Solution   We first compute the slope of the tangent line at $(2, 3)$. With $f(x) = x^2 - 1$, we have from (1)

$$\begin{aligned}
m(2) &= \lim_{\Delta x \to 0} \frac{f(2 + \Delta x) - f(2)}{\Delta x} \\
&= \lim_{\Delta x \to 0} \frac{[(2 + \Delta x)^2 - 1] - 3}{\Delta x} \\
&= \lim_{\Delta x \to 0} \frac{4 + 4\,\Delta x + (\Delta x)^2 - 4}{\Delta x} \\
&= \lim_{\Delta x \to 0} \frac{4\,\Delta x + (\Delta x)^2}{\Delta x} \\
&= \lim_{\Delta x \to 0} (4 + \Delta x) \\
&= 4
\end{aligned}$$

Thus the tangent line at $(2, 3)$ has slope 4. From the point-slope form of an equation of a line, $y - y_1 = m(x - x_1)$, we have

$$y - 3 = 4(x - 2)$$
$$4x - y - 5 = 0$$

Figure 6 shows the parabola and a segment of the tangent line at $(2, 3)$.   ◀

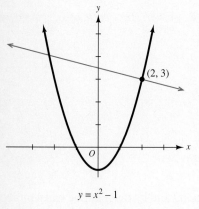

$y = x^2 - 1$

FIGURE 7

2.1.2 Definition of the Normal Line to a Graph

The **normal line** to a graph at a given point is the line perpendicular to the tangent line at that point.

▷   **ILLUSTRATION 1**   The normal line to the graph of Example 1 at $(2, 3)$ is perpendicular to the tangent line at that point. Because the slope of the tangent line at $(2, 3)$ is 4, the slope of the normal line at $(2, 3)$ is $-\frac{1}{4}$, and an equation of this normal line is

$$y - 3 = -\tfrac{1}{4}(x - 2)$$
$$4y - 12 = -x + 2$$
$$x + 4y - 14 = 0$$

The parabola and the normal line at $(2, 3)$ appear in Figure 7.   ◀

▶   **EXAMPLE 2**   **(a)** Find the slope of the tangent line to the graph of

$$f(x) = x^3 - 3x$$

at the point $(x_1, f(x_1))$. **(b)** Find the points on the graph where the tangent line is horizontal and use these points to sketch the graph of f.

Solution

(a)

$$f(x_1) = x_1^3 - 3x_1$$
$$f(x_1 + \Delta x) = (x_1 + \Delta x)^3 - 3(x_1 + \Delta x)$$

From (1),

$$m(x_1) = \lim_{\Delta x \to 0} \frac{f(x_1 + \Delta x) - f(x_1)}{\Delta x}$$

$$= \lim_{\Delta x \to 0} \frac{(x_1 + \Delta x)^3 - 3(x_1 + \Delta x) - (x_1^3 - 3x_1)}{\Delta x}$$

$$= \lim_{\Delta x \to 0} \frac{x_1^3 + 3x_1^2\,\Delta x + 3x_1(\Delta x)^2 + (\Delta x)^3 - 3x_1 - 3\,\Delta x - x_1^3 + 3x_1}{\Delta x}$$

$$= \lim_{\Delta x \to 0} \frac{3x_1^2\,\Delta x + 3x_1(\Delta x)^2 + (\Delta x)^3 - 3\,\Delta x}{\Delta x}$$

Because $\Delta x \neq 0$, the numerator and denominator can be divided by Δx to obtain

$$m(x_1) = \lim_{\Delta x \to 0} \left[3x_1^2 + 3x_1\,\Delta x + (\Delta x)^2 - 3\right]$$
$$m(x_1) = 3x_1^2 - 3 \tag{2}$$

(b) The tangent line is horizontal at points where the slope is zero. Setting $m(x_1) = 0$, we have

$$3x_1^2 - 3 = 0$$
$$x_1^2 = 1$$
$$x_1 = \pm 1$$

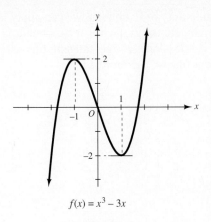

$f(x) = x^3 - 3x$

FIGURE 8

The tangent line is, therefore, horizontal at the points $(-1, 2)$ and $(1, -2)$. Locating these points as well as a few others we obtain the graph shown in Figure 8. ◀

The type of limit in (1) used to define the slope of a tangent line is one of the most important in calculus. It occurs often, and it has a specific name.

2.1.3 Definition of the Derivative of a Function

The **derivative** of the function f is that function, denoted by f', such that its value at a number x in the domain of f is given by

$$f'(x) = \lim_{\Delta x \to 0} \frac{f(x + \Delta x) - f(x)}{\Delta x} \qquad (3)$$

if this limit exists.

If x_1 is a particular number in the domain of f, then

$$f'(x_1) = \lim_{\Delta x \to 0} \frac{f(x_1 + \Delta x) - f(x_1)}{\Delta x} \qquad (4)$$

if this limit exists. Observe that the domain of f' is a subset of the domain of f.

Comparing formulas (1) and (4), note that the slope of the tangent line to the graph of function f at the point $(x_1, f(x_1))$ is precisely the derivative of f evaluated at x_1.

▶ **EXAMPLE 3**   Find the derivative of f if

$$f(x) = \frac{3}{x}$$

Solution   If x is a number in the domain of f, then from (3)

$$f'(x) = \lim_{\Delta x \to 0} \frac{f(x + \Delta x) - f(x)}{\Delta x}$$

$$= \lim_{\Delta x \to 0} \frac{\dfrac{3}{x + \Delta x} - \dfrac{3}{x}}{\Delta x}$$

$$= \lim_{\Delta x \to 0} \frac{3x - 3(x + \Delta x)}{\Delta x(x)(x + \Delta x)}$$

$$= \lim_{\Delta x \to 0} \frac{-3 \, \Delta x}{\Delta x(x)(x + \Delta x)}$$

$$= \lim_{\Delta x \to 0} \frac{-3}{x(x + \Delta x)}$$

$$= -\frac{3}{x^2}$$

Therefore the derivative of f is the function f' defined by $f'(x) = -\dfrac{3}{x^2}$. The domain of f' is the set of all real numbers except 0, which is the same as the domain of f. ◀

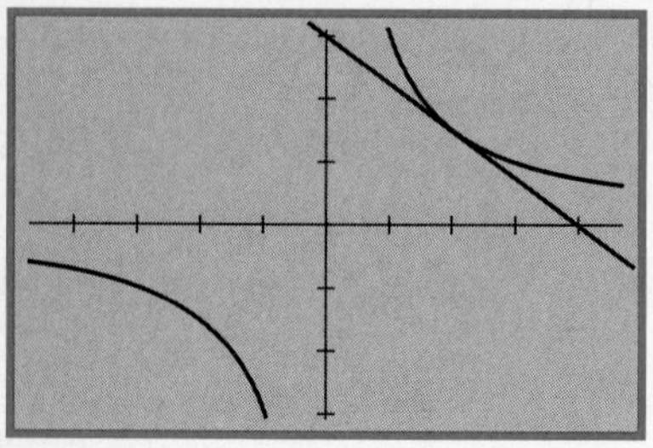

[−4.7, 4.7] by [−3.1, 3.1]

$$f(x) = \frac{3}{x}$$

FIGURE 9

▷ **ILLUSTRATION 2**   For the function f of Example 3 we can apply $f'(x)$ to obtain an equation of the tangent line to the graph of f at a particular point. For instance, at the point $(2, \frac{3}{2})$ the slope of the tangent line is $f'(2) = -\frac{3}{4}$. An equation of this tangent line is, therefore,

$$y - \tfrac{3}{2} = -\tfrac{3}{4}(x - 2)$$
$$4y - 6 = -3x + 6$$
$$3x + 4y - 12 = 0$$

Figure 9 shows the graph of f and this tangent line plotted in the $[−4.7, 4.7]$ by $[−3.1, 3.1]$ window.   ◀

Consider now formula (4), which is

$$f'(x_1) = \lim_{\Delta x \to 0} \frac{f(x_1 + \Delta x) - f(x_1)}{\Delta x}$$

In this formula let

$$x_1 + \Delta x = x \qquad (5)$$

Then

"$\Delta x \to 0$"   is equivalent to   "$x \to x_1$"   (6)

From (4), (5), and (6) we obtain the following formula for $f'(x_1)$:

$$f'(x_1) = \lim_{x \to x_1} \frac{f(x) - f(x_1)}{x - x_1} \qquad (7)$$

if this limit exits. Formula (7) is an alternative formula to (4) for computing $f'(x_1)$.

The quotients $\dfrac{f(x_1 + \Delta x) - f(x_1)}{\Delta x}$ in (4) and $\dfrac{f(x) - f(x_1)}{x - x_1}$ in (7) are called **standard difference quotients** of the function f at the number x_1.

▶ **EXAMPLE 4**   For the function of Example 3, compute $f'(2)$ by applying formula (7).

Solution   From formula (7)

$$f'(2) = \lim_{x \to 2} \frac{f(x) - f(2)}{x - 2}$$
$$= \lim_{x \to 2} \frac{\frac{3}{x} - \frac{3}{2}}{x - 2}$$
$$= \lim_{x \to 2} \frac{3(2 - x)}{2x(x - 2)}$$
$$= \lim_{x \to 2} \frac{-3}{2x}$$
$$= -\frac{3}{4}$$

which agrees with $f'(2)$ in Illustration 2.   ◀

The use of the symbol f' for the derivative of the function f was introduced by the French mathematician Joseph Louis Lagrange (1736–1813) in the eighteenth century. This notation emphasizes that the function f' is derived from the function f and its value at x is $f'(x)$.

If (x, y) is a point on the graph of f, then $y = f(x)$, and y' is also used as a notation for the derivative of $f(x)$. With the function f defined by the equation $y = f(x)$, we can let

$$\Delta y = f(x + \Delta x) - f(x) \tag{8}$$

where Δy is called an *increment* of y and denotes a change in the function value as x changes by Δx. By using (8) and writing $\dfrac{dy}{dx}$ in place of $f'(x)$, formula (3) becomes

$$\frac{dy}{dx} = \lim_{\Delta x \to 0} \frac{\Delta y}{\Delta x}$$

The symbol $\dfrac{dy}{dx}$ as a notation for the derivative was first used by the German mathematician Gottfried Wilhelm Leibniz (1646–1716). In the seventeenth century Leibniz and Sir Isaac Newton (1642–1727), working independently, introduced almost simultaneously the derivative. Leibniz probably thought of dx and dy as small changes in the variables x and y and of the derivative of y with respect to x as the ratio of dy to dx as dy and dx become small. The concept of a limit as we know it today was not known to either Leibniz or Newton.

In the Lagrange notation the value of the derivative at $x = x_1$ is indicated by $f'(x_1)$. With the Leibniz notation we would write

$$\frac{dy}{dx}\bigg]_{x = x_1}$$

You must remember that when $\dfrac{dy}{dx}$ is used as a notation for a derivative, dy and dx have so far in this book not been given independent meaning, although later they will be defined separately. So at this time $\dfrac{dy}{dx}$ is a symbol for a derivative and should not be thought of as a ratio. As a matter of fact, $\dfrac{d}{dx}$ can be considered as an operator (a symbol for the operation of computing the derivative), and when we write $\dfrac{dy}{dx}$, it means $\dfrac{d}{dx}(y)$, that is, the derivative of y with respect to x.

▶ **EXAMPLE 5**   Find $\dfrac{dy}{dx}$ if

$$y = \sqrt{x}$$

Solution We are given $y = f(x)$ where $f(x) = \sqrt{x}$.

$$\frac{dy}{dx} = \lim_{\Delta x \to 0} \frac{\Delta y}{\Delta x}$$

$$= \lim_{\Delta x \to 0} \frac{f(x + \Delta x) - f(x)}{\Delta x}$$

$$= \lim_{\Delta x \to 0} \frac{\sqrt{x + \Delta x} - \sqrt{x}}{\Delta x}$$

To evaluate this limit we rationalize the numerator.

$$\frac{dy}{dx} = \lim_{\Delta x \to 0} \frac{(\sqrt{x + \Delta x} - \sqrt{x})(\sqrt{x + \Delta x} + \sqrt{x})}{\Delta x(\sqrt{x + \Delta x} + \sqrt{x})}$$

$$= \lim_{\Delta x \to 0} \frac{\Delta x}{\Delta x\,(\sqrt{x + \Delta x} + \sqrt{x})}$$

We divide numerator and denominator by Δx (because $\Delta x \neq 0$) and obtain

$$\frac{dy}{dx} = \lim_{\Delta x \to 0} \frac{1}{\sqrt{x + \Delta x} + \sqrt{x}}$$

$$= \frac{1}{2\sqrt{x}} \qquad\qquad \blacktriangleleft$$

Two other notations for the derivative of a function f are

$$\frac{d}{dx}[f(x)] \quad \text{and} \quad D_x[f(x)]$$

Each of these notations allows us to indicate the original function in the expression for the derivative. For instance, we can write the result of Example 5 as

$$\frac{d}{dx}(\sqrt{x}) = \frac{1}{2\sqrt{x}} \quad \text{or as} \quad D_x(\sqrt{x}) = \frac{1}{2\sqrt{x}}$$

Of course, if the function and the variables are denoted by letters other than f, x, and y, the notations for the derivative incorporate those letters. For instance, if the function g is defined by the equation $s = g(t)$, then the derivative of g can be indicated in each of the following ways:

$$g'(t) \qquad \frac{ds}{dt} \qquad \frac{d}{dt}[g(t)] \qquad D_t[g(t)]$$

EXERCISES 2.1

In Exercises 1 through 6, find an equation of the tangent line to the graph of the equation at the given point. Sketch the graph and show a segment of the tangent line at the point.

1. $y = 9 - x^2$; $(2, 5)$ **2.** $y = x^2 + 4$; $(-1, 5)$

3. $y = 2x^2 + 4x$; $(-2, 0)$

4. $y = x^2 - 6x + 9$; $(3, 0)$

5. $y = x^3 + 3$; $(1, 4)$ **6.** $y = 1 - x^3$; $(2, -7)$

In Exercises 7 through 10, (a) find the slope of the tangent line to the graph of the function f at the point $(x_1, f(x_1))$. (b) Find the points on the graph where the tangent line is horizontal and use these points to sketch the graph.

7. $f(x) = 3x^2 - 12x + 8$

8. $f(x) = 7 - 6x - x^2$

9. $f(x) = x^3 - 6x^2 + 9x - 2$

10. $f(x) = 2x^3 - 3x^2$

In Exercises 11 through 16, find equations of the tangent line and normal line to the graph of the equation at the indicated point. Plot on your graphics calculator the graph together with the tangent line and normal line in the same window.

11. $y = \sqrt{x + 1}$; $(3, 2)$ **12.** $y = \sqrt{4 - x}$; $(-5, 3)$

13. $y = 2x - x^3$; $(-2, 4)$ **14.** $y = x^3 - 4x$; $(0, 0)$

15. $y = \dfrac{4}{x^2}$; $(2, 1)$ **16.** $y = -\dfrac{8}{\sqrt{x}}$; $(4, -4)$

17. Given $f(x) = 3x^2 - 7x$. **(a)** On your calculator tabulate values of the standard difference quotient

$$\frac{f(2 + \Delta x) - f(2)}{\Delta x}$$

when Δx is 0.10, 0.09, 0.08, ... 0.01, and -0.10, -0.09, -0.08, ..., -0.01. What does the standard difference quotient appear to be approaching as Δx approaches 0? **(b)** Find $f'(2)$ by applying formula (4) and compare this number with your answer in part (a). **(c)** On your calculator tabulate values of the standard difference quotient

$$\frac{f(x) - f(2)}{x - 2}$$

when x is 2.10, 2.09, 2.08, ..., 2.01, and 1.90, 1.91, 1.92, ..., 1.99. What does the standard difference quotient appear to be approaching as x approaches 2? **(d)** Find $f'(2)$ by applying formula (7) and compare this number with your answer in part (c).

18. Do Exercise 17 if $f(x) = x^3$.

19. Do Exercise 17 if $f(x) = \sqrt{6 - x}$.

20. Do Exercise 17 if $f(x) = \dfrac{1}{4 - x}$.

In Exercises 21 through 30, find $f'(x_1)$ two ways: (a) apply formula (7); (b) apply formula (4).

21. $f(x) = \dfrac{8}{x - 2}$; $x_1 = 6$

22. $f(x) = \dfrac{2}{\sqrt{x}} - 1$; $x_1 = 4$

23. $f(x) = \sin x$; $x_1 = 0$ **24.** $f(x) = \cos x$; $x_1 = 0$

25. $f(x) = \sin x$; $x_1 = \frac{1}{2}\pi$ **26.** $f(x) = \cos x$; $x_1 = \frac{1}{2}\pi$

27. $f(x) = \sec x$; $x_1 = 0$ **28.** $f(x) = \tan x$; $x_1 = 0$

29. $f(x) = \cot x$; $x_1 = \frac{1}{2}\pi$ **30.** $f(x) = \csc x$; $x_1 = \frac{1}{2}\pi$

In Exercises 31 through 36, find $f'(x)$ by applying formula (3).

31. $f(x) = -4$ **32.** $f(x) = 10$

33. $f(x) = 7x + 3$ **34.** $f(x) = 8 - 5x$

35. $f(x) = 4 + 5x - 2x^2$ **36.** $f(x) = 3x^2 - 2x + 1$

In Exercises 37 through 40, find the indicated derivative.

37. $\dfrac{d}{dx}(8 - x^3)$ **38.** $\dfrac{d}{dt}(t^3 + t)$

39. $D_r\left(\dfrac{2r + 3}{3r - 2}\right)$ **40.** $D_x\left(\dfrac{1}{x^2} - x\right)$

In Exercises 41 through 44, find $\dfrac{dy}{dx}$.

41. $y = 3x + \dfrac{6}{x^2}$ **42.** $y = \sqrt[3]{x}$

43. $y = \dfrac{1}{\sqrt{x - 1}}$ **44.** $y = \dfrac{4}{2x - 5}$

45. Find an equation of the tangent line to the curve $y = 2x^2 + 3$ that is parallel to the line $8x - y + 3 = 0$.

46. Find an equation of the tangent line to the curve $y = 3x^2 - 4$ that is parallel to the line $3x + y = 4$.

47. Find an equation of the normal line to the curve $y = 2 - \frac{1}{3}x^2$ that is parallel to the line $x - y = 0$.

48. Find an equation of each normal line to the curve $y = x^3 - 3x$ that is parallel to the line $2x + 18y - 9 = 0$.

49. Prove that there is no line through the point $(1, 5)$ that is tangent to the curve $y = 4x^2$.

50. Prove that there is no line through the point $(1, 2)$ that is tangent to the curve $y = 4 - x^2$.

51. If g is continuous at a and $f(x) = (x - a)g(x)$, find $f'(a)$. *Hint:* use formula (7).

52. If g is continuous at a and $f(x) = (x^2 - a^2)g(x)$, find $f'(a)$. *Hint:* use formula (7).

53. If

$$f''(x) = \lim_{\Delta x \to 0} \frac{f'(x + \Delta x) - f'(x)}{\Delta x}$$

find $f''(x)$ if $f(x) = ax^2 + bx$.

54. Use the formula of Exercise 53 to find $f''(x)$ if $f(x) = a/x$.

55. If $f'(a)$ exists, prove that

$$f'(a) = \lim_{\Delta x \to 0} \frac{f(a + \Delta x) - f(a - \Delta x)}{2\,\Delta x}$$

Hint: $f(a + \Delta x) - f(a - \Delta x)$
$\qquad = f(a + \Delta x) - f(a) + f(a) - f(a - \Delta x)$

56. Let f be a function whose domain is the set of all real numbers and $f(a + b) = f(a) \cdot f(b)$ for all a and b. Furthermore, suppose that $f(0) = 1$ and $f'(0)$ exists. Prove that $f'(x)$ exists for all x and that

$$f'(x) = f'(0) \cdot f(x)$$

57. Plot the parabola $y = \frac{1}{4}x^2$ and its tangent line at the point (2, 1) in the $[-4.7, 4.7]$ by $[-3.1, 3.1]$ window. As you zoom in at the point (2, 1) describe what happens. Why does this occur?

58. Plot the curve $y = \sqrt{x}$ and its tangent line at the point (1, 1) in the $[-1, 3.7]$ by $[-1, 2.1]$ window. As you zoom in at the point (1, 1) describe what happens. Why does this occur?

2.2 DIFFERENTIABILITY AND CONTINUITY

The process of computing the derivative is called *differentiation;* that is, **differentiation** is the operation of deriving a function f' from a function f.

If a function has a derivative at x_1, the function is said to be **differentiable** at x_1. A function is **differentiable on an open interval** if it is differentiable at every number in the open interval. If a function is differentiable at every number in its domain, it is called a **differentiable function.**

▷ **ILLUSTRATION 1**   In Example 3 of Section 2.1, $f(x) = 3/x$ and $f'(x) = -3/x^2$. Because the domain of f is the set of all real numbers except 0, and $f'(x)$ exists at every real number except 0, f is a differentiable function. ◀

▷ **ILLUSTRATION 2**   Let the function g be defined by $g(x) = \sqrt{x}$. The domain of g is $[0, +\infty]$. From Example 5 of Section 2.1,

$$g'(x) = \frac{1}{2\sqrt{x}}$$

Because $g'(0)$ does not exist, g is not differentiable at 0. However, g is differentiable at every other number in its domain. Therefore, g is differentiable on the open interval $(0, +\infty)$. ◀

We begin our discussion of differentiability and continuity with the following example.

▶ **EXAMPLE 1**   Let

$$f(x) = x^{1/3}$$

(a) Show that f is not differentiable at 0 even though it is continuous there. **(b)** Plot the graph of f.

Solution: **(a)** Applying formula (7) of Section 2.1, we have, if the limit exists,

$$f'(0) = \lim_{x \to 0} \frac{f(x) - f(0)}{x - 0}$$

$$= \lim_{x \to 0} \frac{x^{1/3} - 0}{x}$$

$$= \lim_{x \to 0} \frac{1}{x^{2/3}}$$

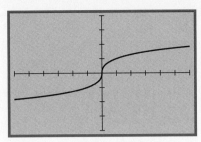

[-6, 6] by [-4, 4]

$f(x) = x^{1/3}$

FIGURE 1

But this limit does not exist. Thus f is not differentiable at 0. However, f is continuous at 0 because

$$\lim_{x \to 0} f(x) = \lim_{x \to 0} x^{1/3}$$
$$= 0$$
$$= f(0)$$

(b) Figure 1 shows the graph of f plotted in the $[-6, 6]$ by $[-4, 4]$ window. ◀

▷ **ILLUSTRATION 3**   For the function f of Example 1, because

$$\lim_{\Delta x \to 0} \frac{f(0 + \Delta x) - f(0)}{\Delta x} = \lim_{\Delta x \to 0} \frac{(\Delta x)^{1/3} - 0}{\Delta x}$$
$$= \lim_{\Delta x \to 0} \frac{1}{(\Delta x)^{2/3}}$$
$$= +\infty$$

it follows from Definition 2.1.1 (ii) that $x = 0$ is the tangent line to the graph of f at the origin. ◀

From Example 1 and Illustration 3, the function defined by $f(x) = x^{1/3}$ has the following properties:

1. f is continuous at zero.
2. f is not differentiable at zero.
3. The graph of f has a vertical tangent line at the point where x is zero.

In the following illustration we have another function that is continuous but not differentiable at zero. The graph of this function does not have a tangent line at the point where x is zero.

▷ **ILLUSTRATION 4**   Let f be the absolute value function defined by

$$f(x) = |x|$$

The graph of this function appears in Figure 2. From formula (7) of Section 2.1, if the limit exists

$$f'(0) = \lim_{x \to 0} \frac{f(x) - f(0)}{x - 0}$$
$$= \lim_{x \to 0} \frac{|x| - 0}{x}$$
$$= \lim_{x \to 0} \frac{|x|}{x}$$

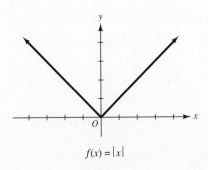

$f(x) = |x|$

FIGURE 2

Because $|x| = x$ if $x > 0$ and $|x| = -x$ if $x < 0$, we consider one-sided limits at 0:

$$\lim_{x \to 0^+} \frac{|x|}{x} = \lim_{x \to 0^+} \frac{x}{x} \qquad \lim_{x \to 0^-} \frac{|x|}{x} = \lim_{x \to 0^-} \frac{-x}{x}$$

$$= \lim_{x \to 0^+} 1 \qquad\qquad = \lim_{x \to 0^-} (-1)$$

$$= 1 \qquad\qquad\qquad = -1$$

Because $\lim_{x \to 0^+} \frac{|x|}{x} \neq \lim_{x \to 0^-} \frac{|x|}{x}$, it follows that the two-sided limit $\lim_{x \to 0} \frac{|x|}{x}$ does not exist. Therefore $f'(0)$ does not exist; so f is not differentiable at 0.

Because Definition 2.1.1 is not satisfied when $x = 0$, the graph of the absolute value function does not have a tangent line at the origin. ◄

Because the functions of Illustration 4 and Example 1 are continuous at a number but not differentiable there, we may conclude that continuity of a function at a number does not imply differentiability of the function at that number. However, differentiability *does* imply continuity, which is given by the next theorem.

2.2.1 Theorem

If a function f is differentiable at x_1, then f is continuous at x_1.

Proof   To prove that f is continuous at x_1 we must show that the three conditions of Definition 1.8.1 hold there. That is, we must show that (i) $f(x_1)$ exists; (ii) $\lim_{x \to x_1} f(x)$ exists; and (iii) $\lim_{x \to x_1} f(x) = f(x_1)$.

By hypothesis, f is differentiable at x_1. Therefore $f'(x_1)$ exists. Because by formula (7) of Section 2.1

$$f'(x_1) = \lim_{x \to x_1} \frac{f(x) - f(x_1)}{x - x_1}$$

$f(x_1)$ must exist; otherwise the above limit has no meaning. Therefore condition (i) holds at x_1. Now consider

$$\lim_{x \to x_1} [f(x) - f(x_1)] = \lim_{x \to x_1} \left[(x - x_1) \cdot \frac{f(x) - f(x_1)}{x - x_1} \right] \tag{1}$$

Because

$$\lim_{x \to x_1} (x - x_1) = 0 \quad \text{and} \quad \lim_{x \to x_1} \frac{f(x) - f(x_1)}{x - x_1} = f'(x_1)$$

we apply the theorem on the limit of a product (1.5.7) to the right side of (1) and obtain

$$\lim_{x \to x_1} [f(x) - f(x_1)] = \lim_{x \to x_1} (x - x_1) \cdot \lim_{x \to x_1} \frac{f(x) - f(x_1)}{x - x_1}$$

$$= 0 \cdot f'(x_1)$$

$$= 0$$

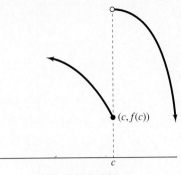

f is not differentiable at c
f is discontinuous at c

FIGURE 3

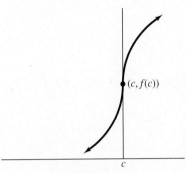

f is not differentiable at c
f is continuous at c

FIGURE 4

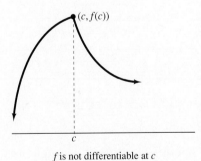

f is not differentiable at c
f is continuous at c

FIGURE 5

By Theorem 1.5.14 this limit is equivalent to

$$\lim_{x \to x_1} f(x) = f(x_1)$$

From this equation it follows that conditions (ii) and (iii) for continuity of f at x_1 hold. Therefore the theorem is proved. ∎

A function f can fail to be differentiable at a number c for one of the following reasons:

1. The function f is discontinuous at c. Refer to Figure 3 for the graph of such a function.
2. The function f is continuous at c, and the graph of f has a vertical tangent line at the point where $x = c$. See Figure 4 for the graph of a function having this property. This situation also occurs in Example 1.
3. The function f is continuous at c, and the graph of f does not have a tangent line at the point where $x = c$. Figure 5 shows the graph of a function satisfying this condition. Observe a "sharp turn" (or corner) in the graph at $x = c$. In Illustration 4, we have another such function.

Before giving an additional example of a function continuous but not differentiable at a number, we introduce the concept of a *one-sided derivative*.

2.2.2 Definition of a One-Sided Derivative

(i) If the function f is defined at x_1, then the **derivative from the right** of f at x_1, denoted by $f'_+(x_1)$, is defined by

$$f'_+(x_1) = \lim_{\Delta x \to 0^+} \frac{f(x_1 + \Delta x) - f(x_1)}{\Delta x}$$

$$\Leftrightarrow f'_+(x_1) = \lim_{x \to x_1^+} \frac{f(x) - f(x_1)}{x - x_1}$$

if the limit exists.

(ii) If the function f is defined at x_1, then the **derivative from the left** of f at x_1, denoted by $f'_-(x_1)$, is defined by

$$f'_-(x_1) = \lim_{\Delta x \to 0^-} \frac{f(x_1 + \Delta x) - f(x_1)}{\Delta x}$$

$$\Leftrightarrow f'_-(x_1) = \lim_{x \to x_1^-} \frac{f(x) - f(x_1)}{x - x_1}$$

if the limit exists.

From this definition and Theorem 1.6.3, it follows that a function f defined on an open interval containing x_1 is differentiable at x_1 if and only if $f'_+(x_1)$ and $f'_-(x_1)$ both exist and are equal. Of course, then $f'(x_1)$, $f'_+(x_1)$, and $f'_-(x_1)$ are all equal.

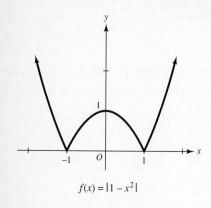

$$f(x) = |1 - x^2|$$

FIGURE 6

▶ **EXAMPLE 2**   Let f be defined by

$$f(x) = |1 - x^2|$$

(a) Sketch the graph of f.   **(b)** Prove that f is continuous at 1.
(c) Determine if f is differentiable at 1.

Solution   By the definition of absolute value, if $x < -1$ or $x > 1$, then $f(x) = -(1 - x^2)$, and if $-1 \leq x \leq 1, f(x) = 1 - x^2$. Therefore f can be defined as follows:

$$f(x) = \begin{cases} x^2 - 1 & \text{if } x < -1 \\ 1 - x^2 & \text{if } -1 \leq x \leq 1 \\ x^2 - 1 & \text{if } 1 < x \end{cases}$$

(a) The graph of f appears in Figure 6.
(b) To prove that f is continuous at 1 we verify the three conditions for continuity.

(i) $f(1) = 0$

(ii) $\displaystyle\lim_{x \to 1^-} f(x) = \lim_{x \to 1^-} (1 - x^2)$ $\displaystyle\lim_{x \to 1^+} f(x) = \lim_{x \to 1^+} (x^2 - 1)$

$$= 0 \qquad\qquad\qquad = 0$$

Thus $\displaystyle\lim_{x \to 1} f(x) = 0$.

(iii) $\displaystyle\lim_{x \to 1} f(x) = f(1)$

Because conditions (i)–(iii) all hold at 1, f is continuous at 1.

(c) $\displaystyle f'_-(1) = \lim_{x \to 1^-} \frac{f(x) - f(1)}{x - 1}$ $\displaystyle f'_+(1) = \lim_{x \to 1^+} \frac{f(x) - f(1)}{x - 1}$

$$= \lim_{x \to 1^-} \frac{(1 - x^2) - 0}{x - 1} \qquad = \lim_{x \to 1^+} \frac{(x^2 - 1) - 0}{x - 1}$$

$$= \lim_{x \to 1^-} \frac{(1 - x)(1 + x)}{x - 1} \qquad = \lim_{x \to 1^+} \frac{(x - 1)(x + 1)}{x - 1}$$

$$= \lim_{x \to 1^-} [-(1 + x)] \qquad = \lim_{x \to 1^+} (x + 1)$$

$$= -2 \qquad\qquad\qquad = 2$$

Because $f'_-(1) \neq f'_+(1)$, it follows that $f'(1)$ does not exist; so f is not differentiable at 1.   ◀

The function of Example 2 is also not differentiable at -1. You are asked to show this in Exercise 32.

▷ **ILLUSTRATION 5**   In Illustration 2 of Section 1.8, we obtained the mathematical model

$$C(x) = \begin{cases} 2x & \text{if } 0 \leq x \leq 10 \\ 1.4x + 6 & \text{if } 10 < x \end{cases}$$

where $C(x)$ dollars is the total cost of x pounds of a product. The graph of C appears in Figure 7. In Section 1.8 we showed that C is continuous at 10.

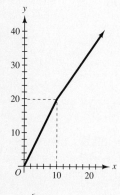

$$C(x) = \begin{cases} 2x & \text{if } 0 \leq x \leq 10 \\ 1.4x + 6 & \text{if } 10 < x \end{cases}$$

FIGURE 7

We now determine whether C is differentiable at 10. Because C is defined piecewise, we compute the one-sided derivatives at 10.

$$C'_-(10) = \lim_{x \to 10^-} \frac{C(x) - C(10)}{x - 10} \qquad C'_+(10) = \lim_{x \to 10^+} \frac{C(x) - C(10)}{x - 10}$$

$$= \lim_{x \to 10^-} \frac{2x - 20}{x - 10} \qquad = \lim_{x \to 10^+} \frac{(1.4x + 6) - 20}{x - 10}$$

$$= \lim_{x \to 10^-} \frac{2(x - 10)}{x - 10} \qquad = \lim_{x \to 10^+} \frac{1.4(x - 10)}{x - 10}$$

$$= \lim_{x \to 10^-} 2 \qquad = \lim_{x \to 10^+} 1.4$$

$$= 2 \qquad = 1.4$$

Because $C'_-(10) \neq C'_+(10)$, C is not differentiable at 10. ◀

▶ **EXAMPLE 3**   Given

$$f(x) = \begin{cases} \dfrac{1}{x} & \text{if } 0 < x < b \\ 1 - \tfrac{1}{4}x & \text{if } b \leq x \end{cases}$$

(a) Determine a value of b so that f is continuous at b. **(b)** Sketch the graph of f with the value of b found in part (a). **(c)** Is f differentiable at the value of b found in part (a)?

Solution

(a) The function f will be continuous at b if $\lim\limits_{x \to b^-} f(x) = f(b)$ and $\lim\limits_{x \to b^+} f(x) = f(b)$.

$$\lim_{x \to b^-} f(x) = \lim_{x \to b^-} \frac{1}{x} \qquad \lim_{x \to b^+} f(x) = \lim_{x \to b^+} (1 - \tfrac{1}{4}x)$$

$$= \frac{1}{b} \qquad = 1 - \tfrac{1}{4}b$$

$f(b) = 1 - \tfrac{1}{4}b$; therefore f will be continuous at b if

$$\frac{1}{b} = 1 - \frac{1}{4}b$$

$$4 = 4b - b^2$$

$$b^2 - 4b + 4 = 0$$

$$(b - 2)^2 = 0$$

$$b = 2$$

Thus

$$f(x) = \begin{cases} \dfrac{1}{x} & \text{if } 0 < x < 2 \\ 1 - \tfrac{1}{4}x & \text{if } 2 \leq x \end{cases}$$

and f is continuous at 2.

(b) The graph of f is sketched in Figure 8.

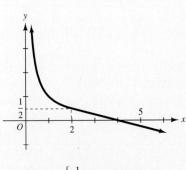

$$f(x) = \begin{cases} \dfrac{1}{x} & \text{if } 0 < x < 2 \\ 1 - \dfrac{1}{4}x & \text{if } 2 \leq x \end{cases}$$

FIGURE 8

(c) To determine if f is differentiable at 2 we compute $f'_-(2)$ and $f'_+(2)$.

$$f'_-(2) = \lim_{x \to 2^-} \frac{f(x) - f(2)}{x - 2} \qquad f'_+(2) = \lim_{x \to 2^+} \frac{f(x) - f(2)}{x - 2}$$

$$= \lim_{x \to 2^-} \frac{\dfrac{1}{x} - \dfrac{1}{2}}{x - 2} \qquad\qquad = \lim_{x \to 2^+} \frac{(1 - \frac{1}{4}x) - \frac{1}{2}}{x - 2}$$

$$= \lim_{x \to 2^-} \frac{2 - x}{2x(x - 2)} \qquad\qquad = \lim_{x \to 2^+} \frac{\frac{1}{2} - \frac{1}{4}x}{x - 2}$$

$$= \lim_{x \to 2^-} \frac{-1}{2x} \qquad\qquad = \lim_{x \to 2^+} \frac{2 - x}{4(x - 2)}$$

$$= -\tfrac{1}{4} \qquad\qquad\qquad = \lim_{x \to 2^+} \frac{-1}{4}$$

$$\qquad\qquad\qquad\qquad\qquad = -\tfrac{1}{4}$$

Because $f'_-(2) = f'_+(2)$, it follows that $f'(2)$ exists, and hence f is differentiable at 2. ◀

▶ **EXAMPLE 4**   In the planning of a coffee shop, the daily profit is estimated to be $16 per place if there are places for 40 to 80 people. However, if the seating capacity is more than 80 places, the daily profit on each place will be decreased by $0.08 times the number of places above 80. **(a)** Find a mathematical model expressing the daily profit as a function of the seating capacity. **(b)** Prove that the function in part (a) is continuous on its domain. **(c)** Determine if the function in part (a) is differentiable at 80.

Solution

(a) Let x places be the seating capacity and $P(x)$ dollars be the daily profit. $P(x)$ is obtained by multiplying x by the number of dollars in the profit per place. When $40 \leq x \leq 80$, $16 is the profit per place; hence $P(x) = 16x$. When $x > 80$, the number of dollars in the profit per place is $16 - 0.08(x - 80)$; thus giving $P(x) = x[16 - 0.08(x - 80)]$; that is, $P(x) = 22.40x - 0.08x^2$. Therefore

$$P(x) = \begin{cases} 16x & \text{if } 40 \leq x \leq 80 \\ 22.40x - 0.08x^2 & \text{if } 80 < x \leq 280 \end{cases}$$

The upper bound of 280 for x is obtained by noting that $22.40x - 0.08x^2 = 0$ when $x = 280$; and $22.40x - 0.08x^2 < 0$ when $x > 280$.

   Even though x, by definition, is a positive integer, to have continuity we let x take on all real values in the interval $[40, 280]$.

(b) Because $P(x)$ is a polynomial on $[40, 80]$ and $(80, 280]$, P is continuous on those intervals. To determine continuity at 80 we compute the one-sided limits at 80:

$$\lim_{x \to 80^-} P(x) = \lim_{x \to 80^-} 16x \qquad \lim_{x \to 80^+} P(x) = \lim_{x \to 80^+} (22.40x - 0.08x^2)$$

$$= 1280 \qquad\qquad\qquad = 1280$$

Because $P(80) = 1280$ and $\lim\limits_{x \to 80} P(x) = 1280$, P is continuous at 80. Thus P is continuous on its domain $[40, 280]$.

(c) To determine if P is differentiable at 80, we compute the one-sided derivatives at 80:

$$P'_-(80) = \lim_{x \to 80^-} \frac{P(x) - P(80)}{x - 80} \qquad P'_+(80) = \lim_{x \to 80^+} \frac{P(x) - P(80)}{x - 80}$$

$$= \lim_{x \to 80^-} \frac{16x - 1280}{x - 80} \qquad = \lim_{x \to 80^+} \frac{(22.40x - 0.08x^2) - 1280}{x - 80}$$

$$= \lim_{x \to 80^-} \frac{16(x - 80)}{x - 80} \qquad = \lim_{x \to 80^+} \frac{-0.08(x^2 - 280x + 16000)}{x - 80}$$

$$= \lim_{x \to 80^-} 16 \qquad = \lim_{x \to 80^+} \frac{-0.08(x - 80)(x - 200)}{x - 80}$$

$$= 16 \qquad = \lim_{x \to 80^+} [-0.08(x - 200)]$$

$$= 9.60$$

Because $P'_-(80) \neq P'_+(80)$, P is not differentiable at 80. ◀

In Section 3.2, we will return to the situation in Example 4 and determine the seating capacity necessary to yield the maximum daily profit.

EXERCISES 2.2

In Exercises 1 through 20, do the following: (a) Sketch the graph of the function; (b) determine if f is continuous at x_1; (c) find $f'_-(x_1)$ and $f'_+(x_1)$ if they exist; (d) determine if f is differentiable at x_1.

1. $f(x) = \begin{cases} x + 2 & \text{if } x \leq -4 \\ -x - 6 & \text{if } -4 < x \end{cases}$ $x_1 = -4$

2. $f(x) = \begin{cases} 3 - 2x & \text{if } x < 2 \\ 3x - 7 & \text{if } 2 \leq x \end{cases}$ $x_1 = 2$

3. $f(x) = |x - 3|$ $x_1 = 3$

4. $f(x) = 1 + |x + 2|$ $x_1 = -2$

5. $f(x) = \begin{cases} -1 & \text{if } x < 0 \\ x - 1 & \text{if } 0 \leq x \end{cases}$ $x_1 = 0$

6. $f(x) = \begin{cases} x & \text{if } x \leq 0 \\ x^2 & \text{if } 0 < x \end{cases}$ $x_1 = 0$

7. $f(x) = \begin{cases} x^2 & \text{if } x \leq 0 \\ -x^2 & \text{if } 0 < x \end{cases}$ $x_1 = 0$

8. $f(x) = \begin{cases} x^2 - 4 & \text{if } x < 2 \\ \sqrt{x - 2} & \text{if } 2 \leq x \end{cases}$ $x_1 = 2$

9. $f(x) = \begin{cases} \sqrt{1 - x} & \text{if } x < 1 \\ (1 - x)^2 & \text{if } 1 \leq x \end{cases}$ $x_1 = 1$

10. $f(x) = \begin{cases} x^2 & \text{if } x < -1 \\ -1 - 2x & \text{if } -1 \leq x \end{cases}$ $x_1 = -1$

11. $f(x) = \begin{cases} 2x^2 - 3 & \text{if } x \leq 2 \\ 8x - 11 & \text{if } 2 < x \end{cases}$ $x_1 = 2$

12. $f(x) = \begin{cases} x^2 - 9 & \text{if } x < 3 \\ 6x - 18 & \text{if } 3 \leq x \end{cases}$ $x_1 = 3$

13. $f(x) = \sqrt[3]{x + 1}$ $x_1 = -1$

14. $f(x) = (x - 2)^{-2}$ $x_1 = 2$

15. $f(x) = \begin{cases} 5 - 6x & \text{if } x \leq 3 \\ -4 - x^2 & \text{if } 3 < x \end{cases}$ $x_1 = 3$

16. $f(x) = \begin{cases} -x^{2/3} & \text{if } x \leq 0 \\ x^{2/3} & \text{if } 0 < x \end{cases}$ $x_1 = 0$

17. $f(x) = \begin{cases} x - 2 & \text{if } x < 0 \\ x^2 & \text{if } 0 \leq x \end{cases}$ $x_1 = 0$

18. $f(x) = \begin{cases} x^3 & \text{if } x \leq 1 \\ x + 1 & \text{if } 1 < x \end{cases}$ $x_1 = 1$

19. $f(x) = \begin{cases} 3x^2 & \text{if } x \leq 2 \\ x^3 & \text{if } 2 < x \end{cases}$ $x_1 = 2$

20. $f(x) = \begin{cases} x^2 + 1 & \text{if } x < -1 \\ 1 - x^2 & \text{if } -1 \leq x \end{cases}$ $x_1 = -1$

Exercises 21 through 26 pertain to the continuous function f whose domain is the set of all real numbers and whose graph is sketched in the accompanying figure. Assume that each part of the graph that appears to be a line segment is a line segment. In each exercise do the following: (a) Define f piecewise; Find (b) $f'_-(-1)$, (c) $f'_+(-1)$, (d) $f'_-(0)$, (e) $f'_+(0)$, (f) $f'_-(1)$, and (g) $f'_+(1)$. (h) At what numbers is f not differentiable?

24.

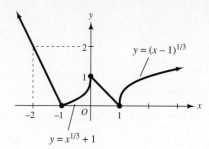

21.

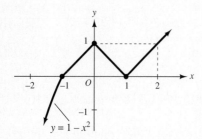

22.

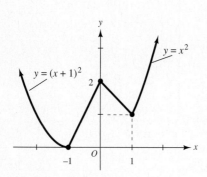

23.

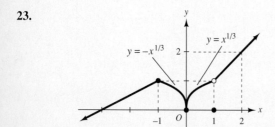

25.

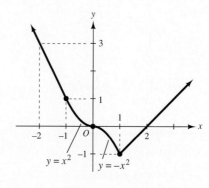

26.

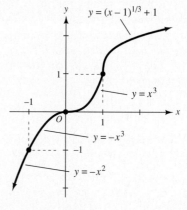

In Exercises 27 through 30, sketch a graph of some continuous function f whose domain is the set of all real numbers and which satisfies the given properties.

27. The range of f is $(-\infty, +\infty)$, and f is differentiable at every number except 0 and 3; $f(-3) = -1$; $f(0) = 0$; $f(3) = 1$; $f'_-(0) = 1$; $f'_+(0) = 0$;
$$\lim_{x \to 3} \frac{f(x) - f(3)}{x - 3} = +\infty.$$

28. The range of f is $[0, +\infty]$, and f is differentiable at every number except -2, 0, and 2; $f(-2) = 0$; $f(0) = 3$; $f(2) = 0$; $f'_-(-2) = -1$; $f'_+(-2) = 1$; $f'_-(2) = -1$; $f'_+(2) = 1$; $\lim_{x \to 0^-} \frac{f(x) - f(0)}{x} = +\infty$;
$$\lim_{x \to 0^+} \frac{f(x) - f(0)}{x} = -\infty.$$

29. The range of f is $(-\infty, +\infty)$, and f is differentiable at every number except -2, 0 and 2; $f(-2) = 3$; $f(-1) = 0$; $f(0) = 0$; $f(1) = 0$; $f(2) = -3$; $f'_-(-2) = 1$; $f'_+(-2) = -1$; $f'_-(2) = -1$; $f'_+(2) = 1$; $\lim\limits_{x \to 0^-} \dfrac{f(x) - f(0)}{x} = -\infty$; $\lim\limits_{x \to 0^+} \dfrac{f(x) - f(0)}{x} = -\infty$.

30. The range of f is $(-\infty, +\infty)$, and f is differentiable at every number except 0 and 4; $f(-2) = 0$; $f(0) = -1$; $f(4) = 1$; $f(5) = 0$; $f'_+(0) = 2$; $f'_-(4) = \frac{1}{2}$; $\lim\limits_{x \to 0^-} \dfrac{f(x) - f(0)}{x} = -\infty$; $\lim\limits_{x \to 4^+} \dfrac{f(x) - f(4)}{x - 4} = -\infty$.

31. For the oil spill in Exercise 53 of Exercises 1.8, determine if the function r is differentiable at 2.

32. Prove that the function of Example 2 is continuous at -1 but not differentiable there.

33. Given
$$f(x) = \begin{cases} x^2 - 7 & \text{if } 0 \le x \le b \\ \dfrac{6}{x} & \text{if } b < x \end{cases}$$
(a) Determine a value of b so that f is continuous at b. **(b)** Sketch the graph of f with the value of b found in part (a). **(c)** Is f differentiable at the value of b found in part (a)?

34. Given $f(x) = \operatorname{sgn} x$. **(a)** Prove that $f'_-(0)$ and $f'_+(0)$ do not exist. **(b)** Prove that $\lim\limits_{x \to 0^-} f'(x) = 0$ and $\lim\limits_{x \to 0^+} f'(x) = 0$. **(c)** Sketch the graph of f.

35. Find the values of a and b such that f is differentiable at 1 and then sketch the graph of f if
$$f(x) = \begin{cases} x^2 & \text{if } x < 1 \\ ax + b & \text{if } 1 \le x \end{cases}$$

36. Find the values of a and b such that f is differentiable at 2 and then sketch the graph of f if
$$f(x) = \begin{cases} ax + b & \text{if } x < 2 \\ 2x^2 - 1 & \text{if } 2 \le x \end{cases}$$

In Exercises 37 through 40, you are to obtain a function as a mathematical model of a particular situation. Even though the independent variable, by definition, will represent a nonnegative integer, allow this variable to represent a nonnegative real number so that you have the necessary continuity requirements.

37. A school-sponsored trip that can accommodate up to 250 students will cost each student $15 if not more than 150 students make the trip; the cost per student, however, will be reduced $0.05 for each student in excess of 150 until the cost reaches $10 per student. **(a)** Find a mathematical model expressing the gross income as a function of the number of students taking the trip. **(b)** Prove that your function in part (a) is continuous on its domain. **(c)** Determine if your function in part (a) is differentiable at 150.

38. Do Exercise 37 if the reduction per student in excess of 150 is $0.07.

39. Orange trees grown in California produce 600 oranges per year if no more than 20 trees are planted per acre. For each additional tree planted per acre, the yield per tree decreases by 15 oranges. **(a)** Find a mathematical model expressing the number of oranges produced per year as a function of the number of trees per acre. **(b)** Prove that your function in part (a) is continuous on its domain. **(c)** Determine if your function in part (a) is differentiable at 20.

40. A private club charges annual membership dues of $100 per member, less $0.50 for each member over 600 and plus $0.50 for each member less than 600. **(a)** Find a mathematical model expressing the club's revenue from annual dues as a function of its membership. **(b)** Prove that your function in part (a) is continuous on its domain. **(c)** Determine if your function in part (a) is differentiable at 600.

41. In Illustration 4 we showed that the absolute value function is not differentiable at 0. Prove that
$$D_x(|x|) = \frac{|x|}{x} \quad \text{if } x \ne 0$$
Hint: Let $|x| = \sqrt{x^2}$.

42. Given $f(x) = [\![x]\!]$, find $f'(x_1)$ if x_1 is not an integer. Prove that $f'(x_1)$ does not exist if x_1 is an integer. If x_1 is an integer, what can you say about $f'_-(x_1)$ and $f'_+(x_1)$?

43. Given $f(x) = (x - 1)[\![x]\!]$. Plot on your graphics calculator the graph of f for x in $[0, 2]$. Find, if they exist: **(a)** $f'_-(1)$; **(b)** $f'_+(1)$; **(c)** $f'(1)$.

44. Given $f(x) = (5 - x)[\![x]\!]$. Plot on your graphics calculator the graph of f for x in $[4, 6]$. Find, if they exist: **(a)** $f'_-(5)$; **(b)** $f'_+(5)$; **(c)** $f'(5)$.

45. Given $f(x) = (x - a)[\![x]\!]$ where a is an integer, show that $f'_-(a) + 1 = f'_+(a)$.

46. Let the function f be defined by
$$f(x) = \begin{cases} \dfrac{g(x) - g(a)}{x - a} & \text{if } x \ne a \\ g'(a) & \text{if } x = a \end{cases}$$
Prove that if $g'(a)$ exists, f is continuous at a.

47. (a) Let $f(x) = |x|$ and $g(x) = -|x|$. Find a formula for $(f + g)(x)$, and show that $f + g$ is differentiable at 0. Use functions f and g as examples to explain why it is possible for the sum of two functions to be differentiable at a number even though neither func-tion is differentiable at the number. **(b)** Let $F(x) = x^{-1}$ and $G(x) = -x^{-1}$. Find a formula for $(F + G)(x)$. Is $F + G$ differentiable at 0? Can functions F and G be used instead of f and g as examples in your explanation in part (a)? Explain.

2.3 THE NUMERICAL DERIVATIVE

The *numerical derivative* will be important to us because its graph can be plotted on a graphics calculator. Furthermore, the numerical derivative can be used to obtain an approximation to the derivative of a function at a particular number whenever that derivative exists.

To lead up to the concept of numerical derivative, recall that $f'(a)$, the derivative of the function f evaluated at the number a, is defined as the limit of a standard difference quotient:

$$f'(a) = \lim_{\Delta x \to 0} \frac{f(a + \Delta x) - f(a)}{\Delta x} \qquad (1)$$

if this limit exists. In Exercise 55 of Exercises 2.1 you were asked to show that if $f'(a)$ exists then

$$f'(a) = \lim_{\Delta x \to 0} \frac{f(a + \Delta x) - f(a - \Delta x)}{2 \Delta x} \qquad (2)$$

If you did not do this exercise when you studied Section 2.1, go back and do it now. The quotient

$$\frac{f(a + \Delta x) - f(a - \Delta x)}{2 \Delta x} \qquad (3)$$

appearing in (2) is called the **symmetric difference quotient** of the function f at the number a. The terminology *symmetric* is appropriate because the quotient is the slope of the secant line through the points $(a - \Delta x, f(a - \Delta x))$ and $(a + \Delta x, f(a + \Delta x))$. See Figure 1. The value of Δx chosen to compute the symmetric difference quotient is called the **tolerance**.

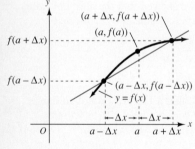

FIGURE 1

▶ **EXAMPLE 1**   Given

$$f(x) = \sqrt{x}$$

(a) Use the result of Example 5 in Section 2.1 to compute the exact value of $f'(4)$. Obtain an approximation to $f'(4)$ by using the symmetric difference quotient of f at 4 with each of the following tolerances: **(b)** 0.1, **(c)** 0.01, and **(d)** 0.001.

Solution

(a) From Example 5 in Section 2.1

$$f'(x) = \frac{1}{2\sqrt{x}}$$

Therefore, $f'(4) = 0.25$.

(b)–(d) From (3), the symmetric difference quotient of f at 4 is

$$\frac{\sqrt{4 + \Delta x} - \sqrt{4 - \Delta x}}{2 \, \Delta x}$$

We evaluate this quotient with the given tolerance Δx.

(b) $\Delta x = 0.1$

$$\frac{\sqrt{4 + 0.1} - \sqrt{4 - 0.1}}{2(0.1)} = 0.2500195366$$

(c) $\Delta x = 0.01$

$$\frac{\sqrt{4 + 0.01} - \sqrt{4 - 0.01}}{2(0.01)} = 0.2500001953$$

(d) $\Delta x = 0.001$

$$\frac{\sqrt{4 + 0.001} - \sqrt{4 - 0.001}}{2(0.001)} = 0.2500000019 \qquad \blacktriangleleft$$

Observe in Example 1 that the symmetric difference quotient of f at 4 gives a good approximation to $f'(4)$, and the smaller the tolerance, the better the approximation. If for a specific tolerance you compare the approximation of $f'(a)$ by the symmetric difference quotient with that by the standard difference quotient in (1), you will observe that the symmetric difference quotient gives a better approximation. You are asked to make some such comparisons in Exercises 1 through 4.

We shall utilize the symmetric difference quotient to compute the *numerical derivative* of a function at a number just as some graphics calculators do with the user choosing the tolerance. We therefore make the following formal definition:

2.3.1 Definition of the Numerical Derivative

The **numerical derivative** of the function f at the number a, denoted by $\text{NDER}(f(x), a)$, is defined by

$$\text{NDER}(f(x), a) = \frac{f(a + \Delta x) - f(a - \Delta x)}{2 \, \Delta x}$$

where the choice of Δx depends on the desired approximation of $\text{NDER}(f(x), a)$ to $f'(a)$.

In this text, we shall compute $\text{NDER}(f(x), a)$ with a tolerance of 0.001; that is,

$$\text{NDER}(f(x), a) = \frac{f(a + 0.001) - f(a - 0.001)}{0.002} \qquad (4)$$

Observe from the statement of Exercise 55 of Exercises 2.1 that $\text{NDER}(f(x), a)$ gives an approximation to $f'(a)$ only if $f'(a)$ exists; that is,

$$\text{NDER}(f(x), a) \approx f'(a) \qquad \text{if } f'(a) \text{ exists} \qquad (5)$$

Consult your users manual on how to obtain the numerical derivative on your particular calculator. If the numerical derivative is not built-in on your calculator, you may use a program or the symmetric difference quotient in (4).

▶ **EXAMPLE 2**   Given

$$f(x) = \frac{3}{x}$$

(a) Approximate $f'(5)$ to five decimal places by computing NDER($f(x)$, 5) on a graphics calculator. (b) Confirm the answer in part (a) analytically by computing $f'(5)$ from the result of Example 3 in Section 2.1.

Solution

(a) On our graphics calculator, we find

$$\text{NDER}\left(\frac{3}{x}, 5\right) = -0.1200000048$$

Therefore, to five decimal places, $f'(5) \approx -0.12000$.

(b) From Example 3 in Section 2.1,

$$f'(x) = -\frac{3}{x^2}$$

Thus $f'(5) = -0.12$, which agrees with our answer in part (a).   ◀

The notation NDER($f(x)$, x) denotes the numerical derivative of the function f at x; that is,

$$\text{NDER}(f(x), x) = \frac{f(x + \Delta x) - f(x - \Delta x)}{2\,\Delta x}$$

For both linear and quadratic functions, NDER($f(x)$, x) is exactly $f'(x)$. You are asked to show this in Exercises 21 and 22.

Your graphics calculator should plot the graph of NDER($f(x)$, x). You will learn the importance of this feature as we proceed through the text.

▶ **EXAMPLE 3**   The function of Example 3 of Section 2.1 is defined by

$$f(x) = \frac{3}{x}$$

Use the graph of NDER($f(x)$, x) to support the value of $f'(x)$ found in Section 2.1.

Solution   Figure 2 shows the result of plotting the graphs of NDER$\left(\frac{3}{x}, x\right)$ and the function f' defined by

$$f'(x) = -\frac{3}{x^2}$$

in the $[-6, 6]$ by $[-7, 1]$ window. The fact that the two graphs appear identical supports the value of $f'(x)$.   ◀

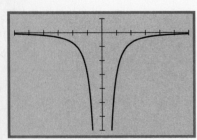

$[-6, 6]$ by $[-7, 1]$

$f'(x) = -\dfrac{3}{x^2}$ and NDER$\left(\dfrac{3}{x}, x\right)$

FIGURE 2

From (5), NDER($f(x)$, a) $\approx f'(a)$ if $f'(a)$ exists. The requirement that $f'(a)$ must exist so that NDER($f(x)$, a) gives an approximation of $f'(a)$ is crucial, as shown in the following example.

▶ **EXAMPLE 4**   Exercise 55 of Exercises 2.1 states that if $f'(a)$ exists then

$$f'(a) = \lim_{\Delta x \to 0} \frac{f(a + \Delta x) - f(a - \Delta x)}{2\,\Delta x}$$

Show by using the absolute value function that it is possible for the limit in the above equation to exist even though $f'(a)$ does not exist.

Solution   With $f(x) = |x|$ and $a = 0$, we have

$$\lim_{\Delta x \to 0} \frac{f(a + \Delta x) - f(a - \Delta x)}{2\,\Delta x} = \lim_{\Delta x \to 0} \frac{|0 + \Delta x| - |0 - \Delta x|}{2\,\Delta x}$$

$$= \lim_{\Delta x \to 0} \frac{|\Delta x| - |-\Delta x|}{2\,\Delta x}$$

$$= \lim_{\Delta x \to 0} 0$$

$$= 0$$

Thus the limit exists and is 0. However, we know from Illustration 4 of Section 2.2 that the derivative of the absolute value function does not exist at 0.   ◀

If you compute NDER($|x|$, 0) on your graphics calculator, you will obtain 0. This result is consistent with what you learned in Example 4, but of course does not give the derivative of the absolute value function at 0. Figure 3 also supports the result of Example 4. This figure is the special case of Figure 1 where $f(x) = |x|$. The symmetric difference quotient is the slope of the secant line through the points $(-\Delta x, |-\Delta x|)$ and $(\Delta x, |\Delta x|)$, which is 0 for any choice of Δx.

The discussion in the preceding paragraph should convince you to be very careful when you use the value of the numerical derivative of function f at a to approximate the value of $f'(a)$. The two values are only approximately equal if $f'(a)$ exists. See Exercises 27 through 29 for other examples demonstrating this fact.

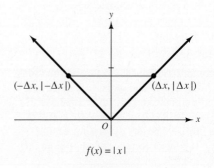

$f(x) = |x|$

FIGURE 3

EXERCISES 2.3

In Exercises 1 through 4, do the following: (a) On your calculator, tabulate values of the symmetric difference quotient $\dfrac{f(2 + \Delta x) - f(2 - \Delta x)}{2\,\Delta x}$ for the given function f when Δx is 0.10, 0.09, 0.08, . . . , 0.01, and $-0.10, -0.09, -0.08, \ldots, -0.01$. What does the symmetric difference quotient appear to be approaching as Δx approaches 0? (b) On your graphics calculator, determine NDER($f(x)$, 2) and compare this number with both your answer in part (a) and the exact value of $f'(2)$ computed in part (b) of the indicated exercise in Exercises 2.1.

(c) Compare your tabulated values in part (a) of this exercise with the corresponding tabulated values in part (a) of the indicated exercise in Exercises 2.1 where the standard difference quotient was used. Which table of values gives the better approximation to $f'(2)$?

1. $f(x) = 3x^2 - 7x$; Exercise 17.
2. $f(x) = x^3$; Exercise 18.
3. $f(x) = \sqrt{6 - x}$; Exercise 19.
4. $f(x) = \dfrac{1}{4 - x}$; Exercise 20.

In Exercises 5 through 8, use the graph of the numerical derivative at x plotted on your graphics calculator to support the value of the derivative found in the indicated exercise of Exercises 2.1.

5. (a) Exercise 33 **(b)** Exercise 35 **(c)** Exercise 37
6. (a) Exercise 34 **(b)** Exercise 36 **(c)** Exercise 38
7. (a) Exercise 39 **(b)** Exercise 41 **(c)** Exercise 43
8. (a) Exercise 40 **(b)** Exercise 42 **(c)** Exercise 44

In Exercises 9 through 20 do the following: (a) Use the numerical derivative of function f at the number x_1, computed on your calculator, to find the slope of the tangent line to the graph of f at the point where $x = x_1$; (b) find an equation of the tangent line to the graph of f at $(x_1, f(x_1))$; (c) plot the graph of f and the tangent line in the same window.

9. $f(x) = (x - 1)^2$; $x_1 = 2$
10. $f(x) = 2 + 2x - x^2$; $x_1 = -1$
11. $f(x) = x^2 - 2x - 4$; $x_1 = 3$
12. $f(x) = (2 - x)^2 + 5$; $x_1 = 4$
13. $f(x) = \sqrt{x^2 - 16}$; $x_1 = -5$
14. $f(x) = \sqrt{25 - x^2}$; $x_1 = 3$
15. $f(x) = \dfrac{x^2 - 1}{x^2 + 4}$; $x_1 = 1$
16. $f(x) = \dfrac{3 - x^2}{1 + x^2}$; $x_1 = -2$
17. $f(x) = x \sin x$; $x_1 = 1$
18. $f(x) = x^2 \cos x$; $x_1 = 2$
19. $f(x) = \sin(\cos x)$; $x_1 = 2$
20. $f(x) = \tan(\sin x)$; $x_1 = 3$

21. Prove that if f is a linear function $\text{NDER}(f(x), x)$ is exactly $f'(x)$.
22. Prove that if f is a quadratic function $\text{NDER}(f(x), x)$ is exactly $f'(x)$.
23. Given: $f(x) = x^2 + 2$. **(a)** Plot the graphs of f and $\text{NDER}(f(x), x)$ in the same window. For what values of x is **(b)** $\text{NDER}(f(x), x) > 0$, and **(c)** $\text{NDER}(f(x), x) < 0$? For what values of x does $f(x)$ appear to be **(d)** increasing as x increases, and **(e)** decreasing as x increases? **(f)** Compare your answers in parts (b) and (d) and in parts (c) and (e).

24. Do Exercise 23 if $f(x) = \dfrac{1}{x^2}$.
25. Do Exercise 23 if $f(x) = \sqrt{4 - x^2}$.
26. Do Exercise 23 if $f(x) = \sqrt{x^2 - 4}$.

27. Given: $f(x) = x^{1/3}$. In Example 1 of Section 2.2, we showed that $f'(0)$ does not exist. **(a)** Compute $\text{NDER}(f(x), 0)$ by Equation (4). **(b)** Support your answer in part (a) by finding $\text{NDER}(f(x), 0)$ on your calculator. **(c)** Explain why $\text{NDER}(f(x), 0)$ exists for this function even though $f'(0)$ does not exist. **(d)** Plot the graph of $\text{NDER}(f(x), x)$. What do you observe when x is 0? **(e)** Is your answer in part (d) consistent with what you learned in Example 1 of Section 2.2? Explain.

28. Given: $f(x) = x^{1/5}$. **(a)** Use formula (7) of Section 2.1 to show that $f'(0)$ does not exist. **(b)** Compute $\text{NDER}(f(x), 0)$ by Equation (4). **(c)** Support your answer in part (b) by finding $\text{NDER}(f(x), 0)$ on your calculator. **(d)** Explain why $\text{NDER}(f(x), 0)$ exists for this function even though $f'(0)$ does not exist. **(e)** Plot the graph of $\text{NDER}(f(x), x)$. What do you observe when x is 0? **(f)** Is your answer in part (e) consistent with your answer in part (a)? Explain.

29. Follow the instructions of Exercise 28 if $f(x) = x^{2/3}$.

30. Compare the computations of $f'(0)$ for the functions of Exercises 27 and 29. Then compare the value of $\text{NDER}(f(x), 0)$ computed in part (a) of Exercise 27 with the value of $\text{NDER}(f(x), 0)$ computed in part (b) of Exercise 29. Explain why you get a similar conclusion for $f'(0)$ for both functions but quite different results for $\text{NDER}(f(x), 0)$.

2.4 THEOREMS ON DIFFERENTIATION OF ALGEBRAIC FUNCTIONS AND HIGHER-ORDER DERIVATIVES

Because the process of computing the derivative of a function from the definition (2.1.3) is usually rather lengthy, we now discuss some theorems that enable us to find derivatives more easily. These theorems are proved from Definition 2.1.3. The statement of the theorem utilizes the Lagrange notation, and following the proof we write the formula with $D_x(f(x))$ notation and in words.

2.4.1 Theorem   The Constant Rule of Differentiation

If c is a constant and if $f(x) = c$ for all x, then

$$f'(x) = 0$$

Proof

$$f'(x) = \lim_{\Delta x \to 0} \frac{f(x + \Delta x) - f(x)}{\Delta x}$$

$$= \lim_{\Delta x \to 0} \frac{c - c}{\Delta x}$$

$$= \lim_{\Delta x \to 0} 0$$

$$= 0$$

$$D_x(c) = 0$$

The derivative of a constant is zero.

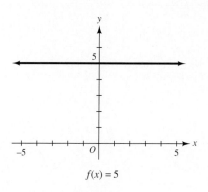

$f(x) = 5$

FIGURE 1

▷ **ILLUSTRATION 1**   If $f(x) = 5$, then from Theorem 2.4.1

$$f'(x) = 0$$

This result is supported by the graph of $f(x) = 5$ in Figure 1. Because the graph is a line parallel to the x axis, the slope of the graph is 0 everywhere. ◀

2.4.2 Theorem   The Power Rule (for Positive Integer Powers) of Differentiation

If n is a positive integer and if $f(x) = x^n$, then

$$f'(x) = nx^{n-1}$$

Proof

$$f'(x) = \lim_{\Delta x \to 0} \frac{f(x + \Delta x) - f(x)}{\Delta x}$$

$$= \lim_{\Delta x \to 0} \frac{(x + \Delta x)^n - x^n}{\Delta x}$$

Applying the binomial theorem to $(x + \Delta x)^n$ we have

$$f'(x) = \lim_{\Delta x \to 0} \frac{\left[x^n + nx^{n-1}\Delta x + \dfrac{n(n - 1)}{2!}x^{n-2}(\Delta x)^2 + \ldots + nx(\Delta x)^{n-1} + (\Delta x)^n \right] - x^n}{\Delta x}$$

$$= \lim_{\Delta x \to 0} \frac{nx^{n-1}\Delta x + \dfrac{n(n - 1)}{2!}x^{n-2}(\Delta x)^2 + \ldots + nx(\Delta x)^{n-1} + (\Delta x)^n}{\Delta x}$$

We divide the numerator and denominator by Δx to obtain

$$f'(x) = \lim_{\Delta x \to 0} \left[nx^{n-1} + \frac{n(n - 1)}{2!}x^{n-2}\Delta x + \ldots + nx(\Delta x)^{n-2} + (\Delta x)^{n-1} \right]$$

Every term except the first has a factor of Δx; therefore every term except the first approaches zero as Δx approaches zero. Thus

$$f'(x) = nx^{n-1}$$

∎

$$D_x(x^n) = nx^{n-1}$$

▷ **ILLUSTRATION 2**   If $f(x) = x^8$, then $f'(x) = 8x^7$.   ◀

▷ **ILLUSTRATION 3**   Let f be the identity function; that is, $f(x) = x$. By Theorem 2.4.2

$$f'(x) = 1 \cdot x^0$$

Observe that if $x = 0$, x^0 becomes 0^0 which is not defined. But if $x \neq 0$, $x^0 = 1$, so that

$$f'(x) = 1 \qquad \text{if } x \neq 0$$

To compute $f'(0)$ for the identity function, we apply formula (7) of Section 2.1:

$$f'(0) = \lim_{x \to 0} \frac{f(x) - f(0)}{x - 0}$$

$$= \lim_{x \to 0} \frac{x - 0}{x}$$

$$= \lim_{x \to 0} 1$$

$$= 1$$

Therefore, for all x, $D_x(x) = 1$.   ◀

2.4.3 Theorem   **The Constant Multiple Rule of Differentiation**

If f is a function, c is a constant, and g is the function defined by

$$g(x) = c \cdot f(x)$$

then if $f'(x)$ exists,

$$g'(x) = c \cdot f(x)$$

Proof

$$g'(x) = \lim_{\Delta x \to 0} \frac{g(x + \Delta x) - g(x)}{\Delta x}$$

$$= \lim_{\Delta x \to 0} \frac{cf(x + \Delta x) - cf(x)}{\Delta x}$$

$$= \lim_{\Delta x \to 0} c \cdot \left[\frac{f(x + \Delta x) - f(x)}{\Delta x} \right]$$

$$= c \cdot \lim_{\Delta x \to 0} \frac{f(x + \Delta x) - f(x)}{\Delta x}$$

$$= cf'(x)$$

∎

$$D_x[c \cdot f(x)] = c \cdot D_x f(x)$$

The derivative of a constant times a function is the constant times the derivative of the function if this derivative exists.

By combining Theorems 2.4.2 and 2.4.3, we obtain the following result: If $f(x) = cx^n$, where n is a positive integer and c is a constant, then

$$f'(x) = cnx^{n-1}$$

$$D_x(cx^n) = cnx^{n-1}$$

▷ **ILLUSTRATION 4**   If $f(x) = 5x^7$, then

$$\begin{aligned} f'(x) &= 5 \cdot 7x^6 \\ &= 35x^6 \end{aligned}$$

◀

2.4.4 Theorem   The Sum Rule of Differentiation

If f and g are functions and if h is the function defined by

$$h(x) = f(x) + g(x)$$

then if $f'(x)$ and $g'(x)$ exist,

$$h'(x) = f'(x) + g'(x)$$

Proof

$$\begin{aligned} h'(x) &= \lim_{\Delta x \to 0} \frac{h(x + \Delta x) - h(x)}{\Delta x} \\ &= \lim_{\Delta x \to 0} \frac{[f(x + \Delta x) + g(x + \Delta x)] - [f(x) + g(x)]}{\Delta x} \\ &= \lim_{\Delta x \to 0} \left[\frac{f(x + \Delta x) - f(x)}{\Delta x} + \frac{g(x + \Delta x) - g(x)}{\Delta x} \right] \\ &= \lim_{\Delta x \to 0} \frac{f(x + \Delta x) - f(x)}{\Delta x} + \lim_{\Delta x \to 0} \frac{g(x + \Delta x) - g(x)}{\Delta x} \\ &= f'(x) + g'(x) \end{aligned}$$

∎

$$D_x[f(x) + g(x)] = D_x f(x) + D_x g(x)$$

The derivative of the sum of two functions is the sum of their derivatives if these derivatives exist.

The result of the preceding theorem can be extended to any finite number of functions by mathematical induction, and this fact is stated as another theorem.

2.4.5 Theorem

The derivative of the sum of a finite number of functions is equal to the sum of their derivatives if these derivatives exist.

From the preceding theorems the derivative of any polynomial function can be found easily.

▶ **EXAMPLE 1**   Find $f'(x)$ if

$$f(x) = 7x^4 - 2x^3 + 8x + 5$$

Solution

$$
\begin{aligned}
f'(x) &= D_x(7x^4 - 2x^3 + 8x + 5) \\
&= D_x(7x^4) + D_x(-2x^3) + D_x(8x) + D_x(5) \\
&= 28x^3 - 6x^2 + 8
\end{aligned}
$$
◀

The derivative of the product of two functions is not what you might hopefully expect; that is, it is not the product of the derivatives, as shown in the following illustration.

▷ **ILLUSTRATION 5**   Let

$$h(x) = (2x^3 - 4x^2)(3x^5 + x^2)$$

We can compute $h'(x)$ by previous theorems if we expand the right side and differentiate the resulting polynomial as follows:

$$
\begin{aligned}
h(x) &= 6x^8 - 12x^7 + 2x^5 - 4x^4 \\
h'(x) &= 48x^7 - 84x^6 + 10x^4 - 16x^3
\end{aligned}
$$

Now let

$$
\begin{aligned}
f(x) &= 2x^3 - 4x^2 \quad \text{so that} \quad f'(x) = 6x^2 - 8x \\
g(x) &= 3x^5 + x^2 \quad \text{so that} \quad g'(x) = 15x^4 + 2x
\end{aligned}
$$

Observe that $h(x) = f(x) \cdot g(x)$ but $h'(x) \neq f'(x) \cdot g'(x)$.   ◀

2.4.6 Theorem   The Product Rule of Differentiation

If f and g are functions and if h is the function defined by

$$h(x) = f(x)g(x)$$

then if $f'(x)$ and $g'(x)$ exist,

$$h'(x) = f(x)g'(x) + g(x)f'(x)$$

Proof

$$
\begin{aligned}
h'(x) &= \lim_{\Delta x \to 0} \frac{h(x + \Delta x) - h(x)}{\Delta x} \\
&= \lim_{\Delta x \to 0} \frac{f(x + \Delta x) \cdot g(x + \Delta x) - f(x) \cdot g(x)}{\Delta x}
\end{aligned}
$$

We now perform a clever bit of manipulation that will lead to limits that define $f'(x)$ and $g'(x)$. We subtract and add $f(x + \Delta x) \cdot g(x)$ in the numerator to obtain

$$h'(x) = \lim_{\Delta x \to 0} \frac{f(x + \Delta x) \cdot g(x + \Delta x) - f(x + \Delta x) \cdot g(x) + f(x + \Delta x) \cdot g(x) - f(x) \cdot g(x)}{\Delta x}$$

$$= \lim_{\Delta x \to 0} \left[f(x + \Delta x) \cdot \frac{g(x + \Delta x) - g(x)}{\Delta x} + g(x) \cdot \frac{f(x + \Delta x) - f(x)}{\Delta x} \right]$$

$$= \lim_{\Delta x \to 0} \left[f(x + \Delta x) \cdot \frac{g(x + \Delta x) - g(x)}{\Delta x} \right] + \lim_{\Delta x \to 0} \left[g(x) \cdot \frac{f(x + \Delta x) - f(x)}{\Delta x} \right]$$

$$= \lim_{\Delta x \to 0} f(x + \Delta x) \cdot \lim_{\Delta x \to 0} \frac{g(x + \Delta x) - g(x)}{\Delta x} + \lim_{\Delta x \to 0} g(x) \cdot \lim_{\Delta x \to 0} \frac{f(x + \Delta x) - f(x)}{\Delta x}$$

Because f is differentiable at x, by Theorem 2.2.1 f is continuous at x; therefore $\lim_{\Delta x \to 0} f(x + \Delta x) = f(x)$. Also, $\lim_{\Delta x \to 0} g(x) = g(x)$ and

$$\lim_{\Delta x \to 0} \frac{g(x + \Delta x) - g(x)}{\Delta x} = g'(x) \qquad \lim_{\Delta x \to 0} \frac{f(x + \Delta x) - f(x)}{\Delta x} = f'(x)$$

thus giving

$$h'(x) = f(x)g'(x) + g(x)f'(x) \qquad\qquad \blacksquare$$

$$D_x[f(x)g(x)] = f(x) \cdot D_x g(x) + g(x) \cdot D_x f(x)$$

The derivative of the product of two functions is the first function times the derivative of the second function plus the second function times the derivative of the first function if these derivatives exist.

▷ **ILLUSTRATION 6**   We apply the product rule to compute $h'(x)$ for the function h of Illustration 5:

$$h(x) = (2x^3 - 4x^2)(3x^5 + x^2)$$

From the product rule,

$$h'(x) = (2x^3 - 4x^2)(15x^4 + 2x) + (3x^5 + x^2)(6x^2 - 8x)$$
$$= (30x^7 - 60x^6 + 4x^4 - 8x^3) + (18x^7 - 24x^6 + 6x^4 - 8x^3)$$
$$= 48x^7 - 84x^6 + 10x^4 - 16x^3$$

which agrees with what we obtained for $h'(x)$ in Illustration 5.   ◀

You no doubt conclude that the computation of $h'(x)$ in Illustration 5 was simpler than the computation in Illustration 6. But remember $h(x)$ in those illustrations is a polynomial. We will be applying the product rule to many functions other than polynomials.

Just as the derivative of the product of two functions is not the product of their derivatives, the derivative of the quotient of two functions is not the quotient of their derivatives, as you see by the next theorem.

2.4.7 Theorem   The Quotient Rule of Differentiation

If f and g are functions and if h is the function defined by

$$h(x) = \frac{f(x)}{g(x)}, \qquad \text{where } g(x) \neq 0$$

then if $f'(x)$ and $g'(x)$ exist,

$$h'(x) = \frac{g(x)f'(x) - f(x)g'(x)}{[g(x)]^2}$$

Proof

$$h'(x) = \lim_{\Delta x \to 0} \frac{h(x + \Delta x) - h(x)}{\Delta x}$$

$$= \lim_{\Delta x \to 0} \frac{\dfrac{f(x + \Delta x)}{g(x + \Delta x)} - \dfrac{f(x)}{g(x)}}{\Delta x}$$

$$= \lim_{\Delta x \to 0} \frac{f(x + \Delta x) \cdot g(x) - f(x) \cdot g(x + \Delta x)}{\Delta x \cdot g(x) \cdot g(x + \Delta x)}$$

As we did in the proof of the product rule, we perform another clever manipulation. This time we subtract and add $f(x) \cdot g(x)$ in the numerator to obtain

$$h'(x) = \lim_{\Delta x \to 0} \frac{f(x + \Delta x) \cdot g(x) - f(x) \cdot g(x) - f(x) \cdot g(x + \Delta x) + f(x) \cdot g(x)}{\Delta x \cdot g(x) \cdot g(x + \Delta x)}$$

$$= \lim_{\Delta x \to 0} \frac{\left[g(x) \cdot \dfrac{f(x + \Delta x) - f(x)}{\Delta x} \right] - \left[f(x) \cdot \dfrac{g(x + \Delta x) - g(x)}{\Delta x} \right]}{g(x) \cdot g(x + \Delta x)}$$

$$= \frac{\displaystyle\lim_{\Delta x \to 0} g(x) \cdot \lim_{\Delta x \to 0} \frac{f(x + \Delta x) - f(x)}{\Delta x} - \lim_{\Delta x \to 0} f(x) \cdot \lim_{\Delta x \to 0} \frac{g(x + \Delta x) - g(x)}{\Delta x}}{\displaystyle\lim_{\Delta x \to 0} g(x) \cdot \lim_{\Delta x \to 0} g(x + \Delta x)}$$

Because g is differentiable at x, then g is continuous at x; thus we have $\lim_{\Delta x \to 0} g(x + \Delta x) = g(x)$. Also, $\lim_{\Delta x \to 0} g(x) = g(x)$ and $\lim_{\Delta x \to 0} f(x) = f(x)$. With these results and the definitions of $f'(x)$ and $g'(x)$ we get

$$h'(x) = \frac{g(x) \cdot f'(x) - f(x) \cdot g'(x)}{g(x) \cdot g(x)}$$

$$= \frac{g(x)f'(x) - f(x)g'(x)}{[g(x)]^2}$$ ∎

$$D_x\left[\frac{f(x)}{g(x)} \right] = \frac{g(x)D_x f(x) - f(x)D_x g(x)}{[g(x)]^2}$$

The derivative of the quotient of two functions is the fraction having as its denominator the square of the original denominator, and as its numerator the denominator times the derivative of the numerator minus the numerator times the derivative of the denominator if these derivatives exist.

▶ *EXAMPLE 2*   Find

$$D_x\left(\frac{2x^3 + 4}{x^2 + 1}\right)$$

Solution

$$D_x\left(\frac{2x^3 + 4}{x^2 + 1}\right) = \frac{(x^2 + 1)(6x^2) - (2x^3 + 4)(2x)}{(x^2 + 1)^2}$$

$$= \frac{6x^4 + 6x^2 - 4x^4 - 8x}{(x^2 + 1)^2}$$

$$= \frac{2x^4 + 6x^2 - 8x}{(x^2 + 1)^2} \qquad \blacktriangleleft$$

> **2.4.8 Theorem   The Power Rule (for Negative Integer Powers) of Differentiation**
>
> If $f(x) = x^{-n}$ where $-n$ is a negative integer and $x \neq 0$, then
>
> $$f'(x) = -nx^{-n-1}$$

Proof   Because we are given that $-n$ is a negative integer, n is a positive integer. We therefore express $f(x)$ as a quotient and apply the quotient rule. We have

$$f(x) = \frac{1}{x^n}$$

$$f'(x) = \frac{x^n \cdot 0 - 1 \cdot nx^{n-1}}{(x^n)^2}$$

$$= \frac{-nx^{n-1}}{x^{2n}}$$

$$= -nx^{n-1-2n}$$

$$= -nx^{-n-1} \qquad \blacksquare$$

▶ *EXAMPLE 3*   Find

$$\frac{d}{dx}\left(\frac{3}{x^5}\right)$$

Solution

$$\frac{d}{dx}\left(\frac{3}{x^5}\right) = \frac{d}{dx}(3x^{-5})$$

$$= 3(-5x^{-6})$$

$$= -\frac{15}{x^6} \qquad \blacktriangleleft$$

If r is any positive or negative integer, then the power rule holds:

$$D_x(x^r) = rx^{r-1}$$

From this formula and the constant product rule,

$$D_x(cx^r) = crx^{r-1}$$

if c is any constant and r is any positive or negative integer.

If the function f is differentiable, then its derivative f' is sometimes called the **first derivative** of f or the first derived function. If the function f' is differentiable, then the derivative of f' is called the **second derivative** of f, or the second derived function. The second derivative of f is denoted by f'' (read as "f double prime"). Similarly, the **third derivative** of f, or the third derived function, is defined as the derivative of f'' provided the derivative of f'' exists. The third derivative of f is denoted by f''' (read as "f triple prime").

The **nth derivative** of the function f, where n is a positive integer greater than 1, is the derivative of the $(n-1)$st derivative of f. We denote the nth derivative of f by $f^{(n)}$. Thus if $f^{(n)}$ is the nth derived function, we can write the function f itself as $f^{(0)}$.

▶ **EXAMPLE 4**   Find all the derivatives of the function f defined by

$$f(x) = 8x^4 + 5x^3 - x^2 + 7$$

Solution

$$f'(x) - 32x^3 + 15x^2 - 2x$$
$$f''(x) = 96x^2 + 30x - 2$$
$$f'''(x) = 192x + 30$$
$$f^{(4)}(x) = 192$$
$$f^{(5)}(x) = 0$$
$$f^{(n)}(x) = 0 \qquad n \geq 5$$

◀

The Leibniz notation for the first derivative is $\dfrac{dy}{dx}$. For the second derivative of y with respect to x the Leibniz notation is $\dfrac{d^2y}{dx^2}$, because it represents $\dfrac{d}{dx}\left[\dfrac{d}{dx}(y)\right]$. The symbol $\dfrac{d^n y}{dx^n}$ is a notation for the nth derivative of y with respect to x.

Other symbols for the nth derivative of f are

$$\frac{d^n}{dx^n}[f(x)] \qquad D_x^n[f(x)]$$

To denote the numerical second derivative of the function f at x we use the notation NDER2 $(f(x), x)$; that is,

$$\text{NDER2}\ (f(x), x) = \text{NDER(NDER}(f(x), x), x)$$

▶ **EXAMPLE 5**   Compute

$$\frac{d}{dx}\left(\frac{1}{x^3}\right) \quad \text{and} \quad \frac{d^2}{dx^2}\left(\frac{1}{x^3}\right)$$

and support the answers graphically.

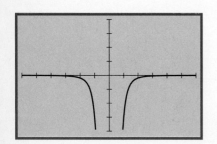

[-6, 6] by [-4, 4]

$f'(x) = -3x^{-4}$ and NDER(x^{-3}, x)

FIGURE 2

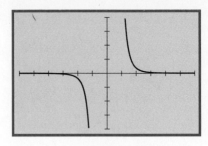

[−6, 6] by [−4, 4]

$f''(x) = 12x^{-5}$ and NDER2 (x^{-3}, x)

FIGURE 3

Solution   Let $\dfrac{1}{x^3} = x^{-3}$.

$$\frac{d}{dx}(x^{-3}) = -3x^{-4}$$

$$\frac{d^2}{dx^2}(x^{-3}) = 12x^{-5}$$

To support our answer graphically, we first plot the graphs of the functions defined by $f'(x) = -3x^{-4}$ and NDER(x^{-3}, x) in the $[-6, 6]$ by $[-4, 4]$ window. Figure 2 shows that the graphs appear identical, which supports our answer for the first derivative. We now plot the graphs of the functions defined by $f''(x) = 12x^{-5}$ and NDER2(x^{-3}, x) or, equivalently, NDER$(-3x^{-4}, x)$ in the $[-6, 6]$ by $[-4, 4]$ window. We obtain Figure 3, which shows that the two graphs appear identical and, therefore, supports our answer for the second derivative.   ◀

EXERCISES 2.4

In Exercises 1 through 24, differentiate the function by applying the theorems of this section.

1. $f(x) = 7x - 5$
2. $g(x) = 8 - 3x$
3. $g(x) = 1 - 2x - x^2$
4. $f(x) = 4x^2 + x + 1$
5. $f(x) = x^3 - 3x^2 + 5x - 2$
6. $f(x) = 3x^4 - 5x^2 + 1$
7. $f(x) = \frac{1}{8}x^8 - x^4$
8. $g(x) = x^7 - 2x^5 + 5x^3 - 7x$
9. $F(t) = \frac{1}{4}t^4 - \frac{1}{2}t^2$
10. $H(x) = \frac{1}{3}x^3 - x + 2$
11. $v(r) = \frac{4}{3}\pi r^3$
12. $G(y) = y^{10} + 7y^5 - y^3 + 1$
13. $F(x) = x^2 + 3x + \dfrac{1}{x^2}$
14. $f(x) = \dfrac{x^3}{3} + \dfrac{3}{x^3}$
15. $g(x) = 4x^4 - \dfrac{1}{4x^4}$
16. $f(x) = x^4 - 5 + x^{-2} + 4x^{-4}$
17. $g(x) = \dfrac{3}{x^2} + \dfrac{5}{x^4}$
18. $H(x) = \dfrac{5}{6x^5}$
19. $f(s) = \sqrt{3}\,(s^3 - s^2)$
20. $g(x) = (2x^2 + 5)(4x - 1)$
21. $f(x) = (2x^4 - 1)(5x^3 + 6x)$
22. $f(x) = (4x^2 + 3)^2$
23. $G(y) = (7 - 3y^3)^2$
24. $F(t) = (t^3 - 2t + 1)(2t^2 + 3t)$

In Exercises 25 through 36, compute the derivative by applying the theorems of this section. In Exercises 25 through 30, support your answer by plotting on your

graphics calculator the graph of your answer and the numerical derivative at x in the same window.

25. $D_x[(x^2 - 3x + 2)(2x^3 + 1)]$
26. $D_x\left(\dfrac{2x}{x + 3}\right)$
27. $D_x\left(\dfrac{x}{x - 1}\right)$
28. $D_y\left(\dfrac{2y + 1}{3y + 4}\right)$
29. $\dfrac{d}{dx}\left(\dfrac{x^2 + 2x + 1}{x^2 - 2x + 1}\right)$
30. $\dfrac{d}{dx}\left(\dfrac{4 - 3x - x^2}{x - 2}\right)$
31. $\dfrac{d}{dt}\left(\dfrac{5t}{1 + 2t^2}\right)$
32. $\dfrac{d}{dx}\left(\dfrac{x^4 - 2x^2 + 5x + 1}{x^4}\right)$
33. $\dfrac{d}{dy}\left(\dfrac{y^3 - 8}{y^3 + 8}\right)$
34. $\dfrac{d}{ds}\left(\dfrac{s^2 - a^2}{s^2 + a^2}\right)$
35. $D_x\left[\dfrac{2x + 1}{x + 5}(3x - 1)\right]$
36. $D_x\left[\dfrac{x^3 + 1}{x^2 + 3}(x^2 - 2x^{-1} + 1)\right]$

In Exercises 37 and 38, find all the derivatives of the function.

37. $f(x) = 6x^5 + 3x^4 - 2x^3 + 5x^2 - 8x + 9$
38. $f(x) = 2x^7 - x^5 + 5x^3 - 8x + 4$

39. Find $D_t{}^3\left(\dfrac{1}{6t^3}\right)$
40. Find $\dfrac{d^4}{dx^4}\left(x^5 - \dfrac{1}{15x^5}\right)$

In Exercises 41 and 42, find $\dfrac{d^2 y}{dx^2}$ and support your answer graphically by plotting the graph of your answer and the numerical second derivative at x in the same window.

41. $y = \dfrac{x^4 + 1}{x^2}$ **42.** $y = \dfrac{3}{x} - \dfrac{1}{3x^3}$

In Exercises 43 through 46, find an equation of either the tangent line or normal line, as indicated, and support your answer by plotting the line and the curve in the same window.

43. The tangent line to the curve $y = x^3 - 4$ at the point (2, 4).

44. The tangent line to the curve $y = \dfrac{8}{x^2 + 4}$ at the point (2, 1).

45. The normal line to the curve $y = \dfrac{10}{14 - x^2}$ at the point (4, −5).

46. The normal line to the curve $y = 4x^2 - 8x$ at the point (1, −4).

47. Find an equation of the line tangent to the curve $y = 3x^2 - 4x$ and parallel to the line $2x - y + 3 = 0$. Support your answer by plotting the curve and the two lines in the same window.

48. Find an equation of each of the tangent lines to the curve $3y = x^3 - 3x^2 + 6x + 4$ that is parallel to the line $2x - y + 3 = 0$. Support your answers by plotting the curve and the lines in the same window.

49. Find an equation of each of the normal lines to the curve $y = x^3 - 4x$ that is parallel to the line $x + 8y - 8 = 0$. Support your answers by plotting the curve and the lines in the same window.

50. Find an equation of the line tangent to the curve $y = x^4 - 6x$ and perpendicular to the line $x - 2y + 6 = 0$. Support your answer by plotting the curve and the two lines in the same window.

51. Find an equation of each of the lines through the point (4, 13) that is tangent to the curve

$y = 2x^2 - 1$. Support your answers by plotting the curve and the lines in the same window.

52. Given $f(x) = \frac{1}{3}x^3 + 2x^2 + 5x + 5$. Show that $f'(x) \geq 0$ for all values of x.

53. If f, g, and h are functions and $\phi(x) = f(x) \cdot g(x) \cdot h(x)$, prove that if $f'(x)$, $g'(x)$, and $h'(x)$ exist,

$$\phi'(x) = f(x) \cdot g(x) \cdot h'(x) + f(x) \cdot g'(x) \cdot h(x) + f'(x) \cdot g(x) \cdot h(x)$$

Hint: Apply the product rule twice.

Use the result of Exercise 53 to differentiate the functions in Exercises 54 through 57.

54. $f(x) = (x^2 + 3)(2x - 5)(3x + 2)$

55. $h(x) = (3x + 2)^2(x^2 - 1)$

56. $g(x) = (3x^3 + x^{-3})(x + 3)(x^2 - 5)$

57. $\phi(x) = (2x^2 + x + 1)^3$

58. If f and g are two functions such that their first and second derivatives exist and h is the function defined by the equation $h(x) = f(x) \cdot g(x)$, prove that

$$h''(x) = f(x) \cdot g''(x) + 2f'(x) \cdot g'(x) + f''(x) \cdot g(x)$$

59. If $y = x^n$, where n is any positive integer, prove by mathematical induction that $\dfrac{d^n y}{dx^n} = n!$

60. Give an alternate proof of the power rule (for positive integer powers) of differentiation by showing that if $f(x) = x^n$, then $f'(a) = na^{n-1}$ by applying formula (7) in Section 2.1 *Hint:* To factor $x^n - a^n$, use formula (12) in Supplementary Section 1.5.

61. Prove that if f and g are two differentiable functions such that $f(0)$ and $g(0)$ are both equal to zero, then the product of f and g cannot be the identity function; that is $f(x) \cdot g(x) \neq x$. *Hint:* Apply the product rule of differentiation.

62. Explain why three theorems on differentiation enable us to differentiate any polynomial. Include the statement of the theorems in your explanation.

2.5 RECTILINEAR MOTION

The derivative of a function f at the number x_1 has an important interpretation as the *instantaneous rate of change of f at x_1*, which we discuss in this section and the next. We begin in this section by considering an application in physics: the motion of a particle on a line. Such a motion is called **rectilinear motion.**

One direction on the line is chosen arbitrarily as positive, and the opposite direction is negative. For simplicity in this discussion, assume that the particle is moving on a horizontal line, with distance to the right as positive and distance to the left as negative. Select some point on the line and denote it by the letter O. Let f be the function determining the directed distance of the particle from O at any particular time.

To be more specific, let s meters (m) be the directed distance of the particle from O at t seconds (sec). Then f is the function defined by the equation

$$s = f(t)$$

which gives the directed distance from the point O to the particle at a particular instant.

▷ **ILLUSTRATION 1**   Let

$$s = t^2 + 2t - 3$$

Then when $t = 0$, $s = -3$; therefore the particle is 3 m to the left of point O when $t = 0$. When $t = 1$, $s = 0$; so the particle is at point O at 1 sec. When $t = 2$, $s = 5$; so the particle is 5 m to the right of point O at 2 sec. When $t = 3$, $s = 12$; so the particle is 12 m to the right of point O at 3 sec.

Figure 1 illustrates the various positions of the particle for specific values of t.

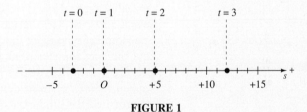

FIGURE 1

Between the time for $t = 1$ and $t = 3$, the particle moves from the point where $s = 0$ to the point where $s = 12$; thus in the 2-second interval the change in the directed distance from O is 12 m. The average velocity of the particle is the ratio of the change in the directed distance from a fixed point to the change in the time. So the number of meters per second in the average velocity of the particle from $t = 1$ to $t = 3$ is $\frac{12}{2} = 6$. From $t = 0$ to $t = 2$, the change in the directed distance from O of the particle is 8 m, and so the number of meters per second in the average velocity of the particle in this 2-second interval is $\frac{8}{2} = 4$.   ◀

In Illustration 1 the average velocity of the particle is obviously not constant; and the average velocity supplies no specific information about the motion of the particle at any particular instant. For example, if a car travels a distance of 100 km in the same direction and it takes 2 hr, we say that the average velocity in traveling that distance is 50 km/hr. However, from this information we cannot determine the speedometer reading of the car at any particular time in the 2-hour period. The speedometer reading at a specific time is referred to as the *instantaneous velocity*. The following discussion enables us to arrive at a definition of what is meant by *instantaneous velocity*.

Let the equation $s = f(t)$ define s (the number of meters in the directed distance of the particle from point O) as a function of t (the number of seconds in the time). When $t = t_1$, $s = s_1$. The change in the directed distance from O is $(s - s_1)$ meters over the interval of time $(t - t_1)$ seconds, and the number of meters per second in the average velocity of the particle over this interval of time is given by

$$\frac{s - s_1}{t - t_1}$$

or, because $s = f(t)$ and $s_1 = f(t_1)$, the average velocity is found from

$$\frac{f(t) - f(t_1)}{t - t_1} \qquad \textbf{(1)}$$

Now the shorter the interval is from t_1 to t, the closer the average velocity will be to what we would intuitively think of as the instantaneous velocity at t_1.

For example, if the speedometer reading of a car as it passes a point P_1 is 80 km/hr and if a point P is, for instance, 10 m from P_1, then the average velocity of the car as it travels this 10 m will very likely be close to 80 km/hr because the variation of the velocity of the car along this short stretch is probably slight. Now if the distance from P_1 to P were shortened to 5 m, the average velocity of the car in this interval would be even closer to the speedometer reading of the car as it passes P_1. We can continue this process, and the speedometer reading at P_1 can be represented as the limit of the average velocity between P_1 and P as P approaches P_1. That is, the *instantaneous velocity* can be defined as the limit of quotient (1) as t approaches t_1, provided the limit exists. This limit is the derivative of the function f at t_1. We have, then, the following definition.

2.5.1 Definition of Instantaneous Velocity

If f is a function given by the equation

$$s = f(t)$$

and a particle is moving along a line such that s is the number of units in the directed distance of the particle from a fixed point on the line at t units of time, then the **instantaneous velocity** of the particle at t units of time is v units of velocity, where

$$v = f'(t) \quad \Leftrightarrow \quad v = \frac{ds}{dt}$$

if it exists.

The instantaneous velocity may be either positive or negative, depending on whether the particle is moving along the line in the positive or the negative direction. When the instantaneous velocity is zero, the particle is at rest.

The **speed** of a particle at any time is defined as the absolute value of the instantaneous velocity. Hence the speed is a nonnegative number. The terms "speed" and "instantaneous velocity" are often confused. Note that the speed indicates only how fast the particle is moving, whereas the instantaneous velocity also tells the direction of motion.

▶ **EXAMPLE 1**   A particle is moving along a horizontal line according to the equation

$$s = t^3 - 12t^2 + 36t - 24 \qquad t \geq 0$$

Determine the intervals of time when the particle is moving to the right and when it is moving to the left. Also determine the instant when the particle reverses its direction.

Solution

$$v = \frac{ds}{dt}$$
$$= 3t^2 - 24t + 36$$
$$= 3(t^2 - 8t + 12)$$
$$= 3(t - 2)(t - 6)$$

The instantaneous velocity is zero when $t = 2$ and when $t = 6$. The particle is, therefore, at rest these two times. The particle is moving to the right when v is positive and moving to the left when v is negative. We determine the sign of v for various intervals of t, and the results are given in Table 1.   ◀

Table 1

	$t - 2$	$t - 6$	Conclusion
$0 \leq t < 2$	$-$	$-$	v is positive; particle is moving to the right
$t = 2$	0	$-$	v is zero; particle is at rest
$2 < t < 6$	$+$	$-$	v is negative; particle is moving to the left
$t = 6$	$+$	0	v is zero; particle is at rest
$6 < t$	$+$	$+$	v is positive; particle is moving to the right

▷ **ILLUSTRATION 2**   To visually interpret the motion of the particle of Example 1, refer to Figure 2 where the motion of the particle is along

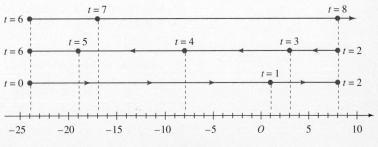

FIGURE 2

Table 2

t	s	v
0	-24	36
1	1	15
2	8	0
3	3	-9
4	-8	-12
5	-19	-9
6	-24	0
7	-17	15
8	8	36

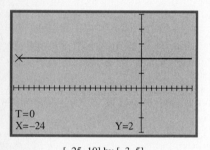

[−25, 10] by [−3, 5]

$x_1(t) = t^3 - 12t^2 + 36t - 24, \quad y_1(t) = 2$

FIGURE 3

the horizontal line in the figure. Above the line, we have indicated in color the particle's behavior, described in Table 1, where the arrow indicates the direction of motion of the particle on the horizontal axis. Table 2 gives values of s and v for integer values of t from 0 to 8. The value of s gives the particle's position on the horizontal line for the particular value of t

We now describe the motion of the particle. At $t = 0$, the particle is 24 units to the left of O and moving to the right; at $t = 1$, the particle is 1 unit to the right of O and still moving to the right; at $t = 2$, the particle is 8 units to the right of O and at rest (it stops for an instant) and then changes direction and starts moving to the left; at $t = 3$, the particle is 3 units to the right of O and moving to the left; at $t = 4$, the particle is 8 units to the left of O and still moving to the left; at $t = 5$, the particle is 19 units to the left of O and still moving to the left; at $t = 6$, the particle is 24 units to the left of O and at rest and then changes direction and starts moving to the right; at $t = 7$, the particle is 17 units to the left of O and is moving to the right; at $t = 8$, the particle is 8 units to the right of O and is moving to the right; from then on the particle continues moving to the right. ◄

Rectilinear motion can be simulated on your graphics calculator. The method involves representing the motion by parametric equations and setting your calculator in parametric mode. If you did not study parametric equations in a precalculus course, see Section 9.1. The following illustration demonstrates the procedure for the rectilinear motion of Example 1 and Illustration 2.

▷ **ILLUSTRATION 3** For clearer visibility, let us simulate the motion of the particle on the line $y = 2$ rather than on the x axis. With our calculator in parametric mode, we let

$$x_1(t) = t^3 - 12t^2 + 36t - 24 \quad \text{and} \quad y_1(t) = 2$$

In the $[-25, 10]$ by $[-3, 5]$ window we let $t_{min} = 0$, $t_{max} = 10$, and $t_{step} = 0.05$. We now press the $\boxed{\text{TRACE}}$ key and then press the left-arrow key and hold it down until the cursor is at $t = 0$. Figure 3 shows the calculator screen as it now appears. Notice the information at the bottom of the screen: $t = 0$, $x = -24$, and $y = 2$.

We are now ready to begin the motion of the particle. We press the right-arrow key and hold it down. The cursor represents the particle moving along the line $y = 2$. Observe that the particle is moving to the right until $t = 2$ and $x = 8$, when it stops and then changes direction. The particle then moves to the left until $t = 6$ and $x = -24$, when it again stops and changes direction. The particle then moves to the right and disappears off the screen to the right. This motion supports our results in Example 1 and Illustration 2. ◄

Rectilinear motion can be visualized another way on your graphics calculator, as shown in the following illustration.

▷ **ILLUSTRATION 4** We consider again the rectilinear motion of Example 1 and Illustrations 2 and 3. With our calculator in parametric mode, we add the following information:

$$x_2(t) = t^3 - 12t^2 + 36t - 24 \quad \text{and} \quad y_2(t) = t$$

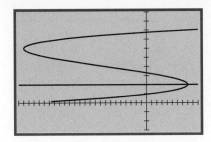

[−25, 10] by [−3, 10]

$x_1(t) = t^3 - 12t^2 + 36t - 24, \quad y_1(t) = 2$

$x_2(t) = t^3 - 12t^2 + 36t - 24, \quad y_2(t) = t$

FIGURE 4

This time we use the $[-25, 10]$ by $[-3, 10]$ window with the t settings the same as in Illustration 3. We plot the graphs for $x_1(t)$, $y_1(t)$ and $x_2(t)$, $y_2(t)$ in the same window and select ⌐SIMUL⌐ (simultaneous) from the ⌐MODE⌐ menu. Figure 4 shows the two graphs: the horizontal line $y = 2$ on which the particle actually moves; and a curve on which the coordinates are $(x_2(t), y_2(t))$, and which represents a vertical amplification of the motion of the particle. We can visualize the particle first moving on the horizontal line as in Illustration 3. Then to visualize the particle moving on the curve (remember, not actually the path of the particle), we first press either the up-arrow or down-arrow key, so that the cursor is on the curve. Then as before, we press the left-arrow key and hold it down until the cursor is at $t = 0$. We now press the right-arrow key and hold it down. This second visualization shows the motion of the particle from left to right, then from right to left, and then from left to right again. Notice on this curve that the particle changes direction at the point where $x = 8$ and $y = 2$ (8 units to right of O at 2 sec) and then again at the point where $x = -24$ and $y = 6$ (24 units to the left of O at 6 sec). ◄

▶ **EXAMPLE 2**   A ball is thrown vertically upward from the ground with an initial velocity of 64 ft/sec. If the positive direction of the distance from the starting point is up, t seconds is the time that has elapsed since the ball was thrown, and s feet is the distance of the ball from the starting point at t seconds, then the equation of motion is

$$s = -16t^2 + 64t$$

(a) Simulate the motion of the ball on a graphics calculator. **(b)** Estimate how high the ball will go and how many seconds it takes for the ball to reach its highest point. **(c)** Confirm the estimations in part **(b)** analytically. **(d)** Find the instantaneous velocity of the ball at 1 sec and 3 sec. **(e)** Find the speed of the ball at 1 sec and 3 sec. **(f)** Find the instantaneous velocity of the ball when it reaches the ground.

Solution
(a) Let us assume that the ball moves on the vertical line $x = 2$. With our calculator in parametric mode, we let

$$x_1(t) = 2 \quad \text{and} \quad y_1(t) = -16t^2 + 64t$$

To determine the values of t of interest, in the given equation we set $s = 0$ and we have

$$-16t(t - 4) = 0$$
$$t = 0 \qquad t = 4$$

The ball is, therefore, on the ground at 0 sec and 4 sec, which indicates $0 \le t \le 4$. In the $[0, 4]$ by $[-25, 100]$ window, we let $t_{\min} = 0$, $t_{\max} = 4$, and $t_{\text{step}} = 0.05$. We now press the ⌐TRACE⌐ key and then press the left-arrow key and hold it down until the cursor is at $t = 0$. Figure 5 shows the calculator screen as it now appears. We press the right-arrow key and observe the ball, represented by the cursor, moving up and down along the vertical line $x = 2$.

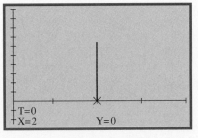

[0, 4] by [−25, 100]

$x_1(t) = 2, \quad y_1(t) = -16t^2 + 64t$

FIGURE 5

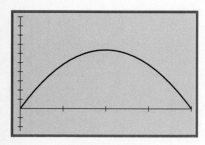

[0, 4] by [−25, 100]

$x_2(t) = t,$ $y_2(t) = -16t^2 + 64t$

FIGURE 6

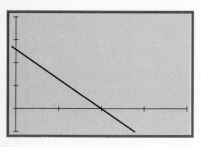

[0, 4] by [−25, 100]

$x_3(t) = t,$ $y_3(t) = -32t + 64$

FIGURE 7

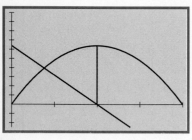

[0, 4] by [−25, 100]

$x_1(t) = 2,$ $y_1(t) = -16t^2 + 64t$
$x_2(t) = t,$ $y_2(t) = -16t^2 + 64t$
$x_3(t) = t,$ $y_3(t) = -32t + 64$

FIGURE 8

(b) By approximating the value of y as 64 and the value of t as 2 when the ball is at its greatest height, we estimate that the ball will reach its highest point of 64 ft at 2 sec.

(c) To confirm our estimations in part (b) analytically, we first compute $v(t)$, the number of feet per second in the instantaneous velocity of the ball at t seconds. Because $v(t) = \dfrac{ds}{dt}$,

$$v(t) = -32t + 64 \qquad (2)$$

Because the ball will reach its greatest height when the direction of motion changes, that is, when $v(t) = 0$, we replace $v(t)$ by 0 in Equation (2) and obtain

$$-32t + 64 = 0$$
$$t = 2$$

From the equation of motion when $t = 2$, $s = 64$. The ball, therefore, reaches a highest point of 64 ft above the starting point at 2 sec. These results confirm our estimations in part (b).

(d) $v(1) = -32(1) + 64 \Leftrightarrow v(1) = 32$; so at the end of 1 sec the ball is rising with an instantaneous velocity of 32 ft/sec. $v(3) = -32(3) + 64 \Leftrightarrow v(3) = -32$; so at the end of 3 sec the ball is falling with an instantaneous velocity of −32 ft/sec.

(e) $|v(t)|$ is the number of feet per second in the speed of the ball at t seconds; $|v(1)| = 32$ and $|v(3)| = 32$.

(f) We determined above that the ball will reach the ground in 4 sec. Because $v(4) = -64$, its instantaneous velocity when it reaches the ground is −64 ft/sec. ◄

▷ **ILLUSTRATION 5**   In Example 2, parametric equations of the path of the ball are given by

$$x_1(t) = 2 \quad \text{and} \quad y_1(t) = -16t^2 + 64t \qquad (3)$$

and plotted in Figure 5. The equation of motion is

$$s = -16t^2 + 64t$$

To plot the graph of this equation in parametric mode, we let

$$x_2(t) = t \quad \text{and} \quad y_2(t) = -16t^2 + 64t \qquad (4)$$

The graph is a parabola whose highest point, the vertex, is at (2, 64). The graph appears in Figure 6. The velocity v of the ball is given by the equation

$$v = -32t + 64$$

whose graph is a line having negative slope. Parametric equations of this line are

$$x_3(t) = t \quad \text{and} \quad y_3(t) = -32t + 64 \qquad (5)$$

The line appears in Figure 7. Refer now to Figure 8 showing the graphs of all three sets of parametric equations in the same window. Notice that the

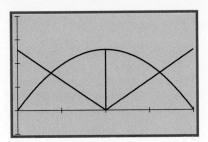

[0, 4] by [−25, 100]

$x_1(t) = 2,\quad y_1(t) = -16t^2 + 64t$

$x_2(t) = t,\quad y_2(t) = -16t^2 + 64t$

$x_4(t) = t,\quad y_4(t) = \left|-32t + 64\right|$

FIGURE 9

velocity is zero (at the point where the line intersects the x axis) when the ball is at its highest point. Also notice that when the ball is rising, the velocity is positive and when the ball is falling, the velocity is negative. Furthermore, the velocity is always decreasing as indicated by the negative slope of the line representing the velocity.

Because the speed of a particle is the absolute value of its velocity, parametric equations for the speed of the ball are

$$x_4(t) = t \quad \text{and} \quad y_4(t) = \left|-32t + 64\right| \tag{6}$$

Figure 9 shows the graphs of (3), (4), and (6) plotted in the same window. Observe that the speed is decreasing when the ball is rising, the speed is zero when the ball reaches its highest point, and the speed is increasing when the ball is falling. ◀

▷ **ILLUSTRATION 6**   Let us now return to the rectilinear motion of Example 1 and Illustrations 2 through 4. Notice in Table 2 that the velocity appears to be decreasing when $0 < t < 4$ and increasing when $4 < t$. This fact can be supported graphically by observing the particle's motion in Illustrations 3 and 4. When $0 \le t \le 2$, $v \ge 0$ and the particle's speed is decreasing; when $2 \le t \le 4$, $v \le 0$ and the particle's speed is increasing; thus for $0 < t < 4$, v is decreasing. When $4 \le t \le 6$, $v \le 0$ and the speed is decreasing; when $6 \le t \le 8$, $v \ge 0$ and the speed is increasing; thus for $4 < t < 8$, v is increasing. ◀

In physics, the instantaneous rate of change of the velocity is called the **instantaneous acceleration.** Therefore, if a particle is moving along a line according to the equation of motion $s = f(t)$, where at t seconds the instantaneous velocity is v meters per second and the instantaneous acceleration is a meters per second per second, then a is the first derivative of v with respect to t or, equivalently, the second derivative of s with respect to t; that is,

$$v = \frac{ds}{dt}$$

$$a = \frac{dv}{dt} \quad \Leftrightarrow \quad a = \frac{d^2s}{dt^2}$$

When $a > 0$, v is increasing, and when $a < 0$, v is decreasing. When $a = 0$, then v is not changing. Because the speed of the particle at t seconds is $|v|$ m/sec, we have the following results:

  (i) If $v \ge 0$ and $a > 0$, the speed is increasing.

  (ii) If $v \ge 0$ and $a < 0$, the speed is decreasing.

  (iii) If $v \le 0$ and $a > 0$, the speed is decreasing.

  (iv) If $v \le 0$ and $a < 0$, the speed is increasing.

▷ **ILLUSTRATION 7**   For the rectilinear motion of Example 1 and Illustrations 2 through 4,

$$s = t^3 - 12t^2 + 36t - 24$$

$$v = \frac{ds}{dt} \quad \Rightarrow \quad v = 3t^2 - 24t + 36$$

$$a = \frac{dv}{dt} \quad \Rightarrow \quad a = 6t - 24$$

Therefore, $a = 6(t - 4)$; so for $0 < t < 4$, $a < 0$ and for $4 < t < 8$, $a > 0$. These results are consistent with our discussion in Illustration 6.   ◀

▷ **ILLUSTRATION 8**   For the ball in Example 2

$$s = -16t^2 + 64t \quad \text{and} \quad v = -32t + 64$$

The acceleration of the ball is a feet per second per second where

$$a = \frac{dv}{dt} \quad \Rightarrow \quad a = -32$$

The acceleration is, therefore, -32 ft/sec². This constant acceleration of the ball in the downward direction, whether the ball is rising or falling, is due to the force of gravity.   ◀

▶ **EXAMPLE 3**   A particle is moving along a horizontal line according to the equation

$$s = 3t^2 - t^3 \qquad t \geq 0 \tag{7}$$

where s meters is the directed distance of the particle from the origin at t seconds. If v meters per second is the instantaneous velocity and a meters per second per second is the instantaneous acceleration at t seconds, find v and a in terms of t. Describe the position and motion of the particle in a table that includes the intervals of time when the particle is moving to the left, when it is moving to the right, when the velocity is increasing, when the velocity is decreasing, when the speed is increasing, when the speed is decreasing, and the particle's position with respect to the origin during these intervals of time. Show the behavior of the motion by a figure similar to Figure 2.

Solution   Because $s = 3t^2 - t^3$ and $v = \dfrac{ds}{dt}$,

$$v = 6t - 3t^2 \tag{8}$$

Because $a = \dfrac{dv}{dt}$,

$$a = 6 - 6t \tag{9}$$

We determine the values of t when any one of the quantities s, v, or a is zero. From (7),

$$s = 0 \quad \text{when} \quad t = 0 \quad \text{or} \quad t = 3$$

From (8),

$$v = 0 \quad \text{when} \quad t = 0 \quad \text{or} \quad t = 2$$

From (9),

$$a = 0 \quad \text{when} \quad t = 1$$

Table 3 gives values of s, v, and a when t is 0, 1, 2, and 3. We have also indicated in the table the sign of s, v, and a in the intervals of t excluding 0, 1, 2, and 3. We then form a conclusion regarding the particle's position and motion for the various values of t.

Table 3

	s	v	a	*Conclusion*
$t = 0$	0	0	6	Particle is at the origin. The velocity is 0 and is increasing. The speed is increasing.
$0 < t < 1$	+	+	+	Particle is at the right of the origin, and it is moving to the right. The velocity is increasing. The speed is increasing.
$t = 1$	2	3	0	Particle is 2 m to the right of the origin, and it is moving to the right at 3 m/sec. The velocity is not changing; so the speed is not changing.
$1 < t < 2$	+	+	−	Particle is at the right of the origin, and it is moving to the right. The velocity is decreasing. The speed is decreasing.
$t = 2$	4	0	−6	Particle is 4 m to the right of the origin, and it is changing its direction of motion from right to left. The velocity is decreasing. The speed is increasing.
$2 < t < 3$	+	−	−	Particle is at the right of the origin, and it is moving to the left. The velocity is decreasing. The speed is increasing.
$t = 3$	0	−9	−12	Particle is at the origin, and it is moving to the left at 9 m/sec. The velocity is decreasing. The speed is increasing.
$3 < t$	−	−	−	Particle is at the left of the origin, and it is moving to the left. The velocity is decreasing. The speed is increasing.

The motion of the particle is along the horizontal line in Figure 10. The particle's behavior as described in Table 3 is indicated in color above the line where the arrow indicates the direction of motion of the particle on the horizontal axis. ◀

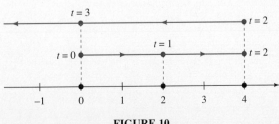

FIGURE 10

You can support the results of Example 3 by simulating the motion of the particle on your graphics calculator as we did in Illustration 3 for the motion of Example 1 and Illustration 2. You are asked to do this in Exercise 24.

▶ **EXAMPLE 4**   A particle is moving along a line according to the equation of motion

$$s = \frac{1}{2}t^2 + \frac{4t}{t + 1}$$

where s meters is the directed distance of the particle from the origin at t seconds. If v meters per second is the instantaneous velocity and a meters per second per second is the instantaneous acceleration at t seconds, find t, s, and v when $a = 0$.

Solution

$$v = \frac{ds}{dt} \qquad\qquad a = \frac{dv}{dt}$$

$$= t + \frac{4}{(t + 1)^2} \qquad = 1 - \frac{8}{(t + 1)^3}$$

Setting $a = 0$ we have

$$\frac{(t + 1)^3 - 8}{(t + 1)^3} = 0$$

$$(t + 1)^3 = 8$$

from which the only real value of t is obtained from the principal cube root of 8, so that $t + 1 = 2$; that is, $t = 1$. When $t = 1$,

$$s = \frac{1}{2}(1)^2 + \frac{4 \cdot 1}{1 + 1} \qquad\qquad v = 1 + \frac{4}{(1 + 1)^2}$$

$$= 2.5 \qquad\qquad\qquad = 2$$

<u>Conclusion:</u>   The acceleration is 0 at 1 sec when the particle is 2.5 m from the origin and moving to the right at a velocity of 2 m/sec.   ◀

EXERCISES 2.5

In Exercises 1 through 8, a particle is moving along a horizontal line according to the given equation, where s meters is the directed distance of the particle from a point O at t seconds. Find the instantaneous velocity v(t) meters per second at t seconds, and then find v(t₁) for the particular value of t₁.

1. $s = 3t^2 + 1$; $t_1 = 3$ **2.** $s = 8 - t^2$; $t_1 = 5$

3. $s = \frac{1}{4t}$; $t_1 = \frac{1}{2}$ **4.** $s = \frac{3}{t^2}$; $t_1 = -2$

5. $s = 2t^3 - t^2 + 5$; $t_1 = -1$

6. $s = 4t^3 + 2t - 1$; $t_1 = \frac{1}{2}$

7. $s = \frac{2t}{4 + t}$; $t_1 = 0$ **8.** $s = \frac{1}{t} + \frac{3}{t^2}$; $t_1 = 2$

In Exercises 9 through 14, a particle is moving along a horizontal line according to the given equation, where s meters is the directed distance of the particle from a point O at t seconds. The positive direction is to the right. Determine the intervals of time when the particle is moving to the right and when it is moving to the left. Also determine when the particle reverses its direction. Show the behavior of the motion by a figure similar to Figure 2, and choose values of t at random but include the values of t when the particle reverses its direction. Support your results by simulating the particle's motion on your graphics calculator.

9. $s = t^3 + 3t^2 - 9t + 4$

10. $s = 2t^3 - 3t^2 - 12t + 8$

11. $s = \frac{2}{3}t^3 + \frac{3}{2}t^2 - 2t + 4$

12. $s = \dfrac{t}{1 + t^2}$ 13. $s = \dfrac{t}{9 + t^2}$ 14. $s = \dfrac{t + 1}{t^2 + 4}$

15. For the rectilinear motion of Exercise 9, plot in the same window the line $y = 2$ on which the particle actually moves and a curve which represents a vertical amplification of the motion of the particle, similar to the one in Illustration 4. Support your results of Exercise 9 by visualizing the particle moving on the curve (not actually the path of the particle). Sketch what you see on the screen of your graphics calculator and describe the particle's motion on the curve.

16. Follow the instructions of Exercise 15 for the rectilinear motion of Exercise 10.

For Exercises 17 through 21, use the following equation of motion from physics for an object moving in a vertical line and subject only to the force of gravity, where the positive direction is upward:

$$s = -16t^2 + v_0 t + s_0 \qquad (10)$$

where s feet is the height of the object at t seconds, s_0 feet is the initial height of the object, and v_0 feet per second is the object's initial velocity.

17. A stone is dropped from a building 256 ft high. (a) Use (10) to write the equation of motion of the stone, and simulate the motion of the stone on your graphics calculator. (b) Find the instantaneous velocity of the stone at 1 sec and 2 sec. (c) Find how long it takes the stone to reach the ground.

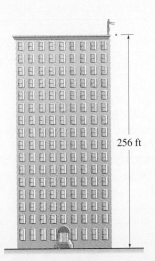

256 ft

(d) What is the speed of the stone when it reaches the ground?

18. In an opera house, the base of a chandelier is 160 ft above the lobby floor. Suppose the phantom of the opera dislocates the chandelier and causes it to fall from rest and crash on the floor below. (a) Use (10) to write an equation of motion of the chandelier, and simulate the motion on your graphics calculator. (b) Find the instantaneous velocity of the chandelier at 1 sec and 1.5 sec. (c) Find how long it takes the chandelier to hit the floor. (d) What is the speed of the chandelier when it hits the floor?

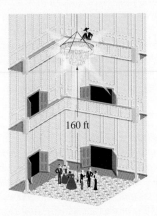

160 ft

19. Do Exercise 18 if the phantom is able to give the chandelier an initial velocity of 48 ft/sec.

20. A ball is thrown vertically upward from the ground with an initial velocity of 32 ft/sec. (a) Use (10) to write the equation of motion of the ball, and simulate the motion of the ball on your graphics calculator. (b) Estimate how high the ball will go and how long it takes the ball to reach its highest point. (c) Confirm your estimations in part (b) analytically. (d) Find the instantaneous velocity of the ball at 0.75 sec and 1.25 sec. (e) Find the speed of the ball at 0.75 sec and 1.25 sec. (f) Find the speed of the ball when it reaches the ground.

21. A rocket is fired vertically upward from the ground with an initial velocity of 560 ft/sec. (a) Use (10) to write the equation of motion of the rocket, and simulate the motion on your graphics calculator. (b) Estimate how high the rocket will go and how long it takes the rocket to reach its highest point. (c) Confirm your estimations in part (b) analytically. (d) Find the instantaneous velocity of the rocket at 10 sec and 25 sec. (e) Find the speed of the rocket at 10 sec and 25 sec. (f) Find the speed of the rocket when it reaches the ground.

22. For the ball of Exercise 20, do the following: (a) Plot in the same window the path of the ball, the graph of the equation of motion, and the graph of the

equation expressing the instantaneous velocity v as a function of t. Sketch what you see on the screen of your graphics calculator and describe why this visualization supports your answer to part (b) in Exercise 20.

23. Follow the instructions of Exercise 22 for the rocket of Exercise 21.

24. Simulate the motion of the particle of Example 3 on your graphics calculator. Explain why this supports the results of Example 3.

In Exercises 25 and 26, a particle is moving along a line according to the given equation, where s feet is the directed distance of the particle from the origin at t seconds. Find the time when the instantaneous acceleration is zero, and then find the directed distance of the particle from the origin and the instantaneous velocity at this time.

25. $s = \frac{1}{3}t^3 - \frac{3}{2}t^2 + 2t + 1; t \ge 0$

26. $s = 2t^3 - 6t^2 + 3t - 4; t \ge 0$

In Exercises 27 and 28, a particle is moving along a horizontal line according to the given equation where at t seconds, s meters is the directed distance of the particle from the origin, v meters per second is the instantaneous velocity of the particle, and a meters per second per second is the instantaneous acceleration of the particle. Find v and a in terms of t. Make a table similar to Table 3 that gives a description of the position and motion of the particle. Include in the table the intervals of time when the particle is moving to the left, when it is moving to the right, when the velocity is increasing, when the velocity is decreasing, when the speed is increasing, when the speed is decreasing, and the position of the particle with respect to the origin during these intervals of time. Show the behavior of the motion by a figure similar to Figure 10.

27. $s = t^3 - 9t^2 + 15t; t \ge 0$

28. $s = \frac{1}{6}t^3 - 2t^2 + 6t - 2; t \ge 0$

29. Simulate the motion of the particle of Exercise 27 on your graphics calculator and explain why this supports your results.

30. Simulate the motion of the particle of Exercise 28 on your graphics calculator and explain why this supports your results.

31. In Equation (10) the coefficient, -16, of t^2 is $\frac{1}{2}(-32)$ where -32 ft/sec^2 is the acceleration due to gravity of an object moving in a vertical line near the surface of the earth when air resistance is neglected. Because the acceleration due to gravity on the moon is -5.5 ft/sec^2, the equation of motion for an object moving in a vertical line near the moon's surface is

$$s = -2.75t^2 + v_0 t + s_0$$

Suppose an astronaut on the moon drops a stone from the edge of a cliff and the stone hits the ground in 4 sec. Then a second astronaut at the bottom of the cliff retrieves the stone and throws it back up to the first astronaut. **(a)** What is the height of the cliff? **(b)** With what velocity does the stone hit the ground? **(c)** With at least what velocity must the second astronaut throw the stone so that it reaches the first astronaut?

32. Instead of on the moon, suppose the two astronauts in Exercise 31 perform the same ritual on Mars, where the acceleration due to gravity is -12 ft/sec^2. Write the corresponding equation of motion and answer the same questions as in Exercise 31 if this time the stone hits the ground in 3 sec.

33. Suppose a sprinter running in a 100-meter race is s meters from the finish line t seconds after the start of the race where

$$s = 100 - \frac{1}{4}(t^2 + 33t)$$

Find the sprinter's speed **(a)** at the start of the race, and **(b)** when the sprinter crosses the finish line.

34. If a ball is given a push so that it has an initial velocity of 24 ft/sec down a certain inclined plane, then $s = 24t + 10t^2$, where s feet is the distance of the ball from the starting point at t seconds and the positive direction is down the inclined plane. **(a)** What is the instantaneous velocity of the ball at t_1 seconds? **(b)** How long does it take for the velocity to increase to 48 ft/sec?

35. A billiard ball is hit and travels in a line. If s centimeters is the distance of the ball from its initial position at t seconds, then $s = 100t^2 + 100t$. If the ball

hits a cushion that is 39 cm from its initial position, at what velocity does it hit the cushion?

36. Two particles, A and B, move to the right along a horizontal line. They start at a point O, s meters is the directed distance of the particle from O at t seconds, and the equations of motion are

$$s = 4t^2 + 5t \qquad \text{(for particle } A\text{)}$$
$$s = 7t^2 + 3t \qquad \text{(for particle } B\text{)}$$

If $t = 0$ at the start, for what values of t will the velocity of particle A exceed the velocity of particle B?

2.6 THE DERIVATIVE AS A RATE OF CHANGE

You learned in Section 2.5 that if a particle is moving along a line according to the equation of motion $s = f(t)$, then the velocity of the particle at t units of time is determined by the derivative of s with respect to t. This concept of velocity in rectilinear motion corresponds to the more general concept of instantaneous rate of change; that is, the rate of change of s per unit change in t is the derivative of s with respect to t.

In a similar way, if a quantity y is a function of a quantity x, we may express the rate of change of y per unit change in x. The discussion is analogous to the discussions of the slope of a tangent line to a graph and the instantaneous velocity of a particle moving along a line.

If the functional relationship between y and x is given by

$$y = f(x)$$

and if x changes from the value x_1 to $x_1 + \Delta x$, then y changes from $f(x_1)$ to $f(x_1 + \Delta x)$. So the change in y, which we denote by Δy, is $f(x_1 + \Delta x) - f(x_1)$ when the change in x is Δx. The average rate of change of y per unit change in x, as x changes from x_1 to $x_1 + \Delta x$, is then

$$\frac{f(x_1 + \Delta x) - f(x_1)}{\Delta x} = \frac{\Delta y}{\Delta x} \tag{1}$$

If the limit of this quotient exists as $\Delta x \to 0$, this limit is what we intuitively think of as the instantaneous rate of change of y per unit change in x at x_1. Accordingly, we have the following definition.

2.6.1 Definition of Instantaneous Rate of Change

If $y = f(x)$, the **instantaneous rate of change of y per unit change in x at x_1** is $f'(x_1)$ or, equivalently, the derivative of y with respect to x at x_1, if it exists.

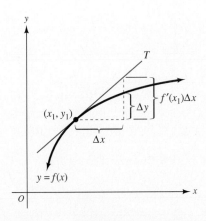

FIGURE 1

To illustrate this definition geometrically, let $f'(x_1)$ be the instantaneous rate of change of y per unit change in x at x_1. Then if $f'(x_1)$ is multiplied by Δx (the change in x), the product is the change that would occur in y if the point (x, y) were to move along the tangent line at (x_1, y_1) of the graph of $y = f(x)$. See Figure 1. The average rate of change of y per unit change in

x is given by the fraction in (1), and when this fraction is multiplied by Δx, the product is Δy, which is the actual change in y caused by a change of Δx in x when the point (x, y) moves along the graph.

▶ **EXAMPLE 1**   Let $V(x)$ cubic centimeters be the volume of a cube having an edge of x centimeters, measured to four significant digits. On a calculator compute the average rate of change of $V(x)$ with respect to x as x changes from **(a)** 3.000 to 3.200; **(b)** 3.000 to 3.100; **(c)** 3.000 to 3.010; **(d)** 3.000 to 3.001. **(e)** What is the instantaneous rate of change of $V(x)$ with respect to x when x is 3.000?

Solution   The average rate of change of $V(x)$ with respect to x as x changes from x_1 to $x_1 + \Delta x$ is

$$\frac{V(x_1 + \Delta x) - V(x_1)}{\Delta x}$$

(a) $x_1 = 3.000, \Delta x = 0.200$

$$\frac{V(3.200) - V(3.000)}{0.200} = \frac{(3.200)^3 - (3.000)^3}{0.200}$$

$$= 28.84$$

(b) $x_1 = 3.000, \Delta x = 0.100$

$$\frac{V(3.100) - V(3.000)}{0.100} = \frac{(3.100)^3 - (3.000)^3}{0.100}$$

$$= 27.91$$

(c) $x_1 = 3.000, \Delta x = 0.010$

$$\frac{V(3.010) - V(3.000)}{0.010} = \frac{(3.010)^3 - (3.000)^3}{0.010}$$

$$= 27.09$$

(d) $x_1 = 3.000, \Delta x = 0.001$

$$\frac{V(3.001) - V(3.000)}{0.001} = \frac{(3.001)^3 - (3.000)^3}{0.001}$$

$$= 27.01$$

In part (a) we see that as the length of the edge of the cube changes from 3.000 cm to 3.200 cm, the average rate of change of the volume is 28.84 cm^3 per centimeter change in the length of the edge. Parts (b)–(d) can be interpreted in a similar way.

(e) The instantaneous rate of change of $V(x)$ with respect to x when x is 3 is $V'(3)$.

$$V'(x) = 3x^2 \qquad V'(3) = 27$$

<u>Conclusion:</u>   When the length of the edge of the cube is 3 cm, the instantaneous rate of change of the volume is 27 cm^3 per centimeter change in the length of the edge.   ◀

▶ **EXAMPLE 2**   In an electric circuit, if E volts is the electromotive force, I amperes is the current, and R ohms is the resistance, then from Ohm's law

   $IR = E$

(a) Assuming that E is a positive constant, show that I decreases at a rate proportional to the inverse square of R. **(b)** What is the instantaneous rate of change of I with respect to R in an electric circuit of 90 volts when the resistance is 15 ohms?

Solution

(a) Solving the given equation for I, we obtain

   $I = E \cdot R^{-1}$

Differentiating I with respect to R, we have

$$\frac{dI}{dR} = -E \cdot R^{-2}$$

$$\frac{dI}{dR} = -\frac{E}{R^2} \tag{2}$$

This equation states that the rate of change of I with respect to R is negative and proportional to $1/R^2$. Therefore, I decreases at a rate proportional to the inverse square of R.

(b) From Equation (2) with $E = 90$ and $R = 15$, we have

$$\frac{dI}{dR} = -\frac{90}{225}$$

$$= -0.4$$

<u>Conclusion:</u>   The current is decreasing at the rate of 0.4 amps per ohm.   ◀

In economics the variation of one quantity with respect to another may be described by either an *average* concept or a *marginal* concept. The average concept expresses the variation of one quantity over a specified range of values of a second quantity, whereas the marginal concept is the instantaneous change in the first quantity that results from a very small unit change in the second quantity. We begin our examples in economics with the definitions of average cost and marginal cost. To define a marginal concept precisely we use the notion of a limit, and this leads to the derivative.

Suppose $C(x)$ dollars is the total cost of producing x units of a commodity. The function C is called a **total cost function.** In normal circumstances x and $C(x)$ are positive. Since x represents the number of units of a commodity, x is usually a nonnegative integer. However, to apply the calculus we assume that x is a nonnegative real number to give the continuity requirements for the function C.

The **average cost** of producing each unit of a commodity is obtained by dividing the total cost by the number of units produced. If $Q(x)$ dollars is the average cost,

$$Q(x) = \frac{C(x)}{x}$$

and Q is called an **average cost function.**

Now suppose that the number of units in a particular output is x_1, and this is changed by Δx. Then the change in the total cost is given by $C(x_1 + \Delta x) - C(x_1)$, and the average change in the total cost with respect to the change in the number of units produced is given by

$$\frac{C(x_1 + \Delta x) - C(x_1)}{\Delta x}$$

Economists use the term *marginal cost* for the limit of this quotient as Δx approaches zero, provided the limit exists. This limit, being the derivative of C at x_1, states that the **marginal cost,** when $x = x_1$, is given by $C'(x_1)$, if it exists. The function C' is called the **marginal cost function,** and $C'(x_1)$ may be interpreted as the rate of change of the total cost when x_1 units are produced.

▷ **ILLUSTRATION 1**   Suppose that $C(x)$ dollars is the total cost of manufacturing x toys, and

$$C(x) = 110 + 4x + 0.02x^2$$

(a) The marginal cost function is C', and

$$C'(x) = 4 + 0.04x$$

(b) The marginal cost when $x = 50$ is $C'(50)$, and

$$C'(50) = 4 + 0.04(50)$$
$$= 6$$

<u>Conclusion:</u>   The rate of change of the total cost, when 50 toys are manufactured, is $6 per toy.

(c) The number of dollars in the actual cost of manufacturing the fifty-first toy is $C(51) - C(50)$, and

$$C(51) - C(50) = [110 + 4(51) + 0.02(51)^2] - [110 + 4(50) + 0.02(50)^2]$$
$$= 366.02 - 360$$
$$= 6.02$$

Note that the answers in (b) and (c) differ by 0.02. This discrepancy occurs because the marginal cost is the instantaneous rate of change of $C(x)$ with respect to a unit change in x. Hence $C'(50)$ is the approximate number of dollars in the cost of producing the fifty-first toy.   ◀

Observe that the computation of $C'(50)$ in Illustration 1 is simpler than computing $C(51) - C(50)$. Economists frequently approximate the cost of producing one additional unit by using the marginal cost function. Specifically, $C'(k)$ dollars is the approximate cost of the $(k + 1)$st unit after the first k units have been produced.

Another function important in economics is the **total revenue function,** denoted by R, and

$$R(x) = px$$

where $R(x)$ dollars is the total revenue received when x units are sold at p dollars per unit.

The **marginal revenue,** when $x = x_1$, is given by $R'(x_1)$, if it exists. The function R' is called the **marginal revenue function.** $R'(x_1)$ may be positive, negative, or zero, and it may be interpreted as the rate of change of the total revenue when x_1 units are sold. $R'(k)$ dollars is the approximate revenue from the sale of the $(k + 1)$st unit after the first k units have been sold.

▶ **EXAMPLE 3**   Suppose that $R(x)$ dollars is the total revenue received from the sale of x tables, and

$$R(x) = 300x - \tfrac{1}{2}x^2$$

Find **(a)** the marginal revenue function; **(b)** the marginal revenue when $x = 40$; **(c)** the actual revenue from the sale of the forty-first table.

Solution

(a) The marginal revenue function is R', and

$$R'(x) = 300 - x$$

(b) The marginal revenue when $x = 40$ is given by $R'(40)$, and

$$R'(40) = 300 - 40$$
$$= 260$$

Conclusion: The rate of change of the total revenue when 40 tables are sold is $260 per table.

(c) The number of dollars in the actual revenue from the sale of the forty-first table is $R(41) - R(40)$, and

$$R(41) - R(40) = \left[300(41) - \frac{(41)^2}{2} \right] - \left[300(40) - \frac{(40)^2}{2} \right]$$
$$= 11{,}459.50 - 11{,}200$$
$$= 259.50$$

Conclusion: The actual revenue from the sale of the forty-first table is $259.50.   ◀

Observe in part (b) of Example 3 we obtained $R'(40) = 260$, and $260 is an approximation of the revenue received from the sale of the forty-first table, which from (c) is $259.50.

Because $f'(x)$ gives the instantaneous rate of change of $f(x)$ with respect to x, $f''(x)$, being the derivative of $f'(x)$, gives the instantaneous rate of change of $f'(x)$ with respect to x. Furthermore, if (x, y) is any point on the graph of $y = f(x)$, then $\dfrac{dy}{dx}$ gives the slope of the tangent line to the graph at the point (x, y). Thus $\dfrac{d^2y}{dx^2}$ is the instantaneous rate of change of the slope of the tangent line with respect to x at the point (x, y).

EXAMPLE 4   Let $m(x)$ be the slope of the tangent line to the curve

$$y = x^3 - 2x^2 + x$$

at the point (x, y). Find the instantaneous rate of change of $m(x)$ with respect to x at the point $(2, 2)$.

Solution

$$m(x) = \frac{dy}{dx}$$

$$= 3x^2 - 4x + 1$$

The instantaneous rate of change of $m(x)$ with respect to x is given by $m'(x)$ or, equivalently, $\dfrac{d^2y}{dx^2}$.

$$m'(x) = \frac{d^2y}{dx^2}$$

$$= 6x - 4$$

At the point $(2, 2)$, $\dfrac{d^2y}{dx^2} = 8$.   ◀

EXERCISES 2.6

1. Let $A(x)$ square centimeters be the area of a square having a side of x centimeters, measured to four significant digits. On your calculator compute the average rate of change of $A(x)$ with respect to x as x changes from **(a)** 4.000 to 4.600; **(b)** 4.000 to 4.300; **(c)** 4.000 to 4.100; **(d)** 4.000 to 4.050. **(e)** What is the instantaneous rate of change of $A(x)$ with respect to x when x is 4.000?

2. The length of a rectangle is 4 in. more than its width, and the 4-in. difference is maintained as the rectangle increases in size. Let $A(w)$ square inches be the area of the rectangle having a width of w inches, measured to four significant digits. On your calculator compute the average rate of change of $A(w)$ with respect to w as w changes from **(a)** 3.000 to 3.200; **(b)** 3.000 to 3.100; **(c)** 3.000 to 3.010; **(d)** 3.000 to 3.001. **(e)** What is the instantaneous rate of change of $A(w)$ with respect to w when w is 3.000?

3. Stefan's law states that a body emits radiant energy to a sink at absolute zero according to the formula $R = kT^4$, where R is the measure of the rate of emission of the radiant energy per square unit of area, T is the measure of the Kelvin temperature of the surface, and k is a constant. Find **(a)** the average rate of change of R with respect to T as T increases from 200 to 300; **(b)** the instantaneous rate of change of R with respect to T when T is 200.

4. Suppose a right-circular cylinder has a constant height of 10.00 in. Let V cubic inches be the volume of the right-circular cylinder and r inches be the radius of its base. Find the average rate of change of V with respect to r as r changes from **(a)** 5.00 to 5.40; **(b)** 5.00 to 5.10; **(c)** 5.00 to 5.01. **(d)** Find the instantaneous rate of change of V with respect to r when r is 5.00.

5. Let r inches be the radius of a circular metal plate of area $A(r)$ square inches and circumference $C(r)$ inches. If heat is expanding the plate, find **(a)** the instantaneous rate of change of $A(r)$ with respect to r, and **(b)** the instantaneous rate of change of $C(r)$ with respect to r. **(c)** Compare your answers in parts (a) and (b) and explain how these rates of change differ.

6. A solid consists of a right-circular cylinder and a hemisphere on each end, and the length of the cylinder is twice its radius. Let r units be the radius of the cylinder and the two hemispheres, and $V(r)$ cubic units be the volume of the solid. Find the instantaneous rate of change of $V(r)$ with respect to r.

7. Let x units be the total length of the solid of Exercise 6, and $V(x)$ cubic units be the volume of the solid in terms of x. Find the instantaneous rate of change of $V(x)$ with respect to x.

8. Boyle's law for the expansion of a gas is $PV = C$, where P weight units per square unit of area is the pressure, V cubic units is the volume of the gas, and C is a constant. **(a)** Show that V decreases at a rate proportional to the inverse square of P. **(b)** Find the instantaneous rate of change of V with respect to P when $P = 4$ and $V = 8$.

9. A person's temperature is $f(t)$ degrees Fahrenheit t days after the start of a ten-day sickness and

$$f(t) = 98.6 + 1.2t - 0.12t^2 \qquad 0 \le t \le 10$$

(a) Find the rate of change of $f(t)$ with respect to t when $0 < t < 10$. What is the person's temperature and the rate of change of the temperature when the person has been sick for **(b)** 3 days and **(c)** 8 days? **(d)** Plot the graph of f, estimate when the temperature is a maximum as well as the maximum temperature.

10. Suppose that a tumor in a person's body is spherical in shape. Find the rate of change of the volume of the tumor with respect to the radius when the radius is **(a)** 0.5 cm and **(b)** 1 cm.

11. A bacterial cell is spherical in shape. Find the rate of change of the volume of the cell with respect to the radius when the radius is **(a)** 1.5 μm (micrometers) and **(b)** 2μm.

12. For the tumor in Exercise 10, find the rate of change of the surface area with respect to the radius when the radius is **(a)** 0.5 cm and **(b)** 1 cm.

13. For the cell in Exercise 11, find the rate of change of the surface area with respect to the radius when the radius is **(a)** 1.5 μm and **(b)** 2 μm.

14. Sand is being dropped onto a conical pile in such a way that the height of the pile is always twice the base radius. Find the rate of change of the volume of the pile with respect to the radius when the height of the pile is **(a)** 4 m and **(b)** 8 m.

15. A cold front is approaching a college campus in such a way that if the temperature is $T(t)$ degrees Fahrenheit t hours after midnight, then

$$T(t) = 0.1(400 - 40t + t^2) \qquad 0 \le t \le 12$$

(a) Find the average rate of change of $T(t)$ with respect to t between 5 A.M. and 6 A.M. **(b)** Find the instantaneous rate of change of $T(t)$ with respect to t at 5 A.M.

16. It is estimated that a worker in a shop that makes picture frames can paint y frames x hours after starting work at 8 A.M., and

$$y = 3x + 8x^2 - x^3 \qquad 0 \le x \le 4$$

(a) Find the rate at which the worker is painting at 10 A.M. **(b)** Find the number of frames that the worker paints between 10 A.M. and 11 A.M.

17. If water is being drained from a swimming pool and $V(t)$ liters is the volume of water in the pool t minutes after the draining starts, where $V(t) = 250(1600 - 80t + t^2)$, find **(a)** the average rate at which the water leaves the pool during the first 5 min, and **(b)** how fast the water is flowing out of the pool 5 min after the draining starts.

18. A stone is dropped into a still pond, and concentric circular ripples spread out. Find the rate of change of the area of the disturbed region when its radius is **(a)** 4 cm and **(b)** 7 cm.

19. The number of dollars in the total cost of manufacturing x watches in a certain plant is given by $C(x) = 1500 + 3x + x^2$. Find **(a)** the marginal cost function; **(b)** the marginal cost when $x = 40$; **(c)** the actual cost of manufacturing the forty-first watch.

20. The total revenue received from the sale of x desks is $R(x)$ dollars, and $R(x) = 200x - \frac{1}{3}x^2$. Find **(a)** the marginal revenue function; **(b)** the marginal revenue when $x = 30$; **(c)** the actual revenue from the sale of the thirty-first desk.

21. If $R(x)$ dollars is the total revenue received from the sale of x television sets and $R(x) = 600x - \frac{1}{20}x^3$, find **(a)** the marginal revenue function; **(b)** the marginal revenue when $x = 20$; **(c)** the actual revenue from the sale of the twenty-first television set.

22. If $C(x)$ dollars is the total cost of manufacturing x paperweights and

$$C(x) = 200 + \frac{50}{x} + \frac{x^2}{5}$$

find **(a)** the marginal cost function; **(b)** the marginal cost when $x = 10$; **(c)** the actual cost of manufacturing the eleventh paperweight.

*In Exercises 23 through 25, we use the concept of relative rate, defined as follows: if $y = f(x)$, the **relative rate of change** of y with respect to x at x_1 is given by $\dfrac{f'(x_1)}{f(x_1)}$ or, equivalently, $\dfrac{dy/dx}{y}$ evaluated at $x = x_1$.*

23. The annual gross earnings of a particular corporation t years from January 1, 1994 is p millions of dollars and $p = \frac{2}{5}t^2 + 2t + 10$. Find **(a)** the rate at which the gross earnings were growing on January 1, 1996; **(b)** the relative rate of growth of the gross earnings January 1, 1996 to the nearest 0.1 percent; **(c)** the rate at which the gross earnings should be growing on January, 1, 2000; **(d)** the anticipated relative rate of growth of the gross earnings on January 1, 2000 to the nearest 0.1 percent.

24. A particular company started doing business on April 1, 1993. The annual gross earnings of the company after t years of operation are p dollars, where $p = 50,000 + 18,000t + 600t^2$. Find **(a)** the rate at which the gross earnings were growing on April 1, 1995, **(b)** the relative rate of growth of the gross earnings on April 1, 1995 to the nearest 0.1 percent; **(c)** the rate at which the gross earnings should be growing on April 1, 2003; **(d)** the anticipated relative rate of growth of the gross earnings on April 1, 2003 to the nearest 0.1 percent.

25. Suppose that the number of people in the population of a particular city t years after January 1, 1995 is expected to be $40t^2 + 200t + 10,000$. Find **(a)** the rate at which the population is expected to be growing on January 1, 2004, **(b)** the expected relative rate of growth of the population on January 1, 2004 to the nearest 0.1 percent; **(c)** the rate at which the population is expected to be growing on January 1, 2010; **(d)** the expected relative rate of growth of the population on January 1, 2010 to the nearest 0.1 percent.

26. Let r be the reciprocal of a number n. Find the instantaneous rate of change of r with respect to n and the relative rate of change of r per unit change in n when n is (a) 4 and (b) 10.

27. The profit of a retail store is $100y$ dollars when x dollars are spent daily on advertising and $y = 2500 + 36x - 0.2x^2$. Use the derivative to determine if it would be profitable for the daily advertising budget to be increased if it is now **(a)** \$60 and **(b)** \$300. **(c)** What is the maximum value for x below which it is profitable to increase the advertising budget?

28. The supply equation for "The Calculus Virgin" tee shirt is $x = 3p^2 + 2p$ where p dollars is the discount price per tee shirt when $1000x$ tee shirts are supplied. **(a)** Find the average rate of change of the supply per \$1 change in the discount price when that price is increased from \$10 to \$11. **(b)** Find the instantaneous (or marginal) rate of change of the supply per \$1 change in the discount price when that price is \$10.

29. Find the slope of the tangent line at each point of the graph of $y = x^4 + x^3 - 3x^2$ where the rate of change of the slope is zero.

30. Find the instantaneous rate of change of the slope of the tangent line to the graph of $y = 2x^3 - 6x^2 - x + 1$ at the point $(3, -2)$.

31. For the oil spill in Exercise 53 of Exercises 1.8 and Exercise 31 of Exercises 2.2, find the rate at which the radius of the spill is changing at **(a)** 0.4 min; **(b)** 2 min; **(c)** 3.2 min.

32. Show that for any linear function f, the average rate of change of $f(x)$ as x changes from x_1 to $x_1 + k$ is the same as the instantaneous rate of change of $f(x)$ at x_1.

33. Prove that at any instant **(a)** the ratio of the instantaneous rate of change of the area of a circle to the rate of change of the radius is equal to the circumference of the circle, and **(b)** the ratio of the instantaneous rate of change of the volume of a sphere to the rate of change of the radius is equal to the surface area of the sphere.

2.7 DERIVATIVES OF THE TRIGONOMETRIC FUNCTIONS

In Section 1.10 we showed that the trigonometric functions are continuous everywhere they are defined. In this section we show that they are also differentiable on their domains. We then use these facts to sketch in a formal manner their graphs, which in precalculus you could obtain by applying only intuitive considerations.

Before computing the derivative of the sine function, we plot the graph of NDER(sin x, x) in the $[-2\pi, 2\pi]$ by $[-4, 4]$ window as shown in Figure 1. Because this graph resembles the graph of the cosine function you became familiar with in precalculus, you may suspect that the derivative of the sine function is the cosine function. We now confirm this suspicion analytically by applying the trigonometric identity

$$\sin(a + b) = \sin a \cos b + \cos a \sin b \qquad (1)$$

as well as Theorems 1.10.2 and 1.10.5.

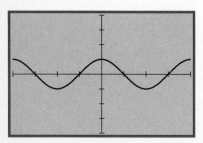

$[-2\pi, 2\pi]$ by $[-4, 4]$

NDER(sin x, x)

FIGURE 1

Let f be the sine function, so that

$$f(x) = \sin x$$

From the definition of a derivative,

$$f'(x) = \lim_{\Delta x \to 0} \frac{f(x + \Delta x) - f(x)}{\Delta x}$$

$$= \lim_{\Delta x \to 0} \frac{\sin(x + \Delta x) - \sin x}{\Delta x}$$

Formula (1) for $\sin(x + \Delta x)$ is used to obtain

$$f'(x) = \lim_{\Delta x \to 0} \frac{\sin x \cos(\Delta x) + \cos x \sin(\Delta x) - \sin x}{\Delta x}$$

$$= \lim_{\Delta x \to 0} \frac{\sin x [\cos(\Delta x) - 1]}{\Delta x} + \lim_{\Delta x \to 0} \frac{\cos x \sin(\Delta x)}{\Delta x}$$

$$= -\lim_{\Delta x \to 0} \frac{1 - \cos(\Delta x)}{\Delta x} \left(\lim_{\Delta x \to 0} \sin x \right) + \left(\lim_{\Delta x \to 0} \cos x \right) \lim_{\Delta x \to 0} \frac{\sin(\Delta x)}{\Delta x} \qquad (2)$$

From Theorems 1.10.5 and 1.10.2,

$$\lim_{\Delta x \to 0} \frac{1 - \cos(\Delta x)}{\Delta x} = 0 \quad \text{and} \quad \lim_{\Delta x \to 0} \frac{\sin(\Delta x)}{\Delta x} = 1 \qquad (3)$$

Substituting from these equations into (2) we get

$$f'(x) = -0 \cdot \sin x + \cos x \cdot 1$$

$$= \cos x$$

We have proved the following theorem.

2.7.1 Theorem   Derivative of the Sine Function

$$D_x(\sin x) = \cos x$$

▶ **EXAMPLE 1**   Find $f'(x)$ if

$$f(x) = x^2 \sin x$$

Solution   We apply the product rule.

$$f'(x) = x^2 D_x(\sin x) + D_x(x^2)\sin x$$

$$= x^2 \cos x + 2x \sin x \qquad ◀$$

We are now ready to obtain the derivative of the cosine function, but first we plot the graph of NDER(cos x, x) in the $[-2\pi, 2\pi]$ by $[-4, 4]$ window as shown in Figure 2. The graph resembles the graph of the sine function reflected through the x axis, which suggests that the derivative of the cosine function may be the negative of the sine function. To confirm this suggestion analytically we proceed as with the sine function. Here we apply the identity

$$\cos(a + b) = \cos a \cos b - \sin a \sin b \qquad (4)$$

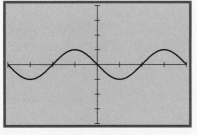

$[-2\pi, 2\pi]$ by $[-4, 4]$

NDER(cos x, x)

FIGURE 2

If g is the cosine function, then

$$g(x) = \cos x$$

$$g'(x) = \lim_{\Delta x \to 0} \frac{g(x + \Delta x) - g(x)}{\Delta x}$$

$$= \lim_{\Delta x \to 0} \frac{\cos(x + \Delta x) - \cos x}{\Delta x}$$

Formula (4) for $\cos(x + \Delta x)$ is used to obtain

$$g'(x) = \lim_{\Delta x \to 0} \frac{\cos x \cos(\Delta x) - \sin x \sin(\Delta x) - \cos x}{\Delta x}$$

$$= \lim_{\Delta x \to 0} \frac{\cos x[\cos(\Delta x) - 1]}{\Delta x} - \lim_{\Delta x \to 0} \frac{\sin x \sin(\Delta x)}{\Delta x}$$

$$= -\lim_{\Delta x \to 0} \frac{1 - \cos(\Delta x)}{\Delta x} \left(\lim_{\Delta x \to 0} \cos x \right) - \left(\lim_{\Delta x \to 0} \sin x \right) \lim_{\Delta x \to 0} \frac{\sin(\Delta x)}{\Delta x} \qquad \textbf{(5)}$$

We substitute from Equations (3) into (5) and obtain

$$g'(x) = -0 \cdot \cos x - \sin x \cdot 1$$

$$= -\sin x$$

We have proved the following theorem.

2.7.2 Theorem   Derivative of the Cosine Function

$$D_x (\cos x) = -\sin x$$

Note the minus sign in front of $\sin x$ for the derivative of $\cos x$; that is, the derivative of $\cos x$ is the negative of $\sin x$ while the derivative of $\sin x$ is $\cos x$.

▶ **EXAMPLE 2**   Find $\dfrac{dy}{dx}$ if

$$y = \frac{\sin x}{1 - 2 \cos x}$$

Solution   We apply the quotient rule.

$$\frac{dy}{dx} = \frac{(1 - 2 \cos x)D_x(\sin x) - \sin x \cdot D_x(1 - 2 \cos x)}{(1 - 2 \cos x)^2}$$

$$= \frac{(1 - 2 \cos x)(\cos x) - \sin x(2 \sin x)}{(1 - 2 \cos x)^2}$$

$$= \frac{\cos x - 2(\cos^2 x + \sin^2 x)}{(1 - 2 \cos x)^2}$$

$$= \frac{\cos x - 2}{(1 - 2 \cos x)^2} \qquad \blacktriangleleft$$

▶ **EXAMPLE 3**   Compute

$$\frac{d^3}{dx^3}(2 \sin x + 3 \cos x - x^3)$$

Solution

$$\frac{d}{dx}(2 \sin x + 3 \cos x - x^3) = 2 \cos x - 3 \sin x - 3x^2$$

$$\frac{d^2}{dx^2}(2 \sin x + 3 \cos x - x^3) = -2 \sin x - 3 \cos x - 6x$$

$$\frac{d^3}{dx^3}(2 \sin x + 3 \cos x - x^3) = -2 \cos x + 3 \sin x - 6 \qquad ◀$$

The derivatives of the tangent, cotangent, secant, and cosecant functions are obtained from trigonometric identities involving the sine and cosine as well as the derivatives of the sine and cosine and theorems on differentiation. For the derivative of the tangent we apply the identities

$$\tan x = \frac{\sin x}{\cos x} \qquad \sec x = \frac{1}{\cos x} \qquad \sin^2 x + \cos^2 x = 1$$

2.7.3 Theorem   Derivative of the Tangent Function

$$D_x(\tan x) = \sec^2 x$$

Proof

$$D_x(\tan x) = D_x\left(\frac{\sin x}{\cos x}\right)$$

$$= \frac{\cos x \cdot D_x(\sin x) - \sin x \cdot D_x(\cos x)}{\cos^2 x}$$

$$= \frac{(\cos x)(\cos x) - (\sin x)(-\sin x)}{\cos^2 x}$$

$$= \frac{\cos^2 x + \sin^2 x}{\cos^2 x}$$

$$= \frac{1}{\cos^2 x}$$

$$= \sec^2 x \qquad ◀$$

2.7.4 Theorem   Derivative of the Cotangent Function

$$D_x(\cot x) = -\csc^2 x$$

The proof of this theorem, analogous to that of Theorem 2.7.3, is left as an exercise (see Exercise 1). You will use the following identities:

$$\cot x = \frac{\cos x}{\sin x} \qquad \csc x = \frac{1}{\sin x}$$

2.7.5 Theorem   Derivative of the Secant Function

$$D_x(\sec x) = \sec x \tan x$$

Proof

$$D_x(\sec x) = D_x\left(\frac{1}{\cos x}\right)$$

$$= \frac{\cos x \cdot D_x(1) - 1 \cdot D_x(\cos x)}{\cos^2 x}$$

$$= \frac{\cos x \cdot 0 - 1 \cdot (-\sin x)}{\cos^2 x}$$

$$= \frac{\sin x}{\cos^2 x}$$

$$= \frac{1}{\cos x} \cdot \frac{\sin x}{\cos x}$$

$$= \sec x \tan x \qquad \blacktriangleleft$$

▶ **EXAMPLE 4**   Compute

$$\frac{d}{dx}(\tan x \sec x)$$

Solution

$$\frac{d}{dx}(\tan x \sec x) = \tan x \cdot \frac{d}{dx}(\sec x) + \frac{d}{dx}(\tan x) \cdot \sec x$$

$$= \tan x(\sec x \tan x) + \sec^2 x(\sec x)$$

$$= \sec x \tan^2 x + \sec^3 x \qquad \blacktriangleleft$$

2.7.6 Theorem   Derivative of the Cosecant Function

$$D_x(\csc x) = -\csc x \cot x$$

The proof of this theorem is also left as an exercise (see Exercise 2).

As promised at the beginning of this section, we now show how the graphs of the trigonometric functions can be sketched by applying the continuity and differentiability of these functions. We first discuss the graphs of the sine and cosine, for each of which the domain is the set of all real numbers and the range is $[-1, 1]$. Let

$$f(x) = \sin x \qquad f'(x) = \cos x$$

To determine where the graph has a horizontal tangent, set $f'(x) = 0$ and get $x = \frac{1}{2}\pi + k\pi$, where k is any integer. At these values of x, $\sin x$ is either $+1$ or -1, and these are the largest and smallest values that $\sin x$ assumes. The graph intersects the x axis at the points where $\sin x = 0$, that is, at the points where $x = k\pi$ and k is any integer. Furthermore, when k is an even integer, $f'(k\pi) = 1$, and when k is an odd integer, $f'(k\pi) = -1$. Thus at the

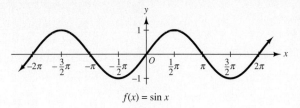

$$f(x) = \sin x$$

FIGURE 3

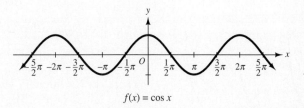

$$f(x) = \cos x$$

FIGURE 4

points of intersection of the graph with the x axis the slope of the tangent line is either 1 or -1. From this information we sketch the graph of the sine function shown in Figure 3.

For the graph of the cosine function we use the identity

$$\cos x = \sin(x + \tfrac{1}{2}\pi)$$

Thus the graph of the cosine is obtained from the graph of the sine by translating the y axis $\tfrac{1}{2}\pi$ units to the right. See Figure 4.

▶ **EXAMPLE 5**   Find an equation of the tangent line to the graph of the cosine function at the point $(\tfrac{3}{2}\pi, 0)$.

Solution   If $f(x) = \cos x$, $f'(x) = -\sin x$. Thus $f'(\tfrac{3}{2}\pi) = -\sin \tfrac{3}{2}\pi$. Because $\sin \tfrac{3}{2}\pi = -1, f'(\tfrac{3}{2}\pi) = 1$. From the point-slope form of an equation of the tangent line having slope 1 and containing the point $(\tfrac{3}{2}\pi, 0)$, we have

$$y - 0 = 1(x - \tfrac{3}{2}\pi)$$
$$y = x - \tfrac{3}{2}\pi$$

◀

We now consider the graph of the tangent function. Because

$$\tan(-x) = -\tan x$$

the graph is symmetric with respect to the origin. Furthermore,

$$\tan(x + \pi) = \tan x$$

and the tangent function is periodic with period π. The tangent function is continuous at all numbers in its domain, which is the set of all real numbers except those of the form $\tfrac{1}{2}\pi + k\pi$, where k is any integer. The range is the set of all real numbers. If k is any integer, $\tan k\pi = 0$. Therefore the graph intersects the x axis at the points $(k\pi, 0)$. Let

$$f(x) = \tan x \qquad f'(x) = \sec^2 x$$

Table 1

x	$\tan x$
0	0
$\frac{1}{6}\pi$	$\dfrac{1}{\sqrt{3}} \approx 0.58$
$\frac{1}{4}\pi$	1
$\frac{1}{3}\pi$	$\sqrt{3} \approx 1.73$

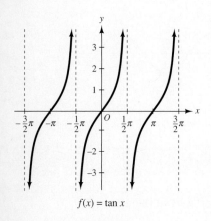

$f(x) = \tan x$

FIGURE 5

Because $f'(k\pi) = \sec^2 k\pi$ and $\sec^2 k\pi = 1$ for k any integer, it follows that where the graph intersects the x axis, the slope of the tangent is 1. Setting $f'(x) = 0$ gives $\sec^2 x = 0$. Because $\sec^2 x \geq 1$ for all x, we conclude that there are no horizontal tangent lines.

Consider the interval $[0, \frac{1}{2}\pi)$ on which the tangent function is defined everywhere.

$$\lim_{x \to \pi/2^-} \tan x = \lim_{x \to \pi/2^-} \frac{\sin x}{\cos x}$$

Because $\lim\limits_{x \to \pi/2^-} \sin x = 1$ and $\lim\limits_{x \to \pi/2^-} \cos x = 0$, where $\cos x$ is approaching zero through positive values,

$$\lim_{x \to \pi/2^-} \tan x = +\infty$$

Therefore the line $x = \frac{1}{2}\pi$ is a vertical asymptote of the graph. Table 1 gives some values of x in the interval $[0, \frac{1}{2}\pi)$ and the corresponding values of $\tan x$. By locating the points having as coordinates the number pairs $(x, \tan x)$ we get the portion of the graph for x in $[0, \frac{1}{2}\pi)$. Because of symmetry with respect to the origin, the portion of the graph for x in $(-\frac{1}{2}\pi, 0]$ is obtained. Since the period is π, we complete the graph shown in Figure 5.

We can get the graph of the cotangent function from that of the tangent function by using the identity

$$\cot x = -\tan(x + \tfrac{1}{2}\pi)$$

From this identity it follows that the graph of the cotangent is obtained from the graph of the tangent by translating the y axis $\frac{1}{2}\pi$ units to the right and then taking a reflection of the graph with respect to the x axis. The graph of the cotangent function appears in Figure 6.

Because

$$\sec(x + 2\pi) = \sec x$$

the secant function is periodic with period 2π. The domain of the secant function is the set of all real numbers except those of the form $\frac{1}{2}\pi + k\pi$,

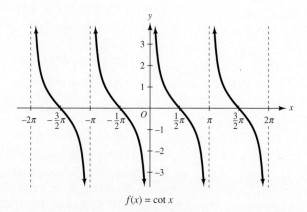

$f(x) = \cot x$

FIGURE 6

where k is any integer. The range is $(-\infty, -1] \cup [1, +\infty)$. The function is continuous at all numbers in its domain. The graph does not intersect the x axis because sec x is never zero.

We use the derivative to determine if the graph has any horizontal tangent lines. Let

$$f(x) = \sec x \qquad f'(x) = \sec x \tan x$$

Setting $f'(x) = 0$ gives sec $x \tan x = 0$. Because sec $x \neq 0, f'(x) = 0$ when $\tan x = 0$, which is when $x = k\pi$, where k is any integer.

We first consider the graph for x in $(-\frac{1}{2}\pi, \frac{1}{2}\pi) \cup (\frac{1}{2}\pi, \frac{3}{2}\pi)$. There are horizontal tangent lines at $x = 0$ and $x = \pi$.

$$\lim_{x \to -\pi/2^+} \sec x = \lim_{x \to -\pi/2^+} \frac{1}{\cos x} \qquad \lim_{x \to \pi/2^-} \sec x = \lim_{x \to \pi/2^-} \frac{1}{\cos x}$$
$$= +\infty \qquad\qquad\qquad\qquad = +\infty$$

$$\lim_{x \to \pi/2^+} \sec x = \lim_{x \to \pi/2^+} \frac{1}{\cos x} \qquad \lim_{x \to 3\pi/2^-} \sec x = \lim_{x \to 3\pi/2^-} \frac{1}{\cos x}$$
$$= -\infty \qquad\qquad\qquad\qquad = -\infty$$

Therefore the lines $x = -\frac{1}{2}\pi, x = \frac{1}{2}\pi$, and $x = \frac{3}{2}\pi$ are vertical asymptotes of the graph.

With the above information and by locating a few points we sketch the graph of the secant function for x in $(-\frac{1}{2}\pi, \frac{1}{2}\pi) \cup (\frac{1}{2}\pi, \frac{3}{2}\pi)$. Because the period is 2π, we obtain the graph shown in Figure 7.

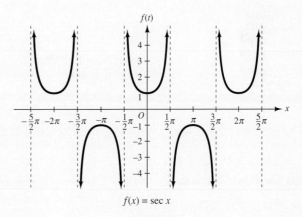

$$f(x) = \sec x$$

FIGURE 7

From the identity

$$\csc x = \sec(x - \tfrac{1}{2}\pi)$$

we get the graph of the cosecant function from that of the secant function by translating the y axis $\frac{1}{2}\pi$ units to the left. The graph of the cosecant function is sketched in Figure 8.

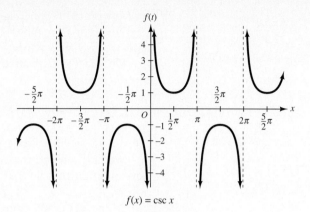

$$f(x) = \csc x$$

FIGURE 8

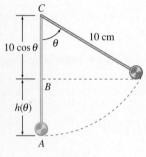

FIGURE 9

▶ **EXAMPLE 6**   A pendulum of length 10 cm has swung so that θ is the radian measure of the angle formed by the pendulum and a vertical line. If $h(\theta)$ centimeters is the vertical height of the end of the pendulum above its lowest position, find the instantaneous rate of change of $h(\theta)$ with respect to θ when $\theta = \frac{1}{6}\pi$.

Solution   Refer to Figure 9. Because $h(\theta) = |\overline{AC}| - |\overline{BC}|$, we have

$$h(\theta) = 10 - 10 \cos \theta$$
$$h'(\theta) = -10(-\sin \theta)$$
$$= 10 \sin \theta$$

Thus $h'(\frac{1}{6}\pi) = 10 \sin \frac{1}{6}\pi$; that is, $h'(\frac{1}{6}\pi) = 5$.

<u>**Conclusion:**</u>   When $\theta = \frac{1}{6}\pi$, the instantaneous rate of change of $h(\theta)$ with respect to θ is 5 cm/rad.   ◀

EXERCISES 2.7

1. Prove: $D_x(\cot x) = -\csc^2 x$.

2. Prove: $D_x(\csc x) = -\csc x \cot x$.

In Exercises 3 through 18, find the derivative of the function.

3. $f(x) = 3 \sin x$ **4.** $g(x) = \sin x + \cos x$

5. $g(x) = \tan x + \cot x$

6. $f(x) = 4 \sec x - 2 \csc x$

7. $f(t) = 2t \cos t$ **8.** $f(x) = 4x^2 \cos x$

9. $g(x) = x \sin x + \cos x$

10. $g(y) = 3 \sin y - y \cos y$ **11.** $h(x) = 4 \sin x \cos x$

12. $f(x) = x^2 \sin x + 2x \cos x$

13. $f(x) = x^2 \cos x - 2x \sin x - 2 \cos x$

14. $h(y) = y^3 - y^2 \cos y + 2y \sin y + 2 \cos y$

15. $f(x) = 3 \sec x \tan x$ **16.** $f(t) = \sin t \tan t$

17. $f(y) = \cos y \cot y$ **18.** $h(x) = \cot x \csc x$

In Exercises 19 through 30, find the derivative.

19. $D_z\left(\dfrac{2 \cos z}{z + 1}\right)$ **20.** $D_t\left(\dfrac{\sin t}{t}\right)$

21. $\dfrac{d}{dx}\left(\dfrac{\sin x}{1 - \cos x}\right)$ **22.** $\dfrac{d}{dx}\left(\dfrac{x + 4}{\cos x}\right)$

23. $\dfrac{d}{dt}\left(\dfrac{\tan t}{\cos t - 4}\right)$ **24.** $\dfrac{d}{dy}\left(\dfrac{\cot y}{1 - \sin y}\right)$

25. $\dfrac{d}{dy}\left(\dfrac{1 + \sin y}{1 - \sin y}\right)$ **26.** $\dfrac{d}{dx}\left(\dfrac{\sin x - 1}{\cos x + 1}\right)$

27. $D_x[(x - \sin x)(x + \cos x)]$

28. $D_z[(z^2 + \cos z)(2z - \sin z)]$

29. $D_t\left(\dfrac{2 \csc t - 1}{\csc t + 2}\right)$ **30.** $D_y\left(\dfrac{\tan y + 1}{\tan y - 1}\right)$

In Exercises 31 through 42, compute NDER($f(x)$, a) on your calculator. Then confirm your answer analytically by computing the exact value of $f'(a)$.

31. $f(x) = x \cos x; \; a = 0$

32. $f(x) = x \sin x; \; a = \frac{3}{2}\pi$

33. $f(x) = \dfrac{\cos x}{x}; \; a = \frac{1}{2}\pi$

34. $f(x) = \dfrac{\sec x}{x^2}; \; a = \pi$

35. $f(x) = x^2 \tan x; \; a = \pi$

36. $f(x) = x^2 \cos x - \sin x; \; a = 0$

37. $f(x) = \sin x(\cos x - 1); \; a = \pi$

38. $f(x) = (\cos x + 1)(x \sin x - 1); \; a = \frac{1}{2}\pi$

39. $f(x) = x \cos x + x \sin x; \; a = \frac{1}{4}\pi$

40. $f(x) = \tan x + \sec x: \; a = \frac{1}{6}\pi$

41. $f(x) = 2 \cot x - \csc x; \; a = \frac{2}{3}\pi$

42. $f(x) = \dfrac{1}{\cot x - 1}; \; a = \frac{3}{4}\pi$

43. (a) Use your calculator to tabulate to four decimal places values of $\dfrac{\sin(\frac{1}{3}\pi + h) - \sin\frac{1}{3}\pi}{h}$ when h is 1, 0.5, 0.1, 0.01, 0.001 and h is $-1, -0.5, -0.1, -0.01, -0.001$. What does the quotient appear to be approaching as h approaches 0? **(b)** Find $\lim\limits_{h \to 0} \dfrac{\sin(\frac{1}{3}\pi + h) - \sin\frac{1}{3}\pi}{h}$ by interpreting it as a derivative.

44. (a) Use your calculator to tabulate to four decimal places values of $\dfrac{\cos(\frac{5}{6}\pi + h) - \cos\frac{5}{6}\pi}{h}$ when h is 1, 0.5, 0.1, 0.01, 0.001 and h is $-1, -0.5, -0.1, -0.01, -0.001$. What does the quotient appear to be approaching as h approaches 0? **(b)** Find $\lim\limits_{h \to 0} \dfrac{\cos(\frac{5}{6}\pi + h) - \cos\frac{5}{6}\pi}{h}$ by interpreting it as a derivative.

45. (a) Use your calculator to tabulate to four decimal places values of $\dfrac{\tan(\frac{1}{4}\pi + h) - \tan\frac{1}{4}\pi}{h}$ when h is 0.1, 0.01, 0.001, 0.0001, 0.00001 and h is $-0.1, -0.01, -0.001, -0.0001, -0.00001$. What does the quotient appear to be approaching as h approaches 0? **(b)** Find $\lim\limits_{h \to 0} \dfrac{\tan(\frac{1}{4}\pi + h) - \tan\frac{1}{4}\pi}{h}$ by interpreting it as a derivative.

46. (a) Use your calculator to tabulate to four decimal places values of $\dfrac{\sec(\frac{1}{6}\pi + h) - \sec\frac{1}{6}\pi}{h}$ when h is 0.1, 0.01, 0.001, 0.0001, 0.00001 and h is $-0.1, -0.01, -0.001, -0.001, -0.0001, -0.00001$. What does the quotient appear to be approaching as h approaches 0? **(b)** Find $\lim\limits_{h \to 0} \dfrac{\sec(\frac{1}{6}\pi + h) - \sec\frac{1}{6}\pi}{h}$ by interpreting it as a derivative.

47. (a) Use your calculator to tabulate to four decimal places values of $\dfrac{\cos x - \cos\frac{1}{6}\pi}{x - \frac{1}{6}\pi}$ when x is $\frac{3}{20}\pi, \frac{19}{120}\pi, \frac{33}{200}\pi, \frac{199}{1200}\pi, \frac{333}{2000}\pi$ and x is $\frac{11}{60}\pi, \frac{7}{40}\pi, \frac{101}{600}\pi, \frac{67}{400}\pi, \frac{1001}{6000}\pi$. What does the quotient appear to be approaching as x approaches $\frac{1}{6}\pi$? **(b)** Find $\lim\limits_{x \to \pi/6} \dfrac{\cos x - \cos\frac{1}{6}\pi}{x - \frac{1}{6}\pi}$ by interpreting it as a derivative.

48. (a) Use your calculator to tabulate to four decimal places values of $\dfrac{\sin x - \sin\frac{1}{3}\pi}{x - \frac{1}{3}\pi}$ when x is $\frac{3}{10}\pi, \frac{19}{60}\pi, \frac{33}{100}\pi, \frac{199}{600}\pi, \frac{333}{1000}\pi$ and x is $\frac{11}{30}\pi, \frac{7}{20}\pi, \frac{101}{300}\pi, \frac{67}{200}\pi, \frac{1001}{3000}\pi$. What does the quotient appear to be approaching as x approaches $\frac{1}{3}\pi$? **(b)** Find $\lim\limits_{x \to \pi/3} \dfrac{\sin x - \sin\frac{1}{3}\pi}{x - \frac{1}{3}\pi}$ by interpreting it as a derivative.

49. (a) Use your calculator to tabulate to four decimal places values of $\dfrac{\csc x - \csc\frac{2}{3}\pi}{x - \frac{2}{3}\pi}$ when x is $\frac{3}{5}\pi, \frac{19}{30}\pi, \frac{33}{50}\pi, \frac{199}{300}\pi, \frac{333}{500}\pi$ and x is $\frac{11}{15}\pi, \frac{7}{10}\pi, \frac{101}{150}\pi, \frac{67}{100}\pi, \frac{1001}{1500}\pi$. What does the quotient appear to be approaching as x approaches $\frac{2}{3}\pi$? **(b)** Find $\lim\limits_{x \to 2\pi/3} \dfrac{\csc x - \csc\frac{2}{3}\pi}{x - \frac{2}{3}\pi}$ by interpreting it as a derivative.

50. (a) Use your calculator to tabulate to four decimal places values of $\dfrac{\cot x - \cot\frac{3}{4}\pi}{x - \frac{3}{4}\pi}$ when x is $\frac{29}{40}\pi, \frac{59}{80}\pi, \frac{299}{400}\pi, \frac{599}{800}\pi, \frac{2999}{4000}\pi$ and x is $\frac{31}{40}\pi, \frac{61}{80}\pi, \frac{301}{400}\pi, \frac{601}{800}\pi, \frac{3001}{4000}\pi$. What does the quotient appear to be approaching as x approaches $\frac{3}{4}\pi$? **(b)** Find $\lim\limits_{x \to 3\pi/4} \dfrac{\cot x - \cot\frac{3}{4}\pi}{x - \frac{3}{4}\pi}$ by interpreting it as a derivative.

51. Find an equation of the tangent line to the graph of the sine function at the point where **(a)** $x = 0$; **(b)** $x = \frac{1}{3}\pi$; **(c)** $x = \pi$.

52. Find an equation of the tangent line to the graph of the cosine function at the point where **(a)** $x = \frac{1}{2}\pi$; **(b)** $x = -\frac{1}{2}\pi$; **(c)** $x = \frac{1}{6}\pi$.

53. Find an equation of the tangent line to the graph of the tangent function at the point where **(a)** $x = 0$; **(b)** $x = \frac{1}{4}\pi$; **(c)** $x = -\frac{1}{4}\pi$.

54. Find an equation of the tangent line to the graph of the secant function at the point where **(a)** $x = \frac{1}{4}\pi$; **(b)** $x = -\frac{1}{4}\pi$; **(c)** $x = \frac{3}{4}\pi$.

In Exercises 55 through 58, a particle is moving along a line according to the equation, where s centimeters is the directed distance of the particle from the origin at t seconds. (a) What are the instantaneous velocity and instantaneous acceleration of the particle at t_1 seconds? (b) Find the instantaneous velocity and instantaneous acceleration of the particle at t_1 seconds for each value of t_1.

55. $s = 4 \sin t$; t_1 is $0, \frac{1}{3}\pi, \frac{1}{2}\pi, \frac{2}{3}\pi$, and π

56. $s = 6 \cos t$; t_1 is $0, \frac{1}{6}\pi, \frac{1}{2}\pi, \frac{5}{6}\pi$, and π

57. $s = -3 \cos t$; t_1 is $0, \frac{1}{6}\pi, \frac{1}{3}\pi, \frac{1}{2}\pi, \frac{2}{3}\pi, \frac{5}{6}\pi$, and π

58. $s = -\frac{1}{2} \sin t$; t_1 is $0, \frac{1}{6}\pi, \frac{1}{3}\pi, \frac{1}{2}\pi, \frac{2}{3}\pi, \frac{5}{6}\pi$, and π

59. If a body of weight W pounds is dragged along a horizontal floor at constant velocity by means of a force of magnitude F pounds and directed at an angle of θ radians with the plane of the floor, then F is given by the equation

$$F = \frac{kW}{k \sin \theta + \cos \theta}$$

where k is a constant called the coefficient of friction. If $k = 0.5$, find the instantaneous rate of change of F with respect to θ when **(a)** $\theta = \frac{1}{4}\pi$; **(b)** $\theta = \frac{1}{2}\pi$.

60. A projectile is shot from a gun at an angle of elevation having radian measure $\frac{1}{2}\alpha$ and an initial velocity of v_0 feet per second. If R feet is the range of the projectile, then

$$R = \frac{v_0^2}{g} \sin \alpha \qquad 0 \le \alpha \le \pi$$

where g ft/sec^2 is the acceleration due to gravity. **(a)** If $v_0 = 480$, find the rate of change of R with respect to α when $\alpha = \frac{1}{2}\pi$ (i.e., the angle of elevation has radian measure $\frac{1}{4}\pi$). Take $g = 32$. **(b)** Find the values of α for which $D_\alpha R > 0$.

61. If k is any positive integer, prove by mathematical induction that

$$D_x{}^n(\sin x) = \begin{cases} \sin x & \text{if } n = 4k \\ \cos x & \text{if } n = 4k + 1 \\ -\sin x & \text{if } n = 4k + 2 \\ -\cos x & \text{if } n = 4k + 3 \end{cases}$$

62. Obtain a formula similar to that in Exercise 61 for $D_x{}^n(\cos x)$.

2.8 THE DERIVATIVE OF A COMPOSITE FUNCTION AND THE CHAIN RULE

To find the derivative of a composite function, we apply the *chain rule*, one of the important computational theorems in calculus. Before stating this theorem, we give three illustrations showing how previous theorems can be used to determine the derivatives of some particular composite functions. In each illustration, we write the final expression for the derivative in a form that may seem unusual to you but that can be easily associated with the chain rule.

▷ **ILLUSTRATION 1** If

$$F(x) = (4x^3 + 1)^2$$

we can obtain $F'(x)$ by applying the product rule as follows:

$$F(x) = (4x^3 + 1)(4x^3 + 1)$$
$$F'(x) = (4x^3 + 1) D_x(4x^3 + 1) + (4x^3 + 1) D_x(4x^3 + 1)$$
$$= (4x^3 + 1)(12x^2) + (4x^3 + 1)(12x^2)$$

Thus

$$F'(x) = 2(4x^3 + 1)(12x^2) \tag{1}$$

Observe that F is the composite function f $\circ$ g, where $f(x) = x^2$ and $g(x) = 4x^3 + 1$; that is,

$$F(x) = f(g(x))$$
$$= f(4x^3 + 1)$$
$$= (4x^3 + 1)^2$$

Because $f'(x) = 2x$ and $g'(x) = 12x^2$, we have from (1)

$$F'(x) = f'(g(x))\, g'(x) \tag{2}$$

◀

▷ **ILLUSTRATION 2**   If

$$G(x) = \sin 2x$$

to find $G'(x)$ we can use the product rule with the trigonometric identities

$$\sin 2x = 2 \sin x \cos x \quad \text{and} \quad \cos 2x = \cos^2 x - \sin^2 x$$

We have

$$G(x) = 2 \sin x \cos x$$
$$G'(x) = (2 \sin x)D_x(\cos x) + (2 \cos x)D_x(\sin x)$$
$$= (2 \sin x)(-\sin x) + (2 \cos x)(\cos x)$$
$$= 2(\cos^2 x - \sin^2 x)$$

Therefore

$$G'(x) = (\cos 2x)(2) \tag{3}$$

If we let $f(x) = \sin x$ and $g(x) = 2x$, then G is the composite function $f \circ g$; that is,

$$G(x) = f(g(x))$$
$$= f(2x)$$
$$= \sin 2x$$

Because $f'(x) = \cos x$ and $g'(x) = 2$, we can write (3) in the form

$$G'(x) = f'(g(x))g'(x) \tag{4}$$

◀

▷ **ILLUSTRATION 3**   If

$$H(x) = (\cos x)^{-1}$$

we can compute $H'(x)$ by first using the identity $(\cos x)^{-1} = \sec x$.

$$H(x) = \sec x$$
$$H'(x) = \sec x \tan x$$
$$= \frac{1}{\cos x} \cdot \frac{\sin x}{\cos x}$$
$$= (-1)\frac{1}{\cos^2 x}(-\sin x)$$

Hence

$$H'(x) = [-1(\cos x)^{-2}](-\sin x) \tag{5}$$

With $f(x) = x^{-1}$ and $g(x) = \cos x$, H is the composite function $f \circ g$; that is,

$$\begin{aligned} H(x) &= f(g(x)) \\ &= f(\cos x) \\ &= (\cos x)^{-1} \end{aligned}$$

Since $f'(x) = -1 \cdot x^{-2}$ and $g'(x) = -\sin x$, we can write (5) in the form

$$H'(x) = f'(g(x))g'(x) \tag{6}$$

◀

Observe that the right-hand sides of (2), (4), and (6) are all $f'(g(x))g'(x)$, which is the right-hand side of the chain rule, stated in the following theorem.

> **2.8.1 Theorem   The Chain Rule**
>
> If the function g is differentiable at x and the function f is differentiable at $g(x)$, then the composite function $f \circ g$ is differentiable at x, and
>
> $$(f \circ g)'(x) = f'(g(x))g'(x) \tag{7}$$

The proof of the chain rule for all differentiable functions is sophisticated and appears in the supplement of this section. A simplified proof pertaining to functions satisfying an additional hypothesis is outlined in Exercise 57.

We now give some illustrations and examples that will help you become familiar with the statement of the chain rule.

▷ **ILLUSTRATION 4**   Let

$$f(x) = x^{10} \quad \text{and} \quad g(x) = 2x^3 - 5x^2 + 4$$

Then the composite function $f \circ g$ is defined by

$$\begin{aligned} (f \circ g)(x) &= f(g(x)) \\ &= (2x^3 - 5x^2 + 4)^{10} \end{aligned}$$

To apply (7) we need to compute $f'(g(x))$ and $g'(x)$. Because $f(x) = x^{10}$, $f'(x) = 10x^9$, thus

$$\begin{aligned} f'(g(x)) &= 10[g(x)]^9 \\ f'(g(x)) &= 10(2x^3 - 5x^2 + 4)^9 \end{aligned} \tag{8}$$

Furthermore, because $g(x) = 2x^3 - 5x^2 + 4$,

$$g'(x) = 6x^2 - 10x \tag{9}$$

Therefore, from (7), (8), and (9) we have

$$(f \circ g)'(x) = f'(g(x))g'(x)$$
$$= 10(2x^3 - 5x^2 + 4)^9(6x^2 - 10x) \qquad \blacktriangleleft$$

▷ **ILLUSTRATION 5**   Let

$$f(x) = \sin x \quad \text{and} \quad g(x) = x^2 + 3$$

Then the composite function $f \circ g$ is defined by

$$(f \circ g)(x) = f(g(x))$$
$$= \sin(x^2 + 3)$$

We compute $f'(g(x))$ and $g'(x)$. Because $f(x) = \sin x, f'(x) = \cos x$. Hence

$$f'(g(x)) = \cos[g(x)]$$
$$f'(g(x)) = \cos(x^2 + 3) \qquad \textbf{(10)}$$

Because $g(x) = x^2 + 3$,

$$g'(x) = 2x \qquad \textbf{(11)}$$

Thus from (7), (10), and (11) we obtain

$$(f \circ g)'(x) = f'(g(x))g'(x)$$
$$= [\cos(x^2 + 3)](2x)$$
$$= 2x \cos(x^2 + 3) \qquad \blacktriangleleft$$

▷ **ILLUSTRATION 6**   Suppose

$$h(x) = \left(\frac{2}{x-1}\right)^5$$

To determine $h'(x)$, let

$$f(x) = x^5 \qquad \text{and} \qquad g(x) = \frac{2}{x-1}$$

Then

$$f'(x) = 5x^4 \qquad\qquad g'(x) = \frac{-2}{(x-1)^2}$$

Because $h(x) = f(g(x))$, we have from the chain rule

$$h'(x) = f'(g(x)) \cdot g'(x)$$
$$= 5\left(\frac{2}{x-1}\right)^4 \cdot \frac{-2}{(x-1)^2}$$
$$= \frac{-160}{(x-1)^6} \qquad \blacktriangleleft$$

When computing derivatives by the chain rule we don't actually write the functions f and g as we did in Illustrations 4, 5, and 6, but we bear them in mind. For instance, in Illustration 6, because $h(x)$ is the fifth power of a quotient, when we apply the chain rule we use the power rule first and then the quotient rule. We could write the computation as follows:

$$h(x) = \left(\frac{2}{x-1}\right)^5$$

$$h'(x) = 5\left(\frac{2}{x-1}\right)^4 \cdot D_x\left(\frac{2}{x-1}\right)$$

$$= 5\left(\frac{2}{x-1}\right)^4 \cdot \frac{-2}{(x-1)^2}$$

$$= \frac{-160}{(x-1)^6}$$

▶ **EXAMPLE 1**   Find $f'(x)$ by the chain rule if

$$f(x) = \frac{1}{4x^3 + 5x^2 - 7x + 8}$$

Solution   We write $f(x) = (4x^3 + 5x^2 - 7x + 8)^{-1}$ and apply the chain rule to obtain

$$f'(x) = -1(4x^3 + 5x^2 - 7x + 8)^{-2} \cdot D_x(4x^3 + 5x^2 - 7x + 8)$$

$$= -1(4x^3 + 5x^2 - 7x + 8)^{-2}(12x^2 + 10x - 7)$$

$$= \frac{-12x^2 - 10x + 7}{(4x^3 + 5x^2 - 7x + 8)^2} \qquad ◀$$

▶ **EXAMPLE 2**   Compute

$$\frac{d}{dx}\left[\left(\frac{2x+1}{3x-1}\right)^4\right]$$

Solution   From the chain rule,

$$\frac{d}{dx}\left[\left(\frac{2x+1}{3x-1}\right)^4\right] = 4\left(\frac{2x+1}{3x-1}\right)^3 \cdot \frac{d}{dx}\left(\frac{2x+1}{3x-1}\right)$$

$$= 4\left(\frac{2x+1}{3x-1}\right)^3 \frac{(3x-1)(2) - (2x+1)(3)}{(3x-1)^2}$$

$$= \frac{4(2x+1)^3(-5)}{(3x-1)^5}$$

$$= -\frac{20(2x+1)^3}{(3x-1)^5} \qquad ◀$$

If the Leibniz notation is used for the derivative, the chain rule can be stated as follows:

If y is a function of u, defined by $y = f(u)$ and $\frac{dy}{du}$ exists, and if u is a function of x, defined by $u = g(x)$ and $\frac{du}{dx}$ exists, then y is a function of x and $\frac{dy}{dx}$ exists and is given by

$$\frac{dy}{dx} = \frac{dy}{du} \cdot \frac{du}{dx} \qquad \qquad \textbf{(12)}$$

Observe from this equation the convenient form for remembering the chain rule. The formal statement suggests a symbolic "division" of du in the numerator and denominator of the right-hand side. However, remember from Section 2.1 when we introduced the Leibniz notation $\dfrac{dy}{dx}$, we emphasized that neither dy nor dx has been given independent meaning. You should, therefore, consider (12) as an equation involving formal differentiation notation.

To write the chain rule another way, let $u = g(x)$. Then

$$(f \circ g)(x) = f(u) \qquad (f \circ g)'(x) = D_x f(u) \qquad f'(g(x)) = f'(u) \qquad g'(x) = D_x u$$

With these substitutions (7) becomes

$$D_x[f(u)] = f'(u) D_x u$$

We shall use this form of the chain rule to state important differentiation formulas. In particular, we have from Theorems 2.7.1–2.7.6 the following formulas involving the derivatives of the trigonometric functions. If u is a differentiable function of x

$$
\begin{array}{ll}
D_x(\sin u) = \cos u\, D_x u & D_x(\cos u) = -\sin u\, D_x u \\
D_x(\tan u) = \sec^2 u\, D_x u & D_x(\cot u) = -\csc^2 u\, D_x u \\
D_x(\sec u) = \sec u \tan u\, D_x u & D_x(\csc u) = -\csc u \cot u\, D_x u
\end{array}
$$

▶ **EXAMPLE 3**   Find $F'(t)$ if

$$F(t) = \tan(3t^2 + 2t)$$

Solution   We use the chain rule and obtain

$$
\begin{aligned}
F'(t) &= \sec^2(3t^2 + 2t) \cdot D_t(3t^2 + 2t) \\
&= \sec^2(3t^2 + 2t) \cdot (6t + 2) \\
&= 2(3t + 1)\sec^2(3t^2 + 2t)
\end{aligned}
$$ ◀

▶ **EXAMPLE 4**   Find $\dfrac{dy}{dx}$ if

$$y = \sin(\cos x)$$

Solution   We apply the chain rule.

$$
\begin{aligned}
\frac{dy}{dx} &= \cos(\cos x)[D_x(\cos x)] \\
&= \cos(\cos x)[-\sin x] \\
&= -\sin x[\cos(\cos x)]
\end{aligned}
$$ ◀

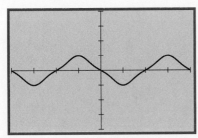

$[-2\pi, 2\pi]$ by $[-4, 4]$

$f(x) = -\sin x\,[\cos(\cos x)]$

and NDER$(\sin(\cos x), x)$

FIGURE 1

Of course the computations of the derivative in the above examples can be supported graphically. To support our answer in Example 4, we plot the graphs of the functions defined by $f(x) = -\sin x[\cos(\cos x)]$ and NDER$(\sin(\cos x), x)$ in the $[-2\pi, 2\pi]$ by $[-4, 4]$ window as shown in Figure 1. The graphs appear identical.

▶ **EXAMPLE 5**   Compute

$$D_x(\sec^4 2x^2)$$

Solution   We use the chain rule twice.

$$\begin{aligned} D_x(\sec^4 2x^2) &= 4 \sec^3 2x^2 [D_x(\sec 2x^2)] \\ &= 4 \sec^3 2x^2 [(\sec 2x^2 \tan 2x^2) \, D_x(2x^2)] \\ &= (4 \sec^4 2x^2 \tan 2x^2)(4x) \\ &= 16x \sec^4 2x^2 \tan 2x^2 \end{aligned}$$ ◀

▶ **EXAMPLE 6**   In Example 3 of Section 1.3, we had the following situation: In a forest a predator feeds on prey, and the predator population is a function f of x, the number of prey in the forest, which in turn is a function g of t, the number of weeks that have elapsed since the end of the hunting season.

$$f(x) = \tfrac{1}{48}x^2 - 2x + 50 \quad \text{and} \quad g(t) = 4t + 52$$

where $0 \le t \le 15$. Determine the rate at which the predator population is growing 11 weeks after the close of the hunting season. Do not express $f \circ g$ in terms of t but use the chain rule.

Solution   The rate at which the predator population is growing 11 weeks after the close of the hunting season is given by $(f \circ g)'(11)$. We use the chain rule to compute $(f \circ g)'(t)$. Because

$$f'(x) = \tfrac{1}{24}x - 2 \quad \text{and} \quad g'(t) = 4$$
$$\begin{aligned}(f \circ g)'(t) &= f'(g(t))g'(t) \\ &= \left[\tfrac{1}{24}(4t + 52) - 2\right] 4\end{aligned}$$

Thus

$$\begin{aligned}(f \circ g)'(11) &= \tfrac{1}{6}(44 + 52) - 8 \\ &= 8\end{aligned}$$

Conclusion: Eleven weeks after the close of the hunting season, the predator population is growing at the rate of 8 animals per week.   ◀

We now give an application of the sine and cosine functions to *simple harmonic motion*. An object moving on a line is said to have **simple harmonic motion** if the measure of its acceleration is always proportional to the measure of its displacement from a fixed point on the line and its acceleration and displacement are oppositely directed. Mathematical models describing simple harmonic motion, either vibrating or oscillating, are given by the functions

$$f(t) = a \sin b(t - c) \tag{13}$$

and

$$f(t) = a \cos b(t - c) \tag{14}$$

where $f(t)$ represents the displacement of the object after t units of time, and a, b, and c are constants.

▷ **ILLUSTRATION 7**   We show that the function defined by Equation (13) describes simple harmonic motion. The displacement is given by

$$f(t) = a \sin b(t - c)$$

and the function giving the acceleration is $f''(t)$, which we compute:

$$f'(t) = ab \cos b(t - c) \quad \text{and} \quad f''(t) = -ab^2 \sin b(t - c)$$

Therefore, $f''(t) = -b^2 f(t)$. Because $-b^2$ is a constant, the acceleration is proportional to the displacement. Furthermore, because $-b^2$ is negative, the acceleration and displacement are oppositely directed. The motion is, therefore, simple harmonic.   ◀

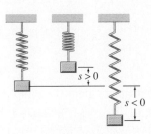

FIGURE 2

An example of simple harmonic motion occurs when a weight is suspended from a spring and is vibrating vertically. Let s centimeters be the directed distance of the weight from its central, or rest, position after t seconds of time. See Figure 2, where a positive value of s indicates that the weight is above its central position. If on a rectangular cartesian coordinate system the values of s are plotted for specific values of t, then if friction is neglected, the resulting graph will have an equation of the form of (13) or (14). The constants a, b, and c are determined by the weight and the spring as well as by how the weight is set into motion. For instance, the further the weight is pulled down before it is released, the greater will be a, the *amplitude* of the motion. Furthermore, the stiffer the spring, the more rapidly the weight will vibrate and thus the smaller will be the *period* of the motion. If P is the period then $P = \dfrac{2\pi}{|b|}$. The *frequency* of a simple harmonic motion is the number of vibrations, or oscillations, per unit of time. If n is the frequency of the motion, $n = \dfrac{1}{P}$.

▶ **EXAMPLE 7**   A weight is vibrating vertically according to the equation

$$s = 8 \cos \tfrac{1}{3} \pi t$$

where s centimeters is the directed distance of the weight from its central position (the origin) at t seconds and the positive direction is upward. **(a)** Find the velocity and acceleration of the motion for any t. **(b)** Show that the motion is simple harmonic. **(c)** Find the amplitude, period, and frequency of the motion. **(d)** Simulate the up-and-down motion of the spring on a graphics calculator. **(e)** Plot the graph of the equation of motion.

Solution

(a) If v centimeters per second is the velocity and a centimeters per second per second is the acceleration.

$$v = \frac{ds}{dt} \qquad\qquad a = \frac{dv}{dt}$$

$$= 8\left(-\sin \tfrac{1}{3}\pi t\right)\left(\tfrac{1}{3}\pi\right) \qquad = -\tfrac{8}{3}\pi\left(\cos \tfrac{1}{3}\pi t\right)\left(\tfrac{1}{3}\pi\right)$$

$$= -\tfrac{8}{3}\pi \sin \tfrac{1}{3}\pi t \qquad\qquad = -\tfrac{8}{9}\pi^2 \cos \tfrac{1}{3}\pi t$$

(b) From the value of s in the given equation and the value of a in part (a), we observe that

$$a = -\tfrac{1}{9}\pi^2 s$$

Because a is proportional to s and oppositely directed, the motion is simple harmonic.

(c) The given equation is the special case of (14) where $a = 8$, $b = \tfrac{1}{3}\pi$ and $c = 0$. The amplitude of the motion is a which is 8; therefore, the maximum displacement is 8 cm. If P is the period, $P = \dfrac{2\pi}{|b|}$; that is, $P = 6$. Therefore, it takes 6 sec for one complete vibration of the weight. Because the frequency n is given by $1/P$, $n = \tfrac{1}{6}$. Thus there is $\tfrac{1}{6}$ of a vibration per second.

(d) To simulate the motion, let us assume that the weight moves on the line $x = 2$. With our calculator in parametric mode, we let

$$x_1(t) = 2 \quad \text{and} \quad y_1(t) = 8\cos\tfrac{1}{3}\pi t$$

The motion continues indefinitely, but let us simulate the motion for $0 \le t \le 12$. In the window $[0, 4]$ by $[-10, 10]$, we let $t_{\min} = 0$, $t_{\max} = 12$, and $t_{\text{step}} = 0.05$. We now press the $\boxed{\text{TRACE}}$ key and then press the left-arrow key and hold it down until the cursor is at $t = 0$. Figure 3 shows the calculator screen as it now appears. We press the right-arrow key and hold it down to observe the weight, represented by the cursor, moving up and down along the vertical line $x = 2$.

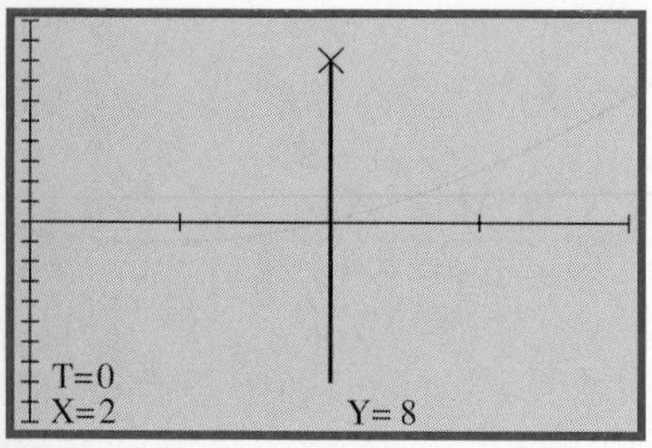

Notice that initially, when $t = 0$, the velocity v is zero, the acceleration a is negative, and $s = 8$ so that the weight is 8 cm above the origin, the central position. In the first 1.5 sec, the velocity is negative but the speed, $|v|$, is increasing. During this time the weight moves downward a distance of 8 cm to its central position because when $t = 1.5$, $s = 0$. Observe that when $t = 1.5$, $a = 0$, so that the acceleration of the weight is zero at its central position. In the next 1.5 sec the motion of the weight continues downward, when its speed is decreasing until after a total of 3 sec the weight is 8 cm below its central position. Then the weight reverses its direction, and its speed increases until it attains its central position, following which the speed decreases until it is back to its starting position after a total of 6 sec. The weight then reverses its direction, and the motion down and up is repeated indefinitely.

(e) Figure 4 shows the graph of the equation of motion plotted in the $[0, 30]$ by $[-10, 10]$ window. ◀

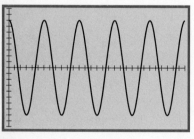

[0, 4] by [−10, 10]

$x_1(t) = 2, \quad y_1(t) = 8\cos\tfrac{1}{3}\pi t$

FIGURE 3

[0, 30] by [−10, 10]

$s = 8\cos\tfrac{1}{3}\pi t$

FIGURE 4

In the above example, we neglected friction, which would cause the weight eventually to come to rest. We discuss *damped harmonic motion*, for which friction is taken into account, in Section 5.4, as an application of the *natural exponential function*.

EXERCISES 2.8

In Exercises 1 through 12, find the derivative of the function.

1. $f(x) = (2x + 1)^3$ **2.** $f(x) = (10 - 5x)^4$

3. $F(x) = (x^2 + 4x - 5)^4$

4. $g(r) = (2r^4 + 8r^2 + 1)^5$

5. $f(t) = (2t^4 - 7t^3 + 2t - 1)^2$

6. $H(z) = (z^3 - 3z^2 + 1)^{-3}$

7. $f(x) = (x^2 + 4)^{-2}$ **8.** $g(x) = \sin x^2$

9. $f(x) = 4 \cos 3x - 3 \sin 4x$

10. $G(x) = \sec^2 x$

11. $h(t) = \frac{1}{3} \sec^3 2t - \sec 2t$ **12.** $f(x) = \cos(3x^2 + 1)$

In Exercises 13 through 16, compute the derivative.

13. $\dfrac{d}{dx} (\sec^2 x \tan^2 x)$ **14.** $\dfrac{d}{dt} (2 \sin^3 t \cos^2 t)$

15. $\dfrac{d}{dt} (\cot^4 t - \csc^4 t)$

16. $\dfrac{d}{dx} [(4x^2 + 7)^2 (2x^3 + 1)^4]$

In Exercises 17 through 24, find the derivative of the function and support your answer by plotting the graphs of your answer and the numerical derivative at x in the same window.

17. $f(x) = \left(\dfrac{x - 7}{x + 2}\right)^2$ **18.** $f(t) = \left(\dfrac{2t^2 + 1}{3t^3 + 1}\right)^2$

19. $g(t) = \sin^2(3t^2 - 1)$ **20.** $g(x) = \tan^2 x^2$

21. $f(x) = (\tan^2 x - x^2)^3$

22. $G(x) = (2 \sin x - 3 \cos x)^3$

23. $F(x) = 4 \cos(\sin 3x)$ **24.** $f(x) = \sin^2(\cos 2x)$

In Exercises 25 and 26, find an equation of the tangent line to the given curve at the indicated point, and support your answer by plotting the curve and the tangent line in the same window.

25. $y = (x^2 - 1)^2$ at the point $(2, 9)$.

26. $y = 4 \tan 2x$ at the point $(\frac{1}{8}\pi, 4)$.

In Exercises 27 through 30, the equation describes the motion of a weight suspended from a spring and vibrating vertically, where s centimeters is the distance of the weight from its central position (the origin) at t seconds and the positive direction is upward. (a) Find the velocity and acceleration of the motion for any t. (b) Show that the motion is simple harmonic. (c) Find the amplitude, period, and frequency of the motion. (d) Simulate the up-and-down motion of the spring on your graphics calculator. (e) Plot the graph of the equation of motion.

27. $s = 6 \sin \frac{1}{4}\pi t$ **28.** $s = 3 \cos \frac{1}{6}\pi t$

29. $s = 4 \cos \pi(2t - \frac{1}{3})$ **30.** $s = 8 \sin \pi(3t + \frac{1}{2})$

In Exercises 31 and 32, a particle is moving along a line according to the given equation of motion, where s meters is the directed distance of the particle from the origin at t seconds. Find (a) the velocity and (b) the acceleration at t seconds, and (c) show that the motion is simple harmonic.

31. $s = b \cos(kt + c)$, where b, k, and c are constants.

32. $s = A \sin 2\pi kt + B \cos 2\pi kt$, where A, B, and k are constants.

In Exercises 33 through 36, a particle is moving along a line according to the given equation of motion, where at t seconds, s feet is the directed distance of the particle from the origin, v feet per second is the velocity and a feet per second per second is the acceleration. (a) Find v and a in terms of t. (b) Show that the motion is simple harmonic. (c) Simulate the motion on your graphics calculator.

33. $s = 5 \sin \pi t + 3 \cos \pi t$

34. $s = \sin(6t - \frac{1}{3}\pi) + \sin(6t + \frac{1}{6}\pi)$

35. $s = 5 - 10 \sin^2 2t$ **36.** $s = 8 \cos^2 6t - 4$

37. (a) For the pendulum of Example 6 in Section 2.7, show that another equation defining $h(\theta)$ is

$$h(\theta) = 20 \sin^2 \frac{1}{2}\theta$$

Hint: Use a trigonometric identity. From this equation find the instantaneous rate of change of $h(\theta)$ with respect to θ when **(b)** $\theta = \frac{1}{6}\pi$; **(c)** $\theta = \frac{1}{3}\pi$; **(d)** $\theta = \frac{1}{2}\pi$.

38. If K square units is the area of a right triangle, 10 units is the length of the hypotenuse, and α is the radian measure of an acute angle, then $K = 25 \sin 2\alpha$. Find the instantaneous rate of change of K with respect to α, when **(a)** $\alpha = \frac{1}{6}\pi$; **(b)** $\alpha = \frac{1}{4}\pi$; **(c)** $\alpha = \frac{1}{3}\pi$.

39. Dulong's law states that if P atmospheres is the absolute pressure of saturated steam at a temperature of T degrees Celsius, then

$$P = \left(\frac{40 + T}{140}\right)^5 \qquad T > 80$$

Find the instantaneous rate of change of P with respect to T, when **(a)** $T = 100$; **(b)** $P = 32$.

40. If at t seconds, q coulombs is the charge on a capacitor and i amperes is the current in the capacitor then i is the rate of change of q with respect to t. Suppose for a certain capacitor

$$q = -\frac{A}{\omega}\cos(\omega t + \phi)$$

where A, ω, and ϕ are constants. Express i in terms of t.

41. A torsional pendulum is made by suspending a horizontal uniform metal disk by a wire from its center. If the disk is rotated and then released, it will execute simple (angular) harmonic motion. Suppose at t seconds the angular displacement of θ radians from the initial position is given by the equation

$$\theta = 0.2\cos\pi(t - 0.5)$$

Determine, to the nearest tenth of a radian per second, how fast the angle is changing at 3.1 sec.

42. Let the function obtained as a mathematical model in Exercise 28 of Exercises 1.3 be denoted by V. Find to the nearest tenth the instantaneous rate of change of $V(x)$ with respect to x when **(a)** $x = 0.9$, **(b)** $x = 1.0$, and **(c)** $x = 1.1$.

43. The electromotive force for an electric circuit with a simplified generator is $E(t)$ volts at t seconds, where $E(t) = 50\sin 120\pi t$. Find the instantaneous rate of change of $E(t)$ with respect to t at **(a)** 0.02 sec and **(b)** 0.2 sec.

44. A wave produced by a simple sound has the equation $P(t) = 0.003\sin 1800\pi t$, where $P(t)$ dynes per square centimeter is the difference between the atmospheric pressure and the air pressure at the eardrum at t seconds. Find the instantaneous rate of change of $P(t)$ with respect to t at **(a)** $\frac{1}{9}$ sec; **(b)** $\frac{1}{8}$ sec; **(c)** $\frac{1}{7}$ sec.

45. The demand equation for a particular toy is $p^2x = 5000$, where x toys are demanded per month when p dollars is the price per toy. It is expected that in t months, where $t \in [0, 6]$, the price of the toy will be p dollars, where $20p = t^2 + 7t + 100$. What is the anticipated rate of change of the demand with respect to time in 5 months? Do not express x in terms of t, but use the chain rule.

46. For the oil spill and function A of Exercise 54 in Exercises 1.8 do the following: **(a)** Prove that A is differentiable at 2. **(b)** Define $A'(t)$. Find the rate at which the area of the spill is changing at **(c)** 0.4 min, **(d)** 2 min, and **(e)** 3.2 min.

47. Given $f(x) = x^3$ and $g(x) = f(x^2)$. Find **(a)** $f'(x^2)$; **(b)** $g'(x)$.

48. Given $f(u) = u^2 + 5u + 5$ and $g(x) = (x + 1)/(x - 1)$. Find the derivative of $f \circ g$

in two ways: **(a)** by first finding $(f \circ g)(x)$ and then finding $(f \circ g)'(x)$; **(b)** by using the chain rule.

49. Derive the formula for the derivative of the cosine function by using the formula for the derivative of the sine function, the chain rule, and the identities

$$\cos x = \sin(\tfrac{1}{2}\pi - x) \quad \text{and} \quad \sin x = \cos(\tfrac{1}{2}\pi - x)$$

50. Use the chain rule to prove that **(a)** the derivative of an even function is an odd function, and **(b)** the derivative of an odd function is an even function, provided that these derivatives exist.

51. Use the result of Exercise 50(a) to prove that if g is an even function and $g'(x)$ exists, then if $h(x) = (f \circ g)(x)$ and f is differentiable everywhere, $h'(0) = 0$.

52. Suppose that f and g are functions such that $f'(x) = \frac{1}{x}$ and $(f \circ g)(x) = x$. Prove that if $g'(x)$ exists, then $g'(x) = g(x)$.

53. Given

$$f(x) = \begin{cases} x^2\sin\dfrac{1}{x} & \text{if } x \neq 0 \\ 0 & \text{if } x = 0 \end{cases}$$

(a) Prove that f is continuous at 0. **(b)** Compute $f'(x)$. **(c)** Prove that f' is discontinuous at 0.

54. If f'' and g'' exist and if $h = f \circ g$, express $h''(x)$ in terms of the derivatives of f and g.

55. Discuss the simple harmonic motion of the weight described by the equation of Exercise 27, as we did in part (d) of Example 7.

56. Follow the instructions of Exercise 55 for the simple harmonic motion of the weight described by the equation of Exercise 28.

57. Suppose that f and g are two functions such that **(i)** $g'(x_1)$ and $f'(g(x_1))$ exist and **(ii)** for all $x \neq x_1$ in some open interval containing x_1, $g(x) - g(x_1) \neq 0$. Then

$$\frac{(f \circ g)(x) - (f \circ g)(x_1)}{x - x_1}$$

$$= \frac{(f \circ g)(x) - (f \circ g)(x_1)}{g(x) - g(x_1)} \cdot \frac{g(x) - g(x_1)}{x - x_1}$$

(a) Prove that as $x \to x_1$, $g(x) \to g(x_1)$ and hence that

$$(f \circ g)'(x_1) = f'(g(x_1))g'(x_1)$$

thus simplifying the proof of the chain rule under the additional hypothesis (ii). **(b)** Explain why the proof of the chain rule given in part (a) applies if $f(x) = x^2$ and $g(x) = x^3$, but that it does not apply if $f(x) = x^2$ and $g(x) = \text{sgn } x$.

2.9 THE DERIVATIVE OF THE POWER FUNCTION FOR RATIONAL EXPONENTS AND IMPLICIT DIFFERENTIATION

In Section 2.4 we showed that the derivative of the **power function,** defined by

$$f(x) = x^r \tag{1}$$

is given by the following formula when r is a positive or negative integer:

$$f'(x) = rx^{r-1} \tag{2}$$

We now prove that this formula holds when r is a rational number, with certain stipulations when $x = 0$.

First consider $x \neq 0$, and $r = 1/q$, where q is a positive integer. Equation (1) then can be written

$$f(x) = x^{1/q} \tag{3}$$

From Definition 2.1.3,

$$f'(x) = \lim_{\Delta x \to 0} \frac{(x + \Delta x)^{1/q} - x^{1/q}}{\Delta x} \tag{4}$$

To evaluate the limit in (4) we must rationalize the numerator. To do this we use the following formula.

$$a^n - b^n = (a - b)(a^{n-1} + a^{n-2}b + a^{n-3}b^2 + \ldots + ab^{n-2} + b^{n-1}) \tag{5}$$

You may recall this formula from your precalculus course. If not, refer to the supplement of Section 1.5 where it is obtained as Equation (12).

The numerator of the fraction in (4) is rationalized by applying (5), where $a = (x + \Delta x)^{1/q}$, $b = x^{1/q}$, and $n = q$. So we multiply the numerator and denominator by

$$[(x + \Delta x)^{1/q}]^{(q-1)} + [(x + \Delta x)^{1/q}]^{(q-2)}x^{1/q} + \ldots + (x^{1/q})^{(q-1)}$$

Then, from (4), $f'(x)$ equals

$$\lim_{\Delta x \to 0} \frac{[(x + \Delta x)^{1/q} - x^{1/q}][(x + \Delta x)^{(q-1)/q} + (x + \Delta x)^{(q-2)/q}x^{1/q} + \ldots + x^{(q-1)/q}]}{\Delta x[(x + \Delta x)^{(q-1)/q} + (x + \Delta x)^{(q-2)/q}x^{1/q} + \ldots + x^{(q-1)/q}]} \tag{6}$$

Now if (5) is applied to the numerator, we get $(x + \Delta x)^{q/q} - x^{q/q}$, which is Δx. So from (6),

$$f'(x) = \lim_{\Delta x \to 0} \frac{\Delta x}{\Delta x[(x + \Delta x)^{(q-1)/q} + (x + \Delta x)^{(q-2)/q}x^{1/q} + \ldots + x^{(q-1)/q}]}$$

$$= \lim_{\Delta x \to 0} \frac{1}{(x + \Delta x)^{(q-1)/q} + (x + \Delta x)^{(q-2)/q}x^{1/q} + \ldots + x^{(q-1)/q}}$$

$$= \frac{1}{x^{(q-1)/q} + x^{(q-1)/q} + \ldots + x^{(q-1)/q}}$$

Because there are exactly q terms in the denominator of the above fraction,

$$f'(x) = \frac{1}{qx^{1-(1/q)}}$$

$$f'(x) = \frac{1}{q}x^{1/q-1} \tag{7}$$

which is formula (2) with $r = 1/q$. We have completed a crucial part of the proof. We have shown that the function defined by (3) is differentiable; furthermore, its derivative is given by (7).

Now, in (1) with $x \neq 0$, let $r = p/q$, where p is any nonzero integer and q is any positive integer; that is, r is any rational number except zero. Then (1) is written as

$$f(x) = x^{p/q} \quad \Leftrightarrow \quad f(x) = (x^{1/q})^p$$

From the chain rule and the power rule for positive and negative integer powers

$$f'(x) = p(x^{1/q})^{p-1} \cdot D_x(x^{1/q})$$

Applying formula (7) for $D_x(x^{1/q})$ we get

$$f'(x) = p(x^{1/q})^{p-1} \cdot \frac{1}{q}x^{1/q-1}$$

$$f'(x) = \frac{p}{q}x^{p/q-1/q + 1/q-1}$$

$$f'(x) = \frac{p}{q}x^{p/q-1}$$

This formula is the same as formula (2) with $r = p/q$.

If $r = 0$ and $x \neq 0$, (1) becomes $f(x) = x^0$; that is, $f(x) = 1$. Thus $f'(x) = 0$, which can be written as $f'(x) = 0 \cdot x^{0-1}$. Therefore (2) holds if $r = 0$ with $x \neq 0$. We have therefore shown that formula (2) holds when r is any rational number and $x \neq 0$.

Now 0 is in the domain of the power function f if and only if r is a positive number, because when $r \leq 0$, $f(0)$ is not defined. Hence we wish to determine for what positive values of $r, f'(0)$ will be given by formula (2). We must exclude the values of r for which $0 < r \leq 1$ because for those values of r, x^{r-1} is not a real number when $x = 0$. Suppose, then, that $r > 1$. By the definition of a derivative.

$$f'(0) = \lim_{x \to 0} \frac{x^r - 0^r}{x - 0}$$
$$= \lim_{x \to 0} x^{r-1}$$

When $r > 1$, $\lim_{x \to 0} x^{r-1}$ exists and equals 0, provided that r is a number such that x^{r-1} is defined on some open interval containing 0. For example, if $r = \frac{3}{2}$, then $x^{r-1} = x^{1/2}$, which is not defined on any open interval containing 0 (since $x^{1/2}$ does not exist when $x < 0$). However, if $r = \frac{5}{3}, x^{r-1} = x^{2/3}$, which is defined on every open interval containing 0. Hence formula (2) gives the derivative of the power function when $x = 0$, provided that r is a number for which x^{r-1} is defined on some open interval containing 0. Thus we have proved the following theorem.

> **2.9.1 Theorem   The Power Rule (for Rational Powers) of Differentiation**
>
> If f is the power function defined by $f(x) = x^r$, where r is any rational number, then f is differentiable and
>
> $$f'(x) = rx^{r-1}$$
>
> For this formula to give $f'(0)$, r must be a number such that x^{r-1} is defined on some open interval containing 0.

▶ **EXAMPLE 1**   Find $f'(x)$ if

$$f(x) = 4\sqrt[3]{x^2}$$

Solution   From Theorem 2.9.1 with $f(x) = 4x^{2/3}$

$$
\begin{aligned}
f'(x) &= 4 \cdot \tfrac{2}{3}(x^{2/3-1}) \\
&= \tfrac{8}{3}x^{-1/3} \\
&= \frac{8}{3x^{1/3}} \\
&= \frac{8}{3\sqrt[3]{x}}
\end{aligned}
$$
◀

The next theorem follows immediately from Theorem 2.9.1 and the chain rule.

> **2.9.2 Theorem**
>
> If f and g are functions such that $f(x) = [g(x)]^r$, where r is any rational number, and if $g'(x)$ exists, then f is differentiable, and
>
> $$f'(x) = r[g(x)]^{r-1}g'(x)$$

▶ **EXAMPLE 2**   Find $f'(t)$ if

$$f(t) = \sqrt{4\sin^2 t + 9\cos^2 t}$$

Solution   We write $f(t) = (4\sin^2 t + 9\cos^2 t)^{1/2}$ and apply Theorem 2.9.2.

$$
\begin{aligned}
f'(t) &= \tfrac{1}{2}(4\sin^2 t + 9\cos^2 t)^{-1/2} \cdot D_t(4\sin^2 t + 9\cos^2 t) \\
&= \frac{8\sin t \cdot D_t(\sin t) + 18\cos t \cdot D_t(\cos t)}{2\sqrt{4\sin^2 t + 9\cos^2 t}} \\
&= \frac{8\sin t \cos t + 18\cos t(-\sin t)}{2\sqrt{4\sin^2 t + 9\cos t}} \\
&= \frac{-10\sin t \cos t}{2\sqrt{4\sin^2 t + 9\cos^2 t}} \\
&= -\frac{5\sin t \cos t}{\sqrt{4\sin^2 t + 9\cos^2 t}}
\end{aligned}
$$
◀

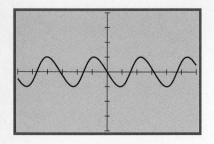

[−6, 6] by [−4, 4]

$$f'(t) = -\frac{5 \sin t \cos t}{\sqrt{4 \sin^2 t + 9 \cos^2 t}}$$

and NDER($\sqrt{4 \sin^2 t + 9 \cos^2 t}$, t)

FIGURE 1

As usual the computations in the above examples can be supported graphically. In particular, the graph in Figure 1, which shows that the graph of our answer and the graph of the numerical derivative of f appear the same, supports our computation in Example 2.

We now discuss another differentiation technique called **implicit differentiation,** which is based on the chain rule.

If $f = \{(x, y) \mid y = 3x^2 + 5x + 1\}$, then the equation

$$y = 3x^2 + 5x + 1$$

defines the function f explicitly. Not all functions, however, can be defined explicitly by an equation. For example, we cannot solve the equation

$$x^6 - 2x = 3y^6 + y^5 - y^2 \qquad \textbf{(8)}$$

for y in terms of x. One or more functions f may exist, however, such that if $y = f(x)$, then Equation (8) is satisfied; that is, such that the equation

$$x^6 - 2x = 3[f(x)]^6 + [f(x)]^5 - [f(x)]^2$$

holds for all values of x in the domain of f. In this case the function f is defined *implicitly* by the given equation.

With the assumption that (8) defines y as at least one differentiable function of x, the derivative of y with respect to x can be found by *implicit differentiation.*

Equation (8) is a special type of equation involving x and y because it can be written so that all the terms involving x are on one side of the equation and all the terms involving y are on the other side. It serves as a first example to illustrate the process of implicit differentiation.

The left side of (8) is a function of x, and the right side is a function of y. Let F be the function defined by the left side, and let G be the function defined by the right side. Thus

$$F(x) = x^6 - 2x \qquad G(y) = 3y^6 + y^5 - y^2$$

where y is a function of x, say $y = f(x)$. So (8) can be written as

$$F(x) = G(f(x))$$

This equation is satisfied by all values of x in the domain of f for which $G(f(x))$ exists.

Then for all values of x for which f is differentiable,

$$D_x(x^6 - 2x) = D_x(3y^6 + y^5 - y^2) \qquad \textbf{(9)}$$

The derivative on the left side of (9) is easily found, and

$$D_x(x^6 - 2x) = 6x^5 - 2 \qquad \textbf{(10)}$$

We find the derivative on the right side of (9) by the chain rule.

$$D_x(3y^6 + y^5 - y^2) = 18y^5 \cdot \frac{dy}{dx} + 5y^4 \cdot \frac{dy}{dx} - 2y \cdot \frac{dy}{dx} \qquad \textbf{(11)}$$

Substituting the values from (10) and (11) into (9) we obtain

$$6x^5 - 2 = (18y^5 + 5y^4 - 2y)\frac{dy}{dx}$$

$$\frac{dy}{dx} = \frac{6x^5 - 2}{18y^5 + 5y^4 - 2y}$$

Observe that by using implicit differentiation we have obtained an expression for $\dfrac{dy}{dx}$ that involves both variables x and y.

In the following illustration the method of implicit differentiation is used to find $\dfrac{dy}{dx}$ from a more general type of equation.

▷ **ILLUSTRATION 1**   Consider the equation

$$3x^4y^2 - 7xy^3 = 4 - 8y \qquad (12)$$

and assume that there exists at least one differentiable function f such that if $y = f(x)$, Equation (12) is satisfied. Differentiating on both sides of (12) (bearing in mind that y is a differentiable function of x) and applying the product rule, the power rule, and the chain rule, we obtain

$$12x^3y^2 + 3x^4(2yD_xy) - 7y^3 - 7x(3y^2D_xy) = 0 - 8\,D_xy$$
$$D_xy(6x^4y - 21xy^2 + 8) = 7y^3 - 12x^3y^2$$
$$D_xy = \frac{7y^3 - 12x^3y^2}{6x^4y - 21xy^2 + 8} \quad ◀$$

Remember we assumed that both (8) and (12) define y as at least one differentiable function of x. It may be that an equation in x and y does not imply the existence of any real-valued function, as is the case for the equation

$$x^2 + y^2 + 4 = 0$$

which is not satisfied by any real values of x and y. Furthermore, it is possible that an equation in x and y may be satisfied by many different functions, some of which are differentiable and some of which are not. A general discussion is beyond the scope of this book but can be found in an advanced calculus text. In subsequent discussions when we state that an equation in x and y defines y implicitly as a function of x, it is assumed that one or more of these functions is differentiable. Example 5, which follows later, illustrates the fact that implicit differentiation gives the derivative of two differentiable functions defined by the given equation.

▶ **EXAMPLE 3**   **(a)** Use implicit differentiation to find the slope of the tangent line to the curve $x^3 + y^3 = 9$ at the point $(1, 2)$. **(b)** Find an equation of the tangent line and support the answer graphically by plotting the curve and the tangent line in the same window.

Solution

(a) We differentiate implicitly with respect to x.

$$3x^2 + 3y^2\frac{dy}{dx} = 0$$
$$\frac{dy}{dx} = -\frac{x^2}{y^2}$$

At the point $(1, 2)$, $\dfrac{dy}{dx} = -\dfrac{1}{4}$.

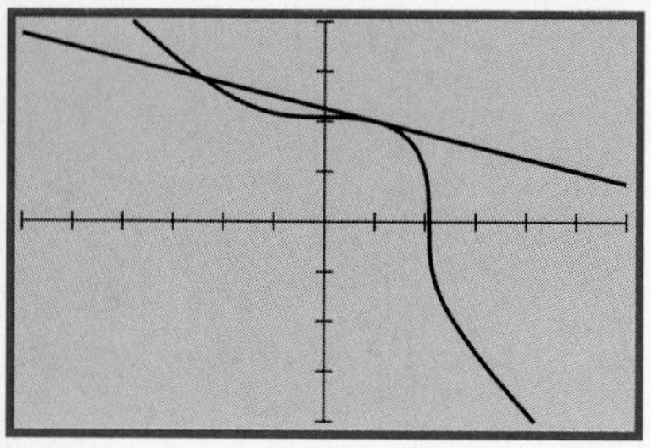

[-6, 6] by [-4, 4]

$y = \sqrt[3]{9 - x^3}$ and $y = \frac{1}{4}(9 - x)$

FIGURE 2

(b) An equation of the tangent line is

$$y - 2 = -\tfrac{1}{4}(x - 1)$$
$$x + 4y - 9 = 0$$

Figure 2 shows the graphs of

$$y = \sqrt[3]{9 - x^3} \quad \text{and} \quad y = \tfrac{1}{4}(9 - x)$$

plotted in the $[-6, 6]$ by $[-4, 4]$ window. The line is tangent to the curve at the point $(1, 2)$, which supports our answer. ◀

▶ **EXAMPLE 4**   Given $x \cos y + y \cos x - 1 = 0$, find $\dfrac{dy}{dx}$.

Solution   Differentiating implicitly with respect to x we get

$$1 \cdot \cos y + x(-\sin y)\frac{dy}{dx} + \frac{dy}{dx}(\cos x) + y(-\sin x) = 0$$

$$\frac{dy}{dx}(\cos x - x \sin y) = y \sin x - \cos y$$

$$\frac{dy}{dx} = \frac{y \sin x - \cos y}{\cos x - x \sin y}$$

◀

▶ **EXAMPLE 5**   Given the equation $x^2 + y^2 = 9$, find **(a)** $\dfrac{dy}{dx}$ by implicit differentiation; **(b)** two functions defined by the equation; **(c)** the derivative of each of the functions obtained in part (b) by explicit differentiation. **(d)** Verify that the result obtained in part (a) agrees with the results obtained in part (c).

Solution

(a) We differentiate implicitly.

$$2x + 2y\frac{dy}{dx} = 0$$

$$\frac{dy}{dx} = -\frac{x}{y}$$

(b) If the given equation is solved for y,

$$y = \sqrt{9 - x^2} \quad \text{and} \quad y = -\sqrt{9 - x^2}$$

Let f_1 and f_2 be the two functions for which

$$f_1(x) = \sqrt{9 - x^2} \quad \text{and} \quad f_2(x) = -\sqrt{9 - x^2}$$

(c) Because $f_1(x) = (9 - x^2)^{1/2}$ and $f_2(x) = -(9 - x^2)^{1/2}$, from the chain rule we obtain

$$f_1'(x) = \tfrac{1}{2}(9 - x^2)^{-1/2}(-2x) \qquad f_2'(x) = -\tfrac{1}{2}(9 - x^2)^{1/2}(-2x)$$

$$= -\frac{x}{\sqrt{9 - x^2}} \qquad\qquad = \frac{x}{\sqrt{9 - x^2}}$$

(d) For $y = f_1(x)$, where $f_1(x) = \sqrt{9 - x^2}$, it follows from part (c) that

$$f_1'(x) = -\frac{x}{\sqrt{9 - x^2}}$$

$$= -\frac{x}{y}$$

which agrees with the answer in part (a).

For $y = f_2(x)$, where $f_2(x) = -\sqrt{9 - x^2}$, we have from part (c)

$$f_2'(x) = \frac{x}{\sqrt{9 - x^2}}$$

$$= -\frac{x}{-\sqrt{9 - x^2}}$$

$$= -\frac{x}{y}$$

which also agrees with the answer in part (a). ◀

The next example illustrates how to compute the second derivative for functions defined implicitly.

▶ **EXAMPLE 6**   Given

$$4x^2 + 9y^2 = 36$$

find $\dfrac{d^2y}{dx^2}$ by implicit differentiation.

Solution   Differentiating implicitly with respect to x we have

$$8x + 18y\frac{dy}{dx} = 0$$

$$\frac{dy}{dx} = \frac{-4x}{9y} \tag{13}$$

To find $\dfrac{d^2y}{dx^2}$ we compute the derivative of a quotient and keep in mind that y is a function of x. Thus

$$\frac{d^2y}{dx^2} = \frac{9y(-4) - (-4x)\left(9 \cdot \dfrac{dy}{dx}\right)}{81y^2}$$

Substituting the value of $\dfrac{dy}{dx}$ from (13) into this equation we get

$$\frac{d^2y}{dx^2} = \frac{-36y + (36x)\dfrac{-4x}{9y}}{81y^2}$$

$$= \frac{-36y^2 - 16x^2}{81y^3}$$

$$= \frac{-4(9y^2 + 4x^2)}{81y^3}$$

Because any values of x and y satisfying this equation must also satisfy the original equation, we can replace $9y^2 + 4x^2$ by 36 and obtain

$$\frac{d^2y}{dx^2} = \frac{-4(36)}{81y^3}$$

$$= -\frac{16}{9y^3}$$

◀

EXERCISES 2.9

In Exercises 1 through 12, find the derivative of the function.

1. $f(x) = 4x^{1/2} + 5x^{-1/2}$

2. $f(x) = 3x^{2/3} - 6x^{1/3} + x^{-1/3}$

3. $g(x) = \sqrt{1 + 4x^2}$ **4.** $f(s) = \sqrt{2 - 3s^2}$

5. $f(x) = (5 - 3x)^{2/3}$ **6.** $g(x) = \sqrt[3]{4x^2 - 1}$

7. $g(y) = \dfrac{1}{\sqrt{25 - y^2}}$ **8.** $f(x) = (5 - 2x^2)^{-1/3}$

9. $h(t) = 2\cos\sqrt{t}$ **10.** $f(x) = 4\sec\sqrt{x}$

11. $g(r) = \cot\sqrt{3r}$ **12.** $g(x) = \sqrt{3\sin x}$

In Exercises 13 through 16, compute the derivative and support your answer by plotting the graphs of your answer and the numerical derivative in the same window.

13. $\dfrac{d}{dt}\left(\sqrt{\dfrac{\sin t}{1 - \sin t}}\right)$ **14.** $\dfrac{d}{dx}\left(\sqrt{\dfrac{\cos x - 1}{\sin x}}\right)$

15. $D_x\left(\sqrt{9 + \sqrt{9 - x}}\right)$ **16.** $D_x\left(\sqrt{x}\tan\sqrt{\dfrac{1}{x}}\right)$

In Exercises 17 through 32, find $\dfrac{dy}{dx}$ by implicit differentiation.

17. $x^2 + y^2 = 16$ **18.** $4x^2 - 9y^2 = 1$

19. $x^3 + y^3 = 8xy$ **20.** $x^2 + y^2 = 7xy$

21. $\dfrac{1}{x} + \dfrac{1}{y} = 1$ **22.** $\dfrac{3}{x} - \dfrac{3}{y} = 2x$

23. $\sqrt{x} + \sqrt{y} = 4$ **24.** $2x^3y + 3xy^3 = 5$

25. $x^2y^2 = x^2 + y^2$ **26.** $(2x + 3)^4 = 3y^4$

27. $y = \cos(x - y)$ **28.** $x = \sin(x + y)$

29. $\sec^2 x + \csc^2 y = 4$ **30.** $\cot xy + xy = 0$

31. $x\sin y + y\cos x = 1$ **32.** $\cos(x + y) = y\sin x$

In Exercises 33 through 36, find an equation of either the tangent line or normal line, as indicated, and support

your answer by plotting the line and the curve in the same window.

33. The tangent line to the curve $y = \sqrt{x^2 + 9}$ at the point $(4, 5)$.

34. The normal line to the curve $y = x\sqrt{16 + x^2}$ at the origin.

35. The normal line to the curve $9x^3 - y^3 = 1$ at the point $(1, 2)$.

36. The tangent line to the curve $16x^4 + y^4 = 32$ at the point $(1, 2)$.

37. At what point of the curve $xy = (1 - x - y)^2$ is the tangent line parallel to the x axis?

38. Two lines through the point $(-1, 3)$ are tangent to the curve $x^2 + 4y^2 - 4x - 8y + 3 = 0$. Find an equation of each line.

In Exercises 39 through 42, do the following: (a) Find two functions defined by the equation; (b) sketch the graph of each function obtained in part (a); (c) sketch the graph of the equation; (d) find the derivative of each function obtained in part (a) and state the domains of the derivatives; (e) find $\dfrac{dy}{dx}$ by implicit differentiation from the given equation, and verify that the result so obtained agrees with your results in part (d); (f) find an equation of each tangent line at the given value of x_1.

39. $y^2 = 4x - 8$; $x_1 = 3$

40. $y^2 - x^2 = 16$; $x_1 = -3$

41. $x^2 - y^2 = 9$; $x_1 = -5$

42. $x^2 + y^2 = 25$; $x_1 = 4$

43. Given $x^2 + y^2 = 1$, show that $\dfrac{d^2y}{dx^2} = -\dfrac{1}{y^3}$.

44. Given $x^{1/2} + y^{1/2} = 2$, show that $\dfrac{d^2y}{dx^2} = \dfrac{1}{x^{3/2}}$.

45. Given $x^3 + y^3 = 1$, show that $\dfrac{d^2y}{dx^2} = \dfrac{-2x}{y^5}$.

46. Given $x^2 + 25y^2 = 100$, show that $\dfrac{d^2y}{dx^2} = -\dfrac{4}{25y^3}$.

47. A particle is moving along a line according to the equation of motion $s = \sqrt{4t^2 + 3}$, with $t \geq 0$. Find the value of t for which the measure of the velocity is **(a)** 0; **(b)** 1; **(c)** 2.

48. A particle is moving along a line according to the equation of motion $s = \sqrt{5 + t^2}$, with $t \geq 0$. Find the value of t for which the measure of the velocity is **(a)** 0; **(b)** 1.

49. Suppose that a liquid is produced by a certain chemical process and that the total cost function C is given by $C(x) = 6 + 4\sqrt{x}$, where $C(x)$ dollars is the total cost of producing x liters of the liquid. Find **(a)** the marginal cost when 16 liters are produced and **(b)** the number of liters produced when the marginal cost is $0.40 per liter.

50. The number of dollars in the total cost of producing x units of a certain commodity is given by $C(x) = 40 + 3x + 9\sqrt{2x}$. Find **(a)** the marginal cost when 50 units are produced and **(b)** the number of units produced when the marginal cost is $4.50.

51. A property development company rents each apartment at p dollars per month when x apartments are rented, and $p = 30\sqrt{300 - 2x}$. If $R(x)$ dollars is the total revenue received from the rental of x apartments, then $R(x) = px$. How many apartments must be rented before the marginal revenue is zero? *Note:* Because x is the number of apartments rented, it is a nonnegative integer. However, to apply calculus, assume that x is a nonnegative real number.

52. The daily production at a particular factory is $f(x)$ units when the capital investment is x thousands of dollars, and $f(x) = 200\sqrt{2x + 1}$. If the current capitalization is $760,000, use the derivative to estimate the change in the daily production if the capital investment is increased by $1000.

53. An airplane is flying parallel to the ground at an altitude of 2 km and at a speed of $4\frac{1}{2}$ km/min. If the plane flies directly over the Statue of Liberty, at what rate is the line-of-sight distance between the plane and the statue changing 20 sec later?

2 km

54. At 8 A.M. a ship sailing due north at 24 knots (nautical miles per hour) is at a point P. At 10 A.M. a second ship sailing due east at 32 knots is at P. At what rate is the distance between the two ships changing at **(a)** 9 A.M. and **(b)** 11 A.M.?

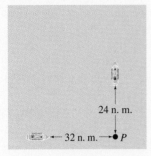

24 n. m.

← 32 n. m. →● P

(a) 9 A.M.

72 n. m.

P ●← 32 n. m. →

(b) 11 A.M.

55. In Exercise 41 of Exercises 2.2, you had to apply the definition of the derivative to prove that

$$D_x(|x|) = \frac{|x|}{x} \quad \text{if } x \neq 0$$

Now use the chain rule and differentiation theorems for the proof. *Hint:* Let $|x| = \sqrt{x^2}$.

56. Find $D_x^2(|x|)$ when it exists. See the hint for Exercise 55.

In Exercises 57 and 58, find the derivative of the function. See the hint for Exercise 55.

57. $f(x) = |x^2 - 4|$ **58.** $g(x) = x|x|$

59. If $f(x) = |x|^3$, find $f'(x)$ and $f''(x)$ when they exist.

60. Given $g(x) = |f(x)|$. Prove that if $f'(x)$ and $g'(x)$ exist, then $|g'(x)| = |f'(x)|$.

61. A rubber ball dropped from a window h feet above the ground rebounds in such a way that t seconds after the ball is dropped, its height is $s(t)$ feet, where

$$s(t) = \frac{h|\cos t|}{(1 + t)^2}$$

Find the rate at which the height of the ball is changing at **(a)** 1.4 sec, **(b)** 1.6 sec, **(c)** 1.8 sec, and **(d)** 2.2 sec.

62. Prove that the sum of the x and y intercepts of any tangent line to the curve $x^{1/2} + y^{1/2} = k^{1/2}$, where k is a constant, is equal to k.

63. Find equations of the tangent lines to the curve $x^{2/3} + y^{2/3} = 1$ at the points where $x = -\frac{1}{8}$. Support your answers by plotting the lines and the curve in the same window.

64. Suppose that $g(x) = \sqrt{9 - x^2}$ and $h(x) = f(g(x))$, where f is differentiable at 3. Prove that $h'(0) = 0$.

65. Show that if $xy = 1$, then $\dfrac{d^2y}{dx^2} \cdot \dfrac{d^2x}{dy^2} = 4$.

66. Let f be the power function defined by $f(x) = x^r$, where r is any rational number. Under the assumption that f is differentiable, use implicit differentiation to show that $f'(x) = rx^{r-1}$. *Hint:* Let $r = \dfrac{p}{q}$, where p and q are integers and $q > 0$. Then replace $f(x)$ by y and write the equation as $y^q = x^p$. Use implicit differentiation to find $\dfrac{dy}{dx}$.

67. For a rigorous proof of Theorem 2.9.1, the power rule (for rational powers) of differentiation, could we have used the procedure of Exercise 66 instead of the one given in this section? Explain.

68. Compute $(f \circ g)'(0)$ if $f(x) = x^6 + 7x^3$ and $g(x) = x^{1/3}$. Explain why the chain rule cannot be applied to perform this computation.

2.10 RELATED RATES

A problem in *related rates* is one involving rates of change of related variables. In real-world applications involving related rates, the variables have a specific relationship for values of t, where t is a measure of time. This relationship is usually expressed in the form of an equation which represents a mathematical model of the situation. We begin with an illustration showing the step-by-step pattern we apply to solve most related-rate problems.

▷ **ILLUSTRATION 1**   A ladder is 25 ft long and leaning against a vertical wall as shown in Figure 1. The bottom of the ladder is pulled horizontally away from the wall at 3 ft/sec. Suppose we wish to determine how fast the top of the ladder is sliding down the wall when the bottom is 15 ft from the wall.

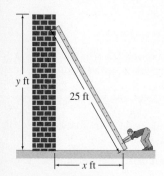

FIGURE 1

Step 1   Begin by defining the variables starting with t.

t: the number of seconds in the time that has elapsed since the ladder started to slide down the wall.

x: the number of feet in the distance from the bottom of the ladder to the wall at t seconds.

y: the number of feet in the distance from the ground to the top of the ladder at t seconds.

Step 2   Write down any numerical facts about x and y and their derivatives with respect to t.

Because the bottom of the ladder is pulled horizontally away from the wall at 3 ft/sec, $\dfrac{dx}{dt} = 3$.

Step 3   Write down what you wish to find.

We wish to find $\dfrac{dy}{dt}$ when $x = 15$.

Step 4   Write an equation to relate x and y.

From the Pythagorean theorem,

$$y^2 = 625 - x^2 \tag{1}$$

Step 5   Differentiate both sides of (1) with respect to t.

$$2y \frac{dy}{dt} = -2x \frac{dx}{dt}$$

$$\frac{dy}{dt} = -\frac{x}{y} \cdot \frac{dx}{dt} \tag{2}$$

Step 6   Substitute the known values of x, y, and $\frac{dx}{dt}$ in the above equation and solve for $\frac{dy}{dt}$.

When $x = 15$, from (1) $y = 20$. Because $\frac{dx}{dt} = 3$, we get from (2)

$$\frac{dy}{dt}\bigg]_{y=20} = -\frac{15}{20} \cdot 3$$

$$= -\frac{9}{4}$$

The minus sign indicates that y decreases as t increases.

Step 7   Write a conclusion.

Conclusion: The top of the ladder is sliding down the wall at the rate of 2.25 ft/sec when the bottom is 15 ft from the wall.   ◄

We now summarize the steps in the above illustration. They give you a procedure to emulate. As you read through the examples that follow refer to these steps to see how they are applied.

Suggestions for Solving a Related-Rate Problem

Read the problem carefully so that you understand it. To gain an understanding, it is often helpful to make up a specific example that involves a similar situation in which all the quantities are known. Another aid is to draw a figure, if feasible, as in Illustration 1 and Examples 1, 2, and 4. Then apply the following steps.

1. Define the variables in the equation you will obtain. Because the variables represent numbers, the definitions of the variables should indicate this fact. For example, if time is measured in seconds, then the variable t should be defined as the number of seconds in the time or, equivalently, t seconds is the time. Be sure to define t first, and the definitions of the other variables should indicate they depend on t.
2. Write down any numerical facts known about the variables and their derivatives with respect to t.
3. Write down what you wish to find.
4. Write an equation to relate the variables that depend on t. This is a mathematical model of the situation.
5. Differentiate with respect to t both sides of the equation found in step 4 to relate the rates of change of the variables.

6. Substitute values of known quantities in the equation of step 5, and solve for the desired quantity.

7. Write a conclusion, consisting of one or more complete sentences, that answers the questions of the problem. Be sure your conclusion contains the correct units of measurement.

▶ **EXAMPLE 1**   Water is flowing at the rate of 2m³/min into a tank in the form of an inverted cone having an altitude of 16 m and a radius of 4 m. How fast is the water level rising when the water is 5 m deep?

Solution   Refer to Figure 2.

Step 1   We define the variables, t first and then the other variables in terms of t.

t: the number of minutes in the time that has elapsed since water started to flow into the tank.

h: the number of meters in the height of the water level at t minutes.

r: the number of meters in the radius of the surface of the water at t minutes.

V: the number of cubic meters in the volume of water in the tank at t minutes. Observe that V, r, and h are all functions of t.

Step 2   Because water is flowing into the tank at the rate of 2 m³/min,
$$\frac{dV}{dt} = 2.$$

Step 3   We wish to find $\dfrac{dh}{dt}$ with $h = 5$.

Step 4   At any time, the volume of water in the tank may be expressed as the volume of a cone, as indicated in Figure 2.

$$V = \tfrac{1}{3}\pi r^2 h \qquad\qquad\qquad\qquad\qquad (3)$$

As stated in Steps 2 and 3, we know $\dfrac{dV}{dt}$, and we wish to find $\dfrac{dh}{dt}$. We therefore want an equation involving V and h. So, we first express r in terms of h by noting that from the similar triangles in Figure 2, we have

$$\frac{r}{h} = \frac{4}{16} \quad\Leftrightarrow\quad r = \frac{1}{4}h$$

Substituting this value of r into (3), we obtain

$$V = \frac{1}{3}\pi\left(\frac{1}{4}h\right)^2(h) \quad\Leftrightarrow\quad V = \frac{1}{48}\pi h^3$$

Step 5   We differentiate both sides of this equation with respect to t:

$$\frac{dV}{dt} = \frac{1}{16}\pi h^2 \cdot \frac{dh}{dt}$$

Step 6   Substituting 2 for $\dfrac{dV}{dt}$ and solving for $\dfrac{dh}{dt}$, we get

$$\frac{dh}{dt} = \frac{32}{\pi h^2}$$

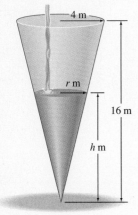

FIGURE 2

Thus

$$\left.\frac{dh}{dt}\right]_{h=5} = \frac{32}{25\pi}$$

$$\approx 0.4074$$

Converting meters to centimeters, 0.4074 m/min = 40.74 cm/min.
Step 7   We write our conclusion.

Conclusion: The water level is rising at the rate of 40.74 cm/min when the water is 5 m deep.   ◀

▶ *EXAMPLE 2*   Two cars, one going due east at the rate of 90 km/hr and the other going due south at the rate of 60 km/hr, are traveling toward the intersection of two roads. At what rate are the cars approaching each other at the instant when the first car is 0.2 km and the second car is 0.15 km from the intersection?

Solution   Refer to Figure 3, where point P is the intersection of the two roads.

Step 1
t: the number of hours in the time that has elapsed since the cars started to approach P.
x: the number of kilometers in the distance of the first car from P at t hours.
y: the number of kilometers in the distance of the second car from P at t hours.
z: the number of kilometers in the distance between the two cars at t hours.
Step 2   Because the first car is approaching P at the rate of 90 km/hr and x is decreasing as t is increasing, $\dfrac{dx}{dt} = -90$. Similarly, $\dfrac{dy}{dt} = -60$.

Step 3   We wish to find $\dfrac{dz}{dt}$ when $x = 0.2$ and $y = 0.15$.

Step 4   From the Pythagorean theorem

$$z^2 = x^2 + y^2 \tag{4}$$

Step 5   Differentiating both sides of (4) with respect to t, we obtain

$$2z\frac{dz}{dt} = 2x\frac{dx}{dt} + 2y\frac{dy}{dt}$$

$$\frac{dz}{dt} = \frac{x\dfrac{dx}{dt} + y\dfrac{dy}{dt}}{z} \tag{5}$$

Step 6   When $x = 0.2$ and $y = 0.15$, it follows from (4) that $z = 0.25$. In (5) we let $\dfrac{dx}{dt} = -90$, $\dfrac{dy}{dt} = -60$, $x = 0.2$, $y = 0.15$, and $z = 0.25$ to get

$$\left.\frac{dz}{dt}\right]_{z=0.25} = \frac{(0.2)(-90) + (0.15)(-60)}{0.25}$$

$$= -108$$

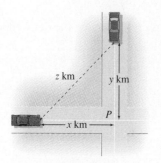

z km y km

P

x km

FIGURE 3

Step 7

<u>Conclusion:</u>   At the instant in question the cars are approaching each other at the rate of 108 km/hr.   ◀

▶   **EXAMPLE 3**   Suppose in a certain market that x thousands of crates of oranges are supplied daily when p dollars is the price per crate, and the supply equation is

$$px - 20p - 3x + 105 = 0$$

If the daily supply is decreasing at the rate of 250 crates per day, at what rate is the price changing when the daily supply is 5000 crates?

Solution   Let t days be the time that has elapsed since the daily supply of oranges started to decrease.

The variables p and x are defined as functions of t in the statement of the example.

Because the daily supply is decreasing at the rate of 250 crates per day, $\dfrac{dx}{dt} = -\dfrac{250}{1000}$; that is, $\dfrac{dx}{dt} = -\dfrac{1}{4}$. We wish to find $\dfrac{dp}{dt}$ when $x = 5$. From the given supply equation, we differentiate implicitly with respect to t and obtain

$$p\frac{dx}{dt} + x\frac{dp}{dt} - 20\frac{dp}{dt} - 3\frac{dx}{dt} = 0$$

$$\frac{dp}{dt} = \frac{3 - p}{x - 20} \cdot \frac{dx}{dt}$$

When $x = 5$, it follows from the supply equation that $p = 6$. Because $\dfrac{dx}{dt} = -\dfrac{1}{4}$, we have from the preceding equation

$$\frac{dp}{dt}\bigg]_{p=6} = \frac{3 - 6}{5 - 20}\left(-\frac{1}{4}\right)$$

$$= -\frac{1}{20}$$

<u>Conclusion:</u>   The price of a crate of oranges is decreasing at the rate of $0.05 per day when the daily supply is 5000 crates.   ◀

▶   **EXAMPLE 4**   An airplane is flying west at 500 ft/sec at an altitude of 4000 ft and a searchlight on the ground lies directly under the path of the plane. If the light is kept on the plane, how fast is the searchlight revolving when the airline distance of the plane from the searchlight is 2000 ft due east?

Solution   Refer to Figure 4 where the searchlight is at point L and at a particular instant the plane is at point P.

Let t seconds be the time that has elapsed since the searchlight spotted the plane.

x: the number of feet due east in the airline distance of the plane from the searchlight at t seconds.

θ: the number of radians in the angle of elevation of the plane at the searchlight at t seconds.

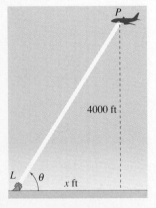

FIGURE 4

We are given $\dfrac{dx}{dt} = -500$, and we wish to find $\dfrac{d\theta}{dt}$ when $x = 2000$.

$$\tan\theta = \frac{4000}{x}$$

Differentiating both sides of this equation with respect to t we obtain

$$\sec^2\theta\,\frac{d\theta}{dt} = -\frac{4000}{x^2}\frac{dx}{dt}$$

Substituting $\dfrac{dx}{dt} = -500$ in the above and dividing by $\sec^2\theta$ gives

$$\frac{d\theta}{dt} = \frac{2{,}000{,}000}{x^2\sec^2\theta} \tag{6}$$

When $x = 2000$, $\tan\theta = 2$. Because $\sec^2\theta = 1 + \tan^2\theta$, $\sec^2\theta = 5$. Substituting these values into (6) we have, when $x = 2000$,

$$\frac{d\theta}{dt} = \frac{2{,}000{,}000}{4{,}000{,}000(5)}$$
$$= \tfrac{1}{10}$$

__Conclusion:__ At the given instant the measurement of the angle is increasing at the rate of $\tfrac{1}{10}$ rad/sec, and this is how fast the searchlight is revolving. ◄

EXERCISES 2.10

In Exercises 1 through 8, x and y are functions of a third variable t.

__1.__ If $2x + 3y = 8$ and $\dfrac{dy}{dt} = 2$, find $\dfrac{dx}{dt}$.

__2.__ If $\dfrac{x}{y} = 10$ and $\dfrac{dx}{dt} = -5$, find $\dfrac{dy}{dt}$.

__3.__ If $xy = 20$ and $\dfrac{dy}{dt} = 10$, find $\dfrac{dx}{dt}$ when $x = 2$.

__4.__ If $2\sin x + 4\cos y = 3$ and $\dfrac{dy}{dt} = 3$, find $\dfrac{dx}{dt}$ at $\left(\tfrac{1}{6}\pi, \tfrac{1}{3}\pi\right)$.

__5.__ If $\sin^2 x + \cos^2 y = \tfrac{5}{4}$ and $\dfrac{dx}{dt} = -1$, find $\dfrac{dy}{dt}$ at $\left(\tfrac{2}{3}\pi, \tfrac{3}{4}\pi\right)$.

__6.__ If $x^2 + y^2 = 25$ and $\dfrac{dx}{dt} = 5$, find $\dfrac{dy}{dt}$ when $y = 4$.

__7.__ If $\sqrt{x} + \sqrt{y} = 5$ and $\dfrac{dy}{dt} = 3$, find $\dfrac{dx}{dt}$ when $x = 1$.

__8.__ If $y(\tan x + 1) = 4$ and $\dfrac{dy}{dt} = -4$, find $\dfrac{dx}{dt}$ when $x = \pi$.

In the related-rate problems in the following exercises, define all your variables precisely as numbers of units of measurement. Use the variable t to represent time and define the other variables as dependent upon t. Be sure to write a conclusion.

__9.__ A child is flying a kite at a height of 40 ft, that is, moving horizontally at a rate of 3 ft/sec. If the string is taut, at what rate is the string being paid out when the length of the string released is 50 ft?

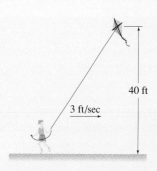

40 ft

3 ft/sec

10. A spherical balloon is being inflated so that its volume is increasing at the rate of 5 m³/min. At what rate is the diameter increasing when the diameter is 12 m?

11. A spherical snowball is being made so that its volume is increasing at the rate of 8 ft³/min. Find the rate at which the radius is increasing when the snowball is 4 ft in diameter.

12. Suppose that when the diameter is 6 ft, the snowball in Exercise 11 stopped growing and started to melt at the rate of $\frac{1}{4}$ ft³/min. Find the rate at which the radius is changing when the radius is 2 ft.

13. Sand is being dropped at the rate of 10 m³/min onto a conical pile. If the height of the pile is always twice the base radius, at what rate is the height increasing when the pile is 8 m high?

14. A light is hung 15 ft above a straight horizontal path. If a man 6 ft tall is walking away from the light at the rate of 5 ft/sec, how fast is his shadow lengthening?

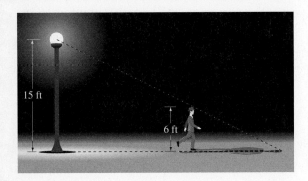

15. In Exercise 14, at what rate is the tip of the man's shadow moving?

16. A man 6 ft tall is walking toward a building at the rate of 5 ft/sec. If there is a light on the ground 50 ft from the building, how fast is the man's shadow on the building growing shorter when he is 30 ft from the building?

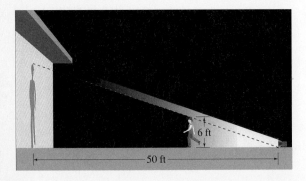

17. Suppose that a tumor in a person's body is spherical in shape. If, when the radius of the tumor is 0.5 cm, the radius is increasing at the rate of 0.001 cm per day, what is the rate of increase of the volume of the tumor at that time?

18. A bacterial cell is spherical in shape. If the radius of the cell is increasing at the rate of 0.01 micrometers per day when it is 1.5 μm, what is the rate of increase of the volume of the cell at that time?

19. For the tumor in Exercise 17, what is the rate of increase of the surface area when its radius is 0.5 cm?

20. For the cell of Exercise 18, what is the rate of increase of the surface area when its radius is 1.5 μm?

21. A water tank in the form of an inverted cone is being emptied at the rate of 6 m³/min. The altitude of the cone is 24 m, and the radius is 12 m. Find how fast the water level is lowering when the water is 10 m deep.

22. A trough is 12 ft long and its ends are in the form of inverted isosceles triangles having an altitude of 3 ft and a base of 3 ft. Water is flowing into the trough at the rate of 2 ft³/min. How fast is the water level rising when the water is 1 ft deep?

23. Boyle's law for the expansion of gas is $PV = C$, where P is the number of pounds per square unit of pressure, V is the number of cubic units of volume of the gas, and C is a constant. At a certain instant the pressure is 3000 lb/ft², the volume is 5 ft³, and the volume is increasing at the rate of 3 ft³/min. Find the rate of change of the pressure at this instant.

24. The adiabatic law (no gain or loss of heat) for the expansion of air is $PV^{1.4} = C$, where P is the number of pounds per square unit of pressure, V is the number of cubic units of volume, and C is a constant. At a specific instant the pressure is 40 lb/in.² and is increasing at the rate of 8 lb/in.² each second. If $C = \frac{5}{16}$, what is the rate of change of the volume at this instant?

25. A stone is dropped into a still pond. Concentric circular ripples spread out, and the radius of the disturbed region increases at the rate of 16 cm/sec. At what rate does the area of the disturbed region increase when its radius is 4 cm?

26. Oil is running into an inverted conical tank at the rate of 3π m³/min. If the tank has a radius of 2.5 m at the top and a depth of 10 m, how fast is the depth of the oil changing when it is 8 m?

27. An automobile traveling at a rate of 30 ft/sec is approaching an intersection. When the automobile is 120 ft from the intersection, a truck traveling at the rate of 40 ft/sec crosses the intersection. The automobile and the truck are on roads that are at right angles to each other. How fast are the automobile and the truck separating 2 sec after the truck leaves the intersection?

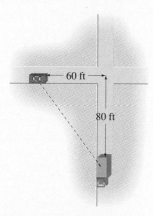

28. A rope is attached to a boat at water level, and a woman on a dock is pulling on the rope at the rate of 50 ft/min. If her hands are 16 ft above the water level, how fast is the boat approaching the dock when the amount of rope out is 20 ft?

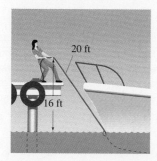

29. This week a factory is producing 50 units of a particular commodity, and the amount being produced is increasing at the rate of 2 units per week. If $C(x)$ dollars is the total cost of producing x units and

$C(x) = 0.08x^3 - x^2 + 10x + 48$, find the current rate at which the production cost is increasing.

30. The demand for a particular breakfast cereal is given by the demand equation $px + 50p = 16,000$, where x thousands of boxes are demanded when p cents is the price per box. If the current price of the cereal is $1.60 per box and the price per box is increasing at the rate of 0.4 cent each week, find the rate of change in the demand.

31. The supply equation for a certain commodity is $x = 1000\sqrt{3p^2 + 20p}$, where x units are supplied per month when p dollars is the price per unit. Find the rate of change in the supply if the current price is $20 per unit and the price is increasing at the rate of $0.50 per month.

32. Suppose that y workers are needed to produce x units of a certain commodity, and $x = 4y^2$. If the production of the commodity this year is 250,000 units and the production is increasing at the rate of 18,000 units per year, what is the current rate at which the labor force should be increased?

33. The demand equation for a particular kind of shirt is $2px + 65p - 4950 = 0$, where x hundreds of shirts are demanded per week when p dollars is the price of a shirt. If the shirt is selling this week at $30 and the price is increasing at the rate of $0.20 per week, find the rate of change in the demand.

34. The measure of one of the acute angles of a right triangle is decreasing at the rate of $\frac{1}{36}\pi$ rad/sec. If the length of the hypotenuse is constant and 40 cm, find how fast the area is changing when the measure of the acute angle is $\frac{1}{6}\pi$.

35. Two trucks, one traveling west and the other traveling south, are approaching an intersection. If both trucks are traveling at the rate of k km/hr, show that they are approaching each other at the rate of $k\sqrt{2}$ km/hr when they are each m kilometers from the intersection.

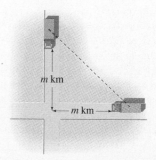

36. A horizontal trough is 16 m long, and its ends are isosceles trapezoids with an altitude of 4 m, a lower base of 4 m, and an upper base of 6 m. Water is being poured into the trough at the rate of 10 m³/min. How fast is the water level rising when the water is 2 m deep?

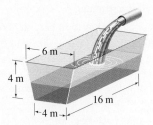

37. In Exercise 36, if the water level is decreasing at the rate of 25 cm/min when the water is 3 m deep, at what rate is water being drawn from the trough?

38. A ladder 7 m long is leaning against a wall. If the bottom of the ladder is pushed horizontally toward the wall at 1.5 m/sec, how fast is the top of the ladder sliding up the wall when the bottom is 2 m from the wall?

39. A ladder 20 ft long is leaning against an embankment inclined 60° to the horizontal. If the bottom of the ladder is being moved horizontally toward the embankment at 1 ft/sec, how fast is the top of the ladder moving when the bottom is 4 ft from the embankment?

40. If a ladder of length 30 ft that is leaning against a wall has its upper end sliding down the wall at the rate of ½ ft/sec, what is the rate of change of the

measure of the acute angle made by the ladder with the ground when the upper end is 18 ft above the ground?

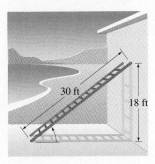

41. An airplane is flying at a constant speed at an altitude of 10,000 ft on a line that will take it directly over an observer on the ground. At a given instant the observer notes that the angle of elevation of the airplane is $\frac{1}{3}\pi$ radians and is increasing at the rate of $\frac{1}{60}$ rad/sec. Find the speed of the airplane.

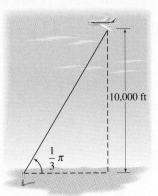

42. A ship is located 4 mi from a straight shore and has a radar transmitter that rotates 32 times per minute. How fast is the radar beam moving along the shoreline when the beam makes an angle of 45° with the shore?

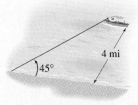

43. After blast-off, a space shuttle climbs vertically and a radar-tracking dish, located 1000 yd from the launch pad, follows the shuttle. How fast is the radar dish revolving 10 sec after blast-off if at that time the velocity of the shuttle is 100 yd/sec and the shuttle is 500 yd above the ground?

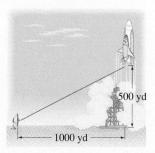

44. Water is poured at the rate of 8 ft³/min into a conical-shaped tank, 20 ft deep and 10 ft in diameter at the top. If the tank has a leak in the bottom and the water level is rising at the rate of 1 in./min, when the water is 16 ft deep, how fast is the water leaking?

45. Show that if the volume of a balloon is decreasing at a rate proportional to its surface area, the radius of the balloon is shrinking at a constant rate.

CHAPTER 2 REVIEW

▶ *SUGGESTIONS FOR REVIEW OF CHAPTER 2*

1. Define the *tangent line* to the graph of the function f at the point $P(x_1, f(x_1))$.

2. Define the *normal line* to a graph at a given point.

3. Define the *derivative* of the function f at a number x in the domain of f.

4. State two formulas giving $f'(x_1)$, the derivative of the function f at the number x_1.

5. What is the geometric interpretation of the derivative of the function f at the number x_1?

6. What is the Lagrange notation for the derivative of the function f at the number x_1? What is the Leibniz notation for a derivative?

7. Is it possible for a function to be differentiable at a number and not continuous there? If your answer is yes, give an example. If your answer is no, state the reason.

8. Is it possible for a function to be continuous at a number and not differentiable there? If your answer is yes, give an example. If your answer is no, state the reason.

9. State a theorem giving the relationship between differentiability and continuity of a function at a number.

10. State three reasons that a function f can fail to be differentiable at a number c and sketch the graph of such a function in each case.

11. Define the *derivative from the right* and the *derivative from the left* of a function f at the number x_1.

12. Make up an example of a function which is not differentiable at a number x_1 because the derivatives from the right and from the left at x_1 are not equal even though they both exist.

13. Make up an example of a function which is not differentiable at a number x_1, for which the graph of the function at the point where $x = x_1$ has a vertical tangent line.

14. Make up an example of a function which is neither continuous nor differentiable at a particular number in its domain.

15. What is the *symmetric difference quotient* of the function f at the number a?

16. Which gives a better approximation of $f'(a)$ for a specific tolerance: the symmetric difference quotient or the standard difference quotient?

17. Define the *numerical derivative* of the function f at the number a.

18. Why is the numerical derivative more important now than before the advent of electronic computers?

19. Does the numerical derivative of a function at a number always give an approximation of the actual derivative of the function at the number? If your answer is yes, explain why. If your answer is no, give an example of a function that justifies your answer.

20. How can you support on your graphics calculator the derivative of a function computed analytically?

21. State the three theorems on differentiation that enable us to differentiate any polynomial.

22. If the function h is the product of the functions f and g, state the product rule for differentiation that expresses the derivative of h in terms of the derivatives of f and g.

23. If the function h is the quotient (f/g) of the functions f and g, state the quotient rule for differentiation that expresses the derivative of h in terms of the derivatives of f and g.

24. If f is a function, what do we mean by the *second derivative* of f? What do we mean by the *third derivative?*

25. How many distinct derivatives does a polynomial function have?

26. What is the Leibniz notation for a second derivative?

27. Suppose a particle is moving on a line according to the equation $s = f(t)$. Define the velocity and acceleration of the particle at $t = t_1$.

28. What is the difference between the velocity and speed of a particle in rectilinear motion?

29. If $s = f(t)$ is an equation of motion of a particle on a horizontal line, how do you simulate the motion on your graphics calculator?

30. Do Suggestion 29 if an object (for example, a ball or a stone) is moving on a vertical line.

31. If $s = f(t)$ is an equation of motion of an object moving on a vertical line, describe how you would determine analytically the following: how high the object will go and how long it takes the object to reach the highest point; the instantaneous velocity of the object at a particular time; the speed of the object at a particular time; the instantaneous velocity of the object when it returns to the starting point.

32. Interpret the derivative of a function f as a rate of change.

33. Suppose $V(x)$ gives the volume of a solid in terms of a measure x. Interpret $V'(x_1)$ as a rate of change.

34. In economics, suppose $C(x)$ gives the total cost of x units of a commodity and $R(x)$ gives the total revenue received when x units are sold. Interpret the marginal cost, $C'(x_1)$, and the marginal revenue, $R'(x_1)$, as rates of change.

35. How do economists apply the derivative to approximate the cost of producing one additional unit after k units have been produced and to approximate the revenue from the sale of one additional unit after k units have been sold?

36. Give examples of applying the derivative as a rate of change in two disciplines other than geometry and economics.

37. State the theorems that give the derivatives of $\sin x$, $\cos x$, $\tan x$, $\cot x$, $\sec x$, and $\csc x$, where x is a real number.

38. What two important limits from Chapter 1 are used to prove the theorems that give the derivatives of sine and cosine?

39. To apply the theorems in Suggestion 37 for the derivatives of the trigonometric functions of θ, where θ is the measure of an angle, why must θ be measured in radians?

40. How are the derivatives of the six trigonometric functions applied to sketch their graphs?

41. Why is calculus necessary to sketch in a formal manner the graphs of the six trigonometric functions, which in precalculus could be obtained by applying only intuitive considerations?

42. If the function h is the composite of the functions f and g, that is $h = f \circ g$, at what numbers must functions f and g be differentiable if h is to be differentiable at the number x_1?

43. State the *chain rule* that gives the formula for the derivative of the composite of the functions f and g.

44. Make up an example showing how the chain rule is used to compute the derivative of a function h, which is the composite of two functions, one of which is a trigonometric function.

45. Make up an example showing how the chain rule is used to compute the derivative of a function h, which is the composite of two algebraic functions, only one of which is a polynomial.

46. What conditions are necessary for the motion of a particle on a horizontal line to be *simple harmonic?*

47. State the formula for the derivative of the power function for rational exponents.

48. Make up an example showing the computation of the derivative of the composite function $f \circ g$, where f is the power function for a non-integer rational exponent and g is a trigonometric function.

49. How do we compute the derivative of the absolute value function by using theorems on differentiation rather than the definition of the derivative? Demonstrate by computing the derivative of $|x - 5|$.

50. Distinguish between defining a function *explicitly* and *implicitly.*

51. What do we mean by *implicit differentiation?*

52. How is the chain rule applied when using implicit differentiation to find $\dfrac{dy}{dx}$ from an equation in x and y?

53. When computing $\dfrac{dy}{dx}$ by implicit differentiation from an equation in x and y, for what functions is $\dfrac{dy}{dx}$ the derivative?

54. What is a problem in *related rates?* Make up an example.

55. When defining the variables in the solution of a related-rate problem, which variable should you define first and why?

56. After defining the first variable in the solution of a related-rate problem, how should you define the other variables?

57. In the solution of a related-rate problem when you obtain an equation relating the variables, with respect to what variable should you differentiate?

58. How is implicit differentiation used in the solution of a related-rate problem?

▶ **MISCELLANEOUS EXERCISES FOR CHAPTER 2**

In Exercises 1 through 14, find the derivative of the function.

1. $f(x) = 5x^3 - 7x^2 + 2x - 3$

2. $g(x) = 5(x^4 + 3x^7)$

3. $g(x) = \dfrac{x^2}{4} + \dfrac{4}{x^2}$

4. $f(x) = \dfrac{4}{x^2} - \dfrac{3}{x^4}$

5. $F(x) = 2x^{1/2} - \dfrac{1}{2}x^{-1/2}$

6. $G(x) = \dfrac{x^2 - 4x + 4}{x - 1}$

7. $G(t) = (3t^2 - 4)(4t^3 + t - 1)$

8. $f(x) = (x^4 - 2x)(4x^2 + 2x + 5)$

9. $g(x) = \dfrac{x^3 + 1}{x^3 - 1}$

10. $h(y) = \dfrac{y^2}{y^3 + 8}$

11. $f(s) = (2s^3 - 3s + 7)^4$

12. $F(x) = (4x^4 - 4x^2 + 1)^{-1/3}$

13. $F(x) = (x^2 - 1)^{3/2}(x^2 - 4)^{1/2}$

14. $g(x) = (x^4 - x)^{-3}(5 - x^2)^{-1}$

In Exercises 15 through 20, compute the derivative.

15. $D_x[(x + 1)\sin x - x \cos x]$

16. $D_t(\sin^2 3t)$

17. $\dfrac{d}{dt}(\sqrt{\tan 4t})$

18. $\dfrac{d}{dx}\left(x \cos\dfrac{1}{x}\right)$

19. $D_w[\sin(\cos 3w) - \sin w \cos 3w]$

20. $D_x[\tan 2x \sec x + \tan(2 \sec x)]$

In Exercises 21 through 24, compute the derivative of the function and support your answer by plotting the graphs of your answer and the numerical derivative at x in the same window.

21. $f(x) = \left(\dfrac{2x}{x^2 + 1}\right)^2$

22. $g(x) = \sqrt{\dfrac{x}{4 - x^2}}$

23. $g(x) = \dfrac{\tan x}{1 + x}$

24. $f(x) = \dfrac{1 + x^2}{\sin x}$

In Exercises 25 through 28, find $\dfrac{dy}{dx}$.

25. $4x^2 + 4y^2 - y^3 = 0$

26. $xy^2 + 2y^3 = x - 2y$

27. $\tan x + \tan y = xy$

28. $\sin(x + y) + \sin(x - y) = 1$

Exercises 29 and 30 pertain to the continuous function f whose domain is the set of all real numbers and whose graph is sketched in the accompanying figure. Assume that each part of the graph that appears to be a line segment is a line segment. In each exercise do the following:
(a) Define f piecewise; Find (b) $f'_-(-2)$, (c) $f'_+(-2)$, (d) $f'_-(0)$, (e) $f'_+(0)$, (f) $f'_-(2)$, and (g) $f'_+(2)$. (h) At what numbers is f not differentiable?

29.

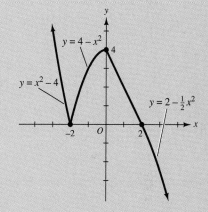

30.

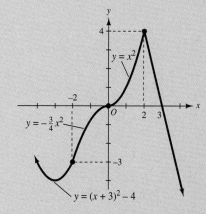

In Exercises 31 and 32, sketch the graph of a continuous function f whose domain is the set of all real numbers and which satisfies the given properties.

31. Function f is differentiable at every number except -2 and 2; $f(x) > 0$ if $x < -2$; $f(-2) = 0$; $0 < f(x) < 3$ if $-2 < x < 2$; $f(0) = 3$; $f(2) = 0$; $f(x) < 0$ if $x > 2$; $f'_+(-2) = 1$; $f'(0) = 0$; $f'_-(2) = -1$; $f'_+(2) = -2$; $\lim\limits_{x \to -2^-} \dfrac{f(x) - f(-2)}{x + 2} = -\infty$.

32. Function f is differentiable at every number except -1, 0, and 1; the range of f is $(-\infty, +\infty)$; $f(-1) = 0$; $f(0) = 1$; $f(1) = 3$; $f'_-(-1) = 1$; $f'_+(-1) = 2$; $f'_-(1) = 0$; $f'_+(1) = 1$; $\lim\limits_{x \to 0} \dfrac{f(x) - f(0)}{x} = +\infty$.

33. Find an equation of the tangent line to the curve $y = x^3 - 3x - 1$ at the point $(2, 1)$ and support your answer by plotting the line and the curve in the same window.

34. Find an equation of the normal line to the curve $y = \dfrac{8x}{x^2 + 3}$ at the point $(3, 2)$ and support your answer by plotting the line and the curve in the same window.

35. Find equations of the tangent lines to the curve $y = 2x^3 + 4x^2 - x$ that have slope $\frac{1}{2}$, and support your answers by plotting the lines and the curve in the same window.

36. Find an equation of the normal line to the curve $x - y = \sqrt{x + y}$ at the point $(3, 1)$.

37. Find equations of the tangent and normal lines to the curve $2x^3 + 2y^3 - 9xy = 0$ at the point $(2, 1)$.

38. Find equations of the tangent and normal lines to the curve $y = 8 \sin^3 2x$ at the point $(\frac{1}{12}\pi, 1)$ and support your answers by plotting the lines and the curve in the same window.

39. Prove that the line tangent to the curve $y = -x^4 + 2x^2 + x$ at the point $(1, 2)$ is also tangent to the curve at another point, and find this point.

40. Prove that the tangent lines to the curves
$$4y^3 - x^2y - x + 5y = 0$$
and
$$x^4 - 4y^3 + 5x + y = 0$$
at the origin are perpendicular.

41. Find $\dfrac{d^3y}{dx^3}$ if $y = \sqrt{3 - 2x}$.

42. Given $\dfrac{dy}{dx} = y^k$, where k is a constant and y is a function of x. Express $\dfrac{d^3y}{dx^3}$ in terms of y and k.

43. Given $f(x) = \frac{1}{12}x^4 + \frac{2}{3}x^3 + \frac{3}{2}x^2 + 8x + 2$. For what values of x is $f''(x) > 0$?

44. Find the rate of change of y with respect to x at the point $(3, 2)$ if $7y^2 - xy^3 = 4$.

In Exercises 45 and 46, a particle is moving along a horizontal line according to the given equation, where s meters is the directed distance of the particle from a point O at t seconds. The positive direction is to the right. Determine the intervals of time when the particle is moving to the right and when it is moving to the left. Also determine when the particle reverses its direction. Show the behavior of the motion by a figure similar to Figure 2 in Section 2.5, and choose values of t at random but include the values of t when the particle reverses its direction. Support your results by simulating the particle's motion on your graphics calculator.

45. $s = 2t^3 + 3t^2 - 12t - 5$ **46.** $s = \dfrac{t - 1}{t^2 - 2t + 5}$

In Exercises 47 and 48, a particle is moving along a horizontal line according to the given equation where at t seconds s meters is the directed distance of the particle from the origin, v meters per second is the instantaneous velocity of the particle, and a meters per second per second is the instantaneous acceleration of the particle. Find v and a in terms of t. Make a table similar to Table 3 in Section 2.5 that gives a description of the position and motion of the particle. Include in the table the intervals of time when the particle is moving to the left, when it is moving to the right, when the velocity is increasing, when the velocity is decreasing, when the speed is increasing, when the speed is decreasing, and the position of the particle with respect to the origin during these intervals of time. Show the behavior of the motion by a figure similar to Figure 10 in Section 2.5. Support your results by simulating the particle's motion on your graphics calculator.

47. $s = 4 - 9t + 6t^2 - t^3$ $t \geq 0$
48. $s = t^3 - 3t^2 - 9t + 13$ $t \geq 0$

In Exercises 49 and 50, a particle is moving along a line according to the given equation, where s feet is the directed distance of the particle from the origin at t seconds. Find the time when the instantaneous acceleration is zero, and then find the directed distance of the particle from the origin and the instantaneous velocity at this time.

49. $s = 9t^2 + 2\sqrt{2t} + 1$, $t \geq 0$
50. $s = \frac{4}{9}t^{3/2} + 2t^{1/2}$ $t \geq 0$

51. A hiker lost in a timberland is sighted by a search party in a helicopter. The searchers drop a bag of food supplies to the hiker from an altitude of 200 ft.

(a) Use Equation (10) in Exercises 2.5 to write an equation of motion of the bag, and simulate the motion on your graphics calculator. (b) Find the instantaneous velocity of the bag at 1 sec and 3 sec. (c) Find how long it takes the bag to hit the ground. (d) What is the speed of the bag when it hits the ground?

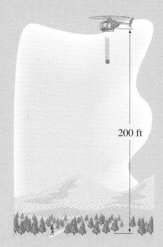

200 ft

52. Do Exercise 51 if the bag of supplies is thrown downward from the helicopter with an initial velocity of 20 ft/sec.

53. A ball is thrown vertically upward from the top of a house 112 ft high with an initial velocity of 96 ft/sec. (a) Use Equation (10) in Exercises 2.5 to write an equation of motion of the ball, and simulate the motion on your graphics calculator. (b) Estimate how high the ball will go and how long it takes the ball to reach its highest point. (c) Confirm your estimations in part (b) analytically. (d) Estimate how long it takes the ball to reach the ground. (e) Confirm your estimate in part (d) analytically. (f) Find the instantaneous velocity of the ball at 2 sec and 4 sec. (g) Find the speed of the ball at 2 sec and 4 sec. (h) Find the instantaneous velocity of the ball when it reaches the ground.

In Exercises 54 through 56, a particle is moving along a line according to the given equation of motion, where at t seconds, s centimeters is the directed distance of the particle from the origin, v centimeters per second is the instantaneous velocity, and a centimeters per second per second is the instantaneous acceleration. (a) Find v and a in terms of t. (b) Show that the motion is simple harmonic. (c) Simulate the motion on your graphics calculator.

54. $s = 5 - 2 \cos^2 t$ **55.** $s = \cos 2t + 2 \sin 2t$

56. $s = \sin(4t + \frac{1}{3}\pi) + \sin(4t + \frac{1}{6}\pi)$

57. A manufacturer can make a profit of $200 on each item if not more than 800 items are produced each week. The profit decreases $0.20 per item over 800. (a) Find a mathematical model expressing the manufacturer's weekly profit as a function of the number of items produced each week. Even though the independent variable, by definition, will represent a nonnegative integer, allow this variable to represent a nonnegative real number so that you have the necessary continuity requirements. (b) Prove that your function in part (a) is continuous on its domain. (c) Determine if your function in part (a) is differentiable at 800.

58. Stefan's law states that a body emits radiant energy according to the formula $R = kT^4$, where R is the measure of the rate of emission of the radiant energy per square unit of area, T is the measure of the Kelvin temperature of the surface, and k is a constant. Find (a) the average rate of change of R with respect to T as T increases from 200 to 300; (b) the instantaneous rate of change of R with respect to T when T is 200.

59. If A square units is the area of an isosceles right triangle for which each leg has a length of x units, find (a) the average rate of change of A with respect to x as x changes from 8.00 to 8.01; (b) the instantaneous rate of change of A with respect to x when x is 8.00.

60. If $y = x^{2/3}$, find the relative rate of change of y with respect to x when (a) $x = 8$, and (b) $x = c$, where c is a constant.

61. The supply equation for a calculator is $y = m^2 + \sqrt{m}$, where $100y$ calculators are supplied when m dollars is the price per calculator. Find (a) the average rate of change of the supply with respect to the price when the price is increased from $16 to $17; (b) the instantaneous (or marginal) rate of change of the supply with respect to the price when the price is $16.

62. The remainder theorem of elementary algebra states that if $P(x)$ is a polynomial in x and r is any real number, then there is a polynomial $Q(x)$ such that $P(x) = Q(x)(x - r) + P(r)$. What is $\lim_{x \to r} Q(x)$?

63. Use the definition of a derivative to find $f'(-5)$ if $f(x) = \dfrac{3}{x + 2}$.

64. Use the definition of a derivative to find $f'(x)$ if $f(x) = 3x^2 - 5x + 1$.

65. Use the definition of a derivative to find $f'(x)$ if $f(x) = \sqrt{4x - 3}$.

66. Use the definition of a derivative to find $f'(5)$ if $f(x) = \sqrt{3x + 1}$.

67. Find $f''(\pi)$ if $f(x) = \sqrt{2 + \cos x}$.

68. Find $f''(x)$ if $f(x) = 3 \sin^2 x - 4 \cos^2 x$.

69. Find $f'(x)$ if $f(x) = (|x + 1| - |x|)^2$.

70. Find $f'(-3)$ if $f(x) = (|x| - x)\sqrt[3]{9x}$.

In Exercises 71 and 72, the equation describes the motion of a weight suspended from a spring and vibrating vertically, where s centimeters is the distance of the weight from its central position (the origin) at t seconds and the positive direction is upward. (a) Find the velocity and acceleration of the motion for any t. (b) Show that the motion is simple harmonic. (c) Find the amplitude, period, and frequency of the motion. (d) Simulate the up-and-down motion of the spring on your graphics calculator. (e) Plot the graph of the equation of motion.

71. $s = 5 \sin \frac{1}{6}\pi t$ **72.** $s = 6 \cos \pi(4t - \frac{1}{2})$

In Exercises 73 and 74, a particle is moving along a line according to the given equation of motion, where at t seconds, s feet is the directed distance of the particle from the origin, v feet per second is the velocity and a feet per second per second is the acceleration. (a) Find v and a in terms of t. (b) Show that the motion is simple harmonic. (c) Simulate the motion on your graphics calculator.

73. $s = 2 \cos(3t + \frac{1}{3}\pi) + 4 \sin(3t - \frac{1}{6}\pi)$

74. $s = 3 - 6 \sin^2 4t$

75. If a particle is moving along a line according to the equation of motion $s = \cos 2t + \cos t$, prove that the motion is not simple harmonic.

76. A particle is moving on a line according to the equation of motion $s = \sqrt{a + bt^2}$, where a and b are positive constants. Prove that the measure of the acceleration of the particle is inversely proportional to s^3 for any t.

77. If $C(x)$ dollars is the total cost of manufacturing x chairs, and $C(x) = x^2 + 40x + 800$, find **(a)** the marginal cost function; **(b)** the marginal cost when 20 chairs are manufactured; **(c)** the actual cost of manufacturing the twenty-first chair.

78. The total revenue received from the sale of x lamps is $R(x)$ dollars and $R(x) = 100x - \frac{1}{6}x^2$. Find **(a)** the marginal revenue function; **(b)** the marginal revenue when $x = 15$; **(c)** the actual revenue from the sale of the sixteenth lamp.

79. In a lake a predator fish feeds on a smaller fish, and the predator population at any time is a function of the number of small fish in the lake at that time. Suppose that when there are x small fish in the lake, the predator population is y, and $y = \frac{1}{60,000}x^2 - \frac{1}{100}x + 40$. If the fishing season ended t weeks ago, $x = 300t + 375$. At what rate is the population of the predator fish growing 10 weeks after the close of the fishing season? Do not express y in terms of t, but use the chain rule.

80. The demand equation for a particular candy bar is

$$px + x + 20p = 3000$$

where $1000x$ candy bars are demanded per week when p cents is the price per bar. If the current price of the candy is 49 cents per bar and the price per bar is increasing at the rate of 0.2 cent each week, find the rate of change in the demand.

81. A ship leaves a port at noon and travels due west at 20 knots. At 6 P.M. a second ship leaves the same port and travels northwest at 15 knots. How fast are the two ships separating when the second ship has traveled 90 nautical miles?

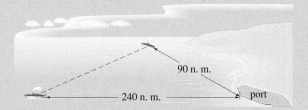

90 n. m.

240 n. m.   port

82. A reservoir is 80 m long and its cross section is an isosceles trapezoid having equal sides of 10 m, an upper base of 17 m, and a lower base of 5 m. At the instant when the water is 5 m deep, find the rate at which the water is leaking out if the water level is falling at the rate of 0.1 m/hr.

83. A funnel in the form of a cone is 10 in. across the top and 8 in. deep. Water is flowing into the funnel at the rate of 12 in.³/sec and out at the rate of 4 in.³/sec. How fast is the surface of the water rising when it is 5 in. deep?

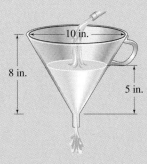

10 in.

8 in.

5 in.

84. As the last car of a train passes under a bridge, an automobile crosses the bridge on a roadway perpendicular to the track and 30 ft above it. The train is traveling at the rate of 80 ft/sec and the automobile is traveling at the rate of 40 ft/sec. How fast are the train and the automobile separating after 2 sec?

Figure for Exercise 84

85. A man 6 ft tall is walking toward a building at the rate of 4 ft/sec. If there is a light on the ground 40 ft from the building, how fast is the man's shadow on the building growing shorter when he is 30 ft from the building?

86. A burn on a person's skin is in the shape of a circle. If the radius of the burn is decreasing at the rate of 0.05 cm per day when it is 1.0 cm, what is the rate of decrease of the area of the burn at that instant?

87. Given

$$f(x) = \begin{cases} x^2 + 2 & \text{if } x \le 3 \\ 20 - x^2 & \text{if } 3 < x \end{cases}$$

(a) Sketch the graph of f. (b) Determine if f is continuous at 3. (c) Determine if f is differentiable at 3.

88. Given

$$f(x) = \begin{cases} x^2 - 16 & \text{if } x < 4 \\ 8x - 32 & \text{if } 4 \le x \end{cases}$$

(a) Sketch the graph of f. (b) Determine if f is continuous at 4. (c) Determine if f is differentiable at 4.

89. Given $f(x) = |x|^3$. (a) Sketch the graph of f. (b) Find $\lim_{x \to 0} f(x)$ if it exists. (c) Find $f'(0)$ if it exists.

90. Given $f(x) = x^2 \operatorname{sgn} x$. (a) Where is f differentiable? (b) Is f' continuous on its domain?

91. Given

$$f(x) = \begin{cases} ax^2 + b & \text{if } x \le 1 \\ \dfrac{1}{|x|} & \text{if } 1 < x \end{cases}$$

Find the values of a and b such that $f'(1)$ exists.

92. Suppose

$$f(x) = \begin{cases} x^3 & \text{if } x < 1 \\ ax^2 + bx + c & \text{if } 1 \le x \end{cases}$$

Find the values of a, b, and c such that $f''(1)$ exists.

93. Show that the tangent line at any point (x_1, y_1) on the circle

$$x^2 + y^2 = r^2$$

is perpendicular to the line through (x_1, y_1) and the center of the circle.

94. If $f(u) = \dfrac{1}{u^2}$ and $g(x) = \dfrac{\sqrt{x}}{\sqrt{2x^3 - 6x + 1}}$, find the derivative of $f \circ g$ in two ways: (a) first find $(f \circ g)(x)$ and then find $(f \circ g)'(x)$; (b) use the chain rule.

95. Suppose $f(x) = 3x + |x|$ and $g(x) = \frac{3}{4}x - \frac{1}{4}|x|$. Prove that neither $f'(0)$ nor $g'(0)$ exists but that $(f \circ g)'(0)$ does exist.

96. Give an example of two functions f and g for which f is differentiable at $g(0)$, g is not differentiable at 0, and $f \circ g$ is differentiable at 0.

97. Give an example of two functions f and g for which f is not differentiable at $g(0)$, g is differentiable at 0, and $f \circ g$ is differentiable at 0.

98. Given

$$f(x) = \begin{cases} 0 & \text{if } x < 0 \\ x^n & \text{if } 0 \le x \end{cases}$$

where n is a positive integer. (a) For what values of n is f continuous for all values of x? (b) For what values of n is f differentiable for all values of x? (c) For what values of n is f' continuous for all values of x?

99. If $f'(x_1)$ exists, prove that

$$\lim_{x \to x_1} \frac{xf(x_1) - x_1 f(x)}{x - x_1} = f(x_1) - x_1 f'(x_1)$$

100. Let f and g be two functions whose domains are the set of all real numbers. Furthermore, suppose that (i) $g(x) = xf(x) + 1$; (ii) $g(a + b) = g(a) \cdot g(b)$ for all a and b; (iii) $\lim_{x \to 0} f(x) = 1$. Prove that $g'(x) = g(x)$.

101. If the two functions f and g are differentiable at the number x_1, is the composite function $f \circ g$ necessarily differentiable at x_1? If your answer is yes, prove it. If your answer is no, give a counterexample.

102. Suppose $g(x) = |f(x)|$. If $f^{(n)}(x)$ exists and $f(x) \ne 0$, prove that

$$g^{(n)}(x) = \frac{f(x)}{|f(x)|} f^{(n)}(x)$$

103. Prove that $D_x{}^n(\sin x) = \sin(x + \frac{1}{2}n\pi)$. *Hint:* Use mathematical induction and the formulas $\sin(x + \frac{1}{2}\pi) = \cos x$ or $\cos(x + \frac{1}{2}\pi) = -\sin x$ after each differentiation.

104. If $y = \dfrac{1}{1 - 2x}$ prove by mathematical induction that

$$\frac{d^n y}{dx^n} = \frac{2^n n!}{(1 - 2x)^{n+1}}$$

BEHAVIOR OF FUNCTIONS AND THEIR GRAPHS, EXTREME FUNCTION VALUES, AND APPROXIMATIONS

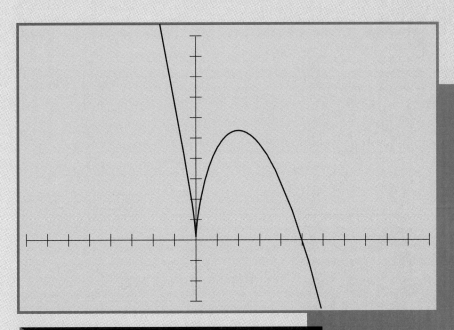

The intrepretation of the derivative as the slope of a tangent line gives us information about the behavior of functions and their graphs. We begin in Section 3.1 by defining and determining maximum and minimum function values. Real-world applications of maxima and minima occur in many diverse fields as you will find out when you study Sections 3.2 and 3.9. In particular, we determine the strongest beam that can be cut from a given cylindrical log, as well as the dimensions of a box requiring the least amount of material for a specific volume.

One of the most important theorems in calculus is the *mean-value theorem*, discussed in Section 3.3. This theorem is used to prove many theorems of both differential and integral calculus, as well as other subjects, such as numerical analysis.

We apply the derivative to techniques of graphing functions in Sections 3.4 through 3.6. These techniques are important because they give us a means of confirming analytically what we can conjecture from a graphics calculator. Sometimes the behavior of a certain graph near certain points is not apparent from what appears on the calculator screen, so that calculus is necessary to determine specific properties of graphs. For example, the derivative reveals where function values are increasing and where they are decreasing. The derivative also enables us to locate points where the tangent line is horizontal and to find intervals on which the graph lies above the tangent line and intervals on which it lies below the tangent line.

We treat limits at infinity in Section 3.7 and apply these limits to find horizontal asymptotes of a graph. In the final section of the chapter we discuss three numerical processes used for approximating function values.

▶ *LOOKING AHEAD*

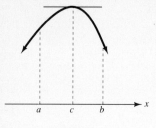

FIGURE 1

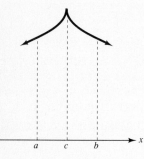

FIGURE 2

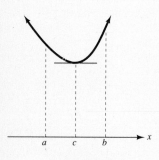

FIGURE 3

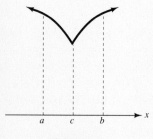

FIGURE 4

3.1 MAXIMUM AND MINIMUM FUNCTION VALUES

An important application of the derivative is to determine where a function attains its *maximum and minimum (extreme) values*. In this section, we begin our treatment of extreme function values by discussing both relative and absolute extrema and the extreme-value theorem, applications of which are presented in the next section.

3.1.1 Definition of a Relative Maximum Value

The function f has a **relative maximum value** at the number c if there exists an open interval containing c, on which f is defined, such that $f(c) \geq f(x)$ for all x in this interval.

Figures 1 and 2 show a portion of the graph of a function having a relative maximum value at c.

3.1.2 Definition of a Relative Minimum Value

The function f has a **relative minimum value** at the number c if there exists an open interval containing c, on which f is defined, such that $f(c) \leq f(x)$ for all x in this interval.

Figures 3 and 4 show a portion of the graph of a function having a relative minimum value at c.

If a function has either a relative maximum or a relative minimum value at c, then the function has a **relative extremum** at c.

The following theorem is used to locate the possible numbers at which a function has a relative extremum.

3.1.3 Theorem

If $f(x)$ exists for all values of x in the open interval (a, b), and if f has a relative extremum at c, where $a < c < b$, and if $f'(c)$ exists, then $f'(c) = 0$.

We defer the proof of this theorem to the end of the section. In geometric terms, the theorem states that if f has a relative extremum at c, and if $f'(c)$ exists, then the graph of f must have a horizontal tangent line at the point where $x = c$. Observe that this situation prevails for the graphs in Figures 1 and 3. The theorem also indicates that if f is a differentiable function, then the only possible numbers c for which f can have a relative extremum are those for which $f'(c) = 0$.

▷ **ILLUSTRATION 1**   Let f be the function defined by

$$f(x) = x^2 - 4x + 5$$
$$f'(x) = 2x - 4$$

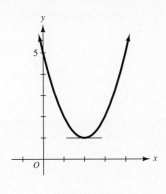

$$f(x) = x^2 - 4x + 5$$

FIGURE 5

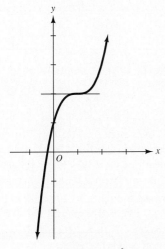

$$f(x) = (x - 1)^3 + 2$$

FIGURE 6

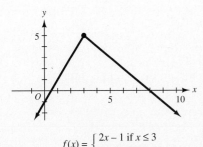

$$f(x) = \begin{cases} 2x - 1 & \text{if } x \leq 3 \\ 8 - x & \text{if } 3 < x \end{cases}$$

FIGURE 7

Because $f'(2) = 0$, f may have a relative extremum at 2. Because $f(2) = 1$ and $1 < f(x)$ when either $x < 2$ or $x > 2$, Definition 3.1.2 guarantees that f has a relative minimum value at 2. Figure 5 shows the graph of f, a parabola whose vertex is at the point $(2, 1)$ where the graph has a horizontal tangent. ◄

Note that $f'(c)$ can equal zero even if f does not have a relative extremum at c, as shown in the following illustration.

▷ **ILLUSTRATION 2**   Consider the function f defined by

$$f(x) = (x - 1)^3 + 2$$
$$f'(x) = 3(x - 1)^2$$

Because $f'(1) = 0$, f may have a relative extremum at 1. However, because $f(1) = 2$ and $2 > f(x)$ when $x < 1$ and $2 < f(x)$ when $x > 1$, neither Definition 3.1.1 nor Definition 3.1.2 applies. So f does not have a relative extremum at 1. The graph of this function, shown in Figure 6, has a horizontal tangent at the point $(1, 2)$, which is consistent with the fact that the derivative is zero there. ◄

A function may have a relative extremum at a number at which the derivative fails to exist. This situation occurs for the functions whose graphs appear in Figures 2 and 4 as well as for the function in the following illustration.

▷ **ILLUSTRATION 3**   Let the function f be defined by

$$f(x) = \begin{cases} 2x - 1 & \text{if } x \leq 3 \\ 8 - x & \text{if } 3 < x \end{cases}$$

The graph of this function appears in Figure 7, showing that f has a relative maximum value at 3. The derivative from the left at 3 is given by $f'_-(3) = 2$, and the derivative from the right at 3 is given by $f'_+(3) = -1$. Therefore we conclude that $f'(3)$ does not exist. ◄

Illustration 3 demonstrates why the condition "$f'(c)$ exists" must be included in the hypothesis of Theorem 3.1.3.

It is possible that a function f can be defined at a number c where $f'(c)$ does not exist and yet f may not have a relative extremum there. The following illustration gives such a function.

▷ **ILLUSTRATION 4**   Let the function f be defined by

$$f(x) = x^{1/3}$$

The domain of f is the set of all real numbers.

$$f'(x) = \frac{1}{3x^{2/3}} \qquad \text{if } x \neq 0$$

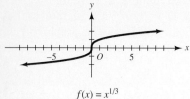

$f(x) = x^{1/3}$

FIGURE 8

Furthermore, $f'(0)$ does not exist. Figure 8 shows the graph of f. The function has no relative extrema. ◀

In summary, then, if a function f is defined at a number c, a necessary condition for f to have a relative extremum there is that either $f'(c) = 0$ or $f'(c)$ does not exist. But this condition is not sufficient.

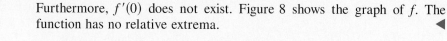

3.1.4 Definition of a Critical Number

If c is a number in the domain of the function f, and if either $f'(c) = 0$ or $f'(c)$ does not exist, then c is a **critical number** of f.

Because of this definition and the previous discussion, a necessary, but not sufficient, condition for a function to have a relative extremum at c is for c to be a critical number.

▶ **EXAMPLE 1**   Given

$$f(x) = x^4 + 4x^3 - 2x^2 - 12x$$

(a) Estimate graphically to the nearest tenth the critical numbers of f.
(b) Confirm the answers in part (a) analytically.

Solution

(a) Because $f(x)$ is a polynomial, $f'(x)$ exists everywhere. The only critical numbers are, therefore, those values of x for which $f'(x) = 0$, that is, the x coordinates of the points on the graph of f for which the tangent line is horizontal. Figure 9 shows the graph of f plotted in the $[-10, 10]$ by $[-10, 10]$ window. On our calculator, the tangent line appears to be horizontal at the points $(-3.0, -9.0)$, $(-1.0, 7.0)$, and $(1.0, -9.0)$. Thus, we estimate the critical numbers to be -3.0, -1.0, and 1.0.

(b) We compute $f'(x)$, set it equal to zero, and solve for x.

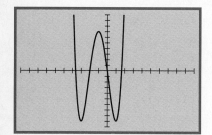

$[-10, 10]$ by $[-10, 10]$

$f(x) = x^4 + 4x^3 - 2x^2 - 12x$

FIGURE 9

$$4x^3 + 12x^2 - 4x - 12 = 0$$
$$x^3 + 3x^2 - x - 3 = 0$$
$$x^2(x + 3) - (x + 3) = 0$$
$$(x + 3)(x^2 - 1) = 0$$
$$x + 3 = 0 \qquad x^2 - 1 = 0$$
$$x = -3 \qquad x^2 = 1$$
$$x = \pm 1$$

We have confirmed the critical numbers to be -3, -1, and 1. ◀

▶ **EXAMPLE 2**

(a) Find the critical numbers of the function defined by

$$f(x) = x^{4/3} + 4x^{1/3}$$

Support the answers in part (a) graphically two ways: **(b)** Plot the graph of f; **(c)** plot the graph of NDER($f(x), x$).

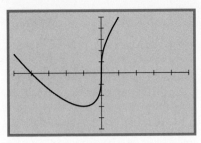

[−5, 5] by [−5, 5]

$f(x) = x^{4/3} + 4x^{1/3}$

FIGURE 10

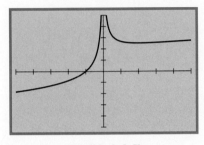

[−5, 5] by [−5, 5]

NDER$(x^{4/3} + 4x^{1/3}, x)$

FIGURE 11

Solution

(a)
$$f'(x) = \tfrac{4}{3}x^{1/3} + \tfrac{4}{3}x^{-2/3}$$
$$= \tfrac{4}{3}x^{-2/3}(x + 1)$$
$$= \frac{4(x + 1)}{3x^{2/3}}$$

When $x = -1$, $f'(x) = 0$, and when $x = 0$, $f'(x)$ does not exist. Both -1 and 0 are in the domain of f; therefore the critical numbers of f are -1 and 0.

(b) Figure 10 shows the graph of f plotted in the $[-5, 5]$ by $[-5, 5]$ window. The graph appears to have a horizontal tangent line at the point $(-1, -3)$ and a vertical tangent line at the point $(0, 0)$. Therefore, the slope of the tangent line is 0 when $x = -1$ and the tangent line has no slope when $x = 0$. These facts support our answers in part (a).

(c) Figure 11 shows the graph of NDER$(f(x), x)$ plotted in the $[-5, 5]$ by $[-5, 5]$ window. Because the graph of f' intersects the x axis at $(-1, 0)$, $f'(-1) = 0$. The graph of f' has the y axis as a vertical asymptote, which indicates that $f'(0)$ does not exist. Again we have supported our answers in part (a).   ◀

▶ **EXAMPLE 3**   Find the critical numbers of the function defined by

$$g(x) = \sin x \cos x$$

Solution   Because $\sin 2x = 2 \sin x \cos x$,

$$g(x) = \tfrac{1}{2} \sin 2x$$
$$g'(x) = \tfrac{1}{2}(\cos 2x)2$$
$$= \cos 2x$$

Since $g'(x)$ exists for all x, the only critical numbers are those for which $g'(x) = 0$. Because $\cos 2x = 0$ when

$$2x = \tfrac{1}{2}\pi + k\pi \qquad \text{where } k \text{ is any integer}$$

the critical numbers of g are $\tfrac{1}{4}\pi + \tfrac{1}{2}k\pi$, where k is any integer.   ◀

We are frequently concerned with a function defined on a given interval, and we wish to find the largest or smallest function value on the interval. These intervals can be either closed, open, or closed at one end and open at the other. The greatest function value on an interval is called the *absolute maximum value*, and the smallest function value on an interval is called the *absolute minimum value*. Following are the precise definitions.

3.1.5 Definition of an Absolute Maximum Value on an Interval

The function f has an **absolute maximum value on an interval** if there is some number c in the interval such that $f(c) \geq f(x)$ for all x in the interval. The number $f(c)$ is then the absolute maximum value of f on the interval.

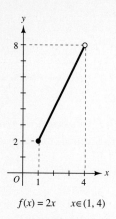

$f(x) = 2x$ $x \in (1, 4)$

FIGURE 12

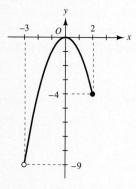

$f(x) = -x^2$ $x \in (-3, 2]$

FIGURE 13

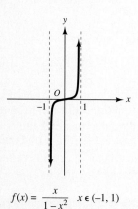

$f(x) = \dfrac{x}{1 - x^2}$ $x \in (-1, 1)$

FIGURE 14

3.1.6 Definition of an Absolute Minimum Value on an Interval

The function f has an **absolute minimum value on an interval** if there is some number c in the interval such that $f(c) \le f(x)$ for all x in the interval. The number $f(c)$ is then the absolute minimum value of f on the interval.

An **absolute extremum** of a function on an interval is either an absolute maximum value or an absolute minimum value of the function on the interval. A function may or may not have an absolute extremum on a particular interval. In each of the following illustrations, a function and an interval are given, and we find the absolute extrema of the function on the interval if there are any.

▷ **ILLUSTRATION 5**   Suppose f is the function defined by

$$f(x) = 2x$$

The graph of f on $[1, 4)$ is sketched in Figure 12. This function has an absolute minimum value of 2 on $[1, 4)$. There is no absolute maximum value of f on $[1, 4)$ because $\lim\limits_{x \to 4^-} f(x) = 8$, but $f(x)$ is always less than 8 on the interval.   ◄

▷ **ILLUSTRATION 6**   Consider the function f defined by

$$f(x) = -x^2$$

The graph of f on $(-3, 2]$ appears in Figure 13. This function has an absolute maximum value of 0 on $(-3, 2]$. There is no absolute minimum value of f on $(-3, 2]$ because $\lim\limits_{x \to -3^+} f(x) = -9$, but $f(x)$ is always greater than -9 on the given interval.   ◄

▷ **ILLUSTRATION 7**   The function f defined by

$$f(x) = \frac{x}{1 - x^2}$$

has neither an absolute maximum value nor an absolute minimum value on $(-1, 1)$. Figure 14 shows the graph of f on $(-1, 1)$. Observe that

$$\lim_{x \to -1^+} f(x) = -\infty \qquad \lim_{x \to 1^-} f(x) = +\infty$$ ◄

▷ **ILLUSTRATION 8**   Let f be the function defined by

$$f(x) = \begin{cases} x + 1 & \text{if } x < 1 \\ x^2 - 6x + 7 & \text{if } 1 \le x \end{cases}$$

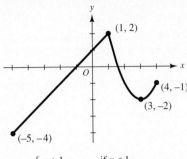

$$f(x) = \begin{cases} x+1 & \text{if } x < 1 \\ x^2 - 6x + 7 & \text{if } 1 \le x \end{cases} \quad x \in [-5, 4]$$

FIGURE 15

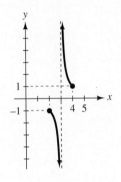

$$f(x) = \frac{1}{x-3} \quad x \in [2, 4], x \ne 3$$

FIGURE 16

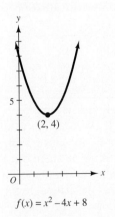

$$f(x) = x^2 - 4x + 8$$

FIGURE 17

The graph of f on $[-5, 4]$ appears in Figure 15. The absolute maximum value of f on $[-5, 4]$ occurs at 1, and $f(1) = 2$; the absolute minimum value of f on $[-5, 4]$ occurs at -5, and $f(-5) = -4$. Note that f has a relative maximum value at 1 and a relative minimum value at 3. Also observe that 1 is a critical number of f because $f'(1)$ does not exist, and 3 is a critical number of f because $f'(3) = 0$. ◄

▷ **ILLUSTRATION 9**   The function f defined by

$$f(x) = \frac{1}{x-3}$$

has neither an absolute maximum value nor an absolute minimum value on $[2, 4]$. See Figure 16 for the graph of f on this interval. $\lim\limits_{x \to 3^-} f(x) = -\infty$; so $f(x)$ can be made less than any negative number by taking $3 - x > 0$ and less than a suitable positive δ. Also, $\lim\limits_{x \to 3^+} f(x) = +\infty$; so $f(x)$ can be made greater than any positive number by taking $x - 3 > 0$ and less than a suitable positive δ. ◄

We may speak of an absolute extremum of a function when no interval is specified. In such a case we are referring to an absolute extremum of the function on its entire domain.

▷ **ILLUSTRATION 10**   The graph of the function f defined by

$$f(x) = x^2 - 4x + 8$$

is the parabola, shown in Figure 17. The lowest point of the parabola is at $(2, 4)$, and the parabola opens upward. The function has an absolute minimum value of 4 at 2. There is no absolute maximum value of f. ◄

Referring back to Illustrations 5–10, we see that the only case in which there are both an absolute maximum function value and an absolute minimum function value is in Illustration 8, where the function is continuous on the closed interval $[-5, 4]$. In the other illustrations, either we do not have a closed interval or we do not have a continuous function. If a function is continuous on a closed interval, a theorem, called the *extreme-value theorem*, assures that the function has both an absolute maximum value and an absolute minimum value on the interval. The proof of this theorem, beyond the scope of this book, can be found in an advanced calculus text.

3.1.7 The Extreme-Value Theorem

If the function f is continuous on the closed interval $[a, b]$, then f has an absolute maximum value and an absolute minimum value on $[a, b]$.

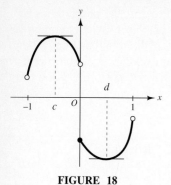

FIGURE 18

The extreme-value theorem states that continuity of a function on a closed interval is a sufficient condition to guarantee that the function has both an absolute maximum value and an absolute minimum value on the interval. However, it is not a necessary condition. For example, the function whose graph appears in Figure 18 has an absolute maximum value at $x = c$ and an absolute minimum value at $x = d$, even though the function is discontinuous on the open interval $(-1, 1)$.

An absolute extremum of a function continuous on a closed interval must be either a relative extremum or a function value at an endpoint of the interval. Because a necessary condition for a function to have a relative extremum at a number c is for c to be a critical number, the absolute maximum value and the absolute minimum value of a continuous function f on a closed interval $[a, b]$ can be determined by the following procedure:

1. Find the function values at the critical numbers of f on (a, b).
2. Find the values of $f(a)$ and $f(b)$.
3. The largest of the values from steps 1 and 2 is the absolute maximum value, and the smallest of the values is the absolute minimum value.

▶ **EXAMPLE 4**   Find the absolute extrema of f on $[-2, 3]$ if

$$f(x) = x^3 - 6x - 1$$

and support the answers graphically.

Solution   Because f is continuous on $[-2, 3]$, the extreme-value theorem applies. To find the critical numbers of f, we first compute $f'(x)$:

$$f'(x) = 3x^2 - 6$$

Because $f'(x)$ exists for all real numbers, the only critical numbers will be the values of x for which $f'(x) = 0$. We set $f'(x) = 0$.

$$3x^2 - 6 = 0$$
$$x = \pm\sqrt{2}$$
$$x \approx \pm 1.41$$

Thus the critical numbers of f are approximately ± 1.41, and each of these numbers is in the given closed interval $[-2, 3]$. The function values at the critical numbers and the endpoints of the interval appear in Table 1.

The absolute maximum value of f on $[-2, 3]$ is therefore 8, which occurs at the right endpoint 3, and the absolute minimum value of f on $[-2, 3]$ is approximately -6.66, which occurs at the critical number 1.41.

Figure 19 shows the graph of f plotted in the $[-2, 3]$ by $[-10, 10]$ window. The graph supports our answers.   ◀

Table 1

x	-2	-1.41	1.41	3
$f(x)$	3	4.66	-6.66	8

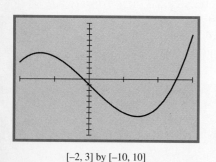

$[-2, 3]$ by $[-10, 10]$

$f(x) = x^3 - 6x - 1$

FIGURE 19

▶ **EXAMPLE 5**   Estimate graphically the absolute extrema of f on $[1, 5]$ if

$$f(x) = (x - 2)^{2/3}$$

and confirm the answers analytically.

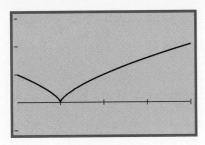

[1, 5] by [−1, 3]

$f(x) = (x - 2)^{2/3}$

FIGURE 20

Table 2

x	1	2	5
$f(x)$	1	0	$\sqrt[3]{9}$

Solution The graph of f plotted in the $[1, 5]$ by $[-1, 3]$ window appears in Figure 20. From the graph, the absolute minimum value is 0 occurring at $x = 2$. The absolute maximum value occurs at the right endpoint 5, and on our calculator, we estimate $f(5)$ to be 2.08.

We confirm the answers analytically by applying the extreme-value theorem because f is continuous on $[1, 5]$.

$$f'(x) = \frac{2}{3(x - 2)^{1/3}}$$

There is no value of x for which $f'(x) = 0$. However, because $f'(x)$ does not exist at 2, we conclude that 2 is a critical number of f; so the absolute extrema occur either at 2 or at one of the endpoints of the interval. The function values at these numbers are given in Table 2.

From the table we conclude that the absolute minimum value of f on $[1, 5]$ is 0 and the absolute maximum value is $\sqrt[3]{9} \approx 2.08$, thus confirming our answers. ◄

Before proving Theorem 3.1.3, as promised, we prove a preliminary theorem used in the proof of Theorem 3.1.3 as well as in the proof of some later theorems.

3.1.8 Theorem

    (i) If $\lim\limits_{x \to c} f(x)$ exists and is positive, there is an open interval containing c such that $f(x) > 0$ for every $x \neq c$ in the interval.

    (ii) If $\lim\limits_{x \to c} f(x)$ exists and is negative, there is an open interval containing c such that $f(x) < 0$ for every $x \neq c$ in the interval.

Proof of part (i) Let $\lim\limits_{x \to c} f(x) = L$, where, by hypothesis, $L > 0$. Applying the definition of a limit (1.5.1) with $\epsilon = \frac{1}{2}L$, there is a $\delta > 0$ such that

$$\text{if } 0 < |x - c| < \delta \quad \text{then} \quad |f(x) - L| < \tfrac{1}{2}L \tag{1}$$

Because $0 < |x - c| < \delta$ is equivalent to the statement

$$x \text{ is in the open interval } (c - \delta, c + \delta) \quad \text{but} \quad x \neq c \tag{2}$$

and $|f(x) - L| < \frac{1}{2}L$ is equivalent to the continued inequality

$$\tfrac{1}{2}L < f(x) < \tfrac{3}{2}L \tag{3}$$

we substitute (2) and (3) in (1) and we have the statement

if x is in the open interval $(c - \delta, c + \delta)$ but $x \neq c$ then

$$\tfrac{1}{2}L < f(x) < \tfrac{3}{2}L$$

Because $L > 0$, this statement means that $f(x) > 0$ for every $x \neq c$ in the open interval $(c - \delta, c + \delta)$. ∎

The proof of part (ii) is similar to the proof of part (i) and is left as an exercise (see Exercise 57).

Proof of Theorem 3.1.3 We wish to show that if $f(x)$ exists for all values of x in the open interval (a, b), and if f has a relative extremum at c, where $a < c < b$, and if $f'(c)$ exists, then $f'(c) = 0$.

Let us assume $f'(c) \neq 0$. Then either $f'(c) > 0$ or $f'(c) < 0$. If $f'(c) > 0$ then

$$\lim_{x \to c} \frac{f(x) - f(c)}{x - c} > 0$$

Therefore by Theorem 3.1.8 (i) there is an open interval I containing c such that

$$\frac{f(x) - f(c)}{x - c} > 0 \qquad (4)$$

for all $x \neq c$ in I. Furthermore,

$$f(x) - f(c) = (x - c)\frac{f(x) - f(c)}{x - c} \quad \text{if} \quad x \neq c \qquad (5)$$

From (4), the quotient on the right side of (5) is positive if x is in I. Therefore, from (5) we can conclude that if x is in I, $f(x) - f(c)$ and $x - c$ have the same sign; that is

$$f(x) > f(c) \quad \text{if} \quad x > c \qquad (6)$$

and

$$f(x) < f(c) \quad \text{if} \quad x < c \qquad (7)$$

From (6) f cannot have a relative maximum value at c and from (7) f cannot have a relative minimum value at c, which contradicts the hypothesis that f has a relative extremum at c.

If $f'(c) < 0$, we get a similar contradiction. You are asked to show this in Exercise 58.

Thus the assumption that $f'(c) \neq 0$ leads to a contradiction. Therefore, $f'(c) = 0$. ∎

EXERCISES 3.1

In Exercises 1 through 8, (a) plot the graph of the function and estimate the critical numbers of the function graphically. (b) Confirm your answers in part (a) analytically.

1. $f(x) = x^3 + 7x^2 - 5x$
2. $g(x) = 2x^3 - 2x^2 - 16x + 1$
3. $g(x) = x^{6/5} - 12x^{1/5}$
4. $f(x) = x^{7/3} + x^{4/3} - 3x^{1/3}$
5. $f(x) = \dfrac{x + 1}{x^2 - 5x + 4}$
6. $f(x) = \dfrac{2x - 9}{x^2 - 9}$
7. $G(x) = (x - 2)^3(x + 1)^2$
8. $F(x) = (5 + x)^3(2 - x)^2$

In Exercises 9 through 14, (a) find the critical numbers of the function f analytically. Support your answers in part (a) graphically two ways: (b) plot the graph of f; (c) plot the graph of $\text{NDER}(f(x), x)$.

9. $f(x) = x^4 + 11x^3 + 34x^2 + 15x - 2$
10. $f(x) = x^4 + 4x^3 - 2x^2 - 12x$
11. $f(t) = (t^2 - 4)^{2/3}$
12. $f(w) = (w^3 - 3w^2 + 4)^{1/3}$
13. $f(x) = \dfrac{x^2 + 4}{x - 2}$
14. $f(x) = \dfrac{x^2 + 2x + 5}{x - 1}$

In Exercises 15 through 18, find the critical numbers of the function.

15. $f(x) = \sin 2x \cos 2x$
16. $f(x) = \sin 2x + \cos 2x$
17. $F(x) = \sec^2 3x$
18. $G(x) = \tan^2 4x$

In Exercises 19 through 38, (a) sketch the graph of the function on the indicated interval; (b) find the absolute extrema of the function on the interval, if there are any, and determine the values of x at which the absolute extrema occur.

19. $f(x) = 4 - 3x; (-1, 2]$

20. $f(x) = x^2 - 2x + 4; (-\infty, +\infty)$

21. $g(x) = \dfrac{1}{x}; [-2, 3]$ 22. $f(x) = \dfrac{1}{x}; [2, 3)$

23. $f(x) = 2\cos x; [-\frac{2}{3}\pi, \frac{1}{3}\pi)$

24. $G(x) = -3\sin x; [0, \frac{3}{4}\pi)$

25. $f(x) = \sqrt{3 + x}; [-3, +\infty)$

26. $f(x) = \sqrt{4 - x^2}; (-2, 2)$

27. $h(x) = \dfrac{4}{(x - 3)^2}; [2, 5)$

28. $g(x) = \dfrac{3x}{9 - x^2}; (-3, 2)$

29. $F(x) = |x - 4| + 1; (0, 6)$

30. $f(x) = |4 - x^2|; (-\infty, +\infty)$

31. $g(x) = \sqrt{4 + 7x}; [0, 3)$

32. $f(x) = \begin{cases} |x + 1| & \text{if } x \neq -1 \\ 3 & \text{if } x = -1 \end{cases}; [-2, 1]$

33. $f(x) = \begin{cases} \dfrac{2}{x - 5} & \text{if } x \neq 5 \\ 2 & \text{if } x = 5 \end{cases}; [3, 5]$

34. $F(x) = U(x) - U(x - 1)$ where
$U(x) = \begin{cases} 0 & \text{if } x < 0 \\ 1 & \text{if } 0 \leq x \end{cases}; (-1, 1)$

35. $f(x) = x - [\![x]\!]; (1, 3)$

36. $h(x) = 2x + [\![2x - 1]\!]; (1, 2]$

37. $g(x) = \sec 3x; [-\frac{1}{6}\pi, \frac{1}{6}\pi]$

38. $f(x) = \tan 2x; [-\frac{1}{4}\pi, \frac{1}{6}\pi]$

In Exercises 39 through 46, find the absolute extrema of the function on the indicated interval by the method of Example 4 and support your answers graphically.

39. (a) $f(x) = x^4 - 8x^2 + 16; [-4, 0]$
    (b) $f(x) = x^4 - 8x^2 + 16; [-3, 2]$

40. (a) $f(x) = x^4 - 8x^2 + 16; [0, 3]$
    (b) $f(x) = x^4 - 8x^2 + 16; [-1, 4]$

41. $f(t) = 2\sin t; [-\pi, \pi]$

42. $g(t) = \frac{1}{2}\csc 2t; [-\frac{1}{4}\pi, \frac{1}{6}\pi]$

43. $g(w) = \dfrac{w}{w + 2}; [-1, 2]$

44. $f(r) = \dfrac{r + 5}{r - 3}; [-5, 2]$

45. $f(x) = (x + 1)^{2/3}; [-2, 1]$

46. $g(x) = 1 - (x - 3)^{2/3}; [-5, 4]$

In Exercises 47 through 52, (a) estimate graphically the absolute extrema of the function on the indicated interval. (b) Confirm your answers analytically by the method of Example 5.

47. $f(x) = x^3 + 5x - 4; [-3, -1]$

48. $g(x) = x^3 + 3x^2 - 9x; [-4, 4]$

49. $g(t) = 2\sec\frac{1}{2}x; [-\frac{1}{3}\pi, \frac{1}{2}\pi]$

50. $f(t) = 3\cos 2t; [\frac{1}{6}\pi, \frac{3}{4}\pi]$

51. $f(x) = (x - 1)^{1/3} + 4; [0, 2]$

52. $f(x) = \dfrac{x + 1}{2x - 3}; [0, 1]$

In Exercises 53 through 56, (a) sketch the graph of the function on the indicated interval. (b) Determine the absolute extrema of the function on the interval.

53. $f(x) = \begin{cases} |x| & \text{if } -3 \leq x \leq 2 \\ 4 - x & \text{if } 2 < x \leq 3 \end{cases}; [-3, 3]$

54. $f(x) = \begin{cases} 2x - 7 & \text{if } -1 \leq x \leq 2 \\ 1 - x^2 & \text{if } 2 < x \leq 4 \end{cases}; [-1, 4]$

55. $F(x) = \begin{cases} 3x - 4 & \text{if } -3 \leq x < 1 \\ x^2 - 2 & \text{if } 1 \leq x \leq 3 \end{cases}; [-3, 3]$

56. $G(x) = \begin{cases} 4 - (x + 5)^2 & \text{if } -6 \leq x \leq -4 \\ 12 - (x + 1)^2 & \text{if } -4 < x \leq 0 \end{cases}; [-6, 0]$

57. Prove part (ii) of Theorem 3.1.8.

58. Prove Theorem 3.1.3 with the assumption that $f'(c) < 0$.

59. If the function f is differentiable everywhere and $f'(c) = 0$, can we conclude that f has a relative extremum at c? Explain.

60. If the function f has a relative extremum at a number c, can we conclude that $f'(c) = 0$? Explain.

61. Describe how you find analytically the absolute extrema of a function continuous on a closed interval.

3.2 APPLICATIONS INVOLVING AN ABSOLUTE EXTREMUM ON A CLOSED INTERVAL

We now apply the extreme-value theorem to problems in which the solution is an absolute extremum of a function on a closed interval. As you learned in the previous section, the theorem assures us that a function continuous on a closed interval has both an absolute maximum value and an absolute

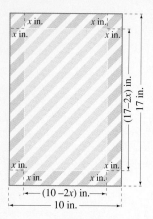

FIGURE 1

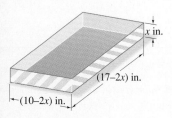

FIGURE 2

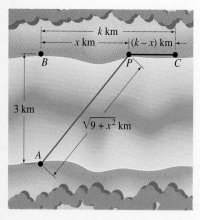

FIGURE 3

minimum value on the interval. We demonstrate the procedure in the following illustration by considering the situation discussed in Example 4 of Section 1.3 and Illustration 2 of Section 1.9.

▷ **ILLUSTRATION 1**   A cardboard box manufacturer wishes to make open boxes from rectangular pieces of cardboard with dimensions 10 in. by 17 in. by cutting equal squares from the four corners and turning up the sides. We wish to find the length of the side of the cut-out square so that the box has the largest possible volume. Figure 1 represents a given piece of cardboard and Figure 2 represents the box. We showed in Example 4 of Section 1.3 that if x inches is the length of the side of the cut-out square and $V(x)$ cubic inches is the volume of the box, then

$$V(x) = 170x - 54x^2 + 4x^3$$

and the domain of V is the closed interval $[0, 5]$. Because V is continuous on $[0, 5]$, we know from the extreme-value theorem that on this interval V has an absolute maximum value, which occurs at either a critical number or at an endpoint of the interval. To find the critical numbers we compute $V'(x)$ and then determine the value of x for which either $V'(x) = 0$ or $V'(x)$ does not exist.

$$V'(x) = 170 - 108x + 12x^2$$

$V'(x)$ exists for all values of x. Setting $V'(x) = 0$, we have

$$2(6x^2 - 54x + 85) = 0$$
$$x = \frac{54 \pm \sqrt{(-54)^2 - 4(6)(85)}}{12}$$

From which we obtain $x = 6.97$ and $x = 2.03$. Thus the only critical number of V in $[0, 5]$ is 2.03. Because $V(0) = 0$ and $V(5) = 0$ while $V(2.03) = 156.03$, the absolute maximum value of V on $[0, 5]$ is 156.03 occurring when $x = 2.03$. This result can be supported on our graphics calculator as we did in Example 4 of Section 1.3.

Conclusion: The largest possible volume is 156.03 in.³, obtained when the length of the side of the cut-out square is 2.03 in.   ◀

▶ **EXAMPLE 1**   Points A and B are opposite each other on the shores of a straight river 3 km wide. Point C is on the same shore as B but k kilometers down the river from B. A telephone company wishes to lay a cable from A to C where the cost per kilometer of the cable on land is \$10,000 and under the water is \$12,500. Let P be a point on the same shore as B and C so that the cable runs from A to P to C. See Figure 3. **(a)** If x kilometers is the distance from B to P, obtain an equation defining $C(x)$ if $C(x)$ dollars is the total cost of laying the cable and state the domain of C. **(b)** If $k = 2$, estimate on a graphics calculator the value of x for which the cost of laying the cable is least as well as the least cost. Then confirm the estimate analytically.

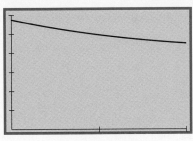

[0, 2] by [0, 60,000]

$C(x) = 12,500\sqrt{9 + x^2} + 10,000\,(2 - x)$

FIGURE 4

Solution

(a) The distance from P to C is $(k - x)$ kilometers, and, from the Pythagorean theorem, the distance from A to P is $\sqrt{3^2 + x^2}$ kilometers. Therefore

$$C(x) = 12{,}500\sqrt{9 + x^2} + 10{,}000(k - x) \tag{1}$$

The domain of C is $[0, k]$.

(b) With $k = 2$ in Equation (1), we have

$$C(x) = 12{,}500\sqrt{9 + x^2} + 10{,}000(2 - x) \tag{2}$$

with $x \in [0, 2]$. The graph of this equation plotted in the $[0, 2]$ by $[0, 60{,}000]$ window appears in Figure 4, which indicates that the absolute minimum value of C on $[0, 2]$ occurs at the right endpoint. Using the trace feature of our calculator, we obtain $C(2) = 45{,}069$. Therefore, we estimate that the cost of laying the cable is least when $x = 2$ and the least cost is \$45,069.

We now confirm this estimate analytically. Because C is continuous on $[0, 2]$, the extreme-value theorem applies; thus C has both an absolute maximum and an absolute minimum value on $[0, 2]$. We wish to find the absolute minimum value. From Equation (2),

$$C'(x) = \frac{12{,}500x}{\sqrt{9 + x^2}} - 10{,}000$$

$C'(x)$ exists for all values of x. Setting $C'(x)$ equal to zero and solving for x we have

$$\frac{12{,}500x}{\sqrt{9 + x^2}} - 10{,}000 = 0$$

$$12{,}500x - 10{,}000\sqrt{9 + x^2} = 0$$

$$5x = 4\sqrt{9 + x^2} \tag{3}$$

$$25x^2 = 16(9 + x^2)$$

$$9x^2 = 16 \cdot 9$$

$$x^2 = 16$$

$$x = \pm 4$$

The number -4 is an extraneous root of Equation (3), and 4 is not in the interval $[0, 2]$, which indicates there are no critical numbers of C in $[0, 2]$. The absolute minimum value of C on $[0, 2]$ must therefore occur at an endpoint of the interval. Computing $C(0)$ and $C(2)$ from Equation (2), we get

$$C(0) = 57{,}500 \quad \text{and} \quad C(2) = 45{,}069$$

Thus the absolute minimum value of C on $[0, 2]$ is 45,069 when $x = 2$, which confirms our estimates.

Conclusion: The cost of the cable is least when the cable goes directly from A to C under the water. ◀

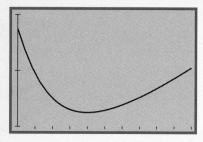

[0, 10] by [120,000, 140,000]

$C(x) = 12,500\sqrt{9 + x^2} + 10,000\,(10 - x)$

FIGURE 5

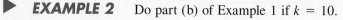

▶ **EXAMPLE 2**   Do part (b) of Example 1 if $k = 10$.

Solution   With $k = 10$ in Equation (1), we have

$$C(x) = 12{,}500\sqrt{9 + x^2} + 10{,}000(10 - x) \tag{4}$$

with $x \in [0, 10]$. Figure 5 shows the graph of this equation plotted in the [0, 10] by [120,000, 140,000] window. We approximate the coordinates of the lowest point on the curve as (4, 122,500). We therefore estimate that the cost of laying the cable in this case is least when $x = 4$ and the least cost is $122,500.

We confirm this estimate analytically the same way we did in Example 1. From Equation (4), we get the same expression for $C'(x)$ as we obtained in Example 1 from Equation (2). Therefore, we again obtain $x = \pm 4$ when we set $C'(x)$ equal to zero and solve for x. Because 4 is in the closed interval [0, 10], 4 is now a critical number of C. Computing $C(0)$, $C(4)$, and $C(10)$ from Equation (4), we get

$$C(0) = 137{,}500 \qquad C(4) = 122{,}500 \qquad C(10) = 130{,}504$$

The absolute minimum value of C on [0, 10] is, therefore, 122,500 when $x = 4$, which confirms our estimates.

<u>Conclusion:</u>   In this case, the cost of the cable is least when the cable goes from A to P on the shore 4 km from B.   ◀

For function C defined by Equation (1) with $x \in [0, k]$, we showed in Example 1 that when $k = 2$, the absolute minimum value of C occurs at the right endpoint of the interval [0, 2] while in Example 2 when $k = 10$, we showed that the absolute minimum value of C occurs in the open interval (0, 10). In Exercise 36 you are asked to determine for what values of k the absolute minimum value of C will occur at a number in the open interval (0, k).

▶ **EXAMPLE 3**   A rectangular field is to be fenced off along the bank of a river where no fence is required along the bank. If the material for the fence costs $12 per running foot for the two ends and $18 per running foot for the side parallel to the river, find the dimensions of the field of largest possible area that can be enclosed with $5400 worth of fence. Support the answer graphically.

Solution   Let x feet be the length of an end of the field, y feet be the length of the side parallel to the river, and A square feet be the area of the field. See Figure 6. Hence

$$A = xy \tag{5}$$

Because the cost of the material for each end is $12 per running foot and the length of an end is x feet, the total cost for the fence for each end is $12x$ dollars. Similarly, the total cost of the fence for the third side is $18y$ dollars. Then

$$12x + 12x + 18y = 5400 \tag{6}$$

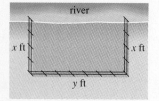

FIGURE 6

To express A in terms of a single variable, we solve (6) for y in terms of x and substitute this value into (5), yielding A as a function of x, and

$$A(x) = x(300 - \tfrac{4}{3}x) \qquad (7)$$

From (6), if $y = 0$, $x = 225$, and if $x = 0$, $y = 300$. Because both x and y must be nonnegative, the value of x that will make A an absolute maximum is in the closed interval $[0, 225]$. Because A is continuous on the closed interval $[0, 225]$, from the extreme-value theorem A has an absolute maximum value on the interval. From (7)

$$A(x) = 300x - \tfrac{4}{3}x^2$$
$$A'(x) = 300 - \tfrac{8}{3}x$$

Because $A'(x)$ exists for all x, the critical numbers of A are found by setting $A'(x) = 0$, which gives

$$x = 112.5$$

The only critical number of A is 112.5, which is in the closed interval $[0, 225]$. Thus the absolute maximum value of A must occur at either 0, 112.5, or 225. Because $A(0) = 0$, $A(225) = 0$, and $A(112.5) = 16,875$, the absolute maximum value of A on $[0, 225]$ is 16,875, occurring when $x = 112.5$ and $y = 150$ (obtained from (6) by substituting 112.5 for x.)

To support our answer graphically, we plot the graph of the function A given by Equation (7) in the $[0, 225]$ by $[0, 20,000]$ window as shown in Figure 7. We determine that the highest point on the graph is $(112.5, 16,875)$, which supports our answer.

<u>Conclusion:</u>   The largest possible area that can be enclosed for $5400 is 16,875 ft^2, obtained when the side parallel to the river is 150 ft long and the ends are each 112.5 ft long.   ◀

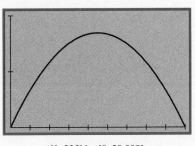

[0, 225] by [0, 20,000]

$A(x) = x(300 - \tfrac{4}{3}x)$

FIGURE 7

▶ **EXAMPLE 4**   In Example 6 of Section 1.3, we had the following situation: In a community of 8000 people, the rate at which a rumor spreads is jointly proportional to the number of people who have heard the rumor and the number of people who have not heard it. When 20 people have heard the rumor, it is being spread at the rate of 200 people per hour. Determine analytically how many people have heard the rumor when the rumor is being spread at the greatest rate.

Solution   In Section 1.3, we obtained the mathematical model

$$f(x) = \tfrac{1}{798}(8000x - x^2)$$

where $f(x)$ people per hour is the rate at which the rumor is spreading when x people have heard it. Because the community has a population of 8000, x is in the closed interval $[0, 8000]$. To have continuity, we allow x to be any real number in this interval. Because $f(x)$ is a polynomial, f is then continuous on $[0, 8000]$, and the extreme-value theorem applies. We compute $f'(x)$:

$$f'(x) = \tfrac{1}{798}(8000 - 2x)$$

The only critical number of f occurs when $f'(x) = 0$, which is when $x = 4000$. Because

$$f(0) = 0 \qquad f(4000) = 20050.1 \qquad f(8000) = 0$$

the absolute maximum value of f occurs when $x = 4000$. This value of x agrees with what we found graphically in Section 1.3.

Conclusion: The rumor is being spread at the greatest rate when 4000 people, half of the population, have heard the rumor. ◀

▶ **EXAMPLE 5** In Example 4 of Section 2.2, we had the following situation: In the planning of a coffee shop, the daily profit is estimated to be $16 per place if there are places for 40 to 80 people. However, if the seating capacity is more than 80 places, the daily profit on each place will be decreased by $0.08 times the number of places above 80. What should be the seating capacity to yield the greatest daily profit?

Solution In Section 2.2, we obtained the mathematical model

$$P(x) = \begin{cases} 16x & \text{if } 40 \leq x \leq 80 \\ 22.40x - 0.08x^2 & \text{if } 80 < x \leq 280 \end{cases}$$

where $P(x)$ dollars is the daily profit of the coffee shop when the seating capacity is x places. Furthermore, in Section 2.2, we let x take on all real values in its domain $[40, 280]$ and showed that P is continuous on that closed interval but not differentiable at 80.

Because of the continuity on $[40, 280]$, the extreme-value theorem guarantees an absolute maximum value of P on the interval. Because $P'(80)$ does not exist, 80 is a critical number of P. To determine any other critical numbers, we compute $P'(x)$:

$$P'(x) = \begin{cases} 16 & \text{if } 40 < x < 80 \\ 22.40 - 0.16x & \text{if } 80 < x < 280 \end{cases}$$

$P'(x) = 0$ when

$$22.40 - 0.16x = 0$$
$$x = 140$$

Thus 140 is also a critical number. We evaluate $P(x)$ at the endpoints of the interval $[40, 280]$ and at the critical numbers:

$$P(40) = 640 \qquad P(80) = 1280 \qquad P(140) = 1568 \qquad P(280) = 0$$

The absolute maximum value of P is, therefore, 1568 occurring when $x = 140$.

Conclusion: The seating capacity should be 140 places, which gives a daily profit of $1568. ◀

▶ **EXAMPLE 6** **(a)** On a graphics calculator, estimate the dimensions of the right-circular cylinder of greatest volume that can be inscribed in a right-circular cone with a radius of 5 cm and a height of 12 cm. **(b)** Confirm the estimates in part (a) analytically.

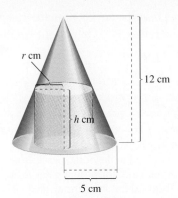

FIGURE 8

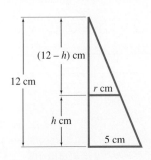

FIGURE 9

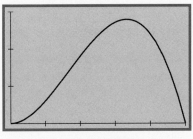

[0, 5] by [0, 150]

$V(r) = \frac{12}{5}\pi(5r^2 - r^3)$

FIGURE 10

Solution

(a) Let r centimeters be the radius of the cylinder, h centimeters be the height of the cylinder, and V cubic centimeters be the volume of the cylinder.

Figure 8 illustrates the cylinder inscribed in the cone, and Figure 9 shows a plane section through the axis of the cone.

If $r = 0$ and $h = 12$, we have a degenerate cylinder, which is the axis of the cone. If $r = 5$ and $h = 0$, we also have a degenerate cylinder, which is a diameter of the base of the cone. The number r is in the closed interval $[0, 5]$ and h is in the closed interval $[0, 12]$.

The following formula expresses V in terms of r and h:

$$V = \pi r^2 h \qquad (8)$$

To express V in terms of a single variable we need another equation involving r and h. From Figure 9, and by similar triangles,

$$\frac{12 - h}{r} = \frac{12}{5}$$

$$h = \frac{60 - 12r}{5} \qquad (9)$$

Substituting from (9) into formula (8) we obtain V as a function of r and write

$$V(r) = \tfrac{12}{5}\pi(5r^2 - r^3) \qquad r \in [0, 5] \qquad (10)$$

Figure 10 shows the graph of V plotted in the $[0, 5]$ by $[0, 150]$ window. We determine that the highest point is $(3.33, 139.63)$. We therefore estimate the radius of the right-circular cylinder to be 3.33 cm and, consequently, from (9) we estimate the height to be 4.01 cm.

(b) To confirm these estimates analytically, we apply the extreme-value theorem because V, defined by Equation (10), is continuous on the closed interval $[0, 5]$. We wish to find the values of r and h that give V its absolute maximum value. From (10)

$$V'(r) = \tfrac{12}{5}\pi(10r - 3r^2)$$

To find the critical numbers of V, we set $V'(r) = 0$ and solve for r:

$$r(10 - 3r) = 0$$

$$r = 0 \qquad r = \tfrac{10}{3}$$

Because $V'(r)$ exists for all values of r, the only critical numbers of V are 0 and $\frac{10}{3}$, both of which are in the closed interval $[0, 5]$. The absolute maximum value of V on $[0, 5]$ must occur at either 0, $\frac{10}{3}$, or 5. From (10) we obtain

$$V(0) = 0 \qquad V(\tfrac{10}{3}) = \tfrac{400}{9}\pi \qquad V(5) = 0$$

The absolute maximum value of V is, therefore, $\frac{400}{9}\pi \approx 139.63$, which occurs when $r = \frac{10}{3} \approx 3.33$. When $r = \frac{10}{3}$, we obtain from (9), $h = 4$. These results confirm our estimates and give us the exact values of r and h.

Conclusion: The greatest volume of an inscribed cylinder in the given cone is $\frac{400}{9}\pi$ cm³, which occurs when the radius is $\frac{10}{3}$ cm and the height is 4 cm.   ◀

EXERCISES 3.2

In these exercises define all your variables precisely as numbers. At the end of each exercise, be sure to write a conclusion.

1. Find the number in the interval $\left[\frac{1}{3}, 2\right]$ such that the sum of the number and its reciprocal is **(a)** a minimum and **(b)** a maximum. Support your answers graphically.

2. Find the number in the interval $[-1, 1]$ such that the difference of the number minus its square is **(a)** a maximum and **(b)** a minimum. Support your answers graphically.

In Exercises 3 through 14, confirm analytically your estimate obtained on your graphics calculator in part (c) of the indicated exercise of Exercises 1.3.

3. Exercise 13   **4.** Exercise 14   **5.** Exercise 15

6. Exercise 16   **7.** Exercise 17   **8.** Exercise 18

9. Exercise 19   **10.** Exercise 20   **11.** Exercise 25

12. Exercise 26   **13.** Exercise 27   **14.** Exercise 28

15. How many students should make the school-sponsored trip in Exercise 37 of Exercises 2.2 for the school to receive the largest gross income?

16. How many students should make the school-sponsored trip in Exercise 38 of Exercises 2.2 for the school to receive the largest gross income?

17. From the mathematical model obtained in Exercise 39 of Exercises 2.2, determine how many orange trees should be planted per acre in California to yield the greatest number of oranges.

18. How many members will give the private club in Exercise 40 of Exercises 2.2 the most revenue from annual dues?

19. (a) Find two nonnegative numbers whose sum is 12 such that their product is an absolute maximum, and support your answers graphically. **(b)** Find two nonnegative numbers whose sum is 12 such that the sum of their squares is an absolute minimum, and support your answers graphically.

20. Suppose that a weight is to be held 10 ft below a horizontal line AB by a wire in the shape of a Y. If the points A and B are 8 ft apart, **(a)** estimate on your graphics calculator to the nearest foot the shortest length of wire that can be used. **(b)** Confirm your estimate in part (a) analytically.

21. An island is at point A, 4 km offshore from the nearest point B on a straight beach. A woman on the island wishes to go to a point C, 6 km down the beach from B. She can go by rowboat at 5 km/hr to a point P between B and C and then walk at 8 km/hr along a straight path from P to C. **(a)** Estimate on your graphics calculator the route from A to C that she can travel in the least time. **(b)** Confirm your estimate in part (a) analytically.

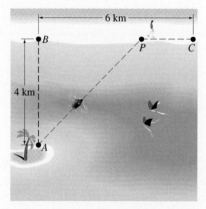

22. Solve Exercise 21 if point C is only 3 km down the beach from B.

23. (a) Use your graphics calculator to estimate the dimensions of the right-circular cylinder of greatest lateral surface area that can be inscribed in a sphere with a radius of 6 in. **(b)** Confirm your estimates in part (a) analytically.

24. (a) Use your graphics calculator to estimate the dimensions of the right-circular cylinder of greatest volume that can be inscribed in a sphere with a radius of 6 in. **(b)** Confirm your estimates in part (a) analytically.

25. Given the circle having the equation $x^2 + y^2 = 9$, find **(a)** the shortest distance from the point $(4, 5)$ to a point on the circle, and **(b)** the longest distance from the point $(4, 5)$ to a point on the circle. **(c)** Support your answers in parts (a) and (b) graphically.

26. **(a)** Find the area of the largest rectangle having two vertices on the x axis and two vertices on or above the x axis and on the parabola $y = 9 - x^2$.
(b) Support your answer in part (a) graphically.

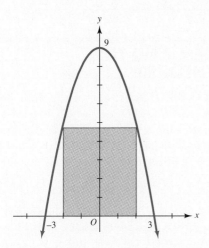

27. Assume that the decrease in a person's blood pressure depends on the amount of a particular drug taken by the person. Thus if x milligrams of the drug is taken, the decrease in blood pressure is a function of x. Suppose that $f(x)$ defines this function and

$$f(x) = \tfrac{1}{2}x^2(k - x)$$

and x is in $[0, k]$, where k is a positive constant. Determine the value of x that causes the greatest decrease in blood pressure.

28. During a cough the radius of a person's trachea (or windpipe) decreases. Suppose that the normal radius of the trachea is R centimeters and the radius of the trachea during a cough is r centimeters, where R is a constant and r is a variable. The velocity of air through the trachea can be shown to be a function of r, and if $V(r)$ centimeters per second is this velocity, then

$$V(r) = kr^2(R - r)$$

where k is a positive constant and r is in $[\tfrac{1}{2}R, R]$. Determine the radius of the trachea during a cough for which the velocity of air through the trachea is greatest.

29. The strength of a rectangular beam is jointly proportional to its breadth and the square of its depth. Find the dimensions of the strongest beam that can be cut from a log in the shape of a right-circular cylinder of radius 72 cm.

27 cm

30. The stiffness of a rectangular beam is jointly proportional to the breadth and the cube of the depth. Find the dimensions of the stiffest beam that can be cut from a log in the shape of a right-circular cylinder of radius a centimeters.

31. A piece of wire 10 ft long is cut into two pieces. One piece is bent into the shape of a circle and the other into the shape of a square. How should the wire be cut so that **(a)** the combined area of the two figures is as small as possible; **(b)** the combined area of the two figures is as large as possible?

32. Solve Exercise 31 if one piece of wire is bent into the shape of an equilateral triangle and the other piece is bent into the shape of a square.

33. If R feet is the range of a projectile, then

$$R = \frac{v_0^2 \sin 2\theta}{g} \qquad 0 \leq \theta \leq \tfrac{1}{2}\pi$$

where v_0 feet per second is the initial velocity, g ft/sec^2 is the acceleration due to gravity, and θ is the radian measure of the angle that the gun makes with the horizontal. Find the value of θ that makes the range a maximum.

34. If a body of weight W pounds is dragged along a horizontal floor at constant velocity by means of a force of magnitude F pounds and directed at an angle of θ radians with the plane of the floor, then F is given by the equation

$$F = \frac{kW}{k \sin \theta + \cos \theta}$$

where k is a constant called the coefficient of friction and $0 < k < 1$. If $0 \leq \theta \leq \tfrac{1}{2}\pi$, find $\cos \theta$ when F is least.

35. Two products A and B are manufactured at a particular factory. If C dollars is the total cost of production for an 8-hour day, then $C = 3x^2 + 42y$, where x machines are used to produce A, y machines are used to produce B, and during an 8-hour day 15 machines are working. **(a)** Determine analytically how many of these machines should be used to produce A and how many should be used to produce B for the total cost to be least. **(b)** Support your answers in part (a) graphically.

36. (a) In Example 1, for what values of k will the absolute minimum value of C occur at a number in the open interval $(0, k)$? **(b)** Examples 1 and 2 and Exercises 21 and 22 are special cases of the following more general problem: Let

$$f(x) = u\sqrt{a^2 + x^2} + v(b - x)$$

where x is in $[0, b]$ and $u > v > 0$. Show that for the absolute minimum value of f to occur at a number in the open interval $(0, b)$, the following inequality must be satisfied: $av < b\sqrt{u^2 - v^2}$.

3.3 ROLLE'S THEOREM AND THE MEAN-VALUE THEOREM

As stated in the introduction to this chapter, one of the most important theorems in calculus is the *mean-value theorem,* which is used to prove many theorems of both differential and integral calculus, as well as of other subjects, such as numerical analysis. The proof of the mean-value theorem is based on a special case of it known as *Rolle's theorem,* which we discuss first.

The French mathematician Michel Rolle (1652–1719) proved that if f is a function continuous on the closed interval $[a, b]$ and differentiable on the open interval (a, b), and if $f(a)$ and $f(b)$ both equal zero, then there is at least one number c between a and b for which $f'(c) = 0$.

Let us see what this means geometrically. Figure 1 shows the graph of a function f satisfying the conditions in the preceding paragraph. We see intuitively that there is at least one point on the curve between the points $(a, 0)$ and $(b, 0)$ where the tangent line is parallel to the x axis; that is, the slope of the tangent line is zero. This situation is illustrated in Figure 1 at the point P. So the abscissa of P is c such that $f'(c) = 0$.

The function, whose graph appears in Figure 1, not only is differentiable on the open interval (a, b) but also is differentiable at the endpoints of the interval. However, the condition that f be differentiable at the endpoints is not necessary for the graph to have a horizontal tangent line at some point in the interval; Figure 2 illustrates this. We see in Figure 2 that the function is not differentiable at a and b; there is, however, a horizontal tangent line at the point where $x = c$, and c is between a and b.

It is necessary, however, that the function be continuous at the endpoints of the interval to guarantee a horizontal tangent line at an interior point. Figure 3 shows the graph of a function continuous on the interval $[a, b)$ but discontinuous at b; the function is differentiable on the open interval (a, b), and the function values are zero at both a and b. However, there is no point at which the graph has a horizontal tangent line.

We now state and prove Rolle's theorem.

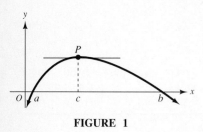

FIGURE 1

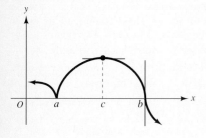

FIGURE 2

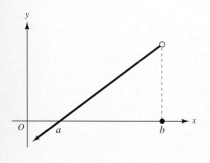

FIGURE 3

3.3.1 Rolle's Theorem

Let f be a function such that

(i) it is continuous on the closed interval $[a, b]$;

(ii) it is differentiable on the open interval (a, b);
(iii) $f(a) = 0$ and $f(b) = 0$.

Then there is a number c in the open interval (a, b) such that

$$f'(c) = 0$$

Proof   We consider two cases.

Case 1: $f(x) = 0$ for all x in $[a, b]$.
  Then $f'(x) = 0$ for all x in (a, b); therefore any number between a and b can be taken for c.

Case 2: $f(x)$ is not zero for some value of x in the open interval (a, b).
  Because f is continuous on the closed interval $[a, b]$, from the extreme-value theorem, f has an absolute maximum value on $[a, b]$ and an absolute minimum value on $[a, b]$. From (iii), $f(a) = 0$ and $f(b) = 0$. Furthermore, $f(x)$ is not zero for some x in (a, b). Hence f will have either a positive absolute maximum value at some c_1 in (a, b) or a negative absolute minimum value at some c_2 in (a, b), or both. Thus for $c = c_1$, or $c = c_2$ as the case may be, there is an absolute extremum at an interior point of the interval $[a, b]$. Therefore the absolute extremum $f(c)$ is also a relative extremum, and because $f'(c)$ exists by hypothesis, it follows from Theorem 3.1.3 that $f'(c) = 0$. This proves the theorem.   ∎

There may be more than one number in the open interval (a, b) for which the derivative of f is zero. This is illustrated geometrically in Figure 4, where there is a horizontal tangent line at the point where $x = c_1$ and also at the point where $x = c_2$, so that both $f'(c_1) = 0$ and $f'(c_2) = 0$.
  The converse of Rolle's theorem is not true. That is, we cannot conclude that if a function f is such that $f'(c) = 0$, with $a < c < b$, then the conditions (i), (ii), and (iii) must hold. Refer to Exercise 36.

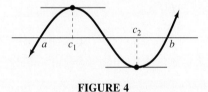

FIGURE 4

▶ ***EXAMPLE 1***   Given

$$f(x) = 4x^3 - 9x$$

verify that the three conditions of the hypothesis of Rolle's theorem are satisfied for each of the following intervals: $[-\frac{3}{2}, 0], [0, \frac{3}{2}]$, and $[-\frac{3}{2}, \frac{3}{2}]$. Then find a suitable choice for c in each of these intervals for which $f'(c) = 0$. Support the choices of c graphically by plotting in the same window the graphs of f and the horizontal tangent line at $(c, f(c))$.

Solution

$$f'(x) = 12x^2 - 9$$

Because $f'(x)$ exists for all values of x, f is differentiable on $(-\infty, +\infty)$ and therefore continuous on $(-\infty, +\infty)$. Conditions (i) and (ii) of Rolle's theorem thus hold on any interval. To determine on which intervals condition (iii) holds, we find the values of x for which $f(x) = 0$. If $f(x) = 0$,

$$4x(x^2 - \tfrac{9}{4}) = 0$$

$$x = -\tfrac{3}{2} \qquad x = 0 \qquad x = \tfrac{3}{2}$$

With $a = -\frac{3}{2}$ and $b = 0$, Rolle's theorem holds on $\left[-\frac{3}{2}, 0\right]$. Similarly, Rolle's theorem holds on $\left[0, \frac{3}{2}\right]$ and $\left[-\frac{3}{2}, \frac{3}{2}\right]$.

To find the suitable values for c, set $f'(x) = 0$ and get

$$12x^2 - 9 = 0$$

$$x = -\tfrac{1}{2}\sqrt{3} \qquad x = \tfrac{1}{2}\sqrt{3}$$

Therefore, in the interval $\left[-\frac{3}{2}, 0\right]$ a suitable choice for c is $-\frac{1}{2}\sqrt{3}$. In the interval $\left[0, \frac{3}{2}\right]$, take $c = \frac{1}{2}\sqrt{3}$. In the interval $\left[-\frac{3}{2}, \frac{3}{2}\right]$ there are two possibilities for c: either $-\frac{1}{2}\sqrt{3}$ or $\frac{1}{2}\sqrt{3}$.

Figure 5, showing in the $[-1.5, 1.5]$ by $[-8, 8]$ window the graphs of f and the horizontal tangent lines at the points where x is $-\frac{1}{2}\sqrt{3} \approx -0.87$ and $\frac{1}{2}\sqrt{3} \approx 0.87$, supports our choices of c. ◀

We now apply Rolle's theorem to prove the mean-value theorem. You should become thoroughly familiar with the content of this theorem.

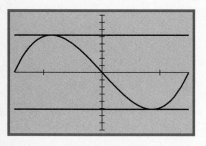

[–1.5, 1.5] by [–8, 8]

$f(x) = 4x^3 - 9x$

FIGURE 5

3.3.2 The Mean-Value Theorem

Let f be a function such that

(i) it is continuous on the closed interval $[a, b]$;
(ii) it is differentiable on the open interval (a, b).

Then there is a number c in the open interval (a, b) such that

$$f'(c) = \frac{f(b) - f(a)}{b - a}$$

Before proving this theorem, we interpret it geometrically. For the graph of the function f, $\dfrac{f(b) - f(a)}{b - a}$ is the slope of the line segment joining the points $A(a, f(a))$ and $B(b, f(b))$. The mean-value theorem states that there is some point on the graph between A and B where the tangent line is parallel to the secant line through A and B; that is, there is some number c in (a, b) such that

$$f'(c) = \frac{f(b) - f(a)}{b - a}$$

Refer to Figure 6.

Take the x axis along the line segment AB and observe that the mean-value theorem is a generalization of Rolle's theorem, which is used in its proof.

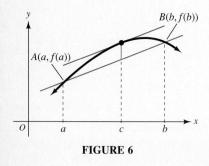

FIGURE 6

Proof of Theorem 3.3.2   An equation of the line through A and B in Figure 6 is

$$y - f(a) = \frac{f(b) - f(a)}{b - a}(x - a)$$

$$\Leftrightarrow \qquad y = \frac{f(b) - f(a)}{b - a}(x - a) + f(a)$$

Now if $F(x)$ measures the vertical distance between a point $(x, f(x))$ on the graph of the function f and the corresponding point on the secant line through A and B, then

$$F(x) = f(x) - \frac{f(b) - f(a)}{b - a}(x - a) - f(a) \tag{1}$$

We show that this function F satisfies the three conditions of the hypothesis of Rolle's theorem.

The function F is continuous on the closed interval $[a, b]$ because it is the sum of f and a linear function, both of which are continuous there. Therefore condition (i) is satisfied by F. Condition (ii) is satisfied by F because f is differentiable on (a, b). From (1), $F(a) = 0$ and $F(b) = 0$. Therefore condition (iii) of Rolle's theorem is satisfied by F.

The conclusion of Rolle's theorem states that there is a c in the open interval (a, b) such that $F'(c) = 0$. But

$$F'(x) = f'(x) - \frac{f(b) - f(a)}{b - a}$$

Thus

$$F'(c) = f'(c) - \frac{f(b) - f(a)}{b - a}$$

Therefore there is a number c in (a, b) such that

$$0 = f'(c) - \frac{f(b) - f(a)}{b - a}$$

$$\Leftrightarrow \quad f'(c) = \frac{f(b) - f(a)}{b - a} \qquad \blacksquare$$

In most cases we cannot find the exact value of the number c guaranteed by the mean-value theorem. The value of c, however, is not significant because the crucial fact of the theorem is that such a number c exists. For this reason, the mean-value theorem is called an **existence theorem.** Many important concepts in mathematics are based on existence theorems, other examples of which are the intermediate-value theorem and the extreme-value theorem. The conclusion of an existence theorem usually assures the existence of one or more numbers having a specific property, and the knowledge that such a number exists is of more significance than being able to identify the number itself.

The following example, presented to demonstrate the conditions of the mean-value theorem, involves a function for which we are able to compute the value of c guaranteed by the theorem.

▶ **EXAMPLE 2**   Given

$$f(x) = x^3 - x^2 - 2x$$

verify that the hypothesis of the mean-value theorem is satisfied for $a = 1$ and $b = 3$. Then find a number c in the open interval $(1, 3)$ such that

$$f'(c) = \frac{f(3) - f(1)}{3 - 1}$$

Support the choice of c graphically by plotting in the same window the graph of f, the tangent line at $x = c$, and the secant line through the points $(1, f(1))$ and $(3, f(3))$.

Solution   Because f is a polynomial function, f is continuous and differentiable everywhere. The hypothesis of the mean-value theorem is, therefore, satisfied for any a and b.

$$f'(x) = 3x^2 - 2x - 2$$

Because $f(1) = -2$ and $f(3) = 12$,

$$\frac{f(3) - f(1)}{3 - 1} = \frac{12 - (-2)}{2}$$

$$= 7$$

We set $f'(c) = 7$ to obtain

$$3c^2 - 2c - 2 = 7$$
$$3c^2 - 2c - 9 = 0$$
$$c = \frac{-(-2) \pm \sqrt{(-2)^2 - 4(3)(-9)}}{2(3)}$$

$$c = \frac{2 + \sqrt{112}}{6} \qquad c = \frac{2 - \sqrt{112}}{6}$$

$$\approx 2.10 \qquad\qquad \approx -1.43$$

Because -1.43 is not in the open interval $(1, 3)$, the only possible value for c is 2.10.

Figure 7 shows the graphs of f, the tangent line at $x = 2.10$, and the secant line through the points $(1, -2)$ and $(3, 12)$ plotted in the $[0, 5]$ by $[-5, 15]$ window. The fact that the tangent line is parallel to the secant line supports our choice of c as 2.10.   ◀

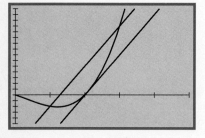

$[0, 5]$ by $[-5, 15]$

$f(x) = x^3 - x^2 - 2x$

FIGURE 7

▶   **EXAMPLE 3**   Given

$$f(x) = x^{2/3}$$

plot the graph of f. Show analytically that there is no number c in the open interval $(-2, 2)$ such that

$$f'(c) = \frac{f(2) - f(-2)}{2 - (-2)}$$

Which condition of the hypothesis of the mean-value theorem fails to hold for f when $a = -2$ and $b = 2$?

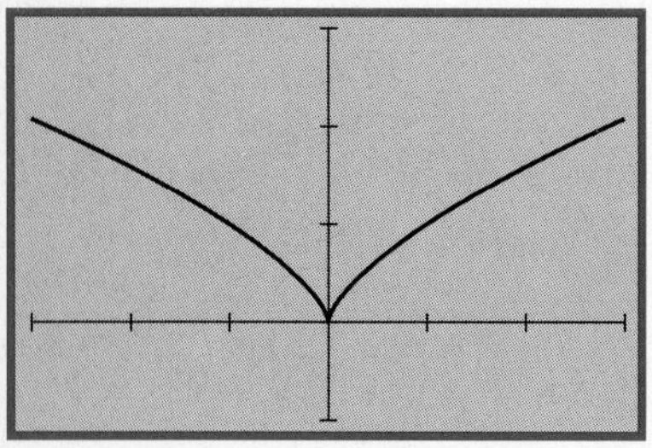

Solution   The graph of f plotted in the $[-3, 3]$ by $[-1, 3]$ window appears in Figure 8.

$$f'(x) = \tfrac{2}{3}x^{-1/3}$$

So

$$f'(c) = \frac{2}{3c^{1/3}}$$

$[-3, 3]$ by $[-1, 3]$

$f(x) = x^{2/3}$

FIGURE 8

Furthermore,

$$\frac{f(2) - f(-2)}{2 - (-2)} = \frac{4^{1/3} - 4^{1/3}}{4}$$

$$= 0$$

There is no number c for which $\dfrac{2}{3c^{1/3}} = 0$.

The function f is continuous on the closed interval $[-2, 2]$; however, f is not differentiable on the open interval $(-2, 2)$ because $f'(0)$ does not exist. Condition (ii) of the hypothesis of the mean-value theorem, therefore, fails to hold for f when $a = -2$ and $b = 2$. ◀

The following example demonstrates the power of the mean-value theorem.

▶ **EXAMPLE 4**   Use the mean-value theorem to prove that if $x > 0$ then $\sin x < x$.

Solution   If $x > 1$, then because $\sin x \leq 1$, $\sin x$ is certainly less than x. Consider then $0 < x \leq 1$ and let

$$f(x) = x - \sin x$$
$$f'(x) = 1 - \cos x$$

Because f is continuous and differentiable everywhere, we conclude from the mean-value theorem with $a = 0$ and $b = x$ that there is some number c, for which $0 < c < x \leq 1$, such that

$$f'(c) = \frac{f(x) - f(0)}{x - 0}$$

Because $f(0) = 0$ and $f'(c) = 1 - \cos c$, we have from this equation,

$$x(1 - \cos c) = f(x) \qquad 0 < c < 1$$

On the left-hand side of this equation both factors are positive. Thus

$$0 < f(x)$$
$$0 < x - \sin x$$
$$\sin x < x \qquad\qquad\qquad\qquad\qquad\qquad\qquad ◀$$

In Exercises 28 through 30 you are to prove some other inequalities by a method similar to the above example.

To further demonstrate the power of the mean-value theorem, we now show its use in the proof of the following theorem needed in Chapter 4.

3.3.3 Theorem

If f is a function such that $f'(x) = 0$ for all values of x in an interval I, then f is constant on I.

Proof   Assume that f is not constant on the interval I. Then there exist two distinct numbers x_1 and x_2 in I, where $x_1 < x_2$, such that $f(x_1) \neq f(x_2)$.

Because, by hypothesis, $f'(x) = 0$ for all x in I, then $f'(x) = 0$ for all x in the closed interval $[x_1, x_2]$. Hence f is differentiable at all x in $[x_1, x_2]$ and f is continuous on $[x_1, x_2]$. Therefore the hypothesis of the mean-value theorem is satisfied, and so there is a number c, with $x_1 < c < x_2$, such that

$$f'(c) = \frac{f(x_1) - f(x_2)}{x_1 - x_2} \tag{2}$$

But because $f'(x) = 0$ for all x in the interval $[x_1, x_2]$, then $f'(c) = 0$, and from (2) it follows that $f(x_1) = f(x_2)$. Yet we assumed that $f(x_1) \neq f(x_2)$. Hence there is a contradiction, and so f is constant on I.   ∎

In the next section you will see another application of the mean-value theorem in the proof of Theorem 3.4.3.

EXERCISES 3.3

In Exercises 1 through 4, verify that the three conditions of the hypothesis of Rolle's theorem are satisfied by the function on the indicated interval. Then find a suitable value for c that satisfies the conclusion of Rolle's theorem. Support your choice of c graphically by plotting in the same window the graphs of f and the horizontal tangent line at (c, f(c)).

1. $f(x) = x^2 - 4x + 3$; $[1, 3]$

2. $f(x) = x^3 - 2x^2 - x + 2$; $[1, 2]$

3. $f(x) = \sin 2x$; $[0, \frac{1}{2}\pi]$

4. $f(x) = 3 \cos^2 x$; $[\frac{1}{2}\pi, \frac{3}{2}\pi]$

In Exercises 5 through 10, do the following: (a) Plot the graph of the function on the indicated interval; (b) test the three conditions of the hypothesis of Rolle's theorem, and determine which conditions are satisfied and which, if any, are not satisfied; (c) if the three conditions in part (b) are satisfied, determine a point at which there is a horizontal tangent line and support your answer graphically.

5. $f(x) = x^{4/3} - 3x^{1/3}$; $[0, 3]$

6. $f(x) = x^{3/4} - 2x^{1/4}$; $[0, 4]$

7. $f(x) = \dfrac{x^2 - x - 12}{x - 3}$; $[-3, 4]$

8. $f(x) = 1 - |x|$; $[-1, 1]$

9. $f(x) = \begin{cases} x^2 - 4 & \text{if } x < 1 \\ 5x - 8 & \text{if } 1 \le x \end{cases}$; $[-2, \frac{8}{5}]$

10. $f(x) = \begin{cases} 3x + 6 & \text{if } x < 1 \\ x - 4 & \text{if } 1 \le x \end{cases}$; $[-2, 4]$

In Exercises 11 through 20, verify that the hypothesis of the mean-value theorem is satisfied for the function on the indicated interval $[a, b]$. Then find a suitable choice

for c that satisfies the conclusion of the mean-value theorem. Support your choice of c by plotting in the same window the graph of f on the closed interval [a, b], the tangent line at (c, f(c)), and the secant line through the points (a, f(a)) and (b, f(b)) and observing that the tangent line and secant line are parallel.

11. $f(x) = x^2 + 2x - 1$; $[0, 1]$

12. $f(x) = x^3 + x^2 - x$; $[-2, 1]$

13. $f(x) = x^{2/3}$; $[0, 1]$

14. $f(x) = \dfrac{x^2 + 4x}{x - 7}$; $[2, 6]$

15. $f(x) = \sqrt{1 + \cos x}$; $[-\frac{1}{2}\pi, \frac{1}{2}\pi]$

16. $f(x) = \sqrt{1 - \sin x}$; $[0, \frac{1}{2}\pi]$

17. $f(x) = x^2$; $[3, 5]$ **18.** $f(x) = x^2$; $[2, 4]$

19. $f(x) = \sin x$; $[0, \frac{1}{2}\pi]$

20. $f(x) = 2 \cos x$; $[\frac{1}{3}\pi, \frac{2}{3}\pi]$

For each of the functions in Exercises 21 through 24, there is no number c in the open interval (a, b) that satisfies the conclusion of the mean-value theorem. In each exercise, determine which part of the hypothesis of the mean-value theorem fails to hold. Sketch the graph of f and the line through the points (a, f(a)) and (b, f(b)).

21. $f(x) = \dfrac{4}{(x - 3)^2}$; $a = 1, b = 6$

22. $f(x) = \dfrac{2x - 1}{3x - 4}$; $a = 1, b = 2$

23. $f(x) = 3(x - 4)^{2/3}$; $a = -4, b = 5$

24. $f(x) = \begin{cases} 2x + 3 & \text{if } x < 3 \\ 15 - 2x & \text{if } 3 \le x \end{cases}$; $a = -1, b = 5$

25. If $f(x) = x^4 - 2x^3 + 2x^2 - x$, then $f'(x) = 4x^3 - 6x^2 + 4x - 1$. Prove by Rolle's theorem that the following equation has at least one real root in the open interval $(0, 1)$:

$$4x^3 - 6x^2 + 4x - 1 = 0$$

26. Prove by Rolle's theorem that the equation $x^3 + 2x + k = 0$, where k is any constant, cannot have more than one real root.

27. Use Rolle's theorem to prove that the equation

$$4x^5 + 3x^3 + 3x - 2 = 0$$

has exactly one root in the open interval $(0, 1)$ *Hint:* First show that the interval $(0, 1)$ contains at least one root of the equation. Then show that the assumption that the interval contains more than one root leads to a contradiction.

28. Use the mean-value theorem to prove that if $x > 0$, then

$$\cos x > 1 - \frac{x^2}{2}$$

Hint: Let $f(x) = \cos x - \left(1 - \frac{x^2}{2}\right)$ and apply the mean-value theorem to function f for $a = 0$ and $b = x$ as we did in Example 4.

29. Use the mean-value theorem to prove that if $x > 0$, then

$$\sin x > x - \frac{x^3}{6}$$

See the hint for Exercise 28.

30. Use the mean-value theorem to prove that if $x > 0$ and $r > 1$, where r is rational, then

$$(1 + x)^r > 1 + rx$$

See the hint for Exercise 28.

31. Use the mean-value theorem to prove that if $a < b$, the arithmetic mean, $\frac{1}{2}(a + b)$, of a and b is in the open interval (a, b). *Hint:* Let $f(x) = x^2$.

32. Use the mean-value theorem to prove that if $0 < a < b$, the geometric mean, $\sqrt{ab}$, of the two numbers a and b is in the open interval (a, b).

Hint: Let $f(x) = \frac{1}{x}$.

33. The speed limit on a particular California freeway is 65 mi/hr. Suppose at point A a highway patrol officer clocks a driver and 30 min later at point B, 35 mi from A, a second officer clocks the driver. Even though both officers determine that the driver was traveling under the speed limit at points A and B, the second officer stops the driver for speeding. Use the mean-value theorem to verify that the driver had indeed been speeding somewhere between A and B. *Hint:* Assume that the driver's equation of motion is $s = f(t)$ and that f is a differentiable function.

34. If $f(x) = \sin^2 x + \cos^2 x$, use Theorem 3.3.3 to show that $f(x) = 1$ for all x in $[-2\pi, 2\pi]$.

35. If the function f is continuous on the closed interval $[a, b]$ and $f'(x) = 1$ for all x in the open interval (a, b), prove that

$$f(x) = x - a + f(a)$$

for all x in $[a, b]$.

36. The converse of Rolle's theorem is not true. Make up an example of a function for which the conclusion of Rolle's theorem is true and for which **(a)** condition (i) is not satisfied but conditions (ii) and (iii) are satisfied; **(b)** condition (ii) is not satisfied but conditions (i) and (iii) are satisfied; **(c)** condition (iii) is not satisfied but conditions (i) and (ii) are satisfied. Sketch the graph showing the horizontal tangent line for each case.

37. Use Rolle's theorem to prove that if every polynomial function of the second degree has at most two real roots, then every polynomial of the third degree has at most three real roots. *Hint:* Show that the assumption that a polynomial of the third degree has four real roots leads to a contradiction.

38. Use the method of Exercise 37 and mathematical induction to prove that a polynomial of the nth degree has at most n real roots.

39. Suppose that $s = f(t)$ is an equation of motion of a particle moving on a line, where f is a differentiable function. Explain why we can conclude that at some instant during any time interval the instantaneous velocity will equal the average velocity during that time interval.

3.4 INCREASING AND DECREASING FUNCTIONS AND THE FIRST-DERIVATIVE TEST

In this section and the following two sections we direct our attention to applying the derivative to properties of graphs of functions. These properties will not only be used to analyze the behavior of functions but also in

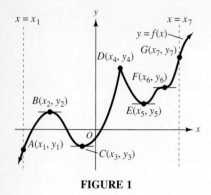

FIGURE 1

Section 3.9 to determine absolute extrema of functions that are not covered by the extreme-value theorem. We begin with a discussion of *increasing* and *decreasing* functions.

Refer to Figure 1 showing the graph of a function f for all x in the closed interval $[x_1, x_7]$ on which f is continuous. The figure shows that as a point moves along the curve from A to B, the function values increase as the abscissa increases, and that as a point moves along the curve from B to C, the function values decrease as the abscissa increases. We say, then, that f is *increasing* on the closed interval $[x_1, x_2]$ and that f is *decreasing* on the closed interval $[x_2, x_3]$. Following are the precise definitions of a function increasing or decreasing on an interval.

3.4.1 Definition of an Increasing Function

A function f defined on an interval is **increasing** on that interval if and only if

$$f(x_1) < f(x_2) \quad \text{whenever} \quad x_1 < x_2$$

where x_1 and x_2 are any numbers in the interval.

The function of Figure 1 is increasing on the following closed intervals: $[x_1, x_2]$; $[x_3, x_4]$; $[x_5, x_6]$; $[x_6, x_7]$; $[x_5, x_7]$.

3.4.2 Definition of a Decreasing Function

A function f defined on an interval is **decreasing** on that interval if and only if

$$f(x_1) > f(x_2) \quad \text{whenever} \quad x_1 < x_2$$

where x_1 and x_2 are any numbers in the interval.

The function of Figure 1 is decreasing on the following closed intervals: $[x_2, x_3]$; $[x_4, x_5]$.

If a function is either increasing on an interval or decreasing on an interval, then it is said to be **monotonic** on the interval.

Before stating a theorem that gives a test for determining if a function is monotonic on an interval, let us see what is happening geometrically. Refer to Figure 1, and observe that when the slope of the tangent line is positive the function is increasing, and when it is negative the function is decreasing. Because $f'(x)$ is the slope of the tangent line to the curve $y = f(x)$, f is increasing when $f'(x) > 0$ and decreasing when $f'(x) < 0$. Also, because $f'(x)$ is the rate of change of the function values $f(x)$ with respect to x, when $f'(x) > 0$, the function values are increasing as x increases; and when $f'(x) < 0$, the function values are decreasing as x increases.

3.4.3 Theorem

Let the function f be continuous on the closed interval $[a, b]$ and differentiable on the open interval (a, b):

(i) if $f'(x) > 0$ for all x in (a, b), then f is increasing on $[a, b]$;
(ii) if $f'(x) < 0$ for all x in (a, b), then f is decreasing on $[a, b]$.

Before proving this theorem we give an illustration demonstrating its content.

▷ **ILLUSTRATION 1**   Figure 2 shows the graphs of

$$f(x) = x^3 - 3x^2 \quad \text{and} \quad f'(x) = 3x^2 - 6x$$

plotted in the same $[-5, 5]$ by $[-5, 5]$ window. Observe that when $x < 0$, $f'(x) > 0$, and f is increasing on $(-\infty, 0]$; when $0 < x < 2$, $f'(x) < 0$ and f is decreasing on $[0, 2]$; when $x > 2$, $f'(x) > 0$ and f is increasing on $[2, +\infty)$. ◀

Proof of Theorem 3.4.3 (i)   Let x_1 and x_2 be any two numbers in $[a, b]$ such that $x_1 < x_2$. Then f is continuous on $[x_1, x_2]$ and differentiable on (x_1, x_2). From the mean-value theorem there is some number c in (x_1, x_2) such that

$$f'(c) = \frac{f(x_2) - f(x_1)}{x_2 - x_1}$$

Because $x_1 < x_2$, then $x_2 - x_1 > 0$. Also, $f'(c) > 0$ by hypothesis. Therefore $f(x_2) - f(x_1) > 0$, and so $f(x_2) > f(x_1)$. We have shown that $f(x_1) < f(x_2)$ whenever $x_1 < x_2$, where x_1 and x_2 are any numbers in the interval $[a, b]$. Therefore, by Definition 3.4.1, f is increasing on $[a, b]$.

The proof of part (ii) is similar and is left as an exercise (see Exercise 51.). ∎

We apply Theorem 3.4.3 in the proof of the *first-derivative test for relative extrema* of a function.

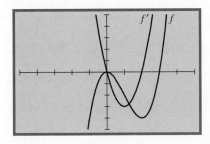

$[-5, 5]$ by $[-5, 5]$

$f(x) = x^3 - 3x^2$ and $f'(x) = 3x^2 - 6x$

FIGURE 2

3.4.4 Theorem   The First-Derivative Test for Relative Extrema

Let the function f be continuous at all points of the open interval (a, b) containing the number c, and suppose that f' exists at all points of (a, b) except possibly at c:

(i) if $f'(x) > 0$ for all values of x in some open interval having c as its right endpoint, and if $f'(x) < 0$ for all values of x in some open interval having c as its left endpoint, then f has a relative maximum value at c;
(ii) if $f'(x) < 0$ for all values of x in some open interval having c as its right endpoint, and if $f'(x) > 0$ for all values of x in some open interval having c as its left endpoint, then f has a relative minimum value at c.

As we did with the previous theorem, we give an illustration demonstrating the content of Theorem 3.4.4 before proving it.

▷ **ILLUSTRATION 2**   Refer again to Figure 2. Notice that $f'(x) > 0$ for all values of x in some open interval having 0 as its right

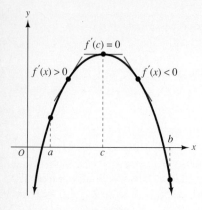

FIGURE 3

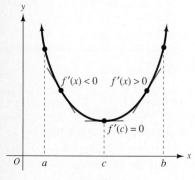

FIGURE 4

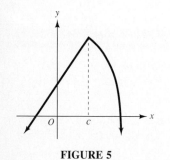

FIGURE 5

endpoint and $f'(x) < 0$ for all values of x in some open interval having 0 as its left endpoint; furthermore, f has a relative maximum value at 0. This demonstrates part (i) of Theorem 3.4.4.

Also in Figure 2, observe that $f'(x) < 0$ for all values of x in some open interval having 2 as its right endpoint and $f'(x) > 0$ for all values of x in some open interval having 2 as its left endpoint; furthermore, f has a relative minimum value at 2. We have demonstrated part (ii) of Theorem 3.4.4. ◀

Proof of Theorem 3.4.4(i)   Let (d, c) (where $d > a$) be the interval having c as its right endpoint for which $f'(x) > 0$ for all x in the interval. From Theorem 3.4.3(i) f is increasing on $[d, c]$. Let (c, e) (where $e < b$) be the interval having c as its left endpoint for which $f'(x) < 0$ for all x in the interval. By Theorem 3.4.3(ii), f is decreasing on $[c, e]$. Because f is increasing on $[d, c]$, we know from Definition 3.4.1 that if x_1 is in $[d, c]$ and $x_1 \neq c$, then $f(x_1) < f(c)$. Also, because f is decreasing on $[c, e]$, we know from Definition 3.4.2 that if x_2 is in $[c, e]$ and $x_2 \neq c$, then $f(c) > f(x_2)$. Therefore, from Definition 3.1.1, f has a relative maximum value at c.

The proof of part (ii) is similar to the proof of part (i) and is left as an exercise (see Exercise 52).   ■

The first-derivative test for relative extrema states that if f is continuous at c and $f'(x)$ changes algebraic sign from positive to negative as x increases through the number c, then f has a relative maximum value at c; and if $f'(x)$ changes algebraic sign from negative to positive as x increases through c, then f has a relative minimum value at c.

Figures 3 and 4 illustrate parts (i) and (ii), respectively, of the first-derivative test when $f'(c)$ exists. Figure 5 shows the graph of a function f that has a relative maximum value at a number c, but $f'(c)$ does not exist; however, $f'(x) > 0$ when $x < c$, and $f'(x) < 0$ when $x > c$. In Figure 6, we have the graph of a function f for which c is a critical number, and $f'(x) < 0$ when $x < c$, and $f'(x) < 0$ when $x > c$; f does not have a relative extremum at c.

Further illustrations of the first-derivative test occur in Figure 1. At x_2 and x_4 the function has a relative maximum value, and at x_3 and x_5 the function has a relative minimum value; even though x_6 is a critical number there is no relative extremum at x_6.

We summarize the procedure for obtaining the relative extrema of a function.

> To determine analytically the relative extrema of f:
>
> **1.** Compute $f'(x)$.
> **2.** Determine the critical numbers of f, that is, the values of x for which $f'(x) = 0$ or for which $f'(x)$ does not exist.
> **3.** Apply the first-derivative test (Theorem 3.4.4).

The following examples demonstrate this procedure.

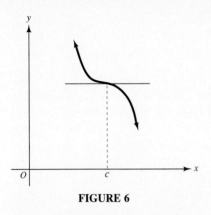

FIGURE 6

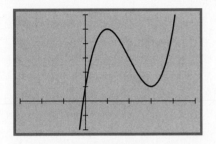

$[-3, 5]$ by $[-2, 6]$

$f(x) = x^3 - 6x^2 + 9x + 1$

FIGURE 7

▶ **EXAMPLE 1**   Plot the graph of the function defined by

$$f(x) = x^3 - 6x^2 + 9x + 1$$

Determine from the graph the relative extrema of f, the values of x at which the relative extrema occur, the intervals on which f is increasing, and the intervals on which f is decreasing. Confirm analytically the information obtained graphically.

Solution   Figure 7 shows the graph of f plotted in the $[-3, 5]$ by $[-2, 6]$ window. From the graph, we determine that f has a relative maximum value of 5 at $x = 1$ and a relative minimum value of 1 at $x = 3$. We also determine from the graph that f is increasing on the intervals $(-\infty, 1]$ and $[3, +\infty)$ and decreasing on the interval $[1, 3]$.

We now confirm this information analytically by first computing the derivative of f:

$$f'(x) = 3x^2 - 12x + 9$$

The only critical numbers are those for which $f'(x) = 0$:

$$3x^2 - 12x + 9 = 0$$
$$3(x - 3)(x - 1) = 0$$
$$x = 3 \qquad x = 1$$

The critical numbers of f are, therefore, 1 and 3. To determine whether f has a relative extremum at these numbers, we apply the first-derivative test and summarize the results in Table 1.

Table 1

	$f(x)$	$f'(x)$	*Conclusion*
$x < 1$		$+$	f is increasing
$x = 1$	5	0	f has a relative maximum value
$1 < x < 3$		$-$	f is decreasing
$x = 3$	1	0	f has a relative minimum value
$3 < x$		$+$	f is increasing

Our conclusions from the table confirm the information we determined graphically.   ◀

▶ **EXAMPLE 2**   Given

$$f(x) = x^{4/3} + 4x^{1/3}$$

Find the relative extrema of f and determine the values of x at which they occur. Also determine the intervals on which f is increasing and on which f is decreasing. Support the answers graphically.

Solution

$$f'(x) = \tfrac{4}{3}x^{1/3} + \tfrac{4}{3}x^{-2/3}$$
$$= \tfrac{4}{3}x^{-2/3}(x + 1)$$

Because $f'(x)$ does not exist when $x = 0$, and $f'(x) = 0$ when $x = -1$, the critical numbers of f are -1 and 0. We apply the first-derivative test and summarize the results in Table 2. In the table, the abbreviation d.n.e. stands for *does not exist*.

Table 2

	$f(x)$	$f'(x)$	*Conclusion*
$x < -1$		$-$	f is decreasing
$x = -1$	-3	0	f has a relative minimum value
$-1 < x < 0$		$+$	f is increasing
$x = 0$	0	d.n.e.	f does not have a relative extremum at $x = 0$
$0 < x$		$+$	f is increasing

We support the information in the table by plotting the graph of f in the $[-7.5, 7.5]$ by $[-5, 5]$ window, as shown in Figure 8. ◀

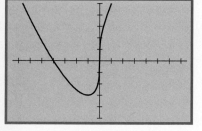

$[-7.5, 7.5]$ by $[-5, 5]$

$f(x) = x^{4/3} + 4x^{1/3}$

FIGURE 8

▶ **EXAMPLE 3**   Given

$$f(x) = \begin{cases} x^2 - 4 & \text{if } x \le 3 \\ 8 - x & \text{if } 3 < x \end{cases}$$

find analytically the relative extrema of f and the values of x at which they occur. Also determine analytically the intervals on which f is increasing and on which f is decreasing. Sketch the graph.

Solution   We compute $f'(x)$:

$$f'(x) = \begin{cases} 2x & \text{if } x < 3 \\ -1 & \text{if } 3 < x \end{cases}$$

Observe that f is continuous at 3. Because $f'_-(3) = 6$ and $f'_+(3) = -1$, $f'(3)$ does not exist. Therefore, 3 is a critical number. Another critical number is 0 because $f'(x) = 0$ when $x = 0$. Table 3 summarizes the results of the first-derivative test. We sketch the graph of f in Figure 9. ◀

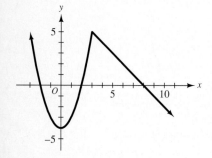

$f(x) = \begin{cases} x^2 - 4 \text{ if } x \le 3 \\ 8 - x \text{ if } 3 < x \end{cases}$

FIGURE 9

Table 3

	$f(x)$	$f'(x)$	*Conclusion*
$x < 0$		$-$	f is decreasing
$x = 0$	-4	0	f has a relative minimum value
$0 < x < 3$		$+$	f is increasing
$x = 3$	5	does not exist	f has a relative maximum value
$3 < x$		$-$	f is decreasing

As we did in Illustrations 1 and 2, we show in the next two examples how the behavior of a function can be read from the graph of its derivative.

▶ **EXAMPLE 4**   Figure 10 shows the graph of the derivative of a function f whose domain is the set of real numbers. From the graph, determine the critical numbers of f, the intervals on which f is increasing and on which f is decreasing, and any relative extrema of f.

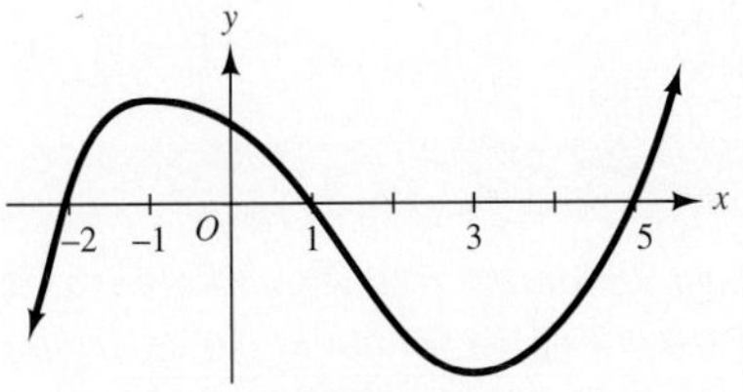

Solution   From the graph, observe that $f'(x)$ exists everywhere and that $f'(-2), f'(1)$, and $f'(5)$ are all zero. Therefore, -2, 1, and 5 are critical numbers of f. Because $f'(x) < 0$ when $x < -2$ or $1 < x < 5$, f is decreasing on the intervals $(-\infty, -2]$ and $[1, 5]$. Because $f'(x) > 0$ when $-2 < x < 1$ or $x > 5$, f is increasing on the intervals $[-2, 1]$ and $[5, +\infty)$. Table 4 summarizes these facts as well as the fact that f has relative minimum values at $x = -2$ and $x = 5$ and a relative maximum value at $x = 1$, obtained by applying the first-derivative test.

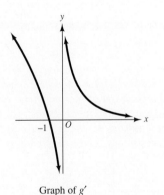

Graph of f'

FIGURE 10

Table 4

	$f'(x)$	*Conclusion*
$x < -2$	$-$	f is decreasing
$x = -2$	0	f has a relative minimum value
$-2 < x < 1$	$+$	f is increasing
$x = 1$	0	f has a relative maximum value
$1 < x < 5$	$-$	f is decreasing
$x = 5$	0	f has a relative minimum value
$5 < x$	$+$	f is increasing

◀

▶ **EXAMPLE 5**   Follow the instructions of Example 4 for the function g, continuous on its domain which is the set of all real numbers and the graph of whose derivative appears in Figure 11.

Solution   From the graph, because $g'(-1) = 0$, -1 is a critical number of g. Because the y axis is an asymptote of the graph of g', $g'(0)$ does not exist even though 0 is in the domain of g. Thus 0 is also a critical number of g. Because $g'(x) > 0$ when either $x < -1$ or $x > 0$, g is increasing on the intervals $(-\infty, -1]$ and $[0, +\infty)$. Because $g'(x) < 0$ when $-1 < x < 0$, g is decreasing on the interval $[-1, 0]$. We incorporate these facts in Table 5, where we have applied the first-derivative test to determine relative extrema.

Graph of g'

FIGURE 11

Table 5

	$g'(x)$	*Conclusion*
$x < -1$	$+$	g is increasing
$x = -1$	0	g has a relative maximum value
$-1 < x < 0$	$-$	g is decreasing
$x = 0$	does not exist	g has a relative minimum value
$0 < x$	$+$	g is increasing

◀

In Section 3.6, we read some additional properties of function f of Example 4 and function g of Example 5 from the graphs of their derivatives; then from these properties as well as those we found in this section, we sketch possible graphs of f and g

EXERCISES 3.4

In Exercises 1 through 18, (a) plot the graph, and determine from the graph (b) the relative extrema of f, (c) the values of x at which the relative extrema occur, (d) the intervals on which f is increasing, and (e) the intervals on which f is decreasing. Confirm analytically the information you obtained graphically.

1. $f(x) = x^2 - 4x - 1$

2. $f(x) = 3x^2 - 3x + 2$

3. $f(x) = x^3 - x^2 - x$

4. $f(x) = x^3 - 9x^2 + 15x - 5$

5. $f(x) = \frac{1}{4}x^4 - x^3 + x^2$ 6. $f(x) = x^4 + 4x$

7. $f(x) = 4 \sin \frac{1}{2}x;\ x \in [-2\pi, 2\pi]$

8. $f(x) = 2 \cos 3x;\ x \in [-\pi, \pi]$

9. $f(x) = \sqrt{x} - \dfrac{1}{\sqrt{x}}$ 10. $f(x) = \dfrac{x - 2}{x + 2}$

11. $f(x) = (1 - x)^2(1 + x)^3$

12. $f(x) = (x + 2)^2(x - 1)^2$

13. $f(x) = x - 3x^{1/3}$ 14. $f(x) = 4x - 6x^{2/3}$

15. $f(x) = x^{2/3} - x^{1/3}$ 16. $f(x) = x^{2/3}(x - 1)^2$

17. $f(x) = x^{5/4} + 10x^{1/4}$ 18. $f(x) = x^{5/3} - 10x^{2/3}$

In Exercises 19 through 32, do the following analytically: (a) find the relative extrema of f; (b) determine the values of x at which the relative extrema occur; (c) determine the intervals on which f is increasing; (d) determine the intervals on which f is decreasing. Support your answers graphically.

19. $f(x) = 2x^3 - 9x^2 + 2$

20. $f(x) = x^3 - 3x^2 - 9x$

21. $f(x) = \frac{1}{5}x^5 - \frac{5}{3}x^3 + 4x + 1$

22. $f(x) = x^5 - 5x^3 - 20x - 2$

23. $f(x) = x + \dfrac{1}{x^2}$ 24. $f(x) = 2x + \dfrac{1}{2x}$

25. $f(x) = 2x \sqrt{3 - x}$ 26. $f(x) = x \sqrt{5 - x^2}$

27. $f(x) = 2 - 3(x - 4)^{2/3}$

28. $f(x) = 2 - (x - 1)^{1/3}$

29. $f(x) = \frac{1}{2}\sec 4x;\ x \in [-\frac{1}{2}\pi, \frac{1}{2}\pi]$

30. $f(x) = 3 \csc 2x;\ x \in [-\pi, \pi]$

31. $f(x) = x^{1/3}(x + 4)^{-2/3}$

32. $f(x) = (x + 1)^{2/3}(x - 2)^{1/3}$

In Exercises 33 through 38, do the following analytically: (a) find the relative extrema of the function; (b) determine the values of x at which the relative extrema occur; (c) determine the intervals on which the function is increasing; (d) determine the intervals on which the function is decreasing. (e) Sketch the graph of the function from your answers in parts (a)–(d).

33. $f(x) = \begin{cases} 2x + 9 & \text{if } x \le -2 \\ x^2 + 1 & \text{if } -2 < x \end{cases}$

34. $f(x) = \begin{cases} 5 - 2x & \text{if } x < 3 \\ 3x - 10 & \text{if } 3 \le x \end{cases}$

35. $f(x) = \begin{cases} 3x + 5 & \text{if } x < -1 \\ x^2 + 1 & \text{if } -1 \le x < 2 \\ 7 - x & \text{if } 2 \le x \end{cases}$

36. $f(x) = \begin{cases} 12 - (x + 5)^2 & \text{if } x \le -3 \\ 5 - x & \text{if } -3 < x \le -1 \\ \sqrt{100 - (x - 7)^2} & \text{if } -1 < x \le 17 \end{cases}$

37. $f(x) = \begin{cases} (x + 9)^2 - 8 & \text{if } x < -7 \\ -\sqrt{25 - (x + 4)^2} & \text{if } -7 \le x \le 0 \\ (x - 2)^2 - 7 & \text{if } 0 < x \end{cases}$

38. $f(x) = \begin{cases} 4 - (x + 5)^2 & \text{if } x < -4 \\ 12 - (x + 1)^2 & \text{if } -4 \le x \end{cases}$

In Exercises 39 through 44, the accompanying figure shows the graph of the derivative of a function f continuous on its domain, which is the set of real numbers. From the graph, determine (a) the critical numbers of f, (b) the intervals on which f is increasing, (c) the intervals on which f is decreasing, and (d) any relative extrema of f.

39.

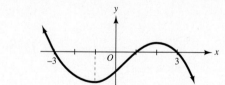

40.

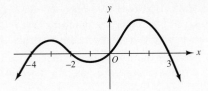

41.

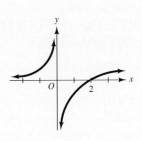

42.

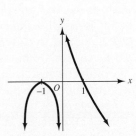

43.

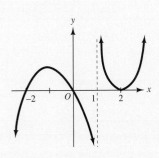

44.

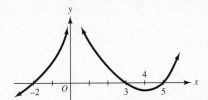

45. Given that the function f is continuous for all values of x, $f(0) = 0$, $f(4) = 2$, $f(8) = 0$, $f'(x) > 0$ if $x < 4$, and $f'(x) < 0$ if $x > 4$, sketch a possible graph of f in each of the following cases where the additional condition is satisfied: **(a)** f' is continuous at 4; **(b)** $f'(x) = \frac{1}{2}$ if $x < 4$, and $f'(x) = -\frac{1}{2}$ if $x > 4$; **(c)** $\lim_{x \to 4^-} f'(x) = 1$, $\lim_{x \to 4^+} f'(x) = -\infty$, and $f'(a) \neq f'(b)$ if $a \neq b$.

46. Given that the function f is continuous for all values of x, $f(3) = 2$, $f'(x) < 0$ if $x < 3$, and $f'(x) > 0$ if $x > 3$, sketch a possible graph of f in each of the following cases, where the additional condition is satisfied: **(a)** f' is continuous at 3; **(b)** $f'(x) = -1$ if $x < 3$, and $f'(x) = 1$ if $x > 3$; **(c)** $\lim_{x \to 3^-} f'(x) = -1$, $\lim_{x \to 3^+} f'(x) = 1$, and $f'(a) \neq f'(b)$ if $a \neq b$.

47. Find a and b such that the function defined by
$$f(x) = x^3 + ax^2 + b$$
will have a relative extremum at $(2, 3)$.

48. Find a, b, and c such that the function defined by
$$f(x) = ax^2 + bx + c$$
will have a relative maximum value of 7 at 1 and the graph of $y = f(x)$ will go through the point $(2, -2)$.

49. Find a, b, c, and d such that the function defined by
$$f(x) = ax^3 + bx^2 + cx + d$$
will have relative extrema at $(1, 2)$ and $(2, 3)$.

50. Given $f(x) = x^p(1 - x)^q$, where p and q are positive integers greater than 1, prove each of the following: **(a)** If p is even, f has a relative minimum value at 0; **(b)** if q is even, f has a relative minimum value at 1; **(c)** f has a relative maximum value at $p/(p + q)$ whether p and q are odd or even.

51. Prove Theorem 3.4.3(ii).

52. Prove Theorem 3.4.4(ii).

53. If $f(x) = x^k$, where k is an odd positive integer, show that f has no relative extrema.

54. Prove that if f is increasing on $[a, b]$ and if g is increasing on $[f(a), f(b)]$, then if $g \circ f$ exists on $[a, b]$, $g \circ f$ is increasing on $[a, b]$.

55. The function f is increasing on the interval I. Prove that **(a)** if $g(x) = -f(x)$, then g is decreasing on I; **(b)** if $h(x) = 1/f(x)$ and $f(x) > 0$ on I, then h is decreasing on I.

56. The function f is differentiable at each number in the closed interval $[a, b]$. Prove that if $f'(a) \cdot f'(b) < 0$, there is a number c in the open interval (a, b) such that $f'(c) = 0$.

57. If $f'(x)$ exists at all numbers in the open interval (a, b) containing the number c and $f'(c) = 0$, can we conclude that f has a relative extremum at c? Explain.

58. Describe how to apply the first-derivative test to determine relative extrema of a function.

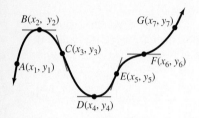

FIGURE 1

3.5 CONCAVITY, POINTS OF INFLECTION, AND THE SECOND-DERIVATIVE TEST

Just as the first derivative gives information about the behavior of a function and its graph, so does the second derivative, as you will learn in this section.

Refer to Figure 1 showing the graph of a function f whose first and second derivatives exist on the closed interval $[x_1, x_7]$. Because both f and f' are differentiable there, f and f' are continuous on $[x_1, x_7]$.

If we consider a point P moving along the graph of Figure 1 from A to G, then the position of P varies as we increase x from x_1 to x_7. As P moves along the graph from A to B, the slope of the tangent line to the graph is positive and is decreasing; that is, the tangent line is turning clockwise, and the graph lies below the tangent line. When the point P is at B, the slope of the tangent line is zero and is still decreasing. As P moves along the graph from B to C, the slope of the tangent line is negative and is still decreasing; the tangent line is still turning clockwise, and the graph is below its tangent line. We say that the graph is *concave downward* from A to C. As P moves along the graph from C to D, the slope of the tangent line is negative and is increasing; that is, the tangent line is turning counterclockwise, and the graph is above its tangent line. At D the slope of the tangent line is zero and is still increasing. From D to E, the slope of the tangent line is positive and increasing; the tangent line is still turning counterclockwise, and the graph is above its tangent line. We say that the graph is *concave upward* from C to E. At the point C the graph changes from concave downward to concave upward. Point C is called a *point of inflection*. We have the following definitions.

3.5.1 Definition of Concave Upward

The graph of a function f is said to be **concave upward** at the point $(c, f(c))$ if $f'(c)$ exists and if there is an open interval I containing c such that for all values of $x \neq c$ in I the point $(x, f(x))$ on the graph is above the tangent line to the graph at $(c, f(c))$.

3.5.2 Definition of Concave Downward

The graph of a function f is said to be **concave downward** at the point $(c, f(c))$ if $f'(c)$ exists and if there is an open interval I containing c such that for all values of $x \neq c$ in I the point $(x, f(x))$ on the graph is below the tangent line to the graph at $(c, f(c))$.

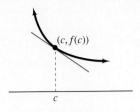

FIGURE 2

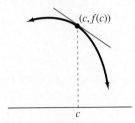

FIGURE 3

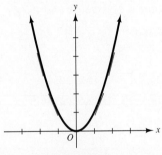

FIGURE 4

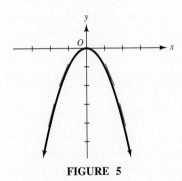

FIGURE 5

▷ **ILLUSTRATION 1**   Figure 2 shows a portion of the graph of a function f concave upward at the point $(c, f(c))$, and Figure 3 shows a portion of the graph of a function f concave downward at the point $(c, f(c))$.   ◀

The graph in Figure 1 is concave downward at all points $(x, f(x))$ for which x is in either of the following open intervals: (x_1, x_3) or (x_5, x_6). Similarly, the graph in Figure 1 is concave upward at all points $(x, f(x))$ for which x is in either (x_3, x_5) or (x_6, x_7).

▷ **ILLUSTRATION 2**   If f is the function defined by $f(x) = x^2$, then $f'(x) = 2x$ and $f''(x) = 2$. Thus $f''(x) > 0$ for all x. Furthermore, because the graph of f, appearing in Figure 4, is above all of its tangent lines, the graph is concave upward at all of its points.

If g is the function defined by $g(x) = -x^2$, then $g'(x) = -2x$ and $g''(x) = -2$. Hence $g''(x) < 0$ for all x. Also, because the graph of g, shown in Figure 5, is below all of its tangent lines, it is concave downward at all of its points.   ◀

The function f of Illustration 2 is such that $f''(x) > 0$ for all x, and the graph of f is concave upward everywhere. For function g of Illustration 2, $g''(x) < 0$ for all x, and the graph of g is concave downward everywhere. These two situations are special cases of the following theorem.

> **3.5.3 Theorem**
>
> Let f be a function that is differentiable on some open interval containing c. Then
>
> **(i)** if $f''(c) > 0$, the graph of f is concave upward at $(c, f(c))$;
> **(ii)** if $f''(c) < 0$, the graph of f is concave downward at $(c, f(c))$.

Proof of (i)

$$f''(c) = \lim_{x \to c} \frac{f'(x) - f'(c)}{x - c}$$

Because $f''(c) > 0$,

$$\lim_{x \to c} \frac{f'(x) - f'(c)}{x - c} > 0$$

Then, by Theorem 3.1.8(i) there is an open interval I containing c such that

$$\frac{f'(x) - f'(c)}{x - c} > 0 \tag{1}$$

for every $x \neq c$ in I.

Now consider the tangent line to the graph of f at the point $(c, f(c))$. An equation of this tangent line is

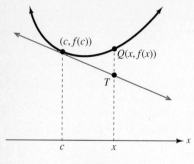

FIGURE 6

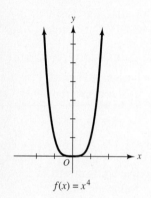

$f(x) = x^4$

FIGURE 7

FIGURE 8

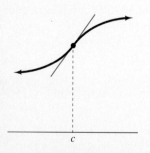

FIGURE 9

$$y = f(c) + f'(c)(x - c) \tag{2}$$

Let x be a number in the interval I such that $x \neq c$, and let Q be the point on the graph of f whose abscissa is x. Through Q draw a line parallel to the y axis, and let T be the point of intersection of this line with the tangent line (see Figure 6).

To prove that the graph of f is concave upward at $(c, f(c))$ we must show that the point Q is above the point T or, equivalently, that the directed distance $\overline{TQ} > 0$ for all values of $x \neq c$ in I. $\overline{TQ}$ equals the ordinate of Q minus the ordinate of T. The ordinate of Q is $f(x)$, and the ordinate of T is obtained from (2); so

$$\overline{TQ} = f(x) - [f(c) + f'(c)(x - c)]$$
$$\overline{TQ} = [f(x) - f(c)] - f'(c)(x - c) \tag{3}$$

From the mean-value theorem there exists some number d between x and c such that

$$f'(d) = \frac{f(x) - f(c)}{x - c}$$

That is,

$$f(x) - f(c) = f'(d)(x - c) \qquad \text{for some } d \text{ between } x \text{ and } c$$

Substituting from this equation into (3) we have

$$\overline{TQ} = f'(d)(x - c) - f'(c)(x - c)$$
$$\overline{TQ} = (x - c)[f'(d) - f'(c)] \tag{4}$$

Because d is between x and c, d is in the interval I, and so by taking $x = d$ in inequality (1) we obtain

$$\frac{f'(d) - f'(c)}{d - c} > 0 \tag{5}$$

To prove that $\overline{TQ} > 0$ we show that both of the factors on the right side of (4) have the same sign. If $x - c > 0$, then $x > c$. And because d is between x and c, then $d > c$; therefore, from inequality (5), $f'(d) - f'(c) > 0$. If $x - c < 0$, then $x < c$ and so $d < c$; therefore, from (5), $f'(d) - f'(c) < 0$. We conclude that $x - c$ and $f'(d) - f'(c)$ have the same sign; therefore $\overline{TQ}$ is a positive number. Thus the graph of f is concave upward at $(c, f(c))$.

The proof of part (ii) is similar and is omitted. ■

The converse of Theorem 3.5.3 is not true. For example, if f is the function defined by $f(x) = x^4$, the graph of f is concave upward at the point $(0, 0)$ but because $f''(x) = 12x^2$, $f''(0) = 0$ (see Figure 7). Accordingly, a sufficient condition for the graph of a function f to be concave upward at the point $(c, f(c))$ is that $f''(c) > 0$, but this is not a necessary condition. Similarly, a sufficient—but not a necessary—condition that the graph of a function f be concave downward at the point $(c, f(c))$ is that $f''(c) < 0$.

If there is a point on the graph of a function at which the sense of concavity changes, and the graph has a tangent line there, then the graph crosses its tangent line at this point, as shown in Figures 8, 9, and 10. Such a point is called a *point of inflection*.

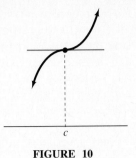

FIGURE 10

3.5.4 Definition of a Point of Inflection

The point $(c, f(c))$ is a **point of inflection** of the graph of the function f if the graph has a tangent line there, and if there exists an open interval I containing c such that if x is in I, then either

(i) $f''(x) < 0$ if $x < c$, and $f''(x) > 0$ if $x > c$; or
(ii) $f''(x) > 0$ if $x < c$ and $f''(x) < 0$ if $x > c$

▷ **ILLUSTRATION 3**   Figure 8 illustrates a point of inflection where condition (i) of Definition 3.5.4 holds; in this case the graph is concave downward at points immediately to the left of the point of inflection, and the graph is concave upward at points immediately to the right of the point of inflection. Condition (ii) is illustrated in Figure 9, where the sense of concavity changes from upward to downward at the point of inflection. Figure 10 gives another illustration of condition (i), where the sense of concavity changes from downward to upward at the point of inflection. Note that in Figure 10 the graph has a horizontal tangent line at the point of inflection.
◀

The graph in Figure 1 has points of inflection at C, E, and F.

A crucial part of the definition of a point of inflection is that the graph must have a tangent line there. Consider, for instance, the function of Example 2 in Section 1.6 defined by

$$h(x) = \begin{cases} 4 - x^2 & \text{if } x \leq 1 \\ 2 + x^2 & \text{if } 1 < x \end{cases}$$

The graph of h appears in Figure 11. Observe that $h''(x) = -2$ if $x < 1$ and $h''(x) = 2$ if $x > 1$. Thus at the point $(1, 3)$ on the graph the sense of concavity changes from downward to upward. However, $(1, 3)$ is not a point of inflection because the graph does not have a tangent line there.

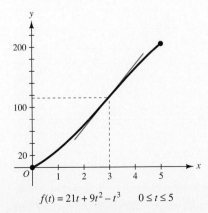

$h(x) = \begin{cases} 4 - x^2 & \text{if } x \leq 1 \\ 2 + x^2 & \text{if } 1 < x \end{cases}$

FIGURE 11

▷ **ILLUSTRATION 4**   Suppose that t hours after starting work at 7 A.M. a factory worker on an assembly line has performed a particular task on $f(t)$ units where

$$f(t) = 21t + 9t^2 - t^3 \qquad 0 \leq t \leq 5$$

Table 1 gives function values for integer values of t from 1 through 5, and Figure 12 shows the graph of f on $[0, 5]$.

Table 1

t	1	2	3	4	5
$f(t)$	29	70	117	164	205

$$f'(t) = 21 + 18t - 3t^2 \qquad f''(t) = 18 - 6t$$
$$= 6(3 - t)$$

Observe that $f''(t) > 0$ if $0 < t < 3$ and $f''(t) < 0$ if $3 < t < 5$. From Definition 3.5.4(ii), the graph of f has a point of inflection at $t = 3$. From Theorem 3.4.3, because $f''(t) > 0$ when $0 < t < 3$, $f'(t)$ is increasing on

$f(t) = 21t + 9t^2 - t^3 \qquad 0 \leq t \leq 5$

FIGURE 12

$[0, 3]$, and because $f''(t) < 0$ when $3 < t < 5$, $f'(t)$ is decreasing on $[3, 5]$. Therefore, since $f'(t)$ is the rate of change of $f(t)$ with respect to t, we conclude that in the first three hours (from 7 A.M. until 10 A.M.) the worker is performing the task at an increasing rate, and during the remaining two hours (from 10 A.M. until noon) the worker is performing the task at a decreasing rate. At $t = 3$ (10 A.M.) the worker is producing most efficiently, and when $3 < t < 5$ (after 10 A.M.) there is a reduction in the worker's production rate. The point at which the worker is producing most efficiently is called the *point of diminishing returns;* this point is a point of inflection of the graph of f.   ◀

Definition 3.5.4 indicates that the second derivative changes sign at a point of inflection but indicates nothing about the value of the second derivative there. The following theorem, however, states that if the second derivative exists at a point of inflection, it must be zero.

3.5.5 Theorem

Suppose the function f is differentiable on some open interval containing c, and $(c, f(c))$ is a point of inflection of the graph of f. Then if $f''(c)$ exists, $f''(c) = 0$.

Proof   Let g be the function such that $g(x) = f'(x)$; then $g'(x) = f''(x)$. Because $(c, f(c))$ is a point of inflection of the graph of f, then $f''(x)$ changes sign at c and so $g'(x)$ changes sign at c. Therefore, by the first-derivative test g has a relative extremum at c, and c is a critical number of g. Because $g'(c) = f''(c)$, and since by hypothesis $f''(c)$ exists, it follows that $g'(c)$ exists. Therefore, by Theorem 3.1.3, $g'(c) = 0$ and $f''(c) = 0$, which is what we wanted to prove.   ∎

The converse of Theorem 3.5.5 is not true. That is, if the second derivative of a function is zero at a number c, the graph of the function does not necessarily have a point of inflection where $x = c$. This fact is demonstrated in the following illustration.

▷   **ILLUSTRATION 5**   Consider the function f whose graph appears in Figure 7 and for which

$$f(x) = x^4 \qquad f'(x) = 4x^3 \qquad f''(x) = 12x^2$$

Observe that $f''(0) = 0$; but because $f''(x) > 0$ if $x < 0$ and $f''(x) > 0$ if $x > 0$, the origin is not a point of inflection. Furthermore, the graph is concave upward everywhere.   ◀

▶   **EXAMPLE 1**   The function in Example 1 of Section 3.4 is defined by

$$f(x) = x^3 - 6x^2 + 9x + 1$$

Find the point of inflection of the graph of f and determine where the graph is concave upward and concave downward. Support the answer by plotting, in the same window, the graph of f and the inflectional tangent.

Solution

$$f'(x) = 3x^2 - 12x + 9 \qquad f''(x) = 6x - 12$$

$f''(x)$ exists for all values of x; so the only possible point of inflection is where $f''(x) = 0$, which occurs at $x = 2$. To determine whether there is a point of inflection at $x = 2$, we must check to see if $f''(x)$ changes sign; at the same time we determine the concavity of the graph for the respective intervals. The results are summarized in Table 2.

Table 2

	$f(x)$	$f'(x)$	$f''(x)$	*Conclusion*
$x < 2$			−	graph of f is concave downward
$x = 2$	3	−3	0	graph of f has a point of inflection
$2 < x$			+	graph of f is concave upward

In Example 1 of Section 3.4, we showed that f has a relative maximum value at 1 and a relative minimum value at 3. Figure 13 shows the graph of f and the inflectional tangent plotted in the $[-1, 8.4]$ by $[-1, 5.2]$ window, which supports the information in Table 2. ◄

The graph of a function may have a point of inflection where the second derivative fails to exist, as shown in the next example.

► **EXAMPLE 2**   Given

$$f(x) = x^{1/3}$$

find the point of inflection of the graph of f, and determine where the graph is concave upward and concave downward. Support the answer graphically.

Solution

$$f'(x) = \tfrac{1}{3}x^{-2/3} \qquad f''(x) = -\tfrac{2}{9}x^{-5/3}$$

Neither $f'(0)$ nor $f''(0)$ exists. In Illustration 3 of Section 2.2, we showed that the y axis is the tangent line to the graph of this function at the origin. Furthermore,

$$f''(x) > 0 \text{ if } x < 0 \quad \text{and} \quad f''(x) < 0 \text{ if } x > 0$$

Therefore, from Definition 3.5.4(ii), f has a point of inflection at the origin. We determine the concavity of the graph from the sign of $f''(x)$ and summarize the results in Table 3.

Table 3

	$f(x)$	$f'(x)$	$f''(x)$	*Conclusion*
$x < 0$		+	+	f is increasing; graph of f is concave upward
$x = 0$	0	does not exist	does not exist	graph of f has a point of inflection
$0 < x$		+	−	f is increasing; graph of f is concave downward

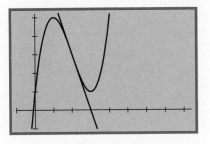

[−1, 8.4] by [−1, 5.2]

$f(x) = x^3 - 6x^2 + 9x + 1$

FIGURE 13

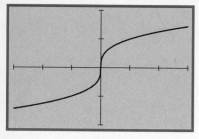

[−3, 3] by [−2, 2]

$f(x) = x^{1/3}$

FIGURE 14

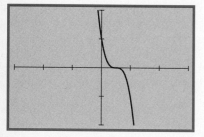

[−3, 3] by [−2, 2]

$f(x) = (1 − 2x)^3$

FIGURE 15

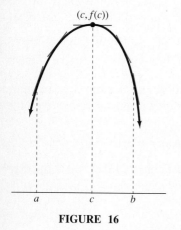

$(c, f(c))$

FIGURE 16

Figure 14, showing the graph of f plotted in the $[−3, 3]$ by $[−2, 2]$ window, supports the information in Table 3. ◀

▶ **EXAMPLE 3** Given

$$f(x) = (1 − 2x)^3$$

Plot the graph, and from the graph, estimate the point of inflection and where the graph is concave upward and concave downward. Confirm the estimates analytically.

Solution Figure 15 shows the graph of f plotted in the $[−3, 3]$ by $[−2, 2]$ window. From the graph we estimate the point of inflection to be at $(0.5, 0)$, the graph concave upward for $x < 0.5$ and the graph concave downward for $x > 0.5$. We now confirm these estimates analytically.

$$f'(x) = −6(1 − 2x)^2 \qquad f''(x) = 24(1 − 2x)$$

Because $f''(x)$ exists for all values of x, the only possible point of inflection is where $f''(x) = 0$, that is, at $x = 0.5$. From the results summarized in Table 4, $f''(x)$ changes sign from $+$ to $−$ at $x = 0.5$; so the graph has a point of inflection there. Note also that because $f'(0.5) = 0$, the graph has a horizontal tangent line at the point of inflection. ◀

Table 4

	$f(x)$	$f'(x)$	$f''(x)$	*Conclusion*
$x < 0.5$			$+$	graph of f is concave upward
$x = 0.5$	0	0	0	graph of f has a point of inflection
$0.5 < x$			$−$	graph of f is concave downward

In Section 3.4 you learned how to determine whether a function has a relative extremum at a critical number c by checking the algebraic sign of the first derivative at numbers in intervals to the left and right of c. Another test for relative extrema, called the *second-derivative test,* involves only the critical number c as well as the second derivative. Before stating the test, we give an informal geometric discussion that should appeal to your intuition.

Suppose that f is a function such that f'' exists on some open interval (a, b) containing c, and that $f'(c) = 0$. Suppose also that $f''(x) < 0$ if x is in (a, b). Then from Theorem 3.5.3(ii) the graph of f is concave downward at all points in (a, b), and from Theorem 3.4.3(ii) f' is decreasing on $[a, b]$. Figure 16 shows the graph of a function having these properties, and a segment of the tangent line is shown at some points in the figure. The slope of the tangent line is decreasing on $[a, b]$, which is consistent with the fact that f' is decreasing on $[a, b]$. Observe that f has a relative maximum value at c.

Now suppose that f is a function having the properties of the function in the previous paragraph except that $f''(x) > 0$ if x is in (a, b). Then from Theorem 3.5.3(i) the graph of f is concave upward at all points in (a, b), and from Theorem 3.4.3(i) f' is increasing on $[a, b]$. The graph of a function

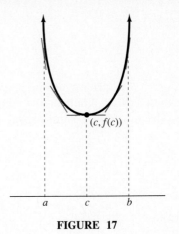

FIGURE 17

having these properties appears in Figure 17. The slopes of the tangent lines, for which some segments are shown in the figure, are increasing on $[a, b]$, and f has a relative minimum value at c.

We now state and prove the *second-derivative test for relative extrema,* which confirms the geometric observations in the preceding two paragraphs.

> **3.5.6 Theorem   The Second-Derivative Test for Relative Extrema**
>
> Let c be a critical number of a function f at which $f'(c) = 0$, and let f'' exist for all values of x in some open interval containing c.
>
> (i) If $f''(c) < 0$, then f has a relative maximum value at c.
> (ii) If $f''(c) > 0$, then f has a relative minimum value at c.

Proof of (i)   By hypothesis, $f''(c)$ exists and is negative; so

$$f''(c) = \lim_{x \to c} \frac{f'(x) - f'(c)}{x - c} < 0$$

Therefore, by Theorem 3.1.8(ii) there is an open interval I containing c such that

$$\frac{f'(x) - f'(c)}{x - c} < 0 \tag{6}$$

for every $x \neq c$ in the interval.

Let I_1 be the open interval containing all values of x in I for which $x < c$; therefore c is the right endpoint of the open interval I_1. Let I_2 be the open interval containing all values of x in I for which $x > c$; so c is the left endpoint of the open interval I_2.

Then if x is in I_1, $x - c < 0$, and from inequality (6) $f'(x) - f'(c) > 0$ or, equivalently, $f'(x) > f'(c)$. If x is in I_2, $x - c > 0$, and from (6) $f'(x) - f'(c) < 0$ or, equivalently, $f'(x) < f'(c)$.

But because $f'(c) = 0$, we conclude that if x is in I_1, $f'(x) > 0$, and if x is in I_2, $f'(x) < 0$. Therefore $f'(x)$ changes algebraic sign from positive to negative as x increases through c; so from the first-derivative test f has a relative maximum value at c.

The proof of part (ii) is similar and is left as an exercise (see Exercise 56).   ∎

▶ **EXAMPLE 4**   Given

$$f(x) = x^4 + \tfrac{4}{3}x^3 - 4x^2$$

find the relative extrema of f by applying the second-derivative test. Use this information to sketch the graph of f. Support the results on a graphics calculator.

Solution   We compute the first and second derivatives of f:

$$f'(x) = 4x^3 + 4x^2 - 8x \qquad f''(x) = 12x^2 + 8x - 8$$

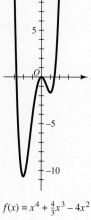

$f(x) = x^4 + \frac{4}{3}x^3 - 4x^2$

FIGURE 18

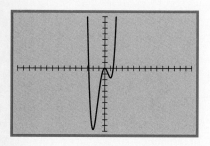

$[-15, 15]$ by $[-11, 9]$

$f(x) = x^4 + \frac{4}{3}x^3 - 4x^2$

FIGURE 19

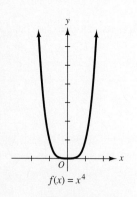

$f(x) = x^4$

FIGURE 20

We set $f'(x) = 0$:

$$4x(x + 2)(x - 1) = 0$$
$$x = 0 \qquad x = -2 \qquad x = 1$$

Thus the critical numbers of f are -2, 0, and 1. We determine whether or not there is a relative extremum at any of these critical numbers by finding the sign of the second derivative there. The results are summarized in Table 5.

Table 5

	$f(x)$	$f'(x)$	$f''(x)$	*Conclusion*
$x = -2$	$-\frac{32}{3}$	0	+	f has a relative minimum value
$x = 0$	0	0	−	f has a relative maximum value
$x = 1$	$-\frac{5}{3}$	0	+	f has a relative minimum value

From the information in this table and by plotting a few more points, we sketch the graph of f shown in Figure 18. Figure 19, showing the graph of f plotted in the $[-15, 15]$ by $[-11, 9]$ window, supports our results. ◄

If $f''(c) = 0$, as well as $f'(c) = 0$, nothing can be concluded regarding a relative extremum of f at c. The following three illustrations justify this statement.

▷ **ILLUSTRATION 6**   If $f(x) = x^4$, then $f'(x) = 4x^3$ and $f''(x) = 12x^2$. Thus $f(0), f'(0)$, and $f''(0)$ all have the value zero. By applying the first-derivative test we see that f has a relative minimum value at 0. The graph of f appears in Figure 20. ◄

▷ **ILLUSTRATION 7**   If $g(x) = -x^4$, then $g'(x) = -4x^3$ and $g''(x) = -12x^2$. Hence $g(0), g'(0)$, and $g''(0)$ are all zero. In this case g has a relative maximum value at 0, as can be seen by applying the first-derivative test. Figure 21 shows the graph of g. ◄

▷ **ILLUSTRATION 8**   If $h(x) = x^3$, then $h'(x) = 3x^2$ and $h''(x) = 6x$; so $h(0), h'(0)$, and $h''(0)$ are all zero. The function h does not have a relative extremum at 0 because if $x < 0$, $h(x) < h(0)$; and if $x > 0$, $h(x) > h(0)$. The graph of h appears in Figure 22. ◄

Illustrations 6–8 give examples of three functions, each of which has zero for its second derivative at a number for which its first derivative is zero; yet at that number, one function has a relative minimum value, another function has a relative maximum value, and the third function has no relative extreme value.

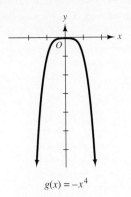

$g(x) = -x^4$

FIGURE 21

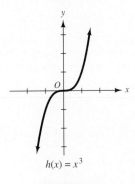

$h(x) = x^3$

FIGURE 22

▶ **EXAMPLE 5**   For the sine function, find the relative extrema by applying the second-derivative test, and find the points of inflection of its graph. Also find the slopes of the inflectional tangents. Plot the graph of the sine function on an interval of length 2π and containing the point of inflection having the smallest positive abscissa. In the same window, plot the inflectional tangent.

Solution   Let

$$f(x) = \sin x \qquad f'(x) = \cos x \qquad f''(x) = -\sin x$$

The functions f, f', and f'' are defined for all x. We obtain the critical numbers by setting $f'(x) = 0$:

$$\cos x = 0$$
$$x = \tfrac{1}{2}\pi + k\pi \qquad k \text{ is any integer}$$

We determine whether or not there is a relative extremum at any of these critical numbers by finding the sign of the second derivative there.

$$f''(\tfrac{1}{2}\pi + k\pi) = -\sin(\tfrac{1}{2}\pi + k\pi)$$
$$= -\cos k\pi$$
$$= \begin{cases} -1 & \text{if } k \text{ is an even integer} \\ 1 & \text{if } k \text{ is an odd integer} \end{cases}$$

We summarize the results of applying the second-derivative test in Table 6.

Table 6

	$f(x)$	$f'(x)$	$f''(x)$	*Conclusion*
$x = \tfrac{1}{2}\pi + k\pi$ (k is an even integer)	1	0	−	f has a relative maximum value
$x = \tfrac{1}{2}\pi + k\pi$ (k is an odd integer)	−1	0	+	f has a relative minimum value

To determine the points of inflection we set $f''(x) = 0$:

$$-\sin x = 0$$
$$x = k\pi \qquad k \text{ is any integer}$$

Because $f''(x)$ changes sign at each of these values of x, the graph has a point of inflection at every point having these abscissas. At each point of inflection,

$$f'(k\pi) = \cos k\pi \qquad k \text{ is any integer}$$
$$= \begin{cases} 1 & \text{if } k \text{ is an even integer} \\ -1 & \text{if } k \text{ is an odd integer} \end{cases}$$

Therefore the slopes of the inflectional tangents are either $+1$ or -1.

Figure 23 shows the graph of the sine function and the inflectional tangent at $(\pi, 0)$ plotted in the $[0, 2\pi]$ by $[-2, 2]$ window.   ◀

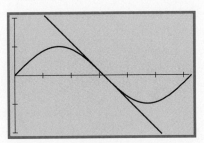

$[0, 2\pi]$ by $[-2, 2]$

$f(x) = \sin x$

FIGURE 23

EXERCISES 3.5

In Exercises 1 through 8, find any points of inflection of the graph of the function and determine where the graph is concave upward and concave downward. Support your answer by plotting in the same window the graph of the function and the inflectional tangents.

1. $f(x) = 2x^3 + 3x^2 - 12x + 1$

2. $g(x) = x^3 - 6x^2 + 20$

3. $g(x) = x^4 - 8x^3$ **4.** $f(x) = x^4 - 2x^3$

5. $F(x) = \dfrac{2}{x^2 + 3}$ **6.** $G(x) = \dfrac{x}{x^2 + 4}$

7. $f(x) = 2 \sin 3x; \; x \in [-\tfrac{1}{2}\pi, \tfrac{1}{2}\pi]$

8. $f(x) = 3 \cos 2x; \; x \in [-\pi, \pi]$

In Exercises 9 through 16, plot the graph of the function and from the graph estimate the point of inflection and where the graph is concave upward and concave downward. Confirm your estimates analytically.

9. $f(x) = x^3 + 9x$ **10.** $g(x) = 2x^3 - 1$

11. $G(x) = (x - 1)^3$ **12.** $F(x) = (x + 2)^3$

13. $f(x) = (x + 2)^{1/3}$ **14.** $g(x) = (x - 1)^{1/3}$

15. $g(x) = \tan \tfrac{1}{2}x; \; x \in (-\pi, \pi)$

16. $f(x) = \cot 2x; \; x \in (0, \tfrac{1}{2}\pi)$

In Exercises 17 through 22, find the point of inflection of the graph of the function, if there is one, and determine where the graph is concave upward and concave downward. Sketch the graph.

17. $f(x) = \begin{cases} x^2 - 1 & \text{if } x < 2 \\ 7 - x^2 & \text{if } 2 \le x \end{cases}$

18. $f(x) = \begin{cases} 2 + x^2 & \text{if } x \le 1 \\ 4 - x^2 & \text{if } 1 < x \end{cases}$

19. $g(x) = \begin{cases} x^2 & \text{if } x \le 0 \\ -x^2 & \text{if } 0 < x \end{cases}$

20. $g(x) = \begin{cases} -x^3 & \text{if } x < 0 \\ x^3 & \text{if } 0 \le x \end{cases}$

21. $F(x) = \begin{cases} x^3 & \text{if } x < 0 \\ x^4 & \text{if } 0 \le x \end{cases}$

22. $G(x) = \begin{cases} x^2 & \text{if } x \le 0 \\ x^4 & \text{if } 0 < x \end{cases}$

In Exercises 23 through 30, sketch a portion of the graph of some function f through the point where $x = c$ if the given conditions are satisfied. Assume that f is continuous on some open interval containing c.

23. **(a)** $f'(x) > 0$ if $x < c$; $f'(x) < 0$ if $x > c$; $f''(x) < 0$ if $x < c$; $f''(x) < 0$ if $x > c$

    (b) $f'(x) > 0$ if $x < c$; $f'(x) < 0$ if $x > c$; $f''(x) > 0$ if $x < c$; $f''(x) > 0$ if $x > c$

24. **(a)** $f'(x) > 0$ if $x < c$; $f'(x) > 0$ if $x > c$; $f''(x) > 0$ if $x < c$; $f''(x) < 0$ if $x > c$

    (b) $f'(x) < 0$ if $x < c$; $f'(x) > 0$ if $x > c$; $f''(x) > 0$ if $x < c$; $f''(x) < 0$ if $x > c$

25. **(a)** $f''(c) = 0$; $f'(c) = 0$; $f''(x) > 0$ if $x < c$; $f''(x) < 0$ if $x > c$

    (b) $f''(c) = 0$; $f'(c) = 0$; $f''(x) > 0$ if $x < c$; $f''(x) > 0$ if $x > c$

26. **(a)** $f'(c) = 0$; $f'(x) > 0$ if $x < c$; $f''(x) > 0$ if $x > c$

    (b) $f'(c) = 0$; $f'(x) < 0$ if $x < c$; $f''(x) > 0$ if $x > c$

27. **(a)** $f''(c) = 0$; $f'(c) = -1$; $f''(x) < 0$ if $x < c$; $f''(x) > 0$ if $x > c$

    (b) $f'(c)$ does not exist; $f''(x) > 0$ if $x < c$; $f''(x) > 0$ if $x > c$

28. **(a)** $f''(c) = 0$; $f'(c) = \tfrac{1}{2}$; $f''(x) > 0$ if $x < c$; $f''(x) < 0$ if $x > c$

    (b) $f'(c)$ does not exist; $f''(x) < 0$ if $x < c$; $f''(x) > 0$ if $x > c$

29. $\lim\limits_{x \to c^-} f'(x) = +\infty$; $\lim\limits_{x \to c^+} f'(x) = 0$; $f''(x) > 0$ if $x < c$; $f''(x) < 0$ if $x > c$

30. $\lim\limits_{x \to c^-} f'(x) = +\infty$; $\lim\limits_{x \to c^+} f'(x) = -\infty$; $f''(x) > 0$ if $x < c$; $f''(x) > 0$ if $x > c$

In Exercises 31 through 38, find the relative extrema of the function by applying the second-derivative test. Use this information to sketch the graph of the function. Support your results on your graphics calculator.

31. $f(x) = -4x^3 + 3x^2 + 18x$

32. $h(x) = 2x^3 - 9x^2 + 27$

33. $g(x) = x^4 - \tfrac{1}{3}x^3 - \tfrac{3}{2}x^2$ **34.** $f(x) = \tfrac{1}{5}x^5 - \tfrac{2}{3}x^3$

35. $f(x) = \cos 3x; \; x \in [-\tfrac{1}{6}\pi, \tfrac{1}{2}\pi]$

36. $g(x) = 2 \sin 4x; \; x \in [0, \tfrac{1}{2}\pi]$

37. $h(x) = 4x^{1/2} + 4x^{-1/2}$ **38.** $f(x) = x\sqrt{x + 3}$

39. Sketch the graph of some function f for which $f(x)$, $f'(x)$, and $f''(x)$ exist and are: **(a)** positive for all x; **(b)** negative for all x.

40. For the cosine function, find **(a)** the relative extrema by applying the second-derivative test; **(b)** the points of inflection of its graph; **(c)** the slopes of the inflectional tangents. **(d)** Plot the graph of the cosine function on an interval of length 2π and containing the point of inflection having the smallest positive abscissa. In the same window, plot the inflectional tangent.

In Exercises 41 and 42, find (a) the points of inflection of the graph of the function, and (b) the slopes of the inflectional tangents. (c) Plot the graph of the function on an interval of length π and containing the point of inflection having the smallest positive abscissa. In the same window, plot the inflectional tangent.

41. the tangent function   **42.** the cotangent function

In Exercises 43 and 44, (a) find the relative extrema of the function by applying the second-derivative test. (b) Plot the graph of the function on an interval of length 2π.

43. the cosecant function   **44.** the secant function

In Exercises 45 through 50, sketch a portion of the graph of a function f through the points $(c, f(c))$, $(d, f(d))$, and $(e, f(e))$ if the given conditions are satisfied. Also draw a segment of the tangent line at each of these points, if there is a tangent line. Assume that $c < d < e$ and f is continuous on some open interval containing c, d, and e.

45. (a) $f'(c) = 0; f'(d) = 1; f''(d) = 0; f'(e) = 0;$
$f''(x) > 0$ if $x < d; f''(x) < 0$ if $x > d$
(b) $f'(c) = 0; f'(d) = -1; f''(d) = 0; f'(e) = 0;$
$f''(e) = 0; f''(x) < 0$ if $x < d; f''(x) > 0$
if $d < x < e; f''(x) < 0$ if $x > e$

46. (a) $f'(c) = 0; f'(d) = -1; f''(d) = 0; f'(e) = 0;$
$f''(x) < 0$ if $x < d; f''(x) > 0$ if $x > d$
(b) $f'(c) = 0; f'(d) = 1; f''(d) = 0; f'(e) = 0;$
$f''(e) = 0; f''(x) > 0$ if $x < d; f''(x) < 0$
if $d < x < e; f''(x) > 0$ if $x > e$

47. (a) $f'(c) = 0; f''(c) = 0; f'(d) = -1; f''(d) = 0;$
$f'(e) = 0; f''(x) > 0$ if $x < c; f''(x) < 0$ if
$c < x < d; f''(x) > 0$ if $x > d$
(b) $f'(c) = 0; \lim_{x \to d^-} f'(x) = +\infty; \lim_{x \to d^+} f'(x) = +\infty;$
$f'(e) = 0; f''(x) > 0$ if $x < d; f''(x) < 0$
if $x > d$

48. (a) $f'(c) = 0; f''(c) = 0; f'(d) = 1; f''(d) = 0;$
$f'(e) = 0; f''(x) < 0$ if $x < c; f''(x) > 0$
if $c < x < d; f''(x) < 0$ if $x > d$
(b) $f'(c) = 0; \lim_{x \to d^-} f'(x) = -\infty; \lim_{x \to d^+} f'(x) = -\infty;$
$f'(e) = 0; f''(x) < 0$ if $x < d; f''(x) > 0$ if
$x > d$

49. (a) $f'(c)$ does not exist; $f'(d) = -1; f''(d) = 0;$
$f'(e) = 0; f''(x) > 0$ if $x < c; f''(x) < 0$
if $c < x < d; f''(x) > 0$ if $x > d$

(b) $f'(c) = 0; f'(d)$ does not exist; $f'(e) = 0;$
$f''(e) = 0; f''(x) < 0$ if $x < d; f''(x) < 0$
if $d < x < e; f''(x) > 0$ if $x > e$

50. (a) $f'(c) = 0; f'(d) = -1; f''(d) = 0; f'(e)$ does not exist; $f''(x) < 0$ if $x < d; f''(x) > 0$
if $d < x < e; f''(x) < 0$ if $x > e$
(b) $f'(c) = 0; f''(c) = 0; f'(d)$ does not exist;
$f'(e) = 0; f''(x) < 0$ if $x < c; f''(x) > 0$
if $c < x < d; f''(x) > 0$ if $x > d$

51. If $f(x) = ax^3 + bx^2$, determine a and b so that the graph of f will have a point of inflection at $(1, 2)$. Support your answer graphically.

52. If $f(x) = ax^3 + bx^2 + cx$, determine a, b, and c so that the graph of f will have a point of inflection at $(1, 2)$ and so that the slope of the inflectional tangent there will be -2. Support your answer graphically.

53. If $f(x) = ax^3 + bx^2 + cx + d$, determine a, b, c, and d so that f will have a relative extremum at $(0, 3)$ and so that the graph of f will have a point of inflection at $(1, -1)$. Support your answer graphically.

54. If $f(x) = ax^4 + bx^3 + cx^2 + dx + e$, determine a, b, c, d, and e so that the graph of f will have a point of inflection at $(1, -1)$, contain the origin, and be symmetric with respect to the y axis. Support your answer graphically.

55. Suppose that $\frac{1}{2}\sqrt{2}$ and $-\frac{1}{2}\sqrt{3}$ are critical numbers of a function f and that $f''(x) = x[\![\frac{1}{2}x^2 + 1]\!]$. At each of these numbers, determine if f has a relative extremum, and if so, whether it is a relative minimum or a relative maximum.

56. Prove part (ii) of the second-derivative test for relative extrema.

57. Suppose that the graph of the function f has a point of inflection at the point $(c, f(c))$. What can you conclude, if anything, about **(a)** the continuity of f at c; **(b)** the continuity of f' at c; **(c)** the continuity of f'' at c?

58. Suppose that f is a function for which $f''(x)$ exists for all x in some open interval I and that at a number c in I, $f''(c) = 0$ and $f'''(c)$ exists and is not zero. Prove that the point $(c, f(c))$ is a point of inflection of the graph of f. *Hint:* the proof is similar to the proof of the second-derivative test.

59. (a) Explain why a point of inflection of the graph of a function representing a worker's productivity can be interpreted as a point of diminishing returns.
(b) Suppose that a worker in a shop that manufac-

tures picture frames can construct y frames x hours after starting work at 8 A.M., and

$$y = 3x + 8x^2 - x^3 \qquad 0 \le x \le 4$$

Determine at what time the worker is performing most efficiently; that is, when does the worker reach the point of diminishing returns?

60. Explain when you would use the second-derivative test to determine relative extrema and when you would use the first-derivative test. In your explanation, indicate the advantages and disadvantages of each test.

3.6 SKETCHING GRAPHS OF FUNCTIONS AND THEIR DERIVATIVES

You learned in Sections 3.4 and 3.5 how properties of graphs of functions can be determined from their derivatives. We now show how these properties can be determined from the graph of the derivative and then used to sketch the graph of the original function.

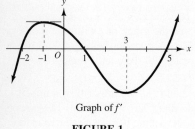

Graph of f'

FIGURE 1

▶ **EXAMPLE 1**   The graph of the derivative of the function f in Example 4 of Section 3.4 is repeated here in Figure 1. From this graph determine the abscissas of any points of inflection of the graph of f and where the graph of f is concave upward and concave downward. Sketch a possible graph of f having these properties as well as the properties obtained in Example 4 of Section 3.4 if the only zeros of f are 3.5 and 6.

Solution   The second derivative f'' evaluated at the number c is the slope of the tangent line at the point where $x = c$ on the graph of f'. Consequently, because the graph of f' has horizontal tangent lines at $x = -1$ and $x = 3$, $f''(-1) = 0$ and $f''(3) = 0$. We observe from Figure 1 that f' is increasing, that is, $f''(x) > 0$ when $x < -1$ and when $x > 3$; therefore, from Theorem 3.5.3(i), the graph of f is concave upward for these values of x. Furthermore, f' is decreasing, that is, $f''(x) < 0$ when $-1 < x < 3$; therefore, from Theorem 3.5.3(ii) the graph of f is concave downward for these values of x. Furthermore, we can conclude from Definition 3.5.4 that the graph of f has points of inflection where $x = -1$ and $x = 3$. We summarize these facts in Table 1.

Table 1

	$f''(x)$	*Conclusion*
$x < -1$	+	Graph of f is concave upward
$x = -1$	0	Graph of f has a point of inflection
$-1 < x < 3$	−	Graph of f is concave downward
$x = 3$	0	Graph of f has a point of inflection
$3 < x$	+	Graph of f is concave upward

Refer now to Table 2 which incorporates the facts from Table 1 above and Table 4 of Section 3.4.

Table 2

	$f'(x)$	$f''(x)$	*Conclusion*
$x < -2$	−	+	f is decreasing; graph of f is concave upward
$x = -2$	0	+	f has a relative minimum value; graph of f is concave upward
$-2 < x < -1$	+	+	f is increasing; graph of f is concave upward
$x = -1$	+	0	f is increasing; graph of f has a point of inflection
$-1 < x < 1$	+	−	f is increasing; graph of f is concave downward
$x = 1$	0	−	f has a relative maximum value; graph of f is concave downward
$1 < x < 3$	−	−	f is decreasing; graph of f is concave downward
$x = 3$	−	0	f is decreasing; graph of f has a point of inflection
$3 < x < 5$	−	+	f is decreasing; graph of f is concave upward
$x = 5$	0	+	f has a relative minimum value; graph of f is concave upward
$5 < x$	+	+	f is increasing; graph of f is concave upward

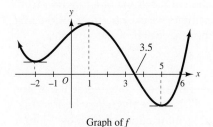

Graph of f

FIGURE 2

Because the only zeros of f are 3.5 and 6, these numbers are the only x intercepts of the graph. With this information and the properties in Table 2, we sketch a possible graph of f shown in Figure 2. ◀

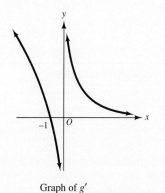

Graph of g'

FIGURE 3

▶ **EXAMPLE 2** Figure 3 shows the graph of the derivative of the function g in Example 5 of Section 3.4. From this graph determine the abscissas of any points of inflection of the graph of g and where the graph of g is concave upward and concave downward. Sketch a possible graph of g having these properties as well as the properties obtained in Example 5 of Section 3.4. Assume the only zeros of g are -2 and 0.

Solution From the graph of g', g' is decreasing, that is $g''(x) < 0$ when $x < 0$ and when $x > 0$. The graph of g is, therefore, concave downward for these values of x. The graph of g is never concave upward. Because $g'(0)$ does not exist, neither does $g''(0)$. Because $g''(x)$ never changes sign, the graph of g has no points of inflection. We incorporate this information with the facts from Table 5 in Section 3.4 to obtain Table 3.

Table 3

	$g'(x)$	$g''(x)$	*Conclusion*
$x < -1$	+	−	g is increasing; graph of g is concave downward
$x = -1$	0	−	g has a relative maximum value; graph of g is concave downward
$-1 < x < 0$	−	−	g is decreasing; graph of g is concave downward
$x = 0$	does not exist	does not exist	g has a relative minimum value
$0 < x$	+	−	g is increasing; graph of g is concave downward

Figure 4 shows a possible graph of g sketched from the properties in Table 3 and from the fact that the only zeros of g are -2 and 0. ◀

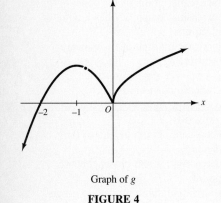

Graph of g

FIGURE 4

In the previous two examples we obtained the graph of a function from the graph of its derivative. In the next example, we sketch graphs of the first and second derivatives of a function from the graph of the function.

▶ **EXAMPLE 3**   The graph of a function f and segments of the inflectional tangents appear in Figure 5. Determine the following information from the figure and incorporate this information in a table similar to Tables 2 and 3: (i) the intervals on which f is increasing; (ii) the intervals on which f is decreasing; (iii) the relative extrema of f; (iv) where the graph of f is concave upward; (v) where the graph of f is concave downward; (vi) the abscissas of any points of inflection of the graph of f. From the table sketch possible graphs of f' and f''.

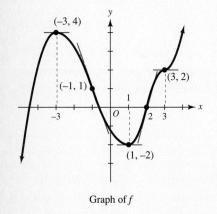

Graph of f

FIGURE 5

Solution   From the figure we obtain the following information:

(i) f is increasing on $(-\infty, -3]$, $[1, 3]$, and $[3, +\infty)$;
(ii) f is decreasing on $[-3, 1]$;
(iii) f has a relative maximum value of 4 at $x = -3$ and a relative minimum value of -2 at $x = 1$;
(iv) the graph of f is concave upward for x in the intervals $(-1, 2)$ and $(3, +\infty)$;
(v) the graph of f is concave downward for x in the intervals $(-\infty, -1)$ and $(2, 3)$.
(vi) the graph of f has points of inflection where $x = -1$, $x = 2$, and $x = 3$.

In Table 4, we incorporate this information along with the signs of f' and f'' on the intervals specified in (i)–(vi).

Table 4

	$f'(x)$	$f''(x)$	*Conclusion*
$x < -3$	$+$	$-$	f is increasing; graph of f is concave downward
$x = -3$	0	$-$	f has a relative maximum value; graph of f is concave downward
$-3 < x < -1$	$-$	$-$	f is decreasing; graph of f is concave downward
$x = -1$	$-$	0	f is decreasing; graph of f has a point of inflection
$-1 < x < 1$	$-$	$+$	f is decreasing; graph of f is concave upward
$x = 1$	0	$+$	f has a relative minimum value; graph of f is concave upward
$1 < x < 2$	$+$	$+$	f is increasing; graph of f is concave upward
$x = 2$	$+$	0	f is increasing; graph of f has a point of inflection
$2 < x < 3$	$+$	$-$	f is increasing; graph of f is concave downward
$x = 3$	0	0	graph of f has a point of inflection with a horizontal tangent line
$3 < x$	$+$	$+$	f is increasing; graph of f is concave upward

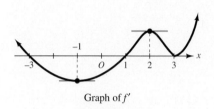

Graph of f'

FIGURE 6

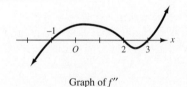

Graph of f''

FIGURE 7

From the table we have sketched possible graphs of f' in Figure 6 and f'' in Figure 7. ◀

EXERCISES 3.6

In Exercises 1 through 6, the accompanying figure shows the graph of the derivative of a function f whose domain is the set of all real numbers and which is continuous everywhere. These graphs are the same as those shown in the indicated exercise of Exercises 3.4. From this graph, determine the abscissas of any points of inflection of the graph of f and where the graph of f is concave upward and concave downward. Incorporate this information and the information obtained in the corresponding exercise of Section 3.4 in a table similar to Tables 2 and 3 of this section. Sketch a possible graph of f having the properties in the table if the only zeros of f are those stated.

1. Refer to Exercise 39 of Exercises 3.4. Zeros of f are $-4, -1, 2,$ and 4.

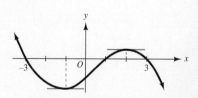

2. Refer to Exercise 40 of Exercises 3.4. Zeros of f are -1, 2, and 4.

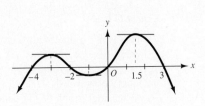

3. Refer to Exercise 41 of Exercises 3.4. Zeros of f are 0 and 4.

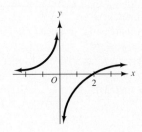

4. Refer to Exercise 42 of Exercises 3.4. Zeros of f are -1 and 1.

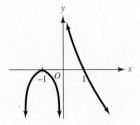

5. Refer to Exercise 43 of Exercises 3.4. Zero of f is 1.

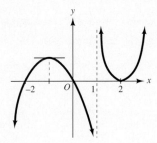

6. Refer to Exercise 44 of Exercises 3.4. Zeros of f are -3 and 0.

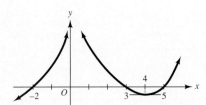

In Exercises 7 through 18, the accompanying figure shows the graph of the derivative of a function f whose domain is the set of all real numbers and which is continuous everywhere. From the graph, determine the following information and incorporate this information in a table similar to Tables 2 and 3 of this section: (i) the intervals on which f is increasing; (ii) the intervals on which f is decreasing; (iii) the relative extrema of f; (iv) where the graph of f is concave upward; (v) where the graph of f is concave downward; (vi) the abscissas of any points of inflection of the graph of f. Sketch a possible graph of f having the properties in the table if the only zeros of f are those stated.

7. Zero of f is 0.

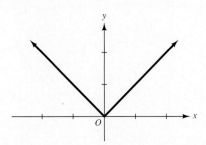

8. Zero of f is 0.

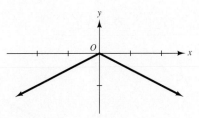

9. Zeros of f are -2, 0, and 2.

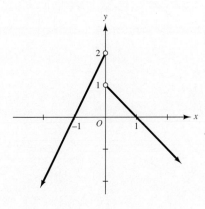

10. Zeros of f are 0 and 4.

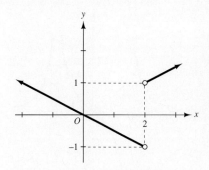

11. Zeros of f are 0 and 3.

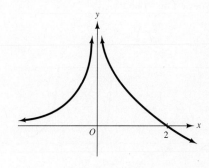

12. Zeros of f are -4, -2, 1, and 5.

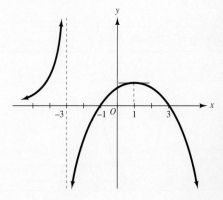

13. Zeros of f are -3, -1, and 1.

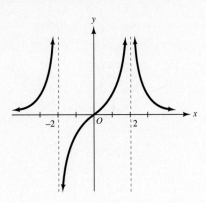

14. Zeros of f are 0 and 3.

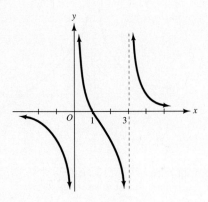

15. Zeros of f are -2 and 2.

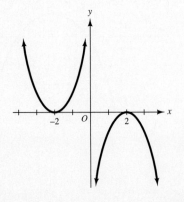

16. Zeros of f are 1 and 3.

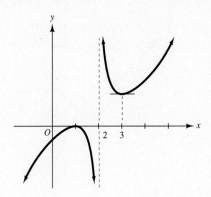

17. Zeros of f are -2, 0, and 2.

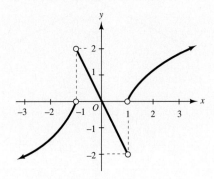

18. Zeros of f are -3, 0, and 3.

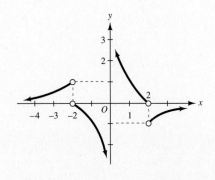

In Exercises 19 through 26, the graph of a function f and segments of the inflectional tangents appear in the accompanying figure. Determine the following information from the figure and incorporate this information in a table similar to Table 4: (i) the intervals on which f is increasing; (ii) the intervals on which f is decreasing; (iii) the relative extrema of f; (iv) where the graph of f is concave upward; (v) where the graph of f is concave downward; (vi) the abscissas of any points of inflection of the graph of f. From the table sketch possible graphs of f' and f''.

19.

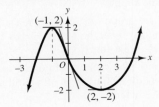

20.

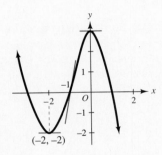

21.

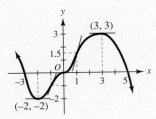

22.

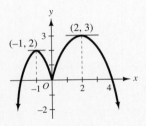

23.

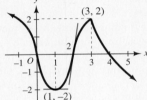

24.

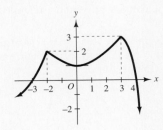

25.

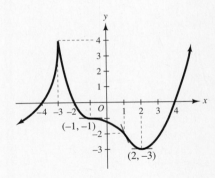

26.

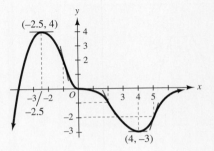

27. If $f(x) = 3x^2 + x|x|$ prove that $f''(0)$ does not exist but the graph of f is concave upward everywhere. Support this result graphically by plotting both the graph of f and the graph of NDER2$(f(x), x)$ in separate windows.

28. Given $f(x) = x^r - rx + k$, where $r > 0$ and $r \neq 1$, prove: **(a)** if $0 < r < 1$, f has a relative maximum value at 1; **(b)** if $r > 1$, f has a relative minimum value at 1.

29. Given $f(x) = x^3 + 3rx + 5$, prove: **(a)** if $r > 0$, f has no relative extrema; **(b)** if $r < 0$, f has both a relative maximum value and a relative minimum value.

30. Given $f(x) = x^2 + rx^{-1}$, prove that regardless of the value of r, f has a relative minimum value and no relative maximum value.

31. Sketch the graph of the equation $x^{2/3} + y^{2/3} = 1$. The graph is not that of a function. The portion of the graph in the first quadrant is, however, the graph of a function. Obtain this portion by properties of graphs you have learned in this chapter, and then complete the graph by symmetry properties. Concavity plays an important part. Support your result by plotting the graphs of the two functions

$$f_1(x) = (1 - x^{2/3})^{3/2} \text{ and } f_2(x) = -(1 - x^{2/3})^{3/2}$$

in the same window.

32. Explain how properties of the graph of a function can be determined from the graphs of the first and second derivatives of the function.

33. Explain how the graph of a function can be used to sketch possible graphs of the first and second derivatives of the function.

3.7 LIMITS AT INFINITY

In Section 1.7 we discussed infinite limits where function values either increased or decreased without bound as the independent variable approached a real number. We now consider limits of functions when the independent variable either increases or decreases without bound. We begin with the function defined by

$$f(x) = \frac{2x^2}{x^2 + 1}$$

Let x take on the values 0, 1, 2, 3, 4, 5, 10, 100, 1000, and so on, allowing x to increase without bound. The corresponding function values, either exact or approximated by a calculator to six decimal places, appear in Table 1. Observe from the table that as x increases through positive values, the function values get closer and closer to 2. This fact is supported by Figure 1, showing the line $y = 2$ and the graph of f plotted in the $[0, 6]$ by $[-1, 3]$ window. Let us examine how close $f(x)$ is to 2 for specific values of x. In particular,

$$2 - f(4) = 2 - 1.882353$$
$$= 0.117647$$

Therefore the difference between 2 and $f(x)$ is 0.117647 when $x = 4$. Furthermore,

$$2 - f(100) = 2 - 1.999800$$
$$= 0.000200$$

Hence the difference between 2 and $f(x)$ is 0.000200 when $x = 100$.

Continuing on, we see intuitively that the value of $f(x)$ can be made as close to 2 as we please by taking x large enough. In other words, the difference between 2 and $f(x)$ can be made as small as we please by taking x any number greater than some sufficiently large positive number. Or,

Table 1

x	$f(x) = \dfrac{2x^2}{x^2 + 1}$
0	0
1	1
2	1.6
3	1.8
4	1.882353
5	1.923077
10	1.980198
100	1.999800
1000	1.999998

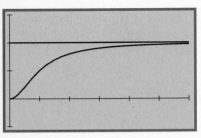

[0, 6] by [−1, 3]

$$f(x) = \frac{2x^2}{x^2 + 1}$$

$$y = 2$$

FIGURE 1

going a step further, for any $\epsilon > 0$, however small, we can find a number $N > 0$ such that if $x > N$, then $|f(x) - 2| < \epsilon$.

When an independent variable x is increasing without bound through positive values, we write "$x \to +\infty$." From the illustrative example above, then, we can say that

$$\lim_{x \to +\infty} \frac{2x^2}{x^2 + 1} = 2$$

3.7.1 Definition of the Limit of f(x) as x Increases without Bound

Let f be a function that is defined at every number in some interval $(a, +\infty)$. The **limit of $f(x)$, as x increases without bound, is L,** written

$$\lim_{x \to +\infty} f(x) = L$$

if for any $\epsilon > 0$, however small, there exists a number $N > 0$ such that

if $x > N$ then $|f(x) - L| < \epsilon$

Note: When $x \to +\infty$ is written, it does not have a similar meaning as, for instance, $x \to 1000$. The symbol $x \to +\infty$ indicates the behavior of the variable x.

Now consider the same function, and let x take on the values $-1, -2, -3, -4, -5, -10, -100, -1000$, and so on, allowing x to decrease through negative values without bound. Table 2 gives the corresponding function values of $f(x)$.

Observe that the function values are the same for the negative numbers as for the corresponding positive numbers. Refer to Figure 2 showing the line $y = 2$ and the graph of f plotted in the $[-6, 0]$ by $[-1, 3]$ window.

We see intuitively that as x decreases without bound $f(x)$ approaches 2; that is, $|f(x) - 2|$ can be made as small as we please by taking x any number less than some negative number having a sufficiently large absolute value. Formally we say that for any $\epsilon > 0$, however small, we can find a number $N < 0$ such that if $x < N$, then $|f(x) - 2| < \epsilon$. Using the symbol $x \to -\infty$ to denote that the variable x is decreasing without bound we write

$$\lim_{x \to -\infty} \frac{2x^2}{x^2 + 1} = 2$$

3.7.2 Definition of the Limit of f(x) as x Decreases without Bound

Let f be a function that is defined at every number in some interval $(-\infty, a)$. The **limit of $f(x)$, as x decreases without bound, is L,** written

$$\lim_{x \to -\infty} f(x) = L$$

if for any $\epsilon > 0$, however small, there exists a number $N < 0$ such that

if $x < N$ then $|f(x) - L| < \epsilon$

Table 2

x	$f(x) = \dfrac{2x^2}{x^2 + 1}$
-1	1
-2	1.6
-3	1.8
-4	1.882353
-5	1.923077
-10	1.980198
-100	1.999800
-1000	1.999998

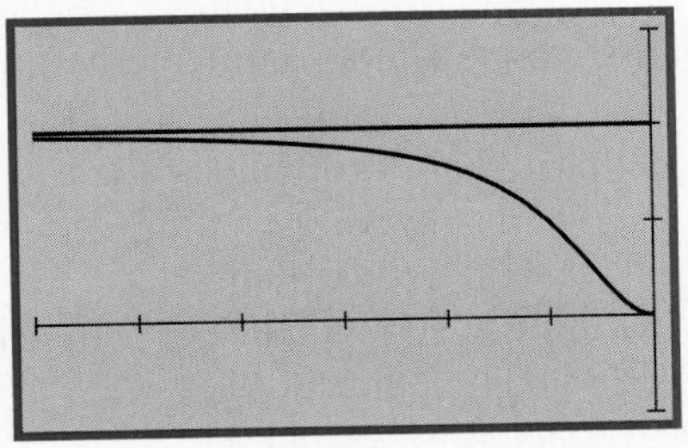

$[-6, 0]$ by $[-1, 3]$

$$f(x) = \frac{2x^2}{x^2 + 1}$$

$$y = 2$$

FIGURE 2

Note: As in the note following Definition 3.7.1, the symbol $x \to -\infty$ indicates only the behavior of the variable x.

Limit Theorems 2, 4, 5, 6, 7, 8, 9, and 10 in Section 1.5 and Limit Theorem 12 in Section 1.7 are valid when "$x \to a$" is replaced by "$x \to +\infty$" or "$x \to -\infty$." We have the following additional limit theorem.

3.7.3 Limit Theorem 13

If r is any positive integer, then

(i) $\displaystyle\lim_{x \to +\infty} \frac{1}{x^r} = 0$

(ii) $\displaystyle\lim_{x \to -\infty} \frac{1}{x^r} = 0$

Proof of (i)   To prove part (i) we must show that Definition 3.7.1 holds for $f(x) = 1/x^r$ and $L = 0$; that is, we must show that for any $\epsilon > 0$ there exists a number $N > 0$ such that

$$\text{if } x > N \quad \text{then} \quad \left| \frac{1}{x^r} - 0 \right| < \epsilon$$

$$\Leftrightarrow \quad \text{if } x > N \quad \text{then} \quad |x|^r > \frac{1}{\epsilon}$$

or equivalently, since $r > 0$,

$$\text{if } x > N \quad \text{then} \quad |x| > \left(\frac{1}{\epsilon} \right)^{1/r}$$

For the above to hold, take $N = (1/\epsilon)^{1/r}$. Thus

$$\text{if } N = \left(\frac{1}{\epsilon} \right)^{1/r} \quad \text{and} \quad x > N \quad \text{then} \quad \left| \frac{1}{x^r} - 0 \right| < \epsilon$$

This proves part (i).   ■

The proof of part (ii) is analogous and is left as an exercise (see Exercise 62).

▶ **EXAMPLE 1**   Given

$$f(x) = \frac{4x - 3}{2x + 5}$$

Find $\displaystyle\lim_{x \to +\infty} f(x)$ and support the answer graphically.

Solution   To apply Limit Theorem 13, we divide the numerator and denominator by x and obtain

$$\lim_{x \to +\infty} \frac{4x - 3}{2x + 5} = \lim_{x \to +\infty} \frac{4 - \dfrac{3}{x}}{2 + \dfrac{5}{x}}$$

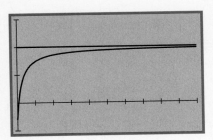

[0, 100] by [−1, 3]

$$f(x) = \frac{4x - 3}{2x + 5}$$

$$y = 2$$

FIGURE 3

$$= \frac{\lim\limits_{x \to +\infty} 4 - \lim\limits_{x \to +\infty} 3 \cdot \lim\limits_{x \to +\infty} \dfrac{1}{x}}{\lim\limits_{x \to +\infty} 2 + \lim\limits_{x \to +\infty} 5 \cdot \lim\limits_{x \to +\infty} \dfrac{1}{x}}$$

$$= \frac{4 - 3 \cdot 0}{2 + 5 \cdot 0}$$

$$= 2$$

We support our answer by plotting the graph of f and the line $y = 2$ in the window [0, 100] by [−1, 3] as shown in Figure 3. ◀

▶ **EXAMPLE 2**   Given

$$f(x) = \frac{2x^2 - x + 5}{4x^3 - 1}$$

Find $\lim\limits_{x \to -\infty} f(x)$ and support the answer graphically.

Solution   To apply Limit Theorem 13, we divide the numerator and denominator by the highest power of x occurring in either numerator or denominator, which is x^3.

$$\lim_{x \to -\infty} \frac{2x^2 - x + 5}{4x^3 - 1} = \lim_{x \to -\infty} \frac{\dfrac{2}{x} - \dfrac{1}{x^2} + \dfrac{5}{x^3}}{4 - \dfrac{1}{x^3}}$$

$$= \frac{\lim\limits_{x \to -\infty} 2 \cdot \lim\limits_{x \to -\infty} \dfrac{1}{x} - \lim\limits_{x \to -\infty} \dfrac{1}{x^2} + \lim\limits_{x \to -\infty} 5 \cdot \lim\limits_{x \to -\infty} \dfrac{1}{x^3}}{\lim\limits_{x \to -\infty} 4 - \lim\limits_{x \to -\infty} \dfrac{1}{x^3}}$$

$$= \frac{2 \cdot 0 - 0 + 5 \cdot 0}{4 - 0}$$

$$= 0$$

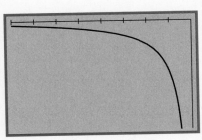

[−80, 0] by [−0.25, 0]

$$f(x) = \frac{2x^2 - x + 5}{4x^3 - 1}$$

FIGURE 4

Figure 4, showing the graph of f in the [−80, 0] by [−0.25, 0] window supports our answer. ◀

▶ **EXAMPLE 3**   Given

$$g(x) = \frac{3x + 4}{\sqrt{2x^2 - 5}}$$

Find $\lim\limits_{x \to +\infty} g(x)$ and support the answer graphically.

Solution   Because the highest power of x is 2 and it appears under the radical sign, we divide the numerator and denominator by $\sqrt{x^2}$, which is $|x|$. We have, then,

$$\lim_{x \to +\infty} \frac{3x + 4}{\sqrt{2x^2 - 5}} = \lim_{x \to +\infty} \frac{\dfrac{3x}{\sqrt{x^2}} + \dfrac{4}{\sqrt{x^2}}}{\dfrac{\sqrt{2x^2 - 5}}{\sqrt{x^2}}}$$

$$= \lim_{x \to +\infty} \frac{\dfrac{3x}{|x|} + \dfrac{4}{|x|}}{\sqrt{2 - \dfrac{5}{x^2}}}$$

Because $x \to +\infty$, $x > 0$; therefore $|x| = x$. Thus we have

$$\lim_{x \to +\infty} \frac{3x + 4}{\sqrt{2x^2 - 5}} = \lim_{x \to +\infty} \frac{\dfrac{3x}{x} + \dfrac{4}{x}}{\sqrt{2 - \dfrac{5}{x^2}}}$$

$$= \frac{\displaystyle\lim_{x \to +\infty} 3 + \lim_{x \to +\infty} 4 \cdot \lim_{x \to +\infty}\left(\dfrac{1}{x}\right)}{\sqrt{\displaystyle\lim_{x \to +\infty} 2 - \lim_{x \to +\infty} 5 \cdot \lim_{x \to +\infty}\left(\dfrac{1}{x^2}\right)}}$$

$$= \frac{3 + 4 \cdot 0}{\sqrt{2 - 5 \cdot 0}}$$

$$= \frac{3}{\sqrt{2}}$$

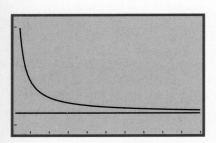

[2, 100] by [2, 3]

$$g(x) = \frac{3x + 4}{\sqrt{2x^2 - 5}}$$

$$y = \frac{3}{\sqrt{2}}$$

FIGURE 5

To support our answer graphically, we plot the graphs of g and the line $y = 3/\sqrt{2}$ in the [2, 100] by [2, 3] window shown in Figure 5.   ◀

▶ **EXAMPLE 4**   For the function of Example 3, find $\lim_{x \to -\infty} g(x)$ and support the answer graphically.

Solution   Again we begin by dividing the numerator and denominator by $|x|$.

$$\lim_{x \to -\infty} \frac{3x + 4}{\sqrt{2x^2 - 5}} = \lim_{x \to -\infty} \frac{\dfrac{3x}{|x|} + \dfrac{4}{|x|}}{\sqrt{2 - \dfrac{5}{x^2}}}$$

Because $x \to -\infty$, $x < 0$; therefore $|x| = -x$. We have, then,

$$\lim_{x \to -\infty} \frac{3x + 4}{\sqrt{2x^2 - 5}} = \lim_{x \to -\infty} \frac{\dfrac{3x}{-x} + \dfrac{4}{-x}}{\sqrt{2 - \dfrac{5}{x^2}}}$$

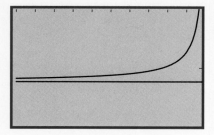

[-100, -2] by [-2.5, -1.5]

$$g(x) = \frac{3x + 4}{\sqrt{2x^2 - 5}}$$

$$y = -\frac{3}{\sqrt{2}}$$

FIGURE 6

$$= \frac{\lim_{x \to -\infty} (-3) - \lim_{x \to -\infty} 4 \cdot \lim_{x \to -\infty} \frac{1}{x}}{\sqrt{\lim_{x \to -\infty} 2 - \lim_{x \to -\infty} 5 \cdot \lim_{x \to -\infty} \frac{1}{x^2}}}$$

$$= \frac{-3 - 4 \cdot 0}{\sqrt{2 - 5 \cdot 0}}$$

$$= -\frac{3}{\sqrt{2}}$$

Figure 6 shows the graph of g and the line $y = -3/\sqrt{2}$ in the $[-100, -2]$ by $[-2.5, -1.5]$ window, which supports our answer. ◄

We consider "infinite" limits at infinity with formal definitions for each of the following:

$$\lim_{x \to +\infty} f(x) = +\infty \qquad \lim_{x \to -\infty} f(x) = +\infty$$
$$\lim_{x \to +\infty} f(x) = -\infty \qquad \lim_{x \to -\infty} f(x) = -\infty$$

For example, $\lim_{x \to +\infty} f(x) = +\infty$ if the function f is defined on some interval $(a, +\infty)$ and if for any number $N > 0$ there exists an $M > 0$ such that if $x > M$, then $f(x) > N$. The other definitions are left as an exercise (see Exercise 61).

► **EXAMPLE 5**   Find

$$\lim_{x \to +\infty} \frac{x^2}{x + 1}$$

Solution   Divide the numerator and denominator by x^2.

$$\lim_{x \to +\infty} \frac{x^2}{x + 1} = \lim_{x \to +\infty} \frac{1}{\dfrac{1}{x} + \dfrac{1}{x^2}}$$

Evaluating the limit of the denominator we have

$$\lim_{x \to +\infty} \left(\frac{1}{x} + \frac{1}{x^2} \right) = \lim_{x \to +\infty} \frac{1}{x} + \lim_{x \to +\infty} \frac{1}{x^2}$$
$$= 0 + 0$$
$$= 0$$

Therefore the limit of the denominator is 0, and the denominator is approaching 0 through positive values.

The limit of the numerator is 1, and so by Limit Theorem 12(i)(1.7.4)

$$\lim_{x \to +\infty} \frac{x^2}{x + 1} = +\infty \qquad ◄$$

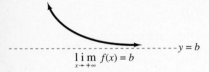

$$\lim_{x \to +\infty} f(x) = b$$

FIGURE 7

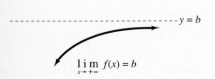

$$\lim_{x \to +\infty} f(x) = b$$

FIGURE 8

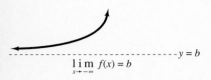

$$\lim_{x \to -\infty} f(x) = b$$

FIGURE 9

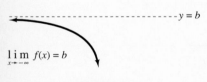

$$\lim_{x \to -\infty} f(x) = b$$

FIGURE 10

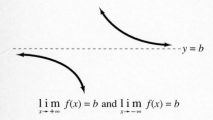

$$\lim_{x \to +\infty} f(x) = b \text{ and } \lim_{x \to -\infty} f(x) = b$$

FIGURE 11

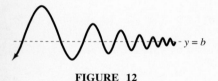

FIGURE 12

▶ **EXAMPLE 6**   Find

$$\lim_{x \to +\infty} \frac{2x - x^2}{3x + 5}$$

Solution

$$\lim_{x \to +\infty} \frac{2x - x^2}{3x + 5} = \lim_{x \to +\infty} \frac{\dfrac{2}{x} - 1}{\dfrac{3}{x} + \dfrac{5}{x^2}}$$

The limits of the numerator and denominator are considered separately.

$$\lim_{x \to +\infty} \left(\frac{2}{x} - 1 \right) = \lim_{x \to +\infty} \frac{2}{x} - \lim_{x \to +\infty} 1 \qquad \lim_{x \to +\infty} \left(\frac{3}{x} + \frac{5}{x^2} \right) = \lim_{x \to +\infty} \frac{3}{x} + \lim_{x \to +\infty} \frac{5}{x^2}$$

$$= 0 - 1 \qquad\qquad\qquad\qquad = 0 + 0$$

$$= -1 \qquad\qquad\qquad\qquad = 0$$

Therefore we have the limit of a quotient in which the limit of the numerator is -1 and the limit of the denominator is 0, where the denominator is approaching 0 through positive values. By Limit Theorem 12(iii),

$$\lim_{x \to +\infty} \frac{2x - x^2}{3x + 5} = -\infty$$ ◀

We discussed vertical asymptotes of a graph as an application of infinite limits in Section 1.7. *Horizontal asymptotes* of a graph provide an application of limits at infinity.

3.7.4 Definition of a Horizontal Asymptote

The line $y = b$ is a **horizontal asymptote** of the graph of the function f if at least one of the following statements is true:

(i) $\lim\limits_{x \to +\infty} f(x) = b$, and for some number N, if $x > N$, then $f(x) \neq b$;

(ii) $\lim\limits_{x \to -\infty} f(x) = b$, and for some number N, if $x < N$, then $f(x) \neq b$.

▷ **ILLUSTRATION 1**   Each of Figures 7 through 10 show a portion of the graph of a function for which the line $y = b$ is a horizontal asymptote. In Figures 7 and 8, part (i) of Definition 3.7.4 applies, and in Figures 9 and 10, part (ii) is true. Both parts (i) and (ii) hold for the function whose graph appears in Figure 11.

Figure 12 shows the graph of a function f for which $\lim\limits_{x \to +\infty} f(x) = b$, but there is no number N such that if $x > N$, then $f(x) \neq b$. Consequently, the line $y = b$ is not a horizontal asymptote of the graph. An example of such a function appears in Exercise 63 of Exercises 5.4.   ◀

▷ **ILLUSTRATION 2**   We motivated our definitions of limits at infinity at the beginning of this section with the function defined by

$$f(x) = \frac{2x^2}{x^2 + 1}$$

and showed that both $\lim\limits_{x \to +\infty} f(x)$ and $\lim\limits_{x \to -\infty} f(x)$ were equal to 2. The line $y = 2$ is, therefore, a horizontal asymptote of the graph of f. The graph plotted along with the line $y = 2$ in Figures 1 and 2 supports this fact. ◀

▶ **EXAMPLE 7**   Find the horizontal asymptotes of the graph of the function defined by

$$f(x) = \frac{x}{\sqrt{x^2 + 1}}$$

and apply them to sketch the graph. Support the results by plotting the graph of f and the asymptotes in the same window.

Solution   We first consider $\lim\limits_{x \to +\infty} f(x)$.

$$\lim_{x \to +\infty} f(x) = \lim_{x \to +\infty} \frac{x}{\sqrt{x^2 + 1}}$$

We divide the numerator and denominator by $\sqrt{x^2}$ and we have

$$\lim_{x \to +\infty} \frac{x}{\sqrt{x^2 + 1}} = \lim_{x \to +\infty} \frac{\dfrac{x}{\sqrt{x^2}}}{\sqrt{\dfrac{x^2}{x^2} + \dfrac{1}{x^2}}}$$

$$= \lim_{x \to +\infty} \frac{\dfrac{x}{|x|}}{\sqrt{1 + \dfrac{1}{x^2}}}$$

Because $x \to +\infty$, $x > 0$; therefore $|x| = x$. Thus

$$\lim_{x \to +\infty} \frac{x}{\sqrt{x^2 + 1}} = \lim_{x \to +\infty} \frac{\dfrac{x}{x}}{\sqrt{1 + \dfrac{1}{x^2}}}$$

$$= \frac{\lim\limits_{x \to +\infty} 1}{\sqrt{\lim\limits_{x \to +\infty} 1 + \lim\limits_{x \to +\infty} \dfrac{1}{x^2}}}$$

$$= \frac{1}{\sqrt{1 + 0}}$$

$$= 1$$

Therefore, by Definition 3.7.4(i), the line $y = 1$ is a horizontal asymptote.

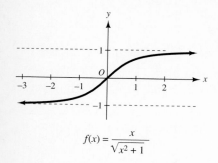

$$f(x) = \frac{x}{\sqrt{x^2 + 1}}$$

FIGURE 13

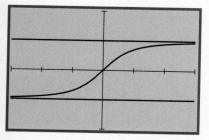

$[-3, 3]$ by $[-2, 2]$

$$f(x) = \frac{x}{\sqrt{x^2 + 1}}$$

$y = 1$ and $y = -1$

FIGURE 14

We now consider $\lim\limits_{x \to -\infty} f(x)$, and again we divide the numerator and denominator by $\sqrt{x^2}$, which is $|x|$. Because $x \to -\infty$, $x < 0$; thus $|x| = -x$. We have, then

$$\lim_{x \to -\infty} f(x) = \lim_{x \to -\infty} \frac{\dfrac{x}{-x}}{\sqrt{1 + \dfrac{1}{x^2}}}$$

$$= \frac{\lim\limits_{x \to -\infty} (-1)}{\sqrt{\lim\limits_{x \to -\infty} 1 + \lim\limits_{x \to -\infty} \dfrac{1}{x^2}}}$$

$$= \frac{-1}{\sqrt{1 + 0}}$$

$$= -1$$

Accordingly, by Definition 3.7.4(ii), the line $y = -1$ is a horizontal asymptote.

With the two horizontal asymptotes as guides, we sketch the graph of f in Figure 13. To support our results, we plot the graph of f and the lines $y = 1$ and $y = -1$ in the $[-3, 3]$ by $[-2, 2]$ window, as shown in Figure 14. ◀

We now define an *oblique asymptote,* one that is neither horizontal nor vertical. Note that the definition of a horizontal asymptote is a special case.

3.7.5 Definition of an Oblique Asymptote

The graph of the function f has the line $y = mx + b$ as an asymptote if either of the following statements is true:

(i) $\lim\limits_{x \to +\infty} [f(x) - (mx + b)] = 0$, and for some number $M > 0$, $f(x) \neq mx + b$ whenever $x > M$;

(ii) $\lim\limits_{x \to -\infty} [f(x) - (mx + b)] = 0$, and for some number $M < 0$, $f(x) \neq mx + b$ whenever $x < M$.

Part (i) of the definition indicates that for any $\epsilon > 0$, there exists a number $N > 0$ such that

if $\ x > N \ $ then $\ \ 0 < |f(x) - (mx + b)| < \epsilon$

that is, we can make the function value $f(x)$ as close to the value of $mx + b$ as we please by taking x sufficiently large. This statement is consistent with our intuitive notion of an asymptote of a graph. A similar statement may be made for part (ii) of the definition.

The graph of a rational function of the form $P(x)/Q(x)$, where the degree of the polynomial $P(x)$ is one more than the degree of $Q(x)$ and $Q(x)$ is not a factor of $P(x)$, has an oblique asymptote. To show this, we let $f(x) = P(x)/Q(x)$ and divide $P(x)$ by $Q(x)$ to express $f(x)$ as the sum of a linear function and a rational function; that is,

$$f(x) = mx + b + \frac{R(x)}{Q(x)}$$

where the degree of the polynomial $R(x)$ is less than the degree of $Q(x)$. Then

$$f(x) - (mx + b) = \frac{R(x)}{Q(x)} \tag{1}$$

When the numerator and denominator of $R(x)/Q(x)$ are divided by the highest power of x appearing in $Q(x)$, there will be a constant term in the denominator and all other terms in the denominator and every term in the numerator will be of the form k/x^r where k is a constant and r is a positive integer. Therefore, as $x \to + \infty$, the limit of the numerator will be zero and the limit of the denominator will be a constant. Thus $\lim\limits_{x \to +\infty} R(x)/Q(x) = 0$. Therefore, from (1)

$$\lim_{x \to +\infty} [f(x) - (mx + b)] = 0$$

from which we conclude from Definition 3.7.5 that the line $y = mx + b$ is an oblique asymptote of the graph of f.

▶ **EXAMPLE 8**   Given

$$h(x) = \frac{x^2 + 3}{x - 1}$$

Find the asymptotes of the graph of h. Support the results by plotting the graph of h and the asymptotes in the same window.

Solution   Because

$$\lim_{x \to 1^-} h(x) = -\infty \quad \text{and} \quad \lim_{x \to 1^+} h(x) = +\infty$$

the line $x = 1$ is a vertical asymptote. There are no horizontal asymptotes because if the numerator and denominator of $h(x)$ are divided by x^2, we obtain

$$\frac{1 + \dfrac{3}{x^2}}{\dfrac{1}{x} - \dfrac{1}{x^2}}$$

and as $x \to +\infty$, or $x \to -\infty$, the limit of the numerator is 1 and the limit of the denominator is 0. However, the degree of the numerator of $h(x)$ is one more than the degree of the denominator, and when we divide the numerator by the denominator, we obtain

$$h(x) = x + 1 + \frac{4}{x - 1}$$

Therefore the line $y = x + 1$ is an oblique asymptote.

Figure 15 shows the graph of h and the asymptotes plotted in the $[-10, 13.5]$ by $[-6, 9.7]$ window, which supports our results.   ◀

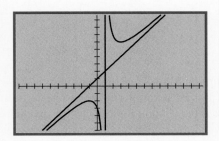

$[-10, 13.5]$ by $[-6, 9.7]$

$$h(x) = \frac{x^2 + 3}{x - 1}$$

$x = 1$ and $y = x + 1$

FIGURE 15

EXERCISES 3.7

In Exercises 1 through 10, do the following: On your calculator tabulate values of $f(x)$ for the specified values of x. (a) What does $f(x)$ appear to be approaching as x increases without bound? (b) What does $f(x)$ appear to be approaching as x decreases without bound? (c) Support your answers in parts (a) and (b) by plotting the graph of f. (d) Confirm your answer in part (a) by finding $\lim_{x \to +\infty} f(x)$. (e) Confirm your answer in part (b) by finding $\lim_{x \to -\infty} f(x)$.

1. $f(x) = \dfrac{4}{x^2}$; x is 1, 2, 4, 6, 8, 10, 100, 1000 and x is $-1, -2, -4, -6, -8, -10, -100, -1000$.

2. $f(x) = \dfrac{3}{x^4}$; x is 1, 2, 4, 6, 8, 10, 100, 1000 and x is $-1, -2, -4, -6, -8, -10, -100, -1000$.

3. $f(x) = \dfrac{1}{x^3}$; x is 1, 2, 4, 6, 8, 10, 100, 1000 and x is $-1, -2, -4, -6, -8, -10, -100, -1000$.

4. $f(x) = -\dfrac{2}{x^3}$; x is 1, 2, 4, 6, 8, 10, 100, 1000 and x is $-1, -2, -4, -6, -8, -10, -100, -1000$.

5. $f(x) = -\dfrac{3x^2}{x^2 + 1}$; x is 0, 1, 2, 4, 6, 8, 10, 100, 1000 and x is $-1, -2, -4, -6, -8, -10, -100, -1000$.

6. $f(x) = \dfrac{x^3}{x^3 + 2}$; x is 2, 4, 6, 8, 10, 100, 1000 and x is $-2, -4, -6, -8, -10, -100, -1000$.

7. $f(x) = \dfrac{4x + 1}{2x - 1}$; x is 2, 6, 10, 100, 1000, 10,000, 100,000 and x is $-2, -6, -10, -100, -1000, -10,000, -100,000$.

8. $f(x) = \dfrac{5x - 3}{10x + 1}$; x is 2, 6, 10, 100, 1000, 10,000, 100,000 and x is $-2, -6, -10, -100, -1000, -10,000, -100,000$.

9. $f(x) = \dfrac{x + 1}{x^2}$; x is 2, 6, 10, 100, 1000, 10,000, 100,000 and x is $-2, -6, -10, -100, -1000, -10,000, -100,000$.

10. $f(x) = \dfrac{x^2}{x + 1}$; x is 2, 6, 10, 100, 1000, 10,000, 100,000 and x is $-2, -6, -10, -100, -1000, -10,000, -100,000$.

In Exercises 11 through 30, find the limit and support your answer graphically.

11. $\lim\limits_{t \to +\infty} \dfrac{2t + 1}{5t - 2}$

12. $\lim\limits_{x \to -\infty} \dfrac{6x - 4}{3x + 1}$

13. $\lim\limits_{x \to -\infty} \dfrac{2x + 7}{4 - 5x}$

14. $\lim\limits_{x \to +\infty} \dfrac{1 + 5x}{2 - 3x}$

15. $\lim\limits_{x \to +\infty} \dfrac{7x^2 - 2x + 1}{3x^2 + 8x + 5}$

16. $\lim\limits_{s \to -\infty} \dfrac{4s^2 + 3}{2s^2 - 1}$

17. $\lim\limits_{x \to +\infty} \dfrac{x + 4}{3x^2 - 5}$

18. $\lim\limits_{x \to +\infty} \dfrac{x^2 + 5}{x^3}$

19. $\lim\limits_{y \to +\infty} \dfrac{2y^2 - 3y}{y + 1}$

20. $\lim\limits_{x \to +\infty} \dfrac{x^2 - 2x + 5}{7x^3 + x + 1}$

21. $\lim\limits_{x \to -\infty} \dfrac{4x^3 + 2x^2 - 5}{8x^3 + x + 2}$

22. $\lim\limits_{x \to +\infty} \dfrac{3x^4 - 7x^2 + 2}{2x^4 + 1}$

23. $\lim\limits_{y \to +\infty} \dfrac{2y^3 - 4}{5y + 3}$

24. $\lim\limits_{x \to -\infty} \dfrac{5x^3 - 12x + 7}{4x^2 - 1}$

25. $\lim\limits_{x \to -\infty} \left(3x + \dfrac{1}{x^2}\right)$

26. $\lim\limits_{t \to +\infty} \left(\dfrac{2}{t^2} - 4t\right)$

27. $\lim\limits_{x \to +\infty} \dfrac{\sqrt{x^2 + 4}}{x + 4}$

28. $\lim\limits_{x \to -\infty} \dfrac{\sqrt{x^2 + 4}}{x + 4}$

29. $\lim\limits_{w \to -\infty} \dfrac{\sqrt{w^2 - 2w + 3}}{w + 5}$

30. $\lim\limits_{y \to -\infty} \dfrac{\sqrt{y^4 + 1}}{2y^2 - 3}$

In Exercises 31 through 34, do the following: (a) Plot the graph of the function f and make a statement regarding the apparent behavior of $f(x)$ as x increases without bound. (b) Confirm your answer in part (a) analytically by computing $\lim\limits_{x \to +\infty} f(x)$.

31. $f(x) = \sqrt{x^2 + 1} - x$

32. $f(x) = \sqrt{x^2 + x} - x$

33. $f(x) = \sqrt{3x^2 + x} - 2x$

34. $f(x) = \dfrac{\sqrt{x + \sqrt{x + \sqrt{x}}}}{\sqrt{x + 1}}$

In Exercises 35 through 46, find the asymptotes of the graph of the function and use them to sketch the graph. Support your results by plotting the graph and the asymptotes in the same window.

35. $f(x) = \dfrac{2x + 1}{x - 3}$

36. $h(x) = 1 + \dfrac{1}{x^2}$

37. $g(x) = 1 - \dfrac{1}{x}$

38. $f(x) = \dfrac{4 - 3x}{x + 1}$

39. $f(x) = \dfrac{2}{\sqrt{x^2 - 4}}$

40. $g(x) = \dfrac{x^2}{4 - x^2}$

41. $G(x) = \dfrac{4x^2}{x^2 - 9}$

42. $F(x) = \dfrac{-3x}{\sqrt{x^2 + 3}}$

43. $h(x) = \dfrac{2x}{6x^2 + 11x - 10}$

44. $h(x) = \dfrac{x}{\sqrt{x^2 - 9}}$

45. $f(x) = \dfrac{4x^2}{\sqrt{x^2 - 2}}$

46. $f(x) = \dfrac{-1}{\sqrt{x^2 + 5x + 6}}$

In Exercises 47 through 54, find the asymptotes of the graph of the function. Support your results by plotting the graph and the asymptotes in the same window.

47. $f(x) = \dfrac{x^2}{x - 1}$

48. $f(x) = \dfrac{x^2 - 3x + 2}{x + 4}$

49. $f(x) = \dfrac{x^2 - 8}{x - 3}$

50. $f(x) = \dfrac{x^2 - 3}{x - 2}$

51. $f(x) = \dfrac{x^2 - 4x - 5}{x + 2}$

52. $f(x) = \dfrac{(x + 1)^3}{(x - 1)^2}$

53. $f(x) = \dfrac{x^3 + 2x^2 + 4}{x^2}$

54. $f(x) = \dfrac{x^3 - 4}{x^2}$

In Exercises 55 and 56, evaluate the limits in parts (a)–(h) from the graph of the function f, sketched in the accompanying figure and whose domain is $(-\infty, +\infty)$.

55. **(a)** $\lim\limits_{x \to -\infty} f(x)$ **(b)** $\lim\limits_{x \to 0^-} f(x)$ **(c)** $\lim\limits_{x \to 0^+} f(x)$

(d) $\lim\limits_{x \to 1^-} f(x)$ **(e)** $\lim\limits_{x \to 1^+} f(x)$ **(f)** $\lim\limits_{x \to 3} f(x)$

(g) $\lim\limits_{x \to 4} f(x)$ **(h)** $\lim\limits_{x \to +\infty} f(x)$

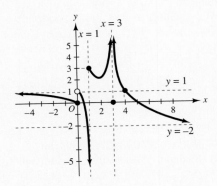

56. **(a)** $\lim\limits_{x \to -\infty} f(x)$ **(b)** $\lim\limits_{x \to -1^-} f(x)$ **(c)** $\lim\limits_{x \to -1^+} f(x)$;

(d) $\lim\limits_{x \to 0} f(x)$ **(e)** $\lim\limits_{x \to 1} f(x)$ **(f)** $\lim\limits_{x \to 2} f(x)$;

(g) $\lim\limits_{x \to 3} f(x)$ **(h)** $\lim\limits_{x \to +\infty} f(x)$

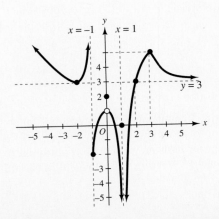

In Exercises 57 and 58, sketch the graph of a function f, satisfying the given properties and whose domain is $(-\infty, +\infty)$.

57. $f(-4) = 0; f(-2) = 0; f(0) = 3; f(2) = -3;$
$f(4) = 0; f(5) = 0; \lim\limits_{x \to -\infty} f(x) = -3; \lim\limits_{x \to -4} f(x) = 0;$
$\lim\limits_{x \to -2} f(x) = +\infty; \lim\limits_{x \to 0} f(x) = 0; \lim\limits_{x \to 2^-} f(x) = +\infty;$
$\lim\limits_{x \to 2^+} f(x) = -\infty; \lim\limits_{x \to 4^-} f(x) = 0; \lim\limits_{x \to 4^+} f(x) = +\infty;$
$\lim\limits_{x \to 5} f(x) = 0; \lim\limits_{x \to +\infty} f(x) = -\infty$

58. $f(-5) = 0; f(-3) = 0; f(-2) = 0; f(0) = 0;$
$f(2) = 3; f(3) = 0; f(4) = 0; \lim\limits_{x \to -\infty} f(x) = -\infty;$
$\lim\limits_{x \to -5} f(x) = 0; \lim\limits_{x \to -3} f(x) = 1; \lim\limits_{x \to -2} f(x) = 0;$
$\lim\limits_{x \to 0^-} f(x) = -\infty; \lim\limits_{x \to 0^+} f(x) = +\infty; \lim\limits_{x \to 2} f(x) = 0;$
$\lim\limits_{x \to 3} f(x) = -\infty; \lim\limits_{x \to +\infty} f(x) = 0$

59. Prove that

$$\lim_{x \to +\infty} \frac{x}{x - 1} = 1$$

by applying Definition 3.7.1; that is, for any $\epsilon > 0$, show that there exists a number $N > 0$ such that if $x > N$, then

$$\left| \frac{x}{x - 1} - 1 \right| < \epsilon$$

60. Prove that

$$\lim_{x \to -\infty} \frac{8x + 3}{2x - 1} = 4$$

by applying Definition 3.7.2; that is, for any $\epsilon > 0$, show that there exists a number $N < 0$ such that if $x < N$, then

$$\left| \frac{8x + 3}{2x - 1} - 4 \right| < \epsilon$$

61. Write a formal definition for each of the following:
(a) $\lim\limits_{x \to +\infty} f(x) = -\infty;$ **(b)** $\lim\limits_{x \to -\infty} f(x) = +\infty;$
(c) $\lim\limits_{x \to -\infty} f(x) = -\infty.$

62. Prove part (ii) of Limit Theorem 13 (3.7.3).

63. Prove that $\lim\limits_{x \to +\infty} (x^2 - 4) = +\infty$ by showing that for any $N > 0$ there exists an $M > 0$ such that if $x > M$ then $x^2 - 4 > N$.

64. Prove that $\lim\limits_{x \to +\infty} (6 - x - x^2) = -\infty$ by applying your definition in Exercise 61(a).

In Exercises 65 through 68, state in words what the indicated symbolism means without using the words limit, approaches, infinity, increasing without bound, or decreasing without bound and without using symbols such as ϵ, N, and M.

65. $\lim\limits_{x \to +\infty} f(x) = L$

66. $\lim\limits_{x \to -\infty} f(x) = L$

67. (a) $\lim\limits_{x \to +\infty} f(x) = +\infty$; (b) $\lim\limits_{x \to -\infty} f(x) = +\infty$

68. (a) $\lim\limits_{x \to +\infty} f(x) = -\infty$; (b) $\lim\limits_{x \to -\infty} f(x) = -\infty$

69. If W is the measure of the weight of an object at a distance x units above the surface of the earth, then

$$W = \left(\frac{R}{R + x} \right)^2 W_0$$

where R units is the radius of the earth and W_0 is the measure of the object's weight at sea level. Determine $\lim\limits_{x \to +\infty} W$ and indicate the significance of this result on space travel.

3.8 SUMMARY OF SKETCHING GRAPHS OF FUNCTIONS

We now summarize the steps, incorporating the properties discussed in this chapter, that you should follow when sketching the graph of a function f.

1. Determine the domain of f.
2. Find any x and y intercepts. When finding the x intercepts you may need to approximate the roots of the equation $f(x) = 0$ on your calculator.
3. Test for symmetry with respect to the y axis and origin.
4. Check for any possible horizontal, vertical, or oblique asymptotes.
5. Compute $f'(x)$ and $f''(x)$.
6. Determine the critical numbers of f. These are the values of x in the domain of f for which either $f'(x)$ does not exist or $f'(x) = 0$.
7. Apply either the first-derivative test or the second-derivative test to determine whether at a critical number there is a relative maximum value, a relative minimum value, or neither.
8. Determine the intervals on which f is increasing by finding the values of x for which $f'(x)$ is positive; determine the intervals on which f is decreasing by finding the values of x for which $f'(x)$ is negative. In locating the intervals on which f is monotonic, also check the critical numbers at which f does not have a relative extremum.
9. Find the critical numbers of f', that is, the values of x for which $f''(x)$ does not exist or $f''(x) = 0$, to obtain possible points of inflection. At each of these values of x check to see if $f''(x)$ changes sign and if the graph has a tangent line there to determine if there actually is a point of inflection.
10. Check for concavity of the graph. Find the values of x for which $f''(x)$ is positive to obtain points at which the graph is concave upward; to obtain points at which the graph is concave downward find the values of x for which $f''(x)$ is negative.
11. Find the slope of each inflectional tangent if that is helpful.

We suggest that you incorporate all the information obtained from the above steps into a table as shown in Sections 3.4–3.6 and in the following examples.

▶ **EXAMPLE 1**   The function in Example 8 of Section 3.7 is defined by

$$f(x) = \frac{x^2 + 3}{x - 1}$$

Sketch the graph of f by following the procedure suggested above. Support the result on a graphics calculator.

Solution   The domain of f is the set of all real numbers except 1. The y intercept is -3 and there are no x intercepts. There is no symmetry with respect to either the y axis or the origin.

In Example 8 of Section 3.7, we determined that the lines $x = 1$ and $y = x + 1$ are asymptotes of the graph.

We now compute $f'(x)$ and $f''(x)$.

$$f'(x) = \frac{2x(x - 1) - (x^2 + 3)}{(x - 1)^2}$$

$$= \frac{x^2 - 2x - 3}{(x - 1)^2}$$

$$f''(x) = \frac{(2x - 2)(x - 1)^2 - 2(x - 1)(x^2 - 2x - 3)}{(x - 1)^4}$$

$$= \frac{8}{(x - 1)^3}$$

Setting $f'(x) = 0$, we get

$$x^2 - 2x - 3 = 0$$
$$(x + 1)(x - 3) = 0$$
$$x = -1 \qquad x = 3$$

$f''(x)$ is never zero. We now make Table 1 by considering the points at which $x = -1$, $x = 1$, and $x = 3$, and the intervals excluding these values of x:

$$x < -1 \qquad -1 < x < 1 \qquad 1 < x < 3 \qquad 3 < x$$

Table 1

	$f(x)$	$f'(x)$	$f''(x)$	Conclusion
$x < -1$		$+$	$-$	f is increasing; graph of f is concave downward
$x = -1$	-2	0	$-$	f has a relative maximum value; graph of f is concave downward
$-1 < x < 1$		$-$	$-$	f is decreasing; graph of f is concave downward
$x = 1$	d.n.e.	d.n.e.	d.n.e.	
$1 < x < 3$		$-$	$+$	f is decreasing; graph of f is concave upward
$x = 3$	6	0	$+$	f has a relative minimum value; graph of f is concave upward
$3 < x$		$+$	$+$	f is increasing; graph of f is concave upward

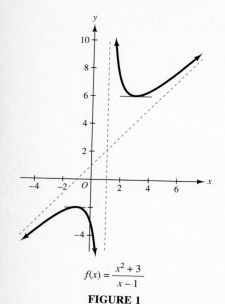

$$f(x) = \frac{x^2 + 3}{x - 1}$$

FIGURE 1

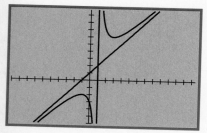

[–10, 13.5] by [–6, 9.7]

$$f(x) = \frac{x^2 + 3}{x - 3}$$

$x = 1$ and $y = x + 1$

FIGURE 2

By indicating the asymptotes and the horizontal tangent lines, locating a few points, and applying the information from Table 1, we sketch the graph of f shown in Figure 1.

Figure 2 (the same as Figure 15 in Section 3.7) shows the graph of f and the asymptotes plotted in the $[-10, 13.5]$ by $[-6, 9.7]$ window, which supports our result.   ◀

▶ **EXAMPLE 2**   Given

$$f(x) = \frac{x^2}{x^2 - 4}$$

(a) Find any asymptotes of the graph of f. **(b)** Plot the graph of f and any asymptotes in the same window. Estimate from the graph the following: the relative extrema of f; the points of inflection of the graph of f; the intervals on which f is increasing and those on which f is decreasing; where the graph is concave upward and where it is concave downward. **(c)** Confirm the estimates in part (b) analytically.

Solution

(a) The domain of f is the set of all real numbers except ± 2. Because 2 and -2 are excluded from the domain, we compute the following limits:

$$\lim_{x \to 2^+} \frac{x^2}{x^2 - 4} = +\infty \qquad \lim_{x \to 2^-} \frac{x^2}{x^2 - 4} = -\infty$$

$$\lim_{x \to -2^+} \frac{x^2}{x^2 - 4} = -\infty \qquad \lim_{x \to -2^-} \frac{x^2}{x^2 - 4} = +\infty$$

Therefore $x = 2$ and $x = -2$ are vertical asymptotes of the graph.

$$\lim_{x \to +\infty} \frac{x^2}{x^2 - 4} = \lim_{x \to +\infty} \frac{1}{1 - \dfrac{4}{x^2}} \qquad \lim_{x \to -\infty} \frac{x^2}{x^2 - 4} = \lim_{x \to -\infty} \frac{1}{1 - \dfrac{4}{x^2}}$$

$$= 1 \qquad\qquad\qquad = 1$$

The line $y = 1$ is, therefore, a horizontal asymptote. The graph has no oblique asymptotes.

(b) Figure 3 shows the graph of f and the asymptotes plotted in the $[-4.7, 4.7]$ by $[-3.1, 3.1]$ window. From the graph we make the following estimates: f has a relative maximum value at the origin; the graph has no points of inflection; f is increasing on $(-\infty, -2)$ and $(-2, 0]$, and f is decreasing on $[0, 2)$ and $(2, +\infty)$; the graph is concave upward when x is in either $(-\infty, -2)$ or $(2, +\infty)$, and the graph is concave downward when x is in $(-2, 2)$.

(c) To confirm the estimates in part (b) analytically, we first compute $f'(x)$ and $f''(x)$:

$$f'(x) = \frac{2x(x^2 - 4) - 2x(x^2)}{(x^2 - 4)^2} \qquad f''(x) = \frac{-8(x^2 - 4)^2 + 8x[2(x^2 - 4)(2x)]}{(x^2 - 4)^4}$$

$$= \frac{-8x}{(x^2 - 4)^2} \qquad\qquad = \frac{24x^2 + 32}{(x^2 - 4)^3}$$

We set $f'(x) = 0$ to obtain $x = 0$; $f''(x)$ is never zero. We construct Table 2 by considering the points at which $x = 0$ and $x = \pm 2$, and the intervals excluding these points:

$$x < -2 \qquad -2 < x < 0 \qquad 0 < x < 2 \qquad 2 < x$$

The information in Table 2 confirms our estimates.

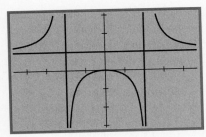

[−4.7, 4.7] by [−3.1, 3.1]

$$f(x) = \frac{x^2}{x^2 - 4}$$

$$y = 1$$

$$x = -2 \text{ and } x = 2$$

FIGURE 3

Table 2

	$f(x)$	$f'(x)$	$f''(x)$	Conclusion
$x < -2$		+	+	f is increasing; graph of f is concave upward
$x = -2$	d.n.e.	d.n.e.	d.n.e.	
$-2 < x < 0$		+	−	f is increasing; graph of f is concave downward
$x = 0$	0	0	−	f has a relative maximum value
$0 < x < 2$		−	−	f is decreasing; graph of f is concave downward
$x = 2$	d.n.e.	d.n.e.	d.n.e.	
$2 < x$		−	+	f is decreasing; graph of f is concave upward

◄

▶ **EXAMPLE 3** Sketch the graph of the function defined by

$$f(x) = x^{2/3} - 2x^{1/3}$$

and indicate any points of inflection. Draw a segment of each inflectional tangent.

Solution We compute $f'(x)$ and $f''(x)$:

$$f'(x) = \tfrac{2}{3}x^{-1/3} - \tfrac{2}{3}x^{-2/3} \qquad f''(x) = -\tfrac{2}{9}x^{-4/3} + \tfrac{4}{9}x^{-5/3}$$

Because $f'(0)$ does not exist, 0 is a critical number of f. Other critical numbers are found by setting $f'(x) = 0$.

$$\frac{2}{3x^{1/3}} - \frac{2}{3x^{2/3}} = 0$$

$$2x^{1/3} - 2 = 0$$

$$x^{1/3} = 1$$

$$x = 1$$

Thus 1 is also a critical number. We can determine if there is a relative extremum at 1 by applying the second-derivative test. We cannot use the second-derivative test at the critical number 0 because $f'(0)$ does not exist.

We apply the first-derivative test at $x = 0$. Table 3 shows the results of these tests.

Because $f''(0)$ does not exist, $(0, 0)$ is a possible point of inflection. To find other possible points of inflection we set $f''(x) = 0$.

$$-\frac{2}{9x^{4/3}} + \frac{4}{9x^{5/3}} = 0$$

$$-2x^{1/3} + 4 = 0$$

$$x^{1/3} = 2$$

$$x = 8$$

To determine if there are points of inflection where x is 0 and 8, we check to see if $f''(x)$ changes sign; at the same time we learn about the concavity of the graph in the respective intervals. At a point of inflection the graph must have a tangent line there. At the origin there is a vertical tangent line because

$$\lim_{x \to 0} f'(x) = \lim_{x \to 0} \frac{2x^{1/3} - 2}{3x^{2/3}}$$

$$= -\infty$$

Table 3 summarizes our results and from them we obtain the graph sketched in Figure 4, which also shows a segment of the inflectional tangent at the point $(8, 0)$. The tangent line at the other point of inflection, the origin, is the y axis.

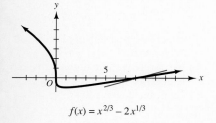

$f(x) = x^{2/3} - 2x^{1/3}$

FIGURE 4

Table 3

	$f(x)$	$f'(x)$	$f''(x)$	Conclusion
$x < 0$		−	−	f is decreasing; graph of f is concave downward
$x = 0$	0	d.n.e.	d.n.e.	f does not have a relative extremum; graph of f has a point of inflection
$0 < x < 1$		−	+	f is decreasing; graph of f is concave upward
$x = 1$	−1	0	+	f has a relative minimum value; graph of f is concave upward
$1 < x < 8$		+	+	f is increasing; graph of f is concave upward
$x = 8$	0	$\frac{1}{6}$	0	f is increasing; graph of f has a point of inflection
$8 < x$		+	−	f is increasing; graph of f is concave downward

◀

When you plot the graph of Example 3 on your graphics calculator, observe that the graph does not reveal the point of inflection at $(8, 0)$ or the change of concavity there. This situation prevails for the graphs of most functions plotted on a graphics calculator. Often, however, by plotting the graph of NDER 2, we can estimate a point of inflection and, consequently, where the concavity changes. We can then confirm this information analytically. The next example demonstrates this procedure.

▶ **EXAMPLE 4**   Given

$$f(x) = 5x^{2/3} - x^{5/3}$$

(a) Plot the graphs of f, NDER$(f(x), x)$, and NDER $2(f(x), x)$ in separate windows and estimate the following: (i) the relative extrema of f; (ii) the intervals on which f is increasing and those on which f is decreasing; (iii) where the graph of f is concave upward and where it is concave downward; (iv) any points of inflection of the graph of f. **(b)** Confirm the estimates in part (a) analytically.

Solution

(a) The graph of f plotted in the $[-8, 10.8]$ by $[-3, 9.4]$ window and the graph of NDER$(f(x), x)$ plotted in the $[-9.4, 9.4]$ by $[-7.2, 5.2]$ window appear in Figures 5 and 6, respectively.

(i) We estimate from Figure 5 that f has a relative minimum value at $x = 0$ and from both Figures 5 and 6 a relative maximum value at $x = 2$.

(ii) From Figure 6, because $f'(x) < 0$ when $x < 0$ and when $x > 2$, we estimate that f is decreasing on the intervals $(-\infty, 0]$ and $[2, +\infty)$. Also from Figure 6, because $f'(x) > 0$ when $0 < x < 2$, we estimate that f is increasing on the interval $[0, 2]$. These estimates are consistent with what we observe about the graph of f in Figure 5.

(iii) From Figure 5, the graph of f appears to be concave downward when $x > 0$. We are not sure about concavity or any points of inflection when $x < 0$. We therefore need to investigate the graph of NDER2 $(f(x), x)$, which is plotted in the $[-6, 6]$ by $[-4, 4]$ window in Figure 7. From this graph, $f''(x) > 0$ when $x < -1$ and $f''(x) < 0$ when $-1 < x < 0$ and when $x > 0$. Thus we estimate that the graph of f is concave upward when $x < -1$ and concave downward when $-1 < x < 0$ and when $x > 0$.

(iv) Because $f''(-1) = 0$ and the graph of f changes concavity at $x = -1$, we estimate that the graph of f has a point of inflection at $x = -1$.

(b) We confirm the estimates in part (a) analytically. By setting $f(x) = 0$, we obtain the zeros of f which are 0 and 5, the x intercepts of the graph. We now compute $f'(x)$ and $f''(x)$:

$$f'(x) = \tfrac{10}{3}x^{-1/3} - \tfrac{5}{3}x^{2/3} \qquad f''(x) = -\tfrac{10}{9}x^{-4/3} - \tfrac{10}{9}x^{-1/3}$$
$$= \tfrac{5}{3}x^{-1/3}(2 - x) \qquad\qquad = -\tfrac{10}{9}x^{-4/3}(1 + x)$$

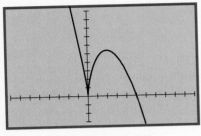

[−8, 10.8] by [−3, 9.4]

$f(x) = 5x^{2/3} - x^{5/3}$

FIGURE 5

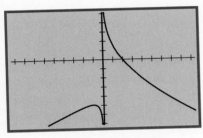

[−9.4, 9.4] by [−7.2, 5.2]

NDER $(5x^{2/3} - x^{5/3}, x)$

FIGURE 6

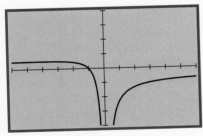

[−6, 6] by [−4, 4]

NDER2 $(5x^{2/3} - x^{5/3}, x)$

FIGURE 7

When $x = 0$, neither $f'(x)$ nor $f''(x)$ exists. We set $f'(x) = 0$ to obtain $x = 2$. Therefore the critical numbers of f are 0 and 2. From $f''(x) = 0$ we obtain $x = -1$. In making Table 4, consider the points at which x is -1, 0, and 2, and the following intervals:

$$x < -1 \qquad -1 < x < 0 \qquad 0 < x < 2 \qquad 2 < x$$

Table 4

	$f(x)$	$f'(x)$	$f''(x)$	Conclusion
$x < -1$		$-$	$+$	f is decreasing; graph of f is concave upward
$x = -1$	6	-5	0	f is decreasing; graph of f has a point of inflection
$-1 < x < 0$		$-$	$-$	f is decreasing; graph of f is concave downward
$x = 0$	0	d.n.e.	d.n.e.	f has a relative minimum value
$0 < x < 2$		$+$	$-$	f is increasing; graph of f is concave downward
$x = 2$	$3\sqrt[3]{4} \approx 4.8$	0	$-$	f has a relative maximum value; graph of f is concave downward
$2 < x$		$-$	$-$	f is decreasing; graph of f is concave downward

From the information in Table 4 and by locating a few points, we sketch the graph of f shown in Figure 8. The table and the graph confirm our estimates in part (a).   ◄

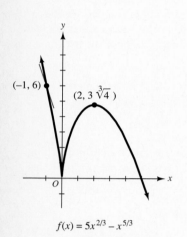

$f(x) = 5x^{2/3} - x^{5/3}$

FIGURE 8

(−1, 6)

$(2, 3\sqrt[3]{4}\,)$

EXERCISES 3.8

In Exercises 1 through 24, sketch the graph of f by first finding the following: the relative extrema of f; the points of inflection of the graph of f; the intervals on which f is increasing and those on which f is decreasing; where the graph of f is concave upward and where it is concave downward; the slope of any inflectional tangent; and the horizontal, vertical, and oblique asymptotes, if there are any. Incorporate this information in a table similar to those in this section. Support your results on your graphics calculator.

1. $f(x) = x^4 - 3x^3 + 3x^2 + 1$ **2.** $f(x) = \frac{1}{4}x^4 - x^3$

3. $f(x) = \frac{1}{4}x^4 - \frac{1}{3}x^3 - x^2 + 1$

4. $f(x) = x^4 - 4x^3 + 16x$

5. $f(x) = \frac{1}{2}x^4 - 2x^3 + 3x^2 + 2$

6. $f(x) = 3x^4 + 4x^3 + 6x^2 - 4$

7. $f(x) = \begin{cases} x^2 & \text{if } x < 0 \\ 2x^2 & \text{if } 0 \leq x \end{cases}$

8. $f(x) = \begin{cases} 2(x - 1)^3 & \text{if } x < 1 \\ (x - 1)^4 & \text{if } 1 \leq x \end{cases}$

9. $f(x) = \begin{cases} -x^4 & \text{if } x < 0 \\ x^4 & \text{if } 0 \leq x \end{cases}$

10. $f(x) = \begin{cases} -x^3 & \text{if } x < 0 \\ x^3 & \text{if } 0 \leq x \end{cases}$

11. $f(x) = \begin{cases} 3(x - 2)^2 & \text{if } x \leq 2 \\ (2 - x)^3 & \text{if } 2 < x \end{cases}$

12. $f(x) = 3x^5 + 5x^3$

13. $f(x) = (x + 1)^3(x - 2)^2$ **14.** $f(x) = x^2(x + 4)^3$

15. $f(x) = \begin{cases} \sin x & \text{if } 0 \leq x < \frac{1}{2}\pi \\ \sin(x - \frac{1}{2}\pi) & \text{if } \frac{1}{2}\pi \leq x \leq \pi \end{cases}$

16. $f(x) = \begin{cases} \cos x & \text{if } -\pi \leq x \leq 0 \\ \cos(\pi - x) & \text{if } 0 < x \leq \pi \end{cases}$

17. $f(x) = \dfrac{x^2}{x - 1}$ **18.** $f(x) = \dfrac{x^2 + 1}{x - 3}$

19. $f(x) = \dfrac{x^2 + 1}{x^2 - 1}$ **20.** $f(x) = \dfrac{x}{x^2 - 4}$

21. $f(x) = \dfrac{2x}{x^2 + 1}$ **22.** $f(x) = \dfrac{x^3}{x^2 - 1}$

23. $f(x) = (x + 1)^{2/3} (x - 2)^{1/3}$

24. $f(x) = \dfrac{x^2 - 4}{x^2 - 9}$

In Exercises 25 through 32, (a) plot the graphs of f,
NDER($f(x), x$) and NDER 2($f(x), x$) in separate win-
dows and estimate the following: (i) the relative extrema
of f; (ii) the intervals on which f is increasing and those
on which f is decreasing; (iii) where the graph of f is con-
cave upward and where it is concave downward; (iv) any
points of inflection of the graph of f. (b) Confirm your es-
timates in part (a) analytically and incorporate the infor-
mation in a table similar to Table 4 of this section. From
the information in this table sketch the graph of f and
compare it to your graph of f plotted in part (a).

25. $f(x) = x^4 + 2x^3 - 13x^2 - 14x + 24$

26. $f(x) = 2x^4 - 15x^3 + 32x^2 - 12x - 16$

27. $f(x) = |25 - x^2|$ **28.** $f(x) = 3\sqrt[3]{x} - x$

29. $f(x) = 4x^{1/3} + x^{4/3}$ **30.** $f(x) = x^2\sqrt{4 - x}$

31. $f(x) = \sin x + \cos x, \ x \in [-\pi, \pi]$

32. $f(x) = 3\sin 2x - 5\cos 2x, \ x \in [-\tfrac{1}{2}\pi, \tfrac{1}{2}\pi]$

33. Before sketching the graph of a function by applying the steps listed at the beginning of this section, why is it advisable to incorporate this information in a table?

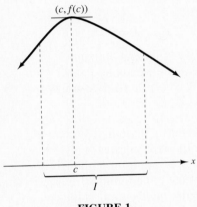

FIGURE 1

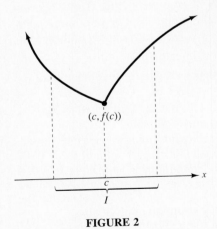

FIGURE 2

3.9 ADDITIONAL APPLICATIONS OF ABSOLUTE EXTREMA

To apply the extreme-value theorem to find a function's absolute extrema, the function must be continuous on a closed interval. In Section 3.2 the applications pertained to such functions. We now deal with applications involving absolute extrema for which the extreme-value theorem cannot be employed. First, however, we present a theorem, which is sometimes useful to determine if a relative extremum is an absolute extremum.

To illustrate the theorem, refer to the functions whose graphs appear in Figures 1 and 2. Each of these functions is continuous on an interval I and each has only one relative extremum, $f(c)$, on I. In both cases, the theorem that follows guarantees that the relative extremum is an absolute extremum.

3.9.1 Theorem

Suppose the function f is continuous on the interval I containing the number c. If $f(c)$ is a relative extremum of f on I and c is the only number in I for which f has a relative extremum, then $f(c)$ is an absolute extremum of f on I.

The proof of this theorem is deferred to the end of the section.

We apply Theorem 3.9.1 in the following examples, dealing with applications for which an absolute extremum is required but for which the extreme-value theorem cannot be utilized. The first example pertains to the situation discussed in Example 5 of Section 1.3. Refer back to that example at this time.

▶ **EXAMPLE 1** If a closed tin can of volume 60 in.^{3} is to be in the form of a right-circular cylinder, find analytically the base radius of the can if the least amount of tin is to be used in its manufacture.

FIGURE 3

Solution   Figure 3 shows the cylindrical can where r inches is the base radius. We wish to determine the base radius for which the total surface area of the can is an absolute minimum. In Example 5 of Section 1.3, we showed that if $S(r)$ square inches is the total surface area,

$$S(r) = \frac{120}{r} + 2\pi r^2$$

The domain of S is $(0, +\infty)$, and S is continuous on its domain.

To determine any relative extrema of S we compute the first and second derivatives:

$$S'(r) = -\frac{120}{r^2} + 4\pi r \qquad S''(r) = \frac{240}{r^3} + 4\pi$$

$S'(r)$ does not exist when $r = 0$, but 0 is not in the domain of S. The only critical numbers are, therefore, those obtained by setting $S'(r) = 0$, from which we have

$$4\pi r^3 = 120$$

$$r = \sqrt[3]{\frac{30}{\pi}}$$

Therefore, $\sqrt[3]{30/\pi}$ is a critical number of S. We apply the second-derivative test and summarize the results in Table 1.

Table 1

	$S'(r)$	$S''(r)$	*Conclusion*
$r = \sqrt[3]{\dfrac{30}{\pi}}$	0	+	S has a relative minimum value

Because S is continuous on its domain and the one and only relative extremum of S on its domain is at $r = \sqrt[3]{30/\pi}$, we conclude from Theorem 3.9.1 that this relative minimum value of S is the absolute minimum value.

To the nearest hundredth, $\sqrt[3]{30/\pi} \approx 2.12$, which agrees with our answer in Example 5 of Section 1.3.

Conclusion: The least amount of tin will be used in the manufacture of the can when the base radius is $\sqrt[3]{30/\pi}$ in. ≈ 2.12 in.   ◀

▶ **EXAMPLE 2**   A closed box with a square base is to have a volume of 2000 in.³ The material for the top and bottom of the box is to cost 3 cents per square inch and the material for the sides is to cost 1.5 cents per square inch. Estimate on a graphics calculator the dimensions of the box so that the total cost of material is least. Confirm the estimate analytically.

Solution   Let x inches be the length of a side of the square base and $C(x)$ dollars be the total cost of the material. The area of the base is x^2 square inches. Let y inches be the depth of the box. See Figure 4. Because the

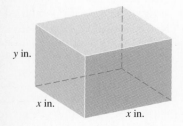

FIGURE 4

volume of the box is the product of the area of the base and the depth

$$x^2 y = 2000$$

$$y = \frac{2000}{x^2} \tag{1}$$

The total number of square inches in the combined area of the top and bottom is $2x^2$, and for the sides it is $4xy$. Therefore the number of cents in the total cost of the material is

$$3(2x^2) + \tfrac{3}{2}(4xy)$$

Replacing y by its equal from (1) we have

$$C(x) = 6x^2 + 6x\left(\frac{2000}{x^2}\right)$$

$$C(x) = 6x^2 + \frac{12,000}{x}$$

The domain of C is $(0, +\infty)$. Figure 5 shows the graph of C plotted in the $[0, 20]$ by $[1000, 5000]$ window. We estimate that the lowest point on the graph is at $x = 10$. From (1), when $x = 10$, $y = 20$. We therefore estimate that the side of the square base should be 10 in. and the depth should be 20 in. for the total cost of the material to be least.

To confirm our estimates analytically, we compute $C'(x)$ and $C''(x)$:

$$C'(x) = 12x - \frac{12,000}{x^2} \qquad C''(x) = 12 + \frac{24,000}{x^3}$$

Observe that $C'(x)$ does not exist when $x = 0$, but 0 is not in the domain of C. Therefore the only critical numbers will be those obtained by setting $C'(x) = 0$, which gives

$$12x - \frac{12,000}{x^2} = 0$$

$$x^3 = 1000$$

The only real solution of this equation is 10. The only critical number is, therefore, 10. To determine if $C(10)$ is a relative minimum value for C, we apply the second-derivative test and summarize the results in Table 2.

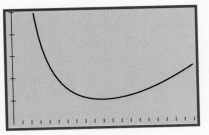

[0, 20] by [1000, 5000]

$$C(x) = 6x^2 + \frac{12,000}{x}$$

FIGURE 5

Table 2

	$C'(x)$	$C''(x)$	*Conclusion*
$x = 10$	0	+	C has a relative minimum value

Because C is continuous on its domain and the one and only relative extremum of C is at $x = 10$, we conclude from Theorem 3.9.1 that the relative minimum value of C is the absolute minimum value. We have, therefore, confirmed our estimates.

Conclusion: The cost of the material will be least when the side of the square base is 10 in. and the depth is 20 in. ◀

In the preceding examples and in the exercises of Section 3.2, the variable for which we wished to find an absolute extremum was expressed as a function of only one variable. Sometimes this procedure is either too difficult or too laborious, or occasionally even impossible. Often the given information enables us to obtain two equations involving three variables. Instead of eliminating one of the variables, it may be more advantageous to differentiate implicitly. The following example illustrates this method. The problem is similar to the one in Example 1, but in this example the volume of the required can is not specified.

▶ **EXAMPLE 3**   If a closed tin can of fixed volume is to be in the form of a right-circular cylinder, find the ratio of the height to the base radius if the least amount of material is to be used in its manufacture.

Solution   We wish to find a relationship between the height and the base radius of the right-circular cylinder in order for the total surface area to be an absolute minimum for a fixed volume. Therefore we consider the volume of the cylinder a constant.

Let V cubic units be the volume of a cylinder (a constant).

We now define the variables.

Let r units be the base radius of the cylinder; $r > 0$. Let h units be the height of the cylinder; $h > 0$. Let S square units be the total surface area of the cylinder (See Figure 6).

We have the following equations:

$$S = 2\pi r^2 + 2\pi rh \tag{2}$$
$$V = \pi r^2 h \tag{3}$$

Because V is a constant, we could solve (3) for either r or h in terms of the other and substitute into (2), which will give S as a function of one variable. The alternative method is to consider S as a function of two variables r and h; however, r and h are not independent of each other. That is, if we choose r as the independent variable, then S depends on r; also, h depends on r.

Differentiating S and V with respect to r and bearing in mind that h is a function of r, we have

$$\frac{dS}{dr} = 4\pi r + 2\pi h + 2\pi r\frac{dh}{dr} \tag{4}$$

$$\frac{dV}{dr} = 2\pi rh + \pi r^2\frac{dh}{dr}$$

Because V is a constant, $\dfrac{dV}{dr} = 0$; therefore, from the above equation,

$$2\pi rh + \pi r^2\frac{dh}{dr} = 0$$

with $r \neq 0$. We divide by r and solve for $\dfrac{dh}{dr}$ to get

$$\frac{dh}{dr} = -\frac{2h}{r} \tag{5}$$

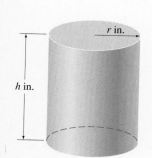

r in.

h in.

FIGURE 6

Substituting from (5) into (4) we obtain

$$\frac{dS}{dr} = 2\pi \left[2r + h + r\left(-\frac{2h}{r} \right) \right]$$

$$\frac{dS}{dr} = 2\pi(2r - h) \tag{6}$$

To find when S has a relative minimum value, we set $\frac{dS}{dr} = 0$ and obtain $2r - h = 0$, which gives

$$r = \tfrac{1}{2}h$$

To determine if this relationship between r and h makes S a relative minimum we apply the second-derivative test. Then from (6),

$$\frac{d^2S}{dr^2} = 2\pi\left(2 - \frac{dh}{dr} \right)$$

Substituting from (5) into this equation we get

$$\frac{d^2S}{dr^2} = 2\pi\left[2 - \left(\frac{-2h}{r} \right) \right]$$

$$= 2\pi\left(2 + \frac{2h}{r} \right)$$

We summarize the results of the second-derivative test in Table 3.

Table 3

	$\dfrac{dS}{dr}$	$\dfrac{d^2S}{dr^2}$	*Conclusion*
$r = \tfrac{1}{2}h$	0	+	S has a relative minimum value

From (2) and (3), S is a continuous function of r on $(0, +\infty)$. Because the one and only relative extremum of S on $(0, +\infty)$ is at $r = \tfrac{1}{2}h$, we conclude from Theorem 3.9.1 that S has an absolute minimum value when $h/r = 2$.

Conclusion: The total surface area of the can will be least for a specific volume when the ratio of the height to the base radius is 2. ◀

Geometric problems involving absolute extrema occasionally are more easily solved by using trigonometric functions as in the next example.

▶ **EXAMPLE 4**   A right-circular cylinder is to be inscribed in a sphere of given radius. Find the ratio of the height to the base radius of the cylinder having the largest lateral surface area.

Solution   Refer to Figure 7, where the measure of the constant radius of the sphere is a.

Let θ radians be the angle at the center of the sphere subtended by the radius of the cylinder, r units be the radius of the cylinder, h units be the

FIGURE 7

height of the cylinder, and S square units be the lateral surface area of the cylinder. From Figure 7,

$$r = a \sin \theta \quad \text{and} \quad h = 2a \cos \theta$$

Because $S = 2\pi rh$,

$$
\begin{aligned}
S &= 2\pi(a \sin \theta)(2a \cos \theta) \\
&= 2\pi a^2 (2 \sin \theta \cos \theta) \\
&= 2\pi a^2 \sin 2\theta
\end{aligned}
$$

Thus S is a function of θ and its domain is $(0, \frac{1}{2}\pi)$.

$$\frac{dS}{d\theta} = 4\pi a^2 \cos 2\theta \quad \text{and} \quad \frac{d^2S}{d\theta^2} = -8\pi a^2 \sin 2\theta$$

Set $\dfrac{dS}{d\theta} = 0$.

$$\cos 2\theta = 0$$

Because $0 < \theta < \frac{1}{2}\pi$,

$$\theta = \tfrac{1}{4}\pi$$

We apply the second-derivative test and summarize the results in Table 4.

Table 4

	$\dfrac{dS}{d\theta}$	$\dfrac{d^2S}{d\theta^2}$	*Conclusion*
$\theta = \frac{1}{4}\pi$	0	−	S has a relative maximum value

Because S is continuous and has only one relative extremum on its domain, we conclude that the relative maximum value is an absolute maximum value.

When $\theta = \frac{1}{4}\pi$,

$$
\begin{array}{ll}
r = a \sin \frac{1}{4}\pi & h = 2a \cos \frac{1}{4}\pi \\
\;\; = \frac{1}{2}\sqrt{2}a & \;\; = \sqrt{2}a
\end{array}
$$

Therefore, $h/r = 2$.

<u>**Conclusion:**</u> For the cylinder having the largest lateral surface area, the ratio of the height to the base radius is 2. ◄

We conclude this section with the proof of Theorem 3.9.1.

Proof of Theorem 3.9.1 We prove the theorem when $f(c)$ is a relative maximum value on the interval I. A similar proof can be given when $f(c)$ is a relative minimum value.

Because $f(c)$ is a relative maximum value of f on I, then by Definition 3.1.1 there is an open interval J, where $J \subset I$, and where J contains c, such that

$$f(c) \geq f(x) \qquad \text{for all } x \in J$$

Because c is the only number in I for which f has a relative maximum value, it follows that

$$f(c) > f(k) \qquad \text{if } k \in J \text{ and } k \neq c \tag{7}$$

To show that $f(c)$ is an absolute maximum value of f on I we show that if d is any number other than c in I, then $f(c) > f(d)$. We assume that

$$f(c) \leq f(d) \tag{8}$$

and show that this assumption leads to a contradiction. Because $d \neq c$, then either $c < d$ or $d < c$. We consider the case that $c < d$ (the proof is similar if $d < c$).

Because f is continuous on I, then f is continuous on the closed interval $[c, d]$. Therefore, by the extreme-value theorem, f has an absolute minimum value on $[c, d]$. Assume this absolute minimum value occurs at e, where $c \leq e \leq d$. From inequality (7) $e \neq c$, and from inequalities (7) and (8) $e \neq d$. Therefore $c < e < d$, and hence f has a relative minimum value at e. But this statement contradicts the hypothesis that c is the only number in I for which f has a relative extremum. Thus our assumption that $f(c) \leq f(d)$ is false. Therefore $f(c) > f(d)$ if $d \in I$ and $d \neq c$, and consequently $f(c)$ is an absolute maximum value of f on I.   ∎

EXERCISES 3.9

In each exercise define all your variables precisely as numbers and be sure to write a conclusion.

1. For the tin can of Example 1, suppose that the cost of material for the top and bottom is twice as much as for the sides. **(a)** Find analytically the height and base radius for the cost of the material to be least. **(b)** Compare your answer in part (a) with your graphical solution to this situation in part (c) of Exercise 21 of Exercises 1.3. Does your graphical solution support your answer in part (a)?

2. **(a)** Do Example 1 analytically if the tin can is open instead of closed. **(b)** Compare your answer in part (a) with your graphical solution to this situation in part (c) of Exercise 22 of Exercises 1.3. Does your graphical solution support your answer in part (a)?

In Exercises 3 and 4, confirm analytically your estimate obtained on your graphics calculator in part (c) of the indicated exercise of Exercises 1.3.

3. Exercise 23

4. Exercise 24

5. A rectangular field having an area of 2700 m² is to be enclosed by a fence, and an additional fence is to be used to divide the field down the middle. The cost of the fence down the middle is $24 per running meter, and the fence along the sides costs $36 per running meter. **(a)** Use your graphics calculator to estimate the dimensions of the field so that the total cost of the fencing material is least. **(b)** Confirm your estimates in part (a) analytically.

6. A rectangular open tank of volume 125 m³ is to have a square base. The cost per square meter for the bottom is $24 and for the sides is $12. **(a)** Use your graphics calculator to estimate the dimensions of the tank for the cost of the material to be least. **(b)** Confirm your estimates in part (a) analytically.

7. A box manufacturer wishes to construct a closed box of volume 288 in.³ where the base is a rectangle having a length three times its width. **(a)** Use your graphics calculator to estimate the dimensions of the box constructed from the least amount of material. **(b)** Confirm your estimates in part (a) analytically.

8. Do Exercise 7 if the box is to have an open top.

9. If salaries are excluded, the number of dollars in the cost per kilometer for operating a truck is $8 + \frac{1}{300}x$, where x kilometers per hour is the average speed of the truck. **(a)** If the combined salary of the driver and the driver's assistant is $27 per hour, estimate on your graphics calculator to the nearest kilometer per hour what the average speed of the truck should be for the cost per kilometer to be least. **(b)** Confirm your estimate in part (a) analytically.

10. The number of dollars in the cost per hour of fuel for a cargo ship is $0.02v^3$, where v knots (nautical miles per hour) is the average speed of the ship. **(a)** If there are additional costs of $400 per hour, estimate to the nearest knot what the average speed of the ship should be for the cost per nautical mile to be least. **(b)** Confirm your estimate in part (a) analytically.

11. An automobile traveling at the rate of 30 ft/sec is approaching an intersection. When the automobile is 120 ft. from the intersection, a truck, traveling at the rate of 40 ft/sec on a road at right angles with the automobile's road, crosses the intersection. **(a)** Determine analytically how long after the truck leaves the intersection until the two vehicles are closest. **(b)** Support your answer in part (a) graphically.

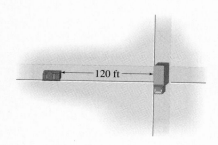

12. Two airplanes A and B are flying horizontally at the same altitude so that the position of B is southwest of A and 20 km to the west and 20 km to the south of A. Suppose plane A is flying due west at 16 km/min and plane B is flying due north at 21.3 km/min. **(a)** Determine analytically in how many seconds the planes will be closest and what their closest distance will be. **(b)** Support your answers in part (a) graphically.

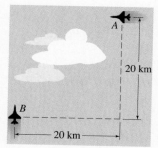

13. Find an equation of the tangent line to the curve $y = x^3 - 3x^2 + 5x$ that has the least slope.

14. A direct current generator has an electromotive force of E volts and an internal resistance of r ohms, where E and r are constants. If R ohms is the external resistance, the total resistance is $(r + R)$ ohms, and if P watts is the power, then

$$P = \frac{E^2 R}{(r + R)^2}$$

Show that the most power is consumed when the external resistance is equal to the internal resistance.

15. In a particular community, a certain epidemic spreads in such a way that x months after the start of the epidemic, P percent of the population is infected, where

$$P = \frac{30x^2}{(1 + x^2)^2}$$

In how many months will the most people be infected, and what percent of the population is this?

16. A cardboard poster containing 32 in.^{2} of printed region is to have a margin of 2 in. at the top and bottom and $\frac{4}{3}$ in. at the sides. Determine the dimensions of the smallest piece of cardboard that can be used to make the poster.

In Exercises 17 and 18, we use the economics term perfect competition. When a company is operating under perfect competition, there are many small firms; so any one firm cannot affect price by increasing production. Therefore, under perfect competition the price of a commodity is constant, and the company can sell as much as it wishes to sell at this constant price.

17. Under perfect competition a firm can sell at a price of $200 per unit all of a particular commodity it produces. If $C(x)$ dollars is the total cost of each day's production when x units are produced, and $C(x) = 2x^2 + 40x + 1400$, find the number of units that should be produced daily for the firm to have the greatest daily total profit. *Hint:* Total profit equals total revenue minus total cost.

18. A company that builds and sells desks is operating under perfect competition and can sell at a price of $400 per desk all the desks it produces. If x desks are produced and sold each week and $C(x)$ dollars is the total cost of the week's production, then $C(x) = 2x^2 + 80x + 6000$. Determine how many desks should be built each week for the manufacturer to have the greatest weekly total profit. What is the greatest weekly total profit? See the hint for Exercise 17.

19. Under a **monopoly,** which means that there is only one producer of a certain commodity, price and hence demand can be controlled by regulating the quantity of the commodity produced. Suppose that under a monopoly x units are demanded daily when p dollars is the price per unit and $x = 140 - p$. If the number of dollars in the total cost of producing x units is given by $C(x) = x^2 + 20x + 300$, find the maximum daily total profit.

20. Find the shortest distance from the point $P(2, 0)$ to a point on the curve $y^2 - x^2 = 1$, and find the point on the curve closest to P.

21. Find the shortest distance from the origin to the line $3x + y = 6$, and find the point P on the line closest to the origin. Then show that the origin lies on the line perpendicular to the given line at P.

22. Find the shortest distance from the point $A(2, \frac{1}{2})$ to a point on the parabola $y = x^2$, and find the point B on the parabola closest to A. Then show that A lies on the normal line of the parabola at B.

23. A Norman window consists of a rectangle surmounted by a semicircle. If the perimeter of a Norman window is to be 32 ft, determine what should be the radius of the semicircle and the height of the rectangle such that the window will admit the most light.

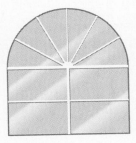

24. Solve Exercise 23 if the window is to be such that the semicircle transmits only half as much light per square foot of area as the rectangle.

25. A steel girder 27 ft long is moved horizontally along a passageway 8 ft wide and into a corridor at right angles to the passageway. How wide must the corridor be for the girder to go around the corner? Neglect the horizontal width of the girder.

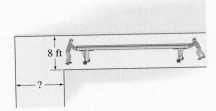

26. If two corridors at right angles to each other are 10 ft and 15 ft wide, respectively, what is the length of the longest steel girder that can be moved horizontally around the corner? Neglect the horizontal width of the girder.

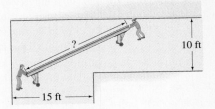

27. A funnel of specific volume is to be in the shape of a right-circular cone. Find the ratio of the height to the base radius if the least amount of material is to be used in its manufacture.

28. A right-circular cone is to be inscribed in a sphere of given radius. Find the ratio of the altitude to the base radius of the cone of largest possible volume.

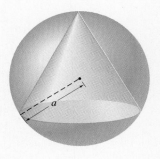

29. A right-circular cone is to be circumscribed about a sphere of given radius. Find the ratio of the altitude to the base radius of the cone of least possible volume.

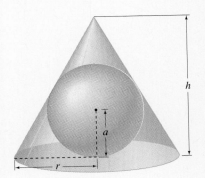

30. Prove by the method of this section that the shortest distance from the point $P_1(x_1, y_1)$ to the line l having the equation $Ax + By + C = 0$ is

$$\frac{\left|Ax_1 + By_1 + C\right|}{\sqrt{A^2 + B^2}}$$

Hint: If s is the number of units from P_1 to a point $P(x, y)$ on l, then s will be an absolute minimum when s^2 is an absolute minimum.

31. The cross section of a trough has the shape of an inverted isosceles triangle. If the lengths of the equal

sides are 15 in., find the size of the vertex angle that will give maximum capacity for the trough.

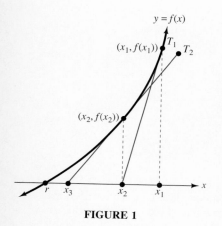

FIGURE 1

3.10 APPROXIMATIONS BY NEWTON'S METHOD, THE TANGENT LINE, AND DIFFERENTIALS

Before the advent of calculators and computers, the roots of an equation of the form $f(x) = 0$ or, equivalently, the zeros of the function f were approximated by numerical techniques involving the derivative. Even though such approximations are now easily accomplished on a graphics calculator by a built-in *solve* feature or the *zoom-in* procedure, we devote this section to a discussion of three of the numerical techniques. The first of these techniques, known as *Newton's method* and devised by Sir Isaac Newton in the seventeenth century, is characteristic of the numerical processes built-in on calculators.

We begin our treatment of Newton's method by giving a geometric interpretation of the concepts involved. Refer to Figure 1, which shows the graph of the equation $y = f(x)$. The number r is an x intercept of the graph. To obtain an approximation of r we first select a number x_1, the choice of which should be reasonably close to the number r. We then consider the tangent line to the graph of f at the point $(x_1, f(x_1))$. The tangent line, denoted by T_1, appears in Figure 1, and T_1 has an x intercept x_2. The number x_2 now serves as a second approximation of r. We then repeat the process with the tangent line T_2 at the point $(x_2, f(x_2))$. The x intercept of T_2 is x_3. We continue the process until we have the required degree of accuracy. For this graph it appears that the numbers x_1, x_2, x_3, and so on are getting closer and closer to the number r. This situation occurs for many functions.

To obtain the successive approximations $x_2, x_3, \ldots$ from the first approximation x_1 we use the equations of the tangent lines. The tangent line T_1 at the point $(x_1, f(x_1))$ has a slope of $f'(x_1)$. Thus an equation of T_1 is

$$y - f(x_1) = f'(x_1)(x - x_1)$$

The x intercept of T_1 is x_2, and we determine x_2 by letting $x = x_2$ and $y = 0$ in the above equation. We get

$$0 - f(x_1) = f'(x_1)(x_2 - x_1)$$

$$x_2 = x_1 - \frac{f(x_1)}{f'(x_1)} \qquad \text{if } f'(x_1) \neq 0$$

With this value of x_2 an equation of T_2 is

$$y - f(x_2) = f'(x_2)(x - x_2)$$

Then in this equation we let $x = x_3$ and $y = 0$, and we have

$$0 - f(x_2) = f'(x_2)(x_3 - x_2)$$

$$x_3 = x_2 - \frac{f(x_2)}{f'(x_2)} \qquad \text{if } f'(x_2) \neq 0$$

Continuing on in this manner we obtain the general formula for the approximation x_{n+1} in terms of the preceding approximation x_n:

$$x_{n+1} = x_n - \frac{f(x_n)}{f'(x_n)} \qquad \text{if } f'(x_n) \neq 0 \tag{1}$$

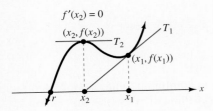

$f'(x_2) = 0$

$(x_2, f(x_2))$

FIGURE 2

Of course, formula (1) is easily adapted for use on a computer or a programmable calculator.

From formula (1) we can obtain the $(n + 1)$st approximation from the nth approximation, provided $f'(x_n) \neq 0$. When $f'(x_n) = 0$, the tangent line is horizontal, and in such a case, unless the tangent line is the x axis itself, it has no x intercept. Figure 2 shows this happening when $f'(x_2) = 0$. So Newton's method is not applicable if $f'(x_n) = 0$ for some x_n. You should also be aware that the value of x_{n+1} obtained from (1) is not necessarily a better approximation of r than x_n. If, for instance, x_1 is not reasonably close to r, then $|f'(x_1)|$ may be small so that the tangent line T_1 is nearly horizontal. Then x_2, the x intercept of T_1, could be farther away from r than x_1. See Figure 3 where this situation occurs.

In the following illustration we show how Newton's method is applied to an equation for which we know the answer.

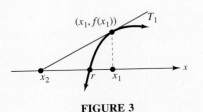

$(x_1, f(x_1))$

FIGURE 3

▷ **ILLUSTRATION 1**   Let us use Newton's method to obtain the positive root of the equation $x^2 = 9$ by starting with a first approximation of 4. We write the equation as $x^2 - 9 = 0$ and let

$$f(x) = x^2 - 9$$

$$f'(x) = 2x$$

From (1) we obtain

$$x_{n+1} = x_n - \frac{f(x_n)}{f'(x_n)}$$

$$x_{n+1} = x_n - \frac{x_n^2 - 9}{2x_n} \tag{2}$$

We now apply (2) with values of n and corresponding values of x_n to compute by a calculator x_{n+1}. We start with $x_1 = 4$.

$$x_2 = x_1 - \frac{x_1{}^2 - 9}{2x_1} \qquad\qquad x_3 = x_2 - \frac{x_2{}^2 - 9}{2x_2}$$

$$= 4 - \frac{16 - 9}{8} \qquad\qquad = 3.125 - \frac{(3.125)^2 - 9}{2(3.125)}$$

$$= 3.125 \qquad\qquad\qquad = 3.0025$$

$$x_4 = x_3 - \frac{x_3{}^2 - 9}{2x_3} \qquad\qquad x_5 = x_4 - \frac{x_4{}^2 - 9}{2x_4}$$

$$= 3.0025 - \frac{(3.0025)^2 - 9}{2(3.0025)} \qquad = 3.0000 - \frac{(3.0000)^2 - 9}{2(3.0000)}$$

$$= 3.0000 \qquad\qquad\qquad = 3.0000$$

Certainly all successive approximations will be 3.0000. Thus the positive root of the equation $x^2 - 9 = 0$ is 3.0000 to four decimal places. ◀

Observe that when x_n is a solution of $f(x) = 0$, $f(x_n) = 0$. Thus from (1),

$$x_{n+1} = x_n - \frac{f(x_n)}{f'(x_n)}$$

$$= x_n - 0$$

$$= x_n$$

Consequently all subsequent approximations are equal to x_n. Note that this situation occurs in Illustration 1, where all approximations after and including x_4 have the same value to four decimal places.

Also observe from (1) that $x_{n+1} = x_n$ implies that $f(x_n) = 0$. Therefore we can conclude that when two successive approximations are equal, we have an approximation for a zero of f.

It is possible, however, that for certain functions, if your initial choice of x_1 is not close enough to the desired zero, you may obtain approximations for a different zero. See Figure 4 for a sketch of the graph of a function where this situation could happen. Note that the indicated choice of x_1 near the desired zero r gives successive approximations $x_2, x_3, x_4, \ldots$ near another zero s. Thus when applying Newton's method you should first draw a rough sketch of the graph of the function to obtain your initial approximation. Refer to the graph as you proceed to make sure you are getting successive approximations to the zero you are seeking.

In summary, when using Newton's method to solve an equation of the form $f(x) = 0$, do the following:

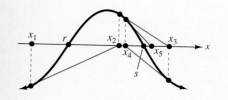

FIGURE 4

1. Make a *good guess* for the first approximation x_1. A graph of f will help to obtain a reasonable choice.
2. Get a second approximation x_2 with the value of x_1 in formula (1). Then use x_2 in (1) to get a third approximation x_3, and so on until $x_{n+1} = x_n$ to the required degree of accuracy.

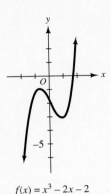

$f(x) = x^3 - 2x - 2$

FIGURE 5

▶ **EXAMPLE 1**   Use Newton's method to find the real root of the equation

$$x^3 - 2x - 2 = 0$$

to four decimal places.

Solution   Let $f(x) = x^3 - 2x - 2$; thus $f'(x) = 3x^2 - 2$. Then from (1) we have

$$x_{n+1} = x_n - \frac{x_n^3 - 2x_n - 2}{3x_n^2 - 2} \qquad (3)$$

The graph of f appears as in Figure 5. Because the graph intersects the x axis at only one point, there is one real root of the given equation. Because $f(1) = -3$ and $f(2) = 2$, this root lies between 1 and 2. A suitable choice for our first approximation is $x_1 = 1.5$. Table 1 shows the results obtained from a calculator by successive approximations computed from (3) with this x_1. We wish the root to be accurate to four decimal places; thus we use five places in the computations. Because x_5 and x_6 are equal (to five decimal places), we round off that number to four places and obtain 1.7693 as the required root.

Table 1

n	x_n	$\dfrac{x_n^3 - 2x_n - 2}{3x_n^2 - 2}$	x_{n+1}
1	1.50000	−0.34211	1.84211
2	1.84211	0.06928	1.77283
3	1.77283	0.00353	1.76930
4	1.76930	0.00001	1.76929
5	1.76929	0.00000	1.76929

◀

▶ **EXAMPLE 2**   Use Newton's method to find to three decimal places the x coordinate of the point of intersection in the first quadrant of the line $y = \frac{1}{3}x$ and the curve $y = \sin x$.

Solution   Figure 6 shows the line and the curve. We wish to find the positive value of x for which

$$\sin x = \tfrac{1}{3}x$$
$$3 \sin x - x = 0$$

Let

$$f(x) = 3 \sin x - x$$
$$f'(x) = 3 \cos x - 1$$

From formula (1),

$$x_{n+1} = x_n - \frac{f(x_n)}{f'(x_n)}$$

$$x_{n+1} = x_n - \frac{3 \sin x_n - x_n}{3 \cos x_n - 1} \qquad (4)$$

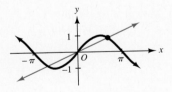

$y = \sin x$ and $y = \frac{1}{3}x$

FIGURE 6

Table 2

n	x_n	$\dfrac{3 \sin x_n - x_n}{3 \cos x_n - 1}$	x_{n+1}
1	2.0000	−0.3237	2.3237
2	2.3237	0.0441	2.2796
3	2.2796	0.0007	2.2789
4	2.2789	0.0000	2.2789

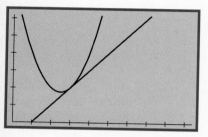

[0, 9.4] by [0, 6.2]

$f(x) = x^2 - 5x + 8$

FIGURE 7

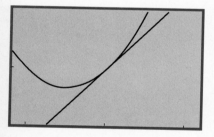

[1.825, 4.175] by [1.225, 2.775]

$f(x) = x^2 - 5x + 8$

FIGURE 8

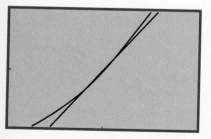

[2.706, 3.294] by [1.806, 2.194]

$f(x) = x^2 - 5x + 8$

FIGURE 9

From Figure 6 it appears that a reasonable choice of x_1 is 2. We use a calculator to compute the successive approximations from formula (4); these appear in Table 2. The results are expressed to four decimal places. Observe that to four decimal places x_4 and x_5 are both equal to 2.2789. Thus to three decimal places the positive value of x for which $\sin x = \frac{1}{3}x$ is 2.279.   ◀

Theorems that state conditions for which Newton's method is applicable, as well as theorems relating to its accuracy, can be found in texts on numerical analysis.

One of the simplest ways that function values can be approximated is called a *linear approximation,* which utilizes the tangent line to the graph of a differentiable function. We begin our discussion of linear approximations with an illustration demonstrating the basic idea.

▷   **ILLUSTRATION 2**   Figure 7 shows the graph of

$$f(x) = x^2 - 5x + 8$$

and the tangent line at the point (3, 2) plotted in the [0, 9.4] by [0, 6.2] window. If we *zoom in* at the point (3, 2) and plot the tangent line, we obtain Figure 8 which has the window [1.825, 4.175] by [1.225, 2.775]. If we *zoom in* again and plot the tangent line, we obtain Figure 9 which has the window [2.706, 3.294] by [1.806, 2.194]. Observe how the tangent line approximates the graph of the function near the point of tangency. Thus if x is in a small open interval containing 3, the corresponding y coordinate on the graph of the function can be approximated by the y coordinate on the tangent line.   ◀

We utilize the concept of the above illustration for a general function f differentiable at a number x_0. An equation of the tangent line to the graph of f at the point $(x_0, f(x_0))$ is

$$y - f(x_0) = f'(x_0)(x - x_0)$$
$$y = f(x_0) + f'(x_0)(x - x_0)$$

Refer to Figure 10 where P is the point $(x_0, f(x_0))$, Q is the point $(x, f(x))$ and R is the point $(x, f(x_0) + f'(x_0)(x - x_0))$. Observe that for a number x sufficiently close to x_0, the point Q on the graph of f is close to the point R on the tangent line. Consequently, if x is close to x_0, $f(x)$ can be approximated by $f(x_0) + f'(x_0)(x - x_0)$; that is,

$$f(x) \approx f(x_0) + f'(x_0)(x - x_0)$$

This approximation is called the **tangent line approximation,** or more concisely the **linear approximation,** of $f(x)$ at x_0.

▶   **EXAMPLE 3**   Given

$$f(x) = \cos^2 x - x + 1 \tag{5}$$

(a) Find the linear approximation of $f(x)$ at 0. **(b)** Support the answer in part (a) graphically. **(c)** Compare the value of $f(x)$ computed from the linear

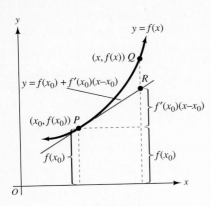

FIGURE 10

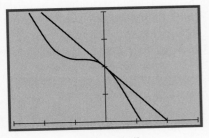

[-3, 3] by [0, 4]

$f(x) = \cos^2 x - x + 1$

FIGURE 11

approximation in part (a) with the function values computed from (5) when x is -0.2, -0.1, -0.01, 0, 0.01, 0.1, and 0.2.

Solution

(a) We compute $f'(x)$:

$$f'(x) = 2 \sin x \cos x - 1$$

The linear approximation of $f(x)$ at 0 is

$$f(x) \approx f(0) + f'(0)(x - 0)$$

Because $f(0) = 2$ and $f'(0) = -1$, we have

$$f(x) \approx 2 - x \tag{6}$$

(b) Figure 11 shows the graph of f and the tangent line at $(0, 2)$ plotted in the $[-3, 3]$ by $[0, 4]$ window, which supports our answer in part (a).

(c) Table 3 compares the values of $f(x)$ computed from (6) with those computed from (5). Observe that the closer x is to 0, the better is the approximation.

Table 3

x	-0.2	-0.1	-0.01	0	0.01	0.1	0.2
$f(x) \approx 2 - x$	2.2	2.1	2.01	2	1.99	1.9	1.8
$f(x) = \cos^2 x - x + 1$	2.16	2.09	2.0099	2	1.9899	1.89	1.76

◀

We now introduce the concept of the *differential,* which also enables us to approximate changes in function values near points where the function is differentiable. You will see that an approximation by differentials is related to a linear approximation. Even though the application of differentials to approximating function values is not very important in the age of technology, differentials are important as a convenient notational device for the computation of *antiderivatives,* as you will learn in the next chapter.

Suppose the function f is defined by the equation

$$y = f(x)$$

At points where f is differentiable

$$f'(x) = \lim_{\Delta x \to 0} \frac{\Delta y}{\Delta x} \tag{7}$$

where

$$\Delta y = f(x + \Delta x) - f(x)$$

From (7) it follows that for any $\epsilon > 0$ there exists a $\delta > 0$ such that

$$\text{if} \quad 0 < |\Delta x| < \delta \quad \text{then} \quad \left| \frac{\Delta y}{\Delta x} - f'(x) \right| < \epsilon$$

$$\Leftrightarrow \text{if} \quad 0 < |\Delta x| < \delta \quad \text{then} \quad \frac{|\Delta y - f'(x)\,\Delta x|}{|\Delta x|} < \epsilon$$

This means that $|\Delta y - f'(x)\,\Delta x|$ is small compared to $|\Delta x|$. That is, for a sufficiently small $|\Delta x|, f'(x)\,\Delta x$ is a good approximation to the value of Δy,

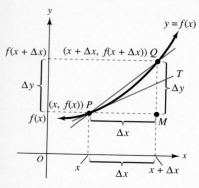

FIGURE 12

and we write

$$\Delta y \approx f'(x)\,\Delta x \tag{8}$$

if $|\Delta x|$ is sufficiently small.

For a graphical interpretation of statement (8), refer to Figure 12. In the figure, an equation of the curve is $y = f(x)$. The line PT is tangent to the curve at $P(x, f(x))$, Q is the point $(x + \Delta x, f(x + \Delta x))$, and the directed distance $\overline{MQ}$ is $\Delta y = f(x + \Delta x) - f(x)$. In the figure, Δx and Δy are both positive; however, they could be negative. For a small value of Δx, the slope of the secant line PQ and the slope of the tangent line at P are approximately equal; that is,

$$\frac{\Delta y}{\Delta x} \approx f'(x)$$

$$\Delta y \approx f'(x)\,\Delta x$$

which is statement (8).

The right side of statement (8) is defined to be the *differential* of y.

3.10.1 Definition of the Differential of the Dependent Variable

If the function f is defined by the equation $y = f(x)$, then the **differential of y,** denoted by dy, is given by

$$dy = f'(x)\,\Delta x \tag{9}$$

where x is in the domain of f' and Δx is an arbitrary increment of x.

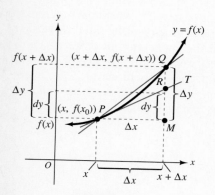

FIGURE 13

Refer now to Figure 13, which is the same as Figure 12 except the vertical line segment MR is shown, where the directed distance $\overline{MR} = dy$. Observe that dy represents the change in y along the tangent line to the graph of the equation $y = f(x)$ at the point $P(x, f(x))$, when x is changed by Δx.

This concept of the differential involves a special type of function of two variables and a detailed study of such functions appears in Chapter 12. The symbol df may be used to represent this function. The variable x can be any number in the domain of f', and Δx can be any number whatsoever. To state that df is a function of the two independent variables x and Δx means that to each ordered pair $(x, \Delta x)$ in the domain of df there corresponds one and only one number in the range of df, and this number can be represented by $df(x, \Delta x)$ so that

$$df(x, \Delta x) = f'(x)\,\Delta x$$

Comparing this equation with (9) we see that when $y = f(x)$, dy and $df(x, \Delta x)$ are two different notations for $f'(x)\,\Delta x$. The dy symbolism is used in subsequent discussions.

▷   **ILLUSTRATION 3**   If $y = 3x^2 - x$, then $f(x) = 3x^2 - x$, so that $f'(x) = 6x - 1$. From Definition 3.10.1, we have

$$dy = (6x - 1)\,\Delta x$$

In particular, if $x = 2$, then $dy = 11\,\Delta x$.   ◀

When $y = f(x)$, Definition 3.10.1 gives us dy, the differential of the dependent variable. We now wish to define the *differential of the independent variable,* or dx. To arrive at a suitable definition consistent with the definition of dy, we consider the identity function defined by $f(x) = x$. For this function, $f'(x) = 1$ and $y = x$; thus from (9), $dy = 1 \cdot \Delta x$; that is,

$$\text{if} \quad y = x \quad \text{then} \quad dy = \Delta x \qquad \qquad \textbf{(10)}$$

For the identity function we would want dx to be equal to dy; that is, because of statement (10) we would want dx to be equal to Δx. This reasoning leads to the following definition.

3.10.2 Definition of the Differential of the Independent Variable

If the function f is defined by the equation $y = f(x)$, then the **differential of x,** denoted by dx, is given by

$$dx = \Delta x$$

where x is any number in the domain of f' and Δx is an arbitrary increment of x.

From Definitions 3.10.1 and 3.10.2,

$$dy = f'(x) \, dx \qquad \qquad \textbf{(11)}$$

Dividing both sides of this equation by dx, we obtain

$$\frac{dy}{dx} = f'(x) \qquad \text{if } dx \neq 0$$

This equation expresses the derivative as the quotient of two differentials. Recall that when we introduced the notation $\dfrac{dy}{dx}$ in Section 2.1, we emphasized that dy and dx had not been given independent meaning at that time.

▶ **EXAMPLE 4**   Given $y = 4x^2 - 3x + 1$, find Δy, dy, and $\Delta y - dy$ for **(a)** any x and Δx; **(b)** $x = 2$, $\Delta x = 0.1$; **(c)** $x = 2$, $\Delta x = 0.01$; **(d)** $x = 2$, $\Delta x = 0.001$.

Solution

(a) Because $y = 4x^2 - 3x + 1$, let

$$f(x) = 4x^2 - 3x + 1$$

Then,

$$\begin{aligned}
\Delta y &= f(x + \Delta x) - f(x) \\
&= 4(x + \Delta x)^2 - 3(x + \Delta x) + 1 - (4x^2 - 3x + 1) \\
&= 4x^2 + 8x \, \Delta x + 4(\Delta x)^2 - 3x - 3 \, \Delta x + 1 - 4x^2 + 3x - 1 \\
&= (8x - 3) \, \Delta x + 4(\Delta x)^2
\end{aligned}$$

From (11),

$$\begin{aligned}
dy &= f'(x) \, dx \\
&= (8x - 3) \, dx \\
&= (8x - 3) \, \Delta x
\end{aligned}$$

Thus

$$\Delta y - dy = 4(\Delta x)^2$$

The results for parts (b), (c), and (d) are given in Table 4.

Table 4

	x	Δx	Δy	dy	$\Delta y - dy$
(b)	2	0.1	1.34	1.3	0.04
(c)	2	0.01	0.1304	0.13	0.0004
(d)	2	0.001	0.013004	0.013	0.000004

◀

Note from Table 4 that the closer Δx is to zero, the smaller is the difference between Δy and dy. Furthermore, observe that for each value of Δx, the corresponding value of $\Delta y - dy$ is smaller than the value of Δx. More generally, dy is an approximation of Δy when Δx is small, and the approximation is of better accuracy than the size of Δx.

For a fixed value of x, say x_0,

$$dy = f'(x_0)\, dx$$

that is, dy is a linear function of dx; consequently dy is usually easier to compute than Δy, as you saw in Example 4. Because

$$f(x_0 + \Delta x) - f(x_0) = \Delta y$$

then

$$f(x_0 + \Delta x) = f(x_0) + \Delta y$$

Thus

$$f(x_0 + \Delta x) \approx f(x_0) + dy$$

We illustrate our results in Figure 14 where the equation of the curve is $y = f(x)$. The line PT is tangent to the curve at $P(x_0, f(x_0))$; Δx and dx are equal and are represented by the directed distance $\overline{PM}$, where M is the point $(x_0 + \Delta x, f(x_0))$. We let Q be the point $(x_0 + \Delta x, f(x_0 + \Delta x))$, and the directed distance $\overline{MQ}$ is Δy. The slope of PT is $f'(x) = dy/dx$. The slope of PT is also $\overline{MR}/\overline{PM}$, and because $\overline{PM} = dx$, we have $dy = \overline{MR}$ and $\overline{RQ} = \Delta y - dy$. Notice that the smaller the value of dx (i.e., the closer the

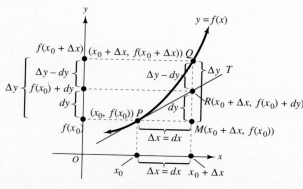

FIGURE 14

point Q is to the point P), then the smaller will be the value of $\Delta y - dy$ (i.e., the smaller will be the length of the line segment RQ).

An equation of the line PT is

$$y = f(x_0) + f'(x_0)(x - x_0)$$

and the ordinate of R is $f(x_0) + dy$. Observe that when we approximate $f(x_0 + \Delta x)$ by $f(x_0) + dy$, we are approximating the ordinate of the point Q on the curve by the ordinate of the point R on the tangent line. Thus using differentials to estimate function values is essentially the same process as linear approximation; only the notation is different.

▶ **EXAMPLE 5** Use differentials to approximate the volume of a spherical shell whose inner radius is 4 in. and whose thickness is $\frac{1}{16}$ in.

Solution We consider the volume of a spherical shell as an increment of the volume of a sphere. See Figure 15. Let r inches be the radius of the sphere, V cubic inches be the volume of the sphere, and ΔV cubic inches be the volume of the spherical shell.

$$V = \tfrac{4}{3}\pi r^3 \qquad dV = 4\pi r^2 \, dr$$

Substituting $r = 4$ and $dr = \frac{1}{16}$ into the above we obtain

$$dV = 4\pi(4)^2 \tfrac{1}{16}$$
$$= 4\pi$$

Therefore $\Delta V \approx 4\pi$.

<u>Conclusion:</u> The approximate volume of the spherical shell is 4π in.^{3} ◀

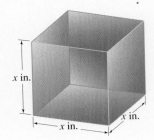

FIGURE 15

▶ **EXAMPLE 6** A closed container in the form of a cube having a volume of 1000 in.^{3} is to be made by using six equal squares of material costing 20 cents per square inch. How accurately must the side of each square be measured so that the total cost of material will be correct to within $3.00?

Solution Figure 16 shows the cube where x inches is the length of a side of the squares and, consequently, the length of the edge of the cube. Let C dollars be the total cost of material. Because the total area of the six squares is $6x^2$ square inches, and the cost of the material is $0.20 per square inch,

$$C = 0.20(6x^2)$$
$$C = 1.2x^2 \tag{12}$$

For the volume of the cube to be 1000 in.^{3}, $x^3 = 1000$; that is, $x = 10$. When $x = 10$, we obtain from (12), $C = 120$. Thus, the cost of the material will be exactly $120 if the length of a side of the squares is 10 in. Because the total cost of material is to be correct to within $3.00, we wish to find $|\Delta x|$ so that $|\Delta C| \le 3$. We shall use the differential dC to approximate ΔC. From (12)

$$dC = 2.4x \, dx$$
$$\Delta C \approx 2.4x \, \Delta x$$

With $x = 10$,

$$|\Delta C| \approx 24|\Delta x|$$

FIGURE 16

Because we want $|\Delta C| \leq 3$, we shall determine when

$$24|\Delta x| \leq 3$$
$$|\Delta x| \leq \tfrac{3}{24}$$
$$|\Delta x| \leq 0.125$$

<u>Conclusion:</u> The side of each square should be measured to within 0.125 in. so that the total cost of material will be correct to within \$3.00.

◀

In Section 2.4 we proved theorems for computing derivatives of algebraic functions. We now restate these theorems with the Leibniz notation, and along with the formula for the derivative we have a corresponding formula for the differential. In these formulas, u and v are functions of x, and it is understood that the formulas hold provided $\dfrac{du}{dx}$ and $\dfrac{dv}{dx}$ exist. When c appears, it is a constant.

$$\text{I} \quad \frac{d(c)}{dx} = 0 \qquad\qquad \text{I}' \quad d(c) = 0$$

$$\text{II} \quad \frac{d(x^n)}{dx} = nx^{n-1} \qquad\qquad \text{II}' \quad d(x^n) = nx^{n-1}\, dx$$

$$\text{III} \quad \frac{d(cu)}{dx} = c\frac{du}{dx} \qquad\qquad \text{III}' \quad d(cu) = c\, du$$

$$\text{IV} \quad \frac{d(u+v)}{dx} = \frac{du}{dx} + \frac{dv}{dx} \qquad\qquad \text{IV}' \quad d(u+v) = du + dv$$

$$\text{V} \quad \frac{d(uv)}{dx} = u\frac{dv}{dx} + v\frac{du}{dx} \qquad\qquad \text{V}' \quad d(uv) = u\, dv + v\, du$$

$$\text{VI} \quad \frac{d\left(\dfrac{u}{v}\right)}{dx} = \frac{v\dfrac{du}{dx} - u\dfrac{dv}{dx}}{v^2} \qquad \text{VI}' \quad d\left(\frac{u}{v}\right) = \frac{v\, du - u\, dv}{v^2}$$

$$\text{VII} \quad \frac{d(u^n)}{dx} = nu^{n-1}\frac{du}{dx} \qquad\qquad \text{VII}' \quad d(u^n) = nu^{n-1}\, du$$

We extend the operation of differentiation to include the process of computing the differential as well as computing the derivative. If $y = f(x)$, dy can be found either by applying formulas I′–VII′ or by finding $f'(x)$ and multiplying it by dx.

EXERCISES 3.10

In Exercises 1 through 4, use Newton's method to find the real root of the equation to four decimal places.

1. $x^3 - 4x^2 - 2 = 0$

2. $6x^3 + 9x + 1 = 0$

3. $x^5 - x + 1 = 0$

4. $x^5 + x - 1 = 0$

In Exercises 5 through 10, use Newton's method to find, to the nearest thousandth, the approximate value of the indicated root.

5. $x^3 - 4x - 8 = 0$; the positive root

6. $x^3 - 2x + 7 = 0$; the negative root

7. $x^4 - 10x + 5 = 0$; the smallest positive root

8. $x^4 - 10x + 5 = 0$; the largest positive root

9. $2x^4 - 2x^3 + x^2 + 3x - 4 = 0$; the negative root

10. $x^4 + x^3 - 3x^2 - x - 4 = 0$; the positive root

In Exercises 11 through 14, use Newton's method to find the value of the radical to five decimal places.

11. $\sqrt{3}$ by solving the equation $x^2 - 3 = 0$

12. $\sqrt{10}$ by solving the equation $x^2 - 10 = 0$

13. $\sqrt[3]{6}$ by solving the equation $x^3 - 6 = 0$

14. $\sqrt[3]{7}$ by solving the equation $x^3 - 7 = 0$

In Exercises 15 through 18, use Newton's method to find to four decimal places the x coordinate of the point of intersection in the first quadrant of the graphs of the two equations.

15. $y = x$; $y = \cos x$

16. $y = \frac{1}{2}x$; $y = \sin x$

17. $y = x^2$; $y = \sin x$

18. $y = x^2$; $y = \cos x$

In Exercises 19 through 24, for the given function f do the following: (a) Find the linear approximation of f(x) at $x = 1$; (b) support your answer in part (a) graphically; (c) compare the values of f(x) computed from the linear approximation in part (a) with the function values computed from the given equations when x is 0.9, 0.99, 1, 1.01, and 1.1.

19. $f(x) = x^2$

20. $f(x) = x^3$

21. $f(x) = 2\sqrt{x}$

22. $f(x) = \dfrac{2}{x^2}$

23. $f(x) = \cos x$

24. $f(x) = \sin x$

In Exercises 25 through 28, (a) find dy and Δy for the values of x and Δx. (b) Sketch the graph and indicate the line segments whose lengths are dy and Δy.

25. $y = x^2$; $x = 2$ and $\Delta x = 0.5$

26. $y = x^3$; $x = 2$ and $\Delta x = 0.5$

27. $y = \sqrt[3]{x}$; $x = 8$ and $\Delta x = 1$

28. $y = \sqrt{x}$; $x = 4$ and $\Delta x = 1$

In Exercises 29 through 34, find (a) Δy; (b) dy; (c) $\Delta y - dy$.

29. $y = x^2 - 3x$; $x = 2$; $\Delta x = 0.03$

30. $y = x^2 - 3x$; $x = -1$; $\Delta x = 0.02$

31. $y = \dfrac{1}{x}$; $x = -2$; $\Delta x = -0.1$

32. $y = \dfrac{1}{x}$; $x = 3$; $\Delta x = -0.2$

33. $y = x^3 + 1$; $x = 1$; $\Delta x = -0.5$

34. $y = x^3 + 1$; $x = -1$; $\Delta x = 0.1$

In Exercises 35 through 42, find dy.

35. $y = (3x^2 - 2x + 1)^3$

36. $y = \dfrac{3x}{x^2 + 2}$

37. $y = x^2\sqrt{2x + 3}$

38. $y = \sqrt{4 - x^2}$

39. $y = \dfrac{2 + \cos x}{2 - \sin x}$

40. $y = x^2 \sin \dfrac{1}{x} - x \cos \dfrac{1}{x}$

41. $y = \tan^2 x \sec^2 x$

42. $y = \cot 2x \csc 2x$

43. The measurement of an edge of a cube is found to be 15 cm with a possible error of 0.01 cm. Use differentials to find the approximate error in computing from this measurement: **(a)** the volume; **(b)** the area of one of the faces.

44. A metal box in the form of a cube is to have an interior volume of 1000 cm^3. The six sides are to be made of metal $\frac{1}{2}$ cm thick. If the cost of the metal to be used is $0.20 per cubic centimeter, use differentials to find the approximate cost of the metal to be used in the manufacture of the box.

45. An open cylindrical tank is to have an outside coating of thickness 2 cm. If the inner radius is 6 m and the altitude is 10 m, find by differentials the approximate amount of coating material to be used.

46. The stem of a particular mushroom is cylindrical in shape, and a stem of height 2 cm and radius r centimeters has a volume of V cubic centimeters, where $V = 2\pi r^2$. Use differentials to find the approximate increase in the volume of the stem when the radius increases from 0.4 cm to 0.5 cm.

47. A burn on a person's skin is in the shape of a circle such that if r centimeters is the radius and A square centimeters is the area of the burn, then $A = \pi r^2$. Use differentials to find the approximate decrease in the area of the burn when the radius decreases from 1 cm to 0.8 cm.

48. A certain bacterial cell is spherical in shape such that if r micrometers is its radius and V cubic micrometers is its volume, then $V = \frac{4}{3}\pi r^3$. Use differentials to find the approximate increase in the volume of the cell when the radius increases from 2.2 μm to 2.3 μm.

49. A tumor in a person's body is spherical in shape such that if r centimeters is the radius and V cubic centimeters is the volume of the tumor, then $V = \frac{4}{3}\pi r^3$. Use differentials to find the approximate increase in the volume of the tumor when the radius increases from 1.5 cm to 1.6 cm.

50. If t seconds is the time for one complete swing of a simple pendulum of length l feet, then $4\pi^2 l = gt^2$,

where $g = 32.2$. A clock having a pendulum of length 1 ft gains 5 min each day. Find the approximate amount by which the pendulum should be lengthened to correct the inaccuracy.

51. The measure of the electrical resistance of a wire is proportional to the measure of its length and inversely proportional to the square of the measure of its diameter. Suppose the resistance of a wire of given length is computed from a measurement of the diameter with a possible 2 percent error. Find the possible percent error in the computed value of the resistance.

52. A contractor agrees to paint both sides of 1000 circular signs each of radius 3 m. Upon receiving the signs it is discovered that the radius of each sign is 1 cm too large. Use differentials to find the approximate percent increase of paint that will be needed.

53. If the possible error in the measurement of the volume of a gas is 0.1 ft^3 and the allowable error in the pressure is $0.001C$ lb/ft^2, find the size of the smallest container for which Boyle's law (Exercise 23 in Exercises 2.10) holds.

54. For the adiabatic law for the expansion of air (Exercise 24 in Exercises 2.10), prove that

$$\frac{dP}{P} = -1.4\frac{dV}{V}$$

55. Show that if Boyle's law holds, then

$$\frac{dP}{P} = -\frac{dV}{V}$$

56. A tightly wound flexible tape of length L feet, fastened at the top of an incline that makes an angle θ with the horizontal, is allowed to unwind down the incline. See the accompanying figure. If T seconds is the time for the tape to completely unwind, then

$$T = \sqrt{\frac{3L}{32}}\, \csc \theta$$

Show that

$$\frac{dT}{T} = -\frac{d\theta}{2 \tan \theta}$$

57. Equations of the form $\tan x + ax = 0$ arise in heat conduction problems. The positive roots of the equation in increasing order are $\alpha_1, \alpha_2, \alpha_3, \ldots$. If $a = 1$, find α_1 and α_2 to four decimal places.

58. Follow the instructions of Exercise 57 if $a = -2$.

In Exercises 59 and 60, obtain an approximation for π to five decimal places by using Newton's method to solve the equation.

59. $\tan x = 0$ **60.** $\cos x + 1 = 0$

61. Explain how the concept of the differential is used to approximate function values.

CHAPTER 3 REVIEW

▶ SUGGESTIONS FOR REVIEW OF CHAPTER 3

1. Explain the difference between a relative extremum and an absolute extremum of a function.

2. Make up an example of a function f having a relative extremum at the point $P(c, f(c))$ and for which the following condition is satisfied:
   (a) the tangent line to the graph of f at P is horizontal;
   (b) the tangent line to the graph of f at P is vertical;
   (c) the graph of f has no tangent line at P.

3. State the extreme-value theorem.

4. Describe how you determine the absolute extrema of a function satisfying the extreme-value theorem.

5. Make up an example of a function satisfying the extreme-value theorem and having the indicated property:
   (a) the function has no critical numbers;
   (b) only one absolute extremum occurs at a critical number;
   (c) both absolute extrema occur at critical numbers;
   (d) the function has exactly two critical numbers but neither absolute extremum occurs at a critical number.

6. Make up an example of a function satisfying the extreme-value theorem and for which the absolute min-

imum value occurs at a critical number c where $f'(c)$ does not exist and

(a) the graph of f has no tangent line at the point $(c, f(c))$;

(b) the graph of f has a vertical tangent line at $(c, f(c))$.

7. What guidelines should you follow when defining the variables used to obtain a function as a mathematical model for a word problem?

8. Why must you state the domain of the function you use as a mathematical model to solve a word problem?

9. To apply the extreme-value theorem to solve a word problem involving an absolute extremum, what requirements must be satisfied by the function you use as a mathematical model?

10. Outline the procedure you use for solving a word problem involving an absolute extremum on a closed interval.

11. State and give the geometric interpretation of Rolle's theorem.

12. State and give the geometric interpretation of the mean-value theorem.

13. Explain why Rolle's theorem is a special case of the mean-value theorem.

14. Both Rolle's theorem and the mean-value theorem require the function f to be continuous on the closed interval $[a, b]$ but differentiable only on the open interval (a, b). Explain why the theorems hold when either or both $f'(a)$ and $f'(b)$ do not exist.

15. Why is the existence of the number c guaranteed by the conclusion of the mean-value theorem more important than the actual value of c? In your answer state situations where only the existence, not the value, of c matters.

16. Make up an example of a function satisfying the hypothesis of the mean-value theorem but for which we cannot find the exact value of the number c guaranteed by the conclusion.

17. Define: the function f is increasing on an interval. How do we determine analytically that f is increasing on the closed interval $[a, b]$?

18. Define: the function f is decreasing on an interval. How do we determine analytically that f is decreasing on the closed interval $[a, b]$?

19. State the first-derivative test for relative extrema.

20. How do we determine analytically the relative extrema of a function?

21. Make up an example of a differentiable function that has exactly two relative extrema. Sketch the graph of your function.

22. Make up an example of a nonlinear differentiable function that has no relative extrema. Sketch the graph of your function.

23. Make up an example of a continuous function that is differentiable everywhere except at the origin, has a relative minimum value at the origin, and whose graph does not have a tangent line at the origin. Sketch the graph of your function.

24. Make up an example of a continuous function that is differentiable everywhere except at the origin, has a relative minimum value at the origin, and whose graph has a tangent line at the origin. Sketch the graph of your function.

25. Make up an example of a continuous function that is differentiable everywhere except at the origin, and such that f does not have a relative extremum at the origin. Sketch the graph of your function.

26. Define: the graph of the function f is concave upward at the point $(c, f(c))$. How do we determine analytically that the graph of a function is concave upward at a particular point?

27. Define: the graph of the function f is concave downward at the point $(c, f(c))$. How do we determine analytically that the graph of a function is concave downward at a particular point?

28. Define: the point $(c, f(c))$ is a point of inflection of the graph of the function f. How do we determine analytically points of inflection of the graph of a function?

29. Sketch the graph of a function f for which the graph has a point of inflection at $(c, f(c))$ where $f''(c) = 0$, $f'(c) = 1$, $f''(x) > 0$ if $x < c$, and $f''(x) < 0$ if $x > c$.

30. Sketch the graph of a function f for which the graph has a point of inflection at $(c, f(c))$ where $f''(c) = 0$, $f'(c) = 0$, $f''(x) < 0$ if $x < c$, and $f''(x) > 0$ if $x > c$.

31. Sketch the graph of a function f for which the graph has a point of inflection at $(c, f(c))$ where $f'(c)$ does not exist, $f''(x) > 0$ if $x < c$, and $f''(x) < 0$ if $x > c$.

32. State the second-derivative test for relative extrema.

33. When is the second-derivative test easier to apply than the first-derivative test? When is the first-derivative test easier to apply? Can either test always be applied? Explain.

34. Make up an example and sketch the graph of a function f for which $f(0)$, $f'(0)$, and $f''(0)$ are each 0 where
(a) f has a relative minimum value at 0;
(b) f has a relative maximum value at 0;
(c) f does not have a relative extremum at 0.

35. Define precisely using ϵ and N notation each of the following: (a) $\lim_{x \to +\infty} f(x) = L$; (b) $\lim_{x \to -\infty} f(x) = L$.

State in words what each of these definitions means without using ϵ and N notation and without using the words *limit, approaches, infinity, increasing without bound,* or *decreasing without bound.*

36. How do you evaluate the limit of a rational function as x either increases or decreases without bound?

37. Make up an example of a function f demonstrating each of the following: **(a)** $\lim\limits_{x \to +\infty} f(x) = 1$; **(b)** $\lim\limits_{x \to -\infty} f(x) = 5$; **(c)** $\lim\limits_{x \to +\infty} f(x) = -2$; **(d)** $\lim\limits_{x \to -\infty} f(x) = 0$; **(e)** $\lim\limits_{x \to +\infty} f(x) = +\infty$; **(f)** $\lim\limits_{x \to +\infty} f(x) = -\infty$.

38. Define a horizontal asymptote of the graph of a function.

39. How can you find any horizontal asymptotes of the graph of a function?

40. Make up an example of a function whose graph has the line $x = 5$ as a vertical asymptote and the line $y = -4$ as a horizontal asymptote.

41. If the line $x = c$ is a vertical asymptote of the graph of the derivative of the function f, what are the possibilities for the behavior of the graph of f at the point $(c, f(c))$? What additional information obtained from the graph of the derivative of f will guarantee a specific behavior of the graph of f at $(c, f(c))$?

42. If the graph of the derivative of the function f reveals that f has a relative extremum at c, what are the possibilities for the behavior of the graph of f at the point $(c, f(c))$? What additional information obtained from the graph of the derivative of f will guarantee a specific behavior of the graph of f at $(c, f(c))$?

43. What is an oblique asymptote of the graph of a function?

44. When does the graph of a rational function have an oblique asymptote, and how do you find an equation of the asymptote?

45. Summarize the steps you should follow when sketching the graph of the function f defined by the equation $y = f(x)$.

46. State a theorem other than the extreme-value theorem that guarantees that a relative extremum of a function on an interval is an absolute extremum of the function on the interval. When solving a problem involving absolute extrema, under what conditions would you use the theorem you just stated instead of the extreme-value theorem?

47. **(a)** Make up an example of a function for which you can apply the theorem stated in the above exercise to determine an absolute extremum, but for which you cannot apply the extreme-value theorem. **(b)** Make up an example of a function for which you can apply either the theorem stated in the above exercise or the extreme-value theorem to determine an absolute extremum on an interval.

48. How do you apply Newton's method to find the zeros of a function? In your answer state the formula for determining x_{n+1} from x_n.

49. How are function values estimated by a linear approximation? What condition (or conditions) must the function f satisfy at the number x_0 in order to estimate $f(x_0)$ by a linear approximation?

50. If $y = f(x)$, define the differentials dy and dx.

51. How are the differential dx and the increment Δx related? How are the differential dy and the increment Δy related?

52. Why can the derivative of a function be expressed as the quotient of two differentials?

53. For what function are the differentials of the independent and dependent variables equal? Show this equality geometrically on a figure containing the graph of the function.

▶ MISCELLANEOUS EXERCISES FOR CHAPTER 3

In Exercises 1 through 10, (a) sketch the graph of the function on the indicated interval. (b) Find the absolute extrema of the function on the interval, if there are any, and determine the values of x at which the absolute extrema occur.

1. $f(x) = \sqrt{5 + x}$; $[-5, +\infty)$
2. $f(x) = \sqrt{4 - x^2}$; $(-2, 2)$
3. $f(x) = |9 - x^2|$; $[-2, 4]$
4. $f(x) = |9 - x^2|$; $[-1, 5]$
5. $f(x) = \dfrac{3}{x - 2}$; $[0, 4]$
6. $f(x) = \dfrac{8}{3 - x}$; $[1, 3]$
7. $f(x) = 2 \sin 3x$; $[-\frac{1}{3}\pi, \frac{1}{3}\pi]$
8. $f(x) = 4 \cos^2 2x$; $[0, \frac{3}{4}\pi]$
9. $f(x) = \begin{cases} 2x + 3 & \text{if } -2 \leq x < 1 \\ x^2 + 4 & \text{if } 1 \leq x \leq 2 \end{cases}$; $[-2, 2]$
10. $f(x) = \begin{cases} 9 - x^2 & \text{if } -3 \leq x < 3 \\ 5x - 15 & \text{if } 3 \leq x \leq 5 \end{cases}$; $[-3, 5]$

In Exercises 11 through 14, (i) estimate on your graphics calculator the absolute extrema of the function on the indicated interval. (ii) Confirm your answers analytically.

11. (a) $f(x) = x^4 - 12x^2 + 36; [-2, 3]$
   (b) $f(x) = x^4 - 12x^2 + 36; [-4, 2]$
12. (a) $f(x) = x^5 - 9x^2 + 5; [-1, 2]$
   (b) $f(x) = x^5 - 9x^2 + 5; [-2, 1]$
13. $f(x) = \sin x + \cos x; [-1, 1]$
14. $f(x) = 2 \cos x + x; [-1, 3]$

In Exercises 15 and 16, verify that the three conditions of the hypothesis of Rolle's theorem are satisfied by the function on the indicated interval. Then find a suitable value for c that satisfies the conclusion of Rolle's theorem. Support your choice of c graphically by plotting in the same window the graphs of f and the horizontal tangent line at (c, f(c)).

15. $f(x) = x^3 - x^2 - 4x + 4; [-2, 1]$
16. $f(x) = 2 \sin 3x; [0, \frac{1}{3}\pi]$

In Exercises 17 through 20, verify that the hypothesis of the mean-value theorem is satisfied by the function on the indicated interval [a, b]. Then find a suitable choice for c that satisfies the conclusion of the mean-value theorem. Support your choice of c by plotting in the same window the graph of f on the closed interval [a, b], the tangent line at (c, f(c)), and the secant line through the points (a, f(a)) and (b, f(b)) and showing that the tangent line and secant line are parallel.

17. $f(x) \sqrt{3 - x}; [-6, -1]$
18. $f(x) = x^3; [-2, 2]$
19. $f(x) = 4 \cos x; [\frac{1}{3}\pi, \frac{2}{3}\pi]$
20. $f(x) = 3 \sin \frac{1}{2}x; [0, \pi]$

21. (a) If f is a polynomial function and $f(a), f(b), f'(a)$ and $f'(b)$ are zero, use Rolle's theorem to prove that there are at least two numbers in the open interval (a, b) that are roots of the equation $f''(x) = 0$.
   (b) Show that the function defined by
   $$f(x) = (x^2 - 4)^2$$
   satisfies part (a) if the interval (a, b) is $(-2, 2)$.
22. If f is the function defined by $f(x) = |2x - 4| - 6$, then $f(-1) = 0$ and $f(5) = 0$. However, $f'(x)$ is never 0. Show why Rolle's theorem does not apply.

For the functions in Exercises 23 and 24, there is no number c in the open interval (a, b) that satisfies the conclusion of the mean-value theorem. In each exercise, determine which part of the hypothesis of the mean-value theorem fails to hold. Sketch the graph of f and the line through the points (a, f(a)) and (b, f(b)).

23. $f(x) = \begin{cases} 4 - x^2 & \text{if } x < 1 \\ 6 - 3x & \text{if } 1 \le x \end{cases}; a = 0, b = 3$
24. $f(x) = 2(x - 2)^{2/3}; a = -6, b = 3$

In Exercises 25 through 32, (a) plot the graph; determine from the graph (b) the relative extrema of f, (c) the values of x at which the relative extrema occur, (d) the intervals on which f is increasing, and (e) the intervals on which f is decreasing. Confirm analytically the information you obtained graphically.

25. $f(x) = x^3 + 3x^2 - 4$
26. $f(x) = x^3 + 2x^2 + x - 5$
27. $f(x) = (x - 3)^{5/3} + 1$
28. $f(x) = (x + 2)^{4/3} - 3$
29. $f(x) = x - \tan x; x \in (-\frac{1}{2}\pi, \frac{1}{2}\pi)$
30. $f(x) = \sin 2x - \cos 2x; x \in [-\frac{3}{8}\pi, \frac{5}{8}\pi]$
31. $f(x) = (x + 1)^{2/3}(x - 3)^2$
32. $f(x) = x\sqrt{25 - x^2}$

In Exercises 33 through 36, do the following analytically: (a) find the relative extrema of f; (b) determine the values of x at which the relative extrema occur; (c) determine the intervals on which f is increasing; (d) determine the intervals on which f is decreasing; (e) find the points of inflection of the graph of f; (f) determine where the graph is concave upward; (g) determine where the graph is concave downward. (h) Sketch the graph of the function from your answers in parts (a)–(g).

33. $f(x) = (x - 4)^2(x + 2)^3$
34. $f(x) = (x - 1)^3(x - 3)$
35. $f(x) = \begin{cases} (1 - x)^3 & \text{if } x \le 1 \\ (x - 1)^3 & \text{if } 1 < x \end{cases}$
36. $f(x) = \begin{cases} x^3 - 3x & \text{if } x < 2 \\ 6 - x^2 & \text{if } 2 \le x \end{cases}$

In Exercises 37 through 44, estimate on your graphics calculator the points of inflection of the graph of the given function and where the graph is concave upward and concave downward. Confirm your estimates analytically.

37. The function of Exercise 25
38. The function of Exercise 26
39. The function of Exercise 27
40. The function of Exercise 28
41. The function of Exercise 29

42. The function of Exercise 30

43. The function of Exercise 31

44. The function of Exercise 32

In Exercises 45 and 46, sketch a portion of the graph of a function f through the point where $x = c$ if the given conditions are satisfied. Assume that f is continuous on some open interval containing c.

45. (a) $f'(x) > 0$ if $x < c$; $f'(x) < 0$ if $x > c$; $f''(x) < 0$ if $x < c$; $f''(x) < 0$ if $x > c$

   (b) $f'(x) < 0$ if $x < c$; $f'(x) > 0$ if $x > c$; $f''(x) < 0$ if $x < c$; $f''(x) < 0$ if $x > c$

   (c) $f'(x) > 0$ if $x < c$; $f'(x) < 0$ if $x > c$; $f''(x) < 0$ if $x < c$; $f''(x) > 0$ if $x > c$

   (d) $f'(c) = 0$; $f''(c) = 0$; $f'(x) < 0$ if $x < c$; $f'(x) < 0$ if $x > c$; $f''(x) > 0$ if $x < c$; $f''(x) < 0$ if $x > c$

46. (a) $f'(c) = -2$; $f''(c) = 0$; $f''(x) < 0$ if $x < c$; $f''(x) > 0$ if $x > c$

   (b) $f'(c)$ does not exist; $f''(x) > 0$ if $x < c$; $f''(x) > 0$ if $x > c$

   (c) $f'(x) < 0$ if $x < c$; $f'(x) > 0$ if $x > c$; $f''(x) > 0$ if $x < c$; $f''(x) < 0$ if $x > c$

   (d) $\lim_{x \to c^-} f'(x) = 1$; $\lim_{x \to c^+} f'(x) = +\infty$; $f''(x) > 0$ if $x < c$; $f''(x) < 0$ if $x > c$

In Exercises 47 and 48, sketch a portion of the graph of a function f through the points $(a, f(a))$, $(b, f(b))$, $(c, f(c))$, and $(d, f(d))$ if the given conditions are satisfied. Also draw a segment of the tangent line at each of these points, if there is a tangent line. Assume that $a < b < c < d$ and that f is continuous on some open interval containing a and d.

47. (a) $f'(a) = 0$; $f'(b) = -1$; $f'(c)$ does not exist; $f'(d) = 0$; $f''(x) < 0$ if $x < b$; $f''(x) > 0$ if $b < x < c$; $f''(x) < 0$ if $x > c$

   (b) $f'(a) = 0$; $f''(a) = 0$; $f'(b) = 1$; $f''(b) = 0$; $f'(c) = 0$; $f'(d)$ does not exist; $f''(x) < 0$ if $x < a$; $f''(x) > 0$ if $a < x < b$; $f''(x) < 0$ if $b < x < d$; $f''(x) > 0$ if $x > d$

48. (a) $f'(a) = 0$; $f'(b) = -1$; $f''(b) = 0$; $f'(c) = 0$; $f''(c) = 0$; $f'(d) = -1$; $f''(d) = 0$; $f''(x) < 0$ if $x < b$; $f''(x) > 0$ if $b < x < c$; $f''(x) < 0$ if $c < x < d$; $f''(x) > 0$ if $x > d$

   (b) $f'(a)$ does not exist; $f'(b) = 0$; $f'(c) = 2$; $f''(c) = 0$; $f'(d) = 0$; $f''(x) < 0$ if $x < a$; $f''(x) > 0$ if $a < x < c$; $f''(x) < 0$ if $x > c$

In Exercises 49 through 52, the accompanying figure shows the graph of the derivative of a function f whose domain is the set of all real numbers and which is contin-

uous everywhere. From the graph, determine the following information and incorporate this information in a table similar to the tables in Section 3.6: (i) the intervals on which f is increasing; (ii) the intervals on which f is decreasing; (iii) the relative extrema of f; (iv) where the graph of f is concave upward; (v) where the graph of f is concave downward; (vi) the points of inflection of the graph of f. Sketch the graph of a function f having the properties in the table if the only zeros of f are those stated.

49. Zeros of f are -4 and 0.

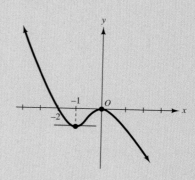

50. Zeros of f are 3 and 5.

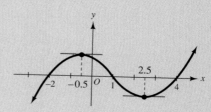

51. Zeros of f are 0 and 3.

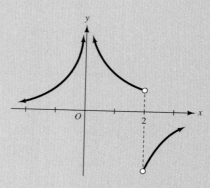

52. Zero of f is -1.

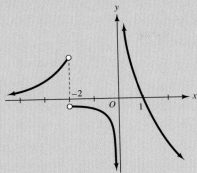

In Exercises 53 through 56, the graph of the function f and segments of the horizontal and inflectional tangents appear in the accompanying figure. Determine the follow-ing information from the figure and incorporate this in-formation in a table similar to the tables in Section 3.6: (i) the intervals on which f is increasing; (ii) the intervals on which f is decreasing; (iii) the relative extrema of f; (iv) where the graph of f is concave upward; (v) where the graph of f is concave downward; (vi) the points of inflection of the graph of f. From the table sketch possible graphs of f' and f''.

53.

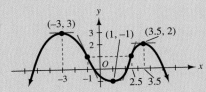

54.

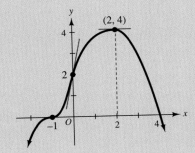

55.

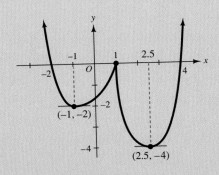

56.

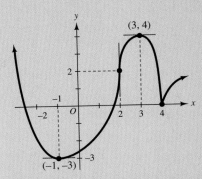

In Exercises 57 through 60, find the limit and support your answer graphically.

57. $\lim\limits_{x \to +\infty} \dfrac{3x^2 + 2x - 5}{x^2 + 4}$

58. $\lim\limits_{x \to -\infty} \dfrac{4x - 3}{5x^2 - x + 1}$

59. $\lim\limits_{x \to -\infty} \dfrac{x^2 + 5}{2x - 4}$

60. $\lim\limits_{x \to +\infty} \left(\dfrac{8x^3 + 7x - 2}{7x^3 + 3x^2 + 5x} \right)^2$

In Exercises 61 and 62, do the following: (a) Plot the graph of the function f and make a statement regarding the apparent behavior of $f(x)$ as x increases without bound. (b) Confirm your answer in part (a) analytically by computing $\lim\limits_{x \to +\infty} f(x)$.

61. $f(x) = \sqrt{x + 1} - \sqrt{x}$

62. $f(x) = \sqrt{x^2 + x} - \sqrt{x^2 + 4}$

In Exercises 63 through 66, find the asymptotes of the graph of the function. Support your results by plotting the graph and the asymptotes in the same window.

63. $f(x) = \dfrac{5x^2}{x^2 - 4}$

64. $f(x) = \dfrac{x}{x^2 - 1}$

65. $f(x) = \dfrac{x^2}{x - 3}$

66. $f(x) = \dfrac{x^2 + 9}{x}$

In Exercises 67 through 70, (a) plot the graphs of f, $NDER(f(x), x)$, and $NDER2(f(x), x)$ in separate windows and estimate the following: (i) the intervals on which f is increasing and those on which f is decreasing; (ii) the rel-ative extrema of f; (iii) where the graph of f is concave upward and where it is concave downward; (iv) any points of inflection of the graph of f. (b) Confirm your es-timates in part (a) analytically and incorporate the infor-mation in a table similar to Table 4 of Section 3.8. From the information in this table sketch the graph of f and compare it to your graph of f plotted in part (a).

67. $f(x) = 2x^4 + 5x^3 - 21x^2 - 45x + 27$

68. $f(x) = 3x^4 + 8x^3 + 3x^2 - 2x$

69. $f(x) = 6\sqrt[3]{x} - x$

70. $f(x) = 2x^{1/3} + x^{4/3}$

71. Find the absolute maximum value attained by the function f if $f(x) = A \sin kx + B \cos kx$, where A, B, and k are positive constants.

72. If $f(x) = ax^3 + bx^2$, determine a and b so that the graph of f will have a point of inflection at $(2, 16)$. Support your answer graphically.

73. If $f(x) = ax^3 + bx^2 + cx$, determine a, b, and c so that the graph of f will have a point of inflection at $(1, -1)$ and so that the slope of the inflectional tangent there will be -3. Support your answer graphically.

74. If $f(x) = \dfrac{x+1}{x^2+1}$, prove that the graph of f has three points of inflection that are collinear. Support your answers by plotting the graph of f and the line containing the points of inflection.

75. If $f(x) = x|x|$, plot the graph of f and prove analytically that the origin is a point of inflection.

76. Let $f(x) = x^n$, where n is a positive integer.
   (a) Prove that the graph of f has a point of inflection at the origin if and only if n is odd and $n > 1$.
   (b) Prove that if n is even, f has a relative minimum value at 0.

In Exercises 77 and 78, confirm analytically your estimate obtained on your graphics calculator in part (d) of the indicated exercise in Miscellaneous Exercises for Chapter 1.

77. **(a)** Exercise 103; **(b)** Exercise 105

78. **(a)** Exercise 104; **(b)** Exercise 106

79. How many items should the manufacturer in Exercise 57 of Miscellaneous Exercises for Chapter 2 produce each week to maximize profit?

80. Find the dimensions of an open box, having a square base and a volume of k cubic inches, that can be constructed with the least amount of material.

81. Two towns A and B are to get their water supply from the same pumping station to be located on the bank of a straight river that is 15 km from town A and 10 km from town B. The points on the river nearest to A and B are 20 km apart and A and B are on the same side of the river.
   (a) Use your graphics calculator to estimate where the pumping station should be located so that the least amount of piping is required.
   (b) Confirm your estimate in part (a) analytically.

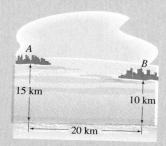

82. A manufacturer offers to deliver to a dealer 300 chairs at $360 per chair and to reduce the price per chair on the entire order by $1 for each additional chair over 300. Find the dollar total involved in the largest possible transaction between the manufacturer and the dealer under these circumstances.

83. Under a monopoly (see Exercise 19 in Exercises 3.9) x units are demanded daily when p dollars is the price per unit and $x^2 + p = 320$. If $20x$ dollars is the total cost of producing x units, find the maximum daily total profit. Support your answer graphically.

84. To construct a closed tin in the form of a right-circular cylinder having a volume of 27 in.^{3}, the circular top and bottom are cut from square pieces of tin.
   (a) Use your graphics calculator to estimate the radius of the can if the least amount of tin is to be used in its manufacture. Include the tin that is wasted when obtaining the top and bottom.
   (b) Confirm your estimate in part (a) analytically and then find what the height of the can should be.

85. If $100x$ units of a particular commodity are demanded when p dollars is the price per unit, $x^2 + p^2 = 36$. Find the maximum total revenue.

86. In a town of population 11,000 the rate of growth of an epidemic is jointly proportional to the number of people infected and the number of people not infected. Determine the number of people infected when the epidemic is growing at a maximum rate.

87. Because of various restrictions, the size of a particular community is limited to 3000 inhabitants, and the rate of increase of the population is jointly proportional to its size and the difference between 3000 and its size. Determine the size of the population for which the rate of growth of the population is a maximum.

88. Find the shortest distance from the point $P(0, 4)$ to a point on the curve $x^2 - y^2 = 16$, and find the point on the curve that is closest to P.

89. A firm operating under perfect competition (see the instructions for Exercises 17 and 18 in Exercises 3.9) manufactures and sells portable radios. The firm can sell at a price of $75 per radio all the radios it produces. If x radios are manufactured each day and $C(x)$ dollars is the daily total cost of production, then $C(x) = x^2 + 25x + 100$. How many radios should be produced each day for the firm to have the greatest daily total profit? What is the greatest daily total profit?

90. Two particles start their motion at the same time. One particle is moving along a horizontal line and its equation of motion is $x = t^2 - 2t$, where x centimeters is the directed distance of the particle from the origin at t seconds. The other particle is moving along a vertical line that intersects the horizontal line at the origin, and its equation of motion is $y = t^2 - 2$, where y centimeters is the directed distance of the particle from the origin at t seconds. Find when the directed distance between the two particles is least, and their velocities at that time.

91. A ladder is to reach over a fence $\frac{27}{8}$ m high to a wall 8 m behind the fence. Find the length of the shortest ladder that may be used.

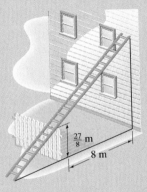

92. Solve Exercise 91 if the fence is h meters high and the wall is w meters behind the fence.

93. Find the volume of the largest right-circular cylinder that can be inscribed in a right-circular cone having a radius of 4 in. and a height of 8 in.

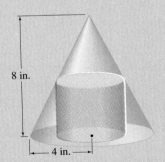

94. A tent is to be in the shape of a cone. Find the ratio of the measure of the radius to the measure of the altitude for a tent of given volume to require the least material.

95. Find the dimensions of the right-circular cone of least volume that can be circumscribed about a right-circular cylinder of radius r centimeters and height h centimeters.

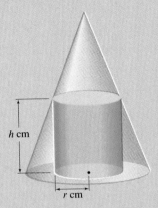

96. One of the acute angles of a triangle is to have a radian measure of $\frac{1}{6}\pi$, and the side opposite this angle is to have a length of 10 in. Prove that of all the triangles satisfying these requirements, the one having the maximum area is isosceles. *Hint:* Express the measure of the area of the triangle in terms of trigonometric functions of one of the other acute angles.

97. In a warehouse, goods weighing 1000 lb are transported along a level floor by securing a heavy rope under a low mobile platform and pulling it with a motorized vehicle. If the rope is directed at an angle of θ radians with the plane of the floor, then the force of magnitude F pounds along the rope is given by

$$F = \frac{1000k}{k \sin \theta + \cos \theta}$$

where k is the constant coefficient of friction and $0 < k < 1$. If $0 \leq \theta \leq \frac{1}{2}\pi$, show that F is least when $\tan \theta = k$.

98. **(a)** Show that among all the rectangles having an area of 81 in.², the square of side 9 in. has the least perimeter, and support your answer graphically.
   (b) Show that among all the rectangles having a perimeter of 36 in., the square of side 9 in. has the greatest area, and support your answer graphically.

99. A piece of wire 20 cm long is cut into two pieces, and each piece is bent into the shape of a square. How should the wire be cut so that the total area of the two squares is as small as possible?

100. A piece of wire 80 cm long is bent to form a rectangle. Find the dimensions of the rectangle so that its area is as large as possible.

101. For a certain commodity, where x units are demanded weekly when p dollars is the price of each unit,

$$10^6 px = 10^9 - 2 \cdot 10^6 x + 18 \cdot 10^3 x^2 - 6x^3$$

The number of dollars in the average cost of producing each unit is given by

$$Q(x) = \tfrac{1}{50}x - 24 + 11 \cdot 10^3 x^{-1}$$

and $x \geq 100$. Find the number of units that should be produced each week and the price of each unit for the total weekly profit to be maximized.

102. Use Newton's method to find to three decimal places the positive root of the equation

$$4x^4 - 3x^3 + 2x - 5 = 0$$

103. Use Newton's method to find to three decimal places the negative root of the equation

$$3x^4 - 4x^3 + 36x^2 + 2x - 8 = 0$$

104. Find to four decimal places by Newton's method the x coordinate of the point of intersection of the curve $y = \sin x$ and the line $y = 2x - 3$.

105. Find to four decimal places the value of x in the interval $(\tfrac{1}{2}\pi, \tfrac{3}{2}\pi)$ for which $\tan x = x$ by applying Newton's method.

In Exercises 106 and 107 for the given function f do the following: (a) Find the linear approximation of f(x) at x = 8; (b) support your answer in part (a) graphically; (c) compare the values of f(x) computed from the linear approximation in part (a) with the function values computed from the given equations when x is 7.9, 7.99, 8, 8.01, and 8.1.

106. $f(x) = \sqrt[3]{x}$ **107.** $f(x) = \sin \tfrac{1}{16}\pi x$

108. If $y = 2x^2 - 3$, **(a)** find dy and Δy for $x = 2$ and $\Delta x = 0.5$. **(b)** Sketch the graph, and indicate the line segments whose lengths are dy and Δy.

109. If $y = 80x - 16x^2$, find the difference $\Delta y - dy$ if **(a)** $x = 2$ and $\Delta x = 0.1$; **(b)** $x = 4$ and $\Delta x = -0.2$.

110. If $x^3 + y^3 - 3xy^2 + 1 = 0$, find dy at the point $(1, 1)$ if $dx = 0.1$.

111. Use differentials to approximate the volume of material needed to make a rubber ball if the radius of the hollow inner core is 2 in. and the thickness of the rubber is $\tfrac{1}{8}$ in.

112. If t seconds is the time for one complete swing of a simple pendulum of length x feet, then $4\pi^2 x = gt^2$, where $g = 32.2$. Use differentials to estimate the effect upon the time if an error of 0.01 ft is made in measuring the length of the pendulum.

113. The measure of the radius of a right-circular cone is $\tfrac{4}{3}$ times the measure of the altitude. Use differentials to estimate how accurately the altitude must be measured if the error in the computed volume is not to exceed 3 percent.

114. Suppose that f and g are two functions that satisfy the hypothesis of the mean-value theorem on $[a, b]$. Furthermore, suppose that $f'(x) = g'(x)$ for all x in the open interval (a, b). Prove that

$$f(x) - g(x) = f(a) - g(a)$$

for all x in $[a, b]$. *Hint:* Let $h(x) = f(x) - g(x)$ and apply Theorem 3.3.3 to function h.

115. Let f and g be two functions that are differentiable at every number in the closed interval $[a, b]$. Suppose further that $f(a) = g(a)$ and $f(b) = g(b)$. Prove that there exists a number c in the open interval (a, b) such that $f'(c) = g'(c)$. *Hint:* Let $h(x) = f(x) - g(x)$ and apply Rolle's theorem to function h.

116. If f is a polynomial function, use Rolle's theorem to show that between any two consecutive roots of the equation $f'(x) = 0$ there is at most one root of the equation $f(x) = 0$.

117. Sketch the graph of a function f on the interval I in each of the following cases: **(a)** I is the open interval $(0, 2)$ and f is continuous on I. At 1, f has a relative maximum value but $f'(1)$ does not exist. **(b)** I is the closed interval $[0, 2]$. The function f has a relative minimum value at 1, but the absolute minimum value of f is at 0. **(c)** I is the open interval $(0, 2)$, and f' has a relative minimum value at 1.

118. If $f(x) = (x^2 + a^2)^p$, where p is a rational number and $p \neq 0$, prove that the graph of f has two points of inflection if $p < \tfrac{1}{2}$, and no point of inflection if $p \geq \tfrac{1}{2}$.

119. (a) If $f(x) = 3|x| + 4|x - 1|$, prove that f has an absolute minimum value of 3.
(b) If $g(x) = 4|x| + 3|x - 1|$, prove that g has an absolute minimum value of 3.
(c) If $a > 0$, $b > 0$, and $h(x) = a|x| + b|x - 1|$, prove that h has an absolute minimum value that is the smaller of the two numbers a and b.

120. If $f(x) = |x|^a \cdot |x - 1|^b$, where a and b are positive rational numbers, prove that f has a relative maximum value of $a^a b^b / (a + b)^{a+b}$.

121. If p and q are rational numbers such that $p + q = 1$, prove that the line $y = x + (ap + bq)$ is an oblique asymptote of the graph of $f(x) = (x + a)^p (x + b)^q$.

THE DEFINITE INTEGRAL AND INTEGRATION

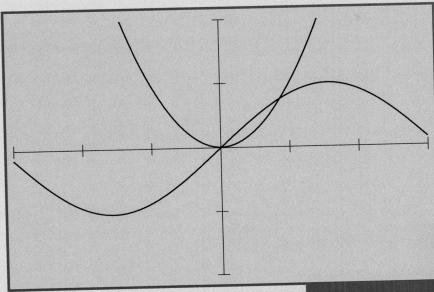

Up to now we have been concerned with the branch of calculus called the *differential calculus* involving the *derivative*. We begin in this chapter our study of the other branch of calculus called the *integral calculus* pertaining to the *definite integral*. You will learn in Section 4.7 that these two branches of calculus are connected by the *fundamental theorems of the calculus*, a landmark discovery in the seventeenth century by Newton and Leibniz, working independently.

A computational tool needed to apply the fundamental theorems is *antidifferentiation*, which we treat in Sections 4.1 and 4.2 and then use in Section 4.3 to solve *separable differential equations* with applications to rectilinear motion.

Just as the derivative is related geometrically to the tangent line of a graph, the definite integral has a geometric interpretation as the *area of a plane region*, which we define in Section 4.4 as a new kind of limit. Then in Section 4.5 we define a *definite integral* in terms of this limit. We develop properties of the definite integral in Sections 4.5 and 4.6 that we use in Section 4.7 to prove the fundamental theorems of the calculus.

We apply the definite integral in Section 4.8 to compute the area of a plane region, and in the final two sections to compute volumes of various kinds of solids. We use *slicing*, *disks*, and *washers* in Section 4.9 and *cylindrical shells* in Section 4.10.

4.1 ANTIDIFFERENTIATION

You are already familiar with *inverse operations*. Addition and subtraction are inverse operations, as are multiplication and division, and raising to powers and extracting roots. In this section we discuss the inverse operation of differentiation called *antidifferentiation*, which involves the computation of an *antiderivative*.

4.1.1 Definition of an Antiderivative

A function F is called an **antiderivative** of the function f on an interval I if $F'(x) = f(x)$ for every value of x in I.

▷ **ILLUSTRATION 1**   If F is the function defined by

$$F(x) = 4x^3 + x^2 + 5$$

then $F'(x) = 12x^2 + 2x$. Thus if f is the function defined by

$$f(x) = 12x^2 + 2x$$

then f is the derivative of F, and F is an antiderivative of f. If G is the function defined by

$$G(x) = 4x^3 + x^2 - 17$$

then G is also an antiderivative of f because $G'(x) = 12x^2 + 2x$. Actually, any function whose function value is given by

$$4x^3 + x^2 + C$$

where C is any constant, is an antiderivative of f.   ◀

▷ **ILLUSTRATION 2**   If C is an arbitrary constant, any function having function values

$$\sin x + C$$

has $\cos x$ as its derivative. Therefore, any such function is an antiderivative of $\cos x$.   ◀

To generalize the discussions in the above illustrations, let the function F be an antiderivative of the function f on an interval I, so that

$$F'(x) = f(x)$$

Then if G is a function defined by

$$G(x) = F(x) + C$$

where C is an arbitrary constant,

$$G'(x) = F'(x)$$
$$= f(x)$$

and G is also an antiderivative of f on the interval I.

We now proceed to prove that if F is any particular antiderivative of f on an interval I, then every antiderivative of f on I is given by $F(x) + C$, where C is an arbitrary constant. First, we need a preliminary theorem whose proof is based on Theorem 3.3.3, which states that if the derivative of a function on an interval is 0 then the function is constant on the interval. Remember, in Section 3.3 we proved this theorem to demonstrate the power of the mean-value theorem.

4.1.2 Theorem

If f and g are two functions defined on an interval I, such that

$$f'(x) = g'(x) \qquad \text{for all } x \text{ in } I$$

then there is a constant K such that

$$f(x) = g(x) + K \qquad \text{for all } x \text{ in } I$$

Proof   Let h be the function defined on I by

$$h(x) = f(x) - g(x)$$

so that for all x in I,

$$h'(x) = f'(x) - g'(x)$$

But, by hypothesis, $f'(x) = g'(x)$ for all x in I. Therefore

$$h'(x) = 0 \qquad \text{for all } x \text{ in } I$$

Because Theorem 3.3.3 applies to the function h, there exists a constant K such that

$$h(x) = K \qquad \text{for all } x \text{ in } I$$

Replacing $h(x)$ by $f(x) - g(x)$ we have

$$f(x) = g(x) + K \qquad \text{for all } x \text{ in } I$$

and the theorem is proved. ∎

The next theorem follows immediately from the above theorem.

4.1.3 Theorem

If F is a particular antiderivative of f on an interval I, then every antiderivative of f on I is given by

$$F(x) + C \tag{1}$$

where C is an arbitrary constant, and all antiderivatives of f on I can be obtained from (1) by assigning particular values to C.

Proof   Let G represent any antiderivative of f on I. Then

$$G'(x) = f(x) \qquad \text{for all } x \text{ in } I \tag{2}$$

Because F is a particular antiderivative of f on I,

$$F'(x) = f(x) \qquad \text{for all } x \text{ in } I \tag{3}$$

From (2) and (3)

$$G'(x) = F'(x) \qquad \text{for all } x \text{ in } I$$

Therefore, from Theorem 4.1.2, there exists a constant K such that

$$G(x) = F(x) + K \qquad \text{for all } x \text{ in } I$$

Because G represents any antiderivative of f on I, all antiderivatives of f can be obtained from $F(x) + C$, where C is an arbitrary constant. We have, therefore, proved the theorem.   ∎

Antidifferentiation is the process of finding the set of all antiderivatives of a given function. The symbol $\int$ denotes the operation of antidifferentiation, and we write

$$\int f(x)\, dx = F(x) + C \tag{4}$$

where

$$F'(x) = f(x)$$

and

$$d\,(F(x)) = f(x)\, dx \tag{5}$$

The expression $F(x) + C$ in (4) is the **general antiderivative** of f.

Leibniz introduced the convention of writing the differential of a function after the antidifferentiation symbol. The advantage of using the differential in this manner will be apparent to you in Section 4.2 when we compute antiderivatives by changing the variable. From (4) and (5), we can write

$$\int d\,(F(x)) = F(x) + C$$

This equation states that when we antidifferentiate the differential of a function, we obtain that function plus an arbitrary constant. So we can think of the $\int$ symbol for antidifferentiation as meaning that operation which is the inverse of the operation denoted by d for computing a differential.

If $\{F(x) + C\}$ is the set of all functions whose differentials are $f(x)\, dx$, it is also the set of all functions whose derivatives are $f(x)$. Antidifferentiation, therefore, is considered as the operation of finding the set of all functions having a given derivative.

Because antidifferentiation is the inverse operation of differentiation, antidifferentiation theorems are obtained from those on differentiation. Thus the following theorems can be proved from the corresponding differentiation theorems.

4.1.4 Theorem

$$\int dx = x + C$$

4.1.5 Theorem

$$\int af(x)\, dx = a \int f(x)\, dx$$

where a is a constant.

Theorem 4.1.5 states that the general antiderivative of a constant times a function is the constant times the general antiderivative of the function.

4.1.6 Theorem

If f and g are defined on the same interval, then

$$\int [f(x) + g(x)]\, dx = \int f(x)\, dx + \int g(x)\, dx$$

Theorem 4.1.6 states that the general antiderivative of the sum of two functions equals the sum of the general antiderivatives of the functions, with the understanding that both functions are defined on the same interval. By extending Theorem 4.1.6 to any finite number of functions and combining it with Theorem 4.1.5, we obtain the next theorem.

4.1.7 Theorem

If $f_1, f_2, \ldots, f_n$ are defined on the same interval,

$$\int [c_1 f_1(x) + c_2 f_2(x) + \ldots + c_n f_n(x)]\, dx$$

$$= c_1 \int f_1(x)\, dx + c_2 \int f_2(x)\, dx + \ldots + c_n \int f_n(x)\, dx$$

where $c_1, c_2, \ldots, c_n$ are constants.

4.1.8 Theorem

If n is a rational number,

$$\int x^n\, dx = \frac{x^{n+1}}{n+1} + C \qquad n \neq -1$$

Proof

$$D_x\left(\frac{x^{n+1}}{n+1}\right) = \frac{(n+1)x^n}{n+1}$$

$$= x^n$$

∎

▷ **ILLUSTRATION 3**   From Theorem 4.1.8 for particular values of n:

$$\int x^2 \, dx = \frac{x^3}{3} + C \qquad\qquad \int x^3 \, dx = \frac{x^4}{4} + C$$

$$\int \frac{1}{x^2} \, dx = \int x^{-2} \, dx \qquad\qquad \int \sqrt[3]{x} \, dx = \int x^{1/3} \, dx$$

$$= \frac{x^{-2+1}}{-2+1} + C \qquad\qquad\qquad = \frac{x^{1/3+1}}{\frac{1}{3}+1} + C$$

$$= \frac{x^{-1}}{-1} + C \qquad\qquad\qquad\quad = \frac{x^{4/3}}{\frac{4}{3}} + C$$

$$= -\frac{1}{x} + C \qquad\qquad\qquad\quad = \tfrac{3}{4}x^{4/3} + C \qquad ◀$$

The next illustration shows how we apply Theorems 4.1.4 through 4.1.8 to antidifferentiate.

▷ **ILLUSTRATION 4**

$$\int (3x + 5) \, dx = \int 3x \, dx + \int 5 \, dx \qquad\qquad \text{(by Theorem 4.1.6)}$$

$$= 3 \int x \, dx + 5 \int dx \qquad\qquad \text{(by Theorem 4.1.5)}$$

$$= 3\left(\frac{x^2}{2} + C_1\right) + 5(x + C_2) \qquad \text{(by Theorems 4.1.8}$$
$$\text{and 4.1.4)}$$

$$= \tfrac{3}{2}x^2 + 5x + (3C_1 + 5C_2)$$

Because $3C_1 + 5C_2$ is an arbitrary constant, it may be denoted by C; so the result can be written as

$$\tfrac{3}{2}x^2 + 5x + C$$

The answer can be checked by finding its derivative.

$$D_x\left(\tfrac{3}{2}x^2 + 5x + C\right) = 3x + 5 \qquad ◀$$

▶ **EXAMPLE 1**   Evaluate

$$\int (5x^4 - 8x^3 + 9x^2 - 2x + 7) \, dx$$

Solution

$$\int (5x^4 - 8x^3 + 9x^2 - 2x + 7) \, dx$$

$$= 5 \int x^4 \, dx - 8 \int x^3 \, dx + 9 \int x^2 \, dx - 2 \int x \, dx + 7 \int dx$$

$$= 5 \cdot \frac{x^5}{5} - 8 \cdot \frac{x^4}{4} + 9 \cdot \frac{x^3}{3} - 2 \cdot \frac{x^2}{2} + 7x + C$$

$$= x^5 - 2x^4 + 3x^3 - x^2 + 7x + C \qquad ◀$$

▶ **EXAMPLE 2** Evaluate

$$\int \sqrt{x}\left(x + \frac{1}{x}\right) dx$$

Solution

$$\int \sqrt{x}\left(x + \frac{1}{x}\right) dx = \int x^{1/2}(x + x^{-1}) \, dx$$

$$= \int (x^{3/2} + x^{-1/2}) \, dx$$

$$= \frac{x^{5/2}}{\frac{5}{2}} + \frac{x^{1/2}}{\frac{1}{2}} + C$$

$$= \tfrac{2}{5}x^{5/2} + 2x^{1/2} + C \qquad \blacktriangleleft$$

▶ **EXAMPLE 3** Evaluate

$$\int \frac{5t^2 + 7}{t^{4/3}} \, dt$$

Solution

$$\int \frac{5t^2 + 7}{t^{4/3}} \, dt = 5 \int \frac{t^2}{t^{4/3}} \, dt + 7 \int \frac{1}{t^{4/3}} \, dt$$

$$= 5 \int t^{2/3} \, dt + 7 \int t^{-4/3} \, dt$$

$$= 5\left(\frac{t^{5/3}}{\frac{5}{3}}\right) + 7\left(\frac{t^{-1/3}}{-\frac{1}{3}}\right) + C$$

$$= 5(\tfrac{3}{5}t^{5/3}) + 7(-3t^{-1/3}) + C$$

$$= 3t^{5/3} - \frac{21}{t^{1/3}} + C \qquad \blacktriangleleft$$

As we did in Illustration 4, antidifferentiation can be checked by computing the derivative of the answer. An antiderivative can be supported graphically by first assigning a specific value to the arbitrary constant C and then plotting the graph of the numerical derivative of that antiderivative. Then in the same window plot the graph of the original function. Your answer is supported if the two graphs appear identical.

▷ **ILLUSTRATION 5** In Example 3, let

$$f(t) = \frac{5t^2 + 7}{t^{4/3}} \qquad \text{and} \qquad F(t) = 3t^{5/3} - \frac{21}{t^{1/3}}$$

Observe that F is the antiderivative of f for $C = 0$. The graphs of f and NDER$(F(t), t)$ are plotted in the $[-10, 10]$ by $[0, 15]$ window in Figure 1. The fact that the graphs appear identical supports our answer in Example 3. ◀

The theorems for the general antiderivative of the sine and cosine functions follow immediately from the corresponding differentiation theorems.

$[-10, 10]$ by $[0, 15]$

$$f(t) = \frac{5t^2 + 7}{t^{4/3}}$$

$$\text{NDER}\left(3t^{5/3} - \frac{21}{t^{1/3}}, t\right)$$

FIGURE 1

4.1.9 Theorem

$$\int \sin x \, dx = -\cos x + C$$

Proof

$$D_x(-\cos x) = -(-\sin x)$$
$$= \sin x \qquad \blacksquare$$

4.1.10 Theorem

$$\int \cos x \, dx = \sin x + C$$

Proof

$$D_x(\sin x) = \cos x \qquad \blacksquare$$

The following theorems are consequences of the differentiation theorems for tangent, cotangent, secant, and cosecant. The proofs are again immediate by computing the derivative of the right-hand side of each equation.

4.1.11 Theorem

$$\int \sec^2 x \, dx = \tan x + C$$

4.1.12 Theorem

$$\int \csc^2 x \, dx = -\cot x + C$$

4.1.13 Theorem

$$\int \sec x \tan x \, dx = \sec x + C$$

4.1.14 Theorem

$$\int \csc x \cot x \, dx = -\csc x + C$$

▶ **EXAMPLE 4**   Evaluate

$$\int (3 \sec x \tan x - 5 \csc^2 x) \, dx$$

Solution We apply Theorems 4.1.13 and 4.1.12.

$$\int (3 \sec x \tan x - 5 \csc^2 x)\, dx = 3 \int \sec x \tan x\, dx - 5 \int \csc^2 x\, dx$$

$$= 3 \sec x - 5(-\cot x) + C$$

$$= 3 \sec x + 5 \cot x + C \qquad \blacktriangleleft$$

Trigonometric identities are often used when computing antiderivatives involving trigonometric functions. The following eight fundamental identities are crucial:

$$\sin x \csc x = 1 \qquad \cos x \sec x = 1 \qquad \tan x \cot x = 1$$

$$\tan x = \frac{\sin x}{\cos x} \qquad \cot x = \frac{\cos x}{\sin x}$$

$$\sin^2 x + \cos^2 x = 1 \qquad \tan^2 x + 1 = \sec^2 x \qquad \cot^2 x + 1 = \csc^2 x$$

▶ **EXAMPLE 5**   Evaluate

$$\int \frac{2 \cot x - 3 \sin^2 x}{\sin x}\, dx$$

Solution

$$\int \frac{2 \cot x - 3 \sin^2 x}{\sin x}\, dx$$

$$= 2 \int \frac{1}{\sin x} \cdot \cot x\, dx - 3 \int \frac{\sin^2 x}{\sin x}\, dx$$

$$= 2 \int \csc x \cot x\, dx - 3 \int \sin x\, dx$$

$$= 2(-\csc x) - 3(-\cos x) + C \quad \text{(from Theorems 4.1.14 and 4.1.9)}$$

$$= -2 \csc x + 3 \cos x + C \qquad \blacktriangleleft$$

▶ **EXAMPLE 6**   Evaluate

$$\int (\tan^2 x + \cot^2 x + 4)\, dx$$

Solution

$$\int (\tan^2 x + \cot^2 x + 4)\, dx$$

$$= \int [(\sec^2 x - 1) + (\csc^2 x - 1) + 4]\, dx$$

$$= \int \sec^2 x\, dx + \int \csc^2 x\, dx + 2 \int dx$$

$$= \tan x - \cot x + 2x + C \quad \text{(from Theorems 4.1.11 and 4.1.12)} \blacktriangleleft$$

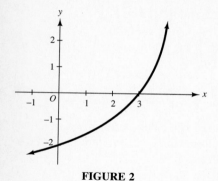

FIGURE 2

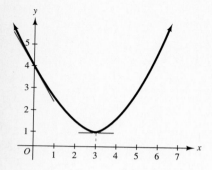

FIGURE 3

In Chapter 3 you learned how to obtain properties of the graph of a function from the graph of its derivative. In a similar way, from the graph of a function f, we can obtain properties of the graph of an antiderivative of f as shown in the next example.

▶ **EXAMPLE 7**   From the graph of the function f sketched in Figure 2, sketch a possible graph of F, an antiderivative of f, if F is continuous everywhere, $F(0) = 4$, and $F(3) = 1$.

Solution   Because F is an antiderivative of f, f is the derivative of F. From Figure 2 we observe that $f(3) = 0$; thus $F'(3) = 0$. Because $f(x) < 0$ when $x < 3$, $F'(x) < 0$ when $x < 3$. Similarly, $F'(x) > 0$ when $x > 3$. Another fact we learn from Figure 2 is that $f(0) = -2$, that is, $F'(0) = -2$. We incorporate this information in Table 1 and from the conclusions in the table we sketch a possible graph of F shown in Figure 3.

Table 1

	$F(x)$	$F'(x)$	Conclusion
$x < 0$		−	F is decreasing
$x = 0$	4	−2	Slope of the tangent line is −2
$0 < x < 3$		−	F is decreasing
$x = 3$	1	0	F has a relative minimum value
$3 < x$		+	F is increasing

◀

Often in applications of antidifferentiation, we need to find a particular antiderivative that satisfies certain conditions called **initial** or **boundary conditions,** depending on whether they occur at one or more than one point. For example, if an equation involving dy/dx is given as well as the initial condition that $y = y_1$ when $x = x_1$, then after the set of all antiderivatives is found, if x and y are replaced by x_1 and y_1, a particular value of the arbitrary constant C is determined. With this value of C, we obtain a particular antiderivative.

▷ **ILLUSTRATION 6**   Suppose we wish to find the particular antiderivative satisfying the equation

$$\frac{dy}{dx} = 2x$$

and the initial condition that $y = 6$ when $x = 2$. From the given equation

$$dy = 2x\,dx$$
$$\int dy = \int 2x\,dx$$
$$y = x^2 + C \qquad \qquad (6)$$

In (6) we substitute 2 for x and 6 for y and get

$$6 = 4 + C$$
$$C = 2$$

When this value of C is substituted back in (6), we obtain

$$y = x^2 + 2$$

which gives the particular antiderivative desired.   ◄

▶ **EXAMPLE 8**   At any point (x, y) on a particular curve the tangent line has a slope equal to $4x - 5$. If the curve contains the point $(3, 7)$, find its equation.

Solution   Because the slope of the tangent line to a curve at any point (x, y) is the value of the derivative at that point, we have

$$\frac{dy}{dx} = 4x - 5$$

$$dy = (4x - 5)\,dx$$

$$\int dy = \int (4x - 5)\,dx$$

$$y = 4\left(\frac{x^2}{2}\right) - 5x + C$$

$$y = 2x^2 - 5x + C \tag{7}$$

Equation (7) represents a *family* of curves. Because we wish to determine the particular curve of this family that contains the point $(3, 7)$, we substitute 3 for x and 7 for y in (7) and get

$$7 = 2(9) - 5(3) + C$$

$$C = 4$$

Replacing C by 4 in (7) we get the required equation, which is

$$y = 2x^2 - 5x + 4 \qquad ◄$$

In Section 2.6 we introduced the marginal cost and marginal revenue functions from economics. They are the first derivatives C' and R' of the total cost function C and the total revenue function R, respectively. Thus C and R can be obtained from C' and R' by antidifferentiation. When finding the function C from C', the arbitrary constant can be evaluated if we know the overhead cost (i.e., the cost when no units are produced) or the cost of production of a specific number of units of the commodity. Because generally the total revenue function is zero when the number of units produced is zero, this fact may be used to evaluate the arbitrary constant when finding the function R from R'.

▶ **EXAMPLE 9**   The marginal cost function C' is determined by a company to be given by

$$C'(x) = 4x^{-1/2} + 1$$

where $C(x)$ dollars is the total cost of producing x units when no more than 25 units are produced. If the cost of producing 4 units is $50, find **(a)** the total cost function and **(b)** the cost of producing 10 units.

Solution (a) Because $C'(x) = 4x^{-1/2} + 1$

$$C(x) = \int (4x^{-1/2} + 1)\, dx$$

$$= 4 \cdot \frac{x^{1/2}}{\frac{1}{2}} + x + k$$

$$= 8x^{1/2} + x + k$$

Because the cost of producing 4 units is \$50, $C(4) = 50$. Thus

$$50 = 8(4)^{1/2} + 4 + k$$

$$k = 30$$

Therefore

$$C(x) = 8x^{1/2} + x + 30 \tag{8}$$

The domain of C is $[0, 25]$; remember that even though x represents the number of units of a commodity, we assume that x is a real number to give the continuity requirements for the functions C and C'.

(b) The cost of producing 10 units is $C(10)$ dollars, and from (8)

$$C(10) = 8(10)^{1/2} + 10 + 30$$

$$= 65.30$$

<u>Conclusion:</u>   The cost of producing 10 units is \$65.30.   ◀

EXERCISES 4.1

In Exercises 1 through 30, perform the antidifferentiation. In Exercises 1 through 8 and 25 through 28, check by finding the derivative of your answer. In Exercises 9 through 12 and 29 and 30, support your answer graphically. In the other exercises, check or support your answer.

1. $\int 3x^4\, dx$

2. $\int 2x^7\, dx$

3. $\int \frac{1}{x^3}\, dx$

4. $\int \frac{3}{t^5}\, dt$

5. $\int 5u^{3/2}\, du$

6. $\int 10\sqrt[3]{x^2}\, dx$

7. $\int \frac{2}{\sqrt[3]{x}}\, dx$

8. $\int \frac{3}{\sqrt{y}}\, dy$

9. $\int 6t^2 \sqrt[3]{t}\, dt$

10. $\int (3u^5 - 2u^3)\, du$

11. $\int y^3(2y^2 - 3)\, dy$

12. $\int x^4(5 - x^2)\, dx$

13. $\int (8x^4 + 4x^3 - 6x^2 - 4x + 5)\, dx$

14. $\int (2 + 3x^2 - 8x^3)\, dx$

15. $\int \sqrt{x}(x + 1)\, dx$

16. $\int \left(\sqrt{x} - \frac{1}{\sqrt{x}}\right) dx$

17. $\int \left(\frac{2}{x^3} + \frac{3}{x^2} + 5\right) dx$

18. $\int \left(3 - \frac{1}{x^4} + \frac{1}{x^2}\right) dx$

19. $\int \frac{x^2 + 4x - 4}{\sqrt{x}}\, dx$

20. $\int \frac{y^4 + 2y^2 - 1}{\sqrt{y}}\, dy$

21. $\int \left(\sqrt[3]{x} + \frac{1}{\sqrt[3]{x}}\right) dx$

22. $\int \frac{27t^3 - 1}{\sqrt[3]{t}}\, dt$

23. $\int (3\sin t - 2\cos t)\, dt$

24. $\int (5\cos x - 4\sin x)\, dx$

25. $\int \frac{\sin x}{\cos^2 x}\, dx$

26. $\int \frac{\cos x}{\sin^2 x}\, dx$

27. $\int (4\csc x \cot x + 2\sec^2 x)\, dx$

28. $\int (3\csc^2 t - 5\sec t \tan t)\, dt$

29. $\int (2\cot^2 \theta - 3\tan^2 \theta)\, d\theta$

30. $\int \frac{3\tan\theta - 4\cos^2\theta}{\cos\theta}\, d\theta$

In Exercises 31 through 36, the graph of a function f is sketched in the accompanying figure. An antiderivative of f is F, which is continuous everywhere and which has the given function value. Sketch a graph of F.

31. (a) $F(0) = 3$;

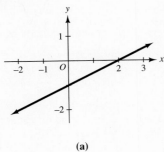

(a)

(b) $F(-2) = 0$

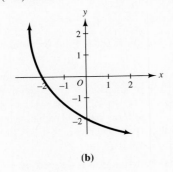

(b)

32. (a) $F(0) = 1$;

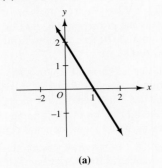

(a)

(b) $F(0) = 2$

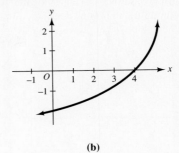

(b)

33. (a) $F(0) = 0$;

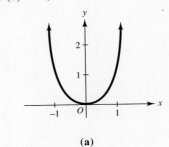

(a)

(b) $F(0) = 0$

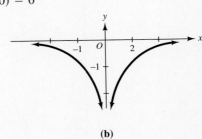

(b)

34. (a) $F(0) = 0$;

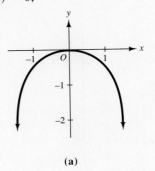

(a)

(b) $F(0) = 0$

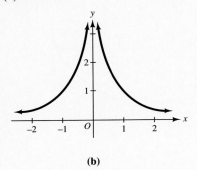

(b)

35. $F(2) = 0$

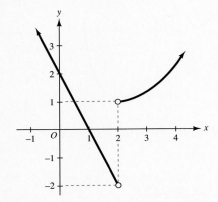

36. $F(-1) = 4$

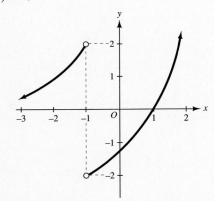

37. The point $(3, 2)$ is on a curve, and at any point (x, y) on the curve the tangent line has a slope equal to $2x - 3$. Find an equation of the curve.

38. The slope of the tangent line at any point (x, y) on a curve is $3\sqrt{x}$. If the point $(9, 4)$ is on the curve, find an equation of the curve.

39. The points $(-1, 3)$ and $(0, 2)$ are on a curve, and at any point (x, y) on the curve $\dfrac{d^2y}{dx^2} = 2 - 4x$. Find an equation of the curve. *Hint:* Let $\dfrac{d^2y}{dx^2} = \dfrac{dy'}{dx}$, and

obtain an equation involving y', x, and an arbitrary constant C_1. From this equation obtain another equation involving y, x, C_1, and C_2. Compute C_1 and C_2 from the conditions.

40. An equation of the tangent line to a curve at the point $(1, 3)$ is $y = x + 2$. If at any point (x, y) on the curve, $\dfrac{d^2y}{dx^2} = 6x$, find an equation of the curve. See the hint for Exercise 39.

41. At any point (x, y) on a curve, $\dfrac{d^2y}{dx^2} = 1 - x^2$, and an equation of the tangent line to the curve at the point $(1, 1)$ is $y = 2 - x$. Find an equation of the curve. See the hint for Exercise 39.

42. At any point (x, y) on a curve, $\dfrac{d^3y}{dx^3} = 2$, and $(1, 3)$ is a point of inflection at which the slope of the inflectional tangent is -2. Find an equation of the curve.

43. The marginal cost function is given by

$$C'(x) = 3x^2 + 8x + 4$$

and the overhead cost is \$6. Find the total cost function.

44. A company has determined that the marginal cost function for the production of a particular commodity is given by $C'(x) = 125 + 10x + \frac{1}{9}x^2$, where $C(x)$ dollars is the total cost of producing x units of the commodity. If the overhead cost is \$250, what is the cost of producing 15 units?

45. The marginal cost function is defined by $C'(x) = 6x$, where $C(x)$ is the number of hundreds of dollars in the total cost of x hundred units of a certain commodity. If the cost of 200 units is \$2000, find **(a)** the total cost function and **(b)** the overhead cost.

46. The marginal revenue function for a certain commodity is $R'(x) = 12 - 3x$. If x units are demanded when p dollars is the price per unit, find **(a)** the total revenue function and **(b)** an equation involving p and x (the demand equation).

47. For a particular article of merchandise, the marginal revenue function is given by $R'(x) = 15 - 4x$. If x units are demanded when p dollars is the price per unit, find **(a)** the total revenue function and **(b)** an equation involving p and x (the demand equation).

48. The efficiency of a factory worker is expressed as a percent. For instance, if the worker's efficiency at a particular time is given as 70 percent, then the worker is performing at 70 percent of her full potential. Suppose that E percent is a factory worker's efficiency t hours after beginning work, and the rate at which E is changing is $(35 - 8t)$ percent per hour. If the worker's efficiency is 81 percent after working 3 hr, find her efficiency after working **(a)** 4 hr and **(b)** 8 hr.

49. The volume of water in a tank is V cubic meters when the depth of the water is h meters. If the rate of change of V with respect to h is $\pi(4h^2 + 12h + 9)$, find the volume of water in the tank when the depth is 3 m.

50. An art collector purchased for $1000 a painting by an artist whose works are currently increasing in value with respect to time according to the formula $\frac{dV}{dt} = 5t^{3/2} + 10t + 50$, where V dollars is the anticipated value of a painting t years after its purchase. If this formula were valid for the next 6 years, what would be the anticipated value of the painting 4 years from now?

51. Let $f(x) = |x|$ and F be defined by

$$F(x) = \begin{cases} -\frac{1}{2}x^2 & \text{if } x < 0 \\ \frac{1}{2}x^2 & \text{if } 0 \le x \end{cases}$$

Show that F is an antiderivative of f on $(-\infty, +\infty)$.

52. Let

$$U(x) = \begin{cases} 0 & \text{if } x < 0 \\ 1 & \text{if } 0 \le x \end{cases}$$

Show that U does not have an antiderivative on $(-\infty, +\infty)$. *Hint:* Assume that U has an antiderivative F on $(-\infty, +\infty)$, and a contradiction is obtained by showing that it follows from the mean-value theorem that there exists a number k such that $F(x) = x + k$ if $x > 0$, and $F(x) = k$ if $x < 0$.

53. Let $f(x) = 1$ for all x in $(-1, 1)$, and let

$$g(x) = \begin{cases} -1 & \text{if } -1 < x \le 0 \\ 1 & \text{if } 0 < x < 1 \end{cases}$$

Then $f'(x) = 0$ for all x in $(-1, 1)$ and $g'(x) = 0$ whenever g' exists in $(-1, 1)$. However, $f(x) \ne g(x) + K$ for x in $(-1, 1)$. Explain why Theorem 4.1.2 does not apply.

54. Let

$$f(x) = \begin{cases} -1 & \text{if } x < 0 \\ 0 & \text{if } x = 0 \\ 1 & \text{if } 0 < x \end{cases}$$

and $F(x) = |x|$. Show that $F'(x) = f(x)$ if $x \ne 0$. Is F an antiderivative of f on $(-\infty, +\infty)$? Explain.

4.2 SOME TECHNIQUES OF ANTIDIFFERENTIATION

Many antiderivatives cannot be found by applying only the theorems of Section 4.1. You must, therefore, learn other techniques of antidifferentiation. In this section, we discuss techniques requiring the *chain rule for antidifferentiation* and those involving a change of variable.

▷ **ILLUSTRATION 1** To differentiate $\frac{1}{10}(1 + x^2)^{10}$, we apply the chain rule for differentiation to obtain

$$D_x[\tfrac{1}{10}(1 + x^2)^{10}] = (1 + x^2)^9 (2x)$$

Now suppose we wish to antidifferentiate $(1 + x^2)^9 (2x)$; that is, we wish to compute

$$\int (1 + x^2)^9(2x \, dx) \tag{1}$$

To lead up to a procedure that can be used in such a situation, let

$$g(x) = 1 + x^2 \qquad g'(x) \, dx = 2x \, dx \tag{2}$$

Then (1) can be written as

$$\int [g(x)]^9[g'(x) \, dx] \tag{3}$$

From Theorem 4.1.8,

$$\int u^9 \, du = \tfrac{1}{10} u^{10} + C \tag{4}$$

Observe that (3) is of the same form as the left-hand side of (4). Thus

$$\int [g(x)]^9 [g'(x) \, dx] = \tfrac{1}{10}[g(x)]^{10} + C$$

and with $g(x)$ and $g'(x) \, dx$ given in (2) we have

$$\int (1 + x^2)^9 (2x \, dx) = \tfrac{1}{10}(1 + x^2)^{10} + C \qquad \blacktriangleleft$$

Justification of the procedure used to obtain the result of Illustration 1 is provided by the following theorem, which is analogous to the chain rule for differentiation and is called the *chain rule for antidifferentiation.*

4.2.1 Theorem   The Chain Rule for Antidifferentiation

Let g be a differentiable function, and let the range of g be an interval I. Suppose that f is a function defined on I and that F is an antiderivative of f on I. Then

$$\int f(g(x))[g'(x) \, dx] = F(g(x)) + C$$

Proof   By hypothesis,

$$F'(g(x)) = f(g(x)) \tag{5}$$

By the chain rule for differentiation.

$$D_x[F(g(x))] = F'(g(x))[g'(x)]$$

Substituting from (5) in this equation we get

$$D_x[F(g(x))] = f(g(x))[g'(x)]$$

from which it follows that

$$\int f(g(x))[g'(x) \, dx] = F(g(x)) + C$$

which is what we wished to prove. $\blacksquare$

As a particular case of Theorem 4.2.1, from Theorem 4.1.8, we have the generalized power formula for antiderivatives, which we now state.

4.2.2 Theorem

If g is a differentiable function, and n is a rational number,

$$\int [g(x)]^n [g'(x) \, dx] = \frac{[g(x)]^{n+1}}{n + 1} + C \qquad n \neq -1$$

▶ **EXAMPLE 1**   Evaluate

$$\int \sqrt{3x + 4} \, dx$$

Solution   To apply Theorem 4.2.2 we first write

$$\int \sqrt{3x + 4} \, dx = \int (3x + 4)^{1/2} \, dx$$

and observe that if

$$g(x) = 3x + 4 \quad \text{then} \quad g'(x) \, dx = 3 \, dx \qquad\qquad (6)$$

Therefore we need a factor of 3 to go with dx to give $g'(x) \, dx$. Hence we write

$$\int (3x + 4)^{1/2} \, dx = \int (3x + 4)^{1/2} \tfrac{1}{3}(3 \, dx)$$

$$= \frac{1}{3} \int (3x + 4)^{1/2}(3 \, dx)$$

Thus from Theorem 4.2.2, with $g(x)$ and $g'(x) \, dx$ given in (6), we have

$$\frac{1}{3} \int (3x + 4)^{1/2} \, (3 \, dx) = \frac{1}{3} \cdot \frac{(3x + 4)^{3/2}}{\frac{3}{2}} + C$$

$$= \tfrac{2}{9}(3x + 4)^{3/2} + C \qquad\qquad ◀$$

▶ **EXAMPLE 2**   Evaluate

$$\int x^2(5 + 2x^3)^8 \, dx$$

and check by differentiating the answer.

Solution   Observe that if

$$g(x) = 5 + 2x^3 \quad \text{then} \quad g'(x) \, dx = 6x^2 \, dx \qquad\qquad (7)$$

Because

$$\int x^2(5 + 2x^3)^8 \, dx = \int (5 + 2x^3)^8(x^2 \, dx)$$

we need a factor of 6 to go with $x^2 \, dx$ to give $g'(x) \, dx$. Therefore we write

$$\int x^2(5 + 2x^3)^8 \, dx = \frac{1}{6} \int (5 + 2x^3)^8(6x^2 \, dx)$$

Applying Theorem 4.2.2 with $g(x)$ and $g'(x) \, dx$ given in (7) we get

$$\frac{1}{6} \int (5 + 2x^3)^8(6x^2 \, dx) = \frac{1}{6} \cdot \frac{(5 + 2x^3)^9}{9} + C$$

$$= \tfrac{1}{54}(5 + 2x^3)^9 + C$$

Checking by differentiation gives

$$D_x[\tfrac{1}{54}(5 + 2x^3)^9] = \tfrac{1}{54} \cdot 9(5 + 2x^3)^8(6x^2)$$
$$= x^2(5 + 2x^3)^8$$

◀

If in the formula of Theorem 4.2.1, f is the cosine function, then F is the sine function and we have

$$\int \cos(g(x))[g'(x)\, dx] = \sin(g(x)) + C \tag{8}$$

We apply this formula in the next example.

▶ **EXAMPLE 3** Evaluate

$$\int x \cos x^2\, dx$$

and support the answer graphically.

Solution If

$$g(x) = x^2 \quad \text{then} \quad g'(x)\, dx = 2x\, dx \tag{9}$$

Because

$$\int x \cos x^2\, dx = \int (\cos x^2)(x\, dx)$$

we need a factor of 2 to go with $x\, dx$ to give $g'(x)\, dx$. Thus we write

$$\int x \cos x^2\, dx = \frac{1}{2} \int (\cos x^2)(2x\, dx)$$

We apply (8) with $g(x)$ and $g'(x)\, dx$ given in (9), and we obtain

$$\frac{1}{2} \int (\cos x^2)(2x\, dx) = \tfrac{1}{2} \sin x^2 + C$$

To support our answer we plot the graph of the function defined by $x \cos x^2$ and the graph of NDER($\tfrac{1}{2} \sin x^2$, x) in the same $[-4.7, 4.7]$ by $[-3.1, 3.1]$ window as shown in Figure 1, which indicates that the two graphs appear identical.

◀

Details of the solutions of the above examples can be shortened by not specifically stating $g(x)$ and $g'(x)\, dx$. The solution of Example 1 then takes the following form:

$$\int \sqrt{3x + 4}\, dx = \frac{1}{3} \int (3x + 4)^{1/2}(3\, dx)$$

$$= \frac{1}{3} \cdot \frac{(3x + 4)^{3/2}}{\frac{3}{2}} + C$$

$$= \tfrac{2}{9}(3x + 4)^{3/2} + C$$

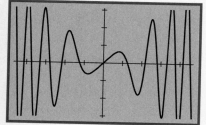

$[-4.7, 4.7]$ by $[-3.1, 3.1]$

$f(x) = x \cos x^2$

NDER ($\tfrac{1}{2} \sin x^2$, x)

FIGURE 1

The solution of Example 2 can be written as

$$\int x^2(5 + 2x^3)^8 \, dx = \frac{1}{6} \int (5 + 2x^3)^8(6x^2 \, dx)$$

$$= \frac{1}{6} \cdot \frac{(5 + 2x^3)^9}{9} + C$$

$$= \tfrac{1}{54}(5 + 2x^3)^9 + C$$

and the solution of Example 3 can be shortened as follows:

$$\int x \cos x^2 \, dx = \frac{1}{2} \int (\cos x^2)(2x \, dx)$$

$$= \tfrac{1}{2} \sin x^2 + C$$

▶ **EXAMPLE 4**   Evaluate

$$\int \frac{4x^2}{(1 - 8x^3)^4} \, dx$$

Solution   Because $d(1 - 8x^3) = -24x^2 \, dx$, we write

$$\int \frac{4x^2}{(1 - 8x^3)^4} \, dx = 4 \int (1 - 8x^3)^{-4}(x^2 \, dx)$$

$$= 4\left(-\frac{1}{24}\right) \int (1 - 8x^3)^{-4}(-24x^2 \, dx)$$

$$= -\frac{1}{6} \cdot \frac{(1 - 8x^3)^{-3}}{-3} + C$$

$$= \frac{1}{18(1 - 8x^3)^3} + C \qquad ◀$$

Sometimes it is possible to compute an antiderivative after a change of variable as demonstrated in the next example.

▶ **EXAMPLE 5**   Evaluate

$$\int x^2 \sqrt{1 + x} \, dx$$

Solution   Let

$$u = 1 + x \qquad du = dx \qquad x = u - 1$$

We have

$$\int x^2 \sqrt{1 + x} \, dx = \int (u - 1)^2 u^{1/2} \, du$$

$$= \int (u^2 - 2u + 1)u^{1/2} \, du$$

$$= \int u^{5/2} \, du - 2 \int u^{3/2} \, du + \int u^{1/2} \, du$$

$$= \frac{u^{7/2}}{\frac{7}{2}} - 2 \cdot \frac{u^{5/2}}{\frac{5}{2}} + \frac{u^{3/2}}{\frac{3}{2}} + C$$

$$= \tfrac{2}{7}(1 + x)^{7/2} - \tfrac{4}{5}(1 + x)^{5/2} + \tfrac{2}{3}(1 + x)^{3/2} + C \qquad ◀$$

▷ **ILLUSTRATION 2**   An alternate method for the solution of Example 5 is to let

$$v = \sqrt{1 + x} \qquad v^2 = 1 + x$$
$$x = v^2 - 1 \qquad dx = 2v \, dv$$

The computation then takes the following form:

$$\int x^2 \sqrt{1 + x} \, dx = \int (v^2 - 1)^2 \cdot v \cdot (2v \, dv)$$

$$= 2 \int v^6 \, dv - 4 \int v^4 \, dv + 2 \int v^2 \, dv$$

$$= \tfrac{2}{7} v^7 - \tfrac{4}{5} v^5 + \tfrac{2}{3} v^3 + C$$

$$= \tfrac{2}{7}(1 + x)^{7/2} - \tfrac{4}{5}(1 + x)^{5/2} + \tfrac{2}{3}(1 + x)^{3/2} + C$$

Checking by differentiation gives

$$D_x\left[\tfrac{2}{7}(1 + x)^{7/2} - \tfrac{4}{5}(1 + x)^{5/2} + \tfrac{2}{3}(1 + x)^{3/2}\right]$$

$$= (1 + x)^{5/2} - 2(1 + x)^{3/2} + (1 + x)^{1/2}$$

$$= (1 + x)^{1/2}[(1 + x)^2 - 2(1 + x) + 1]$$

$$= (1 + x)^{1/2}[1 + 2x + x^2 - 2 - 2x + 1]$$

$$= x^2 \sqrt{1 + x}$$

◀

▶ **EXAMPLE 6**   Evaluate

$$\int \frac{\sin\sqrt{x}}{\sqrt{x}} \, dx$$

Solution   Let

$$u = \sqrt{x} \qquad du = \frac{1}{2\sqrt{x}} \, dx$$

Therefore

$$\int \frac{\sin\sqrt{x}}{\sqrt{x}} \, dx = 2 \int \sin\sqrt{x} \left(\frac{1}{2\sqrt{x}} \, dx\right)$$

$$= 2 \int \sin u \, du$$

$$= -2 \cos u + C$$

$$= -2 \cos \sqrt{x} + C$$

◀

▶ **EXAMPLE 7**   Evaluate

$$\int \sin x \sqrt{1 - \cos x} \, dx$$

Solution Let

$$u = 1 - \cos x \qquad du = \sin x \, dx$$

Thus

$$\int \sin x \sqrt{1 - \cos x} \, dx = \int u^{1/2} \, du$$

$$= \tfrac{2}{3} u^{3/2} + C$$

$$= \tfrac{2}{3}(1 - \cos x)^{3/2} + C \qquad \blacktriangleleft$$

▶ **EXAMPLE 8** Evaluate $\int \tan x \sec^2 x \, dx$ by two methods: **(a)** Let $u = \tan x$; **(b)** Let $v = \sec x$. **(c)** Explain the difference in appearance of the answers in (a) and (b).

Solution

(a) If $u = \tan x$, then $du = \sec^2 x \, dx$. We have

$$\int \tan x \sec^2 x \, dx = \int u \, du$$

$$= \frac{u^2}{2} + C$$

$$= \tfrac{1}{2} \tan^2 x + C$$

(b) If $v = \sec x$, then $dv = \sec x \tan x \, dx$. Thus

$$\int \tan x \sec^2 x \, dx = \int \sec x(\sec x \tan x \, dx)$$

$$= \int v \, dv$$

$$= \frac{v^2}{2} + C$$

$$= \tfrac{1}{2} \sec^2 x + C$$

(c) Because $\sec^2 x = 1 + \tan^2 x$, the functions defined by $\tfrac{1}{2}\tan^2 x$ and $\tfrac{1}{2}\sec^2 x$ differ by a constant; so each serves as an antiderivative of $\tan x \sec^2 x$. Furthermore we can write

$$\tfrac{1}{2}\sec^2 x + C = \tfrac{1}{2}(\tan^2 x + 1) + C$$

$$= \tfrac{1}{2}\tan^2 x + \tfrac{1}{2} + C$$

$$= \tfrac{1}{2}\tan^2 x + K \qquad \text{where } K = \tfrac{1}{2} + C \qquad \blacktriangleleft$$

▶ **EXAMPLE 9** A wound is healing in such a way that t days since Monday the area of the wound has been decreasing at a rate of $-3(t + 2)^{-2}$ square centimeters per day. If on Tuesday the area of the wound was 2 cm², **(a)** what was the area of the wound on Monday, and **(b)** what is the anticipated area of the wound on Friday if it continues to heal at the same rate?

Solution Let A square centimeters be the area of the wound t days since Monday. Then

$$\frac{dA}{dt} = -3(t + 2)^{-2}$$

$$A = -3 \int (t + 2)^{-2} \, dt$$

Because $d(t + 2) = dt$ we obtain

$$A = -3 \cdot \frac{(t + 2)^{-1}}{-1} + C$$

$$A = \frac{3}{t + 2} + C \tag{10}$$

Because on Tuesday the area of the wound was 2 cm², we know that $A = 2$ when $t = 1$. Substituting these values in (10) we obtain

$$2 = 1 + C$$
$$C = 1$$

Therefore from (10),

$$A = \frac{3}{t + 2} + 1 \tag{11}$$

(a) On Monday, $t = 0$. Let A_0 be the value of A when $t = 0$. From (11),

$$A_0 = \tfrac{3}{2} + 1$$
$$= \tfrac{5}{2}$$

<u>Conclusion:</u>   On Monday the area of the wound was 2.5 cm².

(b) On Friday, $t = 4$. Let A_4 be the value of A when $t = 4$. From (11),

$$A_4 = \tfrac{3}{6} + 1$$
$$= \tfrac{3}{2}$$

<u>Conclusion:</u>   On Friday the anticipated area of the wound is 1.5 cm². ◀

EXERCISES 4.2

In Exercises 1 through 44, perform the antidifferentiation. Either check your answer by differentiation or support your answer graphically.

1. $\displaystyle\int \sqrt{1 - 4y} \, dy$

2. $\displaystyle\int \sqrt[3]{3x - 4} \, dx$

3. $\displaystyle\int x\sqrt[3]{x^2 - 9} \, dx$

4. $\displaystyle\int x(2x^2 + 1)^6 \, dx$

5. $\displaystyle\int x^2(x^3 - 1)^{10} \, dx$

6. $\displaystyle\int 3x \sqrt{4 - x^2} \, dx$

7. $\displaystyle\int \frac{y^3}{(1 - 2y^4)^5} \, dy$

8. $\displaystyle\int \frac{s}{\sqrt{3s^2 + 1}} \, ds$

9. $\displaystyle\int (x^2 - 4x + 4)^{4/3} \, dx$

10. $\displaystyle\int x^4 \sqrt{3x^5 - 5} \, dx$

11. $\displaystyle\int x \sqrt{x + 2} \, dx$

12. $\displaystyle\int \frac{t}{\sqrt{t + 3}} \, dt$

13. $\displaystyle\int \frac{2r}{(1 - r)^7} \, dr$

14. $\displaystyle\int x^3(2 - x^2)^{12} \, dx$

15. $\int \sqrt{3 - 2x}\, x^2\, dx$

16. $\int (x^3 + 3)^{1/4} x^5\, dx$

17. $\int \cos 4\theta\, d\theta$

18. $\int \sin \tfrac{1}{3}x\, dx$

19. $\int 6x^2 \sin x^3\, dx$

20. $\int \tfrac{1}{2}t \cos 4t^2\, dt$

21. $\int \sec^2 5x\, dx$

22. $\int \csc^2 2\theta\, d\theta$

23. $\int y \csc 3y^2 \cot 3y^2\, dy$

24. $\int r^2 \sec^2 r^3\, dr$

25. $\int \cos x(2 + \sin x)^5\, dx$

26. $\int \dfrac{4 \sin x}{(1 + \cos x)^2}\, dx$

27. $\int \sqrt{1 + \dfrac{1}{3x}}\, \dfrac{dx}{x^2}$

28. $\int \sqrt{\dfrac{1}{t} - 1}\, \dfrac{dt}{t^2}$

29. $\int 2 \sin x \sqrt[3]{1 + \cos x}\, dx$

30. $\int \sin 2x \sqrt{2 - \cos 2x}\, dx$

31. $\int \cos^2 t \sin t\, dt$

32. $\int \sin^3 \theta \cos \theta\, d\theta$

33. $\int (\tan 2x + \cot 2x)^2\, dx$

34. $\int \dfrac{\sec^2 3\sqrt{t}}{\sqrt{t}}\, dt$

35. $\int \dfrac{x^2 + 2x}{\sqrt{x^3 + 3x^2 + 1}}\, dx$

36. $\int x(x^2 + 1)\sqrt{4 - 2x^2 - x^4}\, dx$

37. $\int \dfrac{y + 3}{(3 - y)^{2/3}}\, dy$

38. $\int \sqrt{3 + s}(s + 1)^2\, ds$

39. $\int \dfrac{(r^{1/3} + 2)^4}{\sqrt[3]{r^2}}\, dr$

40. $\int \left(t + \dfrac{1}{t}\right)^{3/2} \left(\dfrac{t^2 - 1}{t^2}\right)\, dt$

41. $\int \dfrac{x^3}{(x^2 + 4)^{3/2}}\, dx$

42. $\int \dfrac{x^3}{\sqrt{1 - 2x^2}}\, dx$

43. $\int \sin x \sin(\cos x)\, dx$

44. $\int \sec x \tan x \cos(\sec x)\, dx$

45. The marginal cost function for a particular article of merchandise is given by $C'(x) = 3(5x + 4)^{-1/2}$. If the overhead cost is \$10, find the total cost function.

46. For a certain commodity the marginal cost function is given by $C'(x) = 3\sqrt{2x + 4}$. If the overhead cost is zero, find the total cost function.

47. If x units are demanded when p dollars is the price per unit, find an equation involving p and x (the demand equation) of a commodity for which the marginal revenue function is given by
$$R'(x) = 4 + 10(x + 5)^{-2}$$

48. The marginal revenue function for a particular article of merchandise is given by $R'(x) = ab(x + b)^{-2} - c$. Find **(a)** the total revenue function and **(b)** an equation involving p and x (the demand equation) where x units are demanded when p dollars is the price per unit.

49. If q coulombs is the charge of electricity received by a condenser from an electric current of i amperes at t seconds then $i = \dfrac{dq}{dt}$. If $i = 5 \sin 60t$ and $q = 0$ when $t = \tfrac{1}{2}\pi$, find the greatest positive charge on the condenser.

50. Do Exercise 49 if $i = 4 \cos 120t$ and $q = 0$ when $t = 0$.

51. The cost of a certain piece of machinery is \$700, and its value is depreciating with time according to the formula $\dfrac{dV}{dt} = -500(t + 1)^{-2}$, where V dollars is its value t years after its purchase. What is its value 3 years after its purchase?

52. The volume of water in a tank is V cubic meters when the depth of the water is h meters. If the rate of change of V with respect to h is given by $\dfrac{dV}{dh} = \pi(2h + 3)^2$, find the volume of water in the tank when the depth is 3 m.

53. For the first 10 days in December a plant cell grew in such a way that t days after December 1 the volume of the cell was increasing at a rate of $(12 - t)^{-2}$ cubic micrometers per day. If on December 3 the volume of the cell was 3 μm^3, what was the volume on December 8?

54. The volume of a balloon is increasing according to the formula $\dfrac{dV}{dt} = \sqrt{t + 1} + \tfrac{2}{3}t$, where V cubic centimeters is the volume of the balloon at t seconds. If $V = 33$ when $t = 3$, find **(a)** a formula for V in terms of t; **(b)** the volume of the balloon at 8 sec.

55. Evaluate $\int (2x + 1)^3\, dx$ by two methods: **(a)** Expand $(2x + 1)^3$ by the binomial theorem; **(b)** let $u = 2x + 1$. **(c)** Explain the difference in appearance of the answers obtained in (a) and (b).

56. Evaluate $\int x(x^2 + 2)^2\, dx$ by two methods: **(a)** Expand $(x^2 + 2)^2$ and multiply the result by x; **(b)** let $u = x^2 + 2$. **(c)** Explain the difference in appearance of the answers obtained in (a) and (b).

57. Evaluate $\int \dfrac{(\sqrt{x} - 1)^2}{\sqrt{x}} \, dx$ by two methods:
(a) Expand $(\sqrt{x} - 1)^2$ and multiply the result by $x^{-1/2}$; (b) let $u = \sqrt{x} - 1$. (c) Explain the difference in appearance of the answers obtained in (a) and (b).

58. Evaluate $\int \sqrt{x - 1} \, x^2 \, dx$ by two methods: (a) Let $u = x - 1$; (b) let $v = \sqrt{x - 1}$.

59. Evaluate $\int 2 \sin x \cos x \, dx$ by three methods: (a) Let $u = \sin x$; (b) let $v = \cos x$; (c) use the identity $2 \sin x \cos x = \sin 2x$. (d) Explain the difference in appearance of the answers obtained in (a), (b), and (c).

60. Evaluate $\int \csc^2 x \cot x \, dx$ by two methods: (a) Let $u = \cot x$; (b) let $v = \csc x$. (c) Explain the difference in appearance of the answers obtained in (a) and (b).

4.3 DIFFERENTIAL EQUATIONS AND RECTILINEAR MOTION

An equation containing a function and its derivatives, or just its derivatives, is called a *differential equation*. Applications of differential equations occur in many diverse fields. In this section we will apply them to rectilinear motion in physics. Later on we will apply them to exponential growth and decay and logistic growth in chemistry, biology, psychology, sociology, business, and economics.

You were exposed to some simple differential equations in Section 4.1; for instance, in Illustration 6 of that section we had the differential equation.

$$\frac{dy}{dx} = 2x \tag{1}$$

Some other simple differential equations are

$$\frac{dy}{dx} = \frac{2x^2}{3y^3} \tag{2}$$

$$\frac{d^2y}{dx^2} = 4x + 3 \tag{3}$$

The **order** of a differential equation is the order of the derivative of highest order that appears in the equation. Equations (1) and (2) are first-order and (3) is of the second order.

A function f defined by $y = f(x)$ is a **solution** of a differential equation if y and its derivatives satisfy the equation. One of the easiest differential equations to solve is a first-order equation of the form

$$\frac{dy}{dx} = f(x)$$

for which (1) is a particular example. Writing this equation with differentials we have

$$dy = f(x) \, dx \tag{4}$$

Another type of differential equation of the first order is one of the form

$$\frac{dy}{dx} = \frac{g(x)}{h(y)}$$

Equation (2) is a particular example of an equation of this type. If this equation is written with differentials, we have

$$h(y)\, dy = g(x)\, dx \tag{5}$$

In both (4) and (5), the left side involves only the variable y and the right side involves only the variable x. Thus the variables are separated, and we say that these are **separable differential equations.**

Consider Equation (4), which is

$$dy = f(x)\, dx$$

To solve this equation we must find all functions G for which $y = G(x)$ such that the equation is satisfied. So if F is an antiderivative of f, all functions G are defined by $G(x) = F(x) + C$, where C is an arbitrary constant. That is, if

$$d(G(x)) = d(F(x) + C)$$
$$= f(x)\, dx$$

then the **complete solution (or general solution)** of (4) is given by

$$y = F(x) + C$$

This equation represents a family of functions depending on an arbitrary constant C and is called a **one-parameter family.** The graphs of these functions form a one-parameter family of curves in the plane, and just one curve of the family passes through any particular point (x_1, y_1).

▷ **ILLUSTRATION 1**   Suppose we wish to find the complete solution of the differential equation

$$\frac{dy}{dx} = 2x \tag{6}$$

We separate the variables by writing the equation with differentials as

$$dy = 2x\, dx$$

We antidifferentiate on both sides of the equation and obtain

$$\int dy = \int 2x\, dx$$
$$y + C_1 = x^2 + C_2$$

Because $C_2 - C_1$ is an arbitrary constant if C_2 and C_1 are arbitrary, we can replace $C_2 - C_1$ by C, thereby obtaining

$$y = x^2 + C \tag{7}$$

which is the complete solution of differential equation (6).

Equation (7) represents a one-parameter family of functions. Figure 1 shows sketches of the graphs of the functions corresponding to $C = -4$, $C = -1$, $C = 0$, $C = 1$, and $C = 2$.   ◀

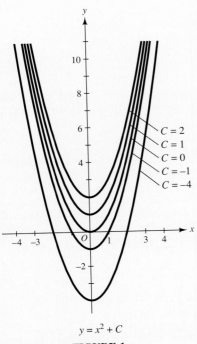

$C = 2$
$C = 1$
$C = 0$
$C = -1$
$C = -4$

$y = x^2 + C$

FIGURE 1

Now consider (5), which is

$$h(y) \, dy = g(x) \, dx$$

If we antidifferentiate on both sides of the equation, we write

$$\int h(y) \, dy = \int g(x) \, dx$$

If H is an antiderivative of h, and G is an antiderivative of g, the complete solution of (5) is given by

$$H(y) = G(x) + C$$

▶ **EXAMPLE 1** Find the complete solution of the differential equation

$$\frac{dy}{dx} = \frac{2x^2}{3y^3}$$

Solution If the given equation is written with differentials, we have

$$3y^3 \, dy = 2x^2 \, dx$$

and the variables are separated. We antidifferentiate on both sides of the equation and obtain

$$\int 3y^3 \, dy = \int 2x^2 \, dx$$

$$\frac{3y^4}{4} = \frac{2x^3}{3} + \frac{C}{12}$$

$$9y^4 = 8x^3 + C$$

which is the complete solution.

At first we wrote the arbitrary constant as $C/12$ so that when we multiplied both sides of the equation by 12, the arbitrary constant became C. ◀

In the following illustration, we show how to obtain a particular solution of a first-order differential equation when an initial condition is given.

▷ **ILLUSTRATION 2** To find the particular solution of differential equation (6) for which $y = 6$ when $x = 2$, we substitute these values in (7) and solve for C, giving $6 = 4 + C$, or $C = 2$. Substituting this value of C in (7) we obtain

$$y = x^2 + 2$$

which is the particular solution desired. ◀

Equation (3) is an example of a particular type of differential equation of the second order

$$\frac{d^2y}{dx^2} = f(x)$$

Two successive antidifferentiations are necessary to solve this equation, and two arbitrary constants occur in the complete solution. The complete solution therefore represents a **two-parameter family** of functions, and the graphs of these functions form a two-parameter family of curves in the plane. The following example shows the method of obtaining the complete solution of an equation of this kind.

▶ **EXAMPLE 2**   Find the complete solution of the differential equation

$$\frac{d^2y}{dx^2} = 4x + 3$$

Solution   Because

$$\frac{d^2y}{dx^2} = \frac{d}{dx}\left(\frac{dy}{dx}\right)$$

and letting $y' = \dfrac{dy}{dx}$, we can write the given equation as

$$\frac{dy'}{dx} = 4x + 3$$

Thus we have, with differentials,

$$dy' = (4x + 3)\, dx$$

Antidifferentiating, we obtain

$$\int dy' = \int (4x + 3)\, dx$$
$$y' = 2x^2 + 3x + C_1$$

Because $y' = \dfrac{dy}{dx}$, we make this substitution in the above equation and get

$$\frac{dy}{dx} = 2x^2 + 3x + C_1$$
$$dy = (2x^2 + 3x + C_1)\, dx$$
$$\int dy = \int (2x^2 + 3x + C_1)\, dx$$
$$y = \tfrac{2}{3}x^3 + \tfrac{3}{2}x^2 + C_1 x + C_2$$

which is the complete solution.   ◀

▶ **EXAMPLE 3**   Find the particular solution of the differential equation in Example 2 for which $y = 2$ and $y' = -3$ when $x = 1$.

Solution   Because $y' = 2x^2 + 3x + C_1$, we substitute -3 for y' and 1 for x, giving $-3 = 2 + 3 + C_1$, or $C_1 = -8$. Substituting this value of C_1 into the complete solution gives

$$y = \tfrac{2}{3}x^3 + \tfrac{3}{2}x^2 - 8x + C_2$$

Because $y = 2$ when $x = 1$, we substitute these values in the above equation and get $2 = \frac{2}{3} + \frac{3}{2} - 8 + C_2$, from which we obtain $C_2 = \frac{47}{6}$. The particular solution desired, then, is

$$y = \tfrac{2}{3}x^3 + \tfrac{3}{2}x^2 - 8x + \tfrac{47}{6}$$

◀

You learned in Section 2.5 that when a particle is moving along a line according to an equation of motion, $s = f(t)$, the instantaneous velocity and acceleration can be determined from the equations

$$v = \frac{ds}{dt} \quad \text{and} \quad a = \frac{dv}{dt}$$

Therefore, if we are given v or a as a function of t, as well as some boundary conditions, we can determine the equation of motion by solving a differential equation. We illustrate the procedure in the next two examples.

▶ **EXAMPLE 4**   A particle is moving on a line where v centimeters per second is the velocity of the particle at t seconds and

$$v = 10 \cos 2\pi t$$

If the positive direction is to the right of the origin and the particle is 5 cm to the right of the origin at the start of the motion, find its position when t is **(a)** 0.3, **(b)** 1.4, **(c)** 2.9, and **(d)** 3.6. Simulate the motion on a graphics calculator and support the answers.

Solution   Let s centimeters be the directed distance of the particle from the origin at t seconds. Because $v = ds/dt$,

$$\frac{ds}{dt} = 10 \cos 2\pi t$$

$$ds = 10 \cos 2\pi t \, dt$$

$$\int ds = 10 \int \cos 2\pi t \, dt$$

$$s = \frac{10}{2\pi} \int \cos 2\pi t (2\pi \, dt)$$

$$s = \frac{5}{\pi} \sin 2\pi t + C$$

Because $s = 5$ when $t = 0$,

$$5 = \frac{5}{\pi} \sin 0 + C$$

$$C = 5$$

The equation of motion is, therefore,

$$s = \frac{5}{\pi} \sin 2\pi t + 5$$

(a) When $t = 0.3$,

$$s = \frac{5}{\pi} \sin 0.6\pi + 5$$

$$\approx 6.51$$

(b) When $t = 1.4$,

$$s = \frac{5}{\pi} \sin 2.8\pi + 5$$

$$\approx 5.94$$

(c) When $t = 2.9$,

$$s = \frac{5}{\pi} \sin 5.8\pi + 5$$

$$\approx 4.06$$

(d) When $t = 3.6$,

$$s = \frac{5}{\pi} \sin 7.2\pi + 5$$

$$\approx 4.06$$

We now simulate the motion on our graphics calculator on the line $y = 1$. With our calculator in parametric mode, we let

$$x(t) = \frac{5}{\pi} \sin 2\pi t + 5 \quad \text{and} \quad y(t) = 1$$

We set our window variables as follows: $t_{\min} = 0$, $t_{\max} = 4$, $t_{\text{step}} = 0.01$, $x_{\min} = 0$, $x_{\max} = 7$, $x_{\text{scl}} = 1$, $y_{\min} = -1$, $y_{\max} = 2$, and $y_{\text{scl}} = 1$. We press the $\boxed{\text{TRACE}}$ key and then press the left-arrow key and hold it down until the cursor is at $t = 0$. Figure 2 shows the calculator screen with the following information at the bottom: $t = 0$, $x = 5$, and $y = 1$. We press the right-arrow key and hold it down and observe the cursor, which represents the particle, moving along the line $y = 1$. At the bottom of the screen, we note the following: when $t = 0.3$, $x = 6.51$; when $t = 1.4$, $x = 5.94$; when $t = 2.9$, $x = 4.06$; when $t = 3.6$, $x = 4.06$. These values support our answers.

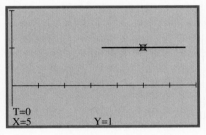

T=0
X=5   Y=1

[0, 7] by [−1, 2]

$x(t) = \frac{5}{\pi} \sin 2\pi t + 5$ and $y(t) = 1$

FIGURE 2

Conclusion: At 0.3 sec, the particle is 6.51 cm from the origin; at 1.4 sec, the particle is 5.94 cm from the origin; at 2.9 sec, the particle is 4.06 cm from the origin; and at 3.6 sec, the particle is again 4.06 cm from the origin. ◀

If an object is moving freely in a vertical line and is being pulled toward the earth by a force of gravity, the acceleration due to *gravity* varies with the distance of the object from the center of the earth. However, for small changes of distances the acceleration due to gravity is almost constant. If the object is near sea level, an approximate value of the acceleration due to gravity is 32 ft/sec² or 9.8 m/sec².

▶ **EXAMPLE 5** A stone is thrown vertically upward from the ground with an initial velocity of 128 ft/sec. Consider that the only force acting is attributed to the acceleration due to gravity. Find **(a)** how high the stone will go, and **(b)** how long it will take for the stone to strike the ground. **(c)** Simulate the motion on a graphics calculator and support the answers in parts (a) and (b). **(d)** Find the speed with which the stone strikes the ground.

Solution The stone's motion is on a vertical line. Figure 3 indicates the behavior of the motion where the arrow indicates the direction of motion of the stone on a vertical line with the positive direction upward.

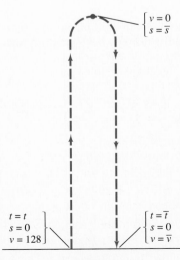

$$\begin{cases} v = 0 \\ s = \overline{s} \end{cases}$$

$$\begin{cases} t = t \\ s = 0 \\ v = 128 \end{cases} \qquad \begin{cases} t = \overline{t} \\ s = 0 \\ v = \overline{v} \end{cases}$$

FIGURE 3

Table 1

t	s	v
0	0	128
	$\bar{s}$	0
$\bar{t}$	0	$\bar{v}$

Let t seconds be the time that has elapsed since the stone was thrown, s feet be the distance of the stone from the ground at t seconds, v feet per second be the velocity of the stone at t seconds, and $|v|$ feet per second be the speed of the stone at t seconds.

When the stone strikes the ground, $s = 0$. Let $\bar{t}$ and $\bar{v}$ be the particular values of t and v when $s = 0$ and $t \neq 0$. The stone will be at its highest point when the velocity is zero. Let $\bar{s}$ be the particular value of s when $v = 0$. Table 1 shows the boundary conditions.

The acceleration due to gravity is in the downward direction and has an approximate constant value of -32 ft/sec^2. Because the acceleration is given by $\dfrac{dv}{dt}$ we have

$$\frac{dv}{dt} = -32$$

$$dv = -32\ dt$$

$$\int dv = -32 \int dt$$

$$v = -32t + C_1$$

Since $v = 128$ when $t = 0$, we substitute these values in the above equation and get $C_1 = 128$. Therefore

$$v = -32t + 128 \tag{8}$$

Because $v = \dfrac{ds}{dt}$,

$$\frac{ds}{dt} = -32t + 128$$

$$ds = (-32t + 128)\ dt$$

$$\int ds = \int (-32t + 128)\ dt$$

$$s = -16t^2 + 128t + C_2$$

Since $s = 0$ when $t = 0$, then $C_2 = 0$, and substituting 0 for C_2 in the above equation gives

$$s = -16t^2 + 128t \tag{9}$$

(a) To find how high the stone will go, we need to determine $\bar{s}$. We first find the value of t for which $v = 0$. From (8), $t = 4$ when $v = 0$. In (9) we substitute 4 for t and $\bar{s}$ for s and get

$$\bar{s} = -16(16) + 128(4)$$
$$= 256$$

<u>Conclusion:</u>   The stone will rise 256 ft.

(b) To find how long it will take for the stone to strike the ground we need to determine $\bar{t}$. In (9) we substitute $\bar{t}$ for t and 0 for s to obtain

$$0 = -16\bar{t}(\bar{t} - 8)$$

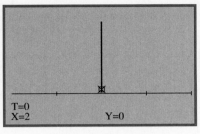

[0, 4] by [−100, 300]

$x(t) = 2$ and $y(t) = -16t^2 + 128t$

FIGURE 4

from which $\bar{t} = 0$ and $\bar{t} = 8$. However, the value 0 occurs when the stone is thrown.

<u>Conclusion:</u>   It takes 8 sec for the stone to strike the ground.

(c) To simulate the motion on our graphics calculator, we assume the stone moves on the vertical line $x = 2$. With our calculator in parametric mode, we let

$$x(t) = 2 \quad \text{and} \quad y(t) = -16t^2 + 128t$$

We set our window variables as follows: $t_{min} = 0$, $t_{max} = 8$, $t_{step} = 0.1$, $x_{min} = 0$, $x_{max} = 4$, $x_{scl} = 1$, $y_{min} = -100$, $y_{max} = 300$, $y_{scl} = 0$. We press the $\boxed{\text{TRACE}}$ key and then press the left-arrow key and hold it down until the cursor is at $t = 0$. Figure 4 shows the calculator screen as it now appears. We press the right-arrow key and observe the stone, represented by the cursor, moving up and down along the line $x = 2$. Observe that the largest value that y assumes is 256, which occurs when $t = 4$, thus supporting our answer in part (a). Also observe that the stone is back on the ground (when $y = 0$) at $t = 8$, which supports our answer in part (b).

(d) To obtain $\bar{v}$ we use (8) and substitute 8 for t and $\bar{v}$ for v and get

$$\bar{v} = -32(8) + 128$$
$$= -128$$

Therefore, $|\bar{v}| = 128$

<u>Conclusion:</u>   The stone strikes the ground with a speed of 128 ft/sec. ◄

EXERCISES 4.3

In Exercises 1 through 14, find the complete solution of the differential equation.

1. $\dfrac{dy}{dx} = 4x - 5$

2. $\dfrac{dy}{dx} = 6 - 3x^2$

3. $\dfrac{dy}{dx} = 3x^2 + 2x - 7$

4. $\dfrac{ds}{dt} = 5\sqrt{s}$

5. $\dfrac{dy}{dx} = 3xy^2$

6. $\dfrac{dy}{dx} = \dfrac{\sqrt{x} + x}{\sqrt{y} - y}$

7. $\dfrac{du}{dv} = \dfrac{3v\sqrt{1 + u^2}}{u}$

8. $\dfrac{dy}{dx} = \dfrac{x^2\sqrt{x^3 - 3}}{y^2}$

9. $\dfrac{dy}{dx} = \dfrac{\sec^2 x}{\tan^2 y}$

10. $\dfrac{du}{dv} = \dfrac{\cos 2v}{\sin 3u}$

11. $\dfrac{d^2y}{dx^2} = 5x^2 + 1$

12. $\dfrac{d^2y}{dx^2} = \sqrt{2x - 3}$

13. $\dfrac{d^2s}{dt^2} = \sin 3t + \cos 3t$

14. $\dfrac{d^2u}{dv^2} = \tan v \sec^2 v$

In Exercises 15 through 20, find the particular solution of the differential equation determined by the initial conditions.

15. $\dfrac{dy}{dx} = x^2 - 2x - 4$; $y = -6$ when $x = 3$

16. $\dfrac{dy}{dx} = (x + 1)(x + 2)$; $y = -\frac{3}{2}$ when $x = -3$

17. $\dfrac{dy}{dx} = \dfrac{\cos 3x}{\sin 2y}$; $y = \frac{1}{3}\pi$ when $x = \frac{1}{2}\pi$

18. $\dfrac{ds}{dt} = \cos \frac{1}{2}t$; $s = 3$ when $t = \frac{1}{3}\pi$

19. $\dfrac{d^2u}{dv^2} = 4(1 + 3v)^2$; $u = -1$ and $\dfrac{du}{dv} = -2$ when $v = -1$

20. $\dfrac{d^2y}{dx^2} = -\dfrac{3}{x^4}$; $y = \dfrac{1}{2}$ and $\dfrac{dy}{dx} = -1$ when $x = 1$

In Exercises 21 through 32, a particle is moving on a line; at t seconds, s feet is the directed distance of the particle from the origin, v feet per second is the velocity of the particle, and a feet per second per second is the acceleration of the particle. Hint for Exercises 29 through 32:

$$a = \frac{dv}{dt} = \frac{dv}{ds}\frac{ds}{dt} = v\frac{dv}{ds}$$

21. $v = \sqrt{2t + 4}$; $s = 0$ when $t = 0$. Express s in terms of t.

22. $v = 4 - t$; $s = 0$ when $t = 2$. Express s in terms of t.

23. $a = 5 - 2t$; $v = 2$ and $s = 0$ when $t = 0$. Express v and s in terms of t.

24. $a = 17$; $v = 0$ and $s = 0$ when $t = 0$. Express v and s in terms of t.

25. $a = t^2 + 2t$; $s = 1$ when $t = 0$ and $s = -3$ when $t = 2$. Express v and s in terms of t.

26. $a = 3t - t^2$; $v = \frac{7}{6}$ and $s = 1$ when $t = 1$. Express v and s in terms of t.

27. $a = -4\sqrt{2}\cos(2t - \frac{1}{4}\pi)$; $v = 2$ and $s = 1$ when $t = 0$. Express v and s in terms of t.

28. $a = 18 \sin 3t$; $v = -6$ and $s = 4$ when $t = 0$. Express v and s in terms of t.

29. $a = 800$; $v = 20$ when $s = 1$. Find an equation involving v and s.

30. $a = 500$; $v = 10$ when $s = 5$. Find an equation involving v and s.

31. $a = 5s + 2$; $v = 4$ when $s = 2$. Find an equation involving v and s.

32. $a = 2s + 1$; $v = 2$ when $s = 1$. Find an equation involving v and s.

In Exercises 33 through 52, be sure to define your variables as numbers and write a conclusion. In Exercises 35 through 43, consider that the only force acting is attributed to the acceleration due to gravity taken as 32 ft/sec² or 9.8 m/sec² in the downward direction.

33. A particle is moving along a line in such a way that if v centimeters per second is the velocity of the particle at t seconds, then $v = 9 \sin 3\pi t$, where the positive direction is to the right of the origin. If the particle is at the origin at the start of the motion, find its position when t is **(a)** 0.6, **(b)** 2.5, **(c)** 4.8, and **(d)** 7.2. Simulate the motion on your graphics calculator and support your answers.

34. Do Exercise 33 if $v = 2 \cos \frac{1}{2}\pi t$.

35. A ball is thrown vertically upward from the ground with an initial velocity of 20 ft/sec. **(a)** How long will the ball be going up, **(b)** how high will the ball go, and **(c)** how long will it take the ball to reach the ground? **(d)** Simulate the motion on your graphics calculator and support your answers in parts (a)–(c). **(e)** With what speed will the ball strike the ground?

36. Do Exercise 35 if the initial velocity is 5 m/sec.

37. A stone is dropped from the top of the Washington Monument, 555 ft high. **(a)** How long will it take the stone to reach the ground, and **(b)** with what speed will it strike the ground?

38. A ball is thrown downward from a window that is 80 ft above the ground with an initial velocity of -64 ft/sec. **(a)** How long will it take the ball to reach the ground, and **(b)** with what speed will it strike the ground?

39. A woman in a hot air balloon drops her binoculars when the balloon is 150 ft above the ground and rising at the rate of 10 ft/sec. **(a)** How long will it take the binoculars to reach the ground, and **(b)** with what speed will it strike the ground?

40. A stone is thrown vertically upward from the top of a house 60 ft above the ground with an initial velocity of 40 ft/sec. **(a)** How long will it take the stone to reach its greatest height, and **(b)** what is its greatest height? **(c)** How long will it take the stone to pass the top of the house on its way down, and **(d)** what is its velocity at that instant? **(e)** How long will it take the stone to reach the ground, and **(f)** with what velocity will it strike the ground?

41. As you are walking in the forest you look up just as a boulder becomes dislodged from the side of a cliff. If your head is 200 ft below the base of the boulder at that instant, **(a)** how much time do you have to get out of the way? **(b)** If you do not get out of the way in time, with what speed will the boulder hit you?

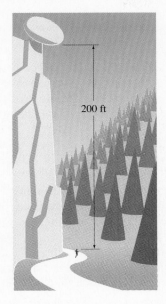

200 ft

42. A ball is thrown vertically upward with an initial velocity of 40 ft/sec from a point 20 ft above the ground. **(a)** If v feet per second is the velocity of the ball when it is s feet from the starting point, express v in terms of s. **(b)** What is the velocity of the ball when it is 36 ft from the ground and rising?

43. A projectile is fired vertically upward with an initial velocity of 150 m/sec from a point 2 m above the ground. **(a)** If s meters is the height of the projectile above the ground t seconds after being fired, express s in terms of t, under the assumption that the only force acting on the projectile is attributed to the acceleration due to gravity. **(b)** How high above the ground is the projectile 4 sec after being fired? **(c)** How long will it take for the projectile to be 500 m above the ground?

44. If a rocket is lifted off the ground with a constant acceleration of 22 m/sec², find **(a)** the velocity of the rocket 30 sec after lift off, and **(b)** how high above the ground the rocket will be at that time.

45. A space shuttle climbs vertically with a constant acceleration of 10 yd/sec². If a radar-tracking dish, 1200 yd from the shuttle's launch pad, follows the shuttle, how fast is the radar dish revolving 8 sec after blast off?

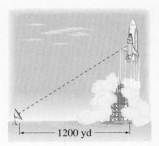

1200 yd

46. If a ball is rolled across level ground with an initial velocity of 20 ft/sec, and if the speed of the ball is decreasing at the rate of 6 ft/sec² due to friction, how far will the ball roll?

47. If the driver of an automobile wishes to increase the speed from 40 km/hr to 100 km/hr while traveling a distance of 200 m, what constant acceleration should be maintained?

48. What constant negative acceleration will enable a driver to decrease the speed from 120 km/hr to 60 km/hr while traveling a distance of 100 m?

49. If the brakes are applied on a car traveling 100 km/hr and the brakes can give the car a constant negative acceleration of 8 m/sec², **(a)** how long will it take the car to come to a stop, and **(b)** how far will the car travel before stopping?

50. A ball started upward from the bottom of an inclined plane with an initial velocity of 6 ft/sec. If there was a constant downward acceleration of 4 ft/sec², how far up the plane did the ball go before starting to roll down?

51. If the brakes on a car can give the car a constant negative acceleration of 8 m/sec², what is the greatest speed it may be going if it is necessary to be able to stop the car within 25 m after the brake is applied?

52. A block of ice slides down a chute with a constant acceleration of 3 m/sec². The chute is 36 m long and it takes 4 sec for the ice to reach the bottom. **(a)** What is the initial velocity of the ice? **(b)** What is the speed of the ice after it has traveled 12 m? **(c)** How long does it take the ice to go the 12 m?

53. The equation $x^2 = 4ay$ represents a one-parameter family of parabolas. Find an equation of another one-parameter family of curves such that at any point (x, y) there is a curve of each family through it and the tangent lines to the two curves at this point are perpendicular. *Hint:* First show that the slope of the tangent line at any point (x, y), not on the y axis, of the parabola of the given family through that point is $2y/x$.

54. Solve Exercise 53 if the given one-parameter family of curves has the equation $x^3 + y^3 = a^3$.

55. If a particle is moving on a line and you know the acceleration as a function of time, what initial condi-

tions must you also know to obtain an equation expressing the distance of the particle from the origin as a function of time? Explain how you find this equation.

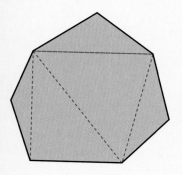

FIGURE 1

4.4 AREA

You probably have an intuitive idea that the *area* of a geometrical figure is a measurement that in some way gives the size of the region enclosed by the figure. For instance, you know that the area of a rectangle is the product of its length and width and the area of a triangle is half the product of the lengths of the base and altitude. The area of a polygon can be defined as the sum of the areas of triangles into which it is decomposed, and it can be proved that the area thus obtained is independent of how the polygon is decomposed into triangles. See Figure 1.

In this section, we define the area of a region in a plane if the region is bounded by a curve. If you are wondering why we are concerned with such an area, the answer is that we are laying the foundation necessary to motivate geometrically the definition of the *definite integral* in the next section. Remember, we motivated geometrically the definition of the derivative of a function as the slope of the tangent line to the graph of the function. Just as with the derivative, after we have defined the definite integral you will learn that we can apply the definition in a wide variety of fields.

In our treatment of area we shall be concerned with the sums of many terms, and so a notation called the sigma notation is introduced to facilitate writing these sums. This notation involves the use of the symbol Σ, the capital sigma of the Greek alphabet. Some examples of the sigma notation are given in the following illustration.

▷ **ILLUSTRATION 1**

$$\sum_{i=1}^{5} i^2 = 1^2 + 2^2 + 3^2 + 4^2 + 5^2$$

$$\sum_{i=-2}^{2} (3i + 2) = [3(-2) + 2] + [3(-1) + 2] + [3 \cdot 0 + 2]$$
$$+ [3 \cdot 1 + 2] + [3 \cdot 2 + 2]$$
$$= (-4) + (-1) + 2 + 5 + 8$$

$$\sum_{j=1}^{n} j^3 = 1^3 + 2^3 + 3^3 + \ldots + n^3$$

$$\sum_{k=3}^{8} \frac{1}{k} = \frac{1}{3} + \frac{1}{4} + \frac{1}{5} + \frac{1}{6} + \frac{1}{7} + \frac{1}{8}$$ ◀

4.4.1 Definition of the Sigma Notation

$$\sum_{i=m}^{n} F(i) = F(m) + F(m + 1) + F(m + 2) + \ldots + F(n - 1) + F(n)$$

where m and n are integers, and $m \leq n$.

The right side of the equation in the definition consists of the sum of $(n - m + 1)$ terms, the first of which is obtained by replacing i by m in $F(i)$, the second by replacing i by $m + 1$ in $F(i)$, and so on, until the last term is obtained by replacing i by n in $F(i)$.

The number m is called the **lower limit** of the sum, and n is called the **upper limit**. The symbol i is called the **index of summation**. It is a "dummy" symbol because any other letter can be used for this purpose. For example,

$$\sum_{k=3}^{5} k^2 = 3^2 + 4^2 + 5^2$$

is equivalent to

$$\sum_{i=3}^{5} i^2 = 3^2 + 4^2 + 5^2$$

▷ **ILLUSTRATION 2**   From Definition 4.4.1,

$$\sum_{i=3}^{6} \frac{i^2}{i + 1} = \frac{3^2}{3 + 1} + \frac{4^2}{4 + 1} + \frac{5^2}{5 + 1} + \frac{6^2}{6 + 1}$$ ◀

Sometimes the terms of a sum involve subscripts, as shown in the next illustration.

▷ **ILLUSTRATION 3**

$$\sum_{i=1}^{n} A_i = A_1 + A_2 + \ldots + A_n$$

$$\sum_{k=4}^{9} kb_k = 4b_4 + 5b_5 + 6b_6 + 7b_7 + 8b_8 + 9b_9$$

$$\sum_{i=1}^{4} f(x_i)\,\Delta x = f(x_1)\,\Delta x + f(x_2)\,\Delta x + f(x_3)\,\Delta x + f(x_4)\,\Delta x$$ ◀

The following theorems involving the sigma notation are useful for computation and are easily proved.

4.4.2 Theorem

$$\sum_{i=1}^{n} c = cn, \text{ where } c \text{ is any constant}$$

Proof

$$\sum_{i=1}^{n} c = c + c + \ldots + c \quad (n \text{ terms})$$
$$= cn$$ ∎

4.4.3 Theorem

$$\sum_{i=1}^{n} c \cdot F(i) = c \sum_{i=1}^{n} F(i), \text{ where } c \text{ is any constant}$$

Proof

$$\sum_{i=1}^{n} c \cdot F(i) = c \cdot F(1) + c \cdot F(2) + c \cdot F(3) + \ldots + c \cdot F(n)$$
$$= c[F(1) + F(2) + F(3) + \ldots + F(n)]$$
$$= c \sum_{i=1}^{n} F(i)$$
∎

4.4.4 Theorem

$$\sum_{i=1}^{n} [F(i) + G(i)] = \sum_{i=1}^{n} F(i) + \sum_{i=1}^{n} G(i)$$

The proof is left as an exercise (see Exercise 43). Theorem 4.4.4 can be extended to the sum of any number of functions.

4.4.5 Theorem

$$\sum_{i=a}^{b} F(i) = \sum_{i=a+c}^{b+c} F(i - c) \tag{1}$$

and

$$\sum_{i=a}^{b} F(i) = \sum_{i=a-c}^{b-c} F(i + c) \tag{2}$$

The proof of theorem 4.4.5 is left as an exercise (see Exercise 44). The following illustration shows the application of this theorem.

▷ **ILLUSTRATION 4**   From Equation (1) of Theorem 4.4.5,

$$\sum_{i=3}^{10} F(i) = \sum_{i=5}^{12} F(i - 2) \quad \text{and} \quad \sum_{i=6}^{11} i^2 = \sum_{i=7}^{12} (i - 1)^2$$

From Equation (2) of Theorem 4.4.5

$$\sum_{i=3}^{10} F(i) = \sum_{i=1}^{8} F(i + 2) \quad \text{and} \quad \sum_{i=6}^{11} i^2 = \sum_{i=1}^{6} (i + 5)^2$$
◀

4.4.6 Theorem

$$\sum_{i=1}^{n} [F(i) - F(i - 1)] = F(n) - F(0)$$

Proof

$$\sum_{i=1}^{n} [F(i) - F(i-1)] = \sum_{i=1}^{n} F(i) - \sum_{i=1}^{n} F(i-1)$$

On the right side of this equation we write the first summation in another form and apply Equation (2) of Theorem 4.4.5 with $c = 1$ to the second summation. Then

$$\sum_{i=1}^{n} [F(i) - F(i-1)] = \left(\sum_{i=1}^{n-1} F(i) + F(n)\right) - \sum_{i=1-1}^{n-1} F[(i+1)-1]$$

$$= \sum_{i=1}^{n-1} F(i) + F(n) - \sum_{i=0}^{n-1} F(i)$$

$$= \sum_{i=1}^{n-1} F(i) + F(n) - \left(F(0) + \sum_{i=1}^{n-1} F(i)\right)$$

$$= F(n) - F(0) \qquad \blacksquare$$

▶ **EXAMPLE 1**   Evaluate

$$\sum_{i=1}^{n} (4^i - 4^{i-1})$$

Solution   From Theorem 4.4.6, where $F(i) = 4^i$, it follows that

$$\sum_{i=1}^{n} (4^i - 4^{i-1}) = 4^n - 4^0$$

$$= 4^n - 1 \qquad ◀$$

The next theorem gives four formulas useful for computation with sigma notation. These formulas can be proved by mathematical induction. They can also be proved without mathematical induction; see Exercises 45–48.

4.4.7 Theorem

If n is a positive integer, then

$$\sum_{i=1}^{n} i = \frac{n(n+1)}{2} \qquad \text{(Formula 1)}$$

$$\sum_{i=1}^{n} i^2 = \frac{n(n+1)(2n+1)}{6} \qquad \text{(Formula 2)}$$

$$\sum_{i=1}^{n} i^3 = \frac{n^2(n+1)^2}{4} \qquad \text{(Formula 3)}$$

$$\sum_{i=1}^{n} i^4 = \frac{n(n+1)(2n+1)(3n^2+3n-1)}{30} \qquad \text{(Formula 4)}$$

▶ **EXAMPLE 2**   Evaluate

$$\sum_{i=1}^{n} i(3i-2)$$

Solution

$$\sum_{i=1}^{n} i(3i - 2) = \sum_{i=1}^{n} (3i^2 - 2i)$$

$$= \sum_{i=1}^{n} (3i^2) + \sum_{i=1}^{n} (-2i) \qquad \text{(by Theorem 4.4.4)}$$

$$= 3 \sum_{i=1}^{n} i^2 - 2 \sum_{i=1}^{n} i \qquad \text{(by Theorem 4.4.3)}$$

$$= 3 \cdot \frac{n(n + 1)(2n + 1)}{6} - 2 \cdot \frac{n(n + 1)}{2} \qquad \text{(by Formulas 2 and 1)}$$

$$= \frac{2n^3 + 3n^2 + n - 2n^2 - 2n}{2}$$

$$= \frac{2n^3 + n^2 - n}{2}$$

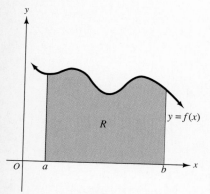

FIGURE 2

Before discussing the area of a plane region, we indicate why we use the terminology "*measure* of the area." The word *measure* refers to a number (no units are included). For example, if the area of a triangle is 20 cm², we say that the square-centimeter measure of the area of the triangle is 20. When the word *measurement* is applied, the units are included. Thus the measurement of the area of the triangle is 20 cm².

Consider now a region R in the plane as shown in Figure 2. The region R is bounded by the x axis, the lines $x = a$ and $x = b$, and the curve having the equation $y = f(x)$, where f is a function continuous on the closed interval $[a, b]$. For simplicity, take $f(x) \geq 0$ for all x in $[a, b]$. We wish to assign a number A to be the measure of the area of R, and we use a limiting process similar to the one used in defining the area of a circle: The area of a circle is defined as the limit of the areas of inscribed regular polygons as the number of sides increases without bound. We realize intuitively that, whatever number is chosen to represent A, that number must be at least as great as the measure of the area of any polygonal region contained in R, and it must be no greater than the measure of the area of any polygonal region containing R.

We first define a polygonal region contained in R. Divide the closed interval $[a, b]$ into n subintervals. For simplicity, we now take each of these subintervals as being of equal length, for instance, Δx. Therefore $\Delta x = (b - a)/n$. Denote the endpoints of these subintervals by $x_0, x_1, x_2, \ldots, x_{n-1}, x_n$, where $x_0 = a$, $x_1 = a + \Delta x, \ldots, x_i = a + i \Delta x, \ldots, x_{n-1} = a + (n - 1) \Delta x, x_n = b$. Let the ith subinterval be denoted by $[x_{i-1}, x_i]$. Because f is continuous on the closed interval $[a, b]$, it is continuous on each closed subinterval. By the extreme-value theorem there is a number in each subinterval for which f has an absolute minimum value. In the ith subinterval let this number be c_i, so that $f(c_i)$ is the absolute minimum value of f on the subinterval $[x_{i-1}, x_i]$. Consider n rectangles, each having a width Δx units and an altitude $f(c_i)$ units (see Figure 3). Let the sum of the areas of these n rectangles be given by S_n square units; then

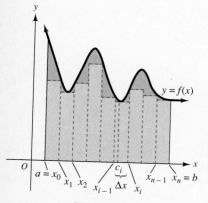

FIGURE 3

$$S_n = f(c_1) \Delta x + f(c_2) \Delta x + \ldots + f(c_i) \Delta x + \ldots + f(c_n) \Delta x$$

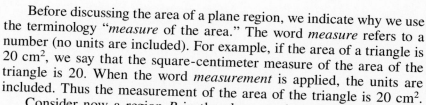

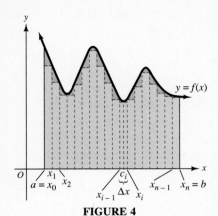

FIGURE 4

or, with the sigma notation,

$$S_n = \sum_{i=1}^{n} f(c_i)\, \Delta x \tag{3}$$

The summation on the right side of (3) gives the sum of the measures of the areas of n inscribed rectangles. Thus, however we define A, it must be such that

$$A \geq S_n$$

In Figure 3 the green region has an area of S_n square units. Now let n increase. Specifically, multiply n by 2; then the number of rectangles is doubled, and the width of each rectangle is halved. This is illustrated in Figure 4, showing twice as many rectangles as Figure 3. By comparing the two figures, notice that the green region in Figure 4 appears to approximate the region R more nearly than that of Figure 3. So the sum of the measures of the areas of the rectangles in Figure 4 is closer to the number we wish to represent the measure of the area of R.

As n increases, the values of S_n found from Equation (3) increase, and successive values of S_n differ from each other by amounts that become arbitrarily small. This is proved in advanced calculus by a theorem that states that if f is continuous on $[a, b]$, then as n increases without bound, the value of S_n given by (3) approaches a limit. It is this limit that we take as the definition of the measure of the area of region R.

4.4.8 Definition of the Area of a Plane Region

Suppose that the function f is continuous on the closed interval $[a, b]$, with $f(x) \geq 0$ for all x in $[a, b]$, and that R is the region bounded by the curve $y = f(x)$, the x axis, and the lines $x = a$ and $x = b$. Divide the interval $[a, b]$ into n subintervals, each of length $\Delta x = (b - a)/n$, and denote the ith subinterval by $[x_{i-1}, x_i]$. Then if $f(c_i)$ is the absolute minimum function value on the ith subinterval, the measure of the **area of region R** is given by

$$A = \lim_{n \to +\infty} \sum_{i=1}^{n} f(c_i)\, \Delta x \tag{4}$$

This equation means that for any $\epsilon > 0$ there is a number $N > 0$ such that if n is a positive integer and

$$\text{if} \quad n > N \quad \text{then} \quad \left| \sum_{i=1}^{n} f(c_i)\, \Delta x - A \right| < \epsilon$$

We could take circumscribed rectangles instead of inscribed rectangles. In this case we take as the measures of the altitudes of the rectangles the absolute maximum value of f on each subinterval. The existence of an absolute maximum value of f on each subinterval is guaranteed by the extreme-value theorem. The corresponding sums of the measures of the areas of the circumscribed rectangles are at least as great as the measure of the area of the region R, and it can be shown that the limit of these sums as n increases without bound is exactly the same as the limit of the sum of the measures of the areas of the inscribed rectangles. This is also proved in advanced calculus. Thus we could define the measure of the area of the region R by

$$A = \lim_{n \to +\infty} \sum_{i=1}^{n} f(d_i) \, \Delta x \tag{5}$$

where $f(d_i)$ is the absolute maximum value of f in $[x_{i-1}, x_i]$.

The measure of the altitude of the rectangle in the ith subinterval actually can be taken as the function value of any number in that subinterval, and the limit of the sum of the measures of the areas of the rectangles is the same no matter what numbers are selected. In Section 4.5 we extend the definition of the measure of the area of a region to be the limit of such a sum.

▶ **EXAMPLE 3**   Find the area of the region bounded by the curve $y = x^2$, the x axis, and the line $x = 3$ by taking inscribed rectangles.

Solution   Figure 5 shows the region and the ith inscribed rectangle. We apply Definition 4.4.8. Divide the closed interval $[0, 3]$ into n subintervals, each of length Δx: $x_0 = 0$, $x_1 = \Delta x$, $x_2 = 2 \, \Delta x$, ..., $x_i = i \, \Delta x$, ..., $x_{n-1} = (n - 1) \, \Delta x$, $x_n = 3$.

$$\Delta x = \frac{3 - 0}{n} \qquad f(x) = x^2$$

$$= \frac{3}{n}$$

Because f is increasing on $[0, 3]$, the absolute minimum value of f on the ith subinterval $[x_{i-1}, x_i]$ is $f(x_{i-1})$. Therefore, from (4)

$$A = \lim_{n \to +\infty} \sum_{i=1}^{n} f(x_{i-1}) \, \Delta x \tag{6}$$

Because $x_{i-1} = (i - 1) \, \Delta x$ and $f(x) = x^2$,

$$f(x_{i-1}) = [(i - 1) \, \Delta x]^2$$

Therefore

$$\sum_{i=1}^{n} f(x_{i-1}) \, \Delta x = \sum_{i=1}^{n} (i - 1)^2 (\Delta x)^3$$

But $\Delta x = 3/n$; so

$$\sum_{i=1}^{n} f(x_{i-1}) \, \Delta x = \sum_{i=1}^{n} (i - 1)^2 \frac{27}{n^3}$$

$$= \frac{27}{n^3} \sum_{i=1}^{n} (i - 1)^2$$

$$= \frac{27}{n^3} \left[\sum_{i=1}^{n} i^2 - 2 \sum_{i=1}^{n} i + \sum_{i=1}^{n} 1 \right]$$

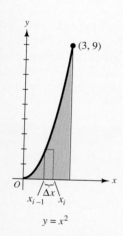

$y = x^2$

FIGURE 5

and using Formulas 2 and 1 and Theorem 4.4.2 we get

$$\sum_{i=1}^{n} f(x_{i-1})\, \Delta x = \frac{27}{n^3}\left[\frac{n(n+1)(2n+1)}{6} - 2 \cdot \frac{n(n+1)}{2} + n\right]$$

$$= \frac{27}{n^3} \cdot \frac{2n^3 + 3n^2 + n - 6n^2 - 6n + 6n}{6}$$

$$= \frac{9}{2} \cdot \frac{2n^2 - 3n + 1}{n^2}$$

Then, from (6),

$$A = \lim_{n \to +\infty} \left[\frac{9}{2} \cdot \frac{2n^2 - 3n + 1}{n^2}\right]$$

$$= \frac{9}{2} \cdot \lim_{n \to +\infty} \left(2 - \frac{3}{n} + \frac{1}{n^2}\right)$$

$$= \tfrac{9}{2}(2 - 0 + 0)$$

$$= 9$$

<u>Conclusion:</u>   The area of the region is 9 square units.   ◄

▶ **EXAMPLE 4**   Find the area of the region in Example 3 by taking circumscribed rectangles.

Solution   Figure 6 shows the region and the ith circumscribed rectangle. With circumscribed rectangles the measure of the altitude of the ith rectangle is the absolute maximum value of f on the ith subinterval $[x_{i-1}, x_i]$, which is $f(x_i)$. From (5),

$$A = \lim_{n \to +\infty} \sum_{i=1}^{n} f(x_i)\, \Delta x \qquad (7)$$

Because $x_i = i\, \Delta x$, then $f(x_i) = (i\, \Delta x)^2$, and so

$$\sum_{i=1}^{n} f(x_i)\, \Delta x = \sum_{i=1}^{n} i^2 (\Delta x)^3$$

$$= \frac{27}{n^3} \sum_{i=1}^{n} i^2$$

$$= \frac{27}{n^3}\left[\frac{n(n+1)(2n+1)}{6}\right]$$

$$= \frac{9}{2} \cdot \frac{2n^2 + 3n + 1}{n^2}$$

Therefore, from (7),

$$A = \lim_{n \to +\infty} \frac{9}{2} \cdot \left(2 + \frac{3}{n} + \frac{1}{n^2}\right)$$

$$= 9 \qquad \text{(as in Example 3)} \qquad ◄$$

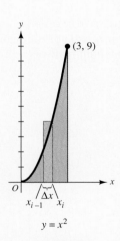

$y = x^2$

FIGURE 6

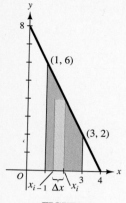

FIGURE 7

▶ **EXAMPLE 5**   Apply Definition 4.4.8 to compute the area of the trapezoidal region bounded by the lines $x = 1$ and $x = 3$, the x axis, and the line $2x + y = 8$. Check by the plane-geometry formula for the area of a trapezoid.

Solution   The region and the ith inscribed rectangle appear in Figure 7. We divide the closed interval $[1, 3]$ into n subintervals, each of length Δx; $x_0 = 1, x_1 = 1 + \Delta x, \ldots, x_i = 1 + i \, \Delta x, \ldots, x_{n-1} = 1 + (n - 1) \, \Delta x$, $x_n = 3$.

$$\Delta x = \frac{3 - 1}{n}$$

$$= \frac{2}{n}$$

Solving the equation of the line for y we obtain $y = -2x + 8$. Therefore $f(x) = -2x + 8$, and because f is decreasing on $[1, 3]$, the absolute minimum value of f on the ith subinterval $[x_{i-1}, x_i]$ is $f(x_i)$. Because $x_i = 1 + i \, \Delta x$ and $f(x) = -2x + 8$, then $f(x_i) = -2(1 + i \, \Delta x) + 8$, that is, $f(x_i) = 6 - 2i \, \Delta x$. From (4),

$$A = \lim_{n \to +\infty} \sum_{i=1}^{n} f(x_i) \, \Delta x$$

$$= \lim_{n \to +\infty} \sum_{i=1}^{n} (6 - 2i \, \Delta x) \, \Delta x$$

$$= \lim_{n \to +\infty} \sum_{i=1}^{n} [6 \, \Delta x - 2i(\Delta x)^2]$$

$$= \lim_{n \to +\infty} \sum_{i=1}^{n} \left[6 \left(\frac{2}{n} \right) - 2i \left(\frac{2}{n} \right)^2 \right]$$

$$= \lim_{n \to +\infty} \left[\frac{12}{n} \sum_{i=1}^{n} 1 - \frac{8}{n^2} \sum_{i=1}^{n} i \right]$$

From Theorem 4.4.2 and Formula 1,

$$A = \lim_{n \to +\infty} \left[\frac{12}{n} \cdot n - \frac{8}{n^2} \cdot \frac{n(n + 1)}{2} \right]$$

$$= \lim_{n \to +\infty} \left(8 - \frac{4}{n} \right)$$

$$= 8$$

<u>Conclusion:</u>   The area is 8 square units.

The plane-geometry formula for the area of a trapezoid is

$$A = \tfrac{1}{2} h(b_1 + b_2)$$

where h, b_1, and b_2 are, respectively, the number of units in the lengths of the altitude and the two bases, which for the trapezoid in Figure 7 are parallel to the y axis. From this formula, we get $A = \tfrac{1}{2}(2)(6 + 2)$; that is, $A = 8$, which agrees with our result.   ◀

EXERCISES 4.4

In Exercises 1 through 12, find the sum.

1. $\sum_{i=1}^{6} (3i - 2)$ **2.** $\sum_{i=1}^{20} (5i + 4)$ **3.** $\sum_{i=1}^{7} (i^2 + 1)$

4. $\sum_{i=1}^{7} (i + 1)^2$ **5.** $\sum_{i=1}^{10} (i - 1)^3$ **6.** $\sum_{i=1}^{10} (i^3 - 1)$

7. $\sum_{i=2}^{5} \frac{i}{i - 1}$ **8.** $\sum_{j=3}^{6} \frac{2}{j(j - 2)}$ **9.** $\sum_{i=-2}^{3} 2^i$

10. $\sum_{i=0}^{3} \frac{1}{1 + i^2}$ **11.** $\sum_{k=1}^{4} \frac{(-1)^{k+1}}{k}$ **12.** $\sum_{k=-2}^{3} \frac{k}{k + 3}$

In Exercises 13 through 20, evaluate the sum by using Theorems 4.4.2 through 4.4.7.

13. $\sum_{i=1}^{25} 2i(i - 1)$ **14.** $\sum_{i=1}^{20} 3i(i^2 + 2)$

15. $\sum_{k=1}^{n} (2^k - 2^{k-1})$ **16.** $\sum_{i=1}^{n} (10^{i+1} - 10^i)$

17. $\sum_{k=1}^{100} \left[\frac{1}{k} - \frac{1}{k + 1}\right]$ **18.** $\sum_{i=1}^{n} 2i(1 + i^2)$

19. $\sum_{i=1}^{n} 4i^2(i - 2)$

20. $\sum_{k=1}^{n} [(3^{-k} - 3^k)^2 - (3^{k-1} - 3^{-k+1})^2]$

In Exercises 21 through 30, use the method of this section to find the area of the region; use inscribed or circumscribed rectangles as indicated. For each exercise draw a figure showing the region and the ith rectangle.

21. The region bounded by $y = x^2$, the x axis, and the line $x = 2$; inscribed rectangles.

22. The region of Exercise 21; circumscribed rectangles.

23. The region above the x axis and to the right of the line $x = 1$ bounded by the x axis, the line $x = 1$, and the curve $y = 4 - x^2$; inscribed rectangles.

24. The region of Exercise 23; circumscribed rectangles.

25. The region above the x axis and to the left of the line $x = 1$ bounded by the curve and lines of Exercise 23; circumscribed rectangles.

26. The region of Exercise 25; inscribed rectangles.

27. The region bounded by $y = x^3$, the x axis, and the lines $x = -1$ and $x = 2$; inscribed rectangles.

28. The region of Exercise 27; circumscribed rectangles.

29. The region bounded by $y = x^3 + x$, the x axis, and the lines $x = -2$ and $x = 1$; circumscribed rectangles.

30. The region of Exercise 29; inscribed rectangles.

31. Use the method of this section to find the area of an isosceles trapezoid whose bases have measures b_1 and b_2 and whose altitude has measure h.

32. The graph of $y = 4 - |x|$ and the x axis from $x = -4$ to $x = 4$ form a triangle. Use the method of this section to find the area of this triangle.

In Exercises 33 through 36, find the area of the region by taking as the measure of the altitude of the ith rectangle $f(m_i)$, where m_i is the midpoint of the ith subinterval. Hint: $m_i = \frac{1}{2}(x_i + x_{i-1})$.

33. The region of Example 3.

34. The region of Exercise 22.

35. The region of Exercise 23.

36. The region of Exercise 26.

In Exercises 37 through 42, a function f and numbers n, a, and b are given. Approximate to four decimal places the area of the region bounded by the curve $y = f(x)$, the x axis, and the lines $x = a$ and $x = b$ by doing the following: Divide the interval $[a, b]$ into n subintervals of equal length Δx units and use a calculator to compute the sum of the areas of n inscribed or circumscribed (as indicated) rectangles each having a width of Δx units.

37. $f(x) = \frac{1}{x}$, $a = 1$, $b = 3$, $n = 10$, inscribed.

38. $f(x) = \frac{1}{x^2}$, $a = 1$, $b = 2$, $n = 12$, circumscribed.

39. $f(x) = \sin x$, $a = \frac{1}{6}\pi$, $b = \frac{5}{6}\pi$, $n = 8$, circumscribed.

40. $f(x) = \cos x$, $a = 0$, $b = \frac{1}{2}\pi$, $n = 6$, inscribed.

41. $f(x) = \sin x$, $a = \frac{1}{6}\pi$, $b = \frac{5}{6}\pi$, $n = 8$, inscribed.

42. $f(x) = \cos x$, $a = 0$, $b = \frac{1}{2}\pi$, $n = 6$, circumscribed.

43. Prove Theorem 4.4.4.   **44.** Prove Theorem 4.4.5.

45. Prove Formula 1 of Theorem 4.4.7 without mathematical induction. Hint: Write two equations: **(i)** equate the sigma summation to $1 + 2 + \cdots + (n - 1) + n$; **(ii)** equate the sigma notation to the sum in (i) in reverse order. Then add the two equations term-by-term and divide both sides of the resulting equation by 2.

46. Prove Formula 2 of Theorem 4.4.7 without mathematical induction. Hint:

$$\sum_{i=1}^{n} [i^3 - (i - 1)^3] = \sum_{i=1}^{n} (3i^2 - 3i + 1)$$

On the left side of this equation use Theorem 4.4.6; on the right side use Theorems 4.4.2, 4.4.3, and 4.4.4 and Formula 1.

47. Prove Formula 3 of Theorem 4.4.7. *Hint*: $i^4 - (i - 1)^4 = 4i^3 - 6i^2 + 4i - 1$, and use a method similar to the one for Exercise 46.

48. Prove Formula 4 of Theorem 4.4.7. (See the hints for Exercises 46 and 47.)

49. Explain Definition 4.4.8 of the area of a plane region in words without using the words *limit* or *approaches* or symbols such as N or ϵ.

4.5 THE DEFINITE INTEGRAL

In Section 4.4, to lead up to the definition of the measure of the area of a plane region as

$$\lim_{n \to +\infty} \sum_{i=1}^{n} f(c_i) \, \Delta x \tag{1}$$

we divided the closed interval $[a, b]$ into n subintervals of equal length Δx and then took c_i as the point in the ith subinterval for which f has an absolute minimum value. We also restricted the function values $f(x)$ to be nonnegative on $[a, b]$ and required f to be continuous on $[a, b]$. The limit in (1) is a special case of a "new kind" of limiting process that leads to the definition of the *definite integral*. We now discuss this "new kind" of limit.

Let f be a function defined on the closed interval $[a, b]$. Divide this interval into n subintervals by choosing *any* $n - 1$ intermediate points between a and b. Let $x_0 = a$ and $x_n = b$, and let $x_1, x_2, \ldots, x_{n-1}$ be the intermediate points so that

$$x_0 < x_1 < x_2 < \ldots < x_{n-1} < x_n$$

The points $x_0, x_1, x_2, \ldots, x_{n-1}, x_n$ are not necessarily equidistant. Let $\Delta_1 x$ be the length of the first subinterval so that $\Delta_1 x = x_1 - x_0$; let $\Delta_2 x$ be the length of the second subinterval so that $\Delta_2 x = x_2 - x_1$; and so forth so that the length of the ith subinterval is $\Delta_i x$, and

$$\Delta_i x = x_i - x_{i-1}$$

A set of all such subintervals of the interval $[a, b]$ is called a **partition** of the interval $[a, b]$. Let Δ be such a partition. Figure 1 illustrates one such partition Δ of $[a, b]$.

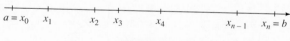

FIGURE 1

The partition Δ contains n subintervals. One of these subintervals is longest; however, there may be more than one such subinterval. The length of the longest subinterval of the partition Δ, called the **norm** of the partition, is denoted by $\|\Delta\|$.

Choose a point in each subinterval of the partition Δ: Let w_1 be the point chosen in $[x_0, x_1]$ so that $x_0 \leq w_1 \leq x_1$. Let w_2 be the point chosen in $[x_1, x_2]$, so that $x_1 \leq w_2 \leq x_2$, and so forth, so that w_i is the point chosen in $[x_{i-1}, x_i]$, and $x_{i-1} \leq w_i \leq x_i$. Form the sum

$$f(w_1) \, \Delta_1 x + f(w_2) \, \Delta_2 x + \ldots + f(w_i) \, \Delta_i x + \ldots + f(w_n) \, \Delta_n x$$

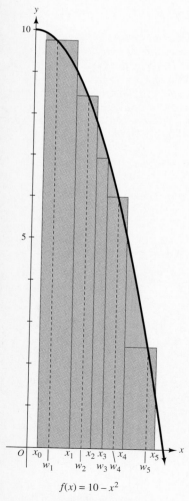

$f(x) = 10 - x^2$

FIGURE 2

or

$$\sum_{i=1}^{n} f(w_i)\, \Delta_i x \qquad\qquad (2)$$

Such a sum is called a **Riemann sum**, named for the mathematician Georg Friedrich Bernhard Riemann (1826–1866).

▷ **ILLUSTRATION 1** Suppose that $f(x) = 10 - x^2$, with $0.25 \le x \le 3$. We will compute the Riemann sum for the function f on $[0.25, 3]$ for the following partition Δ: $x_0 = 0.25$, $x_1 = 1$, $x_2 = 1.5$, $x_3 = 1.75$, $x_4 = 2.25$, $x_5 = 3$, and $w_1 = 0.5$, $w_2 = 1.25$, $w_3 = 1.75$, $w_4 = 2$, $w_5 = 2.75$.

Figure 2 shows the graph of f on $[0.25, 3]$ and the five rectangles the measures of whose areas are the terms of the following Riemann sum:

$$\sum_{i=1}^{5} f(w_i)\, \Delta_i x = f(w_1)\, \Delta_1 x + f(w_2)\, \Delta_2 x + f(w_3)\Delta_3 x + f(w_4)\Delta_4 x + f(w_5)\, \Delta_5 x$$

$$= f(0.5)(1 - 0.25) + f(1.25)(1.5 - 1) + f(1.75)(1.75 - 1.5) + f(2)(2.25 - 1.75) + f(2.75)(3 - 2.25)$$

$$= (9.75)(0.75) + (8.4375)(0.5) + (6.9375)(0.25) + (6)(0.5) + (2.4375)(0.75)$$

$$= 18.09375$$

The norm of partition Δ is the length of the longest subinterval; hence $\|\Delta\| = 0.75$. ◀

In our above definition of (2) as a Riemann sum, the function values are not restricted to nonnegative values. Some of the $f(w_i)$ could, therefore, be negative. In such a case the geometric interpretation of the Riemann sum would be the sum of the measures of the areas of the rectangles lying above the x axis and the negatives of the measures of the areas of the rectangles lying below the x axis. This situation is illustrated in Figure 3. Here

$$\sum_{i=1}^{10} f(w_i)\, \Delta_i x = A_1 + A_2 - A_3 - A_4 - A_5 + A_6 + A_7 - A_8 - A_9 - A_{10}$$

because $f(w_3)$, $f(w_4)$, $f(w_5)$, $f(w_8)$, $f(w_9)$, and $f(w_{10})$ are negative numbers.

Let us now suppose that for the function f in (2) there is a number L such that $\left| \sum_{i=1}^{n} f(w_i)\, \Delta_i x - L \right|$ can be made as small as we please for all partitions Δ whose norms are sufficiently small, and for any w_i in the closed interval $[x_{i-1}, x_i]$, $i = 1, 2, \ldots, n$. In such a case f is said to be *integrable* on $[a, b]$.

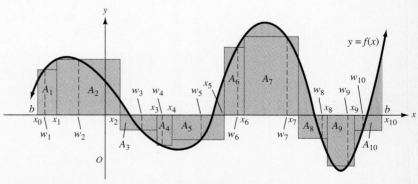

FIGURE 3

4.5.1 Definition of a Function Integrable on a Closed Interval

Let f be a function whose domain includes the closed interval $[a, b]$. Then f is said to be **integrable** on $[a, b]$ if there is a number L satisfying the condition that, for any $\epsilon > 0$, there exists a $\delta > 0$ such that for every partition Δ for which $\|\Delta\| < \delta$, and for any w_i in the closed interval $[x_{i-1}, x_i]$, $i = 1, 2, \ldots, n$, then

$$\left| \sum_{i=1}^{n} f(w_i)\, \Delta_i x - L \right| < \epsilon \tag{3}$$

For such a situation we write

$$\lim_{\|\Delta\| \to 0} \sum_{i=1}^{n} f(w_i)\, \Delta_i x = L \tag{4}$$

This definition states that, for a given function f defined on the closed interval $[a, b]$, we can make the values of the Riemann sums as close to L as we please by taking the norms $\|\Delta\|$ of all partitions Δ of $[a, b]$ sufficiently small for all possible choices of the numbers w_i for which $x_{i-1} \leq w_i \leq x_i$, $i = 1, 2, \ldots, n$.

Observe that the limiting process given by (4) is different from that discussed in Chapter 1. From Definition 4.5.1 the number L in (4) exists if for any $\epsilon > 0$ there exists a $\delta > 0$ such that for every partition Δ for which $\|\Delta\| < \delta$, and for any w_i in the closed interval $[x_{i-1}, x_i]$, $i = 1, 2, \ldots, n$, then inequality (3) holds.

In Definition 1.5.1 we had

$$\lim_{x \to a} f(x) = L \tag{5}$$

if for any $\epsilon > 0$ there exists a $\delta > 0$ such that

$$\text{if} \quad 0 < |x - a| < \delta \quad \text{then} \quad |f(x) - L| < \epsilon$$

In limiting process (4), for a particular $\delta > 0$ there are infinitely many partitions Δ having norm $\|\Delta\| < \delta$. This is analogous to the fact that in limiting process (5), for a given $\delta > 0$ there are infinitely many values of x for which $0 < |x - a| < \delta$. In limiting process (4), however, for each partition Δ there are infinitely many choices of w_i. It is in this respect that the two limiting processes differ.

Theorem 1.5.16 proved in Supplementary Section 1.5 states that if the number L in limiting process (5) exists, it is unique. In a similar manner we can show that if there is a number L satisfying Definition 4.5.1, then it is unique. Now we can define the *definite integral*.

4.5.2 Definition of the Definite Integral

If f is a function defined on the closed interval $[a, b]$, then the **definite integral** of f from a to b, denoted by $\int_a^b f(x)\, dx$, is given by

$$\int_a^b f(x)\, dx = \lim_{\|\Delta\| \to 0} \sum_{i=1}^{n} f(w_i)\, \Delta_i x \tag{6}$$

if the limit exists.

Note that the statement "the function f is integrable on the closed interval $[a, b]$" is synonymous with the statement "the definite integral of f from a to b exists."

In the notation for the definite integral $\int_a^b f(x)\,dx$, $f(x)$ is the **integrand**, a is the **lower limit**, and b is the **upper limit**. The symbol $\int$ is an **integral sign**. The integral sign resembles a capital S, which is appropriate because the definite integral is the limit of a sum. It is the same symbol we have been using to indicate the operation of antidifferentiation. The reason for the common symbol is that a theorem (4.7.2), called the second fundamental theorem of the calculus, enables us to evaluate a definite integral by finding an antiderivative (also called an **indefinite integral**).

The following theorem gives conditions guaranteeing that a function is integrable on a given closed interval.

4.5.3 Theorem

If a function is continuous on the closed interval $[a, b]$, then it is integrable on $[a, b]$.

The proof of this theorem is beyond the scope of this book and can be found in advanced calculus texts. The condition that f is continuous on $[a, b]$, while sufficient to guarantee that f is integrable on $[a, b]$, is not a necessary condition for the existence of the definite integral. That is, a function can be integrable on a closed interval even though it is discontinuous on that interval. You will encounter some such functions when you study *improper integrals* in Chapter 7. At the beginning of this section we stated that the limit used in Definition 4.4.8 to define the measure of the area of a region is a special case of the limit used in Definition 4.5.2 to define the definite integral. In the discussion of area, the interval $[a, b]$ was divided into n subintervals of equal length. Such a partition of the interval $[a, b]$ is called a **regular partition**. If Δx is the length of each subinterval in a regular partition, then each $\Delta_i x = \Delta x$, and the norm of the partition is Δx. Making these substitutions in (6) we have

$$\int_a^b f(x)\,dx = \lim_{\Delta x \to 0} \sum_{i=1}^n f(w_i)\,\Delta x \qquad (7)$$

Furthermore,

$$\Delta x = \frac{b - a}{n} \quad \text{and} \quad n = \frac{b - a}{\Delta x}$$

Thus

$$\lim_{n \to +\infty} \Delta x = 0 \quad \text{and} \quad \lim_{\Delta x \to 0} n = +\infty$$

The reason that $\lim_{\Delta x \to 0} n = +\infty$ is that $b > a$ and Δx approaches zero through positive values (because $\Delta x > 0$). From these limits we conclude that

$$\Delta x \to 0 \quad \text{is equivalent to} \quad n \to +\infty$$

Thus from this statement and (7), we have

$$\int_a^b f(x)\,dx = \lim_{n \to +\infty} \sum_{i=1}^n f(w_i)\,\Delta x \qquad (8)$$

Comparing the limit in Definition 4.4.8 with the limit on the right side of (8), we have in the first case

$$\lim_{n \to +\infty} \sum_{i=1}^{n} f(c_i)\, \Delta x \tag{9}$$

where $f(c_i)$ is the absolute minimum function value on $[x_{i-1}, x_i]$. In the second case we have

$$\lim_{n \to +\infty} \sum_{i=1}^{n} f(w_i)\, \Delta x \tag{10}$$

where w_i is any number in $[x_{i-1}, x_i]$.

If the definite integral $\int_a^b f(x)\, dx$ exists, it is the limit of all Riemann sums of f on $[a, b]$ including those in (9) and (10). Because of this, we redefine the area of a region in a more general way.

4.5.4 Definition of the Area of a Plane Region

Let the function f be continuous on $[a, b]$ and $f(x) \geq 0$ for all x in $[a, b]$. Let R be the region bounded by the curve $y = f(x)$, the x axis, and the lines $x = a$ and $x = b$. Then the measure A of the **area of region R** is given by

$$A = \lim_{\|\Delta\| \to 0} \sum_{i=1}^{n} f(w_i)\, \Delta_i x$$

$$= \int_a^b f(x)\, dx$$

From this definition if the function f is continuous on $[a, b]$ and $f(x) \geq 0$ for all x in $[a, b]$, the definite integral $\int_a^b f(x)\, dx$ can be interpreted geometrically as the measure of the area of the region R shown in Figure 4.

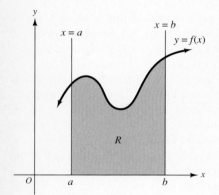

FIGURE 4

▷ **ILLUSTRATION 2**   In Example 3 of Section 4.4, we showed that the area of the region bounded by the graph of $f(x) = x^2$, the x axis, and the line $x = 3$ is 9 square units. Because $f(x) \geq 0$ for all x in $[0, 3]$, we conclude that

$$\int_0^3 x^2\, dx = 9$$

◀

▶ **EXAMPLE 1**   Compute the value of each of the following definite integrals by interpreting it as the measure of the area of a plane region:
(a) $\int_0^3 x\, dx$; **(b)** $\int_{-3}^{3} \sqrt{9 - x^2}\, dx$; **(c)** $\int_{-2}^{2} (2 - |x|)\, dx$.

Solution

(a) With $f(x) = x$, Figure 5 shows the triangular region bounded above by the graph of f, below by the x axis, and on the right by the line $x = 3$. From the formula for the area of a triangle, the number of square units in the area is $\frac{1}{2}(3)(3) = \frac{9}{2}$. Therefore

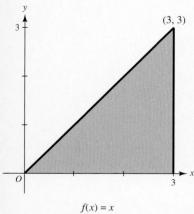

$f(x) = x$

FIGURE 5

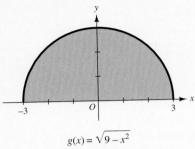

$$g(x) = \sqrt{9 - x^2}$$

FIGURE 6

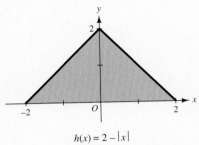

$$h(x) = 2 - |x|$$

FIGURE 7

$$\int_0^3 x \, dx = \frac{9}{2}$$

(b) The integrand of the given definite integral is $\sqrt{9 - x^2}$, which we denote by $g(x)$. The graph of g is a semicircle with center at the origin and radius 3. Figure 6 shows the region bounded above by this semicircle and below by the x axis on the interval $[-3, 3]$. The area of this region is one-half the area of the region enclosed by the complete circle. Because the area of a circular region is given by πr^2, we have

$$\int_{-3}^3 \sqrt{9 - x^2} \, dx = \frac{1}{2} \pi (3)^2$$

$$= \tfrac{9}{2} \pi$$

(c) With $h(x) = 2 - |x|$, we sketch the graph of h on the interval $[-2, 2]$ and obtain Figure 7. Observe that the region bounded by the graph of h and the x axis is a triangle with base 4 and altitude 2. Because the number of square units in the area of this triangular region is $\frac{1}{2}(4)(2) = 4$, we have

$$\int_{-2}^2 (2 - |x|) \, dx = 4 \qquad \blacktriangleleft$$

Just as many graphics calculators can approximate values of numerical derivatives, they can also approximate values of definite integrals. Various numerical techniques are applied for such approximations. You will learn some of these techniques in Section 7.6. We shall denote a calculator approximation of the definite integral $\int_a^b f(x) \, dx$ by the notation

$$\text{NINT}(f(x), a, b)$$

Because of the different techniques used to approximate definite integrals, the values of $\text{NINT}(f(x), a, b)$ may vary depending on the calculator and the tolerance specified. But generally, the answers given by most calculators will agree to at least five significant digits. We shall use a tolerance of 10^{-5} and express answers to six significant digits unless otherwise stated. We will use the equals sign, "$=$", in such computations to mean approximately equal to six significant digits. Consult your user's manual on how to obtain $\text{NINT}(f(x), a, b)$ on your particular calculator.

▷ **ILLUSTRATION 3** To obtain an approximation to the definite integral of Illustration 2, we compute on our graphics calculator

$$\text{NINT}(x^2, 0, 3) = 9.00000$$

which agrees with our answer in Illustration 2. ◀

▷ **ILLUSTRATION 4** In Example 1(b) we obtained the exact value of the definite integral $\int_{-3}^3 \sqrt{9 - x^2} \, dx$ to be $\frac{9}{2} \pi$. On our graphics calculator we compute

$$\text{NINT}(\sqrt{9 - x^2}, -3, 3) = 14.1372$$

Because $\frac{9}{2} \pi \approx 14.1372$, this answer agrees with our answer in Example 1(b). ◀

▶   **EXAMPLE 2**   Obtain an approximation for $\int_0^{2\pi} \sin x \, dx$ by computing NINT($\sin x$, 0, 2π). Interpret the answer in terms of area.

Solution   On our graphics calculator, NINT($\sin x$, 0, 2π) = 0. Thus

$$\int_0^{2\pi} \sin x \, dx = 0$$

The graph of the sine function from 0 to 2π appears in Figure 8. Let A_1 square units and A_2 square units be the areas of the regions bounded by the sine curve and the x axis in the intervals $[0, \pi]$ and $[\pi, 2\pi]$, respectively. Then because A_1 and A_2 are equal, we have

$$\int_0^{2\pi} \sin x \, dx = A_1 - A_2$$

$$= 0$$

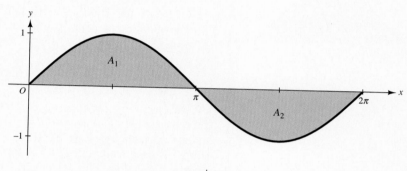

$y = \sin x$

FIGURE 8   ◀

In Definition 4.5.2, because the closed interval $[a, b]$ is given, we assume that $a < b$. To consider the definite integral of a function f from a to b, when $a > b$, or when $a = b$, we have the following definitions.

4.5.5 Definition of $\int_a^b f(x) \, dx$ if $a > b$

If $a > b$ and $\int_b^a f(x) \, dx$ exists, then

$$\int_a^b f(x) \, dx = - \int_b^a f(x) \, dx$$

▷   **ILLUSTRATION 5**   From Illustration 2, $\int_0^3 x^2 \, dx = 9$. Therefore,

$$\int_3^0 x^2 \, dx = - \int_0^3 x^2 \, dx$$

$$= -9$$

◀

4.5.6 Definition of $\int_a^a f(x) \, dx$

If $f(a)$ exists, then

$$\int_a^a f(x) \, dx = 0$$

▷ **ILLUSTRATION 6**

$$\int_1^1 x^2 \, dx = 0$$ ◀

To compute the exact value of a definite integral from the definition by finding the limit of a sum, as we did in Section 4.4 to obtain areas of plane regions, is usually quite tedious and frequently almost impossible. The two fundamental theorems of the calculus, presented in Section 4.7, however, will provide us with a much more convenient method for this computation. To prove these two important theorems we need some properties of the definite integral, which we develop in the remainder of this section and in Section 4.6.

First we need the following two theorems about Riemann sums.

4.5.7 Theorem

If Δ is any partition of the closed interval $[a, b]$, then

$$\lim_{\|\Delta\| \to 0} \sum_{i=1}^{n} \Delta_i x = b - a$$

Proof

$$\sum_{i=1}^{n} \Delta_i x - (b - a) = (b - a) - (b - a)$$
$$= 0$$

Hence, for any $\epsilon > 0$, any choice of $\delta > 0$ guarantees that

$$\text{if} \quad \|\Delta\| < \delta \quad \text{then} \quad \left| \sum_{i=1}^{n} \Delta_i x - (b - a) \right| < \epsilon$$

Thus by Definition 4.5.1,

$$\lim_{\|\Delta\| \to 0} \sum_{i=1}^{n} \Delta_i x = b - a$$ ∎

4.5.8 Theorem

If f is defined on the closed interval $[a, b]$, and if

$$\lim_{\|\Delta\| \to 0} \sum_{i=1}^{n} f(w_i) \, \Delta_i x$$

exists, where Δ is any partition of $[a, b]$, then if k is any constant,

$$\lim_{\|\Delta\| \to 0} \sum_{i=1}^{n} k f(w_i) \, \Delta_i x = k \lim_{\|\Delta\| \to 0} \sum_{i=1}^{n} f(w_i) \, \Delta_i x$$

The proof of this theorem is left as an exercise (see Exercise 54).

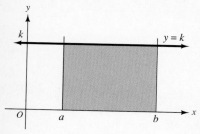

FIGURE 9

▷ **ILLUSTRATION 7**   Refer to Figure 9. If $k > 0$, the definite integral $\int_a^b k\,dx$ gives the measure of the area of the shaded region, which is a rectangle whose dimensions are k units and $(b - a)$ units. This fact is a geometric interpretation of the following theorem when $k > 0$ and $b > a$.   ◀

4.5.9 Theorem

If k is any constant, then

$$\int_a^b k\,dx = k(b - a)$$

Proof   From Definition 4.5.2, if $b > a$

$$\int_a^b f(x)\,dx = \lim_{\|\Delta\| \to 0} \sum_{i=1}^n f(w_i)\,\Delta_i x$$

If $f(x) = k$ for all x in $[a, b]$, we have from this equation

$$\int_a^b k\,dx = \lim_{\|\Delta\| \to 0} \sum_{i=1}^n k\,\Delta_i x$$

$$= k \lim_{\|\Delta\| \to 0} \sum_{i=1}^n \Delta_i x \qquad \text{(by Theorem 4.5.8)}$$

$$= k(b - a) \qquad \text{(by Theorem 4.5.7)}$$

The theorem is also valid if $a \geq b$. You are asked to prove this in Exercise 55.   ■

▶ **EXAMPLE 3**   Evaluate

$$\int_{-3}^5 4\,dx$$

Solution   We apply Theorem 4.5.9.

$$\int_{-3}^5 4\,dx = 4[5 - (-3)]$$

$$= 4(8)$$

$$= 32$$ ◀

4.5.10 Theorem

If the function f is integrable on the closed interval $[a, b]$, and if k is any constant, then

$$\int_a^b kf(x)\,dx = k \int_a^b f(x)\,dx$$

Proof   Because f is integrable on $[a, b]$, $\lim_{\|\Delta\| \to 0} \sum_{i=1}^n f(w_i)\,\Delta_i x$ exists; so by Theorem 4.5.8,

$$\lim_{\|\Delta\| \to 0} \sum_{i=1}^n kf(w_i)\,\Delta_i x = k \lim_{\|\Delta\| \to 0} \sum_{i=1}^n f(w_i)\,\Delta_i x$$

Therefore

$$\int_a^b kf(x)\ dx = k \int_a^b f(x)\ dx$$

∎

4.5.11 Theorem

If the functions f and g are integrable on $[a, b]$, then $f + g$ is integrable on $[a, b]$ and

$$\int_a^b [f(x) + g(x)]\ dx = \int_a^b f(x)\ dx + \int_a^b g(x)\ dx$$

The proof of this theorem appears in the supplement of this section. Observe the similarity of Theorem 4.5.11 to Limit Theorem 4 (1.5.5), the limit of the sum of two functions. The proofs of the two theorems are alike.

The plus sign in the statement of Theorem 4.5.11 can be replaced by a minus sign by applying Theorem 4.5.10 where $k = -1$.

Theorem 4.5.11 can be extended to n functions. That is, if the functions $f_1, f_2, \ldots, f_n$ are all integrable on $[a, b]$, then $(f_1 \pm f_2 \pm \ldots \pm f_n)$ is integrable on $[a, b]$ and

$$\int_a^b [f_1(x) \pm f_2(x) \pm \ldots \pm f_n(x)]\ dx$$

$$= \int_a^b f_1(x)\ dx \pm \int_a^b f_2(x)\ dx \pm \ldots \pm \int_a^b f_n(x)\ dx$$

▶ **EXAMPLE 4** Use the results of Illustration 2, Example 1(a), and properties of the definite integral to find the exact value of

$$\int_0^3 (4x^2 - 2x + 5)\ dx$$

Solution In Illustration 2 and Example 1(a) we showed that

$$\int_0^3 x^2\ dx = 9 \quad \text{and} \quad \int_0^3 x\ dx = \frac{9}{2}$$

From properties of the definite integral

$$\int_0^3 (4x^2 - 2x + 5)\ dx = \int_0^3 4x^2\ dx - \int_0^3 2x\ dx + \int_0^3 5\ dx$$

$$= 4 \int_0^3 x^2\ dx - 2 \int_0^3 x\ dx + 5 \int_0^3 dx$$

$$= 4(9) - 2(\tfrac{9}{2}) + 5(3 - 0)$$

$$= 42$$

◀

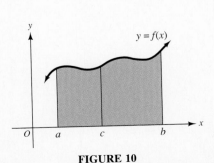

FIGURE 10

▷ **ILLUSTRATION 8** A geometric interpretation of Theorem 4.5.12, which follows, appears in Figure 10 where $f(x) \geq 0$. For all x in $[a, b]$, the measure of the area of the region bounded by the curve $y = f(x)$

and the x axis from a to b is equal to the sum of the measures of the areas of the regions from a to c and from c to b. ◀

4.5.12 Theorem

If the function f is integrable on the closed intervals $[a, b]$, $[a, c]$, and $[c, b]$, then

$$\int_a^b f(x) \, dx = \int_a^c f(x) \, dx + \int_c^b f(x) \, dx$$

where $a < c < b$.

For the proof of Theorem 4.5.12, see the supplement of this section. In the hypothesis of the theorem $a < c < b$. The conclusion of the theorem, however, is true for any ordering of the numbers a, b, and c. This fact is stated in the following theorem whose proof utilizes Theorem 4.5.12.

4.5.13 Theorem

If f is integrable on a closed interval containing the three numbers a, b, and c, then

$$\int_a^b f(x) \, dx = \int_a^c f(x) \, dx + \int_c^b f(x) \, dx \qquad \textbf{(11)}$$

regardless of the order of a, b, and c.

Proof If a, b, and c are distinct, there are six possible orderings of these three numbers: $a < b < c$, $a < c < b$, $b < a < c$, $b < c < a$, $c < a < b$, and $c < b < a$. The second ordering, $a < c < b$, is Theorem 4.5.12. We apply Theorem 4.5.12 to prove that Equation (11) holds for the other orderings.

Suppose that $a < b < c$; then from Theorem 4.5.12

$$\int_a^b f(x) \, dx + \int_b^c f(x) \, dx = \int_a^c f(x) \, dx \qquad \textbf{(12)}$$

From Definition 4.5.5,

$$\int_b^c f(x) \, dx = -\int_c^b f(x) \, dx$$

Substituting from this equation into (12) we obtain

$$\int_a^b f(x) \, dx - \int_c^b f(x) \, dx = \int_a^c f(x) \, dx$$

Thus

$$\int_a^b f(x) \, dx = \int_a^c f(x) \, dx + \int_c^b f(x) \, dx$$

which is the desired result.

The proofs for the other four orderings are similar and left as exercises. See Exercises 43 through 46.

Another possibility is that two of the three numbers are equal; for example, $a = c < b$. Then

$$\int_a^c f(x)\, dx = \int_a^a f(x)\, dx$$

$$= 0 \quad \text{(by Definition 4.5.6)}$$

Also, because $a = c$,

$$\int_c^b f(x)\, dx = \int_a^b f(x)\, dx$$

Therefore

$$\int_a^c f(x)\, dx + \int_c^b f(x)\, dx = 0 + \int_a^b f(x)\, dx$$

which is the desired result. ∎

EXERCISES 4.5

In Exercises 1 through 6, find the Riemann sum for the function on the interval using the partition Δ and the given values of w_i. Sketch the graph of the function on the interval, and show the rectangles, the measure of whose areas are the terms of the Riemann sum. See Illustration 1 and Figure 2.

1. $f(x) = x^2$; $0 \le x \le 3$; Δ: $x_0 = 0$, $x_1 = 0.5$, $x_2 = 1.25$, $x_3 = 2.25$, $x_4 = 3$; $w_1 = 0.25$, $w_2 = 1$, $w_3 = 1.5$, $w_4 = 2.5$

2. $f(x) = x^2$; $0 \le x \le 3$; Δ: $x_0 = 0$, $x_1 = 0.75$, $x_2 = 1.25$, $x_3 = 2$, $x_4 = 2.75$, $x_5 = 3$; $w_1 = 0.5$, $w_2 = 1$, $w_3 = 1.75$, $w_4 = 2.25$, $w_5 = 2.75$

3. $f(x) = 1/x$; $1 \le x \le 3$; Δ: $x_0 = 1$, $x_1 = 1.67$, $x_2 = 2.25$, $x_3 = 2.67$, $x_4 = 3$; $w_1 = 1.25$, $w_2 = 2$, $w_3 = 2.5$, $w_4 = 2.75$

4. $f(x) = 1/(x + 2)$; $-1 \le x \le 3$; Δ: $x_0 = -1$, $x_1 = -0.25$, $x_2 = 0$, $x_3 = 0.5$, $x_4 = 1.25$; $x_5 = 2$, $x_6 = 2.25$, $x_7 = 2.75$, $x_8 = 3$; $w_1 = -0.75$, $w_2 = 0$, $w_3 = 0.25$, $w_4 = 1$, $w_5 = 1.5$, $w_6 = 2$, $w_7 = 2.5$, $w_8 = 3$

5. $f(x) = \sin x$, $0 \le x \le \pi$; Δ: $x_0 = 0$, $x_1 = \frac{1}{4}\pi$, $x_2 = \frac{1}{2}\pi$, $x_3 = \frac{2}{3}\pi$, $x_4 = \frac{3}{4}\pi$, $x_5 = \pi$; $w_1 = \frac{1}{6}\pi$, $w_2 = \frac{1}{3}\pi$, $w_3 = \frac{1}{2}\pi$, $w_4 = \frac{3}{4}\pi$, $w_5 = \frac{5}{6}\pi$

6. $f(x) = 3 \cos \frac{1}{2}x$; $-\pi \le x \le \pi$; Δ: $x_0 = -\pi$, $x_1 = -\frac{1}{2}\pi$, $x_2 = -\frac{1}{3}\pi$, $x_3 = \frac{1}{3}\pi$, $x_4 = \frac{7}{12}\pi$, $x_5 = \pi$; $w_1 = -\frac{2}{3}\pi$, $w_2 = -\frac{1}{3}\pi$, $w_3 = 0$, $w_4 = \frac{1}{2}\pi$, $w_5 = \frac{2}{3}\pi$

In Exercises 7 through 10, approximate the value of the definite integral two ways: (a) use a calculator to compute to four decimal places the corresponding Riemann sum with a regular partition of n subintervals and w_i as the left or right (as indicated) endpoint of each subinterval; (b) use the NINT capability of your calculator. Compare your results.

7. $\displaystyle\int_2^5 \frac{1}{x^2}\, dx$, $n = 9$, w_i is the right endpoint

8. $\displaystyle\int_3^4 \frac{1}{x}\, dx$, $n = 10$, w_i is the left endpoint

9. $\displaystyle\int_{-\pi/3}^{\pi/3} \sec x\, dx$, $n = 8$, w_i is the left endpoint

10. $\displaystyle\int_{\pi/6}^{\pi/3} \csc x\, dx$, $n = 6$, w_i is the right endpoint

In Exercises 11 through 28, (a) determine the exact value of the definite integral by interpreting it as the measure of the area of a plane region. (b) Support your answer by the NINT capability of your calculator.

11. $\displaystyle\int_1^3 (x - 1)\, dx$

12. $\displaystyle\int_{-2}^3 (x + 2)\, dx$

13. $\displaystyle\int_0^2 \sqrt{4 - x^2}\, dx$

14. $\displaystyle\int_{-4}^4 \sqrt{16 - x^2}\, dx$

15. $\displaystyle\int_{-2}^{4} x\,dx$

16. $\displaystyle\int_{0}^{4} (3 - x)\,dx$

17. $\displaystyle\int_{-1}^{2} (5 - 2x)\,dx$

18. $\displaystyle\int_{-1}^{2} (2x + 5)\,dx$

19. $\displaystyle\int_{-2}^{4} |x|\,dx$

20. $\displaystyle\int_{-3}^{3} |1 - x|\,dx$

21. $\displaystyle\int_{0}^{5} (|x + 3| - 5)\,dx$

22. $\displaystyle\int_{-1}^{7} (|x - 2| - 3)\,dx$

23. $\displaystyle\int_{0}^{8} (6 - |x - 2|)\,dx$

24. $\displaystyle\int_{-5}^{0} (3 + |x + 4|)\,dx$

25. $\displaystyle\int_{0}^{2} \sqrt{2x - x^2}\,dx$

26. $\displaystyle\int_{-1}^{5} \sqrt{5 + 4x - x^2}\,dx$

27. $\displaystyle\int_{-\pi}^{\pi} \cos x\,dx$

28. $\displaystyle\int_{\pi/2}^{5\pi/2} \sin x\,dx$

In Exercises 29 and 30, apply Theorem 4.5.9 to determine the exact value of the definite integral.

29. (a) $\displaystyle\int_{2}^{5} 4\,dx$ **(b)** $\displaystyle\int_{-3}^{4} 7\,dx$;   **(c)** $\displaystyle\int_{-5}^{-10} dx$

30. (a) $\displaystyle\int_{5}^{-1} 6\,dx$ **(b)** $\displaystyle\int_{-2}^{2} \sqrt{5}\,dx$;   **(c)** $\displaystyle\int_{3}^{3} dx$

In Exercises 31 through 42, (a) approximate the value of the definite integral by the NINT capability of your calculator. (b) Confirm your answer in part (a) by finding the exact value of the definite integral. Use the following results:

$$\int_{-1}^{2} x^2\,dx = 3 \qquad \int_{-1}^{2} x\,dx = \tfrac{3}{2} \qquad \int_{0}^{\pi} \sin x\,dx = 2$$

$$\int_{0}^{\pi} \cos x\,dx = 0 \qquad \int_{0}^{\pi} \sin^2 x\,dx = \tfrac{1}{2}\pi$$

31. $\displaystyle\int_{-1}^{2} (2x^2 - 4x + 5)\,dx$

32. $\displaystyle\int_{-1}^{2} (8 - x^2)\,dx$

33. $\displaystyle\int_{-1}^{2} (2 - 5x + \tfrac{1}{2}x^2)\,dx$

34. $\displaystyle\int_{-1}^{2} (3x^2 - 4x - 1)\,dx$

35. $\displaystyle\int_{2}^{-1} (2x + 1)^2\,dx$

36. $\displaystyle\int_{-1}^{2} (5x^2 + \tfrac{1}{3}x - \tfrac{1}{2})\,dx$

37. $\displaystyle\int_{-1}^{2} (x - 1)(2x + 3)\,dx$

38. $\displaystyle\int_{2}^{-1} 3x(x - 4)\,dx$

39. $\displaystyle\int_{0}^{\pi} (2 \sin x + 3 \cos x + 1)\,dx$

40. $\displaystyle\int_{0}^{\pi} 3 \cos^2 x\,dx$

41. $\displaystyle\int_{0}^{\pi} (\cos x + 4)^2\,dx$

42. $\displaystyle\int_{\pi}^{0} (\sin x - 2)^2\,dx$

In Exercises 43 through 48, use Theorem 4.5.12 to prove that Theorem 4.5.13 is valid for the given ordering of a, b, and c.

43. $b < a < c$ **44.** $c < a < b$ **45.** $b < c < a$
46. $c < b < a$ **47.** $a = b < c$ **48.** $a < c = b$

49. Express as a definite integral: $\displaystyle\lim_{n \to +\infty} \sum_{i=1}^{n} \frac{8i^2}{n^3}$. *Hint:* Consider the function f for which $f(x) = x^2$.

50. Express as a definite integral: $\displaystyle\lim_{n \to +\infty} \sum_{i=1}^{n} \frac{1}{n + i}$. *Hint:* Consider the function f for which $f(x) = \dfrac{1}{x}$ on $[1, 2]$.

51. Express as a definite integral: $\displaystyle\lim_{n \to +\infty} \sum_{i=1}^{n} \frac{n}{(i + n)^2}$. *Hint:* Consider the function f for which $f(x) = \dfrac{1}{x^2}$ on $[1, 2]$.

52. Show that if f is continuous on $[-1, 2]$, then
$$\int_{-1}^{2} f(x)\,dx + \int_{2}^{0} f(x)\,dx + \int_{0}^{1} f(x)\,dx$$
$$+ \int_{1}^{-1} f(x)\,dx = 0$$

53. Show that if f is continuous on $[-3, 4]$, then
$$\int_{3}^{-1} f(x)\,dx + \int_{4}^{3} f(x)\,dx + \int_{-3}^{4} f(x)\,dx$$
$$+ \int_{-1}^{-3} f(x)\,dx = 0$$

54. Prove Theorem 4.5.8.

55. Prove Theorem 4.5.9 if $a \geq b$.

56. Given that f is integrable on the closed interval $[-r, r]$, prove:
(a) if f is an even function, $\int_{-r}^{r} f(x)\,dx = 2 \int_{0}^{r} f(x)\,dx$;
(b) if f is an odd function, $\int_{-r}^{r} f(x)\,dx = 0$

57. Suppose the function f is continuous on the closed interval $[a, b]$. Under what conditions is the value of the definite integral of f on $[a, b]$ equal to the area of a plane region that includes the graph of f on $[a, b]$ as a boundary? Explain when the value of the definite integral is not equal to the measure of the area of such a plane region.

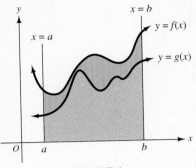

FIGURE 1

4.6 THE MEAN-VALUE THEOREM FOR INTEGRALS

We continue our development of properties of the definite integral in this section. The key theorem of the section is the *mean-value theorem for integrals,* which plays a prominent role in the proof of the *first fundamental theorem of the calculus* in the next section.

▷ **ILLUSTRATION 1**   In Figure 1, $f(x) \geq g(x) \geq 0$ for all x in $[a, b]$. The definite integral $\int_a^b f(x)\, dx$ gives the measure of the area of the region bounded by the graph of f, the x axis, and the lines $x = a$ and $x = b$, while $\int_a^b g(x)\, dx$ gives the measure of the area of the region bounded by the graph of g and the same lines. From the figure we see that the first area is greater than the second. This fact gives a geometric interpretation of the following theorem when $f(x)$ and $g(x)$ are nonnegative on $[a, b]$.   ◀

4.6.1 Theorem

If the functions f and g are integrable on the closed interval $[a, b]$, and if $f(x) \geq g(x)$ for all x in $[a, b]$, then

$$\int_a^b f(x)\, dx \geq \int_a^b g(x)\, dx$$

Proof   Because f and g are integrable on $[a, b]$, then from Theorem 4.5.11 with the plus sign replaced by a minus sign,

$$\int_a^b f(x)\, dx - \int_a^b g(x)\, dx = \int_a^b [f(x) - g(x)]\, dx$$

Let h be the function defined by

$$h(x) = f(x) - g(x)$$

Then $h(x) \geq 0$ for all x in $[a, b]$ because $f(x) \geq g(x)$ for all x in $[a, b]$. We wish to prove that $\int_a^b h(x) \geq 0$. Because

$$\int_a^b h(x)\, dx = \lim_{\|\Delta\| \to 0} \sum_{i=1}^n h(w_i)\, \Delta_i x$$

let us assume that

$$\lim_{\|\Delta\| \to 0} \sum_{i=1}^n h(w_i)\, \Delta_i x = L < 0 \tag{1}$$

Then by Definition 4.5.1, with $\epsilon = -L$, there exists a $\delta > 0$ such that

$$\text{if} \quad \|\Delta\| < \delta \quad \text{then} \quad \left| \sum_{i=1}^n h(w_i)\, \Delta_i x - L \right| < -L \tag{2}$$

But because

$$\sum_{i=1}^n h(w_i)\, \Delta_i x - L \leq \left| \sum_{i=1}^n h(w_i)\, \Delta_i x - L \right|$$

from (2) we have

$$\text{if} \quad \|\Delta\| < \delta \quad \text{then} \quad \sum_{i=1}^{n} h(w_i) \, \Delta_i x - L < -L$$

$$\Leftrightarrow \quad \text{if} \quad \|\Delta\| < \delta \quad \text{then} \quad \sum_{i=1}^{n} h(w_i) \, \Delta_i x < 0$$

But this statement is impossible, because every $h(w_i)$ is nonnegative and every $\Delta_i x > 0$; thus we have a contradiction to our assumption (1). Therefore (1) is false, and

$$\lim_{\|\Delta\| \to 0} \sum_{i=1}^{n} h(w_i) \, \Delta_i x \geq 0$$

$$\int_{a}^{b} h(x) \, dx \geq 0$$

Because $h(x) = f(x) - g(x)$, we have

$$\int_{a}^{b} [f(x) - g(x)] \, dx \geq 0$$

$$\int_{a}^{b} f(x) \, dx - \int_{a}^{b} g(x) \, dx \geq 0$$

$$\int_{a}^{b} f(x) \, dx \geq \int_{a}^{b} g(x) \, dx \qquad \blacksquare$$

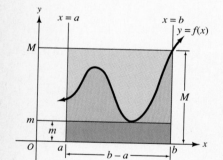

FIGURE 2

▷ **ILLUSTRATION 2**   In Figure 2, $f(x) \geq 0$ for all x in $[a, b]$, and m and M are, respectively, the absolute minimum and absolute maximum function values of f on $[a, b]$. The integral $\int_{a}^{b} f(x) \, dx$ gives the measure of the area of the region bounded by the curve $y = f(x)$, the x axis, and the lines $x = a$ and $x = b$. This area is greater than that of the rectangle whose dimensions are m and $b - a$ and less than that of the rectangle whose dimensions are M and $b - a$. Thus we have a geometric interpretation of the next theorem if $f(x) \geq 0$ for all x in $[a, b]$.   ◀

4.6.2 Theorem

Suppose that the function f is continuous on the closed interval $[a, b]$. If m and M are, respectively, the absolute minimum and absolute maximum function values of f on $[a, b]$ so that

$$m \leq f(x) \leq M \qquad \text{for } a \leq x \leq b$$

then

$$m(b - a) \leq \int_{a}^{b} f(x) \, dx \leq M(b - a)$$

Proof Because f is continuous on $[a, b]$, the extreme-value theorem guarantees the existence of m and M.

By Theorem 4.5.9,

$$\int_a^b m \, dx = m(b - a) \tag{3}$$

and

$$\int_a^b M \, dx = M(b - a) \tag{4}$$

Because f is continuous on $[a, b]$, it follows from Theorem 4.5.3 that f is integrable on $[a, b]$. Then because $f(x) \geq m$ for all x in $[a, b]$, we have from Theorem 4.6.1

$$\int_a^b f(x) \, dx \geq \int_a^b m \, dx$$

which from (3) gives

$$\int_a^b f(x) \, dx \geq m(b - a) \tag{5}$$

Similarly, because $M \geq f(x)$ for all x in $[a, b]$, it follows from Theorem 4.6.1 that

$$\int_a^b M \, dx \geq \int_a^b f(x) \, dx$$

which from (4) gives

$$M(b - a) \geq \int_a^b f(x) \, dx$$

Combining this inequality with (5) we have

$$m(b - a) \leq \int_a^b f(x) \, dx \leq M(b - a) \qquad \blacksquare$$

▶ **EXAMPLE 1** Apply Theorem 4.6.2 to find a closed interval containing the value of $\int_{0.5}^4 (x^3 - 6x^2 + 9x + 1) \, dx$. Use the results of Example 1 of Section 3.4.

Solution Let

$$f(x) = x^3 - 6x^2 + 9x + 1$$

Then from Example 1 of Section 3.4, f has a relative minimum value of 1 at $x = 3$ and a relative maximum value of 5 at $x = 1$. Computing the function values of f at the endpoints of the interval $[0.5, 4]$, we obtain $f(0.5) = 4.125$ and $f(4) = 5$. The absolute minimum value of f on $[0.5, 4]$

is, therefore, 1 and the absolute maximum value is 5. With $m = 1$ and $M = 5$ in Theorem 4.6.2, we have

$$1(4 - 0.5) \leq \int_{0.5}^{4} (x^3 - 6x^2 + 9x + 1) \, dx \leq 5(4 - 0.5)$$

$$3.5 \leq \int_{0.5}^{4} (x^3 - 6x^2 + 9x + 1) \, dx \leq 17.5$$

The closed interval [3.5, 17.5], therefore, contains the value of the definite integral. ◄

In Illustration 4 of Section 4.7, we show that the exact value of the definite integral in the above example is $\frac{679}{64} \approx 10.61$.

▶ **EXAMPLE 2** Apply Theorem 4.6.2 to find a closed interval containing the value of $\int_{\pi/4}^{3\pi/4} \sqrt{\sin x} \, dx$. Support the answer by the NINT capability of a graphics calculator.

Solution If $f(x) = \sqrt{\sin x}$, then

$$f'(x) = \frac{\cos x}{2\sqrt{\sin x}}$$

For x in $[\frac{1}{4}\pi, \frac{3}{4}\pi]$, $f'(x) = 0$ when $x = \frac{1}{2}\pi$. Since $f'(x) > 0$ when $\frac{1}{4}\pi < x < \frac{1}{2}\pi$, and $f'(x) < 0$ when $\frac{1}{2}\pi < x < \frac{3}{4}\pi$, it follows that f has a relative maximum value at $\frac{1}{2}\pi$; and $f(\frac{1}{2}\pi) = 1$. Furthermore, $f(\frac{1}{4}\pi) = \sqrt[4]{2}/\sqrt{2} \approx 0.841$, and $f(\frac{3}{4}\pi) \approx 0.841$. Thus, on $[\frac{1}{4}\pi, \frac{3}{4}\pi]$ the absolute minimum value of f is 0.841 and the absolute maximum value is 1. So, with $m = 0.841$ and $M = 1$ in Theorem 4.6.2

$$0.841[\tfrac{3}{4}\pi - \tfrac{1}{4}\pi] \leq \int_{\pi/4}^{3\pi/4} \sqrt{\sin x} \, dx \leq 1[\tfrac{3}{4}\pi - \tfrac{1}{4}\pi]$$

$$0.420\pi \leq \int_{\pi/4}^{3\pi/4} \sqrt{\sin x} \, dx \leq 0.5\pi$$

$$1.32 \leq \int_{\pi/4}^{3\pi/4} \sqrt{\sin x} \, dx \leq 1.57$$

The value of the definite integral is therefore in the closed interval [1.32, 1.57].

On our graphics calculator we compute

$$\text{NINT}(\sqrt{\sin x}, \pi/4, 3\pi/4) = 1.48861$$

which supports our answer. ◄

We are now ready to discuss the mean-value theorem for integrals. We begin with an illustration that gives a geometric interpretation of the theorem.

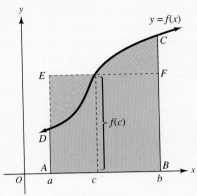

FIGURE 3

▷ **ILLUSTRATION 3**   Consider $f(x) \geq 0$ for all values of x in $[a, b]$. Then $\int_a^b f(x)\, dx$ gives the measure of the area of the region bounded by the curve whose equation is $y = f(x)$, the x axis, and the lines $x = a$ and $x = b$. See Figure 3. The mean-value theorem for integrals states that there is a number c in $[a, b]$ such that the area of the rectangle $AEFB$ of height $f(c)$ units and width $(b - a)$ units is equal to the area of the region $ADCB$. ◀

4.6.3 The Mean-Value Theorem for Integrals

If the function f is continuous on the closed interval $[a, b]$, there exists a number c in $[a, b]$ such that

$$\int_a^b f(x)\, dx = f(c)(b - a)$$

Proof Because f is continuous on $[a, b]$, from the extreme-value theorem f has an absolute maximum value and an absolute minimum value on $[a, b]$.
Let m be the absolute minimum value occurring at $x = x_m$. Thus

$$f(x_m) = m \qquad a \leq x_m \leq b \tag{6}$$

Let M be the absolute maximum value, occurring at $x = x_M$. Thus

$$f(x_M) = M \qquad a \leq x_M \leq b \tag{7}$$

We have, then,

$$m \leq f(x) \leq M \qquad \text{for all } x \text{ in } [a, b]$$

From Theorem 4.6.2

$$m(b - a) \leq \int_a^b f(x)\, dx \leq M(b - a)$$

Dividing by $b - a$ and noting that $b - a$ is positive because $b > a$ we get

$$m \leq \frac{\displaystyle\int_a^b f(x)\, dx}{b - a} \leq M$$

But from (6) and (7), $m = f(x_m)$ and $M = f(x_M)$; so we have

$$f(x_m) \leq \frac{\displaystyle\int_a^b f(x)\, dx}{b - a} \leq f(x_M)$$

From this inequality and the intermediate-value theorem there is some number c in a closed interval containing x_m and x_M such that

$$f(c) = \frac{\displaystyle\int_a^b f(x)\, dx}{b - a}$$

$$\Leftrightarrow \int_a^b f(x)\, dx = f(c)(b - a) \qquad a \leq c \leq b$$

∎

The value of c in the mean-value theorem for integrals is not necessarily unique. The theorem does not provide a method for finding c, but it states that a value of c exists, and this fact is used to prove other theorems. In some particular cases we can find the value of c guaranteed by the theorem, as we show in the following example.

▶ **EXAMPLE 3**   If $f(x) = x^2$, find the value of c to the nearest one-hundredth such that

$$\int_1^3 f(x)\, dx = f(c)(3 - 1)$$

Approximate the value of the definite integral by the NINT capability of a graphics calculator.

Solution   We compute

$$\text{NINT}(x^2, 1, 3) = 8.667$$

Therefore we wish to find c such that

$$f(c)(2) = 8.667$$

that is,

$$c^2 = 4.333$$
$$c = \pm 2.08$$

We reject -2.08 because it is not in the interval $[1, 3]$, and we have

$$\int_1^3 f(x)\, dx = f(2.08)(3 - 1)$$ ◀

The value $f(c)$ given by the mean-value theorem for integrals is called the **mean value** (or **average value**) of f on the interval $[a, b]$. It is a generalization of the arithmetic mean of a finite set of numbers. That is, if $\{f(x_1), f(x_2), \ldots, f(x_n)\}$ is a set of n numbers, then the arithmetic mean is given by

$$\frac{\sum_{i=1}^{n} f(x_i)}{n}$$

To generalize this definition, consider a regular partition of the closed interval $[a, b]$, which is divided into n subintervals of equal length $\Delta x = (b - a)/n$. Let w_i be any point in the ith subinterval. Form the sum:

$$\frac{\sum_{i=1}^{n} f(w_i)}{n} \tag{8}$$

This quotient corresponds to the arithmetic mean of n numbers. Because $\Delta x = (b - a)/n$ we have

$$n = \frac{b - a}{\Delta x} \tag{9}$$

Substituting from (9) into (8) we obtain

$$\frac{\sum\limits_{i=1}^{n} f(w_i)}{\dfrac{b-a}{\Delta x}} = \frac{\sum\limits_{i=1}^{n} f(w_i) \, \Delta x}{b-a}$$

Taking the limit as $n \rightarrow +\infty$ (or $\Delta x \rightarrow 0$) we have, if the limit exists,

$$\lim_{n \rightarrow +\infty} \frac{\sum\limits_{i=1}^{n} f(w_i) \, \Delta x}{b-a} = \frac{\displaystyle\int_a^b f(x) \, dx}{b-a}$$

This result leads to the following definition.

4.6.4 Definition of the Average Value of a Function

If the function f is integrable on the closed interval $[a, b]$, then the **average value** of f on $[a, b]$ is

$$\frac{\displaystyle\int_a^b f(x) \, dx}{b-a}$$

▶ **EXAMPLE 4**   If $f(x) = x^2$, find the average value of f on the interval $[1, 3]$ and interpret the result geometrically.

Solution   In Example 3, we obtained $\text{NINT}(x^2, 1, 3) = 8.667$. Using this number as the value of the definite integral, we have

$$\int_1^3 x^2 \, dx = 8.667$$

So if A.V. is the average value of f on $[1, 3]$.

$$\text{A.V.} = \frac{8.667}{3-1}$$
$$= 4.33$$

In Example 3, we found for this function

$$f(2.08) = 4.33$$

The average value of f, therefore, occurs at $x = 2.08$. Figure 4 shows the graph of f on $[1, 3]$ and the line segment from the point $E(2.08, 0)$ on the x axis to the point $F(2.08, 4.33)$ on the graph of f. The area of rectangle $AGHB$ having height 4.33 and width 2 is equal to the area of region $ACDB$. Consequently, the area of shaded region CGF is equal to the area of shaded region FDH.   ◄

An application of the average value of a function occurs in physics and engineering in connection with the concept of *center of mass,* discussed in Chapter 6.

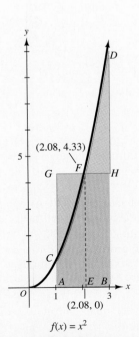

$f(x) = x^2$

FIGURE 4

EXERCISES 4.6

In Exercises 1 through 4, apply Theorem 4.6.1 to determine which of the symbols $\geq$ or $\leq$ should be inserted in the blank to make the inequality correct. Support your answer by the NINT capability of your graphics calculator.

1. $\displaystyle\int_{-1}^{3} (2x^2 - 4)dx$ ——— $\displaystyle\int_{-1}^{3} (x^2 - 6)dx$

2. $\displaystyle\int_{4}^{5} \sqrt{6 - x}\, dx$ ——— $\displaystyle\int_{4}^{5} \sqrt{x - 2}\, dx$

3. $\displaystyle\int_{3\pi/4}^{5\pi/4} \sin^2 x\, dx$ ——— $\displaystyle\int_{3\pi/4}^{5\pi/4} \cos^2 x\, dx$

4. $\displaystyle\int_{0}^{\pi/4} \cos x\, dx$ ——— $\displaystyle\int_{0}^{\pi/4} \sin x\, dx$

In Exercises 5 through 20, apply Theorem 4.6.2 to find a closed interval containing the value of the definite integral. Support your answer by the NINT capability of your graphics calculator.

5. $\displaystyle\int_{0}^{0.5} x^2\, dx$

6. $\displaystyle\int_{-0.5}^{1} x^3\, dx$

7. $\displaystyle\int_{-1}^{1} \sqrt{2 + x}\, dx$

8. $\displaystyle\int_{-2}^{1} (x + 1)^{2/3}\, dx$

9. $\displaystyle\int_{\pi/6}^{\pi/3} \sin x\, dx$

10. $\displaystyle\int_{-\pi/3}^{2\pi/3} \cos x\, dx$

11. $\displaystyle\int_{1.5}^{3} |x - 2|\, dx$

12. $\displaystyle\int_{-1}^{2} \sqrt{x^2 + 5}\, dx$

13. $\displaystyle\int_{-0.5}^{1.5} (\tfrac{1}{4}x^4 - x^3 + x^2)\, dx$

14. $\displaystyle\int_{0}^{1.5} (x - 3x^{1/3})\, dx$

15. $\displaystyle\int_{1}^{2} x\sqrt{5 - x^2}\, dx$

16. $\displaystyle\int_{1.5}^{2.5} x\sqrt{3 - x}\, dx$

17. $\displaystyle\int_{-1}^{1} \frac{x}{x + 2}\, dx$

18. $\displaystyle\int_{0}^{1} \frac{x + 5}{x - 3}\, dx$

19. $\displaystyle\int_{\pi/3}^{\pi/2} (4\cos^3 x - 9\cos x)\, dx$

20. $\displaystyle\int_{-\pi/6}^{\pi/6} \sin^3 x\, dx$

In Exercises 21 through 32, find to the nearest one-hundredth the value of c satisfying the mean-value theorem for integrals. For the value of the definite integral, use the NINT capability of your graphics calculator.

21. $\displaystyle\int_{0}^{2} x^2\, dx$

22. $\displaystyle\int_{2}^{4} x^2\, dx$

23. $\displaystyle\int_{1}^{2} x^3\, dx$

24. $\displaystyle\int_{0}^{5} (x^3 - 1)\, dx$

25. $\displaystyle\int_{1}^{4} (x^2 + 4x + 5)\, dx$

26. $\displaystyle\int_{0}^{4} (x^2 + x - 6)\, dx$

27. $\displaystyle\int_{-2}^{2} (x^3 + 1)\, dx$

28. $\displaystyle\int_{-2}^{1} x^4\, dx$

29. $\displaystyle\int_{2}^{4} \frac{1}{x^2 - 3}\, dx$

30. $\displaystyle\int_{-1}^{3} \frac{1}{x^2 + 5}\, dx$

31. $\displaystyle\int_{\pi/6}^{\pi/4} \tan x\, dx$

32. $\displaystyle\int_{2\pi/3}^{5\pi/6} \cot x\, dx$

In Exercises 33 through 40, apply the mean-value theorem for integrals to prove the inequality.

33. $\displaystyle\int_{0}^{2} \frac{1}{x^2 + 4}\, dx \leq \frac{1}{2}$

34. $\displaystyle\int_{-3}^{3} \frac{1}{x^2 + 6}\, dx \leq 1$

35. $\displaystyle\int_{-\pi/6}^{\pi/6} \cos x^2\, dx \leq \frac{\pi}{3}$

36. $\displaystyle\int_{0}^{\pi} \sin \sqrt{x}\, dx \leq \pi$

37. $\displaystyle 0 \leq \int_{2}^{5} \frac{1}{x^3 + 1}\, dx \leq \frac{1}{3}$

38. $\displaystyle \sqrt{2} \leq \int_{5}^{9} \frac{1}{\sqrt{x - 1}}\, dx \leq 2$

39. $\displaystyle 0 \leq \int_{0}^{2} \sin \tfrac{1}{2}\pi x\, dx \leq 2$

40. $\displaystyle 0 \leq \int_{-1/2}^{1/2} \cos \pi x\, dx \leq 1$

41. Given that $\int_{-1}^{2} x\, dx = \frac{3}{2}$, find the average value of the identity function on the interval $[-1, 2]$. Also find the value of x at which the average value occurs. Describe the geometric interpretation of the results.

42. Find the average value of the function f defined by $f(x) = x^2$ on the interval $[-1, 2]$ given that $\int_{-1}^{2} x^2\, dx = 3$. Also find the value of x at which the average value occurs. Describe the geometric interpretation of the results.

43. Given that $\int_{0}^{\pi} \sin x\, dx = 2$, find the average value of the sine function on the interval $[0, \pi]$. Also find the smallest value of x at which the average value occurs. Describe the geometric interpretation of the results.

44. Find the average value of the function f where $f(x) = \sec^2 x$ on the interval $[0, \frac{1}{4}\pi]$ given that $\int_{0}^{\pi/4} \sec^2 x\, dx = 1$. Also find the value of x at which the average value occurs. Describe the geometric interpretation of the results.

45. Suppose a ball is dropped from rest and after t seconds its velocity is v feet per second. Neglecting air resistance, express v in terms of t as $v = f(t)$, and find the average value of f on $[0, 2]$. *Hint:* Find the value of the definite integral by interpreting it as the measure of the area of a region enclosed by a triangle.

46. Find the average value of the function f defined by $f(x) = \sqrt{49 - x^2}$ on the interval $[0, 7]$. Draw a figure. *Hint:* Find the value of the definite integral by interpreting it as the measure of the area of a region enclosed by a quartercircle.

47. Find the average value of the function f defined by $f(x) = \sqrt{16 - x^2}$ on the interval $[-4, 4]$. Draw a figure. *Hint:* Find the value of the definite integral by interpreting it as the measure of the area of a region enclosed by a semicircle.

48. Suppose that f is integrable on $[-4, 7]$. If the average value of f on the interval $[-4, 7]$ is 4.25, find $\int_{-4}^{7} f(x)\, dx$.

49. Show that $\int_0^1 x\, dx \geq \int_0^1 x^2\, dx$ but $\int_1^2 x\, dx \leq \int_1^2 x^2\, dx$. Do not evaluate the definite integrals.

50. If f is continuous on $[a, b]$, prove that

$$\left| \int_a^b f(x)\, dx \right| \leq \int_a^b |f(x)|\, dx$$

Hint: $-|f(x)| \leq f(x) \leq |f(x)|$.

51. If f is continuous on $[a, b]$ and $\int_a^b f(x)\, dx = 0$, prove that there is at least one number c in $[a, b]$ such that $f(c) = 0$.

52. The following theorem is a generalization of the mean-value theorem for integrals: If f and g are two functions continuous on the closed interval $[a, b]$ and $g(x) > 0$ for all x in the open interval (a, b), then there exists a number c in $[a, b]$ such that

$$\int_a^b f(x) g(x)\, dx = f(c) \int_a^b g(x)\, dx$$

Prove this theorem by a method similar to that for Theorem 4.6.3: Obtain the inequality $m \leq f(x) \leq M$ and then conclude that $mg(x) \leq f(x)g(x) \leq Mg(x)$; apply Theorem 4.6.1 and proceed as in the proof of Theorem 4.6.3.

53. Show that when $g(x) = 1$, the theorem of Exercise 52 becomes the mean-value theorem for integrals.

In Exercises 54 through 58, use the theorem of Exercise 52 to prove the inequality.

54. $\displaystyle\int_0^4 \frac{x\, dx}{x^3 + 2} < \int_0^4 x\, dx$

55. $\displaystyle\int_{-1}^1 \frac{x^2\, dx}{\sqrt{x^2 + 4}} < \int_{-1}^1 x^2\, dx$

56. $\displaystyle\int_0^{\pi} x \sin x\, dx \leq \int_0^{\pi} x\, dx$

57. $\displaystyle\int_{-1/2}^{1/2} \sin^2 \pi x \cos \pi x\, dx \leq \int_{-1/2}^{1/2} \cos \pi x\, dx$

58. $\displaystyle\int_0^1 \frac{x \cos x}{x^2 + 1}\, dx \leq \int_0^1 x\, dx$

4.7 THE FUNDAMENTAL THEOREMS OF THE CALCULUS

Now that you have the necessary background, in this section we will state and prove the two fundamental theorems of the calculus, the link between differential and integral calculus.

Historically, the basic concepts of the definite integral were used by the ancient Greeks, principally Archimedes (287-212 B.C.), more than 2000 years ago. That was many years before the differential calculus was discovered in the seventeenth century when Newton and Leibniz, almost simultaneously but working independently, showed how to find the area of a region bounded by a curve or set of curves by applying antidifferentiation to evaluate a definite integral. This procedure led to the remarkable fundamental theorems. We begin our development of these theorems by discussing definite integrals having a variable upper limit.

Let the function f be continuous on the closed interval $[a, b]$. Then the value of the definite integral $\int_a^b f(x)\, dx$ depends only on f and the numbers a and b, and not on the symbol x, used here as the independent variable. We

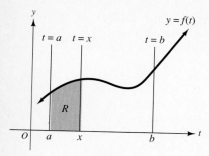

FIGURE 1

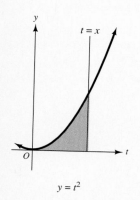

$y = t^2$

FIGURE 2

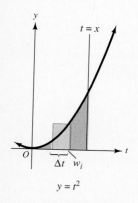

$y = t^2$

FIGURE 3

could have used any other symbol instead of x; for instance from the result of Illustration 2 in Section 4.5

$$\int_0^3 t^2 \, dt = 9 \qquad \int_0^3 u^2 \, du = 9 \qquad \int_0^3 r^2 \, dr = 9$$

Let us now use the symbol x to represent a number in the closed interval $[a, b]$. Then because f is continuous on $[a, b]$, it is continuous on $[a, x]$. Consequently, by Theorem 4.5.3, $\int_a^x f(t) \, dt$ exists. Furthermore, this definite integral is a unique number whose value depends on x. Therefore, $\int_a^x f(t) \, dt$ defines a function F having as its domain all numbers in $[a, b]$ and whose function value at any number x in $[a, b]$ is given by

$$F(x) = \int_a^x f(t) \, dt \tag{1}$$

As a notational observation, if the limits of a definite integral are variables, different symbols are used for these limits and for the independent variable in the integrand. Hence, in (1), because x is the upper limit, we use the letter t as the independent variable in the integrand.

If, in (1), $f(t) \geq 0$ for all values of t in $[a, b]$, then the function value $F(x)$ can be interpreted geometrically as the measure of the area of the region R bounded by the curve whose equation is $y = f(t)$, the t axis, and the lines $t = a$ and $t = x$. (See Figure 1.) Note that $F(a) = \int_a^a f(t) \, dt$, which by Definition 4.5.6 equals 0. In the following illustration, we demonstrate in advance the significance of the *first fundamental theorem of the calculus* by applying this geometric interpretation in a particular case.

▷ **ILLUSTRATION 1**   Let

$$F(x) = \int_0^x t^2 \, dt$$

Figure 2 shows the region bounded above by the graph of $y = t^2$, below by the t axis, and on the sides by the y axis and the line $t = x$. Because the measure of the area of this region is $F(x)$, we can find $F(x)$ by computing the area as the limit of a Riemann sum.

We take a regular partition of the interval $[0, x]$ and choose w_i as the right endpoint of the ith subinterval. We are, therefore, using circumscribed rectangles as shown in Figure 3.

$$F(x) = \lim_{n \to +\infty} \sum_{i=1}^n f(w_i) \, \Delta t$$

Because $f(t) = t^2$ and $w_i = i \, \Delta t$,

$$F(x) = \lim_{n \to +\infty} \sum_{i=1}^n [i^2(\Delta t)^2] \, \Delta t$$

$$= \lim_{n \to +\infty} \sum_{i=1}^n i^2(\Delta t)^3$$

We now replace Δt by x/n:

$$
\begin{aligned}
F(x) &= \lim_{n \to +\infty} \sum_{i=1}^{n} i^2 \left(\frac{x}{n}\right)^3 \\
&= \lim_{n \to +\infty} \frac{x^3}{n^3} \sum_{i=1}^{n} i^2 \\
&= x^3 \lim_{n \to +\infty} \frac{1}{n^3} \cdot \frac{n(n+1)(2n+1)}{6} \\
&= x^3 \lim_{n \to +\infty} \frac{2n^3 + 3n^2 + n}{6n^3} \\
&= x^3 \lim_{n \to +\infty} \frac{2 + \dfrac{3}{n} + \dfrac{1}{n^2}}{6} \\
&= \frac{x^3}{3}
\end{aligned}
$$

Because $F(x) = \frac{1}{3}x^3$, $F'(x) = x^2$, that is,

$$
\frac{d}{dx} \int_0^x t^2 \, dt = x^2
$$

We have shown then that in this particular case when $f(t) = t^2$ and $a = 0$

$$
\frac{d}{dx} \int_a^x f(t) \, dt = f(x)
$$

which is the crucial equation in the statement of the first fundamental theorem of the calculus. ◀

We now state and prove the first fundamental theorem of the calculus, giving the derivative of a function defined as a definite integral having a variable upper limit.

4.7.1 The First Fundamental Theorem of the Calculus

Let the function f be continuous on the closed interval $[a, b]$ and let x be any number in $[a, b]$. If F is the function defined by

$$
F(x) = \int_a^x f(t) \, dt
$$

then

$$
F'(x) = f(x) \tag{2}
$$

$$
\Leftrightarrow \quad \frac{d}{dx} \int_a^x f(t) \, dt = f(x) \tag{3}
$$

(If $x = a$, the derivative in (2) may be a derivative from the right, and if $x = b$, it may be a derivative from the left.)

Proof Consider two numbers x_1 and $x_1 + \Delta x$ in $[a, b]$. Then

$$F(x_1) = \int_a^{x_1} f(t)\, dt$$

and

$$F(x_1 + \Delta x) = \int_a^{x_1 + \Delta x} f(t)\, dt$$

so that

$$F(x_1 + \Delta x) - F(x_1) = \int_a^{x_1 + \Delta x} f(t)\, dt - \int_a^{x_1} f(t)\, dt \qquad (4)$$

By Theorem 4.5.13,

$$\int_a^{x_1} f(t)\, dt + \int_{x_1}^{x_1 + \Delta x} f(t)\, dt = \int_a^{x_1 + \Delta x} f(t)\, dt$$

$$\int_a^{x_1 + \Delta x} f(t)\, dt - \int_a^{x_1} f(t)\, dt = \int_{x_1}^{x_1 + \Delta x} f(t)\, dt$$

Substituting from this equation into (4) we get

$$F(x_1 + \Delta x) - F(x_1) = \int_{x_1}^{x_1 + \Delta x} f(t)\, dt \qquad (5)$$

By the mean-value theorem for integrals there is some number c in the closed interval bounded by x_1 and $x_1 + \Delta x$ such that

$$\int_{x_1}^{x_1 + \Delta x} f(t)\, dt = f(c)\, \Delta x$$

From this equation and (5) we obtain

$$F(x_1 + \Delta x) - F(x_1) = f(c)\, \Delta x$$

$$\frac{F(x_1 + \Delta x) - F(x_1)}{\Delta x} = f(c)$$

Taking the limit as Δx approaches zero we have

$$\lim_{\Delta x \to 0} \frac{F(x_1 + \Delta x) - F(x_1)}{\Delta x} = \lim_{\Delta x \to 0} f(c) \qquad (6)$$

The left side of (6) is $F'(x_1)$. To determine $\lim_{\Delta x \to 0} f(c)$, recall that c is in the closed interval bounded by x_1 and $x_1 + \Delta x$, and because

$$\lim_{\Delta x \to 0} x_1 = x_1 \quad \text{and} \quad \lim_{\Delta x \to 0} (x_1 + \Delta x) = x_1$$

it follows from the squeeze theorem (1.10.1) that $\lim_{\Delta x \to 0} c = x_1$. Thus we have $\lim_{\Delta x \to 0} f(c) = \lim_{c \to x_1} f(c)$. Because f is continuous at x_1, $\lim_{c \to x_1} f(c) = f(x_1)$; thus $\lim_{\Delta x \to 0} f(c) = f(x_1)$, and from (6) we get

$$F'(x_1) = f(x_1) \qquad (7)$$

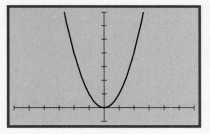

[–6, 6] by [–1, 7]

$$f(x) = x^2$$

FIGURE 4

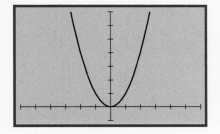

[–6, 6] by [–1, 7]

NDER (NINT (t^2, 0, x), x)

FIGURE 5

If the function f is not defined for values of x less than a but is continuous from the right at a, then in the above argument, if $x_1 = a$ in (6), Δx must approach 0 from the right. Hence the left side of (7) will be $F'_+(x_1)$. Similarly, if f is not defined for values of x greater than b but is continuous from the left at b, then if $x_1 = b$ in (6), Δx must approach 0 from the left. Hence we have $F'_-(x_1)$ on the left side of (7).

Because x_1 is any number in $[a, b]$, Equation (7) states what we wished to prove. ■

Remember that the first fundamental theorem of the calculus states that the definite integral $\int_a^x f(t)\, dt$ with variable upper limit x is an antiderivative of f if f is continuous. We demonstrate this fact graphically in the following illustration for our function of Illustration 1.

▷ **ILLUSTRATION 2**   Figure 4 shows the graph of the function f of Illustration 1, defined by $f(x) = x^2$, plotted in the $[-6, 6]$ by $[-1, 7]$ window. Figure 5 shows the graph of NDER(NINT (t^2, 0, x), x) plotted in the same window. These graphs appear identical, which supports the fact that $\int_0^x t^2\, dt$ is an antiderivative of f. ◀

▶ **EXAMPLE 1**   Compute the following derivatives:

(a) $\dfrac{d}{dx} \displaystyle\int_1^x \dfrac{1}{t^3 + 1}\, dt$ **(b)** $\dfrac{d}{dx} \displaystyle\int_3^{x^2} \sqrt{\cos t}\, dt$

Solution

(a) From (3) with $f(t) = \dfrac{1}{t^3 + 1}$, we have

$$\frac{d}{dx} \int_1^x \frac{1}{t^3 + 1}\, dt = \frac{1}{x^3 + 1}$$

(b) With $u = x^2$ in the chain rule we get

$$\frac{d}{dx} \int_3^{x^2} \sqrt{\cos t}\, dt = \frac{d}{du} \int_3^u \sqrt{\cos t}\, dt \cdot \frac{du}{dx}$$

From (3) with $f(t) = \sqrt{\cos t}$ and because $\dfrac{du}{dx} = 2x$, we have

$$\frac{d}{dx} \int_3^{x^2} \sqrt{\cos t}\, dt = \sqrt{\cos u}\,(2x)$$

$$= 2x \sqrt{\cos x^2}$$

◀

We now apply the first fundamental theorem to prove the *second fundamental theorem of the calculus*.

4.7.2 The Second Fundamental Theorem of the Calculus

Let the function f be continuous on the closed interval $[a, b]$ and let g be a function such that

$$g'(x) = f(x) \tag{8}$$

for all x in $[a, b]$. Then

$$\int_a^b f(t) \, dt = g(b) - g(a)$$

(If $x = a$, the derivative in (8) may be a derivative from the right, and if $x = b$, the derivative in (8) may be a derivative from the left.)

Proof If f is continuous at all numbers in $[a, b]$, we know from the first fundamental theorem that the definite integral $\int_a^x f(t) \, dt$, with variable upper limit x, defines a function F whose derivative on $[a, b]$ is f. Because by hypothesis $g'(x) = f(x)$, it follows from Theorem 4.1.2 that

$$g(x) = \int_a^x f(t) \, dt + k$$

where k is some constant. Letting $x = b$ and $x = a$, successively, in this equation we get

$$g(b) = \int_a^b f(t) \, dt + k \tag{9}$$

and

$$g(a) = \int_a^a f(t) \, dt + k \tag{10}$$

From (9) and (10),

$$g(b) - g(a) = \int_a^b f(t) \, dt - \int_a^a f(t) \, dt$$

But by Definition 4.5.6, $\int_a^a f(t) \, dt = 0$; so

$$g(b) - g(a) = \int_a^b f(t) \, dt$$

which is what we wished to prove.

If f is not defined for values of x greater than b but is continuous from the left at b, the derivative in (8) is a derivative from the left, and we have $g'_-(b) = F'_-(b)$, from which (9) follows. Similarly, if f is not defined for values of x less than a but is continuous from the right at a, then the derivative in (8) is a derivative from the right, and we have $g'_+(a) = F'_+(a)$, from which (10) follows.   ∎

We are now able to find the exact value of a definite integral by applying the second fundamental theorem. In the computation we denote

$$[g(b) - g(a)] \quad \text{by} \quad g(x) \Big]_a^b$$

▷ **ILLUSTRATION 3** We evaluate

$$\int_1^2 x^4 \, dx$$

Because an antiderivative of x^4 is $x^5/5$, we have from the second fundamental theorem

$$\int_1^2 x^4 \, dx = \frac{x^5}{5} \Big]_1^2$$
$$= \tfrac{32}{5} - \tfrac{1}{5}$$
$$= \tfrac{31}{5} \qquad\qquad ◀$$

Because of the connection between definite integrals and antiderivatives, we used the integral sign $\int$ for the notation $\int f(x)\,dx$ for an antiderivative. We now dispense with the terminology of antiderivatives and antidifferentiation and begin to call $\int f(x)\,dx$ an **indefinite integral.** The process of evaluating an indefinite integral or a definite integral is called **integration.**

The difference between an indefinite integral and a definite integral should be emphasized. The indefinite integral $\int f(x)\,dx$ represents all functions whose derivative is $f(x)$. However, the definite integral $\int_a^b f(x)\,dx$ is a number whose value depends on the function f and the numbers a and b, and it is defined as the limit of a Riemann sum. The definition of the definite integral makes no reference to differentiation.

The indefinite integral involves an arbitrary constant; for instance,

$$\int x^2 \, dx = \frac{x^3}{3} + C$$

This arbitrary constant C is called a **constant of integration.** In applying the second fundamental theorem to evaluate a definite integral, we do not need to include the arbitrary constant C in the expression for $g(x)$ because the theorem permits us to select *any* antiderivative, including the one for which $C = 0$.

▷ **ILLUSTRATION 4** From the additive property of definite integrals given by Theorem 4.5.11 and the second fundamental theorem, we have

$$\int_{1/2}^4 (x^3 - 6x^2 + 9x + 1) \, dx$$

$$= \int_{1/2}^4 x^3 \, dx - 6 \int_{1/2}^4 x^2 \, dx + 9 \int_{1/2}^4 x \, dx + \int_{1/2}^4 dx$$

$$= \frac{x^4}{4} - 6 \cdot \frac{x^3}{3} + 9 \cdot \frac{x^2}{2} + x \Big]_{1/2}^4$$

$$= (64 - 128 + 72 + 4) - (\tfrac{1}{64} - \tfrac{1}{4} + \tfrac{9}{8} + \tfrac{1}{2})$$

$$= \tfrac{679}{64}$$

In Example 1 of Section 4.6, we proved that the value of this definite integral is in the interval $[3.5, 17.5]$ in agreement with our result here because $\frac{679}{64} \approx 10.61$. ◀

The following examples further demonstrate the application of the second fundamental theorem. Of course, the answers can be supported by the NINT capability of your graphics calculator.

▶ **EXAMPLE 2**   Evaluate

$$\int_{-1}^{1} (x^{4/3} + 4x^{1/3})\, dx$$

Solution

$$\int_{-1}^{1} (x^{4/3} + 4x^{1/3})\, dx = \frac{3}{7}x^{7/3} + 4 \cdot \frac{3}{4}x^{4/3} \Big]_{-1}^{1}$$
$$= \frac{3}{7} + 3 - (-\frac{3}{7} + 3)$$
$$= \frac{6}{7}$$

◀

▶ **EXAMPLE 3**   Evaluate

$$\int_{0}^{2} 2x^2 \sqrt{x^3 + 1}\, dx$$

Solution

$$\int_{0}^{2} 2x^2 \sqrt{x^3 + 1}\, dx = \frac{2}{3} \int_{0}^{2} \sqrt{x^3 + 1}\, (3x^2\, dx)$$
$$= \frac{2}{3} \cdot \frac{(x^3 + 1)^{3/2}}{\frac{3}{2}} \Big]_{0}^{2}$$
$$= \frac{4}{9}(8 + 1)^{3/2} - \frac{4}{9}(0 + 1)^{3/2}$$
$$= \frac{4}{9}(27 - 1)$$
$$= \frac{104}{9}$$

◀

▶ **EXAMPLE 4**   Evaluate

$$\int_{0}^{3} x \sqrt{1 + x}\, dx$$

Solution   To evaluate the indefinite integral $\int x \sqrt{1 + x}\, dx$ we let

$$u = \sqrt{1 + x} \qquad u^2 = 1 + x \qquad x = u^2 - 1 \qquad dx = 2u\, du$$

Substituting we have

$$\int x \sqrt{1 + x} \, dx = \int (u^2 - 1)u(2u \, du)$$

$$= 2 \int (u^4 - u^2) \, du$$

$$= \tfrac{2}{5}u^5 - \tfrac{2}{3}u^3 + C$$

$$= \tfrac{2}{5}(1 + x)^{5/2} - \tfrac{2}{3}(1 + x)^{3/2} + C$$

Therefore the definite integral

$$\int_0^3 x\sqrt{1 + x} \, dx = \tfrac{2}{5}(1 + x)^{5/2} - \tfrac{2}{3}(1 + x)^{3/2} \Big]_0^3$$

$$= \tfrac{2}{5}(4)^{5/2} - \tfrac{2}{3}(4)^{3/2} - \tfrac{2}{5}(1)^{5/2} + \tfrac{2}{3}(1)^{3/2}$$

$$= \tfrac{64}{5} - \tfrac{16}{3} - \tfrac{2}{5} + \tfrac{2}{3}$$

$$= \tfrac{116}{15} \qquad \blacktriangleleft$$

Another method for evaluating the definite integral in Example 4 is provided by a formula that follows from the second fundamental theorem and the chain rule for antidifferentiation (4.2.1). From these theorems, if F is an antiderivative of f,

$$\int_a^b f(g(x))g'(x) \, dx = F(g(x)) \Big]_a^b$$

$$\Leftrightarrow \int_a^b f(g(x))g'(x) \, dx = F(g(b)) - F(g(a))$$

Thus

$$\int_a^b f(g(x))g'(x) \, dx = F(u) \Big]_{g(a)}^{g(b)}$$

$$\Leftrightarrow \int_a^b f(g(x))g'(x) \, dx = \int_{g(a)}^{g(b)} f(u) \, du \qquad (11)$$

To apply (11), change the variables in the given integral by letting $u = g(x)$. Then $du = g'(x) \, dx$. Then change the x-limits of integration a and b to u-limits, which are $g(a)$ and $g(b)$.

$\triangleright$ **ILLUSTRATION 5** To evaluate the integral of Example 4, let $u = \sqrt{1 + x}$, $x = u^2 - 1$, and $dx = 2u \, du$. Furthermore, when $x = 0$, $u = 1$, and when $x = 3$, $u = 2$. Thus from (11) we have

$$\int_0^3 x\sqrt{1 + x} \, dx = 2 \int_1^2 (u^4 - u^2) \, du$$

$$= \tfrac{2}{5}u^5 - \tfrac{2}{3}u^3 \Big]_1^2$$

$$= \tfrac{64}{5} - \tfrac{16}{3} - \tfrac{2}{5} + \tfrac{2}{3}$$

$$= \tfrac{116}{15} \qquad \blacktriangleleft$$

▶ **EXAMPLE 5** Evaluate

$$\int_0^{\pi/2} \sin^3 x \cos x \, dx$$

Solution Let

$$u = \sin x \qquad du = \cos x \, dx$$

When $x = 0$, $u = 0$; when $x = \frac{1}{2}\pi$, $u = 1$. Therefore

$$\int_0^{\pi/2} \sin^3 x \cos x \, dx = \int_0^1 u^3 \, du$$

$$= \frac{u^4}{4} \bigg]_0^1$$

$$= \tfrac{1}{4} \qquad \blacktriangleleft$$

▶ **EXAMPLE 6** Evaluate

$$\int_{-3}^4 |x + 2| \, dx$$

Solution

$$|x + 2| = \begin{cases} -x - 2 & \text{if } x \le -2 \\ x + 2 & \text{if } -2 \le x \end{cases}$$

From Theorem 4.5.13,

$$\int_{-3}^4 |x + 2| \, dx = \int_{-3}^{-2} (-x - 2) \, dx + \int_{-2}^4 (x + 2) \, dx$$

$$= \left[-\frac{x^2}{2} - 2x \right]_{-3}^{-2} + \left[\frac{x^2}{2} + 2x \right]_{-2}^4$$

$$= [(-2 + 4) - (-\tfrac{9}{2} + 6)] + [(8 + 8) - (2 - 4)]$$

$$= \tfrac{1}{2} + 18$$

$$= \tfrac{37}{2} \qquad \blacktriangleleft$$

▶ **EXAMPLE 7** In an electric circuit, E volts is the electromotive force at t seconds and

$$E = 2 \sin \tfrac{2}{3} \pi t$$

Find the average electromotive force from 0 sec to 4 sec.

Solution   We compute the average value of E on $[0, 4]$. If A.V. is this average value, we have from Definition 4.6.4,

$$\text{A.V.} = \frac{1}{4 - 0} \int_0^4 2 \sin \frac{2}{3} \pi t \, dt$$

$$= \frac{2}{4} \cdot \frac{3}{2\pi} \int_0^4 \sin \frac{2}{3} \pi t \left(\frac{2}{3} \pi \, dt \right)$$

$$= \frac{3}{4\pi} \left[-\cos \frac{2}{3} \pi t \right]_0^4$$

$$= \frac{3}{4\pi} \left(-\cos \frac{8}{3} \pi + \cos 0 \right)$$

$$= \frac{3}{4\pi} \left(\frac{1}{2} + 1 \right)$$

$$= 0.358$$

<u>Conclusion:</u>   The average electromotive force from 0 sec to 4 sec is 0.358 volts.   ◄

EXERCISES 4.7

In Exercises 1 through 34, evaluate the definite integral. In Exercises 1 through 6 and 29 through 34, support your answer by the NINT capability of your graphics calculator.

1. $\displaystyle\int_0^3 (3x^2 - 4x + 1) \, dx$

2. $\displaystyle\int_0^4 (x^3 - x^2 + 1) \, dx$

3. $\displaystyle\int_3^6 (x^2 - 2x) \, dx$

4. $\displaystyle\int_{-1}^3 (3x^2 + 5x - 1) \, dx$

5. $\displaystyle\int_1^2 \frac{x^2 + 1}{x^2} \, dx$

6. $\displaystyle\int_{-3}^5 (y^3 - 4y) \, dy$

7. $\displaystyle\int_0^1 \frac{z}{(z^2 + 1)^3} \, dz$

8. $\displaystyle\int_1^4 \sqrt{x}\,(2 + x) \, dx$

9. $\displaystyle\int_1^{10} \sqrt{5x - 1} \, dx$

10. $\displaystyle\int_0^{\sqrt{5}} t\sqrt{t^2 + 1} \, dt$

11. $\displaystyle\int_{-2}^0 3w\sqrt{4 - w^2} \, dw$

12. $\displaystyle\int_{-1}^3 \frac{1}{(y + 2)^3} \, dy$

13. $\displaystyle\int_0^{\pi/2} \sin 2x \, dx$

14. $\displaystyle\int_0^\pi \cos \tfrac{1}{2}x \, dx$

15. $\displaystyle\int_1^2 t^2 \sqrt{t^3 + 1} \, dt$

16. $\displaystyle\int_1^3 \frac{x}{(3x^2 - 1)^3} \, dx$

17. $\displaystyle\int_0^1 \frac{y^2 + 2y}{\sqrt[3]{y^3 + 3y^2 + 4}} \, dy$

18. $\displaystyle\int_2^4 \frac{w^4 - w}{w^3} \, dw$

19. $\displaystyle\int_0^{15} \frac{w}{(1 + w)^{3/4}} \, dw$

20. $\displaystyle\int_4^5 x^2 \sqrt{x - 4} \, dx$

21. $\displaystyle\int_{-2}^5 |x - 3| \, dx$

22. $\displaystyle\int_{-4}^4 |x - 2| \, dx$

23. $\displaystyle\int_{-1}^1 \sqrt{|x|} - x \, dx$

24. $\displaystyle\int_{-3}^3 \sqrt{3 + |x|} \, dx$

25 $\displaystyle\int_0^3 (x + 2)\sqrt{x + 1} \, dx$

26. $\displaystyle\int_{-2}^1 (x + 1)\sqrt{x + 3} \, dx$

27. $\displaystyle\int_0^1 \frac{x^3 + 1}{x + 1} \, dx$

28. $\displaystyle\int_1^4 \frac{x^5 - x}{3x^3} \, dx$

Hint: Divide the numerator by the denominator.

29. $\displaystyle\int_1^{64} \left(\sqrt{t} - \frac{1}{\sqrt{t}} + \sqrt[3]{t} \right) dt$

30. $\displaystyle\int_0^1 \sqrt{x}\, \sqrt{1 + x\sqrt{x}}\; dx$ **31.** $\displaystyle\int_0^1 \sin \pi x \cos \pi x\; dx$

32. $\displaystyle\int_0^{\pi/6} (\sin 2x + \cos 3x)\; dx$ **33.** $\displaystyle\int_{\pi/8}^{\pi/4} 3 \csc^2 2x\; dx$

34. $\displaystyle\int_0^{1/2} \sec^2 \tfrac{1}{2}\pi t \tan \tfrac{1}{2}\pi t\; dt$

In Exercises 35 through 44, compute the derivative.

35. $\displaystyle\frac{d}{dx}\int_0^x \sqrt{4 + t^6}\; dt$ **36.** $\displaystyle\frac{d}{dx}\int_x^3 \sqrt{1 + t^4}\; dt$

37. $\displaystyle\frac{d}{dx}\int_x^3 \sqrt{\sin t}\; dt$ **38.** $\displaystyle\frac{d}{dx}\int_2^x \frac{1}{t^4 + 4}\; dt$

39. $\displaystyle\frac{d}{dx}\int_{-x}^x \frac{1}{3 + t^2}\; dt$ **40.** $\displaystyle\frac{d}{dx}\int_{-x}^x \cos(t^2 + 1)\; dt$

41. $\displaystyle\frac{d}{dx}\int_1^{x^3} \sqrt[3]{t^2 + 1}\; dt$ **42.** $\displaystyle\frac{d}{dx}\int_0^{x^2} \frac{1}{\sqrt{t^2 + 1}}\; dt$

43. $\displaystyle\frac{d}{dx}\int_2^{\tan x} \frac{1}{1 + t^2}\; dt$ **44.** $\displaystyle\frac{d}{dx}\int_3^{\sin x} \frac{1}{1 - t^2}\; dt$

In Exercises 45 through 48, find the average value of the function f on the interval [a, b]. In Exercises 45 and 46, find the value of x at which the average value occurs and describe the geometric interpretation of the result.

45. $f(x) = 9 - x^2$; $[a, b] = [0, 3]$

46. $f(x) = 8x - x^2$; $[a, b] = [0, 4]$

47. $f(x) = 3x \sqrt{x^2 - 16}$; $[a, b] = [4, 5]$

48. $f(x) = x^2 \sqrt{x - 3}$; $[a, b] = [7, 12]$

49. For the electric circuit of Example 7, find the square root of the average value of E^2 from $t = 0$ to $t = 4$. *Hint:* Use the identity $\sin^2 x = \tfrac{1}{2}(1 - \cos 2x)$.

50. If $f(x) = \sec^2 x$, find the average value of f on the interval $[-\tfrac{1}{4}\pi, \tfrac{1}{4}\pi]$.

51. A ball is dropped from rest, and after t seconds its velocity is v feet per second. Neglecting air resistance, show that the average velocity during the first $\tfrac{1}{2}T$ seconds is one-third of the average velocity during the next $\tfrac{1}{2}T$ seconds.

52. A stone is thrown downward with an initial velocity of v_0 feet per second. Neglect air resistance.
(a) Show that if v feet per second is the velocity of the stone after falling s feet, then $v = \sqrt{v_0^2 + 2gs}$.
(b) Find the average velocity during the first 100 ft of fall if the initial velocity is 60 ft/sec. (Take $g = 32$ and downward as the positive direction.)

53. If an investment earns interest at a rate of $100r(t)$ percent *compounded continuously* over a period of T years, then the average interest rate $100R(T)$ percent over the T years is defined by

$$R(T) = \frac{1}{T}\int_0^T r(t)\; dt$$

Show that

$$R'(T) = \frac{r(T) - R(T)}{T}$$

Note: Interest *compounded continuously* will be defined precisely in Section 5.6.

54. Let

$$I = \int_0^k \frac{f(x)}{f(x) + f(k - x)}\; dx \qquad (12)$$

where f is continuous on $[0, k]$ and $f(x) + f(k - x) \neq 0$ if x is in $[0, k]$. **(a)** Prove that $I = \tfrac{1}{2}k$. *Hint:* Change the variable in (12) by letting $u = k - x$ and show that

$$I = \int_0^k \frac{f(k - u)}{f(u) + f(k - u)}\; du \qquad (13)$$

Change the variable in (13) to x and show that $2I = k$. **(b)** Use the result of part (a) to show that

$$\int_0^{\pi/2} \frac{\sin x}{\sin x + \cos x}\; dx = \frac{1}{4}\pi$$

55. Given

$$F(x) = \int_0^x \frac{1}{1 + t^2}\; dt + \int_0^{1/x} \frac{1}{1 + t^2}\; dt$$

where $x \neq 0$. Prove that F is constant on the intervals $(-\infty, 0)$ and $(0, +\infty)$. *Hint:* Show that $F'(x) = 0$ for all $x \neq 0$.

56. Find a function f such that for any real number x

$$\int_0^x f(t)\; dt = \frac{\cos x}{1 + x^2} - 1$$

Hint: Take the derivative of both sides of the equation.

57. If m and n are positive integers, prove that

$$\int_0^1 x^n (1 - x)^m\; dx = \int_0^1 x^m (1 - x)^n\; dx$$

This integral arises in applications in Probability, Combinatorics, and the Kinetic Theory of Matter.

58. Let f be a function whose derivative f' is continuous on $[a, b]$. Find the average value of the slope of the tangent line of the graph of f on $[a, b]$, and give a geometric interpretation of the result.

59. Find $\displaystyle\int_4^{16} \left[D_x \int_5^x (2\sqrt{t} - 1)\, dt \right] dx.$

60. (a) Given $f(x) = x \sin x$. Plot the graphs of f and NDER(NINT $(f(t), 0, x), x)$ in the same window and show that the graphs appear the same. **(b)** Repeat

part (a) if $f(x) = \sqrt{4 + x^2}$. **(c)** What theorem or theorems do parts (a) and (b) support? Explain.

61. Explain why every continuous function must have an antiderivative. What guarantees this fact?

4.8 AREA OF A PLANE REGION

We defined the area of a plane region as the limit of a Riemann sum in Section 4.4, and in Section 4.5 you learned that such a limit is a definite integral. Now that you have learned some techniques for computing definite integrals we consider more problems involving areas of plane regions.

In the examples that follow we begin by expressing the measure of the required area as the limit of a Riemann sum to reinforce the procedure for setting up such sums for future applications, treated in Sections 4.9 and 4.10 and Chapter 6.

▶ **EXAMPLE 1**   Find the area of the region in the first quadrant bounded by the curve

$$y = x\sqrt{x^2 + 5}$$

the x axis, and the line $x = 2$.

Solution   See Figure 1 showing the region together with one of the rectangular elements of area.

We take a partition of the interval $[0, 2]$. The width of the ith rectangle is $\Delta_i x$ units, and the altitude is $w_i \sqrt{w_i^2 + 5}$ units, where w_i is any number in the ith subinterval. Therefore the measure of the area of the rectangular element is $w_i \sqrt{w_i^2 + 5}\, \Delta_i x$. The sum of the measures of the areas of n such rectangles is

$$\sum_{i=1}^{n} w_i \sqrt{w_i^2 + 5}\, \Delta_i x$$

which is a Riemann sum. The limit of this sum as $\|\Delta\|$ approaches 0 gives the measure of the desired area. The limit of the Riemann sum is a definite integral that we evaluate by the second fundamental theorem of the calculus. Let A square units be the area of the region. Then

$$A = \lim_{\|\Delta\| \to 0} \sum_{i=1}^{n} w_i \sqrt{w_i^2 + 5}\, \Delta_i x$$

$$= \int_0^2 x\sqrt{x^2 + 5}\, dx$$

$$= \frac{1}{2} \int_0^2 \sqrt{x^2 + 5}\,(2x\, dx)$$

$$= \tfrac{1}{2} \cdot \tfrac{2}{3}(x^2 + 5)^{3/2} \Big]_0^2$$

$$= \tfrac{1}{3}[(9)^{3/2} - (5)^{3/2}]$$

$$= \tfrac{1}{3}(27 - 5\sqrt{5})$$

$$\approx 5.27$$

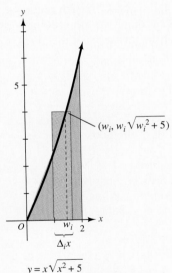

$y = x\sqrt{x^2 + 5}$

FIGURE 1

<u>Conclusion:</u>   The area is $\frac{1}{3}(27 - 5\sqrt{5})$ square units, or approximately 5.27 square units.   ◀

So far we have considered the area of a region for which the function values are nonnegative on $[a, b]$. Suppose now that $f(x) < 0$ for all x in $[a, b]$. Then each $f(w_i)$ is a negative number; so we define the number of square units in the area of the region bounded by $y = f(x)$, the x axis, and the lines $x = a$ and $x = b$ to be

$$\lim_{\|\Delta\| \to 0} \sum_{i=1}^{n} [-f(w_i)]\, \Delta_i x$$

which equals

$$-\int_{a}^{b} f(x)\, dx$$

▶   **EXAMPLE 2**   Find the area of the region bounded by the curve

$$y = x^2 - 4x$$

the x axis, and the lines $x = 1$ and $x = 3$.

Solution   The region, together with a rectangular element of area, appears in Figure 2.

We take a partition of the interval $[1, 3]$; the width of the ith rectangle is $\Delta_i x$. Because $x^2 - 4x < 0$ on $[1, 3]$, the altitude of the ith rectangle is $-(w_i^2 - 4w_i) = 4w_i - w_i^2$. Hence the sum of the measures of the areas of n rectangles is given by

$$\sum_{i=1}^{n} (4w_i - w_i^2)\, \Delta_i x$$

The measure of the desired area is given by the limit of this sum as $\|\Delta\|$ approaches 0; so if A square units is the area of the region,

$$A = \lim_{\|\Delta\| \to 0} \sum_{i=1}^{n} (4w_i - w_i^2)\, \Delta_i x$$

$$= \int_{1}^{3} (4x - x^2)\, dx$$

$$= 2x^2 - \tfrac{1}{3}x^3 \Big]_{1}^{3}$$

$$= \tfrac{22}{3}$$

<u>Conclusion:</u>   The area of the region is $\frac{22}{3}$ square units.   ◀

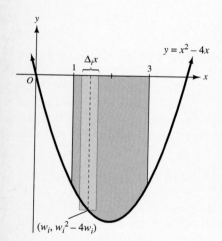

FIGURE 2

▶   **EXAMPLE 3**   Find the area of the region bounded by the curve

$$y = x^3 - 2x^2 - 5x + 6$$

the x axis, and the lines $x = -1$ and $x = 2$.

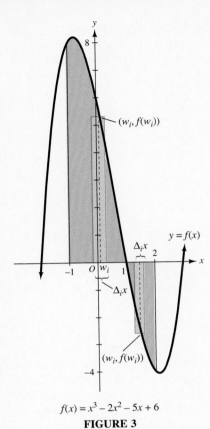

$f(x) = x^3 - 2x^2 - 5x + 6$

FIGURE 3

Solution   The region appears in Figure 3. Let

$$f(x) = x^3 - 2x^2 - 5x + 6$$

Because $f(x) \geq 0$ when x is in the closed interval $[-1, 1]$ and $f(x) \leq 0$ when x is in the closed interval $[1, 2]$, we separate the region into two parts. Let A_1 be the number of square units in the area of the region when x is in $[-1, 1]$, and let A_2 be the number of square units in the area of the region when x is in $[1, 2]$. Then

$$A_1 = \lim_{\|\Delta\| \to 0} \sum_{i=1}^{n} f(w_i)\, \Delta_i x$$

$$= \int_{-1}^{1} f(x)\, dx$$

$$= \int_{-1}^{1} (x^3 - 2x^2 - 5x + 6)\, dx$$

and

$$A_2 = \lim_{\|\Delta\| \to 0} \sum_{i=1}^{n} [-f(w_i)]\, \Delta_i x$$

$$= \int_{1}^{2} -(x^3 - 2x^2 - 5x + 6)\, dx$$

If A square units is the area of the entire region, then

$$A = A_1 + A_2$$

$$= \int_{-1}^{1} (x^3 - 2x^2 - 5x + 6)\, dx - \int_{1}^{2} (x^3 - 2x^2 - 5x + 6)\, dx$$

$$= \left[\tfrac{1}{4}x^4 - \tfrac{2}{3}x^3 - \tfrac{5}{2}x^2 + 6x\right]_{-1}^{1} - \left[\tfrac{1}{4}x^4 - \tfrac{2}{3}x^3 - \tfrac{5}{2}x^2 + 6x\right]_{1}^{2}$$

$$= \left[(\tfrac{1}{4} - \tfrac{2}{3} - \tfrac{5}{2} + 6) - (\tfrac{1}{4} + \tfrac{2}{3} - \tfrac{5}{2} - 6)\right]$$
$$\qquad\qquad - \left[(4 - \tfrac{16}{3} - 10 + 12) - (\tfrac{1}{4} - \tfrac{2}{3} - \tfrac{5}{2} + 6)\right]$$

$$= \tfrac{32}{3} - (-\tfrac{29}{12})$$

$$= \tfrac{157}{12}$$

Conclusion: The area of the region is $\tfrac{157}{12}$ square units.   ◄

Now consider two functions f and g continuous on the closed interval $[a, b]$ and such that $f(x) \geq g(x)$ for all x in $[a, b]$. We wish to find the area of the region bounded by the two curves $y = f(x)$ and $y = g(x)$ and the two lines $x = a$ and $x = b$. Such a situation is shown in Figure 4.

Take a partition of the interval $[a, b]$, with the ith subinterval having a length of $\Delta_i x$. In each subinterval choose a point w_i. Consider the rectangle having altitude $[f(w_i) - g(w_i)]$ units and width $\Delta_i x$ units. A rectangle is shown in Figure 4. There are n such rectangles, one associated with each subinterval. The sum of the measures of the areas of these n rectangles is given by the following Riemann sum:

$$\sum_{i=1}^{n} [f(w_i) - g(w_i)]\, \Delta_i x$$

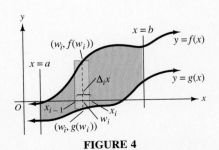

FIGURE 4

This Riemann sum is an approximation to what we intuitively think of as the number representing the "measure of the area" of the region. The smaller the value of $\|\Delta\|$, the better is this approximation. If A square units is the area of the region, we define

$$A = \lim_{\|\Delta\| \to 0} \sum_{i=1}^{n} [f(w_i) - g(w_i)] \, \Delta_i x \tag{1}$$

Because f and g are continuous on $[a, b]$, so too is $f - g$; therefore the limit in (1) exists and is equal to the definite integral

$$\int_a^b [f(x) - g(x)] \, dx$$

▶ **EXAMPLE 4**   Find the area of the region bounded by the curves $y = x^2$ and $y = -x^2 + 4x$.

Solution   To find the points of intersection of the two curves we solve the equations simultaneously and obtain the points $(0, 0)$ and $(2, 4)$. Figure 5 shows the region.

Let

$$f(x) = -x^2 + 4x \quad \text{and} \quad g(x) = x^2$$

Observe that in the interval $[0, 2]$ the curve $y = f(x)$ is above the curve $y = g(x)$. We draw a vertical rectangular element of area, having altitude $[f(w_i) - g(w_i)]$ units and width $\Delta_i x$ units. The measure of the area of this rectangle then is given by $[f(w_i) - g(w_i)] \, \Delta_i x$. The sum of the measures of the areas of n such rectangles is given by the Riemann sum

$$\sum_{i=1}^{n} [f(w_i) - g(w_i)] \, \Delta_i x$$

If A square units is the area of the region, then

$$A = \lim_{\|\Delta\| \to 0} \sum_{i=1}^{n} [f(w_i) - g(w_i)] \, \Delta_i x$$

and the limit of the Riemann sum is a definite integral. Hence

$$A = \int_0^2 [f(x) - g(x)] \, dx$$

$$= \int_0^2 [(-x^2 + 4x) - x^2] \, dx$$

$$= \int_0^2 (-2x^2 + 4x) \, dx$$

$$= -\tfrac{2}{3}x^3 + 2x^2 \Big]_0^2$$

$$= -\tfrac{16}{3} + 8 - 0$$

$$= \tfrac{8}{3}$$

Conclusion: The area of the region is $\tfrac{8}{3}$ square units.   ◀

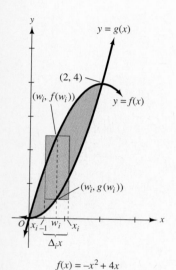

$f(x) = -x^2 + 4x$

$g(x) = x^2$

FIGURE 5

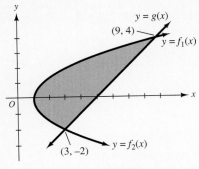

$f_1(x) = \sqrt{2x - 2}$

$f_2(x) = -\sqrt{2x - 2}$

$g(x) = x - 5$

FIGURE 6

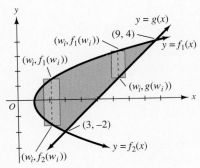

$f_1(x) = \sqrt{2x - 2}$

$f_2(x) = -\sqrt{2x - 2}$

$g(x) = x - 5$

FIGURE 7

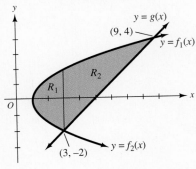

$f_1(x) = \sqrt{2x - 2}$

$f_2(x) = -\sqrt{2x - 2}$

$g(x) = x - 5$

FIGURE 8

▶ **EXAMPLE 5** Find the area of the region bounded by the parabola $y^2 = 2x - 2$ and the line $y = x - 5$.

Solution The two curves intersect at the points $(3, -2)$ and $(9, 4)$. The region is shown in Figure 6.

The equation $y^2 = 2x - 2$ is equivalent to the two equations

$$y = \sqrt{2x - 2} \quad \text{and} \quad y = -\sqrt{2x - 2}$$

with the first equation giving the upper half of the parabola and the second equation giving the bottom half. If

$$f_1(x) = \sqrt{2x - 2} \quad \text{and} \quad f_2(x) = -\sqrt{2x - 2}$$

the equation of the top half of the parabola is $y = f_1(x)$, and the equation of the bottom half is $y = f_2(x)$. If we let $g(x) = x - 5$, the equation of the line is $y = g(x)$.

In Figure 7 we see two vertical rectangular elements of area. Each rectangle has the upper base on the curve $y = f_1(x)$. Because the lower base of the first rectangle is on the curve $y = f_2(x)$, the altitude is $[f_1(w_i) - f_2(w_i)]$ units. Because the lower base of the second rectangle lies on the curve $y = g(x)$, its altitude is $[f_1(w_i) - g(w_i)]$ units. If we wish to solve this problem by using vertical rectangular elements of area, we must divide the region into two separate regions, for instance R_1 and R_2, where R_1 is the region bounded by the curves $y = f_1(x)$ and $y = f_2(x)$ and the line $x = 3$, and where R_2 is the region bounded by the curves $y = f_1(x)$ and $y = g(x)$ and the line $x = 3$ (see Figure 8).

If A_1 square units is the area of region R_1,

$$A_1 = \lim_{\|\Delta\| \to 0} \sum_{i=1}^{n} [f_1(w_i) - f_2(w_i)] \, \Delta_i x$$

$$= \int_1^3 [f_1(x) - f_2(x)] \, dx$$

$$= \int_1^3 [\sqrt{2x - 2} + \sqrt{2x - 2}] \, dx$$

$$= 2 \int_1^3 \sqrt{2x - 2} \, dx$$

$$= \tfrac{2}{3}(2x - 2)^{3/2} \Big]_1^3$$

$$= \tfrac{16}{3}$$

If A_2 square units is the area of region R_2,

$$A_2 = \lim_{\|\Delta\| \to 0} \sum_{i=1}^{n} [f_1(w_i) - g(w_i)] \, \Delta_i x$$

$$= \int_3^9 [f_1(x) - g(x)] \, dx$$

$$= \int_3^9 [\sqrt{2x - 2} - (x - 5)] \, dx$$

$$= \tfrac{1}{3}(2x - 2)^{3/2} - \tfrac{1}{2}x^2 + 5x \Big]_3^9$$

$$= [\tfrac{64}{3} - \tfrac{81}{2} + 45] - [\tfrac{8}{3} - \tfrac{9}{2} + 15]$$

$$= \tfrac{38}{3}$$

Hence $A_1 + A_2 = \tfrac{16}{3} + \tfrac{38}{3}$.

<u>Conclusion:</u>   The area of the entire region is 18 square units.   ◀

▶ **EXAMPLE 6**   Find the area of the region in Example 5 by taking horizontal rectangular elements of area.

Solution   Figure 9 illustrates the region with a horizontal rectangular element of area.

If in the equations of the parabola and the line we solve for x,

$$x = \tfrac{1}{2}(y^2 + 2) \qquad x = y + 5$$

Letting $\phi(y) = \tfrac{1}{2}(y^2 + 2)$ and $\lambda(y) = y + 5$, the equation of the parabola may be written as $x = \phi(y)$ and the equation of the line as $x = \lambda(y)$. Consider the closed interval $[-2, 4]$ on the y axis, and take a partition of this interval. The ith subinterval will have a length of $\Delta_i y$. In the ith subinterval $[y_{i-1}, y_i]$ choose a point w_i. Then the length of the ith rectangular element is $[\lambda(w_i) - \phi(w_i)]$ units and the width is $\Delta_i y$ units. The measure of the area of the region can be approximated by the Reimann sum

$$\sum_{i=1}^{n} [\lambda(w_i) - \phi(w_i)] \, \Delta_i y$$

If A square units is the area of the region, then

$$A = \lim_{\|\Delta\| \to 0} \sum_{i=1}^{n} [\lambda(w_i) - \phi(w_i)] \, \Delta_i y$$

Becasue λ and ϕ are continuous on $[-2, 4]$, so too is $\lambda - \phi$, and the limit of the Riemann sum is a definite integral:

$$A = \int_{-2}^4 [\lambda(y) - \phi(y)] \, dy$$

$$= \int_{-2}^4 [(y + 5) - \tfrac{1}{2}(y^2 + 2)] \, dy$$

$$= \frac{1}{2} \int_{-2}^4 (-y^2 + 2y + 8) \, dy$$

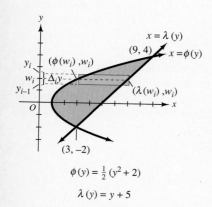

$$\phi(y) = \tfrac{1}{2}(y^2 + 2)$$

$$\lambda(y) = y + 5$$

FIGURE 9

$$= \tfrac{1}{2}\left[-\tfrac{1}{3}y^3 + y^2 + 8y\right]_{-2}^{4}$$

$$= \tfrac{1}{2}[(-\tfrac{64}{3} + 16 + 32) - (\tfrac{8}{3} + 4 - 16)]$$

$$= 18$$

This answer agrees with our solution in Example 5.   ◀

Comparing the solutions in Examples 5 and 6 we see that in the first case there are two definite integrals to evaluate, whereas in the second case there is only one. In general, if possible, the rectangular elements of area should be constructed so that a single definite integral is obtained. The following example illustrates a situation where two definite integrals are necessary.

▶ **EXAMPLE 7**   Find the area of the region bounded by the two curves $y = x^3 - 6x^2 + 8x$ and $y = x^2 - 4x$.

Solution   The points of intersection of the two curves are $(0, 0)$, $(3, -3)$, and $(4, 0)$. The region appears in Figure 10.

Let

$$f(x) = x^3 - 6x^2 + 8x \quad \text{and} \quad g(x) = x^2 - 4x$$

In the interval $[0, 3]$ the curve $y = f(x)$ is above the curve $y = g(x)$, and in the interval $[3, 4]$ the curve $y = g(x)$ is above the curve $y = f(x)$. So the region must be divided into two separate regions R_1 and R_2, where R_1 is the region bounded by the two curves in the interval $[0, 3]$ and R_2 is the region bounded by the two curves in the interval $[3, 4]$. If A_1 square units is the area of R_1 and A_2 square units is the area of R_2,

$$A_1 = \lim_{\|\Delta\| \to 0} \sum_{i=1}^{n} [f(w_i) - g(w_i)] \, \Delta_i x$$

$$A_2 = \lim_{\|\Delta\| \to 0} \sum_{i=1}^{n} [g(w_i) - f(w_i)] \, \Delta_i x$$

so that

$$A_1 + A_2 = \int_0^3 [(x^3 - 6x^2 + 8x) - (x^2 - 4x)] \, dx$$

$$+ \int_3^4 [(x^2 - 4x) - (x^3 - 6x^2 + 8x)] \, dx$$

$$= \int_0^3 (x^3 - 7x^2 + 12x) \, dx + \int_3^4 (-x^3 + 7x^2 - 12x) \, dx$$

$$= \left[\tfrac{1}{4}x^4 - \tfrac{7}{3}x^3 + 6x^2\right]_0^3 + \left[-\tfrac{1}{4}x^4 + \tfrac{7}{3}x^3 - 6x^2\right]_3^4$$

$$= \tfrac{45}{4} + \tfrac{7}{12}$$

$$= \tfrac{71}{6}$$

<u>**Conclusion:**</u>   The required area is $\tfrac{71}{6}$ square units.   ◀

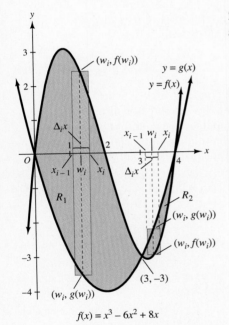

$f(x) = x^3 - 6x^2 + 8x$

$g(x) = x^2 - 4x$

FIGURE 10

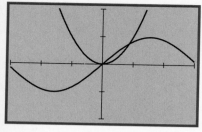

[-3, 3] by [-2, 2]

$f(x) = \sin x$
$g(x) = x^2$

FIGURE 11

In Examples 4 through 7, we computed the coordinates of the points of intersection by solving simultaneously the equations of the curves. In the following example we cannot find the points of intersection that easily.

▶ **EXAMPLE 8**   Find the area of the region bounded by the graphs of $y = x^2$ and $y = \sin x$.

Solution   Refer to Figure 11 showing the two graphs, plotted in the $[-3, 3]$ by $[-2, 2]$ window and intersecting at the origin and at another point in the first quadrant. With $[a, b]$ denoting the interval on which we will compute the area, we know that $a = 0$. We cannot find b algebraically, but we can obtain an approximate value of b by using the intersect or trace and zoom-in features of our graphics calculator. To four significant digits, we get $b = 0.8767$. If $f(x) = \sin x$, $g(x) = x^2$, and A square units is the area of the required region on the interval $[0, 0.8767]$,

$$A = \lim_{\|\Delta\| \to 0} \sum_{i=1}^{n} [f(w_i) - g(w_i)] \, \Delta_i x$$

$$= \int_0^{0.8767} (\sin x - x^2) \, dx$$

We compute this integral by the NINT capability of our graphics calculator and obtain to four significant digits

$$A = 0.1357$$

Conclusion: To four significant digits, the area is 0.1357 square units. ◀

EXERCISES 4.8

In Exercises 1 through 38, find the area of the region bounded by the curves. In each exercise do the following: (a) Draw a figure showing the region and a rectangular element of area; (b) express the area of the region as the limit of a Riemann sum; (c) find the limit in part (b) by the second fundamental theorem of the calculus.

1. $y = 4 - x^2$; x axis

2. $y = x^2 - 2x + 3$; x axis; $x = -2$; $x = 1$

3. $y = 4x - x^2$; x axis; $x = 1$; $x = 3$

4. $y = 6 - x - x^2$; x axis

5. $y = \sqrt{x + 1}$; x axis; y axis; $x = 8$

6. $y = \dfrac{1}{x^2} - x$; x axis; $x = 2$; $x = 3$

7. $y = x^2 + x - 12$; x axis

8. $y = x^2 - 6x + 5$; x axis

9. $y = \sin x$; x axis; $x = \frac{1}{3}\pi$; $x = \frac{2}{3}\pi$

10. $y = \cos x$; x axis; y axis; $x = \frac{1}{6}\pi$

11. $y = \sec^2 x$; x axis; y axis; $x = \frac{1}{4}\pi$

12. $y = \csc^2 x$; x axis; $x = \frac{1}{4}\pi$; $x = \frac{1}{3}\pi$

13. $x^2 = -y$; $y = -4$

14. $y^2 = -x$; $x = -2$; $x = -4$

15. $x^2 + y + 4 = 0$; $y = -8$. Take the elements of area perpendicular to the y axis.

16. The same region as in Exercise 15. Take the elements of area parallel to the y axis.

17. $x^2 - y + 1 = 0$; $x - y + 1 = 0$. Take the elements of area perpendicular to the x axis.

18. The same region as in Exercise 17. Take the elements of area parallel to the x axis.

19. $x^3 = 2y^2$; $x = 0$; $y = -2$

20. $y^3 = 4x$; $x = 0$; $y = -2$

21. $y = 2 - x^2$; $y = -x$

22. $y = x^2$; $y = x^4$

23. $y^2 = x - 1$; $x = 3$

24. $y = x^2$; $x^2 = 18 - y$

25. $y = \sqrt{x}$; $y = x^3$

26. $x = 4 - y^2$; $x = 4 - 4y$

27. $y^3 = x^2$; $x - 3y + 4 = 0$

28. $xy^2 = y^2 - 1$; $x = 1$; $y = 1$; $y = 4$

29. $x = y^2 - 2; x = 6 - y^2$

30. $x = y^2 - y; x = y - y^2$

31. $y = 2x^3 - 3x^2 - 9x; y = x^3 - 2x^2 - 3x$

32. $3y = x^3 - 2x^2 - 15x; y = x^3 - 4x^2 - 11x + 30$

33. $y = x^3 + 3x^2 + 2x; y = 2x^2 + 4x$

34. $y = |x - 1| + 3; y = 0; x = -2; x = 4$

35. $y = \cos x - \sin x; x = 0; y = 0$

36. $y = \sin x; y = -\sin x; x = -\frac{1}{2}\pi; x = \frac{1}{2}\pi$

37. $y = |x|; y = x^2 - 1; x = -1; x = 1$

38. $y = |x + 1| + |x|; y = 0; x = -2; x = 3$

In Exercises 39 through 46, approximate to four significant digits the area of the region bounded by the graphs of the given equations by doing the following: (a) Plot the graphs in a convenient window and find the points of intersection by using the intersection or trace and zoom-in features of your graphics calculator; (b) express the area of the region as the limit of a Riemann sum; (c) approximate the limit in part (b) by the NINT capability of your graphics calculator.

39. $y = x^4 - 2, y = x^2$

40. $y = x^4; y = 4 - x^2$

41. $y = x^2 - 1; y = \sin^2 x$

42. $y = x^2; y = \cos x$

43. $y = x^3; y = 4 - x^2$; the y axis

44. $y = x^3; y = 4 - x^2$; the x axis

45. $y = x^3; y = \tan^2 x - 3; 0 \le x \le \frac{1}{2}\pi$

46. $y = 2 - x^4; y = \sec^2 x$

47. Find by integration the area of the region enclosed by the triangle having vertices at $(5, 1)$, $(1, 3)$, and $(-1, -2)$.

48. Find by integration the area of the region enclosed by the triangle having vertices at $(3, 4)$, $(2, 0)$, and $(0, 1)$.

In Exercises 49 through 57, find the exact area of the described region.

49. The region bounded by the line $x = 4$ and the curve $x^3 - x^2 + 2xy - y^2 = 0$. *Hint:* Solve the quadratic equation in y for y in terms of x, and express y as two functions of x.

50. The region bounded by the three curves $y = x^2$, $x = y^3$, and $x + y = 2$.

51. The region bounded by the three curves $y = x^2$, $y = 8 - x^2$, and $4x - y + 12 = 0$.

52. The region enclosed by the trapezoid having vertices at $(-1, -1)$, $(2, 2)$, $(6, 2)$, and $(7, -1)$.

53. The region bounded by the curve $y = \sin x$, the line $y = 1$, and the y axis to the right of the y axis.

54. The region bounded by the two curves $y = \sin x$ and $y = \cos x$ between two consecutive points of intersection.

55. The region bounded by the curve $y = \tan^2 x$, the x axis, and the line $x = \frac{1}{4}\pi$.

56. The region above the parabola $x^2 = 4py$ and inside the triangle formed by the x axis and the lines $y = x + 8p$ and $y = -x + 8p$ where $p > 0$.

57. The region bounded by the two parabolas $y^2 = 4px$ and $x^2 = 4py$.

58. Find the rate of change of the measure of the area of Exercise 56 with respect to p when $p = \frac{3}{8}$.

59. Find the rate of change of the measure of the area of Exercise 57 with respect to p when $p = 3$.

60. Determine m so that the region above the line $y = mx$ and below the parabola $y = 2x - x^2$ has an area of 36 square units.

61. Determine m so that the region above the curve $y = mx^2$ ($m > 0$), to the right of the y axis, and below the line $y = m$ has an area of K square units, where $K > 0$.

62. If A square units is the area of the region bounded by the parabola $y^2 = 4x$ and the line $y = mx$ ($m > 0$), find the rate of change of A with respect to m.

63. To accelerate the evaporation of a liquid, a circular disk of radius r units is placed in the liquid and then rotated slowly as shown in the accompanying figure. The distance from the center of the disk to the surface of the liquid is h units. The coordinate axes are placed so that the origin is at the center of the disk, the y axis is parallel to the surface of the liquid, and the positive x axis is downward. (a) Show that if $A(h)$ square units is the area of the exposed wetted region,

$$A(h) = \pi r^2 - \pi h^2 - 2\int_h^r \sqrt{r^2 - x^2}\, dx$$

and state the domain of A. (b) Show that to maximize the area of the exposed wetted region, h must be equal to $r/\sqrt{1 + \pi^2}$. *Hint:* To compute $A'(h)$ apply the first fundamental theorem of the calculus.

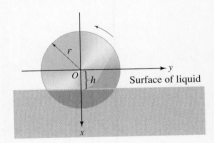

64. When computing the area of a plane region by integration, under what circumstances is it more convenient to use (a) vertical rectangular elements of area and (b) horizontal rectangular elements of area?

FIGURE 1

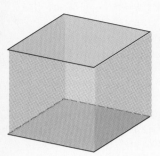

FIGURE 2

FIGURE 3

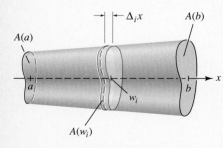

FIGURE 4

4.9 VOLUMES OF SOLIDS BY SLICING, DISKS, AND WASHERS

We led up to the definition of the definite integral by first defining the area of a plane region, and in the development we used the formula for the area of a rectangle. We now use a similar process to obtain volumes of particular kinds of solids. One such solid is a *right cylinder*.

A solid is a **right cylinder** if it is bounded by two congruent plane regions R_1 and R_2 lying in parallel planes and by a lateral surface generated by a line segment, having its endpoints on the boundaries of R_1 and R_2, which moves so that it is always perpendicular to the planes of R_1 and R_2. Figure 1 shows a right cylinder. The height of the cylinder is the perpendicular distance between the planes of R_1 and R_2 and the base is either R_1 or R_2. If the base of the right cylinder is a region enclosed by a rectangle, we have a **rectangular parallelepiped,** appearing in Figure 2, and if the base is a region enclosed by a circle, we have a **right-circular cylinder** as shown in Figure 3.

If the area of the base of a right cylinder is A square units and the height is h units, then if V cubic units is the volume

$$V = Ah$$

We shall use this formula to obtain a method of computing the measure of the volume of a solid for which the area of any plane section (a plane region formed by the intersection of a plane with the solid) perpendicular to an axis is a function of the perpendicular distance of the plane section from a fixed point on the axis. Figure 4 shows such a solid S that lies between the planes perpendicular to the x axis at a and b. We let $A(x)$ square units be the area of the plane section of S perpendicular to the x axis at x. We require A to be continuous on $[a, b]$.

Let Δ be a partition of the closed interval $[a, b]$ given by

$$a = x_0 < x_1 < x_2 < \ldots < x_n = b$$

There are, then, n subintervals of the form $[x_{i-1}, x_i]$, where $i = 1, 2, \ldots,$ n, with the length of the ith subinterval being $\Delta_i x = x_i - x_{i-1}$. Choose any number w_i, with $x_{i-1} \leq w_i \leq x_i$, in each subinterval, and construct the right cylinders of heights $\Delta_i x$ units and plane section areas $A(w_i)$ square units. Figure 5 shows the ith right cylinder, which we call an element of volume. If $\Delta_i V$ cubic units is the volume of the ith element then

$$\Delta_i V = A(w_i) \, \Delta_i x$$

The sum of the measures of the volumes of the n elements is

$$\sum_{i=1}^{n} \Delta_i V = \sum_{i=1}^{n} A(w_i) \, \Delta_i x \qquad \textbf{(1)}$$

which is a Riemann sum. This Riemann sum is an approximation of what we intuitively think of as the number of cubic units in the volume of the solid. The smaller we take the norm $\|\Delta\|$ of the partition, the larger will be n, and the closer this approximation will be to the number V we wish to assign to the measure of the volume. We therefore define V to be the limit of the

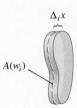

$\Delta_i x$

$A(w_i)$

FIGURE 5

Riemann sum in (1) as $\|\Delta\|$ approaches zero. This limit exists because A is continuous on $[a, b]$. We have, then, the following definition.

4.9.1 Definition of the Volume of a Solid

Let S be a solid such that S lies between planes drawn perpendicular to the x axis at a and b. If the measure of the area of the plane section of S drawn perpendicular to the x axis at x is given by $A(x)$, where A is continuous on $[a, b]$, then the measure of the volume of S is given by

$$V = \lim_{\|\Delta\| \to 0} \sum_{i=1}^{n} A(w_i) \, \Delta_i x$$

$$= \int_a^b A(x) \, dx$$

The terminology **slicing** is used when applying this definition to find the volume of a solid. The process is similar to slicing a loaf of bread into very thin pieces where all the pieces together make up the whole loaf. In the following illustration we show that Definition 4.9.1 is consistent with the formula from solid geometry for the volume of a right-circular cylinder.

▷ **ILLUSTRATION 1**   Figure 6 shows a right-circular cylinder having a height h units and a base radius r units with the coordinate axes chosen so that the origin is at the center of one base and the height is measured along the positive x axis. A plane section at a distance of x units from the origin has an area of $A(x)$ square units where

$$A(x) = \pi r^2$$

An element of volume, shown in Figure 6, is a right cylinder of base area $A(w_i)$ square units and a thickness of $\Delta_i x$ units. Thus if V cubic units is the volume of the right-circular cylinder

$$V = \lim_{\|\Delta\| \to 0} \sum_{i=1}^{n} A(w_i) \, \Delta_i x$$

$$= \int_0^h A(x) \, dx$$

$$= \int_0^h \pi r^2 \, dx$$

$$= \pi r^2 \, x \Big]_0^h$$

$$= \pi r^2 h \qquad \blacktriangleleft$$

In Definition 4.9.1 we can replace x by y. In such a situation S is a solid lying between planes drawn perpendicular to the y axis at c and d, and the measure of the area of the plane section of S drawn perpendicular to the y

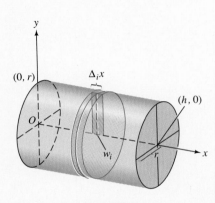

y

$(0, r)$ $\Delta_i x$

$(h, 0)$

O

w_i r x

FIGURE 6

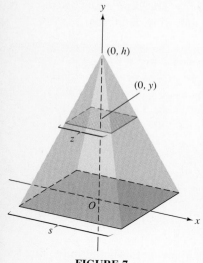

FIGURE 7

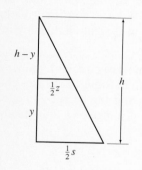

FIGURE 8

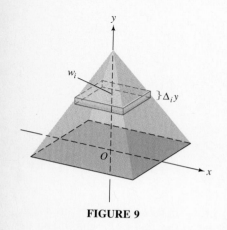

FIGURE 9

axis at y is given by $A(y)$, where A is continuous on $[c, d]$. Then the measure of the volume of S is given by

$$V = \lim_{\|\Delta\| \to 0} \sum_{i=1}^{n} A(w_i) \, \Delta_i y$$

$$= \int_{c}^{d} A(y) \, dy$$

▶ **EXAMPLE 1**   Use slicing to find the volume of a pyramid whose altitude is h units and whose base is a square of side s units.

Solution   Figure 7 shows the pyramid and the coordinate axes chosen so that the center of the base is at the origin and the altitude is measured along the positive side of the y axis. The plane section of the pyramid drawn perpendicular to the y axis at $(0, y)$ is a square. If the length of a side of this square is z units, then by similar triangles (see Figure 8)

$$\frac{\frac{1}{2}z}{h - y} = \frac{\frac{1}{2}s}{h}$$

$$z = \frac{s}{h}(h - y)$$

Therefore, if $A(y)$ square units is the area of the plane section

$$A(y) = \frac{s^2}{h^2}(h - y)^2$$

Figure 9 shows an element of volume which is a right cylinder of area $A(w_i)$ square units and a thickness of $\Delta_i y$ units. Thus if V cubic units is the volume of the pyramid

$$V = \lim_{\|\Delta\| \to 0} \sum_{i=1}^{n} A(w_i) \, \Delta_i y$$

$$= \int_{0}^{h} A(y) \, dy$$

$$= \int_{0}^{h} \frac{s^2}{h^2}(h - y)^2 \, dy$$

$$= \frac{s^2}{h^2} \left[\bigcirc \frac{(h - y)^3}{3} \right]_{0}^{h}$$

$$= \frac{s^2}{h^2} \left[0 + \frac{h^3}{3} \right]$$

$$= \tfrac{1}{3} s^2 h$$

◀

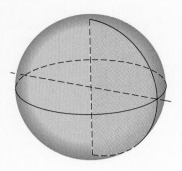

FIGURE 10

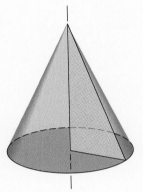

FIGURE 11

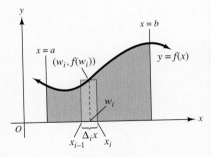

FIGURE 12

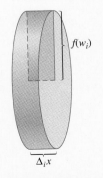

FIGURE 13

We now show how Definition 4.9.1 can be applied to find the volume of a **solid of revolution,** which is a solid obtained by revolving a region in a plane about a line in the plane, called the **axis of revolution,** which may or may not intersect the region. For example, if the region bounded by a semicircle and its diameter is revolved about the diameter, a sphere is generated (see Figure 10). A right-circular cone is generated if the region bounded by a right triangle is revolved about one of its legs (see Figure 11).

Consider first the case where the axis of revolution is a boundary of the region that is revolved. Let the function f be continuous on the closed interval $[a, b]$, and assume that $f(x) \geq 0$ for all x in $[a, b]$. Let R be the region bounded by the curve $y = f(x)$, the x axis, and the lines $x = a$ and $x = b$. Figure 12 shows the region R and the ith rectangle. When the ith rectangle is revolved about the x axis we obtain an element of volume which is a disk whose base is a circle of radius $f(w_1)$ units and whose altitude is $\Delta_i x$ units as shown in Figure 13. If $\Delta_i V$ cubic units is the volume of this disk,

$$\Delta_i V = \pi [f(w_i)]^2 \, \Delta_i x$$

Because there are n rectangles, n disks are obtained in this way, and the sum of the measures of the volumes of these n disks is

$$\sum_{i=1}^{n} \Delta_i V = \sum_{i=1}^{n} \pi [f(w_i)]^2 \, \Delta_i x$$

This is a Riemann sum of the form (1) where $A(w_i) = \pi [f(w_i)]^2$. Therefore if V cubic units is the volume of the solid of revolution, it follows from Definition 4.9.1 that V is the limit of this Riemann sum as $\| \Delta \|$ approaches zero. This limit exists because f^2 is continuous on $[a, b]$, since we assumed that f is continuous there. We have then the following theorem.

4.9.2 Theorem

Let the function f be continuous on the closed interval $[a, b]$, and assume that $f(x) \geq 0$ for all x in $[a, b]$. If S is the solid of revolution obtained by revolving about the x axis the region bounded by the curve $y = f(x)$, the x axis, and the lines $x = a$ and $x = b$, and if V cubic units is the volume of S, then

$$V = \lim_{\| \Delta \| \to 0} \sum_{i=1}^{n} \pi [f(w_i)]^2 \, \Delta_i x$$

$$= \pi \int_{a}^{b} [f(x)]^2 \, dx$$

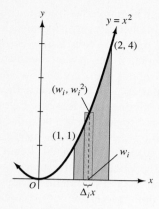

FIGURE 14

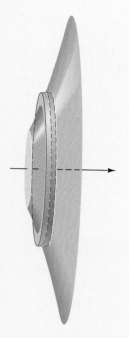

FIGURE 15

▷ **ILLUSTRATION 2**   We find the volume of the solid of revolution generated when the region bounded by the curve $y = x^2$, the x axis, and the lines $x = 1$ and $x = 2$ is revolved about the x axis. Refer to Figure 14, showing the region and a rectangular element of area. Figure 15 shows an element of volume and the solid of revolution. The measure of the volume of the disk is given by

$$\Delta_i V = \pi(w_i{}^2)^2 \, \Delta_i x$$
$$= \pi w_i{}^4 \, \Delta_i x$$

Then

$$V = \lim_{\|\Delta\| \to 0} \sum_{i=1}^{n} \pi w_i{}^4 \, \Delta_i x$$

$$= \pi \int_1^2 x^4 \, dx$$

$$= \pi(\tfrac{1}{5}x^5)\Big]_1^2$$

$$= \tfrac{31}{5}\pi$$

<u>Conclusion:</u>   The volume of the solid of revolution is $\tfrac{31}{5}\pi$ cubic units.

To support our analytic evaluation of the definite integral on our graphics calculator, we compute

$$\text{NINT}(\pi x^4, 1, 2) = 19.47787445$$

which is the same as our exact answer to ten significant digits.   ◀

A theorem similar to Theorem 4.9.2 applies when both the axis of revolution and a boundary of the revolved region are the y axis or any line parallel to either the x axis or the y axis.

▶ **EXAMPLE 2**   Find the volume of the solid generated by revolving about the line $x = 1$ the region bounded by the curve

$$(x - 1)^2 = 20 - 4y$$

and the lines $x = 1$, $y = 1$, and $y = 3$ and to the right of $x = 1$.

Solution   The region and a rectangular element of area are shown in Figure 16. An element of volume and the solid of revolution appear in Figure 17.

In the equation of the curve we solve for x and have

$$x = \sqrt{20 - 4y} + 1$$

Let $g(y) = \sqrt{20 - 4y} + 1$. We take a partition of the interval $[1, 3]$ on the y axis. Then If $\Delta_i V$ cubic units is the volume of the ith disk,

$$\Delta_i V = \pi[g(w_i) - 1]^2 \, \Delta_i y$$
$$= \pi[(\sqrt{20 - 4w_i} + 1) - 1]^2 \, \Delta_i y$$
$$= \pi(20 - 4w_i) \, \Delta_i y$$

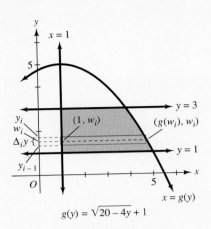

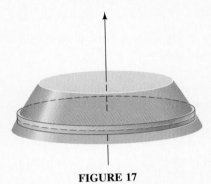

$$g(y) = \sqrt{20 - 4y} + 1$$

FIGURE 16

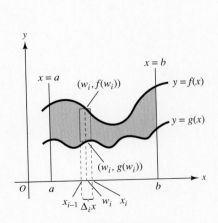

FIGURE 17

If V cubic units is the volume of the solid of revolution,

$$V = \lim_{\|\Delta\| \to 0} \sum_{i=1}^{n} \pi(20 - 4w_i)\,\Delta_i y$$

$$= \pi \int_{1}^{3} (20 - 4y)\,dy$$

$$= \pi \Big[20y - 2y^2 \Big]_{1}^{3}$$

$$= \pi[(60 - 18) - (20 - 2)]$$

$$= 24\pi$$

Conclusion: The volume of the solid of revolution is 24π cubic units. ◀

Now suppose that the axis of revolution is not a boundary of the region being revolved. Let f and g be two continuous functions on the closed interval $[a, b]$, and assume that $f(x) \geq g(x) \geq 0$ for all x in $[a, b]$. Let R be the region bounded by the curves $y = f(x)$ and $y = g(x)$ and the lines $x = a$ and $x = b$. The region R and the ith rectangle are shown in Figure 18, and the solid of revolution appears in Figure 19. When the ith rectangle is revolved about the x axis, we obtain a washer (or circular ring) as in Figure 20. The difference of the areas of the two circular regions is $(\pi[f(w_i)]^2 - \pi[g(w_i)]^2)$ square units and the thickness is $\Delta_i x$ units. If $\Delta_i V$ cubic units is the volume of the washer,

$$\Delta_i V = \pi([f(w_i)]^2 - [g(w_i)]^2)\,\Delta_i x$$

The sum of the measures of the volumes of the n washers formed by revolving the n rectangular elements of area about the x axis is

$$\sum_{i=1}^{n} \Delta_i V = \sum_{i=1}^{n} \pi([f(w_i)]^2 - [g(w_i)]^2)\,\Delta_i x$$

This is a Riemann sum of form (1) where $A(w_i) = \pi[f(w_i)]^2 - \pi[g(w_i)]^2$. From Definition 4.9.1, the number of cubic units in the volume of the solid

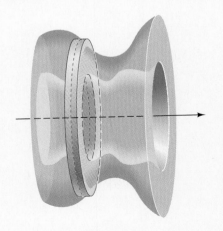

FIGURE 18

FIGURE 19

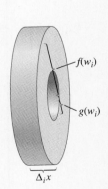

FIGURE 20

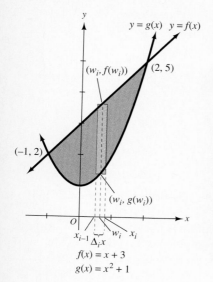

$f(x) = x + 3$

$g(x) = x^2 + 1$

FIGURE 21

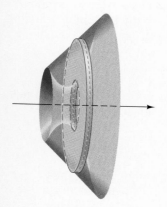

FIGURE 22

of revolution is the limit of this Riemann sum as $\|\Delta\|$ approaches zero. The limit exists since $f^2 - g^2$ is continuous on $[a, b]$ because f and g are continuous there. We have then the following theorem.

4.9.3 Theorem

Let the functions f and g be continuous on the closed interval $[a, b]$, and assume that $f(x) \geq g(x) \geq 0$ for all x in $[a, b]$. Then if V cubic units is the volume of the solid of revolution generated by revolving about the x axis the region bounded by the curves $y = f(x)$ and $y = g(x)$ and the lines $x = a$ and $x = b$,

$$V = \lim_{\|\Delta\|\to 0} \sum_{i=1}^{n} \pi([f(w_i)]^2 - [g(w_i)]^2)\, \Delta_i x$$

$$= \pi \int_{a}^{b} ([f(x)]^2 - [g(x)]^2)\, dx$$

As before, a similar theorem applies when the axis of revolution is the y axis or any line parallel to either the x or y axis.

▶ **EXAMPLE 3**   Find the volume of the solid generated by revolving about the x axis the region bounded by the parabola $y = x^2 + 1$ and the line $y = x + 3$.

Solution   The points of intersection are $(-1, 2)$ and $(2, 5)$. Figure 21 shows the region and a rectangular element of area. An element of volume and the solid of revolution are shown in Figure 22.

If $f(x) = x + 3$ and $g(x) = x^2 + 1$, the measure of the volume of the circular ring is

$$\Delta_i V = \pi([f(w_i)]^2 - [g(w_i)]^2)\, \Delta_i x$$

If V cubic units is the volume of the solid, then

$$V = \lim_{\|\Delta\|\to 0} \sum_{i=1}^{n} \pi([f(w_i)]^2 - [g(w_i)]^2)\, \Delta_i x$$

$$= \pi \int_{-1}^{2} ([f(x)]^2 - [g(x)]^2)\, dx$$

$$= \pi \int_{-1}^{2} [(x + 3)^2 - (x^2 + 1)^2]\, dx$$

$$= \pi \int_{-1}^{2} [-x^4 - x^2 + 6x + 8]\, dx$$

$$= \pi \left[-\tfrac{1}{5}x^5 - \tfrac{1}{3}x^3 + 3x^2 + 8x \right]_{-1}^{2}$$

$$= [(-\tfrac{32}{5} - \tfrac{8}{3} + 12 + 16) - (\tfrac{1}{5} + \tfrac{1}{3} + 3 - 8)]$$

$$= \tfrac{117}{5}\, \pi$$

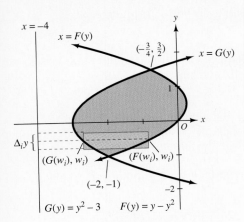

$x = -4$
$x = F(y)$
$(-\frac{3}{4}, \frac{3}{2})$
$x = G(y)$
$\Delta_i y$
$(G(w_i), w_i)$
$(F(w_i), w_i)$
$(-2, -1)$
$G(y) = y^2 - 3$
$F(y) = y - y^2$

FIGURE 23

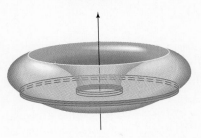

FIGURE 24

Conclusion: The volume of the solid of revolution is $\frac{117}{5}\pi$ cubic units. ◀

▶ **EXAMPLE 4** Find the volume of the solid generated by revolving about the line $x = -4$ the region bounded by the two parabolas $x = y - y^2$ and $x = y^2 - 3$.

Solution The curves intersect at the points $(-2, -1)$ and $(-\frac{3}{4}, \frac{3}{2})$. The region and a rectangular element of area are shown in Figure 23. Figure 24 shows the solid of revolution as well as an element of volume, which is a circular ring.

Let $F(y) = y - y^2$ and $G(y) = y^2 - 3$. The number of cubic units in the volume of the circular ring is

$$\Delta_i V = \pi([4 + F(w_i)]^2 - [4 + G(w_i)]^2)\,\Delta_i y$$

$$V = \lim_{\|\Delta\| \to 0} \sum_{i=1}^{n} \pi([4 + F(w_i)]^2 - [4 + G(w_i)]^2)\,\Delta_i y$$

$$= \pi \int_{-1}^{3/2} [(4 + y - y^2)^2 - (4 + y^2 - 3)^2]\,dy$$

$$= \pi \int_{-1}^{3/2} (-2y^3 - 9y^2 + 8y + 15)\,dy$$

$$= \pi \left[-\tfrac{1}{2}y^4 - 3y^3 + 4y^2 + 15y \right]_{-1}^{3/2}$$

$$= \tfrac{875}{32}\pi$$

Conclusion: The volume of the solid of revolution is $\frac{875}{32}\pi$ cubic units. ◀

We purposely devised the above examples so that the computation could be done easily by hand. In the next example that is not the case. We need to use our graphics calculator.

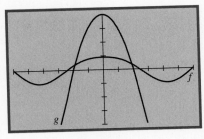

$[-6, 6]$ by $[-4, 4]$

$f(x) = \sin \sqrt{x^2 + 4}$

$g(x) = 4 - x^2$

FIGURE 25

▶ **EXAMPLE 5** Find to four significant digits the volume of the solid generated by revolving about the x axis the region bounded by the graphs of

$$f(x) = \sin \sqrt{x^2 + 4} \quad \text{and} \quad g(x) = 4 - x^2$$

Solution We plot the graphs of the two equations in the $[-6, 6]$ by $[-4, 4]$ window as shown in Figure 25. Because of symmetry with respect to the y axis, we shall obtain one-half the required volume by revolving about the x axis the region bounded by the curves in the first quadrant. We need to take a partition of the interval $[0, b]$ where b is the x coordinate of the point of intersection of the two curves in the first quadrant. We find b by using intersect or trace and zoom-in on our calculator and obtain to four significant digits, $b = 1.905$.

An element of volume is a circular ring. If V cubic units is the required volume

$$\frac{V}{2} = \lim_{\|\Delta\|\to 0} \sum_{i=1}^{n} \pi([g(w_i)]^2 - [f(w_i)]^2)\, \Delta_i x$$

$$= \int_0^{1.905} \pi([g(x)]^2 - [f(x)]^2)\, dx$$

$$= \pi \int_0^{1.905} [(4 - x^2)^2 - \sin^2 \sqrt{x^2 + 4}]\, dx$$

We evaluate the definite integral by the NINT capability of our graphics calculator and obtain

$$\pi\, \text{NINT}((4 - x^2)^2 - \sin^2 \sqrt{x^2 + 4}),\ 0,\ 1.905) = 50.129$$

Therefore

$$\frac{V}{2} = 50.129$$

$$V = 100.26$$

<u>Conclusion:</u>   The volume to four significant digits is 100.3 cubic units.   ◀

As you have seen, computing volumes by disks and washers is a special case of computing volumes by slicing. We now give another example of finding a volume by slicing.

▶ **EXAMPLE 6**   A wedge is cut from a right-circular cylinder with a radius of r centimeters by two planes, one perpendicular to the axis of the cylinder and the other intersecting the first along a diameter of the circular plane section at an angle of measurement 60°. Find the volume of the wedge.

Solution   The wedge appears in Figure 26. The xy plane is taken as the plane perpendicular to the axis of the cylinder, and the origin is at the point of perpendicularity. An equation of the circular plane section is then $x^2 + y^2 = r^2$. Every plane section of the wedge perpendicular to the x axis is a right triangle. An element of volume is a right cylinder having altitude $\Delta_i x$ centimeters, and area of the base given by $\frac{1}{2}\sqrt{3}[f(w_i)]^2$ square centimeters, where $f(x)$ is obtained by solving the equation of the circle for y and setting $y = f(x)$. Therefore, we have $f(x) = \sqrt{r^2 - x^2}$. Thus, if V cubic centimeters is the volume of the wedge,

$$V = \lim_{\|\Delta\|\to 0} \sum_{i=1}^{n} \tfrac{1}{2}\sqrt{3}(r^2 - w_i^2)\, \Delta_i x$$

$$= \tfrac{1}{2}\sqrt{3} \int_{-r}^{r} (r^2 - x^2)\, dx$$

$$= \tfrac{1}{2}\sqrt{3} \left[r^2 x - \tfrac{1}{3}x^3 \right]_{-r}^{r}$$

$$= \tfrac{2}{3}\sqrt{3}\, r^3$$

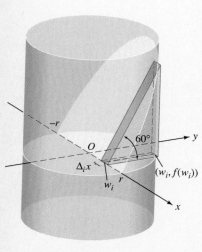

FIGURE 26

<u>Conclusion:</u>   The volume of the wedge is $\tfrac{2}{3}\sqrt{3}\, r^3$ cm³.   ◀

EXERCISES 4.9

In Exercises 1 and 2, derive the formula for the volume of the solid by slicing.

1. A sphere of radius r units.

2. A right-circular cone of altitude h units and base radius a units.

3. Find the volume of the solid of revolution generated when the region bounded by the curve $y = x^3$, the x axis, and the lines $x = 1$ and $x = 2$ is revolved about the x axis.

4. Find the volume of the solid of revolution generated when the region bounded by the curve $y = x^2 + 1$, the x axis, and the lines $x = 2$ and $x = 3$ is revolved about the x axis.

In Exercises 5 through 12, find the volume of the solid of revolution generated when the given region of the figure is revolved about the indicated line. An equation of the curve in the figure is $y^2 = x^3$.

5. OAC about the x axis

6. OAC about the line AC

7. OAC about the line BC

8. OAC about the y axis

9. OBC about the y axis

10. OBC about the line BC

11. OBC about the line AC

12. OBC about the x axis

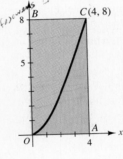

In Exercises 13 through 16, find the volume of the solid of revolution generated by revolving about the indicated line the region bounded by the curve $y = \sqrt{x}$, the x axis, and the line $x = 4$.

13. the line $x = 4$

14. the x axis

15. the y axis

16. the line $y = 2$

17. Derive the formula for the volume of a sphere by revolving about the x axis, the region bounded by the circle $x^2 + y^2 = r^2$ and the x axis.

18. Derive the formula for the volume of a right-circular cone of altitude h units and base radius a units by revolving the region bounded by a right triangle about one of its legs.

19. Derive the formula for the volume of the frustum of a right-circular cone by revolving the line segment from $(0, b)$ to (h, a) about the x axis.

20. Find by slicing the volume of a tetrahedron having three mutually perpendicular faces and three mutually perpendicular edges whose lengths are 3 in., 4 in., and 7 in.

21. The region bounded by the curve $y = \sec x$, the x axis, the y axis, and the line $x = \frac{1}{4}\pi$ is revolved about the x axis. Find the volume of the solid generated.

22. Find the volume of the solid generated when the region bounded by the curve $y = \csc x$, the x axis, and the lines $x = \frac{1}{6}\pi$ and $x = \frac{1}{3}\pi$ is revolved about the x axis.

23. Find the volume of the solid of revolution generated if the region bounded by one arch of the sine curve is revolved about the x axis. *Hint:* Use the identity $\sin^2 x = \frac{1}{2}(1 - \cos 2x)$.

24. The region bounded by the y axis and the curves $y = \sin x$ and $y = \cos x$ for $0 \leq x \leq \frac{1}{4}\pi$ is revolved about the x axis. Find the volume of the solid of revolution generated. *Hint:* Use the following identity: $\cos^2 x - \sin^2 x = \cos 2x$.

25. Find the volume of the solid generated if the region of Exercise 23 is revolved about the line $y = 1$.

26. Find the volume of the solid generated if the region of Exercise 24 is revolved about the line $y = 1$.

27. The region bounded by the curve $y = \cot x$, the line $x = \frac{1}{6}\pi$, and the x axis is revolved about the x axis. Find the volume of the solid generated.

28. The region bounded by the curve $y = \tan x$, the line $x = \frac{1}{3}\pi$, and the x axis is revolved about the x axis. Find the volume of the solid generated.

29. Find the volume of the solid generated by revolving about the line $x = -4$ the region bounded by that line and the parabola $x = 4 + 6y - 2y^2$.

30. Find the volume of the solid generated by revolving about the x axis the region bounded by the parabola $y^2 = 4x$ and the line $y = x$.

31. Find the volume of the solid generated by revolving the region of Exercise 30 about the line $x = 4$.

32. Find the volume of the solid generated by revolving about the y axis the region bounded by the line through $(1, 3)$ and $(3, 7)$, and the lines $y = 3$, $y = 7$, and $x = 0$.

33. Find the volume of the solid generated by revolving about the line $y = -3$ the region bounded by the two parabolas $y = x^2$ and $y = 1 + x - x^2$.

34. Find the volume of the solid generated by revolving about the x axis the region bounded by the loop of the curve whose equation is $2y^2 = x(x^2 - 4)$.

35. Find the volume of the solid generated when the region bounded by one loop of the curve, having the equation $x^2 y^2 = (x^2 - 9)(1 - x^2)$, is revolved about the x axis.

36. An oil tank in the shape of a sphere has a diameter of 60 ft. How much oil does the tank contain if the depth of the oil is 25 ft?

37. The region bounded by the curve $y = \csc x$ and the lines $y = 2$, $x = \frac{1}{6}\pi$, and $x = \frac{5}{6}\pi$ is revolved about the x axis. Find the volume of the solid generated.

38. The region in the first quadrant bounded by the curve $y = \sec x$, the y axis, and the line $y = 2$ is revolved about the x axis. Find the volume of the solid generated.

39. A solid of revolution is formed by revolving about the x axis the region bounded by the curve $y = \sqrt{2x + 4}$, the x axis, the y axis, and the line $x = c$ ($c > 0$). For what value of c will the volume be 12π cubic units?

40. The region in the first quadrant bounded by the coordinate axes, the line $y = 1$, and the curve $y = \cot x$ is revolved about the x axis. Find the volume of the solid generated.

In Exercises 41 through 50, you need to use your graphics calculator to find the volume of the solid generated by revolving the given region about the indicated axis. Express your answer to four significant digits.

41. The region bounded by the graph of $y = \sqrt[4]{x^3 + 4}$, the x axis, the y axis, and the line $x = 2$ about the x axis.

42. The region bounded by the graph of $y = \sqrt[3]{x^4 - 5}$, the x axis, and the lines $x = 2$ and $x = 3$ about the x axis.

43. The region bounded by the graph of $y = \sqrt[4]{x^3 + 4}$, the y axis, and the line $y = 3$ about the y axis.

44. The region bounded by the graph of $y = \sqrt[3]{x^4 - 5}$, the x axis, the y axis, and the line $y = 4$ about the y axis.

45. The region bounded by the graph of $y = \sin x^3$, the y axis, and the line $y = 1$, if $x \in [0, \sqrt[3]{\pi/2}]$ about the x axis.

46. The region bounded by the graph of $y = \tan x^2$, the y axis, and the line $y = 1$, if $x \in [0, \sqrt{\pi/2}]$ about the line $y = 1$.

47. The region of Exercise 45 about the line $y = 2$.

48. The region of Exercise 46 about the line $y = -1$.

49. The region bounded by the graphs of $y = \sin x + 2$ and $y = \tan x$, and the y axis about the x axis.

50. The region bounded by the graphs of $y = x^2 - 1$ and $y = \cos(x^2 + 2)$ about the x axis.

51. The base of a solid is the region enclosed by an ellipse having the equation $3x^2 + y^2 = 6$. Find the volume of the solid if all plane sections perpendicular to the x axis are squares.

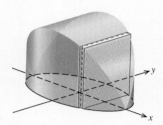

52. The base of a solid is the region enclosed by the hyperbola $25x^2 - 4y^2 = 100$ and the line $x = 4$. Find the volume of the solid if all plane sections perpendicular to the x axis are squares.

53. The base of a solid is the region enclosed by a circle having a radius of 7 cm. Find the volume of the solid if all plane sections perpendicular to a fixed diameter of the base are equilateral triangles.

54. The base of a solid is the region of Exercise 52. Find the volume of the solid if all plane sections perpendicular to the x axis are equilateral triangles.

55. The base of a solid is the region of Exercise 53. Find the volume of the solid if all plane sections perpendicular to a fixed diameter of the base are isosceles triangles of height equal to the distance of the plane section from the center of the circle. The side of the triangle lying in the base of the solid is not one of the two sides of equal length.

56. The base of a solid is the region enclosed by a circle with a radius of r units, and all plane sections perpendicular to a fixed diameter of the base are isosceles right triangles having the hypotenuse in the plane of the base. Find the volume of the solid.

57. Solve Exercise 56 if the isosceles right triangles have one leg in the plane of the base.

58. The base of a solid is the region enclosed by a circle with a radius of 4 in., and each plane section perpendicular to a fixed diameter of the base is an isosceles triangle having an altitude of 10 in. and a chord of the circle as a base. Find the volume of the solid.

59. The base of a solid is the region enclosed by the curve $x = 2\sqrt{y}$ and the lines $x + y = 0$ and $y = 9$. Find the volume of the solid if all plane sections perpendicular to the y axis are squares having a diagonal with one endpoint on the line $x + y = 0$ and the other endpoint on the curve $x = 2\sqrt{y}$.

60. Two right-circular cylinders, each having a radius of r units, have axes that intersect at right angles. Find the volume of the solid common to the two cylinders.

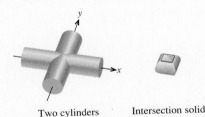

Two cylinders   Intersection solid

61. A wedge is cut from a solid in the shape of a a right-circular cylinder with a radius of r cm by a plane through a diameter of the base inclined to the plane

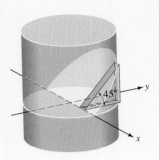

of the base at an angle of measurement 45°. Find the volume of the wedge.

62. A wedge is cut from a solid in the shape of a right-circular cone having a base radius of 5 ft and an altitude of 20 ft by two half planes through the axis of the cone. The angle between the two planes has a measurement of 30°. Find the volume of the wedge cut out.

63. A paraboloid of revolution is obtained by revolving the parabola $y^2 = 4px$ about the x axis. Find the volume of the solid bounded by a paraboloid of revolution and a plane perpendicular to its axis if the plane is 10 cm from the vertex, and if the plane section of intersection is a circle having a radius of 6 cm.

64. Explain the relationship between computing volumes of solids by slicing and computing volumes of solids by disks and washers.

4.10 VOLUMES OF SOLIDS BY CYLINDRICAL SHELLS

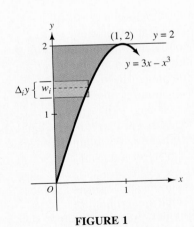

FIGURE 1

In the preceding section we found the volume of a solid of revolution by taking the rectangular elements of area perpendicular to the axis of revolution, and the element of volume was either a disk or a washer. For some solids of revolution this method may not be feasible. For example, suppose we wish to find the exact volume of the solid of revolution obtained by revolving about the y axis the region, shown in Figure 1, bounded by the graph of $y = 3x - x^3$, the y axis, and the line $y = 2$. If an element of area is perpendicular to the y axis as shown in the figure, the element of volume is a disk, and to determine the volume of the solid of revolution involves an integral of the form $\int_0^2 A(y)\, dy$. But to obtain a formula for $A(y)$ requires solving the cubic equation $y = 3x - x^3$ for x in terms of y, which is a laborious undertaking. So we now discuss an alternative procedure for computing the volume of a solid of revolution, which is easier to apply in this and some other situations.

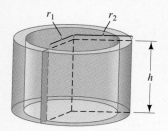

FIGURE 2

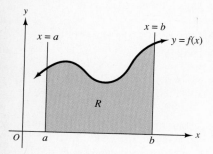

FIGURE 3

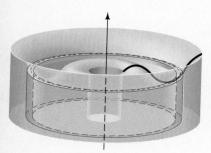

FIGURE 4

The method involves taking the rectangular elements of area parallel to the axis of revolution. Then when an element of area is revolved about the axis of revolution, a *cylindrical shell* is obtained. A **cylindrical shell** is a solid contained between two cylinders having the same center and axis. Such a cylindrical shell is shown in Figure 2.

If the cylindrical shell has an inner radius r_1 units, outer radius r_2 units, and altitude h units, then its volume V cubic units is given by

$$V = \pi r_2^2 h - \pi r_1^2 h$$

(1)

Let R be the region bounded by the curve $y = f(x)$, the x axis, and the lines $x = a$ and $x = b$, where f is continuous on the closed interval $[a, b]$ and $f(x) \geq 0$ for all x in $[a, b]$; further assume that $a \geq 0$. Such a region is shown in Figure 3. If R is revolved about the y axis, a solid of revolution S is generated. Such a solid appears in Figure 4. To find the volume of S when the rectangular elements of area are taken parallel to the y axis we proceed in the following manner.

Let Δ be a partition of the closed interval $[a, b]$ given by

$$a = x_0 < x_1 < x_2 < \ldots < x_{n-1} < x_n = b$$

Let m_i be the midpoint of the ith subinterval $[x_{i-1}, x_i]$. Then we have $m_i = \frac{1}{2}(x_{i-1} + x_i)$. Consider the rectangle having altitude $f(m_i)$ units and width $\Delta_i x$ units. If this rectangle is revolved about the y axis, a cylindrical shell is obtained. Figure 4 shows the cylindrical shell generated by the rectangular element of area.

If $\Delta_i V$ gives the measure of the volume of this cylindrical shell, we have, from formula (1), where $r_1 = x_{i-1}$, $r_2 = x_i$, and $h = f(m_i)$,

$$\Delta_i V = \pi x_i^2 f(m_i) - \pi x_{i-1}^2 f(m_i)$$

$$\Delta_i V = \pi (x_i^2 - x_{i-1}^2) f(m_i)$$

$$\Delta_i V = \pi (x_i - x_{i-1})(x_i + x_{i-1}) f(m_i)$$

Because $x_i - x_{i-1} = \Delta_i x$, and because $x_i + x_{i-1} = 2m_i$, then from this equation

$$\Delta_i V = 2\pi m_i f(m_i) \, \Delta_i x$$

If n rectangular elements of area are revolved about the y axis, n cylindrical shells are obtained. The sum of the measures of their volumes is

$$\sum_{i=1}^{n} \Delta_i V = \sum_{i=1}^{n} 2\pi m_i f(m_i) \, \Delta_i x$$

which is a Riemann sum. The limit of this Riemann sum as $\|\Delta\|$ approaches zero exists because if f is continuous on $[a, b]$ so is the function having values $2\pi x f(x)$. The limit is the definite integral $\int_a^b 2\pi x f(x) \, dx$, and it gives the volume of the solid of revolution. This result is summarized in the following theorem.

4.10.1 Theorem

Let the function f be continuous on the closed interval $[a, b]$, where $a \geq 0$. Assume that $f(x) \geq 0$ for all x in $[a, b]$. If R is the region bounded by the curve $y = f(x)$, the x axis, and the lines $x = a$ and $x = b$, if S is the solid of revolution obtained by revolving R about the y axis, and if V cubic units is the volume of S, then

$$V = \lim_{\|\Delta\| \to 0} \sum_{i=1}^{n} 2\pi m_i f(m_i)\, \Delta_i x$$

$$= 2\pi \int_{a}^{b} x f(x)\, dx$$

While the truth of this theorem should seem plausible because of the discussion preceding its statement, a proof requires showing that the same volume is obtained by the disk method of Theorem 4.9.2. In the February 1984 issue of the *American Mathematical Monthly* (Vol. 91, No. 2) Charles A. Cable of Allegheny College gave such a proof using integration by parts, the subject of Section 7.1.

The formula for the measure of the volume of the cylindrical shell is easily remembered by noticing that $2\pi m_i$, $f(m_i)$, and $\Delta_i x$ are, respectively, the measures of the circumference of the circle having as radius the mean of the inner and outer radii of the shell, the altitude of the shell, and the thickness. Thus the volume of the shell is

$$2\pi\,(\text{mean radius})(\text{altitude})(\text{thickness})$$

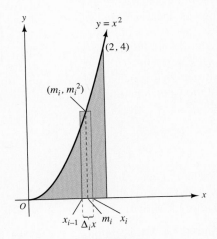

FIGURE 5

▶ **EXAMPLE 1** The region bounded by the curve $y = x^2$, the x axis, and the line $x = 2$ is revolved about the y axis. Find the volume of the solid generated. Take the elements of area parallel to the axis of revolution.

Solution Figure 5 shows the region and a rectangular element of area. Figure 6 shows the solid of revolution and the cylindrical shell obtained by revolving the rectangular element of area about the y axis.

The element of volume is a cylindrical shell the measure of whose volume is

$$\Delta_i V = 2\pi m_i (m_i^2)\, \Delta_i x$$
$$= 2\pi m_i^3\, \Delta_i x$$

Thus

$$V = \lim_{\|\Delta\| \to 0} \sum_{i=1}^{n} 2\pi m_i^3\, \Delta_i x$$

$$= 2\pi \int_{0}^{2} x^3\, dx$$

$$= 2\pi \left(\tfrac{1}{4} x^4 \right) \Big]_{0}^{2}$$

$$= 8\pi$$

FIGURE 6

Conclusion: The volume of the solid of revolution is 8π cubic units. ◀

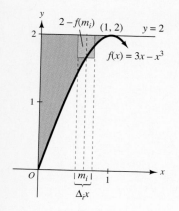

FIGURE 7

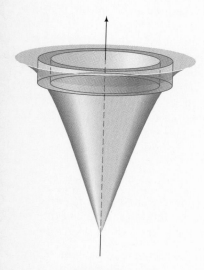

FIGURE 8

In the next example we compute the volume of the solid of revolution discussed at the beginning of this section.

▶   **EXAMPLE 2**   Find the volume of the solid generated by revolving about the y axis the region bounded by the graph of $y = 3x - x^3$, the y axis, and the line $y = 2$.

Solution   Let $f(x) = 3x - x^3$. Figure 7 shows the region and a rectangular element of area parallel to the y axis. The solid of revolution and a cylindrical shell element of volume appear in Figure 8. The mean radius of the cylindrical shell is m_i units, the altitude is $[2 - f(m_i)]$ units, and the thickness is $\Delta_i x$ units. Therefore, if $\Delta_i V$ cubic units is the volume of the shell

$$\Delta_i V = 2\pi m_i [2 - f(m_i)]\, \Delta_i x$$

Thus if V cubic units is the volume of the solid of revolution

$$V = \lim_{\|\Delta\| \to 0} \sum_{i=1}^{n} 2\pi m_i [2 - f(m_i)]\, \Delta_i x$$

$$= 2\pi \int_{0}^{1} x[2 - f(x)]\, dx$$

$$= 2\pi \int_{0}^{1} x(2 - 3x + x^3)\, dx$$

$$= 2\pi \int_{0}^{1} (2x - 3x^2 + x^4)\, dx$$

$$= 2\pi \left[x^2 - x^3 + \frac{x^5}{5} \right]_{0}^{1}$$

$$= 2\pi(1 - 1 + \tfrac{1}{5})$$

$$= \tfrac{2}{5}\pi$$

<u>Conclusion:</u>   The volume is $\tfrac{2}{5}\pi$ cubic units.   ◀

▶   **EXAMPLE 3**   The region bounded by the curve $y = x^2$ and the lines $y = 1$ and $x = 2$ is revolved about the line $y = -3$. Find the volume of the solid generated by taking the rectangular elements of area parallel to the axis of revolution.

Solution   The region and a rectangular element of area appear in Figure 9.

The equation of the curve is $y = x^2$. Solving for x we obtain $x = \pm\sqrt{y}$. Because $x > 0$ for the given region, $x = \sqrt{y}$.

The solid of revolution and a cylindrical shell element of volume are shown in Figure 10. The outer radius of the cylindrical shell is $(y_i + 3)$ units and the inner radius is $(y_{i-1} + 3)$ units. Hence the mean of the inner and outer radii is $(m_i + 3)$ units. Because the altitude and thickness of the cylindrical shell are, respectively, $(2 - \sqrt{m_i})$ units and $\Delta_i y$ units.

$$\Delta_i V = 2\pi(m_i + 3)(2 - \sqrt{m_i})\, \Delta_i y$$

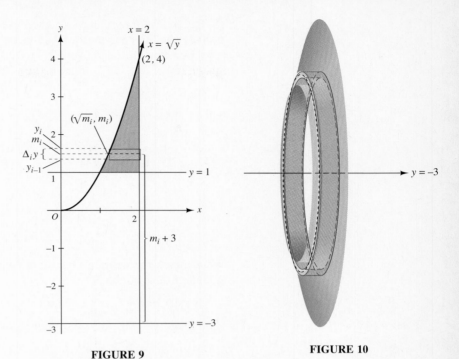

FIGURE 9

FIGURE 10

Hence, if V cubic units is the volume of the solid of revolution,

$$V = \lim_{\|\Delta\| \to 0} \sum_{i=1}^{n} 2\pi(m_i + 3)(2 - \sqrt{m_i}) \, \Delta_i y$$

$$= \int_1^4 2\pi(y + 3)(2 - \sqrt{y}) \, dy$$

$$= 2\pi \int_1^4 (-y^{3/2} + 2y - 3y^{1/2} + 6) \, dy$$

$$= 2\pi \left[-\tfrac{2}{5}y^{5/2} + y^2 - 2y^{3/2} + 6y \right]_1^4$$

$$= \tfrac{66}{5}\pi$$

Conclusion: The volume is $\tfrac{66}{5}\pi$ cubic units.   ◀

▶ **EXAMPLE 4**   Find accurate to four significant digits the volume of the solid generated by revolving the region of Example 5 in Section 4.9 about the y axis.

Solution   In Figure 11 we repeat Figure 25 from Section 4.9, showing the graphs of

$$f(x) = \sin \sqrt{x^2 + 4} \quad \text{and} \quad g(x) = 4 - x^2$$

plotted in the $[-6, 6]$ by $[-4, 4]$ window. Because of symmetry with respect to the y axis, we get the entire solid by revolving only the region bounded by the curves in the first quadrant. We therefore take a partition of the interval

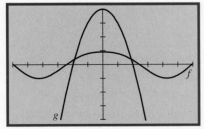

$[-6, 6]$ by $[-4, 4]$

$f(x) = \sin \sqrt{x^2 + 4}$

$g(x) = 4 - x^2$

FIGURE 11

[0, 1.905]. With rectangular elements of area parallel to the axis of revolution we obtain as elements of volume cylindrical shells having a mean radius of m_i units, an altitude of $[g(m_i) - f(m_i)]$ units and a thickness of $\Delta_i x$ units. Therefore, if $\Delta_i V$ cubic units is the volume of the shell

$$\Delta_i V = 2\pi m_i[g(m_i) - f(m_i)]\,\Delta_i x$$

Thus if V cubic units is the volume of the solid of revolution

$$V = \lim_{\|\Delta\|\to 0} \sum_{i=1}^{n} 2\pi m_i[g(m_i) - f(m_i)]\,\Delta_i x$$

$$= \int_{0}^{1.905} 2\pi x[g(x) - f(x)]\,dx$$

$$= \int_{0}^{1.905} 2\pi x[(4 - x^2) - \sin\sqrt{x^2 + 4}]\,dx$$

We evaluate the definite integral to four significant digits on our graphics calculator and obtain

$$\text{NINT}(2\pi x(4 - x^2 - \sin\sqrt{x^2 + 4}), 0, 1.905) = 17.41$$

Conclusion: The volume to four significant digits is 17.41 cubic units. ◀

EXERCISES 4.10

1–12. Solve Exercises 5 through 16 in Section 4.9 by the cylindrical-shell method.

In the figure below, the region bounded by the x axis, the line $x = 1$, and the curve $y = x^2$ is denoted by R_1; the region bounded by the two curves $y = x^2$ and $y^2 = x$ is denoted by R_2; the region bounded by the y axis, the line $y = 1$, and the curve $y^2 = x$ is denoted by R_3. In Exercises 13 through 20, find the volume of the solid generated when the indicated region is revolved about the given line.

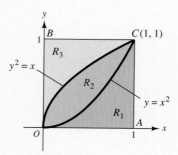

13. R_1 is revolved about the y axis; the rectangular elements are parallel to the axis of revolution.

14. Same as Exercise 13, but the rectangular elements are perpendicular to the axis of revolution.

15. R_2 is revolved about the x axis; the rectangular elements are parallel to the axis of revolution.

16. Same as Exercise 15, but the rectangular elements are perpendicular to the axis of revolution.

17. R_3 is revolved about the line $y = 2$; the rectangular elements are parallel to the axis of revolution.

18. Same as Exercise 17, but the rectangular elements are perpendicular to the axis of revolution.

19. R_2 is revolved about the line $x = -2$; the rectangular elements are parallel to the axis of revolution.

20. Same as Exercise 19, but the rectangular elements are perpendicular to the axis of revolution.

In Exercises 21 through 24, the region bounded by the curves $x = y^2 - 2$ and $x = 6 - y^2$ is revolved about the indicated axis. Find the volume of the solid generated.

21. the x axis

22. the y axis

23. the line $x = 2$

24. the line $y = 2$

25. Find the volume of the solid generated if the region bounded by the parabola $y^2 = 4px$ ($p > 0$) and the line $x = p$ is revolved about $x = p$.

26. Find the volume of the solid generated if the region of Exercise 25 is revolved about the y axis.

27. Find the volume of the solid generated by revolving about the y axis the region bounded by the graph of $y = 3x - x^3$, the x axis, and the line $x = 1$.

28. Find the volume of the solid generated by revolving the region of Exercise 27 about the line $x = 1$.

29. Find the volume of the solid generated by revolving the region of Example 2 about the line $x = 1$.

30. Find the volume of the solid generated by revolving about the y axis the region bounded by the graph of $y = 4x - \frac{1}{8}x^4$, the x axis, the y axis, and the line $x = 2$.

31. Find the volume of the solid generated by revolving the region of Exercise 30 about the line $x = 2$.

32. Find the volume of the solid generated by revolving the region bounded by the graph of $y = 4x - \frac{1}{8}x^4$, the y axis, and the line $y = 6$ about the line $x = 2$.

33. Find the volume of the solid generated by revolving the region of Exercise 32 about the y axis.

34. Find the volume of the solid generated by revolving about the x axis the region bounded by the curves $y = x^3$ and $x = y^3$. Take the rectangular elements of area parallel to the axis of revolution.

35. Find the volume of the solid generated by revolving about the line $y = 1$ the region bounded by that line and the parabola $x^2 = 4y$. Take the rectangular elements of area parallel to the axis of revolution.

36. Find the volume of the solid generated by revolving about the y axis the region bounded by the curve $x^{2/3} + y^{2/3} = a^{2/3}$.

37. Find the volume of the solid generated by revolving about the y axis the region bounded by the curve $y = \sin x^2$, the x axis, and the lines $x = \frac{1}{2}\sqrt{\pi}$ and $x = \sqrt{\pi}$.

38. Find the volume of the solid generated by revolving about the y axis the region in the first quadrant bounded by the curve $y = \cos x^2$ and the coordinate axes.

39. The region in the first quadrant bounded by the curve $x = \cos y^2$, the y axis, and the x axis, with $0 \leq x \leq 1$, is revolved about the x axis. Find the volume of the solid of revolution generated.

40. Find the volume of the solid generated by revolving about the y axis the region bounded by the graph of $y = |x - 3|$, and the lines $x = 1$, $x = 5$, and $y = 0$.

Take the rectangular elements of area parallel to the axis of revolution.

In Exercises 41 through 50, you need to use your graphics calculator to find the volume of the solid generated by revolving about the indicated axis the region of the signified exercise in Exercises 4.9. Use the cylindrical shell method and express your answer to four significant digits.

41. The region of Exercise 41 about the y axis.

42. The region of Exercise 42 about the y axis.

43. The region of Exercise 43 about the x axis.

44. The region of Exercise 44 about the x axis.

45. The region of Exercise 45 about the y axis.

46. The region of Exercise 46 about the line $x = \frac{1}{2}\sqrt{\pi}$.

47. The region of Exercise 47 about the line $x = 2$.

48. The region of Exercise 48 about the line $x = -1$.

49. The region of Exercise 49 about the y axis.

50. The region of Exercise 50 about the line $x = 1$.

51. A hole of radius $2\sqrt{3}$ in. is bored through the center of a spherical shaped solid of radius 4 in. Find the volume of the portion of the solid cut out.

52. A hole of radius 2 cm is bored through a spherical shaped solid of radius 6 cm, and the axis of the hole is a diameter of the sphere. Find the volume of the part of the solid that remains.

53. A solid of revolution is formed by revolving about the y axis the region bounded by the curve $y = \sqrt[3]{x}$, the x axis, and the line $x = c$ ($c > 0$). Take the rectangular elements of area parallel to the axis of revolution to determine the value of c that will give a volume of 12π cubic units.

54. Find the volume of the solid generated by revolving about the y axis the region outside the curve $y = x^2$ and between the lines $y = 2x - 1$ and $y = x + 2$.

55. Explain the circumstances under which computation of volumes of solids of revolution by cylindrical shells is preferable to computation by disks or washers.

CHAPTER 4 REVIEW

▶ *SUGGESTIONS FOR REVIEW OF CHAPTER 4*

1. Define an *antiderivative* of a function f on an interval I.

2. Write an equation satisfied by two functions f and g having the same derivative.

3. How does knowing one antiderivative of a function f on an interval I enable us to obtain all antiderivatives of f on I? Make up a particular example.

4. How do we prove theorems on antidifferentiation?

5. Explain how to antidifferentiate a polynomial function. Make up an example to illustrate your explanation.

6. In economics, what functions can be obtained by antidifferentiating other functions?

7. What is the *chain rule for antidifferentiation*, and how is it related to the chain rule for differentiation?

8. Make up an example to show how the chain rule for antidifferentiation is used as a technique of antidifferentiation.

9. Explain when a change of variable is a convenient technique of antidifferentiation.

10. Make up an example to show how a change of variable is used as a technique of antidifferentiation.

11. What is a *separable differential equation*?

12. What do we mean by the *complete solution* of a differential equation?

13. If an object is moving freely in a vertical line, how do you obtain a differential equation of the motion involving velocity and time?

14. If an object is moving freely in a vertical line, how is knowing the initial velocity used in solving the differential equation of motion?

15. If the velocity of an object is known as a function of time, how do you obtain a differential equation of the motion involving distance and time?

16. If an object is moving freely upward and then comes back down, how do you determine (a) how high the object will go, (b) how long it will take the object to reach the ground, and (c) with what speed the object strikes the ground?

17. How is the sigma notation applied to write a finite sum? Make up an example.

18. Give a precise definition, involving only inscribed rectangles, of the area of the plane region bounded by the graph of a function f, the x axis, and the lines $x = a$ and $x = b$ if f is continuous on the closed interval $[a, b]$ and $f(x) \geq 0$ for all x in $[a, b]$.

19. Answer Suggestion 18 if the definition should involve only circumscribed rectangles.

20. Explain why it seems plausible that the area of the plane region of Suggestions 18 and 19 can be defined by either inscribed or circumscribed rectangles.

21. Make up an example of a nonpolynomial function and choose specific values for a and b to show how your definition in Suggestion 18 is applied.

22. Use the same example you made up in Suggestion 21 to show how your definition in Suggestion 19 is applied.

23. What is a *partition* of the closed interval $[a, b]$ and what is the *norm* of the partition? Make up an example.

24. What is a *Riemann sum*? Make up an example.

25. What is the connection between definite integrals and Riemann sums? Include an example in your answer.

26. What is a *definite integral* and how is it related to the area of a plane region? Include examples in your answer.

27. Make up an example of a definite integral satisfying the following condition and explain how you can determine that your example satisfies the condition without evaluating the definite integral: (a) the value is positive; (b) the value is negative; (c) the value is zero.

28. If a, b, and c are three numbers in a closed interval on which the function f is integrable, state a theorem that gives an equality involving the definite integrals of f on the three closed intervals $[a, b]$, $[a, c]$, and $[b, c]$. Is there a restriction on the order of magnitude of a, b, and c? Explain and make up an example.

29. State a theorem that gives a sufficient condition for a function to be *integrable* on a closed interval $[a, b]$. Is the condition also necessary? Explain.

30. State the hypothesis of a theorem that guarantees that the definite integral of a function f on $[a, b]$ is greater than or equal to the definite integral of a function g on $[a, b]$. Make up an example to illustrate your answer.

31. If the function f is continuous on the closed interval $[a, b]$ and if m and M are, respectively, the absolute minimum and absolute maximum function values on $[a, b]$, what continued inequality is satisfied by the definite integral of f on $[a, b]$? Make up an example to illustrate your answer.

32. State the *mean-value theorem for integrals*. Make up an example to illustrate this theorem.

33. Describe the geometric interpretation of the mean-value theorem for integrals. Use a particular example in your description.

34. If the function f is integrable on the closed interval $[a, b]$, what is the *average value* of f on $[a, b]$? Make up an example to show how the average value of a function on a closed interval is calculated.

35. State the *first fundamental theorem of the calculus*. Make up an example illustrating its application.

36. State the *second fundamental theorem of the calculus*. Make up an example illustrating its application.

37. Why are the two fundamental theorems of the calculus so important?

38. If the function f is differentiable at every number in the closed interval $[a, b]$, can we conclude that the definite integral of f on $[a, b]$ exists? Explain. Make up an example illustrating your answer.

39. If the definite integral of the function f on the closed interval $[a, b]$ exists, can we conclude that f is differ-

entiable at every number in $[a, b]$? Explain. Make up an example illustrating your answer.

40. Explain the difference between a definite integral and an indefinite integral.

41. How do we compute by integration the area of a plane region bounded by the graph of $y = f(x)$, the x axis, and the lines $x = a$ and $x = b$ where f is continuous on $[a, b]$ in each of the following cases: **(i)** $f(x) \geq 0$ for all x in $[a, b]$; **(ii)** $f(x) \leq 0$ for all x in $[a, b]$; **(iii)** $f(x) \geq 0$ for all x in $[a, c]$ and $f(x) \leq 0$ for all x in $[c, b]$?

42. Suppose the graphs of $y = f(x)$ and $y = g(x)$ intersect at the points where $x = a$ and $x = b$ and f and g are continuous on $[a, b]$. How do we compute by integration the area of a plane region bounded by these two graphs in each of the following cases: **(i)** $f(x) \geq g(x)$ for all x in $[a, b]$; **(ii)** $g(x) \geq f(x)$ for all x in $[a, b]$; **(iii)** $f(x) \geq g(x)$ for all x in $[a, c]$ and $g(x) \geq f(x)$ for all x in $[c, b]$?

43. Under what circumstances are you unable to find an exact value of the area of a plane region bounded by the graphs of two continuous functions f and g? Explain how you use your graphics calculator to find an approximate value of the area in such circumstances.

44. Describe how you calculate volumes of solids by slicing. Include an example in your description.

45. Describe how you calculate volumes of solids of revolution by disks. Include an example in your description.

46. Describe how you calculate volumes of solids of revolution by washers. Include an example in your description.

47. How do you determine whether to use disks or washers when calculating volumes of solids? Include an example for each situation.

48. Explain the circumstances when your graphics calculator is indispensable in calculating volumes of solids. Include an example in your explanation.

49. Describe how you calculate volumes of solids of revolution by cylindrical shells. Include an example in your description.

50. Describe how you would decide whether to use cylindrical shells, washers, or disks to compute the volume of a solid of revolution. Include examples in your description.

▶ MISCELLANEOUS EXERCISES FOR CHAPTER 4

In Exercises 1 through 10, perform the antidifferentiation; that is, evaluate the indefinite integral.

1. $\int (2x^3 - x^2 + 3)\, dx$

2. $\int 5x(2 + 3x^2)^8\, dx$

3. $\int x^4 \sqrt{x^5 - 1}\, dx$

4. $\int \sqrt{x}(1 + x^2)\, dx$

5. $\int \frac{s}{\sqrt{2s + 3}}\, ds$

6. $\int x^3 \sqrt{x^2 + 3}\, dx$

7. $\int \tan^2 3\theta\, d\theta$

8. $\int t \csc^2 t^2\, dt$

9. $\int \frac{5\cos^2 x - 3\tan x}{\cos x}\, dx$

10. $\int \sin^3 2\theta \cot 2\theta\, d\theta$

In Exercises 11 through 14, determine the exact value of the definite integral by interpreting it as the measure of the area of a plane region and then computing the area by the method of Section 4.4; use inscribed or circumscribed rectangles as indicated. Check your answer by evaluating the integral by the second fundamental theorem of the calculus. For each exercise draw a figure showing the region and the ith rectangle.

11. $\int_2^4 x^2\, dx$; inscribed rectangles

12. $\int_0^3 x^3\, dx$; inscribed rectangles

13. $\int_1^2 (x^3 - 1)\, dx$; circumscribed rectangles

14. $\int_{-3}^2 (x^2 + 2)\, dx$; circumscribed rectangles

In Exercises 15 through 22, evaluate the definite integral by the second fundamental theorem of the calculus. Support your answer by the NINT capability of your graphics calculator.

15. $\int_2^3 \frac{12x}{(x^2 - 1)^2}\, dx$

16. $\int_{-5}^5 2x\sqrt[3]{x^2 + 2}\, dx$

17. $\int_0^{\pi/6} \frac{\sin 2\theta}{\cos^2 2\theta}\, d\theta$

18. $\int_{\pi/3}^{\pi} \sin^2 \tfrac{1}{2}t \cos \tfrac{1}{2}t\, dt$

19. $\int_{-1}^7 \frac{x^2}{\sqrt{x + 2}}\, dx$

20. $\int_1^2 \frac{y}{\sqrt{5 - y}}\, dy$

21. $\int_0^{\pi/2} (\tan^2 \tfrac{1}{2}x + \sec^2 \tfrac{1}{2}x)\, dx$

22. $\int_{\pi/6}^{\pi/3} (1 - \cos \theta) \csc^2 \theta\, d\theta$

In Exercises 23 through 26, find the complete solution of the differential equation.

23. $x^2 y \dfrac{dy}{dx} = (y^2 - 1)^2$ **24.** $\dfrac{d^2 y}{dx^2} = 12x^2 - 30x$

25. $\dfrac{d^2 y}{dx^2} = \sqrt{2x - 1}$ **26.** $\dfrac{dy}{dx} = \dfrac{x\sqrt{1 - y^2}}{y\sqrt{2x^2 + 1}}$

27. The slope of the tangent line at any point (x, y) on a curve is $10 - 4x$, and the point $(1, -1)$ is on the curve. Find an equation of the curve.

28. The marginal cost function for a particular commodity is given by $C'(x) = 6x - 17$. If the cost of producing 2 units is $25, find the total cost function.

29. The marginal revenue function for a certain article of merchandise is given by $R'(x) = \frac{3}{4}x^2 - 10x + 12$. Find **(a)** the total revenue function and **(b)** an equation involving p and x (the demand equation) where x units are demanded when p dollars is the price per unit.

30. Suppose that a particular company estimates its growth income from sales by the formula

$$\frac{dS}{dt} = 2(t - 1)^{2/3}$$

where S millions of dollars is the gross income from sales t years hence. If the gross income from the current year's sales is $8 million, what should be the expected gross income from sales 2 years from now?

31. The volume of a balloon is increasing according to the formula

$$\frac{dV}{dt} = \sqrt{t + 1} + \frac{2}{3}t$$

where V cubic centimeters is the volume of the balloon at t seconds. If $V = 33$ when $t = 3$, find **(a)** a formula for V in terms of t; **(b)** the volume of the balloon at 8 sec.

32. The enrollment at a certain college has been increasing at the rate of $1000(t + 1)^{-1/2}$ students per year since 1993. If the enrollment in 1996 was 10,000, **(a)** what was the enrollment in 1993, and **(b)** what is the anticipated enrollment in 2001 if it is expected to be increasing at the same rate?

33. It is July 31 and a tumor has been growing inside a person's body in such a way that t days since July 1 the volume of the tumor has been increasing at a rate of $\frac{1}{100}(t + 6)^{1/2}$ cubic centimeters per day. If the volume of the tumor on July 4 was 0.20 cm^3, what is the volume today?

34. After experimentation, a certain manufacturer determined that if x units of a certain article of merchandise are produced per day, the marginal cost is given by $C'(x) = 0.3x - 11$ where $C(x)$ dollars is the total cost of producing x units. If the selling price of the article is fixed at $19 per unit and the overhead cost is $100 per day, find the maximum daily profit that can be obtained.

35. A manufacturer of children's toys has a new toy coming on the market and wishes to determine a selling price for the toy such that the total profit will be a maximum. From analyzing the price and demand of another similar toy, it is anticipated that if x toys are demanded when p dollars is the price per toy, then $\dfrac{dp}{dx} = \dfrac{p^2}{30,000}$, and the demand should be 1800 when the price is $10. If $C(x)$ dollars is the total cost of producing x toys, then $C(x) = x + 7500$. Find the price that should be charged for the manufacturer's total profit to be a maximum.

In Exercises 36 through 38, a particle is moving on a line. At t seconds, s feet is the directed distance of the particle from the origin, v feet per second is the velocity of the particle, and a feet per second per second is the acceleration of the particle.

36. $a = 3t + 4$; $v = 5$ and $s = 0$ when $t = 0$. Express v and s in terms of t.

37. $a = 6 \cos 2t$; $v = 3$ and $s = 4$ when $t = \frac{1}{2}\pi$. Express v and s in terms of t.

38. $a = 3s + 4$; $v = 5$ when $s = 1$. Find an equation involving v and s.

In Exercises 39 through 47, be sure to define your variables as numbers and write a conclusion. In Exercises 40 through 44 and 46, consider that the only force acting is due to the acceleration of gravity taken as 32 ft/sec^2 or 9.8 m/sec^2 in the downward direction.

39. A particle is moving along a line in such a way that if v centimeters per second is the velocity of the particle at t seconds, then $v = 3 \cos 2\pi t$, where the positive direction is to the right of the origin. If the particle is at the origin at the start of the motion, find its position when t is **(a)** 0.2; **(b)** 0.8; **(c)** 1.7; **(d)** 2.25. Simulate the motion on your graphics calculator and support your answers.

40. A stone is thrown vertically upward from the ground with an initial velocity of 25 ft/sec.
(a) How long will the stone be going up?
(b) How high will the stone go?
(c) How long will it take the stone to reach the ground?
(d) Simulate the motion on your graphics calculator and support your answers in parts (a)–(c).
(e) With what speed will the stone strike the ground?

41. Neglecting air resistance, if an object is dropped from an airplane flying horizontally at a height of 30,000 ft above the ocean, **(a)** how long will it take the object to reach the water and **(b)** with what speed will it strike the water?

42. Suppose a bullet is fired directly downward from the airplane in Exercise 41 with a muzzle velocity of 2500 ft/sec. If air resistance is neglected, **(a)** how long will it take the bullet to reach the ocean, and **(b)** with what speed will it strike the ocean?

43. A ball is thrown vertically upward from the top of a house 64 ft above the ground, and the initial velocity is 48 ft/sec.
    (a) How long will it take the ball to reach its greatest height?
    (b) What is its greatest height?
    (c) How long will it take the ball to strike the ground?
    (d) With what velocity will the ball strike the ground?

44. Suppose the ball in Exercise 43 is dropped from the top of the house.
    (a) How long will it take the ball to strike the ground?
    (b) With what velocity will it strike the ground?

45. A rocket is lifted off the ground with a constant acceleration of 25 m/sec^2. Determine **(a)** the velocity of the rocket 1 min after lift off, and **(b)** how high above the ground the rocket will be at that time.

46. A projectile is fired vertically upward with an initial velocity of 200 m/sec from a point 2.5 m above the ground.
    (a) If s meters is the height of the projectile above the ground t seconds after being fired, express s in terms of t.
    (b) How high above the ground is the projectile 3 sec after being fired?
    (c) How long will it take for the projectile to be 600 m above the ground?

47. An automobile traveling at a constant speed of 60 mi/hr along a straight highway fails to stop at a stop sign. If 3 sec later a highway patrol car starts from rest from the stop sign and maintains a constant acceleration of 8 ft/sec^2, how long will it take the patrol car to overtake the automobile, and how far from the stop sign will this occur? Also determine the speed of the patrol car when it overtakes the automobile.

In Exercises 48 and 49, find the sum.

48. $\displaystyle\sum_{i=1}^{100} 2i(i^3 - 1)$ 49. $\displaystyle\sum_{i=1}^{41} (\sqrt[3]{3i - 1} - \sqrt[3]{3i + 2})$

50. Prove that $\displaystyle\sum_{i=1}^{n} i^3 = \left(\sum_{i=1}^{n} i\right)^2$, and verify the formula for $n = 1, 2,$ and 3.

51. Show that each of the following inequalities holds:

    (a) $\displaystyle\int_{-2}^{-1} \frac{dx}{x - 3} \geq \int_{-2}^{-1} \frac{dx}{x}$

    (b) $\displaystyle\int_{1}^{2} \frac{dx}{x} \geq \int_{1}^{2} \frac{dx}{x - 3}$

    (c) $\displaystyle\int_{4}^{5} \frac{dx}{x - 3} \geq \int_{4}^{5} \frac{dx}{x}$

52. Express as a definite integral and evaluate the definite integral: $\displaystyle\lim_{n \to +\infty} \sum_{i=1}^{n} (8\sqrt{i}/n^{3/2})$. *Hint:* Consider the function f for which $f(x) = \sqrt{x}$.

In Exercises 53 and 54, apply Theorem 4.6.2 to find a closed interval containing the value of the definite integral. Support your answer by the NINT capability of your graphics calculator.

53. $\displaystyle\int_{-\pi/2}^{\pi/2} \sqrt{\cos t}\, dt$ 54. $\displaystyle\int_{0}^{3} \sqrt{x^2 - 2x + 6}\, dx$

In Exercises 55 and 56, evaluate the definite integral by the second fundamental theorem of the calculus. Support your answer by the NINT capability of your graphics calculator.

55. $\displaystyle\int_{-3}^{3} |x - 2|^3\, dx$ 56. $\displaystyle\int_{-2}^{2} x|x - 3|\, dx$

In Exercises 57 through 60, compute the derivative.

57. $\displaystyle\frac{d}{dx}\int_{x}^{4} (3t^2 - 4)^{3/2}\, dt$ 58. $\displaystyle\frac{d}{dx}\int_{-x}^{x} \frac{4}{1 + t^2}\, dt$

59. $\displaystyle\frac{d}{dx}\int_{x}^{x^2} \frac{1}{t}\, dt \quad x > 0$

60. $\displaystyle\frac{d}{dx}\int_{1}^{\sec x} \sqrt{t^2 - 1}\, dt \quad 0 < x < \tfrac{1}{2}\pi$

61. Find the average value of the cosine function on the closed interval $[a, a + 2\pi]$.

62. Interpret the mean-value theorem for integrals (4.6.3) in terms of an average function value.

63. If $f(x) = x^2\sqrt{x - 3}$, find the average value of f on $[7, 12]$.

64. **(a)** Find the average value of the function f defined by $f(x) = 1/x^2$ on the interval $[1, r]$.
    (b) If A is the average value found in part (a), find $\displaystyle\lim_{r \to +\infty} A$.

65. A body falls from rest and travels a distance of s feet before striking the ground. If the only force acting is that of gravity, which gives the body an acceleration of g feet per second squared toward the ground, show that the average value of the velocity, expressed as a function of distance, while traveling this distance is $\frac{2}{3}\sqrt{2gs}$ feet per second, and that this average velocity is two-thirds of the final velocity.

66. Suppose a ball is dropped from rest and after t seconds its directed distance from the starting point is s feet and its velocity is v feet per second. Neglect air resistance. When $t = t_1$, $s = s_1$ and $v = v_1$.
(a) Express v as a function of t as $v = f(t)$, and find the average value of f on $[0, t_1]$.
(b) Express v as a function of s as $v = h(s)$, and find the average value of h on $[0, s_1]$.
(c) Write the results of parts (a) and (b) in terms of t_1, and determine which average velocity is larger.

In Exercises 67 through 72, find the area of the region bounded by the curve and lines. In each exercise do the following: (a) Draw a figure showing the region and a rectangular element of area; (b) express the measure of the area of the region as the limit of a Riemann sum; (c) find the limit in part (b) by evaluating a definite integral by the second fundamental theorem of the calculus.

67. $y = 9 - x^2$; x axis; y axis; $x = 2$

68. $y = 3\cos\frac{1}{2}x$; x axis; $x = -\frac{1}{2}\pi$; $x = \frac{1}{2}\pi$

69. $y = 2\sqrt{x - 1}$; x axis; $x = 5$; $x = 17$

70. $y = \dfrac{4}{x^2} - x$; x axis; $x = -2$; $x = -1$

71. $x^2 + y - 5 = 0$; $y = -4$

72. $y = x^2 - 7x$; x axis; $x=2$; $x = 4$

In Exercises 73 through 76, approximate to four significant digits the area of the region bounded by the curves by doing the following: (a) Draw a figure showing the region and a rectangular element of area; (b) express the measure of the area of the region as the limit of a Riemann sum; (c) approximate the limit in part (b) by evaluating a definite integral by the NINT capability of your graphics calculator.

73. $y = 9 - x^2$; $y = x^4$

74. $y = 16 - x^2$; $y = x^3$; the y axis

75. $y = x^2$; $y = \cos^2 x$

76. $y = x^2$; $y = \frac{1}{4}\tan^2 x$; $0 \le x \le \frac{1}{2}\pi$

In Exercises 77 through 81, find the exact area of the described region.

77. The region bounded by the curves $x = y^2$ and $x = y^3$.

78. The region bounded by the curves $y = \sin 2x$ and $y = \sin x$ from $x = 0$ to $x = \frac{1}{3}\pi$.

79. The region bounded by the curves $y = \cos x$ and $y = \sin x$ from $x = \frac{1}{4}\pi$ to $x = \frac{5}{4}\pi$.

80. The region bounded by the loop of the curve $y^2 = x^2(4 - x)$.

81. The region in the first quadrant bounded by the y axis and the curves $y = \sec^2 x$ and $y = 2\tan^2 x$.

82. Suppose that on a particular day in a certain city the Fahrenheit temperature is $f(t)$ degrees t hours since midnight, where

$$f(t) = 60 - 15\sin\frac{1}{12}\pi(8 - t) \qquad 0 \le t \le 24$$

(a) Sketch the graph of f. Find the temperature at (b) 12 midnight; (c) 8 A.M.; (d) 12 noon; (e) 2 P.M.; and (f) 6 P.M. (g) Find the average temperature between 8 A.M. and 6 P.M.

83. Find the volume of the solid generated by revolving about the x axis the region bounded by the curve $y = x^4$, the line $x = 1$, and the x axis.

84. Find the volume of the solid generated if the region of Exercise 83 is revolved about the y axis.

85. The region bounded by the curve $y = \sqrt{\sin x}$, the x axis, and the line $x = \frac{1}{2}\pi$ is revolved about the x axis. Find the volume of the solid generated.

86. The region bounded by the curve $x = \sqrt{\cos y}$, the line $y = \frac{1}{6}\pi$, and the y axis, where $\frac{1}{6}\pi \le y \le \frac{1}{2}\pi$, is revolved about the y axis. Find the volume of the solid generated.

87. The region bounded by the curve $y = \csc x$, the x axis, and the lines $x = \frac{1}{4}\pi$ and $x = \frac{1}{2}\pi$ is revolved about the x axis. Find the volume of the solid generated.

88. Find the volume of the solid of revolution generated when the region bounded by the curve $y = \sqrt{x}$, the x axis, and the line $x = 4$ is revolved about the line $x = 4$. Take the elements of area parallel to the axis of revolution.

89. Find the volume of the solid generated by revolving about the y axis the region bounded by the parabola $x = y^2 + 2$ and the line $x = y + 8$.

90. The region in the first quadrant bounded by the curves $x = y^2$ and $x = y^4$ is revolved about the y axis. Find the volume of the solid generated.

91. The base of a solid is the region bounded by the parabola $y^2 = 8x$ and the line $x = 8$. Find the volume of the solid if every plane section perpendicular to the axis of the base is a square.

92. Use integration to find the volume of the portion of the sphere of radius r units cut off by a plane h units from a pole.

93. Find the volume of the solid generated by revolving the region bounded by the curve $y = |x - 2|$, the x axis, and the lines $x = 1$ and $x = 4$ about the x axis.

94. The base of a solid is the region enclosed by a circle having a radius of r units, and every plane section perpendicular to a fixed diameter of the base is a square for which a chord of the circle is a diagonal. Find the volume of the solid.

95. Find the volume of the solid generated by revolving about the line $y = -1$ the region above the x axis bounded by the line $2y = x + 3$ and the curves $y^2 + x = 0$ and $y^2 - 4x = 0$ from $x = -1$ to $x = 1$.

96. A sphere of radius 10 cm is intersected by two parallel planes on the same side of the center of the sphere. The distance from the center of the sphere to one of the planes is 1 cm, and the distance between the two planes is 6 cm. Find the volume of the solid portion of the sphere between the two planes.

97. Solve Exercise 96 if the two planes lie on opposite sides of the center of the sphere but the other facts are the same.

98. A solid is formed by revolving about the y axis the region bounded by the curve $y^3 = x$, the x axis, and the line $x = c$, where $c > 0$. For what value of c will the volume of the solid be 12π cubic units?

In Exercises 99 through 106, you need to use your graphics calculator to find the volume of the solid generated by revolving the given region about the indicated axis. Take the rectangular elements of area either perpendicular or parallel to the axis of revolution as indicated and express your answer to four significant digits.

99. The region bounded by the graph of $y = \sqrt[3]{x^2 - 7}$ and the x axis; about the x axis; elements perpendicular.

100. The region of Exercise 99; about the y axis; elements parallel.

101. The region of Exercise 99; about the x axis; elements parallel.

102. The region of Exercise 99; about the y axis; elements perpendicular.

103. The region bounded by the graphs of $y = \cos x^2$ and $y = x^3$, and the y axis; about the y axis; elements parallel.

104. The region bounded by the graphs of $y = \cos \sqrt{x}$ and $y = x^2$, and the y axis; about the x axis; elements perpendicular.

105. The region bounded by the graphs of
$$y = x^3 - 6x^2 + 9x - 1 \text{ and } y = x^2 - 2x + 2$$

and not intersected by the line $y = 4$; about the line $y = 4$; elements perpendicular.

106. The region of Exercise 105; about the line $x = -1$; elements parallel.

107. A church steeple is 30 ft high, and every horizontal plane section is a square having sides of length one-tenth of the distance of the plane section from the top of the steeple. Find the volume of the steeple.

108. Find by slicing the volume of a tetrahedron having three mutually perpendicular faces and three mutually perpendicular edges whose lengths are a, b, and c units.

109. The region bounded by a pentagon having vertices at $(-4, 4)$, $(-2, 0)$, $(0, 8)$, $(2, 0)$, and $(4, 4)$ is revolved about the x axis. Find the volume of the solid generated.

110. The region bounded by the curves $y = \tan x$ and $y = \cot x$ and the x axis, where $0 \le x \le \frac{1}{2}\pi$, is revolved about the x axis. Find the volume of the solid generated.

111. The region from $x = 0$ to $x = \frac{1}{2}\pi$ bounded by the curve $y = \sin x$, the line $y = 1$, and the y axis is revolved about the x axis. Find the volume of the solid generated. *Hint:* Use the identity $\sin^2 x = \frac{1}{2}(1 - \cos 2x)$.

112. A wedge is cut from a right-circular cylinder with a radius of r units by two planes, one perpendicular to the axis of the cylinder and the other intersecting the first along a diameter of the circular plane section at an angle of measurement 30°. Find the volume of the wedge.

In Exercises 113 and 114, apply the second fundamental theorem of the calculus to evaluate the definite integral. Then find the value of c satisfying the mean-value theorem for integrals.

113. $\displaystyle\int_0^3 (x^2 + 1)\, dx$ 114. $\displaystyle\int_1^4 \sqrt{x}\, dx$

115. Let f be continuous on $[a, b]$ and $\int_a^b f(t)\, dt \ne 0$. Show that for any number k in $(0, 1)$ there is a number c in (a, b) such that $\int_a^c f(t)\, dt = k \int_a^b f(t)\, dt$. *Hint:* Consider the function F for which $F(x) = \int_a^x f(t)\, dt / \int_a^b f(t)\, dt$, and apply the intermediate-value theorem.

116. Given $F(x) = \displaystyle\int_x^{2x} \frac{1}{t}\, dt$ and $x > 0$. Prove that F is a constant function by showing that $F'(x) = 0$. *Hint:* Use the first fundamental theorem of the calculus after writing the given integral as the difference of two integrals.

117. If $f(x) = x + |x - 1|$ and

$$F(x) = \begin{cases} x & \text{if } x < 1 \\ x^2 - x + 1 & \text{if } 1 \leq x \end{cases}$$

show that F is an antiderivative of f on $(-\infty, +\infty)$.

118. Let f and g be two functions such that for all x in $(-\infty, +\infty)$, $f'(x) = g(x)$ and $g'(x) = -f(x)$. Further suppose that $f(0) = 0$ and $g(0) = 1$. Prove that

$$[f(x)]^2 + [g(x)]^2 = 1$$

Hint: Consider the functions F and G where $F(x) = [f(x)]^2$ and $G(x) = -[g(x)]^2$, and show that $F'(x) = G'(x)$ for all x.

119. Evaluate $\displaystyle\int_0^\pi \left| \cos x + \tfrac{1}{2} \right| \, dx$.

120. Make up an example of a discontinuous function for which the conclusion of the mean-value theorem for integrals **(a)** does not hold and **(b)** does hold.

LOGARITHMIC, EXPONENTIAL, INVERSE TRIGONOMETRIC, AND HYPERBOLIC FUNCTIONS

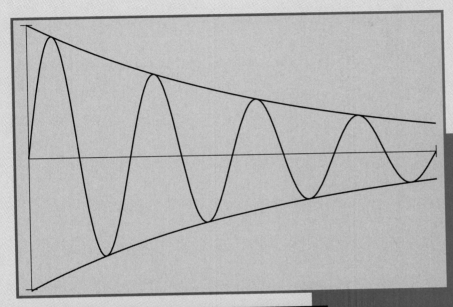

Functions that are not algebraic are called *transcendental*, examples of which are the six trigonometric functions. The *natural logarithmic and exponential functions* are also transcendental and they are featured in this chapter. Because these two functions are inverses of each other, we devote the first section to a treatment of *inverse functions* and their properties. Our discussion includes sufficient conditions for a function to have an inverse, the inverse function theorems, and the derivative of the inverse of a function.

The natural logarithmic function *ln* is defined as an integral in Section 5.2 and the natural exponential function *exp* is defined as its inverse in Section 5.4. With this background we are able to define an irrational power of a real number.

The functions *ln* and *exp* are applied in Section 5.6. The applications include *laws of growth and decay* arising in a wide variety of fields including biology, psychology, sociology, chemistry, physics, business, and economics.

The remaining categories of transcendental functions, *inverse trigonometric functions* and *hyperbolic functions*, are dealt with in the remaining three sections of this chapter. We review the inverse trigonometric functions and obtain their derivatives in Section 5.7. We discuss integrals involving the inverse trigonometric functions in Section 5.8. Hyperbolic functions, which are defined in terms of the natural exponential function, have properties similar to those of the trigonometric functions. These functions are introduced along with their inverses in Section 5.9.

5.1 THE INVERSE OF A FUNCTION

The word *inverse* arose earlier in this text in connection with the inverse calculus operations of differentiation and antidifferentiation. One of a pair of inverse operations essentially "undoes" the other. In the following illustration we use pairs of functions associated with inverse arithmetic operations.

▷ **ILLUSTRATION 1**   (a) Let $f(x) = x + 4$ and $g(x) = x - 4$. Then

$$f(g(x)) = f(x - 4) \qquad g(f(x)) = g(x + 4)$$
$$= (x - 4) + 4 \qquad\qquad = (x + 4) - 4$$
$$= x \qquad\qquad\qquad\quad = x$$

(b) Let $f(x) = 2x$ and $g(x) = \dfrac{x}{2}$. Then

$$f(g(x)) = f\left(\frac{x}{2}\right) \qquad g(f(x)) = g(2x)$$
$$= 2\left(\frac{x}{2}\right) \qquad\qquad = \frac{2x}{2}$$
$$= x \qquad\qquad\qquad = x$$

(c) Let $f(x) = x^3$ and $g(x) = \sqrt[3]{x}$. Then

$$f(g(x)) = f(\sqrt[3]{x}) \qquad g(f(x)) = g(x^3)$$
$$= (\sqrt[3]{x})^3 \qquad\qquad = \sqrt[3]{x^3}$$
$$= x \qquad\qquad\qquad = x$$ ◀

Each pair of functions f and g in Illustration 1 satisfies the following two statements:

$$f(g(x)) = x \qquad \text{for } x \text{ in the domain of } g$$

and

$$g(f(x)) = x \qquad \text{for } x \text{ in the domain of } f$$

Observe that for the functions f and g in these two equations the composite functions $f(g(x))$ and $g(f(x))$ are equal, a relationship that is not generally true for arbitrary functions f and g. You will learn subsequently (in Illustration 5) that each pair of functions in Illustration 1 is a set of *inverse functions,* and that is the reason the two equations are satisfied.

We lead up to the formal definition of the *inverse of a function* by considering some more particular functions. Figure 1 shows the graph of the function defined by

$$f(x) = x^2$$

The domain of f is the set of real numbers and the range is the interval $[0, +\infty)$. Observe that because $f(2) = 4$ and $f(-2) = 4$, the number 4 is

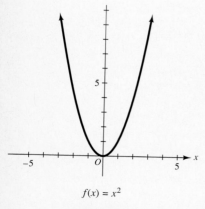

$f(x) = x^2$

FIGURE 1

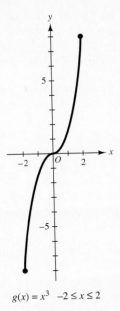

$g(x) = x^3 \quad -2 \le x \le 2$

FIGURE 2

the function value of two distinct numbers in the domain. Furthermore, every number except 0 in the range of this function is the function value of two distinct numbers in the domain. In particular, $\frac{25}{4}$ is the function value of both $\frac{5}{2}$ and $-\frac{5}{2}$, 1 is the function value of both 1 and -1, and 9 is the function value of both 3 and -3.

A different situation occurs with the function g defined by

$$g(x) = x^3 \qquad -2 \le x \le 2$$

The domain of g is the closed interval $[-2, 2]$, and the range is $[-8, 8]$. The graph of g is shown in Figure 2. This function is one for which a number in its range is the function value of one and only one number in the domain. Such a function is called *one-to-one*.

5.1.1 Definition of a One-to-One Function

A function f is said to be **one-to-one** if every number in its range corresponds to exactly one number in its domain; that is, for all x_1 and x_2 in the domain of f

$$\text{if} \quad x_1 \ne x_2, \quad \text{then} \quad f(x_1) \ne f(x_2)$$
$$\Leftrightarrow f(x_1) = f(x_2) \quad \text{only when} \quad x_1 = x_2$$

▷ **ILLUSTRATION 2**   The function defined by $f(x) = x^2$ does not satisfy the above definition because, for instance, 3 and -3 are two distinct numbers in the domain, yet $f(3) = f(-3)$. This function is, therefore, not one-to-one.   ◀

We know that a vertical line can intersect the graph of a function in only one point. For a one-to-one function, it is also true that a horizontal line can intersect the graph in at most one point. Notice that this is the situation for the one-to-one function defined by $g(x) = x^3$, where $-2 \le x \le 2$, whose graph appears in Figure 2. Furthermore, observe in Figure 1 that for the function defined by $f(x) = x^2$, which is not one-to-one, any horizontal line above the x axis intersects the graph in two points. We have, therefore, the following geometric test for determining if a function is one-to-one.

Horizontal-Line Test

A function is one-to-one if and only if every horizontal line intersects the graph of the function in at most one point.

▶ **EXAMPLE 1**   Apply the horizontal-line test to determine if the function is one-to-one:

(a) $f(x) = 4x - 3$ **(b)** $f(x) = (x + 1)^4$

(c) $f(x) = |x|$ **(d)** $f(x) = \dfrac{3x + 4}{x - 2}$

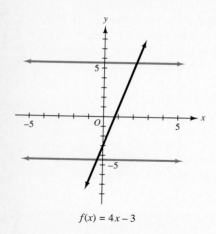

$f(x) = 4x - 3$

FIGURE 3

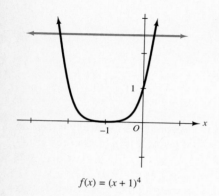

$f(x) = (x + 1)^4$

FIGURE 4

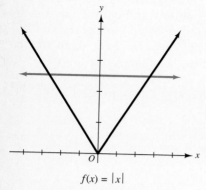

$f(x) = |x|$

FIGURE 5

Solution

(a) This function is linear, and its graph is the line in Figure 3. Because any horizontal line intersects the graph in exactly one point, the function is one-to-one.

(b) The graph of this function, appearing in Figure 4, shows that any horizontal line above the x axis intersects the graph in two points. The function is, therefore, not one-to-one.

(c) The graph of the absolute-value function appears in Figure 5. Observe that any horizontal line above the x axis intersects the graph in two points. Thus the absolute-value function is not one-to-one.

(d) Figure 6 shows the graph of the given rational function and its horizontal asymptote, the line $y = 3$, plotted in the same window. Any horizontal line, except the asymptote, intersects the graph in exactly one point. The function is, therefore, one-to-one. ◀

The following theorem gives a test that can sometimes be applied to show analytically that a function is one-to-one.

5.1.2 Theorem

A function that is monotonic on an interval is one-to-one on the interval.

Proof Assume that the function f is increasing on an interval I. If x_1 and x_2 are two numbers in the interval and $x_1 \neq x_2$, then either $x_1 < x_2$ or $x_2 < x_1$. If $x_1 < x_2$, then from the definition (3.4.1) of an increasing function, $f(x_1) < f(x_2)$; so $f(x_1) \neq f(x_2)$. If $x_2 < x_1$, then $f(x_2) < f(x_1)$; so again $f(x_1) \neq f(x_2)$. Therefore, from Definition 5.1.1, f is one-to-one on the interval. The proof is similar if f is decreasing on an interval. ■

To apply Theorem 5.1.2, we must first determine if the function is increasing or decreasing on an interval. Theorem 3.4.3 can usually be used for this purpose.

▶ **EXAMPLE 2** If

$$f(x) = \frac{2x + 3}{x - 1}$$

prove analytically that f is one-to-one on each of the intervals $(-\infty, 1)$ and $(1, +\infty)$. Support the answer graphically.

Solution The domain of f is the set of all real numbers except 1, or equivalently, the set $(-\infty, 1) \cup (1, +\infty)$. We compute $f'(x)$.

$$f'(x) = \frac{2(x - 1) - (2x + 3)}{(x - 1)^2}$$

$$= -\frac{5}{(x - 1)^2}$$

Because $f'(x) < 0$ for all $x \neq 1$, we conclude from Theorem 3.4.3 that f is decreasing on each of the intervals $(-\infty, 1)$ and $(1, +\infty)$. From Theorem 5.1.2, f is, therefore, one-to-one on each of these intervals.

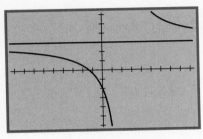

[−9.4, 9.4] by [−6.2, 6.2]

$$f(x) = \frac{3x + 4}{x - 2} \text{ and } y = 3$$

FIGURE 6

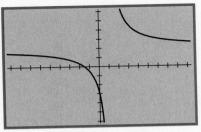

[−9.4, 9.4] by [−6.2, 6.2]

$$f(x) = \frac{2x + 3}{x - 1}$$

FIGURE 7

Figure 7 shows the graph of f plotted in the $[-9.4, 9.4]$ by $[-6.2, 6.2]$ window, which supports the fact that f is not only one-to-one on each of the intervals but is also one-to-one on its domain. ◄

▷ **ILLUSTRATION 3**   Consider the equation

$$y = x^3 \qquad -2 \le x \le 2 \tag{1}$$

This equation defines the one-to-one function g discussed prior to Definition 5.1.1, where

$$g(x) = x^3 \qquad -2 \le x \le 2$$

Function g is the set of ordered pairs (x, y) satisfying (1). If we solve (1) for x, we obtain

$$x = \sqrt[3]{y} \qquad -8 \le y \le 8 \tag{2}$$

which defines a function G where

$$G(y) = \sqrt[3]{y} \qquad -8 \le y \le 8$$

The function G is the set of ordered pairs (y, x) satisfying (2). ◄

The function G of Illustration 3 is called the *inverse* of the function g. In the following formal definition of the inverse of a function, we use the notation f^{-1} to denote the inverse of f. This notation is read "f inverse," and it should not be confused with the use of -1 as an exponent.

5.1.3 Definition of the Inverse of a Function

If f is a one-to-one function that is the set of ordered pairs (x, y), then there is a function f^{-1}, called the **inverse** of f, that is the set of ordered pairs (y, x) defined by

$$x = f^{-1}(y) \quad \text{if and only if} \quad y = f(x)$$

The domain of f^{-1} is the range of f and the range of f^{-1} is the domain of f.

In the preceding definition the requirement that f be a one-to-one function ensures that $f^{-1}(y)$ is unique for each value of y.

Eliminating y from the equations of the definition by writing the equation

$$f^{-1}(y) = x$$

and replacing y by $f(x)$, we obtain

$$f^{-1}(f(x)) = x \tag{3}$$

where x is in the domain of f.

Eliminating x from the same pair of equations by writing the equation

$$f(x) = y$$

and replacing x by $f^{-1}(y)$, we get

$$f(f^{-1}(y)) = y$$

where y is in the domain of f. Because the symbol used for the independent variable is arbitrary, we can replace y by x to obtain

$$f(f^{-1}(x)) = x \qquad \qquad \textbf{(4)}$$

where x is in the domain of f^{-1}.

From Equations (3) and (4) we see that if the inverse of the function f is the function f^{-1}, then the inverse of f^{-1} is f. We state these results formally as the following theorem.

5.1.4 Theorem

If f is a one-to-one function having f^{-1} as its inverse, then f^{-1} is a one-to-one function having f as its inverse. Furthermore,

$$f^{-1}(f(x)) = x \qquad \text{for } x \text{ in the domain of } f$$

and

$$f(f^{-1}(x)) = x \qquad \text{for } x \text{ in the domain of } f^{-1}$$

We use the terminology *inverse functions* when referring to a function and its inverse.

▷ **ILLUSTRATION 4**   In Illustration 3 the function G defined by

$$G(y) = \sqrt[3]{y} \qquad -8 \le y \le 8$$

is the inverse of the function g defined by

$$g(x) = x^3 \qquad -2 \le x \le 2$$

Therefore g^{-1} can be written in place of G, and we have

$$g^{-1}(y) = \sqrt[3]{y} \qquad -8 \le y \le 8$$

or, equivalently, if we replace y by x,

$$g^{-1}(x) = \sqrt[3]{x} \qquad -8 \le x \le 8$$

Observe that the domain of g is $[-2, 2]$, which is the range of g^{-1}; also the range of g is $[-8, 8]$, which is the domain of g^{-1}.   ◀

If a function f has an inverse, then $f^{-1}(x)$ can be found by the method used in the following illustration.

▷ **ILLUSTRATION 5**   Each of the functions f in Illustration 1 is one-to-one. Therefore, $f^{-1}(x)$ exists. For each function we compute $f^{-1}(x)$ from the definition of $f(x)$ by substituting y for $f(x)$ and solving the resulting equation for x. This procedure gives the equation $x = f^{-1}(y)$. We then have the definition of $f^{-1}(y)$, from which we obtain $f^{-1}(x)$.

(a) $f(x) = x + 4$
$y = x + 4$
$x = y - 4$
$f^{-1}(y) = y - 4$
$f^{-1}(x) = x - 4$

(b) $f(x) = 2x$
$y = 2x$
$x = \dfrac{y}{2}$
$f^{-1}(y) = \dfrac{y}{2}$
$f^{-1}(x) = \dfrac{x}{2}$

(c) $f(x) = x^3$
$y = x^3$
$x = \sqrt[3]{y}$
$f^{-1}(y) = \sqrt[3]{y}$
$f^{-1}(x) = \sqrt[3]{x}$

Observe that the function f^{-1} in each part is the function g in the corresponding part of Illustration 1.

▶ **EXAMPLE 3** Find $f^{-1}(x)$ for the function f of Example 1(a) and verify the equations of Theorem 5.1.4 for f and f^{-1}. Plot the graphs of f and f^{-1} in the same window.

Solution In Example 1(a) we showed by the horizontal-line test that the function defined by

$$f(x) = 4x - 3$$

is one-to-one. Therefore f^{-1} exists. To find $f^{-1}(x)$, we write the equation

$$y = 4x - 3$$

and solve for x. We obtain

$$x = \frac{y + 3}{4}$$

Therefore

$$f^{-1}(y) = \frac{y + 3}{4} \quad \Leftrightarrow \quad f^{-1}(x) = \frac{x + 3}{4}$$

We verify the equations of Theorem 5.1.4.

$$f^{-1}(f(x)) = f^{-1}(4x - 3) \qquad f(f^{-1}(x)) = f\left(\frac{x + 3}{4}\right)$$

$$= \frac{(4x - 3) + 3}{4} \qquad\qquad = 4\left(\frac{x + 3}{4}\right) - 3$$

$$= \frac{4x}{4} \qquad\qquad\qquad = (x + 3) - 3$$

$$= x \qquad\qquad\qquad\quad = x$$

Figure 8 shows the graphs of f and f^{-1} plotted in the same window. ◀

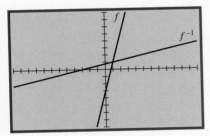

[-12, 12] by [-8, 8]

$f(x) = 4x - 3$ and $f^{-1}(x) = \dfrac{x + 3}{4}$

FIGURE 8

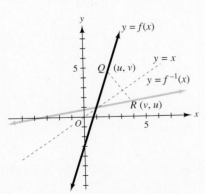

$f(x) = 4x - 3$ and $f^{-1}(x) = \dfrac{x + 3}{4}$

FIGURE 9

Refer to Figure 9 showing the graphs of f and f^{-1} of Example 3 with the point $Q(u, v)$ on the graph of f and the point $R(v, u)$ on the graph of f^{-1}. The line segment QR in the figure is perpendicular to the line $y = x$ and is

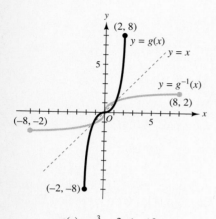

$g(x) = x^3 \quad -2 \le x \le 2$

$g^{-1}(x) = \sqrt[3]{x} \quad -8 \le x \le 8$

FIGURE 10

bisected by it. The point Q is a *reflection of the point R* with respect to the line $y = x$, and the point R is a *reflection of the point Q* with respect to the line $y = x$.

If x and y are interchanged in the equation $y = f(x)$, we obtain the equation $x = f(y)$, and the graph of the equation $x = f(y)$ is a *reflection of the graph* of the equation $y = f(x)$ with respect to the line $y = x$. Because the equation $x = f(y)$ is equivalent to the equation $y = f^{-1}(x)$, the graph of the equation $y = f^{-1}(x)$ is a reflection of the graph of the equation $y = f(x)$ with respect to the line $y = x$. Therefore, if a function has an inverse, the graphs of the functions are reflections of each other with respect to the line $y = x$.

▷ **ILLUSTRATION 6** Functions g and g^{-1} of Illustration 4 are defined by

$$g(x) = x^3 \quad -2 \le x \le 2$$

and

$$g^{-1}(x) = \sqrt[3]{x} \quad -8 \le x \le 8$$

The graphs of g and g^{-1} are sketched in Figure 10. Observe that these graphs are reflections of each other with respect to the line $y = x$. ◀

▶ **EXAMPLE 4** Find $f^{-1}(x)$ for the function f of Example 2, and verify the equations of Theorem 5.1.4. Plot the graphs of f and f^{-1} and the line $y = x$ in the same window and observe that the graphs of f and f^{-1} are reflections of each other with respect to the line $y = x$.

Solution The function f of Example 2 is defined by

$$f(x) = \frac{2x + 3}{x - 1}$$

Because f is one-to-one, as shown in Example 2, f has an inverse f^{-1}. To find $f^{-1}(x)$, we let $y = f(x)$ and solve for x, giving us $x = f^{-1}(y)$. So we have

$$y = \frac{2x + 3}{x - 1}$$

$$xy - y = 2x + 3$$

$$x(y - 2) = y + 3$$

$$x = \frac{y + 3}{y - 2}$$

Therefore

$$f^{-1}(y) = \frac{y + 3}{y - 2} \quad \Leftrightarrow \quad f^{-1}(x) = \frac{x + 3}{x - 2}$$

The domain of f^{-1} is the set of all real numbers except 2. We verify the equations of Theorem 5.1.4.

$$f^{-1}(f(x)) = f^{-1}\left(\frac{2x+3}{x-1}\right) \qquad f(f^{-1}(x)) = f\left(\frac{x+3}{x-2}\right)$$

$$= \frac{\left(\dfrac{2x+3}{x-1}\right)+3}{\left(\dfrac{2x+3}{x-1}\right)-2} \qquad\qquad = \frac{2\left(\dfrac{x+3}{x-2}\right)+3}{\left(\dfrac{x+3}{x-2}\right)-1}$$

$$= \frac{(2x+3)+3(x-1)}{(2x+3)-2(x-1)} \qquad = \frac{2(x+3)+3(x-2)}{(x+3)-(x-2)}$$

$$= \frac{5x}{5} \qquad\qquad\qquad = \frac{5x}{5}$$

$$= x \qquad\qquad\qquad\qquad = x$$

The graphs of f and f^{-1} and the line $y = x$ are plotted in the window $[-9.4, 9.4]$ by $[-6.2, 6.2]$ in Figure 11. We observe that the graphs of the two functions appear to be reflections of each other with respect to the line $y = x$. ◀

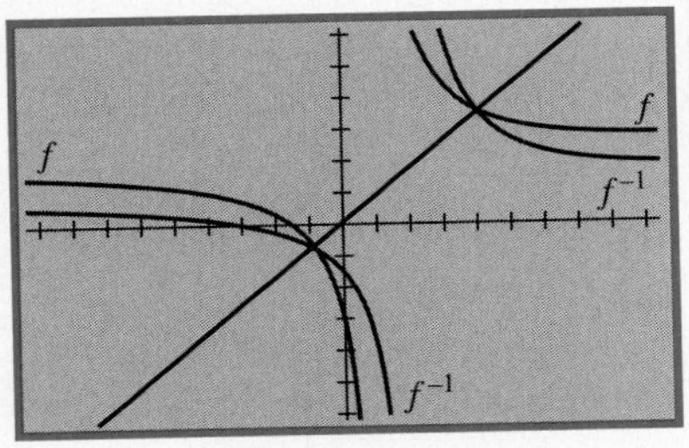

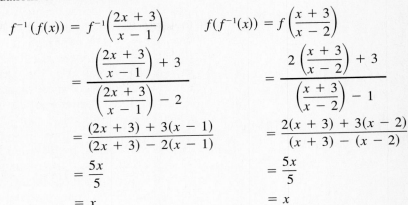

[−9.4, 9.4] by [−6.2, 6.2]

$f(x) = \dfrac{2x+3}{x-1}$ and $f^{-1}(x) = \dfrac{x+3}{x-2}$

$y = x$

FIGURE 11

We can plot the graphs of a function and its inverse on the same screen on our graphics calculator by setting the calculator in parametric mode. The next illustration demonstrates the procedure for the functions g and g^{-1} of Illustration 6.

▷ **ILLUSTRATION 7**   With our calculator in parametric mode, we plot the graph of

$$g(x) = x^3 \qquad -2 \le x \le 2$$

by letting

$$x_1(t) = t \qquad y_1(t) = t^3$$

For the graph of

$$g^{-1}(x) = \sqrt[3]{x} \qquad -8 \le x \le 8$$

we let

$$x_2(t) = t^3 \qquad y_2(t) = t$$

We set our window variables as follows: $t_{\min} = -8$, $t_{\max} = 8$, $t_{\text{step}} = 0.05$, $x_{\min} = -8$, $x_{\max} = 8$, $x_{\text{scl}} = 1$, $y_{\min} = -8$, $y_{\max} = 8$, and $y_{\text{scl}} = 1$. Figure 12, showing the two graphs, supports our graphs in Figure 10. ◀

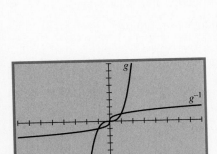

[−8, 8] by [−8, 8]

$g(x) = x^3 \quad -2 \le x \le 2$

$g^{-1}(x) = \sqrt[3]{x} \quad -8 \le x \le 8$

FIGURE 12

Some functions have an inverse for which we cannot obtain an equation defining the inverse function explicitly. For example, let

$$f(x) = x^5 + x^3 + 2x - 2 \tag{5}$$
$$f'(x) = 5x^4 + 3x^2 + 2$$

Because $f'(x) > 0$ for all x, f is an increasing function and therefore has an inverse. However, if we replace $f(x)$ by y in (5), we obtain a fifth-degree equation in x, which we cannot solve for x in terms of y. Nevertheless, even though $f^{-1}(x)$ is not defined explicitly, we can still plot the graph of the inverse function on our graphics calculator in parametric mode as we did in Illustration 7. On some calculators the graphs of both a function and its inverse can be plotted on the same screen with the calculator in function mode. Consult your owners manual under *DrawInv* for this capability.

Some important properties of the inverse function f^{-1} can be determined directly from properties of f. We present some of these properties in the remaining theorems of this section, and in Illustration 12 we return to the function defined by Equation (5).

Information about the continuity and differentiability of the inverse of a function is provided by the *inverse function theorems* that follow. Before stating the inverse function theorem for increasing functions, we present two illustrations giving examples of a function and its inverse that satisfy the conditions of the theorem.

▷ **ILLUSTRATION 8**   In Example 3 we had the function f and its inverse f^{-1} defined by

$$f(x) = 4x - 3 \quad \text{and} \quad f^{-1}(x) = \frac{x + 3}{4}$$

In Figure 8 the graphs of f and f^{-1} are shown plotted in the same window. We observe that both f and f^{-1} are continuous and increasing.   ◀

▷ **ILLUSTRATION 9**   In Illustration 6, the function g and its inverse g^{-1} are defined by

$$g(x) = x^3, \ -2 \le x \le 2 \quad \text{and} \quad g^{-1}(x) = \sqrt[3]{x}, \ -8 \le x \le 8$$

and the graphs of g and g^{-1} appear in Figure 10. Each of these functions is continuous and increasing on its domain.   ◀

5.1.5 Theorem (Inverse Function Theorem)

Suppose that the function f is continuous and increasing on the closed interval $[a, b]$. Then

  (i) f has an inverse f^{-1} defined on $[f(a), f(b)]$;
 (ii) f^{-1} is increasing on $[f(a), f(b)]$;
(iii) f^{-1} is continuous on $[f(a), f(b)]$.

The proof of this theorem appears in the supplement of this section. We now state the inverse function theorem for decreasing functions. The proof is left for the exercises. See Supplementary Exercise 2.

5.1.6 Theorem (Inverse Function Theorem)

Suppose that the function f is continuous and decreasing on the closed interval $[a, b]$. Then

(i) f has an inverse f^{-1} defined on $[f(b), f(a)]$;
(ii) f^{-1} is decreasing on $[f(b), f(a)]$;
(iii) f^{-1} is continuous on $[f(b), f(a)]$.

The inverse function theorems are used to prove the next theorem, which expresses a relationship between the derivatives of a function and its inverse. The statement of the theorem utilizes the Leibniz notation for a derivative, which makes the equation easy to remember.

5.1.7 Theorem

Suppose that the function f is continuous and monotonic on the closed interval $[a, b]$, and let $y = f(x)$. If $f'(x)$ exists and is not zero for all x in $[a, b]$, then the derivative of the inverse function f^{-1}, defined by $x = f^{-1}(y)$, is given by

$$\frac{dx}{dy} = \frac{1}{\dfrac{dy}{dx}}$$

The proof of this theorem also appears in the supplement of this section.

▷ **ILLUSTRATION 10**   We verify Theorem 5.1.7 for the function defined by $f(x) = \sqrt{x}$. If we let $y = f(x)$, we have the equation

$$y = \sqrt{x} \qquad x \geq 0, y \geq 0$$

Because f is one-to-one, f^{-1} exists and is defined by $f^{-1}(y) = y^2$. If we let $x = f^{-1}(y)$, we have the equation

$$x = y^2 \qquad y \geq 0, x \geq 0$$

Because $y = \sqrt{x}$

$$\frac{dy}{dx} = \frac{1}{2\sqrt{x}}$$

and because $x = y^2$

$$\frac{dx}{dy} = 2y$$

Replacing y by $\sqrt{x}$, we get

$$\frac{dx}{dy} = 2\sqrt{x}$$

$$= \frac{1}{\dfrac{1}{2\sqrt{x}}}$$

$$= \frac{1}{\dfrac{dy}{dx}}$$

When $x = 0$, $\dfrac{dy}{dx}$ does not exist; thus the above equation is not satisfied for this value of x. Because the domain of f is the closed interval $[0, +\infty)$, the theorem is valid for this function when x is in the open interval $(0, +\infty)$. ◀

▶ **EXAMPLE 5**   Show that Theorem 5.1.7 holds for the function f of Examples 2 and 4.

Solution   The function is defined by $f(x) = (2x + 3)/(x - 1)$. If we let $y = f(x)$, we have

$$y = \frac{2x + 3}{x - 1} \tag{6}$$

$$\frac{dy}{dx} = -\frac{5}{(x - 1)^2}$$

In the solution of Example 4 we showed that

$$x = \frac{y + 3}{y - 2}$$

We compute $\dfrac{dx}{dy}$ from this equation and get

$$\frac{dx}{dy} = -\frac{5}{(y - 2)^2}$$

In the above equation we substitute the value of y from (6) and obtain

$$\begin{aligned}
\frac{dx}{dy} &= -\frac{5}{\left(\dfrac{2x + 3}{x - 1} - 2\right)^2} \\
&= -\frac{5(x - 1)^2}{(2x + 3 - 2x + 2)^2} \\
&= -\tfrac{5}{25}(x - 1)^2 \\
&= -\tfrac{1}{5}(x - 1)^2 \\
&= \frac{1}{\dfrac{dy}{dx}}
\end{aligned}$$

◀

When applying Theorem 5.1.7 to compute the value of the derivative of the inverse of a function at a particular number, it is more convenient to have the statement of the theorem with f' and $(f^{-1})'$ notations for the derivatives. With this notation we restate Theorem 5.1.7 as Theorem 5.1.8.

5.1.8 Theorem

Suppose the function f is continuous and monotonic on a closed interval $[a, b]$ containing the number c, and let $f(c) = d$. If $f'(c)$ exists and $f'(c) \neq 0$, then $(f^{-1})'(d)$ exists and

$$(f^{-1})'(d) = \frac{1}{f'(c)}$$

▷ **ILLUSTRATION 11**   We show that Theorem 5.1.8 holds for a particular function and particular values of c and d. If f is the function of Illustration 10,

$$f(x) = \sqrt{x} \qquad f'(x) = \frac{1}{2\sqrt{x}}$$

$$f^{-1}(x) = x^2 \qquad (f^{-1})'(x) = 2x \qquad x \geq 0$$

The function f is continuous and monotonic on any closed interval $[a, b]$ for which $0 \leq a < b$. Let $c = 9$, and then $d = f(9)$; that is, $d = 3$. Theorem 5.1.8 states that

$$(f^{-1})'(3) = \frac{1}{f'(9)}$$

This equation is valid because

$$(f^{-1})'(3) = 2 \cdot 3 \qquad \text{and} \qquad f'(9) = \frac{1}{2\sqrt{9}}$$

$$= 6 \qquad\qquad\qquad = \tfrac{1}{6} \qquad ◀$$

▷ **ILLUSTRATION 12**   Consider the function f defined by Equation (5):

$$f(x) = x^5 + x^3 + 2x - 2$$
$$f'(x) = 5x^4 + 3x^2 + 2 \tag{7}$$

As previously stated because $f'(x) > 0$, f is increasing and therefore has an inverse f^{-1}. But we do not have an equation defining explicitly the function values of f^{-1}. We can, however, compute the derivative of f^{-1} at a particular point on the graph of f^{-1}. For instance, because $(0, -2)$ is on the graph of f, the point $(-2, 0)$ is on the graph of f^{-1}. We compute the value of $(f^{-1})'(-2)$ by applying Theorem 5.1.8, which states that

$$(f^{-1})'(-2) = \frac{1}{f'(0)}$$

From (7), $f'(0) = 2$. Thus

$$(f^{-1})'(-2) = \tfrac{1}{2}$$

We now support these results on our graphics calculator. Figure 13 shows the graph of f plotted in the $[-4, 5]$ by $[-5, 1]$ window. Also in the

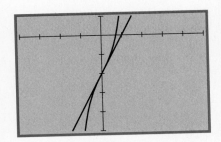

[−4, 5] by [−5, 1]

$f(x) = x^5 + x^3 + 2x - 2$
tangent line at (0, −2)

FIGURE 13

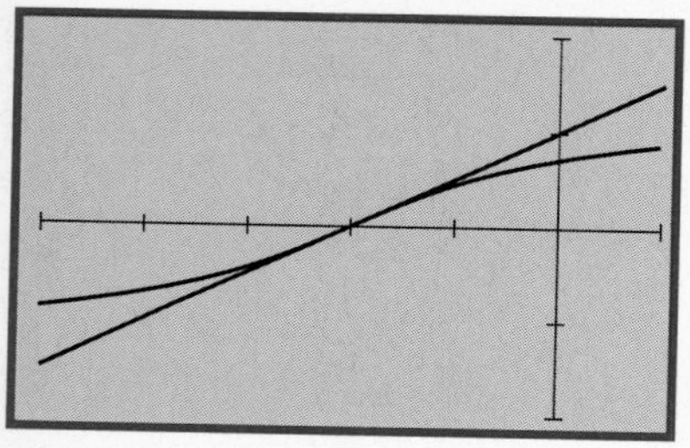

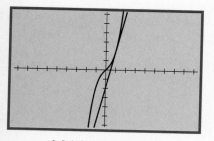

[−5, 1] by [−2, 2]

$x(t) = t^5 + t^3 + 2t - 2$ and $y(t) = t$

tangent line at (−2, 0)

FIGURE 14

figure, we have plotted the tangent line to the graph at the point $(0, -2)$; the tangent line has slope 2.

To plot the graph of f^{-1}, we put our calculator in parametric mode and let

$$x(t) = t^5 + t^3 + 2t - 2 \qquad y(t) = t$$

We set our window variables as follows: $t_{min} = -1$, $t_{max} = 1$, $t_{step} = 0.05$, $x_{min} = -5$, $x_{max} = 1$, $x_{scl} = 1$, $y_{min} = -2$, $y_{max} = 2$, and $y_{scl} = 1$. Figure 14 shows this graph as well as the graph of the tangent line at the point $(-2, 0)$; the tangent line has slope $\frac{1}{2}$.   ◀

▶ **EXAMPLE 6**   For the function f of Illustration 12 find $(f^{-1})'(4)$.

Solution   We are given

$$f(x) = x^5 + x^3 + 2x - 2 \qquad f'(x) = 5x^4 + 3x^2 + 2$$

From Theorem 5.1.8, if $f(c) = 4$, then $(f^{-1})'(4) = \dfrac{1}{f'(c)}$. To compute c we solve the equation

$$c^5 + c^3 + 2c - 2 = 4$$
$$c^5 + c^3 + 2c - 6 = 0$$

We approximate the root of this equation on our graphics calculator by using the root feature or trace and zoom-in and we obtain $c = 1.16124$. Therefore,

$$(f^{-1})'(4) = \frac{1}{f'(1.16124)}$$
$$= \frac{1}{15.1374}$$
$$= 0.06606$$ ◀

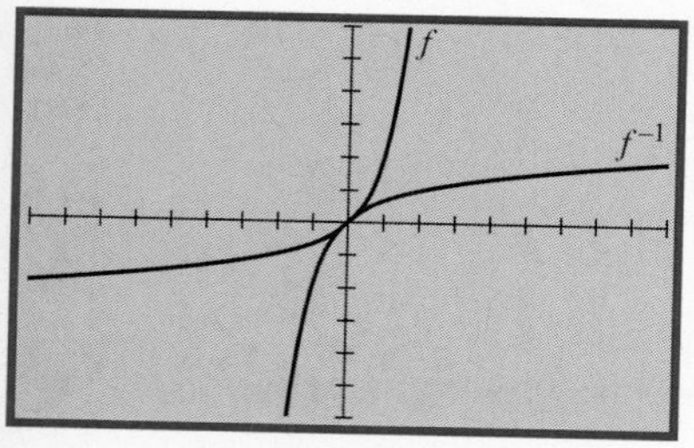

[−9, 9] by [−6, 6]

$f(x) = x^3 + x$

FIGURE 15

▶ **EXAMPLE 7**   Given

$$f(x) = x^3 + x$$

(a) Prove that f has an inverse f^{-1}. **(b)** Find the slope of the tangent line to the graph of f at the point $(1, 2)$. **(c)** Find the slope of the tangent line to the graph of f^{-1} at the point $(2, 1)$. Support the answers in parts (a)–(c) by doing the following: **(d)** Plot the graphs of f and f^{-1} on the same screen; **(e)** plot the graphs of f and its tangent line at $(1, 2)$ on the same screen; **(f)** plot the graphs of f^{-1} and its tangent line at $(2, 1)$ on the same screen.

Solution

$$f'(x) = 3x^2 + 1$$

[−9.4, 9.4] by [−6.2, 6.2]

$f(x) = x^3 + x$
tangent line at (1, 2)

FIGURE 16

(a) Because $f'(x) > 0$ for all real numbers, f is increasing on its domain. Thus f is a one-to-one function, and hence it has an inverse f^{-1}.

(b) The slope of the tangent line to the graph of f at $(1, 2)$ is $f'(1)$ and

$$f'(1) = 4$$

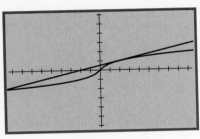

[−9.4, 9.4] by [−6.2, 6.2]

graph of f^{-1} where $f(x) = x^3 + x$
tangent line at (2, 1)

FIGURE 17

(c) The slope of the tangent line to the graph of f^{-1} at (2, 1) is $(f^{-1})'(2)$, and from Theorem 5.1.8

$$(f^{-1})'(2) = \frac{1}{f'(1)}$$

$$= \tfrac{1}{4}$$

(d) The graphs of f and f^{-1} are plotted on the same screen in Figure 15. Observe that the graphs are reflections of each other with respect to the line $y = x$, as expected.

(e) Figure 16 shows the graphs of f and the tangent line at (1, 2) plotted in the $[−9.4, 9.4]$ by $[−6.2, 6.2]$ window. The slope of the tangent line is 4.

(f) The graphs of f^{-1} and the tangent line at (2, 1) are plotted in the $[−9.4, 9.4]$ by $[−6.2, 6.2]$ window in Figure 17. The slope of the tangent line is $\tfrac{1}{4}$. ◀

EXERCISES 5.1

In Exercises 1 through 6, use the horizontal-line test to determine if the function is one-to-one. Either sketch the graph of the function by hand or plot the graph on your graphics calculator.

1. (a) $f(x) = 2x + 3$ **(b)** $f(x) = \tfrac{1}{2}x^2 - 2$
   (c) $g(x) = 4 - x^3$

2. (a) $g(x) = 8 - 4x$ **(b)** $f(x) = 3 - x^2$
   (c) $h(x) = \tfrac{1}{2}x^3 + 1$

3. (a) $f(x) = \sqrt{x + 3}$ **(b)** $g(x) = \dfrac{2}{x + 3}$

   (c) $h(x) = |x - 2|$

4. (a) $f(x) = \sqrt{1 - x^2}$ **(b)** $g(x) = 5$

   (c) $f(x) = \dfrac{1}{2x - 4}$

5. (a) $h(x) = 2 \sin x, -\tfrac{1}{2}\pi \le x \le \tfrac{1}{2}\pi$
   (b) $f(x) = \tfrac{1}{2}\tan x, -\tfrac{1}{2}\pi < x < \tfrac{1}{2}\pi$
   (c) $G(x) = \sec x, x \in [0, \tfrac{1}{2}\pi) \cup [\pi, \tfrac{3}{2}\pi)$

6. (a) $f(x) = 1 - \cos x, 0 \le x \le \pi$
   (b) $F(x) = \cot \tfrac{1}{2}x, 0 < x < 2\pi$
   (c) $g(x) = \csc x, x \in (0, \tfrac{1}{2}\pi] \cup (\pi, \tfrac{3}{2}\pi]$

In Exercises 7 through 18, determine if the function has an inverse. If the inverse exists, do the following: (i) Find it and state its domain and range; (ii) plot the graphs of the function and its inverse on the same screen of your graphics calculator. If the function does not have an inverse, support this fact graphically by verifying that a horizontal line intersects the graph of the function in more than one point.

7. (a) $f(x) = 5x - 7$ **(b)** $g(x) = 1 - x^2$

8. (a) $f(x) = 3x + 6$ **(b)** $g(x) = x^5$

9. (a) $f(x) = (4 - x)^3$ **(b)** $h(x) = \sqrt{2x - 6}$

10. (a) $F(x) = 3(x^2 + 1)$ **(b)** $g(x) = \sqrt{1 - x^2}$

11. (a) $F(x) = \sqrt[3]{x + 1}$ **(b)** $f(x) = (x + 2)^4$

12. (a) $f(x) = |x| + x$ **(b)** $g(x) = 3\sqrt[3]{x} + 1$

13. (a) $f(x) = 2\sqrt[5]{x}$ **(b)** $f(x) = \dfrac{x - 3}{x + 1}$

14. (a) $f(x) = \dfrac{2x - 1}{x}$ **(b)** $g(x) = \dfrac{8}{x^3 + 1}$

15. (a) $g(x) = x^2 + 5, x \ge 0$
   (b) $f(x) = (2x + 1)^3, -\tfrac{1}{2} \le x \le \tfrac{1}{2}$

16. (a) $f(x) = (2x - 1)^2, x \le \tfrac{1}{2}$
   (b) $f(x) = \tfrac{1}{8}x^3, -1 \le x \le 1$

17. $F(x) = \sqrt{9 - x^2}, 0 \le x \le 3$

18. $G(x) = \sqrt{4x^2 - 9}, x \ge \tfrac{3}{2}$

In Exercises 19 through 24, let $y = f(x)$ and $x = f^{-1}(y)$, and verify that

$$\frac{dx}{dy} = \frac{1}{\dfrac{dy}{dx}}$$

19. (a) $f(x) = 4x - 3$ **(b)** $f(x) = \sqrt{x + 1}$

20. (a) $f(x) = 7 - 2x$ **(b)** $f(x) = 8x^3$

21. (a) $f(x) = \tfrac{1}{5}x^5$ **(b)** $f(x) = \sqrt[3]{x - 8}$

22. (a) $f(x) = \sqrt{4 - 3x}$ **(b)** $f(x) = \sqrt[5]{x}$

23. $f(x) = \dfrac{2x - 3}{x + 2}$ **24.** $f(x) = \dfrac{3x + 4}{2x + 6}$

In Exercises 25 through 40, find $(f^{-1})'(d)$.

25. (a) $f(x) = \sqrt{3x + 1}; d = 1$
   (b) $f(x) = x^2 - 16, x \ge 0; d = 9$

26. (a) $f(x) = x^5 + 2; d = 1$
   (b) $f(x) = \sqrt{4 - x}; d = 3$

27. (a) $f(x) = x^3 + 5; d = -3$
   (b) $f(x) = 3x^5 + 2x^3; d = 5$

28. (a) $f(x) = 4x^3 + 2x; d = 6$
   (b) $f(x) = \sin x, -\frac{1}{2}\pi \leq x \leq \frac{1}{2}\pi; d = \frac{1}{2}$

29. (a) $f(x) = \frac{1}{2}\cos^2 x, 0 \leq x \leq \frac{1}{2}\pi; d = \frac{1}{4}$
   (b) $f(x) = 2 \cot x, 0 < x < \pi; d = 2$

30. (a) $f(x) = \tan 2x, -\frac{1}{4}\pi < x < \frac{1}{4}\pi; d = 1$
   (b) $f(x) = \sec \frac{1}{2} x, 0 \leq x < \pi; d = 2$

31. (a) $f(x) = \frac{1}{2} \csc x, 0 < x \leq \frac{1}{2}\pi; d = 1$
   (b) $f(x) = 2x^2 + 8x + 7, x \leq -2; d = 1$

32. (a) $f(x) = x^2 - 6x + 7, x \leq 3; d = 0$
   (b) $f(x) = 2x^3 + x + 20; d = 2$

33. $f(x) = x^3 - \dfrac{2}{x} - 3, x > 0; d = 2$

34. $f(x) = x^3 - \dfrac{2}{x} - 3, x < 0; d = -2$

35. $f(x) = x^4 + x^2 - 4, x \geq 0; d = 1$

36. $f(x) = x^4 + x^2 - 4, x \leq 0; d = -0.5$

37. $f(x) = x + \sqrt{\sin x}, 0 \leq x \leq \pi; d = 3$

38. $f(x) = \cos^2 x + 2x, 0 \leq x \leq \frac{1}{2}\pi; d = 2$

39. $f(x) = \displaystyle\int_{-3}^{x} \sqrt{t + 3}\, dt, x > -3; d = 18$

40. $f(x) = \displaystyle\int_{x}^{2} t\, dt, x < 0; d = -6$

In Exercises 41 through 46, (a) prove that the function f has an inverse, (b) find $f^{-1}(x)$, and (c) verify the equations of Theorem 5.1.4 for f and f^{-1}.

41. $f(x) = 4x - 3$ **42.** $f(x) = 5x + 2$

43. $f(x) = x^3 + 2$ **44.** $f(x) = (x + 2)^3$

45. $f(x) = \dfrac{3x + 1}{2x + 4}$ **46.** $f(x) = \dfrac{x - 3}{3x - 6}$

47. If x degrees is the Celsius temperature, then the number of degrees in the Fahrenheit temperature can be expressed as a function of x. If f is this function, then $f(x)$ degrees is the Fahrenheit temperature and $f(x) = 32 + \frac{9}{5}x$. Determine the inverse function f^{-1} that expresses the number of degrees in the Celsius temperature as a function of the number of degrees in the Fahrenheit temperature.

48. If $f(t)$ dollars is the amount in t years of an investment of $1000 at 12 percent simple interest, then

$$f(t) = 1000(1 + 0.12t)$$

Determine the inverse function f^{-1} that expresses the

number of years that $1000 has been invested at 12 percent simple interest as a function of the amount of the investment.

49. As mentioned in Exercise 51 of Exercises 1.7, according to Einstein's Special Theory of Relativity, if $m(v)$ is the measure of the mass of a particle moving with a velocity of measure v, then

$$m(v) = \frac{m_0}{\sqrt{1 - \left(\dfrac{v}{c}\right)^2}}$$

where m_0 is the constant measure of the particle's rest mass relative to some reference frame and c is the constant measure of the speed of light. Find the inverse function of m that expresses the measure of the velocity of the particle as a function of the measure of its mass.

50. As mentioned in Exercise 39 of Exercises 2.8, Dulong's law states that if $P(T)$ atmospheres is the absolute pressure of saturated steam at a temperature of T degrees Celsius, then

$$P(T) = \left(\frac{40 + T}{140}\right)^5 \qquad T > 80$$

(a) Find the inverse function of P that expresses the number of degrees Celsius in the temperature as a function of the number of atmospheres in the absolute pressure, and indicate the domain of the inverse function. **(b)** Plot in the same window the graphs of P and the inverse function found in part (a).

51. Given $f(x) = x^3 + 3x - 1$. **(a)** Prove that f has an inverse f^{-1}. **(b)** Find the slope of the tangent line to the graph of f at the point $(1, 3)$. **(c)** Find the slope of the tangent line to the graph of f^{-1} at the point $(3, 1)$. Support your answers in parts (a)–(c) by doing the following: **(d)** Plot the graphs of f and f^{-1} on the same screen. **(e)** Plot the graphs of f and its tangent line at $(1, 3)$ on the same screen. **(f)** Plot the graphs of f^{-1} and its tangent line at $(3, 1)$ on the same screen.

52. Given $f(x) = 6 - x - x^3$. **(a)** Prove that f has an inverse f^{-1}. **(b)** Find the slope of the tangent line to the graph of f at the point $(2, -4)$. **(c)** Find the slope of the tangent line to the graph of f^{-1} at the point $(-4, 2)$. Support your answers in parts (a)–(c) by doing the following: **(d)** Plot the graphs of f and f^{-1} on the same screen. **(e)** Plot the graphs of f and its tangent line at $(2, -4)$ on the same screen. **(f)** Plot the graphs of f^{-1} and its tangent line at $(-4, 2)$ on the same screen.

In Exercises 53 and 54, show that function f is its own inverse.

53. $f(x) = \sqrt{16 - x^2}, 0 \le x \le 4$

54. $f(x) = \dfrac{x + 6}{x - 1}$

55. Find the value of k so that the one-to-one function f defined by

$$f(x) = \frac{x + 5}{x + k}$$

will be its own inverse.

In Exercises 56 and 57, show that the function is its own inverse for any constant k.

56. $f(x) = \dfrac{x + k}{x - 1}$

57. $f(x) = \dfrac{kx + 1}{x - k}$

58. Show that the function defined by

$$f(x) = \frac{x + h}{kx - 1}$$

is its own inverse for any values of constants h and k.

In Exercises 59 and 60, (a) show that function f is not one-to-one and hence does not have an inverse; (b) restrict the domain and obtain two one-to-one functions f_1 and f_2 each having the same range as f; (c) find $f_1^{-1}(x)$ and $f_2^{-1}(x)$ and state their domains; (d) plot the graphs of f_1 and f_1^{-1} on the same screen; (e) plot the graphs of f_2 and f_2^{-1} on the same screen.

59. $f(x) = x^2 + 4$

60. $f(x) = x^2 - 9$

61. Given

$$f(x) = \begin{cases} x & \text{if } x < 1 \\ x^2 & \text{if } 1 \le x \le 9 \\ 27\sqrt{x} & \text{if } 9 < x \end{cases}$$

Prove that f has an inverse function and find $f^{-1}(x)$.

62. Given $f(x) = \int_1^x \sqrt{16 - t^4}\, dt, -2 \le x \le 2$. Prove that f has an inverse f^{-1}, and compute $(f^{-1})'(0)$.

63. Given $f(x) = \int_2^x \sqrt{9 + t^4}\, dt$. Prove that f has an inverse f^{-1}, and compute $(f^{-1})'(0)$.

64. Given $f(x) = \displaystyle\int_1^{2x} \frac{dt}{\sqrt{1 + t^4}}$. Prove that f has an inverse and compute $(f^{-1})'(0)$.

65. Given

$$f(x) = \int_{\pi^3}^{x^3} \cos^2 \sqrt[3]{t}\, dt$$

Prove that f has an inverse f^{-1} and compute $(f^{-1})'(0)$.

66. Show that the formula of Theorem 5.1.7 can be written as

$$(f^{-1})'(x) = \frac{1}{f'(f^{-1}(x))}$$

67. Use the formula of Exercise 66 to show that

$$(f^{-1})''(x) = -\frac{f''(f^{-1}(x))}{[f'(f^{-1}(x))]^3}$$

68. Suppose the function f is defined by the equation $y = f(x)$ and you can determine that f has an inverse f^{-1}. However, you cannot compute $f^{-1}(x)$. How can you sketch by hand the graph of f^{-1}? How can you plot on your graphics calculator the graph of f^{-1} without plotting the graph of f?

5.2 THE NATURAL LOGARITHMIC FUNCTION

The definition of the logarithmic function that you encountered in algebra was based on exponents, and the properties of logarithms were then proved from corresponding properties of exponents. Let us briefly review some of these properties and how you learned them in your algebra course.

One property of exponents is

$$a^x \cdot a^y = a^{x+y} \tag{1}$$

If the exponents x and y are positive integers and if a is any real number, (1) follows from the definition of a positive integer exponent and mathematical induction. If the exponents are allowed to be any integers, either positive, negative, or zero, and $a \neq 0$, then (1) will hold if a zero exponent and a negative integer exponent are defined by

$$a^0 = 1 \quad \text{and} \quad a^{-n} = \frac{1}{a^n} \qquad n > 0$$

If the exponents are rational numbers and $a \geq 0$, then (1) holds when $a^{m/n}$ is defined by

$$a^{m/n} = (\sqrt[n]{a})^m$$

It is not quite so simple to define a^x when x is an irrational number. For example, what is meant by $2^{\sqrt{3}}$? In your algebra course, however, you assumed that such a number exists because the definition of the logarithmic function you were given then was based on the assumption that a^x exists if a is any positive number and x is any real number. That definition stated that the equation

$$a^x = N$$

where a is any positive number except 1 and N is any positive number, can be solved for x, and x is uniquely determined by

$$x = \log_a N$$

From this definition and properties of exponents, the following properties of logarithms were proved for M and N any positive numbers:

$$\log_a 1 = 0 \tag{2}$$
$$\log_a MN = \log_a M + \log_a N \tag{3}$$
$$\log_a \frac{M}{N} = \log_a M - \log_a N \tag{4}$$
$$\log_a M^n = n \log_a M \tag{5}$$
$$\log_a a = 1 \tag{6}$$

In this chapter we will be able to fill in the gap left over from algebra; that is, we will define a^x where x is irrational. We begin the process in this section by defining the logarithmic function by using calculus and then proving the properties of logarithms by means of this definition.

Recall the formula

$$\int x^n \, dx = \frac{x^{n+1}}{n+1} + C \qquad n \neq -1$$

This formula does not hold when $n = -1$.

To evaluate $\int x^n \, dx$ for $n = -1$, that is $\int \frac{1}{x} \, dx$, we need a function whose derivative is $\frac{1}{x}$. The first fundamental theorem of the calculus (4.7.1) gives us one; it is

$$\int_a^x \frac{1}{t} \, dt$$

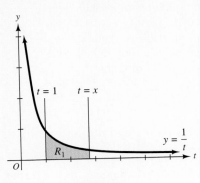

FIGURE 1

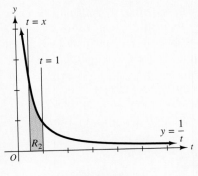

FIGURE 2

where a can be any real number having the same sign as x. To interpret such a function let R_1 be the region bounded by the curve $y = 1/t$, by the t axis, on the left by the line $t = 1$, and on the right by the line $t = x$, where $x > 1$. This region R_1 is shown in Figure 1. The measure of the area of R_1 is a function of x; call it $A(x)$ and define it as a definite integral by

$$A(x) = \int_1^x \frac{1}{t}\, dt$$

Now consider this integral if $0 < x < 1$. From Definition 4.5.5,

$$\int_1^x \frac{1}{t}\, dt = -\int_x^1 \frac{1}{t}\, dt$$

Then the integral $\int_x^1 (1/t)\, dt$ represents the measure of the area of the region R_2 bounded by the curve $y = 1/t$, by the t axis, on the left by the line $t = x$, and on the right by the line $t = 1$. So the integral $\int_1^x (1/t)\, dt$ is then the negative of the measure of the area of the region R_2 shown in Figure 2.

If $x = 1$, the integral $\int_1^x (1/t)\, dt$ becomes $\int_1^1 (1/t)\, dt$, which equals 0 by Definition 4.5.6. In this case the left and right boundaries of the region are the same and the measure of the area is 0.

Thus the integral $\int_1^x (1/t)\, dt$ for $x > 0$ can be interpreted in terms of the measure of the area of a region. Its value depends on x and is used to define the *natural logarithmic function*, denoted by ln.

5.2.1 Definition of the Natural Logarithmic Function

The **natural logarithmic function** is the function defined by

$$\ln x = \int_1^x \frac{1}{t}\, dt \qquad x > 0$$

The domain of the natural logarithmic function is the set of all positive numbers. We read ln x as "the natural logarithm of x."

The natural logarithmic function is differentiable because by applying the first fundamental theorem of the calculus,

$$D_x(\ln x) = D_x\left(\int_1^x \frac{1}{t}\, dt\right)$$

$$= \frac{1}{x}$$

From this result and the chain rule we have the following theorem.

5.2.2 Theorem

If u is a differentiable function of x and $u(x) > 0$, then

$$D_x(\ln u) = \frac{1}{u} \cdot D_x u$$

▶ **EXAMPLE 1**   Find $f'(x)$ if
$$f(x) = \ln(3x^2 - 6x + 8)$$

Solution   From Theorem 5.2.2,

$$f'(x) = \frac{1}{3x^2 - 6x + 8}(6x - 6)$$

$$= \frac{6x - 6}{3x^2 - 6x + 8} \qquad ◀$$

We now show that the natural logarithmic function obeys the properties of logarithms you learned in algebra.

5.2.3 Theorem

$$\ln 1 = 0$$

Proof   If $x = 1$ in Definition 5.2.1,

$$\ln 1 = \int_1^1 \frac{1}{t}\, dt$$

The right side of the above is zero by Definition 4.5.6. Thus

$$\ln 1 = 0 \qquad ∎$$

Theorem 5.2.3 corresponds to the property of logarithms given by (2). The next three theorems correspond to the logarithm properties given by (3), (4), and (5). We postpone the discussion of property (6) because at this time we do not have a base for natural logarithms. Before the statement of each of the three theorems we give an illustration demonstrating the corresponding theorem by computing the natural logarithms of specific numbers from the NINT capability of our graphics calculator.

▷ **ILLUSTRATION 1**   From Definition 5.2.1

$$\ln 2 = \int_1^2 \frac{1}{t}\, dt \qquad \text{NINT}(1/t, 1, 2) = 0.693147$$

$$\ln 3 = \int_1^3 \frac{1}{t}\, dt \qquad \text{NINT}(1/t, 1, 3) = 1.098612$$

$$\ln 6 = \int_1^6 \frac{1}{t}\, dt \qquad \text{NINT}(1/t, 1, 6) = 1.791759$$

From these computations,

$$\ln 2 + \ln 3 = 0.693147 + 1.098612$$

$$= 1.791759$$

$$= \ln 6 \qquad ◀$$

5.2.4 Theorem

If a and b are any positive numbers, then

$$\ln(ab) = \ln a + \ln b$$

Proof   Consider the function f defined by

$$f(x) = \ln(ax)$$

where $x > 0$. Then

$$f'(x) = \frac{1}{ax}(a)$$

$$= \frac{1}{x}$$

The derivatives of $\ln(ax)$ and $\ln x$ are, therefore, equal. Thus from Theorem 4.1.2, a constant K exists such that

$$\ln(ax) = \ln x + K \qquad \text{for all } x > 0 \tag{7}$$

To determine K, we let $x = 1$ in this equation, and we have

$$\ln a = \ln 1 + K$$

Because $\ln 1 = 0$, we obtain $K = \ln a$. Replacing K by $\ln a$ in (7), we obtain

$$\ln(ax) = \ln x + \ln a \qquad \text{for all } x > 0$$

Now, letting $x = b$, we have

$$\ln(ab) = \ln a + \ln b$$ ∎

▷ **ILLUSTRATION 2**   From Illustration 1

$$\ln 6 - \ln 3 = 1.791759 - 1.098612$$

$$= 0.693147$$

$$= \ln 2$$ ◀

5.2.5 Theorem

If a and b are any positive numbers, then

$$\ln \frac{a}{b} = \ln a - \ln b$$

Proof   Because $a = (a/b) \cdot b$,

$$\ln a = \ln\left(\frac{a}{b} \cdot b\right)$$

Applying Theorem 5.2.4 to the right side of this equation we get

$$\ln a = \ln \frac{a}{b} + \ln b$$

$$\ln \frac{a}{b} = \ln a - \ln b$$ ∎

▷ **ILLUSTRATION 3**   From Definition 5.2.1

$$\ln 49 = \int_1^{49} \frac{1}{t} \, dt \qquad \text{NINT}(1/t, 1, 49) = 3.891820$$

$$\ln 7 = \int_1^{7} \frac{1}{t} \, dt \qquad \text{NINT}(1/t, 1, 7) = 1.945910$$

From these computations,

$$2 \ln 7 = 2(1.945910)$$
$$= 3.891820$$
$$= \ln 49$$

◀

5.2.6 Theorem

If a is any positive number and r is any rational number, then

$$\ln a^r = r \ln a$$

Proof   From Theorem 5.2.2, if r is any rational number and $x > 0$,

$$D_x(\ln x^r) = \frac{1}{x^r} \cdot rx^{r-1}$$

$$= \frac{r}{x}$$

and

$$D_x(r \ln x) = \frac{r}{x}$$

Therefore

$$D_x(\ln x^r) = D_x(r \ln x)$$

From this equation the derivatives of $\ln x^r$ and $r \ln x$ are equal; so from Theorem 4.1.2 a constant K exists such that

$$\ln x^r = r \ln x + K \qquad \text{for all } x > 0 \tag{8}$$

To determine K, we substitute 1 for x in (8) and get

$$\ln 1^r = r \ln 1 + K$$

But $\ln 1 = 0$; hence $K = 0$. Replacing K by 0 in (8) gives

$$\ln x^r = r \ln x \qquad \text{for all } x > 0$$

from which it follows that if $x = a$, where a is any positive number, then

$$\ln a^r = r \ln a$$

■

To sketch the graph of the natural logarithmic function by hand we must consider properties of this function. But first, let us plot on our graphics calculator the graph of

$$\text{NINT}(1/t, 1, x)$$

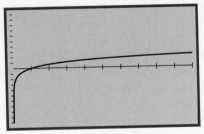

[0.0001, 10] by [−10, 10]

NINT $(1/t, 1, x)$

FIGURE 3

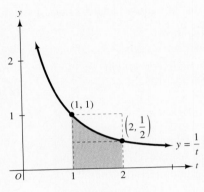

FIGURE 4

Because the domain of ln is the set of positive numbers, we choose a window containing only positive values of x. Figure 3 shows the graph plotted in the [0.0001, 10] by [−10, 10] window. From this figure, the natural logarithmic function appears to be continuous and increasing, and the graph appears to be concave downward. Let us confirm these facts analytically.

With $f(x) = \ln x$, we have

$$f(x) = \int_1^x \frac{1}{t}\, dt \qquad f'(x) = \frac{1}{x} \qquad x > 0$$

Because f is differentiable for all $x > 0$, f is continuous for all $x > 0$. Furthermore, $f'(x) > 0$ for all $x > 0$, and therefore, f is an increasing function.

$$f''(x) = -\frac{1}{x^2}$$

Because $f''(x) < 0$ when $x > 0$, the graph of f is concave downward at every point.

We now determine by geometry an inequality involving ln 2. The definite integral in the equation

$$\ln 2 = \int_1^2 \frac{1}{t}\, dt$$

can be interpreted as the measure of the area of the region appearing in Figure 4. From this figure, we observe that ln 2 is between the measures of the areas of the rectangles, each having a base of length 1 unit and altitudes of lengths $\frac{1}{2}$ units and 1 unit; that is,

$$0.5 < \ln 2 < 1$$

This inequality can be obtained analytically from Theorem 4.6.1 by proceeding as follows. Let $f(t) = 1/t$ and $g(t) = \frac{1}{2}$. Then $f(t) \geq g(t)$ for all t in $[1, 2]$. Because f and g are continuous on $[1, 2]$, they are integrable on $[1, 2]$, and from Theorem 4.6.1,

$$\int_1^2 \frac{1}{t}\, dt \geq \int_1^2 \frac{1}{2}\, dt$$
$$\ln 2 \geq \tfrac{1}{2} \tag{9}$$

Similarly, if $f(t) = 1/t$ and $h(t) = 1$, then $h(t) \geq f(t)$ for all t in $[1, 2]$. Because h and f are continuous on $[1, 2]$, they are integrable there; and again using Theorem 4.6.1 we obtain

$$\int_1^2 1\, dt \geq \int_1^2 \frac{1}{t}\, dt$$
$$1 \geq \ln 2$$

Combining this inequality with (9) we get

$$0.5 \leq \ln 2 \leq 1 \tag{10}$$

The number 0.5 is a lower bound of ln 2 and 1 is an upper bound. In a similar manner we can obtain a lower and upper bound for the natural logarithm of any positive real number. Later you will learn, by applying infinite series, how to compute the natural logarithm of any positive real number to any desired number of decimal places.

The value of ln 2 to five decimal places is given by

$$\ln 2 \approx 0.69315$$

Of course, any calculator with an ☐ ln ☐ key may be used to obtain values of the natural logarithmic function. We can, however, approximate the value of the natural logarithm of any power of 2 by using the value of ln 2 and applying Theorem 5.2.6. In particular

$$
\begin{array}{llll}
\ln 4 = \ln 2^2 & \ln 8 = \ln 2^3 & \ln \tfrac{1}{2} = \ln 2^{-1} & \ln \tfrac{1}{4} = \ln 2^{-2} \\
\quad = 2 \ln 2 & \quad = 3 \ln 2 & \quad = -1 \cdot \ln 2 & \quad = -2 \ln 2 \\
\quad \approx 1.3863 & \quad \approx 2.0795 & \quad \approx -0.69315 & \quad \approx -1.3863
\end{array}
$$

Let us now determine the behavior of the natural logarithmic function for large values of x by considering $\lim\limits_{x \to +\infty} \ln x$.

Because the natural logarithmic function is increasing, if we take p as any positive rational number, we have

$$\text{if} \quad x > 2^p \quad \text{then} \quad \ln x > \ln 2^p \tag{11}$$

From Theorem 5.2.6

$$\ln 2^p = p \ln 2$$

Substituting from this equation into (11) we get

$$\text{if} \quad x > 2^p \quad \text{then} \quad \ln x > p \ln 2$$

Because $\ln 2 \geq \tfrac{1}{2}$, we have from the above

$$\text{if} \quad x > 2^p \quad \text{then} \quad \ln x > \tfrac{1}{2}p$$

Letting $p = 2n$, where $n > 0$, we have

$$\text{if} \quad x > 2^{2n} \quad \text{then} \quad \ln x > n$$

It follows from this statement, by taking $N = 2^{2n}$, that for any $n > 0$

$$\text{if} \quad x > N \quad \text{then} \quad \ln x > n$$

So we may conclude that

$$\lim_{x \to +\infty} \ln x = +\infty \tag{12}$$

To determine the behavior of the natural logarithmic function for positive values of x near zero we investigate $\lim\limits_{x \to 0^+} \ln x$. Because $\ln x = \ln(x^{-1})^{-1}$,

$$\ln x = -\ln \frac{1}{x}$$

The expression "$x \to 0^+$" is equivalent to "$\dfrac{1}{x} \to +\infty$"; so from this equation we write

$$\lim_{x \to 0^+} \ln x = -\lim_{1/x \to +\infty} \ln \frac{1}{x} \tag{13}$$

From (12) we have

$$\lim_{1/x \to +\infty} \ln \frac{1}{x} = +\infty$$

Therefore, from this result and (13) we get

$$\lim_{x \to 0^+} \ln x = -\infty \qquad (14)$$

From (14), (12), and the intermediate-value theorem (1.9.8), the range of the natural logarithmic function is the set of all real numbers. From (14) we conclude that the graph of the natural logarithmic function is asymptotic to the negative part of the y axis through the fourth quadrant.

In summary, the natural logarithmic function satisfies the following properties:

(i) The domain is the set of all positive numbers.
(ii) The range is the set of all real numbers.
(iii) The function is increasing on its entire domain.
(iv) The function is continuous at all numbers in its domain.
(v) The graph of the function is concave downward at all points.
(vi) The graph of the function is asymptotic to the negative part of the y axis through the fourth quadrant.

From these properties and by plotting a few points with a segment of the tangent line at the points, we can sketch the graph of the natural logarithmic function by hand, as shown in Figure 5, where we have plotted the points having abscissas of $\frac{1}{4}, \frac{1}{2}, 1, 2,$ and 4. The slope of the tangent line is found from the formula $D_x(\ln x) = \dfrac{1}{x}$.

We now give more examples of computing derivatives of functions involving the natural logarithm.

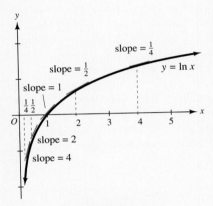

FIGURE 5

▶ **EXAMPLE 2**   Find $\dfrac{dy}{dx}$ if

$$y = \ln[(4x^2 + 3)(2x - 1)]$$

Solution   Applying Theorem 5.2.2, we get

$$\frac{dy}{dx} = \frac{1}{(4x^2 + 3)(2x - 1)} \cdot [8x(2x - 1) + 2(4x^2 + 3)]$$

$$= \frac{24x^2 - 8x + 6}{(4x^2 + 3)(2x - 1)} \qquad (15)$$

◀

▶ **EXAMPLE 3**   Find $\dfrac{dy}{dx}$ if

$$y = \ln\left(\frac{x}{x + 1}\right)$$

Solution   From Theorem 5.2.2,

$$\frac{dy}{dx} = \frac{1}{\dfrac{x}{x+1}} \cdot \frac{(x+1) - x}{(x+1)^2}$$

$$= \frac{x+1}{x} \cdot \frac{1}{(x+1)^2}$$

$$= \frac{1}{x(x+1)} \qquad \blacktriangleleft$$

Observe that when applying theorem 5.2.2, $u(x)$ must be positive; that is, a number in the domain of the derivative must be in the domain of the given function, ln u.

▷   **ILLUSTRATION 4**   In Example 1 the domain of the given function is the set of all real numbers, because $3x^2 - 6x + 8 > 0$ for all x. This can be seen from the fact that the parabola having the equation $y = 3x^2 - 6x + 8$ has its vertex at $(1,5)$ and opens upward. Hence $(6x - 6)/(3x^2 - 6x + 8)$ is the derivative for all values of x.

In Example 2, because $(4x^2 + 3)(2x - 1) > 0$ only when $x > \frac{1}{2}$, the domain of the given function is the interval $(\frac{1}{2}, +\infty)$. Therefore it is understood that fraction (15) is the derivative only if $x > \frac{1}{2}$.

Because $x/(x + 1) > 0$ when either $x < -1$ or $x > 0$, the domain of the function in Example 3 is $(-\infty, -1) \cup (0, +\infty)$; so $1/[x(x + 1)]$ is the derivative if either $x < -1$ or $x > 0$.   ◀

▷   **ILLUSTRATION 5**   In Example 2, if Theorem 5.2.4 is applied before finding the derivative, we have

$$y = \ln(4x^2 + 3) + \ln(2x - 1) \qquad \textbf{(16)}$$

The domain of the function defined by this equation is the interval $(\frac{1}{2}, +\infty)$, which is the same as the domain of the given function. From (16),

$$\frac{dy}{dx} = \frac{8x}{4x^2 + 3} + \frac{2}{2x - 1}$$

and combining the fractions gives

$$\frac{dy}{dx} = \frac{8x(2x - 1) + 2(4x^2 + 3)}{(4x^2 + 3)(2x - 1)}$$

which is equivalent to the first line of the solution of Example 2.   ◀

▷   **ILLUSTRATION 6**   If we apply Theorem 5.2.5 before finding the derivative in Example 3, we have

$$y = \ln x - \ln(x + 1) \qquad \textbf{(17)}$$

Because ln x is defined only when $x > 0$, and $\ln(x + 1)$ is defined only when $x > -1$, the domain of the function defined by (17) is the interval

$(0, +\infty)$. But the domain of the function given in Example 3 consists of the two intervals $(-\infty, -1)$ and $(0, +\infty)$. Computing the derivative from (17) we have

$$\frac{dy}{dx} = \frac{1}{x} - \frac{1}{x+1}$$

$$= \frac{1}{x(x+1)}$$

but remember here that x must be greater than 0, whereas in the solution of Example 3 values of x less than -1 are also included.   ◄

Illustration 6 shows the care that must be taken when applying Theorems 5.2.4, 5.2.5, and 5.2.6 to functions involving the natural logarithm.

► **EXAMPLE 4**   Find $f'(x)$ if

$$f(x) = \ln(2x - 1)^3$$

Solution   From Theorem 5.2.6,

$$f(x) = 3 \ln(2x - 1)$$

Observe that $\ln(2x - 1)^3$ and $3 \ln(2x - 1)$ both have the same domain: $x > 0.5$. Applying Theorem 5.2.2 gives

$$f'(x) = 3 \cdot \frac{1}{2x - 1} \cdot 2$$

$$= \frac{6}{2x - 1}$$ ◄

EXERCISES 5.2

In Exercises 1 through 4, demonstrate the given property of natural logarithms by applying Definition 5.2.1 and the NINT capability of your graphics calculator to compute the indicated natural logarithms.

1. $\ln 68 = \ln 4 + \ln 17$ **2.** $\ln 1000 = 3 \ln 10$

3. $\ln 13 = \ln 117 - \ln 9$ **4.** $\ln 81 = 2 \ln 9$

In Exercises 5 through 30, differentiate the function and simplify the result.

5. $f(x) = \ln(4 + 5x)$ **6.** $g(x) = \ln(1 + 4x^2)$

7. $h(x) = \ln\sqrt{4 + 5x}$ **8.** $f(x) = \ln(8 - 2x)$

9. $f(t) = \ln(3t + 1)^2$ **10.** $h(x) = \ln(8 - 2x)^5$

11. $g(t) = \ln^2(3t + 1)$ **12.** $G(x) = \ln\sqrt{1 + 4x^2}$

13. $f(x) = \ln\sqrt[3]{4 - x^2}$ **14.** $g(y) = \ln(\ln y)$

15. $F(y) = \ln(\sin 5y)$ **16.** $f(x) = x \ln x$

17. $f(x) = \cos(\ln x)$ **18.** $g(x) = \ln \cos \sqrt{x}$

19. $G(x) = \ln(\sec 2x + \tan 2x)$

20. $h(y) = \csc(\ln y)$ **21.** $f(x) = \ln \sqrt{\tan x}$

22. $f(t) = \ln \sqrt[4]{\dfrac{t^2 - 1}{t^2 + 1}}$ **23.** $f(w) = \ln \sqrt{\dfrac{3w + 1}{2w - 5}}$

24. $f(x) = \ln[(5x - 3)^4(2x^2 + 7)^3]$

25. $h(x) = \dfrac{x}{\ln x}$ **26.** $g(x) = \ln(\cos 2x + \sin 2x)$

27. $g(x) = \ln \sqrt[3]{\dfrac{x + 1}{x^2 + 1}}$ **28.** $f(x) = \sqrt[3]{\ln x^3}$

29. $F(x) = \sqrt{x + 1} - \ln(1 + \sqrt{x + 1})$

30. $G(x) = x \ln(x + \sqrt{1 + x^2}) - \sqrt{1 + x^2}$

In Exercises 31 through 36, find $\dfrac{dy}{dx}$ by implicit differentiation.

31. $\ln xy + x + y = 2$ **32.** $\ln \dfrac{y}{x} + xy = 1$

33. $x = \ln(x + y + 1)$

34. $\ln(x + y) - \ln(x - y) = 4$

35. $x + \ln x^2 y + 3y^2 = 2x^2 - 1$

36. $x \ln y + y \ln x = xy$

37. Sketch the graph of $y = \ln x$ by plotting the points having the abscissas $\frac{1}{9}, \frac{1}{3}, 1, 3,$ and 9, and use $\ln 3 \approx 1.1$. At each of the five points find the slope of the tangent line and draw a segment of the tangent line.

In Exercises 38 through 45, sketch the graph of the equation.

38. $x = \ln y$ **39.** $y = \ln(-x)$ **40.** $y = \ln(x + 1)$

41. $y = \ln|x|$ **42.** $y = \ln \dfrac{1}{x - 1}$ **43.** $y = x - \ln x$

44. $y = x + 2 \ln x$ **45.** $y = \ln \sin x$

46. Do Exercise 56 in Exercises 3.10 by taking the natural logarithm of both sides of the given equation before computing the differential.

47. Do Exercise 55 in Exercises 3.10 by taking the natural logarithm of both sides of the equation of Boyle's law before computing the differential.

48. The length of two coaxial cylinders, shown in the accompanying figure, is L centimeters and the radii of the inner and outer cylinders are a and b centimeters, respectively. The capacitance between the cylinders is C farads where

$$C = \frac{2\epsilon_0 L}{\ln \dfrac{b}{a}}$$

where ϵ_0 is an electrical constant. What is $\lim\limits_{a \to b^-} C$?

49. Find an equation of the tangent line to the curve $y = \ln x$ at the point whose abscissa is 2.

50. Find an equation of the normal line to the curve $y = \ln x$ that is parallel to the line $x + 2y - 1 = 0$.

51. Find an equation of the normal line to the graph of $y = x \ln x$ that is perpendicular to the line having the equation $x - y + 7 = 0$.

52. A particle is moving on a line according to the equation of motion $s = (t + 1)^2 \ln(t + 1)$, where s feet is the directed distance of the particle from the starting point at t seconds. Find the velocity and acceleration when $t = 3$.

53. In a television cable, the measure of the speed of the signal is proportional to $x^2 \ln(1/x)$, where x is the ratio of the measure of the radius of the core of the cable to the measure of the thickness of the cable's winding. Find the value of $\ln x$ for which the speed of the signal is greatest.

54. A manufacturer of electric generators began operations on January 1, 1986. During the first year there were no sales because the company concentrated on product development and research. After the first year the sales increased steadily according to the equation $y = x \ln x$, where x is the number of years during which the company has been operating and y is the number of millions of dollars in the sales volume. **(a)** Sketch the graph of the equation. Determine the rate at which the sales were increasing on **(b)** January 1, 1991, and **(c)** January 1, 1996.

55. A particular company has determined that when its weekly advertising expense is x dollars, then if S dollars is its total weekly income from sales, $S = 4000 \ln x$. **(a)** Determine the rate of change of sales income with respect to advertising expense when \$800 is the weekly advertising budget. **(b)** If the weekly advertising budget is increased to \$950, what is the approximate increase in the total weekly income from sales?

56. (a) Plot in the same window the graphs of

$$f(x) = 1 - \frac{1}{x} \qquad g(x) = \ln x \qquad h(x) = x - 1$$

and observe that $f(x) < g(x) < h(x)$.
(b) Confirm your observation in part (a) analytically by establishing the inequality

$$1 - \frac{1}{x} < \ln x < x - 1 \qquad \text{for all } x > 0 \text{ and } x \neq 1$$

by showing that

$$x - 1 - \ln x > 0 \qquad \text{and} \qquad 1 - \ln x - \frac{1}{x} < 0$$

for all $x > 0$ and $x \neq 1$. *Hint:* Let

$$F(x) = x - 1 - \ln x \quad \text{and} \quad G(x) = 1 - \ln x - \frac{1}{x}$$

and determine the signs of $F'(x)$ and $G'(x)$ on the intervals $(0, 1)$ and $(1, +\infty)$.

57. Use the result of Exercise 56 to prove that

$$\lim_{x \to 0} \frac{\ln(1 + x)}{x} = 1$$

58. Establish the limit of Exercise 57 by using the definition of the derivative to find $F'(0)$ if $F(x) = \ln(1 + x)$.

59. Prove that

$$\lim_{x \to 0^+} x \ln x = 0$$

Hint: First show that $x > \ln x$ if $x > 0$, and use this result to show that $-2\sqrt{x} < x \ln x < 0$ if $0 < x < 1$; then use the squeeze theorem.

60. A. P. Hunter, Jr. and A. H. Rubenstein in their article "Market Penetration by New Innovations: the Technological Literature" on pages 197–221 in volume 11 (1978) of "Technological Forecasting and Social Change" show that if $f(t)$ measures the market share of a substitute technology over t units of time, then

$$\ln \frac{f(t)}{1 - f(t)} + \frac{\sigma}{1 - f(t)} = c_1 + c_2 t$$

where σ, c_1, and c_2 are constants. Show that $f'(t)$, the rate of substitution, is given by

$$f'(t) = \frac{c_2 f(t)[1 - f(t)]^2}{\sigma f(t) + [1 - f(t)]}$$

61. Explain how the domain of the derivative of a function involving a natural logarithm may be affected if properties of logarithms are applied to the function before computing the derivative.

5.3 LOGARITHMIC DIFFERENTIATION AND INTEGRALS YIELDING THE NATURAL LOGARITHMIC FUNCTION

For the discussion of both topics of this section, we need a formula for $D_x(\ln|x|)$. To derive such a formula from Theorem 5.2.2, we substitute $\sqrt{x^2}$ for $|x|$ and apply the chain rule. Thus

$$D_x(\ln|x|) = D_x(\ln\sqrt{x^2})$$

$$= \frac{1}{\sqrt{x^2}} \cdot D_x(\sqrt{x^2})$$

$$= \frac{1}{\sqrt{x^2}} \cdot \frac{x}{\sqrt{x^2}}$$

$$= \frac{x}{x^2}$$

$$= \frac{1}{x}$$

From this formula and the chain rule we obtain the following theorem.

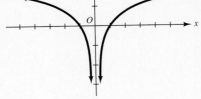

$y = \ln|x|$

FIGURE 1

5.3.1 Theorem

If u is a differentiable function of x,

$$D_x(\ln|u|) = \frac{1}{u} \cdot D_x u$$

In Exercise 41 of Exercises 5.2 you were asked to sketch the graph of $y = \ln|x|$. This graph appears in Figure 1. The slope of the tangent line at each point (x, y) of the graph is $\frac{1}{x}$.

▶ **EXAMPLE 1**   Find $f'(x)$ if

$$f(x) = \ln|x^4 + x^3|$$

Solution   From Theorem 5.3.1

$$f'(x) = \frac{1}{x^4 + x^3}(4x^3 + 3x^2)$$

$$= \frac{x^2(4x + 3)}{x^4 + x^3}$$

$$= \frac{4x + 3}{x^2 + x}$$ ◀

The following example illustrates how the properties of the natural logarithmic function, given in Theorems 5.2.4–5.2.6, can simplify the work involved in differentiating complicated expressions involving products, quotients, and powers.

▶ **EXAMPLE 2**   Find $\dfrac{dy}{dx}$ if

$$y = \frac{\sqrt[3]{x + 1}}{(x + 2)\sqrt{x + 3}}$$

Solution   From the given equation,

$$|y| = \left| \frac{\sqrt[3]{x + 1}}{(x + 2)\sqrt{x + 3}} \right|$$

$$= \frac{|\sqrt[3]{x + 1}|}{|x + 2||\sqrt{x + 3}|}$$

Taking the natural logarithm and applying the properties of logarithms we obtain

$$\ln|y| = \tfrac{1}{3}\ln|x + 1| - \ln|x + 2| - \tfrac{1}{2}\ln|x + 3|$$

Differentiating on both sides implicitly with respect to x and applying Theorem 5.3.1 we get

$$\frac{1}{y} \cdot \frac{dy}{dx} = \frac{1}{3(x + 1)} - \frac{1}{x + 2} - \frac{1}{2(x + 3)}$$

Multiplying on both sides by y we have

$$\frac{dy}{dx} = y \cdot \frac{2(x + 2)(x + 3) - 6(x + 1)(x + 3) - 3(x + 1)(x + 2)}{6(x + 1)(x + 2)(x + 3)}$$

Replacing y by its given value we obtain

$$\frac{dy}{dx} = \frac{(x + 1)^{1/3}}{(x + 2)(x + 3)^{1/2}} \cdot \frac{2x^2 + 10x + 12 - 6x^2 - 24x - 18 - 3x^2 - 9x - 6}{6(x + 1)(x + 2)(x + 3)}$$

$$= \frac{-7x^2 - 23x - 12}{6(x + 1)^{2/3}(x + 2)^2(x + 3)^{3/2}}$$ ◀

The process illustrated in Example 2 is called **logarithmic differentiation,** developed in 1697 by Johann Bernoulli (1667–1748).

From Theorem 5.3.1 we obtain the following one for indefinite integration.

5.3.2 Theorem

$$\int \frac{1}{u}\,du = \ln|u| + C$$

From Theorems 5.3.2 and 4.1.8, for n any rational number,

$$\int u^n\,du = \begin{cases} \dfrac{u^{n+1}}{n+1} + C & \text{if } n \neq -1 \\[2mm] \ln|u| + C & \text{if } n = -1 \end{cases}$$

▶ **EXAMPLE 3** Evaluate

$$\int \frac{x^2}{x^3 + 1}\,dx$$

Solution

$$\int \frac{x^2}{x^3 + 1}\,dx = \frac{1}{3}\int \frac{3x^2}{x^3 + 1}\,dx$$
$$= \tfrac{1}{3}\ln|x^3 + 1| + C$$ ◀

▶ **EXAMPLE 4** Find the exact value of

$$\int_0^2 \frac{x^2 + 2}{x + 1}\,dx$$

and support the answer by the NINT capability of a graphics calculator.

Solution Because $(x^2 + 2)/(x + 1)$ is an improper fraction, we divide the numerator by the denominator and obtain

$$\frac{x^2 + 2}{x + 1} = x - 1 + \frac{3}{x + 1}$$

Therefore,

$$\int_0^2 \frac{x^2 + 2}{x + 1}\,dx = \int_0^2 \left(x - 1 + \frac{3}{x + 1} \right)dx$$
$$= \left. \tfrac{1}{2}x^2 - x + 3\ln|x + 1| \right]_0^2$$
$$= 2 - 2 + 3\ln 3 - 3\ln 1$$
$$= 3\ln 3 - 3\cdot 0$$
$$= 3\ln 3$$

Because $3\ln 3 = \ln 3^3$, the answer can be written as $\ln 27$.

On our graphics calculator, we obtain

$$\text{NINT } ((x^2 + 2)/(x + 1), 0, 2) = 3.295836866$$

which agrees with the value of ln 27.   ◀

▶ **EXAMPLE 5**   Evaluate

$$\int \frac{\ln x}{x} \, dx$$

Solution   Let

$$u = \ln x \qquad du = \frac{1}{x} \, dx$$

Therefore

$$\int \frac{\ln x}{x} \, dx = \int u \, du$$

$$= \frac{u^2}{2} + C$$

$$= \tfrac{1}{2} (\ln x)^2 + C$$ ◀

We have delayed obtaining the formulas for the indefinite integrals of the tangent, cotangent, secant, and cosecant functions until now because they involve the natural logarithmic function.

A formula for the indefinite integral of the tangent function is derived as follows: Because

$$\int \tan u \, du = \int \frac{\sin u}{\cos u} \, du$$

we let

$$v = \cos u \qquad dv = -\sin u \, du$$

and obtain

$$\int \tan u \, du = -\int \frac{dv}{v}$$

$$= -\ln|v| + C$$

$$= -\ln|\cos u| + C$$

$$= \ln|(\cos u)^{-1}| + C$$

$$= \ln|\sec u| + C$$

We have proved the following theorem.

5.3.3 Theorem

$$\int \tan u \, du = \ln|\sec u| + C$$

▷ **ILLUSTRATION 1**

$$\int \tan 3x \, dx = \frac{1}{3} \int \tan 3x (3 \, dx)$$

$$= \tfrac{1}{3} \ln |\sec 3x| + C \qquad \blacktriangleleft$$

The theorem giving the indefinite integral of the cotangent function is proved in a way similar to that of Theorem 5.3.3. See Exercise 45.

5.3.4 Theorem

$$\int \cot u \, du = \ln |\sin u| + C$$

To obtain the formula for $\int \sec u \, du$ we multiply the numerator and denominator of the integrand by $\sec u + \tan u$, and we have

$$\int \sec u \, du = \int \frac{\sec u (\sec u + \tan u)}{\sec u + \tan u} \, du$$

$$= \int \frac{(\sec^2 u + \sec u \tan u)}{\sec u + \tan u} \, du$$

Let

$$v = \sec u + \tan u \qquad dv = (\sec u \tan u + \sec^2 u) \, du$$

Therefore we have

$$\int \sec u \, du = \int \frac{dv}{v}$$

$$= \ln |v| + C$$

$$= \ln |\sec u + \tan u| + C$$

We have proved the following theorem.

5.3.5 Theorem

$$\int \sec u \, du = \ln |\sec u + \tan u| + C$$

In Section 7.5 we obtain a formula for the integral of the secant function by a method that does not depend on the "trick" of multiplying the numerator and denominator by $\sec u + \tan u$ used to prove Theorem 5.3.5.

A formula for $\int \csc u \, du$ can be derived by multiplying the numerator and denominator of the integrand by $\csc u - \cot u$ and proceeding as we did for Theorem 5.3.5. Another procedure is to let

$$\int \csc u \, du = \int \sec(u - \tfrac{1}{2}\pi) \, du$$

and use Theorem 5.3.5 and trigonometric identities. You are asked to provide these derivations in Exercise 45. The formula obtained is given in the next theorem.

5.3.6 Theorem

$$\int \csc u \, du = \ln|\csc u - \cot u| + C$$

▷ **ILLUSTRATION 2**

$$\int \frac{dx}{\sin 2x} = \int \csc 2x \, dx$$

$$= \frac{1}{2} \int \csc 2x (2 \, dx)$$

$$= \tfrac{1}{2} \ln|\csc 2x - \cot 2x| + C$$ ◀

 ▶ **EXAMPLE 6**   Find the exact value of

$$\int_{\pi/8}^{\pi/6} (\csc 4x - \cot 4x) \, dx$$

and support the answer by the NINT capability of a graphics calculator.

Solution

$$\int_{\pi/8}^{\pi/6} (\csc 4x - \cot 4x) \, dx$$

$$= \frac{1}{4} \int_{\pi/8}^{\pi/6} (\csc 4x - \cot 4x)(4 \, dx)$$

$$= \frac{1}{4} \Big[\ln|\csc 4x - \cot 4x| - \ln|\sin 4x| \Big]_{\pi/8}^{\pi/6}$$

$$= \tfrac{1}{4} [(\ln|\csc \tfrac{2}{3}\pi - \cot \tfrac{2}{3}\pi| - \ln|\sin \tfrac{2}{3}\pi|)$$
$$\qquad\qquad - (\ln|\csc \tfrac{1}{2}\pi - \cot \tfrac{1}{2}\pi| - \ln|\sin \tfrac{1}{2}\pi|)]$$

$$= \frac{1}{4} \left[\left(\ln \left| \frac{2}{\sqrt{3}} - \left(-\frac{1}{\sqrt{3}} \right) \right| - \ln \left| \frac{\sqrt{3}}{2} \right| \right) - (\ln|1 - 0| - \ln|1|) \right]$$

$$= \frac{1}{4} \left[\left(\ln \frac{3}{\sqrt{3}} - \ln \frac{\sqrt{3}}{2} \right) - (0 - 0) \right]$$

$$= \frac{1}{4} \left[\ln \sqrt{3} - \ln \frac{\sqrt{3}}{2} \right]$$

$$= \frac{1}{4} \left[\ln \frac{\sqrt{3}}{\frac{\sqrt{3}}{2}} \right] \quad \text{(by Theorem 5.2.5)}$$

$$= \tfrac{1}{4} \ln 2$$

On our graphics calculator, we obtain

$$\text{NINT}(\csc 4x - \cot 4x, \pi/8, \pi/6) = 0.1732867951$$

which agrees with the value of $\frac{1}{4} \ln 2$.   ◀

EXERCISES 5.3

In Exercises 1 through 8, use Theorem 5.3.1 to find $\dfrac{dy}{dx}$.

1. $y = \ln|x^3 + 1|$ **2.** $y = \ln|x^2 - 1|$

3. $y = \ln|\cos 3x|$ **4.** $y = \ln|\sec 2x|$

5. $y = \ln|\tan 4x + \sec 4x|$

6. $y = \ln|\cot 3x - \csc 3x|$

7. $y = \ln\left|\dfrac{3x}{x^2 + 4}\right|$ **8.** $y = \sin(\ln|2x + 1|)$

In Exercises 9 through 14, find $\dfrac{dy}{dx}$ by logarithmic differentiation.

9. $y = x^2(x^2 - 1)^3(x + 1)^4$

10. $y = (5x - 4)(x^2 + 3)(3x^3 - 5)$

11. $y = \dfrac{x^2(x - 1)^2(x + 2)^3}{(x - 4)^5}$

12. $y = \dfrac{x^5(x + 2)}{x - 3}$ **13.** $y = \dfrac{x^3 + 2x}{\sqrt[5]{x^7 + 1}}$

14. $y = \dfrac{\sqrt{1 - x^2}}{(x + 1)^{2/3}}$

In Exercises 15 through 32, evaluate the indefinite integral.

15. $\displaystyle\int \dfrac{1}{3 - 2x}\,dx$ **16.** $\displaystyle\int \dfrac{x}{2 - x^2}\,dx$

17. $\displaystyle\int \dfrac{3x^2}{5x^3 - 1}\,dx$ **18.** $\displaystyle\int \dfrac{2x - 1}{x(x - 1)}\,dx$

19. $\displaystyle\int \dfrac{1}{y \ln y}\,dy$ **20.** $\displaystyle\int \dfrac{\sin 3t}{\cos 3t - 1}\,dt$

21. $\displaystyle\int (\cot 5x + \csc 5x)\,dx$ **22.** $\displaystyle\int \dfrac{\cos 3x + 3}{\sin 3x}\,dx$

23. $\displaystyle\int \dfrac{2 - 3\sin 2x}{\cos 2x}\,dx$ **24.** $\displaystyle\int (\tan 2x - \sec 2x)\,dx$

25. $\displaystyle\int \dfrac{2x^3}{x^2 - 4}\,dx$ **26.** $\displaystyle\int \dfrac{5 - 4y^2}{3 + 2y}\,dy$

27. $\displaystyle\int \dfrac{\ln^2 3x}{x}\,dx$ **28.** $\displaystyle\int \dfrac{(2 + \ln^2 x)}{x(1 - \ln x)}\,dx$

29. $\displaystyle\int \dfrac{2\ln x + 1}{x[(\ln x)^2 + \ln x]}\,dx$

30. $\displaystyle\int \dfrac{3x^5 - 2x^3 + 5x^2 - 2}{x^3 + 1}\,dx$

31. $\displaystyle\int \dfrac{\tan(\ln x)}{x}\,dx$ **32.** $\displaystyle\int \dfrac{\cot \sqrt{t}}{\sqrt{t}}\,dt$

In Exercises 33 through 44, find the exact value of the definite integral and support your answer by the NINT capability of your graphics calculator.

33. $\displaystyle\int_0^2 \dfrac{3x}{x^2 + 4}\,dx$ **34.** $\displaystyle\int_0^2 \dfrac{1}{7x + 10}\,dx$

35. $\displaystyle\int_4^5 \dfrac{x}{4 - x^2}\,dx$ **36.** $\displaystyle\int_1^5 \dfrac{4z^3 - 1}{2z - 1}\,dz$

37. $\displaystyle\int_1^3 \dfrac{2t + 3}{t + 1}\,dt$ **38.** $\displaystyle\int_3^5 \dfrac{2x}{x^2 - 5}\,dx$

39. $\displaystyle\int_0^{\pi/2} \dfrac{\cos t}{1 + 2\sin t}\,dt$ **40.** $\displaystyle\int_1^4 \dfrac{1}{\sqrt{x}(1 + \sqrt{x})}\,dx$

41. $\displaystyle\int_0^{\pi/6} (\tan 2x + \sec 2x)\,dx$

42. $\displaystyle\int_{\pi/12}^{\pi/6} (\cot 3x + \csc 3x)\,dx$

43. $\displaystyle\int_2^4 \dfrac{dx}{x \ln^2 x}$ **44.** $\displaystyle\int_2^4 \dfrac{\ln x}{x}\,dx$

45. (a) Prove Theorem 5.3.4. (b) Prove Theorem 5.3.6 by multiplying the numerator and denominator of the integrand by $\csc u - \cot u$. (c) Prove Theorem 5.3.6 by letting

$$\int \csc u\,du = \int \sec(u - \tfrac{1}{2}\pi)\,du$$

and using Theorem 5.3.5 and trigonometric identities.

46. Prove that $\int \csc u\,du = -\ln|\csc u + \cot u| + C$ in two ways: (a) Use Theorem 5.3.6; (b) multiply the numerator and denominator of the integrand by $\csc u + \cot u$.

In Exercises 47 through 55, give the exact value of the number to be found, and then obtain an approximation of this number to five decimal places on your calculator.

47. If $f(x) = 1/x$, find the average value of f on the interval $[1, 5]$.

48. If $f(x) = (x + 2)/(x - 3)$, find the average value of f on the interval $[4, 6]$.

49. Use Boyle's law for the expansion of a gas (see Exercise 8 in Exercises 2.6) to find the average pressure with respect to the volume as the volume increases from 4 ft^3 to 8 ft^3 and the pressure is 2000 lb/ft^2 when the volume is 4 ft^3.

50. Find the area of the region bounded by the curve $y = x/(2x^2 + 4)$, the x axis, the y axis, and the line $x = 4$.

51. Find the area of the region bounded by the curve $y = 2/(x - 3)$, the x axis, and the lines $x = 4$ and $x = 5$.

52. Find the volume of the solid of revolution generated when the region bounded by the curve $y = 1 - 3/x$, the x axis, and the line $x = 1$ is revolved about the x axis.

53. Find the volume of the solid of revolution generated when the region bounded by the x axis, the curve $y = 1 + 2/\sqrt{x}$, and the lines $x = 1$ and $x = 4$ is revolved about the x axis.

54. An electrical transmission line, consisting of two parallel conducting wires each of radius a units, carries current in opposite directions. If L is the measure of the flux linkage per unit of length of the transmission line and d units is the distance between the two wires, where $d > 2a$, then

$$L = \int_a^{d-a} \frac{\mu_0 I}{2\pi}\left(\frac{1}{x} + \frac{1}{d - x}\right) dx$$

where μ_0 is the constant permeability of the wires and I is the constant electric current. Show that

$$L = \frac{\mu_0 I}{\pi} \ln\left(\frac{d - a}{a}\right)$$

55. Prove that $\lim\limits_{x \to +\infty} \dfrac{\ln x}{x} = 0$ by two methods. **(a)** Let $x = \dfrac{1}{t}$ and use the result of Exercise 59 in Exercises 5.2. **(b)** First prove that $\displaystyle\int_1^x \frac{1}{\sqrt{t}}\, dt \geq \int_1^x \frac{1}{t}\, dt$ by applying Theorem 4.6.1. Then use the squeeze theorem.

56. Explain the difference between Theorem 5.2.2 and Theorem 5.3.1 and why we obtained Theorem 5.3.1 before Theorem 5.3.2.

5.4 THE NATURAL EXPONENTIAL FUNCTION

Because the natural logarithmic function is increasing on its entire domain, then by the inverse function theorem (5.1.5), it has an inverse that is also an increasing function. The inverse of ln is called the *natural exponential function,* denoted by exp, which we now formally define.

5.4.1 Definition of the Natural Exponential Function

The **natural exponential function** is the inverse of the natural logarithmic function; it is, therefore, defined by

$$\exp(x) = y \quad \text{if and only if} \quad x = \ln y$$

The notation $\exp(x)$ denotes "the value of the natural exponential function at x."

The domain of exp is the set of all real numbers and the range is the set of all positive numbers because these sets are, respectively, the range and domain of ln.

Because ln and exp are inverses of each other, we have from Theorem 5.1.4:

$$\ln(\exp(x)) = x \quad \text{and} \quad \exp(\ln x) = x \tag{1}$$

We are now ready to define a^x, where a is a positive number and x is an irrational number. To arrive at a reasonable definition, consistent with the definition of a rational exponent, we consider the case a^r, where $a > 0$ and r is rational. Because exp and ln are inverses of each other

$$a^r = \exp[\ln(a^r)] \tag{2}$$

But by Theorem 5.2.6, where r is rational,

$$\ln a^r = r \ln a \tag{3}$$

Substituting from (3) in (2), we have

$$a^r = \exp(r \ln a)$$

Because the right side of this equation has meaning not only when r is rational but also when r is any real number, we use the equation for our definition.

5.4.2 Definition of a Real Number Exponent

If a is any positive number and x is any real number,

$$a^x = \exp(x \ln a)$$

Furthermore, if $x > 0$, then $0^x = 0$.

In Equation (3) r was restricted to rational numbers, but now, because of this definition, the equation is also valid if r is any real number. We state this fact as a theorem.

5.4.3 Theorem

If a is any positive number and x is any real number,

$$\ln a^x = x \ln a$$

Proof   From Definition 5.4.2

$$a^x = \exp(x \ln a)$$

Thus from Definition 5.4.1,

$$\ln a^x = x \ln a \qquad \blacksquare$$

Even though Definition 5.4.2 tells us what a^x means when x is irrational, the definition does not give us a method of computing an irrational power of a positive number. To obtain a computational procedure we single out the value of the natural exponential function at 1, and give it a formal definition. This number is one of the most important in mathematics.

5.4.4 Definition of the Number e

The number e is the value of the natural exponential function at 1:

$$e = \exp 1$$

The letter e was chosen as the symbol for this number by the Swiss mathematician and physicist Leonhard Euler (1707–1783). Coincidentally, e is the first letter not only of the word "exponent" but also of Euler's last name.

The number e is a *transcendental* number; that is, it cannot be expressed as the root of any polynomial with integer coefficients. The number π is another example of a transcendental number. The proof that e is transcendental was first given in 1873 by Charles Hermite, and its value can be expressed to any required degree of accuracy. In Chapter 8 you will learn a method for doing this. The value of e to seven decimal places is 2.7182818. Thus

$$e \approx 2.7182818$$

The importance of the number e will become apparent as you proceed through this chapter.

5.4.5 Theorem

$$\ln e = 1$$

Proof   By Definition 5.4.4

$$e = \exp 1$$

Therefore

$$\ln e = \ln(\exp 1)$$

Because the natural logarithmic function and the natural exponential function are inverses, it follows that the right side of this equation is 1. Thus

$$\ln e = 1$$

∎

Observe that Theorem 5.4.5 corresponds to property (6) in Section 5.2. The number e is, therefore, the base of natural logarithms. We have now completed showing that the function ln satisfies properties (2)–(6) of logarithms given in Section 5.2.

5.4.6 Theorem

For all values of x,

$$\exp(x) = e^x$$

Proof   By Definition 5.4.2, with $a = e$,

$$e^x = \exp(x \ln e)$$

But by Theorem 5.4.5, $\ln e = 1$, and substituting in the above equation we obtain

$$e^x = \exp(x)$$

∎

From now on we write e^x in place of $\exp(x)$; so from Definition 5.4.1

$$e^x = y \quad \text{if and only if} \quad x = \ln y \tag{4}$$

With e^x in place of $\exp(x)$, (1) becomes

$$\ln e^x = x \quad \text{and} \quad e^{\ln x} = x$$

If we replace $\exp(x \ln a)$ by $e^{x \ln a}$ in the equation of Definition 5.4.2, we have

$$a^x = e^{x \ln a} \quad \text{for every } a > 0 \tag{5}$$

This equation can be used to compute a^x, where $a > 0$, if x is any real number. For values of powers of e use the $\boxed{e^x}$ key on your calculator. Of course, many calculators compute a^x directly. We do the computation both ways in the following example.

▶ **EXAMPLE 1**   Compute on a calculator the value of $2^{\sqrt{3}}$ to five significant digits by first applying equation (5). Support the answer by computing the value directly.

Solution   Because $a^x = e^{x \ln a}$ if $a > 0$

$$2^{\sqrt{3}} = e^{\sqrt{3} \ln 2}$$
$$= e^{(1.73205)(0.693147)}$$
$$= e^{1.20057}$$
$$= 3.3220$$

Computing $2^{\sqrt{3}}$ directly, we obtain $2^{\sqrt{3}} = 3.3220$, which supports our answer.   ◀

Because $0 = \ln 1$, we have from statement (4)

$$\boxed{e^0 = 1}$$

We now state some properties of the natural exponential function as theorems. Observe that these properties are consistent with the properties of exponents you learned in algebra.

5.4.7 Theorem

If a and b are any real numbers,

$$e^a \cdot e^b = e^{a+b}$$

Proof   Let $A = e^a$ and $B = e^b$. Then from statement (4),

$$\ln A = a \quad \text{and} \quad \ln B = b \tag{6}$$

From Theorem 5.2.4,

$$\ln AB = \ln A + \ln B$$

Substituting from (6) into this equation we obtain

$$\ln AB = a + b$$

Thus

$$e^{\ln AB} = e^{a+b}$$

Because $e^{\ln x} = x$ the left side of the above equation is AB; so

$$AB = e^{a+b}$$

Replacing A and B by their values we get

$$e^a \cdot e^b = e^{a+b} \qquad \blacksquare$$

> **5.4.8 Theorem**
>
> If a and b are any real numbers,
>
> $$e^a \div e^b = e^{a-b}$$

The proof is analogous to the proof of Theorem 5.4.7, where Theorem 5.2.4 is replaced by Theorem 5.2.5,

> **5.4.9 Theorem**
>
> If a and b are any real numbers, then
>
> $$(e^a)^b = e^{ab}$$

Proof   If in the equation $x = e^{\ln x}$ we let x be $(e^a)^b$, we have

$$(e^a)^b = e^{\ln (e^a)^b}$$

Applying Theorem 5.4.3 to the exponent in the right side of this equation we obtain

$$(e^a)^b = e^{b \ln e^a}$$

But $\ln e^a = a$, and therefore

$$(e^a)^b = e^{ab} \qquad\qquad\blacksquare$$

Because the natural exponential function is the inverse of the natural logarithmic function, from Theorem 5.1.7 it is differentiable. We obtain the theorem for the derivative of the natural exponential function by implicit differentiation. Let

$$y = e^x$$

Then from statement (4),

$$x = \ln y$$

On both sides of this equation we differentiate implicitly with respect to x to get

$$1 = \frac{1}{y} \cdot \frac{dy}{dx}$$

$$\frac{dy}{dx} = y$$

Replacing y by e^x we obtain

$$\frac{d}{dx} (e^x) = e^x$$

The next theorem follows from this equation and the chain rule.

> **5.4.10 Theorem**
>
> If u is a differentiable function of x,
>
> $$D_x(e^u) = e^u D_x u$$

Observe that the derivative of the function defined by $f(x) = ke^x$, where k is a constant, is itself. The only other function we have previously encountered that has this property is the constant function zero; actually, this is the special case of $f(x) = ke^x$ when $k = 0$. It can be proved that the most general function that is its own derivative is given by $f(x) = ke^x$. See Exercise 59.

▶ **EXAMPLE 2** Find dy/dx if

$$y = e^{1/x^2}$$

Solution From Theorem 5.4.10

$$\frac{dy}{dx} = e^{1/x^2}\left(-\frac{2}{x^3}\right)$$

$$= -\frac{2e^{1/x^2}}{x^3}$$ ◀

▶ **EXAMPLE 3** Find dy/dx if

$$y = e^{2x+\ln x}$$

Solution Because $e^{2x+\ln x} = e^{2x}e^{\ln x}$ and $e^{\ln x} = x$, then

$$y = xe^{2x}$$

Therefore

$$\frac{dy}{dx} = e^{2x} + 2xe^{2x}$$ ◀

The indefinite integration formula given in the following theorem is a consequence of Theorem 5.4.10.

5.4.11 Theorem

$$\int e^u \, du = e^u + C$$

▶ **EXAMPLE 4** Evaluate

$$\int \frac{e^{\sqrt{x}}}{\sqrt{x}} \, dx$$

Solution Let

$$u = \sqrt{x} \qquad du = \frac{1}{2\sqrt{x}} \, dx$$

Therefore

$$\int \frac{e^{\sqrt{x}}}{\sqrt{x}} \, dx = 2 \int e^u \, du$$

$$= 2e^u + C$$

$$= 2e^{\sqrt{x}} + C \qquad \blacktriangleleft$$

Because from (4) $e^x = y$ if and only if $x = \ln y$, the graph of $y = e^x$ is identical to the graph of $x = \ln y$. So we can obtain the graph of $y = e^x$, shown in Figure 1, by interchanging the x and y axes in Figure 5 of Section 5.2.

The graph of $y = e^x$ can be obtained without referring to the graph of the natural logarithmic function. Because the range of the natural exponential function is the set of all positive numbers, it follows that $e^x > 0$ for all values of x. Therefore the graph lies entirely above the x axis. Because $\dfrac{dy}{dx} = e^x > 0$ for all x, the function is increasing for all x. Because $\dfrac{d^2y}{dx^2} = e^x > 0$ for all x, the graph is concave upward at all points.

We have the following two limits:

$$\lim_{x \to +\infty} e^x = +\infty \quad \text{and} \quad \lim_{x \to -\infty} e^x = 0$$

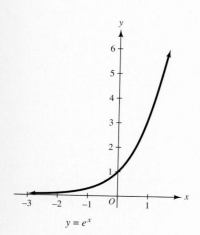

$y = e^x$

FIGURE 1

The proofs of these limits are left as exercises. See Exercises 65 and 66. To plot some specific points use a calculator for powers of e.

Functions having values of the form Ce^{kx}, where C and k are constants, occur frequently in various fields. Some of these applications occur in the exercises of this section and others are discussed in Section 5.6.

Because x^n, where $x > 0$, has been defined for any real number n, we can now prove the theorem for the derivative of the power function if the exponent is any real number.

5.4.12 Theorem

If n is any real number and the function f is defined by

$$f(x) = x^n \qquad \text{where } x > 0$$

then

$$f'(x) = nx^{n-1}$$

Proof   From Definition 5.4.2,

$$f(x) = e^{n \ln x}$$

Thus

$$f'(x) = e^{n \ln x} D_x(n \ln x)$$

$$= e^{n \ln x} \left(\frac{n}{x} \right)$$

$$= x^n \cdot \frac{n}{x}$$

$$= nx^{n-1} \qquad \blacksquare$$

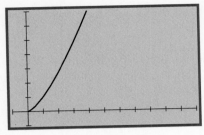

[−1, 11] by [−1, 7]

$f(x) = x^{\sqrt{2}}, x > 0$

FIGURE 2

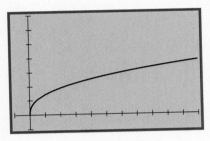

[−1, 11] by [−1, 7]

$f'(x) = \sqrt{2}\, x^{\sqrt{2}-1}$

FIGURE 3

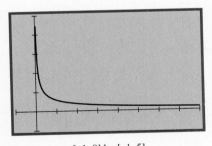

[−1, 8] by [−1, 5]

$f''(x) = \sqrt{2}\,(\sqrt{2}-1)\, x^{\sqrt{2}-2}$

FIGURE 4

▶ **EXAMPLE 5**   Let

$$f(x) = x^{\sqrt{2}} \qquad x \geq 0$$

(a) Prove analytically that f is an increasing function. **(b)** Determine analytically the concavity of the graph of f. **(c)** Plot in separate windows the graphs of f, f', and f'', and show that these graphs support the results of parts (a) and (b).

Solution

(a) From Theorem 5.4.12, if $x > 0$

$$f'(x) = \sqrt{2}\, x^{\sqrt{2}-1}$$

Because $f'(x) > 0$ for all $x > 0$, f is an increasing function.

(b) We compute $f''(x)$ by again applying Theorem 5.4.12.

$$f''(x) = \sqrt{2}(\sqrt{2} - 1)x^{\sqrt{2}-2}$$

Because $f''(x) > 0$ for all $x > 0$, the graph of f is concave upward at all points.

(c) Figures 2, 3, and 4 show the graphs of f, f', and f'' plotted in convenient windows. From Figure 3, we observe that $f'(x) > 0$ for all $x > 0$, which supports the results of part (a). Figure 4 supports the result of part (b) because $f''(x) > 0$. Figure 2 supports both parts (a) and (b). ◀

We have defined the number e as the value of the natural exponential function at 1; that is, $e = \exp 1$. To arrive at another way of defining e, consider the natural logarithmic function

$$f(x) = \ln x$$

We know that the derivative of f is given by $f'(x) = 1/x$; hence $f'(1) = 1$. However, let us apply the definition of the derivative to find $f'(1)$. We have

$$f'(1) = \lim_{\Delta x \to 0} \frac{f(1 + \Delta x) - f(1)}{\Delta x}$$

$$= \lim_{\Delta x \to 0} \frac{\ln(1 + \Delta x) - \ln 1}{\Delta x}$$

$$= \lim_{\Delta x \to 0} \frac{1}{\Delta x} \ln(1 + \Delta x)$$

Therefore

$$\lim_{\Delta x \to 0} \frac{1}{\Delta x} \ln(1 + \Delta x) = 1$$

Replacing Δx by h we have from the above equation and Theorem 5.4.3

$$\lim_{h \to 0} \ln(1 + h)^{1/h} = 1 \tag{7}$$

Now, because the natural exponential function and the natural logarithmic function are inverse functions, we have

$$\lim_{h \to 0}(1 + h)^{1/h} = \lim_{h \to 0} \exp[\ln(1 + h)^{1/h}] \tag{8}$$

Table 1

h	$F(h) = (1 + h)^{1/h}$
1	2
0.5	2.25
0.05	2.6533
0.01	2.7048
0.001	2.7169
0.0001	2.7181

Table 2

h	$F(h) = (1 + h)^{1/h}$
-0.5	4
-0.05	2.7895
-0.01	2.7320
-0.001	2.7196
-0.0001	2.7184

Because the natural exponential function is continuous and $\lim\limits_{h \to 0} \ln(1 + h)^{1/h}$ exists and equals 1, as shown in Equation (7), we can apply Theorem 1.9.1 to the right side of (8) and get

$$\lim_{h \to 0}(1 + h)^{1/h} = \exp\left[\lim_{h \to 0} \ln(1 + h)^{1/h}\right]$$
$$= \exp 1$$

Hence

$$\lim_{h \to 0} (1 + h)^{1/h} = e \tag{9}$$

Equation (9) is sometimes given as the definition of e; however, to use this as a definition it is necessary to prove that the limit exists.

Let us consider the function F defined by

$$F(h) = (1 + h)^{1/h} \tag{10}$$

and determine the function values for some values of h close to zero. These values are obtained from a calculator. When h is positive, the values appear in Table 1, and when h is negative they appear in Table 2.

The two tables lead us to suspect that $\lim\limits_{h \to 0} (1 + h)^{1/h}$ is probably a number that lies between 2.7181 and 2.7184.

In Exercise 55 you are asked to show that

$$\lim_{z \to +\infty}\left(1 + \frac{1}{z}\right)^z = e \quad \text{and} \quad \lim_{z \to -\infty}\left(1 + \frac{1}{z}\right)^z = e$$

In that exercise you are also asked to support these limits graphically.

In Exercise 56 you are asked to plot the graph of the function defined by (10) and from the graph approximate the value of e.

In Section 2.8 you learned that simple harmonic motion continues indefinitely, repeating a cycle every interval of length a period. For instance, in Example 7 of that section a weight suspended by a spring moves vertically upward and downward, and one complete oscillation occurs every interval of 6 sec. In practice, however, friction would cause the amplitude of the motion to decrease until the weight finally came to rest. This is the case of **damped harmonic motion,** which can be described by the product of a sine function and a nonconstant function called a **damping factor,** which causes the decrease in amplitude. Damped harmonic motion plays a prominent part in the design of buildings, bridges, and vehicles. For instance, shock absorbers are used to damp the oscillations when an automobile encounters a bump in the road.

An important damping factor is an exponential function whose values approach zero as the independent variable increases without bound. The following example illustrates the effect of this factor.

▶ **EXAMPLE 6** The function f defined by

$$f(t) = e^{-t/4} \sin 4t \qquad t \geq 0$$

is a mathematical model describing damped harmonic motion. Let

$$F(t) = -e^{-t/4} \qquad G(t) = e^{-t/4}$$

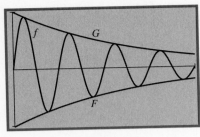

[0, 2π] by [−1, 1]

$F(t) = -e^{-t/4}, f(t) = e^{-t/4} \sin 4t,$
and $G(t) = e^{-t/4}$

FIGURE 5

and do the following: **(a)** Show that $F(t) \leq f(t) \leq G(t)$; **(b)** plot the graphs of the three functions in the $[0, 2\pi]$ by $[-1, 1]$ window; **(c)** prove that $\lim\limits_{t \to +\infty} e^{-t/4} \sin 4t = 0$.

Solution

(a) Because $|\sin 4t| \leq 1$ and $e^{-t/4} > 0$ for all t,

$$|f(t)| \leq e^{-t/4} \qquad \text{for all } t$$

Thus

$$-e^{-t/4} \leq f(t) \leq e^{-t/4} \qquad \text{for all } t \tag{11}$$

That is, $F(t) \leq f(t) \leq G(t)$.

(b) Figure 5 shows the required graphs. Observe that the graph of f is between the graphs of F and G.

(c) Because $\lim\limits_{t \to +\infty} (-e^{-t/4}) = 0$ and $\lim\limits_{t \to +\infty} e^{-t/4} = 0$, we conclude from (11) and the squeeze theorem that $\lim\limits_{t \to +\infty} (e^{-t/4} \sin 4t) = 0$. ◄

EXERCISES 5.4

In Exercises 1 through 4 compute on a calculator the value of a^x for the given values of a and x by first applying Equation (5). Support your answer by computing the value directly.

1. **(a)** $a = 2, x = \sqrt{2}$ **(b)** $a = \sqrt{2}, x = e$

2. **(a)** $a = \sqrt{2}, x = \sqrt{2}$ **(b)** $a = 5, x = \pi$

3. **(a)** $a = e, x = e$ **(b)** $a = \sqrt{3}, x = \pi$

4. **(a)** $a = \pi, x = e$ **(b)** $a = \pi, x = \pi$

In Exercises 5 through 20, find $\dfrac{dy}{dx}$, and support your answer by plotting the graphs of your answer and the numerical derivative in the same window.

5. $y = e^{5x}$ 6. $y = e^{-7x}$ 7. $y = e^{-3x^2}$

8. $y = e^{x^2-3}$ 9. $y = e^{\cos x}$ 10. $y = e^{2 \sin 3x}$

11. $y = e^x \sin e^x$ 12. $y = \dfrac{e^x}{x}$ 13. $y = \tan e^{\sqrt{x}}$

14. $y = e^{e^x}$ 15. $y = \dfrac{e^x - e^{-x}}{e^x + e^{-x}}$

16. $y = \ln \dfrac{e^{4x} - 1}{e^{4x} + 1}$

17. $y = x^5 e^{-3 \ln x}$ 18. $y = \ln(e^x + e^{-x})$

19. $y = \sec e^{2x} + e^{2 \sec x}$ 20. $y = \tan e^{3x} + e^{\tan 3x}$

In Exercises 21 through 24, find $\dfrac{dy}{dx}$ by implicit differentiation.

21. $e^x + e^y = e^{x+y}$ 22. $e^y = \ln(x^3 + 3y)$

23. $y^2 e^{2x} + xy^3 = 1$ 24. $ye^{2x} + xe^{2y} = 1$

In Exercises 25 through 32, evaluate the indefinite integral and support your answer graphically.

25. $\displaystyle\int e^{2-5x} \, dx$ 26. $\displaystyle\int e^{2x+1} \, dx$

27. $\displaystyle\int \dfrac{1 + e^{2x}}{e^x} \, dx$ 28. $\displaystyle\int e^{3x} e^{2x} \, dx$

29. $\displaystyle\int \dfrac{e^{3x}}{(1 - 2e^{3x})^2} \, dx$ 30. $\displaystyle\int x^2 e^{2x^3} \, dx$

31. $\displaystyle\int \dfrac{e^{2x}}{e^x + 3} \, dx$ 32. $\displaystyle\int \dfrac{dx}{1 + e^x}$

In Exercises 33 through 40, evaluate the definite integral. Support your answer by using the NINT capability of your graphics calculator.

33. $\displaystyle\int_0^1 e^2 \, dx$ 34. $\displaystyle\int_1^{e^2} \dfrac{dx}{x}$

35. $\displaystyle\int_e^{e^3} \dfrac{dx}{x}$ 36. $\displaystyle\int_1^e \dfrac{\ln x}{x} \, dx$

37. $\displaystyle\int_e^{e^2} \dfrac{dx}{x(\ln x)^2}$ 38. $\displaystyle\int_0^3 \dfrac{e^x + e^{-x}}{2} \, dx$

39. $\displaystyle\int_0^2 xe^{4-x^2} \, dx$ 40. $\displaystyle\int_1^2 \dfrac{e^x}{e^x + e} \, dx$

41. Plot the graphs of $y = \ln x$ and $y = e^x$ in the same window. For what values of x is **(a)** $\ln x = 0$, **(b)** $e^x = 1$, **(c)** $\ln x = 1$? **(d)** Is e^x ever equal to 0? Describe the behavior of the graph of $y = e^x$ with respect to the x axis.

42. Sketch the graphs of the following equations:
(a) $y = e^{-x}$;   **(b)** $y = e^{|x|}$.

In Exercises 43 and 44, find the exact area of the described region.

43. The region bounded by the curve $y = e^x$, the coordinate axes, and the line $x = 2$.

44. The region bounded by the curve $y = e^x$ and the line through the points $(0, 1)$ and $(1, e)$.

45. Find an equation of the tangent line to the curve $y = e^{-x}$ that is perpendicular to the line $2x - y = 5$.

46. Find an equation of the normal line to the curve $y = e^{2x}$ at the point where $x = \ln 2$.

47. A particle is moving along a line and at t seconds the velocity is v feet per second, where $v = e^3 - e^{2t}$. Find the distance traveled by the particle while $v > 0$ after $t = 0$.

48. A particle is moving along a line, where s feet is the directed distance of the particle from the origin, v feet per second is the velocity of the particle, and a feet per second squared is the acceleration of the particle at t seconds. If $a = e^t + e^{-t}$ and $v = 1$ and $s = 2$ when $t = 0$, find v and s in terms of t.

49. If p pounds per square foot is the atmospheric pressure at a height of h feet above sea level, then $p = 2116e^{-0.0000318h}$. Find the time rate of change of the atmospheric pressure outside an airplane that is 5000 ft high and rising at the rate of 160 ft/sec.

50. At a certain height the gauge on an airplane indicates that the atmospheric pressure is 1500 lb/ft². Applying the formula of Exercise 49, approximate by differentials how much higher the airplane must rise so that the pressure will be 1480 lb/ft².

51. If l feet is the length of an iron rod when t degrees is its temperature, then $l = 60e^{0.00001t}$. Use differentials to find the approximate increase in l when t increases from 0 to 10.

52. A simple electric circuit containing no condensers, a resistance of R ohms, and an inductance of L henrys has the electromotive force cut off when the current is I_0 amperes. The current dies down so that at t seconds the current is i amperes, and $i = I_0 e^{-(R/L)t}$. Show that the rate of change of the current is proportional to the current.

53. An advertising agency determined statistically that if a breakfast food manufacturer increases its budget for television commercials by x thousand dollars, there will be an increase in the total profit of $25x^2 e^{-0.2x}$ hundred dollars. What should be the advertising budget increase in order for the manufacturer to have the greatest profit? What will be the corresponding increase in the company's profit?

54. Let $f(x) = x^\pi$, $x > 0$. **(a)** Prove analytically that f is an increasing function. **(b)** Determine analytically the

concavity of the graph of f. **(c)** Plot in separate windows the graphs of f, f', and f'', and explain why these graphs support your results of parts (a) and (b).

55. (a) By letting $h = \dfrac{1}{z}$ in Equation (9) show that

$$\lim_{z \to +\infty} \left(1 + \frac{1}{z}\right)^z = e \quad \text{and} \quad \lim_{z \to -\infty} \left(1 + \frac{1}{z}\right)^z = e$$

(b) Use a calculator to compute the values of

$$\left(1 + \frac{1}{z}\right)^z \text{ when } z = 10{,}000 \text{ and } z = -10{,}000.$$

Then obtain an approximation of the number e by using these values to find the average value of $(1.0001)^{10{,}000}$ and $(0.9999)^{-10{,}000}$.

(c) Support the limits in part (a) by plotting in the same window the line $y = e$ and the graph of the function defined by

$$f(x) = \left(1 + \frac{1}{x}\right)^x$$

Observe that the line is a horizontal asymptote of the graph.

56. Plot the graph of the function defined by

$$f(x) = (1 + x)^{1/x}$$

in the $[-0.5, 0.5]$ by $[2, 3]$ window. Of course, the graph has a hole on the y axis because $f(0)$ is undefined. However,

$$\lim_{x \to 0} f(x) = e$$

Approximate the value of e to five significant digits by using this graph and the intersect or trace and zoom-in capabilities of your graphics calculator.

In Exercises 57 and 58, the function f is a mathematical model describing damped harmonic motion. In each exercise do the following: (a) Show that $F(t) \le f(t) \le G(t)$. (b) Plot the graphs of the three functions in the $[0, 2\pi]$ by $[-1, 1]$ window. (c) Prove that $\lim\limits_{t \to +\infty} f(t) = 0$.

57. $f(t) = e^{-t/2} \cos 4t$; $F(t) = -e^{-t/2}$; $G(t) = e^{-t/2}$

58. $f(t) = e^{-t/8} \sin 3t$; $F(t) = -e^{-t/8}$; $G(t) = e^{-t/8}$

59. Prove that the most general function equal to its derivative is given by $f(x) = ke^x$. *Hint:* Let $y = f(x)$, and solve the differential equation $\dfrac{dy}{dx} = y$.

60. Prove that

$$\lim_{x \to +\infty} \frac{x}{e^x} = 0$$

Hint: Use the result of Exercise 55 in Exercises 5.3.

In Exercises 61 and 62, do the following analytically: (a) find the relative extrema of f; (b) determine the values of x at which the relative extrema occur; (c) determine the intervals on which f is increasing; (d) determine the intervals on which f is decreasing; (e) determine where the graph of f is concave upward; (f) determine where the graph of f is concave downward; (g) find the slope of any inflectional tangent. Use the information in parts (a) to (f) to sketch the graph of f. In Exercise 62 use the result of Exercise 60 to sketch the graph. Support your answers on your graphics calculator.

61. $f(x) = e^{-x^2}$

62. $f(x) = xe^{-x}$

63. For the function of Example 6, $\lim\limits_{t \to +\infty} f(t) = 0$, but the t axis is not a horizontal asymptote of the graph of f. Why does the definition (3.7.4) of a horizontal asymptote not hold for this function?

64. Prove that the function of Example 5 is continuous from the right at 0 by showing that
$$\lim_{x \to 0^+} x^{\sqrt{2}} = 0$$

65. Prove that
$$\lim_{x \to +\infty} e^x = +\infty$$
by showing that for any $N > 0$ there exists an $M > 0$ such that if $x > M$, then $e^x > N$.

66. Prove that
$$\lim_{x \to -\infty} e^x = 0$$
by showing that for any $\epsilon > 0$ there exists an $N < 0$ such that if $x < N$, then $e^x < \epsilon$.

67. By beginning our treatment of exponential and logarithmic functions in Section 5.2 with the definition of the natural logarithmic function, we were able to define in this section an irrational exponent. This procedure gives us a purely mathematical application of the calculus. Describe as briefly as you can the step-by-step process that led us from the definition (5.2.1) of the natural logarithmic function to the definition (5.4.2) of an irrational exponent.

5.5 OTHER EXPONENTIAL AND LOGARITHMIC FUNCTIONS

In the previous three sections you studied the natural exponential and logarithmic functions, which have the base e. We now discuss exponential and logarithmic functions with other bases.

Recall from Definition 5.4.2, if $a > 0$,
$$a^x = e^{x \ln a} \tag{1}$$

The expression on the left side of this equation is called the *exponential function to the base a.*

> **5.5.1 Definition of the Exponential Function to the Base a**
>
> If a is any positive number and x is any real number, then the function f defined by
> $$f(x) = a^x$$
> is called the **exponential function to the base a.**

The exponential function to the base a satisfies the same properties as the natural exponential function.

▷ **ILLUSTRATION 1**   If x and y are any real numbers and a is positive, then from (1),
$$a^x a^y = e^{x \ln a} e^{y \ln a}$$
$$= e^{x \ln a + y \ln a}$$
$$= e^{(x+y)\ln a}$$
$$= a^{x+y}$$
◀

From Illustration 1 we have the property

$$a^x a^y = a^{x+y}$$

We also have the following properties:

$$a^x \div a^y = a^{x-y}$$
$$(a^x)^y = a^{xy}$$
$$(ab)^x = a^x b^x$$
$$a^0 = 1$$

The proofs of these properties are left as exercises (see Exercises 37 through 40).

To find the derivative of the exponential function to the base a we set $a^x = e^{x \ln a}$ and apply the chain rule.

$$a^x = e^{x \ln a}$$
$$D_x(a^x) = e^{x \ln a} D_x(x \ln a)$$
$$= e^{x \ln a}(\ln a)$$
$$= a^x \ln a$$

Therefore we have the following theorem.

5.5.2 Theorem

If a is any positive number and u is a differentiable function of x,

$$D_x(a^u) = a^u \ln a \, D_x u$$

▶ **EXAMPLE 1**   Find $f'(x)$ if
$$f(x) = 3^{x^2}$$

Solution   From Theorem 5.5.2

$$f'(x) = 3^{x^2}(\ln 3)(2x)$$
$$= 2(\ln 3)x \, 3^{x^2}$$

◀

We now discuss the graph of
$$f(x) = a^x \qquad a > 0$$

We compute the first and second derivatives of f.

$$f'(x) = a^x \ln a \qquad f''(x) = a^x(\ln a)^2$$

Remember that $\ln a > 0$ if $a > 1$ and $\ln a < 0$ if $0 < a < 1$. Thus when $a > 1$, $f'(x) > 0$ and f is an increasing function, and when $0 < a < 1$, $f'(x) < 0$ and f is a decreasing function. Because $f''(x) > 0$ for all x and all $a > 0$, the graph of f is concave upward everywhere. With this information we sketch the graph in Figure 1 when $a > 1$ and in Figure 2 when $0 < a < 1$.

The next theorem, giving the indefinite integration formula for the exponential function to the base a, follows from Theorem 5.5.2.

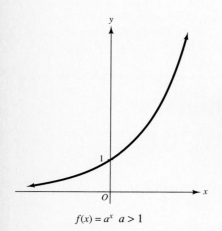

$f(x) = a^x \quad a > 1$

FIGURE 1

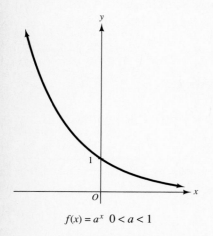

$f(x) = a^x \quad 0 < a < 1$

FIGURE 2

5.5.3 Theorem

If a is any positive number except 1,

$$\int a^u \, du = \frac{a^u}{\ln a} + C$$

▶ **EXAMPLE 2**   Evaluate

$$\int \sqrt{10^{3x}} \, dx$$

Solution   Because $\sqrt{10^{3x}} = 10^{3x/2}$, we apply Theorem 5.5.3 with $u = \frac{3}{2}x$. We have, then,

$$\int \sqrt{10^{3x}} \, dx = \int 10^{3x/2} \, dx$$

$$= \frac{2}{3} \int 10^{3x/2} \left(\frac{3}{2} \, dx \right)$$

$$= \frac{2}{3} \cdot \frac{10^{3x/2}}{\ln 10} + C$$

$$= \frac{2\sqrt{10^{3x}}}{3 \ln 10} + C$$ ◀

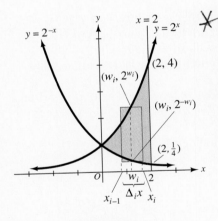

$y = 2^{-x}$

$x = 2$

$y = 2^x$

$(2, 4)$

$(w_i, 2^{w_i})$

$(w_i, 2^{-w_i})$

$(2, \frac{1}{4})$

O w_i 2

x_{i-1} $\Delta_i x$ x_i

FIGURE 3

▶ **EXAMPLE 3**   (a) Sketch the graphs of $y = 2^x$ and $y = 2^{-x}$ on the same set of axes. (b) Find the exact area of the region bounded by these two graphs and the line $x = 2$. (c) Support the answer in part (b) by computing the definite integral by the NINT capability of a graphics calculator.

Solution

(a) The required graphs appear in Figure 3. The region is shaded in the figure.

(b) If A square units is the desired area,

$$A = \lim_{\|\Delta\| \to 0} \sum_{i=1}^{n} [2^{w_i} - 2^{-w_i}] \, \Delta_i x$$

$$= \int_0^2 (2^x - 2^{-x}) \, dx$$

$$= \frac{2^x}{\ln 2} + \frac{2^{-x}}{\ln 2} \bigg]_0^2$$

$$= \frac{4}{\ln 2} + \frac{\frac{1}{4}}{\ln 2} - \frac{1}{\ln 2} - \frac{1}{\ln 2}$$

$$= \frac{9}{4 \ln 2}$$

(c) On our graphics calculator we compute

$$\text{NINT}(2^x - 2^{-x}, 0, 2) = 3.2461$$

This result supports our answer in part (b) because to five significant digits $9/(4 \ln 2) = 3.2461$.   ◀

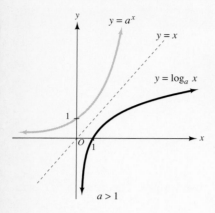

FIGURE 4

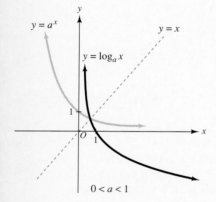

FIGURE 5

We can now define the *logarithmic function to the base a*, denoted by $\log_a$ where a is any positive number other than 1.

5.5.4 Definition of the Logarithmic Function to the Base a

If a is any positive number except 1, the **logarithmic function to the base a** is the inverse of the exponential function to the base a; that is,

$$y = \log_a x \quad \text{if and only if} \quad a^y = x \tag{2}$$

This definition is the same as the one given in algebra; however, (2) has meaning for y any real number because a^y has been defined for real number exponents. If $a = e$, we have the logarithmic function to the base e, which is the natural logarithmic function.

We read $\log_a x$ as "the logarithm of x to the base a."

Because the graph of a function and its inverse are reflections of each other with respect to the line $y = x$, we obtain the graph of $y = \log_a x$ from the graph of $y = a^x$. Figure 4 shows the two graphs if $a > 1$, and Figure 5 shows them if $0 < a < 1$.

The logarithmic function to the base a obeys the same laws as the natural logarithmic function. We list them:

$$\log_a(xy) = \log_a x + \log_a y$$
$$\log_a(x \div y) = \log_a x - \log_a y$$
$$\log_a 1 = 0$$
$$\log_a x^y = y \log_a x$$

The proofs of these properties are left as exercises (see Exercises 41 through 44).

A relationship between logarithms to the base a and natural logarithms follows easily. Let

$$y = \log_a x$$

Then

$$a^y = x$$
$$\ln a^y = \ln x$$
$$y \ln a = \ln x$$
$$y = \frac{\ln x}{\ln a}$$

Replacing y by $\log_a x$ we obtain

$$\log_a x = \frac{\ln x}{\ln a} \tag{3}$$

Most calculators do not have a $\boxed{\log_a x}$ key. Thus (3) is a convenient formula to apply to compute values of $\log_a x$ on a calculator.

Equation (3) sometimes is used as the definition of the logarithmic function to the base a. Because the natural logarithmic function is continuous at all $x > 0$, it follows from (3) that the logarithmic function to the base a is continuous at all $x > 0$.

If in (3) $x = e$, we have

$$\log_a e = \frac{\ln e}{\ln a}$$

$$\log_a e = \frac{1}{\ln a} \tag{4}$$

We now find the derivative of the logarithmic function to the base a by differentiating both sides of (3) with respect to x.

$$D_x(\log_a x) = \frac{1}{\ln a} D_x(\ln x)$$

$$D_x(\log_a x) = \frac{1}{\ln a} \cdot \frac{1}{x} \tag{5}$$

Substituting from (4) into this equation we get

$$D_x(\log_a x) = \frac{\log_a e}{x}$$

By applying the chain rule to this formula and (5) we have the following theorem.

5.5.5 Theorem

If u is a differentiable function of x,

$$D_x(\log_a u) = \frac{\log_a e}{u} \cdot D_x u$$

$$\Leftrightarrow D_x(\log_a u) = \frac{1}{(\ln a)u} \cdot D_x u$$

If in this theorem $a = e$, we have

$$D_x(\log_e u) = \frac{\log_e e}{u} D_x u$$

$$\Leftrightarrow D_x(\ln u) = \frac{1}{u} D_x u$$

which is Theorem 5.2.2 for the derivative of the natural logarithmic function.

▶ **EXAMPLE 4**   Find $\dfrac{dy}{dx}$ if

$$y = \log_{10} \frac{x + 1}{x^2 + 1}$$

Solution   Using a property of logarithms, we write

$$y = \log_{10}(x + 1) - \log_{10}(x^2 + 1)$$

From Theorem 5.5.5

$$\frac{dy}{dx} = \frac{\log_{10} e}{x + 1} - \frac{\log_{10} e}{x^2 + 1} \cdot 2x$$

$$= \log_{10} e\left(\frac{1}{x + 1} - \frac{2x}{x^2 + 1}\right)$$

$$= \frac{\log_{10} e(1 - 2x - x^2)}{(x + 1)(x^2 + 1)}$$

◄

To evaluate integrals involving logarithms to the base a, we first apply formula (3) to change to natural logarithms.

▶ **EXAMPLE 5** Evaluate

$$\int \frac{\log_{10} x}{x} \, dx = \frac{1}{\ln 10} \int \frac{\ln x}{x} \, dx$$

Solution We evaluate the integral on the right as in Example 5, Section 5.3, and we get

$$\int \frac{\log_{10} x}{x} \, dx = \frac{1}{\ln 10} \cdot \frac{(\ln x)^2}{2} + C$$

$$= \frac{(\ln x)^2}{2 \ln 10} + C$$

◄

Theorem 5.4.12 enables us to differentiate a variable to a constant power. In this section you learned how to find the derivative of a constant to a variable power. We now consider the derivative of a function whose value is a variable to a variable power.

▶ **EXAMPLE 6** If $y = x^x$, where $x > 0$, find $\dfrac{dy}{dx}$.

Solution From Definition 5.4.2, if $x > 0$, $x^x = e^{x \ln x}$. Therefore

$$y = e^{x \ln x}$$

$$\frac{dy}{dx} = e^{x \ln x} D_x(x \ln x)$$

$$= e^{x \ln x}\left(x \cdot \frac{1}{x} + \ln x\right)$$

$$= x^x(1 + \ln x)$$

◄

The derivative of a variable to a variable power can also be computed by logarithmic differentiation as shown in the next example.

▶ **EXAMPLE 7** Find the derivative in Example 6 by logarithmic differentiation.

Solution We are given

$$y = x^x$$

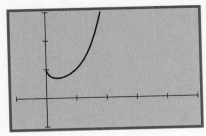

[−1, 5] by [−1, 3]

$y_1 = x^x$

FIGURE 6

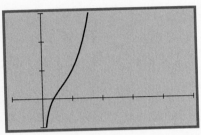

[−1, 5] by [−1, 3]

$y_2 = \text{NDER}(y_1, x)$

FIGURE 7

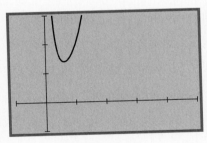

[−1, 5] by [−1, 3]

$y_3 = \text{NDER}(y_2, x)$

FIGURE 8

We take the natural logarithm on both sides of the equation and obtain

$$\ln y = \ln x^x$$
$$\ln y = x \ln x$$

Differentiating on both sides of the above equation with respect to x gives

$$\frac{1}{y} \cdot \frac{dy}{dx} = x \cdot \frac{1}{x} + \ln x$$

$$\frac{dy}{dx} = y(1 + \ln x)$$

$$= x^x(1 + \ln x)$$ ◀

▶ **EXAMPLE 8** Given

$$f(x) = x^x \qquad x > 0$$

Plot the graphs of f, NDER(x^x, x), and NDER2(x^x, x) in convenient windows. From the graphs, estimate any relative extrema of f, the values of x where the relative extrema occur, where f is increasing, where f is decreasing, where the graph of f is concave upward and where it is concave downward, and any points of inflection. Confirm the estimations analytically.

Solution On our graphics calculator, we let

$$y_1 = x^x \qquad y_2 = \text{NDER}(y_1, x) \qquad y_3 = \text{NDER}(y_2, x)$$

By plotting the graphs of y_1, y_2, and y_3 in the $[-1, 5]$ by $[-1, 3]$ window, we obtain Figures 6, 7, and 8, which resemble the graphs of f, f', and f'', respectively. From Figure 7 with the root or trace and zoom-in capabilities of our graphics calculator, we estimate that the graph of f' intersects the x axis at the point where $x = 0.368$. Because $f'(x) < 0$ when $0 < x < 0.368$, and $f'(x) > 0$ when $x > 0.368$, we estimate that f is decreasing when $0 < x < 0.368$ and increasing when $x > 0.368$; furthermore, f has a relative minimum value at 0.368. From Figure 8, $f''(x) > 0$ for all $x > 0$. The graph of f is, therefore, concave upward at all points.

We now confirm these results analytically. From Example 6,

$$f'(x) = x^x(1 + \ln x)$$

Thus

$$f''(x) = D_x(x^x)(1 + \ln x) + x^x D_x(1 + \ln x)$$

$$= [x^x(1 + \ln x)](1 + \ln x) + x^x\left(\frac{1}{x}\right)$$

$$= x^x(1 + \ln x)^2 + x^{x-1}$$

Setting $f'(x) = 0$, we obtain

$$1 + \ln x = 0$$
$$\ln x = -1$$
$$x = e^{-1}$$

To three significant digits, $e^{-1} = 0.368$. The expression for $f'(x)$ is negative when $0 < x < e^{-1}$ and positive when $x > e^{-1}$, and the expression for $f''(x)$ is positive for all $x > 0$. These facts confirm our estimations found graphically. The graph of f in Figure 6 also agrees with our results. ◀

EXERCISES 5.5

In Exercises 1 through 20, find the derivative of the function.

1. $f(x) = 3^{5x}$
2. $f(x) = 6^{-3x}$

3. $f(t) = 4^{3t^2}$
4. $g(x) = 10^{x^2 - 2x}$

5. $f(x) = 4^{\sin 2x}$
6. $f(z) = 2^{\csc 3z}$

7. $g(x) = 2^{5x} 3^{4x^2}$
8. $f(x) = (x^3 + 3)2^{-7x}$

9. $h(x) = \dfrac{\log_{10} x}{x}$
10. $f(t) = \log_{10} \dfrac{t}{t + 1}$

11. $f(x) = \sqrt{\log_a x}$
12. $g(w) = \tan 2^{3w}$

13. $f(t) = \sec 3^{t^2}$
14. $f(x) = x^{\ln x}; \ x > 0$

15. $f(x) = x^{\sqrt{x}}; \ x > 0$
16. $f(x) = x^{x^2}; \ x > 0$

17. $g(z) = z^{\cos z}; \ z > 0$
18. $f(x) = x^{e^x}; \ x > 0$

19. $h(x) = (\sin x)^{\tan x}; \ \sin x > 0$

20. $g(t) = (\cos t)^t; \ \cos t > 0$

In Exercises 21 through 30, evaluate the indefinite integral.

21. $\displaystyle\int 3^{2x} \, dx$
22. $\displaystyle\int a^{nx} \, dx$

23. $\displaystyle\int a^t e^t \, dt$
24. $\displaystyle\int 5^{x^4 + 2x}(2x^3 + 1) \, dx$

25. $\displaystyle\int x^2 10^{x^3} \, dx$
26. $\displaystyle\int a^{z \ln z}(\ln z + 1) \, dz$

27. $\displaystyle\int e^y 2^{e^y} 3^{e^y} \, dy$
28. $\displaystyle\int \dfrac{4^{\ln(1/x)}}{x} \, dx$

29. $\displaystyle\int \dfrac{\log_2 x^2}{x} \, dx$
30. $\displaystyle\int \dfrac{(\log_3 x)^2}{x} \, dx$

In Exercises 31 through 34, compute the value of the logarithm on your calculator to five significant digits.

31. (a) $\log_5 e$ **(b)** $\log_3 7$
32. (a) $\log_6 10$ **(b)** $\log_2 361$
33. (a) $\log_2 10$ **(b)** $\log_{10} e$
34. (a) $\log_3 2$ **(b)** $\log_4 4728$

In Exercises 35 and 36, given $\log_{10} e = 0.4343$ use differentials to find an approximate value of the logarithm to three significant digits; support your answer by computing the value of the logarithm on your calculator.

35. $\log_{10} 997$
36. $\log_{10} 1.015$

In Exercises 37 through 40, prove the property if a and b are any positive numbers and x and y are real numbers.

37. $a^x \div a^y = a^{x-y}$
38. $(a^x)^y = a^{xy}$

39. $(ab)^x = a^x b^x$
40. $a^0 = 1$

In Exercises 41 through 44, prove the property if a is any positive number except 1, and x and y are any positive numbers.

41. $\log_a(xy) = \log_a x + \log_a y$

42. $\log_a(x \div y) = \log_a x - \log_a y$

43. $\log_a 1 = 0$
44. $\log_a x^y = y \log_a x$

45. A company has learned that when it initiates a new sales campaign, the number of sales per day increases. However, the number of extra daily sales per day decreases as the impact of the campaign wears off. For a specific campaign the company has determined that if there are $S(t)$ extra daily sales as a result of the campaign and t days have elapsed since the campaign ended, then $S(t) = 1000(3^{-t/2})$. Find the rate at which the extra daily sales are decreasing when **(a)** $t = 4$ and **(b)** $t = 10$.

46. A company estimates that in t years the number of its employees will be $N(t)$, where $N(t) = 1000(0.8)^{t/2}$. **(a)** How many employees does the company expect to have in 4 years? **(b)** At what rate is the number of employees expected to be changing in 4 years?

47. A particle is moving along a line according to the equation of motion $s = A \cdot 2^{kt} + B \cdot 2^{-kt}$, where A, B, and k are constants and s feet is the directed distance of the particle from the origin at t seconds. Show that if a feet per second squared is the acceleration at t seconds, then a is proportional to s. Why is the motion not simple harmonic?

48. A particle moves along a line according to the equation of motion $s = t^{1/t}$, where s feet is the directed distance of the particle from the origin at t seconds. Find the velocity and acceleration at 2 sec.

49. An historically important abstract painting was purchased in 1934 for $200, and its value has doubled every 10 years since its purchase. If y dollars is the value of the painting t years after its purchase, **(a)** define y in terms of t. **(b)** What was the value of the painting in 1994? **(c)** Find the rate at which the value of the painting was increasing in 1994.

In Exercises 50 through 52, sketch the graph of the equation.

50. (a) $y = 3^x$ **(b)** $y = \log_3 x$

51. (a) $y = 2^x$ **(b)** $y = \log_2 x$

52. (a) $y = 3^{-x}$ **(b)** $y = \log_{1/3} x$

In Exercises 53 through 56, support your answer by computing the definite integral by the NINT *capability of your graphics calculator.*

53. Find the exact area of the region bounded by the graph of $y = 5^x$ and the lines $x = 1$ and $y = 1$.

54. Find the exact area of the region bounded by the graphs of $y = e^x$ and $y = 2^x$ and the line $x = 2$.

55. Find the exact volume of the solid generated by revolving the region of Exercise 53 about the x axis.

56. Find the exact volume of the solid generated by revolving the region of Exercise 54 about the x axis.

57. Find to five significant digits the area of the region bounded by the graphs of $y = \log_{10} x$ and $y = \ln x$ and the line $x = 3$.

58. Find to five significant digits the volume of the solid generated by revolving the region of Exercise 57 about the x axis.

In Exercises 59 and 60, do the following: (a) Plot the graphs of f, $\text{NDER}(f(x), x)$, *and* $\text{NDER } 2(f(x), x)$ *in convenient windows. From the graphs, estimate (b) any relative extrema of* f, *(c) where* f *is increasing, (d) where* f *is decreasing, (e) where the graph of* f *is concave upward and where it is concave downward, and (f) any points of inflection. (g) Confirm your estimations analytically.*

59. $f(x) = x^{\ln x}$ **60.** $f(x) = x^{\sqrt{x}}$

61. In Section 5.4, the functions in Example 6 and Exercises 57 and 58 were mathematical models describing damped harmonic motion where the amplitude decreases to zero as time increases. If the amplitude increases without bound as time increases, we have unbounded harmonic motion and **resonance** occurs. The function defined by

$$f(t) = 2^t \cos 4t \qquad t \geq 0$$

is a mathematical model describing resonance. **(a)** Let

$$F(t) = -2^t \qquad G(t) = 2^t$$

and plot the graphs of f, F, and G in the $[0, \pi]$ by $[-10, 10]$ window. **(b)** From your graphs in part (a) observe that

$$F(t) \leq f(t) \leq G(t)$$

Confirm this continued inequality analytically. **(c)** Desribe the behavior of $f(t)$ as t increases without bound.

62. Do Exercise 61 if $f(t) = 3^{t/3} \sin 8t$, $F(t) = -3^{t/3}$, and $G(t) = 3^{t/3}$. In part (a) plot the graphs in the $[0, 2\pi]$ by $[-10, 10]$ window.

63. Given $f(x) = \frac{1}{2}(a^x + a^{-x})$. Prove that

$$f(b + c) + f(b - c) = 2 f(b) f(c)$$

64. By knowing the values of $\log_{10} 2$ and $\log_{10} 3$, explain why you can compute, without a calculator, $\log_{10} 4$, $\log_{10} 5$, $\log_{10} 6$, $\log_{10} 8$, and $\log_{10} 9$, but not $\log_{10} 7$.

65. The only solution to the equation

$$\log_{10} x = \ln x$$

is $x = 1$. Explain why this is a solution and why there are no others.

66. Describe the common characteristics of the graphs of $y = \log_{10} x$ and $y = \ln x$. Also describe how they differ.

67. Given $f(x) = \log_x 5$. **(a)** Plot the graph of f in a convenient window. *Hint:* First apply Equation (3) of this section. Describe the graph and in your description include: **(i)** where f appears to be increasing, where f appears to be decreasing, and any possible relative extrema of f; **(ii)** where the graph appears to be concave upward, where the graph appears to be concave downward, and any possible points of inflection of the graph. **(b)** Plot the graph of f' in a convenient window. From this graph determine where f is increasing, where f is decreasing, and any relative extrema of f. Are these conclusions consistent with those in part (a)? **(c)** Plot the graph of f'' in a convenient window. From this graph determine where the graph of f is concave upward, where the graph of f is concave downward, and any points of inflection of the graph of f. Are these conclusions consistent with those in part (a)? **(d)** Confirm your conclusions analytically.

5.6 APPLICATIONS OF THE NATURAL EXPONENTIAL FUNCTION

Mathematical models involving differential equations having solutions containing powers of e occur in many fields such as chemistry, physics, biology, psychology, sociology, business, and economics.

We begin by discussing models involving growth and decay that arise when the rate of change of the amount of a quantity with respect to time is proportional to the amount of the quantity present at a given instant. For example, the rate of growth of the population of a community may be proportional to the actual population at any given instant. In biology, under certain circumstances, the rate of growth of a culture of bacteria is proportional to the amount of bacteria present at any specific time. In a chemical reaction, the rate of the reaction is often proportional to the quantity of the substance present; for instance, chemists know from experiments that the rate of decay of radium is proportional to the amount of radium present at a given moment. An application in business occurs when interest is compounded continuously.

In such cases, if the time is represented by t units, and if y units represents the amount of the quantity present at any time, then

$$\frac{dy}{dt} = ky$$

where k is a constant and $y > 0$ for all $t \geq 0$. If y increases as t increases, then $k > 0$, and we have the **law of natural growth.** If y decreases as t increases, then $k < 0$, and we have the **law of natural decay.**

If by definition y is a positive integer (for instance, if y is the population of a certain community), we assume that y can be any positive real number in order for y to be a continuous function of t.

Suppose that we have a mathematical model involving the law of natural growth or decay and the initial condition that $y = y_0$ when $t = 0$. The differential equation is

$$\frac{dy}{dt} = ky$$

Separating the variables we obtain

$$\frac{dy}{y} = k\,dt$$

Integrating we have

$$\int \frac{dy}{y} = k \int dt$$
$$\ln|y| = kt + \bar{c}$$
$$|y| = e^{kt + \bar{c}}$$
$$|y| = e^{\bar{c}} \cdot e^{kt}$$

Letting $e^{\bar{c}} = C$ we have $|y| = Ce^{kt}$, and because y is positive we can omit the absolute-value bars, thereby giving

$$y = Ce^{kt}$$

Because $y = y_0$ when $t = 0$, we obtain $C = y_0$. Thus

$$y = y_0 e^{kt}$$

We have proved the following theorem.

5.6.1 Theorem

Suppose that y is a continuous function of t with $y > 0$ for all $t \geq 0$. Furthermore,

$$\frac{dy}{dt} = ky$$

where k is a constant and $y = y_0$ when $t = 0$. Then

$$y = y_0 e^{kt}$$

Let us consider the statement of this theorem with function notation. With $y = f(t)$ and $f(0) = B$ and $B > 0$ (that is, $y_0 = B$) the theorem states that if

$$f'(t) = kf(t) \qquad t \geq 0 \tag{1}$$

then

$$f(t) = Be^{kt} \qquad t \geq 0 \tag{2}$$

If $k > 0$, then (1) is the law of natural growth and (2) defines a function that has **exponential growth**. With $k > 0$,

$$\lim_{t \to +\infty} f(t) = B \lim_{t \to +\infty} e^{kt}$$

$$= +\infty$$

Thus $f(t)$ increases without bound as t increases without bound. The graph of (2) when $k > 0$ appears in Figure 1.

If $k < 0$, then (1) is the law of natural decay and (2) defines a function that has **exponential decay**. From (2) with $k < 0$,

$$\lim_{t \to +\infty} f(t) = B \lim_{t \to +\infty} e^{kt}$$

$$= 0$$

and $f(t)$ is approaching 0 through positive values. Figure 2 shows the graph of (2) when $k < 0$.

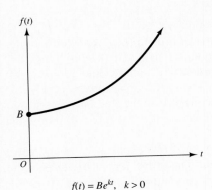

$f(t) = Be^{kt}, \quad k > 0$

FIGURE 1

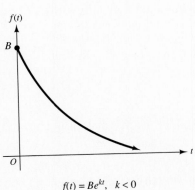

$f(t) = Be^{kt}, \quad k < 0$

FIGURE 2

▶ **EXAMPLE 1**   In a certain culture the rate of growth of bacteria is proportional to the amount present. Initially, 1000 bacteria are present and the amount doubles in 12 min. **(a)** If y bacteria are present at t minutes, express y as a function of t. **(b)** On a graphics calculator, estimate to the nearest minute how long it will take until 10,000 bacteria are present. **(c)** Confirm the estimate in part (b) analytically.

Solution   Table 1 gives the boundary conditions where y bacteria are present at t minutes. Observe that T minutes is the time it will take until 10,000 bacteria are present.

(a) The differential equation is

$$\frac{dy}{dt} = ky$$

Table 1

t	0	12	T
y	1000	2000	10,000

where k is a constant and $y = 1000$ when $t = 0$. From Theorem 5.6.1,

$$y = 1000e^{kt} \tag{3}$$

Because $y = 2000$ when $t = 12$, we obtain from (3)

$$e^{12k} = 2 \tag{4}$$

From (3)

$$y = 1000(e^{12k})^{t/12}$$

Substituting from (4) into this equation, we have

$$y = 1000 \cdot 2^{t/12} \tag{5}$$

(b) Figure 3 shows the graph of Equation (5) and the line $y = 10,000$ plotted in the [0, 100] by [0, 20,000] window. Using intersect, or trace and zoom-in, we determine that the graph and the line intersect at the point where $t = 39.9$. Thus we estimate that it will take 40 min until 10,000 bacteria are present.

(c) To confirm our estimate analytically, in (5) we replace t by T and y by 10,000, and we have

$$10,000 = 1000 \cdot 2^{T/12}$$
$$2^{T/12} = 10$$
$$\ln(2^{T/12}) = \ln 10$$
$$\frac{T}{12} \cdot \ln 2 = \ln 10$$
$$T = \frac{12 \ln 10}{\ln 2}$$
$$T = 39.9$$

which confirms our estimate in part (b).

Conclusion: In 40 min, 10,000 bacteria will be present.   ◀

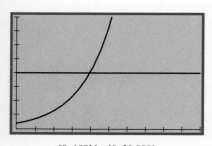

[0, 100] by [0, 20,000]

$y = 1000 \cdot 2^{t/12}$ and $y = 10,000$

FIGURE 3

▶   **EXAMPLE 2**   The rate of increase of the population of a certain city is proportional to the population. In 1950 the population was 50,000 and in 1980 it was 75,000. **(a)** If y is the population t years since 1950, express y as a function of t. **(b)** Estimate on a graphics calculator what the population will be in 2010. **(c)** Confirm the estimate in part (b) analytically.

Solution   Table 2 gives the boundary conditions where y_{60} is the population in 2010.

Table 2

t	0	30	60
y	50,000	75,000	y_{60}

(a) The differential equation is

$$\frac{dy}{dt} = ky$$

where k is a constant and $y = 50,000$ when $t = 0$. From Theorem 5.6.1,

$$y = 50,000e^{kt} \tag{6}$$

Because $y = 75,000$ when $t = 30$, we get from (6)

$$75,000 = 50,000e^{30k}$$
$$e^{30k} = 1.5 \qquad (7)$$

From (6),

$$y = 50,000(e^{30k})^{t/30}$$

Substituting from (7) into this equation, we obtain

$$y = 50,000(1.5)^{t/30} \qquad (8)$$

(b) The graph of Equation (8) is plotted in the $[0, 70]$ by $[0, 150,000]$ window in Figure 4. We use trace and zoom-in to determine that the value of y when $t = 60$ is $112,500$.

(c) Substituting 60 for t and y_{60} for y in (8), we obtain

$$y_{60} = 50,000(1.5)^2$$
$$= 112,500$$

which confirms our estimate in part (b).

Conclusion: The population in 2010 will be $112,500$.   ◀

In the above example, because the population is increasing with time we have a case of exponential growth. If a population decreases with time, which can occur if the death rate is greater than the birth rate, then we have a case of exponential decay (see Exercise 4). The next example provides another situation involving exponential decay. In problems involving exponential decay, the **half-life** of a substance is the time for half of it to decay.

▶ **EXAMPLE 3**   The rate of decay of radium is proportional to the amount present at any time. The half-life of radium is 1690 years and 20 mg of radium are present now. (a) If y milligrams of radium will be present t years from now, express y as a function of t. (b) Estimate on a graphics calculator how much radium will be present 1000 years from now. (c) Confirm the estimate in part (b) analytically.

Solution   We have the boundary conditions given in Table 3, where y_{1000} milligrams of radium will be present 1000 years from now.

(a) The differential equation is

$$\frac{dy}{dt} = ky$$

where k is a constant and $y = 20$ when $t = 0$. From Theorem 5.6.1,

$$y = 20e^{kt} \qquad (9)$$

Because $y = 10$ when $t = 1690$, from (9) we get

$$10 = 20e^{1690k}$$
$$e^{1690k} = \frac{1}{2} \qquad (10)$$

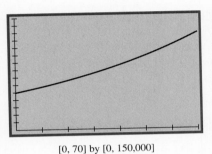

$[0, 70]$ by $[0, 150,000]$

$y = 50,000\,(1.5)^{t/30}$

FIGURE 4

Table 3

t	0	1690	1000
y	20	10	y_{1000}

From (9),

$$y = 20(e^{1690k})^{t/1690}$$

Substituting from (10) into this equation, we obtain

$$y = 20\left(\frac{1}{2}\right)^{t/1690} \tag{11}$$

(b) Figure 5 shows the graph of (11) plotted in the [0, 4000] by [0, 25] window. Applying trace and zoom-in we determine that y is 13.27 when $t = 1000$.

(c) From Equation (11) with $y = y_{1000}$ and $t = 1000$, we have

$$y_{1000} = 20\left(\frac{1}{2}\right)^{1000/1690}$$

$$= 13.27$$

which confirms our estimate in part (b).

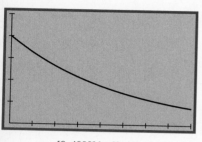

[0, 4000] by [0, 25]

$$y = 20\left(\frac{1}{2}\right)^{t/1690}$$

FIGURE 5

Conclusion: One thousand years from now 13.27 mg of radium will be present. ◀

Observe that Equation (11) in the solution of Example 3 is a special case of the following more general situation: If the half-life of a substance having exponential decay is h years and y_0 units of the substance are present now, then y units will be present in t years, where

$$y = y_0\left(\frac{1}{2}\right)^{t/h}$$

You are asked to prove this in Exercise 34.

▶   **EXAMPLE 4**   A reservoir holding a city's water supply contains 100 million liters of fluoridated water, and the water contains 700 kg of fluoride. To decrease the fluoride content, fresh water runs into the reservoir at the rate of 3 million liters per day, and the mixture of water and fluoride, kept uniform, runs out of the reservoir at the same rate. How many kilograms of fluoride does the reservoir contain 60 days after the pure water started to flow into the reservoir?

Solution   Let t days be the time elapsed since pure water started to flow into the reservoir. Let x kilograms be the weight of the fluoride in the reservoir at t days.

Because 100 million liters of fluoridated water are in the tank at all times, at t days the weight of fluoride per million liters is $x/100$ kilograms. Three million liters of the fluoridated water run out of the reservoir each day; so the reservoir loses $3(x/100)$ kilograms of fluoride per day. Because $\dfrac{dx}{dt}$ is the rate of change of x with respect to t, and x is decreasing as t increases, we have the differential equation

$$\frac{dx}{dt} = -\frac{3x}{100}$$

Table 4

t	0	60
x	700	x_{60}

This equation is of the form $\dfrac{dx}{dt} = kx$, where k is -0.03. We have the initial conditions given in Table 4 where x_{60} kilograms is the weight of the fluoride in the reservoir after 60 days. When $t = 0$, $x = 700$; thus from Theorem 5.6.1

$$x = 700e^{-0.03t}$$

Setting $t = 60$ and $x = x_{60}$ in this equation, we have

$$x_{60} = 700e^{-1.8}$$
$$= 115.71$$

Conclusion: The reservoir contains 116 kg of fluoride 60 days after pure water started to flow into the reservoir.   ◀

The calculus is often very useful to the economist for evaluating certain business decisions. To apply the calculus, however, we must deal with continuous functions. Consider, for example, the following formula, which gives A, the number of dollars in the amount after t years, if P dollars is invested at an annual rate of $100i$ percent, compounded m times per year:

$$A = P\left(1 + \frac{i}{m}\right)^{mt} \tag{12}$$

Let us conceive of a situation in which the interest is continuously compounding; that is, consider formula (12), where we let the number of interest periods per year increase without bound. Then going to the limit in formula (12) we have

$$A = P \lim_{m \to +\infty} \left(1 + \frac{i}{m}\right)^{mt}$$

which can be written as

$$A = P \lim_{m \to +\infty} \left[\left(1 + \frac{i}{m}\right)^{m/i}\right]^{it} \tag{13}$$

To compute this limit by Theorem 1.9.1 we must first determine if

$$\lim_{m \to +\infty} \left(1 + \frac{i}{m}\right)^{m/i}$$

exists. Letting $h = i/m$ we have $m/i = 1/h$; and because $m \to +\infty$ is equivalent to $h \to 0^+$,

$$\lim_{m \to +\infty} \left(1 + \frac{i}{m}\right)^{m/i} = \lim_{h \to 0^+} (1 + h)^{1/h}$$
$$= e$$

Hence, from Theorem 1.9.1

$$\lim_{m \to +\infty} \left[\left(1 + \frac{i}{m}\right)^{m/i}\right]^{it} = \left[\lim_{m \to +\infty} \left(1 + \frac{i}{m}\right)^{m/i}\right]^{it}$$
$$= e^{it}$$

and so (13) becomes

$$A = Pe^{it} \tag{14}$$

By letting t vary through the set of nonnegative real numbers we see that (14) expresses A as a continuous function of t.

Another way of looking at the same situation is to consider an investment of P dollars that increases at a rate proportional to its size. This is the law of natural growth. Then if A dollars is the amount at t years,

$$\frac{dA}{dt} = kA$$

where k is a constant and $A = P$ when $t = 0$. From Theorem 5.6.1

$$A = Pe^{kt}$$

Comparing this equation with (14) we see that they are the same if $k = i$. So if an investment increases at a rate proportional to its size, we say that the interest is **compounded continuously,** and the annual interest rate is the constant of proportionality.

▷ **ILLUSTRATION 1**   If P dollars is invested at a rate of 8 percent per year compounded continuously, and A dollars is the amount of the investment at t years,

$$\frac{dA}{dt} = 0.08A$$

and

$$A = Pe^{0.08t}$$ ◀

If in (14) we take $P = 1$, $i = 1$, and $t = 1$, we get $A = e$, which gives a justification for the economist's interpretation of the number e as the yield on an investment of \$1 for a year at an interest rate of 100 percent compounded continuously.

In the following example we use the terminology *effective annual rate* of interest, which is the rate that gives the same amount of interest compounded once a year.

▶ **EXAMPLE 5**   A bank advertises that interest on savings accounts is computed at 4 percent per year compounded daily. If \$1000 is deposited into a savings account at the bank, find **(a)** an approximate amount at the end of 1 year by taking the interest rate at 4 percent compounded continuously and **(b)** the exact amount at the end of 1 year by considering an annual interest rate of 4 percent compounded 365 times per year. **(c)** Find the effective annual interest rate.

Solution

(a) Let A dollars be the amount at the end of 1 year. From (14) with $P = 1000$, $i = 0.04$, and $t = 1$,

$$A = 1000e^{0.04}$$
$$= 1040.81$$

<u>Conclusion:</u>   \$1040.81 is an approximate amount on deposit at the end of 1 year.

(b) From (12) with $P = 1000$, $i = 0.04$, $m = 365$, and $t = 1$, if A_{365} dollars is the amount,

$$A_{365} = 1000\left(1 + \frac{0.04}{365}\right)^{365}$$

$$= 1040.81$$

Conclusion: The exact amount on deposit at the end of 1 year is $1040.81.
(c) Let i be the effective annual interest rate. Therefore

$$1000(1 + j) = 1040.81$$
$$1 + j = 1.04081$$
$$j = 0.04081$$

Conclusion: The effective annual interest rate is 4.081 percent. ◀

An application of the natural exponential function in physics is afforded by *Newton's law of cooling*, which states that the rate at which a body changes temperature is proportional to the difference between its temperature and that of the surrounding medium.

▶ **EXAMPLE 6** If a body is in air of temperature 35° and the body cools from 120° to 60° in 40 min, use Newton's law of cooling to find the temperature of the body after 100 min.

Solution Let t minutes be the time that has elapsed since the body started to cool. Let y degrees be the temperature of the body at t minutes. Table 5 gives the boundary conditions, where y_{100} degrees is the temperature of the body after 100 min.
From Newton's law of cooling,

$$\frac{dy}{dt} = k(y - 35)$$

where k is a constant and $y > 35$ for all $t \geq 0$. With the substitution $u = y - 35$ and $du/dt = dy/dt$, this equation becomes

$$\frac{du}{dt} = ku$$

When $t = 0$, $y = 120$ and $u = 85$. Thus from Theorem 5.6.1, the solution to this differential equation is

$$u = 85e^{kt}$$

Replacing u by $y - 35$, we have

$$y - 35 = 85e^{kt}$$
$$y = 85e^{kt} + 35 \tag{15}$$

Because $y = 60$ when $t = 40$, we have

Table 5

t	0	40	100
y	120	60	y_{100}

$$60 = 85e^{40k} + 35$$

$$e^{40k} = \frac{5}{17} \tag{16}$$

From (15)

$$y = 85(e^{40k})^{t/40} + 35$$

Substituting from (16) into this equation, we have

$$y = 85\left(\frac{5}{17}\right)^{t/40} + 35$$

Because $y = y_{100}$ when $t = 100$, we obtain from the above equation

$$y_{100} = 85\left(\frac{5}{17}\right)^{5/2} + 35$$

$$= 38.99$$

<u>Conclusion:</u>   After 100 min the temperature of the body is 39°.   ◄

Suppose now that a quantity increases at a rate proportional to the difference between a fixed positive number A and its size. Then if time is represented by t units and y units is the amount of the quantity present at any time,

$$\frac{dy}{dt} = k(A - y) \tag{17}$$

where k is a positive constant and $y < A$ for all $t \geq 0$. With the substitution $u = A - y$ and $du/dt = -dy/dt$, this equation becomes

$$\frac{du}{dt} = -ku$$

If $u = B$ (that is, $y = A - B$) when $t = 0$, then from Theorem 5.6.1 the solution to this equation is

$$u = Be^{-kt}$$

Replacing u by $A - y$, we have

$$A - y = Be^{-kt}$$

$$y = A - Be^{-kt} \tag{18}$$

If in this equation we let $y = f(t)$, it becomes

$$f(t) = A - Be^{-kt}$$

where A, B, and k are positive constants. This equation describes **bounded growth.**

$$\lim_{t \to +\infty} f(t) = \lim_{t \to +\infty} (A - Be^{-kt})$$

$$= A - B \lim_{t \to +\infty} e^{-kt}$$

$$= A - B \cdot 0$$

$$= A$$

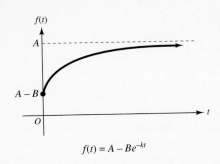

$$f(t) = A - Be^{-kt}$$

FIGURE 6

and $f(t)$ is approaching A through values less than A. Therefore, the line A units above the t axis is a horizontal asymptote of the graph of f. Also note that

$$f(0) = A - Be^{-k \cdot 0}$$
$$= A - B$$

From this information we obtain the graph of f in Figure 6. This graph is sometimes called a **learning curve.** The name is certainly appropriate when $f(t)$ represents the competence at which a person performs a job. As a person's experience increases, the competence increases rapidly at first and then slows down as additional experience has little effect on the skill with which the task is performed.

▶ **EXAMPLE 7**   A new employee performs a job more efficiently each day in such a way that if y units are produced per day after t days on the job,

$$\frac{dy}{dt} = k(80 - y) \tag{19}$$

where k is a positive constant and $y < 80$ for all $t \geq 0$. The employee produces 20 units the first day of work and 50 units per day after being on the job 10 days. **(a)** Express y as a function of t. **(b)** How many units per day can the employee eventually be expected to produce? **(c)** Plot the graph of the function in part (a) and the horizontal asymptote of the graph. **(d)** How many units per day is the employee producing after being on the job 30 days? **(e)** Show that after being on the job 60 days the employee is producing just 1 unit less than full potential.

Solution   The given differential equation (19) is the same as (17) with $A = 80$. Table 6 shows the boundary conditions where y_{30} and y_{60} units are produced per day after being on the job 30 and 60 days, respectively.

(a) The general solution of (19) is of the form of (18) where A is 80:

$$y = 80 - Be^{-kt} \tag{20}$$

Because $y = 20$ when $t = 0$, we obtain from (20)

$$20 = 80 - Be^0$$
$$B = 60$$

Replacing B by 60 in (20), we get

$$y = 80 - 60e^{-kt} \tag{21}$$

From this equation, with $y = 50$ when $t = 10$, we have

$$50 = 80 - 60e^{-10k}$$
$$e^{-10k} = 0.5$$

Substituting this value of e^{-10k} into (21), we have

$$y = 80 - 60(e^{-10k})^{t/10}$$
$$y = 80 - 60(0.5)^{t/10} \tag{22}$$

Table 6

t	0	10	30	60
y	20	50	y_{30}	y_{60}

(b) $\lim_{t \to +\infty} [80 - 60(0.5)^{t/10}] = 80 - 60 \lim_{t \to +\infty} \dfrac{1}{2^{t/10}}$

$$= 80 - 60 \cdot 0$$

$$= 80$$

<u>Conclusion:</u> The employee can eventually be expected to produce 80 units per day.

(c) Figure 7 shows the graph of (22) and its horizontal asymptote, the line $y = 80$, plotted in the $[0, 50]$ by $[0, 90]$ window.

(d) Because $y = y_{30}$ when $t = 30$, we obtain from (22)

$$y_{30} = 80 - 60(0.5)^3$$

$$= 72.5$$

<u>Conclusion:</u> The employee is producing 72 units per day after being on the job 30 days.

(e) From (22), with $y = y_{60}$ when $t = 60$, we get

$$y_{60} = 80 - 60(0.5)^6$$

$$= 79.06$$

<u>Conclusion:</u> After being on the job 60 days, the employee is producing 79 units per day, just 1 unit less than full potential. ◀

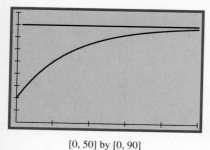

$[0, 50]$ by $[0, 90]$

$y = 80 - 60\,(0.5)^{t/10}$

$y = 80$

FIGURE 7

In Section 7.4 we consider another type of bounded growth, one that gives a model of population growth that takes into account environmental factors.

An important function in statistics, called the **standardized normal probability density function,** is defined by

$$N(x) = \frac{1}{\sqrt{2\pi}}\, e^{-x^2/2}$$

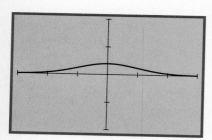

$[-3, 3]$ by $[-2, 2]$

$N(x) = \dfrac{1}{\sqrt{2\pi}}\, e^{-x^2/2}$

FIGURE 8

The graph of N is the bell-shaped curve well known to statisticians. Figure 8 shows this graph plotted in the $[-3, 3]$ by $[-2, 2]$ window. Observe that as x either increases or decreases without bound, $N(x)$ rapidly approaches 0.

The probability that a random choice of x will be in the closed interval $[a, b]$ is denoted by $P([a, b])$, and

$$P([a, b]) = \frac{1}{\sqrt{2\pi}} \int_a^b e^{-x^2/2}\, dx \tag{23}$$

This definite integral is the measure of the area of the region bounded above by the curve $y = N(x)$, below by the x axis, and on the sides by the lines $x = a$ and $x = b$. The definite integral cannot be evaluated by the second fundamental theorem of the calculus because it has been proved that an antiderivative of the integrand cannot be expressed in terms of elementary functions. We can, however, compute an approximate value by the NINT capability of our graphics calculator.

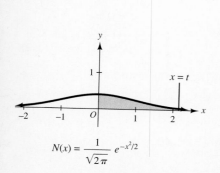

$N(x) = \dfrac{1}{\sqrt{2\pi}}\, e^{-x^2/2}$

FIGURE 9

▶ **EXAMPLE 8**   For the standardized normal probability density function, determine the probability that a random choice of x will be in the interval $[0, 2]$.

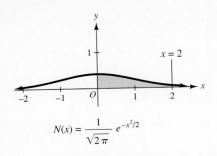

$$N(x) = \frac{1}{\sqrt{2\pi}} e^{-x^2/2}$$

FIGURE 10

Solution   The probability that a random choice of x will be in the interval $[0, 2]$ is $P([0, 2])$, and from (23)

$$P([0, 2]) = \frac{1}{\sqrt{2\pi}} \int_0^2 e^{-x^2/2}\, dx$$

On our graphics calculator we compute $\text{NINT}(N(x), 0, 2) = 0.47725$. Thus

$$P([0, 2]) = 0.47725$$ ◀

Refer now to Figure 9. The shaded region in the first quadrant is bounded by the graph of the standardized normal probability density function, the coordinate axes, and the line $x = t$, where $t > 0$. If $A(t)$ square units is the area of this region, it can be shown, although it is difficult to do so, that $\lim\limits_{t \to +\infty} A(t) = 0.5$. Thus the exact value of $P([0, 2])$, which is the measure of the area of the shaded region in Figure 10, must be less than 0.5. This fact agrees with our result in Example 8.

EXERCISES 5.6

1. The rate of natural increase of the population of a certain city is proportional to the population. In 1955 the population was 40,000, and in 1995 it was 60,000. **(a)** If y is the population t years since 1955, express y as a function of t. **(b)** Estimate on your graphics calculator what the population will be in 2001. **(c)** Estimate on your graphics calculator when the population will be 80,000. **(d)** Confirm your estimates in parts (b) and (c) analytically.

2. Bacteria grown in a certain culture increase at a rate proportional to the number present. There are 1000 bacteria present now and the number will double in 30 min. **(a)** If y bacteria will be present t minutes from now, express y as a function of t. **(b)** Estimate on your graphics calculator how many bacteria will be present in 2 hours. **(c)** Estimate on your graphics calculator when 50,000 bacteria will be present. **(d)** Confirm your estimates in parts (b) and (c) analytically.

3. When a simple electric circuit, containing no capacitors but having inductance and resistance, has the electromotive force removed, the rate of decrease of the current is proportional to the current. The current is i amperes t seconds after the cutoff, $i = 40$ when $t = 0$, and the current dies down to 15 amperes in 0.01 sec. **(a)** Express i as a function of t. **(b)** Estimate on your graphics calculator the current in 0.02 sec. **(c)** Confirm your estimate in part (b) analytically.

4. The population of a town is decreasing at a rate proportional to its size. In 1980 the population was 50,000 and in 1990 it was 44,000. **(a)** If y is the population t years since 1980, express y as a function of

t. **(b)** Estimate on your graphics calculator what the population will be in the year 2000. **(c)** Confirm your estimate in part (b) analytically.

In Exercises 5 through 26, define all your variables precisely as numbers. Use the variable t to represent time and define the other variables in terms of t. Be sure to write a conclusion.

5. After the pre-opening and opening day publicity of a certain exploitation movie stopped, the attendance decreased at a rate proportional to its size. If the opening day's attendance was 5000 and the attendance on the third day was 2000, what is the expected attendance on the sixth day?

6. The population of a particular city doubled from 1900 to 1960. If the rate of natural increase of the population at any time is proportional to the population at the time and the population in 1960 was 60,000, estimate the population in the year 2010.

7. Suppose that the value of a certain antique collection increases with age and its rate of appreciation at any time is proportional to its value at that time. If the value of the collection was \$25,000 10 years ago and its present value is \$35,000, in how many years is its value expected to be \$50,000?

8. After an automobile is 1 year old, its rate of depreciation at any time is proportional to its value at that time. If an automobile was purchased on March 1, 1993, and its values on March 1, 1994 and March 1, 1995, were, respectively, \$7000 and \$5800, what is its expected value on March 1, 1999?

9. In a certain bacterial culture where the rate of growth of bacteria is proportional to the number present, the number triples in 1 hour. If at the end of 4 hours 10 million bacteria were present, how many bacteria were present initially?

10. If the half-life of radium is 1690 years, what percent of the amount present now will be remaining after (a) 100 years and (b) 1000 years?

11. Thirty percent of a radioactive substance disappears in 15 years. Find the half-life of the substance.

12. The winter mortality of a certain species of wildlife in a particular geographical region is proportional to the number of the species present at any time. On December 21, the first day of winter, 2400 of the species were present; 2000 were present 30 days later. How many of the species were expected to survive the winter; that is, how many were expected to be alive on March 21, the first day of spring?

13. A deposit of $5000 is made at a savings bank that advertises that interest on accounts is computed at an annual rate of 5 percent compounded daily. Find (a) an approximate amount at the end of 1 year by taking the interest rate as 5 percent compounded continuously, and (b) the exact amount at the end of 1 year by considering an annual interest rate of 5 percent compounded 365 times a year. (c) What is the effective annual rate of interest?

14. Do Exercise 13 if the bank advertises that interest is computed at an annual rate of 6 percent compounded daily, and (a) take the rate as 6 percent compounded continuously and (b) consider an annual interest rate of 6 percent compounded 365 times a year.

15. If an amount of money invested doubles itself in 10 years at interest compounded continuously, how long will it take for the original amount to triple itself?

16. If the purchasing power of a dollar is decreasing at the rate of 10 percent annually, compounded continuously, how long will it take for the purchasing power to be $0.50?

17. In a certain chemical reaction the rate of conversion of a substance is proportional to the amount of the substance still unreacted at that time. After 10 min one-third of the original amount of the substance has been reacted and 20 g has been reacted after 15 min. What was the original amount of the substance?

18. A tank contains 200 liters of brine in which there are 3 kg of salt per liter. It is desired to dilute this solution by adding brine containing 1 kg of salt per liter, which flows into the tank at the rate of 4 liters/min and the mixture, kept uniform by stirring, runs out at the same rate. When will the tank contain 1.5 kg of salt per liter?

19. There are 100 liters of brine in a tank, and the brine contains 70 kg of dissolved salt. Fresh water runs into the tank at the rate of 3 liters/min, and the mixture, kept uniform by stirring, runs out at the same rate. How many kilograms of salt are there in the tank at the end of 1 hour?

20. Sugar decomposes in water at a rate proportional to the amount still unchanged. If 50 kg of sugar were present initially and at the end of 5 hr this is reduced to 20 kg, how long will it take until 90 percent of the sugar is decomposed?

21. Professor Willard Libby of the University of California at Los Angeles was awarded the Nobel prize in chemistry for discovering a method of determining the date of death of a once-living object. Professor Libby made use of the fact that the tissue of a living organism is composed of two kinds of carbons, a radioactive carbon-14 (commonly written ^{14}C) and a stable carbon-12 (^{12}C), in which the ratio of the amount of ^{14}C to the amount of ^{12}C is approximately constant. When the organism dies, the law of natural decay applies to ^{14}C. If it is determined that the amount of ^{14}C in a piece of charcoal is only 45 percent of its original amount and the half-life of ^{14}C is 5730 years, when did the tree from which the charcoal came die?

22. Refer to Exercise 21. Suppose that after finding a fossil an archaeologist determines that the amount of ^{14}C present in the fossil is 25 percent of its original amount. Using the fact that the half-life of ^{14}C is 5730 years, what is the age of the fossil?

23. Under the conditions of Example 6, after how many minutes will the temperature of the body be 45°?

24. A pot of water was initially boiling at 100° and was cooling in air at a temperature of 0°. After 20 min the temperature of the water was 90°. (a) After how many minutes was the temperature of the water 80°? (b) What was the temperature of the water after 1 hr? Use Newton's law of cooling.

25. If a thermometer is taken from a room in which the temperature is 75° into the open, where the temperature is 35° and the reading of the thermometer is 65° after 30 sec, (a) how long after the removal will the reading be 50°? (b) What is the thermometer reading 3 min after the removal? Use Newton's law of cooling.

26. If a body in air at a temperature of 0° cools from 200° to 100° in 40 min, how many more minutes will it take for the body to cool to 50°? Use Newton's law of cooling.

27. A student has 3 hours to cram for an examination and during this time wishes to memorize a set of 60 facts. According to psychologists, the rate at which a person can memorize a set of facts is proportional to the number of facts remaining to be memorized. Thus if the student memorizes y facts in t minutes,

$$\frac{dy}{dt} = k(60 - y)$$

where k is a positive constant and $y < 60$ for all $t \geq 0$. Assume that zero facts are memorized initially. Suppose that the student memorizes 15 facts in the first 20 min. **(a)** Express y as a function of t. **(b)** Plot the graph of your function in part (a) and the horizontal asymptote of the graph. How many facts will the student memorize in **(c)** 1 hour and **(d)** 3 hours?

28. A new worker on an assembly line can do a particular task in such a way that if y units are completed per day after t days on the assembly line, then

$$\frac{dy}{dt} = k(90 - y)$$

where k is a positive constant and $y < 90$ for all $t \geq 0$. On the day the worker starts, 60 units are completed, and on the fifth day, the worker completes 75 units. **(a)** Express y as a function of t. **(b)** How many units per day can the worker eventually be expected to complete? **(c)** Plot the graph of your function in part (a) and the horizontal asymptote of the graph. **(d)** How many units does the worker complete on the ninth day? **(e)** Show that the worker is producing at almost full potential after 30 days.

29. For the standardized normal probability density function determine to five significant digits the probability that a random choice of x will be in the interval $[0, 1]$.

30. For the standardized normal probability density function, determine to five significant digits the probability that a random choice of x will be in the interval $[-3, 3]$.

31. The error function, denoted by erf, is defined by

$$\operatorname{erf}(x) = \frac{2}{\sqrt{\pi}} \int_0^x e^{-t^2} \, dt$$

Find an approximate value of $\operatorname{erf}(1)$ to five significant digits.

32. For the error function defined in Exercise 31, find an approximate value of $\operatorname{erf}(3)$ to five significant digits.

33. In biology an equation sometimes used to describe the restricted growth of a population is the Gompertz growth equation,

$$\frac{dy}{dt} = ky \ln \frac{a}{y}$$

where a and k are positive constants. Find the general solution of this differential equation.

34. If the half-life of a substance having exponential decay is h years and y_0 units of the substance are present now, then if y units will be present in t years, prove

$$y = y_0 \left(\frac{1}{2}\right)^{t/h}$$

35. Let f be a function describing exponential growth and g be a function describing bounded growth. How do the graphs of these two functions differ? Are the graphs similar in any respect? Why is the graph of g sometimes called a learning curve?

5.7 INVERSE TRIGONOMETRIC FUNCTIONS

Even though you were introduced to inverse trigonometric functions in your precalculus or trigonometry course, we briefly review them here. We will concentrate on the inverse sine, inverse cosine, inverse tangent, and inverse secant functions because these are the most important in calculus.

Recall from Section 5.1 that a function must be one-to-one to have an inverse. Because the six trigonometric functions are all periodic and, therefore, not one-to-one, none of them has an inverse. We can, however, restrict the domains of these functions in such a way to allow for an inverse.

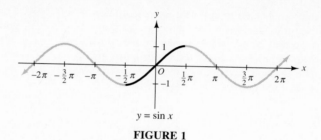

$$y = \sin x$$

FIGURE 1

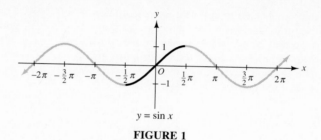

$$F(x) = \sin x \quad -\tfrac{1}{2}\pi \le x \le \tfrac{1}{2}\pi$$

FIGURE 2

We begin with the sine function whose graph appears in Figure 1. Observe from the figure that the sine function is increasing on the interval $\left[-\tfrac{1}{2}\pi, \tfrac{1}{2}\pi\right]$ and consequently, from Theorem 5.1.5 as well as from the horizontal-line test, the function F for which

$$F(x) = \sin x \quad \text{and} \quad -\tfrac{1}{2}\pi \le x \le \tfrac{1}{2}\pi \tag{1}$$

does have an inverse. The graph of F is sketched in Figure 2; its domain is $\left[-\tfrac{1}{2}\pi, \tfrac{1}{2}\pi\right]$ and its range is $[-1, 1]$. The inverse of this function is called the *inverse sine function*.

5.7.1 Definition of the Inverse Sine Function

The **inverse sine function,** denoted by $\sin^{-1}$, is defined by

$$y = \sin^{-1} x \quad \text{if and only if} \quad x = \sin y \text{ and } -\tfrac{1}{2}\pi \le y \le \tfrac{1}{2}\pi$$

The domain of $\sin^{-1}$ is the closed interval $[-1, 1]$ and the range is the closed interval $\left[-\tfrac{1}{2}\pi, \tfrac{1}{2}\pi\right]$.

▷ **ILLUSTRATION 1**

(a) $\sin^{-1} \dfrac{1}{\sqrt{2}} = \dfrac{1}{4}\pi$ (b) $\sin^{-1}\left(-\dfrac{1}{\sqrt{2}}\right) = -\dfrac{1}{4}\pi$ ◀

Of course, approximate inverse sine function values can be obtained on your calculator by using the $\boxed{\sin^{-1}}$ key.

In (1) the domain of F is restricted to the closed interval $\left[-\tfrac{1}{2}\pi, \tfrac{1}{2}\pi\right]$ so that the function is monotonic on its domain and therefore has an inverse function. However, the sine function has period 2π and is increasing on other intervals, for instance, $\left[-\tfrac{5}{2}\pi, -\tfrac{3}{2}\pi\right]$ and $\left[\tfrac{3}{2}\pi, \tfrac{5}{2}\pi\right]$. Also, the function is decreasing on certain closed intervals, in particular the intervals $\left[-\tfrac{3}{2}\pi, -\tfrac{1}{2}\pi\right]$ and $\left[\tfrac{1}{2}\pi, \tfrac{3}{2}\pi\right]$. Any one of these intervals could just as well be chosen for the domain of the function F of Equation (1). The choice of the interval $\left[-\tfrac{1}{2}\pi, \tfrac{1}{2}\pi\right]$, however, is customary because it is the largest interval containing the number 0 on which the function is monotonic.

The use of the symbol -1 to represent the inverse sine function makes it necessary to denote the reciprocal of $\sin x$ by $(\sin x)^{-1}$ to avoid confusion. A similar convention is applied when using any negative exponent with a trigonometric function. For instance,

$$\frac{1}{\tan x} = (\tan x)^{-1} \qquad \frac{1}{\cos^2 x} = (\cos x)^{-2}$$

and so on.

The terminology **arc sine** is sometimes used in place of inverse sine and the notation arc sin x is then used instead of $\sin^{-1} x$. This notation probably comes from the fact that if $t = $ arc sin u, then sin $t = u$, and t units is the length of the arc on the unit circle for which the sine is u. In this text the notation for the inverse trigonometric functions will utilize the symbol -1 rather than the word *arc*. This convention is consistent with the general notation for inverse functions.

We can sketch the graph of the inverse sine function by locating some points from values of $\sin^{-1} x$ such as those given in Table 1. The graph appears in Figure 3.

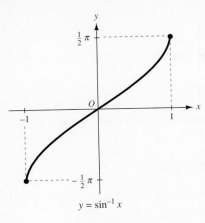

$y = \sin^{-1} x$

FIGURE 3

Table 1

x	-1	$-\dfrac{\sqrt{3}}{2}$	$-\dfrac{1}{2}$	0	$\dfrac{1}{2}$	$\dfrac{\sqrt{3}}{2}$	1
$\sin^{-1} x$	$-\dfrac{1}{2}\pi$	$-\dfrac{1}{3}\pi$	$-\dfrac{1}{6}\pi$	0	$\dfrac{1}{6}\pi$	$\dfrac{1}{3}\pi$	$\dfrac{1}{2}\pi$

From Definition 5.7.1

$$\sin(\sin^{-1} x) = x \qquad \text{for } x \text{ in } [-1, 1]$$
$$\sin^{-1}(\sin y) = y \qquad \text{for } y \text{ in } [-\tfrac{1}{2}\pi, \tfrac{1}{2}\pi]$$

Observe that $\sin^{-1}(\sin y) \neq y$ if y is not in the interval $[-\tfrac{1}{2}\pi, \tfrac{1}{2}\pi]$. For example,

$$\sin^{-1}(\sin \tfrac{3}{4}\pi) = \sin^{-1}\frac{1}{\sqrt{2}} \quad \text{and} \quad \sin^{-1}(\sin \tfrac{7}{4}\pi) = \sin^{-1}\left(-\frac{1}{\sqrt{2}}\right)$$

$$= \tfrac{1}{4}\pi \qquad\qquad\qquad\qquad = -\tfrac{1}{4}\pi$$

▶ **EXAMPLE 1** Find **(a)** $\cos[\sin^{-1}(-\tfrac{1}{2})]$; **(b)** $\sin^{-1}(\cos \tfrac{2}{3}\pi)$.

Solution Because the range of the inverse sine function is $[-\tfrac{1}{2}\pi, \tfrac{1}{2}\pi]$, $\sin^{-1}(-\tfrac{1}{2}) = -\tfrac{1}{6}\pi$.

(a) $\cos[\sin^{-1}(-\tfrac{1}{2})] = \cos(-\tfrac{1}{6}\pi)$ **(b)** $\sin^{-1}(\cos \tfrac{2}{3}\pi) = \sin^{-1}(-\tfrac{1}{2})$

$$= \frac{\sqrt{3}}{2} \qquad\qquad\qquad\qquad = -\tfrac{1}{6}\pi \qquad ◀$$

We now obtain the formula for the derivative of the inverse sine function by applying Theorem 5.1.7 which states that the derivative of a continuous monotonic function and the derivative of its inverse are reciprocals of each other. Let

$$y = \sin^{-1} x$$

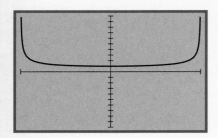

[–1, 1] by [–10, 10]

$$y = \frac{1}{\sqrt{1-x^2}}$$

NDER $(\sin^{-1} x, x)$

FIGURE 4

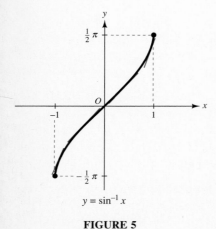

$y = \sin^{-1} x$

FIGURE 5

which is equivalent to

$$x = \sin y \quad \text{and} \quad y \text{ is in } \left[-\tfrac{1}{2}\pi, \tfrac{1}{2}\pi\right]$$

Differentiating on both sides of this equation with respect to y we obtain

$$\frac{dx}{dy} = \cos y \quad \text{and} \quad y \text{ is in } \left[-\tfrac{1}{2}\pi, \tfrac{1}{2}\pi\right] \tag{2}$$

From the identity $\sin^2 y + \cos^2 y = 1$, and replacing $\sin y$ by x, we obtain

$$\cos^2 y = 1 - x^2$$

If y is in $\left[-\tfrac{1}{2}\pi, \tfrac{1}{2}\pi\right]$, $\cos y$ is nonnegative; thus

$$\cos y = \sqrt{1 - x^2} \qquad \text{if } y \text{ is in } \left[-\tfrac{1}{2}\pi, \tfrac{1}{2}\pi\right]$$

Substituting from this equation into (2) we get

$$\frac{dx}{dy} = \sqrt{1 - x^2}$$

Because $\dfrac{dy}{dx}$ is the reciprocal of $\dfrac{dx}{dy}$,

$$D_x(\sin^{-1} x) = \frac{1}{\sqrt{1 - x^2}} \tag{3}$$

We support this result graphically by plotting the graphs of

$$y = \frac{1}{\sqrt{1 - x^2}} \quad \text{and} \quad \text{NDER}(\sin^{-1} x, x)$$

in the same window and showing they appear the same. See Figure 4.

Let us also investigate the geometric interpretation of Equation (3). Refer to Figure 5 showing the graph of the inverse sine function and segments of some tangent lines. Observe that when $-1 < x < 1$, which is the domain of $D_x(\sin^{-1} x)$, the slope of the tangent line is positive. Furthermore, when $x \to -1^+$ or $x \to 1^-$, the slope of the tangent line increases without bound. This information graphically supports the limits

$$\lim_{x \to -1^+} \frac{1}{\sqrt{1 - x^2}} = +\infty \quad \text{and} \quad \lim_{x \to 1^-} \frac{1}{\sqrt{1 - x^2}} = +\infty$$

From (3) and the chain rule we have the following theorem.

5.7.2 Theorem

If u is a differentiable function of x,

$$D_x(\sin^{-1} u) = \frac{1}{\sqrt{1 - u^2}} D_x u$$

▶ **EXAMPLE 2**   Find $f'(x)$ if

$$f(x) = \sin^{-1} x^2$$

Solution From Theorem 5.7.2

$$f'(x) = \frac{1}{\sqrt{1 - (x^2)^2}}(2x)$$

$$= \frac{2x}{\sqrt{1 - x^4}}$$

◀

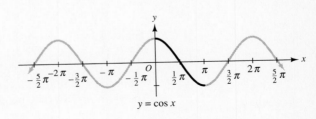

$y = \cos x$

FIGURE 6

To obtain the *inverse cosine function,* we proceed as we did with the inverse sine. We restrict the cosine to an interval on which the function is monotonic. We choose the interval $[0, \pi]$ on which the cosine is decreasing as shown by the graph of the cosine in Figure 6. So let us consider the function G defined by

$$G(x) = \cos x \quad \text{and} \quad 0 \leq x \leq \pi$$

The domain of G is the closed interval $[0, \pi]$ and the range is the closed interval $[-1, 1]$. The graph of G appears in Figure 7. Because G is continuous and decreasing on its domain, it has an inverse, which we now define.

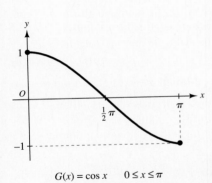

$G(x) = \cos x \quad 0 \leq x \leq \pi$

FIGURE 7

5.7.3 Definition of the Inverse Cosine Function

The **inverse cosine function,** denoted by $\cos^{-1}$, is defined by

$$y = \cos^{-1} x \quad \text{if and only if} \quad x = \cos y \text{ and } 0 \leq y \leq \pi$$

The domain of $\cos^{-1}$ is the closed interval $[-1, 1]$ and the range is the closed interval $[0, \pi]$.

▷ **ILLUSTRATION 2**

(a) $\cos^{-1} \dfrac{1}{\sqrt{2}} = \dfrac{1}{4}\pi$ **(b)** $\cos^{-1}\left(-\dfrac{1}{\sqrt{2}}\right) = \dfrac{3}{4}\pi$

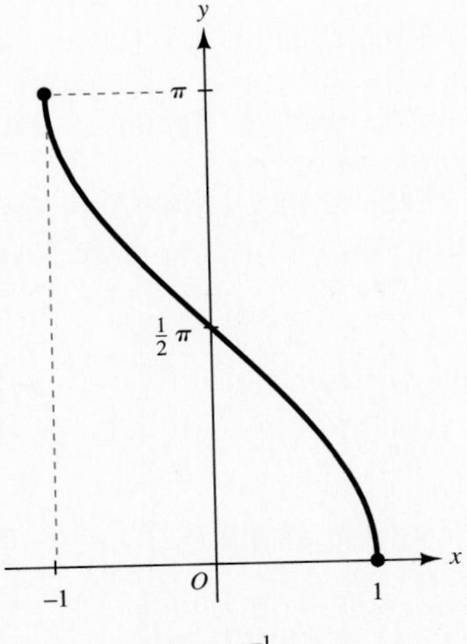

◀

The graph of the inverse cosine function appears in Figure 8. From Definition 5.7.3

$$\cos(\cos^{-1} x) = x \quad \text{for } x \text{ in } [-1, 1]$$
$$\cos^{-1}(\cos y) = y \quad \text{for } y \text{ in } [0, \pi]$$

Notice there is again a restriction on y in order to have the equality $\cos^{-1}(\cos y) = y$. For example, because $\frac{3}{4}\pi$ is in $[0, \pi]$

$$\cos^{-1}(\cos \tfrac{3}{4}\pi) = \tfrac{3}{4}\pi$$

$y = \cos^{-1} x$

FIGURE 8

However,

$$\cos^{-1}(\cos \tfrac{5}{4}\pi) = \cos^{-1}\left(-\frac{1}{\sqrt{2}}\right) \quad \text{and} \quad \cos^{-1}(\cos \tfrac{7}{4}\pi) = \cos^{-1}\left(\frac{1}{\sqrt{2}}\right)$$

$$= \tfrac{3}{4}\pi \qquad\qquad\qquad\qquad\qquad = \tfrac{1}{4}\pi$$

▶ **EXAMPLE 3** Prove

$$\cos^{-1} x = \tfrac{1}{2}\pi - \sin^{-1} x \qquad \text{for } |x| \le 1 \tag{4}$$

Solution   Let x be in $[-1, 1]$, and let

$$t = \cos(\tfrac{1}{2}\pi - \sin^{-1} x) \tag{5}$$

Applying the reduction formula $\cos(\tfrac{1}{2}\pi - v) = \sin v$ with $v = \sin^{-1} x$ on the right side of (5), we get

$$t = \sin(\sin^{-1} x)$$

Because $\sin(\sin^{-1} x) = x$,

$$t = x$$

Replacing t by x in (5) gives

$$x = \cos(\tfrac{1}{2}\pi - \sin^{-1} x) \tag{6}$$

Because $-\tfrac{1}{2}\pi \le \sin^{-1} x \le \tfrac{1}{2}\pi$, by adding $-\tfrac{1}{2}\pi$ to each member we have

$$-\pi \le -\tfrac{1}{2}\pi + \sin^{-1} x \le 0$$

Multiplying each member of this inequality by -1 and reversing the direction of the inequality signs gives

$$0 \le \tfrac{1}{2}\pi - \sin^{-1} x \le \pi$$

From this inequality, (6), and Definition 5.7.3,

$$\cos^{-1} x = \tfrac{1}{2}\pi - \sin^{-1} x \qquad \text{for } |x| \le 1$$

which is (4).   ◀

Observe in the solution of Example 3 that the identity depends on our choosing the range of the inverse cosine function to be $[0, \pi]$.

To derive the formula for the derivative of the inverse cosine function we use (4), which we just proved. Differentiating with respect to x, we have

$$D_x(\cos^{-1} x) = D_x(\tfrac{1}{2}\pi - \sin^{-1} x)$$

$$= -\frac{1}{\sqrt{1 - x^2}} \tag{7}$$

where x is in $(-1, 1)$.

As we did with the derivative of the inverse sine, we support equation (7) by plotting the graphs of

$$y = -\frac{1}{\sqrt{1 - x^2}} \quad \text{and} \quad \text{NDER}(\cos^{-1} x, x)$$

in the same window and showing they appear the same. See Figure 9.

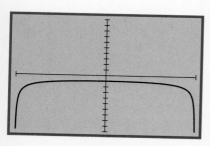

$[-1, 1]$ by $[-10, 10]$

$$y = -\frac{1}{\sqrt{1-x^2}}$$

NDER $(\cos^{-1} x, x)$

FIGURE 9

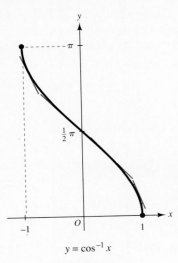

$y = \cos^{-1} x$

FIGURE 10

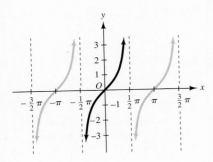

$y = \tan x$

FIGURE 11

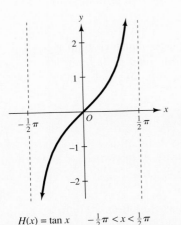

$H(x) = \tan x \quad -\frac{1}{2}\pi < x < \frac{1}{2}\pi$

FIGURE 12

Also as we did before, refer to Figure 10 for the geometric interpretation of Equation (7). The figure, showing the graph of the inverse cosine function and segments of some tangent lines, supports the facts that $D_x(\cos^{-1} x) < 0$ when $-1 < x < 1$ and that

$$\lim_{x \to -1^+} \frac{-1}{\sqrt{1 - x^2}} = -\infty \quad \text{and} \quad \lim_{x \to 1^-} \frac{-1}{\sqrt{1 - x^2}} = -\infty$$

The following theorem results from (7) and the chain rule.

5.7.4 Theorem

If u is a differentiable function of x,

$$D_x(\cos^{-1} u) = -\frac{1}{\sqrt{1 - u^2}} D_x u$$

▶ **EXAMPLE 4** Find $\dfrac{dy}{dx}$ if

$$y = \cos^{-1} e^{2x}$$

Solution From Theorem 5.7.4

$$\frac{dy}{dx} = -\frac{1}{\sqrt{1 - (e^{2x})^2}} (e^{2x})(2)$$

$$= \frac{-2e^{2x}}{\sqrt{1 - e^{4x}}}$$

◀

We now proceed to develop the *inverse tangent function*. Observe from the graph in Figure 11 that the tangent function is continuous and increasing on the open interval $(-\frac{1}{2}\pi, \frac{1}{2}\pi)$. We restrict the tangent function to this interval and let H be the function defined by

$$H(x) = \tan x \quad \text{and} \quad -\frac{1}{2}\pi < x < \frac{1}{2}\pi$$

The domain of H is the open interval $(-\frac{1}{2}\pi, \frac{1}{2}\pi)$ and the range is the set R of real numbers. See Figure 12 for the graph of H. This function has an inverse called the *inverse tangent function.*

5.7.5 Definition of the Inverse Tangent Function

The **inverse tangent function,** denoted by $\tan^{-1}$, is defined by

$$y = \tan^{-1} x \quad \text{if and only if} \quad x = \tan y \text{ and } -\frac{1}{2}\pi < y < \frac{1}{2}\pi$$

The domain of $\tan^{-1}$ is the set R of real numbers and the range is the open interval $(-\frac{1}{2}\pi, \frac{1}{2}\pi)$.

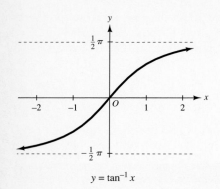

$y = \tan^{-1} x$

FIGURE 13

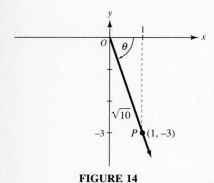

FIGURE 14

▷ **ILLUSTRATION 3**

(a) $\tan^{-1} \sqrt{3} = \frac{1}{3}\pi$ **(b)** $\tan^{-1}\left(-\frac{1}{\sqrt{3}}\right) = -\frac{1}{6}\pi$ **(c)** $\tan^{-1} 0 = 0$

Figure 13 shows the graph of the inverse tangent function. From Definition 5.7.5

$\tan(\tan^{-1} x) = x$ for x in $(-\infty, +\infty)$

$\tan^{-1}(\tan y) = y$ for y in $(-\frac{1}{2}\pi, \frac{1}{2}\pi)$

▷ **ILLUSTRATION 4**

$\tan^{-1}(\tan \frac{1}{4}\pi) = \frac{1}{4}\pi$ and $\tan^{-1}[\tan(-\frac{1}{4}\pi)] = -\frac{1}{4}\pi$

However

$\tan^{-1}(\tan \frac{3}{4}\pi) = \tan^{-1}(-1)$ and $\tan^{-1}(\tan \frac{5}{4}\pi) = \tan^{-1} 1$
$\qquad\qquad\quad = -\frac{1}{4}\pi \qquad\qquad\qquad\qquad = \frac{1}{4}\pi$ ◀

▶ **EXAMPLE 5**   Find the exact value of

$\sec[\tan^{-1}(-3)]$

Solution   We shall do this problem by interpreting $\tan^{-1}(-3)$ as an angle. Let

$\theta = \tan^{-1}(-3)$

Because the range of the inverse tangent function is $(-\frac{1}{2}\pi, \frac{1}{2}\pi)$, and because $\tan \theta$ is negative, $-\frac{1}{2}\pi < \theta < 0$. Thus

$\tan \theta = -3$ and $-\frac{1}{2}\pi < \theta < 0$

Figure 14 shows an angle θ that satisfies these requirements. Observe that the point P selected on the terminal side of θ is $(1, -3)$. From the Pythagorean theorem r is $\sqrt{1^2 + (-3)^2} = \sqrt{10}$. Therefore $\sec \theta = \sqrt{10}$. Hence

$\sec[\tan^{-1}(-3)] = \sqrt{10}$ ◀

For the formula for the derivative of the inverse tangent function, we again apply Theorem 5.1.7. If

$y = \tan^{-1} x$

then

$x = \tan y$ and y is in $(-\frac{1}{2}\pi, \frac{1}{2}\pi)$

Differentiating on both sides of this equation with respect to y we obtain

$\dfrac{dx}{dy} = \sec^2 y$ and y is in $(-\frac{1}{2}\pi, \frac{1}{2}\pi)$ **(8)**

From the identity $\sec^2 y = 1 + \tan^2 y$, and replacing $\tan y$ by x, we have

$\sec^2 y = 1 + x^2$

Substituting from this equation into (8) we get

$$\frac{dx}{dy} = 1 + x^2$$

So from Theorem 5.1.7,

$$D_x(\tan^{-1} x) = \frac{1}{1 + x^2} \tag{9}$$

The domain of the derivative of the inverse tangent function is the set R of real numbers.

In Exercise 58, you are asked to support Equation (9) graphically and to give a geometric interpretation of the equation as we did with Equations (3) and (7) for the derivatives of $\sin^{-1} x$ and $\cos^{-1} x$.

From (9) and the chain rule, we obtain the next theorem.

5.7.6 Theorem

If u is a differentiable function of x,

$$D_x(\tan^{-1} u) = \frac{1}{1 + u^2} D_x u$$

▶ **EXAMPLE 6**   Find $f'(x)$ if

$$f(x) = \tan^{-1} \frac{1}{x + 1}$$

Solution   From Theorem 5.7.6

$$f'(x) = \frac{1}{1 + \dfrac{1}{(x + 1)^2}} \cdot \frac{-1}{(x + 1)^2}$$

$$= \frac{-1}{(x + 1)^2 + 1}$$

$$= \frac{-1}{x^2 + 2x + 2} \qquad ◀$$

Before we define the *inverse secant function*, we direct your attention to the fact that $\cos x \geq 0$ in the range $[-\frac{1}{2}\pi, \frac{1}{2}\pi]$ of $\sin^{-1} x$, which was significant in obtaining formula (3) for the derivative of $\sin^{-1} x$. Furthermore, notice that $\sin x \geq 0$ in the range $[0, \pi]$ of $\cos^{-1} x$, and $\sec x > 0$ in the range $(-\frac{1}{2}\pi, \frac{1}{2}\pi)$ of $\tan^{-1} x$. So that $\tan x$ will be nonnegative in the range of the inverse secant function, we will choose that range to be in the first and third quadrants, which will pay off when we derive the formula for the derivative of the inverse secant function. You will see other advantages of these relationships when we apply inverse trigonometric functions in certain computations, in particular in Section 7.3 pertaining to a technique of integration involving trigonometric substitutions.

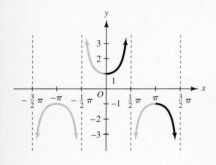

$y = \sec x$

FIGURE 15

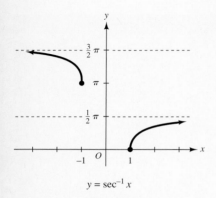

$y = \sec^{-1} x$

FIGURE 16

Refer to Figure 15, showing the graph of the secant function, and observe that the secant is increasing on the interval $[0, \frac{1}{2}\pi)$ and decreasing on the interval $[\pi, \frac{3}{2}\pi)$. Moreover, if $x \in [0, \frac{1}{2}\pi) \cup [\pi, \frac{3}{2}\pi)$, then $\sec x \in (-\infty, -1] \cup [1, +\infty)$. Thus we make the following definition.

5.7.7 Definition of the Inverse Secant Function

The **inverse secant function,** denoted by $\sec^{-1}$, is defined by

$$y = \sec^{-1} x \text{ if and only if } x = \sec y \text{ and } \begin{cases} 0 \le y < \frac{1}{2}\pi & \text{if } x \ge 1 \\ \pi \le y < \frac{3}{2}\pi & \text{if } x \le -1 \end{cases}$$

The domain of $\sec^{-1}$ is $(-\infty, -1] \cup [1, +\infty)$. The range of $\sec^{-1}$ is $[0, \frac{1}{2}\pi) \cup [\pi, \frac{3}{2}\pi)$.

▷ **ILLUSTRATION 5**

(a) $\sec^{-1}(\sqrt{2}) = \frac{1}{4}\pi$ **(b)** $\sec^{-1}(-\sqrt{2}) = \frac{5}{4}\pi$ ◄

See Figure 16 for the graph of the inverse secant function. From Definition 5.7.7

$$\sec(\sec^{-1} x) = x \qquad \text{for } x \text{ in } (-\infty, -1] \cup [1, +\infty)$$
$$\sec^{-1}(\sec y) = y \qquad \text{for } y \text{ in } [0, \frac{1}{2}\pi) \cup [\pi, \frac{3}{2}\pi)$$

▷ **ILLUSTRATION 6**

$$\sec^{-1}(\sec \tfrac{1}{3}\pi) = \tfrac{1}{3}\pi \quad \text{and} \quad \sec^{-1}(\sec \tfrac{4}{3}\pi) = \tfrac{4}{3}\pi$$

However

$$\sec^{-1}(\sec \tfrac{2}{3}\pi) = \tfrac{4}{3}\pi \quad \text{and} \quad \sec^{-1}(\sec \tfrac{5}{3}\pi) = \tfrac{1}{3}\pi \qquad ◄$$

To obtain the formula for the derivative of the inverse secant function, let

$$y = \sec^{-1} x \quad \text{and} \quad |x| \ge 1$$

Then

$$x = \sec y \qquad \text{and } y \text{ is in } [0, \tfrac{1}{2}\pi) \cup [\pi, \tfrac{3}{2}\pi) \tag{10}$$

Differentiating on both sides of (10) with respect to y we get

$$\frac{dx}{dy} = \sec y \tan y \qquad \text{and } y \text{ is in } [0, \tfrac{1}{2}\pi) \cup [\pi, \tfrac{3}{2}\pi) \tag{11}$$

From the identity $\tan^2 y = \sec^2 y - 1$, with $\sec y = x$, we get

$$\tan^2 y = x^2 - 1$$

Because y is in $[0, \frac{1}{2}\pi) \cup [\pi, \frac{3}{2}\pi)$, $\tan y$ is nonnegative. Thus

$$\tan y = \sqrt{x^2 - 1} \qquad \text{if } y \text{ is in } [0, \tfrac{1}{2}\pi) \cup [\pi, \tfrac{3}{2}\pi)$$

Substituting from (10) and this equation in (11) we have

$$\frac{dx}{dy} = x\sqrt{x^2 - 1}$$

Thus from Theorem 5.1.7,

$$D_x(\sec^{-1} x) = \frac{1}{x\sqrt{x^2 - 1}} \tag{12}$$

where $|x| > 1$. From (12) and the chain rule the next theorem follows.

5.7.8 Theorem

If u is a differentiable function of x,

$$D_x(\sec^{-1} u) = \frac{1}{u\sqrt{u^2 - 1}} D_x u$$

▶ **EXAMPLE 7**   Find $f'(x)$ if

$$f(x) = x \sec^{-1} \frac{1}{x}$$

Solution

$$f'(x) = \sec^{-1} \frac{1}{x} + x \left[\frac{1}{\frac{1}{x}\sqrt{\left(\frac{1}{x}\right)^2 - 1}} \left(-\frac{1}{x^2}\right) \right]$$

$$= \sec^{-1} \frac{1}{x} + \frac{x^2}{\frac{\sqrt{1 - x^2}}{\sqrt{x^2}}} \left(-\frac{1}{x^2}\right)$$

$$= \sec^{-1} \frac{1}{x} - \frac{1}{\frac{\sqrt{1 - x^2}}{|x|}}$$

$$= \sec^{-1} \frac{1}{x} - \frac{|x|}{\sqrt{1 - x^2}}   ◀$$

Refer back to Example 3 in which we proved identity (4) involving $\cos^{-1}$ and $\sin^{-1}$. This identity can be used to define the inverse cosine function, and from this definition we can determine that the range of $\cos^{-1}$ is $[0, \pi]$. We use this kind of procedure in the discussion of the two remaining inverse trigonometric functions.

5.7.9 Definition of the Inverse Cotangent Function

The inverse cotangent function, denoted by $\cot^{-1}$, is defined by

$$\cot^{-1} x = \tfrac{1}{2}\pi - \tan^{-1} x \qquad \text{where } x \text{ is any real number}$$

By definition the domain of $\cot^{-1}$ is the set R of real numbers. To obtain the range we write the equation in the definition as

$$\tan^{-1} x = \tfrac{1}{2}\pi - \cot^{-1} x \tag{13}$$

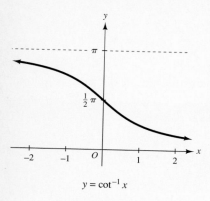

$y = \cot^{-1} x$

FIGURE 17

Because

$$-\tfrac{1}{2}\pi < \tan^{-1} x < \tfrac{1}{2}\pi$$

by substituting from (13) into this inequality we get

$$-\tfrac{1}{2}\pi < \tfrac{1}{2}\pi - \cot^{-1} x < \tfrac{1}{2}\pi$$

Subtracting $\tfrac{1}{2}\pi$ from each member we get

$$-\pi < -\cot^{-1} x < 0$$

Now multiplying each member by -1 and reversing the direction of the inequality signs we obtain

$$0 < \cot^{-1} x < \pi$$

The range of the inverse cotangent function is, therefore, the open interval $(0, \pi)$. Its graph is sketched in Figure 17.

▷ **ILLUSTRATION 7**

(a) $\tan^{-1} 1 = \tfrac{1}{4}\pi$

(b) $\tan^{-1}(-1) = -\tfrac{1}{4}\pi$

(c) $\cot^{-1} 1 = \tfrac{1}{2}\pi - \tan^{-1} 1$
$\qquad = \tfrac{1}{2}\pi - \tfrac{1}{4}\pi$
$\qquad = \tfrac{1}{4}\pi$

(d) $\cot^{-1}(-1) = \tfrac{1}{2}\pi - \tan^{-1}(-1)$
$\qquad = \tfrac{1}{2}\pi - (-\tfrac{1}{4}\pi)$
$\qquad = \tfrac{3}{4}\pi$ ◀

To obtain the formula for the derivative of $\cot^{-1} x$, we differentiate on both sides of the equation in Definition 5.7.9:

$$D_x(\cot^{-1} x) = D_x(\tfrac{1}{2}\pi - \tan^{-1} x)$$

$$= -\frac{1}{1 + x^2}$$

The next theorem follows from this formula and the chain rule.

5.7.10 Theorem

If u is a differentiable function of x,

$$D_x(\cot^{-1} u) = -\frac{1}{1 + u^2} D_x u$$

We now define the *inverse cosecant function* in terms of the inverse secant.

5.7.11 Definition of the Inverse Cosecant Function

The **inverse cosecant function,** denoted by $\csc^{-1}$, is defined by

$$\csc^{-1} x = \tfrac{1}{2}\pi - \sec^{-1} x \qquad \text{for } |x| \geq 1$$

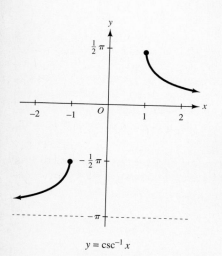

$y = \csc^{-1} x$

FIGURE 18

From the definition the domain of $\csc^{-1}$ is $(-\infty, -1] \cup [1, +\infty)$. The range of $\csc^{-1}$ can be found in a manner similar to that used to determine the range of $\cot^{-1}$. The range of $\csc^{-1}$ is $(-\pi, -\tfrac{1}{2}\pi] \cup (0, \tfrac{1}{2}\pi]$, and you are asked to show this in Exercise 57. The graph of $\csc^{-1}$ appears in Figure 18.

▷ **ILLUSTRATION 8**

(a) $\sec^{-1} 2 = \frac{1}{3}\pi$ **(b)** $\sec^{-1}(-2) = \frac{4}{3}\pi$

(c) $\csc^{-1} 2 = \frac{1}{2}\pi - \sec^{-1} 2$ **(d)** $\csc^{-1}(-2) = \frac{1}{2}\pi - \sec^{-1}(-2)$

$\qquad\qquad = \frac{1}{2}\pi - \frac{1}{3}\pi \qquad\qquad\qquad\qquad = \frac{1}{2}\pi - \frac{4}{3}\pi$

$\qquad\qquad = \frac{1}{6}\pi \qquad\qquad\qquad\qquad\qquad = -\frac{5}{6}\pi$ ◀

From Definition 5.7.11,

$$\csc^{-1} x = \frac{1}{2}\pi - \sec^{-1} x \qquad \text{for } |x| \geq 1$$

Differentiating with respect to x we obtain

$$D_x(\csc^{-1} x) = -\frac{1}{x\sqrt{x^2 - 1}}$$

where $|x| > 1$. From this formula and the chain rule we have the following theorem.

5.7.12 Theorem

If u is a differentiable function of x,

$$D_x(\csc^{-1} u) = -\frac{1}{u\sqrt{u^2 - 1}}D_x u$$

We conclude this section with an example showing an application of inverse trigonometric functions. In the example, an observer is looking at a picture placed high on a wall. See Figure 19. When the observer is far away from the wall, the angle subtended at the observer's eye by the picture is small. As the observer gets closer to the wall, that angle increases until it reaches a maximum value. Then as the observer gets even closer to the wall, the angle gets smaller. When the angle is a maximum, we say that the observer has the "best view" of the picture.

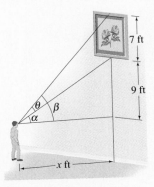

7 ft

9 ft

θ β
α

x ft

FIGURE 19

▶ **EXAMPLE 8**   A picture 7 ft high is placed on a wall with its base 9 ft above the level of the eye of an observer. **(a)** Estimate, to the nearest foot, on a graphics calculator, how far the observer should stand to have the "best view" of the picture. **(b)** Confirm the estimate in part (a) analytically.

Solution

(a) Refer to Figure 19. Let x feet be the distance of the observer from the wall, θ be the radian measure of the angle subtended at the observer's eye by the picture, α be the radian measure of the angle subtended at the observer's eye by the portion of the wall above eye level and below the picture, and $\beta = \alpha + \theta$. From the figure

$$\cot \beta = \frac{x}{16} \quad \text{and} \quad \cot \alpha = \frac{x}{9}$$

Because $0 < \beta < \frac{1}{2}\pi$ and $0 < \alpha < \frac{1}{2}\pi$,

$$\beta = \cot^{-1}\frac{x}{16} \quad \text{and} \quad \alpha = \cot^{-1}\frac{x}{9}$$

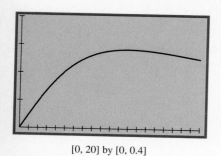

[0, 20] by [0, 0.4]

$$\theta = \tan^{-1}\frac{x}{9} - \tan^{-1}\frac{x}{16}$$

FIGURE 20

Substituting these values of β and α in the equation $\theta = \beta - \alpha$ we get

$$\theta = \cot^{-1}\frac{x}{16} - \cot^{-1}\frac{x}{9} \qquad x > 0 \tag{14}$$

To plot the graph of this equation on our graphics calculator, we first express the right side of the equation in terms of $\tan^{-1}$ because there is no key for $\cot^{-1}$ on our calculator. Applying Definition 5.7.9, we have

$$\theta = \frac{\pi}{2} - \tan^{-1}\frac{x}{16} - \left(\frac{\pi}{2} - \tan^{-1}\frac{x}{9}\right)$$

$$\theta = \tan^{-1}\frac{x}{9} - \tan^{-1}\frac{x}{16}$$

Figure 20 shows the graph of this equation plotted in the $[0, 20]$ by $[0, 0.4]$ window. On our calculator we estimate that the maximum value of θ occurs when $x = 12$.

(b) We wish to determine analytically the value of x that will make θ an absolute maximum. Because x is in the interval $(0, +\infty)$, the absolute maximum value of θ will be a relative maximum value.

We differentiate both sides of Equation (14) with respect to x and obtain

$$\frac{d\theta}{dx} = -\frac{\frac{1}{16}}{1 + \left(\frac{x}{16}\right)^2} + \frac{\frac{1}{9}}{1 + \left(\frac{x}{9}\right)^2}$$

$$= -\frac{16}{16^2 + x^2} + \frac{9}{9^2 + x^2}$$

Setting $\dfrac{d\theta}{dx} = 0$ we obtain

$$9(16^2 + x^2) - 16(9^2 + x^2) = 0$$
$$-7x^2 + 9 \cdot 16(16 - 9) = 0$$
$$x^2 = 9 \cdot 16$$
$$x = \pm 12$$

We reject -12 because it is not in the interval $(0, +\infty)$. Table 2 shows the results of the first-derivative test. Because the relative maximum value of θ is an absolute maximum value, we have confirmed analytically our estimate in part (a).

<u>Conclusion:</u>   To have the best view of the picture, the observer should stand 12 ft from the wall.

Table 2

	$\dfrac{d\theta}{dx}$	*Conclusion*
$0 < x < 12$	$+$	θ is increasing
$x = 12$	0	θ has a relative maximum value
$12 < x < +\infty$	$-$	θ is decreasing

EXERCISES 5.7

In Exercises 1 through 6, determine the exact function value.

1. (a) $\sin^{-1}\frac{1}{2}$ **(b)** $\sin^{-1}(-\frac{1}{2})$
(c) $\cos^{-1}\frac{1}{2}$ **(d)** $\cos^{-1}(-\frac{1}{2})$

2. (a) $\sin^{-1}\dfrac{\sqrt{3}}{2}$ **(b)** $\sin^{-1}\left(-\dfrac{\sqrt{3}}{2}\right)$

(c) $\cos^{-1}\dfrac{\sqrt{3}}{2}$ **(d)** $\cos^{-1}\left(-\dfrac{\sqrt{3}}{2}\right)$

3. (a) $\tan^{-1}\dfrac{1}{\sqrt{3}}$ **(b)** $\tan^{-1}(-\sqrt{3})$

(c) $\sec^{-1}\dfrac{2}{\sqrt{3}}$ **(d)** $\sec^{-1}\left(-\dfrac{2}{\sqrt{3}}\right)$

4. (a) $\cot^{-1}\dfrac{1}{\sqrt{3}}$ **(b)** $\cot^{-1}(-\sqrt{3})$

(c) $\csc^{-1}\dfrac{2}{\sqrt{3}}$ **(d)** $\csc^{-1}\left(-\dfrac{2}{\sqrt{3}}\right)$

5. (a) $\sin^{-1}1$ **(b)** $\sin^{-1}(-1)$ **(c)** $\csc^{-1}1$
(d) $\csc^{-1}(-1)$ **(e)** $\sin^{-1}0$

6. (a) $\cos^{-1}1$ **(b)** $\cos^{-1}(-1)$ **(c)** $\sec^{-1}1$
(d) $\sec^{-1}(-1)$ **(e)** $\cos^{-1}0$

7. Given $x = \sin^{-1}\frac{1}{3}$, find the exact value of each of the following: **(a)** $\cos x$; **(b)** $\tan x$; **(c)** $\cot x$; **(d)** $\sec x$; **(e)** $\csc x$.

8. Given $x = \cos^{-1}\frac{2}{3}$, find the exact value of each of the following: **(a)** $\sin x$; **(b)** $\tan x$; **(c)** $\cot x$; **(d)** $\sec x$; **(e)** $\csc x$.

9. Do Exercise 7 if $x = \sin^{-1}(-\frac{1}{3})$.

10. Do Exercise 8 if $x = \cos^{-1}(-\frac{2}{3})$.

11. Given $y = \tan^{-1}(-2)$, find the exact value of each of the following: **(a)** $\sin y$; **(b)** $\cos y$; **(c)** $\cot y$; **(d)** $\sec y$; **(e)** $\csc y$.

12. Given $t = \sec^{-1}(-3)$, find the exact value of each of the following: **(a)** $\sin t$; **(b)** $\cos t$; **(c)** $\tan t$; **(d)** $\cot t$; **(e)** $\csc t$.

In Exercises 13 through 24, find the exact value of the quantity.

13. (a) $\sin^{-1}(\sin\frac{1}{6}\pi)$ **(b)** $\sin^{-1}[\sin(-\frac{1}{6}\pi)]$
(c) $\sin^{-1}(\sin\frac{5}{6}\pi)$ **(d)** $\sin^{-1}(\sin\frac{11}{6}\pi)$

14. (a) $\sin^{-1}(\sin\frac{1}{3}\pi)$ **(b)** $\sin^{-1}[\sin(-\frac{1}{3}\pi)]$
(c) $\sin^{-1}(\sin\frac{2}{3}\pi)$ **(d)** $\sin^{-1}(\sin\frac{5}{3}\pi)$

15. (a) $\cos^{-1}(\cos\frac{1}{3}\pi)$ **(b)** $\cos^{-1}[\cos(-\frac{1}{3}\pi)]$
(c) $\cos^{-1}(\cos\frac{2}{3}\pi)$ **(d)** $\cos^{-1}(\cos\frac{4}{3}\pi)$

16. (a) $\cos^{-1}(\cos\frac{1}{4}\pi)$ **(b)** $\cos^{-1}[\cos(-\frac{1}{4}\pi)]$
(c) $\cos^{-1}(\cos\frac{3}{4}\pi)$ **(d)** $\cos^{-1}(\cos\frac{5}{4}\pi)$

17. (a) $\tan^{-1}(\tan\frac{1}{6}\pi)$ **(b)** $\tan^{-1}[\tan(-\frac{1}{3}\pi)]$
(c) $\tan^{-1}(\tan\frac{7}{6}\pi)$ **(d)** $\tan^{-1}[\tan(-\frac{4}{3}\pi)]$

18. (a) $\tan^{-1}(\tan\frac{1}{3}\pi)$ **(b)** $\tan^{-1}[\tan(-\frac{1}{6}\pi)]$
(c) $\tan^{-1}(\tan\frac{4}{3}\pi)$ **(d)** $\tan^{-1}[\tan(-\frac{7}{6}\pi)]$

19. (a) $\sec^{-1}(\sec\frac{1}{3}\pi)$ **(b)** $\sec^{-1}[\sec(-\frac{1}{3}\pi)]$
(c) $\sec^{-1}(\sec\frac{2}{3}\pi)$ **(d)** $\sec^{-1}[\sec(\frac{4}{3}\pi)]$

20. (a) $\sec^{-1}(\sec\frac{1}{4}\pi)$ **(b)** $\sec^{-1}[\sec(-\frac{1}{4}\pi)]$
(c) $\sec^{-1}(\sec\frac{3}{4}\pi)$ **(d)** $\sec^{-1}(\sec\frac{5}{4}\pi)$

21. (a) $\tan[\sin^{-1}\frac{1}{2}\sqrt{3}]$ **(b)** $\sin[\tan^{-1}\frac{1}{2}\sqrt{3}]$

22. (a) $\cos[\tan^{-1}(-3)]$ **(b)** $\tan[\sec^{-1}(-3)]$

23. (a) $\cos[\sin^{-1}(-\frac{1}{2})]$ **(b)** $\sin[\cos^{-1}(-\frac{1}{2})]$

24. (a) $\tan[\cot^{-1}(-1)]$ **(b)** $\cot[\tan^{-1}(-1)]$

In Exercises 25 through 30, sketch the graph of the function. Support your graph on your graphics calculator.

25. $f(x) = 2\sin^{-1}x$ **26.** $g(x) = \sin^{-1}2x$
27. $g(x) = \tan^{-1}\frac{1}{2}x$ **28.** $f(x) = \frac{1}{2}\tan^{-1}x$
29. $h(x) = \frac{1}{2}\cos^{-1}3x$ **30.** $h(x) = 3\cos^{-1}\frac{1}{2}x$

31. (a) Sketch the graph of $f(x) = \sin(\sin^{-1}x)$, and support your graph on your graphics calculator. State the domain and range of f. **(b)** Sketch the graph of $g(x) = \sin^{-1}(\sin x)$, and support your graph on your graphics calculator. State the domain and range of g.

32. Do Exercise 31 if $f(x) = \cos(\cos^{-1}x)$ and $g(x) = \cos^{-1}(\cos x)$.

In Exercises 33 through 42, find the derivative of the function.

33. (a) $f(x) = \sin^{-1}\frac{1}{2}x$ **(b)** $g(x) = \tan^{-1}2x$

34. (a) $f(x) = \cos^{-1}3x$ **(b)** $g(x) = \sec^{-1}2x$

35. (a) $F(x) = 2\cos^{-1}\sqrt{x}$
(b) $g(t) = \sec^{-1}5t + \csc^{-1}5t$

36. (a) $g(x) = \frac{1}{2}\sin^{-1}e^x$
(b) $f(y) = \tan^{-1}y^2 + \cot^{-1}y^2$

37. (a) $f(x) = \sin^{-1}\sqrt{1-x^2}$ **(b)** $G(x) = \cot^{-1}\dfrac{2}{x}$

38. (a) $f(w) = 2\tan^{-1}\dfrac{1}{w}$ **(b)** $F(x) = x\cos^{-1}x$

39. (a) $f(x) = \cos^{-1}(\sin x)$
(b) $h(x) = 4\sin^{-1}\frac{1}{2}x + x\sqrt{4-x^2}$

40. (a) $h(x) = \tan^{-1}\dfrac{2x}{1-x^2}$
(b) $g(x) = \sec^{-1}\sqrt{x^2+4}$

41. (a) $f(x) = x\tan^{-1}x - \ln\sqrt{1+x^2}$
(b) $g(x) = \sec^{-1}(2e^{3x})$

42. (a) $f(x) = x\sin^{-1}x + x\cos^{-1}x$
(b) $f(t) = \csc^{-1}\sqrt{t}$

43. A weight is suspended from a spring and vibrating vertically according to the equation

$$y = 2 \sin 4\pi \left(t + \tfrac{1}{8}\right)$$

where y centimeters is the directed distance of the weight from its central position t seconds after the start of the motion and the positive direction is upward. **(a)** Solve the equation for t. **(b)** Use the equation in part (a) to determine the smallest three positive values of t for which the weight is 1 cm above its central position.

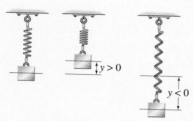

44. A 60-cycle alternating current is described by the equation $x = 20 \sin 120\pi(t - \tfrac{11}{720})$, where x amperes is the current at t seconds. **(a)** Solve the equation for t. **(b)** Use the equation in part (a) to determine the smallest three positive values of t for which the current is 10 amperes.

45. Find equations of the tangent line and normal line to the graph of the equation $y = \sec^{-1}(2x + 1)$ at the point $(\tfrac{1}{2}, \tfrac{1}{3}\pi)$.

46. In Example 8 show that another equation defining θ in terms of x is

$$\theta = \tan^{-1} \frac{7x}{x^2 + 144}$$

Use this equation to determine how far from the wall the observer should stand to get the best view of the picture.

47. A sign 3 ft high is placed on a wall with its base 2 ft above the eye level of a woman attempting to read it. **(a)** Estimate, to the nearest one-hundredth of a foot, on your graphics calculator, how far from the wall the woman should stand to get the best view of the sign; that is, so that the angle subtended at her eye by the sign is a maximum. **(b)** Confirm your estimate in part (a) analytically.

48. Example 8 and Exercise 47 are particular cases of the following more general situation: An object (for instance, a picture or a sign) a feet high is placed on a wall with its base h feet above the eye level of an observer. Show that the observer gets the best view of the object when the distance of the observer from the wall is $\sqrt{b(a + b)}$ feet.

In Exercises 49 through 55, define all your variables precisely as numbers of units of measurement. Use the symbol t to represent time and define the other variables in terms of t. Be sure to write a conclusion.

49. A picture 40 cm high is placed on a wall with its base 30 cm above the level of the eye of an observer. If the observer is approaching the wall at the rate of 40 cm/sec, how fast is the measure of the angle subtended at the observer's eye by the picture changing when the observer is 1 m from the wall?

50. A man on a dock is pulling in at the rate of 2 ft/sec a rowboat by means of a rope. The man's hands are 20 ft above the level of the point where the rope is attached to the boat. How fast is the measure of the angle of depression of the rope changing when there are 52 ft of rope out?

51. A light is 3 km from a straight beach. If the light revolves and makes 2 rpm, find the speed of the light's beam along the beach at a spot 2 km from the point on the beach nearest the light.

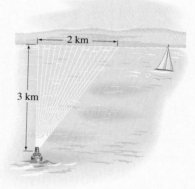

52. A ladder 25 ft long is leaning against a vertical wall. If the bottom of the ladder is pulled horizontally away from the wall so that the top is sliding down at 3 ft/sec, how fast is the measure of the angle between the ladder and the ground changing when the bottom of the ladder is 15 ft from the wall?

53. A woman is walking at the rate of 5 ft/sec along the diameter of a circular courtyard. A light at one end of a diameter perpendicular to her path casts a shadow on the circular wall. How fast is the shadow moving along the wall when the distance from the woman to the center of the courtyard is $\tfrac{1}{2}r$, where r feet is the radius of the courtyard?

Figure for Exercise 53

54. In Exercise 53 how far is the woman from the center of the courtyard when the speed of her shadow along the wall is 9 ft/sec?

55. A rope is attached to a weight and then passes over a hook that is 8 ft above the ground. The rope is pulled over the hook at the rate of $\frac{3}{4}$ ft/sec and drags the weight along level ground. If the length of the rope between the weight and the hook is x feet when the radian measure of the angle between the rope and the floor is θ, find the time rate of change of θ in terms of x.

56. Prove if $x > 0$ that

$$\tan^{-1} x + \tan^{-1} \frac{1}{x} = \frac{1}{2}\pi$$

two ways: **(a)** Use Definition 5.7.9; **(b)** Show that $\tan^{-1} x$ and $\tan^{-1} 1/x$ differ by a constant and then evaluate the constant.

57. Prove that the range of the inverse cosecant function is $(-\pi, -\frac{1}{2}\pi] \cup (0, \frac{1}{2}\pi]$.

58. Support the equation

$$D_x(\tan^{-1} x) = \frac{1}{1 + x^2}$$

on your graphics calculator. Also give a geometric interpretation of this equation as we did with Equations (3) and (7).

59. Given

$$f(x) = \tan^{-1} \frac{1}{x} - \cot^{-1} x$$

(a) Show that $f'(x) = 0$ for all x in the domain of f. **(b)** Prove that there is no constant C for which $f(x) = C$ for all x in the domain of f. **(c)** Why doesn't part (b) contradict Theorem 4.1.2?

In Exercises 60 through 62, an algebraic expression in the variable x is put in the form of a trigonometric expression in the variable θ by a substitution involving an inverse trigonometric function. This kind of substitution is required in Section 7.3.

60. Show that the substitution $\theta = \sin^{-1}(\frac{1}{3}x)$ in the expression $\sqrt{9 - x^2}$ yields $3 \cos \theta$ and explain how the domain of θ is applied.

61. Show that the substitution $\theta = \tan^{-1}(\frac{1}{2}x)$ in the expression $\sqrt{x^2 + 4}$ yields $2 \sec \theta$ and explain how the domain of θ is applied.

62. Show that the substitution $\theta = \sec^{-1}(\frac{1}{5}x)$ in the expression $\sqrt{x^2 - 25}$ yields $5 \tan \theta$ and explain how the domain of θ is applied.

5.8 INTEGRALS YIELDING INVERSE TRIGONOMETRIC FUNCTIONS

From the formulas for the derivatives of the inverse trigonometric functions we obtain some indefinite integral formulas. The following theorem gives three of them.

5.8.1 Theorem

$$\int \frac{du}{\sqrt{1 - u^2}} = \sin^{-1} u + C \qquad (1)$$

$$\int \frac{du}{1 + u^2} = \tan^{-1} u + C \qquad (2)$$

$$\int \frac{du}{u\sqrt{u^2 - 1}} = \sec^{-1} u + C \qquad (3)$$

The proof of each formula is immediate by taking the derivative of the right-hand side. The next theorem gives some more general formulas.

5.8.2 Theorem

$$\int \frac{du}{\sqrt{a^2 - u^2}} = \sin^{-1} \frac{u}{a} + C \qquad \text{where } a > 0 \qquad (4)$$

$$\int \frac{du}{a^2 + u^2} = \frac{1}{a} \tan^{-1} \frac{u}{a} + C \qquad \text{where } a \neq 0 \qquad (5)$$

$$\int \frac{du}{u\sqrt{u^2 - a^2}} = \frac{1}{a} \sec^{-1} \frac{u}{a} + C \qquad \text{where } a > 0 \qquad (6)$$

Proof   These formulas can be proved by finding the derivatives of the right side and obtaining the integrand. We prove formula (4).

$$D_u \left(\sin^{-1} \frac{u}{a} \right) = \frac{1}{\sqrt{1 - \left(\frac{u}{a} \right)^2}} D_u \left(\frac{u}{a} \right)$$

$$= \frac{\sqrt{a^2}}{\sqrt{a^2 - u^2}} \cdot \frac{1}{a}$$

$$= \frac{a}{\sqrt{a^2 - u^2}} \cdot \frac{1}{a} \qquad \text{if } a > 0$$

$$= \frac{1}{\sqrt{a^2 - u^2}} \qquad \text{if } a > 0$$

The proofs of (5) and (6) are left as exercises (see Exercises 32 and 33).   ∎

The formulas of Theorem 5.8.2 can also be proved by making a suitable change of variable and then applying Theorem 5.8.1 (see Exercises 34 through 36). Observe that the formulas of Theorem 5.8.2 include those of Theorem 5.8.1 by taking $a = 1$.

▶ **EXAMPLE 1**   Evaluate

$$\int \frac{dx}{\sqrt{4 - 9x^2}}$$

Solution

$$\int \frac{dx}{\sqrt{4 - 9x^2}} = \frac{1}{3} \int \frac{d(3x)}{\sqrt{4 - (3x)^2}}$$

$$= \frac{1}{3} \sin^{-1} \frac{3x}{2} + C \qquad \blacktriangleleft$$

In the next three examples we complete the square of a quadratic expression to write the integrand in a form that enables us to apply Theorem 5.8.2

▶ **EXAMPLE 2**   Evaluate

$$\int \frac{dx}{3x^2 - 2x + 5}$$

and support the answer graphically.

Solution

$$\int \frac{dx}{3x^2 - 2x + 5} = \int \frac{dx}{3(x^2 - \frac{2}{3}x) + 5}$$

To complete the square of $x^2 - \frac{2}{3}x$ we add $\frac{1}{9}$, and because $\frac{1}{9}$ is multiplied by 3, we actually add $\frac{1}{3}$ to the denominator, and so we also subtract $\frac{1}{3}$ from the denominator. Therefore we have

$$\int \frac{dx}{3x^2 - 2x + 5} = \int \frac{dx}{3(x^2 - \frac{2}{3}x + \frac{1}{9}) + 5 - \frac{1}{3}}$$

$$= \int \frac{dx}{3(x - \frac{1}{3})^2 + \frac{14}{3}}$$

$$= \frac{1}{3} \int \frac{dx}{(x - \frac{1}{3})^2 + \frac{14}{9}}$$

$$= \frac{1}{3} \cdot \frac{3}{\sqrt{14}} \tan^{-1}\left(\frac{x - \frac{1}{3}}{\frac{1}{3}\sqrt{14}}\right) + C$$

$$= \frac{1}{\sqrt{14}} \tan^{-1}\left(\frac{3x - 1}{\sqrt{14}}\right) + C$$

We support our answer graphically by plotting the graphs of

$$y = \frac{1}{3x^2 - 2x + 5} \quad \text{and} \quad \text{NDER}\left(\frac{1}{\sqrt{14}} \tan^{-1}\frac{3x - 1}{\sqrt{14}}, x\right)$$

in the $[-5, 5]$ by $[0, 0.5]$ window as shown in Figure 1. Because the graphs appear to overlap, we have supported our answer.   ◀

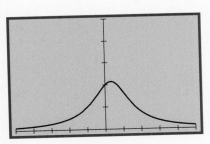

$[-5, 5]$ by $[0, 0.5]$

$$y = \frac{1}{3x^2 - 2x + 5}$$

$$\text{NDER}\left(\frac{1}{\sqrt{14}} \tan^{-1}\frac{3x - 1}{\sqrt{14}}, x\right)$$

FIGURE 1

▶ **EXAMPLE 3**   Use the NINT capability of a graphics calculator to approximate to six significant digits the value of

$$\int_0^1 \frac{(2x + 7)dx}{x^2 + 2x + 5}$$

Confirm the answer analytically.

Solution   On our graphics calculator we compute

$$\text{NINT}\left(\frac{2x + 7}{x^2 + 2x + 5}, 0, 1\right) = 1.27438$$

To confirm our answer analytically we need to evaluate the definite integral. But first we evaluate the indefinite integral.

Because $d(x^2 + 2x + 5) = (2x + 2)\,dx$, we write the numerator as $(2x + 2)\,dx + 5\,dx$ and express the original integral as the sum of two integrals.

$$\int \frac{(2x + 7)\,dx}{x^2 + 2x + 5} = \int \frac{(2x + 2)\,dx}{x^2 + 2x + 5} + 5\int \frac{dx}{x^2 + 2x + 5}$$

$$= \ln\left|x^2 + 2x + 5\right| + 5\int \frac{dx}{(x + 1)^2 + 4}$$

$$= \ln(x^2 + 2x + 5) + \frac{5}{2}\tan^{-1}\frac{x + 1}{2} + C$$

Note: $\left|x^2 + 2x + 5\right| = x^2 + 2x + 5$ because $x^2 + 2x + 5 > 0$ for all x. Therefore

$$\int_0^1 \frac{(2x + 7)\,dx}{x^2 + 2x + 5} = \ln(x^2 + 2x + 5) + \frac{5}{2}\tan^{-1}\frac{x + 1}{2}\Bigg]_0^1$$

$$= \ln 8 + \tfrac{5}{2}\tan^{-1} 1 - (\ln 5 + \tfrac{5}{2}\tan^{-1}\tfrac{1}{2})$$

$$= 1.27438$$

which confirms our answer. ◀

▶ **EXAMPLE 4**   Compute the exact value of

$$\int_0^{2 - \sqrt{2}} \frac{6\,dx}{(2 - x)\sqrt{x^2 - 4x + 3}}$$

Solution   We first evaluate the indefinite integral.

$$\int \frac{6\,dx}{(2 - x)\sqrt{x^2 - 4x + 3}} = \int \frac{6\,dx}{-(x - 2)\sqrt{(x^2 - 4x + 4) - 1}}$$

$$= -6\int \frac{dx}{(x - 2)\sqrt{(x - 2)^2 - 1}}$$

$$= -6\sec^{-1}(x - 2) + C$$

Therefore

$$\int_0^{2-\sqrt{2}} \frac{6\,dx}{(2 - x)\sqrt{x^2 - 4x + 3}} = -6\sec^{-1}(x - 2)\Bigg]_0^{2-\sqrt{2}}$$

$$= -6[\sec^{-1}(-\sqrt{2}) - \sec^{-1}(-2)]$$

$$= -6(\tfrac{5}{4}\pi - \tfrac{4}{3}\pi)$$

$$= \tfrac{1}{2}\pi \qquad ◀$$

▶ **EXAMPLE 5**   Find the exact area of the region in the first quadrant bounded by the curve

$$y = \frac{1}{1 + x^2}$$

the x axis, the y axis, and the line $x = 1$.

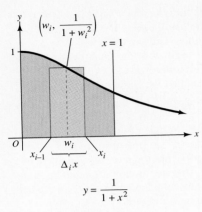

FIGURE 2

Solution Figure 2 shows the region and a rectangular element of area. If A square units is the area of the region,

$$A = \lim_{\|\Delta\| \to 0} \sum_{i=1}^{n} \frac{1}{1 + w_i^2} \Delta_i x$$

$$= \int_0^1 \frac{dx}{1 + x^2}$$

$$= \tan^{-1} x \Big]_0^1$$

$$= \tan^{-1} 1 - \tan^{-1} 0$$

$$= \tfrac{1}{4}\pi - 0$$

$$= \tfrac{1}{4}\pi$$

◀

EXERCISES 5.8

In Exercises 1 through 16, evaluate the indefinite integral. Support your answer either graphically or by showing that the derivative of your answer is the integrand.

1. $\displaystyle\int \frac{dx}{\sqrt{1 - 4x^2}}$

2. $\displaystyle\int \frac{dx}{x^2 + 25}$

3. $\displaystyle\int \frac{dx}{9x^2 + 16}$

4. $\displaystyle\int \frac{dt}{\sqrt{1 - 16t^2}}$

5. $\displaystyle\int \frac{dx}{4x\sqrt{x^2 - 16}}$

6. $\displaystyle\int \frac{x}{x^4 + 16} dx$

7. $\displaystyle\int \frac{r}{\sqrt{16 - 9r^4}} dr$

8. $\displaystyle\int \frac{du}{u\sqrt{16u^2 - 9}}$

9. $\displaystyle\int \frac{e^x}{7 + e^{2x}} dx$

10. $\displaystyle\int \frac{\sin x}{\sqrt{2 - \cos^2 x}} dx$

11. $\displaystyle\int \frac{dx}{(1 + x)\sqrt{x}}$

12. $\displaystyle\int \frac{ds}{\sqrt{2s - s^2}}$

13. $\displaystyle\int \frac{dx}{x^2 - x + 2}$

14. $\displaystyle\int \frac{dx}{\sqrt{3x - x^2 - 2}}$

15. $\displaystyle\int \frac{dx}{\sqrt{15 + 2x - x^2}}$

16. $\displaystyle\int \frac{2\,dt}{(t - 3)\sqrt{t^2 - 6t + 5}}$

In Exercises 17 through 24, compute the exact value of the definite integral. Support your answer by the NINT capability of your graphics calculator.

17. $\displaystyle\int_0^1 \frac{1 + x}{1 + x^2} dx$

18. $\displaystyle\int_2^5 \frac{dx}{x^2 - 4x + 13}$

19. $\displaystyle\int_{-4}^{-2} \frac{dt}{\sqrt{-t^2 - 6t - 5}}$

20. $\displaystyle\int_0^{\sqrt{3}} \frac{x}{\sqrt{12 - x^4}} dx$

21. $\displaystyle\int_0^1 \frac{dx}{e^x + e^{-x}}$

22. $\displaystyle\int_0^{\pi/6} \frac{\sec^2 x}{1 + 9\tan^2 x} dx$

23. $\displaystyle\int_1^e \frac{dx}{x[1 + (\ln x)^2]}$

24. $\displaystyle\int_{1/\sqrt{2}}^1 \frac{dx}{x\sqrt{4x^2 - 1}}$

In Exercises 25 through 28, use the NINT capability of your graphics calculator to approximate to six significant digits the value of the definite integral. Confirm your answer analytically.

25. $\displaystyle\int_{-1}^1 \frac{x}{\sqrt{8 - 2x - x^2}} dx$

26. $\displaystyle\int_0^1 \frac{2 + x}{\sqrt{4 - 2x - x^2}} dx$

27. $\displaystyle\int_0^3 \frac{2x^3}{2x^2 - 4x + 3} dx$

28. $\displaystyle\int_1^4 \frac{x}{x^2 + x + 1} dx$

29. Find the exact area of the region bounded by the curve $y = 8/(x^2 + 4)$, the x axis, the y axis, and the line $x = 2$.

30. Find the exact area of the region bounded by the curves $x^2 = 4ay$ and $y = 8a^3/(x^2 + 4a^2)$.

31. Find the exact area of the region bounded by the curve $y = 1/\sqrt{5 - 4x - x^2}$, the x axis, and the lines $x = -\tfrac{7}{2}$ and $x = -\tfrac{1}{2}$.

In Exercises 32 and 33, prove the formula by showing that the derivative of the right side is equal to the integrand.

32. $\displaystyle\int \frac{du}{a^2 + u^2} = \frac{1}{a}\tan^{-1}\frac{u}{a} + C$

33. $\displaystyle\int \frac{du}{u\sqrt{u^2 - a^2}} = \frac{1}{a}\sec^{-1}\frac{u}{a} + C$ if $a > 0$

In Exercises 34 through 36, prove the indicated formula of Theorem 5.8.2 by making a suitable change of variable and then using Theorem 5.8.1.

34. Formula (4)   **35.** Formula (5)   **36.** Formula (6)

37. In Section 2.8 we stated that a particle moving on a line is said to have *simple harmonic motion* if the measure of its acceleration is always proportional to the measure of its displacement from a fixed point on the line and its acceleration and displacement are oppositely directed. Therefore, if at t seconds s centimeters is the directed distance of the particle from the origin and v centimeters per second is the velocity of the particle, then a differential equation for simple harmonic motion is

$$\frac{dv}{dt} = -k^2 s \qquad (7)$$

where k^2 is the constant of proportionality and the minus sign indicates that the acceleration is opposite in direction from the displacement. Because $\frac{dv}{dt} = \frac{dv}{ds} \cdot \frac{ds}{dt}$, it follows that $\frac{dv}{dt} = v \frac{dv}{ds}$. Thus (7) may be written as

$$v \frac{dv}{ds} = -k^2 s \qquad (8)$$

(a) Solve (8) for v to get $v = \pm k \sqrt{a^2 - s^2}$. *Note:* Take $a^2 k^2$ as the arbitrary constant of integration, and justify this choice. **(b)** Letting $v = ds/dt$ in the solution of part (a) we obtain the differential equation

$$\frac{ds}{dt} = \pm k \sqrt{a^2 - s^2} \qquad (9)$$

Taking $t = 0$ at the instant when $v = 0$ (and hence $s = a$), solve (9) to obtain

$$s = a \cos kt \qquad (10)$$

(c) Show that the largest value for $|s|$ is a. The number a is called the *amplitude* of the motion. **(d)** The particle will oscillate between the points where $s = a$ and $s = -a$. If T seconds is the time for the particle to go from a to $-a$ and return, show that $T = 2\pi/k$. The number T is called the *period* of the motion.

38. A particle is moving on a line according to the equation of motion $s = 5 - 10 \sin^2 2t$, where s centimeters is the directed distance of the particle from the origin at t seconds. **(a)** Use the result of part (b) of Exercise 37 to verify that the motion is simple harmonic. **(b)** Verify that the motion is simple harmonic by showing that differential Equation (7) is satisfied. **(c)** Find the amplitude and period of this motion.

In Exercises 39 through 41, show that the exact value of the definite integral is π. Then approximate π to nine significant digits by the NINT capability of your graphics calculator applied to the definite integral.

39. $\displaystyle\int_0^{0.5} \frac{6}{\sqrt{1 - x^2}}\, dx$ **40.** $\displaystyle\int_0^1 \frac{4}{1 + x^2}\, dx$

41. $\displaystyle\int_{\sqrt{2}}^2 \frac{12}{x\sqrt{x^2 - 1}}\, dx$

42. Prove formulas (a), (b), and (c) by showing that the derivative of the right side is equal to the integrand. Then explain why the formula is equivalent to the corresponding formula of Theorem 5.8.1.

(a) $\displaystyle\int \frac{du}{\sqrt{1 - u^2}} = -\cos^{-1} u + C$

(b) $\displaystyle\int \frac{du}{1 + u^2} = -\cot^{-1} u + C$

(c) $\displaystyle\int \frac{du}{u\sqrt{u^2 - 1}} = -\csc^{-1} u + C$

5.9 HYPERBOLIC FUNCTIONS

Certain combinations of e^x and e^{-x} appear frequently in some applications of mathematics, especially in engineering and physics. These combinations are called *hyperbolic functions,* the two most important of which are the *hyperbolic sine* and *hyperbolic cosine*. At the end of this section we show that values of these functions are related to coordinates of points on an equilateral hyperbola in a manner similar to the way that values of the corresponding trigonometric functions are related to coordinates of points on a circle.

5.9.1 Definition of the Hyperbolic Sine and Hyperbolic Cosine Functions

The **hyperbolic sine function,** denoted by sinh, and the **hyperbolic cosine function,** denoted by cosh, are defined as follows:

$$\sinh x = \frac{e^x - e^{-x}}{2} \qquad \cosh x = \frac{e^x + e^{-x}}{2}$$

where x is any real number.

From the definition the domain of each of these functions is the set R of real numbers. The range of sinh is also the set R. The range of cosh, however, is the set of numbers in the interval $[1, +\infty)$. Because

$$\sinh(-x) = \frac{e^{-x} - e^x}{2} \qquad \cosh(-x) = \frac{e^{-x} + e^x}{2}$$

$$= -\frac{e^x - e^{-x}}{2} \qquad\qquad\qquad = \cosh x$$

$$= -\sinh x$$

the hyperbolic sine is an odd function and the hyperbolic cosine is an even function.

The formulas for the derivatives of the hyperbolic sine and hyperbolic cosine functions are obtained by applying Definition 5.9.1 and differentiating the resulting expressions involving exponential functions. Thus

$$D_x(\sinh x) = D_x\left(\frac{e^x - e^{-x}}{2}\right) \qquad D_x(\cosh x) = D_x\left(\frac{e^x + e^{-x}}{2}\right)$$

$$= \frac{e^x + e^{-x}}{2} \qquad\qquad\qquad = \frac{e^x - e^{-x}}{2}$$

$$= \cosh x \qquad\qquad\qquad\qquad = \sinh x$$

From these formulas and the chain rule we have the following theorem.

5.9.2 Theorem

If u a differentiable function of x,

$$D_x(\sinh u) = \cosh u \, D_x u$$
$$D_x(\cosh u) = \sinh u \, D_x u$$

Because $D_x(\sinh x) > 0$ for all x, the hyperbolic sine function is increasing on its entire domain. With this information, the knowledge that it is an odd function, and some values obtained from a calculator, we have the graph of the hyperbolic sine function shown in Figure 1.

The hyperbolic cosine function is decreasing on the interval $(-\infty, 0]$ because $D_x(\cosh x) < 0$ if $x < 0$, and it is increasing on the interval $[0, +\infty)$ because $D_x(\cosh x) > 0$ if $x > 0$. Furthermore, the hyperbolic cosine is an even function. With these facts and some values of $\cosh x$ from a calculator, we obtain the graph of the hyperbolic cosine function shown in Figure 2.

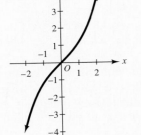

$y = \sinh x$

FIGURE 1

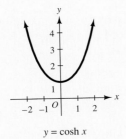

$y = \cosh x$

FIGURE 2

The other four hyperbolic functions are defined in terms of the hyperbolic sine and hyperbolic cosine. Observe that each satisfies an identity analogous to one satisfied by corresponding trigonometric functions.

5.9.3 Definition of the Other Four Hyperbolic Functions

The **hyperbolic tangent, hyperbolic cotangent, hyperbolic secant,** and **hyperbolic cosecant functions,** denoted respectively by tanh, coth, sech, and csch, are defined as follows:

$$\tanh x = \frac{\sinh x}{\cosh x} \qquad \coth x = \frac{\cosh x}{\sinh x}$$

$$\operatorname{sech} x = \frac{1}{\cosh x} \qquad \operatorname{csch} x = \frac{1}{\sinh x}$$

The hyperbolic functions in this definition can be expressed in terms of e^x and e^{-x} by applying Definition 5.9.1:

$$\tanh x = \frac{e^x - e^{-x}}{e^x + e^{-x}} \qquad \coth x = \frac{e^x + e^{-x}}{e^x - e^{-x}}$$

$$\operatorname{sech} x = \frac{2}{e^x + e^{-x}} \qquad \operatorname{csch} x = \frac{2}{e^x - e^{-x}}$$

The graph of the hyperbolic tangent appears in Figure 3. Its domain is the set R of real numbers and its range is the open interval $(-1, 1)$. Figure 4 shows the graph of the hyperbolic cotangent whose domain is $(-\infty, 0) \cup (0, +\infty)$ and whose range is $(-\infty, -1) \cup (1, +\infty)$. Observe from Figures 1 through 4 that none of these functions is periodic, while the corresponding trigonometric functions are periodic.

Identities satisfied by the hyperbolic functions are similar to those involving trigonometric functions. Four of the fundamental identities are given in Definition 5.9.3. The other four fundamental identities are as follows:

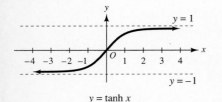

$$y = \tanh x$$

FIGURE 3

$$\tanh x = \frac{1}{\coth x}$$

$$\cosh^2 x - \sinh^2 x = 1$$

$$1 - \tanh^2 x = \operatorname{sech}^2 x$$

$$1 - \coth^2 x = -\operatorname{csch}^2 x$$

The first of these identities follows immediately from the definitions of tanh x and coth x. The other three can be proved by applying the formulas for the functions in terms of e^x and e^{-x}. For example,

$$\cosh^2 x - \sinh^2 x = \left(\frac{e^x + e^{-x}}{2}\right)^2 - \left(\frac{e^x - e^{-x}}{2}\right)^2$$

$$= \tfrac{1}{4}(e^{2x} + 2e^0 + e^{-2x} - e^{2x} + 2e^0 - e^{-2x})$$

$$= 1$$

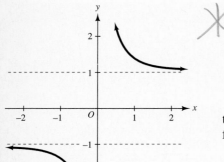

$$y = \coth x$$

FIGURE 4

Other identities can be proved from the eight fundamental identities.

The following two relations can be obtained from Definition 5.9.1:

$$\cosh x + \sinh x = e^x$$
$$\cosh x - \sinh x = e^{-x}$$

These relations are useful to prove the following identities:

$$\sinh(x + y) = \sinh x \cosh y + \cosh x \sinh y$$
$$\cosh(x + y) = \cosh x \cosh y + \sinh x \sinh y$$

If y is replaced by x in these two identities, we have

$$\sinh 2x = 2 \sinh x \cosh x$$
$$\cosh 2x = \cosh^2 x + \sinh^2 x$$

To find the derivative of the hyperbolic tangent, we apply some of the identities.

$$\begin{aligned}
D_x (\tanh x) &= D_x\left(\frac{\sinh x}{\cosh x}\right) \\
&= \frac{\cosh^2 x - \sinh^2 x}{\cosh^2 x} \\
&= \frac{1}{\cosh^2 x} \\
&= \operatorname{sech}^2 x
\end{aligned}$$

The formulas for the derivatives of the remaining three hyperbolic functions are: $D_x(\coth x) = -\operatorname{csch}^2 x$; $D_x(\operatorname{sech} x) = -\operatorname{sech} x \tanh x$; $D_x(\operatorname{csch} x) = -\operatorname{csch} x \coth x$. The proofs of these formulas are left as exercises (see Exercises 11 and 12).

From these formulas and the chain rule we have the following theorem.

5.9.4 Theorem

If u is a differentiable function of x,

$$D_x(\tanh u) = \operatorname{sech}^2 u D_x u$$
$$D_x(\coth u) = -\operatorname{csch}^2 u D_x u$$
$$D_x(\operatorname{sech} u) = -\operatorname{sech} u \tanh u D_x u$$
$$D_x(\operatorname{csch} u) = -\operatorname{csch} u \coth u D_x u$$

Observe that the formulas for the derivatives of the hyperbolic sine, cosine, and tangent all have a plus sign, whereas those for the derivatives of the hyperbolic cotangent, secant, and cosecant all have a minus sign. Otherwise the formulas are similar to the corresponding ones for the derivatives of the trigonometric functions.

▶ **EXAMPLE 1**   Find $f'(x)$ and simplify by hyperbolic-function identities if

$$f(x) = \tfrac{1}{2} \ln \tanh x$$

Solution

$$f'(x) = \frac{1}{2} \cdot \frac{1}{\tanh x} \cdot D_x(\tanh x)$$

$$= \frac{1}{2} \cdot \frac{1}{\tanh x} \cdot \text{sech}^2 x$$

$$= \frac{1}{2} \cdot \frac{\cosh x}{\sinh x} \cdot \frac{1}{\cosh^2 x}$$

$$= \frac{1}{2 \sinh x \cosh x}$$

$$= \frac{1}{\sinh 2x}$$

$$= \text{csch } 2x \qquad \blacktriangleleft$$

The indefinite integration formulas in the next theorem follow from the corresponding differentiation formulas in Theorems 5.9.2 and 5.9.4.

5.9.5 Theorem

$$\int \sinh u \, du = \cosh u + C$$

$$\int \cosh u \, du = \sinh u + C$$

$$\int \text{sech}^2 u \, du = \tanh u + C$$

$$\int \text{csch}^2 u \, du = -\coth u + C$$

$$\int \text{sech } u \tanh u \, du = -\text{sech } u + C$$

$$\int \text{csch } u \coth u \, du = -\text{csch } u + C$$

The techniques applied to integrate hyperbolic functions are similar to those used for trigonometric functions. The next two examples illustrate the procedure.

▶ **EXAMPLE 2**   Evaluate

$$\int \sinh x \cosh^2 x \, dx$$

Solution

$$\int \sinh x \cosh^2 x \, dx = \int \cosh^2 x \, (\sinh x \, dx)$$

$$= \tfrac{1}{3} \cosh^3 x + C \qquad \blacktriangleleft$$

▶ **EXAMPLE 3**   Evaluate to four significant digits and support the answer by a NINT computation on a graphics calculator

$$\int_0^1 \tanh^2 x \, dx$$

Solution

$$\int_0^1 \tanh^2 x \, dx = \int_0^1 (1 - \operatorname{sech}^2 x) \, dx$$

$$= x - \tanh x \Big]_0^1$$

$$= 1 - \tanh 1 + \tanh 0$$

$$= 1 - 0.7616 + 0$$

$$= 0.2384$$

From our graphics calculator

$$\text{NINT}(\tanh^2 x, 0, 1) = 0.2384$$

which supports our answer.   ◀

The graph of the function defined by

$$f(x) = a \cosh \frac{x}{a} \qquad a > 0$$

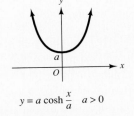

$$y = a \cosh \frac{x}{a} \quad a > 0$$

FIGURE 5

is sketched in Figure 5. The lowest point is at $(0, a)$, the function f is decreasing when $x < 0$ and increasing when $x > 0$, and the graph is concave upward everywhere. You are asked to confirm these properties analytically in Exercise 61. This graph is called a **catenary,** a curve formed by a flexible cable of uniform density hanging freely from two points under its own weight. Some cables of suspension bridges, some attached to telephone poles, and some running above an electric-railroad track, from which the trolley wire is suspended, hang in this shape.

From the graph of the hyperbolic sine in Figure 1, observe that a horizontal line intersects the graph in at most one point. The hyperbolic sine is, therefore, one-to-one. Furthermore, the hyperbolic sine is continuous and increasing on its domain, which you are asked to prove in Exercise 62. Thus this function has an inverse which we now define.

5.9.6 Definition of the Inverse Hyperbolic Sine Function

The **inverse hyperbolic sine function,** denoted by $\sinh^{-1}$, is defined as follows:

$$y = \sinh^{-1} x \quad \text{if and only if} \quad x = \sinh y$$

where y is any real number.

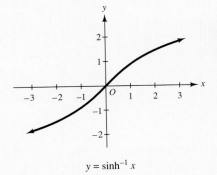

$$y = \sinh^{-1} x$$

FIGURE 6

Both the domain and range of $\sinh^{-1}$ are the set R of real numbers. The graph of this function appears in Figure 6. From the definition

$$\sinh(\sinh^{-1} x) = x \quad \text{and} \quad \sinh^{-1}(\sinh y) = y$$

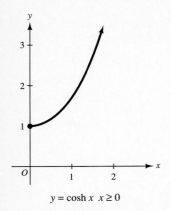

$y = \cosh x \quad x \geq 0$

FIGURE 7

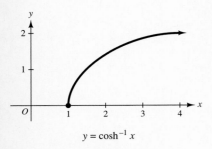

$y = \cosh^{-1} x$

FIGURE 8

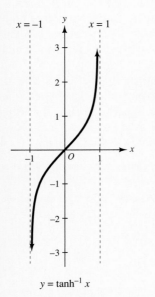

$y = \tanh^{-1} x$

FIGURE 9

In Figure 2 notice that a horizontal line, $y = k$ where $k > 1$, intersects the graph of the hyperbolic cosine function in two points. Thus cosh is not one-to-one and does not have an inverse. In the same way we obtained the inverse trigonometric functions, we restrict the domain and define a new function F as follows:

$$F(x) = \cosh x \qquad x \geq 0$$

The domain of this function is the interval $[0, +\infty)$ and the range is the interval $[1, +\infty)$. Figure 7 shows the graph of F. Because F is continuous and increasing on its domain, it has an inverse, called the *inverse hyperbolic cosine function.*

5.9.7 Definition of the Inverse Hyperbolic Cosine Function

The **inverse hyperbolic cosine function,** denoted by $\cosh^{-1}$, is defined as follows:

$$y = \cosh^{-1} x \quad \text{if and only if} \quad x = \cosh y \text{ and } y \geq 0$$

The domain of $\cosh^{-1}$ is the interval $[1, +\infty)$ and the range is the interval $[0, +\infty)$. The graph of $\cosh^{-1}$ appears in Figure 8. From Definition 5.9.7,

$$\cosh(\cosh^{-1} x) = x \qquad \text{if } x \geq 1$$

and

$$\cosh^{-1}(\cosh y) = y \qquad \text{if } y \geq 0$$

As with the hyperbolic sine, a horizontal line intersects the graphs of both the hyperbolic tangent and hyperbolic cotangent functions in at most one point. You may observe this in Figure 3 for the hyperbolic tangent and in Figure 4 for the hyperbolic cotangent. Both of these functions, therefore, are one-to-one and have an inverse.

5.9.8 Definitions of the Inverse Hyperbolic Tangent and Inverse Hyperbolic Cotangent Functions

The **inverse hyperbolic tangent** and **inverse hyperbolic cotangent functions,** denoted respectively by $\tanh^{-1}$ and $\coth^{-1}$, are defined as follows:

$$y = \tanh^{-1} x \quad \text{if and only if} \quad x = \tanh y$$

where y is any real number;

$$y = \coth^{-1} x \quad \text{if and only if} \quad x = \coth y$$

where $y \in (-\infty, 0) \cup (0, +\infty)$.

The domain of the inverse hyperbolic tangent function is the open interval $(-1, 1)$ and the range is the set R of real numbers. The graph of $\tanh^{-1}$ appears in Figure 9.

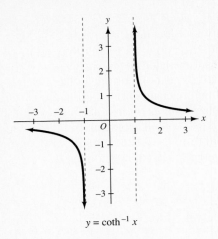

$y = \coth^{-1} x$

FIGURE 10

The domain of the inverse hyperbolic cotangent function is $(-\infty, -1) \cup (1, +\infty)$ and the range is $(-\infty, 0) \cup (0, +\infty)$. Figure 10 shows the graph of $\coth^{-1}$.

We will not concern ourselves with the inverse hyperbolic secant and inverse hyperbolic cosecant functions because they are seldom used.

The inverse hyperbolic functions can be expressed in terms of natural logarithms. This should not surprise you because the hyperbolic functions were defined in terms of the natural exponential function, the inverse of the natural logarithmic function. Following are these expressions for the four inverse hyperbolic functions we have discussed.

$$\sinh^{-1} x = \ln(x + \sqrt{x^2 + 1}) \qquad x \text{ any real number} \qquad (1)$$

$$\cosh^{-1} x = \ln(x + \sqrt{x^2 - 1}) \qquad x \geq 1 \qquad (2)$$

$$\tanh^{-1} x = \frac{1}{2} \ln \frac{1 + x}{1 - x} \qquad |x| < 1 \qquad (3)$$

$$\coth^{-1} x = \frac{1}{2} \ln \frac{x + 1}{x - 1} \qquad |x| > 1 \qquad (4)$$

We prove (1); the proofs of the other three formulas are similar. To prove (1) let

$$y = \sinh^{-1} x$$

Then from Definition 5.9.6, $x = \sinh y$. Applying Definition 5.9.1 to $\sinh y$, we get

$$x = \frac{e^y - e^{-y}}{2}$$

$$2x = e^y - \frac{1}{e^y}$$

from which we get

$$e^{2y} - 2xe^y - 1 = 0$$

Solving this equation for e^y by the quadratic formula, we obtain

$$e^y = \frac{2x \pm \sqrt{4x^2 + 4}}{2}$$

$$e^y = x \pm \sqrt{x^2 + 1}$$

We can reject the minus sign in this equation because $e^y > 0$ for all y and $x - \sqrt{x^2 + 1} < 0$ for all x. Therefore,

$$y = \ln(x + \sqrt{x^2 + 1})$$

and because $y = \sinh^{-1} x$, we have proved (1).

▶ **EXAMPLE 4**   Express each of the following in terms of a natural logarithm: **(a)** $\sinh^{-1} 2$; **(b)** $\tanh^{-1}(-\frac{4}{5})$.

Solution

(a) From (1),

$$\sinh^{-1} 2 = \ln(2 + \sqrt{5})$$

(b) From (3),

$$\tanh^{-1}(-\tfrac{4}{5}) = \frac{1}{2} \ln \frac{\frac{1}{5}}{\frac{9}{5}}$$

$$= \tfrac{1}{2} \ln 3^{-2}$$

$$= -\ln 3 \qquad ◀$$

We now apply Equation (1) to compute the derivative of the inverse hyperbolic sine function.

$$D_x(\sinh^{-1} x) = D_x \ln(x + \sqrt{x^2 + 1})$$

$$= \frac{1 + \dfrac{x}{\sqrt{x^2 + 1}}}{x + \sqrt{x^2 + 1}}$$

$$= \frac{\sqrt{x^2 + 1} + x}{\sqrt{x^2 + 1}(x + \sqrt{x^2 + 1})}$$

$$= \frac{1}{\sqrt{x^2 + 1}}$$

The formulas for the derivatives of the other three inverse hyperbolic functions are found in a similar way from formulas (2), (3), and (4). Their derivations are left as exercises (see Exercises 37 through 39). From these formulas and the chain rule, the next theorem follows.

5.9.9 Theorem

If u is a differentiable function of x,

$$D_x(\sinh^{-1} u) = \frac{1}{\sqrt{u^2 + 1}} D_x u \tag{5}$$

$$D_x(\cosh^{-1} u) = \frac{1}{\sqrt{u^2 - 1}} D_x u \qquad u > 1 \tag{6}$$

$$D_x(\tanh^{-1} u) = \frac{1}{1 - u^2} D_x u \qquad |u| < 1 \tag{7}$$

$$D_x(\coth^{-1} u) = \frac{1}{1 - u^2} D_x u \qquad |u| > 1 \tag{8}$$

▶ **EXAMPLE 5**   Find $\dfrac{dy}{dx}$ if

$$y = \tanh^{-1}(\cos 2x)$$

Solution   From (7)

$$\frac{dy}{dx} = \frac{1}{1 - \cos^2 2x}(-2 \sin 2x)$$

$$= \frac{-2 \sin 2x}{\sin^2 2x}$$

$$= \frac{-2}{\sin 2x}$$

$$= -2 \csc 2x \qquad ◀$$

The main application of inverse hyperbolic functions is in connection with integration, where the formulas in the following theorem are used.

5.9.10 Theorem

$$\int \frac{du}{\sqrt{u^2 + a^2}} = \sinh^{-1}\frac{u}{a} + C$$

$$= \ln(u + \sqrt{u^2 + a^2}) + C \quad \text{if } a > 0 \qquad (9)$$

$$\int \frac{du}{\sqrt{u^2 - a^2}} = \cosh^{-1}\frac{u}{a} + C$$

$$= \ln(u + \sqrt{u^2 - a^2}) + C \quad \text{if } u > a > 0 \qquad (10)$$

$$\int \frac{du}{a^2 - u^2} = \begin{cases} \dfrac{1}{a} \tanh^{-1}\dfrac{u}{a} + C & \text{if } |u| < a \\[2mm] \dfrac{1}{a} \coth^{-1}\dfrac{u}{a} + C & \text{if } |u| > a \end{cases}$$

$$= \frac{1}{2a} \ln\left|\frac{a + u}{a - u}\right| + C \text{ if } u \neq a \text{ and } a \neq 0 \qquad (11)$$

The formulas in this theorem can be proved by computing the derivative of the right side and obtaining the integrand. We demonstrate the procedure by proving (9).

Proof of (9)

$$D_u\!\left(\sinh^{-1}\frac{u}{a}\right) = \frac{1}{\sqrt{\left(\dfrac{u}{a}\right)^2 + 1}} \cdot \frac{1}{a}$$

$$= \frac{\sqrt{a^2}}{\sqrt{u^2 + a^2}} \cdot \frac{1}{a}$$

and because $a > 0$, $\sqrt{a^2} = a$; thus

$$D_u\!\left(\sinh^{-1}\frac{u}{a}\right) = \frac{1}{\sqrt{u^2 + a^2}}$$

To obtain the natural logarithm representation, we use formula (1), and we have

$$\sinh^{-1}\frac{u}{a} = \ln\left(\frac{u}{a} + \sqrt{\left(\frac{u}{a}\right)^2 + 1}\right)$$
$$= \ln\left(\frac{u}{a} + \frac{\sqrt{u^2 + a^2}}{a}\right)$$
$$= \ln(u + \sqrt{u^2 + a^2}) - \ln a$$

Therefore

$$\sinh^{-1}\frac{u}{a} + C = \ln(u + \sqrt{u^2 + a^2}) - \ln a + C$$
$$= \ln(u + \sqrt{u^2 + a^2}) + C_1$$

where $C_1 = C - \ln a$. ∎

In Chapter 7 you will learn other techniques to evaluate the integrals in Theorem 5.9.10. The formulas in the theorem give alternate representations of the integral in question. When evaluating an integral in which one of these forms occurs, the inverse hyperbolic representation may be easier to use and is sometimes less cumbersome to write.

▶ **EXAMPLE 6** Evaluate

$$\int \frac{dx}{\sqrt{x^2 - 6x + 13}}$$

and write the answer in terms of a natural logarithm.

Solution We apply (9) after completing the square.

$$\int \frac{dx}{\sqrt{x^2 - 6x + 13}} = \int \frac{dx}{\sqrt{(x^2 - 6x + 9) + 4}}$$
$$= \int \frac{dx}{\sqrt{(x - 3)^2 + 4}}$$
$$= \ln(x - 3 + \sqrt{x^2 - 6x + 13}) + C \quad ◀$$

▶ **EXAMPLE 7** Find the exact value of

$$\int_6^{10} \frac{dx}{\sqrt{x^2 - 25}}$$

in terms of inverse hyperbolic functions and support the answer by the NINT capability of a graphics calculator.

Solution From formula (10)

$$\int_6^{10} \frac{dx}{\sqrt{x^2 - 25}} = \cosh^{-1}\frac{x}{5}\Big]_6^{10}$$
$$= \cosh^{-1} 2 - \cosh^{-1} 1.2$$

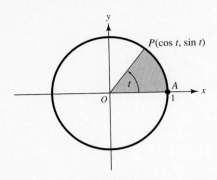

FIGURE 11

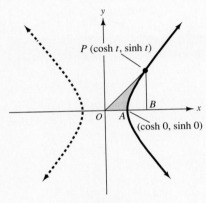

FIGURE 12

On our graphics calculator

$$\text{NINT}\left(\frac{1}{\sqrt{x^2 - 25}}, 6, 10\right) = 0.6945953932$$

To the same number of significant digits,

$$\cosh^{-1} 2 - \cosh^{-1} 1.2 = 0.6945953932$$

which supports our answer.   ◄

As promised, we conclude this section by showing that function values of sinh and cosh have the same relationship to the unit hyperbola $x^2 - y^2 = 1$ as the sine and cosine have to the unit circle $x^2 + y^2 = 1$. This fact justifies calling sinh and cosh hyperbolic functions just as sine and cosine are called *circular functions*.

Recall from your precalculus or trigonometry course (or see Appendix Section A.9) that if t is the radian measure of the angle formed by the x axis and a line from the origin to the point $P(x, y)$ on the unit circle, then

$$\sin t = y \quad \text{and} \quad \cos t = x$$

See Figure 11. Now refer to Figure 12 where t is any real number. The point $P(\cosh t, \sinh t)$ is on the unit hyperbola because

$$\cosh^2 t - \sinh^2 t = 1$$

Observe that because cosh t is never less than 1, all points $(\cosh t, \sinh t)$ are on the right branch of the hyperbola.

We now show how the areas of the shaded regions in Figures 11 and 12 are related. Because the area of a circular sector of radius r units and a central angle of radian measure t is given by $\frac{1}{2}r^2 t$ square units, the area of the circular sector in Figure 11 is $\frac{1}{2}t$ square units, since $r = 1$. The sector AOP in Figure 12 is the region bounded by the x axis, the line OP, and the arc AP of the unit hyperbola. If A_1 square units is the area of sector AOP, A_2 square units is the area of triangle OBP, and A_3 square units is the area of region ABP,

$$A_1 = A_2 - A_3 \tag{12}$$

From the formula for determining the area of a triangle,

$$A_2 = \tfrac{1}{2} \cosh t \sinh t \tag{13}$$

We find A_3 by integration:

$$A_3 = \int_0^t \sinh u \, d(\cosh u)$$

$$= \int_0^t \sinh^2 u \, du$$

$$= \frac{1}{2} \int_0^t (\cosh 2u - 1) \, du$$

$$= \tfrac{1}{4} \sinh 2u - \tfrac{1}{2}u \bigg]_0^t$$

Therefore

$$A_3 = \tfrac{1}{2} \cosh t \sinh t - \tfrac{1}{2}t$$

Substituting from this equation and (13) into (12) we have

$$A_1 = \tfrac{1}{2} \cosh t \sinh t - (\tfrac{1}{2} \cosh t \sinh t - \tfrac{1}{2}t)$$
$$= \tfrac{1}{2}t$$

Thus the measure of the area of circular sector AOP of Figure 11 and the measure of the area of sector AOP of Figure 12 is, in each case, one-half the value of the parameter associated with the point P. For the unit circle, the parameter t is the radian measure of angle AOP. The parameter t for the unit hyperbola is not interpreted as the measure of an angle; the term *hyperbolic radian*, however, is sometimes used in connection with t.

EXERCISES 5.9

In Exercises 1 through 6, (i) determine the exact function value, and (ii) if the exact value is not rational, express the value to four significant digits.

1. (a) $\sinh 0$ (b) $\cosh 0$ (c) $\sinh 1$ (d) $\sinh(-1)$

2. (a) $\tanh 0$ (b) $\operatorname{sech} 0$ (c) $\cosh 1$ (d) $\cosh(-1)$

3. (a) $\tanh 2$ (b) $\tanh(-2)$ (c) $\cosh(\ln 2)$
(d) $\cosh(\ln 0.5)$

4. (a) $\coth(0.5)$ (b) $\coth(-0.5)$ (c) $\sinh(\ln 2)$
(d) $\sinh(\ln 0.5)$

5. (a) $\operatorname{sech} 2$ (b) $\operatorname{sech}(-2)$ (c) $\coth(-1)$
(d) $\operatorname{csch}(\ln 1.5)$

6. (a) $\operatorname{csch} 2$ (b) $\operatorname{csch}(-2)$ (c) $\tanh 1$
(d) $\operatorname{sech}(\ln 1.5)$

In Exercises 7 through 10, prove the identity.

7. (a) $1 - \tanh^2 x = \operatorname{sech}^2 x$
(b) $\sinh(x + y) = \sinh x \cosh y + \cosh x \sinh y$

8. (a) $1 - \coth^2 x = -\operatorname{csch}^2 x$
(b) $\cosh(x + y) = \cosh x \cosh y + \sinh x \sinh y$

9. $\dfrac{1 + \tanh x}{1 - \tanh x} = e^{2x}$ **10.** $\tanh(\ln x) = \dfrac{x^2 - 1}{x^2 + 1}$

11. Prove: $D_x(\coth x) = -\operatorname{csch}^2 x$.

12. Prove: (a) $D_x(\operatorname{sech} x) = -\operatorname{sech} x \tanh x$;
(b) $D_x(\operatorname{csch} x) = -\operatorname{csch} x \coth x$.

In Exercises 13 through 18, find the derivative of the function.

13. (a) $f(x) = \sinh x^2$ (b) $f(w) = \operatorname{sech}^2 4w$

14. (a) $f(x) = \tanh^3 \sqrt{x}$ (b) $g(t) = \cosh t^3$

15. (a) $h(x) = \coth \dfrac{1}{x}$ (b) $g(x) = \ln(\tanh x)$

16. (a) $f(y) = \coth(\ln y)$ (b) $h(x) = e^x \cosh x$

17. (a) $f(x) = \tan^{-1}(\sinh 2x)$ (b) $g(x) = (\cosh x)^x$

18. (a) $g(x) = \sin^{-1}(\tanh x^2)$ (b) $f(x) = x^{\sinh x}, x > 0$

In Exercises 19 through 24, evaluate the indefinite integral.

19. $\displaystyle\int \sinh^4 x \cosh x \, dx$ **20.** $\displaystyle\int x \cosh x^2 \sinh x^2 \, dx$

21. $\displaystyle\int x^2 \operatorname{csch}^2 x^3 \, dx$ **22.** $\displaystyle\int \coth^2 3x \, dx$

23. $\displaystyle\int \tanh 2x \ln(\cosh 2x) \, dx$ **24.** $\displaystyle\int \operatorname{sech}^2 x \tanh^2 x \, dx$

25. Prove: (a) $\int \tanh u \, du = \ln \cosh u + C$;
(b) $\int \operatorname{csch} u \, du = \ln |\tanh \tfrac{1}{2}u| + C$.

26. Prove: (a) $\int \coth u \, du = \ln |\sinh u| + C$;
(b) $\int \operatorname{sech} u \, du = 2 \tan^{-1} e^u + C$.

In Exercises 27 through 32, evaluate to four significant digits the value of the definite integral and support your answer by the NINT capability of your graphics calculator.

27. $\displaystyle\int_0^{\ln 3} \operatorname{sech}^2 t \, dt$ **28.** $\displaystyle\int_0^{\ln 2} \tanh z \, dz$

29. $\displaystyle\int_1^4 \dfrac{\sinh \sqrt{x}}{\sqrt{x}} dx$ **30.** $\displaystyle\int_1^2 x \operatorname{sech}^2 x^2 \, dx$

31. $\displaystyle\int_2^3 \operatorname{sech}^2 x \tanh^5 x \, dx$ **32.** $\displaystyle\int_0^2 \sinh^3 x \cosh x \, dx$

In Exercises 33 through 36, determine the exact function value.

33. (a) $\cosh^{-1} 1$ (b) $\tanh^{-1} \tfrac{1}{2}$

34. (a) $\sinh^{-1} 1$ (b) $\coth^{-1} 2$

35. **(a)** $\sinh^{-1}\frac{1}{2}$ **(b)** $\coth^{-1}(-2)$

36. **(a)** $\cosh^{-1}2$ **(b)** $\tanh^{-1}(-\frac{1}{2})$

In Exercises 37 through 39, prove the formula.

37. Formula (6) **38.** Formula (7)

39. Formula (8)

In Exercises 40 through 48, find the derivative of the function.

40. **(a)** $f(x) = \cosh^{-1}\frac{1}{3}x$ **(b)** $F(x) = \tanh^{-1}x^3$

41. **(a)** $g(x) = \sinh^{-1}4x$ **(b)** $G(x) = \coth^{-1}x^2$

42. **(a)** $h(w) = \coth^{-1}(3w + 1)$
  (b) $f(x) = x^2 \sinh^{-1}x^2$

43. **(a)** $f(x) = \cosh^{-1}(\tan x)$
  (b) $g(x) = \tanh^{-1}(\cos x)$

44. **(a)** $g(x) = \tanh^{-1}(\sin 3x)$
  (b) $F(x) = \coth^{-1}(3 \sin x)$

45. **(a)** $f(z) = (\coth^{-1}z^2)^3$ **(b)** $g(x) = \tanh^{-1}(\sin e^x)$

46. **(a)** $f(t) = \sinh^{-1}e^{2t}$ **(b)** $h(x) = \cosh^{-1}(\ln x)$

47. $G(x) = x \sinh^{-1}x - \sqrt{1 + x^2}$

48. $H(x) = \ln\sqrt{1 - x^2} - x \tanh^{-1}x$

In Exercises 49 through 54, express the indefinite integral in terms of an inverse hyperbolic function and as a natural logarithm.

49. $\displaystyle\int \frac{dx}{\sqrt{4 + x^2}}$

50. $\displaystyle\int \frac{dx}{25 - x^2}$

51. $\displaystyle\int \frac{x}{\sqrt{x^4 - 1}}\, dx$

52. $\displaystyle\int \frac{dx}{\sqrt{25x^2 + 9}}$

53. $\displaystyle\int \frac{dt}{4e^{-t} - e^t}$

54. $\displaystyle\int \frac{dw}{\sqrt{5 - e^{-2w}}}$

In Exercises 55 through 60, find the exact value of the definite integral in terms of inverse hyperbolic functions and support your answer by the NINT capability of your graphics calculator.

55. $\displaystyle\int_3^5 \frac{dx}{\sqrt{x^2 - 4}}$

56. $\displaystyle\int_{-4}^{-3} \frac{dx}{1 - x^2}$

57. $\displaystyle\int_{-1/2}^{1/2} \frac{dx}{1 - x^2}$

58. $\displaystyle\int_{-2}^2 \frac{dx}{\sqrt{16 + x^2}}$

59. $\displaystyle\int_2^3 \frac{dx}{\sqrt{9x^2 - 12x - 5}}$

60. $\displaystyle\int_1^2 \frac{dx}{\sqrt{x^2 + 2x}}$

61. Figure 5 shows the graph of the catenary defined by

$$f(x) = a \cosh \frac{x}{a} \qquad a > 0$$

Confirm analytically that the lowest point is at $(0, a)$, the function f is decreasing when $x < 0$ and increasing when $x > 0$, and the graph is concave upward everywhere.

62. Prove that the hyperbolic sine function is continuous and increasing on its domain.

63. Find the area of the region bounded by the catenary

$$y = 6 \cosh \frac{x}{6}$$

the x axis, the y axis, and the line $x = 6 \ln 6$.

64. Find the volume of the solid of revolution generated if the region of Exercise 63 is revolved about the x axis.

65. A particle is moving on a line according to the equation of motion

$$s = e^{-t/2}(3 \sinh t + 4 \cosh t)$$

where s centimeters is the directed distance of the particle from the origin at t seconds. If v centimeters per second and a centimeters per second per second are the velocity and acceleration, respectively, of the particle at t seconds, **(a)** express v and a as functions of t. **(b)** Show that a is the sum of two numbers, one of which is proportional to s and the other proportional to v.

66. A curve goes through the point $(0, a)$, $a > 0$, and the slope at any point is $\sqrt{y^2/a^2 - 1}$. Prove that the curve is a catenary.

67. A woman wearing a parachute jumps from an airplane, and when her parachute opens, her velocity is 200 ft/sec. If v feet per second is her velocity t seconds after the parachute opens,

$$\frac{324}{g} \cdot \frac{dv}{dt} = 324 - v^2$$

where g is the constant acceleration due to gravity. Solve this differential equation to obtain.

$$t = \frac{18}{g}\left(\coth^{-1}\frac{v}{18} - \coth^{-1}\frac{100}{9}\right)$$

68. The region bounded by the curve

$$y = (16 - x^2)^{-1/2}$$

the x axis, and the lines $x = -2$ and $x = 3$ is revolved about the x axis. **(a)** Show that the exact measure of the volume of the solid generated is

$$\tfrac{1}{4}\pi\left[\tanh^{-1}(\tfrac{3}{4}) - \tanh^{-1}(-\tfrac{1}{2})\right]$$

(b) Use your calculator to approximate the volume accurate to four significant digits.

69. The warehouse shown in the accompanying figure is 100 ft long and 40 ft wide, and x and y are measured in feet. A cross section of the roof is in the shape of the region bounded above by the inverted catenary having the equation

$$y = 31 - 20 \cosh\left(\frac{x}{20}\right)$$

Determine the number of cubic feet of storage space in the warehouse.

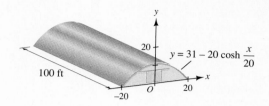

70. Suppose a particle is moving on a line such that s meters is the directed distance of the particle from the origin at t seconds. Explain why the motion is simple harmonic if the equation of motion is

$$s = A \sin kt + B \cos kt$$

but not simple harmonic if

$$s = A \sinh kt + B \cosh kt$$

where A, B, and k are constants.

CHAPTER 5 REVIEW

▶ SUGGESTIONS FOR REVIEW OF CHAPTER 5

1. Define a one-to-one function and state a geometric test for determining if a function is one-to-one. Make up an example illustrating your answer.

2. State a theorem that gives a test that can sometimes be applied to show analytically that a function is one-to-one. Make up an example and show how the test is applied.

3. Define the inverse of a function. Make up an example of an algebraic function and its inverse.

4. State a theorem you can use to determine analytically if two functions are inverses of each other. Apply the theorem to the functions in your answer to Suggestion 3.

5. If you know that a function f has an inverse, how can you sometimes find $f^{-1}(x)$ from $f(x)$? Why is it not always possible to find $f^{-1}(x)$ from $f(x)$? Make up two examples of a function f having an inverse f^{-1}: one where you can find $f^{-1}(x)$ and one where you cannot.

6. State a geometrical property satisfied by the graphs of a function and its inverse. How can you sketch by hand the graph of the inverse of a function from the graph of the function? How can you plot in the same screen on your graphics calculator the graphs of a function and its inverse if you know $f(x)$ but not $f^{-1}(x)$?

7. State a theorem relating the derivatives of a function and its inverse. Make up an example illustrating the theorem.

8. Define the natural logarithmic function and state its domain and range.

9. State the theorems pertaining to the natural logarithmic function that correspond to properties of logarithms you learned in your algebra course.

10. Describe in words only (no figure) the graph of the natural logarithmic function.

11. What do we mean by logarithmic differentiation? Make up an example using logarithmic differentiation.

12. State the formula that gives $\int u^n\, du$ for n any rational number.

13. State four theorems that involve indefinite integrals of trigonometric functions yielding the natural logarithmic function.

14. Define the natural exponential function and state its domain and range.

15. Define what we mean by a^x if a is any positive number and x is any real number. Make up an example applying the definition where x is irrational.

16. Define the number e. Show how e is used to compute an approximate value of your example in Suggestion 15.

17. What is the derivative of the natural exponential function exp? What is the indefinite integral of exp? What is the most general function that is its own derivative? Why is this the only such function?

18. Describe in words only (no figure) the graph of the natural exponential function.

19. Express the number e as a limit. Can this limit be used to define e? Give a reason for your answer.

20. State the theorems pertaining to exponential functions that correspond to properties of exponents you learned in your algebra course.

21. Define the logarithmic function to the base a and state its domain and range.

22. What are the formulas for the derivative and indefinite integral of a^x? Make up an example showing the computation of $f'(x)$ if $f(x) = a^{g(x)}$ where $a > 0$ and g is a transcendental function. Make up an example showing the computation of $\int f(x)\ dx$ if $f(x) = a^{h(x)}h'(x)$ where $a > 0$, and h is a transcendental function.

23. Describe in words only (no figure) the graph of the exponential function to the base a: (i) if $a > 1$; (ii) if $0 < a < 1$.

24. Describe in words only (no figure) the graph of the logarithmic function to the base a: (i) if $a > 1$; (ii) if $0 < a < 1$.

25. Write an equation relating $\log_a x$ and $\ln x$. State two formulas for the derivative of $\log_a x$, one involving $\log_a e$ and the other involving $\ln a$. Make up an example showing the computation of $f'(x)$ if $f(x) = \log_a g(x)$ where g is a transcendental function.

26. Describe how we compute the derivative of a function whose value is a variable to a variable power. Make up an example showing the computation of $f'(x)$ if $f(x) = g(x)^{h(x)}$ where g is a polynomial function and h is a transcendental function.

27. What are the laws of natural growth and natural decay? In your answer include the differential equation giving these laws.

28. Give an example of the law of natural growth in biology and in economics.

29. Give an example of the law of natural decay in chemistry and in business.

30. What is the half-life of a substance? Give an example.

31. Define a function describing exponential growth and a function describing exponential decay.

32. Define a function describing bounded growth. Give an example of bounded growth in business.

33. What is Newton's law of cooling? Make up an example showing how Newton's law of cooling is applied.

34. What is the standardized normal probability density function? How do you compute the probability that a random choice of the independent variable will be in the closed interval $[a, b]$?

35. Define the inverse sine function, state its domain and range, and sketch its graph.

36. Define the inverse cosine function, state its domain and range, and sketch its graph.

37. State an identity involving the inverse sine and inverse cosine functions.

38. Define the inverse tangent function, state its domain and range, and sketch its graph.

39. Define the inverse cotangent function in terms of the inverse tangent function by an identity similar to your answer in Suggestion 37. State the domain and range of the inverse cotangent function.

40. Define the inverse secant function, state its domain and range, and sketch its graph.

41. Define the inverse cosecant function in terms of the inverse secant function by an identity similar to your answer in Suggestion 37. State the domain and range of the inverse cosecant function.

42. State the formulas giving the derivatives of the inverse sine and inverse cosine functions. How are they related? Make up an example illustrating your answer.

43. State the formulas giving the derivatives of the inverse tangent and inverse cotangent functions. How are they related? Make up an example illustrating your answer.

44. State the formulas giving the derivatives of the inverse secant and inverse cosecant functions. How are they related? Make up an example illustrating your answer.

45. Make up an example of an indefinite integral that yields an inverse sine function.

46. Make up an example of an indefinite integral that yields an inverse tangent function.

47. Make up an example of an indefinite integral that yields an inverse secant function.

48. Define the hyperbolic sine and hyperbolic cosine functions and state the domain and range of each. Sketch their graphs.

49. Define the hyperbolic tangent, hyperbolic cotangent, hyperbolic secant, and hyperbolic cosecant functions in terms of the hyperbolic sine and cosine and state the domain and range of each.

50. Write the formulas for the derivatives of each of the six hyperbolic functions and the corresponding indefinite integrals.

51. What is a catenary and what is its equation?

52. Define the inverse hyperbolic sine, inverse hyperbolic cosine, inverse hyperbolic tangent, and inverse hyperbolic cotangent functions and state the domain and range of each. Sketch their graphs.

53. Express the four inverse hyperbolic functions mentioned in Suggestion 52 in terms of natural logarithms.

54. Write the formulas for the derivatives of the four inverse hyperbolic functions mentioned in Suggestion 52.

55. How does the use of inverse hyperbolic functions sometimes shorten the computation in integration? Make up an example illustrating your answer.

▶ MISCELLANEOUS EXERCISES FOR CHAPTER 5

In Exercises 1 through 6, determine if the function has an inverse. If the inverse exists, do the following: (a) Find it and state its domain and range; (b) plot the graphs of the function and its inverse on the same screen of your graphics calculator. If the function does not have an inverse, support this fact graphically by verifying that a horizontal line intersects the graph of the function in more than one point.

1. $f(x) = x^3 - 4$

2. $f(x) = 2\sqrt[3]{x} - 1$

3. $f(x) = 9 - x^2$

4. $f(x) = \sqrt{4 - x^2}$

5. $f(x) = \dfrac{3x - 4}{x}$

6. $f(x) = |2x - 3|$

In Exercises 7 and 8, (a) prove that the function f has an inverse, (b) find $f^{-1}(x)$, and (c) verify the equations of Theorem 5.1.4. for f and f^{-1}.

7. $f(x) = \sqrt[3]{x + 1}$

8. $f(x) = \dfrac{2x - 1}{2x + 1}$

In Exercises 9 through 12, find $(f^{-1})'(d)$.

9. $f(x) = x^2 - 6x + 8, x \geq 3; d = 3$

10. $f(x) = \sqrt{3x + 4}; d = 5$

11. $f(x) = 8x^3 + 6x; d = 4$

12. $f(x) = x^5 + x - 22; d = 12$

In Exercises 13 through 30, differentiate the function and simplify the result.

13. (a) $f(x) = \ln(\cos 3x)$ **(b)** $F(x) = \ln(x^2 + 1)^2$

14. (a) $g(x) = \cos(3 \ln x)$ **(b)** $G(x) = (\ln x^2)^2$

15. (a) $g(t) = \sin e^{4t}$ **(b)** $G(t) = 2^{\tan t}$

16. (a) $f(w) = e^{\sin 4w}$ **(b)** $F(w) = \tan 2^w$

17. (a) $f(x) = \tan^{-1} e^x$ **(b)** $g(x) = e^{\cot^{-1}x}$

18. (a) $F(x) = \cos^{-1} 3^x$ **(b)** $G(x) = 3^{\sin^{-1}x}$

19. (a) $f(w) = \sinh^3 2w$ **(b)** $F(w) = \cosh 2w^3$

20. (a) $g(t) = \tanh(\ln t)$ **(b)** $G(t) = \ln(\coth t)$

21. (a) $F(x) = \text{sech}(\tan x)$ **(b)** $G(x) = \tanh(\sec x)$

22. (a) $f(x) = \sinh^{-1} x^2$ **(b)** $g(x) = \tanh^{-1} 2x$

23. $f(x) = \log_{10}\left(\dfrac{1 + x}{1 - x}\right)^2$

24. $g(x) = \ln \sqrt{\dfrac{2x + 1}{x - 3}}$

25. $g(t) = (\sin t)^{2t}, \sin t > 0$

26. $f(t) = t^{3/\ln t}$

27. $F(x) = \cosh^{-1}\sqrt{x}$

28. $G(x) = \sec^{-1}\sqrt{x^2 + 1}$

29. $f(x) = \cos^{-1}(\tanh 2x)$

30. $g(x) = \coth^{-1}(\csc x)$

In Exercises 31 and 32, find $\dfrac{dy}{dx}$ by logarithmic differentiation.

31. $y = x^3(x^2 + 1)^2(x - 1)^4$

32. $y = \dfrac{\sqrt{4 - x^2}}{\sqrt[3]{x^6 + 8}}$

In Exercises 33 and 34, compute on a calculator the value of a^x for the given values of a and x by first applying the definition of a real number exponent. Support your answer by computing the value directly.

33. (a) $a = 3, x = \sqrt{2}$ **(b)** $a = 2, x = \pi$

34. (a) $a = 7, x = e$ **(b)** $a = e, x = \pi$

In Exercises 35 through 48, evaluate the indefinite integral.

35. $\displaystyle\int \dfrac{3e^{2x}}{1 + e^{2x}} dx$

36. $\displaystyle\int e^{x^2 - 2x}(x - 1) dx$

37. $\displaystyle\int (e^{3x} + 2^{3x}) dx$

38. $\displaystyle\int \dfrac{10^{\ln x^2}}{x} dx$

39. $\displaystyle\int e^x 2^{e^x} dx$

40. $\displaystyle\int \dfrac{10^x + 1}{10^x - 1} dx$

41. $\displaystyle\int \dfrac{4x}{\sqrt{1 - x^4}} dx$

42. $\displaystyle\int \dfrac{dy}{9e^y + e^{-y}}$

43. $\displaystyle\int \dfrac{dx}{x^2 + 2x + 10}$

44. $\displaystyle\int \dfrac{dx}{\sqrt{5 + 4x - x^2}}$

45. $\displaystyle\int \dfrac{dx}{\sqrt{e^{2x} - 8}}$

46. $\displaystyle\int x \coth \tfrac{1}{2}x^2 dx$

47. $\displaystyle\int \tanh^2 3w \, dw$

48. $\displaystyle\int \dfrac{\cosh t}{\sqrt{\sinh t}} dt$

In Exercises 49 through 58, evaluate the definite integral and support your answer by the NINT capability of your graphics calculator.

49. $\displaystyle\int_0^2 x^2 e^{x^3} dx$

50. $\displaystyle\int_0^1 (e^{2x} + 1)^2 dx$

51. $\displaystyle\int_1^8 \dfrac{x^{1/3}}{x^{4/3} + 4} dx$

52. $\displaystyle\int_{1/3}^{1/2} \dfrac{4x^{-3} + 2}{x^{-2} - x} dx$

53. $\displaystyle\int_0^{\ln 2} \dfrac{e^{2x}}{e^x - 5} dx$

54. $\displaystyle\int_e^{e^2} \dfrac{dx}{x(\ln x)}$

55. $\displaystyle\int_1^2 \dfrac{t + 2}{\sqrt{4t - t^2}} dt$

56. $\displaystyle\int_{-1}^1 \dfrac{2x + 6}{x^2 + 2x + 5} dx$

57. $\int_0^1 \sqrt{\cosh^2 y - 1}\ dy$ **58.** $\int_0^2 \text{sech}^2 \tfrac{1}{2}x\ dx$

59. Find $\dfrac{dy}{dx}$ if $ye^x + xe^y + x + y = 0$

60. Show that $\cosh(\ln x) = \dfrac{x^2 + 1}{2x}$.

61. Express the quantity in terms of a natural logarithm:
(a) $\cosh^{-1} 2$; **(b)** $\tanh^{-1} \tfrac{1}{4}$.

62. Prove: **(a)** $\lim\limits_{x \to +\infty} \coth x = 1$; **(b)** $\lim\limits_{x \to +\infty} \text{csch}\ x = 0$.

63. **(a)** Plot in the same window the graph of $y = x^{x-1}$ and the tangent line at the point $(2, 2)$. **(b)** Find an equation of the tangent line.

64. Use differentials to find an approximate value to three decimal places of $\log_{10} 100{,}937$. Use the fact that $\log_{10} e = 0.43429$ with accuracy to five decimal places. Support your answer on your calculator.

65. A particle is moving on a line, where s feet is the directed distance of the particle from the origin, v feet per second is the velocity of the particle, and a feet per second squared is the acceleration of the particle at t seconds. If $a = e^t + e^{-t}$ and $v = 1$ and $s = 2$ when $t = 0$, find v and s in terms of t.

66. The area of the region bounded by the curve $y = e^{-x}$, the coordinate axes, and the line $x = b$ $(b > 0)$ is a function of b. If f is this function, find $f(b)$. Also find $\lim\limits_{b \to +\infty} f(b)$.

67. The volume of the solid of revolution obtained by revolving the region in Exercise 66 about the x axis is a function of b. If g is this function, find $g(b)$. Also find $\lim\limits_{b \to +\infty} g(b)$.

68. Prove that if a rectangle is to have its base on the x axis and two of its vertices on the curve $y = e^{-x^2}$, then the rectangle will have the largest possible area if the two vertices are at the points of inflection of the graph.

69. Given $f(x) = \ln|x|$ and $x < 0$. Show that f has an inverse function. If g is the inverse function, find $g(x)$ and the domain of g.

70. Prove that if $x < 1$, $\ln x < x$. *Hint:* Let $f(x) = x - \ln x$, and show that f is decreasing on $(0, 1)$ and find $f(1)$.

71. When a gas undergoes an adiabatic (no gain or loss of heat) expansion or compression, then the rate of change of the pressure with respect to the volume varies directly as the pressure and inversely as the volume. If the pressure is p pounds per square inch when the volume is v cubic inches, and the initial pressure and volume are p_0 pounds per square inch and v_0 cubic inches, show that $pv^k = p_0 v_0^k$.

72. Find the volume of the solid of revolution generated if the region bounded by the curve $y = 2^{-x}$ and the lines $x = 1$ and $x = 4$ is revolved about the x axis.

73. The half-life of cesium-137 is 30 years, its rate of decay is proportional to the amount present at any time, and 65 mg of cesium are present now.
(a) If y milligrams of cesium will be present t years from now, express y as a function of t.
(b) Estimate on your graphics calculator when only 10 mg of cesium will be present.
(c) Confirm your estimate in part (b) analytically.

74. The rate of natural increase of the population of a certain city is proportional to the population, and the population is expected to double in 60 years. The population is now 120,000.
(a) If y is the expected population t years from now, express y as a function of t.
(b) Estimate on your graphics calculator when the expected population will be 150,000.
(c) Estimate on your graphics calculator the expected population 20 years from now.
(d) Confirm your estimates in parts (b) and (c) analytically.

75. A student studying a foreign language has 50 verbs to memorize. The rate at which the student can memorize these verbs is proportional to the number of verbs remaining to be memorized; that is, if the student memorizes y verbs in t minutes
$$\frac{dy}{dt} = k(50 - y)$$
where k is a positive constant and $y < 50$ for all $t \geq 0$. Assume that initially no verbs are memorized and that 20 verbs are memorized in the first 30 minutes.
(a) Express y as a function of t.
(b) Plot the graph of your function in part (a) and the horizontal asymptote of the graph.
(c) Estimate on your graphics calculator how many verbs the student will memorize in 1 hour.
(d) Estimate on your graphics calculator how long it will be until the student has only one verb left to memorize.
(e) Confirm your estimates in parts (c) and (d) analytically.

In Exercises 76 through 85, define all your variables precisely as numbers. Use the variable t to represent time and define the other variables in terms of t. Be sure to write a conclusion.

76. Interest on a savings account is computed at 10 percent per year compounded continuously. If one wishes to have $1000 in the account at the end of a year by making a single deposit now, what should be the amount of the deposit?

77. How long will it take for an investment to double itself if interest is paid at the rate of 8 percent per year compounded continuously?

78. The charge of electricity on a spherical surface leaks off at a rate proportional to the charge. Initially, the charge of electricity was 8 coulombs and one-fourth leaks off in 15 min. When will there be only 2 coulombs remaining?

79. The rate of bacterial growth in a certain culture is proportional to the number present, and the number doubles in 20 min. If at the end of 1 hour there were 1,500,000 bacteria, how many bacteria were present initially?

80. Refer to Exercise 21 in Exercises 5.6. A paleontologist discovered an insect preserved inside a transparent amber, which is hardened tree pitch, and the amount of ^{14}C present in the insect was determined to be 2 percent of its original amount. Use the fact that the half-life of ^{14}C is 5730 years to determine the age of the insect at the time of discovery.

81. The rate of decay of a radioactive substance is proportional to the amount present. If half of a given deposit of the substance disappears in 1900 years, how long will it take for 95 percent of the deposit to disappear?

82. If the population of a particular country doubles every 25 years, at what percent is it growing per year?

83. A tank contains 60 gal of salt water with 120 lb of dissolved salt. Salt water with 3 lb of salt per gallon flows into the tank at the rate of 2 gal/min, and the mixture, kept uniform by stirring, flows out at the same rate. How long will it be before the tank contains 135 lb of salt?

84. A tank contains 100 liters of fresh water, and brine containing 2 kg of salt per liter flows into the tank at the rate of 3 liters/min. If the mixture, kept uniform by stirring, flows out at the same rate, how many kilograms of salt will the tank contain at the end of 30 min?

85. Use Newton's law of cooling to determine the current temperature of a body in air of temperature 40° if 30 min ago the body's temperature was 150° and 10 min ago it was 90°.

86. Find the point on the graph of $f(x) = e^x$ for which the tangent line to the graph there passes through the origin.

87. In an electric circuit the electromotive force is E volts at t seconds, where $E = 20 \cos 120\pi t$.
(a) Solve the equation for t. Use the equation in part (a) to find the smallest positive value of t for which the electromotive force is (b) 10 volts; (c) 5 volts; (d) −10 volts; (e) −5 volts.

88. A weight is suspended from a spring and vibrating vertically according to the equation

$$y = 4 \sin 2\pi(t + \tfrac{1}{6})$$

where y centimeters is the directed distance of the weight from its central position t seconds after the start of the motion, and the positive direction is upward. (a) Solve the equation for t. Use the equation in part (a) to determine the smallest positive value of t for which the displacement of the weight above its central position is (b) 2 cm and (c) 3 cm.

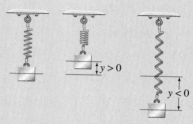

89. Find the area of the region bounded by the line $x = 2\sqrt{2}$, the curve $y = 9/\sqrt{9 - x^2}$, and the two coordinate axes.

90. Find the volume of the solid of revolution generated when the region bounded by the curve $y = \sqrt{\sinh x}$, the x axis, and the lines $x = 0$ and $x = \ln 2$ is revolved about the x axis.

91. A searchlight is $\tfrac{1}{2}$ km from a straight road and it keeps a light trained on an automobile that is traveling at a constant speed of 60 km/hr. Find the rate at which the light beam is changing direction (a) when the car is at the point on the road nearest the searchlight and (b) when the car is $\tfrac{1}{2}$ km down the road from this point.

92. A helicopter leaves the ground at a point 800 ft from an observer and rises vertically at 25 ft/sec. Find the time rate of change of the measure of the observer's angle of elevation of the helicopter when the helicopter is 600 ft above the ground.

93. An airplane is flying at a speed of 300 mi/hr at an altitude of 4 mi. If an observer is on the ground, find the time rate of change of the measure of the observer's angle of elevation of the airplane when the airplane is directly over a point on the ground 2 mi from the observer.

94. A picture 5 ft high is placed on a wall with its base 7 ft above the level of the eye of an observer. If the observer is approaching the wall at the rate of 3 ft/sec, how fast is the measure of the angle subtended at her eye by the picture changing when the observer is 10 ft from the wall?

95. Two points A and B are diametrically opposite each other on the shores of a circular lake 1 km in diameter. A man desires to go from point A to point B. He can row at the rate of 1.5 km/hr and walk at the rate of 5 km/hr. Find the least amount of time it can take him to get from point A to point B.

96. Solve Exercise 95 if the rates of rowing and walking are, respectively, 2 km/hr and 3 km/hr.

97. Prove by using the definition of a derivative that

$$\lim_{x \to 0} \frac{\log_a(1 + x)}{x} = \log_a e$$

(*Note:* Compare with Exercise 57 in Exercises 5.2.)

98. Prove without using the definition of a derivative that

$$\lim_{x \to 0} \frac{a^x - 1}{x} = \ln a$$

Hint: Let $y = a^x - 1$ and express $(a^x - 1)/x$ as a function of y, say $g(y)$. Then show that $y \to 0$ as $x \to 0$, and find $\lim_{y \to 0} g(y)$.

99. Use the results of Exercises 97 and 98 to prove that

$$\lim_{x \to 1} \frac{x^b - 1}{x - 1} = b$$

Hint: Write

$$\frac{x^b - 1}{x - 1} = \frac{e^{b \ln x} - 1}{b \ln x} \cdot \frac{b \ln x}{x - 1}$$

Then let $s = b \ln x$ and $t = x - 1$.

100. Prove by using the definition of a derivative that

$$\lim_{x \to 0} \frac{e^{ax} - 1}{x} = a$$

101. If the domain of f is the set of real numbers and $f'(x) = cf(x)$ for all x where c is a constant, prove that there is a constant k for which $f(x) = ke^{cx}$ for all x. *Hint:* Consider the function g for which $g(x) = f(x)e^{-cx}$, and find $g'(x)$.

102. Prove that

$$D_x^n(\ln x) = (-1)^{n-1} \frac{(n - 1)!}{x^n}$$

Hint: Use mathematical induction.

103. Find $\int_0^t e^{-|x|}\, dx$ if t is any real number.

104. Prove that if $x > 0$, and $\int_1^x t^{h-1}\, dt = 1$, then

$$\lim_{h \to 0} x = \lim_{h \to 0} (1 + h)^{1/h}$$

105. The graph of the equation

$$x = a \sinh^{-1} \sqrt{\frac{a^2}{y^2} - 1} - \sqrt{a^2 - y^2}$$

is called a *tractrix.* Prove that the slope of the curve at any point (x, y) is $-y/\sqrt{a^2 - y^2}$.

106. Do Exercise 51 in the Miscellaneous Exercises for Chapter 4 by evaluating each integral.

107. The *gudermannian,* named for the German mathematician Christoph Gudermann (1798–1852), is the function defined by

$$\text{gd } x = \tan^{-1}(\sinh x)$$

Show that $D_x(\text{gd } x) = \text{sech } x$.

ADDITIONAL APPLICATIONS OF THE DEFINITE INTEGRAL

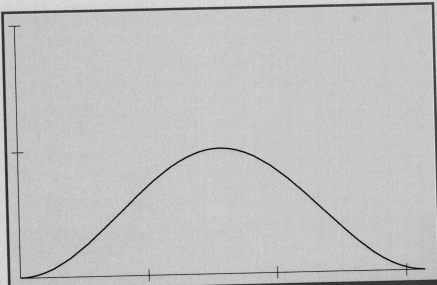

The power of integral calculus in geometry has already been demonstrated by its application to computing the area of a plane region, the volume of a solid of revolution, and the volume of a solid having known parallel plane sections. We present another geometric application in Section 6.1 where we compute the *length of arc* of the graph of a function between two points.

Applications of integration in physics and engineering appear in the other four sections. We determine the *center of mass of a rod* in Section 6.2 and the *center of mass of a lamina* in Section 6.3. The *work* done by a variable force acting on an object is calculated in Section 6.4, while Section 6.5 deals with applying the definite integral to find the force caused by *fluid pressure*, such as water pressure against the side of a container.

6.1 LENGTH OF ARC OF THE GRAPH OF A FUNCTION

In our discussions of areas and volumes, we used the words "measure of the area" and "measure of the volume" to indicate a number without any units of measurement included. In our treatment of *length of arc*, we shall use the word "length" in place of the words "measure of the length." Thus for our purposes the length of an arc is a number without any units of measurement attached to it.

Let the function f be continuous on the closed interval $[a, b]$ and consider the graph of this function defined by the equation $y = f(x)$, of which a sketch appears in Figure 1. The portion of the curve from the point $A(a, f(a))$ to the point $B(b, f(b))$ is called an *arc*. We wish to assign a number to what we intuitively think of as the length of such an arc. If the arc is a line segment from the point (x_1, y_1) to the point (x_2, y_2), we know from the formula for the distance between two points that its length is given by $\sqrt{(x_1 - x_2)^2 + (y_1 - y_2)^2}$. We use this formula for defining the length of an arc in general. Recall from geometry that the circumference of a circle is defined as the limit of the perimeters of regular polygons inscribed in the circle. For other curves we proceed in a similar way.

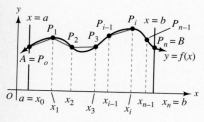

FIGURE 1

Let Δ be a partition of the closed interval $[a, b]$ formed by dividing the interval into n subintervals by choosing any $n - 1$ intermediate numbers between a and b. Let $x_0 = a$ and $x_n = b$, and let $x_1, x_2, x_3, \ldots, x_{n-1}$ be the intermediate numbers so that $x_0 < x_1 < x_2 < \ldots < x_{n-1} < x_n$. Then the ith subinterval is $[x_{i-1}, x_i]$; its length, denoted by $\Delta_i x$, is $x_i - x_{i-1}$, where $i = 1, 2, 3, \ldots, n$. Then if $\|\Delta\|$ is the norm of the partition Δ, each $\Delta_i x \leq \|\Delta\|$.

Associated with each point $(x_i, 0)$ on the x axis is point $P_i(x_i, f(x_i))$ on the curve. Draw a line segment from each point P_{i-1} to the next point P_i, as shown in Figure 2. The length of the line segment from P_{i-1} to P_i is denoted by $|\overline{P_{i-1}P_i}|$ and is given by the distance formula

$$|\overline{P_{i-1}P_i}| = \sqrt{(x_i - x_{i-1})^2 + (y_i - y_{i-1})^2} \tag{1}$$

The sum of the lengths of the line segments is

$$|\overline{P_0P_1}| + |\overline{P_1P_2}| + |\overline{P_2P_3}| + \ldots + |\overline{P_{i-1}P_i}| + \ldots + |\overline{P_{n-1}P_n}|$$

which can be written with sigma notation as

$$\sum_{i=1}^{n} |\overline{P_{i-1}P_i}| \tag{2}$$

It seems plausible that if n is sufficiently large, the sum in (2) will be "close to" what we would intuitively think of as the length of the arc AB. So we define the length of arc as the limit of the sum in (2) as the norm of Δ approaches zero, in which case n increases without bound. We have, then, the following definition.

FIGURE 2

6.1.1 Definition of the Length of Arc of the Graph of a Function

Suppose the function f is continuous on the closed interval $[a, b]$. Further suppose that there exists a number L having the following property:

For any $\epsilon > 0$ there is a $\delta > 0$ such that for every partition Δ of the interval $[a, b]$ it is true that

$$\text{if} \quad \|\Delta\| < \delta \quad \text{then} \quad \left| \sum_{i=1}^{n} |\overline{P_{i-1} P_i}| - L \right| < \epsilon$$

Then we write

$$L = \lim_{\|\Delta\| \to 0} \sum_{i=1}^{n} |\overline{P_{i-1} P_i}| \tag{3}$$

and L is called the **length of arc** of the curve $y = f(x)$ from the point $A(a, f(a))$ to the point $B(b, f(b))$.

If the limit in (3) exists, the arc is said to be **rectifiable**.

We now derive a formula for finding the length L of an arc that is rectifiable. The derivation requires that the derivative of f be continuous on $[a, b]$; such a function is said to be **smooth** on $[a, b]$.

Refer to Figure 3. If P_{i-1} has coordinates (x_{i-1}, y_{i-1}) and P_i has coordinates (x_i, y_i), then the length of the chord $P_{i-1} P_i$ is given by formula (1).

Letting $x_i - x_{i-1} = \Delta_i x$ and $y_i - y_{i-1} = \Delta_i y$ we have

$$|\overline{P_{i-1} P_i}| = \sqrt{(\Delta_i x)^2 + (\Delta_i y)^2}$$

or, equivalently, because $\Delta_i x \neq 0$,

$$|\overline{P_{i-1} P_i}| = \sqrt{1 + \left(\frac{\Delta_i y}{\Delta_i x} \right)^2} \, (\Delta_i x) \tag{4}$$

Because we required that f' be continuous on $[a, b]$, the hypothesis of the mean-value theorem (3.3.2) is satisfied by f; so there is a number z_i in the open interval (x_{i-1}, x_i) such that

$$f(x_i) - f(x_{i-1}) = f'(z_i)(x_i - x_{i-1})$$

Because $\Delta_i y = f(x_i) - f(x_{i-1})$ and $\Delta_i x = x_i - x_{i-1}$, from the above equation we have

$$\frac{\Delta_i y}{\Delta_i x} = f'(z_i)$$

Substituting from this equation into (4) we get

$$|\overline{P_{i-1} P_i}| = \sqrt{1 + [f'(z_i)]^2} \, \Delta_i x$$

For each i from 1 to n there is an equation of this form, so that

$$\sum_{i=1}^{n} |\overline{P_{i-1} P_i}| = \sum_{i=1}^{n} \sqrt{1 + [f'(z_i)]^2} \, \Delta_i x$$

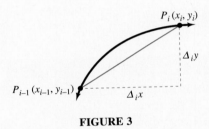

$P_i(x_i, y_i)$

$\Delta_i y$

$P_{i-1}(x_{i-1}, y_{i-1})$

$\Delta_i x$

FIGURE 3

Taking the limit on both sides of this equation as $\|\Delta\|$ approaches zero we obtain

$$\lim_{\|\Delta\|\to 0}\sum_{i=1}^{n}|\overline{P_{i-1}P_i}| = \lim_{\|\Delta\|\to 0}\sum_{i=1}^{n}\sqrt{1 + [f'(z_i)]^2}\,\Delta_i x \qquad (5)$$

if this limit exists.

To show that the limit on the right side of (5) exists, let F be the function defined by

$$F(x) = \sqrt{1 + [f'(x)]^2}$$

Because we are requiring f' to be continuous on $[a, b]$, F is continuous on $[a, b]$. Since $x_{i-1} < z_i < x_i$, for $i = 1, 2, \ldots, n$, on the right side of (5) we have the limit of a Riemann sum which is a definite integral. Therefore from (5)

$$\lim_{\|\Delta\|\to 0}\sum_{i=1}^{n}|\overline{P_{i-1}P_i}| = \int_{a}^{b}\sqrt{1 + [f'(x)]^2}\,dx$$

From (3) the left side is L; therefore

$$L = \int_{a}^{b}\sqrt{1 + [f'(x)]^2}\,dx$$

In this way we have proved the following theorem.

6.1.2 Theorem

If the function f and its derivative f' are continuous on the closed interval $[a, b]$, then the length of arc of the curve $y = f(x)$ from the point $(a, f(a))$ to the point $(b, f(b))$ is given by

$$L = \int_{a}^{b}\sqrt{1 + [f'(x)]^2}\,dx$$

The following theorem, which gives the length of arc of a curve when x is expressed as a function of y, follows from the above theorem by interchanging x and y as well as the functions f and g.

6.1.3 Theorem

If the function g and its derivative g' are continuous on the closed interval $[c, d]$, then the length of arc of the curve $x = g(y)$ from the point $(g(c), c)$ to the point $(g(d), d)$ is given by

$$L = \int_{c}^{d}\sqrt{1 + [g'(y)]^2}\,dy$$

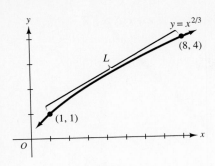

FIGURE 4

▶ **EXAMPLE 1** Find the length of arc of the curve $y = x^{2/3}$ from the point $(1, 1)$ to $(8, 4)$ by using Theorem 6.1.2.

Solution See Figure 4. Because $f(x) = x^{2/3}$, $f'(x) = \frac{2}{3}x^{-1/3}$. From Theorem 6.1.2,

$$L = \int_1^8 \sqrt{1 + \frac{4}{9x^{2/3}}}\, dx$$

$$= \frac{1}{3}\int_1^8 \frac{\sqrt{9x^{2/3} + 4}}{x^{1/3}}\, dx$$

To evaluate this definite integral let $u = 9x^{2/3} + 4$; then $du = 6x^{-1/3}\, dx$. When $x = 1$, $u = 13$; when $x = 8$, $u = 40$. Therefore

$$L = \frac{1}{18}\int_{13}^{40} u^{1/2}\, du$$

$$= \frac{1}{18}\left[\frac{2}{3}u^{3/2}\right]_{13}^{40}$$

$$= \frac{1}{27}(40^{3/2} - 13^{3/2})$$

$$\approx 7.634$$

Conclusion: The length of arc is 7.634. ◀

▶ **EXAMPLE 2** Find the length of arc in Example 1 by using Theorem 6.1.3.

Solution Because $y = x^{2/3}$ and $x > 0$, we solve for x and get $x = y^{3/2}$. Letting $g(y) = y^{3/2}$ we have $g'(y) = \frac{3}{2}y^{1/2}$. Then, from Theorem 6.1.3,

$$L = \int_1^4 \sqrt{1 + \frac{9}{4}y}\, dy$$

$$= \frac{1}{2}\int_1^4 \sqrt{4 + 9y}\, dy$$

$$= \frac{1}{18}\left[\frac{2}{3}(4 + 9y)^{3/2}\right]_1^4$$

$$= \frac{1}{27}(40^{3/2} - 13^{3/2})$$

$$\approx 7.634$$

in agreement with Example 1. ◀

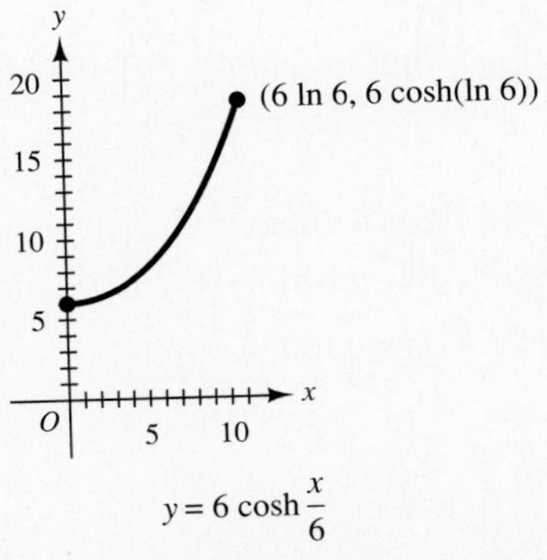

▶ **EXAMPLE 3** Find the length of arc of the catenary defined by

$$y = 6\cosh\left(\frac{x}{6}\right)$$

from the point $(0, 6)$ to the point where $x = 6\ln 6$.

Solution See Figure 5 showing the arc of the catenary.

$$\frac{dy}{dx} = 6\sinh\left(\frac{x}{6}\right) \cdot \frac{1}{6}$$

$$= \sinh\left(\frac{x}{6}\right)$$

$(6\ln 6, 6\cosh(\ln 6))$

$y = 6\cosh\dfrac{x}{6}$

FIGURE 5

If L units is the length of the given arc, from Theorem 6.1.2,

$$L = \int_0^{6\ln 6} \sqrt{1 + \left(\frac{dy}{dx}\right)^2}\, dx$$

$$= \int_0^{6\ln 6} \sqrt{1 + \sinh^2\!\left(\frac{x}{6}\right)}\, dx$$

$$= \int_0^{6\ln 6} \sqrt{\cosh^2\!\left(\frac{x}{6}\right)}\, dx$$

$$= \int_0^{6\ln 6} \cosh\!\left(\frac{x}{6}\right) dx \qquad \left(\text{because } \cosh\left(\frac{x}{6}\right) \geq 1\right)$$

$$= 6 \sinh\!\left(\frac{x}{6}\right)\Big]_0^{6\ln 6}$$

$$= 6 \sinh(\ln 6) - 6 \sinh 0$$

$$= 6 \cdot \frac{e^{\ln 6} - e^{-\ln 6}}{2}$$

$$= 3(6 - \tfrac{1}{6})$$

$$= \tfrac{35}{2}$$

<u>Conclusion:</u>   The length of arc of the catenary is exactly 17.5.   ◄

The definite integral obtained when applying Theorems 6.1.2 and 6.1.3 is often difficult, and most of the time impossible, to evaluate by the second fundamental theorem of the calculus, as we did in the above carefully designed examples. We can, however, use the theorems to set up the definite integral and then compute an approximate value for the length of arc by the NINT capability of our graphics calculator, as we do in the next two examples.

▶   ***EXAMPLE 4***   Find to four significant digits the length of arc of the curve $y = x^3$ from the origin to the point $(2, 8)$.

Solution   Figure 6 shows the arc. With $f(x) = x^3$, $f'(x) = 3x^2$. Thus from Theorem 6.1.2,

$$L = \int_0^2 \sqrt{1 + (3x^2)^2}\, dx$$

$$= \int_0^2 \sqrt{1 + 9x^4}\, dx$$

On our graphics calculator, we obtain to four significant digits

$$\text{NINT}(\sqrt{1 + 9x^4}, 0, 2) = 8.630$$

<u>Conclusion:</u>   The length of arc is 8.630.   ◄

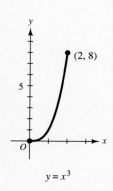

$y = x^3$

FIGURE 6

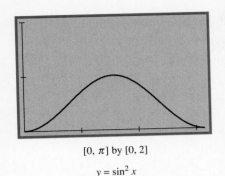

[0, π] by [0, 2]

$y = \sin^2 x$

FIGURE 7

▶ **EXAMPLE 5**   Find to four significant digits the length of arc of the curve $y = \sin^2 x$ from the origin to the point $(\pi, 0)$.

Solution   Figure 7 shows the arc which is the graph of $y = \sin^2 x$ plotted in the $[0, \pi]$ by $[0, 2]$ window. Let $f(x) = \sin^2 x$. Then

$$f'(x) = 2 \sin x \cos x$$
$$= \sin 2x$$

From Theorem 6.1.2

$$L = \int_0^\pi \sqrt{1 + \sin^2 2x} \, dx$$

On our graphics calculator, we obtain

$$\text{NINT}(\sqrt{1 + \sin^2 2x}, 0, \pi) = 3.820$$

<u>Conclusion:</u>   The length of arc is 3.820.   ◀

Using the Leibniz notation for derivatives, the formulas of Theorems 6.1.2 and 6.1.3 can be written as

$$L = \int_a^b \sqrt{1 + \left(\frac{dy}{dx}\right)^2} \, dx \quad \text{and} \quad L = \int_c^d \sqrt{1 + \left(\frac{dx}{dy}\right)^2} \, dy \qquad (6)$$

We now introduce the *arc length function* and the differential of arc length which provide a mnemonic device for remembering these formulas.

If f' is continuous on $[a, b]$, the definite integral $\int_a^x \sqrt{1 + [f'(t)]^2} \, dt$ is a function of x; and it gives the length of arc of the curve $y = f(x)$ from the point $(a, f(a))$ to the point $(x, f(x))$, where x is any number in the closed interval $[a, b]$. Let $s(x)$ denote the length of this arc; s is called the **arc length function** and

$$s(x) = \int_a^x \sqrt{1 + [f'(t)]^2} \, dt$$

From the first fundamental theorem of the calculus,

$$s'(x) = \sqrt{1 + [f'(x)]^2}$$

or, because $s'(x) = \dfrac{ds}{dx}$ and $f'(x) = \dfrac{dy}{dx}$,

$$\frac{ds}{dx} = \sqrt{1 + \left(\frac{dy}{dx}\right)^2}$$

Multiplying by dx we obtain

$$ds = \sqrt{1 + \left(\frac{dy}{dx}\right)^2} \, dx \qquad (7)$$

Similarly, for the length of arc of the curve $x = g(y)$ from the point $(g(c), c)$ to the point $(g(y), y)$,

$$ds = \sqrt{1 + \left(\frac{dx}{dy}\right)^2} \, dy \qquad (8)$$

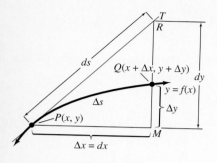

FIGURE 8

Observe that ds (the differential of arc length) is the integrand in formulas (6). Squaring on both sides of either (7) or (8) gives

$$(ds)^2 = (dx)^2 + (dy)^2 \qquad (9)$$

From this equation we get the geometric interpretation of ds, shown in Figure 8. In the figure, line T is tangent to the curve $y = f(x)$ at the point P. $|\overline{PM}| = \Delta x = dx$; $|\overline{MQ}| = \Delta y$; $|\overline{MR}| = dy$; $|\overline{PR}| = ds$; the length of arc PQ is Δs. Figure 8 provides an easy way to remember (9) from which formulas (6) can be obtained.

EXERCISES 6.1

In Exercises 1 through 24, find the exact length of arc by evaluating the resulting definite integral by the second fundamental theoren of the calculus.

1. Compute the length of the segment of the line $y = 3x$ from the point $(1, 3)$ to the point $(2, 6)$ by three methods: **(a)** Use the distance formula; **(b)** use Theorem 6.1.2; **(c)** use Theorem 6.1.3.

2. Compute the length of the segment of the line $x + 3y = 4$ from the point $(-2, 2)$ to the point $(4, 0)$ by three methods: **(a)** Use the distance formula; **(b)** use Theorem 6.1.2; **(c)** use Theorem 6.1.3.

3. Compute the length of the segment of the line $4x + 9y = 36$ between its x and y intercepts by three methods: **(a)** Use the Pythagorean theorem; **(b)** use Theorem 6.1.2; **(c)** use Theorem 6.1.3.

4. Follow the instructions of Exercise 3 for the line $5x - 2y = 10$.

5. Find the length of arc of the curve $9y^2 = 4x^3$ from the origin to the point $(3, 2\sqrt{3})$.

6. Find the length of arc of the curve $x^2 = (2y + 3)^3$ from $(1, -1)$ to $(7\sqrt{7}, 2)$.

7. Find the length of arc of the curve $8y = x^4 + 2x^{-2}$ from the point where $x = 1$ to the point where $x = 2$.

8. Use Theorem 6.1.2 to find the length of arc of the curve $y^3 = 8x^2$ from the point $(1, 2)$ to the point $(27, 18)$.

9. Solve Exercise 8 by using Theorem 6.1.3.

10. Find the length of arc of the curve $y = \frac{2}{3}(x - 5)^{3/2}$ from the point where $x = 6$ to the point where $x = 8$.

11. Find the length of arc of the curve $y = \frac{1}{3}(x^2 + 2)^{3/2}$ from the point where $x = 0$ to the point where $x = 3$.

12. Find the length of arc of the curve $6xy = y^4 + 3$ from the point where $y = 1$ to the point where $y = 2$.

13. Find the length of arc of the curve $y = \frac{1}{3}\sqrt{x}\,(3x - 1)$ from the point where $x = 1$ to the point where $x = 4$.

14. Find the length of arc of the curve $y = \frac{1}{6}x^3 + \frac{1}{2}x^{-1}$ from the point $(2, \frac{19}{12})$ to the point $(5, \frac{314}{15})$.

15. Find the length of arc of the curve $x^{2/3} + y^{2/3} = 1$ in the first quadrant from the point where $x = \frac{1}{8}$ to the point where $x = 1$.

16. Find the length of arc of the curve $x^{2/3} + y^{2/3} = a^{2/3}$ (a is a constant, $a > 1$) in the first quadrant from the point where $x = 1$ to the point where $x = a$.

17. Find the length of the curve $\left(\dfrac{x}{a}\right)^{2/3} + \left(\dfrac{y}{b}\right)^{2/3} = 1$ in the first quadrant from the point where $x = \frac{1}{8}a$ to the point where $x = a$.

18. Find the length of the curve $9y^2 = x^2(2x + 3)$ in the second quadrant from the point where $x = -1$ to the point where $x = 0$.

19. Find the length of the curve $9y^2 = x(x - 3)^2$ in the first quadrant from the point where $x = 1$ to the point where $x = 3$.

20. Find the length of the curve $9y^2 = 4(1 + x^2)^3$ in the first quadrant from the point where $x = 0$ to the point where $x = 2\sqrt{2}$.

21. Find the length of arc of the curve $y = \ln \sec x$ from $x = 0$ to $x = \frac{1}{4}\pi$.

22. Find the length of arc of the curve $y = \ln \csc x$ from $x = \frac{1}{6}\pi$ to $x = \frac{1}{2}\pi$.

23. If

$$f(x) = \int_0^x \sqrt{\cos t}\, dt$$

find the length of arc of the graph of f from the point where $x = 0$ to the point where $x = \frac{1}{2}\pi$. *Hint:* Find $f'(x)$ by the first fundamental theorem of the calculus and use the identity $\cos^2 \frac{1}{2} x = \frac{1}{2}(1 + \cos x)$.

24. If

$$f(x) = \int_0^x \sqrt{\sin t}\; dt$$

find the length of arc of the graph of f from the point where $x = 0$ to the point where $x = \frac{1}{2}\pi$. *Hint:* Use the hint for Exercise 23 and the identity $\sin x = \cos\left(\frac{1}{2}\pi - x\right)$.

In Exercises 25 through 34, find the length of arc to four significant digits by computing the resulting definite integral by the NINT capability of your graphics calculator.

25. The arc of the parabola $y = x^2$ from the origin to the point $(2, 4)$.

26. The arc of the parabola $y = \frac{1}{4}(x - 2)^2 + 1$ from the point $(-2, 5)$ to the point $(4, 2)$.

27. The arc of the sine curve from the origin to the point $(\pi, 0)$.

28. The arc of the cosine curve from the point $(0, 1)$ to the point $(\frac{1}{3}\pi, \frac{1}{2})$.

29. The arc of the curve $y = \frac{1}{3}x^3$ from the origin to the point $(1, \frac{1}{3})$.

30. The arc of the curve $y = \tan x$ from the origin to the point $(\frac{1}{4}\pi, 1)$.

31. The arc of the curve $y = x^3 - 6x^2 + 9x - 1$ from the point $(0, -1)$ to the point $(3, -1)$.

32. The arc of the curve $y = x^3 - 2x^2 - 5x + 6$ from the point $(-2, 0)$ to the point $(3, 0)$.

33. The arc of the curve $y = x^3 - 3x^2 + 3$ between the two points where the graph intersects the positive x axis.

34. The arc of the curve $y = 3 - (x - 1)^4$ between the two points where the graph intersects the x axis.

35. The accompanying figure shows a cable hanging in the form of a catenary between two poles 300 ft apart, and the lowest point of the cable is 200 ft above the ground. The coordinate axes are chosen so that the origin is midway between the bases of the poles on the x axis, and the y axis contains the lowest point of the cable. An equation of the catenary is

$$y = 200 \cosh\left(\frac{x}{200}\right)$$

Find the length of the cable between the two poles.

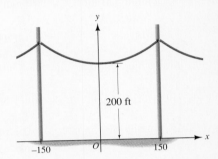

36. Explain why you cannot use Theorem 6.1.2 to compute the length of arc of the graph of $y^3 = x^2$ from the origin to the point $(1, 1)$. Can you use Theorem 6.1.3 to compute this length of arc? If your answer is no, explain why. If your answer is yes, find the length of arc.

6.2 CENTER OF MASS OF A ROD

You learned in Section 4.6 that if the function f is continuous on the closed interval $[a, b]$, the average value of f on $[a, b]$ is given by

$$\frac{\int_a^b f(x)\; dx}{b - a}$$

An important application of the average value of a function occurs in physics in connection with the concept of *center of mass*.

To arrive at a definition of *mass*, consider a particle set into motion along an axis by a force exerted on the particle. So long as the force is acting on the particle, its velocity is increasing; that is, the particle is accelerating. The ratio of the force to the acceleration is constant regardless of the magnitude of the force, and this constant ratio is called the **mass** of the particle. Therefore, if the force is F units, the acceleration is a units, and the mass is M units, then

$$M = \frac{F}{a}$$

We shall be measuring force, mass, and acceleration in units of the British and metric systems. We now discuss these units.

In the British engineering system the unit of force is 1 lb and the unit of acceleration is ft/sec². The unit of mass is defined as the mass of a particle whose acceleration is 1 ft/sec² when the particle is subjected to a force of 1 lb. This unit of mass is called 1 *slug*. Hence

$$1 \text{ slug} = \frac{1 \text{ lb}}{1 \text{ ft/sec}^2}$$

▷ **ILLUSTRATION 1**   The acceleration of a certain particle moving on a horizontal line is 10 ft/sec² when the force is 30 lb. Therefore the mass of the particle is

$$\frac{30 \text{ lb}}{10 \text{ ft/sec}^2} = \frac{3 \text{ lb}}{1 \text{ ft/sec}^2}$$

Thus for every 1 ft/sec² of acceleration, a force of 3 lb must be exerted on the particle. The mass of the particle is then 3 slugs.   ◀

The metric system that has been officially adopted by every major country except the United States is the International System of Units, abbreviated SI for its French name, Système International d'Unités. In the SI system the unit of mass is 1 kilogram (kg) and the unit of acceleration is 1 meter per second squared (m/sec²). The unit of force in the SI system is 1 *newton* (N), which is the force that provides a mass of 1 kg an acceleration of 1 m/sec².

▷ **ILLUSTRATION 2**   A particle of mass 6 kg is subjected to a constant horizontal force of 3 N. The acceleration of the particle is obtained by dividing the force by the mass, and so it is

$$\frac{3 \text{ N}}{6 \text{ kg}} = 0.5 \text{ m/sec}^2 \qquad\qquad ◀$$

In the SI system, the acceleration due to gravity near the surface of the earth is 9.81 m/sec². If M kilograms is the mass of an object, and if F newtons is the force on the object due to gravity near the surface of the earth, then

$$F = 9.81M$$

Another metric system is the centimeter-gram-second system, abbreviated CGS. In the CGS system, the standard unit of mass is the gram, and 1 g = 0.001 kg. The unit of acceleration in the CGS system is 1 cm/sec².

Therefore the unit of force, called 1 *dyne*, is the force that gives a particle of mass 1 g an acceleration of 1 cm/sec². Because

$$1 \text{ kg} = 10^3 \text{g} \quad \text{and} \quad 1 \text{ m/sec}^2 = 10^2 \text{ cm/sec}^2$$

then

$$1 \text{ N} = 10^5 \text{ dynes}$$

Table 1 summarizes the units in the British, SI, and CGS systems.

Table 1

System of Units	Force	Mass	Acceleration
British	pound (lb)	slug	ft/sec²
SI	newton (N)	kilogram (kg)	m/sec²
CGS	dyne	gram (g)	cm/sec²

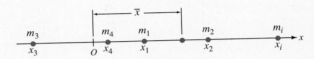

FIGURE 1

Consider now a horizontal rod, of negligible weight and thickness, placed on the x axis. On the rod is a system of n particles located at points $x_1, x_2, \ldots, x_n$. The ith particle ($i = 1, 2, \ldots, n$) is at a directed distance x_i meters from the origin and its mass is m_i kilograms. See Figure 1. The number of kilograms in the total mass of the system is $\sum_{i=1}^{n} m_i$. We define the number of kilogram-meters in the *moment of mass* of the ith particle with respect to the origin as $m_i x_i$. The **moment of mass** for the system is defined as the sum of the moments of mass of all the particles. Hence, if M_0 kilogram-meters is the moment of mass of the system with respect to the origin, then

$$M_0 = \sum_{i=1}^{n} m_i x_i$$

If the measurement of the distance is in feet and of the mass in slugs, then the moment of mass is measured in slug-feet.

We wish to find a point $\bar{x}$ such that if the total mass of the system were concentrated there, its moment of mass with respect to the origin would be equal to the moment of mass of the system with respect to the origin. Then $\bar{x}$ must satisfy the equation

$$\bar{x} \sum_{i=1}^{n} m_i = \sum_{i=1}^{n} m_i x_i$$

$$\bar{x} = \frac{\displaystyle\sum_{i=1}^{n} m_i x_i}{\displaystyle\sum_{i=1}^{n} m_i} \qquad (1)$$

The point $\bar{x}$, called the **center of mass** of the system, is the point where the system will balance. The position of the center of mass is independent of the position of the origin; that is, the location of the center of mass relative to the positions of the particles does not change when the origin is changed. The center of mass is important because the behavior of an entire system of particles can be described by the behavior of the center of mass of the system.

▶ **EXAMPLE 1**   Given four particles of masses 2, 3, 1, and 5 kg located on the x axis at the points having coordinates 5, 2, -3, and -4, respectively, where distance measurement is in meters, find the center of mass of this system.

Solution   If $\bar{x}$ is the coordinate of the center of mass, we have from formula (1)

$$\bar{x} = \frac{2(5) + 3(2) + 1(-3) + 5(-4)}{2 + 3 + 1 + 5}$$

$$= -\frac{7}{11}$$

<u>Conclusion:</u>   The center of mass is $\frac{7}{11}$ m to the left of the origin.   ◀

We now extend the preceding discussion to a rigid horizontal rod having a continuously distributed mass. The rod is said to be **homogeneous** if it has constant linear density, that is, if its mass is directly proportional to its length. In other words, if the segment of the rod whose length is $\Delta_i x$ meters has a mass of $\Delta_i m$ kilograms, and $\Delta_i m = k \Delta_i x$, then the rod is homogeneous. The number k is a constant, and k kilograms per meter is called the **linear density** of the rod.

Suppose that we have a nonhomogeneous rod, in which case the linear density varies along the rod. Let L meters be the length of the rod, and place the rod on the x axis so the left endpoint of the rod is at the origin and the right endpoint is at L. See Figure 2. The linear density at any point x on the rod is $\rho(x)$ kilograms per meter, where ρ is continuous on $[0, L]$. To find the total mass of the rod we consider a partition Δ of the closed interval $[0, L]$ into n subintervals. The ith subinterval is $[x_{i-1}, x_i]$, and its length is $\Delta_i x$ meters. If w_i is any point in $[x_{i-1}, x_i]$, an approximation to the mass of the part of the rod contained in the ith subinterval is $\Delta_i m$ kilograms, where

$$\Delta_i m = \rho(w_i) \, \Delta_i x$$

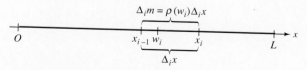

FIGURE 2

The number of kilograms in the total mass of the rod is approximated by

$$\sum_{i=1}^{n} \Delta_i m = \sum_{i=1}^{n} \rho(w_i) \, \Delta_i x$$

The smaller we take the norm of the partition Δ, the closer this Riemann sum will be to what we intuitively think of as the measure of the mass of the rod, and so we define the measure of the mass as the limit of the Riemann sum.

6.2.1 Definition of the Mass of a Rod

A rod of length L meters has its left endpoint at the origin. If $\rho(x)$ kilograms per meter is the linear density at a point x meters from the origin, where ρ is continuous on $[0, L]$, then the total **mass** of the rod is M kilograms, where

$$M = \lim_{\|\Delta\| \to 0} \sum_{i=1}^{n} \rho(w_i) \, \Delta_i x$$

$$= \int_{0}^{L} \rho(x) \, dx \qquad \qquad (2)$$

In this definition, if distance is measured in feet, and mass is measured in slugs, then the density is measured in slugs per foot.

▶ **EXAMPLE 2**   The linear density at any point of a rod 4 m long varies directly as the distance from the point to an external point in the line of the rod and 2 m from an end, where the linear density is 5 kg/m. Find the total mass of the rod.

Solution   Figure 3 shows the rod placed on the x axis. If $\rho(x)$ kilograms per meter is the linear density of the rod at the point x meters from the end having the greater density, then

$$\rho(x) = c(6 - x)$$

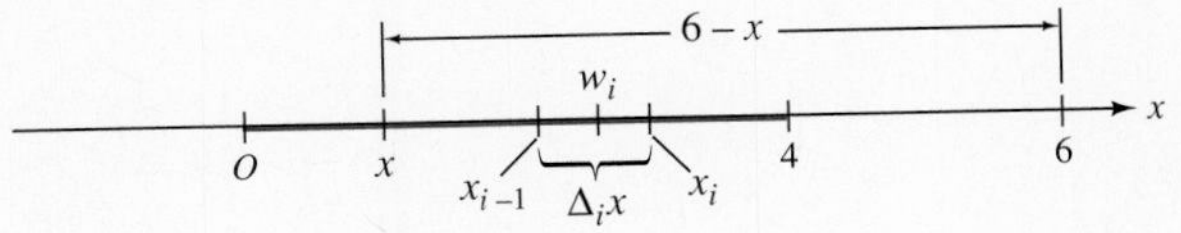

FIGURE 3

where c is the constant of proportionality. Because $\rho(4) = 5$, then $5 = 2c$ or $c = \frac{5}{2}$. Hence $\rho(x) = \frac{5}{2}(6 - x)$. Therefore, if M kilograms is the total mass of the rod, we have from Definition 6.2.1

$$M = \lim_{\|\Delta\| \to 0} \sum_{i=1}^{n} \tfrac{5}{2}(6 - w_i) \, \Delta_i x$$

$$= \int_{0}^{4} \tfrac{5}{2}(6 - x) \, dx$$

$$= \tfrac{5}{2}\left[6x - \tfrac{1}{2}x^2\right]_0^4$$

$$= 40$$

Conclusion: The total mass of the rod is 40 kg.   ◀

Before we obtain a formula for computing the *center of mass* of a rod having a continuously distributed mass, we must define the *moment of mass* of the rod with respect to the origin.

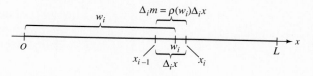

FIGURE 4

We place the rod on the x axis with the left endpoint at the origin and the right endpoint at L. See Figure 4. Let Δ be a partition of $[0, L]$ into n subintervals, with the ith subinterval $[x_{i-1}, x_i]$ having length $\Delta_i x$ meters. If w_i is any point in $[x_{i-1}, x_i]$, an approximation to the moment of mass with respect to the origin of the part of the rod contained in the ith subinterval is $w_i \Delta_i m$ kilogram-meters, where $\Delta_i m = \rho(w_i) \Delta_i x$. The number of kilogram-meters in the moment of mass of the entire rod is approximated by

$$\sum_{i=1}^{n} w_i \, \Delta_i m = \sum_{i=1}^{n} w_i \rho(w_i) \, \Delta_i x$$

The smaller we take the norm of the partition Δ, the closer this Riemann sum will be to what we intuitively think of as the measure of the moment of mass of the rod with respect to the origin. We have, then, the following definition.

6.2.2 Definition of the Moment of Mass of a Rod

A rod of length L meters has its left endpoint at the origin and $\rho(x)$ kilograms per meter is the linear density at a point x meters from the origin, where ρ is continuous on $[0, L]$. The **moment of mass** of the rod with respect to the origin is M_0 kilogram-meters, where

$$M_0 = \lim_{\|\Delta\| \to 0} \sum_{i=1}^{n} w_i \rho(w_i) \, \Delta_i x$$

$$= \int_{0}^{L} x\rho(x) \, dx \qquad\qquad (3)$$

The **center of mass** of the rod is at the point $\bar{x}$ such that if M kilograms is the total mass of the rod, $\bar{x}M = M_0$. Thus, from (2) and (3),

$$\bar{x} = \frac{\displaystyle\int_{0}^{L} x\rho(x) \, dx}{\displaystyle\int_{0}^{L} \rho(x) \, dx} \qquad\qquad (4)$$

▶ **EXAMPLE 3**   Find the center of mass of the rod in Example 2.

Solution   In Example 2, $M = 40$. From (4) with $\rho(x) = \frac{5}{2}(6 - x)$,

$$\bar{x} = \frac{\displaystyle\int_0^4 \frac{5}{2}x(6 - x)\, dx}{40}$$

$$= \frac{1}{16}\left[3x^2 - \frac{1}{3}x^3\right]_0^4$$

$$= \frac{5}{3}$$

Conclusion: The center of mass is $\frac{5}{3}$ m from the end having the greater density.   ◀

▶ **EXAMPLE 4**   Show that the center of mass of a rod of uniform linear density is at the center of the rod.

Solution   Let k kilograms per meter be the uniform linear density where k is a constant. Then from formula (4), if L is the length of the rod

$$\bar{x} = \frac{\displaystyle\int_0^L xk\, dx}{\displaystyle\int_0^L k\, dx} = \frac{\dfrac{kx^2}{2}\Big]_0^L}{kx\Big]_0^L} = \frac{\dfrac{kL^2}{2}}{kL} = \frac{L}{2}$$

Conclusion: The center of mass is at the center of the rod.   ◀

EXERCISES 6.2

In Exercises 1 through 4, a particle is moving on a horizontal line. Find the force exerted on the particle if it has the given mass and acceleration.

1. Mass is 50 slugs; acceleration is 5 ft/sec².
2. Mass is 10 kg; acceleration is 6 m/sec².
3. Mass is 80 g; acceleration is 50 cm/sec².
4. Mass is 22 slugs; acceleration is 4 ft/sec².

In Exercises 5 through 8, a particle is subjected to the given horizontal force, and either the mass or acceleration of the particle is given. Find the other quantity.

5. Force is 6 N; mass is 4 kg.
6. Force is 32 lb; mass is 8 slugs.
7. Force is 24 lb; acceleration is 9 ft/sec².
8. Force is 700 dynes; acceleration is 80 cm/sec².

In Exercises 9 through 12, a system of particles is located on the x axis. The number of kilograms in the mass of each particle and the coordinate of its position are given. Distance is measured in meters. Find the center of mass of each system.

9. $m_1 = 5$ at 2; $m_2 = 6$ at 3; $m_3 = 4$ at 5; $m_4 = 3$ at 8
10. $m_1 = 2$ at -4; $m_2 = 8$ at -1; $m_3 = 4$ at 2; $m_4 = 2$ at 3
11. $m_1 = 2$ at -3; $m_2 = 4$ at -2; $m_3 = 20$ at 4; $m_4 = 10$ at 6; $m_5 = 30$ at 9
12. $m_1 = 5$ at -7; $m_2 = 3$ at -2; $m_3 = 5$ at 0; $m_4 = 1$ at 2; $m_5 = 8$ at 10

In Exercises 13 through 21, find the total mass of the given rod and the center of mass.

13. The length of a rod is 6 m and the linear density of the rod at a point x meters from one end is $(2x + 3)$ kg/m.

14. The length of a rod is 20 cm and the linear density of the rod at a point x centimeters from one end is $(3x + 2)$ g/cm.

15. The length of a rod is 9 in. and the linear density of the rod at a point x inches from one end is $(4x + 1)$ slugs/in.

16. The length of a rod is 3 ft, and the linear density of the rod at a point x feet from one end is $(5 + 2x)$ slugs/ft.

17. The length of a rod is 12 cm, and the measure of the linear density at a point is a linear function of the measure of the distance from the left end of the rod. The linear density at the left end is 3 g/cm and at the right end is 4 g/cm.

18. The length of a rod is 10 m and the measure of the linear density at a point is a linear function of the measure of the distance of the point from the left end of the rod. The linear density at the left end is 2 kg/m and at the right end is 3 kg/m.

19. The measure of the linear density at any point of a rod 6 m long varies directly as the distance from the point to an external point in the line of the rod and 4 m from an end, where the density is 3 kg/m.

20. A rod is 10 ft long, and the measure of the linear density at a point is a linear function of the measure of the distance from the center of the rod. The linear density at each end of the rod is 5 slugs/ft and at the center the linear density is $3\frac{1}{2}$ slugs/ft.

21. The measure of the linear density at a point of a rod varies directly as the third power of the measure of the distance of the point from one end. The length of the rod is 4 ft and the linear density is 2 slugs/ft at the center.

22. The linear density at any point of a rod 5 m long varies directly as the distance from the point to an external point in the line of the rod and 2 m from an end, where the linear density is K kg/m. Find K if the total mass of the rod is 135 kg.

23. The linear density at any point of a rod 3 m long varies directly as the distance from a point to an external point in the line of the rod and 1 m from an end where the linear density is 2 kg/m. If the total mass of the rod is 15 kg, find the center of mass of the rod.

24. The measure of the linear density at a point on a rod varies directly as the fourth power of the measure of the distance of the point from one end. The length of the rod is 2 m. If the total mass of the rod is $\frac{64}{5}$ kg, find the center of mass of the rod.

25. The linear density of a rod at a point x centimeters from one end is $2/(1 + x)$ grams per centimeter. If the rod is 15 cm long, find the mass and center of mass of the rod.

26. The total mass of a rod of length L meters is M kilograms, and the measure of the linear density at a point x meters from the left end is proportional to the measure of the distance of the point from the right end. Show that the linear density at a point on the rod x meters from the left end is $2M(L - x)/L^2$ kilograms per meter.

27. A rod is 6 m long and its mass is 24 kg. If the measure of the linear density at any point of the rod varies directly as the square of the distance of the point from one end, find the largest value of the linear density.

28. A rod is L meters long and the center of mass of the rod is at the point $\frac{3}{4}L$ meters from the left end. If the measure of the linear density at a point is proportional to a power of the measure of the distance of the point from the left end and the linear density at the right end is 20 kg/m, find the linear density at a point x meters from the left end.

29. The weight of an object is the force resulting from gravity exerted on the object. Explain the difference between the weight and the mass of an object. Make up an example for each system of units: British, SI, and CGS.

6.3 CENTER OF MASS OF A LAMINA AND CENTROID OF A PLANE REGION

We regard a thin sheet of continuously distributed mass, for example a piece of paper or a flat strip of tin, as two-dimensional and call such a plane region a **lamina.** In this section we confine our discussion to homogeneous laminae, that is, laminae having constant area density. Laminae of variable area

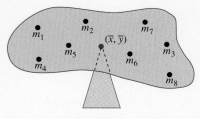

FIGURE 1

density are treated in connection with applications of multiple integrals, the subject of Chapter 13 in the multivariable section of this text.

Let us begin by considering a system of n particles located at the points $(x_1, y_1), (x_2, y_2), \ldots, (x_n, y_n)$, in the xy plane and let their masses be measured by $m_1, m_2, \ldots, m_n$. Imagine the particles are supported by a sheet of negligible weight and thickness. The *center of mass* is the point where the sheet will balance. Refer to Figure 1 showing eight particles placed on the sheet. The label of the ith particle in the figure is m_i, the measure of its mass. The sheet will balance on a fulcrum located at the center of mass denoted by $(\bar{x}, \bar{y})$. To determine the *center of mass* of such a system we must first define the total *mass* of the system and the *moments of mass* of the system with respect to the coordinate axes.

Let the ith particle, located at the point (x_i, y_i), have mass m_i kilograms. The total **mass** of the system is then M kilograms where

$$M = \sum_{i=1}^{n} m_i$$

The moment of mass of the ith particle with respect to the y axis is $m_i x_i$ kilogram-meters and its moment of mass with respect to the x axis is $m_i y_i$ kilogram-meters. If M_y kilogram-meters is the moment of the system of n particles with respect to the y axis, and M_x kilogram-meters is the moment with respect to the x axis, then

$$M_y = \sum_{i=1}^{n} m_i x_i \quad \text{and} \quad M_x = \sum_{i=1}^{n} m_i y_i$$

The center of mass of the system is the point $(\bar{x}, \bar{y})$, where

$$\bar{x} = \frac{M_y}{M} \quad \text{and} \quad \bar{y} = \frac{M_x}{M}$$

The point $(\bar{x}, \bar{y})$ can be interpreted as the point such that, if the total mass M kilograms of the system were concentrated there, the system's moment of mass with respect to the y axis would be $M\bar{x}$ kilogram-meters and its moment of mass with respect to the x axis would be $M\bar{y}$ kilogram-meters.

▶ **EXAMPLE 1**   Find the center of mass of the system of four particles, whose masses have measures 2, 6, 4, and 1, and which are located at the points $(5, -2), (-2, 1), (0, 3),$ and $(4, -1)$, respectively.

Solution

$$M_y = \sum_{i=1}^{4} m_i x_i = 2(5) + 6(-2) + 4(0) + 1(4) = 2$$

$$M_x = \sum_{i=1}^{4} m_i y_i = 2(-2) + 6(1) + 4(3) + 1(-1) = 13$$

$$M = \sum_{i=1}^{4} m_i = 2 + 6 + 4 + 1 = 13$$

Therefore

$$\bar{x} = \frac{M_y}{M} \qquad \bar{y} = \frac{M_x}{M}$$

$$= \tfrac{2}{13} \qquad = \tfrac{13}{13}$$

$$= 1$$

<u>Conclusion:</u> The center of mass is at $(\tfrac{2}{13}, 1)$. ◀

We now extend the concepts of mass, moments of mass, and center of mass to homogeneous laminae. If the homogeneous lamina is a rectangle, we define its center of mass as the center of the rectangle. We apply this definition to obtain the center of mass of a more general homogeneous lamina.

Let L be the homogeneous lamina whose constant area density is k kilograms per square meter and which is bounded by the curve $y = f(x)$, the x axis, and the lines $x = a$ and $x = b$. Assume that the function f is continuous on the closed interval $[a, b]$ and that $f(x) \geq 0$ for all x in $[a, b]$. See Figure 2. Let Δ be a partition of the interval $[a, b]$ into n subintervals. The ith subinterval is $[x_{i-1}, x_i]$ whose midpoint is m_i, and $\Delta_i x = x_i - x_{i-1}$. Associated with the ith subinterval is a rectangular lamina, whose width, altitude, and area density are given by $\Delta_i x$ meters, $f(m_i)$ meters, and k kilograms per square meter, respectively, and whose center of mass is at the point $(m_i, \tfrac{1}{2}f(m_i))$. The area of the rectangular lamina is $f(m_i) \Delta_i x$ square meters; hence $kf(m_i) \Delta_i x$ kilograms is its mass. So the sum of the measures of the masses of n rectangular laminae is the Riemann sum

$$\sum_{i=1}^{n} kf(m_i) \Delta_i x$$

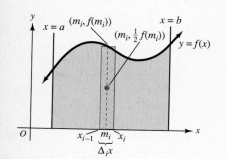

FIGURE 2

In the formal definition (6.3.1) we define the total mass of L as the limit of this Riemann sum.

Let $\Delta_i M_x$ kilogram-meters be the moment of mass of the ith rectangular lamina with respect to the x axis, and $\Delta_i M_y$ kilogram-meters be the moment of mass of this lamina with respect to the y axis. Then

$$\Delta_i M_x = \tfrac{1}{2}f(m_i)[kf(m_i) \Delta_i x] \quad \text{and} \quad \Delta_i M_y = m_i[kf(m_i) \Delta_i x]$$

The Riemann sums of the measures of the moments of mass of n rectangular laminae are

$$\sum_{i=1}^{n} \tfrac{1}{2}k[f(m_i)]^2 \Delta_i x \quad \text{and} \quad \sum_{i=1}^{n} km_i f(m_i) \Delta_i x$$

We formally define the moments of mass of L with respect to the coordinate axes as the limits of these Riemann sums.

6.3.1 Definition of Mass, Moments of Mass, and Center of Mass of a Lamina

Let L be the homogeneous lamina whose constant area density is k kilograms per square meter and which is bounded by the curve $y = f(x)$, the x axis, and the lines $x = a$ and $x = b$. The function f is continuous on $[a, b]$ and $f(x) \geq 0$ for all x in $[a, b]$. If M kilograms is the **total mass of the lamina L,** then

$$M = \lim_{\|\Delta\|\to 0} \sum_{i=1}^{n} kf(m_i) \, \Delta_i x$$

$$= k \int_a^b f(x) \, dx$$

If M_x kilogram-meters is the **moment of mass of the lamina L with respect to the x axis,** then

$$M_x = \lim_{\|\Delta\|\to 0} \sum_{i=1}^{n} \tfrac{1}{2}k[f(m_i)]^2 \, \Delta_i x$$

$$= \tfrac{1}{2}k \int_a^b [f(x)]^2 \, dx$$

If M_y kilogram-meters is the **moment of mass of the lamina L with respect to the y axis,** then

$$M_y = \lim_{\|\Delta\|\to 0} \sum_{i=1}^{n} km_i f(m_i) \, \Delta_i x$$

$$= k \int_a^b xf(x) \, dx$$

If $(\bar{x}, \bar{y})$ is the **center of mass of the lamina L** then

$$\bar{x} = \frac{M_y}{M} \quad \text{and} \quad \bar{y} = \frac{M_x}{M} \tag{1}$$

If we substitute the expressions for M, M_x, and M_y into (1), we obtain

$$\bar{x} = \frac{k \int_a^b xf(x) \, dx}{k \int_a^b f(x) \, dx} \quad \text{and} \quad \bar{y} = \frac{\tfrac{1}{2}k \int_a^b [f(x)]^2 \, dx}{k \int_a^b f(x) \, dx}$$

Dividing both the numerator and denominator by k we get

$$\bar{x} = \frac{\int_a^b xf(x) \, dx}{\int_a^b f(x) \, dx} \quad \text{and} \quad \bar{y} = \frac{\tfrac{1}{2} \int_a^b [f(x)]^2 \, dx}{\int_a^b f(x) \, dx}$$

In these formulas the denominator is the number of square units in the area of the region; so we have expressed a physical problem in terms of a geometric one. That is, $\bar{x}$ and $\bar{y}$ can be considered as the average abscissa and the average ordinate, respectively, of a geometric region. In such a case $\bar{x}$ and $\bar{y}$ depend only on the region, not on the mass of the lamina. So we refer to the center of mass of a plane region instead of to the center of mass of a homogeneous lamina. In such a case the center of mass is called the *centroid* of the region. Instead of moments of mass we consider moments of the region.

6.3.2 Definition of Moments and Centroid of a Plane Region

Let R be the region bounded by the curve $y = f(x)$, the x axis, and the lines $x = a$ and $x = b$. The function f is continuous on $[a, b]$ and $f(x) \geq 0$ for all x in $[a, b]$. If M_x denotes the **moment of R with respect to the x axis** and M_y denotes the **moment of R with respect to the y axis,** then

$$M_x = \lim_{\|\Delta\| \to 0} \sum_{i=1}^{n} \tfrac{1}{2}[f(m_i)]^2 \, \Delta_i x \qquad M_y = \lim_{\|\Delta\| \to 0} \sum_{i=1}^{n} m_i f(m_i) \, \Delta_i x$$

$$= \tfrac{1}{2} \int_a^b [f(x)]^2 \, dx \qquad\qquad = \int_a^b x f(x) \, dx$$

If $(\bar{x}, \bar{y})$ is the **centroid** of the plane region R whose area is A square units, and M_x and M_y are defined as above,

$$\bar{x} = \frac{M_y}{A} \quad \text{and} \quad \bar{y} = \frac{M_x}{A}$$

▶ **EXAMPLE 2**   Find the centroid of the first quadrant region bounded by the curve $y^2 = 4x$, the x axis, and the lines $x = 1$ and $x = 4$.

Solution   Let $f(x) = 2x^{1/2}$. The equation of the curve is then $y = f(x)$. In Figure 3 the region appears together with the ith rectangular element. The centroid of the rectangle is at $(m_i, \tfrac{1}{2}f(m_i))$. The area A square units of the region is given by

$$A = \lim_{\|\Delta\| \to 0} \sum_{i=1}^{n} f(m_i) \, \Delta_i x$$

$$= \int_1^4 f(x) \, dx$$

$$= \int_1^4 2x^{1/2} \, dx$$

$$= \tfrac{4}{3} x^{3/2} \Big]_1^4$$

$$= \tfrac{28}{3}$$

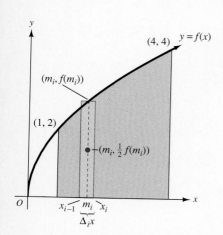

FIGURE 3

We now compute M_y and M_x.

$$M_y = \lim_{\|\Delta\| \to 0} \sum_{i=1}^{n} m_i f(m_i)\, \Delta_i x \qquad M_x = \lim_{\|\Delta\| \to 0} \sum_{i=1}^{n} \tfrac{1}{2} f(m_i) \cdot f(m_i)\, \Delta_i x$$

$$= \int_{1}^{4} x f(x)\, dx \qquad\qquad = \tfrac{1}{2} \int_{1}^{4} [f(x)]^2\, dx$$

$$= \int_{1}^{4} x(2x^{1/2})\, dx \qquad\quad = \tfrac{1}{2} \int_{1}^{4} 4x\, dx$$

$$= 2 \int_{1}^{4} x^{3/2}\, dx \qquad\qquad = x^2 \big]_{1}^{4}$$

$$= \tfrac{4}{5} x^{5/2} \big]_{1}^{4} \qquad\qquad\quad = 15$$

$$= \tfrac{124}{5}$$

Hence

$$\bar{x} = \frac{M_y}{A} \qquad\qquad \bar{y} = \frac{M_x}{A}$$

$$= \frac{\frac{124}{5}}{\frac{28}{3}} \qquad\qquad\quad = \frac{15}{\frac{28}{3}}$$

$$= \tfrac{93}{35} \qquad\qquad\qquad = \tfrac{45}{28}$$

Conclusion: The centroid is at the point $\left(\tfrac{93}{35}, \tfrac{45}{28}\right)$.   ◀

In the following example the region is bounded by two curves instead of one curve and a coordinate axis. The method for finding the centroid is the same as before, but the equations for M_x and M_y are now dependent on the equations defining the two curves.

▶ **EXAMPLE 3**   Find the centroid of the region bounded by the curves $y = x^2$ and $y = 2x + 3$.

Solution   The points of intersection of the two curves are $(-1, 1)$ and $(3, 9)$. The region is shown in Figure 4, together with the ith rectangular element.

Let $f(x) = x^2$ and $g(x) = 2x + 3$. The centroid of the ith rectangular element is at the point $(m_i, \tfrac{1}{2}[f(m_i) + g(m_i)])$, where m_i is the midpoint of the ith subinterval $[x_{i-1}, x_i]$. The measure of the area of the region is given by

$$A = \lim_{\|\Delta\| \to 0} \sum_{i=1}^{n} [g(m_i) - f(m_i)]\, \Delta_i x$$

$$= \int_{-1}^{3} [g(x) - f(x)]\, dx$$

$$= \int_{-1}^{3} [2x + 3 - x^2]\, dx$$

$$= \tfrac{32}{3}$$

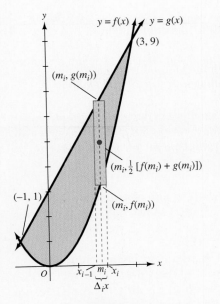

FIGURE 4

We now compute M_y and M_x.

$$M_y = \lim_{\|\Delta\| \to 0} \sum_{i=1}^{n} m_i[g(m_i) - f(m_i)] \, \Delta_i x$$

$$= \int_{-1}^{3} x[g(x) - f(x)] \, dx$$

$$= \int_{-1}^{3} x[2x + 3 - x^2] \, dx$$

$$= \tfrac{32}{3}$$

$$M_x = \lim_{\|\Delta\| \to 0} \sum_{i=1}^{n} \tfrac{1}{2}[g(m_i) + f(m_i)][g(m_i) - f(m_i)] \, \Delta_i x$$

$$= \frac{1}{2} \int_{-1}^{3} [g(x) + f(x)][g(x) - f(x)] \, dx$$

$$= \frac{1}{2} \int_{-1}^{3} [(2x + 3) + x^2][(2x + 3) - x^2] \, dx$$

$$= \frac{1}{2} \int_{-1}^{3} [4x^2 + 12x + 9 - x^4] \, dx$$

$$= \tfrac{544}{15}$$

Therefore

$$\bar{x} = \frac{M_y}{A} \qquad\qquad \bar{y} = \frac{M_x}{A}$$

$$= \frac{\tfrac{32}{3}}{\tfrac{32}{3}} \qquad\qquad = \frac{\tfrac{544}{15}}{\tfrac{32}{3}}$$

$$= 1 \qquad\qquad = \tfrac{17}{5}$$

<u>Conclusion:</u> The centroid is at the point $(1, \tfrac{17}{5})$. ◀

The following theorem can sometimes simplify the problem of finding the centroid of a plane region that can be divided into regions having axes of symmetry.

6.3.3 Theorem

If a line is an axis of symmetry of the plane region R, the centroid of R lies on that line.

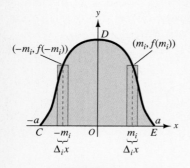

FIGURE 5

Proof   Choose the coordinate axes so that the axis of symmetry is on the y axis and the origin is in the region R. Figure 5 shows this situation. In the figure, R is the region CDE, C is the point $(-a, 0)$, E is the point $(a, 0)$, and an equation of the curve CDE is $y = f(x)$.

Consider a partition of the interval $[0, a]$. Let m_i be the midpoint of the ith subinterval. The moment with respect to the y axis of the rectangular element having an altitude $f(m_i)$ and a width $\Delta_i x$ is $m_i[f(m_i) \, \Delta_i x]$. Because of symmetry, for a similar partition of the interval $[-a, 0]$ there is a corresponding element having as its moment with respect to the y axis $-m_i[f(m_i)\,\Delta_i x]$. The sum of these two moments is 0; therefore $M_y = 0$. Because $\bar{x} = M_y/A$, we conclude that $\bar{x} = 0$. Thus the centroid of the region R lies on the y axis, which is what we wished to prove.   ∎

▶ **EXAMPLE 4**   Find the centroid of the region bounded by the x axis and the semicircle $y = \sqrt{4 - x^2}$.

Solution   Figure 6 shows the region whose area is 2π square units. Because the y axis is an axis of symmetry, the centroid lies on the y axis; thus $\bar{x} = 0$.

The moment of the region with respect to the x axis is given by

$$M_x = \lim_{\|\Delta\|\to 0} \sum_{i=1}^{n} \tfrac{1}{2}\left[\sqrt{4 - m_i^2}\right]^2 \Delta_i x$$

$$= 2 \cdot \tfrac{1}{2}\int_0^2 (4 - x^2)\,dx$$

$$= 4x - \tfrac{1}{3}x^3\Big]_0^2$$

$$= \tfrac{16}{3}$$

Therefore

$$\bar{y} = \frac{\frac{16}{3}}{2\pi}$$

$$= \frac{8}{3\pi}$$

<u>Conclusion:</u>   The centroid is at the point $\left(0, \dfrac{8}{3\pi}\right)$.   ◀

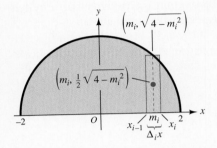

FIGURE 6

An application of centroids is afforded by the *theorem of Pappus* named for the Greek mathematician Pappus of Alexandria who lived in the fourth century.

6.3.4 The Theorem of Pappus for Volumes of Solids of Revolution

If a plane region is revolved about a line in its plane that does not cut the region, then the measure of the volume of the solid of revolution generated is equal to the product of the measure of the area of the region and the measure of the distance traveled by the centroid of the region.

To visualize this theorem, refer to Figure 7 showing the region R bounded by the curves $y = f(x)$ and $y = g(x)$. If A is the measure of the area of R and if $\bar{x}$ is the abscissa of the centroid of R, the theorem states that the measure of the volume V of the solid of revolution obtained by revolving R about the y axis is given by

$$V = 2\pi\,\bar{x}A \tag{2}$$

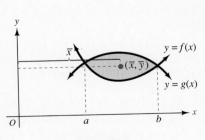

FIGURE 7

You are asked to prove the theorem of Pappus stated as this formula in Exercise 39.

▶ **EXAMPLE 5**   Apply the theorem of Pappus to find the volume of the torus (doughnut shape) generated by revolving a circle with a radius of r units about a line in its plane at a distance of b units from its center, where $b > r$.

Solution   Choose the coordinate axes so that the center of the circle is at the point $(b, 0)$ on the x axis. See Figure 8. The torus shown in Figure 9 is formed by revolving the circle about the y axis. From Theorem 6.3.3, it follows that the centroid of the circular region is at the center of the circle. Therefore, from the theorem of Pappus stated as formula (2), if V cubic units is the volume of the torus

$$V = (2\pi b)(\pi r^2)$$
$$= 2\pi^2 r^2 b$$

Conclusion: The volume is $2\pi^2 r^2 b$ cubic units.   ◀

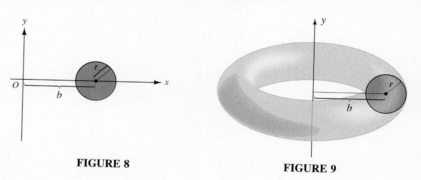

FIGURE 8   **FIGURE 9**

EXERCISES 6.3

1. Find the center of mass of the three particles having masses of 1, 2, and 3 kg located at the points $(-1, 3)$, $(2, 1)$, and $(3, -1)$, respectively.

2. Find the center of mass of the four particles having masses of 2, 3, 3, and 4 kg located at the points $(-1, -2)$, $(1, 3)$, $(0, 5)$, and $(2, 1)$, respectively.

3. The y coordinate of the center of mass of four particles is 5. The particles have masses 2, 5, 4, and m kg located at the points $(3, 2)$, $(-1, 0)$, $(0, 20)$, and $(2, -2)$, respectively. Find m.

4. Find the center of mass of the three particles having masses 3, 7, and 2 kg located at the points $(2, 3)$, $(-1, 4)$, and $(0, 2)$, respectively.

5. Find the center of mass of three particles of equal mass located at the points $(4, -2)$, $(-3, 0)$, and $(1, 5)$.

6. Prove that the center of mass of three particles of equal mass lies at the point of intersection of the medians of the triangle having as vertices the points at which the particles are located.

In Exercises 7 through 14, find the centroid of the region with the indicated boundaries.

7. The parabola $y = 4 - x^2$ and the x axis.

8. The parabola $x = 2y - y^2$ and the y axis.

9. The parabola $y = x^2$ and the line $y = 4$.

10. The parabola $y^2 = 4x$, the y axis, and the line $y = 4$.

11. The curves $y = x^3$ and $y = 4x$ in the first quadrant.

12. The lines $y = 2x + 1$, $x + y = 7$, and $x = 8$.

13. The curves $y = x^2 - 4$ and $y = 2x - x^2$.

14. The curves $y = x^2$ and $y = x^3$.

15. Find the center of mass of the lamina bounded by the parabola $2y^2 = 18 - 3x$ and the y axis if the area density at any point (x, y) is $\sqrt{6 - x}$ kilograms per square meter.

16. Solve Exercise 15 if the area density at any point (x, y) is x kilograms per square meter.

In Exercises 17 through 24, you need to use your graphics calculator to find the centroid of the region of the indicated exercise in Exercises 4.8. Express your answer to four significant digits.

17. Exercise 39
18. Exercise 40
19. Exercise 41
20. Exercise 42
21. Exercise 43
22. Exercise 44
23. Exercise 45
24. Exercise 46

In Exercises 25 through 32, you need to use your graphics calculator to find the centroid of the region of the indicated exercise in Exercises 4.9. Express your answer to four significant digits.

25. Exercise 41
26. Exercise 42
27. Exercise 43
28. Exercise 44
29. Exercise 45
30. Exercise 46
31. Exercise 49
32. Exercise 50

33. Find the value of a if the centroid of the region bounded by the parabola $y^2 = 4px$ and the line $x = a$ is at the point $(p, 0)$.

34. Prove that the distance from the centroid of a triangle to any side of the triangle is equal to one-third of the length of the altitude to that side.

In Exercises 35 through 38, use the theorem of Pappus to find the indicated quantity.

35. The centroid of the region bounded by a semicircle and a diameter line.

36. The volume of a right-circular cone with base radius r units and height h units.

37. The moment with respect to line $y = -r$ of the region bounded by the semicircle $y = \sqrt{r^2 - x^2}$ and the x axis.

38. The volume of the solid of revolution generated by revolving the region of Exercise 37 about the line $x - y = r$. *Hint:* Use the result of Exercise 30 in Exercises 3.9.

39. Prove the theorem of Pappus for volumes of solids of revolution stated as formula (2).

40. Is the centroid of a plane region necessarily a point within the region? Make up an example to illustrate your answer.

6.4 WORK

In physics the term *work* is used to characterize the energy of motion of a body when the body is moved a certain distance due to a force acting on it; so that

work equals force times distance

For example, suppose a constant force of F pounds acts in the direction of motion on an object moving to the right along the x axis from point a to point b. Then if $b - a$ is the number of feet in the distance the object moves, and if W is the number of foot-pounds of work done by the force, W is defined by

$$W = F(b - a) \tag{1}$$

▷ **ILLUSTRATION 1**   If W foot-pounds is the work necessary to lift a 70-lb weight to a height of 3 ft, then

$$W = 70 \cdot 3$$
$$= 210$$

Thus the work done is 210 ft-lb.   ◄

The unit of measurement for work depends on the units of force and distance. In the British system, where the force is measured in pounds and the distance is measured in feet, work is measured in foot-pounds. In the SI system, the unit of force is a newton, the unit of distance is a meter, and the unit of work is a newton-meter, called a *joule*. In the CGS system, the unit of force is a dyne, the unit of distance is a centimeter, and the unit of work is a dyne-centimeter, called an *erg*. For conversion purposes, 1 newton is 10^5 dynes and 1 joule is 10^7 ergs.

The following illustration shows a computation for work using units in the SI system.

▷ **ILLUSTRATION 2**   We wish to find the work done in lifting a rock of mass 8 kg a distance of 4 m. We use the formula $F = Ma$, where F newtons is the force required to give a mass of M kilograms an acceleration of a meters per second squared. The force in this case is the force of gravity and the acceleration is that due to gravity, which is 9.81 m/sec². The mass is 8 kg. Therefore $M = 8$, $a = 9.81$, and

$$F = 8(9.81)$$
$$= 78.5$$

Thus we wish to find the work done by a force of 78.5 N and a distance of 4 m. If W joules is the work,

$$W = (78.5)(4)$$
$$= 314$$

Hence the work done is 314 joules.   ◀

Consider now the work done by a variable force acting along a line in the direction of motion. We wish to define what is meant by the term "work" in such a case.

Suppose that f is continuous on the closed interval $[a, b]$ and $f(x)$ units is the force acting in the direction of motion on an object as it moves to the right along the x axis from point a to point b. Let Δ be a partition of $[a, b]$:

$$a = x_0 < x_1 < x_2 < \ldots < x_{n-1} < x_n = b$$

The ith subinterval is $[x_{i-1}, x_i]$; and if x_{i-1} is close to x_i, the force is almost constant in this subinterval. If we assume that the force is constant in the ith subinterval and if w_i is any point such that $x_{i-1} \le w_i \le x_i$, then if $\Delta_i W$ units of work is done on the object as it moves from the point x_{i-1} to the point x_i, from formula (1) we have

$$\Delta_i W = f(w_i)(x_i - x_{i-1})$$

Replacing $x_i - x_{i-1}$ by $\Delta_i x$ we have

$$\Delta_i W = f(w_i)\,\Delta_i x$$
$$\sum_{i=1}^{n} \Delta_i W = \sum_{i=1}^{n} f(w_i)\,\Delta_i x$$

The smaller we take the norm of the partition Δ, the larger n will be and the closer the Riemann sum will be to what we intuitively think of as the measure of the total work done. We therefore define the measure of the total work as the limit of this Riemann sum.

6.4.1 Definition of Work

Let the function f be continuous on the closed interval $[a, b]$ and $f(x)$ units be the force acting on an object at the point x on the x axis. Then if W units is the work done by the force as the object moves from a to b,

$$W = \lim_{\|\Delta\| \to 0} \sum_{i=1}^{n} f(w_i)\, \Delta_i x$$

$$= \int_a^b f(x)\, dx$$

▶ **EXAMPLE 1**   A particle is moving along the x axis under the action of a force of $f(x)$ pounds when the particle is x feet from the origin. If $f(x) = x^2 + 4$, find the work done as the particle moves from the point where $x = 2$ to the point where $x = 4$.

Solution   We take a partition of the closed interval $[2, 4]$. If W foot-pounds is the work done as the particle moves from the point where $x = 2$ to the point where $x = 4$, then from Definition 6.4.1,

$$W = \lim_{\|\Delta\| \to 0} \sum_{i=1}^{n} f(w_i)\, \Delta_i x$$

$$= \int_2^4 f(x)\, dx$$

$$= \int_2^4 (x^2 + 4)\, dx$$

$$= \frac{x^3}{3} + 4x \Big]_2^4$$

$$= \tfrac{64}{3} + 16 - \left(\tfrac{8}{3} + 8\right)$$

$$= 26\tfrac{2}{3}$$

Conclusion: The work done is $26\tfrac{2}{3}$ ft-lb.   ◀

In the following example we use Hooke's law, named for the British mathematician Robert Hooke (1635–1703). Hooke's law states that if a spring is stretched x units beyond its natural length, but within its elastic limit, it is pulled back with a force equal to kx units, where k is a constant dependent on the material and size of the spring.

▶ **EXAMPLE 2**   A spring has a natural length of 14 cm. If a force of 500 dynes is required to keep the spring stretched 2 cm, how much work is done in stretching the spring from its natural length to a length of 18 cm?

Solution   Place the spring along the x axis with the origin at the point where the stretching starts. See Figure 1. Let $f(x)$ dynes be the force re-

FIGURE 1

quired to stretch the spring x centimeters beyond its natural length. Then by Hooke's law

$$f(x) = kx$$

Because $f(2) = 500$, we have

$$500 = k \cdot 2$$
$$k = 250$$

Thus

$$f(x) = 250x$$

Because the spring is being stretched from 14 cm to 18 cm, we consider a partition of the closed interval $[0, 4]$ on the x axis. Let $\Delta_i x$ centimeters be the length of the ith subinterval and let w_i be any point in that subinterval. If W ergs is the work done in stretching the spring from 14 cm to 18 cm, then

$$W = \lim_{\|\Delta\| \to 0} \sum_{i=1}^{n} f(w_i)\, \Delta_i x$$

$$= \int_0^4 f(x)\, dx$$

$$= \int_0^4 250x\, dx$$

$$= \frac{250}{2} x^2 \Big]_0^4$$

$$= 2000$$

<u>Conclusion:</u>   The work done in stretching the spring is 2000 ergs.   ◀

In Examples 3 and 4, we are concerned with the weight of water. In the SI system the weight density of water is 9810 N/m³, and in the British system it is 62.4 lb/ft³.

▶   **EXAMPLE 3**   A water tank in the form of an inverted right-circular cone is 2 m across the top and 1.5 m deep. If the surface of the water is 0.5 m below the top of the tank, find the work done in pumping the water to the top of the tank.

Solution   Refer to Figure 2. The positive x axis is chosen in the downward direction because the motion is vertical. Take the origin at the top of the tank. We consider a partition of the closed interval $[0.5, 1.5]$ on the x axis and let w_i be any point in the ith subinterval $[x_{i-1}, x_i]$. An element of volume is a circular disk having thickness $\Delta_i x$ meters and radius $f(w_i)$ meters, where the function f is determined by an equation of the line through the points $(0, 1)$ and $(1.5, 0)$ in the form $y = f(x)$. The volume of this element is $\pi[f(w_i)]^2\, \Delta_i x$ cubic meters. With the weight of 1 m³ of water as 9810 N, the weight of the element is $9810\pi[f(w_i)]^2\, \Delta_i x$ newtons, which is the force acting on the element. If x_{i-1} is close to x_i, then the distance the element moves is approximately w_i meters. Thus the work done in pumping the element to the top of the tank is approximately $(9810\pi[f(w_i)]^2\, \Delta_i x) \cdot w_i$

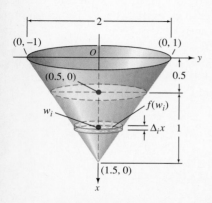

FIGURE 2

joules. So if W joules is the total work done

$$W = \lim_{\|\Delta\| \to 0} \sum_{i=1}^{n} 9810\pi[f(w_i)]^2 \cdot w_i \, \Delta_i x$$

$$= 9810\pi \int_{0.5}^{1.5} [f(x)]^2 x \, dx$$

To determine $f(x)$ we find an equation of the line through $(0, 1)$ and $(1.5, 0)$ by using the slope-intercept form:

$$y = \frac{0 - 1}{1.5 - 0}x + 1 \quad \Leftrightarrow \quad y = -\tfrac{2}{3}x + 1$$

Therefore, $f(x) = -\tfrac{2}{3}x + 1$, and

$$W = 9810\pi \int_{0.5}^{1.5} \left(-\tfrac{2}{3}x + 1\right)^2 x \, dx$$

$$= 9810\pi \int_{0.5}^{1.5} \left(\tfrac{4}{9}x^3 - \tfrac{4}{3}x^2 + x\right) dx$$

$$= 9810\pi \left[\tfrac{1}{9}x^4 - \tfrac{4}{9}x^3 + \tfrac{1}{2}x^2\right]_{0.5}^{1.5}$$

$$= 1090\pi$$

$$\approx 3424$$

Conclusion: The work done is 3424 joules. ◀

▶ **EXAMPLE 4** As a water tank is being raised, water spills out at a constant rate of 2 ft³ per foot of rise. If the weight of the tank is 200 lb and it originally contains 1000 ft³ of water, find the work done in raising the tank 20 ft.

Solution Refer to Figure 3. Here we take the origin at the starting point of the bottom of the tank and the positive x axis is in the upward direction because the motion is vertically upward from O. We consider a partition of the closed interval $[0, 20]$ on the x axis. Let w_i be any point in the ith subinterval $[x_{i-1}, x_i]$. When the bottom of the tank is at w_i, there is $(1000 - 2w_i)$ cubic feet of water in the tank. With the weight of 1 ft³ of water as 62.4 lb the weight of the tank and its contents when it is at w_i is $[200 + 62.4(1000 - 2w_i)]$ pounds or $(62{,}600 - 124.8w_i)$ pounds, which is the force acting on the tank. The work done in raising the tank through the ith subinterval is approximately $(62{,}600 - 124.8w_i) \, \Delta_i x$ foot-pounds. We use the terminology "approximately" because we are assuming that the amount of water in the tank is constant throughout the subinterval. If W foot-pounds is the total work done in raising the tank 20 ft,

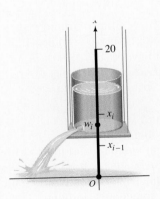

FIGURE 3

$$W = \lim_{\|\Delta\| \to 0} \sum_{i=1}^{n} (62{,}600 - 124.8w_i) \, \Delta_i x$$

$$= \int_{0}^{20} (62{,}600 - 124.8x) \, dx$$

$$= 62{,}600x - 62.4x^2 \Big]_{0}^{20}$$

$$\approx 1{,}230{,}000$$

Conclusion: The work done is 1,230,000 ft-lb. ◀

EXERCISES 6.4

In Exercises 1 and 2, a particle is moving along the x axis under the action of a force of $f(x)$ pounds, directed along the x axis, when the particle is x feet from the origin. Find the work done as the particle moves from the point where $x = a$ to the point where $x = b$.

1. $f(x) = (2x + 1)^2$; $a = 1$; $b = 3$

2. $f(x) = x^2\sqrt{x^3 + 1}$; $a = 0$; $b = 2$

In Exercises 3 and 4, a particle is moving along the x axis under the action of a force of $f(x)$ newtons, directed along the x axis, when the particle is x meters from the origin. Find the work done as the particle moves from the point where $x = a$ to the point where $x = b$.

3. $f(x) = x\sqrt{x + 1}$; $a = 3$; $b = 8$

4. $f(x) = (4x - 1)^2$; $a = 1$; $b = 4$

5. An object is moving along the x axis under the action of a force of $f(x)$ dynes when the object is x centimeters from the origin. If 96 ergs is the work done in moving the object from the origin to the point where $x = K$, and $f(x) = 2x - 3$, find K if $K > 0$.

6. Solve Exercise 5 if 90 ergs is the work done, and $f(x) = 4x - 3$.

7. A spring has a natural length of 8 in. If a force of 20 lb stretches the spring $\frac{1}{2}$ in., find the work done in stretching the spring from 8 in. to 11 in.

8. A spring has a natural length of 10 in., and a 30-lb force stretchs it to $11\frac{1}{2}$ in. **(a)** Find the work done in stretching the spring from 10 in. to 12 in. **(b)** Find the work done in stretching the spring from 12 in. to 14 in.

9. A force of 8 N stretches a spring of natural length 4 m to an additional 50 cm. Find the work done in stretching the spring from its natural length to 5 m.

10. A force of 500 dynes stretches a spring from its natural length of 20 cm to a length of 24 cm. Find the work done in stretching the spring from its natural length to a length of 28 cm.

11. A spring has a natural length of 12 cm. A force of 600 dynes compresses the spring to 10 cm. Find the work done in compressing the spring from 12 cm to 9 cm. Hooke's law holds for compression as well as for extension.

12. A spring has a natural length of 6 in. A 1200-lb force compresses it to $5\frac{1}{2}$ in. Find the work done in compressing it from 6 in. to $4\frac{1}{2}$ in.

13. A tank full of water is in the form of a rectangular parallelepiped 5 ft deep, 15 ft wide, and 25 ft long. Find the work required to pump the water in the tank up to a level 1 ft above the surface of the tank.

14. A trough full of water is 10 ft long, and its cross section is in the shape of an isosceles triangle 2 ft wide across the top and 2 ft high. How much work is done in pumping all the water out of the trough over the top?

15. A hemispherical tank, placed so that the top is a circular region of radius 6 ft, is filled with water to a depth of 4 ft. Find the work done in pumping the water to the top of the tank.

16. A right-circular cylindrical tank with a depth of 12 ft and a radius of 4 ft is half full of oil weighing 60 lb/ft³. Find the work done in pumping the oil to a height 6 ft above the tank.

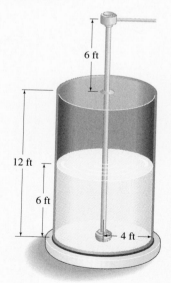

17. A cable 200 ft long and weighing 4 lb/ft is hanging vertically down a well. If a weight of 100 lb is suspended from the lower end of the cable, find the work done in pulling the cable and weight to the top of the well.

18. A bucket weighing 20 lb containing 60 lb of sand is attached to the lower end of a chain 100 ft long and weighing 10 lb that is hanging in a deep well. Find the work done in raising the bucket to the top of the well.

19. Solve Exercise 18 if the sand is leaking out of the bucket at a constant rate and has all leaked out just as soon as the bucket is at the top of the well.

20. As a flour sack is being raised a distance of 9 ft, flour leaks out at such a rate that the number of pounds lost is directly proportional to the square root of the distance traveled. If the sack originally contained 60 lb of flour and it loses a total of 12 lb while being raised the 9 ft, find the work done in raising the sack.

21. A right-circular cylindrical tank with a depth of 10 m and a radius of 5 m is half filled with water. Find the work necessary to pump the water to the top of the tank.

22. A tank in the form of an inverted right-circular cone is 8 m across the top and 10 m deep. If the tank is filled to a height of 9 m with water, find the work done in pumping the water to the top of the tank.

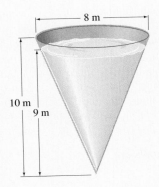

23. If the tank of Exercise 22 is filled to a height of 8 m with oil weighing 950 kg/m³, find the work done in pumping the oil to the top of the tank. *Hint:* The number of newtons of force necessary to lift an element is the product of the number of kilograms of mass (the same as the number of kilograms of weight) and 9.81, the number of meters per second squared in the acceleration due to gravity.

24. If in Exercise 22, only half of the water is to be pumped to the top of the tank, find the work.

25. A 1-horsepower motor can do 550 ft-lb of work per second. If a 0.1 hp motor is used to pump water from a full tank in the shape of a rectangular parallelepiped 2 ft deep, 2 ft wide, and 6 ft long to a point 5 ft above the top of the tank, how long will it take?

26. A meteorite is a miles from the center of the earth and falls to the surface of the earth. The force of gravity is inversely proportional to the square of the distance of a body from the center of the earth. Find the work done by gravity if the weight of the meteorite is w pounds at the surface of the earth. Let R miles be the radius of the earth.

27. A tank in the form of a rectangular parallelepiped 6 ft deep, 4 ft wide, and 12 ft long is full of oil weighing 50 lb/ft³. When one-third of the work necessary to pump the oil to the top of the tank has been done, find by how much the surface of the oil is lowered.

28. A cylindrical water tank of radius 5 ft and height 10 ft is standing on a platform 50 ft high. Find the depth of the water in the tank when one-half of the work required to fill the tank from ground level through a pipe in the bottom has been done.

29. A container is in the shape of the solid of revolution formed by rotating about the x axis (with the positive x axis downward) the region bounded by the curve $y^2 x = e^{-2x}$ and the lines $x = 1$ and $x = 4$. If the container is full of water, find the work done in pumping all the water to a point 1 ft above the top of the container. Distance is measured in feet.

30. If W inch-pounds is the work done by a gas expanding against a piston in a cylinder and P pounds per square inch is the pressure of the gas when the volume of the gas is V cubic inches, show that if V_1 cubic inches and V_2 cubic inches are the initial and final volumes, respectively, then

$$W = \int_{V_1}^{V_2} P \, dV$$

31. Suppose that a piston compresses a gas in a cylinder from an initial volume of 60 in.³ to a volume of 40 in.³ If Boyle's law (Exercise 8 in Exercises 2.6) holds, and the initial pressure is 50 lb/in.², find the work done by the piston. Use the result of Exercise 30.

32. Explain the similarities and differences between the scientific use of the term *work* and Webster's definition of *work* as "bodily or mental effort exerted to do or make something."

6.5 FORCE DUE TO FLUID PRESSURE

Another application of the definite integral in physics is to find the force due to fluid pressure on a plate submerged in the fluid or on a side of a container holding the fluid.

The **pressure** of a fluid is the force per square unit of area exerted by the weight of the fluid. So if ρ is the measure of the weight density of the fluid then the pressure exerted by the fluid at a point h units below the surface of the fluid is P units where

$$P = \rho h \tag{1}$$

Observe from (1) that the size of the container is immaterial so far as fluid pressure is concerned. For example, at a depth of 5 ft in a swimming pool filled with salt water, the pressure is the same as at a depth of 5 ft in the Pacific Ocean, assuming the weight density of the water is the same.

Suppose a flat plate is inserted horizontally into a fluid in a container. If A square units is the area of the submerged plate and F is the measure of the force due to fluid pressure acting on the upper face of the plate, then,

$$F = PA$$

Substituting from (1) into this equation gives

$$F = \rho h A$$

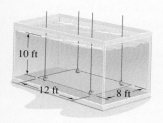

FIGURE 1

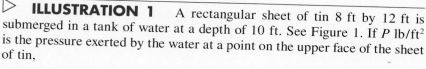

▷   **ILLUSTRATION 1**   A rectangular sheet of tin 8 ft by 12 ft is submerged in a tank of water at a depth of 10 ft. See Figure 1. If P lb/ft² is the pressure exerted by the water at a point on the upper face of the sheet of tin,

$$P = 10\rho$$

The area of the piece of tin is 96 ft². So if F lb is the force due to water pressure acting on the upper face of the sheet of tin

$$F = 96P$$

Substituting 10ρ for P, we get

$$F = 960\rho$$

Because $\rho = 62.4$ in the British system,

$$F = 960(62.4)$$
$$= 60{,}000$$

The force due to water pressure on the upper face of the sheet of tin is, therefore, 60,000 lb.   ◀

Now suppose that a flat plate is submerged vertically in a fluid. Then at points on the plate at different depths the pressure, computed from (1), will be different and will be greater at the bottom of the plate than at the top. To define the force due to fluid pressure on this vertically submerged plate, we use Pascal's principle named for the French mathematician Blaise Pascal (1623–1662).

Pascal's principle: At any point in a fluid, the pressure is the same in all directions.

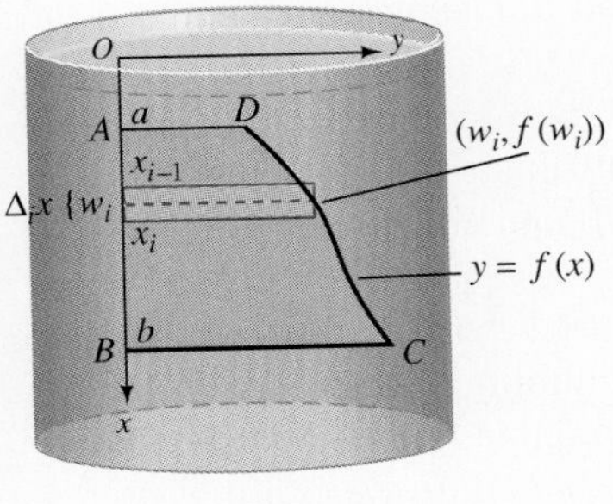

In Figure 2 let $ABCD$ be the region bounded by the x axis, the lines $x = a$ and $x = b$, and the curve $y = f(x)$, where the function f is continuous and $f(x) \geq 0$ on the closed interval $[a, b]$. Choose the coordinate axes so that the y axis lies along the surface of the fluid. Take the x axis vertical with the positive direction downward, so that $f(x)$ units is the length of the plate at a depth of x units.

Let Δ be a partition of the closed interval $[a, b]$ that divides the interval into n subintervals. Choose a point w_i in the ith subinterval, with $x_{i-1} \leq w_i \leq x_i$. Draw n horizontal rectangles. The ith rectangle has a length of $f(w_i)$ units and a width of $\Delta_i x$ units (see Figure 2).

If we rotate each rectangular element through an angle of $90°$, each element becomes a plate submerged horizontally in the fluid at a depth of w_i units below the surface of the fluid and perpendicular to the region $ABCD$. Then the measure of the force on the ith rectangular element is $\rho w_i f(w_i) \, \Delta_i x$. An approximation to the measure of the total force due to fluid pressure on the plate is

$$\sum_{i=1}^{n} \rho w_i f(w_i) \, \Delta_i x$$

which is a Riemann sum. The smaller we take $\| \Delta \|$, the larger n will be and the closer the approximation of this Riemann sum will be to what we wish to be the measure of the total force. We have, then, the following definition.

6.5.1 Definition of Force Due to Fluid Pressure

Suppose that a flat plate is submerged vertically in a fluid for which a measure of its weight density is ρ. The length of the plate at a depth of x units below the surface of the fluid is $f(x)$ units, where f is continuous on the closed interval $[a, b]$ and $f(x) \geq 0$ on $[a, b]$. Then if F is the measure of the **force due to fluid pressure** on the plate

$$F = \lim_{\| \Delta \| \to 0} \sum_{i=1}^{n} \rho w_i f(w_i) \, \Delta_i x$$

$$= \rho \int_{a}^{b} x f(x) \, dx$$

FIGURE 2

▶ **EXAMPLE 1** A trough having a trapezoidal cross section is full of water. If the trapezoid is 3 ft wide at the top, 2 ft wide at the bottom, and 2 ft deep, find the total force due to water pressure on one end of the trough.

Solution Figure 3 illustrates one end of the trough together with a rectangular element of area. Because an equation of the line AB is $y = \frac{3}{2} - \frac{1}{4}x$,

$$f(x) = \frac{3}{2} - \frac{1}{4}x$$

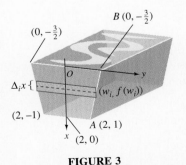

FIGURE 3

If we rotate the rectangular element through 90°, the force on the element is $2\rho w_i f(w_i) \Delta_i x$ pounds. If F pounds is the total force on the side of the trough

$$F = \lim_{\|\Delta\| \to 0} \sum_{i=1}^{n} 2\rho w_i f(w_i) \, \Delta_i x$$

$$= 2\rho \int_0^2 x f(x) \, dx$$

$$= 2\rho \int_0^2 x(\tfrac{3}{2} - \tfrac{1}{4}x) \, dx$$

$$= 2\rho[\tfrac{3}{4}x^2 - \tfrac{1}{12}x^3]_0^2$$

$$= \tfrac{14}{3}\,\rho$$

<u>Conclusion:</u>   With $\rho = 62.4$, the total force is 291 lb.   ◀

▶   **EXAMPLE 2**   The ends of a gasoline tank are semicircular regions, each with a radius of 2 ft. Find the force due to fluid pressure on one end if the tank is full of gasoline having weight density 41 lb/ft³.

Solution   Figure 4 shows one end of the tank together with a rectangular element of area. Solving an equation of the semicircle for y, we get $y = \sqrt{4 - x^2}$. The force on the rectangular element is $2\rho w_i \sqrt{4 - w_i^2}\,\Delta_i x$ pounds. Therefore, if F pounds is the total force on the side of the tank,

$$F = \lim_{\|\Delta\| \to 0} \sum_{i=1}^{n} 2\rho w_i \sqrt{4 - w_i^2} \, \Delta_i x$$

$$= 2\rho \int_0^2 x\sqrt{4 - x^2} \, dx$$

$$= -\tfrac{2}{3}\rho(4 - x^2)^{3/2}\big]_0^2$$

$$= \tfrac{16}{3}\rho$$

<u>Conclusion:</u>   With $\rho = 41$, the total force is 219 lb.   ◀

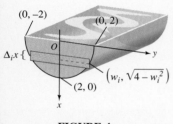

$(0, -2)$

$(0, 2)$

$\Delta_i x \{$

o

y

$\left(w_i, \sqrt{4 - w_i^2}\right)$

$(2, 0)$

x

FIGURE 4

A useful relation exists between the force due to fluid pressure on a plane region and the location of the centroid of the region. Consider the region $ABCD$ in Figure 2 as the flat plate submerged vertically in a fluid as described in Definition 6.5.1. Then from the definition, if F is the measure of the force due to fluid pressure on the plate

$$F = \rho \int_a^b x f(x) \, dx \tag{2}$$

If $\bar{x}$ is the abscissa of the centroid of the region $ABCD$, then $\bar{x} = M_y/A$. Because $M_y = \int_a^b x f(x) \, dx$,

$$\bar{x} = \frac{\displaystyle\int_a^b x f(x) \, dx}{A}$$

$$\int_a^b x f(x) \, dx = \bar{x}A$$

Substituting from this equation into (2), we obtain

$$F = \rho \bar{x} A \tag{3}$$

From (3) it follows that the total force due to fluid pressure against a vertical plane region is the same as it would be if the region were horizontal at a depth $\bar{x}$ units below the surface of the fluid.

▷ **ILLUSTRATION 2** Consider the gasoline tank of Example 2. The ends of the tank are semicircular regions each with a radius of 2 ft. The area of the region is 2π ft^2, and from the result of Example 4 in Section 6.3, the centroid of the region is at a depth of $8/(3\pi)$ ft. Therefore, from (3), if F pounds is the force due to fluid pressure on one end of the trough,

$$F = \rho \frac{8}{3\pi} (2\pi)$$

$$= \tfrac{16}{3} \rho$$

in agreement with the result of Example 2. ◀

Centroids of various simple plane regions may be found in a table. When both the area of the region and the centroid of the region may be obtained directly, (3) is easy to apply and is used in such cases by engineers to find the force due to fluid pressure.

In the next example, we use SI units, where the weight density of water is 9810 N/m^3.

▶ **EXAMPLE 3** A container in the shape of a right-circular cylinder having a base of radius 3 m is on its side at the bottom of a tank full of water. The depth of the tank is 13 m. Find the total force due to water pressure on one end of the container.

Solution Figure 5 shows one end of the container in the tank and a rectangular element of area. The coordinate system is chosen so that the origin is at the center of the circle. An equation of the circle is $x^2 + y^2 = 9$. Solving for x gives $x = \sqrt{9 - y^2}$. The number of newtons in the force on the rectangular element is

$$\rho(10 - w_i)[2\sqrt{9 - w_i^2}] \, \Delta_i y$$

So if F newtons is the total force on the end of the container,

$$F = \lim_{\|\Delta\| \to 0} \sum_{i=1}^{n} \rho \, (10 - w_i)[2\sqrt{9 - w_i^2}] \, \Delta_i y$$

$$= 2\rho \int_{-3}^{3} (10 - y) \sqrt{9 - y^2} \, dy$$

Because $\rho = 9810$, we have

$$F = 196{,}200 \int_{-3}^{3} \sqrt{9 - y^2} \, dy - 19{,}620 \int_{-3}^{3} y \sqrt{9 - y^2} \, dy \tag{4}$$

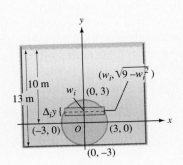

FIGURE 5

To evaluate $\int_{-3}^{3} \sqrt{9 - y^2} \, dy$ requires a technique of integration you will learn in Section 7.3. At present we determine its value by considering it as the measure of the area of the region enclosed by a semicircle of radius 3. Therefore

$$\int_{-3}^{3} \sqrt{9 - y^2} \, dy = \tfrac{9}{2}\pi$$

Substituting this value into (4) and evaluating the second integral we have

$$F = 196{,}200(\tfrac{9}{2}\pi) + 19{,}620\left[\tfrac{1}{3}(9 - y^2)^{3/2}\right]_{-3}^{3}$$
$$= 882{,}900\pi$$

Conclusion: The total force is $882{,}900\pi$ N.   ◄

EXERCISES 6.5

1. A rectangular plate of width 10 ft and depth 8 ft is submerged vertically in a tank of water with the upper edge lying in the surface. Find the force due to water pressure on one side of the plate.

2. A square plate of side 4 ft is submerged vertically in a tank of water and its center is 2 ft below the surface. Find the force due to water pressure on one side of the plate.

3. Solve Exercise 2 if the center of the plate is 4 ft below the surface.

4. A plate in the shape of an isosceles right triangle is submerged vertically in a tank of water, with one leg lying in the surface. The legs are each 6 ft long. Find the force due to water pressure on one side of the plate.

5. A rectangular tank full of water is 2 ft wide and 18 in. deep. Find the force due to water pressure on one end of the tank.

6. The ends of a trough are equilateral triangles having sides with lengths of 2 ft. If the water in the trough is 1 ft deep, find the force due to water pressure on one end.

7. The face of the gate of a dam is in the shape of an isosceles triangle 4 m wide at the top and 3 m high. If the upper edge of the face of the gate is 15 m below the surface of the water, find the total force due to water pressure on the gate.

8. The face of a gate of a dam is vertical and in the shape of an isosceles trapezoid 3 m wide at the top, 4 m wide at the bottom, and 3 m high. If the upper base is 20 m below the surface of the water, find the total force due to water pressure on the gate.

9. The face of a dam adjacent to the water is vertical, and its shape is in the form of an isosceles triangle 250 m wide across the top and 100 m high in the center. If the water is 10 m deep in the center, find the total force on the dam due to water pressure.

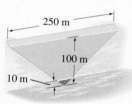

10. An oil tank is in the shape of a right-circular cylinder 4 m in diameter, and its axis is horizontal. If the tank is half full of oil having weight density 7360 N/m³, find the total force on one end due to fluid pressure.

11. An oil tank is in the shape of a right-circular cylinder with a radius of r meters, and its axis is horizontal. If the tank is half full of oil having weight density 7360 N/m³, find r if the total force on one end of the tank due to fluid pressure is 80,000 N.

12. Solve Exercise 4 by using Equation (3).

13. Solve Exercise 5 by using Equation (3).

14. Solve Exercise 6 by using Equation (3).

15. The face of a dam adjacent to the water is vertical and is in the shape of an isosceles trapezoid 90 ft wide at the top, 60 ft wide at the bottom, and 20 ft high. Use Equation (3) to find the total force due to water pressure on the face of the dam.

16. A semicircular plate with a radius of 3 ft is submerged vertically in a tank of water, with its diameter lying in the surface. Use Equation (3) to find the total force due to water pressure on one side of the plate.

17. Find the moment about the lower base of the trapezoid of the force in Exercise 15.

18. A plate in the shape of a region bounded by the parabola $x^2 = 6y$ and the line $2y = 3$ is placed in a water tank with its vertex downward and the line in the surface of the water. Find the total force due to water pressure on one side of the plate if distance is measured in meters.

19. A cylindrical tank is half full of gasoline having weight density 42 lb/ft^3. If the axis is horizontal and the diameter is 6 ft, find the force on an end due to fluid pressure.

20. If the end of a water tank is in the shape of a rectangle and the tank is full, show that the measure of the force due to water pressure on the end is the product of the measure of the area of the end and the measure of the force at the geometrical center.

21. The bottom of a swimming pool is an inclined plane. The pool is 2 ft deep at one end and 8 ft deep at the other. If the width of the pool is 25 ft and the length is 40 ft, find the total force due to water pressure on the bottom.

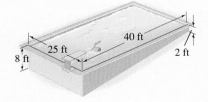

22. The face of a dam adjacent to the water is inclined at an angle of 45° from the vertical. The face is a rectangle of width 80 ft and slant height 40 ft. If the dam is full of water, find the total force due to water pressure on the face.

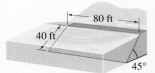

23. The face of a dam adjacent to the water is inclined at an angle of 30° from the vertical. The shape of the face is a rectangle of width 50 ft and slant height of 30 ft. If the dam is full of water, find the total force due to water pressure on the face.

24. Solve Exercise 23 if the face of the dam is an isosceles trapezoid 120 ft wide at the top, 80 ft wide at the bottom, and with a slant height of 40 ft.

25. Explain why dams are constructed so that the walls at the bottom are thicker than the walls at the top.

CHAPTER 6 REVIEW

▶ SUGGESTIONS FOR REVIEW OF CHAPTER 6

1. State two formulas giving the length of arc of the graph of a function f. What conditions must function f satisfy in order to apply these two formulas?

2. Make up an example where either one of the formulas in Suggestion 1 can be applied.

3. Make up an example where only one of the formulas in Suggestion 1 can be applied and explain why the other formula cannot be applied.

4. If $s(x)$ denotes the length of arc of the curve $y = f(x)$ from the point $(a, f(a))$ to the point $(x, f(x))$, where function f satisfies the conditions asked for in Suggestion 1, state a formula involving ds, dx, and dy. Give the geometric interpretation of ds that provides an easy way to remember this formula.

5. How do you find the total mass of a rod if the linear density varies along the rod? Make up an example illustrating your answer.

6. How do you find the center of mass of a rod if the linear density varies along the rod? Make up an example illustrating your answer.

7. If a rod has constant density, where is the center of mass? Justify your answer by applying your answer in Suggestion 6.

8. How do you find the centroid of a plane region bounded by a curve, the x axis, and two vertical lines? Make up an example illustrating your answer.

9. How do you find the centroid of a plane region bounded by two curves? Make up an example illustrating your answer.

10. What is the theorem of Pappus and how can it be used to find the volume of a solid of revolution? Make up an example illustrating your answer.

11. Define the scientific meaning of work. Make up an example.

12. How do we compute the work done by a variable force acting along a line in the direction of motion? Make up an example.

13. How is Hooke's law used to compute the work done by a force used to stretch a spring? Make up an example.

14. How do we compute the work done in pumping a liquid out of a tank? Make up an example.

15. How do we compute the force due to fluid pressure on a plate submerged in the fluid if the face of the plate is horizontal? Make up an example.

16. How do we compute the force due to fluid pressure on a plate submerged in the fluid if the face of the plate is vertical? Make up an example.

17. How do we compute the force exerted by a fluid on a side of a vertical container? Make up an example.

18. What is the relation between the force due to fluid pressure on a plane region and the location of the centroid of the region? Make up an example.

▶ MISCELLANEOUS EXERCISES FOR CHAPTER 6

1. Find the length of arc of the curve $6y^2 = x(x-2)^2$ from $(2, 0)$ to $(8, 4\sqrt{3})$.

2. Find the length of arc of the curve $ay^2 = x^3$ from the origin to $(4a, 8a)$.

3. Find the length of arc of the curve $9x^{2/3} + 4y^{2/3} = 36$ in the second quadrant from the point where $x = -1$ to the point where $x = -\frac{1}{8}$.

4. Find the length of arc of the curve $3y = (x^2 - 2)^{3/2}$ from the point where $x = 3$ to the point where $x = 6$.

5. Three particles of masses 4, 2, and 7 kg are located on the x axis at the points having coordinates -5, 4, and 2, respectively, where the distance is measured in meters. Find the center of mass of the system.

6. Three particles having masses 5, 2, and 8 slugs are located, respectively, at the points $(-1, 3)$, $(2, -1)$, and $(5, 2)$. Find the center of mass, where distance is measured in feet.

7. Find the coordinates of the center of mass of the four particles having equal masses located at the points $(3, 0)$, $(2, 2)$, $(2, 4)$, and $(-1, 2)$.

8. Three particles, each having the same mass, are located on the x axis at the points having coordinates -4, 1, and 5, where the distance is measured in meters. Find the coordinates of the center of mass of the system.

9. The length of a rod is 8 in. and the linear density of the rod at a point x inches from the left end is $2\sqrt{x} + 1$ slugs per inch. Find the total mass of the rod and the center of mass.

10. The length of a rod is 4 m and the linear density of the rod at a point x meters from the left end is $(3x + 1)$ kilograms per meter. Find the total mass of the rod and the center of mass.

11. Find the centroid of the region in the first quadrant bounded by the coordinate axes and the parabola $y = 9 - x^2$.

12. Find the centroid of the region bounded by the parabola $y^2 = x$ and the line $y = x - 2$.

13. Find the centroid of the region bounded by the curves $y = \sqrt{x}$ and $y = x^2$.

14. Find the centroid of the region bounded above by the parabola $4x^2 = 36 - 9y$ and below by the x axis.

15. Use the theorem of Pappus to find the volume of a sphere of radius 4 m.

16. Use the theorem of Pappus to find the volume of a right-circular cone with base radius 2 m and height 3 m.

In Exercises 17 through 20, you need to use your graphics calculator to find the centroid of the region. Express your answer to four significant digits.

17. The region bounded by the graph of $y = \sqrt[3]{x^2 - 7}$ and the x axis.

18. The region bounded by the graphs of
$y = x^3 - 6x^2 + 9x - 1$ and $y = x^2 - 2x + 2$
and not intersected by the line $y = 4$.

19. The region bounded by the graphs of $y = \cos x^2$ and
$y = x^3$, and the y axis.

20. The region bounded by the graphs of $y = \cos \sqrt{x}$
and $y = x^2$, and the y axis.

*In Exercises 21 through 24 find the length of arc to four
significant digits by computing the resulting definite integral by the NINT capability of your graphics calculator.*

21. The arc of the curve $y = 4/x^2$ from the point $(1, 4)$
to the point $(2, 1)$.

22. The arc of the curve $y = 8/x^3$ from the point $(1, 8)$
to the point $(2, 1)$.

23. The arc of the curve $y = \tan x$ from the origin to the
point where $x = 1$.

24. The arc of the sine curve from the point where $x = 1$
to the point where $x = 2$.

25. Find the length of the catenary $y = \cosh x$ from the
point where $x = \ln 2$ to the point where $x = \ln 3$.

26. A force of 500 lb is required to compress a spring
whose natural length is 10 in. to a length of 9 in.
Find the work done to compress the spring to a
length of 8 in.

27. A force of 600 dynes stretches a spring from its natural length of 30 cm to a length of 35 cm. Find the
work done in stretching the spring from its natural
length to a length of 40 cm.

28. The work necessary to stretch a spring from 9 in. to
10 in. is $\frac{3}{2}$ times the work necessary to stretch it from
8 in. to 9 in. What is the natural length of the spring?

29. A cable 20 ft long and weighing 2 lb/ft is hanging
vertically from the top of a pole. Find the work done
in raising the entire cable to the top of the pole.

30. A trough full of water is 6 ft long, and its cross section is in the shape of a semicircle with a diameter of
2 ft at the top. How much work is required to pump
the water out over the top?

31. A tank full of water is in the form of a rectangular
parallelepiped 4 m deep, 15 m wide, and 30 m long.
Find the work required to pump the water in the tank
up to a level 50 cm above the top of the tank.

32. A container has the same shape and dimensions as a
solid of revolution formed by revolving about the y
axis the region in the first quadrant bounded by the

parabola $x^2 = 4py$, the y axis, and the line $y = p$. If
the container is full of water, find the work done in
pumping all the water up to a point $3p$ feet above the
top of the container.

33. A water tank is in the shape of a hemisphere surmounted by a right-circular cylinder. The radius of
both the hemisphere and the cylinder is 4 ft, and the
altitude of the cylinder is 8 ft. If the tank is full of
water, find the work necessary to empty the tank by
pumping it through an outlet at the top of the tank.

34. A hemispherical tank having a diameter of 10 m is
filled with water to a depth of 3 m. Find the work
done in pumping the water to the top of the tank.

35. A plate in the shape of the region bounded by the
parabola $x^2 = 6y$ and the line $2y = 3$ is placed in a
water tank with its vertex downward and the line in
the surface of the water. Find the force due to water
pressure on one side of the plate if distance is measured in feet.

36. A semicircular plate with a radius of 4 ft is submerged vertically in a tank of water, with its diameter lying in the surface. Use Equation (3) of Section
6.5 to find the force due to water pressure on one side
of the plate.

37. A cylindrical tank is half full of gasoline having
weight density 40 lb/ft^3. If the axis is horizontal and
the diameter is 8 ft, find the force on an end due to
fluid pressure.

38. The face of a dam adjacent to the water is inclined at
an angle of 45° from the vertical. The face is a
rectangle of width 100 ft and slant height 60 ft. If
the dam is full of water, find the total force due to
water pressure on the face.

39. The surface of a tank is the same as that of a
paraboloid of revolution obtained by revolving
the parabola $y = x^2$ about the y axis. The vertex
of the parabola is at the bottom of the tank, and the
tank is 36 ft high. If the tank is filled with water to a
depth of 20 ft, find the work done in pumping all of
the water out over the top.

40. If
$$f(x) = \int_0^x \sqrt{\cos t}\, dt$$
find the length of arc of the graph of f from the point
where $x = \frac{1}{3}\pi$ to the point where $x = \frac{1}{2}\pi$. *Hint:* Use
the first fundamental theorem of the calculus and the
identity $\cos^2 \frac{1}{2}x = \frac{1}{2}(1 + \cos x)$.

TECHNIQUES OF INTEGRATION, INDETERMINATE FORMS, AND IMPROPER INTEGRALS

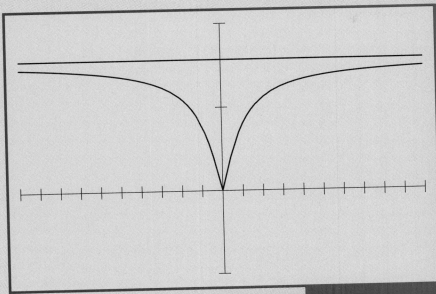

The first five Sections in this chapter pertain to techniques of integration. Even in today's electronic age, when computer algebra systems can be employed to calculate integrals, you need to know certain techniques of integration to express the integrand in a form that the computer can handle or that can be found in a table of integrals. You should, therefore, acquire proficiency in recognizing which technique to apply to a given integral. Furthermore, development of computational skills is important in all branches of mathematics, and the exercises in this chapter provide a good training ground.

Two more applications of integration are introduced in Section 7.4: the law of mass action from chemistry and logistic growth occurring on economics, biology, and sociology.

Numerical methods for finding an approximate value of a definite integral are treated in Section 7.6. Computations by these processes are easily done on your graphics calculator.

Ways for computing certain limits involving indeterminate forms by applying a theorem called L'Hospital's rule are discussed in Sections 7.7 and 7.8.

Prior to Section 7.9 we considered only so-called proper integrals, which are definite integrals of functions continuous on a closed interval. Improper integrals, which either have infinite limits of integration or else have an integrand with an infinite discontinuity within the limits of integration, appear in the final two sections of this chapter.

▶ LOOKING AHEAD

7.1 INTEGRATION BY PARTS

Prior to our discussion of various techniques of integration, we list and number for reference the standard indefinite integration formulas that you learned in previous chapters and that occur frequently.

1. $\displaystyle\int du = u + C$

2. $\displaystyle\int a\, du = au + C$ where a is any constant

3. $\displaystyle\int [f(u) + g(u)]\, du = \int f(u)\, du + \int g(u)\, du$

4. $\displaystyle\int u^n\, du = \frac{u^{n+1}}{n+1} + C$ $n \neq -1$

5. $\displaystyle\int \frac{du}{u} = \ln|u| + C$

6. $\displaystyle\int a^u\, du = \frac{a^u}{\ln a} + C$ where $a > 0$ and $a \neq 1$

7. $\displaystyle\int e^u\, du = e^u + C$

8. $\displaystyle\int \sin u\, du = -\cos u + C$

9. $\displaystyle\int \cos u\, du = \sin u + C$

10. $\displaystyle\int \sec^2 u\, du = \tan u + C$

11. $\displaystyle\int \csc^2 u\, du = -\cot u + C$

12. $\displaystyle\int \sec u \tan u\, du = \sec u + C$

13. $\displaystyle\int \csc u \cot u\, du = -\csc u + C$

14. $\displaystyle\int \tan u\, du = \ln|\sec u| + C$

15. $\displaystyle\int \cot u\, du = \ln|\sin u| + C$

16. $\displaystyle\int \sec u\, du = \ln|\sec u + \tan u| + C$

17. $\displaystyle\int \csc u\, du = \ln|\csc u - \cot u| + C$

18. $\displaystyle\int \frac{du}{\sqrt{a^2 - u^2}} = \sin^{-1}\frac{u}{a} + C$ where $a > 0$

19. $\displaystyle\int \frac{du}{a^2 + u^2} = \frac{1}{a}\tan^{-1}\frac{u}{a} + C$ where $a \neq 0$

20. $\displaystyle\int \frac{du}{u\sqrt{u^2 - a^2}} = \frac{1}{a}\sec^{-1}\frac{u}{a} + C$ where $a > 0$

21. $\displaystyle\int \sinh u\ du = \cosh u + C$

22. $\displaystyle\int \cosh u\ du = \sinh u + C$

23. $\displaystyle\int \operatorname{sech}^2 u\ du = \tanh u + C$

24. $\displaystyle\int \operatorname{csch}^2 u\ du = -\coth u + C$

25. $\displaystyle\int \operatorname{sech} u \tanh u\ du = -\operatorname{sech} u + C$

26. $\displaystyle\int \operatorname{csch} u \coth u\ du = -\operatorname{csch} u + C$

27. $\displaystyle\int \frac{du}{\sqrt{u^2 + a^2}} = \sinh^{-1}\frac{u}{a} + C$

$\qquad\qquad\qquad = \ln(u + \sqrt{u^2 + a^2}) + C$ if $a > 0$

28. $\displaystyle\int \frac{du}{\sqrt{u^2 - a^2}} = \cosh^{-1}\frac{u}{a} + C$

$\qquad\qquad\qquad = \ln(u + \sqrt{u^2 - a^2}) + C$ if $u > a > 0$

29. $\displaystyle\int \frac{du}{a^2 - u^2} = \begin{cases} \dfrac{1}{a}\tanh^{-1}\dfrac{u}{a} + C & \text{if } |u| < a \\[2mm] \dfrac{1}{a}\coth^{-1}\dfrac{u}{a} + C & \text{if } |u| > a \end{cases}$

$\qquad\qquad\quad = \dfrac{1}{2a}\ln\left|\dfrac{a + u}{a - u}\right| + C$ if $u \neq a$ and $a \neq 0$

One of the most widely used techniques of integration is *integration by parts*, obtained from the formula for the derivative of the product of two functions. If f and g are differentiable functions, then

$$D_x[f(x)g(x)] = f(x)g'(x) + g(x)f'(x)$$
$$f(x)g'(x) = D_x[f(x)g(x)] - g(x)f'(x)$$

Integrating on each side of this equation we obtain

$$\int f(x)g'(x)\ dx = \int D_x[f(x)g(x)]\ dx - \int g(x)f'(x)\ dx$$

$$\int f(x)g'(x)\ dx = f(x)g(x) - \int g(x)f'(x)\ dx \qquad (1)$$

We call (1) the **formula for integration by parts.** For computational purposes a more convenient way of writing this formula is obtained by letting

$$u = f(x) \quad \text{and} \quad v = g(x)$$

Then

$$du = f'(x)\, dx \quad \text{and} \quad dv = g'(x)\, dx$$

so that (1) becomes

$$\int u\, dv = uv - \int v\, du \tag{2}$$

This formula expresses the integral $\int u\, dv$ in terms of another integral, $\int v\, du$. By a suitable choice of u and dv, it may be easier to evaluate the second integral than the first. When choosing the substitutions for u and dv, we usually want dv to be the most complicated factor of the integrand that can be integrated directly and u to be a function whose derivative is a simpler function. The method is shown by the following illustrations and examples.

▷ **ILLUSTRATION 1**   We wish to evaluate

$$\int x \ln x\, dx$$

To determine the substitutions for u and dv, bear in mind that to find v we must be able to integrate dv. This suggests letting $dv = x\, dx$ and $u = \ln x$. Then

$$v = \frac{x^2}{2} + C_1 \quad \text{and} \quad du = \frac{dx}{x}$$

From formula (2)

$$\int x \ln x\, dx = \ln x \left(\frac{x^2}{2} + C_1 \right) - \int \left(\frac{x^2}{2} + C_1 \right) \frac{dx}{x}$$

$$= \frac{x^2}{2} \ln x + C_1 \ln x - \frac{1}{2} \int x\, dx - C_1 \int \frac{dx}{x}$$

$$= \frac{x^2}{2} \ln x + C_1 \ln x - \frac{x^2}{4} - C_1 \ln x + C_2$$

$$= \tfrac{1}{2} x^2 \ln x - \tfrac{1}{4} x^2 + C_2 \qquad \blacktriangleleft$$

In Illustration 1 observe that the first constant of integration C_1 does not appear in the final answer. The C_1 is used only to show that all choices for v of the form $\tfrac{1}{2} x^2 + C_1$ produce the same result for $\int x \ln x\, dx$. This situation is true in general, and we prove it as follows: By writing $v + C_1$ in formula (2) we have

$$\int u\, dv = u(v + C_1) - \int (v + C_1)\, du$$

$$= uv + C_1 u - \int v\, du - C_1 \int du$$

$$= uv + C_1 u - \int v\, du - C_1 u$$

$$= uv - \int v\, du$$

Therefore it is not necessary to write C_1 when finding v from dv.

▷ **ILLUSTRATION 2**   We check our result in Illustration 1 by computing the derivative of the answer.

$$D_x\left(\frac{1}{2} x^2 \ln x - \frac{1}{4} x^2\right) = x \ln x + \frac{1}{2} x^2 \left(\frac{1}{x}\right) - \frac{1}{2} x$$
$$= x \ln x + \tfrac{1}{2} x - \tfrac{1}{2} x$$
$$= x \ln x \qquad ◀$$

▷ **ILLUSTRATION 3**   To evaluate

$$\int x^3 e^{x^2} \, dx$$

we make a substitution for the nonlinear exponent which should be a common practice before applying any other technique.

Let $w = x^2$; thus $dw = 2x \, dx$. We have then

$$\int x^3 e^{x^2} \, dx = \frac{1}{2} \int x^2 e^{x^2} (2x \, dx)$$
$$= \frac{1}{2} \int w e^w \, dw$$

We now use integration by parts with $u = w$ and $dv = e^w \, dw$. Then

$$du = dw \quad \text{and} \quad v = e^w$$

From formula (2)

$$\frac{1}{2} \int w e^w \, dw = \frac{1}{2}\left[w e^w - \int e^w \, dw \right]$$
$$= \tfrac{1}{2}[w e^w - e^w] + C$$

Replacing w by x^2, we get

$$\int x^3 e^{x^2} \, dx = \tfrac{1}{2} x^2 e^{x^2} - \tfrac{1}{2} e^{x^2} + C \qquad ◀$$

▶ **EXAMPLE 1**   Evaluate

$$\int x \cos x \, dx$$

and support the answer graphically.

Solution   Let $u = x$ and $dv = \cos x \, dx$. Then

$$du = dx \quad \text{and} \quad v = \sin x$$

Therefore

$$\int x \cos x \, dx = x \sin x - \int \sin x \, dx$$
$$= x \sin x + \cos x + C$$

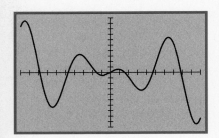

[–10, 10] by [–10, 10]

$y = x \cos x$ and NDER $(x \sin x + \cos x, x)$

FIGURE 1

Figure 1 shows the graphs of

$$y = x \cos x \quad \text{and} \quad \text{NDER}(x \sin x + \cos x, x)$$

plotted in the $[-10, 10]$ by $[-10, 10]$ window. The fact that the graphs appear to overlap supports our answer. ◀

▷ **ILLUSTRATION 4**   In Example 1, if instead of our choices of u and dv as above we let

$$u = \cos x \quad \text{and} \quad dv = x \, dx$$

then

$$du = -\sin x \, dx \quad \text{and} \quad v = \tfrac{1}{2}x^2$$

Thus

$$\int x \cos x \, dx = \frac{x^2}{2} \cos x + \frac{1}{2} \int x^2 \sin x \, dx$$

The integral on the right is more complicated than the one with which we started, because the power of x has increased, thereby indicating that these are not desirable choices for u and dv. ◀

Integration by parts often is used when the integrand involves inverse trigonometric functions and logarithms.

▶ **EXAMPLE 2**   Evaluate

$$\int \tan^{-1} x \, dx$$

Solution   Let $u = \tan^{-1} x$ and $dv = dx$. Then

$$du = \frac{dx}{1 + x^2} \quad \text{and} \quad v = x$$

Thus

$$\int \tan^{-1} x \, dx = x \tan^{-1} x - \int \frac{x \, dx}{1 + x^2}$$
$$= x \tan^{-1} x - \tfrac{1}{2} \ln(1 + x^2) + C \quad ◀$$

In the following example, we have an integral that requires repeated applications of integration by parts.

▶ **EXAMPLE 3**   Evaluate

$$\int (\ln x)^2 \, dx$$

Solution   We let $u = (\ln x)^2$ and $dv = dx$. Then

$$du = 2 \ln x \left(\frac{1}{x} \, dx \right) \quad \text{and} \quad v = x$$

Therefore

$$\int (\ln x)^2 \, dx = x(\ln x)^2 - \int x \left[2 \ln x \left(\frac{1}{x} \right) dx \right]$$

$$= x(\ln x)^2 - 2 \int \ln x \, dx$$

We apply integration by parts again. Let $\overline{u} = \ln x$ and $d\overline{v} = dx$. Then

$$d\overline{u} = \frac{1}{x} dx \quad \text{and} \quad \overline{v} = x$$

So we obtain

$$\int (\ln x)^2 \, dx = x(\ln x)^2 - 2 \left[x \ln x - \int x \left(\frac{1}{x} \, dx \right) \right]$$

$$= x(\ln x)^2 - 2x \ln x + 2 \int dx$$

$$= x(\ln x)^2 - 2x \ln x + 2x + C \qquad \blacktriangleleft$$

▶ **EXAMPLE 4**   Evaluate

$$\int e^x \sin x \, dx$$

Solution   Let $u = e^x$ and $dv = \sin x \, dx$. Then

$$du = e^x \, dx \quad \text{and} \quad v = -\cos x$$

Therefore

$$\int e^x \sin x \, dx = -e^x \cos x + \int e^x \cos x \, dx$$

The integral on the right is similar to the first integral except that cos x appears in place of sin x. We apply integration by parts again by letting $\overline{u} = e^x$ and $d\overline{v} = \cos x \, dx$. So

$$d\overline{u} = e^x \, dx \quad \text{and} \quad \overline{v} = \sin x$$

Thus

$$\int e^x \sin x \, dx = -e^x \cos x + \left(e^x \sin x - \int e^x \sin x \, dx \right)$$

On the right we have the same integral as on the left. So we add $\int e^x \sin x \, dx$ to both sides of the equation and obtain

$$2 \int e^x \sin x \, dx = -e^x \cos x + e^x \sin x + 2C$$

Observe that the right side of the above equation contains an arbitrary constant because on the left side we have an indefinite integral. This arbitrary constant is written as $2C$ so that when we divide on both sides of the equation by 2, the arbitrary constant in the answer becomes C. Thus

$$\int e^x \sin x \, dx = \tfrac{1}{2} e^x (\sin x - \cos x) + C \qquad \blacktriangleleft$$

In applying integration by parts to a specific integral, one pair of choices for u and dv may work while another pair may not. We saw this in Illustration 4, and another case occurs in Illustration 5.

▷ **ILLUSTRATION 5**   In Example 4, in the step where we have

$$\int e^x \sin x \, dx = -e^x \cos x + \int e^x \cos x \, dx$$

if we evaluate the integral on the right by letting $\bar{u} = \cos x$ and $d\bar{v} = e^x \, dx$, we have

$$d\bar{u} = -\sin x \, dx \quad \text{and} \quad \bar{v} = e^x$$

Thus we get

$$\int e^x \sin x \, dx = -e^x \cos x + \left(e^x \cos x + \int e^x \sin x \, dx \right)$$

$$= \int e^x \sin x \, dx$$

which, of course, is correct but leads us nowhere.   ◀

We can support an answer for an indefinite integral by using the NINT capability of our graphics calculator for the corresponding definite integral with a random choice of limits of integration, as shown in the following illustration.

▷ **ILLUSTRATION 6**   Let us evaluate the definite integral obtained from the indefinite integral of Example 4 with 1 and 2 as limits of integration.

$$\int_1^2 e^x \sin x \, dx = \tfrac{1}{2} e^x \left[\sin x - \cos x \right]_1^2$$

$$= \tfrac{1}{2} e^2 (\sin 2 - \cos 2) - \tfrac{1}{2} e (\sin 1 - \cos 1)$$

$$= 4.487560335$$

On our graphics calculator

$$\text{NINT}(e^x \sin x, 1, 2) = 4.487560335$$

which supports our answer above to ten significant digits. Of course, this procedure is not conclusive proof that we have not made an algebraic error when evaluating the indefinite integral but it furnishes powerful support for our answer.   ◀

Integrals involving powers of functions are often evaluated by **reduction formulas,** so called because the formula reduces the exponent of the power. Many of the formulas appearing in a table of integrals are reduction formulas, some of which we shall derive as we proceed through this chapter. We obtain the first one in the following example.

▶ **EXAMPLE 5**   Derive the following reduction formula, where n is any real number:

$$\int x^n e^x \, dx = x^n e^x - n \int x^{n-1} e^x \, dx$$

Solution   We use integration by parts with $u = x^n$ and $dv = e^x \, dx$. Then

$$du = nx^{n-1} \, dx \quad \text{and} \quad v = e^x$$

Therefore,

$$\int x^n e^x \, dx = x^n e^x - \int e^x (nx^{n-1} \, dx)$$

$$= x^n e^x - n \int x^{n-1} e^x \, dx \qquad ◀$$

The reduction formula in the above example appears as Formula 98 in the Table of Integrals on the back endpapers. We apply this reduction formula in the next example.

▶ **EXAMPLE 6**   Use the NINT capability of a graphics calculator to approximate to six significant digits the value of

$$\int_0^2 x^2 e^x \, dx$$

Confirm the answer by applying the reduction formula in Example 5.

Solution   On our graphics calculator we compute

$$\text{NINT}(x^2 e^x, 0, 2) = 12.7781$$

From the reduction formula in Example 5 with $n = 2$, we have

$$\int x^2 e^x \, dx = x^2 e^x - 2 \int x e^x \, dx$$

We apply the reduction formula again with $n = 1$, and we obtain

$$\int x^2 e^x \, dx = x^2 e^x - 2 \left(x e^x - \int e^x \, dx \right)$$

$$= x^2 e^x - 2x e^x + 2e^x + C$$

With this result we evaluate the definite integral.

$$\int_0^2 x^2 e^x \, dx = x^2 e^x - 2x e^x + 2e^x \Big]_0^2$$

$$= (4e^2 - 4e^2 + 2e^2) - 2e^0$$

$$= 2e^2 - 2$$

$$= 12.7781$$

which confirms our answer.   ◀

In Exercises 49 and 50 you are asked to derive the following formulas where a and n are nonzero real numbers. They appear as Formulas 105 and 106 on the back endpapers.

$$\int e^{au} \sin nu \, du = \frac{e^{au}}{a^2 + n^2}(a \sin nu - n \cos nu) + C \qquad \textbf{(3)}$$

$$\int e^{au} \cos nu \, du = \frac{e^{au}}{a^2 + n^2}(a \cos nu + n \sin nu) + C \qquad \textbf{(4)}$$

Integrals of the same form as in (3) and (4) often occur in applications of differential equations involving electricity.

EXERCISES 7.1

In Exercises 1 through 24, evaluate the indefinite integral. As you wish, you may check your answer by differentiation as in Illustration 2, or support your answer on your graphics calculator either graphically as in Example 1 or numerically as in Illustration 6.

1. $\int xe^{3x} \, dx$

2. $\int x \cos 2x \, dx$

3. $\int x \sec x \tan x \, dx$

4. $\int x \, 3^x \, dx$

5. $\int \ln 5x \, dx$

6. $\int \sin^{-1} w \, dw$

7. $\int \frac{(\ln t)^2}{t} \, dt$

8. $\int x \sec^2 x \, dx$

9. $\int x \tan^{-1} x \, dx$

10. $\int \ln(x^2 + 1) \, dx$

11. $\int \frac{xe^x}{(x + 1)^2} \, dx$

12. $\int x^2 \sin 3x \, dx$

13. $\int \sin(\ln y) \, dy$

14. $\int \sin t \ln(\cos t) \, dt$

15. $\int e^x \cos x \, dx$

16. $\int x^5 \, e^{x^2} \, dx$

17. $\int \frac{x^3 \, dx}{\sqrt{1 - x^2}}$

18. $\int \frac{\sin 2x}{e^x} \, dx$

19. $\int x^2 \sinh x \, dx$

20. $\int \frac{e^{2x}}{\sqrt{1 - e^x}} \, dx$

21. $\int \frac{\cot^{-1} \sqrt{z}}{\sqrt{z}} \, dz$

22. $\int \cos^{-1} 2x \, dx$

23. $\int \cos \sqrt{x} \, dx$

24. $\int \tan^{-1} \sqrt{x} \, dx$

In Exercises 25 through 32, find the exact value of the definite integral. Support your answer by the NINT capability of your graphics calculator.

25. $\int_0^2 x^2 3^x \, dx$

26. $\int_{-1}^2 \ln(x + 2) \, dx$

27. $\int_0^{\pi/3} \sin 3w \cos w \, dw$

28. $\int_{-\pi}^{\pi} z^2 \cos 2z \, dz$

29. $\int_1^4 \sqrt{x} \ln x \, dx$

30. $\int_{\pi/4}^{3\pi/4} x \cot x \csc x \, dx$

31. $\int_2^4 \sec^{-1} \sqrt{t} \, dt$

32. $\int_0^1 x \sin^{-1} x \, dx$

In Exercises 33 and 34 use the NINT capability of your graphics calculator to approximate to six significant digits the value of the definite integral and confirm your answer by applying the reduction formula in Example 5.

33. $\int_1^3 x^3 e^x \, dx$

34. $\int_0^4 x^2 e^{x/2} \, dx$

35. Find the area of the region bounded by the curve $y = \ln x$, the x axis, and the line $x = e^2$.

36. Find the volume of the solid generated by revolving the region in Exercise 35 about the x axis.

37. Find the volume of the solid generated by revolving the region in Exercise 35 about the y axis.

38. Find the area of the region bounded by the curve $y = x \csc^2 x$, the x axis, and the lines $x = \frac{1}{6}\pi$ and $x = \frac{1}{4}\pi$.

39. Find the area of the region bounded by the curve $y = 2xe^{-x/2}$, the x axis, and the line $x = 4$.

40. Find the volume of the solid of revolution generated by revolving about the x axis the region of Exercise 39.

41. The linear density of a rod at a point x meters from one end is $2e^{-x}$ kilograms per meter. If the rod is 6 m long, find the mass and center of mass of the rod.

42. Find the centroid of the region bounded by the curve $y = e^x$, the coordinate axes, and the line $x = 3$.

43. Find the centroid of the region in the first quadrant bounded by the curves $y = \sin x$ and $y = \cos x$, and the y axis.

44. The region in the first quadrant bounded by the curve $y = \cos x$ and the lines $y = 1$ and $x = \frac{1}{2}\pi$ is revolved about the line $x = \frac{1}{2}\pi$. Find the volume of the solid generated.

45. A water tank full of water is in the shape of the solid of revolution formed by rotating about the x axis the region bounded by the curve $y = e^{-x}$, the coordinate axes, and the line $x = 4$. Find the work done in pumping all the water to the top of the tank. Distance is measured in feet. Take the positive x axis vertically downward.

46. A particle is moving on a line, and s feet is the directed distance of the particle from the origin at t seconds. If v feet per second is the velocity at t seconds, $s = 0$ when $t = 0$, and $v \cdot s = t \sin t$, find s in terms of t and also s when $t = \frac{1}{2}\pi$.

47. The marginal cost function is C' and $C'(x) = \ln x$, where $x > 1$. Find the total cost function if $C(x)$ dollars is the total cost of producing x units and $C(1) = 5$.

48. A manufacturer has discovered that if $100x$ units of a particular commodity are produced per week, the marginal cost is determined by $x\,2^{x/2}$ and the marginal revenue is determined by $8 \cdot 2^{-x/2}$, where both the production cost and the revenue are in thousands of dollars. If the weekly fixed costs amount to $2000, find the maximum weekly profit that can be obtained.

49. Derive formula (3).   **50.** Derive formula (4).

In Exercises 51 and 52 use the NINT capability of your graphics calculator to approximate to six significant digits the value of the definite integral and confirm your answer by applying either formula (3) or (4) of this section.

51. $\displaystyle\int_{\pi/6}^{\pi/3} e^{4x} \sin 3x \, dx$ **52.** $\displaystyle\int_{\pi/8}^{\pi/4} e^{3x} \cos 4x \, dx$

53. (a) Derive the following formula, where n is any real number:
$$\int x^n \ln x \, dx$$
$$= \begin{cases} \dfrac{x^{n+1}}{(n+1)^2}[(n+1)\ln x - 1] + C & \text{if } n \ne -1 \\ \frac{1}{2}(\ln x)^2 + C & \text{if } n = -1 \end{cases}$$

(b) Use the formula in part (a) to find the exact value of
$$\int_1^3 x^3 \ln x \, dx$$

(c) Support your answer in part (b) by the NINT capability of your graphics calculator.

54. Derive the following formula, where r and q are any real numbers:
$$\int x^r (\ln x)^q \, dx$$
$$= \begin{cases} \dfrac{x^{r+1}(\ln x)^q}{r+1} - \dfrac{q}{r+1}\displaystyle\int x^r(\ln x)^{q-1}\,dx & \text{if } r \ne -1 \\ \dfrac{(\ln x)^{q+1}}{q+1} + C & \text{if } r = -1 \text{ and } q \ne -1 \\ \ln|\ln x| + C & \text{if } r = -1 \text{ and } q = -1 \end{cases}$$

55. If $i(t)$ coulombs per second is the current from a charged capacitor under transient decay through a resistor at t seconds,
$$i(t) = \int_0^t x e^{-x} \, dx$$
If $E(T)$ watts is the energy dissipated for $t \in [0, T]$, then
$$E(T) = R \int_0^T [i(t)]^2 \, dt$$
where R ohms is the resistance. If $R = 50$, how much energy is dissipated when $T = 1$?

56. Describe the integration-by-parts technique. Include in your description the guidelines you should follow when choosing the substitutions for u and dv.

7.2 TRIGONOMETRIC INTEGRALS

Trigonometric integrals involve algebraic operations on trigonometric functions. You have already learned how to evaluate some trigonometric integrals by applying the integration formulas 8–17 listed at the beginning of Section 7.1. We now apply these formulas and trigonometric identities to evaluate integrals involving products of powers of trigonometric functions. We begin with products of powers of sine and cosine and distinguish three cases dependent on whether the exponents are odd or even positive integers.

> **CASE 1** (i) $\int \sin^n x \, dx$ or (ii) $\int \cos^n x \, dx$, where n is a positive odd integer.
>
> **(i)** Factor
>
> $$\begin{aligned} \sin^n x \, dx &= (\sin^{n-1} x)(\sin x \, dx) \\ &= (\sin^2 x)^{(n-1)/2}(\sin x \, dx) \\ &= (1 - \cos^2 x)^{(n-1)/2} \, (\sin x \, dx) \end{aligned}$$
>
> **(ii)** Factor
>
> $$\begin{aligned} \cos^n x \, dx &= (\cos^{n-1} x)(\cos x \, dx) \\ &= (\cos^2 x)^{(n-1)/2} \, (\cos x \, dx) \\ &= (1 - \sin^2 x)^{(n-1)/2} \, (\cos x \, dx) \end{aligned}$$

▷   **ILLUSTRATION 1**   We demonstrate Case 1(ii).

$$\begin{aligned} \int \cos^3 x \, dx &= \int \cos^2 x(\cos x \, dx) \\[1mm] &= \int (1 - \sin^2 x)(\cos x \, dx) \\[1mm] &= \int \cos x \, dx - \int \sin^2 x \cos x \, dx \end{aligned} \qquad (1)$$

For the second integral in (1) observe that because $d(\sin x) = \cos x \, dx$, we have

$$\int \sin^2 x(\cos x \, dx) = \tfrac{1}{3} \sin^3 x + C_1$$

Because the first integral in (1) is $\sin x + C_2$,

$$\int \cos^3 x \, dx = \sin x - \tfrac{1}{3} \sin^3 x + C$$ ◀

▶   **EXAMPLE 1**   Evaluate

$$\int \sin^5 x \, dx$$

and support the answer numerically.

Solution   We proceed as suggested in Case 1(i).

$$\begin{aligned} \int \sin^5 x \, dx &= \int (\sin^2 x)^2 \sin x \, dx \\[1mm] &= \int (1 - \cos^2 x)^2 \sin x \, dx \end{aligned}$$

$$= \int (1 - 2\cos^2 x + \cos^4 x)\sin x \, dx$$

$$= \int \sin x \, dx - 2 \int \cos^2 x \sin x \, dx + \int \cos^4 x \sin x \, dx$$

$$= -\cos x + 2 \int \cos^2 x(-\sin x \, dx) - \int \cos^4 x(-\sin x \, dx)$$

$$= -\cos x + \tfrac{2}{3}\cos^3 x - \tfrac{1}{5}\cos^5 x + C$$

To support the answer numerically we compute the corresponding definite integral with a random choice of limits of integration, for instance, -2 and 3.

$$\int_{-2}^{3} \sin^5 x \, dx = -\cos x + \tfrac{2}{3}\cos^3 x - \tfrac{1}{5}\cos^5 x \Big]_{-2}^{3}$$

$$= -\cos 3 + \tfrac{2}{3}\cos^3 3 - \tfrac{1}{5}\cos^5 3 + \cos(-2) - \tfrac{2}{3}\cos^3(-2) + \tfrac{1}{5}\cos^5(-2)$$

$$= 0.1627341019$$

On our graphics calculator

$$\text{NINT}(\sin^5 x, -2, 3) = 0.1627341019$$

which agrees with the above and gives powerful support for our value of the indefinite integral. ◄

CASE 2 $\int \sin^n x \cos^m x \, dx$, where at least one of the exponents is a positive odd integer. The solution of this case is similar to the method used for Case 1.

(i) If n is odd,

$$\sin^n x \cos^m x \, dx = \sin^{n-1} x \cos^m x(\sin x \, dx)$$

$$= (\sin^2 x)^{(n-1)/2} \cos^m x(\sin x \, dx)$$

$$= (1 - \cos^2 x)^{(n-1)/2} \cos^m x(\sin x \, dx)$$

(ii) If m is odd,

$$\sin^n x \cos^m x \, dx = \sin^n x \cos^{m-1} x(\cos x \, dx)$$

$$= \sin^n x(\cos^2 x)^{(m-1)/2} (\cos x \, dx)$$

$$= \sin^n x(1 - \sin^2 x)^{(m-1)/2} (\cos x \, dx)$$

▷ **ILLUSTRATION 2**   We demonstrate Case 2(i).

$$\int \sin^3 x \cos^4 x \, dx = \int \sin^2 x \cos^4 x(\sin x \, dx)$$

$$= \int (1 - \cos^2 x)\cos^4 x(\sin x \, dx)$$

$$= \int \cos^4 x \sin x \, dx - \int \cos^6 x \sin x \, dx$$

$$= -\tfrac{1}{5}\cos^5 x + \tfrac{1}{7}\cos^7 x + C$$

◄

We cannot follow the procedures of Cases 1 and 2 to integrate powers of sine and cosine when neither exponent is odd. In such a situation we apply one or both of the following identities:

$$\sin^2 x = \frac{1 - \cos 2x}{2} \qquad \cos^2 x = \frac{1 + \cos 2x}{2}$$

CASE 3 (i) $\displaystyle\int \sin^n x \, dx$, (ii) $\displaystyle\int \cos^n x \, dx$, or (iii) $\displaystyle\int \sin^n x \cos^m x \, dx$, where both m and n are positive even integers.

(i) Factor

$$\sin^n x \, dx = (\sin^2 x)^{n/2} \, dx$$
$$= \left(\frac{1 - \cos 2x}{2}\right)^{n/2} dx$$

(ii) Factor

$$\cos^n x \, dx = (\cos^2 x)^{n/2} \, dx$$
$$= \left(\frac{1 + \cos 2x}{2}\right)^{n/2} dx$$

(iii) Factor

$$\sin^n x \cos^m x \, dx = (\sin^2 x)^{n/2}(\cos^2 x)^{m/2} \, dx$$
$$= \left(\frac{1 - \cos 2x}{2}\right)^{n/2} \left(\frac{1 + \cos 2x}{2}\right)^{m/2} dx$$

double angle formulas!

▷ **ILLUSTRATION 3**

$$\int \sin^2 x \, dx = \int \frac{1 - \cos 2x}{2} \, dx$$
$$= \tfrac{1}{2}x - \tfrac{1}{4} \sin 2x + C$$ ◀

▶ **EXAMPLE 2** Evaluate

$$\int \cos^4 x \, dx$$

Solution This integral pertains to Case 3(ii).

$$\int \cos^4 x \, dx = \int \left(\frac{1 + \cos 2x}{2}\right)^2 dx$$
$$= \frac{1}{4} \int dx + \frac{1}{2} \int \cos 2x \, dx + \frac{1}{4} \int \cos^2 2x \, dx$$
$$= \frac{1}{4}x + \frac{1}{4} \sin 2x + \frac{1}{4} \int \frac{1 + \cos 4x}{2} \, dx$$

$$= \frac{1}{4}x + \frac{1}{4}\sin 2x + \frac{1}{8}\int dx + \frac{1}{8}\int \cos 4x \, dx$$

$$= \frac{1}{4}x + \frac{1}{4}\sin 2x + \frac{1}{8}x + \frac{1}{32}\sin 4x + C$$

$$= \frac{3}{8}x + \frac{1}{4}\sin 2x + \frac{1}{32}\sin 4x + C$$

◄

▶ **EXAMPLE 3**   Find the centroid of the region in the first quadrant to the left of the line $x = \frac{1}{2}\pi$ and bounded by the curve $y = \sin x$, the x axis, and the line $x = \frac{1}{2}\pi$.

Solution   We use the symbols A, M_x, M_y, $\bar{x}$, and $\bar{y}$, as defined in Section 6.3. The region and the ith rectangular element are shown in Figure 1. We first compute the area of the region.

$$A = \lim_{\|\Delta\| \to 0} \sum_{i=1}^{n} \sin m_i \, \Delta_i x$$

$$= \int_0^{\pi/2} \sin x \, dx$$

$$= -\cos x \Big]_0^{\pi/2}$$

$$= 1$$

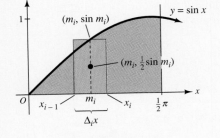

FIGURE 1

We apply Definition 6.3.2 to compute M_x and M_y. To evaluate the integral for M_y we use integration by parts with $u = x$ and $dv = \sin x \, dx$.

$$M_x = \lim_{\|\Delta\| \to 0} \sum_{i=1}^{n} \frac{1}{2}[\sin m_i]^2 \, \Delta_i x \qquad M_y = \lim_{\|\Delta\| \to 0} \sum_{i=1}^{n} m_i \sin m_i \, \Delta_i x$$

$$= \frac{1}{2}\int_0^{\pi/2} \sin^2 x \, dx \qquad\qquad = \int_0^{\pi/2} x \sin x \, dx$$

$$= \frac{1}{2}\int_0^{\pi/2} \frac{1 - \cos 2x}{2} \, dx \qquad = -x \cos x \Big]_0^{\pi/2} + \int_0^{\pi/2} \cos x \, dx$$

$$= \frac{1}{4}\Big[x - \frac{1}{2}\sin 2x\Big]_0^{\pi/2} \qquad = -x \cos x + \sin x \Big]_0^{\pi/2}$$

$$= \frac{1}{4}\Big[\frac{1}{2}\pi\Big] \qquad\qquad\qquad = -\frac{1}{2}\pi \cos \frac{1}{2}\pi + \sin \frac{1}{2}\pi$$

$$= \frac{1}{8}\pi \qquad\qquad\qquad\qquad = 1$$

Therefore

$$\bar{x} = \frac{M_y}{A} \qquad\qquad \bar{y} = \frac{M_x}{A}$$

$$= \frac{1}{1} \qquad\qquad\qquad = \frac{\frac{1}{8}\pi}{1}$$

$$= 1 \qquad\qquad\qquad = \frac{1}{8}\pi$$

<u>**Conclusion:**</u>   The centroid is at the point $(1, \frac{1}{8}\pi)$.   ◄

The next example involves another type of integral containing a product of sine and cosine.

▶ **EXAMPLE 4**   Evaluate

$$\int \sin 3x \cos 2x \, dx$$

Solution   We apply the following trigonometric identity:

$$\sin mx \cos nx = \tfrac{1}{2}\sin(m-n)x + \tfrac{1}{2}\sin(m+n)x$$

$$\int \sin 3x \cos 2x \, dx = \int \left(\frac{1}{2}\sin x + \frac{1}{2}\sin 5x\right) dx$$

$$= \frac{1}{2}\int \sin x \, dx + \frac{1}{2}\int \sin 5x \, dx$$

$$= -\tfrac{1}{2}\cos x - \tfrac{1}{10}\cos 5x + C \qquad ◀$$

To evaluate integrals of the form

$$\int \tan^m x \sec^n x \, dx \quad \text{and} \quad \int \cot^m x \csc^n x \, dx \qquad (2)$$

where m and n are nonnegative integers, we apply the identities

$$1 + \tan^2 x = \sec^2 x \quad \text{and} \quad 1 + \cot^2 x = \csc^2 x$$

▷ **ILLUSTRATION 4**

$$\int \cot^2 x \, dx = \int (\csc^2 x - 1) \, dx$$

$$= \int \csc^2 x \, dx - \int dx$$

$$= -\cot x - x + C \qquad ◀$$

CASE 4 (i) $\int \tan^n x \, dx$ or (ii) $\int \cot^n x \, dx$, where n is a positive integer.

(i) Factor

$$\tan^n x \, dx = \tan^{n-2} x \tan^2 x \, dx$$
$$= \tan^{n-2} x(\sec^2 x - 1) \, dx$$

(ii) Factor

$$\cot^n x \, dx = \cot^{n-2} x \cot^2 x \, dx$$
$$= \cot^{n-2} x(\csc^2 x - 1) \, dx$$

▶ **EXAMPLE 5**   Evaluate

$$\int \tan^3 x \, dx$$

Solution   We use the method suggested by Case 4(i).

$$\int \tan^3 x \, dx = \int \tan x (\sec^2 x - 1) \, dx$$

$$= \int \tan x \sec^2 x \, dx - \int \tan x \, dx$$

$$= \tfrac{1}{2} \tan^2 x + \ln|\cos x| + C \qquad \blacktriangleleft$$

▶ **EXAMPLE 6**   Evaluate

$$\int \cot^4 3x \, dx$$

Solution   This integral pertains to Case 4(ii).

$$\int \cot^4 3x \, dx = \int \cot^2 3x(\csc^2 3x - 1) \, dx$$

$$= \int \cot^2 3x \csc^2 3x \, dx - \int \cot^2 3x \, dx$$

$$= \tfrac{1}{9}(-\cot^3 3x) - \int (\csc^2 3x - 1) \, dx$$

$$= -\tfrac{1}{9} \cot^3 3x + \tfrac{1}{3} \cot 3x + x + C \qquad \blacktriangleleft$$

CASE 5 (i) $\int \sec^n x \, dx$ or (ii) $\int \csc^n x \, dx$, where n is a positive even integer.

(i) Factor

$$\sec^n x \, dx = \sec^{n-2} x(\sec^2 x \, dx)$$
$$= (\sec^2 x)^{(n-2)/2}(\sec^2 x \, dx)$$
$$= (\tan^2 x + 1)^{(n-2)/2}(\sec^2 x \, dx)$$

(ii) Factor

$$\csc^n x \, dx = \csc^{n-2} x(\csc^2 x \, dx)$$
$$= (\csc^2 x)^{(n-2)/2}(\csc^2 x \, dx)$$
$$= (\cot^2 x + 1)^{(n-2)/2}(\csc^2 x \, dx)$$

▶ **EXAMPLE 7**   Evaluate

$$\int \csc^6 x \, dx$$

Solution   We follow the procedure indicated in Case 5(ii).

$$\int \csc^6 x \, dx = \int (\cot^2 x + 1)^2 \csc^2 x \, dx$$

$$= \int \cot^4 x \csc^2 x \, dx + 2 \int \cot^2 x \csc^2 x \, dx + \int \csc^2 x \, dx$$

$$= -\tfrac{1}{5} \cot^5 x - \tfrac{2}{3} \cot^3 x - \cot x + C \qquad \blacktriangleleft$$

CASE 6 (i) $\int \tan^n x \sec^m x \, dx$ or (ii) $\int \cot^n x \csc^m x \, dx$, where m is a positive even integer.

(i) Factor

$$\tan^n x \sec^m x \, dx = \tan^n x \sec^{m-2} x(\sec^2 x \, dx)$$
$$= \tan^n x(\sec^2 x)^{(m-2)/2}(\sec^2 x \, dx)$$
$$= \tan^n x(\tan^2 x + 1)^{(m-2)/2}(\sec^2 x \, dx)$$

(ii) Factor

$$\cot^n x \csc^m x \, dx = \cot^n x \csc^{m-2} x(\csc^2 x \, dx)$$
$$= \cot^n x(\csc^2 x)^{(m-2)/2}(\csc^2 x \, dx)$$
$$= \cot^n x(\cot^2 x + 1)^{(m-2)/2}(\csc^2 x \, dx)$$

▶ **EXAMPLE 8** Evaluate

$$\int \tan^5 x \sec^4 x \, dx$$

Solution We proceed as suggested in Case 6(i).

$$\int \tan^5 x \sec^4 x \, dx = \int \tan^5 x(\tan^2 x + 1)\sec^2 x \, dx$$
$$= \int \tan^7 x \sec^2 x \, dx + \int \tan^5 x \sec^2 x \, dx$$
$$= \tfrac{1}{8} \tan^8 x + \tfrac{1}{6} \tan^6 x + C \qquad ◀$$

CASE 7 (i) $\int \tan^n x \sec^m x \, dx$ or (ii) $\int \cot^n x \csc^m x \, dx$, where n is a positive odd integer.

(i) Factor

$$\tan^n x \sec^m x \, dx = \tan^{n-1} x \sec^{m-1} x(\sec x \tan x \, dx)$$
$$= (\tan^2 x)^{(n-1)/2} \sec^{m-1} x(\sec x \tan x \, dx)$$
$$= (\sec^2 x - 1)^{(n-1)/2} \sec^{m-1} x(\sec x \tan x \, dx)$$

(ii) Factor

$$\cot^n x \csc^m x \, dx = \cot^{n-1} x \csc^{m-1} x(\csc x \cot x \, dx)$$
$$= (\cot^2 x)^{(n-1)/2} \csc^{m-1} x(\csc x \cot x \, dx)$$
$$= (\csc^2 x - 1)^{(n-1)/2} \csc^{m-1} x(\csc x \cot x \, dx)$$

▶ **EXAMPLE 9** Evaluate

$$\int \tan^5 x \sec^7 x \, dx$$

Solution This integral pertains to Case 7(i).

$$\int \tan^5 x \sec^7 x \, dx = \int \tan^4 x \sec^6 x \sec x \tan x \, dx$$

$$= \int (\sec^2 x - 1)^2 \sec^6 x (\sec x \tan x) \, dx$$

$$= \int (\sec^{10} x - 2 \sec^8 x + \sec^6 x)(\sec x \tan x \, dx)$$

$$= \tfrac{1}{11} \sec^{11} x - \tfrac{2}{9} \sec^9 x + \tfrac{1}{7} \sec^7 x + C \qquad \blacktriangleleft$$

We have saved two cases of odd powers of secant and cosecant until last because these cases require a different concept involving integration by parts. The process is illustrated in the following example.

▶ **EXAMPLE 10** Evaluate

$$\int \sec^3 x \, dx$$

Solution For integration by parts, let $u = \sec x$ and $dv = \sec^2 x \, dx$. Then

$$du = \sec x \tan x \, dx \quad \text{and} \quad v = \tan x$$

Therefore

$$\int \sec^3 x \, dx = \sec x \tan x - \int \sec x \tan^2 x \, dx$$

$$\int \sec^3 x \, dx = \sec x \tan x - \int \sec x(\sec^2 x - 1) \, dx$$

$$\int \sec^3 x \, dx = \sec x \tan x - \int \sec^3 x \, dx + \int \sec x \, dx$$

Adding $\int \sec^3 x \, dx$ to both sides we get

$$2 \int \sec^3 x \, dx = \sec x \tan x + \ln|\sec x + \tan x| + 2C$$

$$\int \sec^3 x \, dx = \tfrac{1}{2} \sec x \tan x + \tfrac{1}{2} \ln|\sec x + \tan x| + C \qquad \blacktriangleleft$$

CASE 8 (i) $\int \sec^n x \, dx$ or (ii) $\int \csc^n x \, dx$, where n is a positive odd integer.

Apply integration by parts.

(i) Let $u = \sec^{n-2} x$ and $dv = \sec^2 x \, dx$.
(ii) Let $u = \csc^{n-2} x$ and $dv = \csc^2 x \, dx$.

To integrate an odd power of secant or cosecant you may wish to apply a reduction formula, as given by Formulas 77 and 78 in the Table of Integrals on the back endpapers. You are asked to derive Formula 77 and apply it to evaluate $\int \sec^5 x \, dx$ in Exercise 65.

CASE 9 (i) $\displaystyle\int \tan^n x \sec^m x \, dx$ or (ii) $\displaystyle\int \cot^n x \csc^m x \, dx$, where n is a positive even integer and m is a positive odd integer.

Express the integrand in terms of odd powers of secant or cosecant and then follow the suggestions in Case 8.

(i) Factor

$$\tan^n x \sec^m x \, dx = (\tan^2 x)^{n/2} \sec^m x \, dx$$
$$= (\sec^2 x - 1)^{n/2} \sec^m x \, dx$$

(ii) Factor

$$\cot^n x \csc^m x \, dx = (\cot^2 x)^{n/2} \csc^m x \, dx$$
$$= (\csc^2 x - 1)^{n/2} \csc^m x \, dx$$

▷ **ILLUSTRATION 5**

$$\int \tan^2 x \sec^3 x \, dx = \int (\sec^2 x - 1)\sec^3 x \, dx$$
$$= \int \sec^5 x \, dx - \int \sec^3 x \, dx$$

To evaluate these integrals use integration by parts, as in Example 10, or a reduction formula from a table of integrals.   ◀

EXERCISES 7.2

In Exercises 1 through 34, evaluate the indefinite integral. As you wish, you may check your answer by differentiation or support your answer on your graphics calculator either graphically or numerically as in Example 1.

1. (a) $\displaystyle\int \sin^4 x \cos x \, dx$ **(b)** $\displaystyle\int \cos^3 4x \sin 4x \, dx$

2. (a) $\displaystyle\int \sin^5 x \cos x \, dx$ **(b)** $\displaystyle\int \cos^6 \tfrac{1}{2}x \sin \tfrac{1}{2}x \, dx$

3. (a) $\displaystyle\int \sin^3 x \, dx$ **(b)** $\displaystyle\int \cos^2 \tfrac{1}{2}x \, dx$

4. (a) $\displaystyle\int \cos^5 x \, dx$ **(b)** $\displaystyle\int \sin^2 3x \, dx$

5. (a) $\displaystyle\int \sin^2 x \cos^3 x \, dx$ **(b)** $\displaystyle\int \sqrt{\cos z} \sin^3 z \, dz$

6. (a) $\displaystyle\int \sin^3 x \cos^3 x \, dx$ **(b)** $\displaystyle\int \frac{\cos^3 3x}{\sqrt[3]{\sin 3x}} \, dx$

7. $\displaystyle\int \cos 4x \cos 3x \, dx$

8. $\displaystyle\int \sin 2x \cos 4x \, dx$

9. $\displaystyle\int \sin 3y \cos 5y \, dy$

10. $\displaystyle\int \cos t \cos 3t \, dt$

11. $\displaystyle\int \tan^2 5x \, dx$

12. $\displaystyle\int e^x \tan^2(e^x) \, dx$

13. $\displaystyle\int x \cot^2 2x^2 \, dx$

14. $\displaystyle\int \cot^2 4t \, dt$

15. $\displaystyle\int \cot^3 t \, dt$

16. $\displaystyle\int \tan^4 x \, dx$

17. $\displaystyle\int \tan^6 3x \, dx$

18. $\displaystyle\int \csc^3 x \, dx$

19. $\displaystyle\int \sec^4 x \, dx$

20. $\displaystyle\int \cot^5 2x \, dx$

21. $\displaystyle\int e^x \tan^4(e^x) \, dx$

22. $\displaystyle\int \frac{\sec^4(\ln x)}{x} \, dx$

23. $\displaystyle\int \tan^6 x \sec^4 x\, dx$ **24.** $\displaystyle\int \tan^5 x \sec^3 x\, dx$

25. $\displaystyle\int \cot^2 3x \csc^4 3x\, dx$ **26.** $\displaystyle\int (\sec 5x + \csc 5x)^2\, dx$

27. $\displaystyle\int (\tan 2x + \cot 2x)^2\, dx$ **28.** $\displaystyle\int \frac{dx}{1 + \cos x}$

29. $\displaystyle\int \frac{2 \sin w - 1}{\cos^2 w}\, dw$ **30.** $\displaystyle\int \frac{\tan^3 \sqrt{x}}{\sqrt{x}}\, dx$

31. $\displaystyle\int \frac{\csc^4 x}{\cot^2 x}\, dx$ **32.** $\displaystyle\int \frac{\tan^4 y}{\sec^5 y}\, dy$

33. $\displaystyle\int \frac{\sec^3 x}{\tan^4 x}\, dx$ **34.** $\displaystyle\int \frac{\sin^2 \pi x}{\cos^6 \pi x}\, dx$

In Exercises 35 through 48, find the exact value of the definite integral. Support your answer by the NINT capability of your graphics calculator.

35. $\displaystyle\int_0^{\pi/2} \cos^3 x\, dx$ **36.** $\displaystyle\int_0^{\pi/3} \sin^3 t \cos^2 t\, dt$

37. $\displaystyle\int_0^1 \sin^4 \tfrac{1}{2} \pi x\, dx$ **38.** $\displaystyle\int_0^1 \sin^3 \tfrac{1}{2} \pi t\, dt$

39. $\displaystyle\int_0^1 \sin^2 \pi t \cos^2 \pi t\, dt$ **40.** $\displaystyle\int_0^{\pi/2} \sin^2 \tfrac{1}{2} x \cos^2 \tfrac{1}{2} x\, dx$

41. $\displaystyle\int_0^{\pi/8} \sin 3x \cos 5x\, dx$ **42.** $\displaystyle\int_0^{\pi/6} \sin 2x \cos 4x\, dx$

43. $\displaystyle\int_{\pi/16}^{\pi/12} \tan^3 4x\, dx$ **44.** $\displaystyle\int_{\pi/8}^{\pi/6} 3 \sec^4 2t\, dt$

45. $\displaystyle\int_{-\pi/4}^{\pi/4} \sec^6 x\, dx$ **46.** $\displaystyle\int_0^{\pi/3} \frac{\tan^3 x}{\sec x}\, dx$

47. $\displaystyle\int_{\pi/4}^{\pi/2} \frac{\cos^4 t}{\sin^6 t}\, dt$ **48.** $\displaystyle\int_{\pi/6}^{\pi/4} \cot^3 w\, dw$

49. Find the area of the region bounded by the curve $y = \sin^2 x$ and the x axis from $x = 0$ to $x = \pi$.

50. Find the volume of the solid of revolution generated by revolving one arch of the sine curve about the x axis.

51. Find the volume of the solid of revolution generated if the region of Exercise 49 is revolved about the x axis.

52. The region bounded by the y axis and the curves $y = \sin x$ and $y = \cos x$ for $0 \le x \le \tfrac{1}{4}\pi$ is revolved about the x axis. Find the volume of the solid of revolution generated.

53. Find the volume of the solid of revolution generated if the region of Exercise 49 is revolved about the line $y = 1$.

54. The region in the first quadrant bounded by the curve $y = \cos x$ and the lines $y = 1$ and $x = \tfrac{1}{2}\pi$ is revolved about the x axis. Find the volume of the solid generated.

55. Find the centroid of the region from $x = 1$ to $x = \tfrac{1}{2}\pi$ bounded by the curve $y = \cos x$ and the x axis.

56. Find the centroid of the region in Exercise 52.

57. Find the area of the region bounded by the curve $y = \tan^2 x$, the x axis, and the line $x = \tfrac{1}{4}\pi$.

58. Find the volume of the solid of revolution generated if the region bounded by the curve $y = 3 \csc^3 x$, the x axis, and the lines $x = \tfrac{1}{6}\pi$ and $x = \tfrac{1}{2}\pi$ is revolved about the x axis.

59. Find the volume of the solid of revolution generated if the region bounded by the curve $y = \sec^2 x$, the axes, and the line $x = \tfrac{1}{4}\pi$ is revolved about the x axis.

60. The face of a dam is in the shape of one arch of the curve $y = -100 \cos \frac{1}{200}\pi x$, $x \in [-100, 100]$, and the surface of the water is at the top of the dam. Find the force due to water pressure on the face of the dam if distance is measured in feet.

61. If n is any positive integer, prove that
$$\int_0^\pi \sin^2 nx\, dx = \tfrac{1}{2}\pi$$

62. If n is a positive odd integer, prove that
$$\int_0^\pi \cos^n x\, dx = 0$$

In Exercises 63 and 64, show that the formula is true, where m and n are any positive integers.

63. $\displaystyle\int_{-1}^1 \cos n\pi x \sin m\pi x\, dx = 0$

64. $\displaystyle\int_{-1}^1 \sin n\pi x \sin m\pi x\, dx = \begin{cases} 0 & \text{if } m \ne n \\ 1 & \text{if } m = n \end{cases}$

65. **(a)** Derive the following reduction formula, where $n \ge 2$ and n is an integer:
$$\int \sec^n x\, dx = \frac{1}{n-1} \sec^{n-2} x \tan x + \frac{n-2}{n-1} \int \sec^{n-2} x\, dx$$

(b) Apply the reduction formula in part (a) to evaluate $\displaystyle\int \sec^5 x\, dx$.

66. Apply the reduction formula in Exercise 65 to evaluate each of the following integrals:

(a) $\displaystyle\int \sec^6 x\, dx$ **(b)** $\displaystyle\int \sec^7 x\, dx$

67. (a) Derive the following reduction formula where $n > 1$ and n is an integer:

$$\int \sin^n x \, dx = -\frac{1}{n} \sin^{n-1} x \cos x + \frac{n-1}{n} \int \sin^{n-2} x \, dx$$

(b) Apply the reduction formula in part (a) to evaluate $\int \sin^5 x \, dx$. **(c)** Compare your answer in part (b) with the answer of Example 1, and show that the two answers are equivalent.

68. (a) Derive the following reduction formula where $n > 1$ and n is an integer:

$$\int \cos^n x \, dx = \frac{1}{n} \cos^{n-1} x \sin x + \frac{n-1}{n} \int \cos^{n-2} x \, dx$$

(b) Apply the reduction formula in part (a) to evaluate $\int \cos^4 x \, dx$. **(c)** Compare your answer in part (b) with the answer of Example 2, and show that the two answers are equivalent.

69. (a) Prove:

$$\int \cot x \csc^n x \, dx = -\frac{\csc^n x}{n} + C \quad \text{if } n \neq 0$$

(b) Derive a formula similar to that in part (a) for $\int \tan x \sec^n x \, dx$ if $n \neq 0$.

70. Evaluate

$$\int \sin^3 x \cos^3 x \, dx$$

by three methods:

(a) $\int \sin^3 x \cos^3 x \, dx = \int \sin^3 x \cos^2 x (\cos x \, dx)$

Let $\cos^2 x = 1 - \sin^2 x$ and $u = \sin x$.

(b) $\int \sin^3 x \cos^3 x \, dx = \int \sin^2 x \cos^3 x (\sin x \, dx)$

Let $\sin^2 x = 1 - \cos^2 x$ and $u = \cos x$.

(c) $\int \sin^3 x \cos^3 x \, dx = \frac{1}{8} \int (2 \sin x \cos x)^3 \, dx$

Apply the identity $\sin 2x = 2 \sin x \cos x$.

(d) Explain the difference in appearance of the answers obtained in parts (a)–(c) and why they are equivalent.

7.3 INTEGRATION OF ALGEBRAIC FUNCTIONS BY TRIGONOMETRIC SUBSTITUTION

You have already seen how some techniques of integration require a change-of-variable substitution. In this section you will learn substitutions involving trigonometric functions that lead to trigonometric integrals. We will show with three cases how changing a variable by a trigonometric substitution often enables us to evaluate an integral containing an expression of one of the following forms where $a > 0$:

$$\sqrt{a^2 - x^2} \qquad \sqrt{a^2 + x^2} \qquad \sqrt{x^2 - a^2}$$

> CASE 1 The integrand contains an expression of the form $\sqrt{a^2 - x^2}$, where $a > 0$.
>
> Introduce a new variable θ by letting $x = a \sin \theta$, where
>
> $$0 \leq \theta \leq \tfrac{1}{2}\pi \quad \text{if } x \geq 0 \quad \text{and} \quad -\tfrac{1}{2}\pi \leq \theta < 0 \quad \text{if } x < 0$$

In this case, with $x = a \sin \theta$, $dx = a \cos \theta \, d\theta$, and $\cos \theta \geq 0$ because $-\tfrac{1}{2}\pi \leq \theta \leq \tfrac{1}{2}\pi$. Moreover

$$\begin{aligned}
\sqrt{a^2 - x^2} &= \sqrt{a^2 - a^2 \sin^2 \theta} \\
&= \sqrt{a^2} \sqrt{1 - \sin^2 \theta} \\
&= a\sqrt{\cos^2 \theta} \qquad \text{because } a > 0 \\
&= a \cos \theta \qquad \text{because } \cos \theta \geq 0
\end{aligned}$$

▶ **EXAMPLE 1**   Evaluate

$$\int \frac{\sqrt{9-x^2}}{x^2}\, dx$$

and support the answer numerically.

Solution   Observe that because the denominator is x^2, $x \neq 0$. With the substitution indicated in Case 1, let $x = 3\sin\theta$ where $0 < \theta \leq \frac{1}{2}\pi$ if $x > 0$ and $-\frac{1}{2}\pi \leq \theta < 0$ if $x < 0$. Then $dx = 3\cos\theta\, d\theta$ and

$$\sqrt{9-x^2} = \sqrt{9 - 9\sin^2\theta}$$
$$= 3\sqrt{\cos^2\theta}$$
$$= 3\cos\theta$$

Therefore

$$\int \frac{\sqrt{9-x^2}}{x^2}\, dx = \int \frac{3\cos\theta}{9\sin^2\theta}(3\cos\theta\, d\theta)$$

$$= \int \cot^2\theta\, d\theta$$

$$= \int (\csc^2\theta - 1)\, d\theta$$

$$= -\cot\theta - \theta + C$$

Because $\sin\theta = \frac{1}{3}x$ and $-\frac{1}{2}\pi < \theta < \frac{1}{2}\pi$, $\theta = \sin^{-1}\frac{1}{3}x$. To find $\cot\theta$, refer to Figures 1 (for $x > 0$) and 2 (for $x < 0$). In either case

$$\cot\theta = \frac{\sqrt{9-x^2}}{x}$$

Thus

$$\int \frac{\sqrt{9-x^2}}{x^2}\, dx = -\frac{\sqrt{9-x^2}}{x} - \sin^{-1}\frac{x}{3} + C$$

We support this answer numerically by computing a corresponding definite integral with an arbitrary choice of limits of integration, in this case, 1 and 2.

$$\int_1^2 \frac{\sqrt{9-x^2}}{x^2}\, dx = \left[-\frac{\sqrt{9-x^2}}{x} - \sin^{-1}\frac{x}{3} \right]_1^2$$

$$= -\frac{\sqrt{5}}{2} - \sin^{-1}\frac{2}{3} + \sqrt{8} + \sin^{-1}\frac{1}{3}$$

$$= 1.320502389$$

On our graphics calculator

$$\text{NINT}\left(\frac{\sqrt{9-x^2}}{x^2}, 1, 2 \right) = 1.320502389$$

which agrees with the above and gives powerful support for our value of the indefinite integral.   ◀

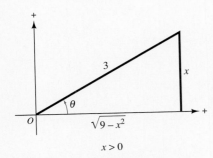

$x > 0$

FIGURE 1

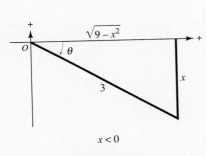

$x < 0$

FIGURE 2

CASE 2 The integrand contains an expression of the form $\sqrt{a^2 + x^2}$, where $a > 0$.

Introduce a new variable θ by letting $x = a \tan \theta$, where

$$0 \leq \theta < \tfrac{1}{2}\pi \quad \text{if } x \geq 0 \quad \text{and} \quad -\tfrac{1}{2}\pi < \theta < 0 \quad \text{if } x < 0$$

With $x = a \tan \theta$, $dx = a \sec^2 \theta \, d\theta$, and because $-\tfrac{1}{2}\pi < \theta < \tfrac{1}{2}\pi$, $\sec \theta \geq 1$. Furthermore

$$\begin{aligned} \sqrt{a^2 + x^2} &= \sqrt{a^2 + a^2 \tan^2 \theta} \\ &= \sqrt{a^2} \sqrt{1 + \tan^2 \theta} \\ &= a \sqrt{\sec^2 \theta} \\ &= a \sec \theta \end{aligned}$$

▶ **EXAMPLE 2**   Evaluate

$$\int \sqrt{x^2 + 5} \, dx$$

and support the answer graphically.

Solution   This integral pertains to Case 2. We let $x = \sqrt{5} \tan \theta$ where $0 \leq \theta < \tfrac{1}{2}\pi$ if $x \geq 0$ and $-\tfrac{1}{2}\pi < \theta < 0$ if $x < 0$. Then $dx = \sqrt{5} \sec^2 \theta \, d\theta$ and

$$\begin{aligned} \sqrt{x^2 + 5} &= \sqrt{5 \tan^2 \theta + 5} \\ &= \sqrt{5} \sqrt{\sec^2 \theta} \\ &= \sqrt{5} \sec \theta \end{aligned}$$

Therefore

$$\int \sqrt{x^2 + 5} \, dx = \int \sqrt{5} \sec \theta (\sqrt{5} \sec^2 \theta \, d\theta)$$

$$= 5 \int \sec^3 \theta \, d\theta$$

For $\sec^3 \theta$, we apply the result of Example 10 in Section 7.2 and obtain

$$\int \sqrt{x^2 + 5} \, dx = \tfrac{5}{2} \sec \theta \tan \theta + \tfrac{5}{2} \ln|\sec \theta + \tan \theta| + C$$

We determine $\sec \theta$ from Figures 3 (for $x \geq 0$) and 4 (for $x < 0$). In either case

$$\sec \theta = \frac{\sqrt{x^2 + 5}}{\sqrt{5}}$$

Hence

$$\int \sqrt{x^2 + 5} \, dx = \frac{5}{2} \cdot \frac{\sqrt{x^2 + 5}}{\sqrt{5}} \cdot \frac{x}{\sqrt{5}} + \frac{5}{2} \ln \left| \frac{\sqrt{x^2 + 5}}{\sqrt{5}} + \frac{x}{\sqrt{5}} \right| + C$$

$$= \tfrac{1}{2} x \sqrt{x^2 + 5} + \tfrac{5}{2} \ln|\sqrt{x^2 + 5} + x| - \tfrac{5}{2} \ln \sqrt{5} + C$$

$$= \tfrac{1}{2} x \sqrt{x^2 + 5} + \tfrac{5}{2} \ln(\sqrt{x^2 + 5} + x) + C_1$$

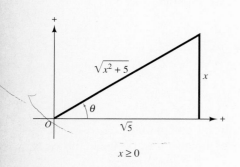

$x \geq 0$

FIGURE 3

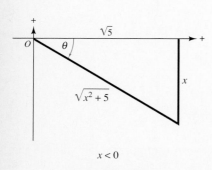

$x < 0$

FIGURE 4

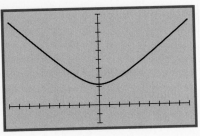

[-9, 9] by [-2, 10]

$y = \sqrt{x^2 + 5}$

NDER $(\frac{1}{2}x \sqrt{x^2 + 5} + \frac{5}{2} \ln (\sqrt{x^2 + 5} + x), x)$

FIGURE 5

Observe that we replaced $-\frac{5}{2} \ln \sqrt{5} + C$ by the arbitrary constant C_1. Also, because $\sqrt{x^2 + 5} + x > 0$, we deleted the absolute-value bars.

Figure 5 shows the graphs of

$$y = \sqrt{x^2 + 5} \quad \text{and} \quad \text{NDER}(\tfrac{1}{2}x \sqrt{x^2 + 5} + \tfrac{5}{2} \ln(\sqrt{x^2 + 5} + x), x)$$

plotted in the $[-9, 9]$ by $[-2, 10]$ window. The fact that the graphs appear to coincide supports our answer. ◀

CASE 3 The integrand contains an expression of the form $\sqrt{x^2 - a^2}$, where $a > 0$.
Introduce a new variable θ by letting $x = a \sec \theta$, where

$$0 \leq \theta < \tfrac{1}{2}\pi \quad \text{if } x \geq a \quad \text{and} \quad \pi \leq \theta < \tfrac{3}{2}\pi \quad \text{if } x \leq -a$$

With $x = a \sec \theta$, $dx = a \sec \theta \tan \theta \, d\theta$, and $\tan \theta \geq 0$ because either $0 \leq \theta < \tfrac{1}{2}\pi$ or $\pi \leq \theta < \tfrac{3}{2}\pi$. Moreover

$$\sqrt{x^2 - a^2} = \sqrt{a^2 \sec^2 \theta - a^2}$$
$$= \sqrt{a^2}\sqrt{\sec^2 \theta - 1}$$
$$= a\sqrt{\tan^2 \theta}$$
$$= a \tan \theta$$

▶ **EXAMPLE 3**   Evaluate

$$\int \frac{dx}{x^3 \sqrt{x^2 - 9}}$$

Solution   We note that $|x|$ must be greater than 3 so that $\sqrt{x^2 - 9}$ is real and not zero. Following the suggestions of Case 3, we let $x = 3 \sec \theta$ where $0 < \theta < \tfrac{1}{2}\pi$ if $x > 3$ and $\pi < \theta < -\tfrac{3}{2}\pi$ if $x < -3$. Then $dx = 3 \sec \theta \tan \theta \, d\theta$ and

$$\sqrt{x^2 - 9} = \sqrt{9 \sec^2 \theta - 9}$$
$$= 3 \sqrt{\tan^2 \theta}$$
$$= 3 \tan \theta$$

Therefore

$$\int \frac{dx}{x^3 \sqrt{x^2 - 9}} = \int \frac{3 \sec \theta \tan \theta \, d\theta}{27 \sec^3 \theta \cdot 3 \tan \theta}$$
$$= \frac{1}{27} \int \cos^2 \theta \, d\theta$$
$$= \frac{1}{54} \int (1 + \cos 2\theta) \, d\theta$$
$$= \tfrac{1}{54}(\theta + \tfrac{1}{2}\sin 2\theta) + C$$
$$= \tfrac{1}{54}(\theta + \sin \theta \cos \theta) + C$$

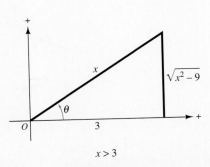

$x > 3$

FIGURE 6

Because $\sec \theta = \frac{1}{3}x$ and θ is in $(0, \tfrac{1}{2}\pi) \cup (\pi, \tfrac{3}{2}\pi)$, $\theta = \sec^{-1} \tfrac{1}{3}x$. When $x > 3, 0 < \theta < \tfrac{1}{2}\pi$, and we obtain $\sin \theta$ and $\cos \theta$ from Figure 6. When

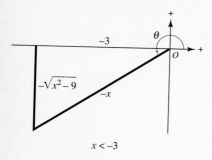

$x < -3$

FIGURE 7

$x < -3$, $\pi < \theta < \frac{3}{2}\pi$, and we obtain $\sin \theta$ and $\cos \theta$ from Figure 7. In either case

$$\sin \theta = \frac{\sqrt{x^2 - 9}}{x} \quad \text{and} \quad \cos \theta = \frac{3}{x}$$

Thus

$$\int \frac{dx}{x^3 \sqrt{x^2 - 9}} = \frac{1}{54}\left(\sec^{-1}\frac{x}{3} + \frac{\sqrt{x^2 - 9}}{x} \cdot \frac{3}{x}\right) + C$$

$$= \frac{1}{54}\sec^{-1}\frac{x}{3} + \frac{\sqrt{x^2 - 9}}{18x^2} + C \qquad \blacktriangleleft$$

Observe in Example 3, the important part played by the range of the inverse secant function. The fact that θ is in either the first or third quadrants enabled us to conclude that $\tan \theta > 0$, so that $\sqrt{\tan^2 \theta} = \tan \theta$. You may recall from Section 5.7 where we chose this range, we indicated that such a range would pay off in this section.

▶ **EXAMPLE 4**   Use a trigonometric substitution to prove that if $u > a > 0$

$$\int \frac{du}{\sqrt{u^2 - a^2}} = \ln(u + \sqrt{u^2 - a^2}) + C$$

Solution   From the substitution indicated in Case 3, we let $u = a \sec \theta$ where $0 < \theta < \frac{1}{2}\pi$. Then $dx = a \sec \theta \tan \theta\, d\theta$ and $\sqrt{u^2 - a^2} = a \tan \theta$. Therefore

$$\int \frac{du}{\sqrt{u^2 - a^2}} = \int \frac{a \sec \theta \tan \theta\, d\theta}{a \tan \theta}$$

$$= \int \sec \theta\, d\theta$$

$$= \ln(\sec \theta + \tan \theta) + C$$

Notice that we do not use absolute-value bars because both $\sec \theta$ and $\tan \theta$ are positive in this case. We determine $\tan \theta$ from Figure 8, where

$$\tan \theta = \frac{\sqrt{u^2 - a^2}}{a}$$

Therefore

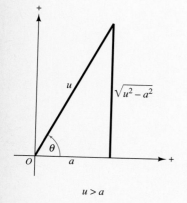

$u > a$

FIGURE 8

$$\int \frac{du}{\sqrt{u^2 - a^2}} = \ln\left(\frac{u}{a} + \frac{\sqrt{u^2 - a^2}}{a}\right) + C_1$$

$$= \ln(u + \sqrt{u^2 - a^2}) - \ln a + C_1$$

$$= \ln(u + \sqrt{u^2 - a^2}) + C$$

where $C = C_1 - \ln a$.   ◀

The indefinite-integration formula in Example 4 appeared in Section 5.9 as the natural logarithm representation of formula (10) in Theorem 5.9.10, which also expresses the integral in terms of an inverse hyperbolic cosine. Most tables of integrals give both forms.

▶ **EXAMPLE 5**   Find the exact value of

$$\int_1^2 \frac{dx}{(6 - x^2)^{3/2}}$$

and support the answer by the NINT capability of a graphics calculator.

Solution   The corresponding indefinite integral pertains to Case 1. We restrict θ to the first quadrant because the limits of the definite integral indicate that $x > 0$. We therefore let $x = \sqrt{6} \sin \theta$ where $0 < \theta < \frac{1}{2}\pi$. Then $dx = \sqrt{6} \cos \theta \, d\theta$ and

$$\begin{aligned}
(6 - x^2)^{3/2} &= (6 - 6 \sin^2 \theta)^{3/2} \\
&= 6\sqrt{6}(1 - \sin^2 \theta)^{3/2} \\
&= 6\sqrt{6}(\cos^2 \theta)^{3/2} \\
&= 6\sqrt{6} \cos^3 \theta
\end{aligned}$$

Hence

$$\begin{aligned}
\int \frac{dx}{(6 - x^2)^{3/2}} &= \int \frac{\sqrt{6} \cos \theta \, d\theta}{6\sqrt{6} \cos^3 \theta} \\
&= \frac{1}{6} \int \frac{d\theta}{\cos^2 \theta} \\
&= \frac{1}{6} \int \sec^2 \theta \, d\theta \\
&= \tfrac{1}{6} \tan \theta + C
\end{aligned}$$

We find $\tan \theta$ from Figure 9 and get

$$\tan \theta = \frac{x}{\sqrt{6 - x^2}}$$

Therefore

$$\begin{aligned}
\int_1^2 \frac{dx}{(6 - x^2)^{3/2}} &= \left. \frac{x}{6\sqrt{6 - x^2}} \right]_1^2 \\
&= \frac{1}{3\sqrt{2}} - \frac{1}{6\sqrt{5}} \\
&= \frac{\sqrt{2}}{6} - \frac{\sqrt{5}}{30} \\
&= \frac{5\sqrt{2} - \sqrt{5}}{30}
\end{aligned}$$

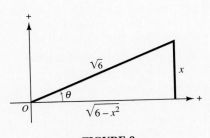

FIGURE 9

To support this answer, we compute on our graphics calculator

$$\text{NINT}(1/(6 - x^2)^{3/2}, 1, 2) = 0.1611666611$$

To the same number of significant digits

$$\frac{5\sqrt{2} - \sqrt{5}}{30} = 0.1611666611$$

which supports our answer.

◀

EXERCISES 7.3

In Exercises 1 through 12, evaluate the indefinite integral, and, if you wish, use your graphics calculator to support your answer either numerically or graphically.

1. $\displaystyle\int \frac{dx}{x^2\sqrt{4-x^2}}$

2. $\displaystyle\int \frac{\sqrt{4-x^2}}{x^2}\, dx$

3. $\displaystyle\int \frac{dx}{x\sqrt{x^2+4}}$

4. $\displaystyle\int \frac{x^2}{\sqrt{x^2+6}}\, dx$

5. $\displaystyle\int \frac{x}{\sqrt{x^2-25}}\, dx$

6. $\displaystyle\int \frac{dx}{(2+x^2)^{3/2}}$

7. $\displaystyle\int \frac{dx}{(4x^2-9)^{3/2}}$

8. $\displaystyle\int \frac{dw}{w^2\sqrt{w^2-7}}$

9. $\displaystyle\int \frac{\sec^2 x}{(4-\tan^2 x)^{3/2}}\, dx$

10. $\displaystyle\int \frac{dz}{(z^2-6z+18)^{3/2}}$

11. $\displaystyle\int \frac{\ln^3 w}{w\sqrt{\ln^2 w-4}}\, dw$

12. $\displaystyle\int \frac{e^{-x}}{(9e^{-2x}+1)^{3/2}}\, dx$

In Exercises 13 through 22, find the exact value of the definite integral and support your answer by the NINT capability of your graphics calculator.

13. $\displaystyle\int_1^4 \frac{dx}{x\sqrt{25-x^2}}$

14. $\displaystyle\int_0^1 \sqrt{1-u^2}\, du$

15. $\displaystyle\int_2^3 \frac{2}{t\sqrt{t^4+25}}\, dt$

16. $\displaystyle\int_1^3 \frac{dx}{x^4\sqrt{16+x^2}}$

17. $\displaystyle\int_2^4 \frac{dx}{\sqrt{4x+x^2}}$

18. $\displaystyle\int_0^4 \frac{dx}{(16+x^2)^{3/2}}$

19. $\displaystyle\int_0^2 \frac{x^3}{\sqrt{16-x^2}}\, dx$

20. $\displaystyle\int_1^3 \frac{dx}{\sqrt{4x-x^2}}$

21. $\displaystyle\int_{-2}^0 \frac{dx}{(5-4x-x^2)^{3/2}}$

22. $\displaystyle\int_2^3 \frac{dx}{x\sqrt{x^4-4}}$

In Exercises 23 through 30, approximate to five significant digits the value of the definite integral by the NINT capability of your graphics calculator. Confirm your answer analytically.

23. $\displaystyle\int_{\sqrt{3}}^{3\sqrt{3}} \frac{dx}{x^2\sqrt{x^2+9}}$

24. $\displaystyle\int_0^1 \frac{x^2}{\sqrt{4-x^2}}\, dx$

25. $\displaystyle\int_4^6 \frac{dx}{x\sqrt{x^2-4}}$

26. $\displaystyle\int_1^3 \frac{dx}{x^4\sqrt{x^2+3}}$

27. $\displaystyle\int_0^5 x^2\sqrt{25-x^2}\, dx$

28. $\displaystyle\int_4^8 \frac{dw}{(w^2-4)^{3/2}}$

29. $\displaystyle\int_0^{\ln 2} \frac{e^t}{(e^{2t}+8e^t+7)^{3/2}}\, dt$

30. $\displaystyle\int_0^1 \frac{\sqrt{16-e^{2x}}}{e^x}\, dx$

In Exercises 31 through 33, use methods previous to this section (i.e., without a trigonometric substitution) to evaluate the integrals.

31. $\displaystyle\int \frac{3}{x\sqrt{4x^2-9}}\, dx$

32. $\displaystyle\int \frac{5x}{\sqrt{3-2x^2}}\, dx$

33. $\displaystyle\int \frac{\sqrt{4-x^2}}{x}\, dx$

34. Find the area of the region bounded by the curve $y = \sqrt{x^2-9}/x^2$, the x axis, and the line $x = 5$.

35. Find the length of arc of the curve $y = \ln x$ from $x = 1$ to $x = 3$.

36. Find the volume of the solid of revolution generated by revolving the region of Exercise 34 about the y axis.

37. Find the volume of the solid of revolution generated when the region to the right of the y axis bounded by the curve $y = x\sqrt[4]{9-x^2}$ and the x axis is revolved about the x axis.

38. Find the length of arc of the parabola $y = x^2$ from $(0, 0)$ to $(1, 1)$.

39. Find the center of mass of a rod 8 cm long if the linear density at a point x centimeters from the left end is $\sqrt{x^2+36}$ grams per centimeter.

40. The linear density of a rod at a point x meters from one end is $\sqrt{9+x^2}$ kilograms per meter. Find the mass and center of mass of the rod if it is 3 m long.

41. Find the centroid of the region bounded by the curve $yx^2 = \sqrt{x^2-9}$, the x axis, and the line $x = 5$.

42. Use integration to obtain πr^2 square units as the area of the region enclosed by a circle of radius r units.

43. A horizontal cylindrical pipe has a 4-ft inner diameter and is closed at one end by a circular gate that just fits over the pipe. If the pipe contains water at a depth of 3 ft, find the force on the gate due to water pressure.

44. A gate in an irrigation ditch is in the shape of a segment of a circle of radius 4 ft. The top of the gate is

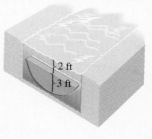

horizontal and 3 ft above the lowest point on the gate. If the water level is 2 ft above the top of the gate, find the force on the gate due to water pressure.

45. An automobile's gasoline tank is in the shape of a right-circular cylinder of radius 8 in. with a horizontal axis. Find the force on one end when the gasoline is 12 in. deep if 0.39 oz/in.^{3} is the weight density of the gasoline.

46. A *tractrix*, which has applications in pursuit problems, is a curve such that the length of the segment of every tangent line from the point of tangency to the point of intersection with the x axis is a positive constant a. See the accompanying figure. Show that an equation of the tractrix is

$$x = a \ln \left(\frac{a + \sqrt{a^2 - y^2}}{y} \right) - \sqrt{a^2 - y^2}$$

Hint: Let $P(x, y)$ be any point on the tractrix and let α be the angle of inclination of the tangent line to the tractrix at P. Show that $\sin \alpha = y/a$, and hence that $\tan \alpha = -y/\sqrt{a^2 - y^2}$. Then solve the differential equation

$$\frac{dy}{dx} = \frac{-y}{\sqrt{a^2 - y^2}}$$

where $y = a$ when $x = 0$.

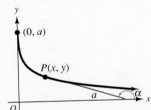

47. Suppose you are at the marina and walking along the edge of a dock while pulling a boat with a rope 15 ft long, so that the boat travels along a tractrix (see Exercise 46). Refer to the accompanying figure where the dock is along the x axis, you are initially at the origin, and the boat is initially at the point (0, 15) on the y axis. **(a)** How far have you walked when the

boat is 12 ft from the dock? Express your answer to two decimal places. **(b)** How far is the boat from the dock when you have walked 20 ft? Express your answer to two decimal places. You will need to use your graphics calculator to solve the equation.

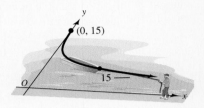

48. Suppose a hound, chasing a rabbit, is moving along the pursuit curve, a tractrix (see Exercise 46), so that it is always going in the direction pointing at the rabbit, and the speed of the hound never exceeds the speed of the rabbit. Refer to the accompanying figure where the rabbit, initially at the origin, is moving along the x axis, and the hound is initially at the point (0, a). Explain why the hound is always the same distance from the rabbit so that it never catches the rabbit.

49. **(a)** Use the trigonometric substitution $x = 2 \sec \theta$ to find the exact value of the definite integral

$$\int_3^4 \frac{dx}{4 - x^2}$$

(b) Explain why you cannot use the trigonometric substitution $x = 2 \sin \theta$ to evaluate the definite integral in part (a).

7.4 INTEGRATION OF RATIONAL FUNCTIONS AND LOGISTIC GROWTH

You know how to combine two or more rational expressions into one rational expression by addition or subtraction. For example

$$\frac{3}{x + 2} + \frac{4}{x - 3} = \frac{7x - 1}{(x + 2)(x - 3)} \tag{1}$$

Suppose you wish to do the reverse, that is, to express a single rational expression as a sum of two or more simpler quotients, called **partial fractions.** You often need to do this when integrating rational functions.

You may have learned in an algebra or precalculus course how to write a rational function as the sum of partial fractions. If you did and need a refresher or if you have never been exposed to partial fractions read Appendix Section A.11 before continuing with this section.

▶ **EXAMPLE 1**   Evaluate

$$\int \frac{7x - 1}{x^2 - x - 6}\, dx$$

and support the answer graphically.

Solution   Factoring the denominator of the integrand, we obtain

$$\frac{7x - 1}{x^2 - x - 6} = \frac{7x - 1}{(x + 2)(x - 3)}$$

Observe that the right-hand side of this equation is the same as the right-hand side of Equation (1). In Illustration 1 of Appendix Section A.11 we decompose this fraction into the partial fractions on the left-hand side of (1). Therefore

$$\int \frac{7x - 1}{x^2 - x - 6}\, dx = \int \frac{3}{x + 2}\, dx + \int \frac{4}{x - 3}\, dx$$
$$= 3 \ln|x + 2| + 4 \ln|x - 3| + C$$
$$= \ln|(x + 2)^3| + \ln|(x - 3)^4| + C$$
$$= \ln|(x + 2)^3(x - 3)^4| + C$$

Figure 1 shows the graphs of

$$y = \frac{7x - 1}{x^2 - x - 6} \quad \text{and} \quad \text{NDER}(\ln|(x + 2)^3(x - 3)^4|, x)$$

plotted in the $[-9.4, 9.4]$ by $[-6.2, 6.2]$ window. Because the graphs appear to overlap we have supported our answer.   ◀

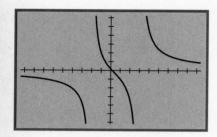

[−9.4, 9.4] by [−6.2, 6.2]

$$y = \frac{7x - 1}{x^2 - x - 6}$$

NDER $(\ln|(x + 2)^3 (x - 3)^4|, x)$

FIGURE 1

▶ **EXAMPLE 2**   Evaluate

$$\int \frac{du}{u^2 - a^2}$$

Solution

$$\frac{1}{u^2 - a^2} \equiv \frac{A}{u - a} + \frac{B}{u + a}$$

Multiplying by $(u - a)(u + a)$ we get

$$1 \equiv A(u + a) + B(u - a)$$
$$1 \equiv (A + B)u + Aa - Ba$$

Equating coefficients we have

$$A + B = 0$$
$$Aa - Ba = 1$$

Solving simultaneously for A and B, we get

$$A = \frac{1}{2a} \qquad B = -\frac{1}{2a}$$

Therefore

$$\int \frac{du}{u^2 - a^2} = \frac{1}{2a} \int \frac{du}{u - a} - \frac{1}{2a} \int \frac{du}{u + a}$$

$$= \frac{1}{2a} \ln|u - a| - \frac{1}{2a} \ln|u + a| + C$$

$$= \frac{1}{2a} \ln\left|\frac{u - a}{u + a}\right| + C \qquad \blacktriangleleft$$

The type of integral of the above example occurs frequently enough for it to be listed as a formula. It is not necessary to memorize it because an integration by partial fractions is fairly simple.

$$\int \frac{du}{u^2 - a^2} = \frac{1}{2a} \ln\left|\frac{u - a}{u + a}\right| + C \tag{2}$$

If we have $\int du/(a^2 - u^2)$, we write

$$\int \frac{du}{a^2 - u^2} = -\int \frac{du}{u^2 - a^2}$$

$$= -\frac{1}{2a} \ln\left|\frac{u - a}{u + a}\right| + C$$

$$= \frac{1}{2a} \ln\left|\frac{u + a}{u - a}\right| + C$$

This is also listed as a formula.

$$\int \frac{du}{a^2 - u^2} = \frac{1}{2a} \ln\left|\frac{u + a}{u - a}\right| + C \tag{3}$$

This formula appeared in Section 5.9 as the natural logarithm representation of formula (11) in Theorem 5.9.10, which also expresses the integral in terms of an inverse hyperbolic tangent or cotangent. You will find both formulas (2) and (3), along with their inverse-hyperbolic-function representations, as Formulas 25 and 26 in the Table of Integrals on the front endpapers.

In Section 5.6 we discussed exponential growth that occurs when the rate of increase of the amount of a quantity is proportional to the amount present at a given instant. It has the mathematical model

$$f(t) = Be^{kt} \tag{4}$$

where k is a positive constant, B units is the amount present initially, and $f(t)$ units is the amount present at t units of time, where $f(t) \geq B$ for $t \geq 0$. We also discussed in Section 5.6 bounded growth that happens when a quantity

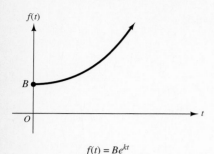

$$f(t) = Be^{kt}$$

FIGURE 2

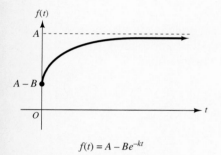

$$f(t) = A - Be^{-kt}$$

FIGURE 3

increases at a rate proportional to the difference between a fixed positive number A and its size. A mathematical model for this bounded growth is

$$f(t) = A - Be^{-kt} \qquad (5)$$

where B and k are positive constants and $A - B \leq f(t) < A$ for $t \geq 0$. Graphs of (4) and (5) are sketched in Figures 2 and 3, respectively.

Consider now the growth of a population that is affected by the environment imposing an upper bound on its size. For instance, space or reproduction may be factors limited by the environment. In such cases a mathematical model of the form (4) does not apply because the population does not increase beyond a certain point. A model that takes into account environmental factors is obtained when a quantity is increasing at a rate that is jointly proportional to its size and the difference between a fixed positive number A and its size. Thus if y units is the amount of the quantity present at t units of time,

$$\frac{dy}{dt} = ky(A - y) \qquad (6)$$

where k is a positive constant, and $0 < y < A$ for $t \geq 0$. To solve (6) we first separate the variables and obtain

$$\frac{dy}{y(A - y)} = k \, dt$$

$$\int \frac{dy}{y(A - y)} = k \int dt \qquad (7)$$

Writing the integrand on the left as the sum of partial fractions gives

$$\frac{1}{y(A - y)} = \frac{1}{A}\left(\frac{1}{y} + \frac{1}{A - y}\right)$$

Thus

$$\int \frac{dy}{y(A - y)} = \frac{1}{A} \int \left(\frac{1}{y} + \frac{1}{A - y}\right) dy$$

$$= \frac{1}{A}(\ln|y| - \ln|A - y|) + C_1$$

Therefore, from (7), we have

$$\frac{1}{A}(\ln|y| - \ln|A - y|) = kt + C_2$$

$$\ln|A - y| - \ln|y| = -Akt - AC_2$$

$$\ln\left|\frac{A - y}{y}\right| = -Akt - AC_2$$

$$\left|\frac{A - y}{y}\right| = e^{-Akt}e^{-AC_2}$$

Because $0 < y < A$, $(A - y)/y > 0$. Therefore we can omit the absolute-value bars and with $B = e^{-AC_2}$ we have

$$A - y = Bye^{-Akt}$$
$$y(1 + Be^{-Akt}) = A$$
$$y = \frac{A}{1 + Be^{-Akt}} \qquad \qquad (8)$$

Letting $y = f(t)$, we write this equation as

$$f(t) = \frac{A}{1 + Be^{-Akt}} \qquad t \geq 0 \qquad (9)$$

where A, B, and k are positive constants. To sketch the graph of f, first consider $\lim_{t \to +\infty} f(t)$. From (9),

$$\lim_{t \to +\infty} f(t) = \frac{A}{1 + B \lim_{t \to +\infty} e^{-Akt}}$$
$$= \frac{A}{1 + B \cdot 0}$$
$$= A$$

and $f(t)$ is approaching A through values less than A. Therefore, the line A units above the t axis is a horizontal asymptote of the graph of f. Because $f(0) = A/(1 + B)$, the graph intersects the $f(t)$ axis at $A/(1 + B)$. In Exercise 44 you are asked to show that the graph of f has a point of inflection at $t = \dfrac{1}{Ak} \ln B$. With this information we sketch the graph shown in Figure 4. It is called a curve of *logistic growth*. Observe that when t is small, the graph is similar to the one for exponential growth in Figure 2, and as t increases the curve is analogous to that shown in Figure 3 for bounded growth.

An application of logistic growth in economics is the distribution of information about a particular product. Logistic growth is used by biologists to describe the spread of a disease and by sociologists to describe the spread of a rumor or joke.

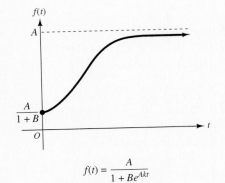

$$f(t) = \frac{A}{1 + Be^{Akt}}$$

FIGURE 4

▶ **EXAMPLE 3**   In a community of 45,000 people, the rate of growth of a flu epidemic is jointly proportional to the number of people who have contracted the flu and the number of people who have not contracted it. (a) If 200 people have the flu at the outbreak of the epidemic and 2800 have it now after 3 weeks, find a mathematical model describing the epidemic. (b) Plot the graph of the mathematical model on a graphics calculator. Estimate from the graph how many people are expected to have the flu (c) after 5 weeks, and (d) after 10 weeks. Confirm the estimates analytically. (e) If the epidemic continues indefinitely, how many people will contract the flu?

Table 1

t	0	3	5	10
y	200	2800	y_5	y_{10}

Solution

(a) If t weeks have elapsed since the outbreak of the epidemic and y people have the flu after t weeks, then

$$\frac{dy}{dt} = ky(45{,}000 - y) \qquad (10)$$

where k is a constant and $0 < y < 45{,}000$ for $t \geq 0$. We have the boundary conditions given in Table 1, where y_5 and y_{10} are the number of people having the flu after 5 weeks and 10 weeks, respectively.

Differential equation (10) is of the form of (6), and its general solution is of the form of (8). Therefore the general solution of (10) is

$$y = \frac{45{,}000}{1 + Be^{-45{,}000kt}} \qquad (11)$$

Because $y = 200$ when $t = 0$, from (11) we get

$$200 = \frac{45{,}000}{1 + Be^0}$$

$$1 + B = 225$$

$$B = 224$$

Substituting this value of B in (11) we obtain

$$y = \frac{45{,}000}{1 + 224e^{-45{,}000kt}} \qquad (12)$$

When $t = 3$, $y = 2800$. Thus from (12) we get

$$2800 = \frac{45{,}000}{1 + 224e^{-135{,}000k}}$$

$$1 + 224e^{-135{,}000k} = \frac{45{,}000}{2800}$$

$$1 + 224e^{-135{,}000k} = 16.0714$$

$$e^{-135{,}000k} = \frac{15.0714}{224}$$

$$-135{,}000k = \ln 0.0672830$$

$$k = -\frac{\ln 0.0672830}{135{,}000}$$

Substituting this value of k in (12) we obtain

$$y = \frac{45{,}000}{1 + 224e^{-0.899616t}} \qquad (13)$$

which is the mathematical model desired.

(b) Figure 5 shows the graph of (13) plotted in the [0, 15] by [0, 50,000] window. Using trace and zoom-in, we estimate that (c) when $t = 5$, $y = 12{,}882$ and (d) when $t = 10$, $y = 43{,}785$. We now confirm these estimates analytically.

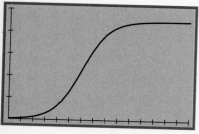

[0, 15] by [0, 50,000]

$$y = \frac{45{,}000}{1 + 224e^{-0.899616t}}$$

FIGURE 5

(c) Because $y = y_5$ when $t = 5$,

$$y_5 = \frac{45,000}{1 + 224e^{-4.49808}}$$

$$= 12,882.2$$

(d) Because $y = y_{10}$ when $t = 10$,

$$y_{10} = \frac{45,000}{1 + 224e^{-8.99616}}$$

$$= 43,785.0$$

These values confirm our estimates.

Conclusion: After 5 weeks, 12,882 people are expected to have the flu, and after 10 weeks, 43,785 are expected to have it.

(e) We compute $\lim\limits_{t \to +\infty} y$.

$$\lim_{t \to +\infty} \frac{45,000}{1 + 224e^{-0.899616t}} = \frac{45,000}{1 + 224 \cdot 0}$$

$$= 45,000$$

Conclusion: The entire community of 45,000 will contract the flu if the epidemic continues indefinitely. ◀

▶ **EXAMPLE 4** In Example 6 of Section 1.3 and Example 4 of Section 3.2, we had the following situation: In a community of 8000 people, the rate at which a rumor spreads is jointly proportional to the number of people who have heard the rumor and the number of people who have not heard it. When 20 people have heard the rumor, it is being spread at the rate of 200 people per hour. **(a)** If 4 people heard the rumor initially, find a mathematical model expressing the number of people who have heard the rumor as a function of the number of hours the rumor has been spreading. Determine how many people have heard the rumor after **(b)** 5 min, **(c)** 15 min, **(d)** 30 min, **(e)** 1 hr, and **(f)** 1 hr 30 min. **(g)** Show that the entire community has heard the rumor within 2 hr. **(h)** Use the answer in Example 4 of Section 3.2 to find how long until the rumor is being spread at the greatest rate.

Solution In Example 6 of Section 1.3 we showed that if $f(x)$ people per hour is the rate at which the rumor is spreading when x people have heard it,

$$f(x) = \frac{1}{798} x(8000 - x)$$

Let us now denote the rate by dx/dt, instead of $f(x)$, so that the spread of the rumor is described by the differential equation

$$\frac{dx}{dt} = \frac{1}{798} x(8000 - x) \tag{14}$$

(a) Differential equation (14) is of the form of (6) with $A = 8000$ and $k = \frac{1}{798}$. Therefore from (8), the general solution of (14), with x replaced by $g(t)$, is

$$g(t) = \frac{8000}{1 + Be^{-(8000/798)t}} \tag{15}$$

Note that $g(t)$ people have heard the rumor when the rumor has been spreading for t hours. Because 4 people heard the rumor initially, $g(0) = 4$. Thus

$$4 = \frac{8000}{1 + Be^0}$$

$$1 + B = 2000$$

$$B = 1999$$

Substituting this value of B in (15) gives us the required mathematical model:

$$g(t) = \frac{8000}{1 + 1999e^{-(8000/798)t}} \tag{16}$$

In parts (b)–(f), because t is measured in hours we convert the indicated time to hours and compute the required function values:

(b) $g(\frac{1}{12}) = 9.2$ **(c)** $g(0.25) = 48.8$ **(d)** $g(0.5) = 559.4$
(e) $g(1) = 7349.5$ **(f)** $g(1.5) = 7995$

Conclusion: In 5 min, 9 people have heard the rumor; in 15 min, 48 people have heard it; in 30 min, 559 people have heard it; in 1 hr, 7349 people have heard it; and in 1 hr 30 min, 7995 people have heard it.

(g) We compute $g(2) = 7999.97$, from which we can safely assume that the entire community of 8000 has heard the rumor within 2 hr.

(h) In Example 4 of Section 3.2, we showed that the rumor is being spread at the greatest rate when 4000 people, half of the population, have heard the rumor. We wish to determine the value of t for which $g(t) = 4000$. Substituting 4000 for $g(t)$ in (16) gives

$$4000 = \frac{8000}{1 + 1999e^{-(8000/798)t}}$$

$$1 + 1999e^{-(8000/798)t} = 2$$

$$e^{-(8000/798)t} = \frac{1}{1999}$$

$$e^{(8000/798)t} = 1999$$

$$\frac{8000t}{798} = \ln 1999$$

$$t = \frac{798 \ln 1999}{8000}$$

$$t = 0.75814$$

Converting 0.75814 hr to minutes gives 45.5 min.

Conclusion: The rumor is being spread at the greatest rate 45.5 min after it began, at which time half the population has heard it. ◀

In chemistry, the *law of mass action* for second-order reactions affords an application of integration that leads to the use of partial fractions. Under certain conditions a substance A reacts with a substance B to form a third substance C in such a way that the rate of change of the amount of C is proportional to the product of the amounts of A and B remaining at any given time.

Suppose that initially there are α grams of A and β grams of B and that r grams of A combine with s grams of B to form $(r + s)$ grams of C. If x grams of substance C is present at t units of time, then C contains $rx/(r + s)$ grams of A and $sx/(r + s)$ grams of B. The number of grams of substance A remaining is then $\alpha - rx/(r + s)$, and the number of grams of substance B remaining is $\beta - sx/(r + s)$. Therefore the law of mass action gives

$$\frac{dx}{dt} = K\left(\alpha - \frac{rx}{r + s}\right)\left(\beta - \frac{sx}{r + s}\right)$$

where K is the constant of proportionality. This equation can be written as

$$\frac{dx}{dt} = \frac{Krs}{(r + s)^2}\left(\frac{r + s}{r}\alpha - x\right)\left(\frac{r + s}{s}\beta - x\right)$$

Letting

$$k = \frac{Krs}{(r + s)^2} \qquad a = \frac{r + s}{r}\alpha \qquad b = \frac{r + s}{s}\beta$$

this equation becomes

$$\frac{dx}{dt} = k(a - x)(b - x) \tag{17}$$

We can separate the variables in (17) and get

$$\frac{dx}{(a - x)(b - x)} = k\,dt$$

If $a = b$, then the left side of the above equation can be integrated by the power formula. If $a \neq b$, partial fractions can be used for the integration.

Table 2

t	0	10	15
x	0	2	x_{15}

▶ **EXAMPLE 5**   A chemical reaction causes a substance A to combine with a substance B to form a substance C so that the law of mass action is obeyed. If in Equation (17) $a = 8$ and $b = 6$, and 2 g of substance C are formed in 10 min, how many grams of C are formed in 15 min?

Solution   If x grams of substance C is present at t minutes, we have the boundary conditions shown in Table 2, where x_{15} grams of substance C is present at 15 min. Equation (17) becomes

$$\frac{dx}{dt} = k(8 - x)(6 - x)$$

Separating the variables we have

$$\int \frac{dx}{(8 - x)(6 - x)} = k \int dt \tag{18}$$

Writing the integrand as the sum of partial fractions gives

$$\frac{1}{(8 - x)(6 - x)} = \frac{A}{8 - x} + \frac{B}{6 - x}$$

$$1 = A(6 - x) + B(8 - x)$$

Substituting 6 for x gives $B = \frac{1}{2}$, and substituting 8 for x gives $A = -\frac{1}{2}$. Hence we write (18) as

$$-\frac{1}{2} \int \frac{dx}{8 - x} + \frac{1}{2} \int \frac{dx}{6 - x} = k \int dt$$

Integrating we have

$$\frac{1}{2} \ln|8 - x| - \frac{1}{2} \ln|6 - x| + \frac{1}{2} \ln|C| = kt$$

$$\ln\left|\frac{6 - x}{C(8 - x)}\right| = -2kt$$

$$\frac{6 - x}{8 - x} = Ce^{-2kt}$$

Substituting $x = 0$, $t = 0$ in this equation gives $C = \frac{3}{4}$. Thus

$$\frac{6 - x}{8 - x} = \frac{3}{4} e^{-2kt} \tag{19}$$

Substituting $x = 2$, $t = 10$ in (19) we have

$$\frac{4}{6} = \frac{3}{4} e^{-20k}$$

$$e^{-20k} = \frac{8}{9}$$

Substituting $x = x_{15}$, $t = 15$ into (19) we get

$$\frac{6 - x_{15}}{8 - x_{15}} = \frac{3}{4} e^{-30k}$$

$$4(6 - x_{15}) = 3(e^{-20k})^{3/2}(8 - x_{15})$$

$$24 - 4x_{15} = 3(\tfrac{8}{9})^{3/2}(8 - x_{15})$$

$$24 - 4x_{15} = \frac{16\sqrt{2}}{9}(8 - x_{15})$$

$$x_{15} = \frac{54 - 32\sqrt{2}}{9 - 4\sqrt{2}}$$

$$x_{15} \approx 2.6$$

<u>Conclusion:</u>   In 15 min 2.6 g of substance C will be formed.   ◄

In the following example one of the factors in the denominator is quadratic. Again refer to Appendix Section A.11 for the procedure for the partial fraction decomposition in such a case.

▶ ***EXAMPLE 6***   Use the NINT capability of a graphics calculator to approximate to six significant digits the value of

$$\int_2^3 \frac{x^2 - x - 5}{(x - 1)(x^2 + 2x + 2)} \, dx$$

Confirm the answer analytically.

Solution On our graphics calculator, we compute

$$\text{NINT}\left(\frac{x^2 - x - 5}{(x - 1)(x^2 + 2x + 2)}, 2, 3\right) = -0.0857470$$

To confirm our answer we evaluate the definite integral by using the partial fraction decomposition from Illustration 3 of Appendix Section A.11. We have

$$\int_2^3 \frac{x^2 - x - 5}{(x - 1)(x^2 + 2x + 2)} \, dx$$

$$= \int_2^3 \frac{2x \, dx}{x^2 + 2x + 2} + 3 \int_2^3 \frac{dx}{x^2 + 2x + 2} - \int_2^3 \frac{dx}{x - 1} \qquad (20)$$

To integrate $\int (2x \, dx)/(x^2 + 2x + 2)$, we observe that the differential of the denominator is $(2x + 2) \, dx$; so we add and subtract 2 in the numerator, thereby giving

$$\int \frac{2x \, dx}{x^2 + 2x + 2} = \int \frac{(2x + 2) \, dx}{x^2 + 2x + 2} - 2 \int \frac{dx}{x^2 + 2x + 2}$$

Substituting from this equation into (20), combining terms, and writing $x^2 + 2x + 2$ as $(x + 1)^2 + 1$, we get

$$\int_2^3 \frac{x^2 - x - 5}{(x - 1)(x^2 + 2x + 2)} \, dx$$

$$= \int_2^3 \frac{(2x + 2) \, dx}{x^2 + 2x + 2} + \int_2^3 \frac{dx}{(x + 1)^2 + 1} - \int_2^3 \frac{dx}{x - 1}$$

$$= \ln\left| x^2 + 2x + 2 \right| + \tan^{-1}(x + 1) - \ln\left| x - 1 \right| \Big]_2^3$$

$$= \ln\left| \frac{x^2 + 2x + 2}{x - 1} \right| + \tan^{-1}(x + 1) \Big]_2^3$$

$$= \ln\tfrac{17}{2} + \tan^{-1} 4 - \ln 10 - \tan^{-1} 3$$

$$= -0.0857470$$

which confirms our answer. ◀

EXERCISES 7.4

In Exercises 1 through 20, evaluate the indefinite integral and, if you wish, use your graphics calculator to support your answer either numerically or graphically.

1. $\displaystyle\int \frac{dx}{x^2 - 4}$

2. $\displaystyle\int \frac{5x - 1}{x^2 - 1} \, dx$

3. $\displaystyle\int \frac{4w - 11}{2w^2 + 7w - 4} \, dw$

4. $\displaystyle\int \frac{4x - 2}{x^3 - x^2 - 2x} \, dx$

5. $\displaystyle\int \frac{x^2}{x^2 + x - 6} \, dx$

6. $\displaystyle\int \frac{9t^2 - 26t - 5}{3t^2 - 5t - 2} \, dt$

Hint for Exercises 5 and 6: Divide numerator by denominator.

7. $\displaystyle\int \frac{dt}{(t + 2)^2(t + 1)}$

8. $\displaystyle\int \frac{3x^2 - x + 1}{x^3 - x^2} \, dx$

9. $\displaystyle\int \frac{dx}{x^3 + 3x^2}$

10. $\displaystyle\int \frac{w^2 + 4w - 1}{w^3 - w} \, dw$

11. $\displaystyle\int \frac{6x^2 - 2x - 1}{4x^3 - x} \, dx$

12. $\displaystyle\int \frac{dx}{2x^3 + x}$

13. $\displaystyle\int \frac{x+4}{x^3+4x}\,dx$

14. $\displaystyle\int \frac{3t}{2t^4+5t^2+2}\,dt$

15. $\displaystyle\int \frac{dx}{16x^4-1}$

16. $\displaystyle\int \frac{dx}{9x^4+x^2}$

17. $\displaystyle\int \frac{x^2+x}{x^3-x^2+x-1}\,dx$

18. $\displaystyle\int \frac{2x^2+3x+2}{x^3+4x^2+6x+4}\,dx$

19. $\displaystyle\int \frac{\sec^2 t(\sec^2 t+1)}{\tan^3 t+1}\,dt$

20. $\displaystyle\int \frac{e^{5x}}{(e^{2x}+1)^2}\,dx$

In Exercises 21 through 26, find the exact value of the definite integral and support your answer by the NINT capability of your graphics calculator.

21. $\displaystyle\int_1^2 \frac{x-3}{x^3+x^2}\,dx$

22. $\displaystyle\int_0^4 \frac{x+4}{2x^2+5x+2}\,dx$

23. $\displaystyle\int_1^3 \frac{x^2-4x+3}{x^3+2x^2+x}\,dx$

24. $\displaystyle\int_1^4 \frac{2x^2+13x+18}{x^3+6x^2+9x}\,dx$

25. $\displaystyle\int_1^4 \frac{4+5x^2}{4x+x^3}\,dx$

26. $\displaystyle\int_0^1 \frac{x\,dx}{x^3+2x^2+x+2}$

In Exercises 27 through 32, use the NINT capability of your graphics calculator to estimate to six significant digits the value of the definite integral. Confirm your answer analytically.

27. $\displaystyle\int_1^2 \frac{5x^2-3x+18}{9x-x^3}\,dx$

28. $\displaystyle\int_3^4 \frac{5x^3-4x}{x^4-16}\,dx$

29. $\displaystyle\int_0^1 \frac{x^2+3x+3}{x^3+x^2+x+1}\,dx$

30. $\displaystyle\int_0^{0.5} \frac{1+t}{1-t^3}\,dt$

31. $\displaystyle\int_{\ln 2}^{\ln 3} \frac{12}{e^{2t}+16}\,dt$

32. $\displaystyle\int_{\pi/6}^{\pi/2} \frac{\cos x}{\sin x+\sin^3 x}\,dx$

33. Find the area of the region bounded by the curve $y=(x-1)/(x^2-5x+6)$, the x axis, and the lines $x=4$ and $x=6$.

34. Find the area of the region in the first quadrant bounded by the curve $(x+2)^2 y=4-x$.

35. Find the volume of the solid of revolution generated by revolving the region in Exercise 33 about the y axis.

36. Find the volume of the solid of revolution generated if the region in Exercise 34 is revolved about the x axis.

37. Find the centroid of the region bounded by the curve $y=(x-1)/(x^2-5x+6)$, the x axis, and the lines $x=4$ and $x=6$.

38. Find the centroid of the region in the first quadrant bounded by the curve $(x+2)^2 y=4-x$.

39. Find the area of the region bounded by the x axis, the y axis, the curve $y(x^2+1)^3=x^3$, and the line $x=1$.

40. Find the area of the region bounded by the x axis, the y axis, the curve $y(x^3+8)=4$, and the line $x=1$.

41. Find the volume of the solid of revolution generated by revolving the region of Exercise 40 about the y axis.

42. Find the abscissa of the centroid of the region of Exercise 40.

43. Use methods previous to those in this section (i.e., without partial fractions) to evaluate the integrals:

(a) $\displaystyle\int \frac{(x^2-4x+6)\,dx}{x^3-6x^2+18x}$

(b) $\displaystyle\int \frac{3x+1}{(x+2)^4}\,dx$

44. Show that the graph of the function f defined by (9) has a point of inflection at $t=\dfrac{1}{Ak}\ln B$ and that $y=\frac{1}{2}A$ at that point.

45. One day on a college campus, when 10,000 people were in attendance, a particular student heard that a certain controversial speaker was going to make an unscheduled appearance. This information was told to friends who in turn related it to others, and the rate of growth of the spread of this information was jointly proportional to the number of people who heard it and the number of people who had not heard it. (a) If after 10 min, 288 people had heard the rumor, find a mathematical model describing the spread of information. (b) Plot the graph of the mathematical model on your graphics calculator. Estimate from the graph how many people had heard the rumor (c) after 15 min and (d) after 20 min. Confirm the estimates analytically. (e) How many people will eventually hear the rumor?

46. Exercise 26 of Exercises 1.3 and Exercise 12 of Exercises 3.2 pertained to the following situation: In a limited environment where 1 million bacteria is the optimum number supportable, the rate of bacterial growth is jointly proportional to the number present and the difference between 1 million and the number present. (a) If 500 bacteria are present initially, find a mathematical model expressing the number of bacteria present as a function of the number of minutes the bacteria have been growing. Determine how many bacteria are present after (b) 30 min, (c) 1 hr, (d) 90 min, (e) 2 hr, and (f) 150 min. (g) Show that the optimum number of 1 million bacteria is present within 7 hr. (h) Use the answer in Exercise 12 of Exercises 3.2 to find how long until the bacteria are growing at the greatest rate. Compare your result with that of Exercise 44.

47. Exercise 27 of Exercises 1.3 and Exercise 13 of Exercises 3.2 pertained to the following situation: Suppose the rate of growth of an epidemic in Fort Bragg, a small town in northern California of population 5000, is jointly proportional to the number of people infected and the number of people not infected.
(a) If 20 people are infected initially, find a mathematical model expressing the number of people infected as a function of the number of days the epidemic has been growing. If the epidemic is not halted, determine how many people will be infected after **(b)** 10 days, **(c)** 20 days, **(d)** 30 days, and **(e)** 60 days. **(f)** Show that if the epidemic is not halted, the entire population of Fort Bragg will be infected within 6 months. **(g)** Use the answer in Exercise 13 of Exercises 3.2 to find in how many days the epidemic will be growing at the greatest rate. Compare your result with that of Exercise 44.

48. At 8 A.M. in Fort Bragg (see Exercise 47) 500 residents heard a radio announcement about a local political scandal. The rate of growth of the spread of information about the scandal was jointly proportional to the number of people who had heard it and the number of people who had not heard it. **(a)** If at 9 A.M. 2000 residents had heard about the scandal, find a mathematical model describing the spread of information. **(b)** Plot the graph of the mathematical model on your graphics calculator. Estimate from the graph **(c)** how many residents had heard about the scandal at 10 A.M., and **(d)** at what time half the population had heard about it. Confirm your estimates analytically. **(e)** Show that by 3 P.M. the entire population had heard about the scandal.

49. The population of Mendocino, a village near Fort Bragg, fluctuates from day to day because of the significant number of tourists who visit the community. On the day the political scandal of Exercise 48 broke, suppose the population of Mendocino was A, and 20 percent of that population heard the 8 A.M. radio announcement. Just as in Fort Bragg, the rate of growth in Mendocino of the spread of information about the scandal was jointly proportional to the number of people who had heard it and the number of people who had not heard it. If at 9 A.M., 50 percent of the Mendocino population had heard about the scandal, at what time had 80 percent of the population heard about it?

50. In a community in which A people are susceptible to a particular virus, the rate of growth of the spread of the virus was jointly proportional to the number of people who had caught the virus and the number of susceptible people who had not caught it. If 10 percent of those susceptible had the virus initially and 25 percent had been infected after 3 weeks, what percent of those susceptible had been infected after 6 weeks?

51. Suppose in Example 5 that $a = 5$ and $b = 4$ and 1 g of substance C is formed in 5 min. How many grams of C are formed in 10 min?

52. Suppose in Example 5 that $a = 6$ and $b = 3$ and 1 g of substance C is formed in 4 min. How long will it take 2 g of substance C to be formed?

53. At any instant the rate at which a substance dissolves is proportional to the product of the amount of the substance present at that instant and the difference between the concentration of the substance in solution at that instant and the concentration of the substance in a saturated solution. A quantity of insoluble material is mixed with 10 lb of salt initially, and the salt is dissolving in a tank containing 20 gal of water. If 5 lb of salt dissolves in 10 min and the concentration of salt in a saturated solution is 3 lb/gal, how much salt will dissolve in 20 min?

54. A manufacturer who began operations four years ago has determined that income from sales has increased steadily at the rate of $\dfrac{t^3 + 3t^2 + 6t + 7}{t^2 + 3t + 2}$ millions of dollars per year, where t is the number of years that the company has been operating. It is estimated that the total income from sales will increase at the same rate for the next 2 years. If the total income from sales for the year just ended was $6 million, what is the total income from sales expected for the period ending 1 year from now? Give the answer to the nearest $100.

55. A particle is moving along a line so that if v centimeters per second is the velocity of the particle at t seconds, then
$$v = \frac{t^2 - t + 1}{(t + 2)^2(t^2 + 1)}$$
Find a formula for the distance traveled by the particle from the time when $t = 0$ to the time when $t = t_1$.

56. A particle is moving along a line so that if v feet per second is the velocity of the particle at t seconds, then
$$v = \frac{t + 3}{t^2 + 3t + 2}$$
Find the distance traveled by the particle from the time when $t = 0$ to the time when $t = 2$.

57. Compare the curve of logistic growth with the curves of exponential growth and bounded growth. How do they differ and how are they similar?

7.5 INTEGRATION BY OTHER SUBSTITUTION TECHNIQUES AND TABLES

We wind up our discussion of techniques of integration by showing how particular substitutions can be employed in certain situations.

If an integrand involves fractional powers of a variable x, the integrand can be simplified by the substitution

$$x = z^n$$

where n is the lowest common denominator of the denominators of the exponents. This substitution is illustrated in the following example.

▶ **EXAMPLE 1**   Evaluate

$$\int \frac{\sqrt{x}\, dx}{1 + \sqrt[3]{x}}$$

Solution   We let $x = z^6$; then $dx = 6z^5\, dz$. So

$$\int \frac{x^{1/2}\, dx}{1 + x^{1/3}} = \int \frac{z^3(6z^5\, dz)}{1 + z^2}$$

$$= 6 \int \frac{z^8}{z^2 + 1}\, dz$$

Dividing the numerator by the denominator we have

$$\int \frac{x^{1/2}\, dx}{1 + x^{1/3}} = 6 \int \left(z^6 - z^4 + z^2 - 1 + \frac{1}{z^2 + 1} \right) dz$$

$$= 6(\tfrac{1}{7}z^7 - \tfrac{1}{5}z^5 + \tfrac{1}{3}z^3 - z + \tan^{-1} z) + C$$

$$= \tfrac{6}{7}x^{7/6} - \tfrac{6}{5}x^{5/6} + 2x^{1/2} - 6x^{1/6} + 6 \tan^{-1} x^{1/6} + C \quad ◀$$

No general rule can be given to determine a substitution that will result in a simpler integrand. The following example shows another situation where we rationalize the given integrand.

▶ **EXAMPLE 2**   Evaluate

$$\int x^5 \sqrt{x^2 + 4}\, dx$$

Solution   Let $z = \sqrt{x^2 + 4}$. Then $z^2 = x^2 + 4$, and $2z\, dz = 2x\, dx$. So

$$\int x^5 \sqrt{x^2 + 4}\, dx = \int (x^2)^2 \sqrt{x^2 + 4}\, (x\, dx)$$

$$= \int (z^2 - 4)^2 z(z\, dz)$$

$$= \int (z^6 - 8z^4 + 16z^2)\, dz$$

$$= \tfrac{1}{7}z^7 - \tfrac{8}{5}z^5 + \tfrac{16}{3}z^3 + C$$
$$= \tfrac{1}{105}z^3[15z^4 - 168z^2 + 560] + C$$
$$= \tfrac{1}{105}(x^2 + 4)^{3/2}[15(x^2 + 4)^2 - 168(x^2 + 4) + 560] + C$$
$$= \tfrac{1}{105}(x^2 + 4)^{3/2}(15x^4 - 48x^2 + 128) + C \qquad \blacktriangleleft$$

If an integrand is a rational function of $\sin x$ and $\cos x$, it can be reduced to a rational function of z by the substitution

$$z = \tan \tfrac{1}{2}x$$

as we will show by an example. To obtain the formulas for $\sin x$ and $\cos x$ in terms of z we use the following identities: $\sin 2y = 2 \sin y \cos y$ and $\cos 2y = 2 \cos^2 y - 1$ with $y = \tfrac{1}{2}x$. We have, then,

$$\sin x = 2 \sin \tfrac{1}{2}x \cos \tfrac{1}{2}x \qquad\qquad \cos x = 2 \cos^2 \tfrac{1}{2}x - 1$$

$$= 2 \cdot \frac{\sin \tfrac{1}{2}x \cos^2 \tfrac{1}{2}x}{\cos \tfrac{1}{2}x} \qquad\qquad = \frac{2}{\sec^2 \tfrac{1}{2}x} - 1$$

$$= 2 \tan \tfrac{1}{2}x \cdot \frac{1}{\sec^2 \tfrac{1}{2}x} \qquad\qquad = \frac{2}{1 + \tan^2 \tfrac{1}{2}x} - 1$$

$$= \frac{2 \tan \tfrac{1}{2}x}{1 + \tan^2 \tfrac{1}{2}x} \qquad\qquad = \frac{2}{1 + z^2} - 1$$

$$= \frac{2z}{1 + z^2} \qquad\qquad = \frac{1 - z^2}{1 + z^2}$$

Because $z = \tan \tfrac{1}{2}x$,

$$dz = \tfrac{1}{2} \sec^2 \tfrac{1}{2}x \, dx$$
$$= \tfrac{1}{2}(1 + \tan^2 \tfrac{1}{2}x) \, dx$$

Thus

$$dx = \frac{2 \, dz}{1 + z^2}$$

We state these results as a theorem.

7.5.1 Theorem

If $z = \tan \tfrac{1}{2}x$, then

$$\sin x = \frac{2z}{1 + z^2} \qquad\qquad \cos x = \frac{1 - z^2}{1 + z^2} \qquad\qquad dx = \frac{2 \, dz}{1 + z^2}$$

▶ **EXAMPLE 3** Use the NINT capability of a graphics calculator to approximate to six significant digits the value of

$$\int_0^{\pi/4} \frac{dx}{1 - \sin x + \cos x}$$

Confirm the answer analytically.

Solution On our graphics calculator, we compute

$$\text{NINT}\left(\frac{1}{1 - \sin x + \cos x}, 0, \pi/4\right) = 0.534800$$

To confirm this answer analytically, we evaluate the indefinite integral by letting $z = \tan \frac{1}{2}x$ and applying the formulas of Theorem 7.5.1.

$$\int \frac{dx}{1 - \sin x + \cos x} = \int \frac{\dfrac{2\,dz}{1 + z^2}}{1 - \dfrac{2z}{1 + z^2} + \dfrac{1 - z^2}{1 + z^2}}$$

$$= 2 \int \frac{dz}{(1 + z^2) - 2z + (1 - z^2)}$$

$$= 2 \int \frac{dz}{2 - 2z}$$

$$= \int \frac{dz}{1 - z}$$

$$= -\ln|1 - z| + C$$

$$= -\ln\left|1 - \tan \frac{1}{2}x\right| + C$$

Therefore

$$\int_0^{\pi/4} \frac{dx}{1 - \sin x + \cos x} = -\ln\left|1 - \tan \frac{1}{2}x\right|\Big]_0^{\pi/4}$$

$$= -\ln\left|1 - \tan \frac{1}{8}\pi\right|$$

$$= 0.534800$$

which confirms our answer.   ◄

► **EXAMPLE 4** Let $z = \tan \frac{1}{2}x$ to evaluate

$$\int \sec x \, dx$$

Solution With $z = \tan \frac{1}{2}x$ and the formulas of Theorem 7.5.1. we have

$$\int \sec x \, dx = \int \frac{dx}{\cos x}$$

$$= \int \frac{2\,dz}{1 + z^2} \cdot \frac{1 + z^2}{1 - z^2}$$

$$= 2 \int \frac{dz}{1 - z^2}$$

$$= \ln\left|\frac{1 + z}{1 - z}\right| + C \qquad \text{(from (3) in Section 7.4)}$$

$$= \ln\left|\frac{1 + \tan \frac{1}{2}x}{1 - \tan \frac{1}{2}x}\right| + C$$ ◄

The value of $\int \sec x \, dx$ from Example 4 can be written in another form by letting $1 = \tan \frac{1}{4}\pi$ and using the trigonometric identity

$$\tan(a + b) = \frac{\tan a + \tan b}{1 - \tan a \tan b}$$

Thus

$$\int \sec x \, dx = \ln \left| \frac{\tan \frac{1}{4}\pi + \tan \frac{1}{2}x}{1 - \tan \frac{1}{4}\pi \cdot \tan \frac{1}{2}x} \right| + C$$

$$\int \sec x \, dx = \ln \left| \tan(\tfrac{1}{4}\pi + \tfrac{1}{2}x) \right| + C \qquad (1)$$

This formula appears in the Table of Integrals on the back endpapers along with the following one from Theorem 5.3.5:

$$\int \sec x \, dx = \ln|\sec x + \tan x| + C$$

which was obtained by multiplying the numerator and denominator of the integrand by $\sec x + \tan x$. Still another formula for this integral is

$$\int \sec x \, dx = \frac{1}{2} \ln\left(\frac{1 + \sin x}{1 - \sin x}\right) + C \qquad (2)$$

You are asked to derive this formula in Exercise 67.

When an integrand has an antiderivative defined explicitly in terms of elementary functions, the indefinite integral is said to be expressed in **closed form.** You have learned a number of techniques of integration that can be applied to obtain a closed-form expression of an indefinite integral. Occasions may arise, however, when these techniques are either not sufficient or else lead to a complicated integration. In such cases you may wish to use a table of integrals. Fairly complete tables of integrals appear in mathematical handbooks. Shorter tables can be found in most calculus textbooks.

Now that computer programs and some calculators can compute antiderivatives and calculators can approximate values of definite integrals, tables of integrals are not as important as they were in the past. Even so you should still learn how to use such a table and you may find it necessary to employ some of the integration techniques to express the integrand in a form found in a table.

The formulas used in the examples and exercises of this section appear in the Table of Integrals on the endpapers of this book. Observe that in the table, the headings indicate the form of the integrand. The five formulas listed under the first heading, *Some Elementary Forms*, are basic. The following example utilizes one of the formulas listed under the second heading, *Rational Forms Containing $a + bu$.*

▶ **EXAMPLE 5** Evaluate

$$\int \frac{x \, dx}{(4 - x)^3}$$

Solution   Formula 10 in the Table of Integrals is

$$\int \frac{u \, du}{(a + bu)^3} = \frac{1}{b^2} \left[\frac{a}{2(a + bu)^2} - \frac{1}{a + bu} \right] + C$$

Using this formula with $u = x$, $a = 4$, and $b = -1$ we have

$$\int \frac{x \, dx}{(4 - x)^3} = \frac{1}{(-1)^2} \left[\frac{4}{2(4 - x)^2} - \frac{1}{4 - x} \right] + C$$

$$= \frac{2}{(4 - x)^2} - \frac{1}{4 - x} + C \qquad \blacktriangleleft$$

▶ **EXAMPLE 6**   Evaluate

$$\int \frac{e^x}{6 - 2e^{2x}} \, dx$$

Solution   By substituting $u = e^x$ and $du = e^x \, dx$, the given integral becomes

$$\int \frac{du}{6 - 2u^2} \qquad\qquad (3)$$

Formula 25 in the table is

$$\int \frac{du}{a^2 - u^2} = \frac{1}{2a} \ln\left|\frac{u + a}{u - a}\right| + C \qquad\qquad (4)$$

This formula can be applied if the coefficient of u^2 in integral (3) is 1 instead of 2. Thus we write

$$\int \frac{du}{6 - 2u^2} = \frac{1}{2} \int \frac{du}{3 - u^2}$$

To the integral on the right side we apply (4) with $a = \sqrt{3}$, and we have

$$\int \frac{du}{6 - 2u^2} = \frac{1}{2} \cdot \frac{1}{2\sqrt{3}} \ln\left|\frac{u + \sqrt{3}}{u - \sqrt{3}}\right| + C$$

Replacing u by e^x gives

$$\int \frac{e^x}{6 - 2e^{2x}} \, dx = \frac{\sqrt{3}}{12} \ln\left|\frac{e^x + \sqrt{3}}{e^x - \sqrt{3}}\right| + C \qquad \blacktriangleleft$$

▶ **EXAMPLE 7**   Evaluate

$$\int \frac{\sqrt{8x - 3x^2}}{x} \, dx$$

Solution   Formula 51 in the table is

$$\int \frac{\sqrt{2au - u^2}}{u} \, du = \sqrt{2au - u^2} + a \cos^{-1}\left(1 - \frac{u}{a}\right) + C \qquad (5)$$

To apply this formula, we first factor the numerator of the given integral.

$$\int \frac{\sqrt{8x - 3x^2}}{x}\, dx = \int \frac{\sqrt{3}\sqrt{\frac{8}{3}x - x^2}}{x}\, dx$$

$$= \sqrt{3} \int \frac{\sqrt{2(\frac{4}{3})x - x^2}}{x}\, dx$$

From formula (5) with $u = x$ and $a = \frac{4}{3}$, we obtain

$$\int \frac{\sqrt{8x - 3x^2}}{x}\, dx = \sqrt{3}\left[\sqrt{\tfrac{8}{3}x - x^2} + \tfrac{4}{3}\cos^{-1}\left(1 - \frac{x}{\frac{4}{3}}\right)\right] + C$$

$$= \sqrt{8x - 3x^2} + \frac{4}{\sqrt{3}}\cos^{-1}\left(1 - \frac{3}{4}x\right) + C \quad \blacktriangleleft$$

In the next example we apply a reduction formula from the Table of Integrals.

▶ **EXAMPLE 8**   Evaluate

$$\int \frac{\sqrt{3 + 4x}}{x}\, dx$$

Solution   Formula 22 from the table is

$$\int \frac{\sqrt{a + bu}}{u}\, du = 2\sqrt{a + bu} + a \int \frac{du}{u\sqrt{a + bu}}$$

From this formula with $u = x$, $a = 3$, and $b = 4$, we have

$$\int \frac{\sqrt{3 + 4x}}{x}\, dx = 2\sqrt{3 + 4x} + 3 \int \frac{dx}{x\sqrt{3 + 4x}} \qquad (6)$$

To evaluate the integral on the right-hand side of this equation we apply the logarithmic form of Formula 20 in the table:

$$\int \frac{du}{u\sqrt{a + bu}}\, du = \frac{1}{\sqrt{a}}\ln\left|\frac{\sqrt{a + bu} - \sqrt{a}}{\sqrt{a + bu} + \sqrt{a}}\right| + C \qquad \text{if } a > 0$$

With this formula and (6), we get

$$\int \frac{\sqrt{3 + 4x}}{x}\, dx = 2\sqrt{3 + 4x} + 3\,\frac{1}{\sqrt{3}}\ln\left|\frac{\sqrt{3 + 4x} - \sqrt{3}}{\sqrt{3 + 4x} + \sqrt{3}}\right| + C$$

$$= 2\sqrt{3 + 4x} + \sqrt{3}\ln\left|\frac{\sqrt{3 + 4x} - \sqrt{3}}{\sqrt{3 + 4x} + \sqrt{3}}\right| + C \quad \blacktriangleleft$$

EXERCISES 7.5

In Exercises 1 through 12, evaluate the indefinite integral. If you wish, use your graphics calculator to support your answer either numerically or graphically.

1. $\displaystyle\int \frac{x}{3 + \sqrt{x}}\, dx$

2. $\displaystyle\int \frac{dx}{\sqrt[3]{x} - x}$

3. $\displaystyle\int \frac{dx}{x\sqrt{1 + 4x}}$

4. $\displaystyle\int x(1 + x)^{2/3}\, dx$

5. $\displaystyle\int \frac{2x^5 + 3x^2}{\sqrt{1 + 2x^3}}\, dx$

6. $\displaystyle\int \frac{dx}{2\sqrt[3]{x} + \sqrt{x}}$

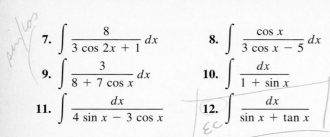

7. $\displaystyle\int \frac{8}{3\cos 2x + 1}\, dx$

8. $\displaystyle\int \frac{\cos x}{3\cos x - 5}\, dx$

9. $\displaystyle\int \frac{3}{8 + 7\cos x}\, dx$

10. $\displaystyle\int \frac{dx}{1 + \sin x}$

11. $\displaystyle\int \frac{dx}{4\sin x - 3\cos x}$

12. $\displaystyle\int \frac{dx}{\sin x + \tan x}$

In Exercises 13 through 18, use the NINT *capability of your graphics calculator to approximate to six significant digits the value of the definite integral. Confirm your answer analytically.*

13. $\displaystyle\int_0^4 \frac{dx}{1 + \sqrt{x}}$

14. $\displaystyle\int_0^1 \frac{x^{3/2}}{x + 1}\, dx$

15. $\displaystyle\int_{1/2}^2 \frac{dx}{\sqrt{2x}(\sqrt{2x} + 9)}$

16. $\displaystyle\int_{16}^{18} \frac{dx}{\sqrt{x} - \sqrt[4]{x^3}}$

17. $\displaystyle\int_0^{\pi/2} \frac{dx}{5\sin x + 3}$

18. $\displaystyle\int_0^{\pi/2} \frac{dx}{3 + \cos 2x}$

In Exercises 19 through 24, find the exact value of the definite integral and support your answer by the NINT *capability of your graphics calculator.*

19. $\displaystyle\int_{\pi/6}^{\pi/3} \frac{3\, dx}{2\sin 2x + 1}$

20. $\displaystyle\int_0^{\pi/4} \frac{8\, dx}{\tan x + 1}$

21. $\displaystyle\int_{-\pi/3}^{\pi/2} \frac{3\, dx}{2\cos x + 1}$

22. $\displaystyle\int_0^{\pi/2} \frac{\sin 2x\, dx}{2 + \cos x}$

23. $\displaystyle\int_0^1 \frac{\sqrt{x}}{1 + \sqrt[3]{x}}\, dx$

24. $\displaystyle\int_2^{11} \frac{x^3\, dx}{\sqrt[3]{x^2 + 4}}$

In Exercises 25 through 48, use the Table of Integrals on the endpapers to evaluate the integral. In Exercises 25 and 26, use one of the Formulas 6–13, where the integrand is a rational form containing a + bu.

25. $\displaystyle\int \frac{x^2}{(6 - x)^2}\, dx$

26. $\displaystyle\int \frac{x}{(5 - 2x)^3}\, dx$

In Exercises 27 and 28, use one of the Formulas 14–23, where the integrand is a form containing $\sqrt{a + bu}$.

27. $\displaystyle\int x\sqrt{1 + 2x}\, dx$

28. $\displaystyle\int \frac{dx}{x^2\sqrt{1 + 2x}}$

In Exercises 29 and 30, use one of the Formulas 24–26, where the integrand is a rational form containing $a^2 \pm u^2$.

29. $\displaystyle\int \frac{dx}{4 - x^2}$

30. $\displaystyle\int \frac{dx}{x^2 - 25}$

In Exercises 31 and 32, use one of the formulas 27–38, where the integrand is a form containing $\sqrt{u^2 \pm a^2}$.

31. $\displaystyle\int \frac{dx}{\sqrt{x^2 + 6x}}$

32. $\displaystyle\int \sqrt{4x^2 + 1}\, dx$

In Exercises 33 and 34, use one of the Formulas 39–48, where the integrand is a form containing $\sqrt{a^2 - u^2}$.

33. $\displaystyle\int \frac{\sqrt{9 - 4x^2}}{x}\, dx$

34. $\displaystyle\int \frac{dx}{x^2\sqrt{25 - 9x^2}}$

In Exercises 35 and 36, use one of the formulas 49–58, where the integrand is a form containing $2au - u^2$.

35. $\displaystyle\int x\sqrt{4x - x^2}\, dx$

36. $\displaystyle\int \frac{x^2}{\sqrt{4x - x^2}}\, dx$

In Exercises 37 through 40, use one of the Formulas 59–88, where the integrand is a form containing trigonometric functions.

37. $\displaystyle\int \sin^5 \theta\, d\theta$

38. $\displaystyle\int \cos^6 x\, dx$

39. $\displaystyle\int t^4 \cos t\, dt$

40. $\displaystyle\int \sin 3w \cos 5w\, dw$

In Exercises 41 and 42, use one of the Formulas 89–94, where the integrand is a form containing an inverse trigonometric function.

41. $\displaystyle\int \sec^{-1} 3x\, dx$

42. $\displaystyle\int \tan^{-1} 4t\, dt$

In Exercises 43 through 46, use one of the Formulas 95–106, where the integrand is a form containing an exponential or logarithmic function.

43. $\displaystyle\int x^2 e^{4x}\, dx$

44. $\displaystyle\int x^3\, 2^x\, dx$

45. $\displaystyle\int x^3 \ln(3x)\, dx$

46. $\displaystyle\int e^{2\theta} \sin 5\theta\, d\theta$

In Exercises 47 and 48, use one of the Formulas 107–124, where the integrand is a form containing a hyperbolic function.

47. $\displaystyle\int 3y \sinh 5y\, dy$

48. $\displaystyle\int e^{3x} \cosh 5x\, dx$

In Exercises 49 through 64, use the Table of Integrals on the endpapers to evaluate the definite integral.

49. $\displaystyle\int_1^2 \frac{dx}{x(5 - x)^2}$

50. $\displaystyle\int_0^3 \frac{x}{(1 + x)^2}\, dx$

51. $\displaystyle\int_0^3 \frac{x^2\, dx}{\sqrt{x^2 + 16}}$

52. $\displaystyle\int_0^2 \frac{dx}{(9 + 4x^2)^{3/2}}$

53. $\displaystyle\int_1^2 x^4 \ln x \, dx$

54. $\displaystyle\int_0^1 x^2 e^{-x} \, dx$

55. $\displaystyle\int_3^4 \sqrt{x^2 + 2x - 15} \, dx$

56. $\displaystyle\int_3^5 x^2 \sqrt{x^2 - 9} \, dx$

57. $\displaystyle\int_1^2 \sqrt{4w - w^2} \, dw$

58. $\displaystyle\int_0^{\pi/3} \sec^5 x \, dx$

59. $\displaystyle\int_{\pi/8}^{\pi/4} \sin 3t \sin 5t \, dt$

60. $\displaystyle\int_0^{\pi/4} \tan^6 \theta \, d\theta$

61. $\displaystyle\int_0^{\pi/2} \sin^3 2x \cos^3 2x \, dx$

62. $\displaystyle\int_5^6 \frac{dw}{w^2\sqrt{w^2 - 16}}$

63. $\displaystyle\int_0^1 x^3 e^{2x} \, dx$

64. $\displaystyle\int_0^{\pi/6} e^{2t} \sin 3t \, dt$

65. Evaluate $\displaystyle\int \frac{dx}{x - \sqrt{x}}$ by two methods: **(a)** Let $x = z^2$;
(b) write $x - \sqrt{x} = \sqrt{x}(\sqrt{x} - 1)$ and let $u = \sqrt{x} - 1$.

66. Use the substitution of this section, $z = \tan \frac{1}{2}x$, to show that $\int \sin x \, dx = -\cos x + C$.

67. Derive formula (2):

$$\int \sec x \, dx = \frac{1}{2} \ln\left(\frac{1 + \sin x}{1 - \sin x}\right) + C$$

Hint: Use the identities

$$\sec x = \frac{1}{\cos x} \quad \text{and} \quad \cos^2 x = 1 - \sin^2 x$$

Let $u = \sin x$, and express the integrand as $du/(1 - u^2)$. Justify the removal of the absolute-value bars.

68. Use the substitution $z = \tan \frac{1}{2}x$ to prove that

$$\int \csc x \, dx = \frac{1}{2} \ln\left(\frac{1 - \cos x}{1 + \cos x}\right) + C$$

Justify the removal of the absolute-value bars.

69. Show that the formula in Exercise 67 is equivalent to the formula $\int \sec x \, dx = \ln|\sec x + \tan x| + C$. *Hint:* Multiply the numerator and denominator of the fraction in the formula by $1 + \sin x$.

70. Show that the formula in Exercise 68 is equivalent to the formula $\int \csc x \, dx = \ln|\csc x - \cot x|$. *Hint:* Use a method similar to that suggested in the hint for Exercise 69.

71. Evaluate the integral

$$\int \frac{\tan \frac{1}{2}x}{\sin x} \, dx$$

by two methods: **(a)** Let $z = \tan \frac{1}{2}x$; **(b)** let $u = \frac{1}{2}x$ and obtain an integral involving trigonometric functions of u.

72. You have had four formulas for $\int \sec x \, dx$. What are they and how are they related?

73. In today's electronic age why should you learn techniques of integration and how to use a table of integrals?

7.6 NUMERICAL INTEGRATION

Let us summarize our treatment of integration so far by listing the various techniques you have learned.

A. The Chain Rule of Antidifferentiation: Section 4.2

B. Integration by Substitution

    1. The u and v substitutions introduced in Section 4.2

    2. Integration of powers of trigonometric functions by trigonometric-identities substitution: Section 7.2

    3. Integration of algebraic functions by trigonometric substitution: Section 7.3

    4. Substitution of $x = z^n$ if the integrand contains fractional powers of x; such as $x = z^6$ if the integrand contains $\sqrt{x}$ and $\sqrt[3]{x}$: Section 7.5

    5. Substitution of $z = \tan \frac{1}{2}x$ if the integrand is a rational function of $\sin x$ and $\cos x$: Section 7.5

C. Integration by Parts: Section 7.1

D. Integration of Rational Functions by Partial Fractions: Section 7.4

With these techniques and a table of integrals or a computer program, we can evaluate any integral that can be expressed in closed form. Suppose, however, we have an integral that cannot be expressed in closed form. Examples of such integrals that arise in statistics are those involving the standardized normal probability density function discussed in Section 5.6 and the error function defined in Exercise 31 of that section:

$$P([a, b]) = \frac{1}{\sqrt{2\pi}} \int_a^b e^{-x^2/2}\, dx \qquad \text{erf}\,(x) = \frac{2}{\sqrt{\pi}} \int_0^x e^{-t^2}\, dt$$

Other examples are

$$\int \sqrt{1 + x^4}\, dx \qquad \int \cos x^2\, dx$$

which turn up in physics, as well as the elliptic integral

$$\int \sqrt{1 - k^2 \sin^2 x}\, dx \qquad 0 < k < 1$$

and

$$\int \frac{\sin x}{x}\, dx \qquad \int \frac{e^x - 1}{x}\, dx \qquad \int \frac{\ln(1 + x)}{x}\, dx \qquad \int \frac{\tan^{-1} x}{x}\, dx$$

Even with computer algebra systems these integrals cannot be expressed in closed form. You will learn in Chapter 8, however, methods of evaluating such nonelementary integrals by infinite series.

Of course, in modern times we can approximate the value of definite integrals by the NINT capability of our graphics calculator. Before the advent of electronic devices, we had to resort to other methods for computing an approximate value of a definite integral. In this section we discuss two of these methods, the *trapezoidal rule* and *Simpson's rule,* which often give fairly good accuracy. We present these rules not only for their historic interest, but because variations of them are used for evaluating a definite integral on graphics calculators, programmable calculators, and computers. The rules also provide a way for us to discuss errors introduced by approximation techniques. Furthermore, they can also be used to calculate definite integrals from function values given in a table as shown in Example 6.

We begin with the trapezoidal rule. Let f be a function continuous on the closed interval $[a, b]$. The definite integral of f on $[a, b]$ is the limit of a Riemann sum; that is,

$$\int_a^b f(x)\, dx = \lim_{\|\Delta\| \to 0} \sum_{i=1}^n f(w_i)\, \Delta_i x$$

We interpret the Riemann sum geometrically as the sum of the measures of the areas of the rectangles lying above the x axis plus the negative of the measures of the areas of the rectangles lying below the x axis (see Figure 3 in Section 4.5).

To approximate the measure of the area of a region we shall use trapezoids instead of rectangles. Let us also use regular partitions and function values at equally spaced points.

Thus for the definite integral $\int_a^b f(x)\,dx$ we divide the interval $[a, b]$ into n subintervals, each of length $\Delta x = (b - a)/n$. This gives the following points: $x_0 = a$, $x_1 = a + \Delta x$, $x_2 = a + 2\,\Delta x$, ... , $x_i = a + i\,\Delta x$, ... , $x_{n-1} = a + (n - 1)\,\Delta x$, $x_n = b$. Then the definite integral $\int_a^b f(x)\,dx$ may be expressed as the sum of n definite integrals as follows:

$$\int_a^b f(x)\,dx = \int_a^{x_1} f(x)\,dx + \int_{x_1}^{x_2} f(x)\,dx + \ldots + \int_{x_{i-1}}^{x_i} f(x)\,dx + \ldots + \int_{x_{n-1}}^b f(x)\,dx \qquad \textbf{(1)}$$

To interpret (1) geometrically, refer to Figure 1, in which $f(x) \geq 0$ for all x in $[a, b]$; however, (1) holds for any function continuous on $[a, b]$.

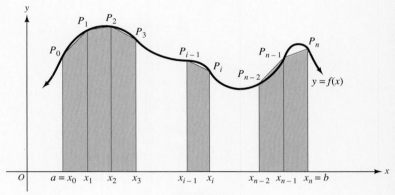

FIGURE 1

Then the integral $\int_a^{x_1} f(x)\,dx$ is the measure of the area of the region bounded by the x axis, the lines $x = a$ and $x = x_1$, and the portion of the curve from P_0 to P_1. This integral may be approximated by the measure of the area of the trapezoid formed by the lines $x = a$, $x = x_1$, $P_0 P_1$, and the x axis. By a formula from geometry the measure of the area of this trapezoid is

$$\tfrac{1}{2}[f(x_0) + f(x_1)]\,\Delta x$$

Similarly, the other integrals on the right side of (1) may be approximated by the measure of the area of a trapezoid. For the ith integral,

$$\int_{x_{i-1}}^{x_i} f(x)\,dx \approx \tfrac{1}{2}[f(x_{i-1}) + f(x_i)]\,\Delta x$$

Using this for each of the integrals on the right side of (1) we have

$$\int_a^b f(x)\,dx \approx \tfrac{1}{2}[f(x_0) + f(x_1)]\,\Delta x + \tfrac{1}{2}[f(x_1) + f(x_2)]\,\Delta x + \ldots$$
$$+ \tfrac{1}{2}[f(x_{n-2}) + f(x_{n-1})]\,\Delta x + \tfrac{1}{2}[f(x_{n-1}) + f(x_n)]\,\Delta x$$

Thus

$$\int_a^b f(x)\,dx \approx \tfrac{1}{2}\Delta x[f(x_0) + 2f(x_1) + 2f(x_2) + \ldots + 2f(x_{n-1}) + f(x_n)]$$

This formula is known as the *trapezoidal rule* and is stated in the following theorem.

7.61 Theorem   The Trapezoidal Rule

If the function f is continuous on the closed interval $[a, b]$ and the numbers $a = x_0, x_1, x_2, \ldots, x_n = b$ form a regular partition of $[a, b]$, then

$$\int_a^b f(x) \, dx \approx \frac{b - a}{2n} [f(x_0) + 2f(x_1) + \ldots + 2f(x_{n-1}) + f(x_n)]$$

▶ **EXAMPLE 1**   (a) Approximate to three decimal places

$$\int_0^3 \frac{dx}{16 + x^2}$$

by using the trapezoidal rule with $n = 6$. **(b)** Compare the result of part (a) with the exact value of the definite integral.

Solution

(a) Because $[a, b] = [0, 3]$ and $n = 6$,

$$\Delta x = \frac{b - a}{n} \qquad\qquad \frac{b - a}{2n} = \frac{3 - 0}{12}$$

$$= \frac{3 - 0}{6} \qquad\qquad\qquad = 0.25$$

$$= 0.5$$

Therefore

$$\int_0^3 \frac{dx}{16 + x^2} \approx 0.25[f(x_0) + 2f(x_1) + 2f(x_2) + 2f(x_3) + 2f(x_4) + 2f(x_5) + f(x_6)]$$

Table 1

i	x_i	$f(x_i)$	k_i	$k_i \cdot f(x_i)$
0	0	0.0625	1	0.0625
1	0.5	0.0615	2	0.1230
2	1	0.0588	2	0.1176
3	1.5	0.0548	2	0.1096
4	2	0.0500	2	0.1000
5	2.5	0.0450	2	0.0900
6	3	0.0400	1	0.0400

$$\sum_{i=0}^{6} k_i f(x_i) = 0.6427$$

where $f(x) = 1/(16 + x^2)$. The computation of the sum in brackets in the above is shown in Table 1, where the entries are obtained from a calculator. Thus

$$\int_0^3 \frac{dx}{16 + x^2} \approx (0.25)(0.6427)$$

$$\approx 0.1607$$

$$\approx 0.161$$

(b) We compute the exact value.

$$\int_0^3 \frac{dx}{16 + x^2} = \frac{1}{4} \tan^{-1} \frac{x}{4} \Big]_0^3$$

$$= \tfrac{1}{4} \tan^{-1} \tfrac{3}{4}$$

This value to three decimal places is 0.161, which agrees with the result of part (a).   ◀

To consider the accuracy of the approximation of a definite integral by the trapezoidal rule, two kinds of errors are introduced. One is the error due to the approximation of the graph of the function by segments of straight lines. The term **truncation error** refers to this kind of error. The other kind of error, which is unavoidable, is called the **round-off error.** It arises because numbers having a finite number of digits are used to approximate numbers. As the value of n (the number of subintervals) increases, the accuracy of the approximation of the area of the region by areas of trapezoids improves; thus the truncation error is reduced. However, as n increases, more computations are necessary; hence there is an increase in the round-off error. By methods discussed in *numerical analysis,* it is possible in a particular problem to determine the value of n that minimizes the combined errors. Obviously the round-off error is affected by how the calculations are performed. The truncation error can be estimated by a theorem. We prove first that as Δx approaches zero and n increases without bound, the limit of the approximation by the trapezoidal rule is the exact value of the definite integral. Let

$$T = \tfrac{1}{2} \Delta x [f(x_0) + 2f(x_1) + \ldots + 2f(x_{n-1}) + f(x_n)]$$

Then

$$T = [f(x_1) + f(x_2) + \ldots + f(x_n)] \Delta x + \tfrac{1}{2}[f(x_0) - f(x_n)] \Delta x$$

$$\Leftrightarrow T = \sum_{i=1}^{n} f(x_i) \Delta x + \tfrac{1}{2}[f(a) - f(b)] \Delta x$$

Therefore, if $n \to +\infty$ and $\Delta x \to 0$,

$$\lim_{\Delta x \to 0} T = \lim_{\Delta x \to 0} \sum_{i=1}^{n} f(x_i) \Delta x + \lim_{\Delta x \to 0} \tfrac{1}{2}[f(a) - f(b)] \Delta x$$

$$= \int_a^b f(x) \, dx + 0$$

Thus we can make the difference between T and the value of the definite integral as small as we please by taking n sufficiently large (and consequently Δx sufficiently small).

The following theorem, which is proved in numerical analysis, gives a method for estimating the truncation error obtained when using the trapezoidal rule. The truncation error is denoted by ϵ_T.

7.6.2 Theorem

Let the function f be continuous on the closed interval $[a, b]$, and f' and f'' both exist on $[a, b]$. If

$$\epsilon_T = \int_a^b f(x) \, dx - T$$

where T is the approximate value of $\int_a^b f(x) \, dx$ found by the trapezoidal rule, then there is some number η in $[a, b]$ such that

$$\epsilon_T = -\tfrac{1}{12}(b - a)f''(\eta)(\Delta x)^2 \tag{2}$$

▶ **EXAMPLE 2** Find bounds for the truncation error in the result of Example 1.

Solution We first find the absolute minimum and absolute maximum values of $f''(x)$ on $[0, 3]$.

$$f(x) = (16 + x^2)^{-1}$$
$$f'(x) = -2x(16 + x^2)^{-2}$$
$$f''(x) = 8x^2(16 + x^2)^{-3} - 2(16 + x^2)^{-2}$$
$$= (6x^2 - 32)(16 + x^2)^{-3}$$
$$f'''(x) = -6x(6x^2 - 32)(16 + x^2)^{-4} + 12x(16 + x^2)^{-3}$$
$$= 24x(16 - x^2)(16 + x^2)^{-4}$$

Because $f'''(x) > 0$ for all x in the open interval $(0, 3)$ then f'' is increasing on the open interval $(0, 3)$. Therefore the absolute minimum value of f'' on $[0, 3]$ is $f''(0)$, and the absolute maximum value of f'' on $[0, 3]$ is $f''(3)$.

$$f''(0) = -\tfrac{1}{128} \qquad f''(3) = \tfrac{22}{15,625}$$

Taking $\eta = 0$ on the right side of (2) we get

$$-\tfrac{3}{12}\left(-\tfrac{1}{128}\right)\tfrac{1}{4} = \tfrac{1}{2048}$$

Taking $\eta = 3$ on the right side of (2) we have

$$-\tfrac{3}{12}\left(\tfrac{22}{15,625}\right)\tfrac{1}{4} = -\tfrac{11}{125,000}$$

Therefore if ϵ_T is the truncation error in the result of Example 1,

$$-\tfrac{11}{125,000} \le \epsilon_T \le \tfrac{1}{2048}$$
$$-0.0001 \le \epsilon_T \le 0.0005$$

◀

If in Theorem 7.6.2 $f(x) = mx + b$, then $f''(x) = 0$ for all x. Therefore $\epsilon_T = 0$; so the trapezoidal rule gives the exact value of the definite integral of a linear function.

Another method for approximating the value of a definite integral is provided by *Simpson's rule* (sometimes referred to as the *parabolic rule*), named after the British mathematician Thomas Simpson (1710–1761). For a given partition of the closed interval $[a, b]$, Simpson's rule usually gives a better approximation than the trapezoidal rule. In the trapezoidal rule, successive points on the graph of $y = f(x)$ are connected by segments of straight lines, whereas in Simpson's rule the points are connected by segments of parabolas. Before Simpson's rule is developed, we state and prove a theorem that will be needed.

7.6.3 Theorem

If $P_0(x_0, y_0)$, $P_1(x_1, y_1)$, and $P_2(x_2, y_2)$ are three noncollinear points on the parabola having the equation $y = Ax^2 + Bx + C$, where $y_0 \ge 0$, $y_1 \ge 0$, $y_2 \ge 0$, $x_1 = x_0 + h$, and $x_2 = x_0 + 2h$, then the measure of the area of the region bounded by the parabola, the x axis, and the lines $x = x_0$ and $x = x_2$ is given by

$$\tfrac{1}{3}h(y_0 + 4y_1 + y_2)$$

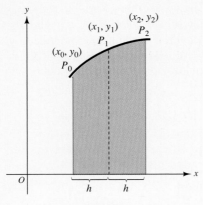

FIGURE 2

Proof The parabola whose equation is $y = Ax^2 + Bx + C$ has a vertical axis. Refer to Figure 2, which shows the region bounded by the parabola, the x axis, and the lines $x = x_0$ and $x = x_2$.

Because P_0, P_1, and P_2 are points on the parabola, their coordinates satisfy the equation of the parabola. So when we replace x_1 by $x_0 + h$, and x_2 by $x_0 + 2h$, we have

$$y_0 = Ax_0^2 + Bx_0 + C$$
$$y_1 = A(x_0 + h)^2 + B(x_0 + h) + C$$
$$ = A(x_0^2 + 2hx_0 + h^2) + B(x_0 + h) + C$$
$$y_2 = A(x_0 + 2h)^2 + B(x_0 + 2h) + C$$
$$ = A(x_0^2 + 4hx_0 + 4h^2) + B(x_0 + 2h) + C$$

Therefore

$$y_0 + 4y_1 + y_2 = A(6x_0^2 + 12hx_0 + 8h^2) + B(6x_0 + 6h) + 6C \quad \textbf{(3)}$$

Now if K square units is the area of the region, then K can be computed by the limit of a Riemann sum, and we have

$$K = \lim_{\|\Delta\| \to 0} \sum_{i=1}^{n} (Aw_i^2 + Bw_i + C) \, \Delta x$$

$$= \int_{x_0}^{x_0 + 2h} (Ax^2 + Bx + C) \, dx$$

$$= \tfrac{1}{3}Ax^3 + \tfrac{1}{2}Bx^2 + Cx \Big]_{x_0}^{x_0 + 2h}$$

$$= \tfrac{1}{3}A(x_0 + 2h)^3 + \tfrac{1}{2}B(x_0 + 2h)^2 + C(x_0 + 2h) - (\tfrac{1}{3}Ax_0^3 + \tfrac{1}{2}Bx_0^2 + Cx_0)$$

$$= \tfrac{1}{3}h[A(6x_0^2 + 12hx_0 + 8h^2) + B(6x_0 + 6h) + 6C]$$

Substituting from (3) in this expression for K we get

$$K = \tfrac{1}{3}h(y_0 + 4y_1 + y_2) \qquad \blacksquare$$

Let the function f be continuous on the closed interval $[a, b]$. Consider a regular partition of the interval $[a, b]$ of n subintervals, where n is even. The length of each subinterval is given by $\Delta x = (b - a)/n$. Let the points on the curve $y = f(x)$ having these partitioning points as abscissas be denoted by $P_0(x_0, y_0)$, $P_1(x_1, y_1)$, ..., $P_n(x_n, y_n)$; see Figure 3, where $f(x) \geq 0$ for all x in $[a, b]$.

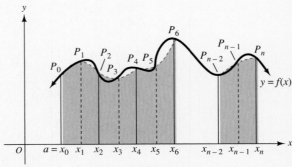

FIGURE 3

We approximate the segment of the curve $y = f(x)$ from P_0 to P_2 by the segment of the parabola with a vertical axis and through P_0, P_1, and P_2. Then by Theorem 7.6.3 the measure of the area of the region bounded by this parabola, the x axis, and the lines $x = x_0$ and $x = x_2$, with $h = \Delta x$, is given by

$$\tfrac{1}{3}\Delta x(y_0 + 4y_1 + y_2) \quad \text{or} \quad \tfrac{1}{3}\Delta x[f(x_0) + 4f(x_1) + f(x_2)]$$

In a similar manner we approximate the segment of the curve $y = f(x)$ from P_2 to P_4 by the segment of the parabola with a vertical axis and through P_2, P_3, and P_4. The measure of the area of the region bounded by this parabola, the x axis, and the lines $x = x_2$ and $x = x_4$ is given by

$$\tfrac{1}{3}\Delta x(y_2 + 4y_3 + y_4) \quad \text{or} \quad \tfrac{1}{3}\Delta x[f(x_2) + 4f(x_3) + f(x_4)]$$

This process is continued until there are $\tfrac{1}{2}n$ such regions, and the measure of the area of the last region is given by

$$\tfrac{1}{3}\Delta x(y_{n-2} + 4y_{n-1} + y_n) \quad \text{or} \quad \tfrac{1}{3}\Delta x[f(x_{n-2}) + 4f(x_{n-1}) + f(x_n)]$$

The sum of the measures of the areas of these regions approximates the measure of the area of the region bounded by the curve whose equation is $y = f(x)$, the x axis, and the lines $x = a$ and $x = b$. The measure of the area of this region is given by the definite integral $\int_a^b f(x)\, dx$. So we have as an approximation to the definite integral

$$\tfrac{1}{3}\Delta x[f(x_0) + 4f(x_1) + f(x_2)] + \tfrac{1}{3}\Delta x[f(x_2) + 4f(x_3) + f(x_4)] + \cdots$$
$$+ \tfrac{1}{3}\Delta x[f(x_{n-4}) + 4f(x_{n-3}) + f(x_{n-2})] + \tfrac{1}{3}\Delta x[f(x_{n-2}) + 4f(x_{n-1}) + f(x_n)]$$

Thus

$$\int_a^b f(x)\, dx \approx \tfrac{1}{3}\Delta x[f(x_0) + 4f(x_1) + 2f(x_2) + 4f(x_3)$$
$$+ 2f(x_4) + \ldots + 2f(x_{n-2}) + 4f(x_{n-1}) + f(x_n)]$$

where $\Delta x = (b - a)/n$.

This formula is called *Simpson's rule* and is given in the next theorem.

7.6.4 Theorem   Simpson's Rule

If the function f is continuous on the closed interval $[a, b]$, n is an even integer, and the numbers $a = x_0, x_1, x_2, \ldots, x_{n-1}, x_n = b$ form a regular partition of $[a, b]$, then

$$\int_a^b f(x)\, dx \approx \frac{b - a}{3n} [f(x_0) + 4f(x_1) + 2f(x_2) + 4f(x_3) + 2f(x_4)$$
$$+ \ldots + 2f(x_{n-2}) + 4f(x_{n-1}) + f(x_n)]$$

▶ **EXAMPLE 3**   (a) Approximate to four decimal places

$$\int_0^1 \frac{dx}{x + 1}$$

by using Simpson's rule with $n = 4$. (b) Compare the result in part (a) with the exact value of the definite integral.

Solution

(a) Applying Simpson's rule with $n = 4$, we have

$$\Delta x = \frac{b - a}{n} \qquad \frac{b - a}{3n} = \frac{1 - 0}{3(4)}$$

$$= \frac{1 - 0}{4} \qquad = \tfrac{1}{12}$$

$$= \tfrac{1}{4}$$

Therefore, if $f(x) = 1/(x + 1)$,

$$\int_0^1 \frac{dx}{x + 1} \approx \tfrac{1}{12}[f(x_0) + 4f(x_1) + 2f(x_2) + 4f(x_3) + f(x_4)]$$

Table 2

i	x_i	$f(x_i)$	k_i	$k_i \cdot f(x_i)$
0	0	1.00000	1	1.00000
1	0.25	0.80000	4	3.20000
2	0.5	0.66667	2	1.33334
3	0.75	0.57143	4	2.28572
4	1	0.50000	1	0.50000

$$\sum_{i=0}^{4} k_i f(x_i) = 8.31906$$

In Table 2, where the entries are obtained from a calculator, we have the computation of the above sum in brackets. Therefore

$$\int_0^1 \frac{dx}{x + 1} \approx \frac{1}{12}(8.31906)$$

$$\approx 0.69325^+$$

Rounding off the result to four decimal places gives

$$\int_0^1 \frac{dx}{x + 1} \approx 0.6933$$

(b) We compute the exact value.

$$\int_0^1 \frac{dx}{x + 1} = \ln|x + 1| \Big]_0^1$$

$$= \ln 2$$

The value of $\ln 2$ to four decimal places is 0.6931, which agrees with the approximation in part (a) in the first three decimal places. And the error in the approximation is -0.0002. ◄

In Simpson's rule, the larger the value of n the smaller will be the value of Δx. So in terms of geometry, the larger the value of n, the smaller will be the truncation error of the approximation because a parabola, containing three points of a curve close to each other, will be close to the curve throughout the subinterval of width Δx.

The following theorem, proved in numerical analysis, gives a method for determining the truncation error, denoted by ϵ_S, in Simpson's rule.

7.6.5 Theorem

Let the function f be continuous on the closed interval $[a, b]$, and f', f'', f''', and $f^{(4)}$ all exist on $[a, b]$. If

$$\epsilon_S = \int_a^b f(x)\, dx - S$$

where S is the approximate value of $\int_a^b f(x)\, dx$ found by Simpson's rule, then there is some number η in $[a, b]$ such that

$$\epsilon_S = -\tfrac{1}{180}(b - a)f^{(4)}(\eta)(\Delta x)^4 \tag{4}$$

▶ **EXAMPLE 4**   Find bounds for the truncation error in Example 3.
Solution

$$f(x) = (x + 1)^{-1}$$
$$f'(x) = -1(x + 1)^{-2}$$
$$f''(x) = 2(x + 1)^{-3}$$
$$f'''(x) = -6(x + 1)^{-4}$$
$$f^{(4)}(x) = 24(x + 1)^{-5}$$
$$f^{(5)}(x) = -120(x + 1)^{-6}$$

Because $f^{(5)}(x) < 0$ for all x in $[0, 1]$, $f^{(4)}$ is decreasing on $[0, 1]$. Thus the absolute minimum value of $f^{(4)}$ is at the right endpoint 1, and the absolute maximum value of $f^{(4)}$ on $[0, 1]$ is at the left endpoint 0.

$$f^{(4)}(0) = 24 \quad \text{and} \quad f^{(4)}(1) = \tfrac{3}{4}$$

Substituting 0 for η in the right side of (4) we get

$$-\tfrac{1}{180}(24)(\tfrac{1}{4})^4 \approx -0.00052$$

Substituting 1 for η in the right side of (4) we have

$$-\tfrac{1}{180} \cdot \tfrac{3}{4}(\tfrac{1}{4})^4 \approx -0.00002$$

So

$$-0.00052 \leq \epsilon_S \leq -0.00002$$

This inequality agrees with the discussion in Example 3 regarding the error in the approximation of $\int_0^1 dx/(x + 1)$ by Simpson's rule because $-0.00052 < -0.0002 < -0.00002$.   ◀

If $f(x)$ is a polynomial of degree three or less, then $f^{(4)}(x) \equiv 0$ and therefore $\epsilon_S = 0$. In other words, Simpson's rule gives an exact result for a polynomial of the third degree or lower. This statement is geometrically obvious if $f(x)$ is of the second or first degree because in the first case the graph of $y = f(x)$ is a parabola, and in the second case the graph is a line.

▶ **EXAMPLE 5**   In Example 8 of Section 5.6 we used the NINT capability of our graphics calculator to show that for the standardized normal probability density function, $P([0, 2])$, the probability that a random choice of x will be in the interval $[0, 2]$, is 0.47725. Now, instead of using NINT, approximate the value of $P([0, 2])$ to three decimal places by **(a)** the trapezoidal rule with $n = 4$ and **(b)** Simpson's rule with $n = 4$.

Solution   From Equation (23) in Section 5.6

$$P([0, 2]) = \frac{1}{\sqrt{2\pi}} \int_0^2 e^{-x^2/2} \, dx \tag{5}$$

(a) We approximate the integral in (5) by the trapezoidal rule with $n = 4$. Because $[a, b] = [0, 2]$, $\Delta x = \frac{1}{2}$. Therefore, with $f(x) = e^{-x^2/2}$,

$$\int_0^2 e^{-x^2/2}\, dx \approx \tfrac{1}{4}[f(0) + 2f(\tfrac{1}{2}) + 2f(1) + 2f(\tfrac{3}{2}) + f(2)]$$

$$= \tfrac{1}{4}[e^0 + 2e^{-1/8} + 2e^{-1/2} + 2e^{-9/8} + e^{-2}]$$

$$\approx 1.191$$

Thus

$$P([0, 2]) \approx \frac{1}{\sqrt{2\pi}}(1.191)$$

$$\approx 0.475$$

(b) If Simpson's rule with $n = 4$ is used to approximate the integral in (5), we have

$$\int_0^2 e^{-x^2/2}\, dx \approx \tfrac{1}{6}[f(0) + 4f(\tfrac{1}{2}) + 2f(1) + 4f(\tfrac{3}{2}) + f(2)]$$

$$= \tfrac{1}{6}[e^0 + 4e^{-1/8} + 2e^{-1/2} + 4e^{-9/8} + e^{-2}]$$

$$\approx 1.196$$

Therefore

$$P([0, 2]) \approx \frac{1}{\sqrt{2\pi}}(1.196)$$

$$\approx 0.477$$

The answers in parts (a) and (b) agree favorably with the answer in Example 8 of Section 5.6, with the answer in part (b) by Simpson's rule agreeing more favorably than the answer in part (a) by the trapezoidal rule. ◄

Numerical methods can be applied to approximate $\int_a^b f(x)\, dx$ even when we do not know a formula for $f(x)$ provided, of course, we have access to some function values. Such function values are often obtained experimentally. The following example involves such a situation.

▶ **EXAMPLE 6**   A particle moving along a horizontal line has a velocity of $v(t)$ meters per second at t seconds. Table 3 gives values of $v(t)$ for $\frac{1}{2}$-sec intervals of time for a period of 4 sec. Use these values and Simpson's rule to approximate the distance the particle travels during the 4 sec.

Table 3

t	0	0.5	1.0	1.5	2.0	2.5	3.0	3.5	4.0
$v(t)$	0	0.15	0.35	0.55	0.78	1.02	1.27	1.57	1.90

Solution   The number of meters the particle travels during the 4 sec is $\int_0^4 v(t)\, dt$. From Simpson's rule with $n = 8$, we have

$$\Delta x = \frac{b - a}{n} \qquad \frac{b - a}{3n} = \frac{4 - 0}{24}$$

$$= \frac{4 - 0}{8} \qquad\qquad = \frac{1}{6}$$

$$= \frac{1}{2}$$

Therefore

$$\int_0^4 v(t)\,dt \approx \tfrac{1}{6}\left[v(0) + 4v(1) + 2v(2) + 4v(3) + 2v(4) + 4v(5) + 2v(6) + 4v(7) + v(8) \right]$$

$$= \tfrac{1}{6}\left[0 + 4(0.15) + 2(0.35) + 4(0.55) + 2(0.78) + 4(1.02) + 2(1.27) + 4(1.57) + 1.90 \right]$$

$$\approx 3.31$$

<u>Conclusion:</u>   The particle travels approximately 3.31 meters during the 4 sec.   ◄

EXERCISES 7.6

In Exercises 1 through 8, (a) compute to three decimal places the approximate value of the definite integral by the trapezoidal rule for the indicated value of n. (b) Compare the result in part (a) with the exact value of the definite integral.

1. $\displaystyle\int_0^2 x^3\, dx;\ n = 4$

2. $\displaystyle\int_0^2 x\sqrt{4 - x^2}\, dx;\ n = 8$

3. $\displaystyle\int_0^\pi \cos x\, dx;\ n = 4$

4. $\displaystyle\int_0^\pi \sin x\, dx;\ n = 6$

5. $\displaystyle\int_1^2 \frac{dx}{x};\ n = 5$

6. $\displaystyle\int_2^{10} \frac{dx}{1 + x};\ n = 8$

7. $\displaystyle\int_0^1 \frac{dx}{\sqrt{1 + x^2}};\ n = 5$

8. $\displaystyle\int_2^3 \sqrt{1 + x^2}\, dx;\ n = 6$

In Exercises 9 through 12, compute to three decimal places the approximate value of the definite integral by the trapezoidal rule for the indicated value of n.

9. $\displaystyle\int_{\pi/2}^{3\pi/2} \frac{\sin x}{x}\, dx;\ n = 6$

10. $\displaystyle\int_0^1 \sqrt{1 + x^3}\, dx;\ n = 4$

11. $\displaystyle\int_0^2 \sqrt{1 + x^4}\, dx;\ n = 6$

12. $\displaystyle\int_0^\pi \frac{\sin x}{1 + x}\, dx;\ n = 6$

In Exercises 13 through 18, find bounds for the truncation error in the approximation of the indicated exercise.

13. Exercise 1   **14.** Exercise 4   **15.** Exercise 3

16. Exercise 6   **17.** Exercise 5   **18.** Exercise 8

19. Approximate $\int_0^2 x^3\, dx$ to three decimal places by Simpson's rule with $n = 4$. Compare the result with those obtained in Exercise 1, and observe that Simpson's rule gives better accuracy than the trapezoidal rule with the same number of subintervals.

20. Approximate $\int_0^\pi \sin x\, dx$ to three decimal places by Simpson's rule with $n = 6$. Compare the result with those obtained in Exercise 4, and observe that Simpson's rule gives better accuracy than the trapezoidal rule with the same number of subintervals.

In Exercises 21 through 24, (a) compute to four decimal places the approximate value of the definite integral by Simpson's rule for the indicated value of n. (b) Compare the result in part (a) with the exact value of the definite integral.

21. $\displaystyle\int_{-1}^0 \frac{dx}{1 - x};\ n = 4$

22. $\displaystyle\int_{-0.5}^0 \frac{dx}{\sqrt{1 - x^2}};\ n = 4$

23. $\displaystyle\int_0^1 \frac{dx}{x^2 + x + 1};\ n = 4$

24. $\displaystyle\int_1^2 \frac{dx}{x + 1};\ n = 8$

In Exercises 25 through 28, find bounds for the truncation error in the approximation of the indicated exercise.

25. Exercise 19

26. Exercise 20

27. Exercise 21

28. Exercise 24

Each of the definite integrals in Exercises 29 through 34 cannot be evaluated exactly in terms of elementary functions. Use Simpson's rule, with the indicated value of n, to find an approximate value of the definite integral. Express the result to four decimal places.

29. $\int_{\pi/2}^{3\pi/2} \dfrac{\sin x}{x}\, dx; \; n = 6$

30. $\int_0^2 \sqrt{1 + x^4}\, dx; \; n = 6$

31. $\int_1^{1.8} \sqrt{1 + x^3}\, dx; \; n = 4$

32. $\int_0^1 \sqrt[3]{1 - x^2}\, dx; \; n = 4$

33. $\int_0^2 \dfrac{dx}{\sqrt{1 + x^3}}; \; n = 8$

34. $\int_0^{\pi/2} \sqrt{\sin x}\, dx; \; n = 6$

35. **(a)** Show that the exact value of the integral $\int_0^2 \sqrt{4 - x^2}\, dx$ is π by interpreting it as the measure of the area of a region. **(b)** Compute to three decimal places the approximate value of the definite integral by the trapezoidal rule with $n = 8$, and compare the result with the exact value.

36. **(a)** Show that the exact value of the integral $\int_0^1 4\sqrt{1 - x^2}\, dx$ is π by interpreting it as the measure of the area of a region. **(b)** Compute to three decimal places the approximate value of the definite integral by Simpson's rule with $n = 6$, and compare the result with the exact value.

37. In Exercise 29 of Exercises 5.6, you used the NINT capability of your graphics calculator to determine $P([0, 1])$ for the standardized normal probability density function. Now, approximate the value of $P([0, 1])$ to three decimal places by **(a)** the trapezoidal rule with $n = 4$ and **(b)** Simpson's rule with $n = 4$.

38. In Exercise 30 of Exercises 5.6, you used the NINT capability of your graphics calculator to determine $P([-3, 3])$ for the standardized normal probability density function. Now, approximate the value of $P([-3, 3])$ to three decimal places by **(a)** the trapezoidal rule with $n = 6$ and **(b)** Simpson's rule with $n = 6$. Comment on your answer in Part (b).

39. In Exercise 27 of Exercises 6.1, you used the NINT capability of your graphics calculator to find to four significant digits the length of arc of the sine curve from the origin to the point $(\pi, 0)$. Now compute this length by Simpson's rule with $n = 8$.

40. In Exercise 28 of Exercises 6.1, you used the NINT capability of your graphics calculator to find to four significant digits the length of arc of the cosine curve from the point $(0, 1)$ to the point $(\frac{1}{3}\pi, \frac{1}{2})$. Now compute this length by Simpson's rule with $n = 8$.

In Exercises 41 and 42, the function values $f(x)$ were obtained experimentally. With the assumption that f is continuous on $[0, 4]$ approximate $\int_0^4 f(x)\, dx$ by (a) the trapezoidal rule and (b) Simpson's rule.

41.

x	0	0.50	1.00	1.50	2.00	2.50	3.00	3.50	4.00
$f(x)$	3.25	4.17	4.60	3.84	3.59	4.23	4.01	3.96	3.75

42.

x	0	0.4	0.8	1.2	1.6	2.0	2.4	2.8	3.2	3.6	4.0
$f(x)$	8.4	8.1	7.9	7.5	7.6	7.2	6.8	6.3	6.5	6.0	5.7

In Exercises 43 and 44, use Simpson's rule to approximate the area of the shaded region in the figure.

43.

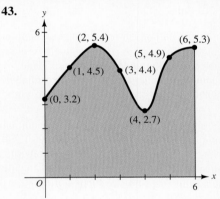

44.

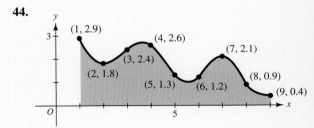

45. A woman took 10 minutes to drive from her home to the supermarket. At every 1-minute interval she observed the speedometer reading given in the following table, where $v(t)$ miles per hour was the speedometer reading t minutes after she left her home. Use Simpson's rule to approximate the distance from the woman's home to the supermarket.

t	0	1	2	3	4	5	6	7	8	9	10
$v(t)$	0	30	33	41	38	32	42	45	41	37	22

46. The shape of a parking lot is irregular and the length of the lot from west to east is 240 ft. At the west end of the lot the width is 150 ft and at the east end it is 175 ft. At 40, 80, 120, 160, and 200 ft from the west end, the widths are 154, 158, 165, 163, and 172 ft, respectively. Use Simpson's rule to approximate the area of the parking lot.

47. Find the area of the region enclosed by the loop of the curve whose equation is $y^2 = 8x^2 - x^5$. Evaluate the definite integral by Simpson's rule with $n = 8$ and express the result to three decimal places.

48. The study of light diffraction (dispersion or bending of light around corners) at a rectangular aperature involves the Fresnel integrals

$$C(t) = \int_0^t \cos \tfrac{1}{2} \pi x^2 \, dx \quad \text{and} \quad S(t) = \int_0^t \sin \tfrac{1}{2} \pi x^2 \, dx$$

Complete the following table of values to four decimal places by Simpson's rule.

t	0.2	0.4	0.6	0.8	1.0
$C(t)$					
$S(t)$					

49. The energy gained by skate-boarding down a frictionless "Gaussian" hill, x meters from the top of the hill after t seconds, is $E(x)$ joules where

$$E(x) = \frac{gM}{\sqrt{2\pi}} \int_0^x e^{-t^2/2} \, dt$$

with $g = 9.8$ and $M = 60$. The velocity of the skate-boarder at t seconds is $\sqrt{2E(x)/M}$. Use Simpson's rule to determine the skate-boarder's velocity 2 m from the top of the hill.

50. Apply Simpson's rule to the definite integral $\int_a^b f(x) \, dx$ where $f(x)$ is a third-degree polynomial to prove the **prismoidal formula:**

$$\int_a^b f(x) \, dx = \frac{b - a}{6} \left[f(a) + 4f\left(\frac{a + b}{2}\right) + f(b) \right]$$

In Exercises 51 through 54, evaluate the definite integral by two methods: (a) use the prismoidal formula given in Exercise 50; (b) use the second fundamental theorem of the calculus.

51. $\int_1^3 (4x^3 - 3x^2 + 1) \, dx$

52. $\int_{-2}^2 (x^3 + x^2 - 4x - 2) \, dx$

53. $\int_{-1}^5 (x^3 + 3x^2 - 2x - 6) \, dx$

54. $\int_2^6 (2x^3 - 2x - 3) \, dx$

55. Suppose that f is a function continuous on the closed-interval $[a, b]$. Let T be the approximate value of $\int_a^b f(x) \, dx$ by using the trapezoidal rule, and let S be the approximate value of $\int_a^b f(x) \, dx$ by using Simpson's rule, where the same partition of the interval $[a, b]$ is used for both approximations. Show that

$$S = \tfrac{2}{3}[T + \Delta x(f(x_1) + f(x_3) + f(x_5) + \ldots + f(x_{n-1}))]$$

where n is even.

56. For polynomials of what degrees do we obtain an exact value of a definite integral by (a) the trapezoidal rule and (b) Simpson's rule? Explain how you arrived at your answer.

7.7 THE INDETERMINATE FORM 0/0 AND CAUCHY'S MEAN-VALUE THEOREM

Throughout this text, you have encountered limits of quotients of functions for which the limits of both the numerator and denominator are zero. For instance

$$\lim_{t \to 0} \frac{\sin t}{t} \quad \text{and} \quad \lim_{x \to 3} \frac{x^2 - 9}{x - 3}$$

are two such limits. To compute these limits, we did not apply immediately the theorem about the limit of a quotient because that theorem requires that the limit of the denominator not be zero. We did, however, follow other procedures. We determined that the first of these limits is 1 by proving

Theorem 1.10.2. We computed the second of these limits by factoring the numerator as the difference of two squares and then dividing numerator and denominator by $x - 3$ to obtain 6 as the limit. We now discuss a more general method that can be applied to limits such as these.

7.7.1 Definition of the Indeterminate Form 0/0

If f and g are two functions such that

$$\lim_{x \to a} f(x) = 0 \quad \text{and} \quad \lim_{x \to a} g(x) = 0$$

then $f(x)/g(x)$ has the **indeterminate form 0/0** at a.

▷ **ILLUSTRATION 1** From Definition 7.7.1 $\dfrac{\sin t}{t}$ has the indeterminate form 0/0 at 0 and $\dfrac{x^2 - 9}{x - 3}$ has the indeterminate form 0/0 at 3. ◀

The general method for finding the limit at the number a of a function having the indeterminate form 0/0 at a involves a theorem known as *L'Hôpital's rule,* named for the French mathematician Guillaume François de L'Hôpital (1661–1707), who wrote the first calculus textbook published in 1696.

7.7.2 Theorem L'Hôpital's Rule

Let f and g be functions differentiable on an open interval I, except possibly at the number a in I. Suppose that for all $x \neq a$ in I, $g'(x) \neq 0$. If $\lim\limits_{x \to a} f(x) = 0$ and $\lim\limits_{x \to a} g(x) = 0$, and

$$\text{if} \quad \lim_{x \to a} \frac{f'(x)}{g'(x)} = L \quad \text{then} \quad \lim_{x \to a} \frac{f(x)}{g(x)} = L$$

The theorem is valid if all the limits are right-hand limits or all the limits are left-hand limits.

Before proving L'Hôpital's rule, we show its application by illustrations and examples.

▷ **ILLUSTRATION 2** Because $\lim\limits_{t \to 0} \sin t = 0$ and $\lim\limits_{t \to 0} t = 0$, we can apply L'Hôpital's rule and obtain

$$\lim_{t \to 0} \frac{\sin t}{t} = \lim_{t \to 0} \frac{\cos t}{1}$$
$$= 1$$

To demonstrate graphically this application of L'Hôpital's rule, refer to Figure 1 showing the graphs of $f(t) = \sin t / t$ and $g(t) = \cos t / 1$ plotted in the same $[-3, 3]$ by $[-2, 2]$ window. The figure supports the fact that both functions have the same limit of 1 as $t \to 0$. At $t = 0$, f has a removable discontinuity and g is continuous. ◀

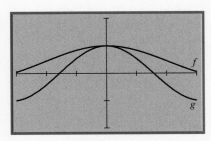

$[-3, 3]$ by $[-2, 2]$

$f(t) = \dfrac{\sin t}{t}$ and $g(t) = \cos t$

FIGURE 1

[0, 12] by [0, 8]

$$f(x) = \frac{x^2 - 9}{x - 3} \text{ and } g(x) = 2x$$

FIGURE 2

▷ **ILLUSTRATION 3** Because

$$\lim_{x \to 3} (x^2 - 9) = 0 \quad \text{and} \quad \lim_{x \to 3} (x - 3) = 0$$

we can apply L'Hôpital's rule and obtain

$$\lim_{x \to 3} \frac{x^2 - 9}{x - 3} = \lim_{x \to 3} \frac{2x}{1}$$
$$= 6$$

Refer to Figure 2 to see a graphical interpretation of this application of L'Hôpital's rule. The figure shows the graphs of $f(x) = (x^2 - 9)/(x - 3)$ and $g(x) = 2x/1$ plotted in the same $[0, 12]$ by $[0, 8]$ window. The figure supports the fact that the limits of both functions are 6 as $x \to 3$. At $x = 3$, f has a removable discontinuity while g is continuous there. ◀

▶ **EXAMPLE 1** Given

$$f(x) = \frac{x}{e^x - 1}$$

(a) Plot the graph of f. What does $f(x)$ appear to be approaching as x approaches 0? **(b)** Confirm the answer in part (a) analytically by computing $\lim_{x \to 0} f(x)$.

Solution

(a) Figure 3 shows the graph of f plotted in the $[-3, 3]$ by $[-1, 3]$ window. Because $f(0)$ does not exist, the graph has a hole (covered by the y axis) at $x = 0$. From the graph, $f(x)$ appears to be approaching 1 as x approaches 0.

(b) Because $\lim_{x \to 0} x = 0$ and $\lim_{x \to 0} (e^x - 1) = 0$, we can apply L'Hôpital's rule, and we have

$$\lim_{x \to 0} \frac{x}{e^x - 1} = \lim_{x \to 0} \frac{1}{e^x}$$
$$= 1$$

which confirms our answer in part (a). ◀

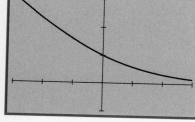

[−3, 3] by [−1, 3]

$$f(x) = \frac{x}{e^x - 1}$$

FIGURE 3

▶ **EXAMPLE 2** Given

$$f(x) = \frac{x^3 - 3x + 2}{1 - x + \ln x}$$

Evaluate $\lim_{x \to 1} f(x)$, if it exists, and support the answer graphically.

Solution We first check to see if we can apply L'Hôpital's rule.

$$\lim_{x \to 1} (x^3 - 3x + 2) = 1 - 3 + 2 \qquad \lim_{x \to 1} (1 - x + \ln x) = 1 - 1 + 0$$
$$= 0 \qquad\qquad\qquad\qquad = 0$$

We therefore apply the rule.

$$\lim_{x \to 1} \frac{x^3 - 3x + 2}{1 - x + \ln x} = \lim_{x \to 1} \frac{3x^2 - 3}{-1 + \dfrac{1}{x}}$$

Now, because $\lim_{x \to 1} (3x^2 - 3) = 0$ and $\lim_{x \to 1} (-1 + 1/x) = 0$, we apply L'Hôpital's rule again, giving

$$\lim_{x \to 1} \frac{3x^2 - 3}{-1 + \dfrac{1}{x}} = \lim_{x \to 1} \frac{6x}{-\dfrac{1}{x^2}}$$

$$= \frac{6}{-1}$$

$$= -6$$

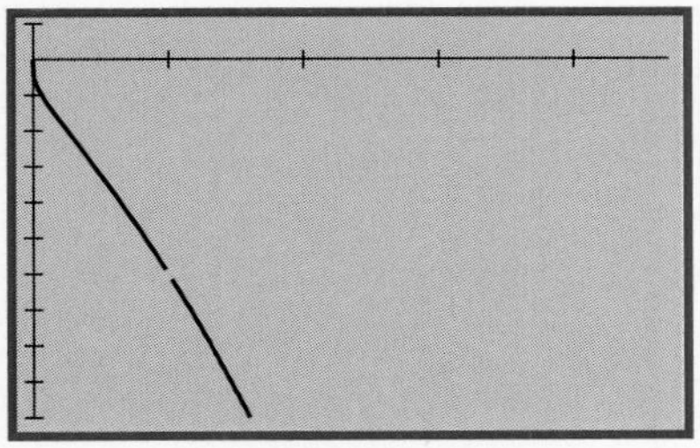

Figure 4 shows the graph of f plotted in the $[0, 4.7]$ by $[-10, 1]$ window. The graph has a hole at $(1, -6)$, which supports our answer. ◀

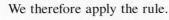

[0, 4.7] by [−10, 1]

$$f(x) = \frac{x^3 - 3x + 2}{1 - x + \ln x}$$

FIGURE 4

To prove Theorem 7.7.2, we need to use *Cauchy's mean-value theorem,* attributed to the French mathematician Augustin L. Cauchy (1789–1857), which extends to two functions the mean-value theorem for a single function. A geometric interpretation of the theorem is postponed until Section 9.1, where derivatives associated with parametric equations are discussed.

7.7.3 Cauchy's Mean-Value Theorem

If f and g are two functions such that

  (i) f and g are continuous on the closed interval $[a, b]$;
  (ii) f and g are differentiable on the open interval (a, b);
  (iii) for all x in the open interval (a, b), $g'(x) \neq 0$,

then there exists a number z in the open interval (a, b) such that

$$\frac{f(b) - f(a)}{g(b) - g(a)} = \frac{f'(z)}{g'(z)}$$

Proof We first show that $g(b) \neq g(a)$. Assume $g(b) = g(a)$. Because g satisfies the two conditions in the hypothesis of the mean-value theorem, there is some number c in (a, b) such that $g'(c) = [g(b) - g(a)]/(b - a)$. But if $g(b) = g(a)$, then there is some number c in (a, b) such that $g'(c) = 0$. But condition (iii) of the hypothesis of this theorem states that for all x in (a, b), $g'(x) \neq 0$. Therefore there is a contradiction. Hence the assumption that $g(b) = g(a)$ is false. Consequently $g(b) - g(a) \neq 0$.

Now consider the function h defined by

$$h(x) = f(x) - f(a) - \left[\frac{f(b) - f(a)}{g(b) - g(a)}\right][g(x) - g(a)]$$

Then

$$h'(x) = f'(x) - \left[\frac{f(b) - f(a)}{g(b) - g(a)}\right]g'(x) \qquad (1)$$

Therefore h is differentiable on (a, b) because f and g are differentiable there, and h is continuous on $[a, b]$ because f and g are continuous there.

$$h(a) = f(a) - f(a) - \left[\frac{f(b) - f(a)}{g(b) - g(a)}\right][g(a) - g(a)]$$

$$= 0$$

$$h(b) = f(b) - f(a) - \left[\frac{f(b) - f(a)}{g(b) - g(a)}\right][g(b) - g(a)]$$

$$= 0$$

Hence the three conditions of the hypothesis of Rolle's theorem are satisfied by the function h. So there exists a number z in the open interval (a, b) such that $h'(z) = 0$. Thus, from (1),

$$f'(z) - \frac{f(b) - f(a)}{g(b) - g(a)}g'(z) = 0$$

Because $g'(z) \neq 0$ on (a, b), we have from the above equation

$$\frac{f(b) - f(a)}{g(b) - g(a)} = \frac{f'(z)}{g'(z)}$$

where z is some number in (a, b). This proves the theorem.   ∎

If $g(x) = x$, then the conclusion of Cauchy's mean-value theorem becomes the conclusion of the former mean-value theorem because then $g'(z) = 1$. So the former mean-value theorem is a special case of Cauchy's mean-value theorem.

► **EXAMPLE 3**   Find all values of z in the interval $(0, 1)$ satisfying the conclusion of Cauchy's mean-value theorem for the functions defined by

$$f(x) = 3x^2 + 3x - 1 \quad \text{and} \quad g(x) = x^3 - 4x + 2$$

Solution

$$f'(x) = 6x + 3 \qquad g'(x) = 3x^2 - 4$$

The functions f and g are differentiable and continuous everywhere, and for all x in $(0, 1)$, $g'(x) \neq 0$. Hence, by Cauchy's mean-value theorem there exists a z in $(0, 1)$ such that

$$\frac{f(1) - f(0)}{g(1) - g(0)} = \frac{6z + 3}{3z^2 - 4}$$

Substituting $f(1) = 5$, $g(1) = -1$, $f(0) = -1$, and $g(0) = 2$ and solving for z we have

$$\frac{5 - (-1)}{-1 - 2} = \frac{6z + 3}{3z^2 - 4}$$

$$6z^2 + 6z - 5 = 0$$

$$z = \frac{-6 \pm \sqrt{36 + 120}}{12}$$

$$= \frac{-6 \pm 2\sqrt{39}}{12}$$

$$= \frac{-3 \pm \sqrt{39}}{6}$$

In the interval $(0, 1)$, $z = \frac{1}{6}(-3 + \sqrt{39}) \approx 0.54083$. ◀

We are now in a position to prove Theorem 7.7.2. We distinguish three cases: (i) $x \to a^+$; (ii) $x \to a^-$; (iii) $x \to a$.

Proof of Theorem 7.7.2(i) Because in the hypothesis it is not assumed that f and g are defined at a, we consider two new functions F and G for which

$$F(x) = \begin{cases} f(x) & \text{if } x \neq a \\ 0 & \text{if } x = a \end{cases} \quad \text{and} \quad G(x) = \begin{cases} g(x) & \text{if } x \neq a \\ 0 & \text{if } x = a \end{cases} \quad (2)$$

Let b be the right endpoint of the open interval I given in the hypothesis. Because f and g are both differentiable on I, except possibly at a, we conclude that F and G are both differentiable on the interval $(a, x]$, where $a < x < b$. Therefore F and G are both continuous on $(a, x]$. The functions are also continuous from the right at a because $\lim_{x \to a^+} F(x) = \lim_{x \to a^+} f(x)$ and $\lim_{x \to a^+} f(x) = 0$, which is $F(a)$; similarly, $\lim_{x \to a^+} G(x) = G(a)$. Therefore F and G are continuous on the closed interval $[a, x]$. So F and G satisfy the three conditions of the hypothesis of Cauchy's mean-value theorem on the interval $[a, x]$. Hence

$$\frac{F(x) - F(a)}{G(x) - G(a)} = \frac{F'(z)}{G'(z)}$$

where z is some number such that $a < z < x$. From (2) and the above equation we have

$$\frac{f(x)}{g(x)} = \frac{f'(z)}{g'(z)}$$

Because $a < z < x$, it follows that as $x \to a^+$, $z \to a^+$; therefore

$$\lim_{x \to a^+} \frac{f(x)}{g(x)} = \lim_{x \to a^+} \frac{f'(z)}{g'(z)}$$

But by hypothesis, this limit is L. Therefore

$$\lim_{x \to a^+} \frac{f(x)}{g(x)} = L$$ ∎

The proof of case (ii) is similar to the proof of case (i) and is left as an exercise (see Exercise 44). Case (iii) follows immediately from cases (i) and (ii).

L'Hôpital's rule also holds if either x increases without bound or x decreases without bound, as given in the next theorem.

7.7.4 Theorem   L'Hôpital's Rule

Let f and g be functions differentiable for all $x > N$, where N is a positive constant, and suppose that for all $x > N$, $g'(x) \neq 0$. If $\lim\limits_{x \to +\infty} f(x) = 0$ and $\lim\limits_{x \to +\infty} g(x) = 0$, and

$$\text{if} \quad \lim_{x \to +\infty} \frac{f'(x)}{g'(x)} = L \quad \text{then} \quad \lim_{x \to +\infty} \frac{f(x)}{g(x)} = L$$

The theorem is also valid if $x \to +\infty$ is replaced by $x \to -\infty$.

Proof   We prove the theorem for $x \to +\infty$. The proof for $x \to -\infty$ is left as an exercise (see Exercise 45).

For all $x > N$, let $x = 1/t$; then $t = 1/x$. Let F and G be the functions defined by $F(t) = f(1/t)$ and $G(t) = g(1/t)$, if $t \neq 0$. Then $f(x) = F(t)$ and $g(x) = G(t)$, where $x > N$ and $0 < t < 1/N$. From Definitions 3.7.1 and 1.6.1 you can show that the statements

$$\lim_{x \to +\infty} f(x) = M \quad \text{and} \quad \lim_{t \to 0^+} F(t) = M$$

have the same meaning. You are asked to prove this in Exercise 42. Because by hypothesis $\lim\limits_{x \to +\infty} f(x) = 0$ and $\lim\limits_{x \to +\infty} g(x) = 0$, we can conclude that

$$\lim_{t \to 0^+} F(t) = 0 \quad \text{and} \quad \lim_{t \to 0^+} G(t) = 0 \tag{3}$$

Using the chain rule in the quotient $F'(t)/G'(t)$, we have

$$\frac{F'(t)}{G'(t)} = \frac{-\dfrac{1}{t^2} f'\left(\dfrac{1}{t}\right)}{-\dfrac{1}{t^2} g'\left(\dfrac{1}{t}\right)}$$

$$= \frac{f'\left(\dfrac{1}{t}\right)}{g'\left(\dfrac{1}{t}\right)}$$

$$= \frac{f'(x)}{g'(x)}$$

Because by hypothesis $\lim\limits_{x \to +\infty} f'(x)/g'(x) = L$, it follows from the above that

$$\lim_{t \to 0^+} \frac{F'(t)}{G'(t)} = L \tag{4}$$

Because for all $x > N$, $g'(x) \neq 0$,

$$G'(t) \neq 0 \quad \text{for all } 0 < t < \frac{1}{N}$$

From this statement, (3), and (4) it follows from Theorem 7.7.2 that

$$\lim_{t \to 0^+} \frac{F(t)}{G(t)} = L$$

But because $F(t)/G(t) = f(x)/g(x)$ for all $x > N$ and $t \neq 0$, then

$$\lim_{x \to +\infty} \frac{f(x)}{g(x)} = L$$

and so the theorem is proved.   ∎

▶ **EXAMPLE 4**   Evaluate the limit if it exists.

$$\lim_{x \to +\infty} \frac{\dfrac{1}{x}}{\tan \dfrac{2}{x}}$$

Solution $\displaystyle\lim_{x \to +\infty} \frac{1}{x} = 0$ and $\displaystyle\lim_{x \to +\infty} \tan \frac{2}{x} = 0$. Thus from L'Hôpital's rule

$$\lim_{x \to +\infty} \frac{\dfrac{1}{x}}{\tan \dfrac{2}{x}} = \lim_{x \to +\infty} \frac{-\dfrac{1}{x^2}}{\left(\sec^2 \dfrac{2}{x}\right)\left(-\dfrac{2}{x^2}\right)}$$

$$= \frac{1}{2} \lim_{x \to +\infty} \frac{1}{\sec^2 \dfrac{2}{x}}$$

$$= \tfrac{1}{2}$$ ◀

Theorems 7.7.2 and 7.7.4 also hold if L is replaced by $+\infty$ or $-\infty$. The proofs of these cases are omitted. Note, however, that if $\displaystyle\lim_{x \to a} f(x) = 0$, $\displaystyle\lim_{x \to a} g(x) = 0$, and $\displaystyle\lim_{x \to a} [f'(x)/g'(x)]$ does not exist and is neither $+\infty$ nor $-\infty$, then $\displaystyle\lim_{x \to a} [f(x)/g(x)]$ may still exist. See Exercise 41 for an example of such a situation.

▶ **EXAMPLE 5**   Prove that if we remove the discontinuity at 0 of the function of Example 1, the resulting function will be differentiable at 0.

Solution   The function of Example 1 is defined by

$$f(x) = \frac{x}{e^x - 1}$$

and we showed there that $\displaystyle\lim_{x \to 0} f(x) = 1$. So we remove the discontinuity by redefining the function to be 1 at 0. If F is this new function,

$$F(x) = \begin{cases} \dfrac{x}{e^x - 1} & \text{if } x \neq 0 \\ 1 & \text{if } x = 0 \end{cases}$$

To show F is differentiable at 0, we compute $F'(0)$.

$$F'(0) = \lim_{x \to 0} \frac{F(x) - F(0)}{x - 0}$$

$$= \lim_{x \to 0} \frac{\dfrac{x}{e^x - 1} - 1}{x}$$

$$= \lim_{x \to 0} \frac{x - e^x + 1}{xe^x - x}$$

Because $\lim_{x \to 0}(x - e^x + 1) = 0$ and $\lim_{x \to 0}(xe^x - x) = 0$, we apply L'Hôpital's rule and get

$$F'(0) = \lim_{x \to 0} \frac{1 - e^x}{e^x + xe^x - 1}$$

Because $\lim_{x \to 0}(1 - e^x) = 0$ and $\lim_{x \to 0}(e^x + xe^x - 1) = 0$, we apply L'Hôpital's rule again and obtain

$$F'(0) = \lim_{x \to 0} \frac{-e^x}{e^x + e^x + xe^x}$$

$$= -\tfrac{1}{2}$$

We have, therefore, shown that F is differentiable at 0.   ◀

EXERCISES 7.7

In Exercises 1 through 10 do the following: (a) Plot the graph of f on your graphics calculator and state what $f(x)$ appears to be approaching as x approaches a; (b) confirm your answer in part (a) analytically by computing $\lim_{x \to a} f(x)$.

1. $f(x) = \dfrac{x}{\tan x}$

$a = 0$

2. $f(x) = \dfrac{\tan x - x}{x - \sin x}$

$a = 0$

3. $f(x) = \dfrac{\sin \pi x}{2 - x}$

$a = 2$

4. $f(x) = \dfrac{\sin^{-1} x}{x}$

$a = 0$

5. $f(x) = \dfrac{2^x - 3^x}{x}$

$a = 0$

6. $f(x) = \dfrac{\tanh 2x}{\tanh x}$

$a = 0$

7. $f(x) = \dfrac{\sin^2 x}{\sin x^2}$

$a = 0$

8. $f(x) = \dfrac{x^3 - 1}{x^3 + 3x - 4}$

$a = 1$

9. $f(x) = \dfrac{x^3 + 8}{x^3 + x^2 + 4}$

$a = -2$

10. $f(x) = \dfrac{3 \cos x}{2x - \pi}$

$a = \pi/2$

In Exercises 11 through 16, find the limit, if it exists, and support your answer graphically.

11. $\lim_{x \to 0} \dfrac{\tan 3x}{\tan 2x}$

12. $\lim_{x \to 1} \dfrac{\ln x}{x - 1}$

13. $\lim_{x \to +\infty} \dfrac{\sin \dfrac{2}{x}}{\dfrac{1}{x}}$

14. $\lim_{\theta \to 0} \dfrac{\theta - \sin \theta}{\tan^3 \theta}$

15. $\lim_{x \to \pi/2} \dfrac{\ln(\sin x)}{(\pi - 2x)^2}$

16. $\lim_{x \to 0} \dfrac{e^x - \cos x}{x \sin x}$

In Exercises 17 through 28, evaluate the limit if it exists.

17. $\displaystyle \lim_{x\to 1^+} \frac{x - 1}{x - 2\sqrt{x - 1} - 1}$

18. $\displaystyle \lim_{x\to 0} \frac{e^{2x^2 - 1}}{\sin^2 x}$

19. $\displaystyle \lim_{z\to +\infty} \frac{1 - e^{1/z}}{-\dfrac{3}{z}}$

20. $\displaystyle \lim_{y\to 0} \frac{y^2}{1 - \cosh y}$

21. $\displaystyle \lim_{t\to 0} \frac{\sin t}{\ln(2e^t - 1)}$

22. $\displaystyle \lim_{z\to 0} \frac{5z}{5^z - e^z}$

23. $\displaystyle \lim_{x\to 0} \frac{(1 + x)^{1/5} - (1 - x)^{1/5}}{(1 + x)^{1/3} - (1 - x)^{1/3}}$

24. $\displaystyle \lim_{x\to +\infty} \frac{\dfrac{1}{x^2} - 2\tan^{-1}\dfrac{1}{x}}{\dfrac{1}{x}}$

25. $\displaystyle \lim_{x\to \pi} \frac{1 + \cos 2x}{1 - \sin x}$

26. $\displaystyle \lim_{x\to 0} \frac{e^x - 10^x}{x}$

27. $\displaystyle \lim_{x\to 0} \frac{\cos x - \cosh x}{x^2}$

28. $\displaystyle \lim_{x\to 0} \frac{\sinh x - \sin x}{\sin^3 x}$

In Exercises 29 through 36, find all values of z in the interval (a, b) satisfying the conclusion of Cauchy's mean-value theorem for the given pair of functions.

29. $f(x) = x^3$, $g(x) = x^2$; $(a, b) = (0, 2)$

30. $f(x) = \dfrac{2x}{1 + x^2}$, $g(x) = \dfrac{1 - x^2}{1 + x^2}$; $(a, b) = (0, 2)$

31. $f(x) = \sin x$, $g(x) = \cos x$; $(a, b) = (0, \pi)$

32. $f(x) = \cos 2x$, $g(x) = \sin x$; $(a, b) = (0, \tfrac{1}{2}\pi)$

33. $f(x) = \ln x$, $g(x) = x^2$; $(a, b) = (1, 3)$

34. $f(x) = \sqrt{x + 5}$, $g(x) = x + 3$; $(a, b) = (-4, -1)$

35. $f(x) = e^{2x}$, $g(x) = e^x$; $(a, b) = (0, 2)$

36. $f(x) = \ln(x + 1)$, $g(x) = \ln x$; $(a, b) = (1, 2)$

37. An electrical circuit has a resistance of R ohms, an inductance of L henrys, and an electromotive force of E volts, where R, L, and E are positive. If i amperes is the current flowing in the circuit t seconds after a switch is turned on, then

$$i = \frac{E}{R}(1 - e^{-Rt/L})$$

If t, E, and L are constants, find $\displaystyle \lim_{R\to 0^+} i$.

38. In a geometric progression, if a is the first term, r is the common ratio of two successive terms, and S is the sum of the first n terms, then if $r \neq 1$,

$$S = \frac{a(r^n - 1)}{r - 1}$$

Find $\displaystyle \lim_{r\to 1} S$. Is the result consistent with the sum of the first n terms if $r = 1$?

39. Given

$$f(x) = \frac{\cos x - 1}{x}$$

Let F be the function obtained from f by removing the discontinuity at 0; that is,

$$F(x) = \begin{cases} f(x) & \text{if } x \neq 0 \\ \displaystyle\lim_{x\to 0} f(x) & \text{if } x = 0 \end{cases}$$

Prove that F is differentiable at 0 by computing $F'(0)$.

40. (a) Prove that if $a > 0$,

$$\lim_{x\to 0} \frac{a^x - 1}{x} = \ln a$$

(b) From the result of part (a) show that if $r > 0$ and $s > 0$, then

$$\lim_{x\to 0} \frac{(rs)^x - 1}{x} = \lim_{x\to 0} \frac{r^x - 1}{x} + \lim_{x\to 0} \frac{s^x - 1}{x}$$

41. Let

$$f(x) = x^2 \sin \frac{1}{x} \quad \text{and} \quad g(x) = x$$

Show that $\displaystyle\lim_{x\to 0} f(x) = 0$, $\displaystyle\lim_{x\to 0} g(x) = 0$, and $\displaystyle\lim_{x\to 0} [f'(x)/g'(x)]$ does not exist and is neither $+\infty$ nor $-\infty$. Also show that $\displaystyle\lim_{x\to 0} [f(x)/g(x)]$ does exist and find this limit. *Hint:* Apply the squeeze theorem.

42. Suppose that f is a function defined for all $x > N$, where N is a positive constant. If $t = 1/x$ and $F(t) = f(1/t)$, where $t \neq 0$, prove that the statements $\displaystyle\lim_{x\to +\infty} f(x) = M$ and $\displaystyle\lim_{t\to 0^+} F(t) = M$ have the same meaning.

43. Find values for a and b such that

$$\lim_{x\to 0} \frac{\sin 3x + ax + bx^3}{x^3} = 0$$

44. Prove Theorem 7.7.2(ii).

45. Prove Theorem 7.7.4 for $x \to -\infty$.

46. Suppose that f and g are two functions such that the function f/g has the indeterminate form $0/0$ at a. Furthermore, suppose that

$$\lim_{x\to a} f'(x) = L_1 \quad \text{and} \quad \lim_{x\to a} g'(x) = L_2$$

What can you conclude about $\displaystyle\lim_{x\to a} [f(x)/g(x)]$ in each of the following cases: **(a)** $L_1 \neq 0$ and $L_2 \neq 0$; **(b)** $L_1 = 0$ and $L_2 \neq 0$; **(c)** $L_1 \neq 0$ and $L_2 = 0$; **(d)** $L_1 = 0$ and $L_2 = 0$?

7.8 OTHER INDETERMINATE FORMS

Another indeterminate form of a quotient of two functions occurs when the numerator increases or decreases without bound and the denominator increases or decreases without bound. For instance, suppose we wish to evaluate, if it exists,

$$\lim_{x \to 0^+} \frac{\ln x}{\dfrac{1}{x}}$$

We cannot apply the theorem involving the limit of a quotient because $\lim_{x \to 0^+} \ln x = -\infty$ and $\lim_{x \to 0^+} (1/x) = +\infty$. In this case we say that the function defined by

$$f(x) = \frac{\ln x}{\dfrac{1}{x}}$$

has the indeterminate form $(-\infty)/(+\infty)$ at $x = 0$. L'Hôpital's rule also applies to an indeterminate form of this type as well as to $(+\infty)/(+\infty)$, $(-\infty)/(-\infty)$, and $(+\infty)/(-\infty)$. The rule is given by the following two theorems, for which the proofs are omitted because they are beyond the scope of this book.

7.8.1 Theorem   L'Hôpital's Rule

Let f and g be functions differentiable on an open interval I, except possibly at the number a in I, and suppose that for all $x \neq a$ in I, $g'(x) \neq 0$. If $\lim_{x \to a} f(x)$ is $+\infty$ or $-\infty$, and $\lim_{x \to a} g(x)$ is $+\infty$ or $-\infty$, and

if $\displaystyle\lim_{x \to a} \frac{f'(x)}{g'(x)} = L$ then $\displaystyle\lim_{x \to a} \frac{f(x)}{g(x)} = L$

The theorem is valid if all the limits are right-hand limits or if all the limits are left-hand limits.

▶ **EXAMPLE 1**   Given

$$f(x) = \frac{\ln x}{\dfrac{1}{x}}$$

(a) Plot the graph of f. What does $f(x)$ appear to be approaching as x approaches 0 from the right? **(b)** Confirm the answer in part (a) analytically by computing $\lim_{x \to 0^+} f(x)$.

Solution

(a) Figure 1 shows the graph of f plotted in the $[0, 3]$ by $[-1, 1]$ window. From the graph $f(x)$ appears to be approaching 0 as x approaches 0 from the right.

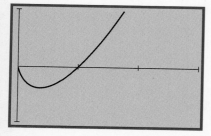

$[0, 3]$ by $[-1, 1]$

$$f(x) = \frac{\ln x}{1/x}$$

FIGURE 1

(b) Because $\lim\limits_{x \to 0^+} \ln x = -\infty$ and $\lim\limits_{x \to 0^+} (1/x) = +\infty$, we apply L'Hôpital's rule and get

$$\lim_{x \to 0^+} \frac{\ln x}{\dfrac{1}{x}} = \lim_{x \to 0^+} \frac{\dfrac{1}{x}}{-\dfrac{1}{x^2}}$$

$$= \lim_{x \to 0^+} (-x)$$

$$= 0$$

which confirms our answer in part (a).   ◀

7.8.2 Theorem   L'Hôpital's Rule

Let f and g be functions differentiable for all $x > N$, where N is a positive constant, and suppose that for all $x > N$, $g'(x) \neq 0$. If $\lim\limits_{x \to +\infty} f(x)$ is $+\infty$ or $-\infty$, and $\lim\limits_{x \to +\infty} g(x)$ is $+\infty$ or $-\infty$, and

$$\text{if} \qquad \lim_{x \to +\infty} \frac{f'(x)}{g'(x)} = L \qquad \text{then} \qquad \lim_{x \to +\infty} \frac{f(x)}{g(x)} = L$$

The theorem is also valid if $x \to +\infty$ is replaced by $x \to -\infty$.

Theorems 7.8.1 and 7.8.2 also hold if L is replaced by $+\infty$ or $-\infty$, and the proofs for these cases are also omitted.

▶ **EXAMPLE 2**   Evaluate, if it exists:

$$\lim_{x \to +\infty} \frac{5x}{\ln(2 + e^x)}$$

Support the answer graphically.

Solution   Because $\lim\limits_{x \to +\infty} 5x = +\infty$ and $\lim\limits_{x \to +\infty} (2 + e^x) = +\infty$, by applying L'Hôpital's rule, we obtain

$$\lim_{x \to +\infty} \frac{5x}{\ln(2 + e^x)} = \lim_{x \to +\infty} \frac{5}{\dfrac{1}{2 + e^x} \cdot (e^x)}$$

$$= \lim_{x \to +\infty} (10 + 5e^x)e^{-x}$$

$$= \lim_{x \to +\infty} (10e^{-x} + 5)$$

$$= 5$$

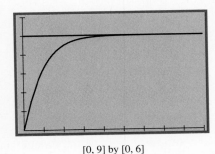

[0, 9] by [0, 6]

$f(x) = \dfrac{5x}{\ln(2 + e^x)}$ and $y = 5$

FIGURE 2

Figure 2 shows the graph of the line $y = 5$ and the function defined by $f(x) = 5x/\ln(2 + e^x)$ plotted in the [0, 9] by [0, 6] window. We have supported our answer because the line appears to be a horizontal asymptote of the graph of f.   ◀

▶ **EXAMPLE 3**   Evaluate, if it exists:

$$\lim_{x \to \pi/2^-} \frac{\sec x}{\sec 3x}$$

Solution $\lim\limits_{x \to \pi/2^-} \sec x = +\infty$, and $\lim\limits_{x \to \pi/2^-} \sec 3x = -\infty$. So from L'Hôpital's rule,

$$\lim_{x \to \pi/2^-} \frac{\sec x}{\sec 3x} = \lim_{x \to \pi/2^-} \frac{\sec x \tan x}{3 \sec 3x \tan 3x}$$

$\lim\limits_{x \to \pi/2^-} \sec x \tan x = +\infty$, and $\lim\limits_{x \to \pi/2^-} 3 \sec 3x \tan 3x = -\infty$. Observe that further applications of L'Hôpital's rule will not help us. The original quotient may, however, be rewritten.

$$\lim_{x \to \pi/2^-} \frac{\sec x}{\sec 3x} = \lim_{x \to \pi/2^-} \frac{\cos 3x}{\cos x}$$

Now, because $\lim\limits_{x \to \pi/2^-} \cos 3x = 0$ and $\lim\limits_{x \to \pi/2^-} \cos x = 0$, we may apply L'Hôpital's rule, giving

$$\lim_{x \to \pi/2^-} \frac{\cos 3x}{\cos x} = \lim_{x \to \pi/2^-} \frac{-3 \sin 3x}{-\sin x}$$

$$= -3 \qquad\qquad ◀$$

The limit in Example 3 can be evaluated without L'Hôpital's rule by using Theorem 1.10.2. You are asked to do this in Exercise 42.

In addition to $0/0$ and $\pm\infty/\pm\infty$, other indeterminate forms are $0 \cdot (+\infty)$, $+\infty - (+\infty)$, 0^0, $(\pm\infty)^0$, and $1^{\pm\infty}$. These indeterminate forms are defined analogously to the other two. For instance, if $\lim\limits_{x \to a} f(x) = +\infty$ and $\lim\limits_{x \to a} g(x) = 0$, then the function defined by $f(x)^{g(x)}$ has the indeterminate form $(+\infty)^0$ at a. To find the limit of a function having one of these indeterminate forms, it must be changed to either the form $0/0$ or $\pm\infty/\pm\infty$ before L'Hôpital's rule can be applied. The following examples illustrate the method.

▶ **EXAMPLE 4**   Evaluate, if it exists:

$$\lim_{x \to 0^+} \sin^{-1} x \csc x$$

Solution   Because $\lim\limits_{x \to 0^+} \sin^{-1} x = 0$ and $\lim\limits_{x \to 0^+} \csc x = +\infty$, the function defined by $f(x) = \sin^{-1} x \csc x$ has the indeterminate form $0 \cdot (+\infty)$ at 0. Before we can apply L'Hôpital's rule we rewrite $\sin^{-1} x \csc x$ as $\sin^{-1} x / \sin x$, and consider $\lim\limits_{x \to 0^+} (\sin^{-1} x / \sin x)$. Now $\lim\limits_{x \to 0^+} \sin^{-1} x = 0$ and

$\lim\limits_{x \to 0^+} \sin x = 0$; so we have the indeterminate form $0/0$. Therefore, from L'Hôpital's rule we obtain

$$\lim_{x \to 0^+} \frac{\sin^{-1} x}{\sin x} = \lim_{x \to 0^+} \frac{\dfrac{1}{\sqrt{1 - x^2}}}{\cos x}$$

$$= \frac{1}{1}$$

$$= 1 \qquad \blacktriangleleft$$

▶ **EXAMPLE 5** Given

$$f(x) = \frac{1}{x^2} - \frac{1}{x^2 \sec x}$$

(a) Plot the graph of f. What does $f(x)$ appear to be approaching as x approaches 0? **(b)** Confirm the answer in part (a) analytically by computing $\lim\limits_{x \to 0} f(x)$.

Solution

(a) Figure 3 shows the graph of f plotted in the $[-3, 3]$ by $[-1, 3]$ window. The graph has a hole (covered by the y axis) at $x = 0$ because $f(0)$ does not exist. From the graph, $f(x)$ appears to be approaching 0.5 as x approaches 0.

(b) Because

$$\lim_{x \to 0} \frac{1}{x^2} = +\infty \quad \text{and} \quad \lim_{x \to 0} \frac{1}{x^2 \sec x} = +\infty$$

we have the indeterminate form $+\infty - (+\infty)$. Rewriting the expression we have

$$\lim_{x \to 0} \left(\frac{1}{x^2} - \frac{1}{x^2 \sec x} \right) = \lim_{x \to 0} \left(\frac{1}{x^2} - \frac{\cos x}{x^2} \right)$$

$$= \lim_{x \to 0} \frac{1 - \cos x}{x^2}$$

$\lim\limits_{x \to 0} (1 - \cos x) = 0$ and $\lim\limits_{x \to 0} x^2 = 0$; so we apply L'Hôpital's rule and obtain

$$\lim_{x \to 0} \frac{1 - \cos x}{x^2} = \lim_{x \to 0} \frac{\sin x}{2x}$$

We apply L'Hôpital's rule once more because $\lim\limits_{x \to 0} \sin x = 0$ and $\lim\limits_{x \to 0} 2x = 0$, and we get

$$\lim_{x \to 0} \frac{\sin x}{2x} = \lim_{x \to 0} \frac{\cos x}{2}$$

$$= \frac{1}{2}$$

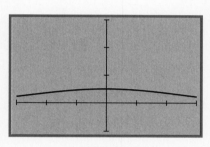

$[-3, 3]$ by $[-1, 3]$

$$f(x) = \frac{1}{x^2} - \frac{1}{x^2 \sec x}$$

FIGURE 3

Therefore

$$\lim_{x \to 0} \left(\frac{1}{x^2} - \frac{1}{x^2 \sec x} \right) = \frac{1}{2}$$

which confirms our answer in part (a).   ◀

For any one of the indeterminate forms 0^0, $(+\infty)^0$, $1^{+\infty}$, the procedure for evaluating the limit is demonstrated in Example 6.

▶   **EXAMPLE 6**   Evaluate, if it exists:

$$\lim_{x \to 0^+} (x + 1)^{\cot x}$$

Support the answer graphically.

Solution   Because $\lim\limits_{x \to 0^+} (x + 1) = 1$ and $\lim\limits_{x \to 0^+} \cot x = +\infty$, we have the indeterminate form $1^{+\infty}$. Let

$$y = (x + 1)^{\cot x} \qquad \qquad \textbf{(1)}$$

Then

$$\ln y = \cot x \ln(x + 1)$$
$$= \frac{\ln(x + 1)}{\tan x}$$

So

$$\lim_{x \to 0^+} \ln y = \lim_{x \to 0^+} \frac{\ln(x + 1)}{\tan x} \qquad \qquad \textbf{(2)}$$

Because $\lim\limits_{x \to 0^+} \ln(x + 1) = 0$ and $\lim\limits_{x \to 0^+} \tan x = 0$, we may apply L'Hôpital's rule to the right side of (2) and obtain

$$\lim_{x \to 0^+} \frac{\ln(x + 1)}{\tan x} = \lim_{x \to 0^+} \frac{\dfrac{1}{x + 1}}{\sec^2 x}$$
$$= 1$$

Therefore substituting 1 on the right side of (2) we have

$$\lim_{x \to 0^+} \ln y = 1 \qquad \qquad \textbf{(3)}$$

Because the exponential function is continuous on its entire domain, which is the set of all real numbers, we may apply Theorem 1.9.1; so

$$\lim_{x \to 0^+} \exp(\ln y) = \exp(\lim_{x \to 0^+} \ln y)$$

Therefore it follows from (3) and this equation that

$$\lim_{x \to 0^+} y = e^1$$

But from (1), $y = (x + 1)^{\cot x}$, and therefore

$$\lim_{x \to 0^+} (x + 1)^{\cot x} = e$$

Figure 4 showing the graph of $f(x) = (x + 1)^{\cot x}$ plotted in the $[0, 3]$ by $[0, 5]$ window supports our answer.   ◀

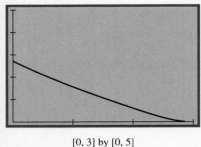

[0, 3] by [0, 5]

$f(x) = (x + 1)^{\cot x}$

FIGURE 4

EXERCISES 7.8

In Exercises 1 through 8 do the following: (a) Estimate the limit, if it exists, by plotting the graph of the function in a convenient window; (b) confirm your answer in part (a) analytically by computing the limit.

1. $\lim\limits_{x \to +\infty} \dfrac{x^2}{e^x}$

2. $\lim\limits_{x \to +\infty} \dfrac{(\ln x)^3}{x}$

3. $\lim\limits_{x \to 0^+} \tan x\,(\ln x)$

4. $\lim\limits_{x \to 0^+} \tan^{-1} x \cot x$

5. $\lim\limits_{x \to 1}\left(\dfrac{1}{\ln x} - \dfrac{1}{x-1}\right)$

6. $\lim\limits_{x \to 0^+} (1 + x)^{\ln x}$

7. $\lim\limits_{x \to 0^+} x^{\sin x}$

8. $\lim\limits_{x \to 2}\left(\dfrac{5}{x^2 + x - 6} - \dfrac{1}{x-2}\right)$

In Exercises 9 through 16, find the limit, if it exists, and support your answer graphically.

9. $\lim\limits_{x \to +\infty} \dfrac{\ln x}{x}$

10. $\lim\limits_{x \to +\infty} \dfrac{\ln(x + 100)}{\ln x}$

11. $\lim\limits_{x \to 0^+} x \csc x$

12. $\lim\limits_{x \to 1/2^+} (2x - 1) \tan \pi x$

13. $\lim\limits_{x \to +\infty} (x^2 - \sqrt{x^4 - x^2 + 2})$

14. $\lim\limits_{x \to 0^+}\left(\dfrac{1}{\sin x} - \dfrac{1}{x}\right)$

15. $\lim\limits_{x \to 0}(1 + 3x)^{1/x}$

16. $\lim\limits_{x \to 0^+} x^{1/\ln x}$

In Exercises 17 through 34, find the limit if it exists.

17. $\lim\limits_{x \to 1/2^-} \dfrac{\ln(1 - 2x)}{\tan \pi x}$

18. $\lim\limits_{x \to \pi/2^-} \dfrac{\ln(\cos x)}{\ln(\tan x)}$

19. $\lim\limits_{x \to +\infty} (e^x + x)^{2/x}$

20. $\lim\limits_{x \to 0^+} (\sinh x)^{\tan x}$

21. $\lim\limits_{x \to 0^+} (\sin x)^{x^2}$

22. $\lim\limits_{x \to 0} (x + e^{2x})^{1/x}$

23. $\lim\limits_{x \to +\infty} \dfrac{x^2 + 2x}{e^{3x} - 1}$

24. $\lim\limits_{x \to +\infty}\left(1 + \dfrac{1}{2x}\right)^{x^2}$

25. $\lim\limits_{x \to 0} (1 + \sinh x)^{2/x}$

26. $\lim\limits_{x \to 2} (x - 2) \tan \tfrac{1}{4}\pi x$

27. $\lim\limits_{x \to 0} [(\cos x)e^{x^2/2}]^{4/x^4}$

28. $\lim\limits_{x \to 0} (\cos x)^{1/x^2}$

29. $\lim\limits_{x \to +\infty} [(x^6 + 3x^5 + 4)^{1/6} - x]$

30. $\lim\limits_{x \to +\infty} \dfrac{\ln(x + e^x)}{3x}$

31. $\lim\limits_{x \to 0^+} \dfrac{e^{-1/x}}{x}$

32. $\lim\limits_{x \to 0^+} x^{x^x}$

33. $\lim\limits_{x \to +\infty} \dfrac{x}{\sqrt{1 + x^2}}$

34. $\lim\limits_{x \to +\infty} (x - \sqrt{x^2 + x})$

35. Plot the graph of

$$f(x) = \dfrac{2^x}{e^x}$$

in a convenient window and from the graph predict the behavior of $f(x)$ as (a) $x \to -\infty$, and

(b) $x \to +\infty$. Confirm your answers in parts (a) and (b) by determining (c) $\lim\limits_{x \to -\infty} f(x)$ and (d) $\lim\limits_{x \to +\infty} f(x)$, respectively.

36. Do Exercise 35 if

$$f(x) = \dfrac{e^x}{3^x}$$

37. Prove that e^x increases faster than x^p for all positive values of p, no matter how large, by evaluating

$$\lim\limits_{x \to +\infty} \dfrac{e^x}{x^p}$$

38. Prove that $\ln x$ increases slower than x^p for all positive values of p, no matter how small, by evaluating

$$\lim\limits_{x \to +\infty} \dfrac{\ln x}{x^p}$$

39. If $f(x) = \begin{cases} (1 - e^{4x})^x & \text{if } x < 0 \\ k & \text{if } 0 \le x \end{cases}$, find k so that f is continuous at $x = 0$.

40. If $f(x) = \begin{cases} (x + 1)^{(\ln k)/x} & \text{if } x \ne 0 \\ 5 & \text{if } x = 0 \end{cases}$, find k so that f is continuous at $x = 0$.

41. If $\lim\limits_{x \to +\infty}\left(\dfrac{nx + 1}{nx - 1}\right)^x = 9$, find n.

42. Evaluate the limit in Example 3 without using L'Hôpital's rule but by using Theorem 1.10.2 and the identities $\cos(\tfrac{1}{2}\pi - t) = \sin t$ and $\sin(\tfrac{1}{2}\pi - t) = \cos t$.

43. (a) Prove that $\lim\limits_{x \to 0} (e^{-1/x^2}/x^n) = 0$ for any positive integer n. (b) If $f(x) = e^{-1/x^2}$, use the result of (a) to prove that the limits of f and all of its derivatives, as x approaches 0, are 0.

44. Suppose $f(x) = \int_1^x e^{3t} \sqrt{9t^4 + 1}\, dt$ and $g(x) = x^n e^{3x}$. If $\lim\limits_{x \to +\infty}\left[\dfrac{f'(x)}{g'(x)}\right] = 1$, find n.

45. If the normal line to the curve $y = x^p$, where $p > 0$, at the point (u, u^p) intersects the x axis at the point $(a, 0)$, prove that

$$\lim\limits_{u \to +\infty} (a - u) = \begin{cases} 0 & \text{if } 0 < p < 0.5 \\ 0.5 & \text{if } p = 0.5 \\ +\infty & \text{if } 0.5 < p \end{cases}$$

46. If the normal line to the curve $y = \ln x$ at the point $(u, \ln u)$ intersects the x axis at the point $(a, 0)$, prove that

$$\lim\limits_{u \to +\infty} (a - u) = 0$$

In Exercises 47 and 48, sketch the graph of f by first finding the local extrema of f and the horizontal asymptotes of the graph, if there are any. Check your graph on your graphics calculator.

47. $f(x) = x^{1/x}$, $x > 0$ **48.** $f(x) = x^x$, $x > 0$

49. Compute $\lim\limits_{x \to +\infty} \log_x(x + 10)$ and support your answer graphically. *Hint:* First express $\log_x(x + 10)$ in terms of natural logarithms by applying Equation (3) in Section 5.5.

50. Given

$$f(x) = \frac{x - \cos x}{x + \sin x}$$

(a) Estimate $\lim\limits_{x \to +\infty} f(x)$, if it exists, by plotting the graph of f in a convenient window. **(b)** Confirm your answer in part (a) analytically by computing the limit. **(c)** Why cannot L'Hôpital's rule be used to compute the limit in part (b)?

51. Determine each of the following limits:

(a) $\lim\limits_{x \to 0^+} (\sin x)^{\csc x}$ **(b)** $\lim\limits_{x \to +\infty} \left(\sin \dfrac{1}{x} \right)^x$

(c) Is $0^{+\infty}$ an indeterminate form? Explain how you arrived at your answer.

7.9 IMPROPER INTEGRALS WITH INFINITE LIMITS OF INTEGRATION

So far in our treatment of the definite integral we have assumed that the integrand was defined on a closed interval. In this section, we extend the definition of the definite integral to consider an infinite interval of integration. We call such an integral an **improper integral.** Another kind of improper integral is discussed in the next section.

▷ **ILLUSTRATION 1**   Consider the problem of finding the area of the region bounded by the curve $y = e^{-x}$, the x axis, and the line $x = b$, where $b > 0$. This region appears in Figure 1. If A square units is the area of the region,

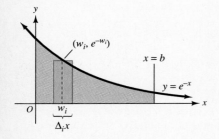

FIGURE 1

$$A = \lim_{\|\Delta\| \to 0} \sum_{i=1}^{n} e^{w_i} \, \Delta_i x$$

$$= \int_0^b e^{-x} \, dx$$

$$= -e^{-x} \Big]_0^b$$

$$= 1 - e^{-b}$$

If we let b increase without bound, then

$$\lim_{b \to +\infty} \int_0^b e^{-x} \, dx = \lim_{b \to +\infty} (1 - e^{-b})$$

$$\lim_{b \to +\infty} \int_0^b e^{-x} \, dx = 1 \qquad \qquad \textbf{(1)}$$

Therefore, no matter how large a value we take for b, the area of the region shown in Figure 1 will always be less than 1 square unit.   ◄

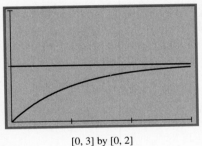

[0, 3] by [0, 2]

$y = \text{NINT}(e^{-t}, 0, x)$ and $y = 1$

FIGURE 2

▷   **ILLUSTRATION 2**   We support our answer in Illustration 1 by plotting the graph of $y = \text{NINT}(e^{-t}, 0, x)$ and the line $y = 1$ in the $[0, 3]$ by $[0, 2]$ window as shown in Figure 2. The figure supports our answer because the line appears to be a horizontal asymptote of the graph.   ◀

Equation (1) states that if $b > 0$, for any $\epsilon > 0$ there exists an $N > 0$ such that

$$\text{if} \quad b > N \quad \text{then} \quad \left| \int_0^b e^{-x} \, dx - 1 \right| < \epsilon$$

In place of (1) we write

$$\int_0^{+\infty} e^{-x} \, dx = 1$$

In general, we have the following definition.

7.9.1 Definition of an Improper Integral with Infinite Upper Limit

If f is continuous for all $x \geq a$, then

$$\int_a^{+\infty} f(x) \, dx = \lim_{b \to +\infty} \int_a^b f(x) \, dx$$

if this limit exists.

The following definition pertains to an improper integral for which the lower limit of integration is infinite.

7.9.2 Definition of an Improper Integral with Infinite Lower Limit

If f is continuous for all $x \leq b$, then

$$\int_{-\infty}^b f(x) \, dx = \lim_{a \to -\infty} \int_a^b f(x) \, dx$$

if this limit exists.

In the above two definitions, if the limits exist, we say that the improper integral is **convergent.** If the limits do not exist, the improper integral is **divergent.**

▶   **EXAMPLE 1**   Evaluate the integral, if it converges:

$$\int_{-\infty}^2 \frac{dx}{(4 - x)^2}$$

Support the answer graphically.

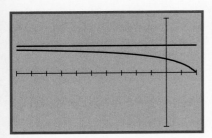

$[-10, 2]$ by $[-1, 1]$

$y = \text{NINT}\left(\dfrac{1}{(4-t)^2}, x, 2\right)$ and $y = 0.5$

FIGURE 3

Solution

$$\int_{-\infty}^{2} \frac{dx}{(4-x)^2} = \lim_{a \to -\infty} \int_{a}^{2} \frac{dx}{(4-x)^2}$$

$$= \lim_{a \to -\infty} \left[\frac{1}{4-x}\right]_{a}^{2}$$

$$= \lim_{a \to -\infty} \left(\frac{1}{2} - \frac{1}{4-a}\right)$$

$$= \tfrac{1}{2} - 0$$

$$= \tfrac{1}{2}$$

We support our answer by plotting the graphs of $y = \text{NINT}(1/(4-t)^2, x, 2)$ and the line $y = 0.5$ in the $[-10, 2]$ by $[-1, 1]$ window as shown in Figure 3, where the line appears to be a horizontal asymptote of the graph. ◀

The following definition pertains to an improper integral for the case when both limits of integration are infinite.

> **7.9.3 Definition of an Improper Integral with Both Lower and Upper Limits Infinite**
>
> If f is continuous for all values of x and c is any real number, then
>
> $$\int_{-\infty}^{+\infty} f(x)\, dx = \lim_{a \to -\infty} \int_{a}^{c} f(x)\, dx + \lim_{b \to +\infty} \int_{c}^{b} f(x)\, dx \qquad (2)$$
>
> if both of these limits exist.

In Exercise 42 you are asked to prove that when the limits exist, the right side of (2) is independent of the choice of c. When Definition 7.9.3 is applied, c is usually taken as 0.

▶ **EXAMPLE 2** Evaluate, if they exist:

(a) $\displaystyle \int_{-\infty}^{+\infty} x\, dx$ **(b)** $\displaystyle \lim_{r \to +\infty} \int_{-r}^{r} x\, dx$

Solution

(a) From Definition 7.9.3 with $c = 0$ we have

$$\int_{-\infty}^{+\infty} x\, dx = \lim_{a \to -\infty} \int_{a}^{0} x\, dx + \lim_{b \to +\infty} \int_{0}^{b} x\, dx$$

$$= \lim_{a \to -\infty} \left[\tfrac{1}{2}x^2\right]_{a}^{0} + \lim_{b \to +\infty} \left[\tfrac{1}{2}x^2\right]_{0}^{b}$$

$$= \lim_{a \to -\infty} \left(-\tfrac{1}{2}a^2\right) + \lim_{b \to +\infty} \tfrac{1}{2}b^2$$

Because neither of these two limits exists, the improper integral diverges.

(b) $\displaystyle\lim_{r\to+\infty}\int_{-r}^{r} x\,dx = \lim_{r\to+\infty}\left[\tfrac{1}{2}x^2\right]_{-r}^{r}$

$\displaystyle\qquad\qquad = \lim_{r\to+\infty}(\tfrac{1}{2}r^2 - \tfrac{1}{2}r^2)$

$\displaystyle\qquad\qquad = \lim_{r\to+\infty} 0$

$\displaystyle\qquad\qquad = 0$ ◀

▶ **EXAMPLE 3**   Evaluate the integral, if it converges:

$$\int_{-\infty}^{+\infty} \frac{dx}{x^2 + 1}$$

Support the answer graphically.

Solution

$$\int_{-\infty}^{+\infty} \frac{dx}{x^2 + 1} = \lim_{a\to-\infty}\int_{a}^{0} \frac{dx}{x^2 + 1} + \lim_{b\to+\infty}\int_{0}^{b} \frac{dx}{x^2 + 1}$$

$$= \lim_{a\to-\infty}\left[\tan^{-1} x\right]_{a}^{0} + \lim_{b\to+\infty}\left[\tan^{-1} x\right]_{0}^{b}$$

$$= \lim_{a\to-\infty}(\tan^{-1} 0 - \tan^{-1} a) + \lim_{b\to+\infty}(\tan^{-1} b - \tan^{-1} 0)$$

$$= 0 - \lim_{a\to-\infty}(\tan^{-1} a) + \lim_{b\to+\infty}(\tan^{-1} b) - 0$$

$$= -\left(-\frac{\pi}{2}\right) + \frac{\pi}{2}$$

$$= \pi$$

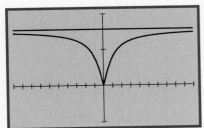

[−10, 10] by [−1, 2]

$y_1 = \text{NINT}\,(1/(t^2 + 1), x, 0)(x < 0)$

$y_2 = \text{NINT}\,(1/(t^2 + 1), 0, x)(x > 0)$

$y = \pi/2$

FIGURE 4

To support our answer we plot the graphs of

$$y_1 = \text{NINT}(1/(t^2 + 1), x, 0)\ (x < 0)$$
$$y_2 = \text{NINT}(1/(t^2 + 1), 0, x)\ (x > 0)$$

and the line $y = \pi/2$ in the $[-10, 10]$ by $[-1, 2]$ window as shown in Figure 4. The fact that the line $y = \pi/2$ appears to be an asymptote of both the graphs of y_1 and y_2 supports our answer. ◀

▶ **EXAMPLE 4**   Evaluate the integral, if it converges:

$$\int_{0}^{+\infty} xe^{-x}\,dx$$

Solution

$$\int_{0}^{+\infty} xe^{-x}\,dx = \lim_{b\to+\infty}\int_{0}^{b} xe^{-x}\,dx$$

To evaluate the integral we use integration by parts with $u = x$, $dv = e^{-x} \, dx$, $du = dx$, and $v = -e^{-x}$. Thus

$$\int_0^{+\infty} xe^{-x} \, dx = \lim_{b \to +\infty} \left[-xe^{-x} - e^{-x} \right]_0^b$$

$$= \lim_{b \to +\infty} (-be^{-b} - e^{-b} + 1)$$

$$= -\lim_{b \to +\infty} \frac{b}{e^b} - 0 + 1 \qquad\qquad \textbf{(3)}$$

To evaluate $\lim\limits_{b \to +\infty} \dfrac{b}{e^b}$, we apply L'Hôpital's rule because $\lim\limits_{b \to +\infty} b = +\infty$ and $\lim\limits_{b \to +\infty} e^b = +\infty$. We have

$$\lim_{b \to +\infty} \frac{b}{e^b} = \lim_{b \to +\infty} \frac{1}{e^b}$$

$$= 0$$

Therefore, from (3),

$$\int_0^{+\infty} xe^{-x} \, dx = 1 \qquad\qquad \blacktriangleleft$$

▶ **EXAMPLE 5**   Is it possible to assign a finite number to represent the measure of the area of the region to the right of the line $x = 1$, below the graph of $y = 1/x$, and above the x axis?

Solution   The region appears in Figure 5. Let L be the number we wish to assign to the measure of the area, if possible. Let A be the measure of the area of the region bounded by the graphs of the equations $y = 1/x$, $y = 0$, $x = 1$, and $x = b$, where $b > 1$. Then

$$A = \lim_{\|\Delta\| \to 0} \sum_{i=1}^n \frac{1}{w_i} \Delta_i x$$

$$= \int_1^b \frac{1}{x} \, dx$$

So we shall let $L = \lim\limits_{b \to +\infty} A$ if this limit exists. But

$$\lim_{b \to +\infty} A = \lim_{b \to +\infty} \int_1^b \frac{1}{x} \, dx$$

$$= \lim_{b \to +\infty} [\ln b - \ln 1]$$

$$= +\infty$$

Therefore it is not possible to assign a finite number to represent the measure of the area of the region.   ◀

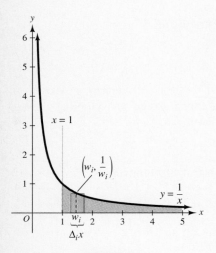

FIGURE 5

▶ **EXAMPLE 6**   Is it possible to assign a finite number to represent the measure of the volume of the solid formed by revolving the region in Example 5 about the x axis?

Solution   The element of volume is a circular disk having a thickness of $\Delta_i x$ and a base radius of $1/w_i$. Let L be the number we wish to assign to the measure of the volume, and let V be the measure of the volume of the solid formed by revolving about the x axis the region bounded by the graphs of the equations $y = 1/x$, $y = 0$, $x = 1$, and $x = b$, where $b > 1$. Then

$$V = \lim_{\|\Delta\| \to 0} \sum_{i=1}^{n} \pi \left(\frac{1}{w_i} \right)^2 \Delta_i x$$

$$= \pi \int_{1}^{b} \frac{1}{x^2} \, dx$$

We shall let $L = \lim_{b \to +\infty} V$, if the limit exists.

$$\lim_{b \to +\infty} V = \lim_{b \to +\infty} \pi \int_{1}^{b} \frac{dx}{x^2}$$

$$= \pi \lim_{b \to +\infty} \left[-\frac{1}{x} \right]_{1}^{b}$$

$$= \pi \lim_{b \to +\infty} \left(-\frac{1}{b} + 1 \right)$$

Thus we assign π to represent the measure of the volume of the solid.   ◀

▶ **EXAMPLE 7**

Determine if $\displaystyle\int_{0}^{+\infty} \sin x \, dx$ is convergent or divergent.

Solution

$$\int_{0}^{+\infty} \sin x \, dx = \lim_{b \to +\infty} \int_{0}^{b} \sin x \, dx$$

$$= \lim_{b \to +\infty} \left[-\cos x \right]_{0}^{b}$$

$$= \lim_{b \to +\infty} (-\cos b + 1).$$

For any integer n, as b takes on all values from $n\pi$ to $2n\pi$, $\cos b$ takes on all values from -1 to 1. Hence $\lim_{b \to +\infty} \cos b$ does not exist. Therefore the improper integral is divergent.   ◀

Example 7 illustrates the case for which an improper integral is divergent where the limit is not infinite.

An application of an improper integral with an infinite limit of integration involves probability. The probability of a particular event occurring is a number in the closed interval $[0, 1]$. If an event is certain to occur, then the probability of its happening is 1; if the event will never occur, then the probability is 0. The surer that an event will occur, the closer its probability is to 1.

Suppose that the set of all possible outcomes of a particular situation is the set of all numbers x in some interval I. For instance, x may be the number of minutes in the waiting time for a table at a particular restaurant, the number of hours in the life of a picture tube for a television set, or the number of inches in a person's height. It is sometimes necessary to determine the probability of x being in some subinterval of I. For example, one may wish to find the probability that a person will have to wait between 20 and 30 minutes for a table at a restaurant, or the probability of a television picture tube lasting more than 2000 hours, or the probability that someone chosen at random will have a height between 66 and 72 inches. Such problems involve evaluating an integral of a function called a *probability density function*. You were introduced to the standardized normal probability density function in Section 5.6. Probability density functions are obtained from statistical experiments. We give a brief informal discussion of them here to show how improper integrals arise.

A **probability density function** is a function f having as its domain the set R of real numbers and that satisfies the following two conditions:

1. $f(x) \geq 0$ for all x in R.

2. $\displaystyle\int_{-\infty}^{+\infty} f(x)\, dx = 1$

We shall consider here the *exponential density function* defined by

$$f(x) = \begin{cases} ke^{-kx} & \text{if } x \geq 0 \\ 0 & \text{if } x < 0 \end{cases} \tag{4}$$

where $k > 0$. To verify that this function qualifies as a probability density function we show that the two properties hold.

1. If $x < 0, f(x) = 0$; if $x \geq 0, f(x) = ke^{-kx}$, and because $k > 0$, $ke^{-kx} > 0$.

2.
$$\begin{aligned}
\int_{-\infty}^{+\infty} f(x)\, dx &= \int_{-\infty}^{0} f(x)\, dx + \int_{0}^{+\infty} f(x)\, dx \\
&= \int_{-\infty}^{0} 0\, dx + \int_{0}^{+\infty} ke^{-kx}\, dx \\
&= 0 + \lim_{b \to +\infty} \left[-\int_{0}^{b} e^{-kx}(-k\, dx) \right] \\
&= \lim_{b \to +\infty} \left[-e^{-kx} \right]_{0}^{b} \\
&= \lim_{b \to +\infty} (-e^{-kb} + 1) \\
&= 1
\end{aligned}$$

If f is a probability density function for a particular event occurring, then the **probability that the event will occur over the closed interval** $[a, b]$ is denoted by $P([a, b])$ and

$$P([a, b]) = \int_{a}^{b} f(x)\, dx$$

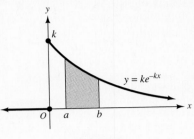

FIGURE 6

Figure 6 shows the graph of the exponential density function. Because $\int_0^{+\infty} ke^{-kx}\, dx = 1$, the measure of the area of the region bounded by $y = ke^{-kx}$, the x axis, and the y axis is 1. The measure of the area of the shaded region in the figure is $P([a, b])$.

▶ **EXAMPLE 8**   For a particular kind of battery the probability density function for x hours to be the life of a battery selected at random is given by

$$f(x) = \begin{cases} \frac{1}{60} e^{-x/60} & \text{if } x \geq 0 \\ 0 & \text{if } x < 0 \end{cases} \qquad (5)$$

Find the probability that the life of a battery selected at random will be **(a)** between 15 and 25 hours and **(b)** at least 50 hours.

Solution   The function defined by (5) is of the form of (4) with $k = \frac{1}{60}$.
(a) The probability that the life of a battery selected at random will be between 15 and 25 hours is $P([15, 25])$, and **(b)** the probability that it will be at least 50 hours is $P([50, +\infty))$.

(a)
$$P([15, 25]) = \int_{15}^{25} \frac{1}{60} e^{-x/60}\, dx$$
$$= -\int_{15}^{25} e^{-x/60}\left(-\frac{1}{60}\, dx\right)$$
$$= -e^{-x/60}\Big]_{15}^{25}$$
$$= -e^{-25/60} + e^{-15/60}$$
$$= 0.120$$

(b)
$$P([50, +\infty)) = \lim_{b \to +\infty} \int_{50}^{b} \frac{1}{60} e^{-x/60}\, dx$$
$$= \lim_{b \to +\infty}\left[-e^{-x/60}\right]_{50}^{b}$$
$$= \lim_{b \to +\infty}\left(-e^{-b/60} + e^{-50/60}\right)$$
$$= 0 + e^{-50/60}$$
$$= 0.435 \qquad \blacktriangleleft$$

EXERCISES 7.9

In Exercises 1 through 18, determine whether the improper integral is convergent or divergent, and if it is convergent, evaluate it. Support your answer graphically.

1. $\int_0^{+\infty} e^{-x/3}\, dx$

2. $\int_{-\infty}^{1} e^x\, dx$

3. $\int_{-\infty}^{0} x5^{-x^2}\, dx$

4. $\int_{1}^{+\infty} 2^{-x}\, dx$

5. $\int_0^{+\infty} x2^{-x}\, dx$

6. $\int_5^{+\infty} \frac{dx}{\sqrt{x-1}}$

7. $\int_{-\infty}^{+\infty} x \cosh x\, dx$

8. $\int_{-\infty}^{0} x^2 e^x\, dx$

9. $\int_5^{+\infty} \frac{x\, dx}{\sqrt[3]{9-x^2}}$

10. $\int_{-\infty}^{+\infty} \frac{3x\, dx}{(3x^2+2)^3}$

11. $\displaystyle\int_{\sqrt{3}}^{+\infty} \frac{3\,dx}{x^2 + 9}$

12. $\displaystyle\int_{e}^{+\infty} \frac{dx}{x \ln x}$

13. $\displaystyle\int_{-\infty}^{+\infty} e^{-|x|}\,dx$

14. $\displaystyle\int_{-\infty}^{+\infty} x e^{-x^2}\,dx$

15. $\displaystyle\int_{e}^{+\infty} \frac{dx}{x(\ln x)^2}$

16. $\displaystyle\int_{-\infty}^{+\infty} \frac{dx}{16 + x^2}$

17. $\displaystyle\int_{1}^{+\infty} \ln x\,dx$

18. $\displaystyle\int_{0}^{+\infty} e^{-x} \cos x\,dx$

19. Evaluate, if they exist:

(a) $\displaystyle\int_{-\infty}^{+\infty} \sin x\,dx$ (b) $\displaystyle\lim_{r \to +\infty} \int_{-r}^{r} \sin x\,dx$

20. Prove that if $\int_{-\infty}^{b} f(x)\,dx$ is convergent, then $\int_{-b}^{+\infty} f(-x)\,dx$ is also convergent and has the same value.

21. Show that the improper integral $\int_{-\infty}^{+\infty} x(1 + x^2)^{-2}\,dx$ is convergent and that the improper integral $\int_{-\infty}^{+\infty} x(1 + x^2)^{-1}\,dx$ is divergent.

22. Prove that the improper integral $\displaystyle\int_{1}^{+\infty} \frac{dx}{x^p}$ is convergent if and only if $p > 1$.

23. Determine if it is possible to assign a finite number to represent the measure of the area of the region bounded by the curve whose equation is $y = 1/(e^x + e^{-x})$ and the x axis. If a finite number can be assigned, find it.

24. Determine if it is possible to assign a finite number to represent the measure of the area of the region bounded by the x axis, the line $x = 2$, and the curve whose equation is $y = 1/(x^2 - 1)$. If a finite number can be assigned, find it.

25. Determine if it is possible to assign a finite number to represent the measure of the volume of the solid formed by revolving about the x axis the region to the right of the line $x = 1$ and bounded by the curve whose equation is $y = 1/x^{3/2}$ and the x axis. If a finite number can be assigned, find it.

26. Determine if it is possible to assign a finite number to represent the measure of the volume of the solid formed by revolving about the x axis the region bounded by the x axis, the y axis, and the curve whose equation is $y = e^{-2x}$. If a finite number can be assigned, find it.

27. For the battery of Example 8, find the probability that the life of a battery selected at random will be **(a)** not more than 50 hours and **(b)** at least 75 hours.

28. For a certain type of light bulb, the probability density function that x hours will be the life of a bulb

selected at random is given by

$$f(x) = \begin{cases} \frac{1}{40} e^{-x/40} & \text{if } x \geq 0 \\ 0 & \text{if } x < 0 \end{cases}$$

Find the probability that the life of a bulb selected at random will be **(a)** between 40 and 60 hours and **(b)** at least 60 hours.

29. In a certain city, the probability density function for x minutes to be the length of a telephone call selected at random is given by

$$f(x) = \begin{cases} \frac{1}{3} e^{-x/3} & \text{if } x \geq 0 \\ 0 & \text{if } x < 0 \end{cases}$$

Find the probability that a telephone call selected at random will last **(a)** between 1 min and 2 min, and **(b)** at least 5 min.

30. For a particular appliance, the probability density function that it will need servicing x months after it is purchased is given by

$$f(x) = \begin{cases} 0.02 e^{-0.02x} & \text{if } x \geq 0 \\ 0 & \text{if } x < 0 \end{cases}$$

If the appliance is guaranteed for a year, what is the probability that a customer selected at random will not need servicing during the 1-year warranty period?

31. Suppose a rocket is launched from the surface of the earth and neglect all resistance except gravity. Then, if v miles per second is the velocity necessary to escape the gravitational field of the earth,

$$v^2 = 2gR^2 \int_{R}^{+\infty} x^{-2}\,dx$$

where g is the gravity constant measured in miles per second per second at the earth's surface and R miles is the radius of the earth. With $g = 0.006094$ and $R = 3963$, approximate the escape velocity to three significant digits.

32. If f is a probability density function, then the *mean* (or *average*) *value* of the probabilities is given by

$$\int_{-\infty}^{+\infty} x f(x)\,dx$$

if it exists. Find the mean of the probabilities obtained from the exponential density function (4).

Exercises 33 through 36 show an application of improper integrals in the field of economics. Suppose a continuous flow of income for which interest is compounded continuously at the annual rate of 100i percent and f(t) dollars is the income per year at any time t years. If the income continues indefinitely, the present value, V dollars, of all future income is defined by

$$V = \int_0^{+\infty} f(t)e^{-it}\, dt$$

33. A continuous flow of income is decreasing with time, and at t years the number of dollars in the annual income is $1000 \cdot 2^{-t}$. Find the present value of this income if it continues indefinitely using an interest rate of 8 percent compounded continuously.

34. Suppose that the owner of a piece of business property holds a permanent lease on the property so that the rent is paid perpetually. If the annual rent is \$12,000 and money is worth 10 percent compounded continuously, find the present value of all future rent payments.

35. The British Consol is a bond with no maturity (i.e., it never comes due), and it affords the holder an annual lump-sum payment. By finding the present value of a flow of payments of R dollars annually and using the current interest rate $100i$ percent, compounded continuously, show that the fair selling price of a British Consol is R/i dollars.

36. The continuous flow of profit for a company is increasing with time, and at t years the number of dollars in the profit per year is proportional to t. Show that the present value of the company is inversely proportional to i^2, where $100i$ percent is the interest rate compounded continuously.

37. The distance of a point mass P (all mass is concentrated at P) from a long wire of uniform mass is b units. The number of units of gravitational force on P due to the wire is F where

$$F = 2kb \int_0^{+\infty} \frac{dx}{(b^2 + x^2)^{3/2}}$$

where k is a positive constant. Show that $F = 2k/b$; that is, F varies inversely as b.

38. The distance of a point mass P from a thin plane of uniform mass is b units. The number of units of gravitational force on P due to the plane is F where

$$F = 2kb \int_{-\infty}^{+\infty} \frac{dx}{x^2 + b^2}$$

where k is a positive constant. Show that $F = 2\pi k$, which indicates that the gravitational force is independent of both the position of P and its distance from the plane.

39. Determine the values of p for which the following improper integral is convergent: $\int_e^{+\infty} \frac{dx}{x(\ln x)^p}$.

40. Determine a value of n for which the improper integral $\int_1^{+\infty} \left(\frac{n}{x+1} - \frac{3x}{2x^2+n} \right) dx$ is convergent, and evaluate the integral for this value of n.

41. Determine a value of n for which the improper integral $\int_1^{+\infty} \left(\frac{nx^2}{x^3+1} - \frac{1}{3x+1} \right) dx$ is convergent, and evaluate the integral for this value of n.

42. Suppose f is continuous for all values of x. Prove that if

$$\lim_{a \to -\infty} \int_a^c f(x)\, dx = L \text{ and } \lim_{b \to +\infty} \int_c^b f(x)\, dx = M$$

then if d is any real number,

$$\lim_{a \to -\infty} \int_a^d f(x)\, dx + \lim_{b \to +\infty} \int_d^b f(x)\, dx = L + M$$

Hint: $\int_a^d f(x)\, dx = \int_a^c f(x)\, dx + \int_c^d f(x)\, dx$
$\int_d^b f(x)\, dx = \int_d^c f(x)\, dx + \int_c^b f(x)\, dx$

43. A *uniform* probability density function is defined by

$$f(x) = \begin{cases} 0 & \text{if } x < c \\ \dfrac{1}{d-c} & \text{if } c \le x \le d \\ 0 & \text{if } d < x \end{cases}$$

where $c < d$. Show that this function qualifies as a probability density function.

44. Explain the difference between

$$\int_{-\infty}^{+\infty} f(x)\, dx \quad \text{and} \quad \lim_{r \to +\infty} \int_{-r}^r f(x)\, dx$$

if f is continuous for all values of x.

7.10 OTHER IMPROPER INTEGRALS

Another type of improper integral is one whose integrand has an infinite discontinuity within the limits of integration. To lead up to the definition of an improper integral with an infinite discontinuity at its lower limit, we investigate what this means in terms of geometry.

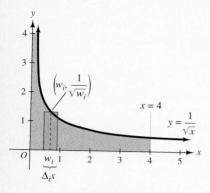

FIGURE 1

Figure 1 shows the region bounded by the curve whose equation is $y = 1/\sqrt{x}$, the x axis, the y axis, and the line $x = 4$. If it is possible to assign a finite number to the measure of the area of this region, it would be given by

$$\lim_{\|\Delta\| \to 0} \sum_{i=1}^{n} \frac{1}{\sqrt{w_i}} \Delta_i x$$

If this limit exists, it is the definite integral denoted by

$$\int_0^4 \frac{dx}{\sqrt{x}} \tag{1}$$

The integrand, however, is discontinuous at the lower limit 0. Furthermore, $\lim_{x \to 0^+} 1/\sqrt{x} = +\infty$, and so we state that the integrand has an infinite discontinuity at the lower limit. Such an integral is improper, and its existence can be determined from the following definition.

7.10.1 Definition of an Improper Integral with an Infinite Discontinuity at Its Lower Limit

If f is continuous at all x in the interval half open on the left $(a, b]$, and if $\lim_{x \to a^+} |f(x)| = +\infty$, then

$$\int_a^b f(x)dx = \lim_{t \to a^+} \int_t^b f(x)\, dx$$

if this limit exists.

▷   **ILLUSTRATION 1**   We determine if a finite number can be assigned to the measure of the area of the region in Figure 1. From the discussion preceding Definition 7.10.1, the measure of the area of the given region will be the improper integral (1) if it exists. By Definition 7.10.1,

$$\int_0^4 \frac{dx}{\sqrt{x}} = \lim_{t \to 0^+} \int_t^4 \frac{dx}{\sqrt{x}}$$

$$= \lim_{t \to 0^+} 2x^{1/2} \Big]_t^4$$

$$= \lim_{t \to 0^+} (4 - 2\sqrt{t})$$

$$= 4 - 0$$

$$= 4$$

We therefore assign 4 to the measure of the area of the given region.   ◄

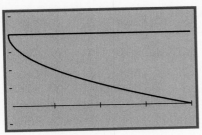

[0.00001, 4] by [−1, 5]

$g(t) = \text{NINT}(1/\sqrt{x}, t, 4)(0 < t \le 4)$

$y = 4$

FIGURE 2

▷ **ILLUSTRATION 2** We support our answer in Illustration 1 by plotting the graph of

$$g(t) = \text{NINT}(1/\sqrt{x}, t, 4)(0 < t \le 4)$$

and the line $y = 4$ in the [0.00001, 4] by [−1, 5] window as shown in Figure 2. Observe that $\lim_{t \to 0^+} g(t)$ appears to be 4. ◀

If the integrand has an infinite discontinuity at the upper limit of integration, we apply the following definition to determine the existence of the improper integral.

7.10.2 Definition of an Improper Integral with an Infinite Discontinuity at Its Upper Limit

If f is continuous at all x in the interval half open on the right $[a, b)$, and if $\lim_{x \to b^-} |f(x)| = +\infty$, then

$$\int_a^b f(x)\, dx = \lim_{t \to b^-} \int_a^t f(x)\, dx$$

if this limit exists.

▶ **EXAMPLE 1** Evaluate the integral, if it is convergent:

$$\int_1^2 \frac{dx}{\sqrt{4 - x^2}}$$

Support the answer graphically.

Solution The integrand has an infinite discontinuity at the upper limit. From Definition 7.10.2

$$\int_1^2 \frac{dx}{\sqrt{4 - x^2}} = \lim_{t \to 2^-} \int_1^t \frac{dx}{\sqrt{4 - x^2}}$$

$$= \lim_{t \to 2^-} \sin^{-1} \frac{x}{2}\Bigg]_1^t$$

$$= \lim_{t \to 2^-} \sin^{-1} \frac{t}{2} - \sin^{-1} \frac{1}{2}$$

$$= \frac{\pi}{2} - \frac{\pi}{6}$$

$$= \frac{\pi}{3}$$

We plot the graph of

$$g(t) = \text{NINT}(1/\sqrt{4 - x^2}, 1, t)\ (1 \le t < 2)$$

and the line $y = \pi/3$ in the [1, 1.99999] by [−1, 2] window as shown in Figure 3. The fact that $\lim_{t \to 2^-} g(t)$ appears to be $\pi/3$ supports our answer.◀

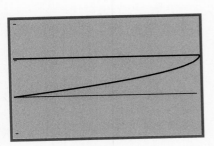

[1, 1.99999] by [−1, 2]

$g(t) = \text{NINT}(1/\sqrt{4 - x^2}, 1, t)(1 \le t < 2)$

$y = \pi/3$

FIGURE 3

If an infinite discontinuity occurs at an interior number in the interval of integration, the existence of the improper integral is determined from the following definition.

7.10.3 Definition of an Improper Integral with an Infinite Discontinuity at an Interior Number

If f is continuous at all x in the interval $[a, b]$ except c, where $a < c < b$, and if $\lim\limits_{x \to c} |f(x)| = +\infty$, then

$$\int_a^b f(x)\, dx = \lim_{t \to c^-} \int_a^t f(x)\, dx + \lim_{s \to c^+} \int_s^b f(x)\, dx$$

if both these limits exist.

▶ **EXAMPLE 2**   Evaluate the integral, if it is convergent:

$$\int_0^2 \frac{dx}{(x - 1)^2}$$

Solution   The integrand has an infinite discontinuity at 1. Applying Definition 7.10.3 we have

$$\int_0^2 \frac{dx}{(x - 1)^2} = \lim_{t \to 1^-} \int_0^t \frac{dx}{(x - 1)^2} + \lim_{s \to 1^+} \int_s^2 \frac{dx}{(x - 1)^2}$$

$$= \lim_{t \to 1^-} \left[-\frac{1}{x - 1} \right]_0^t + \lim_{s \to 1^+} \left[-\frac{1}{x - 1} \right]_s^2$$

$$= \lim_{t \to 1^-} \left[-\frac{1}{t - 1} - 1 \right] + \lim_{s \to 1^+} \left[-1 + \frac{1}{s - 1} \right]$$

Because neither of these limits exists, the improper integral is divergent.   ◀

▷ **ILLUSTRATION 3**   Suppose that in evaluating the integral in Example 2 we had failed to note the infinite discontinuity of the integrand at 1. We would have obtained

$$-\frac{1}{x - 1} \Bigg]_0^2 = -\frac{1}{1} + \frac{1}{-1}$$

$$= -2$$

This is obviously an incorrect result. Because $1/(x - 1)^2$ is never negative, the integral from 0 to 2 could not possibly be a negative number.   ◀

▶ **EXAMPLE 3**   Evaluate the integral, if it is convergent:

$$\int_0^1 x \ln x \, dx$$

Solution   Because the integrand is discontinuous at the lower limit, we proceed as follows where we apply integration by parts:

$$\int_0^1 x \ln x \, dx = \lim_{t \to 0^+} \int_t^1 x \ln x \, dx$$

$$= \lim_{t \to 0^+} \left[\tfrac{1}{2} x^2 \ln x - \tfrac{1}{4} x^2 \right]_t^1$$

$$= \lim_{t \to 0^+} \left[\tfrac{1}{2} \ln 1 - \tfrac{1}{4} - \tfrac{1}{2} t^2 \ln t + \tfrac{1}{4} t^2 \right]$$

Hence

$$\int_0^1 x \ln x \, dx = 0 - \tfrac{1}{4} - \tfrac{1}{2} \lim_{t \to 0^+} t^2 \ln t + 0 \qquad (2)$$

To evaluate

$$\lim_{t \to 0^+} t^2 \ln t = \lim_{t \to 0^+} \frac{\ln t}{\dfrac{1}{t^2}}$$

we apply L'Hôpital's rule, because $\lim_{t \to 0^+} \ln t = -\infty$ and $\lim_{t \to 0^+} 1/t^2 = +\infty$.

$$\lim_{t \to 0^+} \frac{\ln t}{\dfrac{1}{t^2}} = \lim_{t \to 0^+} \frac{\dfrac{1}{t}}{-\dfrac{2}{t^3}}$$

$$= \lim_{t \to 0^+} \left[-\frac{t^2}{2} \right]$$

$$= 0$$

Therefore, from (2),

$$\int_0^1 x \ln x \, dx = -\tfrac{1}{4} \qquad \blacktriangleleft$$

▶ **EXAMPLE 4**   Evaluate the integral, if it is convergent:

$$\int_1^{+\infty} \frac{dx}{x \sqrt{x^2 - 1}}$$

Solution   This integral has both an infinite upper limit and an infinite discontinuity of the integrand at the lower limit. We proceed as follows.

$$\int_1^{+\infty} \frac{dx}{x \sqrt{x^2 - 1}} = \lim_{t \to 1^+} \int_t^2 \frac{dx}{x \sqrt{x^2 - 1}} + \lim_{b \to +\infty} \int_2^b \frac{dx}{x \sqrt{x^2 - 1}}$$

$$= \lim_{t \to 1^+} \left[\sec^{-1} x \right]_t^2 + \lim_{b \to +\infty} \left[\sec^{-1} x \right]_2^b$$

$$= \lim_{t \to 1^+} (\sec^{-1} 2 - \sec^{-1} t) + \lim_{b \to +\infty} (\sec^{-1} b - \sec^{-1} 2)$$

$$= \tfrac{1}{3} \pi - \lim_{t \to 1^+} \sec^{-1} t + \lim_{b \to +\infty} \sec^{-1} b - \tfrac{1}{3} \pi$$

$$= -0 + \tfrac{1}{2} \pi$$

$$= \tfrac{1}{2} \pi \qquad \blacktriangleleft$$

The integral in Example 4 is called an *improper integral of mixed type*.

EXERCISES 7.10

In Exercises 1 through 26, determine whether the improper integral is convergent or divergent. If it is convergent, evaluate it and support your answer graphically.

1. $\displaystyle\int_0^1 \frac{dx}{\sqrt{1-x}}$

2. $\displaystyle\int_0^{16} \frac{dx}{x^{3/4}}$

3. $\displaystyle\int_{-5}^{-3} \frac{x\,dx}{\sqrt{x^2-9}}$

4. $\displaystyle\int_0^4 \frac{x\,dx}{\sqrt{16-x^2}}$

5. $\displaystyle\int_2^4 \frac{dt}{\sqrt{16-t^2}}$

6. $\displaystyle\int_{-4}^1 \frac{dz}{(z+3)^3}$

7. $\displaystyle\int_{\pi/4}^{\pi/2} \sec\theta\,d\theta$

8. $\displaystyle\int_{-2}^0 \frac{dx}{\sqrt{4-x^2}}$

9. $\displaystyle\int_0^{+\infty} \frac{dx}{x^3}$

10. $\displaystyle\int_0^{\pi/2} \tan\theta\,d\theta$

11. $\displaystyle\int_0^{\pi/2} \frac{dy}{1-\sin y}$

12. $\displaystyle\int_0^2 \frac{dx}{(x-1)^{2/3}}$

13. $\displaystyle\int_2^{+\infty} \frac{dx}{x\sqrt{x^2-4}}$

14. $\displaystyle\int_0^4 \frac{dx}{x^2-2x-3}$

15. $\displaystyle\int_0^{+\infty} \ln x\,dx$

16. $\displaystyle\int_0^2 \frac{dx}{\sqrt{2x-x^2}}$

17. $\displaystyle\int_{-2}^0 \frac{dw}{(w+1)^{1/3}}$

18. $\displaystyle\int_{-1}^1 \frac{dx}{x^2}$

19. $\displaystyle\int_{-2}^2 \frac{dx}{x^3}$

20. $\displaystyle\int_0^{+\infty} \frac{e^{-\sqrt{x}}}{\sqrt{x}}\,dx$

21. $\displaystyle\int_{1/2}^2 \frac{dz}{z(\ln z)^{1/5}}$

22. $\displaystyle\int_0^2 \frac{x\,dx}{1-x}$

23. $\displaystyle\int_1^2 \frac{dx}{x\sqrt{x^2-1}}$

24. $\displaystyle\int_0^1 \frac{dx}{x\sqrt{4-x^2}}$

25. $\displaystyle\int_1^{+\infty} \frac{dx}{x^2-1}$

26. $\displaystyle\int_1^3 \frac{dy}{\sqrt[3]{y-2}}$

In Exercises 27 through 29, find the values of n for which the improper integral converges, and evaluate the integral for these values of n.

27. $\displaystyle\int_0^1 x^n\,dx$

28. $\displaystyle\int_0^1 x^n \ln x\,dx$

29. $\displaystyle\int_0^1 x^n \ln^2 x\,dx$

30. Show that it is possible to assign a finite number to represent the measure of the area of the region bounded by the curve whose equation is $y = 1/\sqrt{x}$, the line $x = 1$, and the x and y axes, but that it is not possible to assign a finite number to represent the measure of the volume of the solid of revolution generated if this region is revolved about the x axis.

31. Determine if it is possible to assign a finite number to represent the measure of the volume of the solid formed by revolving about the x axis the region bounded by the curve whose equation is $y = x^{-1/3}$, the line $x = 8$, and the x and y axes.

32. Given the improper integral $\displaystyle\int_a^b \frac{dx}{(x-a)^n}$ where $b > a$. Determine if the integral is convergent or divergent in each case: **(a)** $0 < n < 1$; **(b)** $n = 1$; **(c)** $n > 1$. If the integral is convergent, evaluate it.

33. Use integration to verify that the circumference of the circle $x^2 + y^2 = a^2$ is $2\pi a$.

34. Explain the difference between

$$\lim_{t \to 0^-} \int_{-1}^t \frac{dx}{x} + \lim_{s \to 0^+} \int_s^1 \frac{dx}{x}$$

and

$$\lim_{r \to 0^+} \left[\int_{-1}^{-r} \frac{dx}{x} + \int_r^1 \frac{dx}{x} \right]$$

CHAPTER 7 REVIEW

▶ SUGGESTIONS FOR REVIEW OF CHAPTER 7

1. What is integration by parts? In your answer include the formula for integration by parts.

2. Make up an example of applying integration by parts where the integrand involves the product of two functions.

3. Make up an example of applying integration by parts where the integrand involves a logarithm.

4. Make up an example of applying integration by parts where the integrand involves an inverse trigonometric function.

5. Make up an example of an integral that requires repeated application of integration by parts.

6. Describe the procedure of integrating a positive odd power of sine or cosine. Make up an example illustrating your answer.

7. Answer Suggestion 6 for a positive even power of sine or cosine.

8. Answer Suggestion 6 for a positive integer power, either odd or even, of tangent or cotangent.

9. Answer Suggestion 6 for a positive even power of secant or cosecant.

10. Answer Suggestion 6 for a positive odd power of secant or cosecant.

11. Describe the procedure of integrating a product of powers of tangent and secant where the power of secant is a positive even integer. Make up an example illustrating your answer.

12. Answer Suggestion 11 where the power of tangent is a positive odd integer.

13. What substitution would you make if the integrand contains an expression of the form $\sqrt{a^2 - u^2}$? Explain why this works.

14. Answer Suggestion 13 if the integrand contains an expression of the form $\sqrt{a^2 + u^2}$.

15. Answer Suggestion 13 if the integrand contains an expression of the form $\sqrt{u^2 - a^2}$.

16. How do you decompose a fraction into partial fractions if the denominator has only linear factors and none is repeated? Make up an example.

17. Answer Suggestion 16 if the denominator has only linear factors but some are repeated.

18. Answer Suggestion 16 if the factors of the denominator are linear and quadratic, and none of the quadratic factors is repeated.

19. Answer Suggestion 16 if the factors of the denominator are linear and quadratic and some of the quadratic factors are repeated.

20. What is logistic growth? Make up a differential equation describing logistic growth and write its solution.

21. Sketch a curve of logistic growth. How does this curve compare to a curve of exponential growth and a curve of bounded growth?

22. If an integrand involves fractional powers of a variable x, what substitution would you make to evaluate the integral? Make up an example applying this substitution.

23. If an integrand is a rational function of $\sin x$ and $\cos x$, what substitution would you make so that the integrand is a rational function of a variable z? Make up an example illustrating your answer.

24. What is meant by the closed-form expression of an indefinite integral?

25. Under what circumstances would you need to apply techniques of integration before using a table of integrals to evaluate an indefinite integral? Make up an example illustrating your answer.

26. What is a reduction formula? Make up an example showing the use of a reduction formula to evaluate an indefinite integral.

27. List the many different kinds of substitutions you have learned as techniques of integration.

28. State the trapezoidal rule for approximating the value of a definite integral of a function f on the closed interval $[a, b]$. What necessary condition must function f satisfy in order to apply the trapezoidal rule? Interpret the trapezoidal rule in terms of geometry.

29. Answer Suggestion 28 for Simpson's rule instead of the trapezoidal rule.

30. Explain the difference between a truncation error and a round-off error when applying either the trapezoidal rule or Simpson's rule.

31. What do we mean when we say that the function f/g has the indeterminate form $0/0$ at the number a?

32. State L'Hôpital's rule for $\lim_{x \to a} \dfrac{f(x)}{g(x)}$ if f/g has the indeterminate form $0/0$ at a. Make up an example illustrating the use of this rule.

33. Make up an example using L'Hôpital's rule to compute $\lim_{x \to a} \dfrac{f(x)}{g(x)}$ where both f/g and f'/g' have the indeterminate form $0/0$ at a.

34. State L'Hôpital's rule for $\lim_{x \to a} \dfrac{f(x)}{g(x)}$ if f/g at a has one of the following indeterminate forms: $(+\infty)/(+\infty)$, $(+\infty)/(-\infty)$, $(-\infty)/(+\infty)$, or $(-\infty)/(-\infty)$. Make up an example illustrating the use of this rule.

35. How do you compute $\lim_{x \to a} f(x)^{g(x)}$ if the function defined by $f(x)^{g(x)}$ has the indeterminate form 0^0 at a? Make up an example illustrating your answer.

36. Answer Suggestion 35 if the function defined by $f(x)^{g(x)}$ has the indeterminate form $(+\infty)^0$ at a.

37. Answer Suggestion 35 if the function defined by $f(x)^{g(x)}$ has the indeterminate form $1^{+\infty}$ at a.

38. If f is continuous for all $x \geq a$, define the improper integral $\int_a^{+\infty} f(x)\, dx$. Make up an example illustrating this definition for which the improper integral is (i) convergent, and (ii) divergent.

39. If f is continuous for all $x \leq b$, define the improper integral $\int_{-\infty}^b f(x)\, dx$. Make up an example illustrating this definition for which the improper integral is (i) convergent, and (ii) divergent.

40. If f is continuous for all values of x, define the improper integral $\int_{-\infty}^{+\infty} f(x)\, dx$. Make up an example illustrating this definition for which the improper integral is (i) convergent, and (ii) divergent.

41. Make up an example of a divergent improper integral where the limit is not infinite.

42. What is a probability density function? If f is a probability density function for a particular event occurring, define $P([a, b])$, the probability that the event will occur over the closed interval $[a, b]$. Make up an example illustrating this definition.

43. If f is continuous at all x in the interval $(a, b]$, and if $\lim_{x \to a^+} |f(x)| = +\infty$, define the improper integral $\int_a^b f(x)\, dx$. Make up an example illustrating this definition for which the improper integral is (i) convergent and (ii) divergent.

44. If f is continuous at all x in the interval $[a, b)$, and if $\lim_{x \to b^-} |f(x)| = +\infty$, define the improper integral

$\int_a^b f(x)\, dx$. Make up an example illustrating this definition for which the improper integral is (i) convergent and (ii) divergent.

45. If f is continuous at all x in the interval $[a, b]$ except c, where $a < c < b$, and if $\lim_{x \to c} |f(x)| = +\infty$, define the improper integral $\int_a^b f(x)\, dx$. Make up an example illustrating this definition for which the improper integral is (i) convergent and (ii) divergent.

▶ MISCELLANEOUS EXERCISES FOR CHAPTER 7

In Exercises 1 through 50, evaluate the indefinite integral, and, if you wish, use your graphics calculator to support your answer either numerically or graphically.

1. $\displaystyle\int \tan^2 4x \cos^4 4x\, dx$

2. $\displaystyle\int \frac{5x^2 - 3}{x^3 - x}\, dx$

3. $\displaystyle\int \frac{e^x}{\sqrt{4 - e^x}}\, dx$

4. $\displaystyle\int \frac{dx}{x^2\sqrt{a^2 + x^2}}$

5. $\displaystyle\int \tan^{-1} \sqrt{x}\, dx$

6. $\displaystyle\int \frac{dt}{2t^2 + 5t + 3}$

7. $\displaystyle\int \cos^2 \frac{1}{3}x\, dx$

8. $\displaystyle\int \frac{\sqrt{x + 1} + 1}{\sqrt{x + 1} - 1}\, dx$

9. $\displaystyle\int \frac{x^2 + 1}{(x - 1)^3}\, dx$

10. $\displaystyle\int \frac{dy}{\sqrt{y} + 1}$

11. $\displaystyle\int \sin x \sin 3x\, dx$

12. $\displaystyle\int \cos \theta \cos 2\theta\, d\theta$

13. $\displaystyle\int \frac{dx}{x + x^{4/3}}$

14. $\displaystyle\int t\sqrt{2t - t^2}\, dt$

15. $\displaystyle\int (\sec 3x + \csc 3x)^2\, dx$

16. $\displaystyle\int \frac{dx}{\sqrt{e^x - 1}}$

17. $\displaystyle\int \frac{2t^3 + 11t + 8}{t^3 + 4t^2 + 4t}\, dt$

18. $\displaystyle\int x^3 e^{3x}\, dx$

19. $\displaystyle\int \frac{x^4 + 1}{x^4 - 1}\, dx$

20. $\displaystyle\int \frac{\sqrt{x^2 - 4}}{x^2}\, dx$

21. $\displaystyle\int \sin^4 3x \cos^2 3x\, dx$

22. $\displaystyle\int t \sin^2 2t\, dt$

23. $\displaystyle\int \frac{dr}{\sqrt{3 - 4r - r^2}}$

24. $\displaystyle\int \frac{4x^2 + x - 2}{x^3 - 5x^2 + 8x - 4}\, dx$

25. $\displaystyle\int x^3 \cos x^2\, dx$

26. $\displaystyle\int \frac{y}{9 + 16y^4}\, dy$

27. $\displaystyle\int e^{t/2} \cos 2t\, dt$

28. $\displaystyle\int \frac{du}{u^{5/8} - u^{1/8}}$

29. $\displaystyle\int \frac{\sin x \cos x}{4 + \sin^4 x}\, dx$

30. $\displaystyle\int \frac{dx}{x\sqrt{x^2 + x + 1}}$

31. $\displaystyle\int \frac{\sin x}{1 + \cos^2 x}\, dx$

32. $\displaystyle\int \frac{dx}{x \ln x(\ln x - 1)}$

33. $\displaystyle\int \sqrt{4t - t^2}\, dt$

34. $\displaystyle\int \frac{dx}{\sqrt{1 - x + 3x^2}}$

35. $\displaystyle\int \frac{dx}{x^3 - x}$

36. $\displaystyle\int \frac{dx}{5 + 4 \cos 2x}$

37. $\displaystyle\int \frac{e^x}{\sqrt{4 - 9e^{2x}}}\, dx$

38. $\displaystyle\int \frac{\sqrt{t} - 1}{\sqrt{t} + 1}\, dt$

39. $\displaystyle\int \cot^2 3x \csc^4 3x\, dx$

40. $\displaystyle\int \frac{dx}{x\sqrt{5x - 6 - x^2}}$

41. $\displaystyle\int x^2 \sin^{-1} x\, dx$

42. $\displaystyle\int \frac{\cot x}{3 + 2 \sin x}\, dx$

43. $\displaystyle\int \frac{dx}{\sin x - 2 \csc x}$

44. $\displaystyle\int \cos x \ln(\sin x)\, dx$

45. $\displaystyle\int \frac{\cos 3t}{\sin 3t \sqrt{\sin^2 3t - \frac{1}{4}}}\, dt$

46. $\displaystyle\int \tan x \sin x\, dx$

47. $\displaystyle\int \frac{\sin^{-1} \sqrt{2t}}{\sqrt{1 - 2t}}\, dt$

48. $\displaystyle\int \ln(x^2 + 1)\, dx$

49. $\displaystyle\int \frac{dx}{5 + 4 \sec x}$

50. $\displaystyle\int \frac{dx}{2 + 2 \sin x + \cos x}$

In Exercises 51 through 54, evaluate the indefinite integral.

51. $\displaystyle\int \sin^5 nx\, dx$

52. $\displaystyle\int \tan^n x \sec^4 x\, dx;\ n > 0$

53. $\displaystyle\int x^n \ln x\, dx$

54. $\displaystyle\int \sqrt{\tan x}\, dx$

In Exercises 55 through 84, find the exact value of the definite integral. If you wish, support your answer by the NINT capability of your graphics calculator.

55. $\displaystyle\int_0^{\pi} \sqrt{2 + 2\cos x}\, dx$

56. $\displaystyle\int_{1/2}^{1} \sqrt{\frac{1-x}{x}}\, dx$

57. $\displaystyle\int_1^2 \frac{2x^2 + x + 4}{x^3 + 4x^2}\, dx$

58. $\displaystyle\int_0^1 \frac{dx}{e^x + e^{-x}}$

59. $\displaystyle\int_0^2 \frac{t^3}{\sqrt{4 + t^2}}\, dt$

60. $\displaystyle\int_0^{\pi/2} \sin^3 t \cos^3 t\, dt$

61. $\displaystyle\int_{-2}^{2\sqrt{3}} \frac{x^2}{(16 - x^2)^{3/2}}\, dx$

62. $\displaystyle\int_0^1 \frac{xe^x}{(1+x)^2}\, dx$

63. $\displaystyle\int_0^{\pi/4} \sec^4 x\, dx$

64. $\displaystyle\int_0^2 \frac{1-x}{x^2 + 3x + 2}\, dx$

65. $\displaystyle\int_{\pi/12}^{\pi/8} \cot^3 2y\, dy$

66. $\displaystyle\int_0^2 (2^x + x^2)\, dx$

67. $\displaystyle\int_0^1 \sqrt{2y + y^2}\, dy$

68. $\displaystyle\int_1^2 (\ln x)^2\, dx$

69. $\displaystyle\int_{\sqrt{3}/3}^1 \frac{2x^2 - 2x + 1}{x^3 + x}\, dx$

70. $\displaystyle\int_{\sqrt{2}/2}^1 \frac{x^3}{\sqrt{2 - x^2}}\, dx$

71. $\displaystyle\int_1^{10} \log_{10}\sqrt{ex}\, dx$

72. $\displaystyle\int_0^{2\pi} |\sin x - \cos x|\, dx$

73. $\displaystyle\int_1^2 \frac{x + 2}{(x + 1)^2}\, dx$

74. $\displaystyle\int_0^{\sqrt{\pi/2}} xe^{x^2}\cos x^2\, dx$

75. $\displaystyle\int_0^{\pi} |\cos^3 x|\, dx$

76. $\displaystyle\int_{-\pi/4}^{\pi/4} |\tan^5 x|\, dx$

77. $\displaystyle\int_0^{1/2} \frac{2x\, dx}{x^3 - x^2 - x + 1}$

78. $\displaystyle\int_0^1 x^3\sqrt{1 + x^2}\, dx$

79. $\displaystyle\int_0^{1/2} \frac{x}{\sqrt{1 - 4x^4}}\, dx$

80. $\displaystyle\int_0^{\pi/12} \frac{dx}{\cos^4 3x}$

81. $\displaystyle\int_0^{\pi/2} \frac{dt}{12 + 13\cos t}$

82. $\displaystyle\int_{2\pi/3}^{\pi} \frac{\sin\frac{1}{2}t}{1 + \cos\frac{1}{2}t}\, dt$

83. $\displaystyle\int_0^{16} \sqrt{4 - \sqrt{x}}\, dx$

84. $\displaystyle\int_0^3 \frac{dr}{(r + 2)\sqrt{r + 1}}$

In Exercises 85 and 86, find an approximate value for the integral by using the trapezoidal rule with $n = 4$. Express the result to three decimal places.

85. $\displaystyle\int_0^2 \sqrt{1 + x^2}\, dx$

86. $\displaystyle\int_1^{9/5} \sqrt{1 + x^3}\, dx$

In Exercises 87 and 88, find an approximate value for the integral of the indicated exercise by using Simpson's rule with $n = 4$. Express the result to three decimal places.

87. Exercise 85

88. Exercise 86

89. Find an approximate value of the following integral by two methods and express the result to three decimal places: **(a)** use the trapezoidal rule with $n = 4$; **(b)** use Simpson's rule with $n = 4$:

$$\int_{1/10}^{1/2} \frac{\cos x}{x}\, dx$$

90. The function values $f(x)$ in the following table were obtained experimentally. With the assumption that f is continuous on $[1, 3]$ approximate $\int_1^3 f(x)\, dx$ by **(a)** the trapezoidal rule and **(b)** Simpson's rule.

x	1	1.2	1.4	1.6	1.8	2.0	2.2	2.4	2.6	2.8	3.0
$f(x)$	5.2	5.7	5.8	6.3	6.1	6.4	6.0	6.5	6.8	6.7	6.4

In Exercises 91 through 98 do the following: **(a)** Plot the graph of f on your graphics calculator and state what $f(x)$ appears to be approaching as x approaches a; **(b)** confirm your answer in part (a) analytically by computing $\lim_{x \to a} f(x)$.

91. $f(x) = \dfrac{\tan^{-1} x}{x}$

$a = 0$

92. $f(x) = \dfrac{\tan x}{x}$

$a = 0$

93. $f(x) = \dfrac{x^3 - 8}{x^3 - 2x^2 + 4x - 8}$

$a = 2$

94. $f(x) = \dfrac{\cos \pi x}{2x - 1}$

$a = \frac{1}{2}$

95. $f(x) = \dfrac{\sin 2x}{x - \sin 5x}$

$a = 0$

96. $f(x) = \dfrac{x^3 - 3x + 2}{2x^3 - 3x^2 + 4x - 3}$

$a = 1$

97. $f(x) = \dfrac{\ln(x - 2)}{x - 3}$

$a = 3$

98. $f(x) = \dfrac{x^2}{e^x - 1}$

$a = 0$

In Exercises 99 through 106, do the following: **(a)** Estimate the limit, it if exists, by plotting the graph of the function in a convenient window; **(b)** confirm your answer in part (a) analytically by computing the limit.

99. $\displaystyle\lim_{x \to 0^+} \frac{\ln(\sin x)}{\ln(\cot x)}$

100. $\displaystyle\lim_{x \to +\infty} \frac{\ln x}{x}$

101. $\displaystyle\lim_{x \to +\infty} \frac{x}{e^x}$

102. $\displaystyle\lim_{x \to 0^+} x^{\tan x}$

103. $\lim\limits_{x \to \pi/2} (\sin^2 x)^{\tan x}$

104. $\lim\limits_{x \to -\infty} xe^{2x}$

105. $\lim\limits_{x \to 0^+} \dfrac{\tan 2x}{\sin^2 x}$

106. $\lim\limits_{x \to \pi/2} \left(\dfrac{1}{1 - \sin x} - \dfrac{1}{\cos^2 x} \right)$

In Exercises 107 through 118, find the limit if it exists, and support your answer graphically.

107. $\lim\limits_{x \to 0} (\csc^2 x - x^{-2})$

108. $\lim\limits_{x \to 0} \dfrac{e - (1 + x)^{1/x}}{x}$

109. $\lim\limits_{t \to +\infty} \dfrac{\ln(1 + e^{2t}/t)}{t^{1/2}}$

110. $\lim\limits_{x \to +\infty} x \ln \dfrac{x + 1}{x - 1}$

111. $\lim\limits_{t \to 0^-} (1 + 4t)^{3/t}$

112. $\lim\limits_{y \to +\infty} (1 + e^{2y})^{-2/y}$

113. $\lim\limits_{x \to +\infty} \dfrac{\ln(\ln x)}{\ln(x - \ln x)}$

114. $\lim\limits_{x \to 0} \dfrac{x - \tan^{-1} x}{4x^3}$

115. $\lim\limits_{\theta \to \pi/2} \dfrac{\tan \theta + 3}{\sec \theta - 1}$

116. $\lim\limits_{x \to 0} \left(\dfrac{\sin x}{x} \right)^{1/x}$

117. $\lim\limits_{x \to +\infty} (e^x - x)^{1/x}$

118. $\lim\limits_{x \to \pi/2} (\sin^2 x)^{\tan x}$

In Exercises 119 through 132, determine whether the improper integral is convergent or divergent. If it is convergent, evaluate it and support your answer graphically.

119. $\displaystyle\int_{-2}^{0} \dfrac{dx}{2x + 3}$

120. $\displaystyle\int_{0}^{+\infty} \dfrac{dx}{\sqrt{e^x}}$

121. $\displaystyle\int_{-\infty}^{0} \dfrac{dx}{(x - 2)^2}$

122. $\displaystyle\int_{2}^{4} \dfrac{x}{\sqrt{x - 2}} \, dx$

123. $\displaystyle\int_{0}^{\pi/4} \cot^2 \theta \, d\theta$

124. $\displaystyle\int_{1}^{+\infty} \dfrac{dt}{t^4 + t^2}$

125. $\displaystyle\int_{-\infty}^{3} 4^x \, dx$

126. $\displaystyle\int_{-\infty}^{0} xe^x \, dx$

127. $\displaystyle\int_{0}^{1} \dfrac{(\ln x)^2}{x} \, dx$

128. $\displaystyle\int_{0}^{+\infty} \dfrac{3^{-\sqrt{x}}}{\sqrt{x}} \, dx$

129. $\displaystyle\int_{-\infty}^{+\infty} \dfrac{dx}{4x^2 + 4x + 5}$

130. $\displaystyle\int_{0}^{1} \dfrac{\ln x}{x} \, dx$

131. $\displaystyle\int_{0}^{1} \dfrac{dx}{x + x^3}$

132. $\displaystyle\int_{-3}^{0} \dfrac{dx}{\sqrt{3 - 2x - x^2}}$

133. Find the values of n for which the improper integral

$$\int_{1}^{+\infty} \dfrac{\ln x}{x^n} \, dx$$

converges, and evaluate the integral for those values of n.

134. Evaluate if they exist:

(a) $\displaystyle\int_{-\infty}^{+\infty} \sinh x \, dx$
(b) $\displaystyle\lim_{r \to +\infty} \int_{-r}^{r} \sinh x \, dx$

135. The linear density of a rod 3 m long at a point x meters from one end is ke^{-3x} kilograms per meter. Find the mass and center of mass of the rod.

136. Find the center of mass of a rod 4 m long if the linear density at the point x meters from the left end is $\sqrt{9 + x^2}$ kilograms per meter.

137. Find the length of arc of the parabola $y^2 = 6x$ from $x = 6$ to $x = 12$.

138. Find the area of the region bounded by the curve $y = \sin^{-1} 2x$, the line $x = \frac{1}{4}\sqrt{3}$, and the x axis.

139. Find the area of the region enclosed by one loop of the curve $x^2 = y^4(1 - y^2)$.

140. Find the length of arc of the curve $y = \ln x$ from $x = 1$ to $x = e$.

141. Find the volume of the solid of revolution generated by revolving about the y axis the region bounded by the curve $y = \ln 2x$, the x axis, and the line $x = e$.

142. The region in the first quadrant bounded by the curve $y = \dfrac{5 - x}{(x + 1)^2}$, the x axis, and the y axis is revolved about the x axis. Find the volume of the solid generated.

143. Two chemicals A and B react to form a chemical C, and the rate of change of the amount of C is proportional to the product of the amounts of A and B remaining at any given time. Initially there are 60 lb of chemical A and 60 lb of chemical B, and to form 5 lb of C, 3 lb of A and 2 lb of B are required. After 1 hour, 15 lb of C are formed. **(a)** If x pounds of C are formed at t hours, find an expression for x in terms of t. **(b)** Find the amount of C after 3 hours.

144. A tank is in the shape of the solid of revolution formed by rotating about the x axis the region bounded by the curve $y = \ln x$, the x axis, and the lines $x = e$ and $x = e^2$. If the tank is full of water, find the work done in pumping all the water to the top of the tank. Distance is measured in feet. Take the positive x axis vertically downward.

145. Find the centroid of the region of Exercise 139.

146. Find the centroid of the region enclosed by the loop of the curve $y^2 = x^2 - x^3$.

147. Find the centroid of the region bounded by the y axis and the curves $y = \sin x - \cos x$ and $y = \sin x + \cos x$ from $x = 0$ to $x = \frac{1}{2}\pi$.

148. Find the centroid of the region in the first quadrant bounded by the coordinate axes and the curve $y = \cos x$.

149. The vertical end of a water trough is 3 ft wide at the top and 2 ft deep, and it has the form of the region bounded by the x axis and one arch of the curve $y = 2 \sin \frac{1}{3}\pi x$. If the trough is full of water, find the force due to water pressure on the end.

150. A board is in the shape of a region bounded by a line and one arch of the sine curve. If the board is submerged vertically in water so that the line is the lower boundary 2 ft below the surface of the water, find the force on the board due to water pressure.

151. In a town of population 12,000 the rate of growth of a flu epidemic is jointly proportional to the number of people who have the flu and the number of people who do not have it.
(a) If five days ago 400 people in the town had the flu and today 1000 people have it, find a mathematical model describing the epidemic.
(b) Plot the graph of the mathematical model on your graphics calculator.
Estimate from the graph **(c)** how many people are expected to have the flu tomorrow, and **(d)** in how many days half the population will have the flu. Confirm your estimates analytically.
(e) Show that if the epidemic is not halted, the entire population will have the flu within three and one-half months.

152. Exercise 106 of Miscellaneous Exercises for Chapter 1 and Exercise 78(b) of Miscellaneous Exercises for Chapter 3 pertained to the following situation: A pond can support up to 10,000 fish so that the rate of growth of the fish population is jointly proportional to the number of fish present and the difference between 10,000 and the number present.
(a) If the pond initially contained 400 fish, find a mathematical model expressing the number of fish present as a function of the number of weeks the population has been growing.
Determine how many fish are present after **(b)** 10 weeks, **(c)** 25 weeks, and **(d)** 1 year.
(e) Use the answer in Exercise 78(b) of Miscellaneous Exercises for Chapter 3 to find in how many weeks the growth rate of the fish population is greatest.

153. Determine if it is possible to assign a finite number to represent the measure of the area of the region to the right of the y axis bounded by the curve $4y^2 - xy^2 - x^2 = 0$ and its asymptote. If a finite number can be assigned, find it.

154. Determine if it is possible to assign a finite number to represent the measure of the area of the region bounded by the x axis, the line $x = 1$ and the curve

whose equation is $2xy - y = 1$. If a finite number can be assigned, find it.

155. Determine if it is possible to assign a finite number to represent the measure of the area of the region in the first quadrant and below the curve having the equation $y = e^{-x}$. If a finite number can be assigned, find it.

156. On a certain college campus the probability density function for the length of a telephone call to be x minutes is given by
$$f(x) = \begin{cases} 0.4e^{-0.4x} & \text{if } x \geq 0 \\ 0 & \text{if } x < 0 \end{cases}$$
What is the probability that a telephone call selected at random will last **(a)** between 2 and 3 min; **(b)** at most 3 min; **(c)** at least 10 min?

157. Assume a continuous flow of income for a particular business and that at t years from now the number of dollars in the income per year is given by $1000t - 300$. What is the present value of all future income if 8 percent is the interest rate compounded continuously? *Hint:* See the paragraph preceding Exercise 33 in Exercises 7.9.

158. Given
$$f(x) = \begin{cases} \dfrac{1 - e^{2x}}{2x} & \text{if } x \neq 0 \\ -1 & \text{if } x = 0 \end{cases}$$
(a) Prove that f is continuous at 0. **(b)** Prove that f is differentiable at 0 by computing $f'(0)$.

159. For the function of Exercise 158, find, if they exist: **(a)** $\lim_{x \to +\infty} f(x)$; **(b)** $\lim_{x \to -\infty} f(x)$.

160. Given:
$$f(x) = \begin{cases} \dfrac{e^x - e^{-x}}{e^{2x} - e^{-2x}} & \text{if } x \neq 0 \\ 1 & \text{if } x = 0 \end{cases}$$
(a) Is f continuous at 0?
(b) Find $\lim_{x \to +\infty} f(x)$, if it exists.

161. **(a)** Prove that $\lim_{x \to +\infty} (x^n/e^x) = 0$ for n any positive number. **(b)** Find $\lim_{x \to 0^+} (e^{-1/x}/x^n)$, where n is any positive number, by letting $x = 1/t$ and using the result of part (a).

162. Given the integral $\int_d^{d+6} (x^2 + bx + c)\, dx$, where b, c, and d are constants. Suppose this integral is approximated by using the trapezoidal rule with $n = k$. **(a)** Show that the error in the approximation is exactly $-36/k^2$. **(b)** What is the smallest value of k such that the approximation is accurate to one decimal place?

POLYNOMIAL APPROXIMATIONS, SEQUENCES, AND INFINITE SERIES

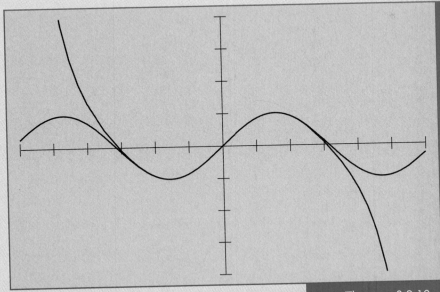

Approximations of functions by power series is the primary objective of this chapter. Prior to our discussion of power series, however, much ground work must be laid. We begin with polynomial approximations in Section 9.1 with an emphasis on Taylor polynomials, which are generalized later in Section 8.9 to Taylor series.

In Section 8.2 we introduce a *sequence function*, which is a function whose domain is a set of positive integers and whose range consists of the elements of a *sequence*. In the supplement of Section 8.2 you will find the proof of the equivalence of convergence and boundedness of monotonic sequences (Theorems 8.2.10 and 8.2.13) based on the completeness property of the real numbers. We define the sum of an *infinite series* as the limit of a particular kind of sequence in Section 8.3, where we also discuss theorems about infinite series. Tests for convergence of infinite series are presented in Section 8.3 as well as in Section 8.4, where we consider series of positive terms, and in Section 8.5 where we are concerned with series whose terms are positive and negative. Section 8.6 contains a summary of the test for convergence or divergence discussed in Sections 8.3 through 8.5.

After our introduction of *power series* in Section 8.7, you will learn in Sections 8.8 through 8.10 how to use them to express as infinite series many functions such as rational, trigonometric, exponential, and logarithmic functions. Power series are applied to approximate irrational numbers such as $\sqrt[3]{29}$, π, e, ln 5, and sin 0.3 as well as to approximate definite integrals for which the integrand has no antiderivative in closed form. For example, power series can be employed to compute values of integrals such as

$$\int_0^{0.5} e^{-t^2}\, dt \qquad \int_0^1 \cos x^2\, dx \qquad \int_0^{0.1} \ln(1 + \sin x)\, dx$$

Furthermore, solutions of many differential equations can be expressed as power series.

► LOOKING AHEAD

8.1 POLYNOMIAL APPROXIMATIONS BY TAYLOR'S FORMULA

While values of polynomial functions can be found by performing a finite number of additions and multiplications, other functions, such as the logarithmic, exponential, and trigonometric functions, cannot be evaluated as easily. We show in this section that many functions can be approximated by polynomials and that the polynomial, instead of the original function, can be used for computations when the difference between the actual function value and the polynomial approximation is sufficiently small.

Various methods can be employed to approximate a given function by polynomials. One of the most widely used involves Taylor's formula, named in honor of the English mathematician Brook Taylor (1685–1731). The following theorem, which can be considered as a generalization of the mean-value theorem, gives Taylor's formula.

8.1.1 Theorem

Let f be a function such that f and its first n derivatives are continuous on the closed interval $[a, b]$. Furthermore, let $f^{(n+1)}(x)$ exist for all x in the open interval (a, b). Then there is a number z in the open interval (a, b) such that

$$f(b) = f(a) + \frac{f'(a)}{1!}(b - a) + \frac{f''(a)}{2!}(b - a)^2 + \ldots$$

$$+ \frac{f^{(n)}(a)}{n!}(b - a)^n + \frac{f^{(n+1)}(z)}{(n + 1)!}(b - a)^{n+1} \tag{1}$$

Equation (1) also holds if $b < a$; in such a case $[a, b]$ is replaced by $[b, a]$, and (a, b) is replaced by (b, a).

Note that when $n = 0$, (1) becomes

$$f(b) = f(a) + f'(z)(b - a)$$

where z is between a and b. This is the mean-value theorem.

We defer the proof of Theorem 8.1.1 until later in this section. If in (1) we replace b by x, we obtain **Taylor's formula**:

$$f(x) = f(a) + \frac{f'(a)}{1!}(x - a) + \frac{f''(a)}{2!}(x - a)^2 + \ldots$$

$$+ \frac{f^{(n)}(a)}{n!}(x - a)^n + \frac{f^{(n+1)}(z)}{(n + 1)!}(x - a)^{n+1} \tag{2}$$

where z is between a and x.

The condition under which (2) holds is that f and its first n derivatives must be continuous on a closed interval containing a and x, and the $(n + 1)$st derivative of f must exist at all points of the corresponding open interval. Formula (2) may be written as

$$f(x) = P_n(x) + R_n(x) \tag{3}$$

where

$$P_n(x) = f(a) + \frac{f'(a)}{1!}(x - a) + \frac{f''(a)}{2!}(x - a)^2 + \ldots + \frac{f^{(n)}(a)}{n!}(x - a)^n \tag{4}$$

and

$$R_n(x) = \frac{f^{(n+1)}(z)}{(n + 1)!}(x - a)^{n+1} \qquad \text{where } z \text{ is between } a \text{ and } x \tag{5}$$

$P_n(x)$ is called the nth-degree **Taylor polynomial** of the function f at the number a, and $R_n(x)$ is called the *remainder*. The term $R_n(x)$ as given in (5) is called the **Lagrange form** of the remainder, named in honor of the French mathematician Joseph L. Lagrange (1736–1813).

The special case of Taylor's formula obtained by taking $a = 0$ in (2) is

$$f(x) = f(0) + \frac{f'(0)}{1!}x + \frac{f''(0)}{2!}x^2 + \ldots + \frac{f^{(n)}(0)}{n!}x^n + \frac{f^{(n+1)}(z)}{(n + 1)!}x^{n+1}$$

where z is between 0 and x. This formula is called **Maclaurin's formula,** named in honor of the Scottish mathematician Colin Maclaurin (1698– 1746). However, the formula was obtained earlier by Taylor and by another British mathematician, James Stirling (1692–1770). The nth degree **Maclaurin polynomial** for a function f, obtained from (4) with $a = 0$, is

$$P_n(x) = f(0) + \frac{f'(0)}{1!}x + \frac{f''(0)}{2!}x^2 + \ldots + \frac{f^{(n)}(0)}{n!}x^n \tag{6}$$

We may approximate a function by means of a Taylor polynomial at a number a or by a Maclaurin polynomial.

▷ **ILLUSTRATION 1**   We compute the nth degree Maclaurin polynomial for the natural exponential function. If $f(x) = e^x$, all the derivatives of f at x are e^x and the derivatives at zero are 1. Therefore, from (6),

$$P_n(x) = 1 + x + \frac{x^2}{2!} + \frac{x^3}{3!} + \ldots + \frac{x^n}{n!} \tag{7}$$

Thus the first four Maclaurin polynomials of the natural exponential function are

$$P_0(x) = 1$$
$$P_1(x) = 1 + x$$
$$P_2(x) = 1 + x + \tfrac{1}{2}x^2$$
$$P_3(x) = 1 + x + \tfrac{1}{2}x^2 + \tfrac{1}{6}x^3$$

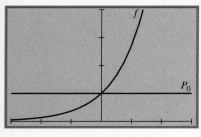

[−3, 3] by [0, 4]

$f(x) = e^x$

$P_0(x) = 1$

FIGURE 1

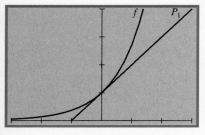

[−3, 3] by [0, 4]

$f(x) = e^x$

$P_1(x) = 1 + x$

FIGURE 2

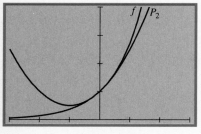

[−3, 3] by [0, 4]

$f(x) = e^x$

$P_2(x) = 1 + x + \frac{1}{2}x^2$

FIGURE 3

Figures 1 through 4 show the graph of $f(x) = e^x$ along with the graphs of $P_0(x)$, $P_1(x)$, $P_2(x)$, and $P_3(x)$, respectively, plotted in the $[-3, 3]$ by $[0, 4]$ window. In Figure 5 the graphs of the four Maclaurin polynomials and the graph of $f(x) = e^x$ are sketched on one coordinate system. Observe how the polynomials approximate e^x for values of x near zero, and notice that as n increases, the approximation improves. Tables 1 and 2 give values of e^x, $P_n(x)$ (when n is 0, 1, 2, and 3) and $e^x - P_n(x)$ for $x = 0.4$ and $x = 0.2$, respectively. From these two values of x it appears that the closer x is to zero, the better is the approximation for a specific $P_n(x)$. ◀

Table 1

n	$e^{0.4}$	$P_n(0.4)$	$e^{0.4} - P_n(0.4)$
0	1.4918	1	0.4918
1	1.4918	1.4	0.0918
2	1.4918	1.48	0.0118
3	1.4918	1.4907	0.0011

Table 2

n	$e^{0.2}$	$P_n(0.2)$	$e^{0.2} - P_n(0.2)$
0	1.2214	1	0.2214
1	1.2214	1.2	0.0214
2	1.2214	1.22	0.0014
3	1.2214	1.2213	0.0001

The Lagrange form of the remainder when $P_n(x)$ is the nth degree Maclaurin polynomial for the natural exponential function is from (5)

$$R_n(x) = \frac{e^z}{(n+1)!}x^{n+1} \qquad \text{where } z \text{ is between } 0 \text{ and } x \qquad \textbf{(8)}$$

In particular, if $P_3(x)$ is used to approximate e^x

$$R_3(x) = \frac{e^z}{4!}x^4 \qquad \text{where } z \text{ is between } 0 \text{ and } x$$

and

$$e^x = P_3(x) + R_3(x)$$

▶ **EXAMPLE 1** Use a Maclaurin polynomial to find the value of $\sqrt{e}$ accurate to four decimal places.

Solution If $f(x) = e^x$, the nth degree Maclaurin polynomial of f is given by (7) and the Lagrange form of the remainder is given by (8). If $x = \frac{1}{2}$ in (8)

$$R_n\left(\frac{1}{2}\right) = \frac{e^z}{(n+1)!}\left(\frac{1}{2}\right)^{n+1} \qquad \text{where } 0 < z < \frac{1}{2}$$

Thus

$$\left| R_n\left(\frac{1}{2}\right) \right| < \frac{e^{1/2}}{2^{n+1}(n+1)!}$$

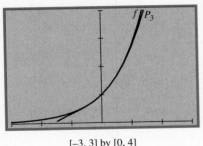

[-3, 3] by [0, 4]

$$f(x) = e^x$$

$$P_3(x) = 1 + x + \frac{1}{2}x^2 + \frac{1}{6}x^3$$

FIGURE 4

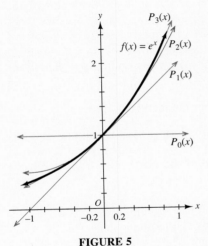

FIGURE 5

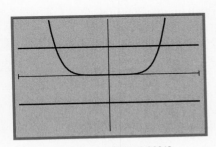

[-1, 1] by [-0.0001, 0.0001]

$$y = e^x - \left(1 + x + \frac{x^2}{2!} + \frac{x^3}{3!} + \frac{x^4}{4!} + \frac{x^5}{5!}\right)$$

$$y = 0.00005 \text{ and } y = -0.00005$$

FIGURE 6

Because $e < 4$, then $e^{1/2} < 2$, and we have

$$\left| R_n\left(\frac{1}{2}\right) \right| < \frac{2}{2^{n+1}(n+1)!} = \frac{1}{2^n(n+1)!}$$

Because our value for $\sqrt{e}$ is to be accurate to four decimal places we want $|R_n(\frac{1}{2})|$ to be less than 0.00005; $|R_n(\frac{1}{2})|$ will be less than 0.00005 if $1/2^n(n+1)! < 0.00005$. When $n = 5$,

$$\frac{1}{2^n(n+1)!} = \frac{1}{(32)(720)}$$
$$= 0.00004$$

Because $0.00004 < 0.00005$, we take $P_5(\frac{1}{2})$ as the approximation of $\sqrt{e}$ accurate to four decimal places. Because from (7)

$$P_5(\tfrac{1}{2}) = 1 + \tfrac{1}{2} + \tfrac{1}{8} + \tfrac{1}{48} + \tfrac{1}{384} + \tfrac{1}{3840}$$

we obtain $\sqrt{e} \approx 1.6487$. ◀

▶ **EXAMPLE 2** Estimate on a graphics calculator the values of x for which $P_5(x)$ approximates e^x accurate to four decimal places.

Solution If $P_5(x)$ is to approximate e^x accurate to four decimal places

$$\left| e^x - P_5(x) \right| < 0.00005$$

Figure 6 shows the graph of $y = e^x - P_5(x)$, that is

$$y = e^x - (1 + x + x^2/2! + x^3/3! + x^4/4! + x^5/5!)$$

and the lines $y = \pm 0.00005$ plotted in the $[-1, 1]$ by $[-0.0001, 0.0001]$ window. Using the *intersect* capability (or trace and zoom-in) of our graphics calculator, we determine that the curve and the line $y = 0.00005$ intersect when $x = -0.5824$ and $x = 0.5667$. Thus we conclude that when $-0.5824 < x < 0.5667$, $P_5(x)$ approximates e^x accurate to four decimal places.

This answer supports our conclusion in Example 1 that $P_5(\frac{1}{2})$ approximates $\sqrt{e}$ accurate to four decimal places. ◀

▷ **ILLUSTRATION 2** We now determine the nth degree Maclaurin polynomial for the sine function. If $f(x) = \sin x$, then

$$f'(x) = \cos x \qquad f''(x) = -\sin x \qquad f'''(x) = -\cos x$$
$$f^{(4)}(x) = \sin x \qquad f^{(5)}(x) = \cos x \qquad f^{(6)}(x) = -\sin x$$

and so on. Thus $f(0) = 0$,

$$f'(0) = 1 \qquad f''(0) = 0 \qquad f'''(0) = -1 \qquad f^{(4)}(0) = 0 \qquad f^{(5)}(0) = 1$$

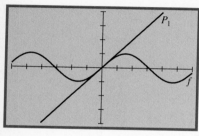

[−6, 6] by [−4, 4]

$f(x) = \sin x$

$P_1(x) = x$

FIGURE 7

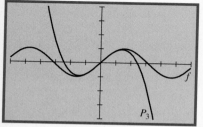

[−6, 6] by [−4, 4]

$f(x) = \sin x$

$P_3(x) = x - \dfrac{x^3}{6}$

FIGURE 8

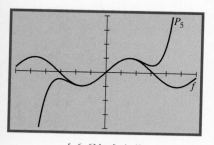

[−6, 6] by [−4, 4]

$f(x) = \sin x$

$P_5(x) = x - \dfrac{x^3}{6} + \dfrac{x^5}{120}$

FIGURE 9

and so on. From (6),

$$P_n(x) = x - \frac{x^3}{3!} + \frac{x^5}{5!} - \frac{x^7}{7!} + \ldots + (-1)^{n-1}\frac{x^{2n-1}}{(2n-1)!}$$

Thus $P_0(x) = 0$,

$$P_1(x) = x \qquad\qquad P_2(x) = x$$

$$P_3(x) = x - \frac{x^3}{6} \qquad\qquad P_4(x) = x - \frac{x^3}{6}$$

$$P_5(x) = x - \frac{x^3}{6} + \frac{x^5}{120} \qquad P_6(x) = x - \frac{x^3}{6} + \frac{x^5}{120}$$

$$P_7(x) = x - \frac{x^3}{6} + \frac{x^5}{120} - \frac{x^7}{5040} \qquad P_8(x) = x - \frac{x^3}{6} + \frac{x^5}{120} - \frac{x^7}{5040}$$

and so on.

Figures 7 through 10 show the graph of the sine function along with the graphs of its Maclaurin polynomials of degrees 1, 3, 5, and 7, respectively, plotted in the $[-6, 6]$ by $[-4, 4]$ window. Figure 11 shows the graphs of these four Maclaurin polynomials and the graph of $f(x) = \sin x$ sketched on the same coordinate system. Notice that the polynomial approximations improve as n increases. ◀

▶ **EXAMPLE 3** **(a)** Determine the accuracy when the seventh degree Maclaurin polynomial of the sine function, $P_7(x)$, is used to approximate sin 0.5. **(b)** Support the answer in part (a) graphically. **(c)** Compute $P_7(0.5)$ to approximate sin 0.5 accurate to the number of decimal places allowed by the answer in part (a).

Solution

(a) From (3) with $f(x) = \sin x$ and $n = 7$, we have

$$\sin x = P_7(x) + R_7(x)$$

Thus

$$\sin 0.5 = P_7(0.5) + R_7(0.5)$$

where from (5) with $x = 0.5$ and $a = 0$

$$R_7(0.5) = \frac{f^{(8)}(z)}{8!}(0.5)^8 \qquad \text{where } z \text{ is between 0 and 0.5}$$

$$= 0.0000001 \sin z$$

Because $|\sin z| < 1$

$$|R_7(0.5)| < 0.0000001$$

We therefore conclude that when $P_7(0.5)$ is used to approximate sin 0.5, our value is accurate to six decimal places.

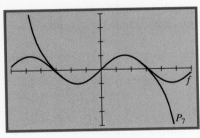

[−6, 6] by [−4, 4]

$$f(x) = \sin x$$

$$P_7(x) = x - \frac{x^3}{6} + \frac{x^5}{120} - \frac{x^7}{5040}$$

FIGURE 10

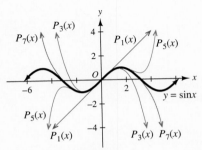

FIGURE 11

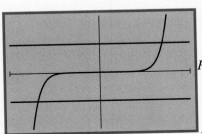

[−1, 1] by [−0.0000002, 0.0000002]

$$y = \sin x - \left(x - \frac{x^3}{6} + \frac{x^5}{120} - \frac{x^7}{5040}\right)$$

$$y = 0.0000001 \text{ and } y = -0.0000001$$

FIGURE 12

(b) To support our answer in part (a) we must show that when $x = 0.5$, $|R_7(x)| < 0.0000001$. Because $R_7(x) = \sin x - P_7(x)$, and from the computation in Illustration 2, for the sine function.

$$P_7(x) = x - \frac{x^3}{6} + \frac{x^5}{120} - \frac{x^7}{5040}$$

we plot the graphs of

$$y = \sin x - \left(x - \frac{x^3}{6} + \frac{x^5}{120} - \frac{x^7}{5040}\right) \quad \text{and} \quad y = \pm0.0000001$$

in the $[−1, 1]$ by $[−0.0000002, 0.0000002]$ window as shown in Figure 12. Using the *intersect* capability (or trace and zoom-in) of our graphics calculator, we determine that the curve and the lines intersect at the points where $x = \pm0.6921$. Because $−0.6921 < 0.5 < 0.6921$ we have supported our answer in part (a).

(c) Substituting 0.5 for x in the expression for $P_7(x)$, we have

$$P_7(0.5) = 0.5 - \frac{(0.5)^3}{6} + \frac{(0.5)^5}{120} - \frac{(0.5)^7}{5040}$$

$$= 0.47942553$$

From part (a), this computation is accurate to six decimal places. Therefore

$$\sin 0.5 = 0.479426 \qquad\blacktriangleleft$$

▶ **EXAMPLE 4**   Find the third-degree Taylor polynomial of the cosine function at $\frac{1}{4}\pi$ and the Lagrange form of the remainder. Plot the graphs of the polynomial and the cosine function in the same window.

Solution   Let $f(x) = \cos x$. Then from (4),

$$P_3(x) = f\left(\frac{\pi}{4}\right) + f'\left(\frac{\pi}{4}\right)\left(x - \frac{\pi}{4}\right) + \frac{f''(\frac{1}{4}\pi)}{2!}\left(x - \frac{\pi}{4}\right)^2 + \frac{f'''(\frac{1}{4}\pi)}{3!}\left(x - \frac{\pi}{4}\right)^3$$

Because $f(x) = \cos x$, $f'(x) = -\sin x$, $f''(x) = -\cos x$, $f'''(x) = \sin x$,

$$f(\tfrac{1}{4}\pi) = \tfrac{1}{2}\sqrt{2} \qquad f'(\tfrac{1}{4}\pi) = -\tfrac{1}{2}\sqrt{2} \qquad f''(\tfrac{1}{4}\pi) = -\tfrac{1}{2}\sqrt{2} \qquad f'''(\tfrac{1}{4}\pi) = \tfrac{1}{2}\sqrt{2}$$

Therefore

$$P_3(x) = \tfrac{1}{2}\sqrt{2} - \tfrac{1}{2}\sqrt{2}(x - \tfrac{1}{4}\pi) - \tfrac{1}{4}\sqrt{2}(x - \tfrac{1}{4}\pi)^2 + \tfrac{1}{12}\sqrt{2}(x - \tfrac{1}{4}\pi)^3$$

Because $f^{(4)}(x) = \cos x$, we obtain from (5)

$$R_3(x) = \tfrac{1}{24}(\cos z)(x - \tfrac{1}{4}\pi)^4 \qquad \text{where } z \text{ is between } \tfrac{1}{4}\pi \text{ and } x$$

Because $|\cos z| \leq 1$, we conclude that $|R_3(x)| \leq \tfrac{1}{24}(x - \tfrac{1}{4}\pi)^4$ for all x.

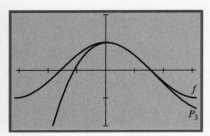

$[-\pi, \pi]$ by $[-2, 2]$

$f(x) = \cos x$

$P_3(x) = \frac{1}{2}\sqrt{2} - \frac{1}{2}\sqrt{2}\ (x - \frac{1}{4}\pi)$

$-\frac{1}{4}\sqrt{2}\ (x - \frac{1}{4}\pi)^2 + \frac{1}{12}\sqrt{2}\ (x - \frac{1}{4}\pi)^3$

FIGURE 13

Figure 13 shows the graphs of $P_3(x)$ and $f(x) = \cos x$ plotted in the $[-\pi, \pi]$ by $[-2, 2]$ window. Observe how the graph of the polynomial approximates the graph of the cosine function near $x = \frac{1}{4}\pi$. ◀

▶ **EXAMPLE 5**   Use the third-degree Taylor polynomial of the cosine function at $\frac{1}{4}\pi$ found in Example 4 to compute an approximate value of $\cos 47°$, and determine the accuracy of the result.

Solution $47° \sim \frac{47}{180}\pi$ radians. Thus in the solution of Example 4, take $x = \frac{47}{180}\pi$ and $x - \frac{1}{4}\pi = \frac{1}{90}\pi$, and

$$\cos 47° = \frac{1}{2}\sqrt{2}[1 - \frac{1}{90}\pi - \frac{1}{2}(\frac{1}{90}\pi)^2 + \frac{1}{6}(\frac{1}{90}\pi)^3] + R_3(\frac{47}{180}\pi) \qquad (9)$$

where

$$R_3(\tfrac{47}{180}\pi) = \tfrac{1}{24}\cos z(\tfrac{1}{90}\pi)^4 \qquad \text{where } \tfrac{1}{4}\pi < z < \tfrac{47}{180}\pi$$

Because $0 < \cos z < 1$,

$$0 < R_3(\tfrac{47}{180}\pi) < \tfrac{1}{24}(\tfrac{1}{90}\pi)^4 < 0.00000007 \qquad (10)$$

Taking $\frac{1}{90}\pi \approx 0.0349066$ we obtain from (9)

$$\cos 47° \approx 0.681998$$

which is accurate to six decimal places because of inequality (10). ◀

We now prove Theorem 8.1.1. There are several known proofs of this theorem, although none is very well motivated. The one following makes use of Cauchy's mean-value theorem (7.7.3).

Proof of Theorem 8.1.1   Let F and G be two functions defined by

$$F(x) = f(b) - f(x) - f'(x)(b - x) - \frac{f''(x)}{2!}(b - x)^2 - \ldots - \frac{f^{(n-1)}(x)}{(n - 1)!}(b - x)^{n-1} - \frac{f^{(n)}(x)}{n!}(b - x)^n \quad (11)$$

and

$$G(x) = \frac{(b - x)^{n+1}}{(n + 1)!} \qquad (12)$$

It follows that $F(b) = 0$ and $G(b) = 0$. Differentiating in (11) we get

$$F'(x) = -f'(x) + f'(x) - f''(x)(b - x) + \frac{2f''(x)(b - x)}{2!} - \frac{f'''(x)(b - x)^2}{2!} + \frac{3f'''(x)(b - x)^2}{3!}$$

$$-\frac{f^{(4)}(x)(b - x)^3}{3!} + \ldots + \frac{(n - 1)f^{(n-1)}(x)(b - x)^{n-2}}{(n - 1)!} - \frac{f^{(n)}(x)(b - x)^{n-1}}{(n - 1)!}$$

$$+ \frac{nf^{(n)}(x)(b - x)^{n-1}}{n!} - \frac{f^{(n+1)}(x)(b - x)^n}{n!}$$

Combining terms we see that the sum of every odd-numbered term with the following even-numbered term is zero; so only the last term remains.

Therefore

$$F'(x) = -\frac{f^{(n+1)}(x)}{n!}(b - x)^n \tag{13}$$

Differentiating in (12) we obtain

$$G'(x) = -\frac{1}{n!}(b - x)^n \tag{14}$$

Checking the hypothesis of Cauchy's mean-value theorem we see that

(i) F and G are continuous on $[a, b]$;
(ii) F and G are differentiable on (a, b);
(iii) for all x in (a, b), $G'(x) \neq 0$.

So by the conclusion of the theorem

$$\frac{F(b) - F(a)}{G(b) - G(a)} = \frac{F'(z)}{G'(z)}$$

where z is in (a, b). But $F(b) = 0$ and $G(b) = 0$. So

$$F(a) = \frac{F'(z)}{G'(z)}G(a) \tag{15}$$

for some z in (a, b).

Letting $x = a$ in (12), $x = z$ in (13), and $x = z$ in (14) and substituting into (15) we obtain

$$F(a) = -\frac{f^{(n+1)}(z)}{n!}(b - z)^n\left[-\frac{n!}{(b - z)^n}\right]\frac{(b - a)^{n+1}}{(n + 1)!}$$

$$F(a) = \frac{f^{(n+1)}(z)}{(n + 1)!}(b - a)^{n+1} \tag{16}$$

If $x = a$ in (11), we obtain

$$F(a) = f(b) - f(a) - f'(a)(b - a) - \frac{f''(a)}{2!}(b - a)^2 - \ldots - \frac{f^{(n-1)}(a)}{(n - 1)!}(b - a)^{n-1} - \frac{f^{(n)}(a)}{n!}(b - a)^n$$

Substituting from (16) into the above equation, we get

$$f(b) = f(a) + f'(a)(b - a) + \frac{f''(a)}{2!}(b - a)^2 + \ldots + \frac{f^{(n)}(a)}{n!}(b - a)^n + \frac{f^{(n+1)}(z)}{(n + 1)!}(b - a)^{n+1}$$

which is the desired result. The theorem holds if $b < a$ because the conclusion of Cauchy's mean-value theorem is unaffected if a and b are interchanged. ∎

There are other forms of the remainder in Taylor's formula. Depending on the function, one form of the remainder may be more desirable to use than another. The following theorem, known as *Taylor's formula with integral form of the remainder*, expresses the remainder as an integral.

> **8.1.2 Theorem   Taylor's Formula with Integral Form of the Remainder**
>
> If f is a function whose first $n + 1$ derivatives are continuous on a closed interval containing a and x, then $f(x) = P_n(x) + R_n(x)$, where $P_n(x)$ is the nth-degree Taylor polynomial of f at a and $R_n(x)$ is the remainder given by
>
> $$R_n(x) = \frac{1}{n!} \int_a^x (x - t)^n f^{(n+1)}(t)\, dt$$

The proof of this theorem is left as an exercise (see Exercise 40).

You have seen how a function can be approximated by a succession of Taylor polynomials. The values of these polynomials for a given value of x can be thought of as a *sequence* of numbers, the subject matter of the next section. The nth degree Taylor polynomial is the sum of $n + 1$ terms, and as n increases without bound, the sum may or may not approach a limit. Such considerations form the basis of *infinite series,* defined in Section 8.3 and the principal topic of this chapter.

EXERCISES 8.1

In Exercises 1 through 10, find the Maclaurin polynomial of the stated degree for the function f with the Lagrange form of the remainder. Plot the graphs of f and the polynomial in the same window and observe how the graph of the polynomial approximates the graph of f near the point where x = 0.

1. $f(x) = \dfrac{1}{x - 2}$; degree 4

2. $f(x) = \dfrac{1}{x + 3}$; degree 5

3. $f(x) = e^{-x}$; degree 5

4. $f(x) = \tan x$; degree 3

5. $f(x) = \cos x$; degree 6

6. $f(x) = \cosh x$; degree 4

7. $f(x) = \sinh x$; degree 4

8. $f(x) = e^{-x^2}$; degree 3

9. $f(x) = (1 + x)^{3/2}$; degree 3

10. $f(x) = (1 - x)^{-1/2}$; degree 4

In Exercises 11 through 18, find the Taylor polynomial of the stated degree at the given number a for the function f with the Lagrange form of the remainder. Plot the graphs of f and the polynomial in the same window and observe how the graph of the polynomial approximates the graph of f near the point where x = a.

11. $f(x) = x^{3/2}$; $a = 4$; degree 3

12. $f(x) = \sqrt{x}$; $a = 4$; degree 4

13. $f(x) = \sin x$; $a = \frac{1}{6}\pi$; degree 3

14. $f(x) = \cos x$; $a = \frac{1}{3}\pi$; degree 4

15. $f(x) = \ln x$; $a = 1$; degree 5

16. $f(x) = \ln(x + 2)$; $a = -1$; degree 3

17. $f(x) = \ln \cos x$; $a = \frac{1}{3}\pi$; degree 3

18. $f(x) = x \sin x$; $a = \frac{1}{6}\pi$; degree 5

19. Compute the value of e accurate to five decimal places, and prove that your answer has the required accuracy. Support your answer graphically.

20. Do Exercise 19 for the value of $e^{-1/2}$.

21. Compute $\sin 31°$ accurate to three decimal places by using a Taylor polynomial and prove that your answer has the required accuracy. Support your answer graphically.

22. Compute $\cos 59°$ accurate to three decimal places by using a Taylor polynomial and prove that your answer has the required accuracy. Support your answer graphically.

23. Estimate the error that results when $\cos x$ is replaced by $1 - \frac{1}{2}x^2$ if $|x| < 0.1$.

24. Estimate the error that results when $\sin x$ is replaced by $x - \frac{1}{6}x^3$ if $|x| < 0.05$.

25. Estimate the error that results when $\sqrt{1 + x}$ is replaced by $1 + \frac{1}{2}x$ if $0 < x < 0.01$.

26. Estimate the error that results when $1/\sqrt{x}$ is replaced by $\frac{3}{2} - \frac{1}{2}x$ if $0.99 < x < 1.01$. *Hint:* Let $\frac{3}{2} - \frac{1}{2}x = 1 - \frac{1}{2}(x - 1)$.

27. Estimate the error that results when e^x is replaced by $1 + x + \frac{1}{2}x^2$ if $|x| < 0.01$.

28. Use the Maclaurin polynomial for the function defined by $f(x) = \ln(1 + x)$ to compute the value of $\ln 1.2$ accurate to four decimal places.

29. Use the Maclaurin polynomial for the function defined by

$$f(x) = \ln \frac{1 + x}{1 - x}$$

to compute the value of $\ln 1.2$ accurate to four decimal places. Compare the computation with that of Exercise 28.

30. Show that if $0 \le x \le \frac{1}{2}$,

$$\sin x = x - \frac{x^3}{3!} + R(x)$$

where $|R(x)| < \frac{1}{3840}$.

31. Use the result of Exercise 30 to find an approximate value of $\int_0^{1/\sqrt{2}} \sin x^2 \, dx$, and estimate the error.

32. Show that the formula $(1 + x)^{3/2} \approx 1 + \frac{3}{2}x$ is accurate to three decimal places if $-0.03 \le x \le 0$.

33. Show that the formula $(1 + x)^{-1/2} \approx 1 - \frac{1}{2}x$ is accurate to two decimal places if $-0.1 \le x \le 0$.

34. Sketch the graphs of $y = \sin x$ and $y = mx$ on the same set of axes. Note that if m is positive and close to zero, then the graphs intersect at a point whose abscissa is close to π. By finding the second-degree Taylor polynomial at π for the function f defined by $f(x) = \sin x - mx$, show that an approximate solution of the equation $\sin x = mx$, when m is positive and close to zero, is given by $x \approx \pi/(1 + m)$.

35. Use the method described in Exercise 34 to find an approximate solution of the equation $\cot x = mx$ when m is positive and close to zero.

36. (a) Use the first-degree Maclaurin polynomial to approximate e^k if $0 < k < 0.01$. **(b)** Estimate the error in terms of k.

37. Apply Taylor's formula to express the polynomial

$$P(x) = x^4 - x^3 + 2x^2 - 3x + 1$$

as a polynomial in powers of $x - 1$.

38. (a) Differentiate term by term the nth degree Maclaurin polynomial for e^x and compare the new polynomial with the one for e^x. **(b)** Integrate term by term the nth degree Maclaurin polynomial for e^x, determine the constant of integration, and compare the new polynomial with the one for e^x.

39. (a) Differentiate term by term the nth degree Maclaurin polynomial for $\sin x$ and compare the new polynomial with the one for $\cos x$. **(b)** Integrate term by term the nth degree Maclaurin polynomial for $\sin x$, determine the constant of integration, and compare the new polynomial with the one for $-\cos x$.

40. Prove Theorem 8.1.2. *Hint:* From Theorem 4.7.2 $\int_a^x f'(t) \, dt = f(x) - f(a)$. Solve for $f(x)$ and integrate $\int_a^x f'(t) \, dt$ by parts by letting $u = f'(t)$ and $dv = dt$. Repeat this process, and the desired result follows by mathematical induction.

41. (a) Prove that the terms of the nth degree Maclaurin polynomial of an odd function contain only odd powers of x. **(b)** Prove that the terms of the nth degree Maclaurin polynomial of an even function contain only even powers of x.

42. When using a Taylor polynomial in powers of $x - a$ to approximate a function value at a particular number x_1, what facts influence your choice of a? Illustrate your answer for the functions defined by $f(x) = e^x$ and $g(x) = \sin x$.

8.2 SEQUENCES

You have often encountered *sequences* of numbers in mathematics. For instance, the numbers

2, 4, 6, 8, 10

form a sequence. This sequence is called **finite** because it has a last number. If a set of numbers forming a sequence has no last number, the sequence is said to be **infinite.** For example,

$$\frac{1}{3}, \frac{2}{5}, \frac{3}{7}, \frac{4}{9}, \cdots \tag{1}$$

is an infinite sequence; the three dots with no number following indicate that there is no last number. Because calculus is concerned with infinite sequences, the word "sequence" in this text means an infinite sequence. We begin by defining a *sequence function*.

8.2.1 Definition of a Sequence Function

A **sequence function** is a function whose domain is the set

$$\{1, 2, 3, \ldots, n, \ldots\}$$

of all positive integers.

The numbers in the range of a sequence function are called **elements**. A **sequence** consists of the elements of a sequence function listed in order.

▷ **ILLUSTRATION 1**   Let f be the function defined by

$$f(n) = \frac{n}{2n + 1} \qquad n \in \{1, 2, 3, 4, \ldots\}$$

Then f is a sequence function, and

$$f(1) = \tfrac{1}{3} \qquad f(2) = \tfrac{2}{5} \qquad f(3) = \tfrac{3}{7} \qquad f(4) = \tfrac{4}{9} \qquad f(5) = \tfrac{5}{11}$$

and so on. The elements of the sequence defined by f are then $\tfrac{1}{3}, \tfrac{2}{5}, \tfrac{3}{7}, \tfrac{4}{9}, \tfrac{5}{11}$, and so on; and the sequence is (1). Some of the ordered pairs in the sequence function f are $(1, \tfrac{1}{3})$, $(2, \tfrac{2}{5})$, $(3, \tfrac{3}{7})$, $(4, \tfrac{4}{9})$, and $(5, \tfrac{5}{11})$. ◀

Usually the nth element $f(n)$ of the sequence is stated when the elements are listed in order. Thus the elements of sequence (1) can be written as

$$\frac{1}{3}, \frac{2}{5}, \frac{3}{7}, \frac{4}{9}, \ldots, \frac{n}{2n + 1}, \ldots$$

Because the domain of every sequence function is the same, the notation $\{f(n)\}$ may be used to denote a sequence. So sequence (1) may be denoted by $\{n/(2n + 1)\}$. The subscript notation $\{a_n\}$ is also used to denote the sequence for which $f(n) = a_n$.

The graph of a sequence function may be plotted in various ways on a graphics calculator. Some calculators have a built-in capability of obtaining a sequence graph (consult your owner's manual). If your calculator does not have that capability, one procedure for the sequence $\{f(n)\}$ is to plot the graph of the corresponding real-valued function $f(x)$ for $x \geq 1$; then the y coordinates on the graph for positive-integer values of x are the elements of the sequence. Another procedure involving parametric and dot mode is demonstrated in the following illustration.

▷ **ILLUSTRATION 2**   To plot the graph of the sequence function of Illustration 1, we first make sure that the calculator is in parametric and dot mode. We then let

$$x = t \quad \text{and} \quad y = \frac{t}{2t + 1}$$

and set our window variables: $t_{\min} = 1$, $t_{\max} = 25$, $t_{\text{step}} = 1$, $x_{\min} = 0$, $x_{\max} = 25$, $x_{\text{scl}} = 1$, $y_{\min} = 0$, $y_{\max} = 1$, and $y_{\text{scl}} = 0.5$. The resulting graph appears in Figure 1. Remember the y coordinates of the points are the elements of the sequence. ◀

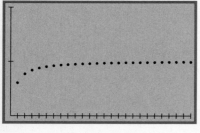

[0, 25] by [0, 1]

$$x = t \text{ and } y = \frac{t}{2t + 1}$$

FIGURE 1

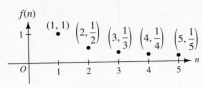

FIGURE 2

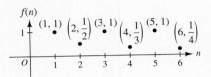

FIGURE 3

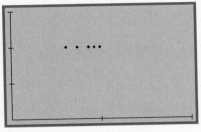

[0, 1] by [0, 3]

$$x = \frac{t}{2t + 1} \quad \text{and } y = 2$$

FIGURE 4

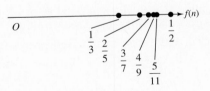

FIGURE 5

A sequence

$$a_1, a_2, a_3, \ldots, a_n, \ldots$$

is said to be **equal** to a sequence

$$b_1, b_2, b_3, \ldots, b_n, \ldots$$

if and only if $a_i = b_i$ for every positive integer i. Remember that a sequence consists of an ordering of elements. Therefore it is possible for two sequences to have the same elements and be unequal. This situation is shown in the following illustration.

▷ **ILLUSTRATION 3**   The sequence $\{1/n\}$ has as its elements the reciprocals of the positive integers

$$1, \frac{1}{2}, \frac{1}{3}, \frac{1}{4}, \ldots, \frac{1}{n}, \ldots \tag{2}$$

The sequence for which

$$f(n) = \begin{cases} 1 & \text{if } n \text{ is odd} \\ \dfrac{2}{n + 2} & \text{if } n \text{ is even} \end{cases}$$

has as its elements

$$1, \tfrac{1}{2}, 1, \tfrac{1}{3}, 1, \tfrac{1}{4}, \ldots \tag{3}$$

The elements of sequences (2) and (3) are the same, but the sequences are not equal. The graphs of the sequence functions for sequences (2) and (3) appear in Figures 2 and 3, respectively. ◀

We can plot on a number line the points corresponding to successive elements of a sequence. We show this in Figure 4 for sequence (1) on the horizontal line $y = 2$. To obtain this figure we set the calculator in parametric and dot mode and let

$$x = \frac{t}{2t + 1} \quad \text{and} \quad y = 2$$

with the following window variables: $t_{\min} = 1$, $t_{\max} = 10$, $t_{\text{step}} = 1$, $x_{\min} = 0$, $x_{\max} = 1$, $x_{\text{scl}} = 0.5$, $y_{\min} = 0$, $y_{\max} = 3$, and $y_{\text{scl}} = 1$. In Figure 5, we have located on a number line the five points representing the first five elements of the sequence. Observe in both Figures 4 and 5 that successive elements of the sequence get closer and closer to $\tfrac{1}{2}$, even though no element in the sequence has the value $\tfrac{1}{2}$. Intuitively we see that the element will be as close to $\tfrac{1}{2}$ as we please by taking the number of the element sufficiently large. Or stating this another way, $|n/(2n + 1) - \tfrac{1}{2}|$ can be made less than any given positive ϵ by taking n large enough. Because of this we state that the limit of the sequence $\{n/(2n + 1)\}$ is $\tfrac{1}{2}$.

In general, if there is a number L such that $|a_n - L|$ is arbitrarily small for n sufficiently large, the sequence $\{a_n\}$ is said to have the limit L.

8.2.2 Definition of the Limit of a Sequence

A sequence $\{a_n\}$ has the limit L if for any $\epsilon > 0$ there exists a number $N > 0$ such that if n is an integer and

if $n > N$ then $|a_n - L| < \epsilon$

and we write

$$\lim_{n \to +\infty} a_n = L$$

Compare this definition with Definition 3.7.1 of the limit of $f(x)$ as x increases without bound. The two definitions are almost identical; however, when we state that $\lim\limits_{x \to +\infty} f(x) = L$, the function f is defined for all real numbers greater than some real number r, while when we consider $\lim\limits_{n \to +\infty} a_n$, n is restricted to positive integers. The next theorem then follows immediately from Definition 3.7.1. In Exercise 56 you are asked to write the formal proof.

8.2.3 Theorem

If $\lim\limits_{x \to +\infty} f(x) = L$, and f is defined for every positive integer, then also $\lim\limits_{n \to +\infty} f(n) = L$, when n is restricted to positive integers.

▷ **ILLUSTRATION 4**   We apply Theorem 8.2.3 for sequence (1) where $f(n) = n/(2n + 1)$, so that $f(x) = x/(2x + 1)$.

$$\lim_{x \to +\infty} \frac{x}{2x + 1} = \lim_{x \to +\infty} \frac{1}{2 + \dfrac{1}{x}}$$

$$= \tfrac{1}{2}$$

Thus from Theorem 8.2.3, $\lim\limits_{n \to +\infty} f(n) = \tfrac{1}{2}$ when n is restricted to positive integers.   ◀

▷ **ILLUSTRATION 5**   Consider the sequence $\{(-1)^{n+1}/n\}$. Note that the nth element of this sequence is $(-1)^{n+1}/n$, and $(-1)^{n+1}$ is equal to $+1$ when n is odd and to -1 when n is even. Hence the elements of the sequence can be written

$$1, -\frac{1}{2}, \frac{1}{3}, -\frac{1}{4}, \frac{1}{5}, \ldots, \frac{(-1)^{n+1}}{n}, \ldots$$

Figure 6 shows points corresponding to successive elements of the sequence located on a number line. In the figure $a_1 = 1$, $a_2 = -\frac{1}{2}$, $a_3 = \frac{1}{3}$, $a_4 = -\frac{1}{4}$, $a_5 = \frac{1}{5}$, $a_6 = -\frac{1}{6}$, $a_7 = \frac{1}{7}$, $a_8 = -\frac{1}{8}$, $a_9 = \frac{1}{9}$, $a_{10} = -\frac{1}{10}$. The limit of the sequence is 0, and the elements oscillate about 0.   ◀

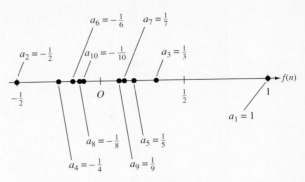

FIGURE 6

If a sequence $\{a_n\}$ has a limit, the sequence is said to be **convergent,** and a_n **converges** to that limit. If the sequence is not convergent, it is **divergent.**

▶ **EXAMPLE 1**   Determine whether the sequence is convergent or divergent and support the answer graphically:

$$\left\{ \frac{4n^2}{2n^2 + 1} \right\}$$

Solution   We wish to determine if $\lim\limits_{n \to +\infty} 4n^2/(2n^2 + 1)$ exists. We let $f(x) = 4x^2/(2x^2 + 1)$, and investigate $\lim\limits_{x \to +\infty} f(x)$.

$$\lim_{x \to +\infty} \frac{4x^2}{2x^2 + 1} = \lim_{x \to +\infty} \frac{4}{2 + \dfrac{1}{x^2}}$$

$$= 2$$

Therefore, by Theorem 8.2.3, $\lim\limits_{n \to +\infty} f(n) = 2$. Thus the given sequence is convergent and $4n^2/(2n^2 + 1)$ converges to 2.

Figure 7 showing the graph of f and the line $y = 2$ plotted in the $[1, 20]$ by $[0, 4]$ window supports our answer because the line appears to be a horizontal asymptote of the graph of f.

We could also support our answer by plotting the graph of the corresponding sequence function and observing that the y coordinates of successive points get closer and closer to 2.   ◀

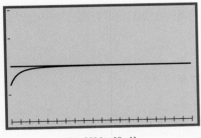

$[1, 20]$ by $[0, 4]$

$f(x) = \dfrac{4x^2}{2x^2 + 1}$ and $y = 2$

FIGURE 7

▶ **EXAMPLE 2**   Determine whether the sequence is convergent or divergent:

$$\left\{ n \sin \frac{\pi}{n} \right\}$$

Solution   We wish to determine whether $\lim\limits_{n \to +\infty} n \sin(\pi/n)$ exists. We let $f(x) = x \sin(\pi/x)$ and investigate $\lim\limits_{x \to +\infty} f(x)$. Because $f(x)$ can be written as $[\sin(\pi/x)]/(1/x)$ and $\lim\limits_{x \to +\infty} \sin(\pi/x) = 0$ and $\lim\limits_{x \to +\infty} (1/x) = 0$, L'Hôpital's rule can be applied to obtain

$$\lim_{x \to +\infty} f(x) = \lim_{x \to +\infty} \frac{-\dfrac{\pi}{x^2} \cos \dfrac{\pi}{x}}{-\dfrac{1}{x^2}}$$

$$= \lim_{x \to +\infty} \pi \cos \frac{\pi}{x}$$

$$= \pi$$

Therefore $\lim\limits_{n \to +\infty} f(n) = \pi$. So the given sequence is convergent and $n \sin(\pi/n)$ converges to π. ◀

▶ **EXAMPLE 3**   Prove that if $|r| < 1$, the sequence $\{r^n\}$ is convergent and r^n converges to zero.

Solution First we consider $r = 0$. Then the sequence is $\{0\}$ and $\lim\limits_{n \to +\infty} 0 = 0$. Thus the sequence is convergent and the nth element converges to zero.

If $0 < |r| < 1$, we must show that Definition 8.2.2 holds with $L = 0$. Therefore, we must show that for any $\epsilon > 0$ there exists a number $N > 0$ such that if n is an integer and

$$\text{if } n > N \quad \text{then} \quad |r^n - 0| < \epsilon \tag{4}$$
$$\Leftrightarrow \text{ if } n > N \quad \text{then} \quad |r|^n < \epsilon$$
$$\Leftrightarrow \text{ if } n > N \quad \text{then} \quad \ln|r|^n < \ln \epsilon$$
$$\Leftrightarrow \text{ if } n > N \quad \text{then} \quad n \ln|r| < \ln \epsilon$$

Because $0 < |r| < 1$, $\ln|r| < 0$. The above statement is equivalent to

$$\text{if } n > N \quad \text{then} \quad n > \frac{\ln \epsilon}{\ln|r|}$$

Therefore, if $N = \ln \epsilon / \ln|r|$, (4) follows. Hence, $\lim\limits_{n \to +\infty} r^n = 0$. Thus the sequence $\{r^n\}$ is convergent and r^n converges to zero. ◀

The following theorem incorporates the limit theorems for sequences that are analogous to limit theorems for functions. The proofs are omitted because they are similar to the proofs of the corresponding theorems for limits of functions.

8.2.4 Theorem

If $\{a_n\}$ and $\{b_n\}$ are convergent sequences and c is a constant, then

  (i) the constant sequence $\{c\}$ has c as its limit;

 (ii) $\lim\limits_{n \to +\infty} c a_n = c \lim\limits_{n \to +\infty} a_n$;

(iii) $\lim\limits_{n \to +\infty} (a_n \pm b_n) = \lim\limits_{n \to +\infty} a_n \pm \lim\limits_{n \to +\infty} b_n$;

 (iv) $\lim\limits_{n \to +\infty} a_n b_n = \left(\lim\limits_{n \to +\infty} a_n \right) \left(\lim\limits_{n \to +\infty} b_n \right)$;

  (v) $\lim\limits_{n \to +\infty} \dfrac{a_n}{b_n} = \dfrac{\lim\limits_{n \to +\infty} a_n}{\lim\limits_{n \to +\infty} b_n}$ if $\lim\limits_{n \to +\infty} b_n \neq 0$, and every $b_n \neq 0$.

▶ **EXAMPLE 4**   Apply Theorem 8.2.4 to prove that the sequence

$$\left\{ \frac{4n^3}{2n^2 + 1} \sin \frac{\pi}{n} \right\}$$

is convergent, and find its limit.

Solution

$$\frac{4n^3}{2n^2 + 1} \sin \frac{\pi}{n} = \frac{4n^2}{2n^2 + 1} \cdot n \sin \frac{\pi}{n}$$

In Example 1 the sequence $\{4n^2/(2n^2 + 1)\}$ was shown to be convergent and $\lim_{n \to +\infty} [4n^2/(2n^2 + 1)] = 2$. In Example 2 we showed that the sequence $\{n \sin(\pi/n)\}$ is convergent and $\lim_{n \to +\infty} [n \sin(\pi/n)] = \pi$. Hence, by Theorem 8.2.4(iv),

$$\lim_{n \to +\infty} \left[\frac{4n^2}{2n^2 + 1} \cdot n \sin \frac{\pi}{n} \right] = \lim_{n \to +\infty} \frac{4n^2}{2n^2 + 1} \cdot \lim_{n \to +\infty} n \sin \frac{\pi}{n}$$

$$= 2 \cdot \pi$$

Thus the given sequence is convergent, and its limit is 2π.   ◀

Certain kinds of sequences are given special names.

8.2.5 Definition of Increasing and Decreasing Sequences

A sequence $\{a_n\}$ is

(i) **increasing** if $a_n \le a_{n+1}$ for all n;

(ii) **decreasing** if $a_n \ge a_{n+1}$ for all n.

A sequence is **monotonic** if it is either increasing or decreasing.

If $a_n < a_{n+1}$ (a special case of $a_n \le a_{n+1}$), the sequence is **strictly increasing**; if $a_n > a_{n+1}$, the sequence is **strictly decreasing.**

▶ **EXAMPLE 5**   Apply Definition 8.2.5 to determine if the sequence is increasing, decreasing, or not monotonic:

(a) $\left\{ \frac{n}{2n + 1} \right\}$ (b) $\left\{ \frac{1}{n} \right\}$ (c) $\left\{ \frac{(-1)^{n+1}}{n} \right\}$

Solution

(a) The elements of the sequence can be written

$$\frac{1}{3}, \frac{2}{5}, \frac{3}{7}, \frac{4}{9}, \ldots, \frac{n}{2n + 1}, \frac{n + 1}{2n + 3}, \ldots$$

Note that a_{n+1} is obtained from a_n by replacing n by $n + 1$.

Look at the first four elements of the sequence and observe that the elements increase as n increases. Thus we suspect in general that

$$\frac{n}{2n + 1} \le \frac{n + 1}{2n + 3} \tag{5}$$

Inequality (5) can be verified if an equivalent inequality can be found that we know is valid. Multiplying each member of (5) by $(2n + 1)(2n + 3)$ we obtain the following equivalent inequalities:

$$n(2n + 3) \leq (n + 1)(2n + 1)$$
$$2n^2 + 3n \leq 2n^2 + 3n + 1 \tag{6}$$

Inequality (6) obviously holds because the right member is 1 greater than the left member. Therefore inequality (5) holds; so the given sequence is increasing.

(b) The elements of the sequence can be written

$$1, \frac{1}{2}, \frac{1}{3}, \frac{1}{4}, \ldots, \frac{1}{n}, \frac{1}{n + 1}, \ldots$$

Because

$$\frac{1}{n} > \frac{1}{n + 1}$$

for all n, the sequence is decreasing.

(c) The elements of the sequence can be written

$$1, -\frac{1}{2}, \frac{1}{3}, -\frac{1}{4}, \ldots, \frac{(-1)^{n+1}}{n}, \frac{(-1)^{n+2}}{n + 1}, \ldots$$

Because $a_1 = 1$ and $a_2 = -\frac{1}{2}, a_1 > a_2$. But $a_3 = \frac{1}{3}$; thus $a_2 < a_3$. In a more general sense, consider three consecutive elements

$$a_n = \frac{(-1)^{n+1}}{n} \qquad a_{n+1} = \frac{(-1)^{n+2}}{n + 1} \qquad a_{n+2} = \frac{(-1)^{n+3}}{n + 2}$$

If n is odd, $a_n > a_{n+1}$ and $a_{n+1} < a_{n+2}$; for instance, $a_1 > a_2$ and $a_2 < a_3$. If n is even, $a_n < a_{n+1}$ and $a_{n+1} > a_{n+2}$; for instance, $a_2 < a_3$ and $a_3 > a_4$. Hence the sequence is neither increasing nor decreasing; thus it is not monotonic. ◀

The answers in Example 5 can be supported graphically by plotting the graph of the corresponding sequence function. Figure 1 supports the answer in part (a) that the sequence is increasing, and Figure 2 supports the answer in part (b) that the sequence is decreasing.

For many sequences $\{f(n)\}$ we can determine if the sequence is monotonic by computing $f'(x)$ and applying Theorem 3.4.3 as shown in the following illustration.

▷ **ILLUSTRATION 6**
(a) For the sequence $\{n/(2n + 1)\}$ of Example 5(a) let

$$f(x) = \frac{x}{2x + 1} \qquad f'(x) = \frac{1}{(2x + 1)^2}$$

Because $f'(x) > 0$ for all $x \geq 1$, the sequence is increasing.
(b) For the sequence $\{1/n\}$ of Example 5(b) let

$$f(x) = \frac{1}{x} \qquad f'(x) = -\frac{1}{x^2}$$

Because $f'(x) < 0$ for all $x \geq 1$, the sequence is decreasing. ◀

8.2.6 Definition of Upper and Lower Bounds of a Sequence

The number C is a **lower bound** of the sequence $\{a_n\}$ if $C \le a_n$ for all positive integers n, and the number D is an **upper bound** of the sequence $\{a_n\}$ if $a_n \le D$ for all positive integers n.

▷ **ILLUSTRATION 7**   The number zero is a lower bound of the sequence $\{n/(2n + 1)\}$ whose elements are

$$\frac{1}{3}, \frac{2}{5}, \frac{3}{7}, \frac{4}{9}, \ldots, \frac{n}{2n + 1}, \ldots$$

Another lower bound of this sequence is $\frac{1}{3}$. Actually any number that is less than or equal to $\frac{1}{3}$ is a lower bound of this sequence.   ◄

▷ **ILLUSTRATION 8**   For the sequence $\{1/n\}$ whose elements are

$$1, \frac{1}{2}, \frac{1}{3}, \frac{1}{4}, \ldots, \frac{1}{n}, \ldots$$

1 is an upper bound; 26 is also an upper bound. Any number that is greater than or equal to 1 is an upper bound of this sequence, and any nonpositive number will serve as a lower bound.   ◄

Observe from Illustrations 7 and 8 that a sequence may have many upper and lower bounds.

8.2.7 Definition of Greatest Lower Bound and Least Upper Bound of a Sequence

If A is a lower bound of a sequence $\{a_n\}$ and if A has the property that for every lower bound C of $\{a_n\}$, $C \le A$, then A is the **greatest lower bound** of the sequence. Similarly, if B is an upper bound of a sequence $\{a_n\}$ and if B has the property that for every upper bound D of $\{a_n\}$, $B \le D$, then B is the **least upper bound** of the sequence.

▷ **ILLUSTRATION 9**   For the sequence $\{n/(2n + 1)\}$ of Illustration 7, $\frac{1}{3}$ is the greatest lower bound because every lower bound of the sequence is less than or equal to $\frac{1}{3}$. Furthermore, $\frac{1}{2}$ is an upper bound of the sequence because

$$\frac{n}{2n + 1} = \frac{1}{2 + \dfrac{1}{n}} < \frac{1}{2}$$

for all n, and because every upper bound of the sequence is greater than or equal to $\frac{1}{2}$, this number is the least upper bound.   ◄

▷ **ILLUSTRATION 10**   The least upper bound of the sequence $\{1/n\}$ of Illustration 8 is 1 because every upper bound of the sequence is greater than or equal to 1. The greatest lower bound of this sequence is 0.   ◄

8.2.8 Definition of a Bounded Sequence

A sequence is **bounded** if and only if it has an upper bound and a lower bound.

Because the sequence $\{1/n\}$ of Illustration 10 has both an upper and lower bound, it is bounded. This sequence is also decreasing and hence is a bounded monotonic sequence. Furthermore, because $\lim\limits_{n \to +\infty} (1/n) = 0$, this sequence is convergent. Theorem 8.2.10, which follows shortly, guarantees that a bounded monotonic sequence is convergent. In contrast, the sequence $\{n\}$ is monotonic because it is increasing, but is not bounded because it has no upper bound. The sequence is also divergent because $\lim\limits_{n \to +\infty} n = +\infty$.

The following important property of the real-number system will be used in the proof of Theorem 8.2.10.

8.2.9 The Axiom of Completeness

Every nonempty set of real numbers that has a lower bound has a greatest lower bound. Also, every nonempty set of real numbers that has an upper bound has a least upper bound.

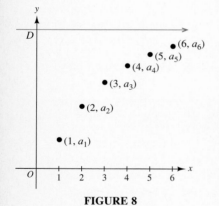

FIGURE 8

The second sentence in the statement of the axiom of completeness is unnecessary because it can be proved from the first sentence. It is included in the axiom here to expedite the discussion.

Suppose $\{a_n\}$ is a bounded increasing sequence, and let D be an upper bound of the sequence. Then if the points (n, a_n) are located on a rectangular cartesian coordinate system, these points will all lie below the line $y = D$. Furthermore, because the sequence is increasing, the points will get closer and closer to the line $y = D$ as n increases. See Figure 8. Therefore, the elements a_n increase toward D as n increases. Intuitively then, the sequence $\{a_n\}$ appears to have a limit that is either D or some number less than D. This situation is indeed the case and is guaranteed by the following theorem, which is proved in the supplement of this section.

8.2.10 Theorem

A bounded monotonic sequence is convergent.

This theorem states that if $\{a_n\}$ is a bounded monotonic sequence, there exists a number L such that $\lim\limits_{n \to +\infty} a_n = L$, but it does not state how to find L. For this reason Theorem 8.2.10 is called an *existence theorem*. Many important concepts in mathematics are based on existence theorems. In particular, for many sequences the limit cannot be found by direct use of the definition or by use of limit theorems, but the knowledge that such a limit exists can be valuable to a mathematician.

If you read the proof of Theorem 8.2.10, you will learn that the limit of a bounded increasing sequence is the least upper bound B of the sequence. Therefore, if D is an upper bound of the sequence, $\lim\limits_{n \to +\infty} a_n = B \le D$. We have, then, the following theorem.

8.2.11 Theorem

Let $\{a_n\}$ be an increasing sequence, and suppose that D is an upper bound of this sequence. Then $\{a_n\}$ is convergent, and

$$\lim_{n \to +\infty} a_n \leq D$$

In proving Theorem 8.2.10 for the case when the bounded monotonic sequence is decreasing, the limit of the sequence is the greatest lower bound. The next theorem follows in a way similar to that of Theorem 8.2.11.

8.2.12 Theorem

Let $\{a_n\}$ be a decreasing sequence, and suppose that C is a lower bound of this sequence. Then $\{a_n\}$ is convergent, and

$$\lim_{a \to +\infty} a_n \geq C$$

▶ **EXAMPLE 6**   Apply Theorem 8.2.10 to prove that the sequence is convergent:

$$\left\{\frac{2^n}{n!}\right\}$$

Solution   The elements of the given sequence are

$$\frac{2^1}{1!}, \frac{2^2}{2!}, \frac{2^3}{3!}, \frac{2^4}{4!}, \ldots, \frac{2^n}{n!}, \frac{2^{n+1}}{(n+1)!}, \ldots$$

$1! = 1, 2! = 2, 3! = 6, 4! = 24$. Hence the elements of the sequence can be written as

$$2, 2, \frac{4}{3}, \frac{2}{3}, \ldots, \frac{2^n}{n!}, \frac{2^{n+1}}{(n+1)!}, \ldots$$

Then $a_1 = a_2 > a_3 > a_4$; so the given sequence may be decreasing. We must check to see if $a_n \geq a_{n+1}$; that is, we must determine if

$$\frac{2^n}{n!} \geq \frac{2^{n+1}}{(n+1)!} \tag{7}$$

$$\Leftrightarrow \quad 2^n(n+1)! \geq 2^{n+1}n!$$

$$\Leftrightarrow \quad 2^n n! \, (n+1) \geq 2 \cdot 2^n n!$$

$$\Leftrightarrow \quad n+1 \geq 2 \tag{8}$$

When $n = 1$, inequality (8) becomes $2 = 2$, and (8) obviously holds when $n > 2$. Because inequality (7) is equivalent to (8), it follows that the given sequence is decreasing and hence monotonic. An upper bound for the given sequence is 2, and a lower bound is 0. Therefore the sequence is bounded.

The sequence $\{2^n/n!\}$ is therefore a bounded monotonic sequence, and by Theorem 8.2.10 it is convergent.   ◀

Theorem 8.2.10 states that a sufficient condition for a monotonic sequence to be convergent is that it be bounded. This condition is also necessary and is given in the following theorem, whose proof also appears in the supplement of this section.

8.2.13 Theorem

A convergent monotonic sequence is bounded.

Theorems 8.2.10 and 8.2.13 are converses of each other and together they state: for a monotonic sequence, convergence and boundedness are equivalent. This fact will be useful in our treatment of infinite series later in this chapter.

EXERCISES 8.2

In Exercises 1 through 20, write the first four elements of the sequence and determine whether it is convergent or divergent. If the sequence converges, find its limit and support your answer graphically.

1. $\left\{ \dfrac{n+1}{2n-1} \right\}$ **2.** $\left\{ \dfrac{2n^2+1}{3n^2-n} \right\}$ **3.** $\left\{ \dfrac{n^2+1}{n} \right\}$

4. $\left\{ \dfrac{3n^3+1}{2n^2+n} \right\}$ **5.** $\left\{ \dfrac{3-2n^2}{n^2+1} \right\}$ **6.** $\left\{ \dfrac{e^n}{n} \right\}$

7. $\left\{ \dfrac{\ln n}{n^2} \right\}$ **8.** $\left\{ \dfrac{\log_b n}{n} \right\}, b > 1$ **9.** $\{\tanh n\}$

10. $\{\sinh n\}$ **11.** $\left\{ \dfrac{n}{n+1}\sin\dfrac{n\pi}{2} \right\}$ **12.** $\left\{ \dfrac{\sinh n}{\sin n} \right\}$

13. $\left\{ \dfrac{1}{\sqrt{n^2+1}-n} \right\}$ **14.** $\{\sqrt{n+1}-\sqrt{n}\}$

15. $\left\{ \left(1+\dfrac{1}{3n}\right)^n \right\}$ *Hint: Use* $\lim\limits_{x\to 0}(1+x)^{1/x} = e.$

16. $\left\{ \left(1+\dfrac{2}{n}\right)^n \right\}$ See Hint for Exercise 15.

17. $\{2^{1/n}\}$ **18.** $\left\{ \left(\dfrac{1}{2}\right)^{1/n} \right\}$ **19.** $\left(\dfrac{n}{2^n}\right)$ **20.** $\{\cos n\pi\}$

In Exercises 21 through 24, estimate on your graphics calculator the limit of the convergent sequence. Confirm your estimate analytically.

21. **(a)** $\left\{ \dfrac{3}{n+1} \right\}$ **(b)** $\left\{ \dfrac{8n}{2n+3} \right\}$

22. **(a)** $\left\{ \dfrac{4}{2n-1} \right\}$ **(b)** $\left\{ \dfrac{1-7n}{2n+5} \right\}$

23. **(a)** $\left\{ \dfrac{3n^2}{6n^2+1} \right\}$ **(b)** $\left\{ \dfrac{n^2-1}{2+n} \right\}$

24. **(a)** $\left\{ \dfrac{9-2n}{3+n} \right\}$ **(b)** $\left\{ \dfrac{6n}{n^2+4} \right\}$

25. Show that the sequences

$$\left\{ \dfrac{n^2}{n+3} \right\} \quad \text{and} \quad \left\{ \dfrac{n^2}{n+4} \right\}$$

are both divergent, but that the sequence

$$\left\{ \dfrac{n^2}{n+3} - \dfrac{n^2}{n+4} \right\}$$

is convergent.

26. Prove that the sequence $\{n/c^n\}$ is convergent if $|c| > 1$ and divergent if $0 < |c| \le 1.$

In Exercises 27 through 42, determine if the sequence is increasing, decreasing, or not monotonic.

27. $\left\{ \dfrac{3n-1}{4n+5} \right\}$ **28.** $\left\{ \dfrac{2n-1}{4n-1} \right\}$ **29.** $\left\{ \dfrac{1-2n^2}{n^2} \right\}$

30. $\{\sin n\pi\}$ **31.** $\{\cos \frac{1}{3}n\pi\}$ **32.** $\left\{ \dfrac{n^3-1}{n} \right\}$

33. $\left\{ \dfrac{1}{n+\sin n^2} \right\}$ **34.** $\left\{ \dfrac{2^n}{1+2^n} \right\}$ **35.** $\left\{ \dfrac{5^n}{1+5^{2n}} \right\}$

36. $\left\{ \dfrac{(2n)!}{5^n} \right\}$ **37.** $\left\{ \dfrac{n!}{3^n} \right\}$ **38.** $\left\{ \dfrac{n}{2^n} \right\}$

39. $\left\{ \dfrac{n^n}{n!} \right\}$ **40.** $\{n^2 + (-1)^n n\}$

41. $\left\{ \dfrac{n!}{1 \cdot 3 \cdot 5 \cdot \ldots \cdot (2n-1)} \right\}$

42. $\left\{ \dfrac{1 \cdot 3 \cdot 5 \cdot \ldots \cdot (2n-1)}{2^n \cdot n!} \right\}$

In Exercises 43 and 44, determine if the sequence is bounded.

43. $\left\{ \dfrac{n^2+3}{n+1} \right\}$ **44.** $\{3 - (-1)^{n-1}\}$

In Exercises 45 through 54, prove that the sequence is convergent by using Theorem 8.2.10.

45. The sequence of Exercise 27

46. $\left\{ \dfrac{n}{3^{n+1}} \right\}$ **47.** $\left\{ \dfrac{1 \cdot 3 \cdot 5 \cdot \ldots \cdot (2n - 1)}{2 \cdot 4 \cdot 6 \cdot \ldots \cdot (2n)} \right\}$

48. The sequence of Exercise 34

49. The sequence of Exercise 35

50. The sequence of Exercise 38

51. The sequence of Exercise 41

52. The sequence of Exercise 42

53. $\left\{ \dfrac{n^2}{2^n} \right\}$ **54.** $\{k^{1/n}\}, \, k > 1$

55. Make up an example of a sequence that is bounded and convergent but not monotonic.

56. Prove Theorem 8.2.3.

57. Given the sequence

$$\left\{ \frac{1 - \left(1 - \dfrac{1}{n}\right)^a}{1 - \left(1 - \dfrac{1}{n}\right)^b} \right\} \quad \begin{array}{l} a \text{ and } b \text{ are constants} \\ \text{and } b \neq 0 \end{array}$$

Determine whether the sequence is convergent or divergent. If the sequence converges, find its limit.

58. Prove that if the sequence $\{a_n\}$ is convergent then $\lim\limits_{n \to +\infty} a_n$ is unique. *Hint:* Assume that $\lim\limits_{n \to +\infty} a_n$ has two different values, L and M, and show that this is impossible by taking $\epsilon = \frac{1}{2} |L - M|$ in Definition 8.2.2.

59. Prove that if $|r| < 1$, the sequence $\{nr^n\}$ is convergent and nr^n converges to zero.

60. Prove that if the sequence $\{a_n\}$ is convergent and $\lim\limits_{n \to +\infty} a_n = L$, then the sequence $\{|a_n|\}$ is also convergent and $\lim\limits_{n \to +\infty} |a_n| = |L|$.

61. Prove that if the sequence $\{a_n\}$ is convergent and $\lim\limits_{n \to +\infty} a_n = L$, then the sequence $\{a_n{}^2\}$ is also convergent and $\lim\limits_{n \to +\infty} a_n{}^2 = L^2$.

62. Prove that the sequence $\{a_n\}$ is convergent, where $a_n > 0$ for all n, and $a_{n+1} < ka_n$ with $0 < k < 1$.

63. Explain what it means to say: "For a monotonic sequence, convergence and boundedness are equivalent."

64. If the sequence $\{a_n\}$ is divergent, can we conclude that $\lim\limits_{n \to +\infty} a_n = +\infty$? Justify your answer and illustrate by an example.

8.3 INFINITE SERIES OF CONSTANT TERMS

An important part of the study of calculus involves representing functions as "infinite sums." To do this requires extending the familiar operation of addition of a finite set of numbers to addition of infinitely many numbers. To carry this out we deal with a limiting process by considering sequences.

Let us associate with the sequence

$$u_1, u_2, u_3, \ldots, u_n, \ldots$$

an "infinite sum" denoted by

$$u_1 + u_2 + u_3 + \ldots + u_n + \ldots$$

But what is the meaning of such an expression? That is, what do we mean by the "sum" of an infinite number of terms, and under what circumstances does such a sum exist? To get an intuitive idea of the concept of such a sum, suppose a piece of string of length 2 ft is cut in half. One of these halves of length 1 ft is set aside and the other piece is cut in half again. One of the resulting pieces of length $\frac{1}{2}$ ft is set aside and the other piece is cut in half so that two pieces, each of length $\frac{1}{4}$ ft, are obtained. One of the pieces of length $\frac{1}{4}$ ft is set aside and then the other piece is cut in half; so two pieces, each of length $\frac{1}{8}$ ft, are obtained. Again one of the pieces is set aside and the other is cut in half. If this procedure is continued indefinitely, the number of feet in the sum of the lengths of the pieces set aside can be considered as the infinite sum

$$1 + \frac{1}{2} + \frac{1}{4} + \frac{1}{8} + \frac{1}{16} + \ldots + \frac{1}{2^{n-1}} + \ldots \tag{1}$$

Because we started with a piece of string 2 ft in length, our intuition indicates that the infinite sum (1) should be 2. We demonstrate that this is indeed the case in Illustration 2. However, we first need some preliminary definitions.

From the sequence

$$u_1, u_2, u_3, \ldots, u_n, \ldots$$

we form a new sequence $\{s_n\}$ by adding successive elements of $\{u_n\}$:

$$s_1 = u_1$$
$$s_2 = u_1 + u_2$$
$$s_3 = u_1 + u_2 + u_3$$
$$s_4 = u_1 + u_2 + u_3 + u_4$$
$$\vdots$$
$$s_n = u_1 + u_2 + u_3 + u_4 + \ldots + u_n$$

The sequence $\{a_n\}$ obtained in this manner from the sequence $\{s_n\}$ is a *sequence of partial sums* called an *infinite series*.

8.3.1 Definition of an Infinite Series

If $\{u_n\}$ is a sequence and

$$s_n = u_1 + u_2 + u_3 + \ldots + u_n$$

then $\{s_n\}$ is a **sequence of partial sums** called an **infinite series** denoted by

$$\sum_{n=1}^{+\infty} u_n = u_1 + u_2 + u_3 + \ldots + u_n + \ldots$$

The numbers $u_1, u_2, u_3, \ldots, u_n, \ldots$ are the **terms** of the infinite series.

▷ **ILLUSTRATION 1**   Consider the sequence $\{1/2^{n-1}\}$:

$$1, \frac{1}{2}, \frac{1}{4}, \frac{1}{8}, \frac{1}{16}, \ldots, \frac{1}{2^{n-1}}, \ldots$$

From this sequence let us form a sequence of partial sums:

$$s_1 = 1 \qquad\qquad\qquad\qquad s_1 = 1$$

$$s_2 = 1 + \frac{1}{2} \qquad\qquad \Leftrightarrow \quad s_2 = \frac{3}{2}$$

$$s_3 = 1 + \frac{1}{2} + \frac{1}{4} \qquad\qquad \Leftrightarrow \quad s_3 = \frac{7}{4}$$

$$s_4 = 1 + \frac{1}{2} + \frac{1}{4} + \frac{1}{8} \qquad \Leftrightarrow \quad s_4 = \frac{15}{8}$$

$$s_5 = 1 + \frac{1}{2} + \frac{1}{4} + \frac{1}{8} + \frac{1}{16} \quad \Leftrightarrow \quad s_5 = \frac{31}{16}$$

$$\vdots$$

$$s_n = 1 + \frac{1}{2} + \frac{1}{4} + \frac{1}{8} + \frac{1}{16} + \ldots + \frac{1}{2^{n-1}}$$

This sequence of partial sums $\{s_n\}$ is the infinite series denoted by

$$\sum_{n=1}^{+\infty} \frac{1}{2^{n-1}} = 1 + \frac{1}{2} + \frac{1}{4} + \frac{1}{8} + \frac{1}{16} + \ldots + \frac{1}{2^{n-1}} + \ldots$$

Observe that this is the infinite sum (1) obtained at the beginning of this section in the discussion of repeatedly cutting the string of length 2 ft. It is an example of a *geometric series* discussed later in this section. ◀

When $\{s_n\}$ is a sequence of partial sums,

$$s_{n-1} = u_1 + u_2 + u_3 + \ldots + u_{n-1}$$

Thus

$$s_n = s_{n-1} + u_n$$

We use this formula in the following example.

▶ **EXAMPLE 1** Given the infinite series

$$\sum_{n=1}^{+\infty} u_n = \sum_{n=1}^{+\infty} \frac{1}{n(n+1)}$$

(a) find the first four elements of the sequence of partial sums $\{s_n\}$, and
(b) find a formula for s_n in terms of n.

Solution

(a) Because $s_n = s_{n-1} + u_n$

$$s_1 = u_1 \qquad s_2 = s_1 + u_2 \qquad s_3 = s_2 + u_3 \qquad s_4 = s_3 + u_4$$

$$= \frac{1}{1 \cdot 2} \qquad = \frac{1}{2} + \frac{1}{2 \cdot 3} \qquad = \frac{2}{3} + \frac{1}{3 \cdot 4} \qquad = \frac{3}{4} + \frac{1}{4 \cdot 5}$$

$$= \tfrac{1}{2} \qquad\quad = \tfrac{2}{3} \qquad\qquad = \tfrac{3}{4} \qquad\qquad = \tfrac{4}{5}$$

(b) Because $u_k = \dfrac{1}{k(k+1)}$ we have, by partial fractions,

$$u_k = \frac{1}{k} - \frac{1}{k+1}$$

Therefore,

$$u_1 = 1 - \tfrac{1}{2} \qquad u_2 = \tfrac{1}{2} - \tfrac{1}{3} \qquad u_3 = \tfrac{1}{3} - \tfrac{1}{4}$$

$$\vdots$$

$$u_{n-1} = \frac{1}{n-1} - \frac{1}{n} \qquad u_n = \frac{1}{n} - \frac{1}{n+1}$$

Thus, because $s_n = u_1 + u_2 + \ldots + u_{n-1} + u_n$,

$$s_n = \left(1 - \frac{1}{2}\right) + \left(\frac{1}{2} - \frac{1}{3}\right) + \left(\frac{1}{3} - \frac{1}{4}\right) + \ldots + \left(\frac{1}{n-1} - \frac{1}{n}\right) + \left(\frac{1}{n} - \frac{1}{n+1}\right)$$

Upon removing parentheses and combining terms we obtain

$$s_n = 1 - \frac{1}{n+1}$$

By taking n as 1, 2, 3, and 4, we see that the previous results agree. ◀

The method in the solution of the above example applies only to a special case. Generally, it is not possible to obtain such an expression for s_n.

8.3.2 Definition of the Sum of an Infinite Series

Let $\displaystyle\sum_{n=1}^{+\infty} u_n$ denote a given infinite series for which $\{s_n\}$ is the sequence of partial sums. If $\displaystyle\lim_{n \to +\infty} s_n$ exists and is equal to S, then the series is **convergent** and S is the **sum** of the series. If $\displaystyle\lim_{n \to +\infty} s_n$ does not exist, the series is **divergent,** and the series does not have a sum.

Essentially this definition states that an infinite series is convergent if and only if the corresponding sequence of partial sums is convergent. If an infinite series has a sum S, we also say that the series converges to S.

Observe that the sum of a convergent series is the limit of a sequence of partial sums and is not obtained by ordinary addition. For a convergent series, the symbolism

$$\sum_{n=1}^{+\infty} u_n$$

is utilized to denote both the series and the sum of the series. The use of the same symbol should not be confusing because the correct interpretation will be apparent from the context in which it is employed.

▷ **ILLUSTRATION 2** The infinite series of Illustration 1 is

$$\sum_{n=1}^{+\infty} \frac{1}{2^{n-1}} = 1 + \frac{1}{2} + \frac{1}{4} + \frac{1}{8} + \frac{1}{16} + \ldots + \frac{1}{2^{n-1}} + \ldots \tag{2}$$

and the sequence of partial sums is $\{s_n\}$, where

$$s_n = 1 + \frac{1}{2} + \frac{1}{4} + \frac{1}{8} + \ldots + \frac{1}{2^{n-1}} \tag{3}$$

To determine if infinite series (2) has a sum we must compute $\lim_{n \to +\infty} s_n$. To find a formula for s_n we use the identity from algebra:

$$a^n - b^n = (a - b)(a^{n-1} + a^{n-2}b + a^{n-3}b^2 + \ldots + ab^{n-2} + b^{n-1})$$

Applying this identity with $a = 1$ and $b = \frac{1}{2}$ we have

$$1 - \frac{1}{2^n} = \left(1 - \frac{1}{2}\right)\left(1 + \frac{1}{2} + \frac{1}{2^2} + \frac{1}{2^3} + \ldots + \frac{1}{2^{n-1}}\right)$$

$$\Leftrightarrow \quad 1 + \frac{1}{2} + \frac{1}{4} + \frac{1}{8} + \ldots + \frac{1}{2^{n-1}} = \frac{1 - \dfrac{1}{2^n}}{\dfrac{1}{2}}$$

Comparing this equation and (3) we obtain

$$s_n = 2\left(1 - \frac{1}{2^n}\right)$$

Because $\lim_{n \to +\infty} \dfrac{1}{2^n} = 0$ we have

$$\lim_{n \to +\infty} s_n = 2$$

Therefore infinite series (2) has the sum 2. ◀

▶ **EXAMPLE 2** Determine if the infinite series of Example 1 has a sum.

Solution In the solution of Example 1 we showed that the sequence of partial sums for the given series is $\{s_n\} = \{1 - 1/(n + 1)\}$. Therefore

$$\lim_{n \to +\infty} s_n = \lim_{n \to +\infty} \left(1 - \frac{1}{n + 1}\right)$$
$$= 1$$

So the infinite series has a sum equal to 1, and we write

$$\sum_{n=1}^{+\infty} \frac{1}{n(n + 1)} = \frac{1}{2} + \frac{1}{6} + \frac{1}{12} + \frac{1}{20} + \ldots + \frac{1}{n(n + 1)} + \ldots$$
$$= 1 \qquad \blacktriangleleft$$

▶ **EXAMPLE 3**   Write with sigma notation the infinite series that is the following sequence of partial sums:

$$\{s_n\} = \left\{\frac{1}{2^n}\right\}$$

Also determine if the infinite series is convergent or divergent; if it is convergent, find its sum.

Solution   Because $s_1 = \frac{1}{2}$, then $u_1 = \frac{1}{2}$. If $n > 1$,

$$u_n = s_n - s_{n-1}$$

$$= \frac{1}{2^n} - \frac{1}{2^{n-1}}$$

$$= -\frac{1}{2^n}$$

Therefore the infinite series is

$$\frac{1}{2} - \sum_{n=2}^{+\infty} \frac{1}{2^n}$$

Because

$$\lim_{n \to +\infty} s_n = \lim_{n \to +\infty} \frac{1}{2^n}$$

$$= 0$$

the series is convergent and its sum is 0.   ◀

As mentioned above, in most cases it is not possible to obtain an expression for s_n in terms of n; so we must have other methods for determining whether or not a given infinite series has a sum or, equivalently, whether a given infinite series is convergent or divergent.

8.3.3 Theorem

If the infinite series $\sum\limits_{n=1}^{+\infty} u_n$ is convergent, then $\lim\limits_{n \to +\infty} u_n = 0$.

Proof   Let $\{s_n\}$ be the sequence of partial sums for the given series and denote the sum of the series by S. From Definition 8.3.2, $\lim\limits_{n \to +\infty} s_n = S$ and $\lim\limits_{n \to +\infty} s_{n-1} = S$. Because $u_n = s_n - s_{n-1}$

$$\lim_{n \to +\infty} u_n = \lim_{n \to +\infty} (s_n - s_{n-1})$$

$$= \lim_{n \to +\infty} s_n - \lim_{n \to +\infty} s_{n-1}$$

$$= S - S$$

$$= 0$$

■

Theorem 8.3.3 provides a simple test for divergence: if $\lim\limits_{n \to +\infty} u_n \neq 0$, then $\sum\limits_{n=1}^{+\infty} u_n$ is divergent.

▶ **EXAMPLE 4**   Prove that the following two series are divergent:

(a) $\displaystyle\sum_{n=1}^{+\infty} \frac{n^2 + 1}{n^2} = 2 + \frac{5}{4} + \frac{10}{9} + \frac{17}{16} + \dots$

(b) $\displaystyle\sum_{n=1}^{+\infty} (-1)^{n+1}3 = 3 - 3 + 3 - 3 + \dots$

Solution

(a) $\displaystyle\lim_{n \to +\infty} u_n = \lim_{n \to +\infty} \frac{n^2 + 1}{n^2}$

$\displaystyle \qquad = \lim_{n \to +\infty} \frac{1 + \dfrac{1}{n^2}}{1}$

$\qquad = 1$

$\qquad \neq 0$

Therefore, by Theorem 8.3.3, the series is divergent.

(b) $\displaystyle\lim_{n \to +\infty} u_n = \lim_{n \to +\infty} (-1)^{n+1}3$, which does not exist. Therefore, by Theorem 8.3.3, the series is divergent. ◀

The converse of Theorem 8.3.3 is false. That is, if $\displaystyle\lim_{n \to +\infty} u_n = 0$, it does not follow that the series is necessarily convergent. In other words, it is possible to have a divergent series for which $\displaystyle\lim_{n \to +\infty} u_n = 0$. An example of such a series is

$$\sum_{n=1}^{+\infty} \frac{1}{n} = 1 + \frac{1}{2} + \frac{1}{3} + \frac{1}{4} + \dots + \frac{1}{n} + \dots$$

called the **harmonic series.** Clearly, $\displaystyle\lim_{n \to +\infty} (1/n) = 0$, but this series diverges, which we now prove as a theorem.

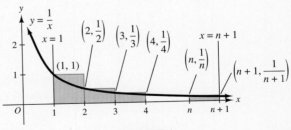

FIGURE 1

8.3.4 Theorem

The harmonic series is divergent.

Proof   The nth term, $1/n$, of the harmonic series can be interpreted geometrically as the number of square units in the area of a rectangle having width of 1 unit and length of $1/n$ unit. See Figure 1 indicating n such rectangles circumscribing the region bounded above by the graph of $y = 1/x$, below by the x axis, and on the sides by the lines $x = 1$ and $x = n + 1$. The sum of the areas of the n rectangles is

$$1 + \frac{1}{2} + \frac{1}{3} + \cdots + \frac{1}{n}$$

which is s_n, the nth partial sum of the harmonic series. The area of the region is

$$\int_1^{n+1} \frac{1}{x} \, dx = \ln(n + 1)$$

Therefore

$$s_n > \ln(n + 1)$$

Thus the sequence $\{s_n\}$ is not bounded. But since $\{s_n\}$ is an increasing sequence, and from Section 8.2 we know that convergence and boundedness are equivalent for a monotonic sequence, it follows that the sequence $\{s_n\}$ is divergent. Therefore, because its sequence of partial sums diverges, the harmonic series diverges. ∎

An infinite series of the form

$$\sum_{n=1}^{+\infty} ar^{n-1} = a + ar + ar^2 + \ldots + ar^{n-1} + \ldots \qquad (4)$$

is called a **geometric series.** Infinite series (2), discussed in Illustrations 1 and 2, is a geometric series with $a = 1$ and $r = \frac{1}{2}$.

8.3.5 Theorem

The geometric series converges to the sum $a/(1 - r)$ if $|r| < 1$ and diverges if $|r| \geq 1$.

Proof The nth partial sum of the geometric series (4) is given by

$$s_n = a(1 + r + r^2 + \ldots + r^{n-1}) \qquad (5)$$

From the identity

$$1 - r^n = (1 - r)(1 + r + r^2 + \ldots + r^{n-1})$$

(5) can be written as

$$s_n = \frac{a(1 - r^n)}{1 - r} \qquad \text{if } r \neq 1 \qquad (6)$$

In Example 3 of Section 8.2, we showed that $\lim\limits_{n \to +\infty} r^n = 0$ if $|r| < 1$. Therefore, from (6), if $|r| < 1$

$$\lim_{n \to +\infty} s_n = \frac{a}{1 - r}$$

So if $|r| < 1$, the geometric series converges and its sum is $a/(1 - r)$.

If $r = \pm 1$, the limit of the nth term is not zero. Hence the geometric series diverges when $|r| = 1$.

If $|r| > 1$, $\lim\limits_{n \to +\infty} ar^{n-1} = a \lim\limits_{n \to +\infty} r^{n-1}$. Clearly, $\lim\limits_{n \to +\infty} r^{n-1} \neq 0$ because $|r^{n-1}|$ can be made as large as we please by taking n large enough. Therefore, by Theorem 8.3.3, the series is divergent. This completes the proof. ∎

The following example illustrates how Theorem 8.3.5 can be applied to express a nonterminating repeating decimal as a common fraction.

▶ **EXAMPLE 5**   Express 0.3333 . . . as a common fraction.

Solution

$$0.3333 \ldots = \frac{3}{10} + \frac{3}{100} + \frac{3}{1000} + \frac{3}{10,000} + \cdots + \frac{3}{10^n} + \cdots$$

This is a geometric series in which $a = \frac{3}{10}$ and $r = \frac{1}{10}$. Because $|r| < 1$, it follows from Theorem 8.3.5 that the series converges and its sum is $a/(1 - r)$. Therefore

$$0.3333 \ldots = \frac{\frac{3}{10}}{1 - \frac{1}{10}}$$

$$= \tfrac{1}{3}$$

◀

We conclude this section with four theorems that extend certain properties of finite sums to convergent infinite series. The first of these theorems states that if an infinite series is multiplied term by term by a nonzero constant, its convergence or divergence is not affected.

8.3.6 Theorem

Let c be any nonzero constant.

(i) If the series $\displaystyle\sum_{n=1}^{+\infty} u_n$ is convergent and its sum is S, then the series

$\displaystyle\sum_{n=1}^{+\infty} cu_n$ is also convergent and its sum is $c \cdot S$.

(ii) If the series $\displaystyle\sum_{n=1}^{+\infty} u_n$ is divergent, then the series $\displaystyle\sum_{n=1}^{+\infty} cu_n$ is also

divergent.

Proof   Let the nth partial sum of the series $\displaystyle\sum_{n=1}^{+\infty} u_n$ be s_n. Therefore

$s_n = u_1 + u_2 + \ldots + u_n$. The nth partial sum of the series $\displaystyle\sum_{n=1}^{+\infty} cu_n$ is

$c(u_1 + u_2 + \ldots + u_n) = cs_n$.

Proof of (i)   If the series $\displaystyle\sum_{n=1}^{+\infty} u_n$ is convergent, then $\displaystyle\lim_{n \to +\infty} s_n$ exists and is S.
Therefore

$$\lim_{n \to +\infty} cs_n = c \lim_{n \to +\infty} s_n$$

$$= c \cdot S$$

Hence the series $\displaystyle\sum_{n=1}^{+\infty} cu_n$ is convergent and its sum is $c \cdot S$.

Proof of (ii)   If the series $\displaystyle\sum_{n=1}^{+\infty} u_n$ is divergent, then $\displaystyle\lim_{n\to+\infty} s_n$ does not exist. Now suppose that the series $\displaystyle\sum_{n=1}^{+\infty} cu_n$ is convergent. Then $\displaystyle\lim_{n\to+\infty} cs_n$ exists. But $s_n = cs_n/c$; so

$$\lim_{n\to+\infty} s_n = \lim_{n\to+\infty} \frac{1}{c}(cs_n)$$

$$= \frac{1}{c} \lim_{n\to+\infty} cs_n$$

Thus $\displaystyle\lim_{n\to+\infty} s_n$ must exist, which is a contradiction. Therefore the series $\displaystyle\sum_{n=1}^{+\infty} cu_n$ is divergent.   ■

▶ **EXAMPLE 6**   Determine whether the series is convergent or divergent:

$$\sum_{n=1}^{+\infty} \frac{1}{4n}$$

Solution

$$\sum_{n=1}^{+\infty} \frac{1}{4n} = \frac{1}{4} + \frac{1}{8} + \frac{1}{12} + \frac{1}{16} + \ldots + \frac{1}{4n} + \ldots$$

Because $\displaystyle\sum_{n=1}^{+\infty} \frac{1}{n}$ is the harmonic series that is divergent, then by Theorem 8.3.6(ii) with $c = \frac{1}{4}$, the given series is divergent.   ◀

Another property of finite sums is

$$\sum_{k=1}^{n} (a_k \pm b_k) = \sum_{k=1}^{n} a_k \pm \sum_{k=1}^{n} b_k$$

and its extension to convergent infinite series is given by the following theorem.

8.3.7 Theorem

If $\displaystyle\sum_{n=1}^{+\infty} a_n$ and $\displaystyle\sum_{n=1}^{+\infty} b_n$ are convergent infinite series whose sums are S and T, respectively, then

(i) $\displaystyle\sum_{n=1}^{+\infty} (a_n + b_n)$ is a convergent series and its sum is $S + T$;

(ii) $\displaystyle\sum_{n=1}^{+\infty} (a_n - b_n)$ is a convergent series and its sum is $S - T$.

The proof of this theorem is left as an exercise (see Exercise 60).

The next theorem is a corollary of the above theorem and is sometimes used to prove that a series is divergent.

8.3.8 Theorem

If the series $\displaystyle\sum_{n=1}^{+\infty} a_n$ is convergent and the series $\displaystyle\sum_{n=1}^{+\infty} b_n$ is divergent,

then the series $\displaystyle\sum_{n=1}^{+\infty} (a_n + b_n)$ is divergent.

Proof Assume that $\displaystyle\sum_{n=1}^{+\infty} (a_n + b_n)$ is convergent and its sum is S. Let the sum

of the series $\displaystyle\sum_{n=1}^{+\infty} a_n$ be T. Then because

$$\sum_{n=1}^{+\infty} b_n = \sum_{n=1}^{+\infty} [(a_n + b_n) - a_n]$$

we conclude from Theorem 8.3.7(ii) that $\displaystyle\sum_{n=1}^{+\infty} b_n$ is convergent and its sum is

$S - T$. But this is a contradiction to the hypothesis that $\displaystyle\sum_{n=1}^{+\infty} b_n$ is divergent.

Hence $\displaystyle\sum_{n=1}^{+\infty} (a_n + b_n)$ is divergent. ∎

▶ **EXAMPLE 7** Determine whether the series is convergent or divergent:

$$\sum_{n=1}^{+\infty} \left(\frac{1}{4n} + \frac{1}{4^n} \right)$$

Solution In Example 6 the series $\displaystyle\sum_{n=1}^{+\infty} \frac{1}{4n}$ was proved to be divergent.

Because the series $\displaystyle\sum_{n=1}^{+\infty} \frac{1}{4^n}$ is a geometric series with $|r| = \frac{1}{4} < 1$, it is

convergent. Hence, by Theorem 8.3.8, the given series is divergent. ◀

If both series $\displaystyle\sum_{n=1}^{+\infty} a_n$ and $\displaystyle\sum_{n=1}^{+\infty} b_n$ are divergent, the series $\displaystyle\sum_{n=1}^{+\infty} (a_n + b_n)$ may

or may not be convergent. For example, if $a_n = \dfrac{1}{n}$ and $b_n = \dfrac{1}{n}$, then

$a_n + b_n = \dfrac{2}{n}$ and $\displaystyle\sum_{n=1}^{+\infty} \frac{2}{n}$ is divergent. But if $a_n = \dfrac{1}{n}$ and $b_n = -\dfrac{1}{n}$, then

$a_n + b_n = 0$ and $\displaystyle\sum_{n=1}^{+\infty} 0$ is convergent.

The final theorem of this section states that the convergence or divergence of an infinite series is not affected by changing a finite number of terms.

8.3.9 Theorem

If $\displaystyle\sum_{n=1}^{+\infty} a_n$ and $\displaystyle\sum_{n=1}^{+\infty} b_n$ are two infinite series, differing only in their first m terms (i.e., $a_k = b_k$ if $k > m$), then either both series converge or both series diverge.

Proof   Let $\{s_n\}$ and $\{t_n\}$ be the sequences of partial sums of the series $\displaystyle\sum_{n=1}^{+\infty} a_n$ and $\displaystyle\sum_{n=1}^{+\infty} b_n$, respectively. Then

$$s_n = a_1 + a_2 + \ldots + a_m + a_{m+1} + a_{m+2} + \ldots + a_n$$

and

$$t_n = b_1 + b_2 + \ldots + b_m + b_{m+1} + b_{m+2} + \ldots + b_n$$

Because $a_k = b_k$ if $k > m$, then if $n \geq m$,

$$s_n - t_n = (a_1 + a_2 + \ldots + a_m) - (b_1 + b_2 + \ldots + b_m)$$

So

$$\text{if}\quad n \geq m \quad\text{then}\quad s_n - t_n = s_m - t_m \tag{7}$$

We wish to show that either both $\lim\limits_{n \to +\infty} s_n$ and $\lim\limits_{n \to +\infty} t_n$ exist or do not exist. Suppose that $\lim\limits_{n \to +\infty} t_n$ exists. From (7),

$$\text{if}\quad n \geq m \quad\text{then}\quad s_n = t_n + (s_m - t_m)$$

Thus

$$\lim_{n \to +\infty} s_n = \lim_{n \to +\infty} t_n + (s_m - t_m)$$

Hence, when $\lim\limits_{n \to +\infty} t_n$ exists, $\lim\limits_{n \to +\infty} s_n$ also exists and both series converge. Now suppose that $\lim\limits_{n \to +\infty} t_n$ does not exist and $\lim\limits_{n \to +\infty} s_n$ exists. From (7),

$$\text{if}\quad n \geq m \quad\text{then}\quad t_n = s_n + (t_m - s_m)$$

Because $\lim\limits_{n \to +\infty} s_n$ exists, it follows that

$$\lim_{n \to +\infty} t_n = \lim_{n \to +\infty} s_n + (t_m - s_m)$$

and so $\lim\limits_{n \to +\infty} t_n$ has to exist, which is a contradiction. Hence, if $\lim\limits_{n \to +\infty} t_n$ does not exist, then $\lim\limits_{n \to +\infty} s_n$ does not exist, and both series diverge.   ∎

▶ **EXAMPLE 8** Determine whether the series is convergent or divergent:

$$\sum_{n=1}^{+\infty} \frac{1}{n + 4}$$

Solution The given series is

$$\frac{1}{5} + \frac{1}{6} + \frac{1}{7} + \ldots + \frac{1}{n + 4} + \ldots$$

which can be written as

$$0 + 0 + 0 + 0 + \frac{1}{5} + \frac{1}{6} + \frac{1}{7} + \ldots + \frac{1}{n} + \ldots \tag{8}$$

Now the harmonic series, which is known to be divergent, is

$$1 + \frac{1}{2} + \frac{1}{3} + \frac{1}{4} + \frac{1}{5} + \frac{1}{6} + \frac{1}{7} + \ldots + \frac{1}{n} + \ldots$$

Series (8) differs from the harmonic series only in the first four terms. Hence, by Theorem 8.3.9, series (8) is also divergent. ◀

▶ **EXAMPLE 9** Determine whether the series is convergent or divergent:

$$\sum_{n=1}^{+\infty} \frac{[\![\cos \frac{3}{n} \pi + 2]\!]}{3^n}$$

Solution The given series can be written as

$$\frac{[\![\cos 3\pi + 2]\!]}{3} + \frac{[\![\cos \frac{3}{2} \pi + 2]\!]}{3^2} + \frac{[\![\cos \pi + 2]\!]}{3^3} + \frac{[\![\cos \frac{3}{4} \pi + 2]\!]}{3^4}$$

$$+ \frac{[\![\cos \frac{3}{5} \pi + 2]\!]}{3^5} + \frac{[\![\cos \frac{1}{2} \pi + 2]\!]}{3^6} + \frac{[\![\cos \frac{3}{7} \pi + 2]\!]}{3^7} + \ldots$$

$$= \frac{1}{3} + \frac{2}{3^2} + \frac{1}{3^3} + \frac{1}{3^4} + \frac{1}{3^5} + \frac{2}{3^6} + \frac{2}{3^7} + \frac{2}{3^8} + \ldots \tag{9}$$

Consider the geometric series with $a = \frac{2}{3}$ and $r = \frac{1}{3}$:

$$\frac{2}{3} + \frac{2}{3^2} + \frac{2}{3^3} + \frac{2}{3^4} + \frac{2}{3^5} + \frac{2}{3^6} + \frac{2}{3^7} + \frac{2}{3^8} + \ldots \tag{10}$$

which is convergent. Because series (9) differs from series (10) only in the first five terms, then from Theorem 8.3.9 series (9) is also convergent. ◀

As a consequence of Theorem 8.3.9, for a given infinite series a finite number of terms can be added or subtracted without affecting its convergence or divergence. For instance, in Example 8 the given series may be thought of as being obtained from the harmonic series by subtracting the first four terms. And because the harmonic series is divergent, the given series is divergent. In Example 9 we could consider the convergent geometric series

$$\frac{2}{3^6} + \frac{2}{3^7} + \frac{2}{3^8} + \cdots \qquad \textbf{(11)}$$

and obtain the given series (9) by adding five terms. Because series (11) is convergent, then series (9) is convergent.

EXERCISES 8.3

In Exercises 1 through 8, find the first four elements of the sequence of partial sums $\{s_n\}$, and find a formula for s_n in terms of n. Also determine whether the infinite series is convergent or divergent; if it is convergent, find its sum.

1. $\displaystyle\sum_{n=1}^{+\infty} \frac{1}{(2n-1)(2n+1)}$ **2.** $\displaystyle\sum_{n=1}^{+\infty} n$

3. $\displaystyle\sum_{n=1}^{+\infty} \frac{5}{(3n+1)(3n-2)}$ **4.** $\displaystyle\sum_{n=1}^{+\infty} \frac{2}{(4n-3)(4n+1)}$

5. $\displaystyle\sum_{n=1}^{+\infty} \ln \frac{n}{n+1}$ **6.** $\displaystyle\sum_{n=1}^{+\infty} \frac{2n+1}{n^2(n+1)^2}$

7. $\displaystyle\sum_{n=1}^{+\infty} \frac{2}{5^{n-1}}$ **8.** $\displaystyle\sum_{n=1}^{+\infty} \frac{2^{n-1}}{3^n}$

In Exercises 9 through 13, write with sigma notation the infinite series that is the given sequence of partial sums. Also determine whether the infinite series is convergent or divergent; if it is convergent, find its sum.

9. $\{s_n\} = \left\{\dfrac{2n}{3n+1}\right\}$ **10.** $\{s_n\} = \left\{\dfrac{n^2}{n+1}\right\}$

11. $\{s_n\} = \left\{\dfrac{1}{3^n}\right\}$ **12.** $\{s_n\} = \{3^n\}$

13. $\{s_n\} = \{\ln(2n+1)\}$

In Exercises 14 through 24, write the first four terms of the infinite series and determine whether the series is convergent or divergent. If the series is convergent, find its sum.

14. $\displaystyle\sum_{n=1}^{+\infty} \frac{n}{n+1}$ **15.** $\displaystyle\sum_{n=1}^{+\infty} \frac{2n+1}{3n+2}$

16. $\displaystyle\sum_{n=1}^{+\infty} [1+(-1)^n]$ **17.** $\displaystyle\sum_{n=1}^{+\infty} \left(\frac{2}{3}\right)^n$ **18.** $\displaystyle\sum_{n=1}^{+\infty} \frac{3n^2}{n^2+1}$

19. $\displaystyle\sum_{n=1}^{+\infty} \ln \frac{1}{n}$ **20.** $\displaystyle\sum_{n=1}^{+\infty} \frac{2}{3^{n-1}}$ **21.** $\displaystyle\sum_{n=1}^{+\infty} (-1)^{n+1} \frac{3}{2^n}$

22. $\displaystyle\sum_{n=1}^{+\infty} \tan^n \frac{\pi}{6}$ **23.** $\displaystyle\sum_{n=1}^{+\infty} e^{-n}$ **24.** $\displaystyle\sum_{n=1}^{+\infty} \frac{\sinh n}{n}$

In Exercises 25 through 44, determine whether the series is convergent or divergent. If the series is convergent, find its sum.

25. $\displaystyle\sum_{n=1}^{+\infty} \frac{1}{n+2}$ **26.** $\displaystyle\sum_{n=3}^{+\infty} \frac{1}{n-1}$ **27.** $\displaystyle\sum_{n=1}^{+\infty} \frac{3}{2n}$

28. $\displaystyle\sum_{n=1}^{+\infty} \frac{2}{3n}$ **29.** $\displaystyle\sum_{n=1}^{+\infty} \frac{3}{2^n}$ **30.** $\displaystyle\sum_{n=1}^{+\infty} \frac{2}{3^n}$

31. $\displaystyle\sum_{n=1}^{+\infty} \frac{4}{3}\left(\frac{5}{7}\right)^n$ **32.** $\displaystyle\sum_{n=1}^{+\infty} \frac{7}{5}\left(\frac{3}{4}\right)^n$

33. $\displaystyle\sum_{n=1}^{+\infty} \frac{\left[\!\left[\sin \frac{4}{n}\pi + 3 \right]\!\right]}{4^n}$ **34.** $\displaystyle\sum_{n=1}^{+\infty} \frac{\left[\!\left[\cos \frac{1}{n}\pi + 1 \right]\!\right]}{2^n}$

35. $\displaystyle\sum_{n=1}^{+\infty} \left(\frac{1}{2n} + \frac{1}{2^n}\right)$ **36.** $\displaystyle\sum_{n=1}^{+\infty} \left(\frac{1}{3^n} + \frac{1}{3n}\right)$

37. $\displaystyle\sum_{n=1}^{+\infty} \left(\frac{1}{2^n} + \frac{1}{3^n}\right)$ **38.** $\displaystyle\sum_{n=1}^{+\infty} \left(\frac{1}{3^n} - \frac{1}{4^n}\right)$

39. $\displaystyle\sum_{n=1}^{+\infty} (e^{-n} + e^n)$ **40.** $\displaystyle\sum_{n=1}^{+\infty} (2^{-n} + 3^n)$

41. $\displaystyle\sum_{n=1}^{+\infty} \left(\frac{1}{2n} - \frac{1}{3n}\right)$ **42.** $\displaystyle\sum_{n=1}^{+\infty} \left(\frac{3}{2n} - \frac{2}{3n}\right)$

43. $\displaystyle\sum_{n=1}^{+\infty} \left(\frac{3}{2^n} - \frac{2}{3^n}\right)$ **44.** $\displaystyle\sum_{n=1}^{+\infty} \left(\frac{5}{4^n} + \frac{4}{5^n}\right)$

Exercises 45 through 48, express the nonterminating repeating decimal as a common fraction.

45. $0.27\ 27\ 27 \ldots$ **46.** $2.045\ 45\ 45 \ldots$

47. $1.234\ 234\ 234 \ldots$ **48.** $0.4653\ 4653\ 4653 \ldots$

49. The path of each swing, after the first, of a pendulum bob is 0.93 as long as the path of the previous swing (from one side to the other side). If the path of the first swing is 56 cm long, and air resistance eventually brings the pendulum to rest, how far does the bob travel before it comes to rest?

50. After a woman riding a bicycle stops pedaling, the front wheel rotates 200 times during the first 10 sec.

Then in each succeeding 10-sec time period the wheel rotates four-fifths as many times as it did the previous period. Determine the number of rotations of the wheel before the bicycle stops.

51. A ball is dropped from a height of 12 ft, and each time it strikes the ground, it bounces back to a height of three-fourths the distance from which it fell. Find the total distance traveled by the ball before it comes to rest.

52. What is the total distance traveled by a tennis ball before coming to rest if it is dropped from a height of 199 ft and if, after each fall, it rebounds eleven-twentieths of the distance from which it fell?

53. **(a)** Prove that it takes a ball $\sqrt{h}/4$ seconds to reach the ground if it is dropped from a height of h feet. **(b)** Use the result of part (a) to determine how long it takes the ball of Exercise 51 to stop bouncing.

54. Use the result of part (a) of Exercise 53 to determine how long it takes the tennis ball of Exercise 52 to stop bouncing.

55. An equilateral triangle has sides of length 4 units. Another equilateral triangle is constructed by drawing line segments through the midpoints of the sides of the first triangle. If this procedure can be repeated an unlimited number of times, what is the total perimeter of all the triangles formed?

56. Find an infinite geometric series whose sum is 6 and such that each term is four times the sum of all the terms that follow it.

57. Plot on your graphics calculator the sequence of the first 100 partial sums of the harmonic series. From your graph estimate

(a) $\displaystyle\sum_{n=1}^{25} \frac{1}{n}$ **(b)** $\displaystyle\sum_{n=1}^{50} \frac{1}{n}$ **(c)** $\displaystyle\sum_{n=1}^{75} \frac{1}{n}$ **(d)** $\displaystyle\sum_{n=1}^{100} \frac{1}{n}$

58. Plot on your graphics calculator the sequence of the first 1000 partial sums of the harmonic series. From your graph estimate

(a) $\displaystyle\sum_{n=1}^{250} \frac{1}{n}$ **(b)** $\displaystyle\sum_{n=1}^{500} \frac{1}{n}$ **(c)** $\displaystyle\sum_{n=1}^{750} \frac{1}{n}$ **(d)** $\displaystyle\sum_{n=1}^{1000} \frac{1}{n}$

59. Use your graphics calculator any way you wish to determine the first element of the sequence of partial sums of the harmonic series which is at least 10.

60. Prove Theorem 8.3.7.

61. **(a)** If an infinite series is divergent, can we conclude that its nth term does not approach 0 as n increases without bound? **(b)** If the nth term of an infinite series does not approach 0 as n increases without bound, can we conclude that the series is divergent? Justify your answers in (a) and (b) by stating a theorem or giving an example.

8.4 INFINITE SERIES OF POSITIVE TERMS

Infinite series, all of whose terms are positive, have special properties. In particular, the sequence of partial sums of such a series is increasing and has a lower bound of 0. If the sequence of partial sums also has an upper bound, then the sequence is monotonic and bounded. Because boundedness and convergence of a monotonic sequence are equivalent, the sequence of partial sums is convergent, and therefore the series is convergent. Thus we have the following theorem.

8.4.1 Theorem

An infinite series of positive terms is convergent if and only if its sequence of partial sums has an upper bound.

▶ **EXAMPLE 1** Prove that the series is convergent by applying Theorem 8.4.1:

$$\sum_{n=1}^{+\infty} \frac{1}{n!}$$

Solution We must find an upper bound for the sequence of partial sums of the series $\sum_{n=1}^{+\infty} \dfrac{1}{n!}$.

$$s_1 = 1 \qquad s_2 = 1 + \frac{1}{1 \cdot 2} \qquad s_3 = 1 + \frac{1}{1 \cdot 2} + \frac{1}{1 \cdot 2 \cdot 3}$$

$$\vdots$$

$$s_n = 1 + \frac{1}{1 \cdot 2} + \frac{1}{1 \cdot 2 \cdot 3} + \ldots + \frac{1}{1 \cdot 2 \cdot 3 \cdot \ldots \cdot n} \qquad (1)$$

Now consider the first n terms of the geometric series with $a = 1$ and $r = \frac{1}{2}$:

$$\sum_{k=1}^{n} \frac{1}{2^{k-1}} = 1 + \frac{1}{2} + \frac{1}{2^2} + \ldots + \frac{1}{2^{n-1}} \qquad (2)$$

By Theorem 8.3.5 the geometric series with $a = 1$ and $r = \frac{1}{2}$ has the sum $a/(1 - r) = 2$. Hence summation (2) is less than 2. Observe that each term of summation (1) is less than or equal to the corresponding term of summation (2); that is,

$$\frac{1}{k!} \leq \frac{1}{2^{k-1}}$$

This is true because $k! = 1 \cdot 2 \cdot 3 \cdot \ldots \cdot k$, which in addition to the factor 1 contains $k - 1$ factors each greater than or equal to 2. Hence

$$s_n = \sum_{k=1}^{n} \frac{1}{k!} \leq \sum_{k=1}^{n} \frac{1}{2^{k-1}} < 2$$

From the above, $\{s_n\}$ has an upper bound of 2. Therefore, by Theorem 8.4.1, the given series is convergent.   ◀

In Example 1, we compared the terms of the given series with those of a known convergent series. This procedure is a particular case of the following theorem known as the *comparison test*.

8.4.2 Theorem   Comparison Test

Let the series $\sum_{n=1}^{+\infty} u_n$ be a series of positive terms.

(i) If $\sum_{n=1}^{+\infty} v_n$ is a series of positive terms known to be convergent, and $u_n \leq v_n$ for all positive integers n, then $\sum_{n=1}^{+\infty} u_n$ is convergent.

(ii) If $\sum_{n=1}^{+\infty} w_n$ is a series of positive terms known to be divergent, and $u_n \geq w_n$ for all positive integers n, then $\sum_{n=1}^{+\infty} u_n$ is divergent.

Proof of (i)   Let $\{s_n\}$ be the sequence of partial sums for the series $\sum\limits_{n=1}^{+\infty} u_n$ and $\{t_n\}$ be the sequence of partial sums for the series $\sum\limits_{n=1}^{+\infty} v_n$. Because $\sum\limits_{n=1}^{+\infty} v_n$ is a series of positive terms that is convergent, it follows from Theorem 8.4.1 that the sequence $\{t_n\}$ has an upper bound; call it B. Because $u_n \leq v_n$ for all positive integers n, we can conclude that $s_n \leq t_n \leq B$ for all positive integers n. Therefore B is an upper bound of the sequence $\{s_n\}$. And because the terms of the series $\sum\limits_{n=1}^{+\infty} u_n$ are all positive, it follows from Theorem 8.4.1 that $\sum\limits_{n=1}^{+\infty} u_n$ is convergent.

Proof of (ii)   Assume that $\sum\limits_{n=1}^{+\infty} u_n$ is convergent. Then because both $\sum\limits_{n=1}^{+\infty} u_n$ and $\sum\limits_{n=1}^{+\infty} w_n$ are infinite series of positive terms and $w_n \leq u_n$ for all positive integers n, it follows from part (i) that $\sum\limits_{n=1}^{+\infty} w_n$ is convergent. However, this contradicts the hypothesis; so our assumption is false. Therefore $\sum\limits_{n=1}^{+\infty} u_n$ is divergent.   ■

As you learned in Section 8.3, the convergence or divergence of an infinite series is not affected by discarding a finite number of terms. Therefore, when applying the comparison test, if $u_i \leq w_i$ or $u_i \geq w_i$ when $i > m$, the test is valid regardless of how the first m terms of the two series compare.

▶ **EXAMPLE 2**   Determine whether the series is convergent or divergent:

$$\sum_{n=1}^{+\infty} \frac{4}{3^n + 1}$$

Solution   The given series is

$$\frac{4}{4} + \frac{4}{10} + \frac{4}{28} + \frac{4}{82} + \ldots + \frac{4}{3^n + 1} + \ldots$$

Comparing the nth term of this series with the nth term of the convergent geometric series

$$\frac{4}{3} + \frac{4}{9} + \frac{4}{27} + \frac{4}{81} + \ldots + \frac{4}{3^n} + \ldots \qquad r = \tfrac{1}{3} < 1$$

we have

$$\frac{4}{3^n + 1} < \frac{4}{3^n}$$

for every positive integer n. Therefore, by part (i) of the comparison test, the given series is convergent.   ◀

▶ **EXAMPLE 3** Determine whether the series is convergent or divergent:

$$\sum_{n=1}^{+\infty} \frac{1}{\sqrt{n}}$$

Solution The given series is

$$\sum_{n=1}^{+\infty} \frac{1}{\sqrt{n}} = \frac{1}{\sqrt{1}} + \frac{1}{\sqrt{2}} + \frac{1}{\sqrt{3}} + \ldots + \frac{1}{\sqrt{n}} + \ldots$$

Comparing the nth term of this series with the nth term of the divergent harmonic series we have

$$\frac{1}{\sqrt{n}} \geq \frac{1}{n} \qquad \text{for every positive integer } n$$

So by part (ii) of the comparison test the given series is divergent. ◀

The *limit comparison test,* which follows, is a consequence of the comparison test and is often easier to apply.

8.4.3 Theorem   Limit Comparison Test

Let $\displaystyle\sum_{n=1}^{+\infty} u_n$ and $\displaystyle\sum_{n=1}^{+\infty} v_n$ be two series of positive terms.

  (i) If $\displaystyle\lim_{n \to +\infty} \frac{u_n}{v_n} = c > 0$, then the two series either both converge or both diverge.

  (ii) If $\displaystyle\lim_{n \to +\infty} \frac{u_n}{v_n} = 0$, and if $\displaystyle\sum_{n=1}^{+\infty} v_n$ converges, then $\displaystyle\sum_{n=1}^{+\infty} u_n$ converges.

  (iii) If $\displaystyle\lim_{n \to +\infty} \frac{u_n}{v_n} = +\infty$, and if $\displaystyle\sum_{n=1}^{+\infty} v_n$ diverges, then $\displaystyle\sum_{n=1}^{+\infty} u_n$ diverges.

Proof of (i) Because $\displaystyle\lim_{n \to +\infty} (u_n/v_n) = c$, there exists an $N > 0$ such that

$$\text{if } n > N \quad \text{then} \quad \left| \frac{u_n}{v_n} - c \right| < \frac{c}{2}$$

$$\Leftrightarrow \text{ if } n > N \quad \text{then} \quad -\frac{c}{2} < \frac{u_n}{v_n} - c < \frac{c}{2}$$

$$\Leftrightarrow \text{ if } n > N \quad \text{then} \quad \frac{c}{2} < \frac{u_n}{v_n} < \frac{3c}{2} \tag{3}$$

From the right-hand inequality (3),

$$u_n < \tfrac{3}{2} c v_n \tag{4}$$

If $\displaystyle\sum_{n=1}^{+\infty} v_n$ is convergent, so is $\displaystyle\sum_{n=1}^{+\infty} \tfrac{3}{2} c v_n$. It follows from inequality (4) and the

comparison test that $\displaystyle\sum_{n=1}^{+\infty} u_n$ is convergent.

From the left-hand inequality (3),

$$v_n < \frac{2}{c} u_n \tag{5}$$

If $\sum_{n=1}^{+\infty} u_n$ is convergent, so is $\sum_{n=1}^{+\infty} \frac{2}{c} u_n$. From inequality (5) and the comparison

test it follows that $\sum_{n=1}^{+\infty} v_n$ is convergent.

If $\sum_{n=1}^{+\infty} v_n$ is divergent $\sum_{n=1}^{+\infty} u_n$ can be shown to be divergent by assuming

that $\sum_{n=1}^{+\infty} u_n$ is convergent and getting a contradiction by applying inequality

(5) and the comparison test.

In a similar manner, if $\sum_{n=1}^{+\infty} u_n$ is divergent, it follows that $\sum_{n=1}^{+\infty} v_n$ is

divergent because a contradiction is obtained from inequality (4) and the

comparison test if $\sum_{n=1}^{+\infty} v_n$ is assumed to be convergent.

We have therefore proved part (i). The proofs of parts (ii) and (iii) are
left as exercises (see Exercises 57 and 58). ∎

CAUTION: Be sure you apply part (ii) of the limit comparison test
correctly. When $\lim_{n \to +\infty} \frac{u_n}{v_n} = 0$, the convergence of the series $\sum_{n=1}^{+\infty} v_n$ implies

the convergence of the series $\sum_{n=1}^{+\infty} u_n$, but the divergence of the v-series does

not imply that the u-series diverges.

▶ **EXAMPLE 4** Solve Example 2 by the limit comparison test.

Solution Let u_n be the nth term of the given series $\sum_{n=1}^{+\infty} \frac{4}{3^n + 1}$ and v_n be

the nth term of the convergent geometric series $\sum_{n=1}^{+\infty} \frac{4}{3^n}$. Therefore

$$\lim_{n \to +\infty} \frac{u_n}{v_n} = \lim_{n \to +\infty} \frac{\dfrac{4}{3^n + 1}}{\dfrac{4}{3^n}}$$

$$= \lim_{n \to +\infty} \frac{3^n}{3^n + 1}$$

$$= \lim_{n \to +\infty} \frac{1}{1 + 3^{-n}}$$

$$= 1$$

Hence, by part (i) of the limit comparison test, the given series is convergent.   ◀

▶   **_EXAMPLE 5_**   Solve Example 3 by the limit comparison test.

Solution   Let u_n be the nth term of the given series $\displaystyle\sum_{n=1}^{+\infty} \frac{1}{\sqrt{n}}$ and v_n be the

nth term of the divergent harmonic series. Then

$$\lim_{n \to +\infty} \frac{u_n}{v_n} = \lim_{n \to +\infty} \frac{\dfrac{1}{\sqrt{n}}}{\dfrac{1}{n}}$$

$$= \lim_{n \to +\infty} \sqrt{n}$$

$$= +\infty$$

Therefore, by part (iii) of the limit comparison test, the given series is divergent.   ◀

▶   **_EXAMPLE 6_**   Determine whether the series is convergent or divergent:

$$\sum_{n=1}^{+\infty} \frac{n^3}{n!}$$

Solution   In Example 1 we proved that the series $\displaystyle\sum_{n=1}^{+\infty} \frac{1}{n!}$ is convergent. By

the limit comparison test with $u_n = \dfrac{n^3}{n!}$ and $v_n = \dfrac{1}{n!}$,

$$\lim_{n \to +\infty} \frac{u_n}{v_n} = \lim_{n \to +\infty} \frac{\dfrac{n^3}{n!}}{\dfrac{1}{n!}}$$

$$= \lim_{n \to +\infty} n^3$$

$$= +\infty$$

Part (iii) of the limit comparison test is not applicable because $\displaystyle\sum_{n=1}^{+\infty} v_n$ converges. However, there is a way that the limit comparison test can be used. The given series can be written as

$$\frac{1^3}{1!} + \frac{2^3}{2!} + \frac{3^3}{3!} + \frac{4^3}{4!} + \frac{5^3}{5!} + \ldots + \frac{n^3}{n!} + \ldots$$

Because Theorem 8.3.9 allows us to subtract a finite number of terms without affecting the behavior (convergence or divergence) of a series, we discard the first three terms and obtain

$$\frac{4^3}{4!} + \frac{5^3}{5!} + \frac{6^3}{6!} + \ldots + \frac{(n + 3)^3}{(n + 3)!} + \ldots$$

Now let $u_n = \dfrac{(n + 3)^3}{(n + 3)!}$ and, as before, let $v_n = \dfrac{1}{n!}$. Then

$$\lim_{n \to +\infty} \frac{u_n}{v_n} = \lim_{n \to +\infty} \frac{\dfrac{(n + 3)^3}{(n + 3)!}}{\dfrac{1}{n!}}$$

$$= \lim_{n \to +\infty} \frac{(n + 3)^3 n!}{(n + 3)!}$$

$$= \lim_{n \to +\infty} \frac{(n + 3)^3 n!}{n!(n + 1)(n + 2)(n + 3)}$$

$$= \lim_{n \to +\infty} \frac{(n + 3)^2}{(n + 1)(n + 2)}$$

$$= \lim_{n \to +\infty} \frac{n^2 + 6n + 9}{n^2 + 3n + 2}$$

$$= \lim_{n \to +\infty} \frac{1 + \dfrac{6}{n} + \dfrac{9}{n^2}}{1 + \dfrac{3}{n} + \dfrac{2}{n^2}}$$

$$= 1$$

From part (i) of the limit comparison test, the given series is convergent. ◀

Before stating the next theorem, we give an illustration of a particular case.

▷ **ILLUSTRATION 1**   Consider the geometric series

$$1 + \frac{1}{2} + \frac{1}{4} + \frac{1}{8} + \frac{1}{16} + \frac{1}{32} + \ldots + \frac{1}{2^{n-1}} + \ldots \tag{6}$$

which converges to 2 as shown in Illustration 2 of Section 8.3. Regroup the terms of this series to obtain

$$\left(1 + \frac{1}{2}\right) + \left(\frac{1}{4} + \frac{1}{8}\right) + \left(\frac{1}{16} + \frac{1}{32}\right) + \ldots + \left(\frac{1}{4^{n-1}} + \frac{1}{2 \cdot 4^{n-1}}\right) + \ldots$$

which is the series

$$\frac{3}{2} + \frac{3}{8} + \frac{3}{32} + \ldots + \frac{3}{2 \cdot 4^{n-1}} + \ldots \tag{7}$$

Because series (7) is the geometric series with $a = \frac{3}{2}$ and $r = \frac{1}{4}$, it is convergent and its sum is

$$\frac{a}{1 - r} = \frac{\frac{3}{2}}{1 - \frac{1}{4}}$$

$$= 2$$

We have shown that series (7), which is obtained from the convergent series (6) by regrouping the terms, is also convergent, and its sum is the same as that of series (6). ◀

8.4.4 Theorem

If $\sum_{n=1}^{+\infty} u_n$ is a given convergent series of positive terms, its terms can be grouped in any manner, and the resulting series also will be convergent and will have the same sum as the given series.

Proof   Let $\{s_n\}$ be the sequence of partial sums for the given convergent series of positive terms. Then $\lim_{n\to+\infty} s_n$ exists; let this limit be S. Consider a series $\sum_{n=1}^{+\infty} v_n$ whose terms are obtained by grouping the terms of $\sum_{n=1}^{+\infty} u_n$ in some manner. For example $\sum_{n=1}^{+\infty} v_n$ may be the series

$$u_1 + (u_2 + u_3) + (u_4 + u_5 + u_6) + (u_7 + u_8 + u_9 + u_{10}) + \ldots$$

or it may be the series

$$(u_1 + u_2) + (u_3 + u_4) + (u_5 + u_6) + (u_7 + u_8) + \ldots$$

and so forth. Let $\{t_m\}$ be the sequence of partial sums for the series $\sum_{n=1}^{+\infty} v_n$. Each partial sum of the sequence $\{t_m\}$ is also a partial sum of the sequence $\{s_n\}$. Therefore, as m increases without bound, so does n. Because $\lim_{n\to+\infty} s_n = S$, we conclude that $\lim_{n\to+\infty} t_m = S$. This proves the theorem. ∎

Theorem 8.4.4 as well as the following one state properties of the sum of a convergent series of positive terms similar to properties that hold for the sum of a finite number of terms.

8.4.5 Theorem

If $\sum_{n=1}^{+\infty} u_n$ is a given convergent series of positive terms, the order of the terms can be rearranged, and the resulting series also will be convergent and will have the same sum as the given series.

Proof   Let $\{s_n\}$ be the sequence of partial sums for the given convergent series of positive terms, and let $\lim_{n\to+\infty} s_n = S$. Let $\sum_{n=1}^{+\infty} v_n$ be a series formed by rearranging the order of the terms of $\sum_{n=1}^{+\infty} u_n$. For example, $\sum_{n=1}^{+\infty} v_n$ may be the series

$$u_4 + u_3 + u_7 + u_1 + u_9 + u_5 + \ldots$$

Let $\{t_n\}$ be the sequence of partial sums for the series $\sum_{n=1}^{+\infty} v_n$. Each partial sum of the sequence $\{t_n\}$ will be less than S because it is the sum of n terms of the infinite series $\sum_{n=1}^{+\infty} u_n$. Therefore S is an upper bound of the sequence $\{t_n\}$.

Furthermore, because all the terms of the series $\sum_{n=1}^{+\infty} v_n$ are positive, $\{t_n\}$ is a monotonic increasing sequence. Hence, by Theorem 8.2.11 the sequence $\{t_n\}$ is convergent, and $\lim\limits_{n \to +\infty} t_n = T \le S$. Now because the given series $\sum_{n=1}^{+\infty} u_n$ can be obtained from the series $\sum_{n=1}^{+\infty} v_n$ by rearranging the order of the terms, we can use the same argument and conclude that $S \le T$. If both inequalities, $T \le S$ and $S \le T$, must hold, it follows that $S = T$. This proves the theorem. ∎

The following series, known as the **p series** or the **hyperharmonic series**, is often used in the comparison test:

$$\frac{1}{1^p} + \frac{1}{2^p} + \frac{1}{3^p} + \ldots + \frac{1}{n^p} + \ldots \qquad \text{where } p \text{ is a constant} \qquad (8)$$

In the following illustration we prove that the p series diverges if $p \le 1$ and converges if $p > 1$.

▷ **ILLUSTRATION 2**   If $p = 1$, the p series is the harmonic series, which diverges. If $p < 1$, then $n^p \le n$; so

$$\frac{1}{n^p} \ge \frac{1}{n} \qquad \text{for every positive integer } n$$

Therefore, by the comparison test, the p series diverges if $p < 1$.

If $p > 1$, we group the terms as follows:

$$\frac{1}{1^p} + \left(\frac{1}{2^p} + \frac{1}{3^p}\right) + \left(\frac{1}{4^p} + \frac{1}{5^p} + \frac{1}{6^p} + \frac{1}{7^p}\right) + \left(\frac{1}{8^p} + \frac{1}{9^p} + \ldots + \frac{1}{15^p}\right) + \ldots \qquad (9)$$

Consider the series

$$\frac{1}{1^p} + \frac{2}{2^p} + \frac{4}{4^p} + \frac{8}{8^p} + \ldots + \frac{2^{n-1}}{(2^{n-1})^p} + \ldots \qquad (10)$$

This is a geometric series whose ratio is $2/2^p = 1/2^{p-1}$, which is a positive number less than 1. Hence series (10) is convergent. We now rewrite the terms of series (10) to get

$$\frac{1}{1^p} + \left(\frac{1}{2^p} + \frac{1}{2^p}\right) + \left(\frac{1}{4^p} + \frac{1}{4^p} + \frac{1}{4^p} + \frac{1}{4^p}\right) + \left(\frac{1}{8^p} + \frac{1}{8^p} + \ldots + \frac{1}{8^p}\right) + \ldots \qquad (11)$$

By comparing series (9) and series (11) we see that the group of terms in each set of parentheses after the first group is less in sum for (9) than it is for (11). Therefore, by the comparison test, series (9) is convergent. Because (9) is merely a regrouping of the terms of the p series when $p > 1$, it follows from Theorem 8.4.4 that the p series is convergent if $p > 1$. ◀

Note that the series in Example 3 is the p series where $p = \frac{1}{2} < 1$; therefore it is divergent.

▶ **EXAMPLE 7**   Determine whether the series is convergent or divergent:

$$\sum_{n=1}^{+\infty} \frac{1}{(n^2 + 2)^{1/3}}$$

Solution   Because for large values of n the number $n^2 + 2$ is close to the number n^2, so is the number $1/(n^2 + 2)^{1/3}$ close to the number $1/n^{2/3}$. The series $\sum_{n=1}^{+\infty} \frac{1}{n^{2/3}}$ is divergent because it is the p series with $p = \frac{2}{3} < 1$. From the limit comparison test with $u_n = \dfrac{1}{(n^2 + 2)^{1/3}}$ and $v_n = \dfrac{1}{n^{2/3}}$,

$$\lim_{n \to +\infty} \frac{u_n}{v_n} = \lim_{n \to +\infty} \frac{\dfrac{1}{(n^2 + 2)^{1/3}}}{\dfrac{1}{n^{2/3}}}$$

$$= \lim_{n \to +\infty} \frac{n^{2/3}}{(n^2 + 2)^{1/3}}$$

$$= \lim_{n \to +\infty} \left(\frac{n^2}{n^2 + 2}\right)^{1/3}$$

$$= \lim_{n \to +\infty} \left(\frac{1}{1 + \dfrac{2}{n^2}}\right)^{1/3}$$

$$= 1$$

The given series is, therefore, divergent.   ◀

Another theorem sometimes used to test an infinite series of positive terms for convergence is the *integral test*, which utilizes the theory of improper integrals.

8.4.6 Theorem   Integral Test

Let f be a function that is continuous, decreasing, and positive valued for all $x \geq 1$. Then the infinite series

$$\sum_{n=1}^{+\infty} f(n) = f(1) + f(2) + f(3) + \ldots + f(n) + \ldots$$

is convergent if the improper integral $\displaystyle\int_{1}^{+\infty} f(x)\, dx$ exists, and it is divergent if $\displaystyle\lim_{b \to +\infty} \int_{1}^{b} f(x)\, dx = +\infty$.

Proof If i is a positive integer and $i \geq 2$, then by the mean-value theorem for integrals (4.6.3) there exists a number c such that $i - 1 \leq c \leq i$ and

$$\int_{i-1}^{i} f(x)\, dx = f(c) \cdot 1 \tag{12}$$

Because f is a decreasing function,

$$f(i - 1) \geq f(c) \geq f(i)$$

and so from (12),

$$f(i - 1) \geq \int_{i-1}^{i} f(x)\, dx \geq f(i)$$

Therefore, if n is a positive integer and $n \geq 2$,

$$\sum_{i=2}^{n} f(i - 1) \geq \sum_{i=2}^{n} \int_{i-1}^{i} f(x)\, dx \geq \sum_{i=2}^{n} f(i)$$

$$\Leftrightarrow \sum_{i=1}^{n-1} f(i) \geq \int_{1}^{n} f(x)\, dx \geq \sum_{i=1}^{n} f(i) - f(1) \tag{13}$$

Figures 1 and 2 show the geometric interpretation of the above discussion for $n = 6$. Figure 1 shows the graph of a function f satisfying the hypothesis. The sum of the measures of the areas of the shaded rectangles is $f(1) + f(2) + f(3) + f(4) + f(5)$, which is the left member of inequality (13) when $n = 6$. Clearly, the sum of the measures of the areas of these rectangles is greater than the measure of the area given by the definite integral when $n = 6$. In Figure 2 the sum of the measures of the areas of the shaded rectangles is $f(2) + f(3) + f(4) + f(5) + f(6)$, which is the right member of inequality (13) when $n = 6$. This sum is less than the value of the definite integral when $n = 6$.

If the given improper integral exists, let L be its value. Then

$$\int_{1}^{n} f(x)\, dx \leq L \tag{14}$$

From the second and third members of inequality (13) and from (14),

$$\sum_{i=1}^{n} f(i) \leq f(1) + \int_{1}^{n} f(x)\, dx \leq f(1) + L \tag{15}$$

Consider now the infinite series $\sum_{n=1}^{+\infty} f(n)$. Let the sequence of partial sums of this series be $\{s_n\}$, where $s_n = \sum_{i=1}^{n} f(i)$. From (15), $\{s_n\}$ has an upper bound of $f(1) + L$. Hence, by Theorem 8.4.1, $\sum_{n=1}^{+\infty} f(n)$ is convergent.

Suppose that $\lim\limits_{b \to +\infty} \int_{1}^{b} f(x)\, dx = +\infty$. From (13)

$$\sum_{i=1}^{n-1} f(i) \geq \int_{1}^{n} f(x)\, dx$$

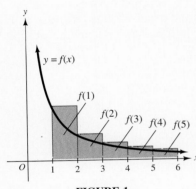

FIGURE 1

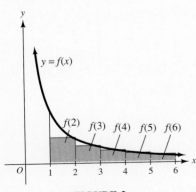

FIGURE 2

for all positive integers n. Therefore

$$\lim_{n \to +\infty} s_n = \lim_{n \to +\infty} \sum_{i=1}^{n} f(i)$$

$$= +\infty$$

Hence $\sum_{n=1}^{+\infty} f(n)$ is divergent. ∎

▶ **EXAMPLE 8** Determine whether the series is convergent or divergent:

$$\sum_{n=1}^{+\infty} ne^{-n}$$

Solution Let $f(x) = xe^{-x}$. Then

$$f'(x) = e^{-x} - xe^{-x}$$

$$= e^{-x}(1 - x)$$

Because $f'(x) < 0$ if $x > 1$, it follows from Theorem 3.4.3 that f is decreasing if $x \geq 1$. Furthermore, f is continuous and positive valued for all $x \geq 1$. Thus the hypothesis of the integral test is satisfied. By applying integration by parts,

$$\int xe^{-x}\, dx = -e^{-x}(x + 1) + C$$

Hence

$$\int_{1}^{+\infty} xe^{-x}\, dx = \lim_{b \to +\infty} \left[-e^{-x}(x + 1) \right]_{1}^{b}$$

$$= \lim_{b \to +\infty} \left[-\frac{b + 1}{e^{b}} + \frac{2}{e} \right]$$

Because $\lim_{b \to +\infty} (b + 1) = +\infty$ and $\lim_{b \to +\infty} e^{b} = +\infty$, L'Hôpital's rule can be used to obtain

$$\lim_{b \to +\infty} \frac{b + 1}{e^{b}} = \lim_{b \to +\infty} \frac{1}{e^{b}}$$

$$= 0$$

Therefore

$$\int_{1}^{+\infty} xe^{-x}\, dx = \frac{2}{e}$$

Thus the given series is convergent. ◀

If the summation index for an infinite series starts with $n = k$ rather than $n = 1$, the integral test is modified as follows:

If f is a function that is continuous, decreasing, and positive valued for all $x \geq k$, then the infinite series $\sum\limits_{n=k}^{+\infty} f(n)$ is convergent if the improper integral $\int_{k}^{+\infty} f(x)\, dx$ exists and is divergent if $\lim\limits_{b \to +\infty} \int_{k}^{b} f(x)\, dx = +\infty$.

The proof is identical to that of Theorem 8.4.6.

▶ **EXAMPLE 9**   Determine whether the series is convergent or divergent:

$$\sum_{n=2}^{+\infty} \frac{1}{n \sqrt{\ln n}}$$

Solution   The function f defined by

$$f(x) = \frac{1}{x \sqrt{\ln x}}$$

is continuous and positive valued for all $x \geq 2$. Also, if $2 \leq x_1 < x_2$, then $f(x_1) > f(x_2)$; so f is decreasing for all $x \geq 2$. Therefore the integral test can be applied.

$$\int_{2}^{+\infty} \frac{dx}{x \sqrt{\ln x}} = \lim_{b \to +\infty} \int_{2}^{b} (\ln x)^{-1/2} \frac{dx}{x}$$

$$= \lim_{b \to +\infty} \left[2\sqrt{\ln x} \right]_{2}^{b}$$

$$= \lim_{b \to +\infty} \left[2\sqrt{\ln b} - 2\sqrt{\ln 2} \right]$$

$$= +\infty$$

Thus the given series is divergent.   ◀

EXERCISES 8.4

In Exercises 1 through 24, determine whether the series is convergent or divergent by applying either the comparison test or the limit comparison test.

1. $\sum\limits_{n=1}^{+\infty} \dfrac{1}{n\,2^n}$

2. $\sum\limits_{n=1}^{+\infty} \dfrac{1}{\sqrt{2n+1}}$

3. $\sum\limits_{n=1}^{+\infty} \dfrac{1}{n^n}$

4. $\sum\limits_{n=1}^{+\infty} \dfrac{n^2}{4n^3+1}$

5. $\sum\limits_{n=1}^{+\infty} \dfrac{3n+1}{2n^2+5}$

6. $\sum\limits_{n=1}^{+\infty} \dfrac{3}{\sqrt{n^3+n}}$

7. $\sum\limits_{n=1}^{+\infty} \dfrac{\cos^2 n}{3^n}$

8. $\sum\limits_{n=1}^{+\infty} \dfrac{1}{\ln(n+1)}$

9. $\sum\limits_{n=1}^{+\infty} \dfrac{1}{\sqrt{n^2+4n}}$

10. $\sum\limits_{n=1}^{+\infty} \dfrac{|\sin n|}{n^2}$

11. $\sum\limits_{n=1}^{+\infty} \dfrac{n!}{(n+2)!}$

12. $\sum\limits_{n=1}^{+\infty} \dfrac{1}{\sqrt{n^3+1}}$

13. $\sum\limits_{n=1}^{+\infty} \dfrac{n}{5n^2+3}$

14. $\sum\limits_{n=1}^{+\infty} \dfrac{(n-1)!}{(n+1)!}$

15. $\sum\limits_{n=1}^{+\infty} \dfrac{n!}{(2n)!}$

16. $\sum\limits_{n=1}^{+\infty} \sin \dfrac{1}{n}$

17. $\sum\limits_{n=1}^{+\infty} \dfrac{|\csc n|}{n}$

18. $\sum\limits_{n=1}^{+\infty} \dfrac{1}{n+\sqrt{n}}$

19. $\displaystyle\sum_{n=2}^{+\infty} \frac{1}{n\sqrt{n^2 - 1}}$

20. $\displaystyle\sum_{n=1}^{+\infty} \frac{2^n}{n!}$

21. $\displaystyle\sum_{n=1}^{+\infty} \frac{3}{2n - \sqrt{n}}$

22. $\displaystyle\sum_{n=1}^{+\infty} \frac{\sqrt{n}}{n^2 + 1}$

23. $\displaystyle\sum_{n=1}^{+\infty} \frac{\ln n}{n^2 + 2}$

24. $\displaystyle\sum_{n=1}^{+\infty} \frac{1}{3^n - \cos n}$

In Exercises 25 through 32, apply the integral test to determine whether the series is convergent or divergent.

25. $\displaystyle\sum_{n=1}^{+\infty} \frac{1}{2n + 1}$

26. $\displaystyle\sum_{n=1}^{+\infty} \frac{2}{(3n + 5)^2}$

27. $\displaystyle\sum_{n=1}^{+\infty} \frac{1}{(n + 2)^{3/2}}$

28. $\displaystyle\sum_{n=2}^{+\infty} \frac{n}{n^2 - 2}$

29. $\displaystyle\sum_{n=3}^{+\infty} \frac{4}{n^2 - 4}$

30. $\displaystyle\sum_{n=1}^{+\infty} \frac{2n + 3}{(n^2 + 3n)^2}$

31. $\displaystyle\sum_{n=1}^{+\infty} e^{-5n}$

32. $\displaystyle\sum_{n=1}^{+\infty} \frac{2n}{n^4 + 1}$

In Exercises 33 through 46, use any method to determine whether the series is convergent or divergent.

33. $\displaystyle\sum_{n=1}^{+\infty} \frac{\ln n}{n}$

34. $\displaystyle\sum_{n=2}^{+\infty} \frac{1}{n \ln n}$

35. $\displaystyle\sum_{n=1}^{+\infty} \frac{\tan^{-1} n}{n^2 + 1}$

36. $\displaystyle\sum_{n=1}^{+\infty} ne^{-n^2}$

37. $\displaystyle\sum_{n=1}^{+\infty} n^2 e^{-n}$

38. $\displaystyle\sum_{n=1}^{+\infty} ne^{-n}$

39. $\displaystyle\sum_{n=2}^{+\infty} \frac{\ln n}{n^3}$

40. $\displaystyle\sum_{n=1}^{+\infty} \cot^{-1} n$

41. $\displaystyle\sum_{n=1}^{+\infty} \text{csch } n$

42. $\displaystyle\sum_{n=1}^{+\infty} \frac{e^{\tan^{-1} n}}{n^2 + 1}$

43. $\displaystyle\sum_{n=1}^{+\infty} \frac{e^{1/n}}{n^2}$

44. $\displaystyle\sum_{n=1}^{+\infty} \text{sech}^2 n$

45. $\displaystyle\sum_{n=1}^{+\infty} \ln\!\left(\frac{n + 3}{n}\right)$

46. $\displaystyle\sum_{n=2}^{+\infty} \frac{1}{n(\ln n)^3}$

47. $\displaystyle\sum_{n=1}^{+\infty} \frac{(n + 1)^2}{(n + 2)!}$

48. $\displaystyle\sum_{n=1}^{+\infty} \frac{1}{(n + 2)(n + 4)}$

49. If $\displaystyle\sum_{n=1}^{+\infty} a_n$ and $\displaystyle\sum_{n=1}^{+\infty} b_n$ are two convergent series of positive terms, use the limit comparison test to prove that the series $\displaystyle\sum_{n=1}^{+\infty} a_n b_n$ is also convergent.

50. Use the integral test to show that the p series diverges if $p \leq 1$ and converges if $p > 1$.

51. Prove that the series $\displaystyle\sum_{n=2}^{+\infty} \frac{1}{n(\ln n)^p}$ is convergent if and only if $p > 1$.

52. Prove that the series $\displaystyle\sum_{n=3}^{+\infty} \frac{1}{n(\ln n)[\ln(\ln n)]^p}$ is convergent if and only if $p > 1$.

53. Prove that the series $\displaystyle\sum_{n=1}^{+\infty} \frac{\ln n}{n^p}$ is convergent if and only if $p > 1$.

54. If s_k is the kth partial sum of the harmonic series, prove that $\ln(k + 1) < s_k < 1 + \ln k$. *Hint:* $\dfrac{1}{m + 1} \leq \dfrac{1}{x} \leq \dfrac{1}{m}$ if $0 < m \leq x \leq m + 1$. Integrate each member of the inequality from m to $m + 1$; let m take on successively the values $1, 2, \ldots, n - 1$, and add the results.

55. Use the method of Exercise 54 to estimate the sum
$$\sum_{m=50}^{100} \frac{1}{m} = \frac{1}{50} + \frac{1}{51} + \ldots + \frac{1}{100}$$

56. Suppose that f is a function such that $f(n) > 0$ for any positive integer n. Furthermore suppose that if p is some positive number, $\displaystyle\lim_{n \to +\infty} n^p f(n)$ exists and is positive. Prove that the series $\displaystyle\sum_{n=1}^{+\infty} f(n)$ is convergent if $p > 1$ and divergent if $0 < p \leq 1$.

57. Prove Theorem 8.4.3(ii).

58. Prove Theorem 8.4.3(iii).

59. Explain why Theorem 8.4.1 does not hold for an infinite series of both positive and negative terms. *Hint:* Consider the series $\displaystyle\sum_{n=1}^{+\infty} (-1)^{n+1}$.

8.5 INFINITE SERIES OF POSITIVE AND NEGATIVE TERMS

One type of infinite series having both positive and negative terms is an *alternating series,* whose terms are alternately positive and negative.

8.5.1 Definition of an Alternating Series

If $a_n > 0$ for all positive integers n, then the series

$$\sum_{n=1}^{+\infty} (-1)^{n+1} a_n = a_1 - a_2 + a_3 - a_4 + \ldots + (-1)^{n+1} a_n + \ldots \quad (1)$$

and the series

$$\sum_{n=1}^{+\infty} (-1)^n a_n = -a_1 + a_2 - a_3 + a_4 - \ldots + (-1)^n a_n + \ldots \quad (2)$$

are called **alternating series.**

▷ **ILLUSTRATION 1** An example of an alternating series of the form (1), where the first term is positive, is

$$\sum_{n=1}^{+\infty} (-1)^{n+1} \frac{1}{n} = 1 - \frac{1}{2} + \frac{1}{3} - \frac{1}{4} + \ldots + (-1)^{n+1} \frac{1}{n} + \ldots$$

An alternating series of the form (2), where the first term is negative, is

$$\sum_{n=1}^{+\infty} (-1)^n \frac{1}{n!} = -1 + \frac{1}{2!} - \frac{1}{3!} + \frac{1}{4!} - \ldots + (-1)^n \frac{1}{n!} + \ldots \quad ◀$$

The following theorem, called the *alternating-series test,* states that an alternating series is convergent if its terms decrease in absolute value and the limit of its nth term is zero. The theorem is also known as Leibniz's test for alternating series because Leibniz formulated it in 1705.

8.5.2 Theorem Alternating-Series Test

Suppose we have the alternating series $\displaystyle\sum_{n=1}^{+\infty} (-1)^{n+1} a_n$

$\left[\text{or } \displaystyle\sum_{n=1}^{+\infty} (-1)^n a_n \right]$, where $a_n > 0$ and $a_{n+1} < a_n$ for all positive

integers n. If $\displaystyle\lim_{n \to +\infty} a_n = 0$, the alternating series is convergent.

Proof Assume that the first term of the alternating series is positive. This assumption is not a loss of generality because if this is not the case, then we discard the first term, which does not affect the convergence of the series.

Thus we have the alternating series $\displaystyle\sum_{n=1}^{+\infty} (-1)^{n+1} a_n$. Consider the partial sum

$$s_{2n} = (a_1 - a_2) + (a_3 - a_4) + \ldots + (a_{2n-1} - a_{2n})$$

Because by hypothesis $a_{n+1} < a_n$, each quantity in parentheses is positive. Therefore

$$0 < s_2 < s_4 < s_6 < \ldots < s_{2n} < \ldots \quad (3)$$

We can also write s_{2n} as

$$s_{2n} = a_1 - (a_2 - a_3) - (a_4 - a_5) - \ldots - (a_{2n-2} - a_{2n-1}) - a_{2n}$$

Because $a_{n+1} < a_n$, again each quantity in parentheses is positive. Therefore

$$s_{2n} < a_1 \qquad \text{for every positive integer } n \qquad\qquad (4)$$

From (3) and (4),

$$0 < s_{2n} < a_1 \qquad \text{for every positive integer } n$$

Thus the sequence $\{s_{2n}\}$ is bounded. Furthermore, from (3), the sequence $\{s_{2n}\}$ is increasing. Because $\{s_{2n}\}$ is a bounded montotonic sequence, it is convergent. Suppose S is the limit of this sequence; that is, $\lim\limits_{n\to+\infty} s_{2n} = S$. Then from Theorem 8.2.11, $S \leq a_1$. Because $s_{2n+1} = s_{2n} + a_{2n+1}$,

$$\lim_{n\to+\infty} s_{2n+1} = \lim_{n\to+\infty} s_{2n} + \lim_{n\to+\infty} a_{2n+1}$$

But, by hypothesis, $\lim\limits_{n\to+\infty} a_{2n+1} = 0$; so $\lim\limits_{n\to+\infty} s_{2n+1} = \lim\limits_{n\to+\infty} s_{2n}$. Therefore the sequence of partial sums of the even-numbered terms and the sequence of partial sums of the odd-numbered terms have the same limit S.

We now show that $\lim\limits_{n\to+\infty} s_n = S$. Because $\lim\limits_{n\to+\infty} s_{2n} = S$, then for any $\epsilon > 0$ there exists an integer $N_1 > 0$ such that

$$\text{if} \quad 2n \geq N_1 \quad \text{then} \quad |s_{2n} - S| < \epsilon$$

And because $\lim\limits_{n\to+\infty} s_{2n+1} = S$, there exists an integer $N_2 > 0$ such that

$$\text{if} \quad 2n + 1 \geq N_2 \quad \text{then} \quad |s_{2n+1} - S| < \epsilon$$

If N is the larger of the two integers N_1 and N_2, it follows that if n is any integer, either odd or even, and

$$\text{if} \quad n \geq N \quad \text{then} \quad |s_n - S| < \epsilon$$

Therefore $\lim\limits_{n\to+\infty} s_n = S$; so the alternating series is convergent. ∎

▶ **EXAMPLE 1**   Prove that the following alternating series is convergent:

$$\sum_{n=1}^{+\infty} (-1)^{n+1} \frac{1}{n}$$

Solution   The given series is

$$1 - \frac{1}{2} + \frac{1}{3} - \frac{1}{4} + \ldots + (-1)^{n+1} \frac{1}{n} + (-1)^{n+2} \frac{1}{n+1} + \ldots$$

Because $\dfrac{1}{n+1} < \dfrac{1}{n}$ for all positive integers n, and $\lim\limits_{n\to+\infty} \dfrac{1}{n} = 0$, then from the alternating-series test the given series is convergent. ◀

▶ **EXAMPLE 2**   Determine whether the series is convergent or divergent:

$$\sum_{n=1}^{+\infty} (-1)^n \frac{n+2}{n(n+1)}$$

Solution   The given series is an alternating series.

$$\lim_{n \to +\infty} a_n = \lim_{n \to +\infty} \frac{n+2}{n(n+1)}$$

$$= \lim_{n \to +\infty} \frac{\dfrac{1}{n} + \dfrac{2}{n^2}}{1 + \dfrac{1}{n}}$$

$$= 0$$

Before the alternating-series test can be applied, we must also show that $a_{n+1} < a_n$ or, equivalently, $\dfrac{a_{n+1}}{a_n} < 1$.

$$\frac{a_{n+1}}{a_n} = \frac{\dfrac{n+3}{(n+1)(n+2)}}{\dfrac{n+2}{n(n+1)}}$$

$$= \frac{n(n+3)}{(n+2)^2}$$

$$= \frac{n^2 + 3n}{n^2 + 4n + 4}$$

$$< 1$$

By the alternating-series test, the given series is convergent.   ◀

8.5.3 Definition of the Remainder After k Terms

If an infinite series is convergent and its sum is S, then the **remainder after k terms,** obtained by approximating the sum of the series by the kth partial sum s_k, is denoted by R_k, and

$$R_k = S - s_k$$

This definition is used in the statement of the next theorem which gives a method for determining an upper bound for the error introduced when the sum of a convergent alternating series is approximated by the sum of a finite number of terms of the series.

8.5.4 Theorem

Consider the alternating series

$$\sum_{n=1}^{+\infty} (-1)^{n+1} a_n \left[\text{or} \sum_{n=1}^{+\infty} (-1)^n a_n \right]$$

where $a_n > 0$ and $a_{n+1} < a_n$ for all positive integers n, and $\lim_{n \to +\infty} a_n = 0$. If R_k is the remainder obtained by approximating the sum of the series by the sum of the first k terms, $|R_k| < a_{k+1}$.

The proof of this theorem appears in the supplement of this section. To demonstrate the content of the theorem, we apply it in the following illustration to an alternating series whose exact sum we can compute.

▷ **ILLUSTRATION 2** Let us consider the geometric series with $a = 1$ and $r = -\frac{1}{2}$:

$$\sum_{n=1}^{+\infty} \left(-\frac{1}{2}\right)^{n-1} = 1 - \frac{1}{2} + \frac{1}{4} - \frac{1}{8} + \ldots + \left(-\frac{1}{2}\right)^{n-1} + \ldots$$

From Theorem 8.3.5 the sum of this series is

$$\frac{1}{1 - (-\frac{1}{2})} = \frac{2}{3}$$
$$= 0.66667$$

to five significant digits. Suppose we approximate the sum of the series by the first ten terms:

$$1 - \tfrac{1}{2} + \tfrac{1}{4} - \tfrac{1}{8} + \tfrac{1}{16} - \tfrac{1}{32} + \tfrac{1}{64} - \tfrac{1}{128} + \tfrac{1}{256} - \tfrac{1}{512} = 0.66602$$

The error is $0.66667 - 0.66602 = 0.00065$. Theorem 8.5.4 states that the error is less than the absolute value of the eleventh term, which is

$$\tfrac{1}{1024} = 0.00098$$

and $0.00065 < 0.00098$. ◀

▶ **EXAMPLE 3** A series for computing $\ln(1 + x)$ if x is in the interval $(-1, 1]$ is

$$\ln(1 + x) = \sum_{n=1}^{+\infty} (-1)^{n+1} \frac{x^n}{n}$$

Find an upper bound for the error when the first three terms of this series are used to approximate the value of $\ln 1.1$.

Solution We use the given series with $x = 0.1$ to obtain

$$\ln 1.1 = 0.1 - \frac{(0.1)^2}{2} + \frac{(0.1)^3}{3} - \frac{(0.1)^4}{4} + \ldots$$

This series satisfies the conditions of Theorem 8.5.4; so if R_3 is the difference between the actual value of $\ln 1.1$ and the sum of the first three terms, then

$$|R_3| < 0.000025$$

Thus the sum of the first three terms will yield a value of $\ln 1.1$ accurate to at least four decimal places. From the first three terms we get

$$\ln 1.1 \approx 0.0953 \qquad ◀$$

If all the terms of a given infinite series are replaced by their absolute values and the resulting series is convergent, then the given series is said to be *absolutely convergent*.

8.5.5 Definition of Absolutely Convergent

The infinite series $\displaystyle\sum_{n=1}^{+\infty} u_n$ is **absolutely convergent** if the series $\displaystyle\sum_{n=1}^{+\infty} |u_n|$ is convergent.

▷ **ILLUSTRATION 3**   Consider the series

$$\sum_{n=1}^{+\infty} (-1)^{n+1} \frac{2}{3^n} = \frac{2}{3} - \frac{2}{3^2} + \frac{2}{3^3} - \frac{2}{3^4} + \ldots + (-1)^{n+1} \frac{2}{3^n} + \ldots \quad \textbf{(5)}$$

This series will be absolutely convergent if the series

$$\sum_{n=1}^{+\infty} \frac{2}{3^n} = \frac{2}{3} + \frac{2}{3^2} + \frac{2}{3^3} + \frac{2}{3^4} + \ldots + \frac{2}{3^n} + \ldots$$

is convergent. Because this is the geometric series with $r = \frac{1}{3} < 1$, it is convergent. Therefore series (5) is absolutely convergent.   ◀

▷ **ILLUSTRATION 4**   In Example 1 we proved that the series

$$\sum_{n=1}^{+\infty} (-1)^{n+1} \frac{1}{n}$$

is convergent. This series is not absolutely convergent because the series of absolute values is the harmonic series, which is divergent.   ◀

The series in Illustration 4, sometimes called the **alternating harmonic series,** is an example of a *conditionally convergent* series.

8.5.6 Definition of Conditionally Convergent

A series that is convergent, but not absolutely convergent, is **conditionally convergent.**

The significance of conditional convergence is shown in the following illustration.

▷ **ILLUSTRATION 5**   Consider the alternating harmonic series:

$$1 - \frac{1}{2} + \frac{1}{3} - \frac{1}{4} + \frac{1}{5} - \frac{1}{6} + \ldots + (-1)^{n+1} \frac{1}{n} + \ldots \quad \textbf{(6)}$$

which is conditionally convergent. Let us rearrange and group the terms of this series as follows:

$$(1 - \tfrac{1}{2}) - \tfrac{1}{4} + (\tfrac{1}{3} - \tfrac{1}{6}) - \tfrac{1}{8} + (\tfrac{1}{5} - \tfrac{1}{10}) - \tfrac{1}{12} + \ldots$$
$$= \tfrac{1}{2} - \tfrac{1}{4} + \tfrac{1}{6} - \tfrac{1}{8} + \tfrac{1}{10} - \tfrac{1}{12} + \ldots$$
$$= \tfrac{1}{2} (1 - \tfrac{1}{2} + \tfrac{1}{3} - \tfrac{1}{4} + \tfrac{1}{5} - \tfrac{1}{6} + \ldots) \quad \textbf{(7)}$$

Observe that the infinite series in parentheses above is the same as infinite series (6). Because series (6) is convergent, it has a sum which is ln 2 from Example 3 where $x = 1$. Series (7) also has a sum, but obviously the sum of series (7) is one-half of the sum of series (6). This situation arises because series (6) is only conditionally convergent rather than absolutely convergent. ◀

From Illustration 5, it is apparent that you cannot rearrange the order of the terms of a conditionally convergent series and preserve the sum. Recall, however, from Theorem 8.4.5 that for a convergent series of only positive terms, we *can* rearrange the order of the terms without affecting the sum of the series.

The next theorem allows us to prove that an infinite series of both positive and negative terms is convergent by showing it is absolutely convergent.

8.5.7 Theorem

If the series $\sum\limits_{n=1}^{+\infty} |u_n|$ is convergent, then the series $\sum\limits_{n=1}^{+\infty} u_n$ is convergent.

Proof   If to each member of the inequality

$$-|u_n| \leq u_n \leq |u_n|$$

we add $|u_n|$, we obtain

$$0 \leq u_n + |u_n| \leq 2|u_n| \tag{8}$$

Because the series $\sum\limits_{n=1}^{+\infty} |u_n|$ is convergent, so is the series $\sum\limits_{n=1}^{+\infty} 2|u_n|$. Then by inequality (8) and the comparison test, we can conclude that the series $\sum\limits_{n=1}^{+\infty} (u_n + |u_n|)$ is convergent. The series $\sum\limits_{n=1}^{+\infty} u_n$ can be written as follows:

$$\sum_{n=1}^{+\infty} u_n = \sum_{n=1}^{+\infty} (u_n + |u_n| - |u_n|)$$

$$\sum_{n=1}^{+\infty} u_n = \sum_{n=1}^{+\infty} (u_n + |u_n|) - \sum_{n=1}^{+\infty} |u_n|$$

The right-hand side of the above equality is the difference of two convergent series. Therefore, $\sum\limits_{n=1}^{+\infty} u_n$ is convergent. ∎

▶ **EXAMPLE 4**   Determine whether the series is convergent or divergent:

$$\sum_{n=1}^{+\infty} \frac{\cos \frac{1}{3} n\pi}{n^2}$$

Solution Denoting the given series by $\displaystyle\sum_{n=1}^{+\infty} u_n$, we have

$$\sum_{n=1}^{+\infty} u_n = \frac{\frac{1}{2}}{1^2} - \frac{\frac{1}{2}}{2^2} - \frac{1}{3^2} - \frac{\frac{1}{2}}{4^2} + \frac{\frac{1}{2}}{5^2} + \frac{1}{6^2} + \frac{\frac{1}{2}}{7^2} - \ldots + \frac{\cos \frac{1}{3}n\pi}{n^2} + \ldots$$

$$= \frac{1}{2} - \frac{1}{8} - \frac{1}{9} - \frac{1}{32} + \frac{1}{50} + \frac{1}{36} + \frac{1}{98} - \ldots$$

This is a series of positive and negative terms. We can prove this series is convergent if we can show that it is absolutely convergent.

$$\sum_{n=1}^{+\infty} |u_n| = \sum_{n=1}^{+\infty} \frac{\left|\cos \frac{1}{3}n\pi\right|}{n^2}$$

Because $\left|\cos \frac{1}{3}n\pi\right| \leq 1$ for all n

$$\frac{\left|\cos \frac{1}{3}n\pi\right|}{n^2} \leq \frac{1}{n^2} \qquad \text{for all positive integers } n$$

The series $\displaystyle\sum_{n=1}^{+\infty} \frac{1}{n^2}$ is the p series, with $p = 2$, and is therefore convergent. So by the comparison test $\displaystyle\sum_{n=1}^{+\infty} |u_n|$ is convergent. The given series is therefore absolutely convergent; hence, by Theorem 8.5.7 it is convergent.

Observe that the terms of the series $\displaystyle\sum_{n=1}^{+\infty} |u_n|$ neither increase monotonically nor decrease monotonically. For example, $|u_4| = \frac{1}{32}$, $|u_5| = \frac{1}{50}$, $|u_6| = \frac{1}{36}$; and so $|u_5| < |u_4|$, but $|u_6| > |u_5|$. ◀

The *ratio test,* given in the next theorem, is used frequently to determine whether a given series is absolutely convergent.

8.5.8 Theorem Ratio Test

Let $\displaystyle\sum_{n=1}^{+\infty} u_n$ be a given infinite series for which every u_n is nonzero:

(i) if $\displaystyle\lim_{n \to +\infty} \left|\frac{u_{n+1}}{u_n}\right| = L < 1$, the series is absolutely convergent;

(ii) if $\displaystyle\lim_{n \to +\infty} \left|\frac{u_{n+1}}{u_n}\right| = L > 1$ or if $\displaystyle\lim_{n \to +\infty} \left|\frac{u_{n+1}}{u_n}\right| = +\infty$, the series is divergent;

(iii) if $\displaystyle\lim_{n \to +\infty} \left|\frac{u_{n+1}}{u_n}\right| = 1$, no conclusion regarding convergence may be made from this test.

Proof of (i)   It is given that $L < 1$. Let R be a number such that $L < R < 1$. Let $R - L = \epsilon < 1$. Because $\displaystyle\lim_{n \to +\infty} \left|\frac{u_{n+1}}{u_n}\right| = L$, there exists an integer $N > 0$ such that

$$\text{if} \quad n \geq N \quad \text{then} \quad \left|\left|\frac{u_{n+1}}{u_n}\right| - L\right| < \epsilon$$

Therefore

$$\text{if} \quad n \geq N \quad \text{then} \quad 0 < \left| \frac{u_{n+1}}{u_n} \right| < L + \epsilon = R \tag{9}$$

Let n take on the successive values N, $N + 1$, $N + 2$, $\ldots$, and so forth. We obtain, from (9),

$$|u_{N+1}| < R|u_N|$$
$$|u_{N+2}| < R|u_{N+1}| < R^2|u_N|$$
$$|u_{N+3}| < R|u_{N+2}| < R^3|u_N|$$
$$\cdots$$

In general,

$$|u_{N+k}| < R^k|u_N| \qquad \text{for every positive integer } k \tag{10}$$

The series

$$\sum_{k=1}^{+\infty} |u_N| R^k = |u_N|R + |u_N|R^2 + \ldots + |u_N|R^n + \ldots$$

is convergent because it is a geometric series whose ratio is less than 1. So from (10) and the comparison test it follows that the series $\displaystyle\sum_{k=1}^{+\infty} |u_{N+k}|$ is convergent. The series $\displaystyle\sum_{k=1}^{+\infty} |u_{N+k}|$ differs from the series $\displaystyle\sum_{n=1}^{+\infty} |u_n|$ in only the first N terms. Therefore $\displaystyle\sum_{n=1}^{+\infty} |u_n|$ is convergent; so the given series is absolutely convergent.

Proof of (ii) If $\displaystyle\lim_{n \to +\infty} \left| \frac{u_{n+1}}{u_n} \right| = L > 1$ or $\displaystyle\lim_{n \to +\infty} \left| \frac{u_{n+1}}{u_n} \right| = +\infty$, then in either case there is an integer $N > 0$ such that if $n \geq N$, then $\left| \dfrac{u_{n+1}}{u_n} \right| > 1$. Let n take on the successive values N, $N + 1$, $N + 2$, $\ldots$, and so on. We obtain

$$|u_{N+1}| > |u_N|$$
$$|u_{N+2}| > |u_{N+1}| > |u_N|$$
$$|u_{N+3}| > |u_{N+2}| > |u_N|$$
$$\cdots$$

Thus if $n > N$, then $|u_n| > |u_N|$. Hence $\displaystyle\lim_{n \to +\infty} u_n \neq 0$; so the given series is divergent.

Proof of (iii) If the ratio test is applied to the p series, we have

$$\lim_{n \to +\infty} \left| \frac{u_{n+1}}{u_n} \right| = \lim_{n \to +\infty} \left| \frac{\dfrac{1}{(n+1)^p}}{\dfrac{1}{n^p}} \right|$$

$$= \lim_{n \to +\infty} \left| \left(\frac{n}{n+1} \right)^p \right|$$

$$= 1$$

Because the p series diverges if $p \le 1$ and converges if $p > 1$, we have shown that it is possible to have both convergent and divergent series for which $\lim\limits_{n \to +\infty} \left| \dfrac{u_{n+1}}{u_n} \right| = 1$. This proves part (iii).   ∎

▶ **EXAMPLE 5**   Determine whether the series is convergent or divergent:

$$\sum_{n=1}^{+\infty} (-1)^{n+1} \frac{n}{2^n}$$

Solution $u_n = (-1)^{n+1} \dfrac{n}{2^n}$ and $u_{n+1} = (-1)^{n+2} \dfrac{n+1}{2^{n+1}}$. Therefore

$$\left| \frac{u_{n+1}}{u_n} \right| = \frac{n+1}{2^{n+1}} \cdot \frac{2^n}{n}$$

$$= \frac{n+1}{2n}$$

So

$$\lim_{n \to +\infty} \left| \frac{u_{n+1}}{u_n} \right| = \lim_{n \to +\infty} \frac{1 + \dfrac{1}{n}}{2}$$

$$= \frac{1}{2}$$

$$< 1$$

Therefore, by the ratio test, the given series is absolutely convergent and hence, by Theorem 8.5.7, it is convergent.   ◀

▶ **EXAMPLE 6**   In Example 2 we showed that the series

$$\sum_{n=1}^{+\infty} (-1)^n \frac{n+2}{n(n+1)}$$

is convergent. Is this series absolutely convergent or conditionally convergent?

Solution   To test for absolute convergence we apply the ratio test. In the solution of Example 2, we showed that the ratio

$$\frac{|u_{n+1}|}{|u_n|} = \frac{n^2 + 3n}{n^2 + 4n + 4}$$

Hence

$$\lim_{n \to +\infty} \left| \frac{u_{n+1}}{u_n} \right| = \lim_{n \to +\infty} \frac{1 + \dfrac{3}{n}}{1 + \dfrac{4}{n} + \dfrac{4}{n^2}}$$

$$= 1$$

So the ratio test fails. Because

$$|u_n| = \frac{n+2}{n(n+1)}$$

$$= \frac{n+2}{n+1} \cdot \frac{1}{n}$$

$$> \frac{1}{n}$$

the comparison test can be applied. And because the series $\sum_{n=1}^{+\infty} \frac{1}{n}$ is the harmonic series, which diverges, we conclude that the series $\sum_{n=1}^{+\infty} |u_n|$ is divergent and hence $\sum_{n=1}^{+\infty} u_n$ is not absolutely convergent. Therefore the series is conditionally convergent.   ◄

Note that the ratio test does not include all possibilities for $\lim\limits_{n\to+\infty} \left| \frac{u_{n+1}}{u_n} \right|$ because it is possible that the limit does not exist and is not $+\infty$. The discussion of such cases is beyond the scope of this book.

The proof of the ratio test was based on using the comparison test with the geometric series. Another test whose proof is similar is the *root test*.

8.5.9 Theorem   Root Test

Let $\sum_{n=1}^{+\infty} u_n$ be a given infinite series for which every u_n is nonzero:

(i) if $\lim\limits_{n\to+\infty} \sqrt[n]{|u_n|} = L < 1$, the series is absolutely convergent;

(ii) if $\lim\limits_{n\to+\infty} \sqrt[n]{|u_n|} = L > 1$, or if $\lim\limits_{n\to+\infty} \sqrt[n]{|u_n|} = +\infty$, the series is divergent;

(iii) if $\lim\limits_{n\to+\infty} \sqrt[n]{|u_n|} = 1$, no conclusion regarding convergence may be made from this test.

Because of the similarity of the proof of the root test with that of the ratio test, we leave the proof for you to do as an exercise (see Exercises 50 through 52).

► **EXAMPLE 7**   Apply the root test to determine whether the series is convergent or divergent:

$$\sum_{n=1}^{+\infty} (-1)^n \frac{3^{2n+1}}{n^{2n}}$$

Solution By applying the root test we have

$$\lim_{n\to+\infty} \sqrt[n]{|u_n|} = \lim_{n\to+\infty} \left(\frac{3^{2n+1}}{n^{2n}}\right)^{1/n}$$

$$= \lim_{n\to+\infty} \frac{3^{2+(1/n)}}{n^2}$$

$$= 0$$

$$< 1$$

Therefore, by the root test, the given series is absolutely convergent. Hence by Theorem 8.5.7 it is convergent. ◄

The ratio test and the root test are closely related. The ratio test, however, is usually easier to apply; if the terms of the series contain factorials, this is certainly the case. A series for which the ratio test fails, but for which the root test can be used to show convergence, appears in Exercise 49. If the terms of a series contain powers, as in Example 7, the root test may be favored over the ratio test. The next example provides another series for which the root test is the better one to apply.

► **EXAMPLE 8** Determine whether the series is convergent or divergent:

$$\sum_{n=1}^{+\infty} \frac{1}{[\ln(n+1)]^n}$$

Solution All the terms of the series are positive.

$$\lim_{n\to+\infty} \sqrt[n]{|u_n|} = \lim_{n\to+\infty} \sqrt[n]{\left|\frac{1}{[\ln(n+1)]^n}\right|}$$

$$= \lim_{n\to+\infty} \left|\frac{1}{\ln(n+1)}\right|$$

$$= 0$$

$$< 1$$

From the root test, the given series is convergent. ◄

EXERCISES 8.5

In Exercises 1 through 14, determine whether the alternating series is convergent or divergent.

1. $\sum_{n=1}^{+\infty} (-1)^{n+1} \frac{1}{2n}$

2. $\sum_{n=1}^{+\infty} (-1)^n \frac{1}{n^2}$

3. $\sum_{n=1}^{+\infty} (-1)^n \frac{3}{n^2+1}$

4. $\sum_{n=1}^{+\infty} (-1)^{n+1} \frac{4}{3n-2}$

5. $\sum_{n=2}^{+\infty} (-1)^n \frac{1}{\ln n}$

6. $\sum_{n=1}^{+\infty} (-1)^{n+1} \sin \frac{\pi}{n}$

7. $\sum_{n=1}^{+\infty} (-1)^{n+1} \frac{n^2}{n^3+2}$

8. $\sum_{n=1}^{+\infty} (-1)^{n+1} \frac{\ln n}{n}$

9. $\sum_{n=1}^{+\infty} (-1)^{n+1} \frac{\ln n}{n^2}$

10. $\sum_{n=1}^{+\infty} (-1)^n \frac{e^n}{n}$

11. $\sum_{n=1}^{+\infty} (-1)^n \frac{3^n}{n^2}$

12. $\sum_{n=1}^{+\infty} (-1)^n \frac{\sqrt{n}}{3n-1}$

13. $\sum_{n=1}^{+\infty} (-1)^n \frac{n}{2^n}$

14. $\sum_{n=1}^{+\infty} (-1)^{n+1} \frac{3^n}{1+3^{2n}}$

In Exercises 15 through 22, find an upper bound for the error if the sum of the first four terms is used as an approximation to the sum of the infinite series.

15. $\sum_{n=1}^{+\infty} (-1)^{n+1} \frac{1}{n}$

16. $\sum_{n=1}^{+\infty} (-1)^n \frac{2}{n^2}$

17. $\sum_{n=1}^{+\infty} (-1)^{n+1} \frac{1}{(2n-1)^2}$

18. $\sum_{n=1}^{+\infty} (-1)^{n+1} \frac{n}{(n+1)^2}$

19. $\sum_{n=1}^{+\infty} (-1)^n \frac{1}{n^2}$

20. $\sum_{n=1}^{+\infty} (-1)^{n+1} \frac{1}{n^n}$

21. $\sum_{n=1}^{+\infty} (-1)^{n+1} \frac{1}{(n+1)\ln(n+1)}$

22. $\sum_{n=1}^{+\infty} (-1)^n \frac{1}{n!}$

In Exercises 23 through 30, find the sum of the infinite series, accurate to three decimal places.

23. $\sum_{n=1}^{+\infty} (-1)^{n+1} \frac{1}{2^n}$

24. $\sum_{n=1}^{+\infty} (-1)^{n+1} \frac{1}{n^4}$

25. $\sum_{n=1}^{+\infty} (-1)^{n+1} \frac{1}{n!}$

26. $\sum_{n=1}^{+\infty} (-1)^{n+1} \frac{2}{3^n}$

27. $\sum_{n=1}^{+\infty} (-1)^{n+1} \frac{1}{(2n)^3}$

28. $\sum_{n=1}^{+\infty} (-1)^n \frac{1}{(2n+1)^3}$

In Exercises 29 through 50, determine if the series is absolutely convergent, conditionally convergent, or divergent. Prove your answer.

29. $\sum_{n=1}^{+\infty} \left(-\frac{2}{3}\right)^n$

30. $\sum_{n=1}^{+\infty} (-1)^n \frac{2^n}{n^3}$

31. $\sum_{n=1}^{+\infty} (-1)^{n+1} \frac{2^n}{n!}$

32. $\sum_{n=1}^{+\infty} n\left(\frac{2}{3}\right)^n$

33. $\sum_{n=1}^{+\infty} \frac{n^2}{n!}$

34. $\sum_{n=1}^{+\infty} (-1)^{n+1} \frac{1}{(2n-1)!}$

35. $\sum_{n=1}^{+\infty} (-1)^n \frac{n!}{2^{n+1}}$

36. $\sum_{n=1}^{+\infty} (-1)^{n+1} \frac{1}{n(n+2)}$

37. $\sum_{n=1}^{+\infty} \frac{1-2\sin n}{n^3}$

38. $\sum_{n=1}^{+\infty} (-1)^n \frac{1}{(n+1)^3}$

39. $\sum_{n=1}^{+\infty} (-1)^{n+1} \frac{3^n}{n!}$

40. $\sum_{n=1}^{+\infty} (-1)^n \frac{n^2+1}{n^3}$

41. $\sum_{n=2}^{+\infty} (-1)^{n+1} \frac{1}{n(\ln n)^2}$

42. $\sum_{n=1}^{+\infty} \frac{\cos n}{n^2}$

43. $\sum_{n=1}^{+\infty} \frac{\sin \pi n}{n}$

44. $\sum_{n=2}^{+\infty} (-1)^{n+1} \frac{n}{\ln n}$

45. $\sum_{n=2}^{+\infty} \frac{1}{(\ln n)^n}$

46. $\sum_{n=1}^{+\infty} \frac{\left(1+\frac{1}{n}\right)^{2n}}{e^n}$

47. $\sum_{n=1}^{+\infty} \frac{n^n}{n!}$

48. $\sum_{n=1}^{+\infty} \frac{1\cdot 3\cdot 5\cdot \ldots \cdot (2n-1)}{1\cdot 4\cdot 7\cdot \ldots \cdot (3n-2)}$

49. Given the series $\sum_{n=1}^{+\infty} \frac{1}{2^{n+1+(-1)^n}}$. **(a)** Show that the ratio test fails for this series. **(b)** Use the root test to determine whether the series is convergent or divergent.

50. Prove part (i) of the root test (Theorem 8.5.9). *Hint:* Because $L < 1$, let R be a number such that $L < R < 1$, and let $R - L = \epsilon < 1$. Show that there is an integer N such that if $n > N$, then $|u_n| < R^n$. Then use the comparison test.

51. Prove part (ii) of the root test. See the Hint for Exercise 50.

52. Prove part (iii) of the root test by applying it to the two series $\sum_{n=1}^{+\infty} \frac{1}{n}$ and $\sum_{n=1}^{+\infty} \frac{1}{n^2}$. *Hint:* Determine $\lim_{n\to\infty} \sqrt[n]{n}$ by letting $\sqrt[n]{n} = e^{(\ln n)/n}$ and using L'Hôpital's rule to find $\lim_{n\to+\infty} \frac{\ln n}{n}$.

53. Prove that if $\sum_{n=1}^{+\infty} u_n$ is absolutely convergent, then $\sum_{n=1}^{+\infty} u_n^2$ is convergent.

54. Do you suspect that the converse of Exercise 53 is true or false? Justify your answer by proving it if the converse is true or giving an example if the converse is false.

8.6 A SUMMARY OF TESTS FOR CONVERGENCE OR DIVERGENCE OF AN INFINITE SERIES

Sections 8.3 through 8.5 contain a number of tests to determine convergence or divergence of an infinite series of constant terms. To gain proficiency in recognizing and applying the appropriate test requires considerable practice that you will gain by doing the exercises of this section. To assist you, we list the tests that you might attempt step-by-step in the indicated order. If a particular step is not applicable or no conclusion can be made, continue on to the next one. Of course, sometimes more than one test can be used, but hopefully you will select the most efficient one,

1. Compute $\lim\limits_{n \to +\infty} u_n$. If $\lim\limits_{n \to +\infty} u_n \neq 0$, then the series diverges. If $\lim\limits_{n \to +\infty} u_n = 0$, no conclusion can be made.

2. Examine the series to determine if it is one of the special types:

   (i)   A geometric series: $\sum\limits_{n=1}^{+\infty} ar^{n-1}$. It converges to the sum $\dfrac{a}{1-r}$ if $|r| < 1$; it diverges if $|r| \geq 1$.

   (ii) A p series: $\sum\limits_{n=1}^{+\infty} \dfrac{1}{n^p}$ (where p is a constant). It converges if $p > 1$; it diverges if $p \leq 1$.

   (iii) An alternating series: $\sum\limits_{n=1}^{+\infty} (-1)^{n+1} a_n$ or $\sum\limits_{n=1}^{+\infty} (-1)^n a_n$. Apply the alternating-series test (Theorem 8.5.2): If $a_n > 0$ and $a_{n+1} < a_n$ for all positive integers n, and $\lim\limits_{n \to +\infty} a_n = 0$, then the alternating series is convergent.

3. Try the ratio test (Theorem 8.5.8): Let $\sum\limits_{n=1}^{+\infty} u_n$ be a given infinite series for which every u_n is nonzero:

   (i)   if $\lim\limits_{n \to +\infty} \left| \dfrac{u_{n+1}}{u_n} \right| = L < 1$, the series is absolutely convergent;

   (ii) if $\lim\limits_{n \to +\infty} \left| \dfrac{u_{n+1}}{u_n} \right| = L > 1$ or if $\lim\limits_{n \to +\infty} \left| \dfrac{u_{n+1}}{u_n} \right| = +\infty$, the series is divergent;

   (iii) if $\lim\limits_{n \to +\infty} \left| \dfrac{u_{n+1}}{u_n} \right| = 1$, no conclusion regarding convergence may be made from this test.

4. Try the root test (Theorem 8.5.9): Let $\sum\limits_{n=1}^{+\infty} u_n$ be a given infinite series for which every u_n is nonzero:

   (i)   if $\lim\limits_{n \to +\infty} \sqrt[n]{|u_n|} = L < 1$, the series is absolutely convergent;

   (ii) if $\lim\limits_{n \to +\infty} \sqrt[n]{|u_n|} = L > 1$, or if $\lim\limits_{n \to +\infty} \sqrt[n]{|u_n|} = +\infty$, the series is divergent;

   (iii) if $\lim\limits_{n \to +\infty} \sqrt[n]{|u_n|} = 1$, no conclusion regarding convergence may be made from this test.

5. Try the integral test (Theorem 8.4.6): Let f be a function that is continuous, decreasing, and positive valued for all $x \geq 1$. Then the infinite series

$$\sum_{n=1}^{+\infty} f(n) = f(1) + f(2) + f(3) + \ldots + f(n) + \ldots$$

is convergent if the improper integral $\displaystyle\int_{1}^{+\infty} f(x)\, dx$ exists, and it is divergent if $\lim\limits_{b \to +\infty} \displaystyle\int_{1}^{b} f(x)\, dx = +\infty$.

6. Try the comparison test (Theorem 8.4.2): Let the series $\sum\limits_{n=1}^{+\infty} u_n$ be a series of positive terms.

(i) If $\sum\limits_{n=1}^{+\infty} v_n$ is a series of positive terms known to be convergent, and $u_n \leq v_n$ for all positive integers n, then $\sum\limits_{n=1}^{+\infty} u_n$ is convergent.

(ii) If $\sum\limits_{n=1}^{+\infty} w_n$ is a series of positive terms known to be divergent, and $u_n \geq w_n$ for all positive integers n, then $\sum\limits_{n=1}^{+\infty} u_n$ is divergent.

or the limit comparison test (Theorem 8.4.3): Let $\sum\limits_{n=1}^{+\infty} u_n$ and $\sum\limits_{n=1}^{+\infty} v_n$ be two series of positive terms.

(i) If $\lim\limits_{n\to+\infty} \dfrac{u_n}{v_n} = c > 0$, then the two series either both converge or both diverge.

(ii) If $\lim\limits_{n\to+\infty} \dfrac{u_n}{v_n} = 0$, and if $\sum\limits_{n=1}^{+\infty} v_n$ converges, then $\sum\limits_{n=1}^{+\infty} u_n$ converges.

(iii) If $\lim\limits_{n\to+\infty} \dfrac{u_n}{v_n} = +\infty$, and if $\sum\limits_{n=1}^{+\infty} v_n$ diverges, then $\sum\limits_{n=1}^{+\infty} u_n$ diverges.

EXERCISES 8.6

The following exercises provide a review of Sections 8.3 through 8.5.

In Exercises 1 and 2, find the first four elements of the sequence of partial sums $\{s_n\}$, and find a formula for s_n in terms of n. Also determine whether the infinite series is convergent or divergent; if it is convergent, find its sum.

1. $\sum\limits_{n=1}^{+\infty} \dfrac{3}{4^{n+1}}$

2. $\sum\limits_{n=1}^{+\infty} \ln\left(\dfrac{2n-1}{2n+1}\right)$

In Exercises 3 through 12, determine whether the series is convergent or divergent. If the series is convergent, find its sum.

3. $\sum\limits_{n=1}^{+\infty} \left(\dfrac{3}{4}\right)^n$

4. $\sum\limits_{n=1}^{+\infty} e^{-2n}$

5. $\sum\limits_{n=1}^{+\infty} \dfrac{n-1}{n+1}$

6. $\sum\limits_{n=0}^{+\infty} [(-1)^n + (-1)^{n+1}]$

7. $\sum\limits_{n=0}^{+\infty} \sin^n \tfrac{1}{3}\pi$

8. $\sum\limits_{n=0}^{+\infty} \cos^n \tfrac{1}{3}\pi$

9. $\sum\limits_{n=1}^{+\infty} \dfrac{1}{(3n-1)(3n+2)}$ *Hint: To find the sum, first find the sequence of partial sums.*

10. $\sum\limits_{n=1}^{+\infty} \dfrac{3}{2}\left(\dfrac{1}{5}\right)^n$

11. $\sum\limits_{n=1}^{+\infty} \dfrac{\left[\!\left[\sin \dfrac{3}{n}\pi + 2\right]\!\right]}{3^n}$

12. $\sum\limits_{n=1}^{+\infty} \left(\dfrac{1}{4^n} + \dfrac{1}{3^n}\right)$

In Exercises 13 through 30, determine whether the series is convergent or divergent.

13. $\sum\limits_{n=1}^{+\infty} \dfrac{2}{n^2 + 6n}$

14. $\sum\limits_{n=1}^{+\infty} \dfrac{1}{(2n+1)^3}$

15. $\sum\limits_{n=1}^{+\infty} \cos\left(\dfrac{\pi}{2n^2 - 1}\right)$

16. $\sum\limits_{n=1}^{+\infty} \dfrac{3 + \sin n}{n^2}$

17. $\sum\limits_{n=1}^{+\infty} \dfrac{(n!)^2}{(2n)!}$

18. $\sum\limits_{n=1}^{+\infty} \dfrac{n}{\sqrt{3n+2}}$

19. $\sum\limits_{n=1}^{+\infty} (-1)^n \ln\dfrac{1}{n}$

20. $\sum\limits_{n=1}^{+\infty} \dfrac{(-1)^{n+1}}{1 + \sqrt{n}}$

21. $\sum\limits_{n=2}^{+\infty} \dfrac{1}{n(\ln n)^2}$

22. $\sum\limits_{n=1}^{+\infty} \dfrac{\ln n}{n^2}$

23. $\sum\limits_{n=1}^{+\infty} \left(\dfrac{2}{5n} - \dfrac{3}{2n}\right)$

24. $\sum\limits_{n=0}^{+\infty} \dfrac{n!}{10^n}$

25. $\sum\limits_{n=1}^{+\infty} \dfrac{1}{1 + 2\ln n}$

26. $\sum\limits_{n=1}^{+\infty} \dfrac{|\sec n|}{n^{3/4}}$

27. $\sum\limits_{n=1}^{+\infty} \dfrac{\cos n}{n^3}$

28. $\sum\limits_{n=1}^{+\infty} n3^{-n^2}$

29. $\displaystyle\sum_{n=1}^{+\infty} \frac{1}{2^n + \sin n}$

30. $\displaystyle\sum_{n=1}^{+\infty} \frac{(n+2)^2}{(n+3)!}$

In Exercises 31 through 40, determine if the series is absolutely convergent, conditionally convergent, or divergent. Prove your answer.

31. $\displaystyle\sum_{n=0}^{+\infty} (-1)^n \frac{n^2}{3^n}$

32. $\displaystyle\sum_{n=0}^{+\infty} (-1)^n \frac{5^{2n+1}}{(2n+1)!}$

33. $\displaystyle\sum_{n=1}^{+\infty} (-1)^{n-1} \frac{1}{(n+1)^{3/4}}$

34. $\displaystyle\sum_{n=1}^{+\infty} (-1)^{n-1} \frac{6^n}{5^{n+1}}$

35. $\displaystyle\sum_{n=1}^{+\infty} (-1)^n \frac{n!}{10n}$

36. $\displaystyle\sum_{n=1}^{+\infty} (-1)^n \frac{\sqrt{2n-1}}{n}$

37. $\displaystyle\sum_{n=1}^{+\infty} (-1)^{n-1} \frac{2^{3n}}{n^n}$

38. $\displaystyle\sum_{n=1}^{+\infty} (-1)^{n-1} \frac{1}{[\ln(n+2)]^n}$

39. $\displaystyle\sum_{n=1}^{+\infty} c_n$, where $c_n = \begin{cases} -\dfrac{1}{n} & \text{if } n \text{ is a perfect square} \\[2mm] \dfrac{1}{n^2} & \text{if } n \text{ is not a perfect square} \end{cases}$

40. $\displaystyle\sum_{n=1}^{+\infty} c_n$, where $c_n = \begin{cases} -\dfrac{1}{n} & \text{if } \frac{1}{4}n \text{ is an integer} \\[2mm] \dfrac{1}{n^2} & \text{if } \frac{1}{4}n \text{ is not an integer} \end{cases}$

41. Express the nonterminating repeating decimal 1.324 24 24 . . . as a common fraction.

42. A ball is dropped from a height of 18 ft, and each time it strikes the ground it bounces back to a height of two-thirds of the distance from which it fell. Find the total distance traveled by the ball before it comes to rest.

43. Use the result of part (a) of Exercise 55 in Exercises 8.3 to determine how long it takes the ball of Exercise 42 to stop bouncing.

44. The path of each swing, after the first, of a pendulum bob is 80 percent as long as the path of the previous swing from one side to the other side. If the path of the first swing is 18 in. long, and air resistance eventually brings the pendulum to rest, how far does the bob travel before it comes to rest?

8.7 POWER SERIES

The infinite series you have studied so far have involved constant terms. We now discuss an important type of series of variable terms called *power series,* which can be considered as a generalization of a polynomial function. You will learn in the remaining sections of this chapter how power series can be used to calculate function values such as $\sin x$, e^x, $\ln x$, and $\sqrt{x}$, which cannot be evaluated by the familiar operations of arithmetic used for determining rational function values.

8.7.1 Definition of a Power Series

A **power series** in $x - a$ is a series of the form

$$c_0 + c_1(x-a) + c_2(x-a)^2 + \ldots + c_n(x-a)^n + \ldots \quad (1)$$

We use the notation $\displaystyle\sum_{n=0}^{+\infty} c_n(x-a)^n$ to represent series (1). (Note that we take $(x-a)^0 = 1$, even when $x = a$, for convenience in writing the general term.) If x is a particular number, the power series (1) becomes an infinite series of constant terms. A special case of (1) is obtained when $a = 0$, and the series becomes a power series in x, which is

$$\sum_{n=0}^{+\infty} c_n x^n = c_0 + c_1 x + c_2 x^2 + \ldots + c_n x^n + \ldots \quad (2)$$

In addition to power series in $x - a$ and x, there are power series of the form

$$\sum_{n=0}^{+\infty} c_n[\phi(x)]^n = c_0 + c_1\phi(x) + c_2[\phi(x)]^2 + \ldots + c_n[\phi(x)]^n + \ldots$$

where ϕ is a function of x. Such a series is called a power series in $\phi(x)$. In this book we are concerned exclusively with power series of the forms (1) and (2), and when the term "power series" is used, we mean either of these forms. Our discussion of the theory of power series is confined to series (2). The more general power series (1) can be obtained from (2) by the translation $x = \bar{x} - a$; therefore our results can be applied to series (1) as well.

In dealing with an infinite series of constant terms we were concerned with the question of convergence or divergence of the series. In considering a power series we ask, For what values of x does the power series converge? For each value of x for which the power series converges, the series represents the number that is the sum of the series. A power series in x, therefore, defines a function having as its domain all values of x for which the power series converges.

We shall use the notation $P_n(x)$ to represent a power series' partial sum whose highest power is n. This notation is consistent with the use of $P_n(x)$ in Section 8.1 to represent an nth degree Taylor polynomial.

▷ **ILLUSTRATION 1**   Consider the geometric series for which $a = 1$ and $r = x$, which is $\sum\limits_{n=0}^{+\infty} x^n$. By Theorem 8.3.5 this series converges to the sum $1/(1 - x)$ if $|x| < 1$. The power series $\sum\limits_{n=0}^{+\infty} x^n$, therefore, defines the function f for which $f(x) = 1/(1 - x)$ and whose domain is the open interval $(-1, 1)$. Thus we write

$$1 + x + x^2 + x^3 + \ldots + x^n + \ldots = \frac{1}{1 - x} \quad \text{if } |x| < 1 \quad \textbf{(3)}$$

Figure 1 shows the graphs of

$$f(x) = \frac{1}{1 - x} \quad \text{and} \quad P_{10}(x) = \sum_{n=0}^{10} x^n$$

plotted in the $[-2, 2]$ by $[-1, 10]$ window. Observe that the graph of $P_{10}(x)$ approximates the graph of f when $|x| < 1$, which supports the fact that the power series converges to $1/(1 - x)$ if $|x| < 1$.   ◀

Series (3) can be used to form other power series whose sums can be determined.

▷ **ILLUSTRATION 2**   If in (3) x is replaced by $-x$, we have

$$1 - x + x^2 - x^3 + \ldots + (-1)^n x^n + \ldots = \frac{1}{1 + x} \quad \text{if } |x| < 1 \quad \textbf{(4)}$$

Replace x by x^2 in (3) and get

$$1 + x^2 + x^4 + x^6 + \ldots + x^{2n} + \ldots = \frac{1}{1 - x^2} \quad \text{if } |x| < 1 \quad \textbf{(5)}$$

If x is replaced by $-x^2$ in (3), we obtain

$$1 - x^2 + x^4 - x^6 + \ldots + (-1)^n x^{2n} + \ldots = \frac{1}{1 + x^2} \quad \text{if } |x| < 1 \quad \textbf{(6)}$$

◀

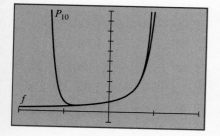

$[-2, 2]$ by $[-1, 10]$

$$f(x) = \frac{1}{1 - x}$$

$$P_{10}(x) = \sum_{n=0}^{10} x^n$$

FIGURE 1

In Exercises 1 through 3 you are asked to support graphically that power series (4) through (6) converge to the corresponding rational function if $|x| < 1$.

We now show by means of three examples how the ratio test can be used to determine the values of x for which a power series is convergent. Some series, such as the one in Example 2, converge for every value of x. Of course, every power series (2) is convergent for $x = 0$, but, as you will see in Example 3, some series converge for no other value of x.

▶ **EXAMPLE 1** Find the values of x for which the power series is convergent:

$$\sum_{n=1}^{+\infty} (-1)^{n+1} \frac{2^n x^n}{n 3^n}$$

Solution For the given series,

$$u_n = (-1)^{n+1} \frac{2^n x^n}{n 3^n} \quad \text{and} \quad u_{n+1} = (-1)^{n+2} \frac{2^{n+1} x^{n+1}}{(n+1) 3^{n+1}}$$

So

$$\lim_{n \to +\infty} \left| \frac{u_{n+1}}{u_n} \right| = \lim_{n \to +\infty} \left| \frac{2^{n+1} x^{n+1}}{(n+1) 3^{n+1}} \cdot \frac{n 3^n}{2^n x^n} \right|$$

$$= \lim_{n \to +\infty} \frac{2}{3} |x| \frac{n}{n+1}$$

$$= \tfrac{2}{3} |x|$$

Therefore the power series is absolutely convergent when $\frac{2}{3}|x| < 1$ or, equivalently, when $|x| < \frac{3}{2}$. The series is divergent when $\frac{2}{3}|x| > 1$ or, equivalently, when $|x| > \frac{3}{2}$. When $\frac{2}{3}|x| = 1$ (i.e., when $x = \pm\frac{3}{2}$), the ratio test fails. When $x = \frac{3}{2}$, the given power series becomes the alternating harmonic series

$$\frac{1}{1} - \frac{1}{2} + \frac{1}{3} - \frac{1}{4} + \ldots + (-1)^{n+1} \frac{1}{n} + \ldots$$

which is convergent, as shown in Example 1 of Section 8.5. When $x = -\frac{3}{2}$, we have

$$-\frac{1}{1} - \frac{1}{2} - \frac{1}{3} - \frac{1}{4} - \ldots - \frac{1}{n} - \ldots$$

the negative of the harmonic series, which is divergent. We conclude, then, that the given power series is absolutely convergent when $-\frac{3}{2} < x < \frac{3}{2}$ and is conditionally convergent when $x = \frac{3}{2}$. If $x \leq -\frac{3}{2}$ or $x > \frac{3}{2}$, the series is divergent. ◀

When $n!$ is used in representing the nth term of a power series, as in the next example, we take $0! = 1$ so that the expression for the nth term will hold when $n = 0$.

▶ **EXAMPLE 2** Find the values of x for which the power series is convergent:

$$\sum_{n=0}^{+\infty} \frac{x^n}{n!}$$

Solution   For the given series,

$$u_n = \frac{x^n}{n!} \quad \text{and} \quad u_{n+1} = \frac{x^{n+1}}{(n+1)!}.$$

So by applying the ratio test,

$$\lim_{n \to +\infty} \left| \frac{u_{n+1}}{u_n} \right| = \lim_{n \to +\infty} \left| \frac{x^{n+1}}{(n+1)!} \cdot \frac{n!}{x^n} \right|$$

$$= |x| \lim_{n \to +\infty} \frac{1}{n+1}$$

$$= 0$$

$$< 1$$

Therefore the given power series is absolutely convergent for all x.   ◄

► **EXAMPLE 3**   Find the values of x for which the power series is convergent:

$$\sum_{n=0}^{+\infty} n!\, x^n$$

Solution   For the given series, $u_n = n!\, x^n$ and $u_{n+1} = (n+1)!\, x^{n+1}$. Applying the ratio test we have

$$\lim_{n \to +\infty} \left| \frac{u_{n+1}}{u_n} \right| = \lim_{n \to +\infty} \left| \frac{(n+1)!\, x^{n+1}}{n!\, x^n} \right|$$

$$= \lim_{n \to +\infty} |(n+1)x|$$

$$= \begin{cases} 0 & \text{if } x = 0 \\ +\infty & \text{if } x \neq 0 \end{cases}$$

It follows that the series is divergent for all values of x except 0.   ◄

► **EXAMPLE 4**   Use the root test to find the values of x for which the power series is convergent:

$$\sum_{n=1}^{+\infty} n^3 x^n$$

Solution   To use the root test we compute $\lim_{n \to +\infty} \sqrt[n]{|u_n|}$.

$$\lim_{n \to +\infty} \sqrt[n]{|n^3 x^n|} = \lim_{n \to +\infty} n^{3/n} |x| \tag{7}$$

To determine $\lim_{n \to +\infty} n^{3/n}$, let $y = n^{3/n}$. Then $\ln y = \frac{3}{n} \ln n$. Thus

$$\lim_{n \to +\infty} \ln y = \lim_{n \to +\infty} \frac{3 \ln n}{n} \tag{8}$$

To compute the limit on the right-hand side of (8) we first find $\lim\limits_{z \to +\infty} \dfrac{3 \ln z}{z}$, where values of z are real numbers. Because $\lim\limits_{z \to +\infty} \ln z = +\infty$ and $\lim\limits_{z \to +\infty} z = +\infty$, we apply L'Hôpital's rule and get

$$\lim_{z \to +\infty} \frac{3 \ln z}{z} = \lim_{z \to +\infty} \frac{3}{z}$$
$$= 0$$

Thus from Theorem 8.2.3, $\lim\limits_{n \to +\infty} \dfrac{3 \ln n}{n} = 0$; hence, from (8),

$$\lim_{n \to +\infty} \ln y = 0$$
$$\lim_{n \to +\infty} y = 1$$

Substituting this result in (7) we have

$$\lim_{n \to +\infty} \sqrt[n]{|n^3 x^n|} = |x|$$

Therefore the power series is absolutely convergent when $|x| < 1$. The series is divergent when $|x| > 1$. When $x = 1$, the given power series becomes $\sum\limits_{n=1}^{+\infty} n^3$, which is divergent because $\lim\limits_{n \to +\infty} n^3 \neq 0$. Similarly, the power series is divergent when $x = -1$. ◀

Refer back to Example 1, which provides an illustration of the following theorem. The power series in that example is convergent for $x = \frac{3}{2}$ and is absolutely convergent for all values of x for which $|x| < \frac{3}{2}$.

8.7.2 Theorem

If the power series $\sum\limits_{n=0}^{+\infty} c_n x^n$ is convergent for $x = x_1$ $(x_1 \neq 0)$, then it is absolutely convergent for all values of x for which $|x| < |x_1|$.

Proof If $\sum\limits_{n=0}^{+\infty} c_n x_1{}^n$ is convergent, then $\lim\limits_{n \to +\infty} c_n x_1{}^n = 0$. Therefore, if we take $\epsilon = 1$ in Definition 3.7.1, there exists an integer $N > 0$ such that

$$\text{if } n \geq N \text{ then } |c_n x_1{}^n| < 1$$

Now if x is any number such that $|x| < |x_1|$, then if $n \geq N$

$$|c_n x^n| = \left| c_n x_1{}^n \frac{x^n}{x_1{}^n} \right|$$
$$|c_n x^n| = |c_n x_1{}^n| \left| \frac{x}{x_1} \right|^n$$
$$|c_n x^n| < \left| \frac{x}{x_1} \right|^n \tag{9}$$

The series

$$\sum_{n=N}^{+\infty} \left| \frac{x}{x_1} \right|^n \tag{10}$$

is convergent because it is a geometric series with $r = |x/x_1| < 1$ (because $|x| < |x_1|$). Compare the series $\sum\limits_{n=N}^{+\infty} |c_n x^n|$, where $|x| < |x_1|$, with series (10). From (9) and the comparison test, $\sum\limits_{n=N}^{+\infty} |c_n x^n|$ is convergent for $|x| < |x_1|$. So the given power series is absolutely convergent for all values of x for which $|x| < |x_1|$.   ∎

The next theorem is a corollary of Theorem 8.7.2. The power series of Example 1 again provides an illustration of the content of the theorem because the series is divergent for $x = -\frac{3}{2}$ as well as for all values of x for which $|x| > |-\frac{3}{2}|$.

8.7.3 Theorem

If the power series $\sum\limits_{n=0}^{+\infty} c_n x^n$ is divergent for $x = x_2$, it is divergent for all values of x for which $|x| > |x_2|$.

Proof Suppose that the given power series is convergent for some number x for which $|x| > |x_2|$. Then by Theorem 8.7.2 the series must converge when $x = x_2$. However, this contradicts the hypothesis. Therefore the given power series is divergent for all values of x for which $|x| > |x_2|$.   ∎

From Theorems 8.7.2 and 8.7.3, we prove the following key theorem of this section.

8.7.4 Theorem

Let $\sum\limits_{n=0}^{+\infty} c_n x^n$ be a given power series. Then exactly one of the following conditions holds:

  (i) the series converges only when $x = 0$;
  (ii) the series is absolutely convergent for all values of x;
  (iii) there exists a number $R > 0$ such that the series is absolutely convergent for all values of x for which $|x| < R$ and is divergent for all values of x for which $|x| > R$.

Proof If x is replaced by zero in the given power series, we have $c_0 + 0 + 0 + \ldots$, which is obviously convergent. Therefore every power series of the form $\sum\limits_{n=0}^{+\infty} c_n x^n$ is convergent when $x = 0$. If this is the only value of x for which the series converges, then condition (i) holds.

Suppose that the given series is convergent for $x = x_1$ where $x_1 \neq 0$. Then from Theorem 8.7.2 the series is absolutely convergent for all values of x for which $|x| < |x_1|$. Now if in addition there is no value of x for which the given series is divergent, then the series is absolutely convergent for all values of x. This is condition (ii).

If the given series is convergent for $x = x_1$ where $x_1 \neq 0$ and is divergent for $x = x_2$ where $|x_2| > |x_1|$, from Theorem 8.7.3 the series is

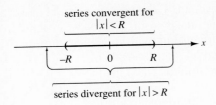

series convergent for $|x| < R$

series divergent for $|x| > R$

FIGURE 2

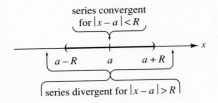

series convergent for $|x - a| < R$

series divergent for $|x - a| > R$

FIGURE 3

divergent for all values of x for which $|x| > |x_2|$. Hence $|x_2|$ is an upper bound of the set of values of $|x|$ for which the series is absolutely convergent. Therefore, by the axiom of completeness (8.2.9) this set of numbers has a least upper bound, which is the number R of condition (iii). This proves that exactly one of the three conditions holds. ∎

Figure 2 illustrates on the number line part (iii) of Theorem 8.7.4.

If instead of the power series $\sum_{n=1}^{+\infty} c_n x^n$ we have the series $\sum_{n=0}^{+\infty} c_n (x - a)^n$, then in conditions (i) and (iii) of Theorem 8.7.4 x is replaced by $x - a$. The conditions become

(i) the series converges only when $x = a$;

(iii) there exists a number $R > 0$ such that the series is absolutely convergent for all values of x for which $|x - a| < R$ and is divergent for all values of x for which $|x - a| > R$. (See Figure 3 for an illustration of this on the number line.)

The number R of condition (iii) of Theorem 8.7.4 is called the **radius of convergence** of the power series. If condition (i) holds, $R = 0$; if condition (ii) holds, we write $R = +\infty$. If $R > 0$, the set of all values of x for which a given power series is convergent is called the **interval of convergence** of the power series.

▷ **ILLUSTRATION 3** For the power series of Example 1, $R = \frac{3}{2}$, and the interval of convergence is $(-\frac{3}{2}, \frac{3}{2}]$. In Example 2, $R = +\infty$, and the interval of convergence is written as $(-\infty, +\infty)$. ◄

If the radius of convergence of a power series in x is R, where $R > 0$, the interval of convergence is $(-R, R)$, $[-R, R]$, $(-R, R]$, or $[-R, R)$ whereas for a power series in $x - a$, the interval of convergence is $(a - R, a + R)$, $[a - R, a + R]$, $(a - R, a + R]$, or $[a - R, a + R)$.

A given power series then defines a function having the interval of convergence as its domain. We now summarize the procedure for determining the interval of convergence.

> **Procedure for Determining the Interval of Convergence of a Power Series in x − a**
>
> 1. Apply the ratio test (or sometimes the root test) to find the radius of convergence R of the series. Some series converge absolutely for all values of x, as in Example 2 where $R = +\infty$, and some series converge only at one number, as in Example 3, where $R = 0$.
>
> 2. If $R > 0$, the series converges absolutely for all x in the interval $(a - R, a + R)$ and diverges for $|x - a| > R$. Test for convergence at the endpoints of the interval $(a - R, a + R)$ by the methods summarized in Section 8.6; of course, no conclusion regarding convergence at the endpoints can be made from either the ratio test or the root test.

▶ **EXAMPLE 5** Determine the interval of convergence of

$$\sum_{n=1}^{+\infty} n(x-2)^n$$

Solution The given power series is

$$(x-2) + 2(x-2)^2 + \ldots + n(x-2)^n + (n+1)(x-2)^{n+1} + \ldots$$

Applying the ratio test we have

$$\lim_{n \to +\infty} \left| \frac{u_{n+1}}{u_n} \right| = \lim_{n \to +\infty} \left| \frac{(n+1)(x-2)^{n+1}}{n(x-2)^n} \right|$$

$$= |x-2| \lim_{n \to +\infty} \frac{n+1}{n}$$

$$= |x-2|$$

The given series then will be absolutely convergent if $|x-2| < 1$ or, equivalently, $-1 < x-2 < 1$ or, equivalently, $1 < x < 3$.

When $x = 1$, the series is $\sum_{n=1}^{+\infty} (-1)^n n$, which is divergent because $\lim_{n \to +\infty} u_n \neq 0$. When $x = 3$, the series is $\sum_{n=1}^{+\infty} n$, which is also divergent because $\lim_{n \to +\infty} u_n \neq 0$. Therefore the interval of convergence is $(1, 3)$. So the given power series defines a function having the interval $(1, 3)$ as its domain.

◀

▶ **EXAMPLE 6** Determine the interval of convergence of

$$\sum_{n=1}^{+\infty} \frac{x^n}{2 + n^2}$$

Solution The given power series is

$$\frac{x}{2 + 1^2} + \frac{x^2}{2 + 2^2} + \frac{x^3}{2 + 3^2} + \ldots + \frac{x^n}{2 + n^2} + \frac{x^{n+1}}{2 + (n+1)^2} + \ldots$$

Applying the ratio test we have

$$\lim_{n \to +\infty} \left| \frac{u_{n+1}}{u_n} \right| = \lim_{n \to +\infty} \left| \frac{x^{n+1}}{2 + (n+1)^2} \cdot \frac{2 + n^2}{x^n} \right|$$

$$= |x| \lim_{n \to +\infty} \frac{2 + n^2}{2 + n^2 + 2n + 1}$$

$$= |x|$$

So the given series will be absolutely convergent if $|x| < 1$ or, equivalently, $-1 < x < 1$. When $x = 1$, the series is

$$\frac{1}{2 + 1^2} + \frac{1}{2 + 2^2} + \frac{1}{2 + 3^2} + \ldots + \frac{1}{2 + n^2} + \ldots$$

Because $\dfrac{1}{2 + n^2} < \dfrac{1}{n^2}$ for all positive integers n, and because $\displaystyle\sum_{n=1}^{+\infty} \dfrac{1}{n^2}$ is a convergent p series, from the comparison test the given power series is convergent when $x = 1$. When $x = -1$, the series is $\displaystyle\sum_{n=1}^{+\infty} \dfrac{(-1)^n}{2 + n^2}$, which is convergent because we have just seen that it is absolutely convergent. Hence the interval of convergence of the given power series is $[-1, 1]$. ◀

You have learned that the ratio test will not reveal anything about the convergence or divergence of a power series at the endpoints of the interval of convergence. Furthermore, at an endpoint a power series may be either absolutely convergent, conditionally convergent, or divergent. If a power series converges absolutely at one endpoint, we can prove that the series is absolutely convergent at each endpoint (see Exercise 37). We can also prove that if a power series converges at one endpoint and diverges at the other, the series is conditionally convergent at the endpoint at which it converges (see Exercise 38). For some power series, convergence or divergence at the endpoints cannot be determined by methods of elementary calculus.

EXERCISES 8.7

1. (a) Support graphically on your graphics calculator that the power series in (4) converges to

$f(x) = \dfrac{1}{1 + x}$, if $|x| < 1$, by plotting the graphs of f and $P_{10}(x)$ in the same window. **(b)** Use series (4) to find a power-series representation for $\dfrac{1}{1 + 2x}$ and support your answer graphically.

2. (a) Support graphically on your graphics calculator that the power series in (5) converges to

$f(x) = \dfrac{1}{1 - x^2}$, if $|x| < 1$, by plotting the graphs of f and $P_{10}(x)$ in the same window. **(b)** Use series (5) to find a power-series representation for $\dfrac{1}{1 - 4x^2}$ and support your answer graphically.

3. (a) Support graphically on your graphics calculator that the power series in (6) converges to

$f(x) = \dfrac{1}{1 + x^2}$, if $|x| < 1$, by plotting the graphs of f and $P_{10}(x)$ in the same window. **(b)** Use series (6) to find a power-series representation for $\dfrac{1}{1 + 9x^2}$ and support your answer graphically.

4. (a) Use series (4) to find a power-series representation for $f(x) = \dfrac{1}{1 + x^3}$. **(b)** Support graphically on your graphics calculator that the power series in

part (a) converges to $f(x)$, if $|x| < 1$, by plotting the graphs of f and $P_{10}(x)$ in the same window.

In Exercises 5 through 32, determine the interval of convergence of the power series.

5. $\displaystyle\sum_{n=0}^{+\infty} \dfrac{x^n}{n + 1}$

6. $\displaystyle\sum_{n=0}^{+\infty} \dfrac{x^n}{n^2 + 1}$

7. $\displaystyle\sum_{n=0}^{+\infty} \dfrac{x^n}{n^2 - 3}$

8. $\displaystyle\sum_{n=0}^{+\infty} \dfrac{n^2 x^n}{2^n}$

9. $\displaystyle\sum_{n=1}^{+\infty} \dfrac{2^n x^n}{n^2}$

10. $\displaystyle\sum_{n=1}^{+\infty} \dfrac{x^n}{2^n \sqrt{n}}$

11. $\displaystyle\sum_{n=1}^{+\infty} \dfrac{n x^n}{3^n}$

12. $\displaystyle\sum_{n=1}^{+\infty} (-1)^n \dfrac{x^{2n}}{(2n)!}$

13. $\displaystyle\sum_{n=1}^{+\infty} (-1)^{n+1} \dfrac{x^{2n-1}}{(2n - 1)!}$

14. $\displaystyle\sum_{n=1}^{+\infty} \dfrac{n + 1}{n^{2n}} x^n$

15. $\displaystyle\sum_{n=0}^{+\infty} \dfrac{(x + 3)^n}{2^n}$

16. $\displaystyle\sum_{n=0}^{+\infty} \dfrac{x^n}{(n + 1)5^n}$

17. $\displaystyle\sum_{n=1}^{+\infty} (-1)^n \dfrac{x^n}{(2n - 1)3^{2n-1}}$

18. $\displaystyle\sum_{n=1}^{+\infty} (-1)^{n+1} \dfrac{(n + 1)x^n}{n!}$

19. $\displaystyle\sum_{n=1}^{+\infty} (-1)^{n+1} \dfrac{(x - 1)^n}{n}$

20. $\displaystyle\sum_{n=1}^{+\infty} \dfrac{(x + 2)^n}{(n + 1)2^n}$

21. $\displaystyle\sum_{n=0}^{+\infty} (\sinh 2n)x^n$

22. $\displaystyle\sum_{n=1}^{+\infty} \dfrac{x^n}{\ln(n + 1)}$

23. $\displaystyle\sum_{n=2}^{+\infty} (-1)^{n+1} \dfrac{x^n}{n(\ln n)^2}$

24. $\displaystyle\sum_{n=1}^{+\infty} \dfrac{(x + 5)^{n-1}}{n^2}$

25. $\displaystyle\sum_{n=1}^{+\infty} \dfrac{n^2}{5^n} (x - 1)^n$

26. $\displaystyle\sum_{n=0}^{+\infty} \dfrac{4^{n+1} x^{2n}}{n + 3}$

27. $\displaystyle\sum_{n=1}^{+\infty} \frac{\ln n(x-5)^n}{n+1}$ 28. $\displaystyle\sum_{n=1}^{+\infty} \frac{x^n}{n^n}$

29. $\displaystyle\sum_{n=1}^{+\infty} (-1)^n \frac{1 \cdot 3 \cdot 5 \cdot \ldots \cdot (2n-1)}{2 \cdot 4 \cdot 6 \cdot \ldots \cdot 2n} x^{2n+1}$

30. $\displaystyle\sum_{n=1}^{+\infty} n^n(x-3)^n$ 31. $\displaystyle\sum_{n=1}^{+\infty} \frac{n! x^n}{n^n}$

32. $\displaystyle\sum_{n=1}^{+\infty} \frac{(-1)^{n+1} 1 \cdot 3 \cdot 5 \cdot \ldots \cdot (2n-1)}{2 \cdot 4 \cdot 6 \cdot \ldots \cdot 2n} x^n$

33. The description of the vapor state of an ideal gas, useful in refrigeration engineering, is determined in thermodynamics by the virial equations of state:

$$Z = 1 + \frac{B}{V} + \frac{C}{V^2} + \frac{D}{V^3} + \ldots$$

$$Z = 1 + \overline{B}P + \overline{C}P^2 + \overline{D}P^3 + \ldots$$

where $B, C, D, \ldots, \overline{B}, \overline{C}, \overline{D}, \ldots$ are constants,

and where Z is the compressibility factor, and V and P are, respectively, measures of the volume and pressure of the gas. Furthermore, $Z = PV/RT$, where T is the measure of the temperature of the gas and R is the universal gas constant. By comparing the two power series, show that

$$\overline{B} = \frac{B}{RT} \qquad \overline{C} = \frac{C - B^2}{R^2 T^2} \qquad \overline{D} = \frac{D + 2B^3 - 3BC}{R^3 T^3}$$

34. If $\displaystyle\sum_{n=1}^{+\infty} a_n$ is an absolutely convergent series, prove that $\displaystyle\sum_{n=1}^{+\infty} a_n x^n$ is absolutely convergent when $|x| \le 1$.

35. If a and b are positive integers, find the radius of convergence of the power series $\displaystyle\sum_{n=1}^{+\infty} \frac{(n+a)!}{n!(n+b)!} x^n$.

36. Prove that if $\displaystyle\lim_{n \to +\infty} \sqrt[n]{|u_n|} = L \; (L \ne 0)$, then the radius of convergence of $\displaystyle\sum_{n=1}^{+\infty} u_n x^n$ is $1/L$.

37. Prove that if a power series converges absolutely at one endpoint of its interval of convergence, then the series is absolutely convergent at each endpoint.

38. Prove that if a power series converges at one endpoint of its interval of convergence and diverges at the other endpoint, then the series is conditionally convergent at the endpoint at which it converges.

39. Prove that if the radius of convergence of the power series $\displaystyle\sum_{n=1}^{+\infty} u_n x^n$ is r, then the radius of convergence of the series $\displaystyle\sum_{n=1}^{+\infty} u_n x^{2n}$ is $\sqrt{r}$.

40. (a) Suppose the power series $\displaystyle\sum_{n=0}^{+\infty} c_n x^n$ is convergent for $x = 2$. Explain why we can conclude that the series is convergent for $x = 1$ but not necessarily convergent for $x = 3$. (b) Suppose the series $\displaystyle\sum_{n=0}^{+\infty} c_n(x-4)^n$ is convergent for $x = 2$. Explain why we can conclude that the series is convergent for $x = 3$ but not necessarily convergent for $x = 1$.

8.8 DIFFERENTIATION AND INTEGRATION OF POWER SERIES

Power series can be obtained from other power series by differentiation and integration. You will learn in this section that if R (where $R \ne 0$) is the radius of convergence of a power series that defines a function f, then f is differentiable on the open interval $(-R, R)$ and the derivative of f can be obtained by differentiating the power series term by term. Furthermore, we will show that f is integrable on every closed subinterval of $(-R, R)$, and the integral of f is evaluated by integrating the power series term by term. First we need two preliminary theorems.

8.8.1 Theorem

If $\displaystyle\sum_{n=0}^{+\infty} c_n x^n$ is a power series having a radius of convergence of $R > 0$, then $\displaystyle\sum_{n=1}^{+\infty} n c_n x^{n-1}$ also has R as its radius of convergence.

This theorem, whose proof appears in the supplement of this section, states that the series, obtained by differentiating each term of a given power series term by term, will have the same radius of convergence as the given series. In the following illustration we verify the theorem for a particular power series.

▷ **ILLUSTRATION 1**   Consider the power series

$$\sum_{n=0}^{+\infty} \frac{x^{n+1}}{(n+1)^2} = x + \frac{x^2}{4} + \frac{x^3}{9} + \ldots + \frac{x^{n+1}}{(n+1)^2} + \frac{x^{n+2}}{(n+2)^2} + \ldots$$

The radius of convergence is found by applying the ratio test.

$$\lim_{n \to +\infty} \left| \frac{u_{n+1}}{u_n} \right| = \lim_{n \to +\infty} \left| \frac{(n+1)^2 x^{n+2}}{(n+2)^2 x^{n+1}} \right|$$

$$= |x| \lim_{n \to +\infty} \left| \frac{n^2 + 2n + 1}{n^2 + 4n + 4} \right|$$

$$= |x|$$

Hence the power series is convergent when $|x| < 1$; so its radius of convergence $R = 1$.

The series obtained by differentiating the given series term by term is

$$\sum_{n=0}^{+\infty} \frac{(n+1)x^n}{(n+1)^2} = \sum_{n=0}^{+\infty} \frac{x^n}{n+1}$$

$$= 1 + \frac{x}{2} + \frac{x^2}{3} + \frac{x^3}{4} + \ldots + \frac{x^n}{n+1} + \frac{x^{n+1}}{n+2} + \ldots$$

Applying the ratio test for this power series we have

$$\lim_{n \to +\infty} \left| \frac{u_{n+1}}{u_n} \right| = \lim_{n \to +\infty} \left| \frac{(n+1)x^{n+1}}{(n+2)x^n} \right|$$

$$= |x| \lim_{n \to +\infty} \left| \frac{n+1}{n+2} \right|$$

$$= |x|$$

This series is convergent when $|x| < 1$; thus its radius of convergence $R' = 1$. Because $R = R'$, we have verified Theorem 8.8.1 for this series. ◄

8.8.2 Theorem

If the radius of convergence of the power series $\sum_{n=0}^{+\infty} c_n x^n$ is $R > 0$, then R is also the radius of convergence of $\sum_{n=2}^{+\infty} n(n-1)c_n x^{n-2}$.

Proof   The desired result follows when Theorem 8.8.1 is applied to the series $\sum_{n=1}^{+\infty} nc_n x^{n-1}$ ∎

We now state the important theorem regarding term-by-term differentiation of a power series. Theorems 8.8.1 and 8.8.2 play a crucial part in the proof of the theorem, found in the supplement of this section.

8.8.3 Theorem

Let $\displaystyle\sum_{n=0}^{+\infty} c_n x^n$ be a power series whose radius of convergence is $R > 0$. If f is the function defined by

$$f(x) = \sum_{n=0}^{+\infty} c_n x^n$$

then $f'(x)$ exists for every x in the open interval $(-R, R)$ and

$$f'(x) = \sum_{n=1}^{+\infty} n c_n x^{n-1}$$

In Theorem 8.8.3, if the series for $f'(x)$ converges at R (or $-R$), then R (or $-R$) is in the domain of f'. The proof of this fact is beyond the scope of this book.

The following example involves an application of Theorem 8.8.3.

▶ **EXAMPLE 1**   Let f be the function defined by the power series of Illustration 1. **(a)** Find the domain of f; **(b)** write the power series that defines the function f' and find the domain of f'.

Solution

(a) $\displaystyle f(x) = \sum_{n=0}^{+\infty} \frac{x^{n+1}}{(n+1)^2}$

The domain of f is the interval of convergence of the power series. In Illustration 1 we showed that the radius of convergence of the power series is 1; that is, the series converges when $|x| < 1$. Consider now the power series when $|x| = 1$. When $x = 1$, the series is

$$1 + \frac{1}{4} + \frac{1}{9} + \ldots + \frac{1}{(n+1)^2} + \ldots$$

which is convergent because it is the p series with $p = 2$. When $x = -1$, we have the series $\displaystyle\sum_{n=0}^{+\infty} \frac{(-1)^{n+1}}{(n+1)^2}$, which is convergent because it is absolutely convergent. Hence the domain of f is the interval $[-1, 1]$.

(b) From Theorem 8.8.3, f' is defined by

$$f'(x) = \sum_{n=0}^{+\infty} \frac{x^n}{n+1} \tag{1}$$

and $f'(x)$ exists for every x in the open interval $(-1, 1)$. In Illustration 1 we showed that the radius of convergence of the power series in (1) is 1. We now consider the power series in (1) when $x = \pm 1$. When $x = 1$, the series is

$$1 + \frac{1}{2} + \frac{1}{3} + \frac{1}{4} + \ldots + \frac{1}{n+1} + \ldots$$

which is the harmonic series and hence is divergent. When $x = -1$, the series is

$$1 - \frac{1}{2} + \frac{1}{3} - \frac{1}{4} + \ldots + (-1)^n \frac{1}{n+1} + \ldots$$

which is the convergent alternating harmonic series. Therefore the domain of f' is the interval $[-1, 1)$. ◀

Example 1 illustrates the fact that if a function f is defined by a power series and this power series is differentiated term by term, the resulting power series, which defines f', has the same radius of convergence but not necessarily the same interval of convergence.

▶ **EXAMPLE 2**   Obtain a power-series representation of

$$\frac{1}{(1-x)^2}$$

Solution   We apply Theorem 8.8.3. From (3) in Section 8.7

$$\frac{1}{1-x} = 1 + x + x^2 + x^3 + \ldots + x^n + \ldots \qquad \text{if } |x| < 1$$

Differentiating on both sides of the above we get

$$\frac{1}{(1-x)^2} = 1 + 2x + 3x^2 + \ldots + nx^{n-1} + \ldots \qquad \text{if } |x| < 1 \quad ◀$$

▶ **EXAMPLE 3**   Show that for all real values of x

$$e^x = \sum_{n=0}^{+\infty} \frac{x^n}{n!}$$

$$= 1 + x + \frac{x^2}{2!} + \frac{x^3}{3!} + \ldots + \frac{x^n}{n!} + \ldots$$

Solution   In Example 2 of Section 8.7 we showed that the power series $\sum_{n=0}^{+\infty} \frac{x^n}{n!}$ is absolutely convergent for all real values of x. Therefore, if f is the function defined by

$$f(x) = \sum_{n=0}^{+\infty} \frac{x^n}{n!} \qquad\qquad\qquad (2)$$

the domain of f is the set of all real numbers; that is, the interval of convergence is $(-\infty, +\infty)$. From Theorem 8.8.3, for all real values of x,

$$f'(x) = \sum_{n=1}^{+\infty} \frac{nx^{n-1}}{n!}$$

Because $\dfrac{n}{n!} = \dfrac{1}{(n-1)!}$, the above can be written as

$$f'(x) = \sum_{n=1}^{+\infty} \frac{x^{n-1}}{(n-1)!}$$

$$\Leftrightarrow f'(x) = \sum_{n=0}^{+\infty} \frac{x^n}{n!}$$

From this equality and (2), $f'(x) = f(x)$ for all real values of x. Therefore the function f satisfies the differential equation

$$\frac{dy}{dx} = y$$

for which, as shown in Section 5.6, the general solution is $y = Ce^x$. Hence for some constant C, $f(x) = Ce^x$. From (2), $f(0) = 1$. (Remember that we take $x^0 = 1$ even when $x = 0$ for convenience in writing the general term.) Therefore $C = 1$; so $f(x) = e^x$, and we have the desired result. ◀

Observe that $P_n(x)$ for the power series for e^x in the above example is the nth degree Maclaurin polynomial for e^x obtained in Illustration 1 of Section 8.1. You will learn in Section 8.9 that this series is called the *Maclaurin series* for e^x.

▶   **EXAMPLE 4**   **(a)** From the result of Example 3, find a power-series representation of e^{-x}. **(b)** Use the series in part (a) to find the value of e^{-1} correct to five decimal places. Compare the result with a calculator value of e^{-1}.

Solution

(a) If x is replaced by $-x$ in the series for e^x, we have

$$e^{-x} = 1 - x + \frac{x^2}{2!} - \frac{x^3}{3!} + \ldots + (-1)^n\frac{x^n}{n!} + \ldots$$

for all real values of x.
(b) If $x = 1$ in the series for e^{-x},

$$e^{-1} = 1 - 1 + \frac{1}{2!} - \frac{1}{3!} + \frac{1}{4!} - \frac{1}{5!} + \frac{1}{6!} - \frac{1}{7!} + \frac{1}{8!} - \frac{1}{9!} + \frac{1}{10!} - \ldots$$

$$\approx 1 - 1 + 0.5 - 0.166667 + 0.041667 - 0.008333 + 0.001389$$
$$- 0.000198 + 0.000025 - 0.000003 + 0.0000003 - \ldots$$

This is a convergent alternating series for which $|u_{n+1}| < |u_n|$. So if the first ten terms are used to approximate the sum, by Theorem 8.5.4 the error is less than the absolute value of the eleventh term. Adding the first ten terms we obtain 0.367880. Rounding off to five decimal places gives

$$e^{-1} \approx 0.36788$$

Our calculator gives the same value to five decimal places. ◀

In computation with infinite series two kinds of errors occur. One is the error given by the remainder after the first n terms. The other is the *round-off error* that occurs when each term of the series is approximated by a decimal with a finite number of places. In particular, in Example 4 we wanted the result accurate to five decimal places; so each term was rounded off to six decimal places. After computing the sum, we rounded off this result to five decimal places. Of course, the error given by the remainder can be reduced by considering additional terms of the series, while the round-off error can be reduced by using more decimal places.

If you take a course in differential equations, you will learn that it is possible to express solutions of many differential equations as power series. In the following example we have this situation.

▶ **EXAMPLE 5**   Show that

$$y = x + \sum_{n=0}^{+\infty} \frac{x^n}{n!} \tag{3}$$

is a solution of the differential equation $\dfrac{d^2y}{dx^2} - y + x = 0$.

Solution   The power series in (3) is convergent for all values of x. Therefore, from Theorem 8.8.3 for all x,

$$\frac{dy}{dx} = 1 + \sum_{n=1}^{+\infty} \frac{nx^{n-1}}{n!} \qquad \frac{d^2y}{dx^2} = \sum_{n=2}^{+\infty} \frac{(n-1)x^{n-2}}{(n-1)!}$$

$$= 1 + \sum_{n=1}^{+\infty} \frac{x^{n-1}}{(n-1)!} \qquad = \sum_{n=2}^{+\infty} \frac{x^{n-2}}{(n-2)!}$$

$$= \sum_{n=0}^{+\infty} \frac{x^n}{n!}$$

Thus

$$\frac{d^2y}{dx^2} - y + x = \sum_{n=0}^{+\infty} \frac{x^n}{n!} - \left(x + \sum_{n=0}^{+\infty} \frac{x^n}{n!} \right) + x$$

$$= 0$$

Hence the differential equation is satisfied; so (3) is a solution. ◀

The following theorem regarding term-by-term integration of a power series is a consequence of Theorem 8.8.3.

8.8.4 Theorem

Let $\displaystyle\sum_{n=0}^{+\infty} c_n x^n$ be a power series whose radius of convergence is $R > 0$. If f is the function defined by

$$f(x) = \sum_{n=0}^{+\infty} c_n x^n$$

then f is integrable on every closed subinterval of $(-R, R)$, and the integral of f is evaluated by integrating the given power series term by term; that is, if x is in $(-R, R)$, then

$$\int_0^x f(t)\, dt = \sum_{n=0}^{+\infty} \frac{c_n}{n+1} x^{n+1}$$

Furthermore, R is the radius of convergence of the resulting series.

Proof   Let g be the function defined by

$$g(x) = \sum_{n=0}^{+\infty} \frac{c_n}{n+1} x^{n+1}$$

Because the terms of the power-series representation of $f(x)$ are the derivatives of the terms of the power-series representation of $g(x)$, the two series have, by Theorem 8.8.1, the same radius of convergence. By Theorem 8.8.3

$$g'(x) = f(x) \qquad \text{for every } x \text{ in } (-R, R)$$

By Theorem 8.8.2, $f'(x) = g''(x)$ for every x in $(-R, R)$. Because f is differentiable on $(-R, R)$, f is continuous there; consequently f is continuous on every closed subinterval of $(-R, R)$. From the second fundamental theorem of the calculus, we conclude that if x is in $(-R, R)$, then

$$\int_0^x f(t)\, dt = g(x) - g(0)$$

$$= g(x)$$

$$\Leftrightarrow \int_0^x f(t)\, dt = \sum_{n=0}^{+\infty} \frac{c_n}{n+1} x^{n+1} \qquad\blacksquare$$

Theorem 8.8.4 often is used to compute a definite integral that cannot be evaluated directly by finding an antiderivative of the integrand. Examples 6 and 7, which follow, illustrate the technique. The definite integral appearing in these two examples is similar to the one that represents the measure of the area of a region under the "normal probability curve."

▶ **EXAMPLE 6**

(a) Find a power-series representation of $\displaystyle\int_0^x e^{-t^2}\, dt$ and determine its radius of convergence. **(b)** Plot in the same window the graphs of $\text{NINT}(e^{-t^2}, 0, x)$ and the polynomial consisting of the first ten nonzero terms of the series in part (a).

Solution

(a) From Example 4,

$$e^{-x} = \sum_{n=0}^{+\infty} \frac{(-1)^n x^n}{n!}$$

for all values of x. If x is replaced by t^2,

$$e^{-t^2} = 1 - t^2 + \frac{t^4}{2!} - \frac{t^6}{3!} + \cdots + (-1)^n \frac{t^{2n}}{n!} + \cdots \quad \text{for all values of } t$$

Applying Theorem 8.8.4 we integrate term by term and obtain

$$\int_0^x e^{-t^2} \, dt = \sum_{n=0}^{+\infty} \int_0^x (-1)^n \frac{t^{2n}}{n!} \, dt$$

$$= x - \frac{x^3}{3} + \frac{x^5}{2! \cdot 5} - \frac{x^7}{3! \cdot 7} + \cdots + (-1)^n \frac{x^{2n+1}}{n!(2n+1)} + \cdots$$

The power series represents the integral for all values of x; the radius of convergence R is, therefore, $+\infty$.

(b) Because the power-series expansion of $\int_0^x e^{-t^2} \, dt$ contains only odd powers of x, the sum of the first ten nonzero terms is given by $P_{19}(x)$.

Figure 1 shows the graphs of

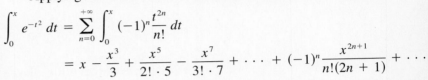

$$\text{NINT}(e^{-t^2}, 0, x) \quad \text{and} \quad P_{19}(x) = \sum_{n=0}^{9} (-1)^n \frac{x^{2n+1}}{n!(2n+1)}$$

plotted in the $[-5, 5]$ by $[-5, 5]$ window. Observe how the graph of the polynomial approximates the graph of the integral. ◄

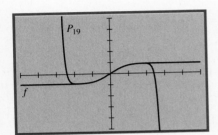

$[-5, 5]$ by $[-5, 5]$

$$f(x) = \text{NINT}(e^{-t^2}, 0, x)$$

$$P_{19}(x) = \sum_{n=0}^{9} (-1)^n \frac{x^{2n+1}}{n!(2n+1)}$$

FIGURE 1

► **EXAMPLE 7**   (a) Use the result of Example 6 to compute accurate to three decimal places the value of $\int_0^{1/2} e^{-t^2} \, dt$. (b) Support the answer in part (a) by the NINT capability of a graphics calculator.

Solution

(a) We replace x by $\frac{1}{2}$ in the power series obtained in Example 6 to obtain

$$\int_0^{1/2} e^{-t^2} \, dt = \frac{1}{2} - \frac{1}{24} + \frac{1}{320} - \frac{1}{5376} + \cdots$$

$$\approx 0.5 - 0.0417 + 0.0031 - 0.0002 + \cdots$$

This is a convergent alternating series with $|u_{n+1}| < |u_n|$. Thus if we use the first three terms to approximate the sum, by Theorem 8.5.4 the error is less than the absolute value of the fourth term. From the first three terms,

$$\int_0^{1/2} e^{-t^2} \, dt \approx 0.461$$

(b) On our graphics calculator,

$$\text{NINT}(e^{-t^2}, 0, 0.5) = 0.461$$

to three decimal places, which supports our answer in part (a). ◄

▶ **EXAMPLE 8**   Obtain a power-series representation of $\tan^{-1} x$.

Solution   From series (6) in Section 8.7,

$$\frac{1}{1 + x^2} = 1 - x^2 + x^4 - x^6 + \ldots + (-1)^n x^{2n} + \ldots \qquad \text{if } |x| < 1$$

We apply Theorem 8.8.4 and integrate term by term to obtain

$$\int_0^x \frac{1}{1 + t^2}\, dt = x - \frac{x^3}{3} + \frac{x^5}{5} - \ldots + (-1)^n \frac{x^{2n+1}}{2n + 1} + \ldots$$

Therefore

$$\tan^{-1} x = \sum_{n=0}^{+\infty} (-1)^n \frac{x^{2n+1}}{2n + 1} \qquad \text{if } |x| < 1 \tag{4} \blacktriangleleft$$

Although Theorem 8.8.4 allows us to conclude that the power series (4) represents $\tan^{-1} x$ only for values of x such that $|x| < 1$, the interval of convergence of the power series is $[-1, 1]$ and the power series represents $\tan^{-1} x$ for all x in its interval of convergence. You are asked to show this in Exercise 82 of the Miscellaneous Exercises for this chapter. Therefore

$$\tan^{-1} x = \sum_{n=0}^{+\infty} (-1)^n \frac{x^{2n+1}}{2n + 1}$$
$$= x - \frac{x^3}{3} + \frac{x^5}{5} - \ldots \qquad \text{if } |x| \le 1 \tag{5}$$

Figure 2 shows the graphs of

$$f(x) = \tan^{-1} x \quad \text{and} \quad P_{19}(x) = \sum_{n=0}^{9} (-1)^n \frac{x^{2n+1}}{2n + 1}$$

plotted in the $[-2, 2]$ by $[-3, 3]$ window. Observe that the graph of the polynomial approximates the graph of $\tan^{-1} x$ when $|x| \le 1$, which supports (5).

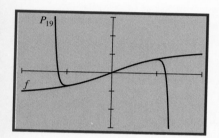

[−2, 2] by [−3, 3]

$$f(x) = \tan^{-1} x$$

$$P_{19}(x) = \sum_{n=0}^{9} (-1)^n \frac{x^{2n+1}}{2n + 1}$$

FIGURE 2

▷ **ILLUSTRATION 2**   If $x = 1$ in (5),

$$\frac{\pi}{4} = 1 - \frac{1}{3} + \frac{1}{5} - \frac{1}{7} + \ldots + (-1)^n \frac{1}{2n + 1} + \ldots \qquad \blacktriangleleft$$

The series in Illustration 2 is not suitable for computing π because it converges too slowly. The following example gives a better method.

▶ **EXAMPLE 9**   Prove that

$$\tfrac{\pi}{4} = \tan^{-1} \tfrac{1}{2} + \tan^{-1} \tfrac{1}{3}$$

Apply this formula and the power series for $\tan^{-1} x$ of Example 8 to compute the value of π, accurate to five significant digits.

Solution Let $\alpha = \tan^{-1} \frac{1}{2}$ and $\beta = \tan^{-1} \frac{1}{3}$. Then

$$\tan(\alpha + \beta) = \frac{\tan \alpha + \tan \beta}{1 - \tan \alpha \tan \beta}$$

$$= \frac{\frac{1}{2} + \frac{1}{3}}{1 - \frac{1}{2} \cdot \frac{1}{3}}$$

$$= \frac{3 + 2}{6 - 1}$$

$$= 1$$

$$= \tan \frac{\pi}{4}$$

Therefore, because $0 < \alpha + \beta < \frac{1}{2}\pi$,

$$\frac{\pi}{4} = \alpha + \beta$$

$$\frac{\pi}{4} = \tan^{-1} \frac{1}{2} + \tan^{-1} \frac{1}{3} \tag{6}$$

From formula (5) with $x = \frac{1}{2}$,

$$\tan^{-1} \frac{1}{2} = \frac{1}{2} - \frac{1}{3}\left(\frac{1}{2}\right)^3 + \frac{1}{5}\left(\frac{1}{2}\right)^5 - \frac{1}{7}\left(\frac{1}{2}\right)^7 + \frac{1}{9}\left(\frac{1}{2}\right)^9 - \frac{1}{11}\left(\frac{1}{2}\right)^{11} + \frac{1}{13}\left(\frac{1}{2}\right)^{13} - \frac{1}{15}\left(\frac{1}{2}\right)^{15} + \cdots$$

$$\approx 0.500000 - 0.041667 + 0.006250 - 0.001116 + 0.000217$$
$$- 0.000044 + 0.000009 - 0.000002 + \cdots$$

Because the series is alternating and $|u_{n+1}| < |u_n|$, then from Theorem 8.5.4, if the first seven terms are used to approximate the sum of the series, the error is less than the absolute value of the eighth term. Therefore

$$\tan^{-1} \frac{1}{2} \approx 0.463648$$

From formula (5) with $x = \frac{1}{3}$,

$$\tan^{-1} \frac{1}{3} = \frac{1}{3} - \frac{1}{3}\left(\frac{1}{3}\right)^3 + \frac{1}{5}\left(\frac{1}{3}\right)^5 - \frac{1}{7}\left(\frac{1}{3}\right)^7 + \frac{1}{9}\left(\frac{1}{3}\right)^9 - \frac{1}{11}\left(\frac{1}{3}\right)^{11} + \cdots$$

$$\approx 0.333333 - 0.012346 + 0.000823 - 0.000065 + 0.000006 + 0.0000005 + \cdots$$

If the first five terms are used to approximate the sum,

$$\tan^{-1} \frac{1}{3} \approx 0.321751$$

By substituting the values of $\tan^{-1} \frac{1}{2}$ and $\tan^{-1} \frac{1}{3}$ into (6),

$$\frac{\pi}{4} \approx 0.463648 + 0.321751$$

$$\approx 0.78540$$

We multiply by 4 and to five significant digits $\pi \approx 3.1416$. ◀

EXERCISES 8.8

In Exercises 1 through 10, do the following: (a) Find the radius of convergence of the power series and the domain of f; (b) verify Theorem 8.8.1 for the function f by writing the power series that defines the function f' and finding its radius of convergence; (c) find the domain of f'.

1. $f(x) = \displaystyle\sum_{n=1}^{+\infty} \frac{x^n}{n^2}$

2. $f(x) = \displaystyle\sum_{n=1}^{+\infty} (-1)^{n-1} \frac{x^n}{n}$

3. $f(x) = \displaystyle\sum_{n=1}^{+\infty} \frac{x^n}{\sqrt{n}}$

4. $f(x) = \displaystyle\sum_{n=2}^{+\infty} \frac{(x-2)^n}{\sqrt{n-1}}$

5. $f(x) = \displaystyle\sum_{n=1}^{+\infty} (-1)^{n-1} \dfrac{x^{2n-1}}{(2n-1)!}$ **6.** $f(x) = \displaystyle\sum_{n=0}^{+\infty} \dfrac{x^{2n}}{(n!)^2}$

7. $f(x) = \displaystyle\sum_{n=1}^{+\infty} (n+1)(3x-1)^n$ **8.** $f(x) = \displaystyle\sum_{n=1}^{+\infty} \dfrac{x^{2n-2}}{(2n-2)!}$

9. $f(x) = \displaystyle\sum_{n=1}^{+\infty} \dfrac{(x-1)^n}{n3^n}$ **10.** $f(x) = \displaystyle\sum_{n=2}^{+\infty} (-1)^n \dfrac{(x-3)^n}{n(n-1)}$

11. Use the result of Example 2 to find a power-series representation of $\dfrac{1}{(1-x)^3}$.

12. Use the result of Example 3 to find a series representation of $e^{\sqrt{x}}$.

13. Obtain a power-series representation of $\dfrac{1}{(1+x)^2}$ if $|x| < 1$ by differentiating series (4) of Section 8.7 term by term.

14. Obtain a power-series representation of $\dfrac{x}{(1+x^2)^2}$ if $|x| < 1$ by differentiating series (6) of Section 8.7 term by term.

15. Given $\cosh x = \displaystyle\sum_{n=0}^{+\infty} \dfrac{x^{2n}}{(2n)!}$ for all x. Obtain a power-series representation for $\sinh x$ by integrating the given series term by term from 0 to x.

16. Find a power-series representation for $\tanh^{-1} x$ by integrating term by term from 0 to x a power-series representation for $(1 - t^2)^{-1}$.

17. **(a)** Use the result of Example 3 to find a power-series representation for e^{x^2}. **(b)** Differentiate term by term the series found in part (a) to find a power-series representation for xe^{x^2}.

18. Let f be defined by $f(x) = \displaystyle\sum_{n=0}^{+\infty} (-1)^n \dfrac{x^n}{3^n(n+2)}$.

(a) Find the domain of f. **(b)** Find $f'(x)$ and find the domain of f'.

19. Use the result of Example 4(a) to find the value of $1/\sqrt{e}$ correct to five decimal places and compare your result with the value obtained on your calculator.

20. If $f(x) = \displaystyle\sum_{n=0}^{+\infty} (-1)^n \dfrac{x^{2n}}{3^n}$, find $f'(\tfrac{1}{2})$ correct to four decimal places.

21. Use the results of Examples 3 and 4(a) to find a power-series representation of (a) $\sinh x$ and (b) $\cosh x$.

22. Show that each of the power series in parts (a) and (b) of Exercise 21 can be obtained from the other by term-by-term differentiation.

In Exercises 23 through 27, show that the power series is a solution of the differential equation.

23. $y = \displaystyle\sum_{n=0}^{+\infty} \dfrac{2^n}{n!}x^n; \ \dfrac{dy}{dx} - 2y = 0$

24. $y = \displaystyle\sum_{n=0}^{+\infty} \dfrac{1}{2^n n!}x^{2n}; \ \dfrac{dy}{dx} - xy = 0$

25. $y = \displaystyle\sum_{n=1}^{+\infty} \dfrac{(-1)^{n+1}}{(2n-1)!}x^{2n-1}; \ \dfrac{d^2y}{dx^2} + y = 0$

26. $y = x + \displaystyle\sum_{n=0}^{+\infty} (-1)^n \dfrac{x^{2n}}{(2n)!}; \ \dfrac{d^2y}{dx^2} + y - x = 0$

27. $y = \displaystyle\sum_{n=0}^{+\infty} (-1)^n \dfrac{2^n n!}{(2n+1)!}x^{2n+1}; \ \dfrac{d^2y}{dx^2} + x\dfrac{dy}{dx} + y = 0$

28. Use the result of Example 2 to find the sum of the series $\displaystyle\sum_{n=1}^{+\infty} \dfrac{n}{2^n}$.

In Exercises 29 through 32, find a power-series representation of the integral and determine its radius of convergence. Support your answer graphically.

29. $\displaystyle\int_0^x e^t \, dt$ **30.** $\displaystyle\int_0^x \dfrac{dt}{t^2 + 4}$

31. $\displaystyle\int_2^x \dfrac{dt}{4 - t}$ **32.** $\displaystyle\int_0^x \tan^{-1}t \, dt$

In Exercises 33 through 36, compute accurate to three decimal places the value of the integral by two methods: (a) Use the second fundamental theorem of the calculus; (b) use the result of the indicated exercise.

33. $\displaystyle\int_0^1 e^t \, dt$; Exercise 29   **34.** $\displaystyle\int_0^1 \dfrac{dt}{t^2 + 4}$; Exercise 30

35. $\displaystyle\int_2^3 \dfrac{dt}{4 - t}$; Exercise 31

36. $\displaystyle\int_0^{1/3} \tan^{-1} t \, dt$; Exercise 32

37. Given

$$f(t) = \begin{cases} \dfrac{e^t - 1}{t} & \text{if } t \neq 0 \\ 1 & \text{if } t = 0 \end{cases}$$

(a) Prove that f is continuous at 0. **(b)** Find a power-series representation of $\int_0^x f(t) \, dt$ and determine its radius of convergence. **(c)** Plot in the same window the graphs of $\text{NINT}(f(t), 0, x)$ and the polynomial consisting of the first ten nonzero terms of your series in part (b).

38. Do Exercise 37 if

$$f(t) = \begin{cases} \dfrac{\tan^{-1} t}{t} & \text{if } t \neq 0 \\ 1 & \text{if } t = 0 \end{cases}$$

39. For the function of Exercise 37, use your series in part (b) of that exercise to compute $\int_0^1 f(t)\,dt$ accurate to three decimal places and support your answer by the NINT capability of your graphics calculator.

40. For the function of Exercise 38, use your series in part (b) of that exercise to compute $\int_0^{1/4} f(t)\,dt$ accurate to three decimal places and support your answer by the NINT capability of your graphics calculator.

In Exercises 41 through 46, compute accurate to three decimal places the value of the definite integral by using series, and support your answer by the NINT capability of your graphics calculator.

41. $\displaystyle\int_0^{1/2} \frac{dx}{1 + x^3}$

42. $\displaystyle\int_0^{1/3} \frac{dx}{1 + x^4}$

43. $\displaystyle\int_0^{1/2} \tan^{-1} x^2\,dx$

44. $\displaystyle\int_0^{1/2} e^{-x^3}\,dx$

45. $\displaystyle\int_0^1 x \sinh \sqrt{x}\,dx$

46. $\displaystyle\int_0^{1/2} \cosh x^2\,dx$

47. Use the power series in (4) to compute $\tan^{-1} \frac{1}{4}$ accurate to four decimal places, and compare your result with the value obtained on your calculator.

48. If $f'(x) = \displaystyle\sum_{n=0}^{+\infty} (-1)^n \frac{(x-1)^n}{n!}$ and $f(1) = 0$, find $f(\frac{5}{4})$ accurate to three decimal places.

49. If $g'(x) = \displaystyle\sum_{n=0}^{+\infty} (-1)^n \frac{x^n}{n^2 + 3}$ and $g(0) = 0$, find $g(1)$ accurate to two decimal places.

50. Find a power series for xe^x by multiplying the series for e^x by x, and then integrate the resulting series term by term from 0 to 1 and show that $\displaystyle\sum_{n=1}^{+\infty} \frac{1}{n!(n+2)} = \frac{1}{2}$.

51. **(a)** Find a power-series representation for $x^2 e^{-x}$.
(b) By differentiating term by term the power series in part (a), show that $\displaystyle\sum_{n=1}^{+\infty} (-2)^{n+1} \frac{n+2}{n!} = 4$.

52. **(a)** Find a power-series representation for $\dfrac{e^x - 1}{x}$.
(b) By differentiating term by term the power series in part (a), show that $\displaystyle\sum_{n=1}^{+\infty} \frac{n}{(n+1)!} = 1$.

53. By integrating term by term from 0 to x a power-series representation for $t \tan^{-1} t$, show that
$$\sum_{n=1}^{+\infty} (-1)^{n+1} \frac{x^{2n+1}}{(2n-1)(2n+1)} = \tfrac{1}{2}[(x^2+1)\tan^{-1}x - x]$$

54. **(a)** Find a power-series representation for e^{-x^2}.
(b) By differentiating the power series in part (a) twice term by term, show that
$$\sum_{n=1}^{+\infty} (-1)^{n+1} \frac{2n+1}{2^n n!} = 1$$

55. Suppose a function f has the power-series representation $\displaystyle\sum_{n=0}^{+\infty} c_n x^n$, where the radius of convergence $R > 0$. If $f'(x) = f(x)$ and $f(0) = 1$, find the power series by using only properties of power series and nothing about the exponential function.

56. **(a)** Use only properties of power series to find a power-series representation of the function f if $f(x) > 0$ and $f'(x) = 2xf(x)$ for all x, and $f(0) = 1$.
(b) Verify your result in part (a) by solving the differential equation $\dfrac{dy}{dx} = 2xy$ with the initial condition $y = 1$ when $x = 0$.

57. Suppose a function f has the power-series representation $\displaystyle\sum_{n=0}^{+\infty} c_n x^n$. If f is an even function, show that $c_n = 0$ when n is odd.

58. Find the power series in x of $f(x)$ if $f''(x) = -f(x)$, $f(0) = 0$, and $f'(0) = 1$. Also, find the radius of convergence of the resulting series.

59. Assume that the constant 0 has a power-series representation $\displaystyle\sum_{n=0}^{+\infty} c_n x^n$, where the radius of convergence $R > 0$. Prove that $c_n = 0$ for all n.

60. Discuss the importance of differentiation and integration of power series. Include in your discussion an example of how each operation is applied.

8.9 TAYLOR SERIES

You have seen how certain rational functions as well as some transcendental functions, such as e^x and $\tan^{-1} x$, can be expressed as power series. We now show how to find power-series representations of functions that have derivatives of all orders, that is, functions that are *infinitely differentiable*.

Suppose f is a function defined by a power series; that is

$$f(x) = c_0 + c_1x + c_2x^2 + c_3x^3 + \ldots + c_nx^n + \ldots \tag{1}$$

whose radius of convergence $R > 0$. From successive applications of Theorem 8.8.3, f is infinitely differentiable on $(-R, R)$. Consecutive differentiations of f give

$$f'(x) = c_1 + 2c_2x + 3c_3x^2 + 4c_4x^3 + \ldots + nc_nx^{n-1} + \ldots \tag{2}$$
$$f''(x) = 2c_2 + 2 \cdot 3c_3x + 3 \cdot 4c_4x^2 + \ldots + (n-1)nc_nx^{n-2} + \ldots \tag{3}$$
$$f'''(x) = 2 \cdot 3c_3 + 2 \cdot 3 \cdot 4c_4x + \ldots + (n-2)(n-1)nc_nx^{n-3} + \ldots \tag{4}$$
$$f^{(4)}(x) = 2 \cdot 3 \cdot 4c_4 + \ldots + (n-3)(n-2)(n-1)nc_nx^{n-4} + \ldots \tag{5}$$

etc. If $x = 0$ in $(1) - (5)$

$$f(0) = c_0 \quad f'(0) = c_1 \quad f''(0) = 2!c_2 \quad f'''(0) = 3!c_3 \quad f^{(4)}(0) = 4!c_4$$

So that

$$c_0 = f(0) \qquad c_1 = f'(0) \qquad c_2 = \frac{f''(0)}{2!} \qquad c_3 = \frac{f'''(0)}{3!} \qquad c_4 = \frac{f^4(0)}{4!}$$

In general,

$$c_n = \frac{f^{(n)}(0)}{n!} \qquad \text{for every positive integer } n$$

This formula also holds when $n = 0$ if we take $f^{(0)}(0)$ to be $f(0)$ and $0! = 1$. So from this formula and (1) the power series of f in x can be written as

$$\sum_{n=0}^{+\infty} \frac{f^{(n)}(0)}{n!}x^n = f(0) + f'(0)x + \frac{f''(0)}{2!}x^2 + \ldots + \frac{f^{(n)}(0)}{n!}x^n + \ldots \tag{6}$$

In a more general sense, consider the function f as a power series in $x - a$; that is,

$$f(x) = \sum_{n=0}^{+\infty} c_n(x - a)^n$$
$$= c_0 + c_1(x - a) + c_2(x - a)^2 + \ldots + c_n(x - a)^n + \ldots \tag{7}$$

If the radius of convergence of this series is R, then f is infinitely differentiable on $(a - R, a + R)$. Successive differentiations of the function in (7) give

$$f'(x) = c_1 + 2c_2(x - a) + 3c_3(x - a)^2 + 4c_4(x - a)^3 + \ldots + nc_n(x - a)^{n-1} + \ldots$$
$$f''(x) = 2c_2 + 2 \cdot 3c_3(x - a) + 3 \cdot 4c_4(x - a)^2 + \ldots + (n-1)nc_n(x - a)^{n-2} + \ldots$$
$$f'''(x) = 2 \cdot 3c_3 + 2 \cdot 3 \cdot 4c_4(x - a) + \ldots + (n-2)(n-1)nc_n(x - a)^{n-3} + \ldots$$

etc. Letting $x = a$ in the power-series representations of f and its derivatives we get

$$c_0 = f(a) \qquad c_1 = f'(a) \qquad c_2 = \frac{f''(a)}{2!} \qquad c_3 = \frac{f'''(a)}{3!}$$

and in general

$$c_n = \frac{f^{(n)}(a)}{n!} \tag{8}$$

From this formula and (7) the power series of f in $x - a$ can be written as

$$\sum_{n=0}^{+\infty} \frac{f^{(n)}(a)}{n!}(x - a)^n = f(a) + f'(a)(x - a) + \frac{f''(a)}{2!}(x - a)^2 + \ldots + \frac{f^{(n)}(a)}{n!}(x - a)^n + \ldots \qquad (9)$$

The series in (9) is called the **Taylor series** of f at a. The special case of (9), when $a = 0$, is (6), which is called the **Maclaurin series.**

Observe that the nth partial sum of infinite series (9) is the nth degree Taylor polynomial of the function f at the number a, discussed in Section 8.1.

▶ **EXAMPLE 1** Find the Maclaurin series for e^x.

Solution If $f(x) = e^x$, $f^{(n)}(x) = e^x$ for all x; therefore $f^{(n)}(0) = 1$ for all n. So From (6) we have the Maclaurin series:

$$e^x = 1 + x + \frac{x^2}{2!} + \frac{x^3}{3!} + \ldots + \frac{x^n}{n!} + \ldots \qquad (10) \quad ◀$$

Note that the series for e^x in the above example is the same as the one in Example 3 of Section 8.8.

▶ **EXAMPLE 2** (a) Find the Taylor series for $\sin x$ at a. (b) Use the answer in part (a) to write the Taylor series for $\sin x$ at $\frac{1}{4}\pi$.

Solution

(a) If $f(x) = \sin x$, then $f'(x) = \cos x$, $f''(x) = -\sin x$, $f'''(x) = -\cos x$, $f^{(4)}(x) = \sin x$, and so forth. Thus, from formula (8), $c_0 = \sin a$, $c_1 = \cos a$, $c_2 = (-\sin a)/2!$, $c_3 = (-\cos a)/3!$, $c_4 = (\sin a)/4!$, and so on. The required Taylor series is obtained from (9), and it is

$$\sin x = \sin a + (\cos a)(x - a) - (\sin a)\frac{(x - a)^2}{2!} - (\cos a)\frac{(x - a)^3}{3!} + (\sin a)\frac{(x - a)^4}{4!} + \ldots$$

(b) With $a = \frac{1}{4}\pi$ in the above series, we have

$$\sin x = \sin \tfrac{1}{4}\pi + (\cos \tfrac{1}{4}\pi)(x - \tfrac{1}{4}\pi) - (\sin \tfrac{1}{4}\pi)\frac{(x - \tfrac{1}{4}\pi)^2}{2!} - (\cos \tfrac{1}{4}\pi)\frac{(x - \tfrac{1}{4}\pi)^3}{3!} + (\sin \tfrac{1}{4}\pi)\frac{(x - \tfrac{1}{4}\pi)^4}{4!} + \ldots$$

$$= \frac{\sqrt{2}}{2} + \frac{\sqrt{2}}{2} \cdot (x - \tfrac{1}{4}\pi) - \frac{\sqrt{2}}{2} \cdot \frac{(x - \tfrac{1}{4}\pi)^2}{2!} - \frac{\sqrt{2}}{2} \cdot \frac{(x - \tfrac{1}{4}\pi)^3}{3!} + \frac{\sqrt{2}}{2} \cdot \frac{(x - \tfrac{1}{4}\pi)^4}{4!} + \ldots$$

$$= \frac{\sqrt{2}}{2}\left[1 + (x - \tfrac{1}{4}\pi) - \frac{(x - \tfrac{1}{4}\pi)^2}{2!} - \frac{(x - \tfrac{1}{4}\pi)^3}{3!} + \frac{(x - \tfrac{1}{4}\pi)^4}{4!} + \ldots \right] \qquad (11)$$

◀

We can deduce that a power-series representation of a function is unique. That is, if two functions have the same function values in some interval containing the number a, and if both functions have a power-series representation in $x - a$, then these series must be the same because the coefficients in the series are obtained from the values of the functions and their derivatives at a. Therefore, if a function has a power-series representation in $x - a$, this series must be its Taylor series at a. Hence the Taylor series for a given function does not have to be obtained by using formula (9). Any method that gives a power series in $x - a$ representing the function will be the Taylor series of the function at a.

▶ **EXAMPLE 3**   Use series (10) to find the Taylor series for e^x at a.

Solution   We write $e^x = e^a e^{x-a}$ and use series (10) where x is replaced by $x - a$. Then

$$e^x = e^a \left[1 + (x - a) + \frac{(x - a)^2}{2!} + \frac{(x - a)^3}{3!} + \ldots + \frac{(x - a)^n}{n!} + \ldots \right] \quad ◀$$

A natural question that arises is: If a function has a Taylor series in $x - a$ having radius of convergence $R > 0$, does this series represent the function for all values of x in the interval $(a - R, a + R)$? For most elementary functions the answer is yes. However, there are functions for which the answer is no. The following example shows this.

▶ **EXAMPLE 4**   Let f be the function defined by

$$f(x) = \begin{cases} e^{-1/x^2} & \text{if } x \neq 0 \\ 0 & \text{if } x = 0 \end{cases}$$

Find the Maclaurin series for f, and show that it converges for all values of x but that it represents $f(x)$ only when $x = 0$.

Solution   Note that f is continuous at $x = 0$ because $\lim_{x \to 0} e^{-1/x^2} = 0$ and $f(0) = 0$. To find $f'(0)$, we apply the definition of a derivative.

$$f'(0) = \lim_{x \to 0} \frac{e^{-1/x^2} - 0}{x - 0}$$

$$= \lim_{x \to 0} \frac{\dfrac{1}{x}}{e^{1/x^2}}$$

Because $\lim_{x \to 0} (1/x) = +\infty$ and $\lim_{x \to 0} e^{1/x^2} = +\infty$, we can use L'Hôpital's rule. Therefore

$$f'(0) = \lim_{x \to 0} \frac{-\dfrac{1}{x^2}}{e^{1/x^2}\left(-\dfrac{2}{x^3}\right)}$$

$$= \lim_{x \to 0} \frac{x}{2e^{1/x^2}}$$

$$= 0$$

By a similar method, using the definition of a derivative and L'Hôpital's rule, we get 0 for every derivative. So $f^{(n)}(0) = 0$ for all n. Therefore the Maclaurin series for the given function is $0 + 0 + 0 + \ldots + 0 + \ldots$. This series converges to 0 for all x; but, if $x \neq 0$, $f(x) \neq 0$. ◀

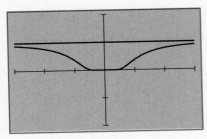

[−3, 3] by [−2, 2]

$$f(x) = \begin{cases} e^{-1/x^2} & \text{if } x \neq 0 \\ 0 & \text{if } x = 0 \end{cases}$$

$$y = 1$$

FIGURE 1

Figure 1 shows the graph of the function of Example 4 and its horizontal asymptote $y = 1$ plotted in the $[-3, 3]$ by $[-2, 2]$ window. Observe that the graph is tangent to the x axis at the origin which supports the fact that $f'(0) = 0$. The "flatness" of the graph at the origin is consistent with the fact that higher-order derivatives are also 0 when $x = 0$.

The following theorem gives a test for determining whether a function is represented by its Taylor series.

8.9.1 Theorem

Let f be a function such that f and all of its derivatives exist in some interval $(a - r, a + r)$. Then the function is represented by its Taylor series

$$\sum_{n=0}^{+\infty} \frac{f^{(n)}(a)}{n!}(x - a)^n$$

for all x such that $|x - a| < r$ if and only if

$$\lim_{n \to +\infty} R_n(x) = \lim_{n \to +\infty} \frac{f^{(n+1)}(z_n)}{(n + 1)!}(x - a)^{n+1}$$

$$= 0$$

where each z_n is between x and a.

Proof   In the interval $(a - r, a + r)$, the function f satisfies the hypothesis of Theorem 8.1.1 for which

$$f(x) = P_n(x) + R_n(x) \tag{12}$$

where $P_n(x)$ is the nth-degree Taylor polynomial of f at a and $R_n(x)$ is the remainder, given by

$$R_n(x) = \frac{f^{(n+1)}(z_n)}{(n + 1)!}(x - a)^{n+1} \tag{13}$$

where each z_n is between x and a.

Now $P_n(x)$ is the nth partial sum of the Taylor series of f at a. So if we show that $\lim_{n \to +\infty} P_n(x)$ exists and equals $f(x)$ if and only if $\lim_{n \to +\infty} R_n(x) = 0$, the theorem will be proved. From (12),

$$P_n(x) = f(x) - R_n(x)$$

If $\lim_{n \to +\infty} R_n(x) = 0$, it follows from this equation that

$$\lim_{n \to +\infty} P_n(x) = f(x) - \lim_{n \to +\infty} R_n(x)$$

$$= f(x) - 0$$

$$= f(x)$$

Now under the hypothesis that $\lim_{n \to +\infty} P_n(x) = f(x)$ we wish to show that $\lim_{n \to +\infty} R_n(x) = 0$. From (12),

$$R_n(x) = f(x) - P_n(x)$$

Thus

$$\lim_{n \to +\infty} R_n(x) = f(x) - \lim_{n \to +\infty} P_n(x)$$
$$= f(x) - f(x)$$
$$= 0$$

This proves the theorem.

∎

Theorem 8.9.1 also holds for other forms of the remainder $R_n(x)$ besides the Lagrange form.

It is often difficult to apply Theorem 8.9.1 because the values of z_n are arbitrary. However, sometimes an upper bound for $R_n(x)$ can be found, and it may be possible to prove that the limit of the upper bound is zero as $n \to +\infty$. The following limit is helpful in some cases:

$$\lim_{n \to +\infty} \frac{x^n}{n!} = 0 \qquad \text{for all } x \tag{14}$$

This follows from Example 2 of Section 8.7, where we showed that the power series $\sum_{n=0}^{+\infty} \dfrac{x^n}{n!}$ is convergent for all values of x and hence the limit of its nth term must be zero. In a similar manner, because $\sum_{n=0}^{+\infty} \dfrac{(x-a)^n}{n!}$ is convergent for all values of x,

$$\lim_{n \to +\infty} \frac{(x-a)^n}{n!} = 0 \qquad \text{for all } x \tag{15}$$

▶ **EXAMPLE 5**   Apply Theorem 8.9.1 to show that the Maclaurin series for e^x, found in Example 1, represents the function for all values of x.

Solution   The Maclaurin series for e^x is series (10) and

$$R_n(x) = \frac{e^{z_n}}{(n+1)!} x^{n+1}$$

where each z_n is between 0 and x.

We must show that $\lim_{n \to +\infty} R_n = 0$ for all x. There are three cases: $x > 0$, $x < 0$, and $x = 0$.

If $x > 0$, then $0 < z_n < x$; hence $e^{z_n} < e^x$. So

$$0 < \frac{e^{z_n}}{(n+1)!} x^{n+1} < e^x \frac{x^{n+1}}{(n+1)!} \tag{16}$$

From (14), $\lim_{n \to +\infty} \dfrac{x^{n+1}}{(n+1)!} = 0$, and so

$$\lim_{n \to +\infty} e^x \frac{x^{n+1}}{(n+1)!} = 0$$

Therefore, from (16) and the squeeze theorem it follows that $\lim\limits_{n \to +\infty} R_n(x) = 0$.

If $x < 0$, then $x < z_n < 0$ and $0 < e^{z_n} < 1$. Therefore, if $x^{n+1} > 0$,

$$0 < \frac{e^{z_n}}{(n+1)!} x^{n+1} < \frac{x^{n+1}}{(n+1)!}$$

and if $x^{n+1} < 0$,

$$\frac{x^{n+1}}{(n+1)!} < \frac{e^{z_n}}{(n+1)!} x^{n+1} < 0$$

In either case, because $\lim\limits_{n \to +\infty} \dfrac{x^{n+1}}{(n+1)!} = 0$, we conclude that $\lim\limits_{n \to +\infty} R_n = 0$.

Finally, if $x = 0$, the series has the sum of 1, which is e^0. Hence series (10) represents e^x for all values of x. ◀

From the above example we can write

$$e^x = \sum_{n=0}^{+\infty} \frac{x^n}{n!}$$
$$= 1 + x + \frac{x^2}{2!} + \frac{x^3}{3!} + \ldots \qquad \text{for all } x$$

and this agrees with Example 3 of Section 8.8.

▶ **EXAMPLE 6** Show that the Taylor series for $\sin x$ at a, found in Example 2(a), represents the function for all values of x.

Solution We will apply Theorem 8.9.1; that is, we will show that

$$\lim_{n \to +\infty} R_n(x) = \lim_{n \to +\infty} \frac{f^{(n+1)}(z_n)}{(n+1)!}(x-a)^{n+1}$$
$$= 0$$

Because $f(x) = \sin x$, $f^{(n+1)}(z_n)$ will be one of the following numbers: $\cos z_n$, $\sin z_n$, $-\cos z_n$, or $-\sin z_n$. In any case, $|f^{(n+1)}(z_n)| \leq 1$. Hence

$$0 < |R_n(x)| \leq \frac{|x-a|^{n+1}}{(n+1)!} \tag{17}$$

From (15), $\lim\limits_{n \to +\infty} \dfrac{|x-a|^{n+1}}{(n+1)!} = 0$. Thus, by the squeeze theorem and (17) it follows that $\lim\limits_{n \to +\infty} R_n(x) = 0$. ◀

In Example 2(b), we obtained Taylor series (11) for $\sin x$ at $\frac{1}{4}\pi$; from Example 6 we know that this series represents $\sin x$ for all values of x. The graph of the sine function and the Taylor polynomials $P_1(x)$, $P_2(x)$, $P_3(x)$,

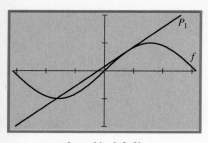

$[-\pi, \pi]$ by $[-2, 2]$

$f(x) = \sin x$

$$P_1(x) = \frac{\sqrt{2}}{2}\left[1 + \left(x - \frac{1}{4}\pi\right)\right]$$

FIGURE 2

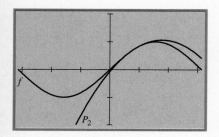

$[-\pi, \pi]$ by $[-2, 2]$

$f(x) = \sin x$

$$P_2(x) = \frac{\sqrt{2}}{2}\left[1 + \left(x - \frac{1}{4}\pi\right) - \frac{\left(x - \frac{1}{4}\pi\right)^2}{2!}\right]$$

FIGURE 3

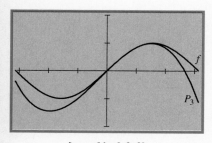

$[-\pi, \pi]$ by $[-2, 2]$

$f(x) = \sin x$

$$P_3(x) = \frac{\sqrt{2}}{2}\left[1 + \left(x - \frac{1}{4}\pi\right) - \frac{\left(x - \frac{1}{4}\pi\right)^2}{2!}\right. $$
$$\left. - \frac{\left(x - \frac{1}{4}\pi\right)^3}{3!}\right]$$

FIGURE 4

$P_4(x)$, and $P_5(x)$ at $\frac{1}{4}\pi$ are plotted in Figures 2 through 6, respectively. Observe how close the graphs of the polynomials are to the graph of the sine function at $\frac{1}{4}\pi$, and how the polynomial approximations improve as n increases.

▶ **EXAMPLE 7** Use the Taylor series for $\sin x$ at $\frac{1}{4}\pi$ to compute the value of $\sin 47°$ accurate to four decimal places. Compare the result with a calculator value of $\sin 47°$.

Solution We first express $47°$ in radians: $47°$ is equivalent to $\frac{47}{180}\pi$ radians. From series (11) with $x = \frac{47}{180}\pi$ and $x - \frac{1}{4}\pi = \frac{1}{90}\pi$, we have

$$\sin \tfrac{47}{180}\pi = \tfrac{1}{2}\sqrt{2} + \tfrac{1}{2}\sqrt{2}\cdot\tfrac{1}{90}\pi - \tfrac{1}{2}\sqrt{2}\cdot\tfrac{1}{2}(\tfrac{1}{90}\pi)^2 - \tfrac{1}{2}\sqrt{2}\cdot\tfrac{1}{6}(\tfrac{1}{90}\pi)^3 + \ldots$$
$$\approx \tfrac{1}{2}\sqrt{2}(1 + 0.03490 - 0.00061 - 0.000002 + \ldots)$$

Taking $\sqrt{2} \approx 1.41421$ and using the first three terms of the series we get

$$\sin \tfrac{47}{180}\pi \approx (0.70711)(1.03429)$$
$$\approx 0.73136$$

Rounding off to four decimal places gives $\sin 47° \approx 0.7314$. The error introduced by using the first three terms is $R_2(\frac{47}{180}\pi)$, and from (17),

$$\left|R_2\left(\frac{47}{180}\pi\right)\right| \le \frac{(\frac{1}{90}\pi)^3}{3!} \approx 0.00001$$

The result, then, is between $0.73136 - 0.00001$ and $0.73136 + 0.00001$; that is, the result is between 0.73135 and 0.73137. Thus to four decimal place accuracy, we have

$$\sin \tfrac{47}{180}\pi \approx 0.7314$$

On our calculator we obtain $\sin 47° = 0.731354$ in agreement to four decimal places. ◀

By letting $a = 0$ in the Taylor series for $\sin x$ found in Example 2(a), we have the Maclaurin series:

$$\sin x = \sum_{n=0}^{+\infty} \frac{(-1)^n x^{2n+1}}{(2n+1)!}$$
$$= x - \frac{x^3}{3!} + \frac{x^5}{5!} - \frac{x^7}{7!} + \ldots \qquad \text{for all } x$$

By differentiating this series term by term (see Exercise 1), we obtain the Maclaurin series for $\cos x$:

$$\cos x = \sum_{n=0}^{+\infty} \frac{(-1)^n x^{2n}}{(2n)!}$$
$$= 1 - \frac{x^2}{2!} + \frac{x^4}{4!} - \frac{x^6}{6!} + \ldots \qquad \text{for all } x$$

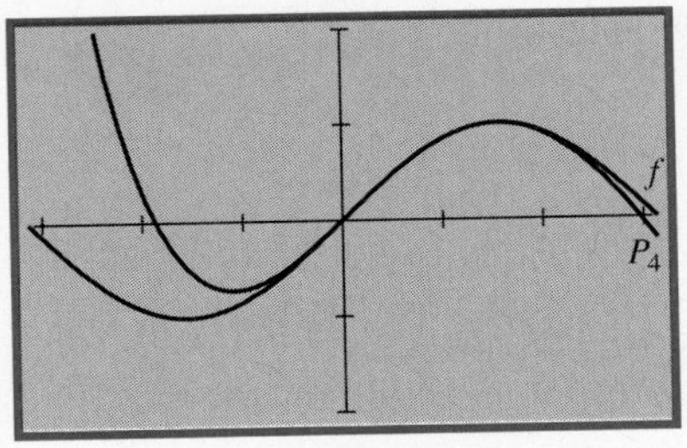

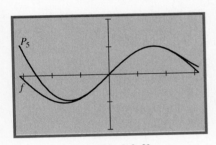

$[-\pi, \pi]$ by $[-2, 2]$

$$f(x) = \sin x$$

$$P_4(x) = \frac{\sqrt{2}}{2}\left[1 + \left(x - \frac{1}{4}\pi\right) - \frac{\left(x - \frac{1}{4}\pi\right)^2}{2!}\right.$$

$$\left. - \frac{\left(x - \frac{1}{4}\pi\right)^3}{3!} + \frac{\left(x - \frac{1}{4}\pi\right)^4}{4!}\right]$$

FIGURE 5

$[-\pi, \pi]$ by $[-2, 2]$

$$f(x) = \sin x$$

$$P_5(x) = \frac{\sqrt{2}}{2}\left[1 + (x - \tfrac{1}{4}\pi) - \frac{(x - \tfrac{1}{4}\pi)^2}{2!}\right.$$

$$- \frac{(x - \tfrac{1}{4}\pi)^3}{3!} + \frac{(x - \tfrac{1}{4}\pi)^4}{4!}$$

$$\left. + \frac{(x - \tfrac{1}{4}\pi)^5}{5!}\right]$$

FIGURE 6

▶ **EXAMPLE 8**   Use series to evaluate to five decimal places

$$\int_{0.5}^{1} \frac{\sin x}{x}\, dx$$

Support the answer by the NINT capability of a graphics calculator.

Solution   An antiderivative of the integrand in terms of elementary functions cannot be found. However, from the Maclaurin series for $\sin x$,

$$\frac{\sin x}{x} = \frac{1}{x} \cdot \sin x$$

$$= \frac{1}{x}\left(x - \frac{x^3}{3!} + \frac{x^5}{5!} - \frac{x^7}{7!} + \frac{x^9}{9!} - \cdots\right)$$

$$= 1 - \frac{x^2}{3!} + \frac{x^4}{5!} - \frac{x^6}{7!} + \frac{x^8}{9!} - \cdots$$

which is true for all $x \neq 0$. Using term-by-term integration we get

$$\int_{0.5}^{1} \frac{\sin x}{x}\, dx = x - \frac{x^3}{3 \cdot 3!} + \frac{x^5}{5 \cdot 5!} - \frac{x^7}{7 \cdot 7!} + \frac{x^9}{9 \cdot 9!} - \cdots\bigg]_{0.5}^{1}$$

$$\approx (1 - 0.0555555 + 0.0016667 - 0.0000283 + 0.0000003 - \cdots)$$

$$- (0.5 - 0.0069444 + 0.0000521 - 0.0000002 + \cdots)$$

Each set of parentheses contains a convergent alternating series with $|u_{n+1}| < |u_n|$. In the first set of parentheses we use the first four terms because the error obtained is less than 0.0000003, and in the second set, we use the first three terms where the error obtained is less than 0.0000002. Doing the computation and rounding off to five decimal places we get

$$\int_{0.5}^{1} \frac{\sin x}{x}\, dx \approx 0.45298$$

On our graphics calculator, we obtain

$$\text{NINT}((\sin x)/x, 0.5, 1) = 0.45298$$

which supports our answer.   ◀

EXERCISES 8.9

1. Obtain the Maclaurin series for $\cos x$ by differentiating term by term the Maclaurin series for $\sin x$.

2. Obtain the Maclaurin series for $\sinh x$ by applying formula (6), and prove that the series represents $\sinh x$ for all values of x.

3. Obtain the Maclaurin series for $\cosh x$ by applying formula (6), and prove that the series represents $\cosh x$ for all values of x.

4. Obtain the Maclaurin series for $\cosh x$ by performing operations on the Maclaurin series for e^x and e^{-x}.

5. Obtain the Maclaurin series for $\sinh x$ by performing operations on the Maclaurin series for e^x and e^{-x}.

6. Obtain the Maclaurin series for $\sinh x$ by differentiating term by term the Maclaurin series for $\cosh x$. Also differentiate the Maclaurin series for $\sinh x$ to obtain the one for $\cosh x$.

7. Find the Taylor series for e^x at 3 by using the Maclaurin series for e^x.

8. Find the Taylor series for e^{-x} at 2 by using the Maclaurin series for e^x.

In Exercises 9 through 14, find a power-series representation for the function at the number a, and determine its radius of convergence. Support your answer on your graphics calculator.

9. $f(x) = \ln x$; $a = 1$ **10.** $f(x) = \sqrt[4]{x}$; $a = 1$

11. $f(x) = \sqrt[3]{x}$; $a = 8$ **12.** $f(x) = \sin x$; $a = \frac{1}{6}\pi$

13. $f(x) = \cos x$; $a = \frac{1}{3}\pi$ **14.** $f(x) = 2^x$; $a = 0$

15. Find the Maclaurin series for $\sin^2 x$.
Hint: $\sin^2 x = \frac{1}{2}(1 - \cos 2x)$.

16. Find the Maclaurin series for $\cos^2 x$.
Hint: $\cos^2 x = \frac{1}{2}(1 + \cos 2x)$.

17. Find the first three nonzero terms of the Maclaurin series for $\tan x$.

18. Find the first three nonzero terms of the Taylor series for $\cot x$ at $\frac{1}{2}\pi$.

19. Use the answer in Exercise 17 and term-by-term differentiation to find the first three nonzero terms of the Maclaurin series for $\sec^2 x$.

20. Use the answer in Exercise 18 and term-by-term differentiation to find the first three nonzero terms of the Taylor series for $\csc^2 x$ at $\frac{1}{2}\pi$.

21. Use the answer in Exercise 17 and term-by-term integration to find the first three nonzero terms of the Maclaurin series for $\ln \sec x$.

22. Use the answer in Exercise 18 and term-by-term integration to find the first three nonzero terms of the Taylor series for $\ln \sin x$ at $\frac{1}{2}\pi$.

In Exercises 23 through 28, use a power series to compute to the indicated accuracy the value of the quantity and compare the result with your calculator value.

23. $\cos 58°$; four decimal places

24. $\sqrt[5]{e}$; four decimal places

25. $\sqrt[5]{30}$; five decimal places

26. $\sinh \frac{1}{2}$; five decimal places

27. $\ln (0.9)$; four decimal places

28. $\sqrt[3]{29}$; three decimal places

29. Use the Maclaurin series for e^x to compute the value of e correct to seven decimal places, and prove that your answer has the required accuracy.

In Exercises 30 through 33, use series to evaluate accurate to three decimal places the definite integral. Support your answer by the NINT capability of your graphics calculator.

30. $\displaystyle\int_0^1 \sqrt{x}e^{-x^2} \, dx$ **31.** $\displaystyle\int_0^{1/2} \sin x^2 \, dx$

32. $\displaystyle\int_0^1 \cos \sqrt{x} \, dx$ **33.** $\displaystyle\int_0^{0.1} \ln(1 + \sin x) \, dx$

34. (a) Find a Maclaurin series for $\int_0^x f(t) \, dt$ where

$$f(t) = \begin{cases} \dfrac{\sin t}{t} & \text{if } t \neq 0 \\ 1 & \text{if } t = 0 \end{cases}$$

Observe that f is continuous at 0 because $\lim_{t \to 0} f(t) = f(0)$. **(b)** Plot in the same window the graphs of $\text{NINT}(f(t), 0, x)$ and the Maclaurin polynomial consisting of the first ten nonzero terms of your series in part (a). **(c)** Apply your series in part (a) to compute $\int_0^{1/3} f(t) \, dt$ accurate to three decimal places and support your answer by the NINT capability of your graphics calculator.

35. (a) Find a Maclaurin series for $\int_0^x g(t) \, dt$ where

$$g(t) = \begin{cases} \dfrac{1 - \cos t}{t} & \text{if } t \neq 0 \\ 0 & \text{if } t = 0 \end{cases}$$

Observe that g is continuous at 0 because $\lim_{t \to 0} g(t) = g(0)$. **(b)** Plot in the same window the graphs of $\text{NINT}(g(t), 0, x)$ and the Maclaurin polynomial consisting of the first ten nonzero terms of your series in part (a). **(c)** Apply your series in part (a) to compute $\int_0^1 g(t) \, dt$ accurate to three decimal places and support your answer by the NINT capability of your graphics calculator.

36. The function E defined by

$$E(x) = \frac{2}{\sqrt{\pi}} \int_0^x e^{-t^2} \, dt$$

is called the *error function*, and it is important in mathematical statistics. Find the Maclaurin series for the error function.

37. Determine a_n ($n = 0, 1, 2, 3, 4$) so that the polynomial

$$f(x) = 3x^4 - 17x^3 + 35x^2 - 32x + 17$$

is written in the form

$$f(x) = a_4(x - 1)^4 + a_3(x - 1)^3 + a_2(x - 1)^2 + a_1(x - 1) + a_0$$

38. Determine a_n ($n = 0, 1, 2, 3$) so that the polynomial

$$f(x) = 4x^3 - 5x^2 + 2x - 3$$

is written in the form

$$f(x) = a_3(x + 2)^3 + a_2(x + 2)^2 + a_1(x + 2) + a_0$$

39. When using a Taylor series of a function f at a to compute a particular function value, what determines your choice of a? Make up an example to illustrate your answer.

8.10 POWER SERIES FOR NATURAL LOGARITHMS AND THE BINOMIAL SERIES

We wind up our treatment of infinite series in this section by discussing and applying two basic series: (i) a series for computing natural logarithms and (ii) the binomial series.

To lead up to the series for computing natural logarithms, we first obtain a power-series representation of $\ln(1 + x)$ in the following illustration.

▷ **ILLUSTRATION 1**   Consider the function f defined by

$$f(t) = \frac{1}{1 + t}$$

A power-series representation of this function is given by series (4) in Section 8.7, which is

$$\frac{1}{1 + t} = 1 - t + t^2 - t^3 + \ldots + (-1)^n t^n + \ldots \qquad \text{if } |t| < 1$$

We integrate term by term to obtain

$$\int_0^x \frac{dx}{1 + t} = \sum_{n=0}^{+\infty} \int_0^x (-1)^n t^n \, dt \qquad \text{if } |x| < 1$$

Therefore

$$\ln(1 + x) = x - \frac{x^2}{2} + \frac{x^3}{3} - \frac{x^4}{4} + \ldots + (-1)^n \frac{x^{n+1}}{n + 1} + \ldots \qquad \text{if } |x| < 1$$

$$\Leftrightarrow \quad \ln(1 + x) = \sum_{n=1}^{+\infty} (-1)^{n-1} \frac{x^n}{n} \qquad \text{if } |x| < 1 \tag{1}$$

Because $|x| < 1$, $|1 + x| = 1 + x$. Thus the absolute-value bars are not needed when writing $\ln(1 + x)$. ◀

In Illustration 1, Theorem 8.8.4 allows us to conclude that power series (1) represents the function only for values of x in the open interval $(-1, 1)$. The power series is, however, convergent at the right endpoint 1, as we showed in Example 1 of Section 8.5. When $x = -1$, the power series becomes the negative of the harmonic series and is divergent. Hence the interval of convergence of power series (1) is $(-1, 1]$.

In the following illustration we show that power series (1) represents $\ln(1 + x)$ at $x = 1$ by proving that the sum of the series $\sum_{n=1}^{+\infty} \frac{(-1)^{n-1}}{n}$ is $\ln 2$.

▷ **ILLUSTRATION 2**   For the infinite series $\sum_{n=1}^{+\infty} \frac{(-1)^{n-1}}{n}$ the nth

partial sum is

$$s_n = 1 - \frac{1}{2} + \frac{1}{3} - \frac{1}{4} + \ldots + (-1)^{n-1} \frac{1}{n} \tag{2}$$

It follows from Definition 8.3.2 that if we show $\lim_{n \to +\infty} s_n = \ln 2$, we will have proved that the sum of the series is $\ln 2$.

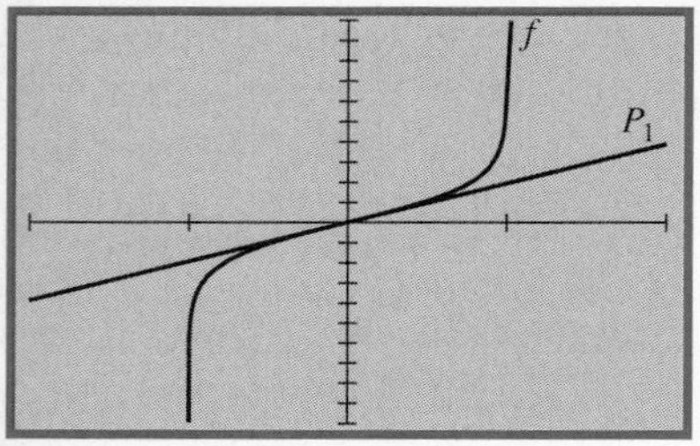

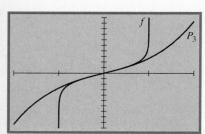

[−2, 2] by [−10, 10]

$f(x) = \ln \dfrac{1+x}{1-x}$

$P_1(x) = 2x$

FIGURE 1

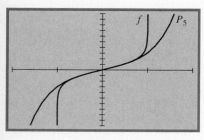

[−2, 2] by [−10, 10]

$f(x) = \ln \dfrac{1+x}{1-x}$

$P_3(x) = 2\left(x + \dfrac{x^3}{3}\right)$

FIGURE 2

[−2, 2] by [−10, 10]

$f(x) = \ln \dfrac{1+x}{1-x}$

$P_5(x) = 2\left(x + \dfrac{x^3}{3} + \dfrac{x^5}{5}\right)$

FIGURE 3

From algebra comes the following formula for the sum of a finite geometric series:

$$a + ar + ar^2 + ar^3 + \ldots + ar^{n-1} = \frac{a - ar^n}{1 - r}$$

From this formula with $a = 1$ and $r = -t$,

$$1 - t + t^2 - t^3 + \ldots + (-t)^{n-1} = \frac{1 - (-t)^n}{1 + t}$$

which may be written as

$$1 - t + t^2 - t^3 + \ldots + (-1)^{n-1}t^{n-1} = \frac{1}{1+t} + (-1)^{n+1}\frac{t^n}{1+t}$$

Integrating from 0 to 1 we get

$$\int_0^1 [1 - t + t^2 - t^3 + \ldots + (-1)^{n-1}t^{n-1}]\,dt = \int_0^1 \frac{dt}{1+t} + (-1)^{n+1}\int_0^1 \frac{t^n}{1+t}\,dt$$

which gives

$$1 - \frac{1}{2} + \frac{1}{3} - \frac{1}{4} + \ldots + (-1)^{n-1}\frac{1}{n} = \ln 2 + (-1)^{n+1}\int_0^1 \frac{t^n}{1+t}\,dt \qquad \textbf{(3)}$$

Referring to (2), we see that the left side of (3) is s_n. Letting

$$R_n = (-1)^{n+1}\int_0^1 \frac{t^n}{1+t}\,dt$$

(3) may be written as

$$s_n = \ln 2 + R_n \qquad \textbf{(4)}$$

Because $\dfrac{t^n}{1+t} \le t^n$ for all t in $[0, 1]$ then from Theorem 4.6.1

$$\int_0^1 \frac{t^n}{1+t}\,dt \le \int_0^1 t^n\,dt$$

Hence

$$0 \le |R_n| = \int_0^1 \frac{t^n}{1+t}\,dt \le \int_0^1 t^n\,dt = \frac{1}{n+1}$$

Because $\lim\limits_{n\to+\infty} \dfrac{1}{n+1} = 0$, it follows from the above inequality and the squeeze theorem that $\lim\limits_{n\to+\infty} R_n = 0$. Therefore, from (4)

$$\begin{aligned}\lim_{n\to+\infty} s_n &= \ln 2 + \lim_{n\to+\infty} R_n \\ &= \ln 2\end{aligned}$$

Thus

$$\begin{aligned}\sum_{n=1}^{+\infty} (-1)^{n-1}\frac{1}{n} &= 1 - \frac{1}{2} + \frac{1}{3} - \frac{1}{4} + \ldots \qquad \textbf{(5)}\\ &= \ln 2\end{aligned}$$

◀

From Illustrations 1 and 2 we can conclude that power series (1) represents $\ln(1 + x)$ for all x in its interval of convergence $(-1, 1]$.

Although the sum of series (5) is $\ln 2$, this series converges too slowly to apply it to calculate $\ln 2$. We need another series for computation of natural logarithms, and we now proceed to obtain one.

From (1),

$$\ln(1 + x) = x - \frac{x^2}{2} + \frac{x^3}{3} - \ldots + (-1)^{n-1} \frac{x^n}{n} + \ldots \qquad \text{for } x \text{ in } (-1, 1] \qquad (6)$$

If x is replaced by $-x$ in this series,

$$\ln(1 - x) = -x - \frac{x^2}{2} - \frac{x^3}{3} - \frac{x^4}{4} - \ldots - \frac{x^n}{n} - \ldots \qquad \text{for } x \text{ in } [-1, 1) \qquad (7)$$

Subtracting term by term (7) from (6) we obtain

$$\ln \frac{1 + x}{1 - x} = 2\left(x + \frac{x^3}{3} + \frac{x^5}{5} + \ldots + \frac{x^{2n-1}}{2n - 1} + \ldots\right) \text{ if } |x| < 1 \qquad (8)$$

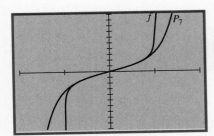

[−2, 2] by [−10, 10]

$$f(x) = \ln \frac{1+x}{1-x}$$

$$P_7(x) = 2\left(x + \frac{x^3}{3} + \frac{x^5}{5} + \frac{x^7}{7}\right)$$

FIGURE 4

The graphs of $f(x) = \ln \frac{1 + x}{1 - x}$ and the polynomials $P_1(x)$, $P_3(x)$, $P_5(x)$, and $P_7(x)$ of series (8) are plotted in Figures 1 through 4, respectively, showing how the graphs of the polynomials approximate the graph of f when $|x| < 1$.

Series (8) can be used to compute the natural logarithm of any positive number. To apply the series to compute $\ln y$ we let

$$y = \frac{1 + x}{1 - x} \quad \text{and then} \quad x = \frac{y - 1}{y + 1} \quad \text{and} \quad |x| < 1 \qquad (9)$$

▶ **EXAMPLE 1**   Compute $\ln 2$ accurate to five decimal places and compare with the value obtained on a calculator.

Solution   From (9), if $y = 2$ then $x = \frac{1}{3}$. Thus from (8),

$$\ln 2 = 2\left(\frac{1}{3} + \frac{1}{3^4} + \frac{1}{5 \cdot 3^5} + \frac{1}{7 \cdot 3^7} + \frac{1}{9 \cdot 3^9} + \frac{1}{11 \cdot 3^{11}} + \ldots\right)$$

$$= 2\left(\frac{1}{3} + \frac{1}{81} + \frac{1}{1215} + \frac{1}{15,309} + \frac{1}{177,147} + \frac{1}{1,948,617} + \ldots\right)$$

$$\approx 2(0.333333 + 0.012346 + 0.000823 + 0.000065 + 0.000006 + 0.000001 + \ldots)$$

Using the first six terms in parentheses, multiplying by 2, and rounding off to five decimal places we get.

$$\ln 2 \approx 0.69315$$

which agrees with the value obtained on our calculator.   ◀

To obtain the *binomial series,* we consider first the binomial theorem that you learned in algebra. The binomial theorem expresses $(a + b)^m$, where m is a positive integer, as a sum of powers of a and b as follows:

$$(a + b)^m = a^m + ma^{m-1}b + \frac{m(m-1)}{2!}a^{m-2}b^2 + \ldots$$

$$+ \frac{m(m-1) \cdot \ldots \cdot (m-k+1)}{k!}a^{m-k}b^k + \ldots + b^m$$

We now take $a = 1$ and $b = x$ and apply the binomial theorem to the expression $(1 + x)^m$, where m is not a positive integer. We obtain the power series

$$1 + mx + \frac{m(m-1)}{2!}x^2 + \frac{m(m-1)(m-2)}{3!}x^3 + \ldots$$

$$+ \frac{m(m-1)(m-2) \cdot \ldots \cdot (m-n+1)}{n!}x^n + \ldots \quad \textbf{(10)}$$

This is the Maclaurin series for $(1 + x)^m$ called the **binomial series.** To find the radius of convergence of this series, we apply the ratio test and get

$$\lim_{x \to +\infty} \left| \frac{u_n + 1}{u_n} \right| = \lim_{n \to +\infty} \left| \frac{\dfrac{m(m-1) \cdot \ldots \cdot (m-n+1)(m-n)}{(n+1)!}x^{n+1}}{\dfrac{m(m-1) \cdot \ldots \cdot (m-n+1)}{n!}x^n} \right|$$

$$= \lim_{n \to +\infty} \left| \frac{m-n}{n+1} \right| |x|$$

$$= \lim_{n \to +\infty} \left| \frac{\dfrac{m}{n} - 1}{1 + \dfrac{1}{n}} \right| |x|$$

$$= |x|$$

So the series is convergent if $|x| < 1$. We now prove that series (10) represents $(1 + x)^m$ for all real numbers m if x is in the open interval $(-1, 1)$. This is not done by calculating $R_n(x)$ and showing that its limit is zero because that is quite difficult, as you will soon see if you attempt to do so. Instead we use the following method. Let

$$f(x) = 1 + \sum_{n=1}^{+\infty} \frac{m(m-1) \cdot \ldots \cdot (m-n+1)}{n!}x^n \quad |x| < 1 \quad \textbf{(11)}$$

We wish to show that $f(x) = (1 + x)^m$, where $|x| < 1$. By Theorem 8.8.3,

$$f'(x) = \sum_{n=1}^{+\infty} \frac{m(m-1) \cdot \ldots \cdot (m-n+1)}{(n-1)!}x^{n-1} \quad |x| < 1 \quad \textbf{(12)}$$

Multiplying on both sides of (12) by x we get, from Theorem 8.3.6,

$$xf'(x) = \sum_{n=1}^{+\infty} \frac{m(m-1) \cdot \ldots \cdot (m-n+1)}{(n-1)!}x^n \quad \textbf{(13)}$$

By rewriting the right side of (12),

$$f'(x) = m + \sum_{n=2}^{+\infty} \frac{m(m-1) \cdot \ldots \cdot (m-n+1)}{(n-1)!}x^{n-1}$$

Rewriting this summation with the lower limit decreased by 1 and n replaced by $n + 1$, we have

$$f'(x) = m + \sum_{n=1}^{+\infty} (m - n) \frac{m(m - 1) \cdot \ldots \cdot (m - n + 1)}{n!} x^n$$

In (13) we multiply the numerator and the denominator by n to obtain

$$xf'(x) = \sum_{n=1}^{+\infty} n \frac{m(m - 1) \cdot \ldots \cdot (m - n + 1)}{n!} x^n$$

The series for $f'(x)$ and $xf'(x)$ are absolutely convergent for $|x| < 1$. So by Theorem 8.3.7 they can be added term by term and the resulting series will also be absolutely convergent for $|x| < 1$. From the addition,

$$(1 + x)f'(x) = m\left[1 + \sum_{n=1}^{+\infty} \frac{m(m - 1) \cdot \ldots \cdot (m - n + 1)}{n!} x^n\right]$$

Because by (11) the expression in brackets is $f(x)$, we have

$$(1 + x)f'(x) = mf(x)$$

$$\frac{f'(x)}{f(x)} = \frac{m}{1 + x}$$

The left side of the above equation is $D_x[\ln f(x)]$; thus

$$\frac{d}{dx}[\ln f(x)] = \frac{m}{1 + x}$$

However, we also know that

$$\frac{d}{dx}[\ln(1 + x)^m] = \frac{m}{1 + x}$$

Because $\ln f(x)$ and $\ln(1 + x)^m$ have the same derivative, they differ by a constant. Hence

$$\ln f(x) = \ln(1 + x)^m + C$$

From (11), $f(0) = 1$. Therefore $C = 0$; so

$$f(x) = (1 + x)^m$$

We have proved the following general binomial theorem.

8.10.1 Binomial Theorem

If m is any real number, then

$$(1 + x)^m = 1 + \sum_{n=1}^{+\infty} \frac{m(m - 1)(m - 2) \cdot \ldots \cdot (m - n + 1)}{n!} x^n$$

for all values of x such that $|x| < 1$.

If m is a positive integer, the binomial series terminates after a finite number of terms.

▶ **EXAMPLE 2**   Express as a power series in x:

$$\frac{1}{\sqrt{1+x}}$$

Solution   From the binomial theorem, when $|x| < 1$

$$(1 + x)^{-1/2} = 1 - \frac{1}{2}x + \frac{(-\frac{1}{2})(-\frac{1}{2} - 1)}{2!}x^2 + \frac{(-\frac{1}{2})(-\frac{1}{2} - 1)(-\frac{1}{2} - 2)}{3!}x^3$$

$$+ \dots + \frac{(-\frac{1}{2})(-\frac{3}{2})(-\frac{5}{2}) \cdot \dots \cdot (-\frac{1}{2} - n + 1)}{n!}x^n + \dots$$

$$= 1 - \frac{1}{2}x + \frac{1 \cdot 3}{2^2 \cdot 2!}x^2 - \frac{1 \cdot 3 \cdot 5}{2^3 \cdot 3!}x^3 + \dots$$

$$+ (-1)^n \frac{1 \cdot 3 \cdot 5 \cdot \dots \cdot (2n - 1)}{2^n n!}x^n + \dots \quad ◀$$

▶ **EXAMPLE 3**   From the result of Example 2, obtain a binomial series for $(1 - x^2)^{-1/2}$, and use it to find a power series for $\sin^{-1} x$. Support the answer graphically.

Solution   We replace x by $-x^2$ in the series for $(1 + x)^{-1/2}$ and get for $|x| < 1$

$$(1 - x^2)^{-1/2} = 1 + \frac{1}{2}x^2 + \frac{1 \cdot 3}{2^2 \cdot 2!}x^4 + \frac{1 \cdot 3 \cdot 5}{2^3 \cdot 3!}x^6 + \dots + \frac{1 \cdot 3 \cdot 5 \cdot \dots \cdot (2n - 1)}{2^n n!}x^{2n} + \dots$$

We integrate term by term to obtain

$$\int_0^x \frac{dt}{\sqrt{1 - t^2}} = x + \frac{1}{2} \cdot \frac{x^3}{3} + \frac{1 \cdot 3}{2^2 \cdot 2!} \cdot \frac{x^5}{5} + \frac{1 \cdot 3 \cdot 5}{2^3 \cdot 3!} \cdot \frac{x^7}{7} + \dots + \frac{1 \cdot 3 \cdot 5 \cdot \dots \cdot (2n - 1)}{2^n n!} \cdot \frac{x^{2n+1}}{2n + 1} + \dots$$

Therefore

$$\sin^{-1} x = x + \sum_{n=1}^{+\infty} \frac{1 \cdot 3 \cdot 5 \cdot \dots \cdot (2n - 1)}{2^n n!} \cdot \frac{x^{2n+1}}{2n + 1} \quad \text{for } |x| < 1$$

Figure 5 shows the graphs of

$$f(x) = \sin^{-1} x \quad \text{and} \quad P_7(x) = x + \frac{1}{6}x^3 + \frac{3}{40}x^5 + \frac{5}{112}x^7$$

plotted in the $[-2, 2]$ by $[-2, 2]$ window. The fact that the graph of $P_7(x)$ approximates the graph of f for $|x| < 1$ supports our answer. ◀

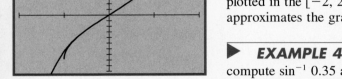

$[-2, 2]$ by $[-2, 2]$

$f(x) = \sin^{-1} x$

$P_7(x) = x + \frac{1}{6}x^3 + \frac{3}{40}x^5 + \frac{5}{112}x^7$

FIGURE 5

▶ **EXAMPLE 4**   Apply the power series obtained in Example 3 to compute $\sin^{-1} 0.35$ accurate to four decimal places, and compare with the value obtained on a calculator.

Solution   With $x = 0.35$ in $P_7(x)$, giving the first four nonzero terms in the series for $\sin^{-1} x$, we have

$$P_7(0.35) = 0.35 + \frac{1}{6}(0.35)^3 + \frac{3}{40}(0.35)^5 + \frac{5}{112}(0.35)^7$$

$$\approx 0.35 + 0.00715 + 0.00039 + 0.00003$$

$$\approx 0.3576$$

On our calculator we obtain the same value to four decimal places. ◀

▶ **EXAMPLE 5** (a) Express $(1 - \sqrt{x})^{2/3}$ as a series in x. (b) From the result of part (a), compute accurate to three decimal places the value of

$$\int_0^{1/4} (1 - \sqrt{x})^{2/3} \, dx$$

Support the answer by the NINT capability of a graphics calculator.

Solution

(a) We apply the binomial theorem with $m = \frac{2}{3}$ to get

$$(1 + x)^{2/3} = 1 + \frac{\frac{2}{3}}{1!}x + \frac{\frac{2}{3}(-\frac{1}{3})}{2!}x^2 + \frac{\frac{2}{3}(-\frac{1}{3})(-\frac{4}{3})}{3!}x^3 + \frac{\frac{2}{3}(-\frac{1}{3})(-\frac{4}{3})(-\frac{7}{3})}{4!}x^4 + \dots \quad \text{if } |x| < 1$$

$$= 1 + \frac{2}{3}x - \frac{1}{9}x^2 + \frac{4}{81}x^3 - \frac{7}{243}x^4 + \dots \quad \text{if } |x| < 1$$

Replacing x by $-\sqrt{x}$ results in

$$(1 - \sqrt{x})^{2/3} = 1 - \frac{2}{3}x^{1/2} - \frac{1}{9}x - \frac{4}{81}x^{3/2} - \frac{7}{243}x^2 - \dots \quad \text{if } 0 \le x < 1$$

(b) Integrating the above series term by term, we obtain

$$\int_0^{1/4} (1 - \sqrt{x})^{2/3} \, dx = x - \frac{4}{9}x^{3/2} - \frac{1}{18}x^2 - \frac{8}{405}x^{5/2} - \frac{7}{729}x^3 - \dots \Big]_0^{1/4}$$

$$= \frac{1}{4} - \frac{4}{9} \cdot \frac{1}{8} - \frac{1}{18} \cdot \frac{1}{16} - \frac{8}{405} \cdot \frac{1}{32} - \frac{7}{729} \cdot \frac{1}{64} - \dots$$

$$= 0.2500 - 0.0555 - 0.0035 - 0.0006 - 0.00002 - \dots$$

$$\approx 0.190$$

On our graphics calculator, we get to three decimal places

$$\text{NINT}((1 - \sqrt{x})^{2/3}, 0, 0.25) = 0.190$$

which supports our answer. ◀

EXERCISES 8.10

In Exercises 1 through 4, use power series (8) to compute the natural logarithm accurate to four decimal places and compare with the value obtained on a calculator.

1. $\ln 3$ **2.** $\ln 0.8$ **3.** $\ln 1.4$ **4.** $\ln 2.5$

5. (a) Show that $\ln x = \ln a + \ln\left(1 + \frac{x - a}{a}\right)$ where $a > 0$. **(b)** Use the equation in part (a) and series (1) for $\ln(1 + x)$ to obtain the Taylor series for $\ln x$ at a where $a > 0$.

6. (a) Use the result of part (b) of Exercise 5 to write the Taylor series for $\ln x$ at 1. **(b)** Use the series found in part (a) to compute $\ln 0.8$ to four decimal places. Compare the computation with that for Exercise 2.

7. (a) Use the result of part (b) of Exercise 5 to write the Taylor series for $\ln x$ at 2. **(b)** Given $\ln 2 = 0.6931$, use the series found in part (a) to compute $\ln 3$ accurate to four decimal places. Compare the computation with that for Exercise 1.

8. Find a power-series representation for $\ln(1 + ax)$ by integrating term by term from 0 to x a power-series representation for $\frac{1}{1 + at}$.

In Exercises 9 through 18, use a binomial series to find the Maclaurin series for the function and determine its radius of convergence. Support your answer on your graphics calculator.

9. $f(x) = \sqrt{1 + x}$ **10.** $f(x) = (3 - x)^{-2}$

11. $f(x) = (4 + x)^{-1/2}$ **12.** $f(x) = \sqrt[3]{8 + x}$

13. $f(x) = \sqrt[3]{1 - x^3}$ **14.** $f(x) = (4 + x^2)^{-1}$

15. $f(x) = (9 + x^4)^{-1/2}$ **16.** $f(x) = \dfrac{x}{\sqrt{1 - x}}$

17. $f(x) = \dfrac{x^2}{\sqrt{1 + x}}$ **18.** $f(x) = \dfrac{x}{\sqrt[3]{1 + x^2}}$

19. **(a)** Express $\sqrt[4]{1 + x^2}$ as a power series in x by first obtaining a power series for $\sqrt[4]{1 + x}$ and then replacing x by x^2. **(b)** Use the result of part (a) to compute accurate to three decimal places the value of $\int_0^{1/2} \sqrt[4]{1 + x^2} \, dx$. Support your answer by the NINT capability of your graphics calculator.

20. **(a)** Express $(1 - x^3)^{-1/2}$ as a power series in x by first obtaining a power series for $(1 - x)^{-1/2}$ and then replacing x by x^3. **(b)** Use the result of part (a) to compute accurate to three decimal places the value of $\int_0^{1/2} (1 - x^3)^{-1/2} \, dx$. Support your answer by the NINT capability of your graphics calculator.

In Exercises 21 through 26, use series to compute accurate to three decimal places the value of the definite integral. Support your answer by the NINT capability of your graphics calculator.

21. $\int_0^{1/3} \sqrt{1 + x^3} \, dx$ **22.** $\int_0^{2/5} \sqrt[3]{1 + x^4} \, dx$

23. $\int_0^1 \sqrt[3]{8 + x^2} \, dx$ **24.** $\int_0^{1/2} \sqrt{1 - x^3} \, dx$

25. $\int_0^{1/2} \dfrac{dx}{\sqrt{1 + x^4}}$ **26.** $\int_0^{1/3} \dfrac{dx}{\sqrt[3]{x^2 + 1}}$

27. Given

$$f(t) = \begin{cases} \dfrac{\ln(1 + t)}{t} & \text{if } t \neq 0 \\ 1 & \text{if } t = 0 \end{cases}$$

(a) Prove that f is continuous at 0. **(b)** Find a power-series representation of $\int_0^x f(t) \, dt$ and determine its radius of convergence. **(c)** Plot in the same window the graphs of NINT($f(t)$, 0, x) and the polynomial consisting of the first ten nonzero terms of your series in part (b).

28. Do Exercise 27 if

$$f(t) = \begin{cases} \dfrac{\sin^{-1} t}{t} & \text{if } t \neq 0 \\ 1 & \text{if } t = 0 \end{cases}$$

29. For the function of Exercise 27, use your series in part (b) of that exercise to compute $\int_0^{1/3} f(t) \, dt$, and support your answer by the NINT capability of your graphics calculator.

30. For the function of Exercise 28, use your series in part (b) of that exercise to compute $\int_0^{1/2} f(t) \, dt$, and support your answer by the NINT capability of your graphics calculator.

31. Obtain the Maclaurin series for $\sinh^{-1} x$ by integrating term by term the binomial series for $(1 + t^2)^{-1/2}$ and determine its radius of convergence.

32. Obtain the Maclaurin series for $\tanh^{-1} x$ by integrating term by term the binomial series for $(1 - t^2)^{-1}$ and determine the radius of convergence.

In Exercises 33 through 36, use a Maclaurin series to compute an approximate value of the quantity accurate to four decimal places and compare your result with the value found on your calculator. In Exercise 35 use the series found in Exercise 31, and in Exercise 36 use the series found in Exercise 32.

33. $\sin^{-1} 0.24$ **34.** $\sin^{-1} (-0.62)$

35. $\sinh^{-1} (-0.15)$ **36.** $\tanh^{-1} 0.27$

37. By integrating term by term from 0 to x a power-series representation for $\ln(1 - t)$, show that

$$\sum_{n=2}^{+\infty} \frac{x^n}{(n - 1)n} = x + (1 - x) \ln(1 - x)$$

38. By integrating term by term from 0 to x a power-series representation for $\ln(1 + t)$, show that

$$\sum_{n=0}^{+\infty} \frac{(-1)^n}{(n + 1)(n + 2)} = 2 \ln 2 - 1$$

39. The relativistic expression for KE, the measure of the kinetic energy of a particle, obtained by subtracting the measure of the rest energy from the measure of the total energy is

$$KE = \frac{m_0 c^2}{\sqrt{1 - \dfrac{v^2}{c^2}}} - m_0 c^2 \qquad \textbf{(14)}$$

where m_0 is the measure of the rest mass of the particle, c is the measure of the speed of light in a vacuum, and v is the measure of the velocity of the particle. For small values of v, compared with c, the measure of the Newtonian kinetic energy is given by

$$KE = \tfrac{1}{2} m_0 v^2$$

Deduce this fact by expanding $(1 - v^2/c^2)^{-1/2}$ by the binomial theorem and substituting in (14) to obtain

$$KE = \frac{1}{2} m_0 v^2 + \frac{3}{8} m_0 \frac{v^4}{c^2} + \frac{5}{16} m_0 \frac{v^6}{c^4} + \dots$$

40. Find the Maclaurin series for $\int_0^x \dfrac{t^p}{\sqrt{1 - t^2}} \, dt$ if p is a nonnegative integer. Determine the radius of convergence of the series.

41. Explain how you can use the answer for Exercise 32 to obtain series (8) for $\ln \dfrac{1 + x}{1 - x}$.

CHAPTER 8 REVIEW

▶ *SUGGESTIONS FOR REVIEW OF CHAPTER 8*

1. What is Taylor's formula and under what conditions does the formula hold? What is Maclaurin's formula?

2. What is the nth degree Taylor polynomial and the Lagrange form of the remainder for a function f?

3. Make up an example of the computation of the third-degree Taylor polynomial and the Lagrange form of the remainder for a rational function, where your choice of a is not zero. Explain how you estimate the error when the polynomial is used to compute a function value.

4. Answer Suggestion 3 for an exponential function.

5. Answer Suggestion 3 for a trigonometric function.

6. What is a sequence function? What is a sequence? How do you plot the graph of a sequence function?

7. Define the limit of a sequence. What do we mean by a convergent sequence and a divergent sequence? Give an example of a convergent sequence and show why it is convergent; do the same for a divergent sequence.

8. Define an increasing sequence, and give an example; do the same for a decreasing sequence. Give an example of a sequence that is not monotonic.

9. What is a lower bound of a sequence? Give an example of a sequence having a lower bound, and state its greatest lower bound.

10. What is an upper bound of a sequence? Give an example of a sequence having an upper bound, and state its least upper bound.

11. What two properties are equivalent for monotonic sequences? Give an example of an increasing sequence and state these equivalent properties for your example; do the same for a decreasing sequence.

12. What is a sequence of partial sums of an infinite series? Why is this sequence important?

13. What do we mean by a convergent infinite series and a divergent infinite series? Give an example of a convergent infinite series and show why it is convergent; do the same for a divergent infinite series.

14. What is the harmonic series? Is it convergent or divergent and why?

15. What is a geometric series? Which geometric series are convergent and which are divergent? Give an example of a convergent geometric series and a divergent one. What is the sum of a convergent geometric series? Illustrate by an example.

16. State some properties of finite sums that can be extended to convergent infinite series. Demonstrate each of these properties for infinite series by giving an example.

17. State the comparison test. Give an example showing how the comparison test can be used to show an infinite series is convergent; do the same to show an infinite series is divergent.

18. Answer Suggestion 17 for the limit comparison test.

19. What is a p series? Which p series are convergent and which are divergent? Give an example of a convergent p series and a divergent one.

20. State the integral test. Give an example showing how the integral test can be applied to show an infinite series is convergent; do the same to show an infinite series is divergent.

21. What is an alternating series? Give an example of a convergent alternating series and an example of an alternating series that is divergent.

22. What is the alternating-series test? Give an example showing how the alternating-series test is used to prove convergence.

23. How do you estimate the error introduced when the sum of a convergent alternating series is approximated by a finite number of terms of the series? Give an example illustrating your answer.

24. Define absolute convergence and conditional convergence of an infinite series. Give an example of an infinite series of positive and negative terms and show how absolute convergence is applied. Give an example of an infinite series of positive and negative terms that is conditionally convergent.

25. What is the ratio test? Give an example showing how the ratio test is applied to prove that an infinite series is (i) absolutely convergent and (ii) divergent. Give an example of an infinite series for which no conclusion regarding convergence can be made from the ratio test.

26. Answer Suggestion 25 for the root test.

27. List and describe all the tests you know for determining convergence or divergence of an infinite series of constant terms.

28. Define a power series in x. Define a power series in $x - a$.

29. How do you determine the values of x for which a power series converges? Give an example to illustrate your answer.

30. Suppose R is the radius of convergence of a power series in x. For what values of x are you certain that

the power series is absolutely convergent? For what values of x are you certain that the power series is divergent? For what values of x is convergence or divergence of the power series questionable, and how do you determine convergence or divergence for those values of x?

31. Answer Suggestion 30 if R is the radius of convergence of a power series in $x - a$.

32. State the theorem that allows us to differentiate a power series term by term. Are the intervals of convergence of the two series necessarily the same? Are the radii of convergence necessarily the same? Give an example illustrating your answer.

33. State the theorem that allows us to integrate a power series term by term. Are the intervals of convergence of the two series necessarily the same? Are the radii of convergence necessarily the same? Gave an example illustrating your answer.

34. Give an example of obtaining a power-series representation of a rational function by term-by-term integration of a power series.

35. Give two examples of computing the value of an irrational number (not involving a radical) by a power series.

36. What is the Taylor series of a function f at the number a? Give an example of a function and its Taylor series at a nonzero number.

37. What is the Maclaurin series of a function f? Give an example of a function and its Maclaurin series.

38. State two reasons for studying Taylor series. Give an example for each reason.

39. How can you determine if a function is represented by its Taylor series? Give an example illustrating your answer.

40. Why is a power-series representation of $\ln(1 + x)$ not convenient for computing the natural logarithm of a number? What is a better series for such a computation? Give an example illustrating your answer.

41. State the binomial series. How is this series related to the binomial expansion you learned in an algebra course? Give a particular example.

42. Give an example showing the application of a binomial series to a problem other than computation of a radical.

▶ MISCELLANEOUS EXERCISES FOR CHAPTER 8

See Exercises 8.6 for a review of Sections 8.3 through 8.5. The following exercises provide a review of Sections 8.1, 8.2, and 8.7 through 8.10.

In Exercises 1 through 6, find the Taylor or Maclaurin polynomial of the stated degree at the given number a for the function f with the Lagrange form of the remainder. Plot the graphs of f and the polynomial in the same window and observe how the graph of the polynomial approximates the graph of f near the point where $x = a$.

1. $f(x) = \sin^2 x$; $a = 0$; degree 5
2. $f(x) = e^{x^2}$; $a = 0$; degree 4
3. $f(x) = x^{-1/2}$; $a = 9$; degree 4
4. $f(x) = (1 + x^2)^{-1}$; $a = 1$; degree 3
5. $f(x) = xe^x$; $a = 0$; degree 6
6. $f(x) = x \cos x$; $a = \frac{1}{4}\pi$; degree 5

7. Compute $\sin^2 0.3$ accurate to four decimal places by using a Maclaurin polynomial, and prove that your answer has the required accuracy. Support your answer graphically.

8. Compute $\sqrt[3]{e}$ accurate to five decimal places by using a Taylor polynomial, and prove that your answer has the required accuracy. Support your answer graphically.

9. Evaluate $\lim\limits_{x \to 0^+} \dfrac{e^{-x^2/2} - \cos x}{x^4}$ two ways:
   (a) Apply L'Hôpital's rule; (b) express both $e^{-x^2/2}$ and $\cos x$ as a Maclaurin polynomial of degree 4.

10. Apply Taylor's formula to express the polynomial

$$P(x) = 4x^3 + 5x^2 - 2x + 1$$

as a polynomial in powers of $x + 2$.

In Exercises 11 through 18, write the first four elements of the sequence and determine whether it is convergent or divergent. If the sequence converges, find its limit and support your answer graphically.

11. $\left\{ \dfrac{3n}{n + 2} \right\}$ 12. $\left\{ \dfrac{(-1)^{n-1}}{(n + 1)^2} \right\}$ 13. $\left\{ \dfrac{n^2 - 1}{n^2 + 1} \right\}$

14. $\left\{ \dfrac{n^2}{\ln(n + 1)} \right\}$ 15. $\{2 + (-1)^n\}$

16. $\left\{ \dfrac{n + 3n^2}{4 + 2n^3} \right\}$ 17. $\left\{ \left(1 + \dfrac{1}{n}\right)^{2n} \right\}$

18. $\left\{ \dfrac{(n + 2)^2}{n + 4} - \dfrac{(n + 2)^2}{n} \right\}$

In Exercises 19 through 22, estimate on your graphics calculator the limit of the convergent sequence. Confirm your estimate analytically.

19. $\left\{\dfrac{5}{n^2 + 4}\right\}$ **20.** $\left\{\dfrac{6n}{2n - 1}\right\}$

21. $\left\{\dfrac{3 - 4n}{1 + 2n}\right\}$ **22.** $\left\{\dfrac{3}{n + 1}\right\}$

In Exercises 23 and 24 prove that the sequence is convergent by applying Theorem 8.2.10.

23. $\left\{\dfrac{3n}{2^{n-1}}\right\}$ **24.** $\left\{\dfrac{1 \cdot 4 \cdot 7 \cdot \ldots \cdot (3n - 2)}{3 \cdot 6 \cdot 9 \cdot \ldots \cdot (3n)}\right\}$

In Exercises 25 through 36, find the interval of convergence of the power series.

25. $\displaystyle\sum_{n=1}^{+\infty} \dfrac{x^n}{\sqrt{n}}$ **26.** $\displaystyle\sum_{n=1}^{+\infty} \dfrac{(x - 2)^n}{n}$

27. $\displaystyle\sum_{n=1}^{+\infty} \dfrac{x^n}{3^n(n^2 + n)}$ **28.** $\displaystyle\sum_{n=0}^{+\infty} \dfrac{x^n}{2^n}$

29. $\displaystyle\sum_{n=0}^{+\infty} \dfrac{n!}{2^n}(x - 3)^n$ **30.** $\displaystyle\sum_{n=1}^{+\infty} \dfrac{(-1)^{n-1}x^{2n-1}}{(2n - 1)!}$

31. $\displaystyle\sum_{n=1}^{+\infty} \dfrac{n^2}{6^n}(x + 1)^n$ **32.** $\displaystyle\sum_{n=1}^{+\infty} n(2x - 1)^n$

33. $\displaystyle\sum_{n=1}^{+\infty} \dfrac{(-1)^{n-1}(x - 1)^n}{n\,2^n}$ **34.** $\displaystyle\sum_{n=1}^{+\infty} n^n x^n$

35. $\displaystyle\sum_{n=0}^{+\infty} (\sin 2n)x^n$

36. $\displaystyle\sum_{n=1}^{+\infty} (-1)^{n+1} \dfrac{x^n}{(n + 1)\ln(n + 1)}$

In Exercises 37 through 40 do the following: (a) Find the radius of convergence of the power series and the domain of f; (b) write the power series that defines the function f' and state its radius of convergence; (c) find the domain of f'.

37. $f(x) = \displaystyle\sum_{n=1}^{+\infty} (-1)^n \dfrac{x^{2n}}{2n}$ **38.** $f(x) = \displaystyle\sum_{n=1}^{+\infty} \dfrac{x^n}{n^3}$

39. $f(x) = \displaystyle\sum_{n=0}^{+\infty} \dfrac{x^n}{(n!)^2}$ **40.** $f(x) = \displaystyle\sum_{n=1}^{+\infty} \dfrac{(x + 1)^n}{n\,2^n}$

In Exercises 41 and 42, find a power-series representation of the integral and determine its radius of convergence. Support your answer graphically.

41. $\displaystyle\int_0^x \dfrac{dt}{t^2 + 16}$ **42.** $\displaystyle\int_3^x \dfrac{dt}{t - 1}$

In Exercises 43 and 44, compute accurate to three decimal places the value of the definite integral by two methods: (a) Use the second fundamental theorem of the calculus; (b) use the series obtained in the indicated exercise.

43. $\displaystyle\int_0^3 \dfrac{dt}{t^2 + 16}$; Exercise 41   **44.** $\displaystyle\int_3^4 \dfrac{dt}{t - 1}$; Exercise 42

For Exercises 45 and 46, use the respective series obtained in Exercises 34 and 35 of Exercises 8.9 to compute, accurate to three decimal places, the value of the definite integral. Support your answer by the NINT capability of your graphics calculator.

45. $\displaystyle\int_0^{0.5} f(t)\, dt$, where $f(t) = \begin{cases} \dfrac{\sin t}{t} & \text{if } t \neq 0 \\ 1 & \text{if } t = 0 \end{cases}$

46. $\displaystyle\int_0^{0.25} g(t)\, dt$, where $g(t) = \begin{cases} \dfrac{1 - \cos t}{t} & \text{if } t \neq 0 \\ 0 & \text{if } t = 0 \end{cases}$

47. (a) Find a Maclaurin series for $\int_0^x f(t)\, dt$ where

$$f(t) = \begin{cases} \dfrac{\cosh t - 1}{t} & \text{if } t \neq 0 \\ 0 & \text{if } t = 0 \end{cases}$$

(b) Prove that f is continuous at 0. **(c)** Plot in the same window the graphs of $\text{NINT}(f(t), 0, x)$ and the Maclaurin polynomial consisting of the first ten nonzero terms of your series in part (a). **(d)** Use your series in part (a) to compute $\int_0^1 f(t)\, dt$ accurate to three decimal places and support your answer by the NINT capability of your graphics calculator.

In Exercises 48 through 50 use series to evaluate accurate to three decimal places the definite integral, and support your answer by the NINT capability of your graphics calculator.

48. $\displaystyle\int_0^{1/2} \dfrac{dx}{1 + x^5}$ **49.** $\displaystyle\int_0^{1/4} \sqrt{x} \sin x \, dx$

50. $\displaystyle\int_0^1 e^{-x^2} \, dx$

In Exercises 51 through 58, use a power series to compute accurate to four decimal places the value of the quantity and compare with the value obtained on your calculator.

51. $\sqrt[4]{e}$ **52.** $\sin^{-1} 0.1$ **53.** $\tan^{-1} \tfrac{1}{5}$ **54.** $\sqrt[3]{130}$

55. $\cos 3°$ **56.** $\sin 0.3$ **57.** $\ln 5$ **58.** $\sinh 0.3$

In Exercises 59 through 62, use two different infinite series to approximate the value of the irrational number to four significant digits.

59. π **60.** e **61.** $\dfrac{1}{\sqrt{3}}$ **62.** $\ln 1.3$

In Exercises 63 through 66, find the Maclaurin series for the function, and find its interval of convergence. Support your answer graphically.

63. $f(x) = \sqrt{x + 1}$ **64.** $f(x) = \dfrac{1}{2 - x}$

65. $f(x) = a^x, a > 0$ **66.** $f(x) = \sin^3 x$

In Exercises 67 through 70, find the Taylor series for the function at the indicated number, and find its interval of convergence. Support your answer graphically.

67. $f(x) = \sin 3x; -\frac{1}{3}$ **68.** $f(x) = \dfrac{1}{x}; 2$

69. $f(x) = \ln|x|; -1$ **70.** $f(x) = e^{x-2}; 2$

71. Find $\displaystyle\lim_{n \to +\infty} \int_0^1 \dfrac{x^n}{x + 1}\, dx$.

72. Find the Maclaurin series for $(1 + x)^n$ where n is a positive integer, and show that the series is the same as the expansion of this expression you learn how to derive in an algebra course by the binomial theorem.

73. Obtain the Maclaurin series for $\cos^2 x$ from the Maclaurin series for $\cos 2x$. *Hint:* $\cos 2x = 2\cos^2 x - 1$.

74. Obtain the first three nonzero terms of the Maclaurin series for $\sin 2x$ from the Maclaurin series for $\sin x$ and $\cos x$. *Hint:* $\sin 2x = 2 \sin x \cos x$.

Exercises 75 through 79 pertain to the functions J_0 and J_1 defined by power series as follows:

$$J_0(x) = \sum_{n=0}^{+\infty} (-1)^n \frac{x^{2n}}{n!\, n!\, 2^{2n}}$$

$$J_1(x) = \sum_{n=0}^{+\infty} (-1)^n \frac{x^{2n+1}}{n!\, (n + 1)!\, 2^{2n+1}}$$

The functions J_0 and J_1 are called Bessel functions of the first kind of orders zero and one, respectively.

75. Show that both J_0 and J_1 converge for all real values of x.

76. Show that $y = J_0(x)$ is a solution of the differential equation

$$x\frac{d^2y}{dx^2} + \frac{dy}{dx} + xy = 0$$

77. Show that $J_0'(x) = -J_1(x)$

78. Show that $D_x(xJ_1(x)) = xJ_0(x)$.

79. Show that $y = J_1(x)$ is a solution of the differential equation

$$x^2\frac{d^2y}{dx^2} + x\frac{dy}{dx} + (x^2 - 1)y = 0$$

80. In quantum mechanics, the measure E of the average energy per oscillator is given by

$$E = \frac{\displaystyle\sum_{n=0}^{+\infty} N_0 nhF e^{-nhF/kT}}{\displaystyle\sum_{n=0}^{+\infty} N_0 e^{-nhF/kT}}$$

where T is the measure of the temperature, h is Planck's constant, k is the universal gas constant, F is the constant frequency, and N_0 is the number of oscillators at the lowest energy.

(a) Let $x = e^{-hF/kT}$, and show that

$$E = hFx\left(\frac{1 + 2x + 3x^2 + 4x^3 + \cdots}{1 + x + x^2 + x^3 + \cdots}\right)$$

(b) Use the result of part (a) and power series for $(1 - x)^{-1}$ and $(1 - x)^{-2}$ to show that

$$E = \frac{hF}{e^{hF/kT} - 1}$$

81. Show that if $x = e^{-\alpha hF}$ and $\alpha = 1/kT$, then E, defined in Exercise 80, satisfies the equations:

$$E = -\frac{d}{d\alpha} \ln \sum_{n=0}^{+\infty} x^n \quad \text{and} \quad E = -\frac{d}{d\alpha} \ln(1 - x)^{-1}$$

82. In Example 8 of Section 8.8, we obtained

$$\tan^{-1} x = \sum_{n=0}^{+\infty} (-1)^n \frac{x^{2n+1}}{2n + 1} \text{ if } |x| < 1.$$ Show that the interval of convergence of this power series is $[-1, 1]$ and that the power series represents $\tan^{-1} x$ for all x in its interval of convergence.

PARAMETRIC EQUATIONS, PLANE CURVES, AND POLAR GRAPHS

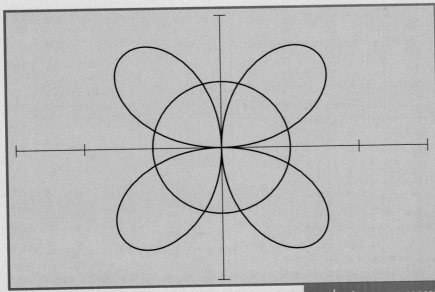

So far we have dealt with curves that are graphs of functions involving rectangular cartesian coordinates. In this chapter we are concerned with other plane curves. Section 9.1 is devoted to curves defined by parametric equations, and in Section 9.3 the curves are polar graphs defined in terms of polar coordinates.

You learned in Chapter 6 how to apply the definite integral to determine the length of arc of the graph of a function. Here we apply integration in Section 9.2 to find the length of arc of a curve defined by parametric equations and in Section 9.4 to find the length of arc of a polar graph. The computation of the area of a plane region bounded by polar graphs is another application of integration treated in Section 9.4. In the final section of the chapter we give a unified treatment of conic sections by defining a conic in terms of its eccentricity. This approach leads naturally to polar equations of conics.

▶ LOOKING AHEAD

9.1 PARAMETRIC EQUATIONS AND PLANE CURVES

Suppose a particle moves in a plane so that the coordinates (x, y) of its position at any time t are given by the equations

$$x = f(t) \quad \text{and} \quad y = g(t) \tag{1}$$

Then for every number t in the domain common to f and g the particle is at a point $(f(t), g(t))$ and these points trace a **plane curve** C traveled by the particle. Equations (1) are called **parametric equations** of C and the variable t is called a **parameter.** The curve C is also called a **graph;** that is, the set of all points (x, y) satisfying (1) is the graph of the parametric equations.

If the parameter t is eliminated from the pair of Equations (1), we obtain one equation in x and y, called a **cartesian equation** of C. The elimination of the parameter may lead to a cartesian equation whose graph contains more points than the graph defined by the parametric equations. This situation occurs in Example 3.

▶   **EXAMPLE 1**   Find a cartesian equation of the curve defined by the parametric equations

$$x = 2t - 3 \quad \text{and} \quad y = 4t - 1$$

and sketch the curve.

Solution   We eliminate t from the two equations by solving the first equation for t to obtain

$$t = \tfrac{1}{2}x + \tfrac{3}{2}$$

and substituting in the second equation:

$$y = 4(\tfrac{1}{2}x + \tfrac{3}{2}) - 1$$
$$y = 2x + 5$$

The graph of this equation is a line with slope 2 and y intercept 5. This line appears in Figure 1. Observe from the parametric equations that as t increases so do x and y. Thus a particle moving on the line goes upward and to the right, indicated in the figure by the arrowhead.   ◀

In general, the graph of any pair of parametric equations of the form

$$x = at + b \quad \text{and} \quad y = ct + d$$

where either $a \neq 0$ or $c \neq 0$, is a line.

▶   **EXAMPLE 2**   Find a cartesian equation of the graph of the parametric equations

$$x = 2 \cos t \qquad \text{and} \qquad y = 2 \sin t \qquad 0 \le t \le 2\pi$$

and sketch the graph.

Solution   To eliminate t from the two parametric equations, we square on both sides of each equation and add, which gives

$$x^2 + y^2 = 4 \cos^2 t + 4 \sin^2 t$$
$$x^2 + y^2 = 4(\cos^2 t + \sin^2 t)$$
$$x^2 + y^2 = 4$$

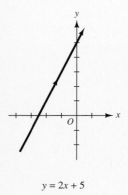

$y = 2x + 5$

FIGURE 1

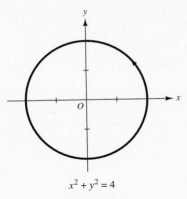

$x^2 + y^2 = 4$

FIGURE 2

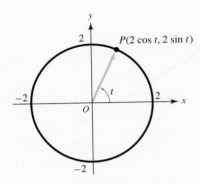

FIGURE 3

The graph of this equation is a circle with center at the origin and radius 2. By letting t take on all numbers in the closed interval $[0, 2\pi]$, we obtain the entire circle starting at the point $(2, 0)$ and moving along the circle in the counterclockwise direction, as indicated in Figure 2.   ◄

While the parameter for a set of parametric equations often represents time, this need not be the case. For instance, in Example 2, the parameter t may represent the radian measure of the angle measured from the positive side of the x axis to the line segment from the origin to the point (x, y) on the circle, as indicated in Figure 3.

▶ **EXAMPLE 3**   Given the parametric equations

$$x = \cosh t \quad \text{and} \quad y = \sinh t$$

(a) Sketch the graph defined by these equations and **(b)** find a cartesian equation of the graph.

Solution

(a) Squaring on both sides of the two parametric equations and subtracting we have

$$x^2 - y^2 = \cosh^2 t - \sinh^2 t$$

From the identity $\cosh^2 t - \sinh^2 t = 1$, this equation becomes

$$x^2 - y^2 = 1$$

whose graph is the unit hyperbola. Observe, however, that for any real number t, $\cosh t$ is never less than 1. Thus the curve defined by the given parametric equations consists of only the points on the right branch of the hyperbola. This curve appears in Figure 4. The "dashed" curve in the figure is the left branch of the unit hyperbola.

(b) A cartesian equation is

$$x^2 - y^2 = 1 \qquad x \geq 1$$ ◄

If a plane curve C is defined by an equation of the form $y = f(x)$, where f is continuous, then parametric equations for C may be obtained by letting

$$x = t \quad \text{and} \quad y = f(t)$$

where t is in the domain of f. Other substitutions for x may also give parametric equations for C provided x assumes every value in the domain of f.

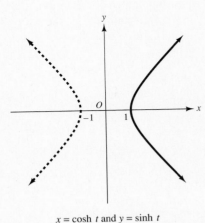

$x = \cosh t$ and $y = \sinh t$

FIGURE 4

▷ **ILLUSTRATION 1**   The parabola having the equation $y = x^2$ is also defined by the parametric equations

$$x = t \quad \text{and} \quad y = t^2$$

as well as by the parametric equations

$$x = t^3 \quad \text{and} \quad y = t^6$$

However, the parametric equations

$$x = t^2 \quad \text{and} \quad y = t^4$$

define only the right-hand side of the parabola where $x \geq 0$.   ◀

To plot the graph of a pair of parametric equations on your graphics calculator, consult the users manual for your particular calculator. Some calculators require you to set the calculator in parametric mode, while other calculators may utilize a parametric plot format. In any case, you will need to enter into the calculator equations defining x and y as functions of t. Furthermore, you must indicate the smallest and largest values of t under consideration. We shall denote these values by $t_{\min}$ and $t_{\max}$.

▷ **ILLUSTRATION 2**   To plot the graph of the parametric equations of Example 2, we enter

$$x = 2 \cos t \quad \text{and} \quad y = 2 \sin t$$

and let $t_{\min} = 0$ and $t_{\max} = 2\pi$. In the window $[-4.5, 4.5]$ by $[-3, 3]$, we obtain the circle shown in Figure 5.   ◀

Parametric equations can be used to define a curve described by a physical motion. As an example, we consider a **cycloid,** the curve traced by a point on the circumference of a circle as the circle rolls along a line. Let the radius of the circle be a and the fixed line on which the circle rolls be the x axis. Let the origin be one of the points at which the given point P comes in contact with the x axis, after which the circle has rolled through an angle of t radians as shown in Figure 6. The circle has rolled a distance of $|\overline{OT}|$ units, which is also the length of the arc PT on the circumference of the circle. Thus $|\overline{OT}| = at$. The coordinates of C, the center of the circle, are then (at, a). From right triangle PAC, $|\overline{PA}| = a \sin t$ and $|\overline{AC}| = a \cos t$. Thus

$$x = |\overline{OT}| - |\overline{PA}| \quad \text{and} \quad y = |\overline{TC}| - |\overline{AC}|$$
$$x = at - a \sin t \quad \text{and} \quad y = a - a \cos t$$

Parametric equations of the cycloid are, therefore,

$$x = a(t - \sin t) \quad \text{and} \quad y = a(1 - \cos t) \tag{2}$$

where t is any real number. A portion of the cycloid is sketched in Figure 7.

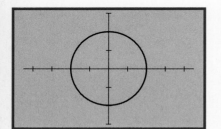

[−4.5, 4.5] by [−3, 3]

$x = 2 \cos t$ and $y = 2 \sin t$

FIGURE 5

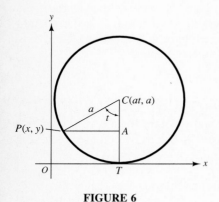

FIGURE 6

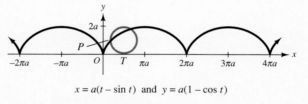

$x = a(t - \sin t)$ and $y = a(1 - \cos t)$

FIGURE 7

We now define some terminology pertaining to plane curves that will be useful later.

9.1.1 Definition of a Smooth Curve

A plane curve C defined by the parametric equations

$$x = f(t) \quad \text{and} \quad y = g(t) \qquad a \le t \le b$$

is said to be **smooth** on the closed interval $[a, b]$ if f' and g' are continuous on $[a, b]$ and $f'(t)$ and $g'(t)$ are not both zero at every number in the open interval (a, b).

▷ **ILLUSTRATION 3**   For the circle of Example 2 shown in Figure 2

$$f(t) = 2 \cos t \qquad g(t) = 2 \sin t$$
$$f'(t) = -2 \sin t \qquad g'(t) = 2 \cos t$$

Because f' and g' are continuous for all t and $f'(t)$ and $g'(t)$ are not both zero anywhere, the circle is a smooth curve.   ◄

If an interval I can be partitioned into a finite number of subintervals on which curve C is smooth, then C is said to be **piecewise smooth** on I.

▷ **ILLUSTRATION 4**   For the cycloid defined by parametric equations (2) and shown in Figure 7

$$f(t) = a(t - \sin t) \qquad g(t) = a(1 - \cos t)$$
$$f'(t) = a(1 - \cos t) \qquad g'(t) = a \sin t$$

The functions f' and g' are continuous for all t, but $f'(t)$ and $g'(t)$ are both zero if $t = 2\pi n$, where n is any integer. The cycloid, therefore, is not smooth. However, the cycloid is piecewise smooth because it is smooth in each subinterval $[2\pi n, 2\pi(n + 1)]$, where n is any integer.   ◄

9.1.2 Definition of a Closed Curve

A plane curve C defined by the parametric equations

$$x = f(t) \quad \text{and} \quad y = g(t) \qquad a \le t \le b$$

is said to be **closed** if the initial point $A(f(a), g(a))$ and the terminal point $B(f(b), g(b))$ coincide.

Figure 8 shows a smooth closed curve where points A and B coincide. A curve that does not cross itself is called a *simple* curve.

9.1.3 Definition of a Simple Curve

A plane curve C defined by the parametric equations

$$x = f(t) \quad \text{and} \quad y = g(t) \qquad a \le t \le b$$

is said to be **simple** between points $A(f(a), g(a))$ and $B(f(b), g(b))$ if $(f(t_1), g(t_1))$ is not the same point as $(f(t_2), g(t_2))$ for all distinct t_1 and t_2 in the open interval (a, b).

FIGURE 8

(a) Simple but not closed

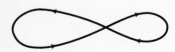

(b) Closed but not simple

(c) Neither simple nor closed

FIGURE 9

Circles and ellipses are examples of smooth simple closed curves. The curve of Figure 8 is another smooth simple closed curve. Figure 9 provides examples of smooth curves that may or may not be simple and closed. In (a) the curve is simple but not closed; in (b) the curve is closed but not simple; and in (c) the curve is neither simple nor closed.

Suppose a smooth curve C is defined parametrically by

$$x = f(t) \quad \text{and} \quad y = g(t) \tag{3}$$

and that this pair of equations defines at least one differentiable function h for which $y = h(x)$. Then the derivative of each such function h, denoted by dy/dx, is related to dx/dt and dy/dt by the following equation given by the chain rule:

$$\frac{dy}{dt} = \frac{dy}{dx} \cdot \frac{dx}{dt}$$

If $dx/dt \neq 0$, we can divide on both sides of this equation by dx/dt and obtain

$$\frac{dy}{dx} = \frac{\dfrac{dy}{dt}}{\dfrac{dx}{dt}} \tag{4}$$

Note that this equation expresses the derivative of y with respect to x in terms of the parameter t for all differentiable functions h, such that $y = h(x)$, with $x = f(t)$ and $y = g(t)$.

Because $\dfrac{d^2y}{dx^2} = \dfrac{d}{dx}\left(\dfrac{dy}{dx}\right)$, then $\dfrac{d^2y}{dx^2} = \dfrac{d(y')}{dx}$. Thus from (4)

$$\frac{d^2y}{dx^2} = \frac{\dfrac{d(y')}{dt}}{\dfrac{dx}{dt}} \tag{5}$$

▶ **EXAMPLE 4**   Given the parametric equations

$$x = 4 - t^2 \quad \text{and} \quad y = t^2 + 4t$$

find $\dfrac{dy}{dx}$ and $\dfrac{d^2y}{dx^2}$ without eliminating t.

Solution   Because $\dfrac{dy}{dt} = 2t + 4$ and $\dfrac{dx}{dt} = -2t$, we have, from (4)

$$\frac{dy}{dx} = \frac{2t + 4}{-2t}$$

$$= -1 - \frac{2}{t}$$

Since $y' = -1 - 2/t$, $d(y')/dt = 2/t^2$. Then from (5)

$$\frac{d^2y}{dx^2} = \frac{d(y')/dt}{dx/dt}$$

$$= \frac{2/t^2}{-2t}$$

$$= -\frac{1}{t^3} \quad \blacktriangleleft$$

From (4), the slope of the tangent line at a point on curve C defined by parametric equations (3) is $(dy/dt)/(dx/dt)$. Therefore, the graph has a horizontal tangent line at a point where $dy/dt = 0$ and $dx/dt \neq 0$. The graph has a vertical tangent line at a point where $dx/dt = 0$ and $dy/dt \neq 0$.

Table 1

t	x	y
-4	-12	0
-3	-5	-3
-2	0	-4
-1	3	-3
0	4	0
1	3	5
2	0	12
3	-5	21

▶ **EXAMPLE 5** For the graph of the parametric equations of Example 4, **(a)** find the horizontal and vertical tangent lines, and **(b)** determine the concavity. **(c)** Sketch the graph. **(d)** Support the graph on a graphics calculator.

Solution

(a) From Example 4,

$$x = 4 - t^2 \quad \text{and} \quad y = t^2 + 4t$$

$$\frac{dx}{dt} = -2t \quad \text{and} \quad \frac{dy}{dt} = 2t + 4$$

When $t = -2$, $dy/dt = 0$ and $dx/dt \neq 0$. Thus the graph has a horizontal tangent line at $(0, -4)$. When $t = 0$, $dx/dt = 0$ and $dy/dt \neq 0$. The graph, therefore, has a vertical tangent line at $(4, 0)$.

(b) Also from the solution of Example 4,

$$\frac{d^2y}{dx^2} = -\frac{1}{t^3}$$

Because $d^2y/dx^2 > 0$ when $t < 0$, the graph is concave upward for these values of t. Similarly, the graph is concave downward when $t > 0$ because then $d^2y/dx^2 < 0$.

(c) Table 1 gives values of x and y for particular values of t. With points obtained from these values, and knowing the horizontal and vertical tangent lines as well as the concavity, we sketch the graph shown in Figure 10.

(d) Figure 11, showing the graph plotted in the $[-20, 10]$ by $[-5, 15]$ window supports our graph sketched by hand. ◀

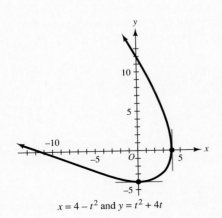

$x = 4 - t^2$ and $y = t^2 + 4t$

FIGURE 10

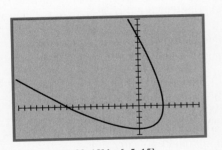

$[-20, 10]$ by $[-5, 15]$

$x = 4 - t^2$ and $y = t^2 + 4t$

FIGURE 11

As promised in Section 7.7 where we stated and proved Cauchy's mean-value theorem, we now give a geometric interpretation of the theorem. Recall that the theorem states that if f and g are two functions such that (i) f and g are continuous on $[a, b]$, (ii) f and g are differentiable on (a, b), and (iii) for all x in (a, b), $g'(x) \neq 0$, then there exists a number z in the open interval (a, b) such that

$$\frac{f(b) - f(a)}{g(b) - g(a)} = \frac{f'(z)}{g'(z)}$$

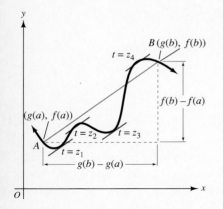

FIGURE 12

Figure 12 shows a curve having the parametric equations $x = g(t)$ and $y = f(t)$, where $a \le t \le b$. The slope of the curve in the figure at a particular point is given by

$$\frac{dy}{dx} = \frac{f'(t)}{g'(t)}$$

and the slope of the line segment through the points $A(g(a), f(a))$ and $B(g(b), f(b))$ is given by

$$\frac{f(b) - f(a)}{g(b) - g(a)}$$

Cauchy's mean-value theorem states that the slopes are equal for at least one value of t between a and b. For the curve shown in Figure 12 four values of t satisfy the conclusion of the theorem: $t = z_1, t = z_2, t = z_3$, and $t = z_4$.

EXERCISES 9.1

In Exercises 1 through 10, sketch the graph of the parametric equations and find a cartesian equation of the graph.

1. $x = 4 \cos t, y = 4 \sin t; t \in [0, 2\pi]$
2. $x = 4 \cos t, y = 4 \sin t; t \in [0, \pi]$
3. $x = 4 \cos t, y = 4 \sin t; t \in [-\frac{1}{2}\pi, \frac{1}{2}\pi]$
4. $x = 9 \cos t, y = 4 \sin t; t \in [0, 2\pi]$
5. $x = 4 \cos t, y = 25 \sin t; t \in [0, 2\pi]$
6. $x = 4 \cos t, y = 25 \sin t; t \in [-\frac{1}{2}\pi, \frac{1}{2}\pi]$
7. $x = 4 \sec t, y = 9 \tan t; t \in (-\frac{1}{2}\pi, \frac{1}{2}\pi)$
8. $x = 4 \tan t, y = 9 \sec t; t \in [0, \frac{1}{2}\pi) \cup [\pi, \frac{3}{2}\pi)$
9. $x = 3 - 2t, y = 4 + t$
10. $x = 2t - 5, y = t + 1$

In Exercises 11 through 16, find $\frac{dy}{dx}$ and $\frac{d^2y}{dx^2}$ without eliminating the parameter.

11. $x = 3t, y = 2t^2$
12. $x = 1 - t^2, y = 1 + t$
13. $x = t^2 e^t, y = t \ln t$
14. $x = e^{2t}, y = 1 + \cos t$
15. $x = a \cos t, y = b \sin t$
16. $x = a \cosh t, y = b \sinh t$

In Exercises 17 through 21, for the graph of the parametric equations, (a) find the horizontal and vertical tangent lines, and (b) determine the concavity. (c) Sketch the graph. (d) Support your graph on your calculator.

17. $x = 4t^2 - 4t, y = 1 - 4t^2$
18. $x = t^2 + t, y = t^2 - t$
19. $x = 2t^3, y = 4t^2$
20. $x = 2t^2, y = 3t^3$

21. $x = \dfrac{3t}{1 + t^3}, y = \dfrac{3t^2}{1 + t^3}; t \ne -1$
    (the folium of Descartes)

22. Plot the folium of Descartes of Exercise 21 on your graphics calculator and determine the portion of the folium generated when **(a)** $t < -1$; **(b)** $-1 < t \le 0$; **(c)** $t > 0$.

23. Find a cartesian equation of the folium of Descartes of Exercise 21. *Hint:* Eliminate t by evaluating $x^3 + y^3$.

24. A projectile moves so that the coordinates of its position at any time t are given by the parametric equations $x = 60t$ and $y = 80t - 16t^2$. Sketch the path of the projectile and check your graph on your graphics calculator.

25. Find an equation of the tangent line at the point where $t = \frac{1}{3}\pi$ on the curve defined by the parametric equations $x = 2 \sin t$ and $y = 5 \cos t$.

26. Find an equation of the tangent line at the point where $t = \frac{1}{6}\pi$ on the curve defined by the parametric equations $x = 1 + 3 \sin t$ and $y = 2 - 5 \cos t$.

27. Find $\dfrac{dy}{dx}, \dfrac{d^2y}{dx^2}$, and $\dfrac{d^3y}{dx^3}$ at the point on the cycloid having Equations (2) for which y has its largest value when x is in the closed interval $[0, 2\pi a]$.

28. Show that the slope of the tangent line at $t = t_1$ to the cycloid having Equations (2) is $\cot \frac{1}{2}t_1$. Deduce, then, that the tangent line is vertical when $t = 2n\pi$, where n is any integer.

29. Find the area of the region bounded by the x axis and one arch of the cycloid having Equations (2).

30. Find the centroid of the region of Exercise 29.

31. Parametric equations for the *trochoid* are

$$x = at - b \sin t \quad \text{and} \quad y = a - b \cos t$$

(a) If $a > b > 0$, show that the trochoid has no vertical tangent line. Plot the trochoid on your graphics calculator for $t \in [-\pi, \pi]$ if **(b)** $a = 3$ and $b = 1$ and **(c)** $a = 1$ and $b = 3$. Sketch what appears on your calculator screen. Verify that for your sketch in part (b) where $a > b$, the trochoid has no vertical tangent line, while for your sketch in part (c) where $a < b$, the trochoid has two vertical tangent lines.

32. A *hypocycloid* is the curve traced by a point P on a circle of radius b that is rolling inside a fixed circle of radius a, $a > b$. If the origin is at the center of the fixed circle, $A(a, 0)$ is one of the points at which the point P comes in contact with the fixed circle, B is the moving point of tangency of the two circles, and the parameter t is the number of radians in the angle AOB, prove that parametric equations of the hypocycloid are

$$x = (a - b)\cos t + b \cos \frac{a - b}{b} t$$

and

$$y = (a - b)\sin t - b \sin \frac{a - b}{b} t$$

33. Plot on your graphics calculator the hypocycloid in Exercise 32 if **(a)** $a = 6$ and $b = 2$ for $t \in [-\pi, \pi]$; **(b)** $a = 12$ and $b = 2$ for $t \in [-\pi, \pi]$. Sketch what appears on your calculator screen. How many cusps does the hypocycloid have in each case?

34. Plot on your graphics calculator the hypocycloid in Exercise 32 if **(a)** $a = 8$ and $b = 7$ for $t \in [-8\pi, 8\pi]$; **(b)** $a = 8$ and $b = 3$ for $t \in [-4\pi, 4\pi]$. Sketch what appears on your calculator screen. How many cusps does the hypocycloid have in each case?

35. If $a = 4b$ in Exercise 32, we have a *hypocycloid of four cusps*. **(a)** Show that parametric equations of this curve are $x = a \cos^3 t$ and $y = a \sin^3 t$. Plot on your graphics calculator the hypocycloid of four cusps if **(b)** $a = 4$ for $t \in [-\pi, \pi]$ and **(c)** $a = 8$ for $t \in [-\pi, \pi]$. Sketch what appears on your calculator screen.

36. (a) From the parametric equations of Exercise 35, find a cartesian equation of the hypocycloid of four cusps. **(b)** Use your cartesian equation in part (a) to sketch the graph of this hypocycloid.

37. In Exercise 44 of Exercises 7.3 we defined a tractrix: a curve such that the length of the segment of every tangent line from the point of tangency to the point of intersection with the x axis is a positive constant a. In that exercise we obtained the cartesian equation of the tractrix:

$$x = a \ln \frac{a + \sqrt{a^2 - y^2}}{y} - \sqrt{a^2 - y^2}$$

(a) Show that parametric equations of the tractrix are

$$x = t - a \tanh \frac{t}{a} \quad \text{and} \quad y = a \operatorname{sech} \frac{t}{a}$$

Hint: Substitute the value of y in terms of the parameter t in the cartesian equation, simplify using hyperbolic identities, and obtain the value of x in terms of the parameter t.
(b) Use the parametric equations in part (a) to plot the tractrix for which $a = 4$ on your graphics calculator. Sketch what appears on your calculator screen.

38. Prove that the parameter t in the parametric equations of a tractrix (see Exercise 37) is the x intercept of the tangent line.

39. Explain the importance of parametric equations in the study of plane curves.

9.2 LENGTH OF ARC OF A PLANE CURVE

In Section 6.1 we obtained a formula for finding the length of arc of the graph of a function. We now develop a method for computing the length of arc of a general plane curve, not necessarily the graph of a function.

Let C be the curve having parametric equations

$$x = f(t) \quad \text{and} \quad y = g(t)$$

and suppose that f and g are continuous on the closed interval $[a, b]$. We wish to assign a number L to represent the number of units in the length of arc of C from $t = a$ to $t = b$. We proceed as in Section 6.1.

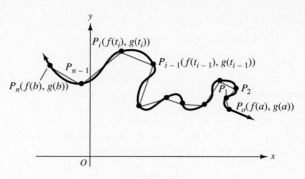

FIGURE 1

Let Δ be a partition of the closed interval $[a, b]$ formed by dividing the interval into n subintervals by choosing $n - 1$ numbers between a and b. Let $t_0 = a$ and $t_n = b$, and let $t_1, t_2, \ldots, t_{n-1}$ be intermediate numbers:

$$t_0 < t_1 < \ldots < t_{n-1} < t_n$$

The ith subinterval is $[t_{i-1}, t_i]$ and the number of units in its length, denoted by $\Delta_i t$, is $t_i - t_{i-1}$, where $i = 1, 2, \ldots, n$. Let $\| \Delta \|$ be the norm of the partition; so each $\Delta_i t \leq \| \Delta \|$.

Associated with each number t_i is a point $P_i(f(t_i), g(t_i))$ on C. From each point P_{i-1} draw a line segment to the next point P_i. See Figure 1. The number of units in the length of the line segment from P_{i-1} to P_i is denoted by $|\overline{P_{i-1}P_i}|$. From the distance formula we have

$$|\overline{P_{i-1}P_i}| = \sqrt{[f(t_i) - f(t_{i-1})]^2 + [g(t_i) - g(t_{i-1})]^2} \tag{1}$$

The sum of the numbers of units of lengths of the n line segments is

$$\sum_{i=1}^{n} |\overline{P_{i-1}P_i}|$$

Our intuitive notion of the length of arc from $t = a$ to $t = b$ leads us to define the number of units of the length of arc as the limit of this sum as $\| \Delta \|$ approaches zero.

9.2.1 Definition of Length of Arc of a Plane Curve

Let the curve C have parametric equations $x = f(t)$ and $y = g(t)$. Suppose there exists a number L having the following property: For any $\epsilon > 0$ there is a $\delta > 0$ such that for every partition Δ of the interval $[a, b]$ for which $\| \Delta \| < \delta$, then

$$\left| \sum_{i=1}^{n} |\overline{P_{i-1}P_i}| - L \right| < \epsilon$$

Then we write

$$L = \lim_{\|\Delta\| \to 0} \sum_{i=1}^{n} |\overline{P_{i-1}P_i}|$$

and L units is called the **length of arc** of the curve C from the point $(f(a), g(a))$ to the point $(f(b), g(b))$.

The arc of the curve is rectifiable if the limit in Definition 9.2.1 exists. If f' and g' are continuous on $[a, b]$, we proceed as follows to find a formula for evaluating this limit.

Because f' and g' are continuous on $[a, b]$, they are continuous on each subinterval of the partition Δ. So the hypothesis of the mean-value theorem is satisfied by f and g on each $[t_{i-1}, t_i]$; therefore there are numbers z_i and w_i in the open interval (t_{i-1}, t_i) such that

$$f(t_i) - f(t_{i-1}) = f'(z_i)\,\Delta_i t \quad \text{and} \quad g(t_i) - g(t_{i-1}) = g'(w_i)\,\Delta_i t$$

Substituting from these equations into (1) we obtain

$$|\overline{P_{i-1}P_i}| = \sqrt{[f'(z_i)\,\Delta_i t]^2 + [g'(w_i)\,\Delta_i t]^2}$$
$$|\overline{P_{i-1}P_i}| = \sqrt{[f'(z_i)]^2 + [g'(w_i)]^2}\,\Delta_i t \tag{2}$$

where z_i and w_i are in the open interval (t_{i-1}, t_i). Then from Definition 9.2.1 and (2), if the limit exists,

$$L = \lim_{\|\Delta\| \to 0} \sum_{i=1}^{n} \sqrt{[f'(z_i)]^2 + [g'(w_i)]^2}\,\Delta_i t \tag{3}$$

The sum in (3) is not a Riemann sum because z_i and w_i are not necessarily the same numbers. So we cannot apply the definition of a definite integral to evaluate the limit in (3). However, there is a theorem that can be applied to evaluate this limit. We state the theorem, but a proof is not given because it is beyond the scope of this book. You can find a proof in an advanced calculus text.

9.2.2 Theorem

If the functions F and G are continuous on the closed interval $[a, b]$, then the function $\sqrt{F^2 + G^2}$ is also continuous on $[a, b]$, and if Δ is a partition of the interval $[a, b]$, and z_i and w_i are any numbers in (t_{i-1}, t_i), then

$$\lim_{\|\Delta\| \to 0} \sum_{i=1}^{n} \sqrt{[F(z_i)]^2 + [G(w_i)]^2}\,\Delta_i t = \int_a^b \sqrt{[F(t)]^2 + [G(t)]^2}\,dt$$

Applying this theorem to (3) where F is f' and G is g', we have

$$L = \int_a^b \sqrt{[f'(t)]^2 + [g'(t)]^2}\,dt$$

This result gives the following theorem.

9.2.3 Theorem

Let the curve C have parametric equations $x = f(t)$ and $y = g(t)$, and suppose that f' and g' are continuous on the closed interval $[a, b]$. Then if L units is the length of arc of the curve C from the point $(f(a), g(a))$ to the point $(f(b), g(b))$,

$$L = \int_a^b \sqrt{[f'(t)]^2 + [g'(t)]^2}\,dt$$

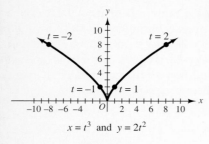

$x = t^3$ and $y = 2t^2$

FIGURE 2

▶ **EXAMPLE 1**   Find the length of arc of the curve having parametric equations

$$x = t^3 \quad \text{and} \quad y = 2t^2$$

for each of the cases: **(a)** from $t = 0$ to $t = 1$; **(b)** from $t = -2$ to $t = 0$.

Solution   The curve is sketched in Figure 2. The curve has parametric equations $x = f(t)$ and $y = g(t)$ where

$$f(t) = t^3 \qquad g(t) = 2t^2$$
$$f'(t) = 3t^2 \qquad g'(t) = 4t$$

We apply Theorem 9.2.3 in parts (a) and (b) where L_a units is the length of arc from $t = 0$ to $t = 1$ and L_b units is the length of arc from $t = -2$ to $t = 0$.

(a) $L_a = \displaystyle\int_0^1 \sqrt{9t^4 + 16t^2}\, dt$ $\qquad$ **(b)** $L_b = \displaystyle\int_{-2}^0 \sqrt{9t^4 + 16t^2}\, dt$

$\qquad = \displaystyle\int_0^1 \sqrt{t^2}\sqrt{9t^2 + 16}\, dt$ $\qquad\qquad = \displaystyle\int_{-2}^0 \sqrt{t^2}\sqrt{9t^2 + 16}\, dt$

$\qquad = \displaystyle\int_0^1 t\sqrt{9t^2 + 16}\, dt$ $\qquad\qquad\quad = \displaystyle\int_{-2}^0 -t\sqrt{9t^2 + 16}\, dt$

need dt!

$\qquad = \frac{1}{18} \cdot \frac{2}{3}(9t^2 + 16)^{3/2}\Big]_0^1$ $\qquad\quad = -\frac{1}{18} \cdot \frac{2}{3}(9t^2 + 16)^{3/2}\Big]_{-2}^0$

$\qquad = \frac{1}{27}\big[(25)^{3/2} - (16)^{3/2}\big]$ $\qquad\quad = -\frac{1}{27}\big[(16)^{3/2} - (52)^{3/2}\big]$

$\qquad = \frac{1}{27}(125 - 64)$ $\qquad\qquad\qquad = \frac{1}{27}(104\sqrt{13} - 64)$

$\qquad = \frac{61}{27}$ $\qquad\qquad\qquad\qquad\quad \approx 11.5$

Observe in the third integral in part (a) we replaced $\sqrt{t^2}$ by t because $0 \le t \le 1$. However, in the third integral in part (b) we replaced $\sqrt{t^2}$ by $-t$ because $-2 \le t \le 0$. ◀

▶ **EXAMPLE 2**   Derive the formula for the circumference of a circle of radius a by computing the length of arc of

$$x = a \cos t \quad \text{and} \quad y = a \sin t \qquad 0 \le t \le 2\pi$$

Solution   With $f(t) = a \cos t$ and $g(t) = a \sin t$, $f'(t) = -a \sin t$ and $g'(t) = a \cos t$. If L is the circumference of the circle, from Theorem 9.2.3, we have

$$L = \int_0^{2\pi} \sqrt{(-a \sin t)^2 + (a \cos t)^2}\, dt$$

$$= \int_0^{2\pi} \sqrt{a^2(\sin^2 t + \cos^2 t)}\, dt$$

$$= \sqrt{a^2}\int_0^{2\pi} dt$$

$$= a\, t\Big]_0^{2\pi}$$

$$= 2\pi a$$

◀

Just as occurred when computing the length of arc of the graph of a function, the definite integral obtained by applying Theorem 9.2.3 is often either difficult or impossible to evaluate by the second fundamental theorem of the calculus. With the NINT capability of our graphics calculator, we can, however, approximate the value as we do in the next example.

▶ **EXAMPLE 3**   Plot the curve having parametric equations

$$x = \sin t \quad \text{and} \quad y = e^t \qquad 0 \le t \le \pi$$

and find its length to four significant digits.

Solution   Figure 3 shows the curve plotted in the $[0, 2]$ by $[0, 25]$ window. Let $f(t) = \sin t$ and $g(t) = e^t$, so that $f'(t) = \cos t$ and $g'(t) = e^t$. From Theorem 9.2.3, if L is the length of the given curve,

$$L = \int_0^\pi \sqrt{\cos^2 t + e^{2t}} \, dt$$

On our graphics calculator,

$$\text{NINT}(\sqrt{\cos^2 t + e^{2t}}, 0, \pi) = 22.40$$

<u>Conclusion:</u>   The length of arc is 22.40.   ◀

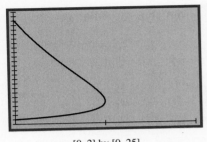

$[0, 2]$ by $[0, 25]$

$x = \sin t$ and $y = e^t$ $0 \le t \le \pi$

FIGURE 3

EXERCISES 9.2

In Exercises 1 through 14, find the exact length of arc of the curve defined by the given set of parametric equations. Plot the curve on your graphics calculator and observe if the apparent length of arc as shown on your graph supports your answer.

1. $x = \frac{1}{2}t^2 + t, y = \frac{1}{2}t^2 - t$; from $t = 0$ to $t = 1$
2. $x = 3t^2, y = 2t^3$; from $t = 0$ to $t = 3$
3. $x = t^2 + 2t, y = t^2 - 2t$; from $t = 0$ to $t = 2$
4. $x = t^3, y = 3t^2$; from $t = -2$ to $t = 0$
5. $x = 2t^2, y = 2t^3$; from $t = 1$ to $t = 2$
6. $x = t, y = \cosh t$; from $t = 0$ to $t = 3$
7. $x = 3e^{2t}, y = -4e^{2t}$; from $t = 0$ to $t = \ln 5$
8. $x = t^2 + 3, y = 3t^2$; from $t = 1$ to $t = 4$
9. $x = e^t \cos t, y = e^t \sin t$; from $t = 0$ to $t = 1$
10. $x = \ln \sin t, y = t + 1$; from $t = \frac{1}{6}\pi$ to $t = \frac{1}{2}\pi$
11. $x = \tan^{-1} t, y = \frac{1}{2}\ln(t^2 + 1)$; from $t = 0$ to $t = 1$
12. $x = 2(\cos t + t \sin t), y = 2(\sin t - t \cos t)$; from $t = 0$ to $t = \frac{1}{3}\pi$
13. $x = 4 \sin 2t, y = 4 \cos 2t$; from $t = 0$ to $t = \pi$
14. $x = e^{-t} \cos t, y = e^{-t} \sin t$; from $t = 0$ to $t = \pi$

In Exercises 15 through 22, use the NINT capability of your graphics calculator to find an approximate value to

four significant digits of the length of arc of the curve defined by the given set of parametric equations.

15. $x = t + 2, y = 4t^2 + t$; from $t = 0$ to $t = 3$
16. $x = 2t^2 + 3t, y = 2t - 1$; from $t = 1$ to $t = 2$
17. $x = 3 \cos t, y = 2 \sin t$; from $t = 0$ to $t = \frac{1}{2}\pi$
18. $x = 2 \sec t, y = 3 \tan t$; from $t = 0$ to $t = \frac{1}{4}\pi$
19. $x = 8 \tan t, y = 6 \sec t$; from $t = \frac{3}{4}\pi$ to $t = \pi$
20. $x = e^t, y = \ln t$; from $t = 1$ to $t = 5$
21. $x = 4 - t^2, y = t^2 + 4t$; from $t = -4$ to $t = 4$
22. $x = 3t, y = 4t^3$; from $t = -1$ to $t = 1$
23. Find the length of the entire hypocycloid of four cusps:

$$x = a \cos^3 t \quad \text{and} \quad y = a \sin^3 t$$

24. Find the length of one arch of the cycloid

$$x = a(t - \sin t) \quad \text{and} \quad y = a(1 - \cos t)$$

25. Find the length of the tractrix

$$x = t - a \tanh \frac{t}{a} \quad \text{and} \quad y = a \operatorname{sech} \frac{t}{a}$$

from $t = a$ to $t = 2a$.

26. Find the distance traveled by a thumbtack in the tread of a bicycle tire if the radius of the tire is 40 cm and the bicycle goes a distance of 50π m. *Hint:* The path of the thumbtack is a cycloid.

27. (a) Show that the curve defined by the parametric equations

$$x = a \sin t \quad \text{and} \quad y = b \cos t \quad a > b$$

is an ellipse.

(b) If C is the circumference of the ellipse of part (a), show that

$$C = 4 \int_0^{\pi/2} a\sqrt{1 - k^2 \sin^2 t} \; dt$$

where $k^2 = (a^2 - b^2)/a^2 < 1$. This integral is called an *elliptic integral* and cannot be evaluated exactly in terms of elementary functions.

28. (a) Use the formula of Exercise 27(b) and the NINT capability of your graphics calculator to determine the circumference of the ellipse defined by the parametric equations

$$x = 5 \sin t \quad \text{and} \quad y = 4 \cos t$$

(b) Plot the ellipse on your graphics calculator. Support your answer in part (a) by finding the perimeters of the inscribed rhombus and the circumscribed rectangle and showing that the circumference of the ellipse is between these two perimeters.

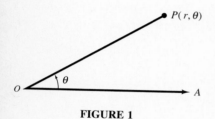

FIGURE 1

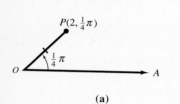

(a)

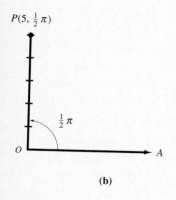

(b)

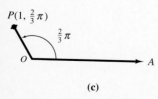

(c)

FIGURE 2

9.3 POLAR COORDINATES AND POLAR GRAPHS

Until now, we have located a point in a plane by its rectangular cartesian coordinates. Other coordinate systems give the position of a point in a plane, and the polar coordinate system is one of them. This system is important because certain curves have simpler equations in polar coordinates. Furthermore, all three conics (the parabola, ellipse, and hyperbola) have one equation, as you will learn in Section 9.5. This equation is applied in the derivation of Kepler's laws in physics and in the study of the motion of planets in astronomy.

Cartesian coordinates are numbers, the abscissa and ordinate, and these numbers are directed distances from two fixed lines. Polar coordinates consist of a directed distance and the measure of an angle relative to a fixed point and a fixed ray (or half line). The fixed point is called the **pole** (or origin), designated by the letter O. The fixed ray is called the **polar axis** (or polar line), which we label OA. The ray OA is usually drawn horizontally and to the right, and it extends indefinitely. See Figure 1.

Let P be any point in the plane distinct from O. Let θ be the radian measure of a directed angle AOP, positive when measured counterclockwise and negative when measured clockwise, having as its initial side the ray OA and as its terminal side the ray OP. Then if r is the undirected distance from O to P (that is, $r = |\overline{OP}|$), one set of polar coordinates of P is given by r and θ, and we write these coordinates as (r, θ).

▶ **EXAMPLE 1** Locate each of the following points having the given set of polar coordinates: **(a)** $(2, \frac{1}{4}\pi)$; **(b)** $(5, \frac{1}{2}\pi)$; **(c)** $(1, \frac{2}{3}\pi)$; **(d)** $(3, \frac{7}{6}\pi)$; **(e)** $(4, -\frac{1}{3}\pi)$; **(f)** $(\frac{5}{2}, -\pi)$.

Solution

(a) The point $(2, \frac{1}{4}\pi)$ is determined by first drawing the angle with radian measure $\frac{1}{4}\pi$, having its vertex at the pole and its initial side along the polar axis. The point on the terminal side that is 2 units from the pole is the point $(2, \frac{1}{4}\pi)$. See Figure 2(a). In a similar manner we obtain the points appearing in Figure 2(b)–(f). ◀

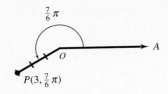

$P(3, \frac{7}{6}\pi)$

(d)

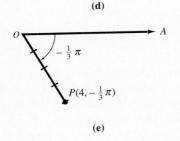

$P(4, -\frac{1}{3}\pi)$

(e)

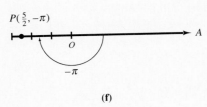

$P(\frac{5}{2}, -\pi)$

(f)

FIGURE 2

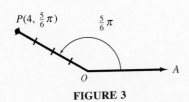

FIGURE 3

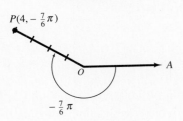

FIGURE 4

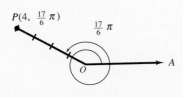

FIGURE 5

▷ **ILLUSTRATION 1**   Figure 3 shows the point $(4, \frac{5}{6}\pi)$. Another set of polar coordinates for this point is $(4, -\frac{7}{6}\pi)$; see Figure 4. Furthermore the polar coordinates $(4, \frac{17}{6}\pi)$ also yield the same point, as shown in Figure 5. ◀

Actually the coordinates $(4, \frac{5}{6}\pi + 2k\pi)$, where k is any integer, give the same point as $(4, \frac{5}{6}\pi)$. Thus a given point has an unlimited number of sets of polar coordinates, unlike the rectangular cartesian coordinate system in which a one-to-one correspondence between the coordinates and the position of points in the plane exists. A further example is obtained by considering sets of polar coordinates for the pole. If $r = 0$ and θ is any real number, we have the pole, designated by $(0, \theta)$.

We now consider polar coordinates for which r is negative. In this case, instead of being on the terminal side of the angle, the point is on the extension of the terminal side, which is the ray from the pole extending in the direction opposite to the terminal side. Hence if P is on the extension of the terminal side of the angle of radian measure θ, a set of polar coordinates of P is (r, θ), where $r = -|\overline{OP}|$.

▷ **ILLUSTRATION 2**   The point $(-4, -\frac{1}{6}\pi)$ shown in Figure 6 is the same point as $(4, \frac{5}{6}\pi)$, $(4, -\frac{7}{6}\pi)$, and $(4, \frac{17}{6}\pi)$ in Illustration 1. Still another set of polar coordinates for this point is $(-4, \frac{11}{6}\pi)$; see Figure 7.

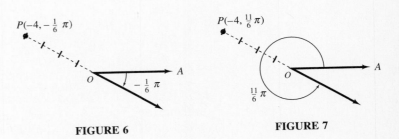

FIGURE 6   **FIGURE 7**   ◀

The angle is usually measured in radians: thus a set of polar coordinates of a point is an ordered pair of real numbers. For each ordered pair of real numbers there is a unique point having this set of polar coordinates. However, we have seen that a particular point can be given by an unlimited number of ordered pairs of real numbers. If the point P is not the pole, and r and θ are restricted so that $r > 0$ and $0 \le \theta < 2\pi$, P has a unique set of polar coordinates.

Sometimes we wish to refer to both the rectangular cartesian coordinates and the polar coordinates of a point. To do this, we take the origin of the first system and the pole of the second system coincident, the polar axis as the positive side of the x axis and the ray for which $\theta = \frac{1}{2}\pi$ as the positive side of the y axis.

Suppose P is a point whose representation in the rectangular cartesian coordinate system is (x, y) and (r, θ) is a polar coordinate representation

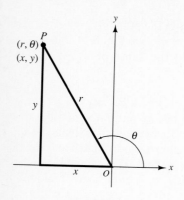

FIGURE 8

of P. As a particular case, suppose P is in the second quadrant and $r > 0$, as indicated in Figure 8. Then

$$\cos \theta = \frac{x}{|\overline{OP}|} \qquad \sin \theta = \frac{y}{|\overline{OP}|}$$

$$= \frac{x}{r} \qquad\qquad = \frac{y}{r}$$

Thus

$$x = r \cos \theta \quad \text{and} \quad y = r \sin \theta \tag{1}$$

These equations hold for P in any quadrant and r positive or negative. From the equations we can not only obtain the rectangular cartesian coordinates of a point when its polar coordinates are known, but we can also obtain a polar equation of a curve from its rectangular cartesian equation.

To derive equations that give a set of polar coordinates of a point when its rectangular cartesian coordinates are known, we square on both sides of each equation in (1), equate the sum of the left members to the sum of the right members, and solve for r to get

$$r = \pm \sqrt{x^2 + y^2} \tag{2}$$

From the equations in (1) and dividing, we have

$$\frac{r \sin \theta}{r \cos \theta} = \frac{y}{x}$$

$$\tan \theta = \frac{y}{x} \qquad \text{if } x \neq 0 \tag{3}$$

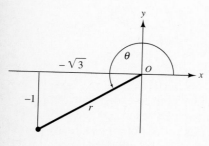

FIGURE 9

▷ **ILLUSTRATION 3**   Figure 9 shows the point whose cartesian co-ordinate representation is $(-\sqrt{3}, -1)$. To obtain polar coordinates (r, θ) for which $r > 0$ and $0 \leq \theta < 2\pi$, we apply (2) and (3):

$$r = \sqrt{3 + 1} \qquad \tan \theta = \frac{-1}{-\sqrt{3}}$$

$$= 2 \qquad\qquad \theta = \tfrac{7}{6}\pi \qquad (\text{since } \pi < \theta < \tfrac{3}{2}\pi)$$

Thus the point is $(2, \tfrac{7}{6}\pi)$.   ◀

An equation in polar coordinates is called a **polar equation** to distin-guish it from a **cartesian equation,** the term used when an equation is given in rectangular cartesian coordinates.

▶ **EXAMPLE 2**   Find a cartesian equation of a graph having the polar equation

$$r^2 = 4 \sin 2\theta$$

Solution   Because $\sin 2\theta = 2 \sin \theta \cos \theta$ we have $\sin 2\theta = 2(y/r)(x/r)$ where $r \neq 0$. With this substitution and $r^2 = x^2 + y^2$, we obtain from the given polar equation

$$x^2 + y^2 = 4(2)\frac{y}{r} \cdot \frac{x}{r}$$

$$x^2 + y^2 = \frac{8xy}{r^2}$$

$$x^2 + y^2 = \frac{8xy}{x^2 + y^2}$$

$$(x^2 + y^2)^2 = 8xy$$

◀

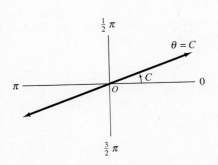

FIGURE 10

The graph of an equation in polar coordinates, called a **polar graph,** consists of those points, and only those points, having at least one pair of polar coordinates that satisfy the equation. We now discuss properties of such graphs and obtain them by hand and on a graphics calculator.

The equation

$$\theta = C$$

where C is a constant, is satisfied by all points having polar coordinates (r, C) whatever the value of r. Therefore, the graph of this equation is a line containing the pole and making an angle of radian measure C with the polar axis. See Figure 10. The same line is given by the equation

$$\theta = C \pm k\pi$$

where k is any integer.

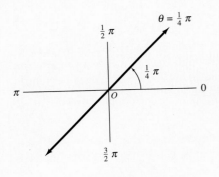

FIGURE 11

▷ **ILLUSTRATION 4**

(a) The graph of the equation

$$\theta = \tfrac{1}{4}\pi$$

appears in Figure 11. It is the line passing through the pole and making an angle of radian measure $\frac{1}{4}\pi$ with the polar axis. The same line is given by the equations

$$\theta = \tfrac{5}{4}\pi \qquad \theta = \tfrac{9}{4}\pi \qquad \theta = -\tfrac{3}{4}\pi \qquad \theta = -\tfrac{7}{4}\pi$$

and so on.

(b) Figure 12 shows the graph of the equation

$$\theta = \tfrac{2}{3}\pi$$

It is the line passing through the pole and making an angle of radian measure $\frac{2}{3}\pi$ with the polar axis. Other equations of this line are

$$\theta = \tfrac{5}{3}\pi \qquad \theta = \tfrac{8}{3}\pi \qquad \theta = -\tfrac{1}{3}\pi \qquad \theta = -\tfrac{4}{3}\pi$$

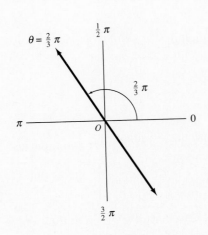

FIGURE 12

and so on.   ◀

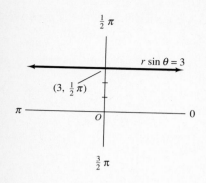

FIGURE 13

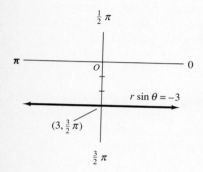

FIGURE 14

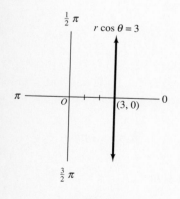

FIGURE 15

In general, the polar form of an equation of a line is not as simple as the cartesian form. However, if the line is parallel to either the polar axis or the $\frac{1}{2}\pi$ axis, the equation is fairly simple.

If a line is parallel to the polar axis and contains the point B whose cartesian coordinates are $(0, b)$ and polar coordinates are $(b, \frac{1}{2}\pi)$, then a cartesian equation is $y = b$. If we replace y by $r \sin \theta$, we have

$$r \sin \theta = b$$

which is a polar equation of any line parallel to the polar axis. If b is positive, the line is above the polar axis. If b is negative, it is below the polar axis.

▷ **ILLUSTRATION 5**   In Figure 13 we have the graph of the equation

$$r \sin \theta = 3$$

and in Figure 14 we have the graph of the equation

$$r \sin \theta = -3$$ ◀

Now consider a line parallel to the $\frac{1}{2}\pi$ axis or, equivalently, perpendicular to the polar axis. If the line goes through the point A whose cartesian coordinates are $(a, 0)$ and polar coordinates are $(a, 0)$, a cartesian equation is $x = a$. Replacing x by $r \cos \theta$ we obtain

$$r \cos \theta = a$$

which is an equation of any line perpendicular to the polar axis. If a is positive, the line is to the right of the $\frac{1}{2}\pi$ axis. If a is negative, the line is to the left of the $\frac{1}{2}\pi$ axis.

▷ **ILLUSTRATION 6**   Figure 15 shows the graph of the equation

$$r \cos \theta = 3$$

and Figure 16 shows the graph of the equation

$$r \cos \theta = -3$$ ◀

The graph of the equation

$$r = C$$

where C is any constant, is a circle whose center is at the pole and radius is $|C|$. The same circle is given by the equation

$$r = -C$$

▷ **ILLUSTRATION 7**   In Figure 17, we have the graph of the equation

$$r = 4$$

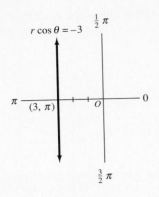

FIGURE 16

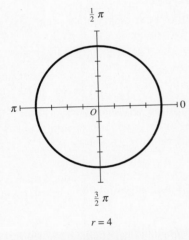

$r = 4$

FIGURE 17

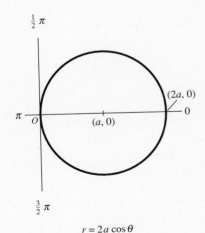

$r = 2a \cos \theta$

FIGURE 18

a circle with center at the pole and radius 4. The same circle is given by the equation

$$r = -4$$

although the use of such an equation is uncommon.   ◄

As with the line, the general polar equation of a circle is not as simple as the cartesian form. However, further special cases of an equation of a circle are worth considering in polar form.

If a circle contains the origin (the pole) and has its center at the point having cartesian coordinates (a, b), then a cartesian equation of the circle is

$$x^2 + y^2 - 2ax - 2by = 0$$

A polar equation of this circle is

$$(r \cos \theta)^2 + (r \sin \theta)^2 - 2a(r \cos \theta) - 2b(r \sin \theta) = 0$$
$$r^2(\cos^2 \theta + \sin^2 \theta) - 2ar \cos \theta - 2br \sin \theta = 0$$
$$r^2 - 2ar \cos \theta - 2br \sin \theta = 0$$
$$r(r - 2a \cos \theta - 2b \sin \theta) = 0$$
$$r = 0 \qquad r - 2a \cos \theta - 2b \sin \theta = 0$$

Because the graph of the equation $r = 0$ is the pole and the pole ($r = 0$ when $\theta = \tan^{-1}(-a/b)$) is on the graph of $r - 2a \cos \theta - 2b \sin \theta = 0$, a polar equation of the circle is

$$r = 2a \cos \theta + 2b \sin \theta$$

When $b = 0$ in this equation, we have

$$\boxed{r = 2a \cos \theta}$$

This is a polar equation of the circle of radius $|a|$ units, tangent to the $\frac{1}{2}\pi$ axis, and with its center on the polar axis or its extension. If $a > 0$, the circle is to the right of the pole as in Figure 18, and if $a < 0$, the circle is to the left of the pole.

If $a = 0$ in the equation $r = 2a \cos \theta + 2b \sin \theta$, we have

$$\boxed{r = 2b \sin \theta}$$

which is a polar equation of the circle of radius $|b|$ units, with its center on the $\frac{1}{2}\pi$ axis or its extension and tangent to the polar axis. If $b > 0$, the circle is above the pole, and if $b < 0$, the circle is below the pole.

► **EXAMPLE 3**   Sketch the graph of each of the following equations:
(a) $r = 5 \cos \theta$; **(b)** $r = -6 \sin \theta$.

Solution

(a) The equation

$$r = 5 \cos \theta$$

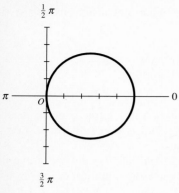

$r = 5 \cos\theta$

FIGURE 19

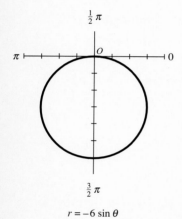

$r = -6 \sin \theta$

FIGURE 20

is of the form $r = 2a \cos \theta$ with $a = \frac{5}{2}$. Thus the graph is a circle with center at the point having polar coordinates $(\frac{5}{2}, 0)$ and tangent to the $\frac{1}{2}\pi$ axis. The graph appears in Figure 19.

(b) The equation

$$r = -6 \sin \theta$$

is of the form $r = 2b \sin \theta$ with $b = -3$. The graph is the circle with center at the point having polar coordinates $(3, \frac{3}{2}\pi)$ and tangent to the polar axis. Figure 20 shows the graph.   ◀

Summary of Polar Equations of Lines and Circles

C, a, and b are constants

$\theta = C$	Line containing pole; making angle of radian measure C with polar axis.
$r \sin \theta = b$	Line parallel to polar axis; above polar axis if $b > 0$; below polar axis if $b < 0$.
$r \cos \theta = a$	Line parallel to $\frac{1}{2}\pi$ axis; to right of $\frac{1}{2}\pi$ axis if $a > 0$; to left of $\frac{1}{2}\pi$ axis if $a < 0$.
$r = C$	Circle; center at pole; radius is C.
$r = 2a \cos \theta$	Circle; radius is $|a|$; tangent to $\frac{1}{2}\pi$ axis; center on polar axis or its extension.
$r = 2b \sin \theta$	Circle; radius is $|b|$; tangent to polar axis; center on $\frac{1}{2}\pi$ axis or its extension.

Before discussing other polar graphs, we state the following symmetry tests, which can be proved from the definition of symmetry of a graph given in Appendix Section A.2.

Symmetry Tests

A polar graph is

   (i) symmetric with respect to the polar axis if an equivalent equation is obtained when (r, θ) is replaced by either $(r, -\theta)$ or $(-r, \pi - \theta)$;
  (ii) symmetric with respect to the $\frac{1}{2}\pi$ axis if an equivalent equation is obtained when (r, θ) is replaced by either $(r, \pi - \theta)$ or $(-r, -\theta)$;
 (iii) symmetric with respect to the pole if an equivalent equation is obtained when (r, θ) is replaced by either $(-r, \theta)$ or $(r, \pi + \theta)$.

▷   **ILLUSTRATION 8**   For the graph of the equation

$$r = 4 \cos 2\theta$$

we test for symmetry with respect to the polar axis, the $\frac{1}{2}\pi$ axis, and the pole.

To test for symmetry with respect to the polar axis, we replace (r, θ) by $(r, -\theta)$ and obtain $r = 4 \cos(-2\theta)$, which is equivalent to $r = 4 \cos 2\theta$. So the graph is symmetric with respect to the polar axis.

Table 1

θ	r
0	-1
$\frac{1}{6}\pi$	$1 - \sqrt{3}$
$\frac{1}{3}\pi$	0
$\frac{1}{2}\pi$	1
$\frac{2}{3}\pi$	2
$\frac{5}{6}\pi$	$1 + \sqrt{3}$
π	3

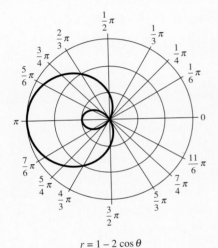

$r = 1 - 2 \cos \theta$

FIGURE 21

To test for symmetry with respect to the $\frac{1}{2}\pi$ axis, we replace (r, θ) by $(r, \pi - \theta)$ in the given equation and get $r = 4 \cos(2(\pi - \theta))$ or, equivalently, $r = 4 \cos(2\pi - 2\theta)$, which is equivalent to $r = 4 \cos 2\theta$. Therefore the graph is symmetric with respect to the $\frac{1}{2}\pi$ axis.

To test for symmetry with respect to the pole, we replace (r, θ) by $(-r, \theta)$ and obtain the equation $-r = 4 \cos 2\theta$, which is not equivalent to the given equation. But we must also determine if the other set of coordinates works. We replace (r, θ) by $(r, \pi + \theta)$ and obtain $r = 4 \cos 2(\pi + \theta)$ or equivalently, $r = 4 \cos(2\pi + 2\theta)$, which is equivalent to the equation $r = 4 \cos 2\theta$. Therefore the graph is symmetric with respect to the pole. ◀

When sketching a polar graph, we determine if it contains the pole by substituting 0 for r and solving for θ.

▶ **EXAMPLE 4**   Sketch the graph of the equation

$$r = 1 - 2 \cos \theta$$

Solution   Because we obtain an equivalent equation when (r, θ) is replaced by $(r, -\theta)$, the graph is symmetric with respect to the polar axis.

If $r = 0$, we obtain $\cos \theta = \frac{1}{2}$, and if $0 \leq \theta \leq \pi$, then $\theta = \frac{1}{3}\pi$. Thus the point $(0, \frac{1}{3}\pi)$, the pole, is on the graph. Table 1 gives coordinates of some other points on the graph. From these points we sketch one half of the graph; the remainder is sketched from its symmetry with respect to the polar axis. The graph appears in Figure 21. ◀

In Figure 21, the graph is sketched on a polar coordinate system. You are asked to sketch some polar graphs on a polar coordinate system in Exercises 51 through 60.

The following theorem shows how to define a polar graph by a pair of parametric equations.

9.3.1 Theorem

The graph of the polar equation $r = f(\theta)$ is defined by the parametric equations

$$x = f(t)\cos t \quad \text{and} \quad y = f(t)\sin t$$

Proof   Let (x, y) be the cartesian representation of a point P whose polar representation is (r, θ). Then

$$x = r \cos \theta \quad \text{and} \quad y = r \sin \theta$$

Because $r = f(\theta)$, we have

$$x = f(\theta)\cos \theta \quad \text{and} \quad y = f(\theta)\sin \theta$$

Replacing θ by t so that the parameter is t, we have

$$x = f(t)\cos t \quad \text{and} \quad y = f(t)\sin t \quad \blacksquare$$

The parametric equations in Theorem 9.3.1 are used by some computers and graphics calculators to plot polar graphs. Other graphics calculators allow you to plot a polar graph directly from the equation $r = f(\theta)$ with the calculator in polar mode.

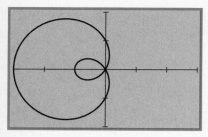

[−3, 3] by [−2, 2]

$r = 1 - 2 \cos \theta$

FIGURE 22

▷ **ILLUSTRATION 9** To plot the graph of Example 4 on our graphics calculator by using the parametric equations of Theorem 9.3.1, because $f(\theta) = 1 - 2 \cos \theta$, we let

$$x = (1 - 2 \cos t)\cos t \quad \text{and} \quad y = (1 - 2 \cos t)\sin t$$

With our calculator in parametric and radian mode and $0 \le t \le 2\pi$, we select $[-3, 3]$ by $[-2, 2]$ as our window and obtain the graph shown in Figure 22, which agrees with the curve in Figure 21. ◀

The polar graph in Example 4 and Illustration 9 is called a *limaçon,* a French word from the Latin *limax* meaning snail or slug. A *limaçon* is the graph of an equation of the form

$$r = a \pm b \cos \theta \quad \text{or} \quad r = a \pm b \sin \theta$$

where $a > 0$ and $b > 0$. There are four types of limaçons, depending on the ratio a/b.

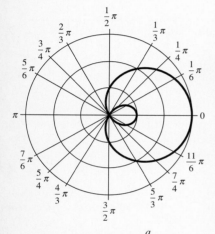

$r = a + b \cos \theta \quad 0 < \dfrac{a}{b} < 1$

(a) limaçon with a loop

Types of Limaçons

From the equation $r = a + b \cos \theta$ where $a > 0$ and $b > 0$:

1. $0 < \dfrac{a}{b} < 1$ **Limaçon with a loop.** See Figure 23(a).

2. $\dfrac{a}{b} = 1$ **Cardioid** (heart-shaped). See Figure 23(b).

3. $1 < \dfrac{a}{b} < 2$ **Limaçon with a dent.** See Figure 23(c).

4. $2 \le \dfrac{a}{b}$ **Convex limaçon** (no dent). See Figure 23(d).

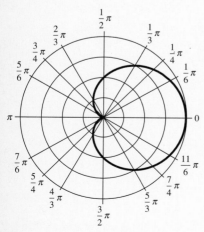

$r = a + b \cos \theta \quad \dfrac{a}{b} = 1$

(b) cardioid

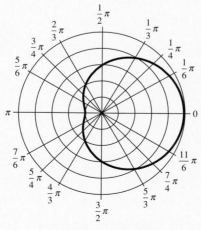

$r = a + b \cos \theta \quad 1 < \dfrac{a}{b} < 2$

(c) limaçon with a dent

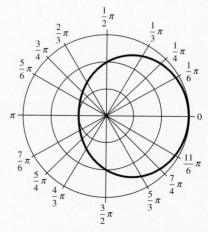

$r = a + b \cos \theta \quad 2 \le \dfrac{a}{b}$

(d) convex limaçon

FIGURE 23

Later in this section when horizontal and vertical tangent lines of polar graphs are discussed, the reason that limaçons of type 3 have a dent and those of type 4 have no dent will be apparent.

From the equation of a limaçon, we can also determine its symmetry and the direction in which it points.

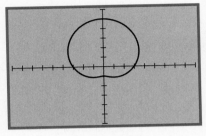

[−9, 9] by [−6, 6]

$r = 3 + 2 \sin \theta$

FIGURE 24

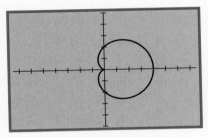

[−7.5, 7.5] by [−5, 5]

$r = 2 + 2 \cos \theta$

FIGURE 25

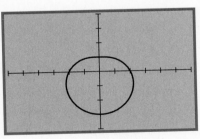

[−6, 6] by [−4, 4]

$r = 2 - \sin \theta$

FIGURE 26

Symmetry and Direction of a Limaçon

$a > 0$ and $b > 0$

$r = a + b \cos \theta$	Symmetry with respect to polar axis; points to right.
$r = a - b \cos \theta$	Symmetry with respect to polar axis; points to left.
$r = a + b \sin \theta$	Symmetry with respect to the $\frac{1}{2}\pi$ axis; points upward.
$r = a - b \sin \theta$	Symmetry with respect to the $\frac{1}{2}\pi$ axis; points downward.

▶ **EXAMPLE 5**   For each of the following limaçons, determine the type, its symmetry, and the direction it points, and plot the limaçon: **(a)** $r = 3 + 2 \sin \theta$; **(b)** $r = 2 + 2 \cos \theta$; **(c)** $r = 2 - \sin \theta$.

Solution

(a) The equation $r = 3 + 2 \sin \theta$ is of the form $r = a + b \sin \theta$ with $a = 3$ and $b = 2$. Because $\dfrac{a}{b} = \dfrac{3}{2}$ and $1 < \dfrac{3}{2} < 2$, the graph is a limaçon with a dent. It is symmetric with respect to the $\frac{1}{2}\pi$ axis and points upward. We plot the graph in the $[-9, 9]$ by $[-6, 6]$ window and obtain the limaçon in Figure 24.

(b) The equation $r = 2 + 2 \cos \theta$ is of the form $r = a + b \cos \theta$ with $a = 2$ and $b = 2$. Because $\dfrac{a}{b} = 1$, the graph is a cardioid. It is symmetric with respect to the polar axis and points to the right. We plot the cardioid in the $[-7.5, 7.5]$ by $[-5, 5]$ window as shown in Figure 25.

(c) The equation $r = 2 - \sin \theta$ is of the form $r = a - b \sin \theta$ with $a = 2$ and $b = 1$. Because $\dfrac{a}{b} = 2$, the graph is a convex limaçon. It is symmetric with respect to the $\frac{1}{2}\pi$ axis and points downward. The graph appears in Figure 26.   ◀

The graph of an equation of the form

$$r = a \cos n\theta \quad \text{or} \quad r = a \sin n\theta$$

is a **rose,** having n leaves if n is odd and $2n$ leaves if n is even.

▶   *EXAMPLE 6*   Describe and plot the graph of the equation

$$r = 4 \cos 2\theta$$

Solution   The equation is of the form $r = a \cos n\theta$ where n is 2. Because n is even, the graph is a four-leafed rose. The length of a leaf is 4. In Illustration 8, we proved that the graph is symmetric with respect to the polar axis, the $\frac{1}{2}\pi$ axis, and the pole. The graph contains the pole because when $r = 0$ we have

$$\cos 2\theta = 0$$

from which we obtain, for $0 \leq \theta \leq 2\pi$,

$$\theta = \tfrac{1}{4}\pi \qquad \theta = \tfrac{3}{4}\pi \qquad \theta = \tfrac{5}{4}\pi \qquad \theta = \tfrac{7}{4}\pi$$

We plot the graph in the $[-7.5, 7.5]$ by $[-5, 5]$ window as shown in Figure 27. The graph agrees with our description.   ◀

Observe that if in the equations for a rose we take $n = 1$, we get

$$r = a \cos \theta \quad \text{or} \quad r = a \sin \theta$$

which are equations for a circle. A circle can, therefore, be considered as a one-leafed rose.

Other polar graphs that occur frequently are *spirals* (see Exercises 37 through 40) and *lemniscates* (see Exercises 41 through 44). The graph in the next example is called *a spiral of Archimedes.*

▶   *EXAMPLE 7*   Describe and plot the graph of the equation

$$r = \theta \qquad \theta \geq 0$$

Solution   We first observe that there is no symmetry for the graph. Furthermore, as θ increases so does r. When $r = 0$, $\theta = 0$; so the pole is on the graph. When $\theta = n\pi$, where n is any integer, the graph intersects the polar axis or its extension, and when $\theta = \frac{1}{2}n\pi$, where n is any odd integer, the graph intersects the $\frac{1}{2}\pi$ axis or its extension. We plot the graph in the $[-42, 42]$ by $[-28, 28]$ window shown in Figure 28, which agrees with our description.   ◀

A formula for finding the slope of a tangent line to a polar graph is given by the following theorem.

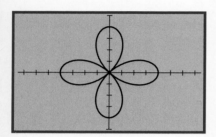

$[-7.5, 7.5]$ by $[-5, 5]$

$r = 4 \cos 2\theta$

FIGURE 27

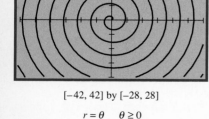

$[-42, 42]$ by $[-28, 28]$

$r = \theta \quad \theta \geq 0$

FIGURE 28

9.3.2 Theorem

If m is the slope of the tangent line to the graph of $r = f(\theta)$ at the point (r, θ)

$$m = \frac{\sin \theta \dfrac{dr}{d\theta} + r \cos \theta}{\cos \theta \dfrac{dr}{d\theta} - r \sin \theta}$$

Proof From Theorem 9.3.1, the graph of $r = f(\theta)$ is defined by the parametric equations

$$x = f(\theta)\cos \theta \quad \text{and} \quad y = f(\theta)\sin \theta$$

where θ is the parameter. From formula (4) of Section 9.1.

$$\frac{dy}{dx} = \frac{\dfrac{dy}{d\theta}}{\dfrac{dx}{d\theta}}$$

$$= \frac{f'(\theta)\sin \theta + f(\theta)\cos \theta}{f'(\theta)\cos \theta + f(\theta)(-\sin \theta)}$$

Replacing dy/dx by m, $f(\theta)$ by r, and $f'(\theta)$ by $dr/d\theta$, we get

$$m = \frac{\sin \theta \dfrac{dr}{d\theta} + r \cos \theta}{\cos \theta \dfrac{dr}{d\theta} - r \sin \theta} \qquad \blacksquare$$

The formula in Theorem 9.3.2 can be used to determine where a polar graph has horizontal and vertical tangent lines. This information is helpful when sketching polar graphs. The procedure is applied to two of the limaçons in Example 5 in the following illustration and the next example.

▷ **ILLUSTRATION 10**   The limaçon in Example 5(c) has the equation

$$r = 2 - \sin \theta$$

With this value of r and $dr/d\theta = -\cos \theta$, we have from Theorem 9.3.2

$$
\begin{aligned}
m &= \frac{\sin \theta(-\cos \theta) + (2 - \sin \theta)\cos \theta}{\cos \theta(-\cos \theta) - (2 - \sin \theta)\sin \theta} \\[2mm]
&= \frac{-\sin \theta \cos \theta + 2 \cos \theta - \sin \theta \cos \theta}{-\cos^2 \theta - 2 \sin \theta + \sin^2 \theta} \\[2mm]
&= \frac{2 \cos \theta - 2 \sin \theta \cos \theta}{-(1 - \sin^2 \theta) - 2 \sin \theta + \sin^2 \theta} \\[2mm]
&= \frac{2 \cos \theta(1 - \sin \theta)}{2 \sin^2 \theta - 2 \sin \theta - 1}
\end{aligned}
\qquad (4)
$$

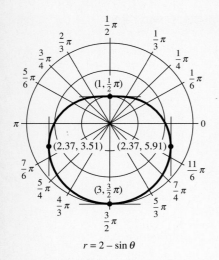

$r = 2 - \sin \theta$

FIGURE 29

The horizontal tangent lines of this limaçon occur when $m = 0$. Thus we equate the numerator of (4) to zero and solve for θ.

$$2 \cos \theta (1 - \sin \theta) = 0$$

$$\cos \theta = 0 \qquad\qquad 1 - \sin \theta = 0$$

$$\theta = \tfrac{1}{2}\pi \qquad \theta = \tfrac{3}{2}\pi \qquad\qquad \sin \theta = 1$$

$$\theta = \tfrac{1}{2}\pi$$

Therefore the curve has a horizontal tangent line at the points $(1, \tfrac{1}{2}\pi)$ and $(3, \tfrac{3}{2}\pi)$. The vertical tangent lines occur when the denominator of (4) is zero and the numerator is not zero. We solve the resulting equation.

$$2 \sin^2 \theta - 2 \sin \theta - 1 = 0$$

$$\sin \theta = \frac{-b \pm \sqrt{b^2 - 4ac}}{2a}$$

$$= \frac{2 \pm \sqrt{4 + 8}}{4}$$

$$\sin \theta = 1.3660 \qquad\qquad \sin \theta = -0.3660$$

$$\text{no solution} \qquad\qquad \theta \approx 3.51 \qquad \theta \approx 5.91$$

Hence the curve has a vertical tangent line at the points having polar coordinates $(2.37, 3.51)$ and $(2.37, 5.91)$. Figure 29 shows the limaçon and the horizontal and vertical tangent lines. ◀

▶ **EXAMPLE 8** Determine the points at which the limaçon in Example 5(a) has horizontal and vertical tangent lines. Sketch the graph and show these tangent lines.

Solution The limaçon has the equation

$$r = 3 + 2 \sin \theta$$

With this value of r and $dr/d\theta = 2 \cos \theta$, we have from Theorem 9.3.2

$$m = \frac{\sin \theta (2 \cos \theta) + (3 + 2 \sin \theta)\cos \theta}{\cos \theta (2 \cos \theta) - (3 + 2 \sin \theta)\sin \theta}$$

$$= \frac{2 \sin \theta \cos \theta + 3 \cos \theta + 2 \sin \theta \cos \theta}{2 \cos^2 \theta - 3 \sin \theta - 2 \sin^2 \theta}$$

$$= \frac{4 \sin \theta \cos \theta + 3 \cos \theta}{2 - 2 \sin^2 \theta - 3 \sin \theta - 2 \sin^2 \theta}$$

$$= -\frac{\cos \theta (4 \sin \theta + 3)}{4 \sin^2 \theta + 3 \sin \theta - 2} \qquad\qquad (5)$$

To determine the horizontal tangent lines we equate the numerator of (5) to zero.

$$\cos \theta (4 \sin \theta + 3) = 0$$

$$\cos \theta = 0 \qquad\qquad 4 \sin \theta + 3 = 0$$

$$\theta = \tfrac{1}{2}\pi \qquad \theta = \tfrac{3}{2}\pi \qquad\qquad \sin \theta = -\tfrac{3}{4}$$

$$\theta \approx 3.99 \qquad \theta \approx 5.44$$

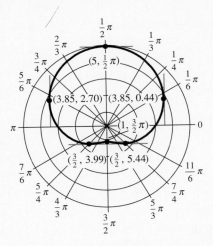

$r = 3 + 2 \sin \theta$

FIGURE 30

Thus the curve has a horizontal tangent line at the points $(5, \frac{1}{2}\pi)$, $(1, \frac{3}{2}\pi)$, $(\frac{3}{2}, 3.99)$ and $(\frac{3}{2}, 5.44)$.

The vertical tangent lines are found by equating the demominator of (5) to zero.

$$4 \sin^2 \theta + 3 \sin \theta - 2 = 0$$

$$\sin \theta = \frac{-b \pm \sqrt{b^2 - 4ac}}{2a}$$

$$= \frac{-3 \pm \sqrt{41}}{8}$$

$\sin \theta = 0.4254$ $\sin \theta = -1.1754$

$\theta \approx 0.44$ $\theta \approx 2.70$ no solution

Therefore the curve has a vertical tangent line at the points with polar coordinates $(3.85, 0.44)$ and $(3.85, 2.70)$.

Refer to Figure 30, which shows the limaçon and the horizontal and vertical tangent lines. ◀

Observe from Figure 30 that the limaçon has a dent. This fact is apparent because of the four horizontal tangent lines. The limaçon of Figure 29 has no dent; it has only two horizontal tangent lines.

EXERCISES 9.3

In Exercises 1 through 4, locate the point having the given set of polar coordinates.

1. (a) $(3, \frac{1}{6}\pi)$ **(b)** $(2, \frac{2}{3}\pi)$ **(c)** $(1, \pi)$
    (d) $(4, \frac{5}{4}\pi)$ **(e)** $(5, \frac{11}{6}\pi)$

2. (a) $(4, \frac{1}{3}\pi)$ **(b)** $(3, \frac{3}{4}\pi)$ **(c)** $(1, \frac{7}{6}\pi)$
    (d) $(2, \frac{3}{2}\pi)$ **(e)** $(5, \frac{5}{3}\pi)$

3. (a) $(1, -\frac{1}{4}\pi)$ **(b)** $(3, -\frac{5}{6}\pi)$ **(c)** $(-1, \frac{1}{4}\pi)$
    (d) $(-3, \frac{5}{6}\pi)$ **(e)** $(-2, -\frac{1}{2}\pi)$

4. (a) $(5, -\frac{2}{3}\pi)$ **(b)** $(2, -\frac{7}{6}\pi)$ **(c)** $(-5, \frac{2}{3}\pi)$
    (d) $(-2, \frac{7}{6}\pi)$ **(e)** $(-4, -\frac{5}{4}\pi)$

In Exercises 5 and 6, find the rectangular cartesian coordinates of the points whose polar coordinates are given.

5. (a) $(3, \pi)$ **(b)** $(\sqrt{2}, -\frac{3}{4}\pi)$
    (c) $(-4, \frac{2}{3}\pi)$ **(d)** $(-1, -\frac{7}{6}\pi)$

6. (a) $(-2, -\frac{1}{2}\pi)$ **(b)** $(-1, \frac{1}{4}\pi)$
    (c) $(2, -\frac{7}{6}\pi)$ **(d)** $(2, \frac{7}{4}\pi)$

In Exercises 7 and 8, find a set of polar coordinates of the points whose rectangular cartesian coordinates are given. Take $r > 0$ and $0 \le \theta < 2\pi$.

7. (a) $(1, -1)$ **(b)** $(-\sqrt{3}, 1)$
    (c) $(2, 2)$ **(d)** $(-5, 0)$

8. (a) $(3, -3)$ **(b)** $(-1, \sqrt{3})$
    (c) $(0, -2)$ **(d)** $(-2, -2\sqrt{3})$

In Exercises 9 through 12, find a cartesian equation of the graph having the given polar equation.

9. (a) $r^2 = 2 \sin 2\theta$ **(b)** $r^2 = \cos \theta$

10. (a) $r^2 \cos 2\theta = 10$ **(b)** $r^2 = 4 \cos 2\theta$

11. (a) $r \cos \theta = -1$ **(b)** $r = \dfrac{6}{2 - 3 \sin \theta}$

12. (a) $r = 2 \sin 3\theta$ **(b)** $r = \dfrac{4}{3 - 2 \cos \theta}$

In Exercises 13 through 20, sketch the graph of the equation.

13. (a) $\theta = \frac{1}{3}\pi$ **(b)** $r = \frac{1}{3}\pi$

14. (a) $\theta = \frac{3}{4}\pi$ **(b)** $r = \frac{3}{4}\pi$

15. (a) $\theta = 2$ **(b)** $r = 2$

16. (a) $\theta = -3$ **(b)** $r = -3$

17. (a) $r \cos \theta = 4$ **(b)** $r = 4 \cos \theta$

18. (a) $r \sin \theta = 2$ **(b)** $r = 2 \sin \theta$

19. (a) $r \sin \theta = -4$ **(b)** $r = -4 \sin \theta$

20. (a) $r \cos \theta = -5$ **(b)** $r = -5 \cos \theta$

In Exericises 21 through 30, determine the type of limaçon, its symmetry, and the direction in which it points. Plot the limaçon.

21. $r = 4(1 - \cos \theta)$ **22.** $r = 3(1 - \sin \theta)$

23. $r = 2(1 + \sin \theta)$ **24.** $r = 3(1 + \cos \theta)$

25. $r = 2 - 3 \sin \theta$

26. $r = 4 - 3 \sin \theta$

27. $r = 3 - 2 \cos \theta$

28. $r = 3 - 4 \cos \theta$

29. $r = 4 + 2 \sin \theta$

30. $r = 6 + 2 \cos \theta$

In Exercises 31 through 50, describe and plot the graph of the equation.

31. $r = 2 \sin 3\theta$

32. $r = 4 \sin 5\theta$

33. $r = 2 \cos 4\theta$

34. $r = 3 \cos 2\theta$

35. $r = 4 \sin 2\theta$

36. $r = 3 \cos 3\theta$

37. $r = e^{\theta}$ (logarithmic spiral)

38. $r = e^{\theta/3}$ (logarithmic spiral)

39. $r = \dfrac{1}{\theta}$ (reciprocal spiral)

40. $r = 2\theta$ (spiral of Archimedes)

41. $r^2 = 9 \sin 2\theta$ (lemniscate)

42. $r^2 = 16 \cos 2\theta$ (lemniscate)

43. $r^2 = -25 \cos 2\theta$ (lemniscate)

44. $r^2 = -4 \sin 2\theta$ (lemniscate)

45. $r = 2 \sin \theta \tan \theta$ (cissoid)

46. $r^2 = 8\theta$ (Fermat's spiral)

47. $r = 2 \sec \theta - 1$ (conchoid of Nicomedes)

48. $r = 2 \csc \theta + 3$ (conchoid of Nicomedes)

49. $r = |\sin 2\theta|$

50. $r = 2|\cos \theta|$

51. Polar graphs can be sketched on polar graph paper using a polar coordinate system as in Figure 21. Construct such a system with ruler, compass, and protractor. On this system sketch the graph of $r = 1 + 4 \sin \theta$.

52. Follow the instructions of Exercise 51 for the graph of $r = 2 + \cos \theta$.

In Exercises 53 through 60, determine the points at which the graph has horizontal and vertical tangent lines. Sketch the graph and show these tangent lines. For your sketches you may wish to use a polar coordinate system as suggested in Exercise 51.

53. $r = 4 + 3 \sin \theta$

54. $r = 2 + \cos \theta$

55. $r = 4 - 2 \cos \theta$

56. $r = 3 - 2 \sin \theta$

57. $r = \cos 2\theta$

58. $r = 2 \sin 3\theta$

59. $r^2 = 4 \sin 2\theta$

60. $r^2 = 9 \cos 2\theta$

In Exercises 61 through 64, plot the graphs of the two equations in the same window. Then use intersect (or trace and zoom-in) to approximate to two significant digits the rectangular cartesian coordinates of the points of intersection of the graphs. An analytic method for obtaining points of intersection of polar graphs is discussed in Section 9.4.

61. $\begin{cases} r = 3 \\ r = 2(1 + \cos \theta) \end{cases}$

62. $\begin{cases} r = 2 \cos \theta \\ r = 2 \sin \theta \end{cases}$

63. $\begin{cases} r = 2 \sin 3\theta \\ r = 4 \sin \theta \end{cases}$

64. $\begin{cases} r = 2 \cos 2\theta \\ r = 2 \sin \theta \end{cases}$

65. Explain why a one-to-one correspondence exists between the position of a point in the plane and its rectangular cartesian coordinates but no such correspondence exists for the point's polar coordinates. In your explanation give two points as examples: one in the first quadrant and one in the second quadrant.

9.4 LENGTH OF ARC AND AREA OF A REGION FOR POLAR GRAPHS

The formula of Theorem 9.2.3 for the length of arc L of a curve C, having parametric equations $x = f(t)$ and $y = g(t)$, from the point $(f(a), g(a))$ to the point $(f(b), g(b))$ is

$$L = \int_a^b \sqrt{[f'(t)]^2 + [g'(t)]^2}\, dt$$

where f' and g' are continuous on the closed interval $[a, b]$. Replacing $f'(t)$ by dx/dt and $g'(t)$ by dy/dt, this formula becomes

$$L = \int_a^b \sqrt{\left(\frac{dx}{dt}\right)^2 + \left(\frac{dy}{dt}\right)^2}\, dt \tag{1}$$

Suppose now that we wish to find the length of arc of a curve C whose polar equation is $r = F(\theta)$. If (x, y) is the cartesian representation of a point

P on C and (r, θ) is a polar representation of P, then from Theorem 9.3.1, parametric equations of C, where θ is the parameter, are

$$x = F(\theta)\cos \theta \quad \text{and} \quad y = F(\theta)\sin \theta \qquad (2)$$

Therefore, if F' is continuous on the closed interval $[\alpha, \beta]$, the formula for the length of arc of C is obtained from (1) by taking $t = \theta$ to get

$$L = \int_{\alpha}^{\beta} \sqrt{\left(\frac{dx}{d\theta}\right)^2 + \left(\frac{dy}{d\theta}\right)^2}\, d\theta \qquad (3)$$

From parametric equations (2)

$$\frac{dx}{d\theta} = F'(\theta)\cos \theta - F(\theta)\sin \theta \quad \text{and} \quad \frac{dy}{d\theta} = F'(\theta)\sin \theta + F(\theta)\cos \theta$$

Therefore

$$\left(\frac{dx}{d\theta}\right)^2 + \left(\frac{dy}{d\theta}\right)^2 = (F'(\theta)\cos \theta - F(\theta)\sin \theta)^2 + (F'(\theta)\sin \theta + F(\theta)\cos \theta)^2$$

The right-hand side of this equation can be simplified so that

$$\left(\frac{dx}{d\theta}\right)^2 + \left(\frac{dy}{d\theta}\right)^2 = [F'(\theta)]^2 + [F(\theta)]^2 \qquad (4)$$

You are asked to verify this equation in Exercise 50. Substituting from (4) into (3) and replacing $F'(\theta)$ by $dr/d\theta$ and $F(\theta)$ by r, we obtain the following formula for the length of arc of a polar graph:

$$L = \int_{\alpha}^{\beta} \sqrt{\left(\frac{dr}{d\theta}\right)^2 + r^2}\, d\theta \qquad (5)$$

▶ **EXAMPLE 1**   Find the length of the cardioid $r = 2(1 + \cos \theta)$.

Solution   The cardioid appears in Figure 1. To obtain the length of the entire curve we can let θ take on values from 0 to 2π or we can utilize the symmetry of the curve and find half the length by letting θ take on values from 0 to π.

Because $r = 2(1 + \cos \theta)$, $\dfrac{dr}{d\theta} = -2 \sin \theta$. Substituting into (5), integrating from 0 to π, and multiplying by 2 we have

$$L = 2\int_0^{\pi} \sqrt{(-2 \sin \theta)^2 + 4(1 + \cos \theta)^2}\, d\theta$$

$$= 4\int_0^{\pi} \sqrt{\sin^2 \theta + 1 + 2 \cos \theta + \cos^2 \theta}\, d\theta$$

$$= 4\sqrt{2}\int_0^{\pi} \sqrt{1 + \cos \theta}\, d\theta$$

To evaluate this integral, we use the identity $\cos^2 \tfrac{1}{2}\theta = \tfrac{1}{2}(1 + \cos \theta)$, so that $\sqrt{1 + \cos \theta} = \sqrt{2}\,|\cos \tfrac{1}{2}\theta|$. Because $0 \le \theta \le \pi$, $0 \le \tfrac{1}{2}\theta \le \tfrac{1}{2}\pi$;

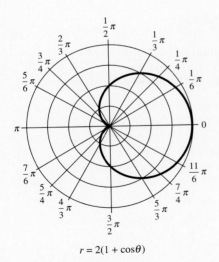

$r = 2(1 + \cos\theta)$

FIGURE 1

thus $\cos \frac{1}{2}\theta \geq 0$. Therefore $\sqrt{1 + \cos \theta} = \sqrt{2} \cos \frac{1}{2}\theta$. So

$$L = 4\sqrt{2} \int_0^\pi \sqrt{2} \cos \tfrac{1}{2}\theta \, d\theta$$

$$= 16 \sin \tfrac{1}{2}\theta \Big]_0^\pi$$

$$= 16 \qquad \blacktriangleleft$$

As with our previous formulas for length of arc, the formula for the length of arc of a polar graph most of the time leads to a definite integral either difficult or impossible to evaluate by the second fundamental theorem of the calculus. Our graphics calculator, however, provides us with an approximate value as in the next example.

▶ **EXAMPLE 2**   Find the length of the limaçon

$$r = 2 - \sin \theta$$

Solution   We plotted this limaçon in Example 5(c) of Section 9.3. Figure 2 shows the graph. From (5)

$$L = \int_0^{2\pi} \sqrt{\left(\frac{dr}{d\theta}\right)^2 + r^2} \, d\theta$$

$$= \int_0^{2\pi} \sqrt{\cos^2 \theta + (2 - \sin \theta)^2} \, d\theta$$

$$= \int_0^{2\pi} \sqrt{\cos^2 \theta + 4 - 4\sin \theta + \sin^2 \theta} \, d\theta$$

$$= \int_0^{2\pi} \sqrt{5 - 4\sin \theta} \, d\theta$$

On our graphics calulator

$$\text{NINT}(\sqrt{5 - 4\sin \theta}, 0, 2\pi) = 13.36489322$$

Thus to five significant digits, the length of the limaçon is 13.365.   ◀

We now develop a method for finding the area of a region bounded by two lines through the pole and a polar graph.

Let the function f be continuous and nonnegative on the closed interval $[\alpha, \beta]$. Let R be the region bounded by the curve whose equation is $r = f(\theta)$ and by the lines $\theta = \alpha$ and $\theta = \beta$. Then the region R is the region AOB shown in Figure 3.

Consider a partition Δ of $[\alpha, \beta]$ defined by

$$\alpha = \theta_0 < \theta_1 < \theta_2 < \ldots < \theta_{i-1} < \theta_i < \ldots < \theta_{n-1} < \theta_n = \beta$$

Thus we have n subintervals of the form $[\theta_{i-1}, \theta_i]$, $i = 1, 2, \ldots, n$. Let w_i be a value of θ in the ith subinterval $[\theta_{i-1}, \theta_i]$. See Figure 4, where the ith subinterval is shown together with $\theta = w_i$. The radian measure of the angle between the lines $\theta = \theta_{i-1}$ and $\theta = \theta_i$ is denoted by $\Delta_i\theta$. The number of square units in the area of the circular sector of radius $f(w_i)$ units and central angle of radian measure $\Delta_i \theta$ is given by

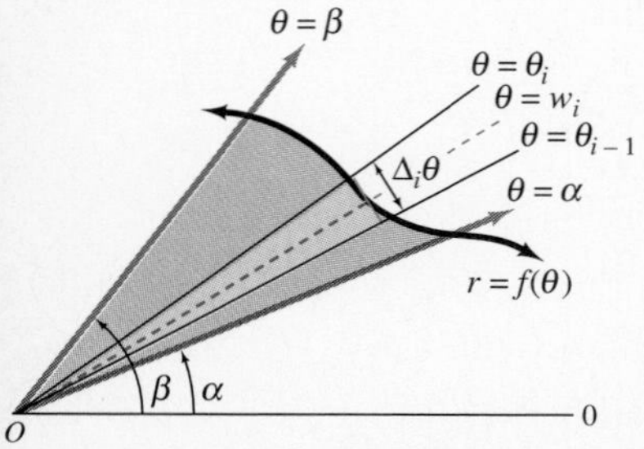

$$\tfrac{1}{2}[f(w_i)]^2 \, \Delta_i\theta$$

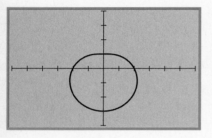

[−6, 6] by [−4, 4]

$r = 2 - \sin \theta$

FIGURE 2

FIGURE 3

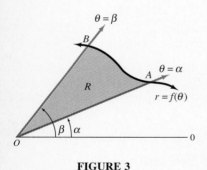

FIGURE 4

There is such a circular sector for each of the n subintervals. The sum of the measures of the areas of these n circular sectors is

$$\tfrac{1}{2}[f(w_1)]^2\, \Delta_1\theta + \tfrac{1}{2}[f(w_2)]^2\, \Delta_2\theta + \ldots + \tfrac{1}{2}[f(w_i)]^2\, \Delta_i\theta + \ldots + \tfrac{1}{2}[f(w_n)]^2\, \Delta_n\theta$$

which can be written, using sigma notation, as

$$\sum_{i=1}^{n} \tfrac{1}{2}[f(w_i)]^2\, \Delta_i\theta \tag{6}$$

Let $\|\Delta\|$ be the norm of the partition Δ; that is, $\|\Delta\|$ is the measure of the largest $\Delta_i\theta$. Then if A square units is the area of region R, A is the limit of Riemann sum (6) as $\|\Delta\|$ approaches 0, which is a definite integral as stated in the following theorem.

9.4.1 Theorem

Let R be the region bounded by the lines $\theta = \alpha$ and $\theta = \beta$ and the curve whose equation is $r = f(\theta)$, where f is continuous and nonnegative on the closed interval $[\alpha, \beta]$. Then if A square units is the area of region R,

$$A = \lim_{\|\Delta\| \to 0} \sum_{i=1}^{n} \tfrac{1}{2}[f(w_i)]^2\, \Delta_i\theta$$
$$= \frac{1}{2}\int_{\alpha}^{\beta} [f(\theta)]^2\, d\theta$$

▶ **EXAMPLE 3** Find the area of the region bounded by the cardioid of Example 1: $r = 2 + 2\cos\theta$.

Solution The region together with an element of area appears in Figure 5. Because the graph is symmetric with respect to the polar axis, we take

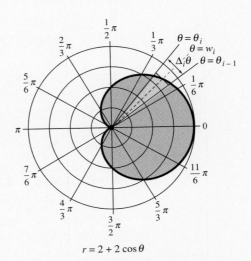

$$r = 2 + 2\cos\theta$$

FIGURE 5

the θ limits from 0 to π that determine the area of the region bounded by the curve above the polar axis. Then the area of the entire region is obtained by multiplying that area by 2. Thus, if A square units is the required area,

$$A = 2 \lim_{\|\Delta\| \to 0} \sum_{i=1}^{n} \tfrac{1}{2}(2 + 2 \cos w_i)^2 \, \Delta_i \theta$$

$$= 2 \int_{0}^{\pi} \tfrac{1}{2}(2 + 2 \cos \theta)^2 \, d\theta$$

$$= 4 \int_{0}^{\pi} (1 + 2 \cos \theta + \cos^2 \theta) \, d\theta$$

$$= 4 \left[\theta + 2 \sin \theta + \tfrac{1}{2}\theta + \tfrac{1}{4} \sin 2\theta \right]_{0}^{\pi}$$

$$= 4(\pi + 0 + \tfrac{1}{2}\pi + 0 - 0)$$

$$= 6\pi$$

◀

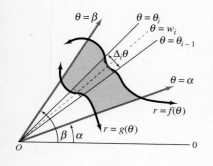

FIGURE 6

Consider now the region bounded by the lines $\theta = \alpha$ and $\theta = \beta$ and the two curves whose equations are $r = f(\theta)$ and $r = g(\theta)$, where f and g are continuous on the closed interval $[\alpha, \beta]$ and $f(\theta) \geq g(\theta)$ on $[\alpha, \beta]$. See Figure 6. We wish to find the area of this region. We take a partition of the interval $[\alpha, \beta]$ with w_i a value of θ in the ith subinterval $[\theta_{i-1}, \theta_i]$. The measure of the area of an element is the difference of the measures of the areas of two circular sectors:

$$\tfrac{1}{2}[f(w_i)]^2 \, \Delta_i \theta - \tfrac{1}{2}[g(w_i)]^2 \, \Delta_i \theta = \tfrac{1}{2}([f(w_i)]^2 - [g(w_i)]^2) \, \Delta_i \theta$$

The sum of the measures of the areas of n such elements is given by

$$\sum_{i=1}^{n} \tfrac{1}{2}([f(w_i)]^2 - [g(w_i)]^2) \, \Delta_i \theta$$

Hence, if A square units is the area of the region desired, we have

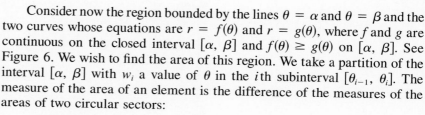

$$A = \lim_{\|\Delta\| \to 0} \sum_{i=1}^{n} \tfrac{1}{2}([f(w_i)]^2 - [g(w_i)]^2) \, \Delta_i \theta$$

Because f and g are continuous on $[\alpha, \beta]$, so also is $f - g$; therefore the limit exists and is equal to a definite integral. Thus

$$A = \frac{1}{2} \int_{\alpha}^{\beta} ([f(\theta)]^2 - [g(\theta)]^2) \, d\theta$$

▶ **EXAMPLE 4**   Find the area of the region inside the circle $r = 3 \sin \theta$ and outside the limaçon $r = 2 - \sin \theta$.

Solution   We first find the points of intersection of the two curves. Equating the right-hand sides of the two equations, we get

$$3 \sin \theta = 2 - \sin \theta$$

$$\sin \theta = \tfrac{1}{2}$$

$$\theta = \tfrac{1}{6}\pi \qquad \theta = \tfrac{5}{6}\pi$$

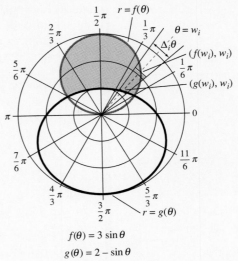

$$f(\theta) = 3 \sin \theta$$
$$g(\theta) = 2 - \sin \theta$$

FIGURE 7

The curves are sketched and the region is shown together with an element of area in Figure 7.

If we let $f(\theta) = 3 \sin \theta$ and $g(\theta) = 2 - \sin \theta$, then the equation of the circle is $r = f(\theta)$, and the equation of the limaçon is $r = g(\theta)$.

Instead of taking the limits from $\frac{1}{6}\pi$ to $\frac{5}{6}\pi$ we use the property of symmetry with respect to the $\frac{1}{2}\pi$ axis and take the limits from $\frac{1}{6}\pi$ to $\frac{1}{2}\pi$ and multiply by 2. Then, if A square units is the area of the given region,

$$A = 2 \lim_{\|\Delta\| \to 0} \sum_{i=1}^{n} \tfrac{1}{2}([f(w_i)]^2 - [g(w_i)]^2)\, \Delta_i \theta$$

$$= 2 \cdot \tfrac{1}{2} \int_{\pi/6}^{\pi/2} ([f(\theta)]^2 - [g(\theta)]^2)\, d\theta$$

$$= \int_{\pi/6}^{\pi/2} [9 \sin^2 \theta - (2 - \sin \theta)^2]\, d\theta$$

$$= 8 \int_{\pi/6}^{\pi/2} \sin^2 \theta\, d\theta + 4 \int_{\pi/6}^{\pi/2} \sin \theta\, d\theta - 4 \int_{\pi/6}^{\pi/2} d\theta$$

$$= 4 \int_{\pi/6}^{\pi/2} (1 - \cos 2\theta)\, d\theta + \Big[-4 \cos \theta - 4\theta\Big]_{\pi/6}^{\pi/2}$$

$$= 4\theta - 2 \sin 2\theta - 4 \cos \theta - 4\theta \Big]_{\pi/6}^{\pi/2}$$

$$= -2 \sin 2\theta - 4 \cos \theta \Big]_{\pi/6}^{\pi/2}$$

$$= (-2 \sin \pi - 4 \cos \tfrac{1}{2}\pi) - (-2 \sin \tfrac{1}{3}\pi - 4 \cos \tfrac{1}{6}\pi)$$

$$= 2 \cdot \tfrac{1}{2}\sqrt{3} + 4 \cdot \tfrac{1}{2}\sqrt{3}$$

$$= 3\sqrt{3}$$

◀

In the above example, we found the points of intersection of the two polar graphs by solving the two equations simultaneously. This procedure does not always give every point of intersection, as it does when dealing with

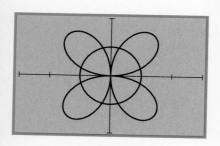

[−3, 3] by [−2, 2]

$r = 2 \sin 2\theta$ and $r = 1$

FIGURE 8

equations in cartesian coordinates. Because a point has an unlimited number of sets of polar coordinates, it is possible to have as the intersection of two polar graphs a point for which no single pair of polar coordinates satisfies both equations. This situation occurs in the following illustration.

▷ **ILLUSTRATION 1**   Figure 8 shows the graphs of the four-leafed rose, $r = 2 \sin 2\theta$, and the circle, $r = 1$, plotted in the same $[−3, 3]$ by $[−2, 2]$ window. Observe that the graphs intersect in eight points.

Solving the two equations simultaneously gives

$$2 \sin 2\theta = 1$$
$$\sin 2\theta = \tfrac{1}{2}$$

Therefore

$$2\theta = \tfrac{1}{6}\pi \qquad 2\theta = \tfrac{5}{6}\pi \qquad 2\theta = \tfrac{13}{6}\pi \qquad 2\theta = \tfrac{17}{6}\pi$$
$$\theta = \tfrac{1}{12}\pi \qquad \theta = \tfrac{5}{12}\pi \qquad \theta = \tfrac{13}{12}\pi \qquad \theta = \tfrac{17}{12}\pi$$

We have, therefore, obtained four points of intersection: $(1, \tfrac{1}{12}\pi)$, $(1, \tfrac{5}{12}\pi)$, $(1, \tfrac{13}{12}\pi)$, and $(1, \tfrac{17}{12}\pi)$. The other four points are obtained by taking another form of the equation of the circle $r = 1$; that is, consider the equation $r = -1$, which is an equation of the same circle. Solving this equation simultaneously with the equation of the four-leafed rose, we have

$$\sin 2\theta = -\tfrac{1}{2}$$

Then we get

$$2\theta = \tfrac{7}{6}\pi \qquad 2\theta = \tfrac{11}{6}\pi \qquad 2\theta = \tfrac{19}{6}\pi \qquad 2\theta = \tfrac{23}{6}\pi$$
$$\theta = \tfrac{7}{12}\pi \qquad \theta = \tfrac{11}{12}\pi \qquad \theta = \tfrac{19}{12}\pi \qquad \theta = \tfrac{23}{12}\pi$$

Thus we have the points: $(-1, \tfrac{7}{12}\pi)$, $(-1, \tfrac{11}{12}\pi)$, $(-1, \tfrac{19}{12}\pi)$, and $(-1, \tfrac{23}{12}\pi)$. Incidentally, $(-1, \tfrac{7}{12}\pi)$ also can be written as $(1, \tfrac{19}{12}\pi)$, $(-1, \tfrac{11}{12}\pi)$ can be written as $(1, \tfrac{23}{12}\pi)$, $(-1, \tfrac{19}{12}\pi)$ can be written as $(1, \tfrac{7}{12}\pi)$, and $(-1, \tfrac{23}{12}\pi)$ can be written as $(1, \tfrac{11}{12}\pi)$.

Figure 9 shows the two graphs sketched on a polar coordinate system where the eight points of intersection are labeled with their polar coordinates. ◀

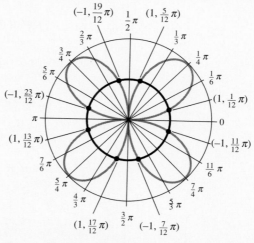

$r = 2 \sin 2\theta$ and $r = 1$

FIGURE 9

If you plot the two graphs of the previous illustration in simultaneous mode on your graphics calculator, you will observe that the second group of four points are not reached at the same time because the two graphs do not have the same value of θ for these points.

While plotting two polar graphs will indicate the number of points of intersection, the polar coordinates of these points are not always easily found by the trace and zoom-in features of your calculator. However, we do have a general method for finding the points of intersection analytically. The method is based on the fact that if an equation of a polar graph is $r = f(\theta)$, then the same curve is given by

$$(-1)^n r = f(\theta + n\pi) \tag{7}$$

where n is any integer.

▷ **ILLUSTRATION 2** Consider the graphs of Illustration 1. The graph of the equation $r = 2 \sin 2\theta$ also has the equation (by taking $n = 1$ in (7))

$$(-1)r = 2 \sin 2(\theta + \pi) \quad \Leftrightarrow \quad -r = 2 \sin 2\theta$$

If we take $n = 2$ in (7), the graph of $r = 2 \sin 2\theta$ also has the equation

$$(-1)^2 r = 2 \sin 2(\theta + 2\pi) \quad \Leftrightarrow \quad r = 2 \sin 2\theta$$

which is the same as the original equation. Taking any other integer n, we get either $r = 2 \sin 2\theta$ or $r = -2 \sin 2\theta$. The graph of the equation $r = 1$ also has the equation, by taking $n = 1$ in (7), $r = -1$. Other integer values of n in (7) applied to the equation $r = 1$ give either $r = 1$ or $r = -1$. ◀

One other remark is necessary regarding intersections of polar graphs. Because $(0, \theta)$, represents the pole for any θ, you can determine if the pole is a point of intersection by setting $r = 0$ in each equation and solving for θ.

General Method for Finding All Points of Intersection of the Polar Graphs of the Equations $r = f(\theta)$ and $r = g(\theta)$

1. Use (7) to determine all the distinct equations of the graphs:

$$r = f_1(\theta), r = f_2(\theta), r = f_3(\theta), \ldots \tag{8}$$
$$r = g_1(\theta), r = g_2(\theta), r = g_3(\theta), \ldots \tag{9}$$

2. Solve each equation (8) simultaneously with each equation (9).
3. Check to see if the pole is a point of intersection by setting $r = 0$ in each equation, thereby giving

$$f(\theta) = 0 \quad \text{and} \quad g(\theta) = 0$$

If each of these equations has a solution for θ, not necessarily the same, then the pole lies on both graphs.

▶ **EXAMPLE 5** Find the area of the region inside the four-leafed rose $r = 2 \sin 2\theta$ and outside the circle $r = 1$.

Solution In Illustration 1, we found the eight points of intersection of the two graphs and sketched them in Figure 9. From the figure observe that, because of symmetry, one-fourth of the required area is obtained by taking

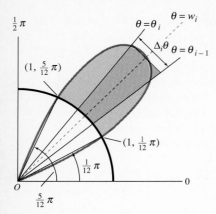

FIGURE 10

the θ limits from $\frac{1}{12}\pi$ to $\frac{5}{12}\pi$. This region and an element of area appear in Figure 10. Thus if A square units is the required area,

$$A = 4 \lim_{\|\Delta\| \to 0} \sum_{i=1}^{n} \frac{1}{2}[(2 \sin 2\, w_i)^2 - \frac{1}{2}(1)^2]\, \Delta_i \theta$$

$$= 4 \cdot \frac{1}{2} \int_{\pi/12}^{5\pi/12} (4 \sin^2 2\theta - 1)\, d\theta$$

$$= 2 \int_{\pi/12}^{5\pi/12} (2 - 2\cos 4\theta - 1)\, d\theta$$

$$= 2 \int_{\pi/12}^{5\pi/12} (1 - 2\cos 4\theta)\, d\theta$$

$$= 2\left[\theta - \frac{1}{2}\sin 4\theta \right]_{\pi/12}^{5\pi/12}$$

$$= 2\left[\frac{5}{12}\pi - \frac{1}{2}\sin \frac{5}{3}\pi - \frac{1}{12}\pi + \frac{1}{2}\sin \frac{1}{3}\pi \right]$$

$$= 2\left[\frac{1}{3}\pi - \frac{1}{2}(-\frac{1}{2}\sqrt{3}) + \frac{1}{2}(\frac{1}{2}\sqrt{3}) \right]$$

$$= \frac{2}{3}\pi + \sqrt{3}$$

◀

EXERCISES 9.4

In Exercises 1 through 4, use the length of arc formula to find the circumference of the circle having the given polar equation.

1. $r = 5 \cos \theta$

2. $r = 4 \sin \theta$

3. $r = a, a > 0$

4. $r = a \sin \theta, a > 0$

In Exercises 5 through 12, find the exact length of arc of the given polar graph.

5. The entire curve $r = 4 + 4 \cos \theta$

6. The entire curve $r = 1 - \sin \theta$

7. The entire curve $r = 3 \cos^2 \frac{1}{2}\theta$

8. $r = 3\theta$; from $\theta = 0$ to $\theta = 2\pi$

9. $r = e^{2\theta}$; from $\theta = 0$ to $\theta = 4$

10. $r = 3\theta^2$; from $\theta = 0$ to $\theta = \pi$

11. $r = 2 \sin^3 \frac{1}{3}\theta$; from $\theta = 0$ to $\theta = 6\pi$

12. $r = \sin^2 \frac{1}{2}\theta$; from $\theta = 0$ to $\theta = \frac{1}{2}\pi$

In Exercises 13 through 20, use the NINT capability of your graphics calculator to find an approximate value to four significant digits of the length of arc of the given polar graph.

13. The limaçon $r = 3 + \cos \theta$

14. The limaçon $r = 3 - 2 \sin \theta$

15. The loop of the limaçon $r = 2 - 3 \sin \theta$

16. The loop of the limaçon $r = 1 + 2 \cos \theta$

17. One leaf of the rose $r = 2 \sin 3\theta$

18. One leaf of the rose $r = 3 \cos 4\theta$

19. The lemniscate $r^2 = 25 \cos 2\theta$

20. The lemniscate $r^2 = 4 \sin 2\theta$

In Exercises 21 through 26, find the exact area of the region enclosed by the graph of the equation.

21. $r = 3 \cos \theta$

22. $r = 2 - \sin \theta$

23. $r = 4 \cos 3\theta$

24. $r = 4 \sin^2 \frac{1}{2}\theta$

25. $r^2 = 4 \sin 2\theta$

26. $r = 4 \sin^2 \theta \cos \theta$

27. Find the area of the region enclosed by the graph of the equation $r = \theta$ from $\theta = 0$ to $\theta = \frac{3}{2}\pi$.

28. Find the area of the region enclosed by the graph of $r = e^{\theta}$ and the lines $\theta = 0$ and $\theta = 1$.

In Exercises 29 through 32, find the area of the region enclosed by one loop of the graph of the equation.

29. $r = 3 \cos 2\theta$

30. $r = 4(1 - 2 \cos \theta)$

31. $r = 1 + 3 \sin \theta$

32. $r = 4 \sin 3\theta$

In Exercises 33 through 36, find the area of the intersection of the regions enclosed by the graphs of the two equations.

33. $\begin{cases} r = 2 \\ r = 3 - 2 \cos \theta \end{cases}$

34. $\begin{cases} r = 4 \sin \theta \\ r = 4 \cos \theta \end{cases}$

35. $\begin{cases} r = 3 \sin 2\theta \\ r = 3 \cos 2\theta \end{cases}$

36. $\begin{cases} r^2 = 2 \cos 2\theta \\ r = 1 \end{cases}$

In Exercises 37 through 40, find the exact area of the region inside the graph of the first equation and outside the graph of the second equation.

37. $\begin{cases} r = 3 \\ r = 3(1 - \cos \theta) \end{cases}$

38. $\begin{cases} r^2 = 4 \sin 2\theta \\ r = \sqrt{2} \end{cases}$

39. $\begin{cases} r = 2 \sin \theta \\ r = \sin \theta + \cos \theta \end{cases}$

40. $\begin{cases} r = 4 \sin \theta \\ r = 2 \end{cases}$

41. **(a)** Find the coordinates of all points of intersection of the limaçon $r = 1 + 4 \cos \theta$ and the circle $r = 1$.
(b) Find the area of the region inside the loop of the limaçon and outside the circle.

42. **(a)** Find the coordinates of all points of intersection of the limaçon $r = 1 - 3 \sin \theta$ and the circle $r = 1$.
(b) Find the area of the region inside the loop of the limaçon and outside the circle.

43. **(a)** Find the coordinates of all points of intersection of the rose $r = 4 \cos 2\theta$ and the circle $r = 2$.
(b) Find the area of the region inside the rose and outside the circle.

44. **(a)** Find the coordinates of all points of intersection of the rose $r = 2 \sin 2\theta$ and the circle $r = 2 \sin \theta$.
(b) Find the area of the region inside the circle and outside the rose.

45. The face of a bow tie is the region enclosed by the graph of the equation $r^2 = 4 \cos 2\theta$. How much material is necessary to cover the face of the tie?

46. Determine the value of a for which the area of the region enclosed by the cardioid $r = a(1 - \cos \theta)$ is 9π square units.

47. Find the area of the region swept out by the radius vector of the spiral $r = a\theta$ during its second revolution that was not swept out during its first revolution.

48. Find the area of the region swept out by the radius vector of the spiral of Exercise 47 during its third revolution that was not swept out during its second revolution.

49. Find the area of the region inside the cardioid $r = a(1 + \cos \theta)$ and outside the circle $r = 2a \cos \theta$.

50. Verify Equation (4).

51. Suppose a classmate computes the area of the region in Exercise 49 as

$$\tfrac{1}{2} a^2 \int_0^{2\pi} [(1 + \cos \theta)^2 - 4 \cos^2 \theta] \, d\theta$$

How would you explain the classmate's error?

9.5 A UNIFIED TREATMENT OF CONIC SECTIONS AND POLAR EQUATIONS OF CONICS

You may have studied conics in a precalculus course where each of the three types of conics was defined separately. For either a review or first exposure of that procedure refer to Appendix Sections A.4 through A.8. An alternative approach is to start with a definition that gives a common property of conics and then introduce each of the conics as a special case of the general definition. We state this definition in the following theorem. The positive constant e in the statement of the theorem is the **eccentricity** of the conic.

9.5.1 Theorem

A conic section can be defined as the set of all points P in a plane such that the ratio of the undirected distance of P from a fixed point to the undirected distance of P from a fixed line that does not contain the fixed point is a positive constant e. Furthermore, if $e = 1$, the conic is a parabola; if $0 < e < 1$, it is an ellipse; and if $e > 1$, it is a hyperbola.

Proof If $e = 1$, we see by comparing the definition of a parabola as a set of points equidistant from a focus and a directrix (Definition A.4.1) with the statement of this theorem that the set is a parabola having the fixed point as its focus and the fixed line as its directrix.

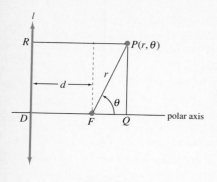

FIGURE 1

Suppose now that $e \neq 1$. We first obtain a polar equation of the set of points described. Let F denote the fixed point and l denote the fixed line. We take the pole at F and the polar axis and its extension perpendicular to l. We first consider the situation when the line l is to the left of the point F. Let D be the point of intersection of l with the extension of the polar axis, and let d denote the undirected distance from F to l. Refer to Figure 1. Let $P(r, \theta)$ be any point in the set to the right of l and on the terminal side of the angle of measure θ. Draw perpendiculars PQ and PR to the polar axis and line l, respectively. The point P is in the set described if and only if

$$|\overline{FP}| = e|\overline{RP}| \tag{1}$$

Because P is to the right of l, $\overline{RP} > 0$; thus $|\overline{RP}| = \overline{RP}$. Furthermore, $|\overline{FP}| = r$ because $r > 0$. Thus from (1),

$$r = e(\overline{RP}) \tag{2}$$

However, $\overline{RP} = \overline{DQ}$, and because $\overline{DQ} = \overline{DF} + \overline{FQ}$, we have

$$\overline{RP} = d + r \cos \theta$$

Substituting this expression for $\overline{RP}$ in (2) we get

$$r = e(d + r \cos \theta)$$

Solving for r gives

$$r = \frac{ed}{1 - e \cos \theta} \tag{3}$$

We obtain a cartesian representation of this equation by first replacing $\cos \theta$ by x/r. We have

$$r = \frac{ed}{1 - \dfrac{ex}{r}}$$

$$r = \frac{edr}{r - ex}$$

$$r - ex = ed$$

$$r = e(x + d)$$

We now replace r by $\pm \sqrt{x^2 + y^2}$ and get

$$\pm\sqrt{x^2 + y^2} = e(x + d)$$

Squaring on both sides of this equation gives

$$x^2 + y^2 = e^2x^2 + 2e^2\, dx + e^2d^2$$

$$y^2 + x^2(1 - e^2) = 2e^2\, dx + e^2d^2$$

Because $e \neq 1$, we can divide on both sides of this equation by $1 - e^2$ and obtain

$$x^2 - \frac{2e^2d}{1 - e^2}x + \frac{1}{1 - e^2}y^2 = \frac{e^2d^2}{1 - e^2}$$

Completing the square for the terms involving x by adding $e^4 d^2/(1 - e^2)^2$ on both sides of the above equation we get

$$\left(x - \frac{e^2 d}{1 - e^2} \right)^2 + \frac{1}{1 - e^2} y^2 = \frac{e^2 d^2}{(1 - e^2)^2}$$

Dividing both sides of this equation by $e^2 d^2/(1 - e^2)^2$ gives us an equation of the form

$$\frac{(x - h)^2}{\dfrac{e^2 d^2}{(1 - e^2)^2}} + \frac{y^2}{\dfrac{e^2 d^2}{1 - e^2}} = 1 \tag{4}$$

where

$$h = \frac{e^2 d}{1 - e^2} \tag{5}$$

Now let

$$\frac{e^2 d^2}{(1 - e^2)^2} = a^2 \qquad \text{where } a > 0 \tag{6}$$

Then (4) can be written as

$$\frac{(x - h)^2}{a^2} + \frac{y^2}{a^2(1 - e^2)} = 1 \tag{7}$$

If $0 < e < 1$, then $a^2(1 - e^2) > 0$ and we can let

$$b^2 = a^2(1 - e^2) \quad \text{where } 0 < e < 1 \tag{8}$$

Substituting from (8) in (7), we get

$$\frac{(x - h)^2}{a^2} + \frac{y^2}{b^2} = 1$$

which is an equation of an ellipse having its principal axis on the x axis and its center at $(h, 0)$, where $h > 0$.

If $e > 1$, then $a^2(e^2 - 1) > 0$, and we can let

$$b^2 = a^2(e^2 - 1) \qquad \text{where } e > 1 \tag{9}$$

Substituting from this equation in (7), we obtain

$$\frac{(x - h)^2}{a^2} - \frac{y^2}{b^2} = 1$$

which is an equation of a hyperbola having its principal axis on the x axis and its center at $(h, 0)$, where $h < 0$.

In a similar manner we can derive an equation of a central conic (an ellipse or hyperbola) from (1) when $e \neq 1$ if the line l is to the right of the point F at the pole. In this case instead of Equation (3) we have

$$r = \frac{ed}{1 + e \cos \theta} \tag{10}$$

The derivation of (10) is left as an exercise (see Exercise 33).

We can also derive an equation of a central conic from (1) when $e \neq 1$ if the line l is parallel to the polar axis and the point F is at the pole. In this case instead of Equation (3) we obtain

$$r = \frac{ed}{1 \pm e \sin \theta} \tag{11}$$

where e and d are, respectively, the eccentricity and undirected distance between F and l. The plus sign is taken when l is above F, and the minus sign is taken when it is below F. The derivations of (11) are left as exercises (see Exercises 34 and 35).

We can reverse the steps in going from (1) to (7). Thus if P is any point on a central conic, Equation (1) is satisfied.

Therefore we conclude that a conic can be defined by the described set of points. ∎

In Appendix Sections A.7 and A.8, we defined the eccentricity e of a central conic by the equation

$$e = \frac{c}{a} \quad \Leftrightarrow \quad c = ae$$

To show that the number e in the statement of Theorem 9.5.1 satisfies this equation for an ellipse, we substitute from (8) in the equation $c^2 = a^2 - b^2$; to show that the same equation is satisfied for a hyperbola, we substitute from (9) in the equation $c^2 = a^2 + b^2$. For an ellipse, we have

$$c^2 = a^2 - a^2(1 - e^2)$$

and for a hyperbola, we have

$$c^2 = a^2 + a^2(e^2 - 1)$$

In both cases, we obtain

$$c^2 = a^2 e^2$$
$$c = ae$$

In the proof of Theorem 9.5.1 we showed that when the conic is a parabola, the fixed point F mentioned in the theorem is the focus of the parabola and the fixed line is the directrix. In Exercise 40, you are asked to show that the point F is one of the foci when we have a central conic. If (7) is an equation of an ellipse, the point F is the left-hand focus, and if (7) is an equation of a hyperbola, F is the right-hand focus.

Consider now the standard form of a cartesian equation of a central conic having its principal axis on the x axis and its center at the origin:

$$\frac{x^2}{a^2} + \frac{y^2}{a^2(1 - e^2)} = 1 \tag{12}$$

The fixed line l mentioned in Theorem 9.5.1 is the directrix of the central conic corresponding to the focus at F. When the conic defined by Equation (12) is an ellipse, the directrix corresponding to the focus at $(-c, 0)$ or, equivalently, $(-ae, 0)$ has the equation

$$x = -ae - d$$

From (6) when $0 < e < 1$, $d = a(1 - e^2)/e$, so this equation becomes

$$x = -ae - \frac{a(1 - e^2)}{e}$$

$$x = -\frac{a}{e}$$

Similarly, when the conic defined by (12) is a hyperbola, the directrix corresponding to the focus at $(c, 0)$ or, equivalently, $(ae, 0)$ has the equation

$$x = ae - d$$

Again from (6), when $e > 1$, $d = a(e^2 - 1)/e$, so the above equation of the directrix can be written as

$$x = \frac{a}{e}$$

Hence we have shown that if (12) is an equation of an ellipse, a focus and its corresponding directrix are $(-ae, 0)$ and $x = -a/e$; and if (12) is an equation of a hyperbola, a focus and its corresponding directrix are $(ae, 0)$ and $x = a/e$.

Because (12) contains only even powers of x and y, its graph is symmetric with respect to both the x and y axes. Therefore, if there is a focus at $(-ae, 0)$ having a corresponding directrix of $x = -a/e$, by symmetry there is also a focus at $(ae, 0)$ having a corresponding directrix of $x = a/e$. Similarly, for a focus at $(ae, 0)$ and a corresponding directrix of $x = a/e$, there is also a focus at $(-ae, 0)$ and a corresponding directrix of $x = -a/e$. These results are summarized in the following theorem.

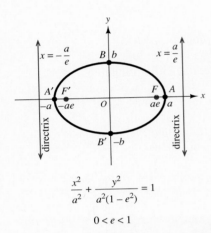

$$\frac{x^2}{a^2} + \frac{y^2}{a^2(1 - e^2)} = 1$$

$$0 < e < 1$$

FIGURE 2

9.5.2 Theorem

The central conic having the equation

$$\frac{x^2}{a^2} + \frac{y^2}{a^2(1 - e^2)} = 1 \tag{13}$$

where $a > 0$, has a focus at $(-ae, 0)$, whose corresponding directrix is $x = -a/e$, and a focus at $(ae, 0)$, whose corresponding directrix is $x = a/e$.

Figures 2 and 3 show sketches of the graph of (13) together with the foci and directrices in the respective cases of an ellipse and a hyperbola.

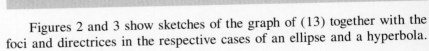

▶ **EXAMPLE 1**   The ellipse of Example 1 in Section A.7 has the equation

$$\frac{x^2}{25} + \frac{y^2}{16} = 1$$

(a) Find the eccentricity and directrices of this ellipse. **(b)** Sketch the ellipse and show the directrices and foci. Also choose any three points P on

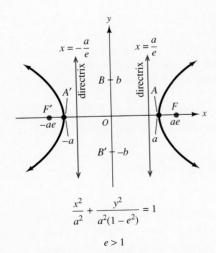

$$\frac{x^2}{a^2} + \frac{y^2}{a^2(1 - e^2)} = 1$$

$$e > 1$$

FIGURE 3

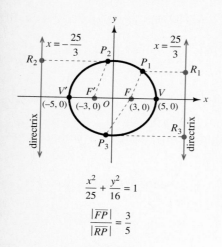

$$\frac{x^2}{25} + \frac{y^2}{16} = 1$$

$$\frac{|\overline{FP}|}{|\overline{RP}|} = \frac{3}{5}$$

FIGURE 4

the ellipse and draw the line segments whose lengths are the undirected distances from P to a focus and its corresponding directrix. Observe that the ratio of these distances is e.

Solution

(a) From the equation of the ellipse, $a = 5$ and $b = 4$. For an ellipse, $c^2 = a^2 - b^2$; thus $c = 3$. Because $e = c/a$, $e = 3/5$. Because $a/e = 25/3$, it follows from Theorem 9.5.2 that the directrix corresponding to the focus at $(3, 0)$ has the equation $x = 25/3$, and the directrix corresponding to the focus at $(-3, 0)$ has the equation $x = -25/3$.

(b) Figure 4 shows the ellipse, the directrices, and the foci, as well as three points P_1, P_2, and P_3 on the ellipse. For each of these points,

$$\frac{|\overline{FP}|}{|\overline{RP}|} = \frac{3}{5} \qquad \blacktriangleleft$$

▶ **EXAMPLE 2** The hyperbola of Example 1 in Section A.8 has the equation

$$\frac{x^2}{9} - \frac{y^2}{16} = 1$$

(a) Find the eccentricity and directrices of this hyperbola. **(b)** Sketch the hyperbola and show the directrices and foci. Also choose any three points P on the hyperbola and draw the line segments whose lengths are the undirected distances from P to a focus and its corresponding directrix. Observe that the ratio of these distances is e.

Solution

(a) From the equation of the hyperbola, $a = 3$ and $b = 4$. For a hyperbola, $c^2 = a^2 + b^2$; thus $c = 5$. Because $e = c/a$, $e = 5/3$. Because $a/e = 9/5$, we conclude from Theorem 9.5.2 that the directrix corresponding to the focus at $(5, 0)$ has the equation $x = 9/5$, and the directrix corresponding to the focus at $(-5, 0)$ has the equation $x = -9/5$.

(b) Figure 5 shows the hyperbola, the directrices, and the foci, as well as three points P_1, P_2, and P_3 on the hyperbola. For each of these points,

$$\frac{|\overline{FP}|}{|\overline{RP}|} = \frac{5}{3} \qquad \blacktriangleleft$$

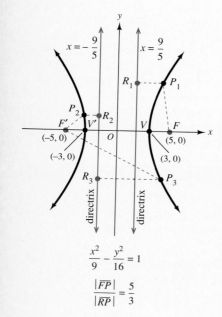

$$\frac{x^2}{9} - \frac{y^2}{16} = 1$$

$$\frac{|\overline{FP}|}{|\overline{RP}|} = \frac{5}{3}$$

FIGURE 5

In the proof of Theorem 9.5.1, you learned that all three types of conics have polar equations of the same form. When a focus is at the pole and the corresponding directrix is either perpendicular or parallel to the polar axis, an equation of the conic has the form of (3), (10), or (11). We have, therefore, the following theorem.

9.5.3 Theorem

The numbers e and d are, respectively, the eccentricity and the undirected distance between the focus and the corresponding directrix of a conic.

(i) If a focus of the conic is at the pole and the corresponding directrix is perpendicular to the polar axis, then an equation of the conic is

$$r = \frac{ed}{1 \pm e \cos \theta} \tag{14}$$

where the plus sign is taken when the directrix corresponding to the focus at the pole is to the right of the focus and the minus sign is taken when it is to the left of the focus.

(ii) If a focus of the conic is at the pole and the corresponding directrix is parallel to the polar axis, then an equation of the conic is

$$r = \frac{ed}{1 \pm e \sin \theta} \tag{15}$$

where the plus sign is taken when the directrix corresponding to the focus at the pole is above the focus, and the minus sign is taken when it is below the focus.

▶ **EXAMPLE 3**   A parabola has its focus at the pole and its vertex at $(4, \pi)$. Find a polar equation of the parabola and an equation of the directrix. Sketch the parabola and show the directrix. Check the graph on a graphics calculator.

Solution   Because the focus is at the pole and the vertex is at $(4, \pi)$, the polar axis and its extension are along the axis of the parabola. Furthermore, the vertex is to the left of the focus; so the directrix is also to the left of the focus. Hence an equation of the parabola is of the form of (14) with the minus sign. Because the vertex is at $(4, \pi)$, $\frac{1}{2}d = 4$; thus $d = 8$. The eccentricity $e = 1$, and therefore we obtain the equation

$$r = \frac{8}{1 - \cos \theta}$$

An equation of the directrix is given by $r \cos \theta = -d$, and because, $d = 8$, this equation is $r \cos \theta = -8$.

Figure 6 shows the parabola and the directrix. We obtain the same graph on our graphics calculator.   ◀

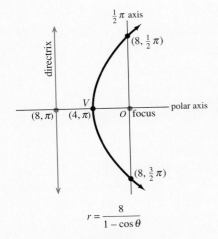

$$r = \frac{8}{1 - \cos \theta}$$

FIGURE 6

▶ **EXAMPLE 4**   An equation of a conic is

$$r = \frac{5}{3 + 2 \sin \theta}$$

Identify the conic, find the eccentricity, write an equation of the directrix corresponding to the focus at the pole, and find the vertices. Sketch the curve and check the graph on a graphics calculator.

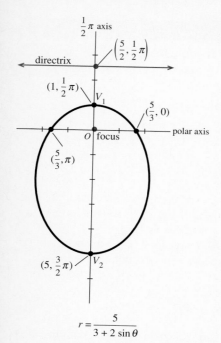

$$r = \frac{5}{3 + 2 \sin \theta}$$

FIGURE 7

Solution Dividing the numerator and denominator of the fraction in the given equation by 3 we obtain

$$r = \frac{\frac{5}{3}}{1 + \frac{2}{3} \sin \theta}$$

which is of the form of (15) with the plus sign. The eccentricity $e = \frac{2}{3}$. Because $e < 1$, the conic is an ellipse. Because $ed = \frac{5}{3}$, $d = \frac{5}{3} \div \frac{2}{3}$; thus $d = \frac{5}{2}$. The $\frac{1}{2}\pi$ axis and its extension are along the principal axis. The directrix corresponding to the focus at the pole is above the focus, and an equation of it is $r \sin \theta = \frac{5}{2}$. When $\theta = \frac{1}{2}\pi$, $r = 1$; and when $\theta = \frac{3}{2}\pi$, $r = 5$. The vertices are therefore at $(1, \frac{1}{2}\pi)$ and $(5, \frac{3}{2}\pi)$.

The ellipse, as sketched, appears in Figure 7. We obtain the same curve on our graphics calculator. ◀

▶ **EXAMPLE 5** The polar axis and its extension are along the principal axis of a hyperbola having a focus at the pole. The corresponding directrix is to the left of the focus. If the hyperbola contains the point $(1, \frac{2}{3}\pi)$ and $e = 2$, find **(a)** a polar equation of the hyperbola, **(b)** the vertices, **(c)** the center, **(d)** an equation of the directrix corresponding to the focus at the pole. **(e)** Sketch the hyperbola and check the graph on a graphics calculator.

Solution An equation of the hyperbola is of the form of (14) with the minus sign, where $e = 2$. We have, then,

$$r = \frac{2d}{1 - 2 \cos \theta}$$

(a) Because the point $(1, \frac{2}{3}\pi)$ lies on the hyperbola, its coordinates satisfy the equation. Therefore

$$1 = \frac{2d}{1 - 2(-\frac{1}{2})}$$

from which we obtain $d = 1$. Hence an equation of the hyperbola is

$$r = \frac{2}{1 - 2 \cos \theta} \tag{16}$$

(b) The vertices are the points on the hyperbola for which $\theta = 0$ and $\theta = \pi$. From (16), when $\theta = 0$, $r = -2$; and when $\theta = \pi$, $r = \frac{2}{3}$. Consequently, the left vertex V_1 is at the point $(-2, 0)$, and the right vertex V_2 is at the point $(\frac{2}{3}, \pi)$.

(c) The center C of the hyperbola is the point on the principal axis halfway between the two vertices. This is the point $(\frac{4}{3}, \pi)$.

(d) An equation of the directrix corresponding to the focus at the pole is given by $r \cos \theta = -d$. Because $d = 1$, this equation is $r \cos \theta = -1$.

(e) As an aid in sketching the hyperbola, we first draw the two asymptotes. These are lines through the center of the hyperbola that are parallel to the lines $\theta = \theta_1$ and $\theta = \theta_2$, where θ_1 and θ_2 are the values of θ in the interval $[0, 2\pi)$ for which r is not defined. From (16), r is not defined when $1 - 2 \cos \theta = 0$. Therefore $\theta_1 = \frac{1}{3}\pi$ and $\theta_2 = \frac{5}{3}\pi$. Figure 8 shows the hyperbola, as well as the two asymptotes and the directrix corresponding to the focus at the pole. Our graphics calculator gives the same graph. ◀

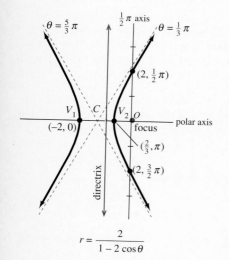

$$r = \frac{2}{1 - 2 \cos \theta}$$

FIGURE 8

EXERCISES 9.5

In Exercises 1 through 8, (a) find the eccentricity, foci, and directrices of the central conic. (b) Sketch the conic and show the foci and directrices. Also choose any three points P (in different quadrants) on the conic and draw the line segments whose lengths are the undirected distances from P to a focus and its corresponding directrix. Observe that the ratio of these distances is e.

1. $4x^2 + 9y^2 = 36$ **2.** $4x^2 + 9y^2 = 4$

3. $25x^2 + 4y^2 = 100$ **4.** $16x^2 + 9y^2 = 144$

5. $4x^2 - 25y^2 = 100$ **6.** $x^2 - 9y^2 = 9$

7. $16x^2 - 9y^2 = 144$ **8.** $4y^2 - x^2 = 16$

In Exercises 9 and 10, the polar equation represents a conic having a focus at the pole. Identify the conic.

9. (a) $r = \dfrac{3}{1 - \cos \theta}$ **(b)** $r = \dfrac{6}{4 + 5 \sin \theta}$

     (c) $r = \dfrac{5}{4 - \cos \theta}$ **(d)** $r = \dfrac{4}{1 + \sin \pi}$

10. (a) $r = \dfrac{1}{1 - \sin \theta}$ **(b)** $r = \dfrac{2}{3 + \sin \theta}$

     (c) $r = \dfrac{3}{2 + 4 \cos \theta}$ **(d)** $r = \dfrac{5}{1 - \cos \pi}$

In Exercises 11 through 22, the graph of the equation is a conic having a focus at the pole. (a) Find the eccentricity; (b) identify the conic; (c) write an equation of the directrix corresponding to the focus at the pole; and (d) sketch the curve and check your graph on your graphics calculator.

11. $r = \dfrac{2}{1 - \cos \theta}$ **12.** $r = \dfrac{4}{1 + \cos \theta}$

13. $r = \dfrac{5}{2 + \sin \theta}$ **14.** $r = \dfrac{4}{1 - 3 \cos \theta}$

15. $r = \dfrac{6}{3 - 2 \cos \theta}$ **16.** $r = \dfrac{1}{2 + \sin \theta}$

17. $r = \dfrac{9}{5 - 6 \sin \theta}$ **18.** $r = \dfrac{1}{1 - 2 \sin \theta}$

19. $r = \dfrac{10}{7 - 2 \sin \theta}$ **20.** $r = \dfrac{7}{3 + 4 \cos \theta}$

21. $r = \dfrac{10}{4 + 5 \cos \theta}$ **22.** $r = \dfrac{1}{5 - 3 \sin \theta}$

In Exercises 23 through 28, find a polar equation of the conic having a focus at the pole and satisfying the given conditions.

23. Parabola; vertex at $(4, \frac{3}{2}\pi)$

24. Ellipse; $e = \frac{1}{2}$; corresponding vertex at $(4, \pi)$

25. Hyperbola; $e = \frac{4}{3}$; $r \cos \theta = 9$ is the directrix corresponding to the focus at the pole

26. Hyperbola; vertices at $(1, \frac{1}{2}\pi)$ and $(3, \frac{1}{2}\pi)$

27. Ellipse; vertices at $(3, 0)$ and $(1, \pi)$

28. Parabola; vertex at $(6, \frac{1}{2}\pi)$

29. (a) Find a polar equation of the hyperbola having a focus at the pole and the corresponding directrix to the left of the focus if the point $(2, \frac{4}{3}\pi)$ is on the hyperbola and $e = 3$. **(b)** Write an equation of the directrix that corresponds to the focus at the pole.

30. (a) Find a polar equation of the hyperbola for which $e = 3$ and which has the line $r \sin \theta = 3$ as the directrix corresponding to a focus at the pole. **(b)** Find the polar equations of the two lines through the pole that are parallel to the asymptotes of the hyperbola.

31. Find the area of the region inside the ellipse $r = 6/(2 - \sin \theta)$ and above the parabola $r = 3/(1 + \sin \theta)$.

32. For the ellipse and parabola of Exercise 31, find the area of the region inside the ellipse and below the parabola.

33. Show that an equation of a conic having its principal axis along the polar axis and its extension, a focus at the pole, and the corresponding directrix to the right of the focus is $r = ed/(1 + e \cos \theta)$.

34. Show that an equation of a conic having its principal axis along the $\frac{1}{2}\pi$ axis and its extension, a focus at the pole, and the corresponding directrix above the focus is $r = ed/(1 + e \sin \theta)$.

35. Show that an equation of a conic having its principal axis along the $\frac{1}{2}\pi$ axis and its extension, a focus at the pole, and the corresponding directrix below the focus is $r = ed/(1 - e \sin \theta)$.

36. Show that the equation $r = k \csc^2 \frac{1}{2}\theta$, where k is a constant, is a polar equation of a parabola.

37. A comet is moving in a parabolic orbit around the sun at the focus of the parabola. When the comet is 80 million miles from the sun, the line segment from the sun to the comet makes an angle of $\frac{1}{3}\pi$ radians with the axis of the orbit. **(a)** Find an equation of the comet's orbit. **(b)** How close does the comet come to the sun?

38. The orbit of a planet is in the form of an ellipse having the equation $r = p/(1 + e \cos \theta)$ where the pole is at the sun. Find the average measure of the distance of the planet from the sun with respect to θ.

39. A satellite is traveling around the earth in an elliptical orbit having the center of the earth at one focus and an eccentricity of $\frac{1}{3}$. The closest distance that the satellite gets to the earth is 300 mi. Find the farthest distance that the satellite gets from the earth. Assume the earth's radius is 4000 mi.

40. Show that the point F mentioned in the proof of Theorem 9.5.1 is one of the foci when the conic is either an ellipse or a hyperbola. *Hint:* Use (7), which is the cartesian equation of a central conic having its center at $(h, 0)$, the value of h from Equation (5), the value of a from Equation (6), and the fact that $c = ae$.

41. Show that if α is the angle between the asymptotes of a hyperbola of eccentricity e then

$$\alpha = 2 \tan^{-1} \sqrt{e^2 - 1}$$

42. Describe how the shape of a conic changes as the eccentricity takes on the following values: 0.01, 0.10, 0.50, 0.99, 1.00, $\sqrt{2}$, 1.50, 2.00.

CHAPTER 9 REVIEW

▶ *SUGGESTIONS FOR REVIEW OF CHAPTER 9*

1. How do you find a cartesian equation of the graph of a pair of parametric equations?

2. How can you represent the graph of a function by a set of parametric equations?

3. If $x = f(t)$ and $y = g(t)$, how do you compute dy/dx and d^2y/dx^2? Make up an example to illustrate your answer.

4. How do you find horizontal and vertical tangent lines of the graph of a pair of parametric equations?

5. What is a cycloid? Define a cycloid by a pair of parametric equations.

6. What is the formula for the length of arc of a plane curve defined by the parametric equations $x = f(t)$ and $y = g(t)$?

7. Place a polar coordinate system and a rectangular cartesian coordinate system in the same diagram and show the relationships between the two sets of coordinates.

8. If a point P has polar coordinates (r, θ), where $r > 0$ and $0 < \theta < \frac{1}{2}\pi$, give two other sets of polar coordinates of P, one set for which $r < 0$ and one set for which $r > 0$.

9. Answer Suggestion 8 if $r < 0$ and $\frac{1}{2}\pi < \theta < \pi$.

10. How do you obtain a cartesian equation of a graph from its polar equation?

11. Write a polar equation of **(a)** a line containing the pole, **(b)** a line parallel to the polar axis, and **(c)** a line parallel to the $\frac{1}{2}\pi$ axis. Sketch each line.

12. Write a polar equation of **(a)** a circle whose center is at the pole, **(b)** a circle tangent to the $\frac{1}{2}\pi$ axis and center on the polar axis; **(c)** a circle tangent to the polar axis and center on the $\frac{1}{2}\pi$ axis. Sketch each circle.

13. Define the graph of the polar equation $r = f(\theta)$ by a pair of parametric equations. Make up an example illustrating your answer.

14. Write a polar equation for each of the four types of limaçons and sketch the limaçons.

15. Write a polar equation of **(a)** a three-leafed rose and **(b)** a four-leafed rose. Sketch the roses.

16. What is the formula for the length of arc of a polar graph?

17. What is the formula for the area of a region bounded by polar graphs?

18. Why is it more difficult to find points of intersection of polar graphs than to find points of intersection of graphs of cartesian equations?

19. State the definition that gives a common property of conics involving the eccentricity e. How does the value of e determine the type of conic?

20. Write an equation of an ellipse whose focus is at the pole and for which the corresponding directrix is perpendicular to the polar axis if **(a)** the directrix is to the right of the focus and **(b)** the directrix is to the left of the focus. Sketch each ellipse.

21. Write an equation of a hyperbola whose focus is at the pole and for which the corresponding directrix is parallel to the polar axis if **(a)** the directrix is above the focus and **(b)** the directrix is below the focus. Sketch each hyperbola.

22. Write an equation of a parabola whose focus is at the pole and **(a)** the corresponding directrix is perpendicular to the polar axis and to the left of the focus and **(b)** the corresponding directrix is parallel to the polar axis and above the focus. Sketch each parabola.

► MISCELLANEOUS EXERCISES FOR CHAPTER 9

In Exercises 1 through 4, (a) sketch the graph of the parametric equations and check your graph on your graphics calculator; (b) find a cartesian equation of the graph.

1. $x = 2 - t, y = 2t$

2. $x = t^2, y = t^3 + 1$

3. $x = 2t^3, y = 3t^2 - 4$

4. $x = 4 \cos t - 2, y = 4 \sin t + 3$

In Exercises 5 and 6, find $\dfrac{dy}{dx}$ and $\dfrac{d^2y}{dx^2}$ without eliminating the parameter.

5. $x = 9t^2 - 1, y = 3t + 1$ **6.** $x = e^{2t}, y = e^{-3t}$

In Exercises 7 and 8, find equations of the horizontal and vertical tangent lines, and then sketch the graph of the given pair of parametric equations.

7. $x = 12 - t^2, y = 12t - t^3$

8. $x = \dfrac{2at^2}{1 + t^2}, y = \dfrac{2at^3}{1 + t^2}, a > 0$
(the cissoid of Diocles)

In Exercises 9 and 10, locate the point having the given set of polar coordinates; then give two other sets of polar coordinates of the same point, one with the same value of r and one with an r having opposite sign.

9. (a) $(2, \frac{3}{4}\pi)$ **(b)** $(-3, \frac{7}{6}\pi)$

10. (a) $(4, -\frac{1}{3}\pi)$ **(b)** $(-1, \frac{1}{4}\pi)$

In Exercises 11 and 12, find the rectangular cartesian coordinates of the point whose polar coordinates are given.

11. (a) $(1, \frac{1}{2}\pi)$ **(b)** $(2, -\frac{1}{3}\pi)$
(c) $(4, \frac{5}{4}\pi)$ **(d)** $(-3, \frac{1}{6}\pi)$

12. (a) $(5, \pi)$ **(b)** $(-2, \frac{5}{6}\pi)$
(c) $(-\sqrt{2}, \frac{1}{4}\pi)$ **(d)** $(1, \frac{4}{3}\pi)$

In Exercises 13 and 14, find a set of polar coordinates of the point whose rectangular cartesian coordinates are given. Take $r > 0$ and $0 \le \theta < 2\pi$.

13. (a) $(-4, 4)$ **(b)** $(1, -\sqrt{3})$
(c) $(0, 6)$ **(d)** $(-2\sqrt{3}, -2)$

14. (a) $(-4, 0)$ **(b)** $(\sqrt{3}, 1)$
(c) $(-2, -2)$ **(d)** $(3, -3\sqrt{3})$

In Exercises 15 through 18, find a polar equation of the graph having the given cartesian equation.

15. $4x^2 - 9y^2 = 36$ **16.** $2xy = 1$

17. $x^2 + y^2 - 9x + 8y = 0$ **18.** $y^4 = x^2(a^2 - y^2)$

In Exercises 19 through 22, find a cartesian equation of the graph having the given polar equation.

19. $r^2 \sin 2\theta = 4$ **20.** $r(1 - \cos \theta) = 2$

21. $r^2 = \sin^2 \theta$ **22.** $r = a \tan^2 \theta$

In Exercises 23 through 26, sketch the graph of the equation.

23. (a) $\theta = \frac{1}{4}\pi$ **(b)** $r = 4$

24. (a) $\theta = \frac{2}{3}$ **(b)** $r = \frac{3}{2}$

25. (a) $r \cos \theta = 3$ **(b)** $r = 3 \cos \theta$

26. (a) $r \sin \theta = 6$ **(b)** $r = 6 \sin \theta$

In Exercises 27 through 32, determine the type of limaçon, its symmetry, and the direction in which it points. Plot the limaçon on your graphics calculator.

27. $r = 3 + 2 \cos \theta$ **28.** $r = 2 + 3 \sin \theta$

29. $r = 2(1 - \cos \theta)$ **30.** $r = 3(1 + \sin \theta)$

31. $r = 1 - 2 \sin \theta$ **32.** $r = 2 - \cos \theta$

In Exercises 33 through 38, describe and plot the graph of the equation on your graphics calculator.

33. $r = 3 \sin 2\theta$ **34.** $r = 3 \cos 2\theta$

35. $r = \sqrt{|\cos \theta|}$ **36.** $r = |\sin 2\theta|$

37. $r^2 = -\sin 2\theta$ **38.** $r^2 = 16 \cos \theta$

39. Describe and plot the graph of each of the following equations: **(a)** $r\theta = 3$ (reciprocal spiral); **(b)** $3r = \theta$ (spiral of Archimedes).

40. Show by hand that the equations $r = 1 + \sin \theta$ and $r = \sin \theta - 1$ have the same graph. Then check your graphs on your graphics calculator.

41. Find the exact length of arc of the curve having parametric equations $x = 2 - t$ and $y = t^2$ from $t = 0$ to $t = 3$.

42. Find the exact length of arc of the curve having parametric equations $x = t^2$ and $y = t^3$ from $t = 1$ to $t = 2$.

43. Find the exact length of arc of the cardioid $r = 4(1 - \sin \theta)$.

44. Find the exact length of arc of the polar graph $r = 3 \sec \theta$ from $\theta = 0$ to $\theta = \frac{1}{4}\pi$.

45. Find the area of the region enclosed by **(a)** the loop of the limaçon $r = 4(1 + 2 \cos \theta)$ and **(b)** the outer part of the limaçon.

46. Find the area of one leaf of the rose $r = 2 \sin 3\theta$.

47. Find the area of the region inside the graph of $r = 2a \sin \theta$ and outside the graph of $r = a$.

48. Find the area of the region inside the graph of the lemniscate $r^2 = 2 \sin 2\theta$ and outside the graph of the circle $r = 1$.

49. Find the area of the region swept out by the radius vector of the logarithmic spiral $r = e^{k\theta}$, $k > 0$, as θ varies from 0 to 2π.

50. Find the area of the intersection of the regions enclosed by the graphs of the two equations $r = a \cos \theta$ and $r = a(1 - \cos \theta)$, where $a > 0$.

51. Find a polar equation of the circle having its center at (r_0, θ_0) and a radius of a units. *Hint:* Apply the law of cosines to the triangle having vertices at the pole, (r_0, θ_0) and (r, θ).

52. Find the area enclosed by one loop of the curve $r = a \sin n\theta$, where n is a positive integer.

In Exercises 53 through 56, the equation is that of a conic having a focus at the pole. (a) Find the eccentricity; (b) identify the conic; (c) write an equation of the directrix that corresponds to the focus at the pole; (d) sketch the curve.

53. $r = \dfrac{2}{2 - \sin \theta}$

54. $r = \dfrac{5}{3 + 3 \sin \theta}$

55. $r = \dfrac{4}{2 + 3 \cos \theta}$

56. $r = \dfrac{4}{3 - 2 \cos \theta}$

In Exercises 57 through 60, find a polar equation of the conic satisfying the conditions, and sketch the graph.

57. A focus at the pole; vertices at $(2, \pi)$ and $(4, \pi)$

58. A focus at the pole; a vertex at $(6, \frac{1}{2}\pi)$; $e = \frac{3}{4}$

59. A focus at the pole; a vertex at $(3, \frac{3}{2}\pi)$; $e = 1$

60. The line $r \sin \theta = 6$ is the directrix corresponding to the focus at the pole and $e = \frac{5}{3}$

In Exercises 61 through 64, use the NINT capability of your graphics calculator to find an approximate value to four significant digits of the length of arc of the given curve.

61. $x = 2t^3$, $y = t - 2$; from $t = 2$ to $t = 3$

62. $x = e^t$, $y = \cos t$; from $t = -\frac{1}{2}\pi$ to $t = \frac{1}{2}\pi$

63. The entire limaçon $r = 4 - 2 \sin \theta$

64. One leaf of the rose $r = 4 \cos 3\theta$

65. The orbit of the planet Mercury around the sun is elliptical in shape with the sun at one focus, a semimajor axis of length 36 million miles, and an eccentricity of 0.206. Find **(a)** how close Mercury gets to the sun and **(b)** the greatest possible distance between Mercury and the sun.

66. A satellite is traveling around the earth in an elliptical orbit having the earth at one focus and an eccentricity of $\frac{1}{2}$. The closest distance that the satellite gets to the earth is 200 mi. Find the farthest distance that the satellite gets from the earth. Assume the earth's radius is 4000 mi.

67. A comet is moving in a parabolic orbit around the sun at the focus F of the parabola. An observation of the comet is made when it is at point P_1, 15 million miles from the sun, and a second observation is made when it is at point P_2, 5 million miles from the sun. The line segments FP_1 and FP_2 are perpendicular. With this information there are two possible orbits for the comet. Find how close the comet comes to the sun for each orbit.

68. If the distance between the two directrices of an ellipse is three times the distance between the foci, find the eccentricity.

69. Find a polar equation of the parabola containing the point $(2, \frac{1}{3}\pi)$, whose focus is at the pole and whose vertex is on the extension of the polar axis.

70. Find the area of the region bounded by the two parabolas $r = 2/(1 - \cos \theta)$ and $r = 2/(1 + \cos \theta)$.

71. A focal chord of a conic is a line segment passing through a focus and having its endpoints on the conic. Prove that if two focal chords of a parabola are perpendicular, the sum of the reciprocals of the measures of their lengths is a constant. *Hint:* Use polar coordinates.

72. A focal chord of a conic is divided into two segments by the focus. Prove that the sum of the reciprocals of the measures of the lengths of the two segments is the same, regardless of what chord is taken. *Hint:* Use polar coordinates.

73. An *epicycloid* is the curve traced by a point P on the circumference of a circle of radius b which is rolling externally on a fixed circle of radius a. If the origin is at the center of the fixed circle, $A(a, 0)$ is one of the points at which the given point P comes in contact with the fixed circle, B is the moving point of tangency of the two circles, and the parameter t is the radian measure of the angle AOB, prove that parametric equations of the epicycloid are

$$x = (a + b) \cos t - b \cos \frac{a + b}{b} t$$

and

$$y = (a + b) \sin t - b \sin \frac{a + b}{b} t$$

74. Plot on your graphics calculator the epicyloid in Exercise 73 if **(a)** $a = 4$ and $b = 2$ for $t \in [-\pi, \pi]$; **(b)** $a = 24$ and $b = 3$ for $t \in [-2\pi, 2\pi]$; **(c)** $a = 8$ and $b = 3$ for $t \in [-4\pi, 4\pi]$. Sketch what appears on your calculator screen.

VECTORS AND PLANES, LINES, AND SURFACES IN SPACE

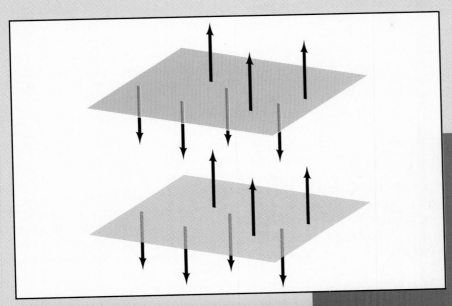

Our approach to vectors in this chapter is modern and serves as an introduction both to the viewpoint of linear algebra and to that of classical vector analysis. In Section 10.1 and 10.2 we define vectors as ordered pairs and ordered triples of real numbers. In these sections as well as in Sections 10.3 and 10.5 we perform operations on vectors by applying algebraic operations on their real coordinates. Applications include subject matter from physics, engineering, navigation, and geometry.

Topics from solid analytical geometry are included in this chapter because their discussion is simplified by the use of vectors. These topics, appearing in Sections 10.4 and 10.6, include planes, lines, cylinders, surfaces of revolution, and quadric surfaces.

10.1 VECTORS IN THE PLANE

Applications of mathematics are often concerned with quantities that possess both magnitude and direction. An example of such a quantity is *velocity*. For instance, the velocity of an airplane has magnitude, the airplane's speed, and direction, the airplane's course. Other examples of such quantities are *force, displacement,* and *acceleration.* Physicists and engineers refer to a directed line segment as a *vector,* and quantities having both magnitude and direction are called **vector quantities.** In contrast, a quantity that has magnitude but not direction is called a **scalar quantity.** Examples of scalar quantities are length, area, volume, cost, profit, and speed. The study of vectors is called **vector analysis.**

The approach to vector analysis can be on either a geometric or an analytic basis. If the geometric approach is taken, we first define a directed line segment as a line segment from a point P to a point Q and denote this directed line segment by $\overrightarrow{PQ}$. The point P is called the **initial point,** and the point Q is called the **terminal point.** Then two directed line segments $\overrightarrow{PQ}$ and $\overrightarrow{RS}$ are said to be equal if they have the same *length* and *direction,* and we write $\overrightarrow{PQ} = \overrightarrow{RS}$ (see Figure 1). The directed line segment $\overrightarrow{PQ}$ is called the **vector** from P to Q. A vector is denoted by a single letter, set in boldface type, such as **A**. In some books, a letter in lightface type, with an arrow above it, is used to indicate a vector, for example $\vec{A}$. When doing your work, you may use that notation or $\underline{A}$ to distinguish the symbol for a vector from the symbol for a real number.

Continuing with the geometric approach to vector analysis, note that if the directed line segment $\overrightarrow{PQ}$ is the vector **A**, and $\overrightarrow{PQ} = \overrightarrow{RS}$, the directed line segment $\overrightarrow{RS}$ is also the vector **A**. Then a vector is considered to remain unchanged if it is moved parallel to itself. With this interpretation of a vector, we can assume for convenience that every vector has its initial point at some fixed reference point. By taking this point as the origin of a rectangular cartesian coordinate system, a vector can be defined analytically in terms of real numbers. Such a definition permits the study of vector analysis from a purely algebraic viewpoint.

In this book we use the analytic approach while the geometric interpretation is used for illustrative purposes. A vector in the plane is denoted by an ordered pair of real numbers and the notation $\langle x, y \rangle$ is used instead of (x, y) to avoid confusing the notation for a vector with the notation for a point. V_2 is the set of all such ordered pairs.

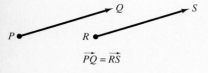

$\overrightarrow{PQ} = \overrightarrow{RS}$

FIGURE 1

10.1.1 Definition of a Vector in the Plane

A **vector in the plane** is an ordered pair of real numbers $\langle x, y \rangle$. The numbers x and y are the **components** of the vector $\langle x, y \rangle$.

From this definition two vectors $\langle a_1, a_2 \rangle$ and $\langle b_1, b_2 \rangle$ are **equal** if and only if $a_1 = b_1$ and $a_2 = b_2$.

A one-to-one correspondence exists between the vectors $\langle x, y \rangle$ in the plane and the points (x, y) in the plane. Let the vector **A** be the ordered pair of real numbers $\langle a_1, a_2 \rangle$. If A is the point (a_1, a_2), then the vector **A** may be represented geometrically by the directed line segment $\overrightarrow{OA}$. Such a directed line segment is called a **representation** of vector **A**. Any directed line

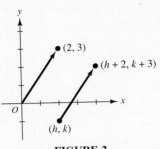

FIGURE 2

segment equal to $\overrightarrow{OA}$ is also a representation of vector **A**. The particular representation of a vector with its initial point at the origin is called the **position representation** of the vector.

▷ **ILLUSTRATION 1** The vector $\langle 2, 3 \rangle$ has as its position representation the directed line segment from the origin to the point $(2, 3)$. The representation of the vector $\langle 2, 3 \rangle$ whose initial point is (h, k) has as its terminal point $(h + 2, k + 3)$; refer to Figure 2. ◀

The vector $\langle 0, 0 \rangle$ is called the **zero vector,** denoted by **0**; that is,

$$\mathbf{0} = \langle 0, 0 \rangle$$

Any point is a representation of the zero vector.

10.1.2 Definition of Magnitude and Direction of a Vector

The **magnitude** of a vector **A**, denoted by $\|\mathbf{A}\|$, is the length of any of its representations, and the **direction** of a nonzero vector is the direction of any of its representations.

10.1.3 Theorem

If **A** is the vector $\langle a_1, a_2 \rangle$, then $\|\mathbf{A}\| = \sqrt{a_1^2 + a_2^2}$.

Proof Because by Definition 10.1.2 $\|\mathbf{A}\|$ is the length of any of the representations of **A**, then $\|\mathbf{A}\|$ will be the length of the position representation of **A**, which is the distance from the origin to the point (a_1, a_2). So from the formula for the distance between two points,

$$\|\mathbf{A}\| = \sqrt{(a_1 - 0)^2 + (a_2 - 0)^2}$$
$$= \sqrt{a_1^2 + a_2^2} \qquad \blacksquare$$

Observe that $\|\mathbf{A}\|$ is a nonnegative number and not a vector. From Theorem 10.1.3, $\|\mathbf{0}\| = 0$.

▷ **ILLUSTRATION 2** If $\mathbf{A} = \langle -3, 5 \rangle$, then

$$\|\mathbf{A}\| = \sqrt{(-3)^2 + 5^2}$$
$$= \sqrt{34} \qquad ◀$$

▶ **EXAMPLE 1** Let the vector **A** be $\langle -4, 5 \rangle$ and the point P be $(6, -2)$. **(a)** Draw the position representation of **A** and also the particular representation of **A** having P as its initial point. **(b)** Find the magnitude of **A**.

Solution

(a) Let A be the point $(-4, 5)$. Figure 3 shows $\overrightarrow{OA}$, which is the position representation of vector **A**. Let $\overrightarrow{PQ}$ be the particular representation of vector **A** having P as its initial point. If $Q = (x, y)$, then

$$x - 6 = -4 \qquad y + 2 = 5$$
$$x = 2 \qquad y = 3$$

Therefore $Q = (2, 3)$ and $\overrightarrow{PQ}$ appears in Figure 3.

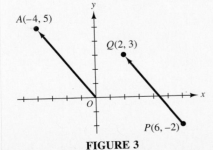

FIGURE 3

(b) From Theorem 10.1.3,

$$\|\mathbf{A}\| = \sqrt{(-4)^2 + 5^2}$$
$$= \sqrt{41}$$

◀

The **direction angle** of any nonzero vector is the angle θ measured from the positive side of the x axis counterclockwise to the position representation of the vector. If θ is measured in radians, $0 \leq \theta < 2\pi$. If $\mathbf{A} = \langle a_1, a_2 \rangle$, then

$$\tan \theta = \frac{a_2}{a_1} \qquad \text{if } a_1 \neq 0 \tag{1}$$

If $a_1 = 0$ and $a_2 > 0$, then $\theta = \frac{1}{2}\pi$; if $a_1 = 0$ and $a_2 < 0$, then $\theta = \frac{3}{2}\pi$. Figures 4 through 6 show the direction angle θ for specific vectors whose position representations are drawn.

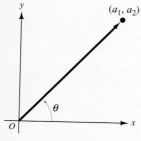

FIGURE 4

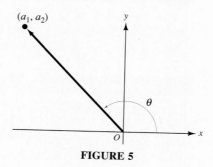

FIGURE 5

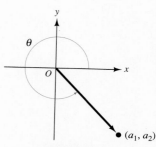

FIGURE 6

▶ **EXAMPLE 2** Find the radian measure of the direction angle of each of the following vectors **(a)** $\langle -1, 1 \rangle$; **(b)** $\langle 0, -5 \rangle$; **(c)** $\langle 1, -2 \rangle$.

Solution The position representations of the vectors in (a), (b), and (c) appear in Figures 7, 8, and 9, respectively.

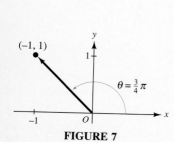

FIGURE 7

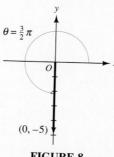

FIGURE 8

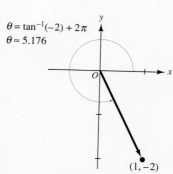

FIGURE 9

(a) $\tan \theta = -1$, and $\frac{1}{2}\pi < \theta < \pi$; so $\theta = \frac{3}{4}\pi$.
(b) $\tan \theta$ does not exist, and $a_2 < 0$; thus $\theta = \frac{3}{2}\pi$.
(c) $\tan \theta = -2$, and $\frac{3}{2}\pi < \theta < 2\pi$; therefore $\theta = \tan^{-1}(-2) + 2\pi$; that is, $\theta \approx 5.176$.

◀

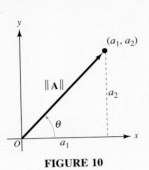

FIGURE 10

Observe that if $\mathbf{A} = \langle a_1, a_2 \rangle$ and θ is the direction angle of $\mathbf{A}$, then

$$a_1 = \| \mathbf{A} \| \cos \theta \qquad \text{and} \qquad a_2 = \| \mathbf{A} \| \sin \theta \qquad (2)$$

See Figure 10, where the point (a_1, a_2) is in the first quadrant.

If the vector $\mathbf{A} = \langle a_1, a_2 \rangle$, then the representation of $\mathbf{A}$ whose initial point is (x, y) has as its endpoint $(x + a_1, y + a_2)$. In this way a vector may be thought of as a translation of the plane into itself. Figure 11 illustrates five representations of the vector $\mathbf{A} = \langle a_1, a_2 \rangle$. In each case $\mathbf{A}$ translates the point (x_i, y_i) into the point $(x_i + a_1, y_i + a_2)$.

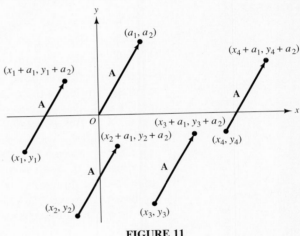

FIGURE 11

▶ **EXAMPLE 3** Suppose P is the point $(-1, 8)$ and Q is the point $(3, 2)$. Find the vector $\mathbf{A}$ having $\overrightarrow{PQ}$ as a representation. Draw $\overrightarrow{PQ}$ and the position representation of $\mathbf{A}$.

Solution Figure 12 shows the directed line segment $\overrightarrow{PQ}$. Let the vector $\mathbf{A} = \langle a_1, a_2 \rangle$. Because $\overrightarrow{PQ}$ is a representation of vector $\mathbf{A}$, the vector $\mathbf{A}$ translates the point $P(-1, 8)$ into the point $Q(3, 2)$. But vector $\langle a_1, a_2 \rangle$ translates the point $(-1, 8)$ into the point $\langle -1 + a_1, 8 + a_2 \rangle$. Thus

$$-1 + a_1 = 3 \qquad 8 + a_2 = 2$$
$$a_1 = 4 \qquad a_2 = -6$$

Therefore $\mathbf{A} = \langle 4, -6 \rangle$. Figure 12 also shows the position representation of $\mathbf{A}$. ◀

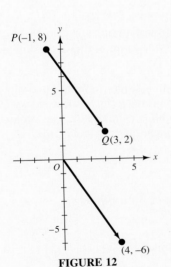

FIGURE 12

The following definition gives the method for adding two vectors.

10.1.4 Definition of the Sum of Two Vectors

The **sum** of vectors $\mathbf{A} = \langle a_1, a_2 \rangle$ and $\mathbf{B} = \langle b_1, b_2 \rangle$ is the vector $\mathbf{A} + \mathbf{B}$ defined by

$$\mathbf{A} + \mathbf{B} = \langle a_1 + b_1, a_2 + b_2 \rangle$$

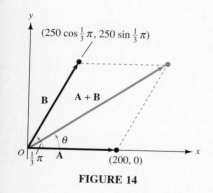

FIGURE 13

▷ **ILLUSTRATION 3**   If $\mathbf{A} = \langle 3, -1 \rangle$ and $\mathbf{B} = \langle -4, 5 \rangle$, then

$$\mathbf{A} + \mathbf{B} = \langle 3 + (-4), -1 + 5 \rangle$$
$$= \langle -1, 4 \rangle$$

◀

The geometric interpretation of the sum of two vectors is shown in Figure 13. Let $\mathbf{A} = \langle a_1, a_2 \rangle$ and $\mathbf{B} = \langle b_1, b_2 \rangle$, and let P be the point (x, y). Then $\mathbf{A}$ translates P into the point $(x + a_1, y + a_2) = Q$. The vector $\mathbf{B}$ translates Q into the point $((x + a_1) + b_1, (y + a_2) + b_2)$ or, equivalently, $(x + (a_1 + b_1), y + (a_2 + b_2)) = R$. Furthermore,

$$\mathbf{A} + \mathbf{B} = \langle a_1 + b_1, a_2 + b_2 \rangle$$

Therefore the vector $\mathbf{A} + \mathbf{B}$ translates the point P into the point $(x + (a_1 + b_1), y + (a_2 + b_2)) = R$. Thus, in Figure 13 $\overrightarrow{PQ}$ is a representation of the vector $\mathbf{A}$, $\overrightarrow{QR}$ is a representation of the vector $\mathbf{B}$, and $\overrightarrow{PR}$ is a representation of the vector $\mathbf{A} + \mathbf{B}$. The representations of the vectors $\mathbf{A}$ and $\mathbf{B}$ are adjacent sides of a parallelogram, and the representation of the vector $\mathbf{A} + \mathbf{B}$ is a diagonal of the parallelogram. This diagonal is called the **resultant** of the vectors $\mathbf{A}$ and $\mathbf{B}$. The rule for the addition of vectors is sometimes referred to as the **parallelogram law.**

Force is a vector quantity where the magnitude is expressed in force units and the direction angle is determined by the direction of the force. It is shown in physics that two forces applied to an object at a particular point can be replaced by an equivalent force that is their resultant.

▶ **EXAMPLE 4**   Two forces of magnitudes 200 lb and 250 lb make an angle of $\frac{1}{3}\pi$ with each other and are applied to an object at the same point. Find **(a)** the magnitude of the resultant force and **(b)** the angle it makes with the force of 200 lb.

Solution   Refer to Figure 14, where the axes are chosen so that the position representation of the force of 200 lb is along the positive side of the x axis. The vector $\mathbf{A}$ represents this force, and $\mathbf{A} = \langle 200, 0 \rangle$. The vector $\mathbf{B}$ represents the force of 250 lb. From formulas (2), if $\mathbf{B} = \langle b_1, b_2 \rangle$, then

$$b_1 = 250 \cos \tfrac{1}{3}\pi \qquad b_2 = 250 \sin \tfrac{1}{3}\pi$$
$$= 125 \qquad\qquad \approx 216.5$$

Thus $\mathbf{B} = \langle 125, 216.5 \rangle$. The resultant force is $\mathbf{A} + \mathbf{B}$, and

$$\mathbf{A} + \mathbf{B} = \langle 200, 0 \rangle + \langle 125, 216.5 \rangle$$
$$= \langle 325, 216.5 \rangle$$

(a) $\| \mathbf{A} + \mathbf{B} \| = \sqrt{(325)^2 + (216.5)^2}$
$$\approx 390.5$$

(b) If θ is the angle the vector $\mathbf{A} + \mathbf{B}$ makes with $\mathbf{A}$, then

$$\tan \theta = \frac{216.5}{325}$$
$$\tan \theta \approx 0.6662$$
$$\theta \approx 0.5877$$

◀

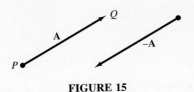

FIGURE 15

If $\mathbf{A} = \langle a_1, a_2 \rangle$, then the **negative of A,** denoted by $-\mathbf{A}$, is the vector $\langle -a_1, -a_2 \rangle$.

If the directed line segment $\overrightarrow{PQ}$ is a representation of the vector $\mathbf{A}$, then the directed line segment $\overrightarrow{QP}$ is a representation of $-\mathbf{A}$. Any directed line segment parallel to $\overrightarrow{PQ}$, having the same length as $\overrightarrow{PQ}$, and whose direction is opposite that of $\overrightarrow{PQ}$ is also a representation of $-\mathbf{A}$. See Figure 15.

10.1.6 Definition of the Difference of Two Vectors

The **difference** of vectors $\mathbf{A}$ and $\mathbf{B}$, denoted by $\mathbf{A} - \mathbf{B}$, is the vector obtained by adding $\mathbf{A}$ to the negative of $\mathbf{B}$; that is,

$$\mathbf{A} - \mathbf{B} = \mathbf{A} + (-\mathbf{B})$$

Thus if $\mathbf{A} = \langle a_1, a_2 \rangle$ and $\mathbf{B} = \langle b_1, b_2 \rangle$, then $-\mathbf{B} = \langle -b_1, -b_2 \rangle$, and

$$\mathbf{A} - \mathbf{B} = \langle a_1 - b_1, a_2 - b_2 \rangle$$

▷ **ILLUSTRATION 4**   If $\mathbf{A} = \langle 4, -2 \rangle$ and $\mathbf{B} = \langle 6, -3 \rangle$, then

$$
\begin{aligned}
\mathbf{A} - \mathbf{B} &= \langle 4, -2 \rangle - \langle 6, -3 \rangle \\
&= \langle 4, -2 \rangle + \langle -6, 3 \rangle \\
&= \langle -2, 1 \rangle
\end{aligned}
$$
◀

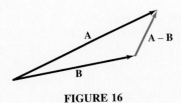

FIGURE 16

To interpret the difference of two vectors geometrically, let the representations of vectors $\mathbf{A}$ and $\mathbf{B}$ have the same initial point. Then the directed line segment from the endpoint of the representation of $\mathbf{B}$ to the endpoint of the representation of $\mathbf{A}$ is a representation of the vector $\mathbf{A} - \mathbf{B}$. This obeys the parallelogram law $\mathbf{B} + (\mathbf{A} - \mathbf{B}) = \mathbf{A}$. See Figure 16.

The following example, involving the difference of two vectors, is concerned with air navigation. The *air speed* of a plane refers to its speed relative to the air, and the *ground speed* is its speed relative to the ground. When there is a wind, the velocity of the plane relative to the ground is the resultant of the vector representing the wind's velocity and the vector representing the velocity of the plane relative to the air. In navigation, the *course* of a ship or airplane is the angle measured in degrees clockwise from the north to the direction in which the carrier is traveling. The angle is considered positive even though it is in the clockwise sense.

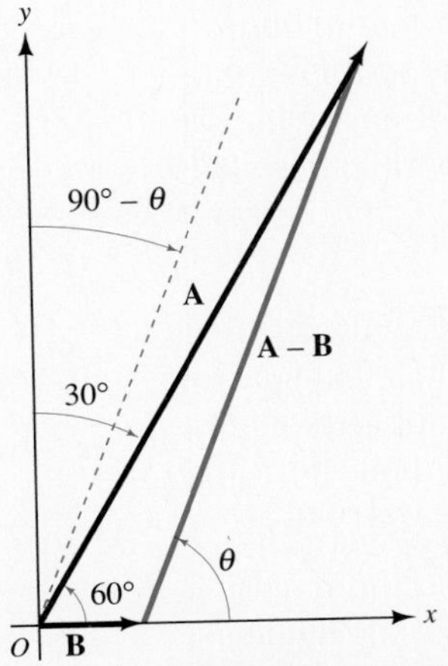

▶ **EXAMPLE 5**   An airplane can fly at an air speed of 300 mi/hr. If a wind is blowing toward the east at 50 mi/hr, what should be the plane's compass heading in order for its true course to be 30°? What will be the plane's ground speed if it flies this course?

Solution   Refer to Figure 17, showing position representations of the vectors $\mathbf{A}$ and $\mathbf{B}$ as well as a representation of $\mathbf{A} - \mathbf{B}$. The vector $\mathbf{A}$ represents the velocity of the plane relative to the ground on a course of 30°. The direction angle of $\mathbf{A}$ is 60°. The vector $\mathbf{B}$ represents the velocity of the

FIGURE 17

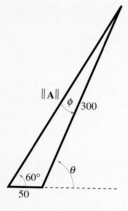

FIGURE 18

wind. Because **B** has a magnitude of 50 and a direction angle of 0°, **B** = $\langle 50, 0 \rangle$. The vector **A** − **B** represents the velocity of the plane relative to the air; thus $\| \mathbf{A} - \mathbf{B} \| = 300$. Let θ be the direction angle of **A** − **B**. From Figure 17 we obtain the triangle shown in Figure 18. Applying the law of sines to this triangle, we get

$$\frac{\sin \phi}{50} = \frac{\sin 60°}{300}$$

$$\sin \phi = \frac{50 \sin 60°}{300}$$

$$\sin \phi = 0.1433$$

$$\phi = 8.3°$$

Therefore

$$\theta = 60° + 8.3°$$
$$\quad = 68.3°$$

Again applying the law of sines to the triangle in Figure 18, we have

$$\frac{\| \mathbf{A} \|}{\sin(180° - \theta)} = \frac{300}{\sin 60°}$$

$$\| \mathbf{A} \| = \frac{300 \sin 111.7°}{\sin 60°}$$

$$\| \mathbf{A} \| = 322$$

Conclusion: The plane's compass heading should be $90° - \theta$, which is 21.7°, and if the plane flies this course, its ground speed will be 322 mi/hr.

◀

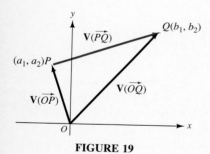

FIGURE 19

Suppose P is the point (a_1, a_2) and Q is the point (b_1, b_2). We shall use the notation $\mathbf{V}(\overrightarrow{PQ})$ to denote the vector having the directed line segment $\overrightarrow{PQ}$ as a representation. See Figure 19, showing representations of the vectors $\mathbf{V}(\overrightarrow{PQ})$, $\mathbf{V}(\overrightarrow{OP})$, and $\mathbf{V}(\overrightarrow{OQ})$. Observe that

$$\mathbf{V}(\overrightarrow{PQ}) = \mathbf{V}(\overrightarrow{OQ}) - \mathbf{V}(\overrightarrow{OP})$$
$$\mathbf{V}(\overrightarrow{PQ}) = \langle b_1, b_2 \rangle - \langle a_1, a_2 \rangle$$

$$\mathbf{V}(\overrightarrow{PQ}) = \langle b_1 - a_1, b_2 - a_2 \rangle$$

▷ **ILLUSTRATION 5**   If P is the point $(-6, 7)$ and Q is the point $(2, 9)$, then

$$\mathbf{V}(\overrightarrow{PQ}) = \langle 2 - (-6), 9 - 7 \rangle$$
$$\quad = \langle 8, 2 \rangle$$

◀

Another operation with vectors is *scalar multiplication,* involving the product of a vector and a scalar (a real number).

10.1.7 Definition of the Product of a Vector and a Scalar

If c is a scalar and $\mathbf{A}$ is the vector $\langle a_1, a_2 \rangle$, then the **product** of c and $\mathbf{A}$, denoted by $c\mathbf{A}$, is the vector given by

$$c\mathbf{A} = c\langle a_1, a_2 \rangle$$
$$= \langle ca_1, ca_2 \rangle$$

▷ **ILLUSTRATION 6** If $\mathbf{A} = \langle 4, -5 \rangle$, then

$$3\mathbf{A} = 3\langle 4, -5 \rangle$$
$$= \langle 12, -15 \rangle$$

◄

In Exercise 45 you are asked to show that if $\mathbf{A}$ is any vector and c is any scalar

$$0(\mathbf{A}) = \mathbf{0} \qquad \text{and} \qquad c(\mathbf{0}) = \mathbf{0}$$

The magnitude of the vector $c\mathbf{A}$ is computed as follows:

$$\| c\mathbf{A} \| = \sqrt{(ca_1)^2 + (ca_2)^2}$$
$$= \sqrt{c^2(a_1^2 + a_2^2)}$$
$$= \sqrt{c^2}\sqrt{a_1^2 + a_2^2}$$
$$= |c|\,\|\mathbf{A}\|$$

Therefore the magnitude of $c\mathbf{A}$ is the absolute value of c times the magnitude of $\mathbf{A}$.

The geometric interpretation of the vector $c\mathbf{A}$ is given in Figures 20 and 21. If $c > 0$, then $c\mathbf{A}$ is a vector whose representation has a length c times the magnitude of $\mathbf{A}$ and the same direction as $\mathbf{A}$; an example of this appears in Figure 20, where $c = 3$. If $c < 0$, then $c\mathbf{A}$ is a vector whose representation has a length that is $|c|$ times the magnitude of $\mathbf{A}$ and a direction opposite to that of $\mathbf{A}$. This situation is shown in Figure 21, where $c = -\frac{1}{2}$.

The following theorem gives laws satisfied by the operations of vector addition and scalar multiplication of any vectors in V_2.

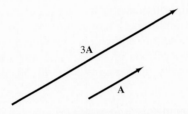

FIGURE 20

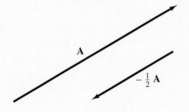

FIGURE 21

10.1.8 Theorem

If $\mathbf{A}$, $\mathbf{B}$, and $\mathbf{C}$ are any vectors in V_2, and c and d are any scalars, then vector addition and scalar multiplication satisfy the following properties:

(i) $\mathbf{A} + \mathbf{B} = \mathbf{B} + \mathbf{A}$ (commutative law)

(ii) $\mathbf{A} + (\mathbf{B} + \mathbf{C}) = (\mathbf{A} + \mathbf{B}) + \mathbf{C}$ (associative law)

(iii) There is a vector $\mathbf{0}$ in V_2 for which $\mathbf{A} + \mathbf{0} = \mathbf{A}$ (existence of additive identity)

(iv) There is a vector $-\mathbf{A}$ in V_2 such that $\mathbf{A} + (-\mathbf{A}) = \mathbf{0}$ (existence of negative)

(v) $(cd)\mathbf{A} = c(d\mathbf{A})$ (associative law)

(vi) $c(\mathbf{A} + \mathbf{B}) = c\mathbf{A} + c\mathbf{B}$ (distributive law)

(vii) $(c + d)\mathbf{A} = c\mathbf{A} + d\mathbf{A}$ (distributive law)

(viii) $1(\mathbf{A}) = \mathbf{A}$ (existence of scalar multiplicative identity)

Proof We give the proofs of (i) and (vi) and leave the others as exercises (see Exercises 46 through 50). In the proof of (i) we use the commutative law for real numbers and in the proof of (vi) we use the distributive law for real numbers. Let $\mathbf{A} = \langle a_1, a_2 \rangle$ and $\mathbf{B} = \langle b_1, b_2 \rangle$.

Proof of (i)

$$
\begin{aligned}
\mathbf{A} + \mathbf{B} &= \langle a_1, a_2 \rangle + \langle b_1, b_2 \rangle \\
&= \langle a_1 + b_1, a_2 + b_2 \rangle \\
&= \langle b_1 + a_1, b_2 + a_2 \rangle \\
&= \langle b_1, b_2 \rangle + \langle a_1, a_2 \rangle \\
&= \mathbf{B} + \mathbf{A}
\end{aligned}
$$

Proof of (vi)

$$
\begin{aligned}
c(\mathbf{A} + \mathbf{B}) &= c(\langle a_1, a_2 \rangle + \langle b_1, b_2 \rangle) \\
&= c(\langle a_1 + b_1, a_2 + b_2 \rangle) \\
&= \langle c(a_1 + b_1), c(a_2 + b_2) \rangle \\
&= \langle ca_1 + cb_1, ca_2 + cb_2 \rangle \\
&= \langle ca_1, ca_2 \rangle + \langle cb_1, cb_2 \rangle \\
&= c\langle a_1, a_2 \rangle + c\langle b_1, b_2 \rangle \\
&= c\mathbf{A} + c\mathbf{B} \qquad \blacksquare
\end{aligned}
$$

Theorem 10.1.8 is important because every algebraic law for the operations of vector addition and scalar multiplication of vectors in V_2 can be derived from the eight properties stated in the theorem. These laws are similar to the laws of arithmetic of real numbers. Furthermore, in linear algebra, a *real vector space* is defined as a set of vectors together with a set of real numbers (*scalars*) and the two operations of vector addition and scalar multiplication that satisfy the eight properties given in Theorem 10.1.8.

> ### 10.1.9 Definition of a Real Vector Space
>
> A **real vector space** V is a set of elements, called *vectors,* together with a set of real numbers, called *scalars,* with two operations called *vector addition* and *scalar multiplication* such that for every pair of vectors $\mathbf{A}$ and $\mathbf{B}$ in V and for every scalar c, a vector $\mathbf{A} + \mathbf{B}$ and a vector $c\mathbf{A}$ are defined so that properties (i)–(viii) of Theorem 10.1.8 are satisfied.

From this definition, V_2 is a real vector space.

We now take an arbitrary vector in V_2 and write it in a special form.

$$
\langle a_1, a_2 \rangle = \langle a_1, 0 \rangle + \langle 0, a_2 \rangle
$$
$$
\langle a_1, a_2 \rangle = a_1 \langle 1, 0 \rangle + a_2 \langle 0, 1 \rangle \tag{3}
$$

Because the magnitude of each of the two vectors $\langle 1, 0 \rangle$ and $\langle 0, 1 \rangle$ is one unit, they are called **unit vectors.** We introduce the following notations for these two unit vectors:

$$
\mathbf{i} = \langle 1, 0 \rangle \qquad \mathbf{j} = \langle 0, 1 \rangle
$$

With these notations, we have from (3)

$$
\langle a_1, a_2 \rangle = a_1 \mathbf{i} + a_2 \mathbf{j} \tag{4}
$$

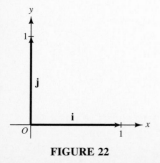

FIGURE 22

The position representation of each of the vectors $\mathbf{i}$ and $\mathbf{j}$ is shown in Figure 22. Equation (4) states that any vector in V_2 can be written as a linear combination of $\mathbf{i}$ and $\mathbf{j}$. Because of this statement and the fact that $\mathbf{i}$ and $\mathbf{j}$ are independent (their position representations are not collinear), the vectors $\mathbf{i}$ and $\mathbf{j}$ are said to form a **basis** for the vector space V_2. See Exercise 52 for an example of a basis consisting of nonunit vectors. The number of elements in a basis of a vector space is called the **dimension** of the vector space. Therefore V_2 is a two-dimensional vector space.

▷ **ILLUSTRATION 7**   From (4),

$$\langle 3, -4 \rangle = 3\mathbf{i} - 4\mathbf{j}$$ ◄

Let $\mathbf{A}$ be the vector $\langle a_1, a_2 \rangle$ and θ the direction angle of $\mathbf{A}$. See Figure 23, where the point (a_1, a_2) is in the second quadrant and the position representation of $\mathbf{A}$ is shown. Because $\mathbf{A} = a_1\mathbf{i} + a_2\mathbf{j}$, $a_1 = \|\mathbf{A}\| \cos \theta$, and $a_2 = \|\mathbf{A}\| \sin \theta$, we can write

$$\mathbf{A} = \|\mathbf{A}\| \cos \theta\, \mathbf{i} + \|\mathbf{A}\| \sin \theta\, \mathbf{j}$$

$$\mathbf{A} = \|\mathbf{A}\|(\cos \theta\, \mathbf{i} + \sin \theta\, \mathbf{j}) \qquad (5)$$

This equation expresses the vector $\mathbf{A}$ in terms of its magnitude, the cosine and sine of its direction angle, and the unit vectors $\mathbf{i}$ and $\mathbf{j}$.

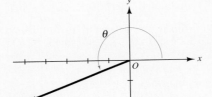

FIGURE 23

▶ **EXAMPLE 6**   Express the vector $\langle -5, -2 \rangle$ in the form of (5).

Solution   Refer to Figure 24, which shows the position representation of the vector $\langle -5, -2 \rangle$.

$$\|\langle -5, -2 \rangle\| = \sqrt{(-5)^2 + (-2)^2}$$
$$= \sqrt{29}$$

$$\cos \theta = -\frac{5}{\sqrt{29}} \qquad \text{and} \qquad \sin \theta = -\frac{2}{\sqrt{29}}$$

Therefore from (5)

$$\langle -5, -2 \rangle = \sqrt{29}\left(-\frac{5}{\sqrt{29}}\mathbf{i} - \frac{2}{\sqrt{29}}\mathbf{j} \right)$$ ◄

FIGURE 24

10.1.10 Theorem

If the nonzero vector $\mathbf{A} = a_1\mathbf{i} + a_2\mathbf{j}$, then the unit vector $\mathbf{U}$ having the same direction as $\mathbf{A}$ is given by

$$\mathbf{U} = \frac{a_1}{\|\mathbf{A}\|}\mathbf{i} + \frac{a_2}{\|\mathbf{A}\|}\mathbf{j}$$

Proof   We must show that the vector $\mathbf{U}$ is a unit vector having the same direction as $\mathbf{A}$.

$$\|\mathbf{U}\| = \sqrt{\left(\frac{a_1}{\|\mathbf{A}\|}\right)^2 + \left(\frac{a_2}{\|\mathbf{A}\|}\right)^2} \qquad \mathbf{U} = \frac{1}{\|\mathbf{A}\|}(a_1\mathbf{i} + a_2\mathbf{j})$$
$$= \frac{\sqrt{a_1^2 + a_2^2}}{\|\mathbf{A}\|} \qquad\qquad = \frac{1}{\|\mathbf{A}\|}(\mathbf{A})$$
$$= \frac{\|\mathbf{A}\|}{\|\mathbf{A}\|}$$
$$= 1$$

Because $\|\mathbf{U}\| = 1$, $\mathbf{U}$ is a unit vector, and because $\mathbf{U}$ is a positive scalar times the vector $\mathbf{A}$, the direction of $\mathbf{U}$ is the same as the direction of $\mathbf{A}$. ∎

▶ **EXAMPLE 7** Given $\mathbf{A} = 3\mathbf{i} + \mathbf{j}$ and $\mathbf{B} = -2\mathbf{i} + 4\mathbf{j}$, find the unit vector having the same direction as $\mathbf{A} - \mathbf{B}$.

Solution

$$\mathbf{A} - \mathbf{B} = (3\mathbf{i} + \mathbf{j}) - (-2\mathbf{i} + 4\mathbf{j})$$
$$= 5\mathbf{i} - 3\mathbf{j}$$

Thus

$$\|\mathbf{A} - \mathbf{B}\| = \sqrt{5^2 + (-3)^2}$$
$$= \sqrt{34}$$

By Theorem 10.1.10, the desired unit vector is

$$\mathbf{U} = \frac{5}{\sqrt{34}}\mathbf{i} - \frac{3}{\sqrt{34}}\mathbf{j} \qquad ◀$$

EXERCISES 10.1

In Exercises 1 through 4, (a) draw the position representation of the vector $\mathbf{A}$ and also the particular representation through the point P. (b) Find the magnitude of $\mathbf{A}$.

1. $\mathbf{A} = \langle 3, 4 \rangle$; $P = (2, 1)$
2. $\mathbf{A} = \langle -2, 5 \rangle$; $P = (-3, 4)$
3. $\mathbf{A} = \langle e, -\frac{1}{2} \rangle$; $P = (-2, -e)$
4. $\mathbf{A} = \langle 4, 0 \rangle$; $P = (2, 6)$

In Exercises 5 and 6, find the exact radian measure of the direction angle of the vector. In part (c) also approximate the radian measure to the nearest hundredth.

5. (a) $\langle 1, -1 \rangle$ (b) $\langle -3, 0 \rangle$ (c) $\langle 5, 2 \rangle$
6. (a) $\langle \sqrt{3}, 1 \rangle$ (b) $\langle 0, 4 \rangle$ (c) $\langle -3, 2 \rangle$

In Exercises 7 through 10, find the vector $\mathbf{A}$ having $\overrightarrow{PQ}$ as a representation. Draw $\overrightarrow{PQ}$ and the position representation of $\mathbf{A}$.

7. $P = (3, 7)$; $Q = (5, 4)$ 8. $P = (5, 4)$; $Q = (3, 7)$
9. $P = (-5, -3)$; $Q = (0, 3)$
10. $P = (-\sqrt{2}, 0)$; $Q = (0, 0)$

In Exercises 11 through 14, find the point S so that $\overrightarrow{PQ}$ and $\overrightarrow{RS}$ are each representations of the same vector.

11. $P = (2, 5)$; $Q = (1, 6)$; $R = (-3, 2)$
12. $P = (-2, 0)$; $Q = (-3, -4)$; $R = (4, 2)$
13. $P = (0, 3)$; $Q = (5, -2)$; $R = (7, 0)$
14. $P = (-1, 4)$; $Q = (2, -3)$; $R = (-5, -2)$

In Exercises 15 and 16, find the sum of the pairs of vectors and illustrate geometrically.

15. (a) $\langle 2, 4 \rangle$, $\langle -3, 5 \rangle$ (b) $\langle -3, 0 \rangle$, $\langle 4, -5 \rangle$
16. (a) $\langle 0, 3 \rangle$, $\langle -2, 3 \rangle$ (b) $\langle 2, 3 \rangle$, $\langle -\sqrt{2}, -1 \rangle$

In Exercises 17 and 18, subtract the second vector from the first and illustrate geometrically.

17. (a) $\langle -3, -4 \rangle$, $\langle 6, 0 \rangle$ (b) $\langle 1, e \rangle$, $\langle -3, 2e \rangle$
18. (a) $\langle 0, 5 \rangle$, $\langle 2, 8 \rangle$ (b) $\langle 3, 7 \rangle$, $\langle 3, 7 \rangle$

In Exercises 19 and 20, find the vector or scalar if $\mathbf{A} = \langle 2, 4 \rangle$, $\mathbf{B} = \langle 4, -3 \rangle$, and $\mathbf{C} = \langle -3, 2 \rangle$.

19. (a) $\mathbf{A} + \mathbf{B}$ (b) $\|\mathbf{C} - \mathbf{B}\|$ (c) $\|7\mathbf{A} - \mathbf{B}\|$
20. (a) $\mathbf{A} - \mathbf{B}$ (b) $\|\mathbf{C}\|$ (c) $\|2\mathbf{A} + 3\mathbf{B}\|$

In Exercises 21 through 24, find the given vector or scalar if $\mathbf{A} = 2\mathbf{i} + 3\mathbf{j}$ and $\mathbf{B} = 4\mathbf{i} - \mathbf{j}$.

21. (a) $5\mathbf{A}$ (b) $-6\mathbf{B}$ (c) $\mathbf{A} + \mathbf{B}$ (d) $\|\mathbf{A} + \mathbf{B}\|$
22. (a) $-2\mathbf{A}$ (b) $3\mathbf{B}$ (c) $\mathbf{A} - \mathbf{B}$ (d) $\|\mathbf{A} - \mathbf{B}\|$
23. (a) $\|\mathbf{A}\| + \|\mathbf{B}\|$ (b) $5\mathbf{A} - 6\mathbf{B}$
    (c) $\|5\mathbf{A} - 6\mathbf{B}\|$ (d) $\|5\mathbf{A}\| - \|6\mathbf{B}\|$
24. (a) $\|\mathbf{A}\| - \|\mathbf{B}\|$ (b) $3\mathbf{B} - 2\mathbf{A}$
    (c) $\|3\mathbf{B} - 2\mathbf{A}\|$ (d) $\|3\mathbf{B}\| - \|2\mathbf{A}\|$

In Exercises 25 and 26, $\mathbf{A} = -4\mathbf{i} + 2\mathbf{j}$, $\mathbf{B} = -\mathbf{i} + 3\mathbf{j}$, and $\mathbf{C} = 5\mathbf{i} - \mathbf{j}$.

25. Find: (a) $5\mathbf{A} - 2\mathbf{B} - 2\mathbf{C}$; (b) $\|5\mathbf{A} - 2\mathbf{B} - 2\mathbf{C}\|$.
26. Find: (a) $3\mathbf{B} - 2\mathbf{A} - \mathbf{C}$; (b) $\|3\mathbf{B} - 2\mathbf{A} - \mathbf{C}\|$.

In Exercises 27 and 28, $\mathbf{A} = 8\mathbf{i} + 5\mathbf{j}$ *and* $\mathbf{B} = 3\mathbf{i} - \mathbf{j}$.

27. Find a unit vector having the same direction as $\mathbf{A} + \mathbf{B}$.

28. Find a unit vector having the same direction as $\mathbf{A} - \mathbf{B}$.

In Exercises 29 through 32, write the given vector in the form $r(\cos\theta\,\mathbf{i} + \sin\theta\,\mathbf{j})$, *where r is the magnitude and* θ *is the direction angle. Also find a unit vector having the same direction.*

29. (a) $3\mathbf{i} - 4\mathbf{j}$ (b) $2\mathbf{i} + 2\mathbf{j}$

30. (a) $8\mathbf{i} + 6\mathbf{j}$ (b) $2\sqrt{5}\mathbf{i} + 4\mathbf{j}$

31. (a) $-4\mathbf{i} + 4\sqrt{3}\mathbf{j}$ (b) $-16\mathbf{i}$

32. (a) $3\mathbf{i} - 3\mathbf{j}$ (b) $2\mathbf{j}$

33. If $\mathbf{A} = -2\mathbf{i} + \mathbf{j}$, $\mathbf{B} = 3\mathbf{i} - 2\mathbf{j}$, and $\mathbf{C} = 5\mathbf{i} - 4\mathbf{j}$, find scalars h and k such that $\mathbf{C} = h\mathbf{A} + k\mathbf{B}$.

34. If $\mathbf{A} = 5\mathbf{i} - 2\mathbf{j}$, $\mathbf{B} = -4\mathbf{i} + 3\mathbf{j}$, and $\mathbf{C} = -6\mathbf{i} + 8\mathbf{j}$, find scalars h and k such that $\mathbf{B} = h\mathbf{C} - k\mathbf{A}$.

35. If $\mathbf{A} = \mathbf{i} - 2\mathbf{j}$, $\mathbf{B} = -2\mathbf{i} + 4\mathbf{j}$, and $\mathbf{C} = 7\mathbf{i} - 5\mathbf{j}$, show that $\mathbf{C}$ cannot be written in the form $h\mathbf{A} + k\mathbf{B}$, where h and k are scalars.

36. Two forces of magnitudes 340 lb and 475 lb make an angle of 34.6° with each other and are applied to an object at the same point. Find (a) the magnitude of the resultant force and (b) to the nearest tenth of a degree the angle it makes with the force of 475 lb.

37. Two forces of magnitudes 60 lb and 80 lb make an angle of 30° with each other and are applied to an object at the same point. Find (a) the magnitude of the resultant force and (b) to the nearest degree the angle it makes with the force of 60 lb.

38. A force of magnitude 22 lb and one of magnitude 34 lb are applied to an object at the same point and make an angle of θ with each other. If the resultant force has a magnitude of 46 lb, find θ to the nearest degree.

39. A force of magnitude 112 lb and one of 84 lb are applied to an object at the same point, and the resultant force has a magnitude of 162 lb. Find to the nearest tenth of a degree the angle made by the resultant force with the force of 112 lb.

40. A plane has an air speed of 350 mi/hr. In order for the actual course of the plane to be due north, the compass heading is 340°. If the wind is blowing from the west, (a) what is the speed of the wind? (b) What is the plane's ground speed?

41. In an airplane that has an air speed of 250 mi/hr, a pilot wishes to fly due north. If there is a wind blowing at 60 mi/hr toward the east, (a) what should be the plane's compass heading? (b) What will be the plane's ground speed if it flies this course?

42. A boat can travel 15 knots relative to the water. On a river whose current is 3 knots toward the west the boat has a compass heading of south. What is the speed of the boat relative to the land and what is its course?

43. A swimmer who can swim at a speed of 1.5 mi/hr relative to the water leaves the south bank of a river and is headed north directly across the river. If the river's current is toward the east at 0.8 mi/hr, (a) in what direction is the swimmer going? (b) What is the swimmer's speed relative to the land? (c) If the distance across the river is 1 mile, how far down the river does the swimmer reach the north bank?

44. Suppose the swimmer in Exercise 43 wishes to reach the point directly north across the river. (a) In what direction should the swimmer head? (b) What will be the swimmer's speed relative to the land if this direction is taken?

45. Prove that if $\mathbf{A}$ is any vector and c is any scalar then $0(\mathbf{A}) = \mathbf{0}$ and $c(\mathbf{0}) = \mathbf{0}$.

46. Prove Theorem 10.1.8(ii).

47. Prove Theorem 10.1.8(iii) and (viii).

48. Prove Theorem 10.1.8(iv).

49. Prove Theorem 10.1.8(v).

50. Prove Theorem 10.1.8(vii).

51. Given $\mathbf{A} = \langle 2, -5 \rangle$; $\mathbf{B} = \langle 3, 1 \rangle$; $\mathbf{C} = \langle -4, 2 \rangle$.
(a) Find $\mathbf{A} + (\mathbf{B} + \mathbf{C})$ and illustrate geometrically.
(b) Find $(\mathbf{A} + \mathbf{B}) + \mathbf{C}$ and illustrate geometrically.

52. Two vectors are said to be *independent* if and only if their position representations are not collinear. Furthermore, two vectors $\mathbf{A}$ and $\mathbf{B}$ are said to form a *basis* for the vector space V_2 if and only if any vector in V_2 can be written as a linear combination of $\mathbf{A}$ and $\mathbf{B}$. A theorem can be proved which states that two vectors form a basis for the vector space V_2 if they are independent. Show that this theorem holds for the two vectors $\langle 2, 5 \rangle$ and $\langle 3, -1 \rangle$ by doing the following: (a) Verify that the vectors are independent by showing that their position representations are not collinear; (b) verify that the vectors form a basis by showing that any vector $a_1\mathbf{i} + a_2\mathbf{j}$ can be written as $c(2\mathbf{i} + 5\mathbf{j}) + d(3\mathbf{i} - \mathbf{j})$, where c and d are scalars. *Hint:* Find c and d in terms of a_1 and a_2.

53. Refer to the first two sentences of Exercise 52. A theorem can be proved which states that two vectors form a basis for the vector space V_2 only if they are independent. Show that this theorem holds for the two vectors $\langle 3, -2 \rangle$ and $\langle -6, 4 \rangle$ by doing the following: (a) Verify that the vectors are dependent (not independent) by showing that their position representations are collinear; (b) verify that the vectors do not form a basis by taking a particular vector and showing that it cannot be written in the form $c(3\mathbf{i} - 2\mathbf{j}) + d(-6\mathbf{i} + 4\mathbf{j})$, where c and d are scalars.

54. A set of vectors $\mathbf{V}_1, \mathbf{V}_2, \mathbf{V}_3, \ldots, \mathbf{V}_n$ is said to be *linearly dependent* if and only if there are scalars $k_1, k_2, k_3, \ldots, k_n$, not all zero, such that

$$k_1\mathbf{V}_1 + k_2\mathbf{V}_2 + k_3\mathbf{V}_3 + \ldots + k_n\mathbf{V}_n = \mathbf{0}$$

Show that if $\mathbf{V}_1 = 3\mathbf{i} - 2\mathbf{j}$, $\mathbf{V}_2 = \mathbf{i} + 4\mathbf{j}$, and $\mathbf{V}_3 = 2\mathbf{i} + 5\mathbf{j}$, then $\mathbf{V}_1$, $\mathbf{V}_2$, and $\mathbf{V}_3$ are linearly dependent.

55. Let $\overrightarrow{PQ}$ be a representation of vector $\mathbf{A}$, $\overrightarrow{QR}$ be a representation of vector $\mathbf{B}$, and $\overrightarrow{RS}$ be a representation of vector $\mathbf{C}$. Prove that if $\overrightarrow{PQ}$, $\overrightarrow{QR}$, and $\overrightarrow{RS}$ are sides of a triangle, then $\mathbf{A} + \mathbf{B} + \mathbf{C} = \mathbf{0}$.

56. Prove analytically the triangle inequality for vectors:

$$\| \mathbf{A} + \mathbf{B} \| \le \| \mathbf{A} \| + \| \mathbf{B} \|$$

57. Explain the difference between a vector quantity and a scalar quantity.

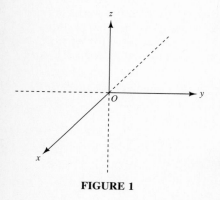

FIGURE 1

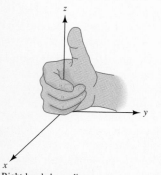

Right-handed coordinate system

FIGURE 2

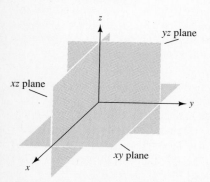

FIGURE 3

10.2 VECTORS IN THREE-DIMENSIONAL SPACE

So far we have been concerned with the one-dimensional number space R, the number line, and the two-dimensional number space R^2, the number plane. We identified the real numbers in R with points on a horizontal axis and the real-number pairs in R^2 with points in a geometric plane. Now, prior to extending a vector to three dimensions, we discuss the *three-dimensional number space.*

10.2.1 Definition of the Three-Dimensional Number Space

The set of all ordered triples of real numbers is called the **three-dimensional number space,** denoted by R^3. Each ordered triple (x, y, z) is called a **point** in the three-dimensional number space.

To represent R^3 in a geometric three-dimensional space, consider the directed distances of a point from three mutually perpendicular planes. The planes are formed by first taking three mutually perpendicular lines that intersect at a point, the **origin,** denoted by the letter O. These lines, called the coordinate axes, are designated as the x axis, y axis, and z axis. Usually the x and y axes are taken in a horizontal plane, and the z axis is vertical. A positive direction, selected on each axis as in Figure 1, gives a **right-handed coordinate system.** This terminology follows from the fact that if you hold your right hand so that your fingers are curled from the positive x axis toward the positive y axis then your thumb points in the direction of the positive z axis. See Figure 2. The three axes determine three coordinate planes: the xy plane containing the x and y axes, the xz plane containing the x and z axes, and the yz plane containing the y and z axes, as shown in Figure 3.

An ordered triple of real numbers (x, y, z) is associated with each point P in a geometric three-dimensional space. The directed distance of P from the yz plane is the **x coordinate,** its directed distance from the xz plane is the **y coordinate,** and the **z coordinate** is the directed distance of P from the xy plane. These three coordinates are called the **rectangular cartesian**

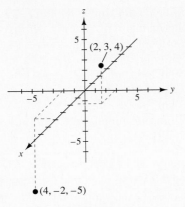

FIGURE 4

coordinates of P and a one-to-one correspondence, called a **rectangular cartesian coordinate system,** exists between all such ordered triples of real numbers and the points in a geometric three-dimensional space. Hence we identify R^3 with the geometric three-dimensional space. The points $(2, 3, 4)$ and $(4, -2, -5)$ are located in Figure 4. The three coordinate planes divide the space into eight parts called **octants.** The first octant is the one in which all three coordinates are positive.

A line is parallel to a plane if and only if the distance from any point on the line to the plane is the same.

▷ **ILLUSTRATION 1**   A line parallel to the yz plane, one parallel to the xz plane, and one parallel to the xy plane appear in Figures 5, 6, and 7, respectively.   ◀

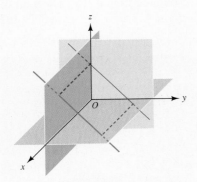

Line parallel to the yz plane

FIGURE 5

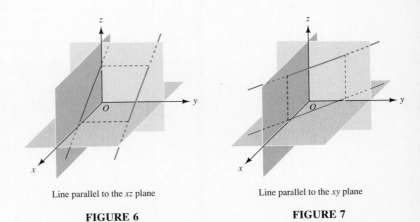

Line parallel to the xz plane

FIGURE 6

Line parallel to the xy plane

FIGURE 7

The next theorem follows immediately.

> **10.2.2 Theorem**
> **(i)** A line is parallel to the yz plane if and only if all points on the line have equal x coordinates.
> **(ii)** A line is parallel to the xz plane if and only if all points on the line have equal y coordinates.
> **(iii)** A line is parallel to the xy plane if and only if all points on the line have equal z coordinates.

As a special case, we consider all lines lying in a given plane as being parallel to the plane, in which case the distance from any point on the line to the plane is zero.

In three-dimensional space, if a line is parallel to each of two intersecting planes, it is parallel to the line of intersection of the two planes. Also, if a given line is parallel to a second line, then the given line is parallel to any plane containing the second line. The next theorem follows from these two geometrical facts and from Theorem 10.2.2.

10.2.3 Theorem

(i) A line is parallel to the x axis if and only if all points on the line have equal y coordinates and equal z coordinates.
(ii) A line is parallel to the y axis if and only if all points on the line have equal x coordinates and equal z coordinates.
(iii) A line is parallel to the z axis if and only if all points on the line have equal x coordinates and equal y coordinates.

▷ **ILLUSTRATION 2**   A line parallel to the x axis, one parallel to the y axis, and one parallel to the z axis appear in Figures 8, 9, and 10, respectively. ◀

The formulas for finding the directed distance from one point to another on a line parallel to a coordinate axis are obtained from the definition of directed distance given in Appendix Section A.2 and are stated in the following theorem.

10.2.4 Theorem

(i) If $A(x_1, y, z)$ and $B(x_2, y, z)$ are two points on a line parallel to the x axis, then the directed distance from A to B, denoted by $\overline{AB}$, is given by

$$\overline{AB} = x_2 - x_1$$

(ii) If $C(x, y_1, z)$ and $D(x, y_2, z)$ are two points on a line parallel to the y axis, then the directed distance from C to D, denoted by $\overline{CD}$, is given by

$$\overline{CD} = y_2 - y_1$$

(iii) If $E(x, y, z_1)$ and $F(x, y, z_2)$ are two points on a line parallel to the z axis, then the directed distance from E to F, denoted by $\overline{EF}$, is given by

$$\overline{EF} = z_2 - z_1$$

▷ **ILLUSTRATION 3**   The directed distance $\overline{PQ}$ from the point $P(2, -5, -4)$ to the point $Q(2, -3, -4)$ is given by Theorem 10.2.4(ii).

$$\overline{PQ} = (-3) - (-5)$$
$$= 2$$

◀

The next theorem gives a formula for determining the undirected distance between any two points in three-dimensional space.

10.2.5 Theorem

The undirected distance between the two points $P_1(x_1, y_1, z_1)$ and $P_2(x_2, y_2, z_2)$ is given by

$$|\overline{P_1 P_2}| = \sqrt{(x_2 - x_1)^2 + (y_2 - y_1)^2 + (z_2 - z_1)^2}$$

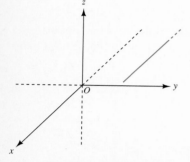

Line parallel to the x axis

FIGURE 8

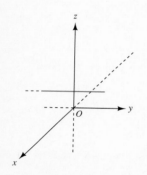

Line parallel to the y axis

FIGURE 9

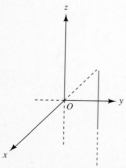

Line parallel to the z axis

FIGURE 10

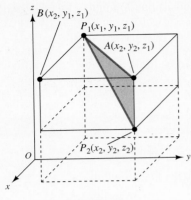

FIGURE 11

Proof   We construct a rectangular parallelepiped having P_1 and P_2 as opposite vertices and faces parallel to the coordinate planes (see Figure 11).
By the Pythagorean theorem,

$$|\overline{P_1P_2}|^2 = |\overline{P_1A}|^2 + |\overline{AP_2}|^2 \qquad (1)$$

Because

$$|\overline{P_1A}|^2 = |\overline{P_1B}|^2 + |\overline{BA}|^2$$

we obtain, by substituting from this equation into (1),

$$|\overline{P_1P_2}|^2 = |\overline{P_1B}|^2 + |\overline{BA}|^2 + |\overline{AP_2}|^2$$

Applying Theorem 10.2.4 (i), (ii), and (iii) to the right side we obtain

$$|\overline{P_1P_2}|^2 = (x_2 - x_1)^2 + (y_2 - y_1)^2 + (z_2 - z_1)^2$$
$$|\overline{P_1P_2}| = \sqrt{(x_2 - x_1)^2 + (y_2 - y_1)^2 + (z_2 - z_1)^2}$$ ∎

▶ **EXAMPLE 1**   Find the undirected distance between the points $P(-3, 4, -1)$ and $Q(2, 5, -4)$.

Solution   From Theorem 10.2.5,

$$|\overline{PQ}| = \sqrt{(2 + 3)^2 + (5 - 4)^2 + (-4 + 1)^2}$$
$$= \sqrt{35}$$ ◀

The formula for the distance between two points in R^3 is merely an extension of the corresponding formula for the distance between two points in R^2. It is noteworthy that the undirected distance between two points x_2 and x_1 in R is given by

$$|x_2 - x_1| = \sqrt{(x_2 - x_1)^2}$$

The formulas for the coordinates of the midpoint of a line segment are derived by forming congruent triangles and proceeding in a manner analogous to the two-dimensional case. These formulas are given in the following theorem and the proof is left as an exercise (see Exercise 18).

10.2.6 Theorem

The coordinates of the midpoint of the line segment having endpoints $P_1(x_1, y_1, z_1)$ and $P_2(x_2, y_2, z_2)$ are given by

$$\overline{x} = \frac{x_1 + x_2}{2} \qquad \overline{y} = \frac{y_1 + y_2}{2} \qquad \overline{z} = \frac{z_1 + z_2}{2}$$

10.2.7 Definition of the Graph of an Equation in R^3

The **graph of an equation in R^3** is the set of all points (x, y, z) whose coordinates are numbers satisfying the equation.

A **surface** is the graph of an equation in R^3. One particular surface is the *sphere*.

10.2.8 Definition of a Sphere

A **sphere** is the set of all points in three-dimensional space equidistant from a fixed point. The fixed point is called the **center** of the sphere and the measure of the constant distance is called the **radius** of the sphere.

10.2.9 Theorem

An equation of the sphere of radius r and center at (h, k, l) is

$$(x - h)^2 + (y - k)^2 + (z - l)^2 = r^2 \tag{2}$$

Proof   Let the point (h, k, l) be denoted by C (see Figure 12). The point $P(x, y, z)$ is a point on the sphere if and only if $|\overline{CP}| = r$; that is

$$\sqrt{(x - h)^2 + (y - k)^2 + (z - l)^2} = r$$

Squaring on both sides of the above equation we obtain the desired result.   ∎

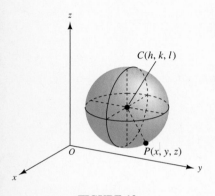

FIGURE 12

If the center of the sphere is at the origin, then $h = 0, k = 0, l = 0$; so an equation of this sphere is

$$x^2 + y^2 + z^2 = r^2$$

If we expand and regroup the terms of (2) we have

$$x^2 + y^2 + z^2 - 2hx - 2ky - 2lz + (h^2 + k^2 + l^2 - r^2) = 0$$

This equation is of the form

$$x^2 + y^2 + z^2 + Gx + Hy + Iz + J = 0 \tag{3}$$

where G, H, I, and J are constants. Equation (3) is called the **general form** of an equation of a sphere, whereas (2) is called the **center-radius form.** Because every sphere has a center and a radius, its equation can be put in the center-radius form and hence the general form.

Any equation of the form (3) can be put in the form

$$(x - h)^2 + (y - k)^2 + (z - l)^2 = K \tag{4}$$

where

$$h = -\tfrac{1}{2}G \qquad k = -\tfrac{1}{2}H \qquad l = -\tfrac{1}{2}I \qquad K = \tfrac{1}{4}(G^2 + H^2 + I^2 - 4J)$$

You are asked to show this in Exercise 19.

If $K > 0$, then (4) is of the form of Equation (2); so the graph of the equation is a sphere having its center at (h, k, l) and radius $\sqrt{K}$. If $K = 0$, the graph of the equation is the point (h, k, l). If $K < 0$, the graph is the empty set because the sum of the squares of three real numbers is nonnegative. We state this result as a theorem.

10.2.10 Theorem

The graph of any second-degree equation in x, y, and z, of the form

$$x^2 + y^2 + z^2 + Gx + Hy + Iz + J = 0$$

is either a sphere, a point, or the empty set.

▶ **EXAMPLE 2**   Determine the graph of the equation

$$x^2 + y^2 + z^2 - 6x - 4y + 2z = 2$$

Solution   Regrouping terms and completing the squares we have

$$x^2 - 6x + 9 + y^2 - 4y + 4 + z^2 + 2z + 1 = 2 + 9 + 4 + 1$$
$$(x - 3)^2 + (y - 2)^2 + (z + 1)^2 = 16$$

The graph is a sphere having its center at $(3, 2, -1)$ and radius 4.   ◀

Figure 13 shows the sphere of Example 2.

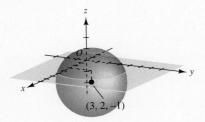

FIGURE 13

▶ **EXAMPLE 3**   Find an equation of the sphere having the points $A(-5, 6, -2)$ and $B(9, -4, 0)$ as endpoints of a diameter.

Solution   The center of the sphere is the midpoint of the line segment AB. Let this point be $C(\bar{x}, \bar{y}, \bar{z})$. By Theorem 10.2.6 we get

$$\bar{x} = \frac{9 - 5}{2} \qquad \bar{y} = \frac{-4 + 6}{2} \qquad \bar{z} = \frac{0 - 2}{2}$$
$$= 2 \qquad\qquad = 1 \qquad\qquad = -1$$

Thus C is the point $(2, 1, -1)$. The radius of the sphere is $|\overline{CB}|$. Hence

$$r = \sqrt{(9 - 2)^2 + (-4 - 1)^2 + (0 + 1)^2}$$
$$= \sqrt{75}$$

Therefore, from Theorem 10.2.9 an equation of the sphere is

$$(x - 2)^2 + (y - 1)^2 + (z + 1)^2 = 75$$
$$x^2 + y^2 + z^2 - 4x - 2y + 2z - 69 = 0$$

◀

In Section 10.1 we defined a vector in the plane as an ordered pair of real numbers. We now extend this definition to a vector in three-dimensional space.

10.2.11 Definition of a Vector in Three-Dimensional Space

A **vector in three-dimensional space** is an ordered triple of real numbers $\langle x, y, z \rangle$. The numbers x, y, and z are the **components** of the vector $\langle x, y, z \rangle$.

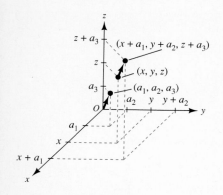

FIGURE 14

The two vectors $\langle a_1, a_2, a_3 \rangle$ and $\langle b_1, b_2, b_3 \rangle$ are **equal** if and only if $a_1 = b_1$, $a_2 = b_2$, and $a_3 = b_3$.

V_3 denotes the set of all ordered triples $\langle x, y, z \rangle$ for which x, y, and z are real numbers. Just as for vectors in V_2, a vector in V_3 can be represented by a directed line segment. If $\mathbf{A} = \langle a_1, a_2, a_3 \rangle$, then the directed line segment having its initial point at the origin and its terminal point at the point (a_1, a_2, a_3) is called the **position representation** of $\mathbf{A}$. A directed line segment having its initial point at (x, y, z) and its terminal point at the point $(x + a_1, y + a_2, z + a_3)$ is also a representation of the vector $\mathbf{A}$. See Figure 14.

The **zero vector** is the vector $\langle 0, 0, 0 \rangle$ and is denoted by $\mathbf{0}$. Any point is a representation of the zero vector.

The **magnitude** of a vector is the length of any of its representations. If the vector $\mathbf{A} = \langle a_1, a_2, a_3 \rangle$, the magnitude of $\mathbf{A}$ is denoted by $\| \mathbf{A} \|$, and

$$\| \mathbf{A} \| = \sqrt{a_1{}^2 + a_2{}^2 + a_3{}^2}$$

The **direction** of a nonzero vector in V_3 is given by three angles, called the *direction angles* of the vector.

10.2.12 Definition of the Direction Angles of a Vector

The **direction angles** of a nonzero vector are the three angles that have the smallest nonnegative radian measures α, β, and γ measured from the positive x, y, and z axes, respectively, to the position representation of the vector.

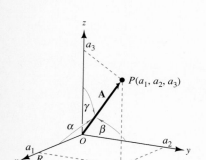

FIGURE 15

The radian measure of each direction angle of a vector is greater than or equal to 0 and less than or equal to π. The direction angles having radian measures α, β, and γ of the vector $\mathbf{A} = \langle a_1, a_2, a_3 \rangle$ are shown in Figure 15. In this figure the components of $\mathbf{A}$ are all positive numbers, and the direction angles of this vector all have positive radian measure less than $\frac{1}{2}\pi$. From the figure we see that triangle POR is a right triangle and

$$\cos \alpha = \frac{a_1}{\| \mathbf{A} \|}$$

It can be shown that the same formula holds if $\frac{1}{2}\pi \leq \alpha \leq \pi$. Similar formulas can be found for $\cos \beta$ and $\cos \gamma$, and we have

$$\cos \alpha = \frac{a_1}{\| \mathbf{A} \|} \qquad \cos \beta = \frac{a_2}{\| \mathbf{A} \|} \qquad \cos \gamma = \frac{a_3}{\| \mathbf{A} \|} \tag{5}$$

The three numbers $\cos \alpha$, $\cos \beta$, and $\cos \gamma$ are called the **direction cosines** of vector $\mathbf{A}$. The zero vector has no direction angles and hence no direction cosines.

▷ **ILLUSTRATION 4** We find the magnitude and direction cosines of the vector $\mathbf{A} = \langle 3, 2, -6 \rangle$.

$$\| \mathbf{A} \| = \sqrt{(3)^2 + (2)^2 + (-6)^2}$$
$$= 7$$

From Equations (5),

$$\cos \alpha = \tfrac{3}{7} \qquad \cos \beta = \tfrac{2}{7} \qquad \cos \gamma = -\tfrac{6}{7} \qquad \blacktriangleleft$$

If the magnitude of a vector and its direction cosines are known, the vector is uniquely determined because from (5)

$$a_1 = \|\mathbf{A}\| \cos \alpha \qquad a_2 = \|\mathbf{A}\| \cos \beta \qquad a_3 = \|\mathbf{A}\| \cos \gamma \qquad \textbf{(6)}$$

The three direction cosines of a vector are not independent of each other, as we see by the following theorem.

10.2.13 Theorem

If $\cos \alpha$, $\cos \beta$, and $\cos \gamma$ are the direction cosines of a vector,

$$\cos^2 \alpha + \cos^2 \beta + \cos^2 \gamma = 1$$

Proof   If $\mathbf{A} = \langle a_1, a_2, a_3 \rangle$, the direction cosines of $\mathbf{A}$ are given by (5) and

$$\cos^2 \alpha + \cos^2 \beta + \cos^2 \gamma = \frac{a_1{}^2}{\|\mathbf{A}\|^2} + \frac{a_2{}^2}{\|\mathbf{A}\|^2} + \frac{a_3{}^2}{\|\mathbf{A}\|^2}$$

$$= \frac{a_1{}^2 + a_2{}^2 + a_3{}^2}{\|\mathbf{A}\|^2}$$

$$= \frac{\|\mathbf{A}\|^2}{\|\mathbf{A}\|^2}$$

$$= 1 \qquad\qquad \blacksquare$$

▷ **ILLUSTRATION 5**   We verify Theorem 10.2.13 for the vector of Illustration 4.

$$\cos^2 \alpha + \cos^2 \beta + \cos^2 \gamma = (\tfrac{3}{7})^2 + (\tfrac{2}{7})^2 + (-\tfrac{6}{7})^2$$

$$= \tfrac{9}{49} + \tfrac{4}{49} + \tfrac{36}{49}$$

$$= 1 \qquad\qquad \blacktriangleleft$$

The vector $\mathbf{A} = \langle a_1, a_2, a_3 \rangle$ is a unit vector if $\|\mathbf{A}\| = 1$, and from Equations (5) the components of a unit vector are its direction cosines.

The operations of addition, subtraction, and scalar multiplication of vectors in V_3 are given definitions analogous to the corresponding definitions for vectors in V_2.

If $\mathbf{A} = \langle a_1, a_2, a_3 \rangle$, $\mathbf{B} = \langle b_1, b_2, b_3 \rangle$, and c is a scalar, then

$$\mathbf{A} + \mathbf{B} = \langle a_1 + b_1, a_2 + b_2, a_3 + b_3 \rangle \qquad\qquad -\mathbf{A} = \langle -a_1, -a_2, -a_3 \rangle$$

$$\mathbf{A} - \mathbf{B} = \mathbf{A} + (-\mathbf{B}) \qquad\qquad\qquad\qquad\quad c\mathbf{A} = c\langle a_1, a_2, a_3 \rangle$$

$$\qquad\quad = \langle a_1 - b_1, a_2 - b_2, a_3 - b_3 \rangle \qquad\qquad\quad = \langle ca_1, ca_2, ca_3 \rangle$$

▶ **EXAMPLE 4**   Given $\mathbf{A} = \langle 5, -2, 6 \rangle$ and $\mathbf{B} = \langle 8, -5, -4 \rangle$, find $\mathbf{A} + \mathbf{B}$, $\mathbf{A} - \mathbf{B}$, $3\mathbf{A}$, and $-5\mathbf{B}$.

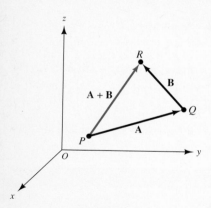

FIGURE 16

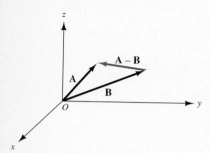

FIGURE 17

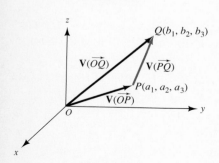

FIGURE 18

Solution

$$A + B = \langle 5 + 8, -2 + (-5), 6 + (-4) \rangle$$
$$= \langle 13, -7, 2 \rangle$$
$$A - B = \langle 5 - 8, -2 - (-5), 6 - (-4) \rangle$$
$$= \langle -3, 3, 10 \rangle$$
$$3A = 3\langle 5, -2, 6 \rangle \qquad -5B = -5\langle 8, -5, -4 \rangle$$
$$= \langle 15, -6, 18 \rangle \qquad\qquad = \langle -40, 25, 20 \rangle \qquad \blacktriangleleft$$

The geometric interpretation of the sum of two vectors in V_3 is similar to that for vectors in V_2. See Figure 16. If P is the point (x, y, z), and $A = \langle a_1, a_2, a_3 \rangle$, and $\overrightarrow{PQ}$ is a representation of A, then Q is the point $(x + a_1, y + a_2, z + a_3)$. Let $B = \langle b_1, b_2, b_3 \rangle$, and let $\overrightarrow{QR}$ be a representation of B. Then $(x + (a_1 + b_1), y + (a_2 + b_2), z + (a_3 + b_3))$ is the point R. Therefore $\overrightarrow{PR}$ is a representation of the vector $A + B$, and the parallelogram law holds.

The difference of two vectors in V_3 is also interpreted geometrically as it is in V_2. See Figure 17. A representation of the vector $A - B$ is obtained by choosing representations of A and B having the same initial point. Then a representation of the vector $A - B$ is the directed line segment from the terminal point of the representation of B to the terminal point of the representation of A.

Figure 18 shows the points $P(a_1, a_2, a_3)$, and $Q(b_1, b_2, b_3)$, and the directed line segments $\overrightarrow{PQ}$, $\overrightarrow{OP}$, and $\overrightarrow{OQ}$. Observe that

$$V(\overrightarrow{PQ}) = V(\overrightarrow{OQ}) - V(\overrightarrow{OP})$$
$$= \langle b_1, b_2, b_3 \rangle - \langle a_1, a_2, a_3 \rangle$$

Therefore

$$\boxed{V(\overrightarrow{PQ}) = \langle b_1 - a_1, b_2 - a_2, b_3 - a_3 \rangle}$$

▷ **ILLUSTRATION 6**   Figure 19 shows the directed line segment $\overrightarrow{PQ}$, where P is the point $(1, 3, 5)$ and Q is the point $(2, -1, 4)$.

$$V(\overrightarrow{PQ}) = \langle 2 - 1, -1 - 3, 4 - 5 \rangle$$
$$= \langle 1, -4, -1 \rangle \qquad \blacktriangleleft$$

Suppose that $A = \langle a_1, a_2, a_3 \rangle$ is a nonzero vector having direction cosines $\cos \alpha$, $\cos \beta$, and $\cos \gamma$, and let c be any nonzero scalar. Then $cA = \langle ca_1, ca_2, ca_3 \rangle$; and if $\cos \alpha_1$, $\cos \beta_1$, and $\cos \gamma_1$ are the direction cosines of cA, we have, from Equations (5),

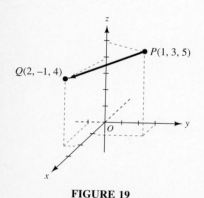

FIGURE 19

$$\cos \alpha_1 = \frac{ca_1}{\|cA\|} \qquad \cos \beta_1 = \frac{ca_2}{\|cA\|} \qquad \cos \gamma_1 = \frac{ca_3}{\|cA\|}$$

$$\cos \alpha_1 = \frac{c}{|c|}\frac{a_1}{\|A\|} \qquad \cos \beta_1 = \frac{c}{|c|}\frac{a_2}{\|A\|} \qquad \cos \gamma_1 = \frac{c}{|c|}\frac{a_3}{\|A\|}$$

$$\cos \alpha_1 = \frac{c}{|c|}\cos \alpha \qquad \cos \beta_1 = \frac{c}{|c|}\cos \beta \qquad \cos \gamma_1 = \frac{c}{|c|}\cos \gamma \quad (7)$$

Thus if $c > 0$, then from Equations (7) the direction cosines of vector $c\mathbf{A}$ are the same as the direction cosines of $\mathbf{A}$. And if $c < 0$, the direction cosines of $c\mathbf{A}$ are the negatives of the direction cosines of $\mathbf{A}$. Therefore, if c is a nonzero scalar, the vector $c\mathbf{A}$ is a vector whose magnitude is $|c|$ times the magnitude of $\mathbf{A}$. If $c > 0$, $c\mathbf{A}$ has the same direction as $\mathbf{A}$, whereas if $c < 0$, the direction of $c\mathbf{A}$ is opposite that of $\mathbf{A}$.

The operations of vector addition and scalar multiplication of any vectors in V_3 satisfy the properties given in Theorem 10.1.8; you are asked to prove them in Exercises 47 and 48. From this fact and Definition 10.1.9, V_3 is a real vector space. The three unit vectors

$$\mathbf{i} = \langle 1, 0, 0 \rangle \qquad \mathbf{j} = \langle 0, 1, 0 \rangle \qquad \mathbf{k} = \langle 0, 0, 1 \rangle$$

form a basis for the vector space V_3 because any vector $\langle a_1, a_2, a_3 \rangle$ can be written in terms of them as follows:

$$\langle a_1, a_2, a_3 \rangle = a_1 \langle 1, 0, 0 \rangle + a_2 \langle 0, 1, 0 \rangle + a_3 \langle 0, 0, 1 \rangle$$

Hence, if $\mathbf{A} = \langle a_1, a_2, a_3 \rangle$, we also can write

$$\mathbf{A} = a_1 \mathbf{i} + a_2 \mathbf{j} + a_3 \mathbf{k} \tag{8}$$

Because there are three elements in a basis, V_3 is a three-dimensional vector space.

Substituting from (6) into (8) we have

$$\mathbf{A} = \|\mathbf{A}\| \cos \alpha \, \mathbf{i} + \|\mathbf{A}\| \cos \beta \, \mathbf{j} + \|\mathbf{A}\| \cos \gamma \, \mathbf{k}$$

$$\mathbf{A} = \|\mathbf{A}\|(\cos \alpha \, \mathbf{i} + \cos \beta \, \mathbf{j} + \cos \gamma \, \mathbf{k}) \tag{9}$$

This equation enables us to express any nonzero vector in terms of its magnitude and direction cosines.

▶ **EXAMPLE 5** Express the vector of Illustration 4 in terms of its magnitude and direction cosines.

Solution In Illustration 4, we have $\mathbf{A} = \langle 3, 2, -6 \rangle$, $\|\mathbf{A}\| = 7$, $\cos \alpha = \frac{3}{7}$, $\cos \beta = \frac{2}{7}$, and $\cos \gamma = -\frac{6}{7}$. Hence, from (9),

$$\mathbf{A} = 7(\tfrac{3}{7}\mathbf{i} + \tfrac{2}{7}\mathbf{j} - \tfrac{6}{7}\mathbf{k}) \qquad\qquad ◀$$

10.2.14 Theorem

If the nonzero vector $\mathbf{A} = a_1 \mathbf{i} + a_2 \mathbf{j} + a_3 \mathbf{k}$, then the unit vector $\mathbf{U}$ having the same direction as $\mathbf{A}$ is given by

$$\mathbf{U} = \frac{a_1}{\|\mathbf{A}\|}\mathbf{i} + \frac{a_2}{\|\mathbf{A}\|}\mathbf{j} + \frac{a_3}{\|\mathbf{A}\|}\mathbf{k}$$

The proof of this theorem is analogous to the proof of Theorem 10.1.10 for a vector in V_2 and is left as an exercise (see Exercise 55).

▶ **EXAMPLE 6** Given the points $R(2, -1, 3)$ and $S(3, 4, 6)$, find the unit vector having the same direction as $\mathbf{V}(\overrightarrow{RS})$.

Solution

$$\mathbf{V}(\overrightarrow{RS}) = \langle 3 - 2, 4 - (-1), 6 - 3 \rangle \quad \|\mathbf{V}(\overrightarrow{RS})\| = \sqrt{1^2 + 5^2 + 3^2}$$
$$= \mathbf{i} + 5\mathbf{j} + 3\mathbf{k} \qquad\qquad\qquad = \sqrt{35}$$

Therefore, by Theorem 10.2.14, the desired unit vector is

$$\mathbf{U} = \frac{1}{\sqrt{35}}\mathbf{i} + \frac{5}{\sqrt{35}}\mathbf{j} + \frac{3}{\sqrt{35}}\mathbf{k} \qquad \blacktriangleleft$$

Operations with vectors, such as addition and scalar multiplication, as well as determining the magnitude of a vector and a unit vector having the same direction can be done on some computers and calculators. Refer to the users manual of the specific utility for the method of performing certain vector operations.

EXERCISES 10.2

In Exercises 1 through 5, points A and B are opposite vertices of a rectangular parallelepiped having its faces parallel to the coordinate planes. In each exercise, (a) sketch the figure, (b) find the coordinates of the other six vertices, (c) find the length of the diagonal AB.

1. $A(0, 0, 0)$; $B(7, 2, 3)$ **2.** $A(1, 1, 1)$; $B(3, 4, 2)$
3. $A(-1, 1, 2)$; $B(2, 3, 5)$
4. $A(2, -1, -3)$; $B(4, 0, -1)$
5. $A(1, -1, 0)$; $B(3, 3, 5)$

6. The vertex opposite one corner of a room is 18 ft east, 15 ft south, and 12 ft up from the first corner. **(a)** Sketch the figure; **(b)** determine the length of the diagonal joining two opposite vertices; **(c)** find the coordinates of all eight vertices of the room.

In Exercises 7 through 11, find (a) the undirected distance between the points A and B and (b) the midpoint of the line segment joining A and B.

7. $A(3, 4, 2)$; $B(1, 6, 3)$
8. $A(4, -3, 2)$; $B(-2, 3, -5)$
9. $A(2, -4, 1)$; $B\left(\frac{1}{2}, 2, 3\right)$
10. $A(-2, -\frac{1}{2}, 5)$; $B(5, 1, -4)$
11. $A(-5, 2, 1)$; $B(3, 7, -2)$

12. Prove that the three points $(1, -1, 3)$, $(2, 1, 7)$, and $(4, 2, 6)$ are the vertices of a right triangle, and find its area.

13. A line is drawn through the point $(6, 4, 2)$ perpendicular to the yz plane. Find the coordinates of the points on this line at a distance of 10 units from the point $(0, 4, 0)$.

14. Solve Exercise 13 if the line is drawn perpendicular to the xy plane.

15. Prove that the three points $(-3, 2, 4)$, $(6, 1, 2)$, and $(-12, 3, 6)$ are collinear by using the distance formula.

16. Find the vertices of the triangle whose sides have midpoints at $(3, 2, 3)$, $(-1, 1, 5)$ and $(0, 3, 4)$.

17. For the triangle having vertices at $A(2, -5, 3)$, $B(-1, 7, 0)$, and $C(-4, 9, 7)$ find **(a)** the length of each side and **(b)** the midpoint of each side.

18. Prove Theorem 10.2.6.

19. Show that any equation of the form
$$x^2 + y^2 + z^2 + Gx + Hy + Iz + J = 0$$
can be put in the form
$$(x - h)^2 + (y - k)^2 + (z - l)^2 = K$$

In Exercises 20 through 25, determine the graph of the equation.

20. $x^2 + y^2 + z^2 - 8y + 6z - 25 = 0$
21. $x^2 + y^2 + z^2 - 8x + 4y + 2z - 4 = 0$
22. $x^2 + y^2 + z^2 - x - y - 3z + 2 = 0$
23. $x^2 + y^2 + z^2 - 6z + 9 = 0$
24. $x^2 + y^2 + z^2 - 8x + 10y - 4z + 13 = 0$
25. $x^2 + y^2 + z^2 - 6x + 2y - 4z + 19 = 0$

In Exercises 26 through 28, find an equation of the sphere satisfying the conditions.

26. A diameter is the line segment having endpoints at $(6, 2, -5)$ and $(-4, 0, 7)$.

27. It is concentric with the sphere having the equation $x^2 + y^2 + z^2 - 2y + 8z - 9 = 0$ and has radius 3.

28. It contains the points $(0, 0, 4)$, $(2, 1, 3)$, and $(0, 2, 6)$ and has its center in the yz plane.

In Exercises 29 through 34, $\mathbf{A} = \langle 1, 2, 3 \rangle$,
$\mathbf{B} = \langle 4, -3, -1 \rangle$, $\mathbf{C} = \langle -5, -3, 5 \rangle$, and $\mathbf{D} = \langle -2, 1, 6 \rangle$.

29. Find **(a)** $\mathbf{A} + 5\mathbf{B}$; **(b)** $7\mathbf{C} - 5\mathbf{D}$;
(c) $\| 7\mathbf{C} \| - \| 5\mathbf{D} \|$; **(d)** $\| 7\mathbf{C} - 5\mathbf{D} \|$.

30. Find **(a)** $2\mathbf{A} - \mathbf{C}$; **(b)** $\| 2\mathbf{A} \| - \| \mathbf{C} \|$;
(c) $4\mathbf{B} + 6\mathbf{C} - 2\mathbf{D}$; **(d)** $\| 4\mathbf{B} \| + \| 6\mathbf{C} \| - \| 2\mathbf{D} \|$.

31. Find **(a)** $\mathbf{C} + 3\mathbf{D} - 8\mathbf{A}$; **(b)** $\| \mathbf{A} \| \| \mathbf{B} \| (\mathbf{C} - \mathbf{D})$.

32. Find **(a)** $3\mathbf{A} - 2\mathbf{B} + \mathbf{C} - 12\mathbf{D}$; **(b)** $\| \mathbf{A} \| \mathbf{C} - \| \mathbf{B} \| \mathbf{D}$.

33. Find scalars a and b such that
$$a(\mathbf{A} + \mathbf{B}) + b(\mathbf{C} + \mathbf{D}) = \mathbf{0}$$

34. Find scalars a, b, and c such that
$$a\mathbf{A} + b\mathbf{B} + c\mathbf{C} = \mathbf{D}$$

In Exercises 35 through 38, find the direction cosines of
the vector $\mathbf{V}(\overrightarrow{P_1 P_2})$ and check the answers by verifying
that the sum of their squares is 1.

35. $P_1(3, -1, -4)$; $P_2(7, 2, 4)$

36. $P_1(-2, 6, 5)$; $P_2(2, 4, 1)$

37. $P_1(4, -3, -1)$; $P_2(-2, -4, -8)$

38. $P_1(1, 3, 5)$; $P_2(2, -1, 4)$

39. Use the points P_1 and P_2 of Exercise 35 and find the
point Q such that $\mathbf{V}(\overrightarrow{P_1 P_2}) = 3\mathbf{V}(\overrightarrow{P_1 Q})$.

40. Use the points P_1 and P_2 of Exercise 38 and find the
point R such that $\mathbf{V}(\overrightarrow{P_1 R}) = -2\mathbf{V}(\overrightarrow{P_2 R})$.

41. Given $P_1(3, 2, -4)$ and $P_2(-5, 4, 2)$, find the point
P_3 such that $4\mathbf{V}(\overrightarrow{P_1 P_2}) = -3\mathbf{V}(\overrightarrow{P_2 P_3})$.

42. Given $P_1(7, 0, -2)$ and $P_2(2, -3, 5)$, find the point
P_3 such that $\mathbf{V}(\overrightarrow{P_1 P_3}) = 5\mathbf{V}(\overrightarrow{P_2 P_3})$.

In Exercises 43 and 44, express the vector in terms of its
magnitude and direction cosines.

43. (a) $-6\mathbf{i} + 2\mathbf{j} + 3\mathbf{k}$ **(b)** $-2\mathbf{i} + \mathbf{j} - 3\mathbf{k}$

44. (a) $2\mathbf{i} - 2\mathbf{j} + \mathbf{k}$ **(b)** $3\mathbf{i} + 4\mathbf{j} - 5\mathbf{k}$

In Exercises 45 and 46, find the unit vector having the
same direction as $\mathbf{V}(\overrightarrow{P_1 P_2})$.

45. (a) $P_1(4, -1, -6)$ and $P_2(5, 7, -2)$
(b) $P_1(-2, 5, 3)$ and $P_2(-4, 7, 5)$

46. (a) $P_1(3, 0, -1)$ and $P_2(-3, 8, -1)$
(b) $P_1(-8, -5, 2)$ and $P_2(-3, -9, 4)$

In Exercises 47 and 48, prove the property if $\mathbf{A}$, $\mathbf{B}$, and $\mathbf{C}$
are any vectors in V_3 and c and d are any scalars.

47. (a) $\mathbf{A} + \mathbf{B} = \mathbf{B} + \mathbf{A}$ (commutative law)
(b) There is a vector $\mathbf{0}$ in V_3 for which $\mathbf{A} + \mathbf{0} = \mathbf{A}$
(existence of additive identity)
(c) There is a vector $-\mathbf{A}$ in V_3 such that
$\mathbf{A} + (-\mathbf{A}) = \mathbf{0}$ (existence of negative)
(d) $c(\mathbf{A} + \mathbf{B}) = c\mathbf{A} + c\mathbf{B}$ (distributive law)

48. (a) $\mathbf{A} + (\mathbf{B} + \mathbf{C}) = (\mathbf{A} + \mathbf{B}) + \mathbf{C}$ (associative law)
(b) $(cd)\mathbf{A} = c(d\mathbf{A})$ (associative law)
(c) $(c + d)\mathbf{A} = c\mathbf{A} + d\mathbf{A}$ (distributive law)
(d) $1(\mathbf{A}) = \mathbf{A}$

49. Prove by analytic geometry that the four diagonals
joining opposite vertices of a rectangular parallelepiped bisect each other.

50. If P, Q, R, and S are four points in three-dimensional
space and A, B, C, and D are the midpoints of PQ,
QR, RS, and SP, respectively, prove by analytic geometry that $ABCD$ is a parallelogram.

51. Prove by analytic geometry that the four diagonals of
a rectangular parallelepiped have the same length.

52. Three vectors in V_3 are said to be *independent* if and
only if their position representations do not lie in a
plane, and three vectors, $\mathbf{E}_1$, $\mathbf{E}_2$, and $\mathbf{E}_3$ are said to
form a *basis* for the vector space V_3 if and only if any
vector in V_3 can be written as a linear combination of
$\mathbf{E}_1$, $\mathbf{E}_2$, and $\mathbf{E}_3$. A theorem can be proved which
states that three vectors form a basis for the vector
space V_3 if they are independent. Show that this theo-
rem holds for the three vectors $\langle 1, 0, 0 \rangle$, $\langle 1, 1, 0 \rangle$, and
$\langle 1, 1, 1 \rangle$ by doing the following: **(a)** Verify that the
vectors are independent by showing that their posi-
tion representations are not coplanar; **(b)** verify that
the vectors form a basis by showing that any vector
$\mathbf{A}$ can be written
$$\mathbf{A} = r\langle 1, 0, 0 \rangle + s\langle 1, 1, 0 \rangle + t\langle 1, 1, 1 \rangle \quad \textbf{(10)}$$
where r, s, and t are scalars. **(c)** If $\mathbf{A} = \langle 6, -2, 5 \rangle$,
find the particular values of r, s, and t such that (10)
holds.

53. See Exercise 52. **(a)** Verify that the vectors $\langle 2, 0, 1 \rangle$,
$\langle 0, -1, 0 \rangle$, and $\langle 1, -1, 0 \rangle$ form a basis for V_3 by
showing that any vector $\mathbf{A}$ can be written
$$\mathbf{A} = r\langle 2, 0, 1 \rangle + s\langle 0, -1, 0 \rangle + t\langle 1, -1, 0 \rangle \quad \textbf{(11)}$$
where r, s, and t are scalars. **(b)** If $\mathbf{A} = \langle -2, 3, 5 \rangle$,
find the particular values of r, s, and t such that (11)
holds.

54. Refer to the first sentence of Exercise 52. A theorem
can be proved which states that three vectors form a
basis for the vector space V_3 only if they are independent. Show that this theorem is valid for the three
vectors $\mathbf{F}_1 = \langle 1, 0, 1 \rangle$, $\mathbf{F}_2 = \langle 1, 1, 1 \rangle$, and
$\mathbf{F}_3 = \langle 2, 1, 2 \rangle$ by doing the following: **(a)** Verify that
$\mathbf{F}_1$, $\mathbf{F}_2$, and $\mathbf{F}_3$ are not independent by showing that
their position representations are coplanar; **(b)** verify
that the vectors do not form a basis by showing that
every vector in V_3 cannot be written as a linear combination of $\mathbf{F}_1$, $\mathbf{F}_2$, and $\mathbf{F}_3$.

55. Prove Theorem 10.2.14.

56. If the radian measure of each direction angle of a
vector is the same, what is the measure? Explain how
you arrived at your answer.

10.3 DOT PRODUCT

So far, we have defined the following operations with vectors: addition and subtraction, and multiplication of a vector by a scalar. Each of these operations results in a vector. We now define a multiplication operation on two vectors, called the *dot product,* which yields a scalar and not a vector.

10.3.1 Definition of Dot Product

The **dot product** of two vectors **A** and **B**, denoted by **A** · **B** is defined as follows:

(i) If $\mathbf{A} = \langle a_1, a_2 \rangle$ and $\mathbf{B} = \langle b_1, b_2 \rangle$ are two vectors in V_2

$$\mathbf{A} \cdot \mathbf{B} = a_1 b_1 + a_2 b_2$$

(ii) If $\mathbf{A} = \langle a_1, a_2, a_3 \rangle$ and $\mathbf{B} = \langle b_1, b_2, b_3 \rangle$ are two vectors in V_3

$$\mathbf{A} \cdot \mathbf{B} = a_1 b_1 + a_2 b_2 + a_3 b_3$$

The dot product is sometimes called the **inner product** or **scalar product,** not to be confused with scalar multiplication which gives the product of a scalar and a vector.

▷ **ILLUSTRATION 1** If $\mathbf{A} = \langle 2, -3 \rangle$ and $\mathbf{B} = \langle -\frac{1}{2}, 4 \rangle$, then

$$\mathbf{A} \cdot \mathbf{B} = \langle 2, -3 \rangle \cdot \langle -\tfrac{1}{2}, 4 \rangle$$
$$= (2)\left(-\tfrac{1}{2}\right) + (-3)(4)$$
$$= -13$$

◀

▷ **ILLUSTRATION 2** If $\mathbf{A} = \langle 4, 2, -6 \rangle$ and $\mathbf{B} = \langle -5, 3, -2 \rangle$, then

$$\mathbf{A} \cdot \mathbf{B} = \langle 4, 2, -6 \rangle \cdot \langle -5, 3, -2 \rangle$$
$$= 4(-5) + 2(3) + (-6)(-2)$$
$$= -2$$

◀

Dot products involving the unit vectors **i**, **j**, and **k** are useful and easily verified (see Exercises 5 and 6):

$$\mathbf{i} \cdot \mathbf{i} = 1 \qquad \mathbf{j} \cdot \mathbf{j} = 1 \qquad \mathbf{k} \cdot \mathbf{k} = 1$$
$$\mathbf{i} \cdot \mathbf{j} = 0 \qquad \mathbf{i} \cdot \mathbf{k} = 0 \qquad \mathbf{j} \cdot \mathbf{k} = 0$$

The following theorem states that dot multiplication is commutative and distributive with respect to vector addition.

10.3.2 Theorem

If **A**, **B**, and **C** are any vectors in V_2 or V_3, then

(i) $\mathbf{A} \cdot \mathbf{B} = \mathbf{B} \cdot \mathbf{A}$ (commutative law)
(ii) $\mathbf{A} \cdot (\mathbf{B} + \mathbf{C}) = \mathbf{A} \cdot \mathbf{B} + \mathbf{A} \cdot \mathbf{C}$ (distributive law)

The proofs are left as exercises (see Exercises 7 and 8).

Because $\mathbf{A} \cdot \mathbf{B}$ is a scalar, the expression $(\mathbf{A} \cdot \mathbf{B}) \cdot \mathbf{C}$ is meaningless. Hence we do not consider associativity of dot multiplication.

Other laws of dot multiplication are given in the following theorem.

10.3.3 Theorem

If $\mathbf{A}$ and $\mathbf{B}$ are any vectors in V_2 or V_3, and c is any scalar, then

(i) $c(\mathbf{A} \cdot \mathbf{B}) = (c\mathbf{A}) \cdot \mathbf{B}$
(ii) $\mathbf{0} \cdot \mathbf{A} = 0$
(iii) $\mathbf{A} \cdot \mathbf{A} = \|\mathbf{A}\|^2$

The proofs are left as exercises (see Exercises 9 and 10).

We now consider what is meant by the angle between two vectors, and this leads to another expression for the dot product of two vectors.

10.3.4 Definition of the Angle Between Two Vectors

Let $\mathbf{A}$ and $\mathbf{B}$ be two nonzero vectors.

(i) If $\mathbf{A}$ is not a scalar multiple of $\mathbf{B}$ and if $\overrightarrow{OP}$ is the position representation of $\mathbf{A}$ and $\overrightarrow{OQ}$ is the position representation of $\mathbf{B}$, then the **angle between the vectors** $\mathbf{A}$ and $\mathbf{B}$ is the angle of positive measure between $\overrightarrow{OP}$ and $\overrightarrow{OQ}$ interior to the triangle determined by the points O, P, and Q.
(ii) If $\mathbf{A} = c\mathbf{B}$, where c is a scalar, then if $c > 0$ the angle between the vectors has radian measure 0; if $c < 0$, the angle between the vectors has radian measure π.

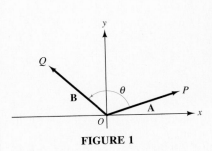

FIGURE 1

The symbol used to denote the angle between two vectors is also used to denote the measure of that angle. From the definition, if θ is the radian measure of the angle between two vectors, then $0 \le \theta \le \pi$. Figure 1 shows the angle θ between the vectors $\mathbf{A}$ and $\mathbf{B}$ (where $\mathbf{A}$ is not a scalar multiple of $\mathbf{B}$) in V_2, and Figure 2 shows the angle when the vectors are in V_3.

10.3.5 Theorem

If θ is the angle between the two nonzero vectors $\mathbf{A}$ and $\mathbf{B}$, then

$$\mathbf{A} \cdot \mathbf{B} = \|\mathbf{A}\| \|\mathbf{B}\| \cos \theta$$

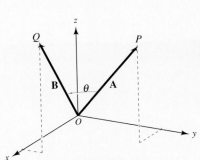

FIGURE 2

Proof Figure 3 shows the position representation $\overrightarrow{OP}$ of $\mathbf{A}$, the position representation $\overrightarrow{OQ}$ of $\mathbf{B}$, the representation $\overrightarrow{PQ}$ of $\mathbf{B} - \mathbf{A}$, and the angle θ at the origin in triangle POQ. From the law of cosines

$$\cos \theta = \frac{\|\mathbf{A}\|^2 + \|\mathbf{B}\|^2 - \|\mathbf{B} - \mathbf{A}\|^2}{2\|\mathbf{A}\| \|\mathbf{B}\|} \tag{1}$$

From properties of the dot product in Theorems 10.3.2 and 10.3.3,

$$\|\mathbf{B} - \mathbf{A}\|^2 = (\mathbf{B} - \mathbf{A}) \cdot (\mathbf{B} - \mathbf{A})$$
$$= (\mathbf{B} - \mathbf{A}) \cdot \mathbf{B} - (\mathbf{B} - \mathbf{A}) \cdot \mathbf{A}$$
$$= \mathbf{B} \cdot \mathbf{B} - \mathbf{A} \cdot \mathbf{B} - \mathbf{B} \cdot \mathbf{A} + \mathbf{A} \cdot \mathbf{A}$$
$$= \|\mathbf{B}\|^2 - 2\mathbf{A} \cdot \mathbf{B} + \|\mathbf{A}\|^2 \tag{2}$$

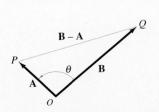

FIGURE 3

Substituting from (2) into (1), we get

$$\cos \theta = \frac{\| \mathbf{A} \|^2 + \| \mathbf{B} \|^2 - (\| \mathbf{B} \|^2 - 2\mathbf{A} \cdot \mathbf{B} + \| \mathbf{A} \|^2)}{2\| \mathbf{A} \| \| \mathbf{B} \|}$$

$$\cos \theta = \frac{2\mathbf{A} \cdot \mathbf{B}}{2\| \mathbf{A} \| \| \mathbf{B} \|}$$

$$\mathbf{A} \cdot \mathbf{B} = \| \mathbf{A} \| \| \mathbf{B} \| \cos \theta \qquad \blacksquare$$

Theorem 10.3.5 states that the dot product of two vectors is the product of the magnitudes of the vectors and the cosine of the angle between them.

▶ **EXAMPLE 1**   Given the vectors

$$\mathbf{A} = 6\mathbf{i} - 3\mathbf{j} + 2\mathbf{k} \quad \text{and} \quad \mathbf{B} = 2\mathbf{i} + \mathbf{j} - 3\mathbf{k}$$

find $\cos \theta$ if θ is the angle between $\mathbf{A}$ and $\mathbf{B}$.

Solution   We first compute $\mathbf{A} \cdot \mathbf{B}$, $\| \mathbf{A} \|$, and $\| \mathbf{B} \|$.

$$\begin{array}{llll}
\mathbf{A} \cdot \mathbf{B} = \langle 6, -3, 2 \rangle \cdot \langle 2, 1, -3 \rangle & \qquad \| \mathbf{A} \| = \sqrt{36 + 9 + 4} & \qquad \| \mathbf{B} \| = \sqrt{4 + 1 + 9} \\
\qquad = 12 - 3 - 6 & \qquad \quad = \sqrt{49} & \qquad \quad = \sqrt{14} \\
\qquad = 3 & \qquad \quad = 7 &
\end{array}$$

From Theorem 10.3.5,

$$\begin{aligned}
\cos \theta &= \frac{\mathbf{A} \cdot \mathbf{B}}{\| \mathbf{A} \| \| \mathbf{B} \|} \\
&= \frac{3}{7\sqrt{14}}
\end{aligned} \qquad \blacktriangleleft$$

You learned in Section 10.1 that if two nonzero vectors are scalar multiples of each other, they have either the same or opposite directions. This fact gives us the following definition.

10.3.6 Definition of Parallel Vectors

Two vectors are said to be **parallel** if and only if one of the vectors is a scalar multiple of the other.

▷ **ILLUSTRATION 3**   The vectors $\langle 3, -4, 8 \rangle$ and $\langle \frac{3}{4}, -1, 2 \rangle$ are parallel because $\langle 3, -4, 8 \rangle = 4 \langle \frac{3}{4}, -1, 2 \rangle$.   ◀

If $\mathbf{A}$ is any vector, $\mathbf{0} = 0\mathbf{A}$; thus, from Definition 10.3.6 the zero vector is parallel to any vector.

As an exercise you are to show that two nonzero vectors are parallel if and only if the radian measure of the angle between them is 0 or π (see Exercise 49).

If $\mathbf{A}$ and $\mathbf{B}$ are nonzero vectors, then from Theorem 10.3.5

$$\cos \theta = 0 \quad \text{if and only if} \quad \mathbf{A} \cdot \mathbf{B} = 0$$

Because $0 \le \theta \le \pi$, it follows from this statement that

$$\theta = \tfrac{1}{2}\pi \quad \text{if and only if} \quad \mathbf{A} \cdot \mathbf{B} = 0$$

We have, then, the following definition.

10.3.7 Definition of Orthogonal Vectors

Two vectors $\mathbf{A}$ and $\mathbf{B}$ are said to be **orthogonal** (**perpendicular**) if and only if $\mathbf{A} \cdot \mathbf{B} = 0$.

▷ **ILLUSTRATION 4**   The vectors $\langle -4, 5, 0 \rangle$ and $\langle 10, 8, 3 \rangle$ are orthogonal because

$$\langle -4, 5, 0 \rangle \cdot \langle 10, 8, 3 \rangle = (-4)(10) + (5)(8) + (0)(3)$$
$$= 0 \qquad \blacktriangleleft$$

If $\mathbf{A}$ is any vector, $\mathbf{0} \cdot \mathbf{A} = 0$, and therefore the zero vector is orthogonal to any vector.

▶ **EXAMPLE 2**   Given $\mathbf{A} = 3\mathbf{i} + 2\mathbf{j}$ and $\mathbf{B} = 2\mathbf{i} + k\mathbf{j}$, where k is a scalar, find **(a)** k such that $\mathbf{A}$ and $\mathbf{B}$ are orthogonal; **(b)** k such that $\mathbf{A}$ and $\mathbf{B}$ are parallel.

Solution

(a) By Definition 10.3.7, $\mathbf{A}$ and $\mathbf{B}$ are orthogonal if and only if $\mathbf{A} \cdot \mathbf{B} = 0$; that is,

$$(3)(2) + 2(k) = 0$$
$$k = -3$$

(b) From Definition 10.3.6, $\mathbf{A}$ and $\mathbf{B}$ are parallel if and only if there is some scalar c such that $\langle 3, 2 \rangle = c\langle 2, k \rangle$; that is,

$$3 = 2c \quad \text{and} \quad 2 = ck$$

Solving these two equations simultaneously we obtain $k = \tfrac{4}{3}$. ◀

▶ **EXAMPLE 3**   Prove by using vectors that the points $A(4, 9, 1)$, $B(-2, 6, 3)$, and $C(6, 3, -2)$ are the vertices of a right triangle.

Solution   Triangle CAB appears in Figure 4. From the figure it looks as if the angle at A is the one that may be a right angle. We shall find $\mathbf{V}(\overrightarrow{AB})$ and $\mathbf{V}(\overrightarrow{AC})$ and if the dot product of these two vectors is zero, the angle is a right angle.

$$\mathbf{V}(\overrightarrow{AB}) = \langle -2 - 4, 6 - 9, 3 - 1 \rangle \qquad \mathbf{V}(\overrightarrow{AC}) = \langle 6 - 4, 3 - 9, -2 - 1 \rangle$$
$$= \langle -6, -3, 2 \rangle \qquad\qquad\qquad\qquad = \langle 2, -6, -3 \rangle$$
$$\mathbf{V}(\overrightarrow{AB}) \cdot \mathbf{V}(\overrightarrow{AC}) = \langle -6, -3, 2 \rangle \cdot \langle 2, -6, -3 \rangle$$
$$= -12 + 18 - 6$$
$$= 0$$

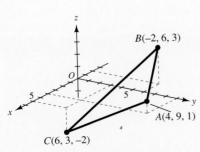

FIGURE 4

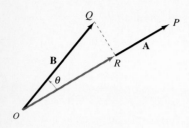

FIGURE 5

Conclusion: $\mathbf{V}(\overrightarrow{AB})$ and $\mathbf{V}(\overrightarrow{AC})$ are orthogonal; thus the angle at A in triangle CAB is a right angle, and CAB is a right triangle. ◀

A geometric interpretation of the dot product is obtained from the *scalar projection* of one vector onto another. See Figure 5, where $\overrightarrow{OP}$ and $\overrightarrow{OQ}$ are the position representations of vectors $\mathbf{A}$ and $\mathbf{B}$, respectively. Point R is the foot of the perpendicular from Q to the line containing $\overrightarrow{OP}$. The scalar projection of $\mathbf{B}$ onto $\mathbf{A}$ is the magnitude of the vector having $\overrightarrow{OR}$ as its position representation.

10.3.8 Definition of the Scalar Projection of One Vector onto Another

If $\mathbf{A}$ and $\mathbf{B}$ are nonzero vectors, the **scalar projection** of $\mathbf{B}$ onto $\mathbf{A}$ is defined to be $\|\mathbf{B}\| \cos \theta$, where θ is the angle between $\mathbf{A}$ and $\mathbf{B}$.

Observe that the scalar projection may be either positive or negative, depending on the sign of $\cos \theta$.

From Theorem 10.3.5,

$$\mathbf{A} \cdot \mathbf{B} = \|\mathbf{A}\|(\|\mathbf{B}\| \cos \theta) \tag{3}$$

Thus the dot product of $\mathbf{A}$ and $\mathbf{B}$ is the magnitude of $\mathbf{A}$ multiplied by the scalar projection of $\mathbf{B}$ onto $\mathbf{A}$. See Figure 6(a) and (b). Because dot multiplication is commutative, $\mathbf{A} \cdot \mathbf{B}$ is also the magnitude of $\mathbf{B}$ multiplied by the scalar projection of $\mathbf{A}$ onto $\mathbf{B}$.

If $\mathbf{B} = b_1 \mathbf{i} + b_2 \mathbf{j} + b_3 \mathbf{k}$, then

$$\mathbf{i} \cdot \mathbf{B} = b_1 \qquad \mathbf{j} \cdot \mathbf{B} = b_2 \qquad \mathbf{k} \cdot \mathbf{B} = b_3$$

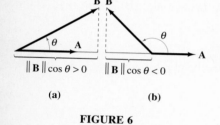

$\|\mathbf{B}\| \cos \theta > 0$ (a) $\|\mathbf{B}\| \cos \theta < 0$ (b)

FIGURE 6

Hence the dot product of $\mathbf{B}$ and one of the unit vectors $\mathbf{i}$, $\mathbf{j}$, or $\mathbf{k}$ gives the component of $\mathbf{B}$ in the direction of that unit vector. To generalize this result, let $\mathbf{U}$ be any unit vector. Then from (3), if θ is the angle between $\mathbf{U}$ and $\mathbf{B}$,

$$\mathbf{U} \cdot \mathbf{B} = \|\mathbf{U}\|\|\mathbf{B}\| \cos \theta$$
$$= \|\mathbf{B}\| \cos \theta$$

Therefore $\mathbf{U} \cdot \mathbf{B}$ is the scalar projection of $\mathbf{B}$ onto $\mathbf{U}$, which is called the *component* of the vector $\mathbf{B}$ in the direction of $\mathbf{U}$. More generally, the **component** of a vector $\mathbf{B}$ in the direction of a vector $\mathbf{A}$ is the scalar projection of $\mathbf{B}$ onto a unit vector in the direction of $\mathbf{A}$.

The following theorem can be used to compute the scalar projection of one vector onto another.

10.3.9 Theorem

The scalar projection of the vector $\mathbf{B}$ onto the vector $\mathbf{A}$ is

$$\frac{\mathbf{A} \cdot \mathbf{B}}{\|\mathbf{A}\|}$$

Proof   From Definition 10.3.8, the scalar projection of **B** onto **A** is
$\|\mathbf{B}\| \cos \theta$, where θ is the angle between **A** and **B**. From Theorem 10.3.5,

$$\|\mathbf{A}\| \|\mathbf{B}\| \cos \theta = \mathbf{A} \cdot \mathbf{B}$$

$$\|\mathbf{B}\| \cos \theta = \frac{\mathbf{A} \cdot \mathbf{B}}{\|\mathbf{A}\|} \qquad \blacksquare$$

Refer again to Figure 5. If **C** is the vector having $\overrightarrow{OR}$ as its position
representation, then **C** is called the **vector projection** of **B** onto **A**. To
determine **C**, we multiply $\|\mathbf{B}\| \cos \theta$ by the unit vector having the same
direction as **A**. Thus

$$\mathbf{C} = (\|\mathbf{B}\| \cos \theta) \frac{\mathbf{A}}{\|\mathbf{A}\|}$$

$$= \frac{\|\mathbf{A}\| (\|\mathbf{B}\| \cos \theta)}{\|\mathbf{A}\|^2} \mathbf{A}$$

$$= \left(\frac{\mathbf{A} \cdot \mathbf{B}}{\|\mathbf{A}\|^2} \right) \mathbf{A} \qquad \text{(from Theorem 10.3.5)}$$

We state this result as a theorem.

> **10.3.10 Theorem**
>
> The vector projection of the vector **B** onto the vector **A** is
>
> $$\left(\frac{\mathbf{A} \cdot \mathbf{B}}{\|\mathbf{A}\|^2} \right) \mathbf{A}$$

▷ **ILLUSTRATION 5**   In Example 1, for the vectors

$$\mathbf{A} = 6\mathbf{i} - 3\mathbf{j} + 2\mathbf{k} \quad \text{and} \quad \mathbf{B} = 2\mathbf{i} + \mathbf{j} - 3\mathbf{k}$$

we computed $\mathbf{A} \cdot \mathbf{B} = 3$ and $\|\mathbf{A}\| = 7$.

The component of **B** in the direction of **A** is the scalar projection of **B**
onto **A**, which from Theorem 10.3.9 is

$$\frac{\mathbf{A} \cdot \mathbf{B}}{\|\mathbf{A}\|} = \frac{3}{7}$$

From Theorem 10.3.10, the vector projection of **B** onto **A** is

$$\left(\frac{\mathbf{A} \cdot \mathbf{B}}{\|\mathbf{A}\|^2} \right) \mathbf{A} = \frac{3}{49} (6\mathbf{i} - 3\mathbf{j} + 2\mathbf{k})$$

$$= \frac{18}{49} \mathbf{i} - \frac{9}{49} \mathbf{j} + \frac{6}{49} \mathbf{k} \qquad \blacktriangleleft$$

▶ **EXAMPLE 4**   Given the vectors

$$\mathbf{A} = -5\mathbf{i} + \mathbf{j} \quad \text{and} \quad \mathbf{B} = 4\mathbf{i} + 2\mathbf{j}$$

Find: **(a)** the scalar projection of **B** onto **A**; **(b)** the vector projection of **B**
onto **A**. **(c)** Show on a figure the position representations of **A**, **B**, and the
vector projection of **B** onto **A**.

Solution We first compute $\mathbf{A} \cdot \mathbf{B}$ and $\|\mathbf{A}\|$.

$$\mathbf{A} \cdot \mathbf{B} = \langle -5, 1 \rangle \cdot \langle 4, 2 \rangle \qquad \|\mathbf{A}\| = \sqrt{(-5)^2 + 1^2}$$
$$= -20 + 2 \qquad\qquad\qquad = \sqrt{26}$$
$$= -18$$

(a) From Theorem 10.3.9, the scalar projection of $\mathbf{B}$ onto $\mathbf{A}$ is

$$\frac{\mathbf{A} \cdot \mathbf{B}}{\|\mathbf{A}\|} = -\frac{18}{\sqrt{26}}$$

(b) From Theorem 10.3.10, the vector projection of $\mathbf{B}$ onto $\mathbf{A}$ is

$$\left(\frac{\mathbf{A} \cdot \mathbf{B}}{\|\mathbf{A}\|^2} \right) \mathbf{A} = -\tfrac{18}{26}(-5\mathbf{i} + \mathbf{j})$$
$$= -\tfrac{9}{13}(-5\mathbf{i} + \mathbf{j})$$
$$= \tfrac{45}{13}\mathbf{i} - \tfrac{9}{13}\mathbf{j}$$

(c) Figure 7 shows the position representations of $\mathbf{A}$, $\mathbf{B}$, and $\mathbf{C}$, where $\mathbf{C}$ is the vector projection of $\mathbf{B}$ onto $\mathbf{A}$. ◄

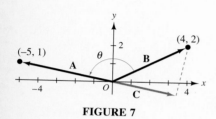

FIGURE 7

▶ **EXAMPLE 5** Find the distance from the point $P(4, 1, 6)$ to the line through the points $A(8, 3, 2)$ and $B(2, -3, 5)$.

Solution Figure 8 shows the point P and the line through A and B. The point M is the foot of the perpendicular line from P to the line through A and B. Let d units be the distance $|\overline{PM}|$. Thus from the Pythagorean theorem,

$$d = \sqrt{|\overline{AP}|^2 - |\overline{AM}|^2} \tag{4}$$

To apply (4) we need to compute $|\overline{AP}|$, which is the magnitude of $\mathbf{V}(\overrightarrow{AP})$, and $|\overline{AM}|$, which is the scalar projection of $\mathbf{V}(\overrightarrow{AP})$ onto $\mathbf{V}(\overrightarrow{AB})$. We first find $\mathbf{V}(\overrightarrow{AP})$ and $\mathbf{V}(\overrightarrow{AB})$.

$$\mathbf{V}(\overrightarrow{AP}) = \langle 4 - 8, 1 - 3, 6 - 2 \rangle \qquad \mathbf{V}(\overrightarrow{AB}) = \langle 2 - 8, -3 - 3, 5 - 2 \rangle$$
$$= \langle -4, -2, 4 \rangle \qquad\qquad\qquad = \langle -6, -6, 3 \rangle$$

We compute $|\overline{AP}|$ by finding $\|\mathbf{V}(\overrightarrow{AP})\|$, and we compute $|\overline{AM}|$ by Theorem 10.3.9 with $\mathbf{A} = \mathbf{V}(\overrightarrow{AB})$ and $\mathbf{B} = \mathbf{V}(\overrightarrow{AP})$.

$$|\overline{AP}| = \|\mathbf{V}(\overrightarrow{AP})\| \qquad\qquad |\overline{AM}| = \frac{\mathbf{V}(\overrightarrow{AB}) \cdot \mathbf{V}(\overrightarrow{AP})}{\|\mathbf{V}(\overrightarrow{AB})\|}$$

$$= \sqrt{(-4)^2 + (-2)^2 + 4^2} \qquad = \frac{\langle -6, -6, 3 \rangle \cdot \langle -4, -2, 4 \rangle}{\sqrt{(-6)^2 + (-6)^2 + 3^2}}$$

$$= \sqrt{36} \qquad\qquad\qquad\qquad = \frac{24 + 12 + 12}{\sqrt{81}}$$

$$= 6 \qquad\qquad\qquad\qquad\qquad = \tfrac{48}{9}$$

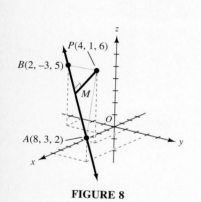

FIGURE 8

Substituting these values of $|\overline{AP}|$ and $|\overline{AM}|$ in (4) we get

$$d = \sqrt{6^2 - (\tfrac{48}{9})^2}$$
$$= 6\sqrt{1 - \tfrac{64}{81}}$$
$$= \tfrac{2}{3}\sqrt{17}$$ ◄

You learned in Section 6.4 that if a constant force of F pounds moves an object a distance d feet along a line and the force is acting in the direction of motion, then if W is the number of foot-pounds in the work done by the force, $W = Fd$. Suppose, however, that the constant force is not directed along the line of motion. In this case the physicist defines the **work** done as the *product of the component of the force along the line of motion times the displacement.* If the object moves from the point A to the point B, we call the vector, having $\overrightarrow{AB}$ as a representation, the **displacement vector** and denote it by $\mathbf{V}(\overrightarrow{AB})$. So if the magnitude of a constant force vector $\mathbf{F}$ is expressed in pounds and the distance from A to B is expressed in feet, and θ is the angle between the vectors $\mathbf{F}$ and $\mathbf{V}(\overrightarrow{AB})$, then if W is the number of foot-pounds in the work done by the force $\mathbf{F}$ in moving an object from A to B,

$$W = (\|\mathbf{F}\| \cos \theta) \|\mathbf{V}(\overrightarrow{AB})\|$$
$$= \|\mathbf{F}\| \|\mathbf{V}(\overrightarrow{AB})\| \cos \theta$$
$$= \mathbf{F} \cdot \mathbf{V}(\overrightarrow{AB})$$

▶ **EXAMPLE 6**   Suppose that a force $\mathbf{F}$ has a magnitude of 6 lb and $\frac{1}{6}\pi$ is the radian measure of the angle giving its direction. Find the work done by $\mathbf{F}$ in moving an object along a line from the origin to the point $P(7, 1)$, where distance is measured in feet.

Solution   Figure 9 shows the position representations of $\mathbf{F}$ and $\mathbf{V}(\overrightarrow{OP})$. Because $\mathbf{F} = \langle 6 \cos \frac{1}{6}\pi, 6 \sin \frac{1}{6}\pi \rangle$, and $\mathbf{V}(\overrightarrow{OP}) = \langle 7, 1 \rangle$, then if W ft-lb is the work done,

$$\mathbf{W} = \mathbf{F} \cdot \mathbf{V}(\overrightarrow{OP})$$
$$= \langle 6 \cos \tfrac{1}{6}\pi, 6 \sin \tfrac{1}{6}\pi \rangle \cdot \langle 7, 1 \rangle$$
$$= \langle 3\sqrt{3}, 3 \rangle \cdot \langle 7, 1 \rangle$$
$$= 21\sqrt{3} + 3$$
$$\approx 39.37$$

Conclusion: The work done is approximately 39.37 ft-lb.   ◀

Vectors have geometric representations independent of the coordinate system used. Because of this, vector analysis can be used to prove certain theorems of plane geometry as illustrated in the following example.

▶ **EXAMPLE 7**   Prove by vector analysis that the altitudes of a triangle meet in a point.

Solution   Let ABC be a triangle having altitudes AP and BQ intersecting at point S. Draw a line through C and S intersecting AB at point R. We wish to prove that RC is perpendicular to AB (see Figure 10).

Let $\overrightarrow{AB}, \overrightarrow{BC}, \overrightarrow{AC}, \overrightarrow{AS}, \overrightarrow{BS}, \overrightarrow{CS}$ be representations of vectors. Let $\mathbf{V}(\overrightarrow{AB})$ be the vector having directed line segment $\overrightarrow{AB}$ as a representation. In a similar manner let $\mathbf{V}(\overrightarrow{BC}), \mathbf{V}(\overrightarrow{AC}), \mathbf{V}(\overrightarrow{AS}), \mathbf{V}(\overrightarrow{BS})$, and $\mathbf{V}(\overrightarrow{CS})$ be the vectors having the directed line segment in parentheses as a representation.

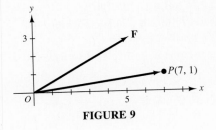

FIGURE 9

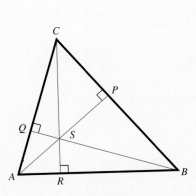

FIGURE 10

Because AP is an altitude of the triangle,

$$\mathbf{V}(\overrightarrow{AS}) \cdot \mathbf{V}(\overrightarrow{BC}) = 0 \tag{5}$$

Also, because BQ is an altitude of the triangle,

$$\mathbf{V}(\overrightarrow{BS}) \cdot \mathbf{V}(\overrightarrow{AC}) = 0 \tag{6}$$

To prove that RC is perpendicular to AB we shall show $\mathbf{V}(\overrightarrow{CS}) \cdot \mathbf{V}(\overrightarrow{AB}) = 0$.

$$
\begin{aligned}
\mathbf{V}(\overrightarrow{CS}) \cdot \mathbf{V}(\overrightarrow{AB}) &= \mathbf{V}(\overrightarrow{CS}) \cdot [\mathbf{V}(\overrightarrow{AC}) + \mathbf{V}(\overrightarrow{CB})] \\
&= \mathbf{V}(\overrightarrow{CS}) \cdot \mathbf{V}(\overrightarrow{AC}) + \mathbf{V}(\overrightarrow{CS}) \cdot \mathbf{V}(\overrightarrow{CB}) \\
&= [\mathbf{V}(\overrightarrow{CB}) + \mathbf{V}(\overrightarrow{BS})] \cdot \mathbf{V}(\overrightarrow{AC}) + [\mathbf{V}(\overrightarrow{CA}) + \mathbf{V}(\overrightarrow{AS})] \cdot \mathbf{V}(\overrightarrow{CB}) \\
&= \mathbf{V}(\overrightarrow{CB}) \cdot \mathbf{V}(\overrightarrow{AC}) + \mathbf{V}(\overrightarrow{BS}) \cdot \mathbf{V}(\overrightarrow{AC}) + \mathbf{V}(\overrightarrow{CA}) \cdot \mathbf{V}(\overrightarrow{CB}) + \mathbf{V}(\overrightarrow{AS}) \cdot \mathbf{V}(\overrightarrow{CB})
\end{aligned}
$$

Replacing $\mathbf{V}(\overrightarrow{CA})$ by $-\mathbf{V}(\overrightarrow{AC})$ and using (5) and (6) we obtain

$$
\begin{aligned}
\mathbf{V}(\overrightarrow{CS}) \cdot \mathbf{V}(\overrightarrow{AB}) &= \mathbf{V}(\overrightarrow{CB}) \cdot \mathbf{V}(\overrightarrow{AC}) + 0 + [-\mathbf{V}(\overrightarrow{AC})] \cdot \mathbf{V}(\overrightarrow{CB}) + 0 \\
&= 0
\end{aligned}
$$

Conclusion: Altitudes AP, BQ, and RC meet in a point.   ◀

EXERCISES 10.3

In Exercises 1 through 4, find $\mathbf{A} \cdot \mathbf{B}$.

1. (a) $\mathbf{A} = \langle -1, 2 \rangle$, $\mathbf{B} = \langle -4, 3 \rangle$
   (b) $\mathbf{A} = 2\mathbf{i} - \mathbf{j}$, $\mathbf{B} = \mathbf{i} + 3\mathbf{j}$

2. (a) $\mathbf{A} = \langle \frac{1}{3}, -\frac{1}{2} \rangle$, $\mathbf{B} = \langle \frac{5}{2}, \frac{4}{3} \rangle$
   (b) $\mathbf{A} = -2\mathbf{i}$, $\mathbf{B} = -\mathbf{i} + \mathbf{j}$

3. (a) $\mathbf{A} = \langle \frac{2}{5}, \frac{1}{4}, -\frac{3}{2} \rangle$, $\mathbf{B} = \langle \frac{1}{2}, \frac{3}{5}, \frac{1}{2} \rangle$
   (b) $\mathbf{A} = 3\mathbf{j} - 2\mathbf{k}$, $\mathbf{B} = \mathbf{i} + \mathbf{j} - 3\mathbf{k}$

4. (a) $\mathbf{A} = \langle 4, 0, 2 \rangle$, $\mathbf{B} = \langle 5, 2, -1 \rangle$
   (b) $\mathbf{A} = 3\mathbf{i} - 2\mathbf{j} + \mathbf{k}$; $\mathbf{B} = 6\mathbf{i} + 7\mathbf{j} + 2\mathbf{k}$

5. Show that $\mathbf{i} \cdot \mathbf{i} = 1$, $\mathbf{i} \cdot \mathbf{k} = 0$, and $\mathbf{j} \cdot \mathbf{k} = 0$.

6. Show that $\mathbf{j} \cdot \mathbf{j} = 1$, $\mathbf{k} \cdot \mathbf{k} = 1$, and $\mathbf{i} \cdot \mathbf{j} = 0$.

In Exercises 7 through 10, prove the theorem for vectors in V_3.

7. Theorem 10.3.2(i)   **8.** Theorem 10.3.2(ii)
9. Theorem 10.3.3(i)   **10.** Theorem 10.3.3(ii), (iii)

In Exercises 11 and 12, if θ *is the angle between* $\mathbf{A}$ *and* $\mathbf{B}$, *find* $\cos \theta$.

11. (a) $\mathbf{A} = \langle 4, 3 \rangle$, $\mathbf{B} = \langle 1, -1 \rangle$
   (b) $\mathbf{A} = 5\mathbf{i} - 12\mathbf{j}$, $\mathbf{B} = 4\mathbf{i} + 3\mathbf{j}$

12. (a) $\mathbf{A} = \langle -2, -3 \rangle$, $\mathbf{B} = \langle 3, 2 \rangle$
   (b) $\mathbf{A} = 2\mathbf{i} + 4\mathbf{j}$, $\mathbf{B} = -5\mathbf{j}$

13. Find k such that the radian measure of the angle between the vectors in Example 2 is $\frac{1}{4}\pi$.

14. Given $\mathbf{A} = k\mathbf{i} - 2\mathbf{j}$ and $\mathbf{B} = k\mathbf{i} + 6\mathbf{j}$, where k is a scalar. Find k such that $\mathbf{A}$ and $\mathbf{B}$ are orthogonal.

15. Given $\mathbf{A} = 5\mathbf{i} - k\mathbf{j}$ and $\mathbf{B} = k\mathbf{i} + 6\mathbf{j}$, where k is a scalar. Find **(a)** k such that $\mathbf{A}$ and $\mathbf{B}$ are orthogonal; **(b)** k such that $\mathbf{A}$ and $\mathbf{B}$ are parallel.

16. Find k such that the vectors in Exercise 14 have opposite directions.

17. If $\mathbf{A} = -8\mathbf{i} + 4\mathbf{j}$ and $\mathbf{B} = 7\mathbf{i} - 6\mathbf{j}$, find **(a)** the scalar projection of $\mathbf{A}$ onto $\mathbf{B}$ and **(b)** the vector projection of $\mathbf{A}$ onto $\mathbf{B}$.

18. For the vectors of Exercise 17, find **(a)** the scalar projection of $\mathbf{B}$ onto $\mathbf{A}$ and **(b)** the vector projection of $\mathbf{B}$ onto $\mathbf{A}$.

19. Find the component of the vector $\mathbf{A} = 5\mathbf{i} - 6\mathbf{j}$ in the direction of the vector $\mathbf{B} = 7\mathbf{i} + \mathbf{j}$.

20. For the vectors $\mathbf{A}$ and $\mathbf{B}$ of Exercise 19, find the component of $\mathbf{B}$ in the direction of $\mathbf{A}$.

In Exercises 21 through 26, $\mathbf{A} = \langle -4, -2, 4 \rangle$; $\mathbf{B} = \langle 2, 7, -1 \rangle$; $\mathbf{C} = \langle 6, -3, 0 \rangle$, *and* $\mathbf{D} = \langle 5, 4, -3 \rangle$.

21. Find **(a)** $\mathbf{A} \cdot (\mathbf{B} + \mathbf{C})$; **(b)** $(\mathbf{A} \cdot \mathbf{B})(\mathbf{C} \cdot \mathbf{D})$; **(c)** $\mathbf{A} \cdot \mathbf{D} - \mathbf{B} \cdot \mathbf{C}$; **(d)** $(\mathbf{D} \cdot \mathbf{B})\mathbf{A} - (\mathbf{D} \cdot \mathbf{A})\mathbf{B}$.

22. Find **(a)** $\mathbf{A} \cdot \mathbf{B} + \mathbf{A} \cdot \mathbf{C}$; **(b)** $(\mathbf{A} \cdot \mathbf{B})(\mathbf{B} \cdot \mathbf{C})$; **(c)** $(\mathbf{A} \cdot \mathbf{B})\mathbf{C} + (\mathbf{B} \cdot \mathbf{C})\mathbf{D}$; **(d)** $(2\mathbf{A} + 3\mathbf{B}) \cdot (4\mathbf{C} - \mathbf{D})$.

23. Find **(a)** $\cos \theta$ if θ is the angle between $\mathbf{A}$ and $\mathbf{C}$; **(b)** the component of $\mathbf{C}$ in the direction of $\mathbf{A}$; **(c)** the vector projection of $\mathbf{C}$ onto $\mathbf{A}$.

24. Find **(a)** cos θ if θ is the angle between **B** and **D**;
(b) the component of **B** in the direction of **D**;
(c) the vector projection of **B** onto **D**.

25. Find **(a)** the scalar projection of **A** onto **B**;
(b) the vector projection of **A** onto **B**.

26. Find **(a)** the scalar projection of **D** onto **C**;
(b) the vector projection of **D** onto **C**.

27. Find the distance from the point $(2, -1, -4)$ to the line through the points $(3, -2, 2)$ and $(-9, -6, 6)$.

28. Find the distance from the point $(3, 2, 1)$ to the line through the points $(1, 2, 9)$ and $(-3, -6, -3)$.

29. Prove by using vectors that the points $(2, 2, 2)$, $(2, 0, 1)$, $(4, 1, -1)$, and $(4, 3, 0)$ are the vertices of a rectangle.

30. Prove by using vectors that the points $(2, 2, 2)$, $(0, 1, 2)$, $(-1, 3, 3)$, and $(3, 0, 1)$ are the vertices of a parallelogram.

31. Find the area of the triangle having vertices at $(-2, 3, 1)$, $(1, 2, 3)$, and $(3, -1, 2)$.

32. Prove by using vectors that the points $(-2, 1, 6)$, $(2, 4, 5)$, and $(-1, -2, 1)$ are the vertices of a right triangle, and find the area of the triangle.

33. Find two unit vectors each having a representation whose initial point is $(2, 4)$ and which is tangent to the parabola $y = x^2$ there.

34. Find two unit vectors each having a representation whose initial point is $(2, 4)$ and which is normal to the parabola $y = x^2$ there.

35. If $\mathbf{A} = 3\mathbf{i} + 5\mathbf{j} - 3\mathbf{k}$, $\mathbf{B} = -\mathbf{i} - 2\mathbf{j} + 3\mathbf{k}$, and $\mathbf{C} = 2\mathbf{i} - \mathbf{j} + 4\mathbf{k}$, find the component of **B** in the direction of $\mathbf{A} - 2\mathbf{C}$.

36. Find the cosines of the angles of the triangle having vertices at $A(0, 0, 0)$, $B(4, -1, 3)$, and $C(1, 2, 3)$.

37. A vector **F** represents a force that has a magnitude of 8 lb and $\frac{1}{3}\pi$ is the radian measure of its direction angle. Find the work done by the force in moving an object **(a)** along the x axis from the origin to the point $(6, 0)$ and **(b)** along the y axis from the origin to the point $(0, 6)$. Distance is measured in feet.

38. A vector **F** represents a force that has a magnitude of 10 lb and $\frac{1}{4}\pi$ is the radian measure of its direction angle. Find the work done by the force in moving an object along the y axis from the point $(0, -2)$ to the point $(0, 5)$. Distance is measured in feet.

39. A vector **F** represents a force that has a magnitude of 9 lb and $\frac{2}{3}\pi$ is the radian measure of its direction angle. Find the work done by the force in moving an object from the origin to the point $(-4, -2)$. Distance is measured in feet.

40. Two forces represented by the vectors $\mathbf{F}_1$ and $\mathbf{F}_2$ act on a particle and cause it to move along a line from the point $(2, 5)$ to the point $(7, 3)$. If $\mathbf{F}_1 = 3\mathbf{i} - \mathbf{j}$ and $\mathbf{F}_2 = -4\mathbf{i} + 5\mathbf{j}$, the magnitudes of the forces are measured in pounds, and distance is measured in feet, find the work done by the two forces acting together.

41. If a force has the vector representation $\mathbf{F} = 3\mathbf{i} - 2\mathbf{j} + \mathbf{k}$, find the work done by the force in moving an object from the point $P_1(-2, 4, 3)$ along a line to the point $P_2(1, -3, 5)$. The magnitude of the force is measured in pounds and distance is measured in feet.

42. If a force has the vector representation $\mathbf{F} = 5\mathbf{i} - 3\mathbf{k}$, find the work done by the force in moving an object from the point $P_1(4, 1, 3)$ along a line to the point $P_2(-5, 6, 2)$. The magnitude of the force is measured in pounds and distance is measured in feet.

43. A force is represented by the vector **F**, it has a magnitude of 10 lb, and direction cosines of **F** are $\cos \alpha = \frac{1}{6}\sqrt{6}$ and $\cos \beta = \frac{1}{3}\sqrt{6}$. If the force moves an object from the origin along a line to the point $(7, -4, 2)$, find the work done. Distance is measured in feet.

44. If **A** and **B** are nonzero vectors, prove that the vector $\mathbf{A} - c\mathbf{B}$ is orthogonal to **B** if $c = \mathbf{A} \cdot \mathbf{B}/\|\mathbf{B}\|^2$.

45. If $\mathbf{A} = 12\mathbf{i} + 9\mathbf{j} - 5\mathbf{k}$ and $\mathbf{B} = 4\mathbf{i} + 3\mathbf{j} - 5\mathbf{k}$, use the result of Exercise 44 to find the value of the scalar c so that the vector $\mathbf{B} - c\mathbf{A}$ is orthogonal to **A**.

46. For the vectors of Exercise 45, use the result of Exercise 44 to find the value of the scalar d so that the vector $\mathbf{A} - d\mathbf{B}$ is orthogonal to **B**.

47. Prove: If **A** and **B** are any vectors, then the vectors $\|\mathbf{B}\|\mathbf{A} + \|\mathbf{A}\|\mathbf{B}$ and $\|\mathbf{B}\|\mathbf{A} - \|\mathbf{A}\|\mathbf{B}$ are orthogonal.

48. Prove that if **A** and **B** are any nonzero vectors and $\mathbf{C} = \|\mathbf{B}\|\mathbf{A} + \|\mathbf{A}\|\mathbf{B}$, then the angle between **A** and **C** has the same measure as the angle between **B** and **C**.

49. Prove that two nonzero vectors are parallel if and only if the radian measure of the angle between them is 0 or π.

50. Prove by vector analysis that the medians of a triangle meet in a point.

51. Prove by vector analysis that the line segment joining the midpoints of two sides of a triangle is parallel to the third side and its length is one-half the length of the third side.

52. Prove by vector analysis that the line segment joining the midpoints of the nonparallel sides of a trapezoid is parallel to the parallel sides and its length is one-half the sum of the lengths of the parallel sides.

53. Snell's law of refraction pertains to light traveling from one medium, such as air, to a denser medium, such as water. The law states that the part of the light ray that passes through the denser medium will be refracted ("bent") toward the normal. See the accompanying figure where θ_1 is the angle of incidence and θ_2 is the angle of refraction. From Snell's law

$$\sin \theta_1 = \mu \sin \theta_2$$

where μ is the index of refraction of the denser medium. Show that if **A** is a unit vector along the incident ray, **B** is a unit vector along the refracted ray, **F** is a unit vector in the interface, and **N** is the unit normal vector to the interface as shown in the figure, then

$$\mathbf{A} \cdot \mathbf{F} + \mu \mathbf{B} \cdot \mathbf{F} = 0$$

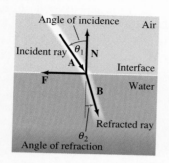

54. Prove the **Cauchy–Schwarz inequality:** If **A** and **B** are any vectors, then

$$|\mathbf{A} \cdot \mathbf{B}| \leq \|\mathbf{A}\| \|\mathbf{B}\|$$

where equality holds if and only if there exists a scalar c such that $\mathbf{A} = c\mathbf{B}$, that is, **A** and **B** are parallel.

55. Prove: If **A** and **B** are any vectors, then

$$\|\mathbf{A} + \mathbf{B}\|^2 = \|\mathbf{A}\|^2 + 2\mathbf{A} \cdot \mathbf{B} + \|\mathbf{B}\|^2$$

Hint: Use Theorem 10.3.3(iii).

56. Prove the **Pythagorean theorem:**

$$\|\mathbf{A} + \mathbf{B}\|^2 = \|\mathbf{A}\|^2 + \|\mathbf{B}\|^2$$

if and only if **A** and **B** are orthogonal. *Hint:* Use the identity in Exercise 55.

57. Prove the **parallelogram law:** If **A** and **B** are any vectors, then

$$\|\mathbf{A} + \mathbf{B}\|^2 + \|\mathbf{A} - \mathbf{B}\|^2 = 2\|\mathbf{A}\|^2 + 2\|\mathbf{B}\|^2$$

What is the geometric interpretation of this identity?

Hint: See the accompanying figure showing the parallelogram determined by representations of vectors **A** and **B**.

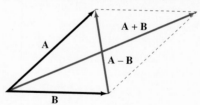

58. Prove the **polarization identity:** If **A** and **B** are any vectors, then

$$\|\mathbf{A} + \mathbf{B}\|^2 - \|\mathbf{A} - \mathbf{B}\|^2 = 4\mathbf{A} \cdot \mathbf{B}$$

What is the geometric interpretation of this identity? *Hint:* See the accompanying figure for Exercise 57.

59. In electromagnetic theory, it is sometimes necessary to do the following: If **E** and **H** are two given vectors, write **E** as the sum of two vectors $\mathbf{E}_1$ and $\mathbf{E}_2$, such that $\mathbf{E}_1$ is parallel to **H** and $\mathbf{E}_2$ is orthogonal to **H**. Define $\mathbf{E}_1$ and $\mathbf{E}_2$ in such a situation.

60. Vector notation along with the dot product can be used to store data. For example, suppose an investment company sells shares of three stocks X, Y, and Z. Let the components a_1, a_2, and a_3 of a vector **A** be, respectively, the number of shares of X, Y, and Z sold on a specific day. Let the components s_1, s_2, and s_3 of a vector **S** be, respectively, the number of dollars in the selling price per share of X, Y, and Z on that day. Then if R dollars is the total revenue earned for the three stocks on that day, $R = \mathbf{A} \cdot \mathbf{S}$. Find the total revenue earned from the three stocks on each day of the week where **A** and **S** are given in Table 1. Note: Since a company is not limited to trading just three stocks, this example can be generalized to trading n stocks where the vectors **A** and **S** each have n components, so that $\mathbf{A} = \langle a_1, a_2, a_3, \ldots, a_n \rangle$ and $\mathbf{S} = \langle s_1, s_2, s_3, \ldots, s_n \rangle$ and

$$\mathbf{A} \cdot \mathbf{S} = a_1 s_1 + a_2 s_2 + a_3 s_3 + \ldots + a_n s_n$$

Table 1

Day	A	S
Mon.	$\langle 250, 180, 310 \rangle$	$\langle 25.50, 16.80, 54.55 \rangle$
Tues.	$\langle 185, 210, 215 \rangle$	$\langle 27.50, 14.60, 61.25 \rangle$
Wed.	$\langle 400, 120, 180 \rangle$	$\langle 21.20, 21.50, 66.50 \rangle$
Thurs.	$\langle 355, 165, 200 \rangle$	$\langle 23.40, 18.50, 62.30 \rangle$
Fri.	$\langle 370, 145, 240 \rangle$	$\langle 22.60, 19.10, 61.75 \rangle$

10.4 PLANES AND LINES IN R^3

The graph of an equation in two variables, x and y, is a curve in R^2. The simplest such curve is a line whose general equation is of the form $Ax + By + C = 0$, an equation of the first degree. In R^3, the graph of an equation in three variables, x, y, and z, is a surface. In Section 10.2 you studied one particular surface, the sphere, and in Section 10.6, you will encounter other surfaces. In this section we concentrate on the simplest surface, a *plane*, and you will learn that an equation of a plane is of the first degree in three variables. You will also learn that *lines* in R^3 are defined by pairs of equations, each equation representing a plane containing the line.

10.4.1 Definition of a Plane

If $\mathbf{N}$ is a given nonzero vector and P_0 is a given point, then the set of all points P for which $\mathbf{V}(\overrightarrow{P_0P})$ and $\mathbf{N}$ are orthogonal is defined to be a **plane** through P_0 having $\mathbf{N}$ as a **normal vector.**

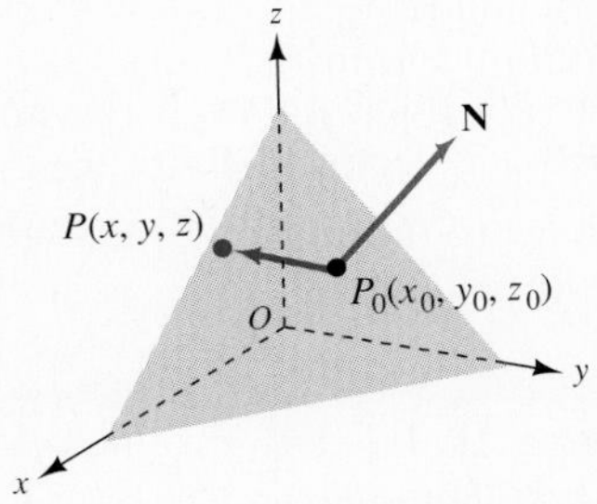

Figure 1 shows a portion of a plane through the point $P_0(x_0, y_0, z_0)$ and the representation of the normal vector $\mathbf{N}$ having its initial point at P_0.

In plane analytic geometry we can obtain an equation of a line if a point on the line and its direction (slope) are given. In an analogous manner, in solid analytic geometry an equation of a plane can be determined by knowing a point in the plane and the direction of a normal vector.

10.4.2 Theorem

If $P_0(x_0, y_0, z_0)$ is a point in a plane and $\langle a, b, c \rangle$ is a normal vector to the plane then an equation of the plane is
$$a(x - x_0) + b(y - y_0) + c(z - z_0) = 0$$

Proof Refer to Figure 1 where $\mathbf{N} = \langle a, b, c \rangle$. Let $P(x, y, z)$ be any point in the plane. $\mathbf{V}(\overrightarrow{P_0P})$ is the vector having $\overrightarrow{P_0P}$ as a representation; so

$$\mathbf{V}(\overrightarrow{P_0P}) = \langle x - x_0, y - y_0, z - z_0 \rangle \tag{1}$$

From Definition 10.4.1 and the fact that the dot product of two orthogonal vectors is zero we have

$$\mathbf{V}(\overrightarrow{P_0P}) \cdot \langle a, b, c \rangle = 0$$

From (1) and the above equation,

$$a(x - x_0) + b(y - y_0) + c(z - z_0) = 0$$

which is the desired equation. ∎

z

$\mathbf{N}$

$P(x, y, z)$

$P_0(x_0, y_0, z_0)$

O

y

x

FIGURE 1

▶ **EXAMPLE 1** Find an equation of the plane containing the point $(2, 1, 3)$ and having $3\mathbf{i} - 4\mathbf{j} + \mathbf{k}$ as a normal vector.

Solution   From Theorem 10.4.2 where the point (x_0, y_0, z_0) is $(2, 1, 3)$ and the vector $\langle a, b, c \rangle$ is $\langle 3, -4, 1 \rangle$, we have as an equation of the required plane

$$3(x - 2) - 4(y - 1) + (z - 3) = 0$$
$$3x - 4y + z - 5 = 0 \qquad \blacktriangleleft$$

10.4.3 Theorem

If a, b, and c are not all zero, the graph of an equation of the form

$$ax + by + cz + d = 0$$

is a plane and $\langle a, b, c \rangle$ is a normal vector to the plane.

Proof   Suppose that $b \neq 0$. Then the point $(0, -d/b, 0)$ is on the graph of the equation because its coordinates satisfy the equation. The given equation can be written as

$$a(x - 0) + b\left(y + \frac{d}{b}\right) + c(z - 0) = 0$$

which from Theorem 10.4.2 is an equation of a plane through the point $(0, -d/b, 0)$ and for which $\langle a, b, c \rangle$ is a normal vector. This proves the theorem if $b \neq 0$. A similar argument holds if $b = 0$ and either $a \neq 0$ or $c \neq 0$.
$\blacksquare$

The equations of Theorems 10.4.2 and 10.4.3 are called *cartesian equations of a plane.* The equation of Theorem 10.4.2 is analogous to the point-slope form of an equation of a line in two dimensions. The equation of Theorem 10.4.3 is the general first-degree equation in three variables and is called a *linear equation.*

A plane is determined by three noncollinear points, by a line and a point not on the line, by two intersecting lines, or by two parallel lines.

▶ **EXAMPLE 2**   Find an equation of the plane through the points $P(1, 3, 2)$, $Q(3, -2, 2)$, and $R(2, 1, 3)$.

Solution   From Theorem 10.4.3 the graph of the linear equation

$$ax + by + cz + d = 0 \qquad \textbf{(2)}$$

is a plane. If this equation is satisfied by the coordinates of points P, Q, and R, the plane will contain the points. Replacing x, y, and z in (2) by the coordinates of the three points we have the equations

$$a + 3b + 2c + d = 0$$
$$3a - 2b + 2c + d = 0$$
$$2a + b + 3c + d = 0$$

We solve this system of equations for a, b, and c in terms of d, and we obtain

$$a = -\tfrac{5}{9}d \qquad b = -\tfrac{2}{9}d \qquad c = \tfrac{1}{9}d$$

Replacing a, b, and c in (2) by these values we have

$$-\tfrac{5}{9}dx - \tfrac{2}{9}dy + \tfrac{1}{9}dz + d = 0$$

Multiplying on both sides of this equation by $-9/d$ we get

$$5x + 2y - z - 9 = 0$$

which is the required equation.   ◄

To sketch a plane from its equation it is convenient to find the points at which the plane intersects each of the coordinate axes. The x coordinate of the point at which the plane intersects the x axis is called the x *intercept* of the plane; the y coordinate of the point at which the plane intersects the y axis is called the y *intercept* of the plane; and the z *intercept* of the plane is the z coordinate of the point at which the plane intersects the z axis.

▷ **ILLUSTRATION 1**   We wish to sketch the plane having the equation

$$2x + 4y + 3z = 8$$

By substituting zero for y and z we obtain $x = 4$; so the x intercept of the plane is 4. The y intercept and the z intercept are obtained in a similar manner; they are 2 and $\tfrac{8}{3}$, respectively. Locating the points corresponding to these intercepts and connecting them with lines we have Figure 2. Note that only a portion of the plane appears in the figure.   ◄

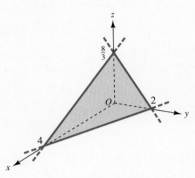

Plane: $2x + 4y + 3z = 8$

FIGURE 2

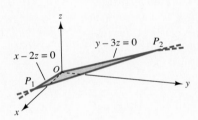

Plane: $3x + 2y - 6z = 0$

FIGURE 3

▷ **ILLUSTRATION 2**   To sketch the plane having the equation

$$3x + 2y - 6z = 0$$

first notice that because the equation is satisfied when x, y, and z are all zero, the plane intersects each of the axes at the origin. If $x = 0$ in the given equation, we obtain $y - 3z = 0$, which is a line in the yz plane; this is the line of intersection of the yz plane with the given plane. Similarly, the line of intersection of the xz plane with the given plane is obtained by setting $y = 0$, and we get $x - 2z = 0$. Sketching each of these two lines and a line segment from a point on one of the lines to a point on the other line, we obtain Figure 3.   ◄

In Illustration 2 the line in the yz plane and the line in the xz plane used to sketch the plane are called the **traces** of the given plane in the yz plane and the xz plane, respectively. The equation $x = 0$ is an equation of the yz plane because the point (x, y, z) is in the yz plane if and only if $x = 0$. Similarly, the equations $y = 0$ and $z = 0$ are equations of the xz plane and the xy plane, respectively.

A plane parallel to the yz plane has an equation of the form $x = k$, where k is a constant. Figure 4 shows the plane having the equation $x = 3$.

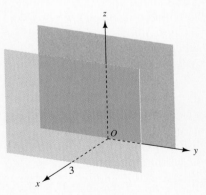

Plane: $x = 3$

FIGURE 4

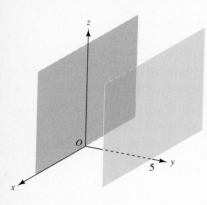

Plane: $y = 5$

FIGURE 5

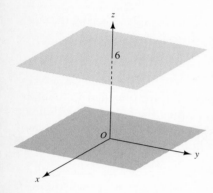

Plane: $z = 6$

FIGURE 6

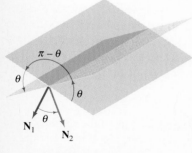

Angle between two planes

FIGURE 7

A plane parallel to the xz plane has an equation of the form $y = k$, and a plane parallel to the xy plane has an equation of the form $z = k$. Figures 5 and 6 show the planes having the equations $y = 5$ and $z = 6$, respectively.

10.4.4 Definition of an Angle Between Two Planes

An **angle between two planes** is defined to be the angle between normal vectors of the planes.

There are two angles between two planes. If one of these angles is θ, the other is the supplement of θ. Figure 7 shows two planes and the two angles between them.

▶ **EXAMPLE 3** Find the radian measure of the acute angle between the planes

$$5x - 2y + 5z - 12 = 0 \quad \text{and} \quad 2x + y - 7z + 11 = 0$$

Solution Let $\mathbf{N}_1$ be a normal vector to the first plane and $\mathbf{N}_2$ be a normal vector to the second plane. Then

$$\mathbf{N}_1 = 5\mathbf{i} - 2\mathbf{j} + 5\mathbf{k} \quad \text{and} \quad \mathbf{N}_2 = 2\mathbf{i} + \mathbf{j} - 7\mathbf{k}$$

From Definition 10.4.4, an angle between the two planes is the angle between $\mathbf{N}_1$ and $\mathbf{N}_2$. Thus from Theorem 10.3.5, if θ is the radian measure of this angle,

$$
\begin{aligned}
\cos \theta &= \frac{\mathbf{N}_1 \cdot \mathbf{N}_2}{\|\mathbf{N}_1\| \|\mathbf{N}_2\|} \\
&= \frac{\langle 5, -2, 5 \rangle \cdot \langle 2, 1, -7 \rangle}{\sqrt{25 + 4 + 25} \ \sqrt{4 + 1 + 49}} \\
&= \frac{10 - 2 - 35}{\sqrt{54} \ \sqrt{54}} \\
&= -\tfrac{27}{54} \\
&= -\tfrac{1}{2}
\end{aligned}
$$

Therefore $\theta = \tfrac{2}{3}\pi$. The acute angle between the two planes is the supplement of θ which is $\tfrac{1}{3}\pi$. ◀

10.4.5 Definition of Parallel Planes

Two planes are **parallel** if and only if their normal vectors are parallel.

Recall that two vectors are parallel if and only if one of the vectors is a scalar multiple of the other. Thus from Definition 10.4.5, if we have one plane with a normal vector $\mathbf{N}_1$ and another plane with a normal vector $\mathbf{N}_2$,

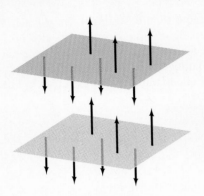

FIGURE 8

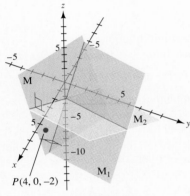

FIGURE 9

then the two planes are parallel if and only if

$$\mathbf{N}_1 = k\mathbf{N}_2$$

where k is a constant. Figure 8 shows two parallel planes and representations of some of their normal vectors.

10.4.6 Definition of Perpendicular Planes

Two planes are **perpendicular** if and only if their normal vectors are orthogonal.

From this definition and the fact that two vectors are orthogonal if and only if their dot product is zero, two planes having normal vectors $\mathbf{N}_1$ and $\mathbf{N}_2$ are perpendicular if and only if

$$\mathbf{N}_1 \cdot \mathbf{N}_2 = 0 \tag{3}$$

▶ **EXAMPLE 4**   Find an equation of the plane containing the point $P(4, 0, -2)$ and perpendicular to each of the planes

$$x - y + z = 0 \quad \text{and} \quad 2x + y - 4z - 5 = 0$$

Solution   Let M be the required plane and $\langle a, b, c \rangle$, $a \neq 0$, be a normal vector of M. Let M_1 be the plane having the equation $x - y + z = 0$. By Theorem 10.4.3, a normal vector of M_1 is $\langle 1, -1, 1 \rangle$. Because M and M_1 are perpendicular, then from (3)

$$\langle a, b, c \rangle \cdot \langle 1, -1, 1 \rangle = 0$$
$$a - b + c = 0 \tag{4}$$

Let M_2 be the plane having the equation $2x + y - 4z - 5 = 0$. A normal vector of M_2 is $\langle 2, 1, -4 \rangle$. Because M and M_2 are perpendicular,

$$\langle a, b, c \rangle \cdot \langle 2, 1, -4 \rangle = 0$$
$$2a + b - 4c = 0$$

Solving this equation and (4) simultaneously for b and c in terms of a we get $b = 2a$ and $c = a$. Therefore a normal vector of M is $\langle a, 2a, a \rangle$. Because $P(4, 0, -2)$ is a point in M, then from Theorem 10.4.2 an equation of M is

$$a(x - 4) + 2a(y - 0) + a(z + 2) = 0$$

Because $a \neq 0$, we divide by a and combine terms to obtain

$$x + 2y + z - 2 = 0$$

Figure 9 shows the three planes and the point P.   ◀

Consider now the plane having the equation $ax + by + d = 0$ and the xy plane whose equation is $z = 0$. Normal vectors to these planes are $\langle a, b, 0 \rangle$ and $\langle 0, 0, 1 \rangle$, respectively. Because $\langle a, b, 0 \rangle \cdot \langle 0, 0, 1 \rangle = 0$, the two planes are perpendicular. This means that a plane having an equation with

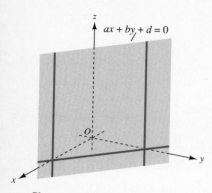

Plane perpendicular to the xy plane

FIGURE 10

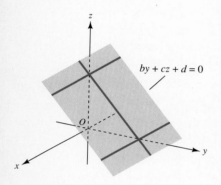

Plane perpendicular to the yz plane

FIGURE 11

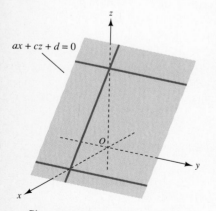

Plane perpendicular to the xz plane

FIGURE 12

no z term is perpendicular to the xy plane. Figure 10 illustrates this. In a similar manner we can conclude that a plane having an equation with no x term is perpendicular to the yz plane (see Figure 11), and a plane having an equation with no y term is perpendicular to the xz plane (see Figure 12).

Vectors can be used to find the distance from a point to a plane. The following example illustrates the procedure.

▶ **EXAMPLE 5**　Find the distance from the point $(1, 4, 6)$ to the plane

$$2x - y + 2z + 10 = 0$$

Solution　Let P be the point $(1, 4, 6)$ and choose any point Q in the plane. For simplicity choose the point Q as the point where the plane intersects the x axis, that is, the point $(-5, 0, 0)$. The vector having $\overrightarrow{PQ}$ as a representation is given by

$$\mathbf{V}(\overrightarrow{PQ}) = -6\mathbf{i} - 4\mathbf{j} - 6\mathbf{k}$$

A normal vector to the given plane is

$$\mathbf{N} = 2\mathbf{i} - \mathbf{j} + 2\mathbf{k}$$

The negative of $\mathbf{N}$ is also a normal vector to the given plane and

$$-\mathbf{N} = -2\mathbf{i} + \mathbf{j} - 2\mathbf{k}$$

We are not certain which of the two vectors, $\mathbf{N}$ or $-\mathbf{N}$, makes the smaller angle with vector $\mathbf{V}(\overrightarrow{PQ})$. Let $\mathbf{N}'$ be the one of the two vectors $\mathbf{N}$ or $-\mathbf{N}$ that makes an angle of radian measure $\theta < \frac{1}{2}\pi$ with $\mathbf{V}(\overrightarrow{PQ})$. Figure 13 shows a portion of the given plane containing the point $Q(-5, 0, 0)$, the representation of the vector $\mathbf{N}'$ having its initial point at Q, the point $P(1, 4, 6)$, the directed line segment $\overrightarrow{PQ}$, and the point R, which is the foot of the perpendicular from P to the plane. For simplicity the coordinate axes are not included in this figure. The distance $|\overrightarrow{RP}|$ is the required distance, which we call d. Because d is an undirected distance it is nonnegative. We see from Figure 13 that d is the absolute value of the scalar projection of $\mathbf{V}(\overrightarrow{PQ})$ onto $\mathbf{N}'$. Thus from Theorem 10.3.9 we get

$$d = \frac{|\mathbf{N}' \cdot \mathbf{V}(\overrightarrow{PQ})|}{\|\mathbf{N}'\|}$$

Because we have the absolute value of the dot product in the numerator and the magnitude of $\mathbf{N}'$ in the denominator we can replace $\mathbf{N}'$ by $\mathbf{N}$, and we have

$$\begin{aligned}
d &= \frac{|\mathbf{N} \cdot \mathbf{V}(\overrightarrow{PQ})|}{\|\mathbf{N}\|} \\
&= \frac{|\langle 2, -1, 2\rangle \cdot \langle -6, -4, -6\rangle|}{\sqrt{4 + 1 + 4}} \\
&= \frac{|-12 + 4 - 12|}{\sqrt{9}} \\
&= \tfrac{20}{3}
\end{aligned}$$

◀

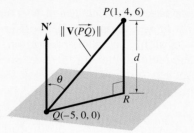

FIGURE 13

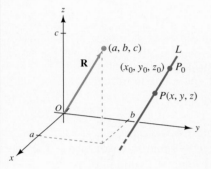

FIGURE 14

We now discuss lines in R^3. Let L be a line that contains a given point $P_0(x_0, y_0, z_0)$ and is parallel to the representations of a given vector $\mathbf{R} = \langle a, b, c \rangle$. Figure 14 shows L and the position representation of $\mathbf{R}$. Line L is the set of points $P(x, y, z)$ such that $\mathbf{V}(\overrightarrow{P_0 P})$ is parallel to $\mathbf{R}$. So P is on L if and only if there is a nonzero scalar t such that

$$\mathbf{V}(\overrightarrow{P_0 P}) = t\mathbf{R}$$

Because $\mathbf{V}(\overrightarrow{P_0 P}) = \langle x - x_0, y - y_0, z - z_0 \rangle$, we obtain from this equation

$$\langle x - x_0, y - y_0, z - z_0 \rangle = t \langle a, b, c \rangle$$

from which it follows that

$$x - x_0 = ta \qquad y - y_0 = tb \qquad z - z_0 = tc$$

$$x = x_0 + ta \qquad y = y_0 + tb \qquad z = z_0 + tc \qquad \textbf{(5)}$$

Letting the parameter t be any real number, P may be any point on L. Therefore Equations (5) represent the line L; these equations are called **parametric equations** of the line.

▷ **ILLUSTRATION 3**   From Equations (5), parametric equations of the line L, parallel to the representations of the vector $\mathbf{R} = \langle 11, 8, 10 \rangle$ and containing the point $(8, 12, 6)$, are

$$x = 8 + 11t \qquad y = 12 + 8t \qquad z = 6 + 10t$$

Figure 15 shows the line and the position representation of $\mathbf{R}$.   ◀

If none of the numbers a, b, or c is zero, we can eliminate t from Equations (5) and obtain

$$\frac{x - x_0}{a} = \frac{y - y_0}{b} = \frac{z - z_0}{c} \qquad \textbf{(6)}$$

These equations are called **symmetric equations** of the line. Equations (6) are equivalent to the system of three equations

$$b(x - x_0) = a(y - y_0)$$
$$c(x - x_0) = a(z - z_0)$$
$$c(y - y_0) = b(z - z_0)$$

Actually, these three equations are not independent because any one of them can be derived from the other two. Each of the equations is an equation of a plane containing the line L represented by Equations (6). Any two of these planes have as their intersection the line L; hence any two of the equations define the line. However, an unlimited number of planes contain a given line, and because any two of them will determine the line, an unlimited number of pairs of equations represent a line.

The vector $\mathbf{R} = \langle a, b, c \rangle$ determines the direction of the line having symmetric equations (6), and the numbers a, b, and c are called **direction numbers** of the line. Any vector parallel to $\mathbf{R}$ has either the same or the

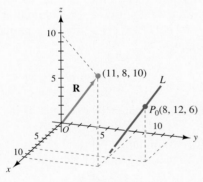

FIGURE 15

opposite direction as **R**; hence such a vector can be used in place of **R** in the above discussion. Because the components of any vector parallel to **R** are proportional to the components of **R**, any set of three numbers proportional to a, b, and c also can serve as a set of direction numbers of the line. So a line has an unlimited number of sets of direction numbers. A set of direction numbers of a line is written in brackets as $[a, b, c]$.

▷ **ILLUSTRATION 4** If $[2, 3, -4]$ represents a set of direction numbers of a line, other sets of direction numbers of the same line can be represented as $[4, 6, -8]$, $[1, \frac{3}{2}, -2]$, and $[2/\sqrt{29}, 3/\sqrt{29}, -4/\sqrt{29}]$. ◀

▷ **ILLUSTRATION 5** A set of direction numbers of the line of Illustration 3 is $[11, 8, 10]$, and the line contains the point $(8, 12, 6)$. Thus, from (6), symmetric equations of this line are

$$\frac{x - 8}{11} = \frac{y - 12}{8} = \frac{z - 6}{10}$$ ◀

▶ **EXAMPLE 6** Find two sets of symmetric equations of the line through the points $(-3, 2, 4)$ and $(6, 1, 2)$.

Solution Let P_1 be the point $(-3, 2, 4)$ and P_2 be the point $(6, 1, 2)$. Then the required line is parallel to the representations of the vector $\mathbf{V}(\overrightarrow{P_1 P_2})$, and so the components of this vector constitute a set of direction numbers of the line. $\mathbf{V}(\overrightarrow{P_1 P_2}) = \langle 9, -1, -2 \rangle$. Taking P_0 as the point $(-3, 2, 4)$ we have, from (6), the equations

$$\frac{x + 3}{9} = \frac{y - 2}{-1} = \frac{z - 4}{-2}$$

Another set of symmetric equations of this line, obtained by taking P_0 as the point $(6, 1, 2)$, is

$$\frac{x - 6}{9} = \frac{y - 1}{-1} = \frac{z - 2}{-2}$$

Figure 16 shows this line and the points P_1 and P_2 on the line. ◀

If one of the numbers a, b, or c is zero, we cannot use symmetric equations (6). Suppose, however, that $b = 0$ and neither a nor c is zero. Then equations of the line are

$$\frac{x - x_0}{a} = \frac{z - z_0}{c} \quad \text{and} \quad y = y_0$$

A line having these symmetric equations lies in the plane $y = y_0$ and hence is parallel to the xz plane. Figure 17 shows such a line.

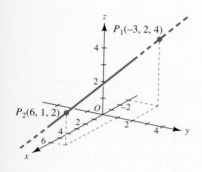

Line: $\dfrac{x + 3}{9} = \dfrac{y - 2}{-1} = \dfrac{z - 4}{-2}$

FIGURE 16

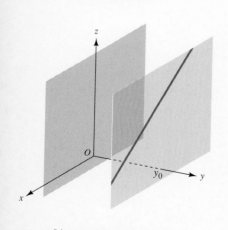

Line parallel to the xz plane

FIGURE 17

▶ **EXAMPLE 7**   Given the two planes

$$x + 3y - z - 9 = 0 \quad \text{and} \quad 2x - 3y + 4z + 3 = 0$$

For the line of intersection of these two planes, find **(a)** a set of symmetric equations, **(b)** a set of parametric equations, and **(c)** the direction cosines of a vector whose representations are parallel to it.

Solution

(a) A set of symmetric equations is of the form (6). To obtain this form we solve the pair of given equations for x and y in terms of z. The computation is as follows:

$$
\begin{array}{ll}
\begin{array}{l}
x + 3y - z - 9 = 0 \\
\underline{2x - 3y + 4z + 3 = 0} \;(+) \\
3x \qquad + 3z - 6 = 0 \\
\qquad\qquad x = -z + 2
\end{array}
&
\begin{array}{l}
2x + 6y - 2z - 18 = 0 \\
\underline{2x - 3y + 4z + \;\;3 = 0} \;(-) \\
\qquad 9y - 6z - 21 = 0 \\
\qquad\qquad y = \tfrac{2}{3}z + \tfrac{7}{3}
\end{array}
\end{array}
$$

We now solve each equation for z and obtain

$$\frac{x-2}{-1} = z \qquad \frac{y - \tfrac{7}{3}}{\tfrac{2}{3}} = z$$

Thus a set of symmetric equations is

$$\frac{x-2}{-1} = \frac{y - \tfrac{7}{3}}{\tfrac{2}{3}} = \frac{z-0}{1}$$

$$\Leftrightarrow \qquad \frac{x-2}{-3} = \frac{y - \tfrac{7}{3}}{2} = \frac{z-0}{3}$$

(b) A set of parametric equations is obtained by setting each of the ratios in part (a) equal to t, and we have

$$\frac{x-2}{-3} = t \qquad \frac{y - \tfrac{7}{3}}{2} = t \qquad \frac{z-0}{3} = t$$

$$x = 2 - 3t \qquad y = \tfrac{7}{3} + 2t \qquad z = 3t$$

(c) From the symmetric equations in part (a), a set of direction numbers of the line is $[-3, 2, 3]$. Therefore the vector $\langle -3, 2, 3 \rangle$ has its representations parallel to the line. Because $\sqrt{(-3)^2 + 2^2 + 3^2} = \sqrt{22}$, the direction cosines of this vector are

$$\cos\alpha = -\frac{3}{\sqrt{22}} \qquad \cos\beta = \frac{2}{\sqrt{22}} \qquad \cos\gamma = \frac{3}{\sqrt{22}} \quad ◀$$

▶ **EXAMPLE 8**   Find equations of the line through the point $(1, -1, 1)$ perpendicular to the line

$$3x = 2y = z \tag{7}$$

and parallel to the plane

$$x + y - z = 0 \tag{8}$$

Solution   Let $[a, b, c]$ be a set of direction numbers of the required line. Equations (7) can be written as

$$\frac{x - 0}{\frac{1}{3}} = \frac{y - 0}{\frac{1}{2}} = \frac{z - 0}{1}$$

which are symmetric equations of the line. A set of direction numbers of this line is $[\frac{1}{3}, \frac{1}{2}, 1]$. Because the required line is perpendicular to this line, it follows that the vectors $\langle a, b, c \rangle$ and $\langle \frac{1}{3}, \frac{1}{2}, 1 \rangle$ are orthogonal. So

$$\langle a, b, c \rangle \cdot \langle \tfrac{1}{3}, \tfrac{1}{2}, 1 \rangle = 0$$
$$\tfrac{1}{3}a + \tfrac{1}{2}b + c = 0 \tag{9}$$

A normal vector to the plane (8) is $\langle 1, 1, -1 \rangle$. Because the required line is parallel to this plane, it is perpendicular to representations of the normal vector. Hence the vectors $\langle a, b, c \rangle$ and $\langle 1, 1, -1 \rangle$ are orthogonal; so

$$\langle a, b, c \rangle \cdot \langle 1, 1, -1 \rangle = 0$$
$$a + b - c = 0$$

Assuming $c \neq 0$, we solve this equation and (9) simultaneously for a and b in terms of c and get $a = 9c$ and $b = -8c$. The required line then has the set of direction numbers $[9c, -8c, c]$ and contains the point $(1, -1, 1)$. Therefore symmetric equations of the line are

$$\frac{x - 1}{9c} = \frac{y + 1}{-8c} = \frac{z - 1}{c}$$

$$\Leftrightarrow \quad \frac{x - 1}{9} = \frac{y + 1}{-8} = \frac{z - 1}{1} \qquad \blacktriangleleft$$

In the following example we use the concept of **skew lines**, which are two lines that do not lie in one plane.

▶ **EXAMPLE 9**   If l_1 is the line through $A(1, 2, 7)$ and $B(-2, 3, -4)$ and l_2 is the line through $C(2, -1, 4)$ and $D(5, 7, -3)$, prove that l_1 and l_2 are skew lines.

Solution   To show that two lines do not lie in one plane we demonstrate that they do not intersect and are not parallel. Parametric equations of a line are

$$x = x_0 + ta \qquad y = y_0 + tb \qquad z = z_0 + tc$$

where $[a, b, c]$ is a set of direction numbers of the line and (x_0, y_0, z_0) is any point on the line. Because $\mathbf{V}(\overrightarrow{AB}) = \langle -3, 1, -11 \rangle$, a set of direction numbers of l_1 is $[-3, 1, -11]$. Taking A as the point P_0 we have as parametric equations of l_1

$$x = 1 - 3t \qquad y = 2 + t \qquad z = 7 - 11t \tag{10}$$

Because $\mathbf{V}(\overrightarrow{CD}) = \langle 3, 8, -7 \rangle$ and l_2 contains the point C, parametric equations of l_2 are

$$x = 2 + 3s \qquad y = -1 + 8s \qquad z = 4 - 7s \tag{11}$$

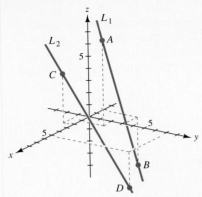

$L_1: x = 1 - 3t \quad y = 2 + t \quad z = 7 - 11t$
$L_2: x = 2 + 3s \quad y = -1 + 8s \quad z = 4 - 7s$

FIGURE 18

Because the sets of direction numbers are not proportional, l_1 and l_2 are not parallel. For the lines to intersect, a value of t and a value of s must give the same point (x_1, y_1, z_1) in both sets of Equations (10) and (11). Therefore we equate the right sides of the respective equations and obtain

$$1 - 3t = 2 + 3s$$
$$2 + t = -1 + 8s$$
$$7 - 11t = 4 - 7s$$

Solving the first two equations simultaneously we obtain $s = \frac{8}{27}$ and $t = -\frac{17}{27}$. This set of values does not satisfy the third equation; hence the two lines do not intersect. Thus l_1 and l_2 are skew lines.

Figure 18 shows lines l_1, through points A and B, and l_2, through points C and D.   ◄

EXERCISES 10.4

*In Exercises 1 through 6, find an equation of the plane containing the point P and having the vector **N** as a normal vector.*

1. $P(3, 1, 2); \mathbf{N} = \langle 1, 2, -3 \rangle$

2. $P(-3, 2, 5); \mathbf{N} = \langle 6, -3, -2 \rangle$

3. $P(0, -1, 2); \mathbf{N} = \langle 0, 1, -1 \rangle$

4. $P(-1, 8, 3); \mathbf{N} = \langle -7, -1, 1 \rangle$

5. $P(2, 1, -1); \mathbf{N} = -\mathbf{i} + 3\mathbf{j} + 4\mathbf{k}$

6. $P(1, 0, 0); \mathbf{N} = \mathbf{i} + \mathbf{k}$

In Exercises 7 and 8, find an equation of the plane containing the three points.

7. $(3, 4, 1), (1, 7, 1), (-1, -2, 5)$

8. $(0, 0, 2), (2, 4, 1), (-2, 3, 3)$

In Exercises 9 through 14, sketch the plane and find two unit vectors normal to the plane.

9. $2x - y + 2z - 6 = 0$

10. $4x - 4y + 2z - 9 = 0$

11. $4x + 3y - 12z = 0$ **12.** $y + 2z - 4 = 0$

13. $3x + 2z - 6 = 0$ **14.** $z = 5$

In Exercises 15 through 20, find an equation of the plane satisfying the conditions.

15. Perpendicular to the line through the points $(2, 2, -4)$ and $(7, -1, 3)$ and containing the point $(-5, 1, 2)$.

16. Parallel to the plane $4x - 2y + z - 1 = 0$ and containing the point $(2, 6, -1)$.

17. Perpendicular to the plane $x + 3y - z - 7 = 0$ and containing the points $(2, 0, 5)$ and $(0, 2, -1)$.

18. Perpendicular to each of the planes $x - y + z = 0$ and $2x + y - 4z - 5 = 0$ and containing the point $(4, 0, -2)$.

19. Perpendicular to the yz plane, containing the point $(2, 1, 1)$, and making an angle of radian measure $\cos^{-1} \frac{2}{3}$ with the plane $2x - y + 2z - 3 = 0$.

20. Containing the point $P(-3, 5, -2)$ and perpendicular to the representations of the vector $\mathbf{V}(\overrightarrow{OP})$.

In Exercises 21 through 23, find the acute angle between the two planes.

21. $2x - y - 2z - 5 = 0$ and $6x - 2y + 3z + 8 = 0$

22. $2x - 5y + 3z - 1 = 0$ and $y - 5z + 3 = 0$

23. $3x + 4y = 0$ and $4x - 7y + 4z - 6 = 0$

24. Find the distance from the plane $2x + 2y - z - 6 = 0$ to the point $(2, 2, -4)$.

25. Find the distance from the plane $5x + 11y + 2z - 30 = 0$ to the point $(-2, 6, 3)$.

26. Find the perpendicular distance between the parallel planes $4x - 8y - z = -9$ and $4x - 8y - z = 6$.

27. Find the perpendicular distance between the parallel planes $4y - 3z - 6 = 0$ and $8y - 6z - 27 = 0$.

28. If a, b, and c are nonzero and are the x intercept, y intercept, and z intercept, respectively, of a plane, prove that an equation of the plane is

$$\frac{x}{a} + \frac{y}{b} + \frac{z}{c} = 1$$

This is the *intercept form* of an equation of a plane.

In Exercises 29 through 36, find parametric and symmetric equations for the line satisfying the conditions.

29. Through the two points $(1, 2, 1)$ and $(5, -1, 1)$.

30. Through the point $(5, 3, 2)$ with direction numbers $[4, 1, -1]$.

31. Through the origin and perpendicular to the line $\frac{1}{4}(x - 10) = \frac{1}{3}y = \frac{1}{2}z$ at their intersection.

32. Through the origin and perpendicular to the lines having direction numbers $[4, 2, 1]$ and $[-3, -2, 1]$.

33. Perpendicular to the lines having direction numbers $[-5, 1, 2]$ and $[2, -3, -4]$ at the point $(-2, 0, 3)$.

34. Through the point $(-3, 1, -5)$ and perpendicular to the plane $4x - 2y + z - 7 = 0$.

35. Through the point $(4, -5, 20)$ and perpendicular to the plane $x + 3y - 6z - 8 = 0$.

36. Through the point $(2, 0, -4)$ and parallel to each of the planes $2x + y - z = 0$ and $x + 3y + 5z = 0$.

37. Find a set of symmetric equations for the line
$$\begin{cases} 4x - 3y + z - 2 = 0 \\ 2x + 5y - 3z + 4 = 0 \end{cases}$$

38. Show that the lines
$$\frac{x + 1}{2} = \frac{y + 4}{-5} = \frac{z - 2}{3}$$
$$\frac{x - 3}{-2} = \frac{y + 14}{5} = \frac{z - 8}{-3}$$
are coincident.

39. Prove that the line $\frac{1}{2}(x - 3) = \frac{1}{3}(y + 2) = \frac{1}{4}(z + 1)$ lies in the plane $x - 2y + z = 6$.

40. Prove that the line $x + 1 = -\frac{1}{2}(y - 6) = z$ lies in the plane $3x + y - z = 3$.

The planes through a line perpendicular to the coordinate planes are called the **projecting planes** *of the line. In Exercises 41 through 44, find equations of the projecting planes of the line and sketch the line.*

41. $\begin{cases} 3x - 2y + 5z - 30 = 0 \\ 2x + 3y - 10z - 6 = 0 \end{cases}$

42. $\begin{cases} x + y - 3z + 1 = 0 \\ 2x - y - 3z + 14 = 0 \end{cases}$

43. $\begin{cases} x - 2y - 3z + 6 = 0 \\ x + y + z - 1 = 0 \end{cases}$

44. $\begin{cases} 2x - y + z - 7 = 0 \\ 4x - y + 3z - 13 = 0 \end{cases}$

45. Find the cosine of the smallest angle between the vector whose representations are parallel to the line $x = 2y + 4$, $z = -y + 4$, and the vector whose representations are parallel to the line $x = y + 7$, $2z = y + 2$.

46. Find an equation of the plane containing the point $(6, 2, 4)$ and the line $\frac{1}{5}(x - 1) = \frac{1}{6}(y + 2) = \frac{1}{7}(z - 3)$.

In Exercises 47 and 48, find an equation of the plane containing the given intersecting lines.

47. $\dfrac{x - 2}{4} = \dfrac{y + 3}{-1} = \dfrac{z + 2}{3}$
$$\begin{cases} 3x + 2y + z + 2 = 0 \\ x - y + 2z - 1 = 0 \end{cases}$$

48. $\dfrac{x}{2} = \dfrac{y - 2}{3} = \dfrac{z - 1}{1}$ and $\dfrac{x}{1} = \dfrac{y - 2}{-1} = \dfrac{z - 1}{1}$

49. Show that the lines
$$\begin{cases} 3x - y - z = 0 \\ 8x - 2y - 3z + 1 = 0 \end{cases}$$
$$\begin{cases} x - 3y + z + 3 = 0 \\ 3x - y - z + 5 = 0 \end{cases}$$
are parallel, and find an equation of the plane determined by these lines.

50. Show that the lines
$$\frac{x + 2}{5} = \frac{y - 1}{-2} = z + 4$$
$$\frac{x - 3}{-5} = \frac{y + 4}{2} = \frac{z - 3}{-1}$$
are parallel, and find an equation of the plane determined by these lines.

51. Find the coordinates of the point of intersection of the line $\frac{1}{4}(x - 2) = -\frac{1}{2}(y + 3) = \frac{1}{7}(z - 1)$ and the plane $5x - y + 2z - 12 = 0$.

52. Find equations of the line through the point $(1, -1, 1)$, perpendicular to the line $3x = 2y = z$, and parallel to the plane $x + y - z = 0$.

53. Find equations of the line through the point $(3, 6, 4)$, intersecting the z axis, and parallel to the plane $x - 3y + 5z - 6 = 0$.

54. Find the perpendicular distance from the origin to the line $x = -2 + \frac{6}{7}t$, $y = 7 - \frac{2}{7}t$, $z = 4 + \frac{3}{7}t$.

55. Find the perpendicular distance from the point $(-1, 3, -1)$ to the line $x - 2z = 7$, $y = 1$.

56. Find equations of the line through the origin, perpendicular to the line $x = y - 5$, $z = 2y - 3$, and intersecting the line $y = 2x + 1$, $z = x + 2$.

57. Prove that the lines
$$\frac{x - 1}{5} = \frac{y - 2}{-2} = \frac{z + 1}{-3}$$
$$\frac{x - 2}{1} = \frac{y + 1}{-3} = \frac{z + 3}{2}$$
are skew lines.

58. Find equations of the line through the point $(3, -4, -5)$ that intersects each of the skew lines of Exercise 57.

59. Prove that the perpendicular distance between the parallel planes $ax + by + cz + d_1 = 0$ and $ax + by + cz + d_2 = 0$ is given by

$$\frac{|d_1 - d_2|}{\sqrt{a^2 + b^2 + c^2}}$$

60. Prove that the undirected distance from the plane $ax + by + cz + d = 0$ to the point (x_0, y_0, z_0) is

given by

$$\frac{|ax_0 + by_0 + cz_0 + d|}{\sqrt{a^2 + b^2 + c^2}}$$

61. What are symmetric equations of a line if the two direction numbers a and b are zero?

62. Describe how vectors are used to determine the distance from a point to a plane.

63. Describe how vectors are used to determine the distance from a point to a line in R^3.

10.5 CROSS PRODUCT

Cross product, a vector operation for vectors in V_3, has applications in geometry, planetary motion, electricity, magnetism, and mechanics. We now introduce this operation along with its properties.

If **A** and **B** are two nonparallel vectors, representations of the two vectors with the same initial point determine a plane as indicated in Figure 1. The cross product of **A** and **B** yields a vector whose representations are perpendicular to this plane.

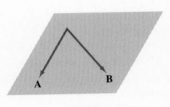

FIGURE 1

10.5.1 Definition of Cross Product

If $\mathbf{A} = \langle a_1, a_2, a_3 \rangle$ and $\mathbf{B} = \langle b_1, b_2, b_3 \rangle$, then the **cross product** of **A** and **B**, denoted by $\mathbf{A} \times \mathbf{B}$, is given by

$$\mathbf{A} \times \mathbf{B} = \langle a_2 b_3 - a_3 b_2, a_3 b_1 - a_1 b_3, a_1 b_2 - a_2 b_1 \rangle$$

Observe that this definition pertains only to vectors in V_3. There is no cross product for vectors in V_2. The cross product also is called the **vector product.** The operation of obtaining the cross product is called **cross multiplication** or **vector multiplication.**

▷ **ILLUSTRATION 1**   If $\mathbf{A} = \langle 2, 1, -3 \rangle$ and $\mathbf{B} = \langle 3, -1, 4 \rangle$, then from Definition 10.5.1,

$$\mathbf{A} \times \mathbf{B} = \langle 2, 1, -3 \rangle \times \langle 3, -1, 4 \rangle$$
$$= \langle (1)(4) - (-3)(-1), (-3)(3) - (2)(4), (2)(-1) - (1)(3) \rangle$$
$$= \langle 4 - 3, -9 - 8, -2 - 3 \rangle$$
$$= \langle 1, -17, -5 \rangle$$
$$= \mathbf{i} - 17\mathbf{j} - 5\mathbf{k} \qquad ◀$$

There is a mnemonic device for remembering the cross-product formula that makes use of determinant notation. A second-order determinant is defined by the equation

$$\begin{vmatrix} a & b \\ c & d \end{vmatrix} = ad - bc$$

where a, b, and c are real numbers. For example,

$$\begin{vmatrix} 3 & 6 \\ -2 & 5 \end{vmatrix} = 3(5) - (6)(-2)$$

$$= 27$$

Therefore the cross-product formula can be written as

$$\mathbf{A} \times \mathbf{B} = \begin{vmatrix} a_2 & a_3 \\ b_2 & b_3 \end{vmatrix} \mathbf{i} - \begin{vmatrix} a_1 & a_3 \\ b_1 & b_3 \end{vmatrix} \mathbf{j} + \begin{vmatrix} a_1 & a_2 \\ b_1 & b_2 \end{vmatrix} \mathbf{k}$$

The right side of the above expression can be written symbolically as

$$\begin{vmatrix} \mathbf{i} & \mathbf{j} & \mathbf{k} \\ a_1 & a_2 & a_3 \\ b_1 & b_2 & b_3 \end{vmatrix}$$

which is the notation for a third-order determinant. However, observe that the first row contains vectors and not real numbers as is customary with determinant notation.

▷ **ILLUSTRATION 2**   We use the mnemonic device employing determinant notation to find the cross product of the vectors of Illustration 1.

$$\mathbf{A} \times \mathbf{B} = \begin{vmatrix} \mathbf{i} & \mathbf{j} & \mathbf{k} \\ 2 & 1 & -3 \\ 3 & -1 & 4 \end{vmatrix}$$

$$= \begin{vmatrix} 1 & -3 \\ -1 & 4 \end{vmatrix} \mathbf{i} - \begin{vmatrix} 2 & -3 \\ 3 & 4 \end{vmatrix} \mathbf{j} + \begin{vmatrix} 2 & 1 \\ 3 & -1 \end{vmatrix} \mathbf{k}$$

$$= [(1)(4) - (-3)(-1)]\mathbf{i} - [(2)(4) - (-3)(3)]\mathbf{j} + [(2)(-1) - (1)(3)]\mathbf{k}$$

$$= \mathbf{i} - 17\mathbf{j} - 5\mathbf{k}$$ ◀

10.5.2 Theorem

If $\mathbf{A}$ is any vector in V_3, then

(i) $\mathbf{A} \times \mathbf{A} = \mathbf{0}$
(ii) $\mathbf{0} \times \mathbf{A} = \mathbf{0}$
(iii) $\mathbf{A} \times \mathbf{0} = \mathbf{0}$

Proof of (i)   If $\mathbf{A} = \langle a_1, a_2, a_3 \rangle$, then by Definition 10.5.1,

$$\mathbf{A} \times \mathbf{A} = \langle a_2 a_3 - a_3 a_2, a_3 a_1 - a_1 a_3, a_1 a_2 - a_2 a_1 \rangle$$

$$= \langle 0, 0, 0 \rangle$$

$$= \mathbf{0}$$

The proofs of (ii) and (iii) are left as exercises (see Exercise 13).   ■

By applying Definition 10.5.1 to pairs of unit vectors $\mathbf{i}$, $\mathbf{j}$, and $\mathbf{k}$ we obtain the following:

$$\mathbf{i} \times \mathbf{i} = \mathbf{0} \qquad \mathbf{j} \times \mathbf{j} = \mathbf{0} \qquad \mathbf{k} \times \mathbf{k} = \mathbf{0}$$
$$\mathbf{i} \times \mathbf{j} = \mathbf{k} \qquad \mathbf{j} \times \mathbf{k} = \mathbf{i} \qquad \mathbf{k} \times \mathbf{i} = \mathbf{j}$$
$$\mathbf{j} \times \mathbf{i} = -\mathbf{k} \qquad \mathbf{k} \times \mathbf{j} = -\mathbf{i} \qquad \mathbf{i} \times \mathbf{k} = -\mathbf{j}$$

As an aid in remembering the above cross products, first notice that the cross product of any one of the unit vectors $\mathbf{i}$, $\mathbf{j}$, or $\mathbf{k}$ with itself is the zero vector. The other six cross products can be obtained from Figure 2 by applying the following rule: The cross product of two consecutive vectors in the clockwise direction is the next vector; and the cross product of two consecutive vectors in the counterclockwise direction is the negative of the next vector.

We can easily show that cross multiplication of two vectors is not commutative because in particular $\mathbf{i} \times \mathbf{j} \neq \mathbf{j} \times \mathbf{i}$. However, $\mathbf{i} \times \mathbf{j} = \mathbf{k}$ and $\mathbf{j} \times \mathbf{i} = -\mathbf{k}$; so $\mathbf{i} \times \mathbf{j} = -(\mathbf{j} \times \mathbf{i})$. In general, if $\mathbf{A}$ and $\mathbf{B}$ are any vectors in V_3, $\mathbf{A} \times \mathbf{B} = -(\mathbf{B} \times \mathbf{A})$, which we state and prove as a theorem.

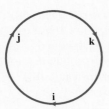

FIGURE 2

10.5.3 Theorem

If $\mathbf{A}$ and $\mathbf{B}$ are any vectors in V_3,

$$\mathbf{A} \times \mathbf{B} = -(\mathbf{B} \times \mathbf{A})$$

Proof If $\mathbf{A} = \langle a_1, a_2, a_3 \rangle$ and $\mathbf{B} = \langle b_1, b_2, b_3 \rangle$, then by Definition 10.5.1,

$$\mathbf{A} \times \mathbf{B} = \langle a_2 b_3 - a_3 b_2, a_3 b_1 - a_1 b_3, a_1 b_2 - a_2 b_1 \rangle$$
$$= -1 \langle a_3 b_2 - a_2 b_3, a_1 b_3 - a_3 b_1, a_2 b_1 - a_1 b_2 \rangle$$
$$= -(\mathbf{B} \times \mathbf{A}) \qquad \blacksquare$$

Cross multiplication of vectors is not associative as shown by the following particular case:

$$\mathbf{i} \times (\mathbf{i} \times \mathbf{j}) = \mathbf{i} \times \mathbf{k} \qquad (\mathbf{i} \times \mathbf{i}) \times \mathbf{j} = \mathbf{0} \times \mathbf{j}$$
$$= -\mathbf{j} \qquad\qquad\qquad = \mathbf{0}$$

Thus

$$\mathbf{i} \times (\mathbf{i} \times \mathbf{j}) \neq (\mathbf{i} \times \mathbf{i}) \times \mathbf{j}$$

Cross multiplication of vectors is distributive with respect to vector addition, as given by the following theorem.

10.5.4 Theorem

If $\mathbf{A}$, $\mathbf{B}$, and $\mathbf{C}$ are any vectors in V_3, then

$$\mathbf{A} \times (\mathbf{B} + \mathbf{C}) = \mathbf{A} \times \mathbf{B} + \mathbf{A} \times \mathbf{C}$$

To prove this theorem let $\mathbf{A} = \langle a_1, a_2, a_3 \rangle$, $\mathbf{B} = \langle b_1, b_2, b_3 \rangle$, and $\mathbf{C} = \langle c_1, c_2, c_3 \rangle$, and then show that the components of the vector on the left side of the equation are the same as the components of the vector on the right side. The details are left as an exercise (see Exercise 39).

10.5.5 Theorem

If **A** and **B** are any two vectors in V_3 and c is a scalar, then

(i) $(c\mathbf{A}) \times \mathbf{B} = \mathbf{A} \times (c\mathbf{B})$;

(ii) $(c\mathbf{A}) \times \mathbf{B} = c(\mathbf{A} \times \mathbf{B})$.

The proof of this theorem is left as an exercise (see Exercise 40).

Theorems 10.5.4 and 10.5.5 can be applied to compute the cross product of two vectors by using laws of algebra, provided the order of the vectors in cross multiplication is not changed because that is prohibited by Theorem 10.5.3. The following illustration demonstrates this procedure.

▷ **ILLUSTRATION 3**   We find the cross product of the vectors in Illustration 1 by applying Theorems 10.5.4 and 10.5.5.

$$
\begin{aligned}
\mathbf{A} \times \mathbf{B} &= (2\mathbf{i} + \mathbf{j} - 3\mathbf{k}) \times (3\mathbf{i} - \mathbf{j} + 4\mathbf{k}) \\
&= 6(\mathbf{i} \times \mathbf{i}) - 2(\mathbf{i} \times \mathbf{j}) + 8(\mathbf{i} \times \mathbf{k}) + 3(\mathbf{j} \times \mathbf{i}) - 1(\mathbf{j} \times \mathbf{j}) \\
&\qquad\qquad + 4(\mathbf{j} \times \mathbf{k}) - 9(\mathbf{k} \times \mathbf{i}) + 3(\mathbf{k} \times \mathbf{j}) - 12(\mathbf{k} \times \mathbf{k}) \\
&= 6(\mathbf{0}) - 2(\mathbf{k}) + 8(-\mathbf{j}) + 3(-\mathbf{k}) - 1(\mathbf{0}) + 4(\mathbf{i}) - 9(\mathbf{j}) + 3(-\mathbf{i}) - 12(\mathbf{0}) \\
&= -2\mathbf{k} - 8\mathbf{j} - 3\mathbf{k} + 4\mathbf{i} - 9\mathbf{j} - 3\mathbf{i} \\
&= \mathbf{i} - 17\mathbf{j} - 5\mathbf{k}
\end{aligned}
$$
◀

The procedure of Illustration 3 provides a method for computing the cross product without having to remember the formula of Definition 10.5.1 or to use determinant notation. Actually all the steps shown need not be included because the various cross products of the unit vectors can be obtained immediately from Figure 2 and the corresponding rule.

Two *triple products* sometimes arise in applications of vectors. One is the product $\mathbf{A} \cdot (\mathbf{B} \times \mathbf{C})$ called the **triple scalar product** of the vectors **A**, **B**, and **C**. Actually, the parentheses are not needed because $\mathbf{A} \cdot \mathbf{B} \times \mathbf{C}$ can be interpreted only one way since $\mathbf{A} \cdot \mathbf{B}$ is a scalar.

10.5.6 Theorem

If **A**, **B**, and **C** are vectors in V_3, then

$$\mathbf{A} \cdot \mathbf{B} \times \mathbf{C} = \mathbf{A} \times \mathbf{B} \cdot \mathbf{C}$$

This theorem can be proved by letting

$$\mathbf{A} = \langle a_1, a_2, a_3 \rangle \qquad \mathbf{B} = \langle b_1, b_2, b_3 \rangle \qquad \mathbf{C} = \langle c_1, c_2, c_3 \rangle$$

and then by showing that the scalar on the left side of the equation is equal to the scalar on the right. The details are left as an exercise (see Exercise 41).

▷ **ILLUSTRATION 4**   We verify Theorem 10.5.6 for

$$\mathbf{A} = \langle 1, -1, 2 \rangle \qquad \mathbf{B} = \langle 3, 4, -2 \rangle \qquad \mathbf{C} = \langle -5, 1, -4 \rangle$$

$$\begin{aligned}
\mathbf{B} \times \mathbf{C} &= (3\mathbf{i} + 4\mathbf{j} - 2\mathbf{k}) \times (-5\mathbf{i} + \mathbf{j} - 4\mathbf{k}) \\
&= 3\mathbf{k} - 12(-\mathbf{j}) - 20(-\mathbf{k}) - 16\mathbf{i} + 10\mathbf{j} - 2(-\mathbf{i}) \\
&= -14\mathbf{i} + 22\mathbf{j} + 23\mathbf{k}
\end{aligned}$$

$$\begin{aligned}
\mathbf{A} \cdot (\mathbf{B} \times \mathbf{C}) &= \langle 1, -1, 2 \rangle \cdot \langle -14, 22, 23 \rangle \\
&= -14 - 22 + 46 \\
&= 10
\end{aligned}$$

$$\begin{aligned}
\mathbf{A} \times \mathbf{B} &= (\mathbf{i} - \mathbf{j} + 2\mathbf{k}) \times (3\mathbf{i} + 4\mathbf{j} - 2\mathbf{k}) \\
&= 4\mathbf{k} - 2(-\mathbf{j}) - 3(-\mathbf{k}) + 2\mathbf{i} + 6\mathbf{j} + 8(-\mathbf{i}) \\
&= -6\mathbf{i} + 8\mathbf{j} + 7\mathbf{k}
\end{aligned}$$

$$\begin{aligned}
(\mathbf{A} \times \mathbf{B}) \cdot \mathbf{C} &= \langle -6, 8, 7 \rangle \cdot \langle -5, 1, -4 \rangle \\
&= 30 + 8 - 28 \\
&= 10
\end{aligned}$$

This verifies the theorem for these three vectors.   ◀

The triple product $\mathbf{A} \times (\mathbf{B} \times \mathbf{C})$ is called the **triple vector product.**

10.5.7 Theorem

If $\mathbf{A}$, $\mathbf{B}$, and $\mathbf{C}$ are vectors in V_3, then

$$\mathbf{A} \times (\mathbf{B} \times \mathbf{C}) = (\mathbf{A} \cdot \mathbf{C})\mathbf{B} - (\mathbf{A} \cdot \mathbf{B})\mathbf{C}$$

The proof of this theorem is similar to the proof of Theorem 10.5.6. By using components of the vectors $\mathbf{A}$, $\mathbf{B}$, and $\mathbf{C}$ we can show that the vector on the left side of the equation is the same as the vector on the right. The computation is left as an exercise (see Exercise 42).

▷ **ILLUSTRATION 5**   We verify Theorem 10.5.7 for the vectors $\mathbf{A}$, $\mathbf{B}$, and $\mathbf{C}$ of Illustration 4. Because $\mathbf{B} \times \mathbf{C} = -14\mathbf{i} + 22\mathbf{j} + 23\mathbf{k}$

$$\begin{aligned}
\mathbf{A} \times (\mathbf{B} \times \mathbf{C}) &= \begin{vmatrix} \mathbf{i} & \mathbf{j} & \mathbf{k} \\ 1 & -1 & 2 \\ -14 & 22 & 23 \end{vmatrix} \\
&= -23\mathbf{i} - 28\mathbf{j} + 22\mathbf{k} - 14\mathbf{k} - 44\mathbf{i} - 23\mathbf{j} \\
&= -67\mathbf{i} - 51\mathbf{j} + 8\mathbf{k} \qquad\qquad (1)
\end{aligned}$$

$$\begin{aligned}
\mathbf{A} \cdot \mathbf{C} &= \langle 1, -1, 2 \rangle \cdot \langle -5, 1, -4 \rangle & \mathbf{A} \cdot \mathbf{B} &= \langle 1, -1, 2 \rangle \cdot \langle 3, 4, -2 \rangle \\
&= -5 - 1 - 8 & &= 3 - 4 - 4 \\
&= -14 & &= -5
\end{aligned}$$

Thus

$$(\mathbf{A} \cdot \mathbf{C})\mathbf{B} - (\mathbf{A} \cdot \mathbf{B})\mathbf{C} = -14\langle 3, 4, -2\rangle - (-5)\langle -5, 1, -4\rangle$$
$$= \langle -42, -56, 28\rangle - \langle 25, -5, 20\rangle$$
$$= \langle -67, -51, 8\rangle$$
$$= -67\mathbf{i} - 51\mathbf{j} + 8\mathbf{k}$$

By comparing this result with (1), Theorem 10.5.7 is verified for these three vectors. ◄

The next theorem is used for a geometric interpretation of the cross product.

> **10.5.8 Theorem**
>
> If $\mathbf{A}$ and $\mathbf{B}$ are two vectors in V_3 and θ is the angle between $\mathbf{A}$ and $\mathbf{B}$, then
>
> $$\|\mathbf{A} \times \mathbf{B}\| = \|\mathbf{A}\|\|\mathbf{B}\| \sin \theta$$

Proof From Theorem 10.3.3(iii),

$$\|\mathbf{A} \times \mathbf{B}\|^2 = (\mathbf{A} \times \mathbf{B}) \cdot (\mathbf{A} \times \mathbf{B}) \qquad (2)$$

With the notation $\mathbf{U}$, $\mathbf{V}$, and $\mathbf{W}$ as the vectors, from Theorem 10.5.6

$$(\mathbf{U} \times \mathbf{V}) \cdot \mathbf{W} = \mathbf{U} \cdot (\mathbf{V} \times \mathbf{W})$$

If in this equation we let $\mathbf{U} = \mathbf{A}$, $\mathbf{V} = \mathbf{B}$, and $\mathbf{W} = \mathbf{A} \times \mathbf{B}$, we have

$$(\mathbf{A} \times \mathbf{B}) \cdot (\mathbf{A} \times \mathbf{B}) = \mathbf{A} \cdot [(\mathbf{B} \times (\mathbf{A} \times \mathbf{B})]$$

Applying Theorem 10.5.7 to the vector in brackets on the right side we get

$$(\mathbf{A} \times \mathbf{B}) \cdot (\mathbf{A} \times \mathbf{B}) = \mathbf{A} \cdot [(\mathbf{B} \cdot \mathbf{B})\mathbf{A} - (\mathbf{B} \cdot \mathbf{A})\mathbf{B}]$$
$$= (\mathbf{A} \cdot \mathbf{A})(\mathbf{B} \cdot \mathbf{B}) - (\mathbf{A} \cdot \mathbf{B})(\mathbf{A} \cdot \mathbf{B})$$
$$= \|\mathbf{A}\|^2\|\mathbf{B}\|^2 - (\mathbf{A} \cdot \mathbf{B})^2 \qquad (3)$$

From Theorem 10.3.5, if θ is the angle between $\mathbf{A}$ and $\mathbf{B}$,

$$\mathbf{A} \cdot \mathbf{B} = \|\mathbf{A}\|\|\mathbf{B}\| \cos \theta$$

Substituting from this equation into (3) we have

$$(\mathbf{A} \times \mathbf{B}) \cdot (\mathbf{A} \times \mathbf{B}) = \|\mathbf{A}\|^2\|\mathbf{B}\|^2 - \|\mathbf{A}\|^2\|\mathbf{B}\|^2 \cos^2 \theta$$
$$= \|\mathbf{A}\|^2\|\mathbf{B}\|^2 (1 - \cos^2 \theta)$$

Substituting from (2) into the above, and because $1 - \cos^2 \theta = \sin^2 \theta$, we have

$$\|\mathbf{A} \times \mathbf{B}\|^2 = \|\mathbf{A}\|^2\|\mathbf{B}\|^2 \sin^2 \theta$$

Because $0 \le \theta \le \pi$, $\sin \theta \ge 0$. Therefore, we take the square root of both sides and get

$$\|\mathbf{A} \times \mathbf{B}\| = \|\mathbf{A}\|\|\mathbf{B}\| \sin \theta \qquad \blacksquare$$

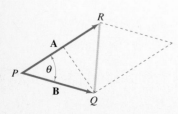

FIGURE 3

We consider now a geometric interpretation of $\|\mathbf{A} \times \mathbf{B}\|$. Let $\overrightarrow{PR}$ be a representation of $\mathbf{A}$ and $\overrightarrow{PQ}$ be a representation of $\mathbf{B}$. Then the angle between the vectors $\mathbf{A}$ and $\mathbf{B}$ is the angle at P in triangle RPQ (see Figure 3).

Let the radian measure of this angle be θ. Therefore the area of the parallelogram having $\overrightarrow{PR}$ and $\overrightarrow{PQ}$ as adjacent sides is $\|\mathbf{A}\|\|\mathbf{B}\|\sin\theta$ square units because the altitude of the parallelogram has length $\|\mathbf{B}\|\sin\theta$ units and the length of the base is $\|\mathbf{A}\|$ units. So from Theorem 10.5.8, $\|\mathbf{A}\times\mathbf{B}\|$ square units is the area of this parallelogram.

▶ **EXAMPLE 1**   Show that the quadrilateral having vertices at $P(1, -2, 3)$, $Q(4, 3, -1)$, $R(2, 2, 1)$, and $S(5, 7, -3)$ is a parallelogram, and find its area.

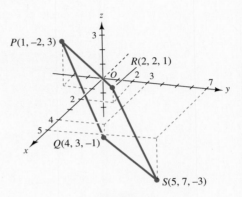

FIGURE 4

Solution   Figure 4 shows the quadrilateral $PQSR$.

$\mathbf{V}(\overrightarrow{PQ}) = \langle 4 - 1, 3 + 2, -1 - 3 \rangle$ $\mathbf{V}(\overrightarrow{PR}) = \langle 2 - 1, \ 2 + 2, \ 1 - 3 \rangle$

$\qquad\quad = \langle 3, 5, -4 \rangle$ $\qquad\qquad\quad = \langle 1, 4, -2 \rangle$

$\mathbf{V}(\overrightarrow{RS}) = \langle 5 - 2, 7 - 2, -3 - 1 \rangle$ $\mathbf{V}(\overrightarrow{QS}) = \langle 5 - 4, 7 - 3, -3 + 1 \rangle$

$\qquad\quad = \langle 3, 5, -4 \rangle$ $\qquad\qquad\quad = \langle 1, 4, -2 \rangle$

Because $\mathbf{V}(\overrightarrow{PQ}) = \mathbf{V}(\overrightarrow{RS})$ and $\mathbf{V}(\overrightarrow{PR}) = \mathbf{V}(\overrightarrow{QS})$, it follows that $\overrightarrow{PQ}$ is parallel to $\overrightarrow{RS}$ and $\overrightarrow{PR}$ is parallel to $\overrightarrow{QS}$. Therefore $PQSR$ is a parallelogram.

Let $\mathbf{A} = \mathbf{V}(\overrightarrow{PR})$ and $\mathbf{B} = \mathbf{V}(\overrightarrow{PQ})$; then

$\mathbf{A}\times\mathbf{B} = (\mathbf{i} + 4\mathbf{j} - 2\mathbf{k}) \times (3\mathbf{i} + 5\mathbf{j} - 4\mathbf{k})$

$= 3(\mathbf{i}\times\mathbf{i}) + 5(\mathbf{i}\times\mathbf{j}) - 4(\mathbf{i}\times\mathbf{k}) + 12(\mathbf{j}\times\mathbf{i}) + 20(\mathbf{j}\times\mathbf{j})$
$\qquad\qquad\qquad - 16(\mathbf{j}\times\mathbf{k}) - 6(\mathbf{k}\times\mathbf{i}) - 10(\mathbf{k}\times\mathbf{j}) + 8(\mathbf{k}\times\mathbf{k})$

$= 3(\mathbf{0}) + 5(\mathbf{k}) - 4(-\mathbf{j}) + 12(-\mathbf{k}) + 20(\mathbf{0}) - 16(\mathbf{i}) - 6(\mathbf{j}) - 10(-\mathbf{i}) + 8(\mathbf{0})$

$= -6\mathbf{i} - 2\mathbf{j} - 7\mathbf{k}$

Thus

$$\|\mathbf{A}\times\mathbf{B}\| = \sqrt{36 + 4 + 49}$$
$$= \sqrt{89}$$

Conclusion: The area of the parallelogram is $\sqrt{89}$ square units.   ◀

10.5.9 Theorem

If $\mathbf{A}$ and $\mathbf{B}$ are two vectors in V_3, $\mathbf{A}$ and $\mathbf{B}$ are parallel if and only if $\mathbf{A}\times\mathbf{B} = \mathbf{0}$.

Proof   If either **A** or **B** is the zero vector, then from Theorem 10.5.2, **A** × **B** = **0**. Because the zero vector is parallel to any vector, the theorem holds.

If neither **A** nor **B** is the zero vector, $\|\mathbf{A}\| \neq 0$ and $\|\mathbf{B}\| \neq 0$. Therefore by Theorem 10.5.8, $\|\mathbf{A} \times \mathbf{B}\| = 0$ if and only if $\sin\theta = 0$. Because $\|\mathbf{A} \times \mathbf{B}\| = 0$ if and only if **A** × **B** = **0** and $\sin\theta = 0$ ($0 \leq \theta \leq \pi$) if and only if $\theta = 0$ or $\theta = \pi$, we can conclude that

$$\mathbf{A} \times \mathbf{B} = \mathbf{0} \quad \text{if and only if} \quad \theta = 0 \text{ or } \theta = \pi$$

However, two nonzero vectors are parallel if and only if the radian measure of the angle between the two vectors is 0 or π, from which the theorem follows. ∎

10.5.10 Theorem

If **A** and **B** are two vectors in V_3, then the vector **A** × **B** is orthogonal to both **A** and **B**.

Proof   From Theorem 10.5.6,

$$\mathbf{A} \cdot \mathbf{A} \times \mathbf{B} = \mathbf{A} \times \mathbf{A} \cdot \mathbf{B}$$

From Theorem 10.5.2(i), **A** × **A** = **0**. Therefore, from the above equation,

$$\mathbf{A} \cdot \mathbf{A} \times \mathbf{B} = \mathbf{0} \cdot \mathbf{B}$$
$$= 0$$

Because the dot product of **A** and **A** × **B** is zero, **A** and **A** × **B** are orthogonal. Also from Theorem 10.5.6,

$$\mathbf{A} \times \mathbf{B} \cdot \mathbf{B} = \mathbf{A} \cdot \mathbf{B} \times \mathbf{B}$$

Again applying Theorem 10.5.2(i) we get **B** × **B** = **0**; thus from the above equation,

$$\mathbf{A} \times \mathbf{B} \cdot \mathbf{B} = \mathbf{A} \cdot \mathbf{0}$$
$$= 0$$

Therefore, because the dot product of **A** × **B** and **B** is zero, **A** × **B** and **B** are orthogonal and the theorem is proved. ∎

From Theorem 10.5.10 we can conclude that if representations of the vectors **A**, **B**, and **A** × **B** have the same initial point, then the representation of **A** × **B** is perpendicular to the plane formed by the representations of **A** and **B**.

▶ **EXAMPLE 2**   Given the points $P(-1, -2, -3)$, $Q(-2, 1, 0)$, and $R(0, 5, 1)$, find a unit vector whose representations are perpendicular to the plane through the points P, Q, and R.

Solution   Let $\mathbf{A} = \mathbf{V}(\overrightarrow{PQ})$ and $\mathbf{B} = \mathbf{V}(\overrightarrow{PR})$. Then

$$\mathbf{A} = \langle -2 + 1, 1 + 2, 0 + 3 \rangle \qquad \mathbf{B} = \langle 0 + 1, 5 + 2, 1 + 3 \rangle$$
$$= \langle -1, 3, 3 \rangle \qquad\qquad\qquad = \langle 1, 7, 4 \rangle$$

The plane through P, Q, and R is the plane formed by $\overrightarrow{PQ}$ and $\overrightarrow{PR}$, which are, respectively, representations of vectors $\mathbf{A}$ and $\mathbf{B}$. Therefore any representation of the vector $\mathbf{A} \times \mathbf{B}$ is perpendicular to this plane.

$$\mathbf{A} \times \mathbf{B} = (-\mathbf{i} + 3\mathbf{j} + 3\mathbf{k}) \times (\mathbf{i} + 7\mathbf{j} + 4\mathbf{k})$$
$$= -9\mathbf{i} + 7\mathbf{j} - 10\mathbf{k}$$

The desired vector is a unit vector parallel to $\mathbf{A} \times \mathbf{B}$. To find this unit vector we apply Theorem 10.2.14 and divide $\mathbf{A} \times \mathbf{B}$ by $\| \mathbf{A} \times \mathbf{B} \|$ to obtain

$$\frac{\mathbf{A} \times \mathbf{B}}{\| \mathbf{A} \times \mathbf{B} \|} = -\frac{9}{\sqrt{230}}\mathbf{i} + \frac{7}{\sqrt{230}}\mathbf{j} - \frac{10}{\sqrt{230}}\mathbf{k} \qquad \blacktriangleleft$$

The next two examples show how the cross product can be applied to find an equation of a plane. These examples involve the same information as in Examples 2 and 4 of Section 10.4.

▶ **EXAMPLE 3**   Find an equation of the plane through the points $P(1, 3, 2)$, $Q(3, -2, 2)$, and $R(2, 1, 3)$.

Solution $\mathbf{V}(\overrightarrow{QR}) = -\mathbf{i} + 3\mathbf{j} + \mathbf{k}$ and $\mathbf{V}(\overrightarrow{PR}) = \mathbf{i} - 2\mathbf{j} + \mathbf{k}$. A normal vector to the required plane is the cross product $\mathbf{V}(\overrightarrow{QR}) \times \mathbf{V}(\overrightarrow{PR})$, which is

$$(-\mathbf{i} + 3\mathbf{j} + \mathbf{k}) \times (\mathbf{i} - 2\mathbf{j} + \mathbf{k}) = 5\mathbf{i} + 2\mathbf{j} - \mathbf{k}$$

So if $P_0 = (1, 3, 2)$ and $\mathbf{N} = \langle 5, 2, -1 \rangle$, from Theorem 10.4.2 an equation of the required plane is

$$5(x - 1) + 2(y - 3) - (z - 2) = 0$$
$$5x + 2y - z - 9 = 0$$

This result agrees with that in Example 2 of Section 10.4.   ◀

▶ **EXAMPLE 4**   Find an equation of the plane containing the point $(4, 0, -2)$ and perpendicular to each of the planes

$$x - y + z = 0 \qquad \text{and} \qquad 2x + y - 4z - 5 = 0$$

Solution   By Theorem 10.4.3, a normal vector to the plane $x - y + z = 0$ is $\langle 1, -1, 1 \rangle$ and a normal vector to the plane $2x + y - 4z - 5 = 0$ is $\langle 2, 1, -4 \rangle$. Thus a normal vector to the required plane is orthogonal to both $\langle 1, -1, 1 \rangle$ and $\langle 2, 1, -4 \rangle$. By Theorem 10.5.10, such a vector is

$$\langle 1, -1, 1 \rangle \times \langle 2, 1, -4 \rangle = \begin{vmatrix} \mathbf{i} & \mathbf{j} & \mathbf{k} \\ 1 & -1 & 1 \\ 2 & 1 & -4 \end{vmatrix}$$
$$= 3\mathbf{i} + 6\mathbf{j} + 3\mathbf{k}$$

The required plane contains the point $(4, 0, -2)$ and has $\langle 3, 6, 3 \rangle$ as a normal vector. From Theorem 10.4.2, an equation of this plane is

$$3(x - 4) + 6(y - 0) + 3(z + 2) = 0$$
$$x + 2y + z - 2 = 0$$

This equation agrees with that in Example 4 of Section 10.4.   ◀

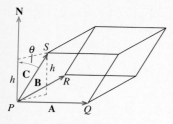

FIGURE 5

A geometric interpretation of the triple scalar product is obtained by considering a parallelepiped having the edges $\overrightarrow{PQ}$, $\overrightarrow{PR}$, and $\overrightarrow{PS}$ and letting $\mathbf{A} = \mathbf{V}(\overrightarrow{PQ})$, $\mathbf{B} = \mathbf{V}(\overrightarrow{PR})$, and $\mathbf{C} = \mathbf{V}(\overrightarrow{PS})$. See Figure 5. The vector $\mathbf{A} \times \mathbf{B}$ is a normal vector to the plane of $\overrightarrow{PQ}$ and $\overrightarrow{PR}$. The vector $-(\mathbf{A} \times \mathbf{B})$ is also a normal vector to this plane. We are not certain which of the two vectors, $\mathbf{A} \times \mathbf{B}$ or $-(\mathbf{A} \times \mathbf{B})$, makes the smaller angle with $\mathbf{C}$. Let $\mathbf{N}$ be the one of the two vectors $\mathbf{A} \times \mathbf{B}$ or $-(\mathbf{A} \times \mathbf{B})$ that makes an angle of radian measure $\theta < \frac{1}{2}\pi$ with $\mathbf{C}$. Then the representations of $\mathbf{N}$ and $\mathbf{C}$ having their initial points at P are on the same side of the plane of $\overrightarrow{PQ}$ and $\overrightarrow{PR}$ as shown in Figure 5. The area of the base of the parallelepiped is $\|\mathbf{A} \times \mathbf{B}\|$ square units. If h units is the length of the altitude of the parallelepiped, and if V cubic units is the volume of the parallelepiped,

$$V = \|\mathbf{A} \times \mathbf{B}\|h \tag{4}$$

Consider now the dot product $\mathbf{N} \cdot \mathbf{C}$. By Theorem 10.3.5,

$$\mathbf{N} \cdot \mathbf{C} = \|\mathbf{N}\| \|\mathbf{C}\| \cos \theta$$

But $h = \|\mathbf{C}\| \cos \theta$; thus

$$\mathbf{N} \cdot \mathbf{C} = \|\mathbf{N}\|h \tag{5}$$

Because $\mathbf{N}$ is either $\mathbf{A} \times \mathbf{B}$ or $-(\mathbf{A} \times \mathbf{B})$, $\|\mathbf{N}\| = \|\mathbf{A} \times \mathbf{B}\|$. Thus, from (5),

$$\mathbf{N} \cdot \mathbf{C} = \|\mathbf{A} \times \mathbf{B}\|h$$

Comparing this equation and (4) we have

$$V = \mathbf{N} \cdot \mathbf{C}$$

We conclude that the measure of the volume of the parallelepiped is either $(\mathbf{A} \times \mathbf{B}) \cdot \mathbf{C}$ or $-(\mathbf{A} \times \mathbf{B}) \cdot \mathbf{C}$; that is,

$$\boxed{V = |\mathbf{A} \times \mathbf{B} \cdot \mathbf{C}|}$$

▶ **EXAMPLE 5** Find the volume of the parallelepiped having vertices $P(5, 4, 5)$, $Q(4, 10, 6)$, $R(1, 8, 7)$, and $S(2, 6, 9)$ and edges $\overrightarrow{PQ}$, $\overrightarrow{PR}$, and $\overrightarrow{PS}$.

Solution Figure 6 shows the parallelepiped. Let $\mathbf{A} = \mathbf{V}(\overrightarrow{PQ})$; then $\mathbf{A} = \langle -1, 6, 1 \rangle$. Let $\mathbf{B} = \mathbf{V}(\overrightarrow{PR})$; then $\mathbf{B} = \langle -4, 4, 2 \rangle$. Let $\mathbf{C} = \mathbf{V}(\overrightarrow{PS})$; then $\mathbf{C} = \langle -3, 2, 4 \rangle$. Thus

$$\mathbf{A} \times \mathbf{B} = (-\mathbf{i} + 6\mathbf{j} + \mathbf{k}) \times (-4\mathbf{i} + 4\mathbf{j} + 2\mathbf{k})$$
$$= 8\mathbf{i} - 2\mathbf{j} + 20\mathbf{k}$$

Therefore

$$\mathbf{A} \times \mathbf{B} \cdot \mathbf{C} = \langle 8, -2, 20 \rangle \cdot \langle -3, 2, 4 \rangle$$
$$= -24 - 4 + 80$$
$$= 52$$

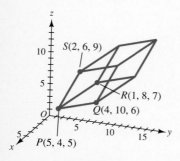

FIGURE 6

Conclusion: The volume is 52 cubic units. ◀

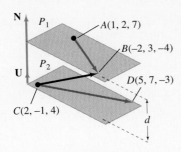

N P_1 $A(1, 2, 7)$

      $B(-2, 3, -4)$

U P_2

            $D(5, 7, -3)$

$C(2, -1, 4)$

                   d

FIGURE 7

▶ **EXAMPLE 6**   Find the distance between the two skew lines l_1 and l_2 of Example 9 in Section 10.4.

Solution   The line l_1 contains the points $A(1, 2, 7)$ and $B(-2, 3, -4)$. The line l_2 contains the points $C(2, -1, 4)$ and $D(5, 7, -3)$. Because l_1 and l_2 are skew lines, there are parallel planes P_1 and P_2 containing the lines l_1 and l_2, respectively. See Figure 7. Let d units be the distance between planes P_1 and P_2. The distance between l_1 and l_2 is also d units. A normal vector to the two planes is

$$\mathbf{N} = \mathbf{V}(\overrightarrow{AB}) \times \mathbf{V}(\overrightarrow{CD})$$

Let $\mathbf{U}$ be a unit vector in the direction of $\mathbf{N}$. Then

$$\mathbf{U} = \frac{\mathbf{V}(\overrightarrow{AB}) \times \mathbf{V}(\overrightarrow{CD})}{\|\mathbf{V}(\overrightarrow{AB}) \times \mathbf{V}(\overrightarrow{CD})\|} \tag{6}$$

Now we take two points, one in each plane (for instance, B and C). Then the scalar projection of $\mathbf{V}(\overrightarrow{CB})$ onto $\mathbf{N}$ is $\mathbf{V}(\overrightarrow{CB}) \cdot \mathbf{U}$, and

$$d = |\mathbf{V}(\overrightarrow{CB}) \cdot \mathbf{U}| \tag{7}$$

We now perform the computations.

$$\mathbf{V}(\overrightarrow{AB}) = \langle -2 - 1, 3 - 2, -4 - 7 \rangle \qquad \mathbf{V}(\overrightarrow{CD}) = \langle 5 - 2, 7 + 1, -3 - 4 \rangle$$
$$= \langle -3, 1, -11 \rangle \qquad\qquad\qquad = \langle 3, 8, -7 \rangle$$

Thus

$$\mathbf{V}(\overrightarrow{AB}) \times \mathbf{V}(\overrightarrow{CD}) = \begin{vmatrix} \mathbf{i} & \mathbf{j} & \mathbf{k} \\ -3 & 1 & -11 \\ 3 & 8 & -7 \end{vmatrix}$$
$$= 27(3\mathbf{i} - 2\mathbf{j} - \mathbf{k})$$

Therefore, from (6),

$$\mathbf{U} = \frac{27(3\mathbf{i} - 2\mathbf{j} - \mathbf{k})}{\sqrt{27^2(3^2 + 2^2 + 1^2)}}$$

$$\mathbf{U} = \frac{1}{\sqrt{14}}(3\mathbf{i} - 2\mathbf{j} - \mathbf{k}) \tag{8}$$

Furthermore

$$\mathbf{V}(\overrightarrow{CB}) = \langle -2 - 2, 3 + 1, -4 - 4 \rangle$$
$$\mathbf{V}(\overrightarrow{CB}) = \langle -4, 4, -8 \rangle$$

Substituting from this equation and (8) into (7) we get

$$d = \left| \langle -4, 4, -8 \rangle \cdot \frac{1}{\sqrt{14}} \langle 3, -2, -1 \rangle \right|$$

$$= \frac{1}{\sqrt{14}} |-12 - 8 + 8|$$

$$= \frac{12}{\sqrt{14}}$$

$$\approx 3.21$$

◀

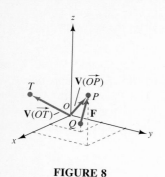

FIGURE 8

We conclude this section with an application of the cross product in mechanics to compute a *torque vector*. See Figure 8 where a force vector $\mathbf{F}$, having the representation $\overrightarrow{QP}$, is applied at point P on an object lying along $\overrightarrow{OP}$. $\mathbf{F}$ causes the object to rotate about a line perpendicular to the plane determined by $\overrightarrow{OP}$ and $\overrightarrow{QP}$. The **torque vector,** whose position representation is $\overrightarrow{OT}$, is the moment of $\mathbf{F}$ about O; it yields the magnitude and direction of the rotative resultant evoked by $\mathbf{F}$. This torque vector is defined by

$$\mathbf{V}(\overrightarrow{OT}) = \mathbf{V}(\overrightarrow{OP}) \times \mathbf{F}$$

▶ **EXAMPLE 7** A force $\mathbf{F}$ of magnitude 15 lb is applied at an angle of 40° at the right endpoint P of a 5-foot bar, as indicated in Figure 9. Find the magnitude of the torque vector induced by $\mathbf{F}$ on the left endpoint O.

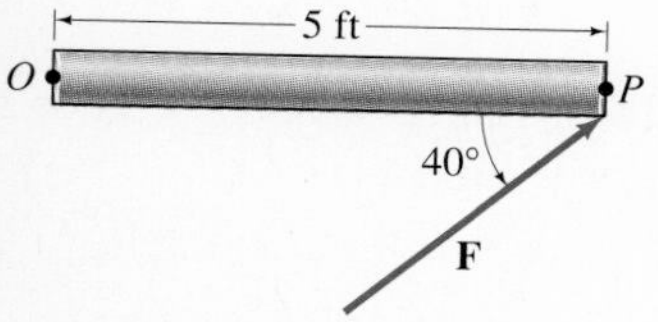

Solution The magnitude of the torque vector is given by $\| \mathbf{V}(\overrightarrow{OP}) \times \mathbf{F} \|$, and by Theorem 10.5.8

$$\| \mathbf{V}(\overrightarrow{OP}) \times \mathbf{F} \| = \| \mathbf{V}(\overrightarrow{OP}) \| \, \| \mathbf{F} \| \sin 40°$$
$$= (5)(15)\sin 40°$$
$$= 48.21$$

FIGURE 9

<u>Conclusion:</u> The magnitude of the torque vector is 48.21 ft-lb. ◀

EXERCISES 10.5

In Exercises 1 through 12, $\mathbf{A} = \langle 1, 2, 3 \rangle$, $\mathbf{B} = \langle 4, -3, -1 \rangle$, $\mathbf{C} = \langle -5, -3, 5 \rangle$, $\mathbf{D} = \langle -2, 1, 6 \rangle$, $\mathbf{E} = \langle 4, 0, -7 \rangle$, *and* $\mathbf{F} = \langle 0, 2, 1 \rangle$

1. Find $\mathbf{A} \times \mathbf{B}$.
2. Find $\mathbf{D} \times \mathbf{E}$.
3. Find $(\mathbf{C} \times \mathbf{D}) \cdot (\mathbf{E} \times \mathbf{F})$.
4. Find $(\mathbf{C} \times \mathbf{E}) \cdot (\mathbf{D} \times \mathbf{F})$.
5. Verify Theorem 10.5.3 for vectors $\mathbf{A}$ and $\mathbf{B}$.
6. Verify Theorem 10.5.4 for vectors $\mathbf{A}$, $\mathbf{B}$, and $\mathbf{C}$.
7. Verify Theorem 10.5.5(i) for $\mathbf{A}$ and $\mathbf{B}$ and $c = 3$.
8. Verify Theorem 10.5.5(ii) for $\mathbf{A}$ and $\mathbf{B}$ and $c = 3$.
9. Verify Theorem 10.5.6 for vectors $\mathbf{A}$, $\mathbf{B}$, and $\mathbf{C}$.
10. Verify Theorem 10.5.7 for vectors $\mathbf{A}$, $\mathbf{B}$, and $\mathbf{C}$.
11. Find $(\mathbf{A} + \mathbf{B}) \times (\mathbf{C} - \mathbf{D})$ and $(\mathbf{D} - \mathbf{C}) \times (\mathbf{A} + \mathbf{B})$, and verify that they are equal.
12. Find $\| \mathbf{A} \times \mathbf{B} \| \| \mathbf{C} \times \mathbf{D} \|$.
13. Prove Theorem 10.5.2(ii) and (iii).
14. Given the unit vectors $\mathbf{A} = \frac{4}{9}\mathbf{i} + \frac{7}{9}\mathbf{j} - \frac{4}{9}\mathbf{k}$ and $\mathbf{B} = -\frac{2}{3}\mathbf{i} + \frac{2}{3}\mathbf{j} + \frac{1}{3}\mathbf{k}$. If θ is the angle between $\mathbf{A}$ and $\mathbf{B}$, find $\sin \theta$ in two ways: (**a**) by using the cross product (Theorem 10.5.8); (**b**) by using the dot product and a trigonometric identity.
15. Follow the instructions of Exercise 14 for the two unit vectors

$$\mathbf{A} = \frac{1}{\sqrt{3}}\mathbf{i} - \frac{1}{\sqrt{3}}\mathbf{j} + \frac{1}{\sqrt{3}}\mathbf{k}$$

$$\mathbf{B} = \frac{1}{3\sqrt{3}}\mathbf{i} + \frac{5}{3\sqrt{3}}\mathbf{j} + \frac{1}{3\sqrt{3}}\mathbf{k}$$

16. Show that the quadrilateral having vertices at $(-2, 1, -1)$, $(1, 1, 3)$, $(-5, 4, 0)$ and $(8, 4, -4)$ is a parallelogram, and find its area.
17. Show that the quadrilateral having vertices at $(1, -2, 3)$, $(4, 3, -1)$, $(2, 2, 1)$, and $(5, 7, -3)$ is a parallelogram, and find its area.
18. Find the area of the parallelogram $PQRS$ if $\mathbf{V}(\overrightarrow{PQ}) = 3\mathbf{i} - 2\mathbf{j}$ and $\mathbf{V}(\overrightarrow{PS}) = 3\mathbf{j} + 4\mathbf{k}$.
19. Find the area of the triangle having vertices at $(0, 2, 2)$, $(8, 8, -2)$, and $(9, 12, 6)$.
20. Find the area of the triangle having vertices at $(4, 5, 6)$, $(4, 4, 5)$, and $(3, 5, 5)$.

In Exercises 21 and 22, use the cross product to find an equation of the plane containing the three points.

21. $(-2, 2, 2)$, $(-8, 1, 6)$, $(3, 4, -1)$
22. $(2, 3, 0)$, $(2, 0, 4)$, $(0, 3, 4)$
23. Do Exercise 18 in Exercises 10.4 by using the cross product.
24. Find a unit vector whose representations are perpendicular to the plane containing $\overrightarrow{PQ}$ and $\overrightarrow{PR}$ if $\overrightarrow{PQ}$ is a representation of the vector $\mathbf{i} + 3\mathbf{j} - 2\mathbf{k}$ and $\overrightarrow{PR}$ is a representation of the vector $2\mathbf{i} - \mathbf{j} - \mathbf{k}$.

In Exercises 25 through 27, find a unit vector whose representations are perpendicular to the plane through the points, P, Q, and R.

25. $P(5, 2, -1)$, $Q(2, 4, -2)$, $R(11, 1, 4)$

26. $P(-2, 1, 0)$, $Q(2, -2, -1)$, $R(-5, 0, 2)$

27. $P(1, 4, 2)$, $Q(3, 2, 4)$, $R(4, 3, 1)$

28. Find the volume of the parallelepiped having edges $\overrightarrow{PQ}$, $\overrightarrow{PR}$, and $\overrightarrow{PS}$ if the points P, Q, R, and S are, respectively, $(1, 3, 4)$, $(3, 5, 3)$, $(2, 1, 6)$, and $(2, 2, 5)$.

29. Find the volume of the parallelepiped $PQRS$ if the vectors $\mathbf{V}(\overrightarrow{PQ})$, $\mathbf{V}(\overrightarrow{PR})$, and $\mathbf{V}(\overrightarrow{PS})$ are, respectively, $\mathbf{i} + 3\mathbf{j} + 2\mathbf{k}$, $2\mathbf{i} + \mathbf{j} - \mathbf{k}$, and $\mathbf{i} - 2\mathbf{j} + \mathbf{k}$.

30. Find an equation of the plane containing the endpoints of the position representations of the vectors $2\mathbf{i} - \mathbf{j} + 3\mathbf{k}, -\mathbf{i} + \mathbf{j} + 2\mathbf{k}$, and $5\mathbf{i} + \mathbf{j} - \mathbf{k}$.

In Exercises 31 and 32, find the perpendicular distance between the two skew lines.

31. $\dfrac{x - 1}{5} = \dfrac{y - 2}{3} = \dfrac{z + 1}{2}$

$\dfrac{x + 2}{4} = \dfrac{y + 1}{2} = \dfrac{z - 3}{-3}$

32. $\dfrac{x + 1}{2} = \dfrac{y + 2}{-4} = \dfrac{z - 1}{-3}$

$\dfrac{x - 1}{5} = \dfrac{y - 1}{3} = \dfrac{z + 1}{2}$

33. In the accompanying figure, a bolt at point Q is turned by applying at point P a force $\mathbf{F}$ of 25 lb at an angle of 70° to the wrench, which is 8 in. long. Find the magnitude of the torque vector induced by the force on the bolt.

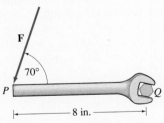

34. A force $\mathbf{F}$ of 30 lb in the downward direction is applied at point P, the left end of the lever arm of the stapler shown in the accompanying figure. The length of the lever arm is 6 in. and in rest position the lever

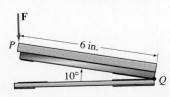

arm makes an angle of 10° with the horizontal base of the stapler at point Q. Find the magnitude of the torque vector exerted by $\mathbf{F}$ on Q.

35. If θ is the angle between vectors $\mathbf{A}$ and $\mathbf{B}$ in V_3, prove that

$$\tan \theta = \frac{\|\mathbf{A} \times \mathbf{B}\|}{\mathbf{A} \cdot \mathbf{B}}$$

36. If $\mathbf{A}$ and $\mathbf{B}$ are vectors in V_3, prove that

$$\mathbf{A} \cdot (\mathbf{A} \times \mathbf{B}) = 0$$

37. If $\mathbf{A}$ and $\mathbf{B}$ are vectors in V_3, prove that

$$(\mathbf{A} - \mathbf{B}) \times (\mathbf{A} + \mathbf{B}) = 2(\mathbf{A} \times \mathbf{B})$$

38. Let P, Q, and R be three noncollinear points in R^3 and let $\overrightarrow{OP}$, $\overrightarrow{OQ}$, and $\overrightarrow{OR}$ be the position representations of vectors $\mathbf{A}$, $\mathbf{B}$, and $\mathbf{C}$, respectively. Prove that the representations of the vector $\mathbf{A} \times \mathbf{B} + \mathbf{B} \times \mathbf{C} + \mathbf{C} \times \mathbf{A}$ are perpendicular to the plane containing the points P, Q, and R.

39. Prove Theorem 10.5.4.   40. Prove Theorem 10.5.5.

41. Prove Theorem 10.5.6.   42. Prove Theorem 10.5.7.

43. Let P, Q, and R be three noncollinear points in R^3 and let $\overrightarrow{OP}$, $\overrightarrow{OQ}$, and $\overrightarrow{OR}$ be the position representations of vectors $\mathbf{A}$, $\mathbf{B}$, and $\mathbf{C}$, respectively. Prove that the distance from the origin to the plane determined by the three points is given by

$$\frac{|\mathbf{A} \cdot \mathbf{B} \times \mathbf{C}|}{\|(\mathbf{B} - \mathbf{A}) \times (\mathbf{C} - \mathbf{A})\|}$$

44. Let $\overrightarrow{OP}$ be the position representation of vector $\mathbf{A}$, $\overrightarrow{OQ}$ be the position representation of vector $\mathbf{B}$, and $\overrightarrow{OR}$ be the position representation of vector $\mathbf{C}$. Prove that the area of triangle PQR is $\frac{1}{2}\|(\mathbf{B} - \mathbf{A}) \times (\mathbf{C} - \mathbf{A})\|$.

45. If $\mathbf{A}$, $\mathbf{B}$, and $\mathbf{C}$ are vectors in V_3, prove that

$$(\mathbf{A} \times \mathbf{B}) \times \mathbf{C} = (\mathbf{C} \cdot \mathbf{A})\mathbf{B} - (\mathbf{C} \cdot \mathbf{B})\mathbf{A}$$

46. If $\mathbf{A}$, $\mathbf{B}$, and $\mathbf{C}$ are vectors in V_3, prove **Jacobi's identity**

$$\mathbf{A} \times (\mathbf{B} \times \mathbf{C}) + \mathbf{B} \times (\mathbf{C} \times \mathbf{A}) + \mathbf{C} \times (\mathbf{A} \times \mathbf{B}) = 0$$

Hint: Apply Theorem 10.5.7 to each term.

47. If $\mathbf{A}$, $\mathbf{B}$, and $\mathbf{C}$ are vectors in V_3, prove that

$$(\mathbf{A} \times \mathbf{B}) \times \mathbf{C} = \mathbf{A} \times (\mathbf{B} \times \mathbf{C})$$

if and only if $\mathbf{B} \times (\mathbf{C} \times \mathbf{A}) = 0$.

Hint: Apply Jacobi's identity in Exercise 46.

48. Describe the geometric interpretations of the cross product, the triple scalar product, and the triple vector product.

10.6 SURFACES

We have already discussed two kinds of surfaces, a plane and a sphere. The purpose of this section is to introduce other surfaces that play an important part in our treatment of the calculus of functions of more than one variable in Chapters 12 through 14.

A **surface** is represented by an equation in three variables if the coordinates of every point on the surface satisfy the equation and if every point whose coordinates satisfy the equation lies on the surface. One kind of surface is a *cylinder*.

10.6.1 Definition of a Cylinder

A **cylinder** is a surface generated by a line moving along a given plane curve in such a way that it always remains parallel to a fixed line not lying in the plane of the given curve. The moving line is called a **generator** of the cylinder and the given plane curve is called a **directrix** of the cylinder. Any position of a generator is called a **ruling** of the cylinder.

We confine this discussion to cylinders having a directrix in a coordinate plane and rulings perpendicular to that plane. If the rulings of a cylinder are perpendicular to the plane of a directrix, the cylinder is said to be perpendicular to the plane.

The familiar right-circular cylinder is one for which a directrix is a circle in a plane perpendicular to the cylinder and whose rulings are parallel to the axis of the cylinder.

▷ **ILLUSTRATION 1**   Figure 1 shows a right-circular cylinder whose directrix is $x^2 + y^2 = 4$ in the xy plane and whose rulings are parallel to the z axis. In Figure 2, we have a cylinder whose directrix is the parabola $y^2 = 8x$ in the xy plane and whose rulings are parallel to the z axis. The cylinder is called a **parabolic cylinder.** An **elliptic cylinder** appears in Figure 3; its directrix is the ellipse $9x^2 + 16y^2 = 144$ in the xy plane, and its rulings are parallel to the z axis. Figure 4 shows a **hyperbolic cylinder** having as a directrix the hyperbola $25x^2 - 4y^2 = 100$ in the xy plane and rulings parallel to the z axis.   ◀

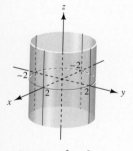

Cylinder: $x^2 + y^2 = 4$

FIGURE 1

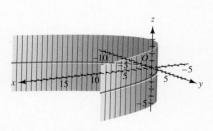

Cylinder: $y^2 = 8x$

FIGURE 2

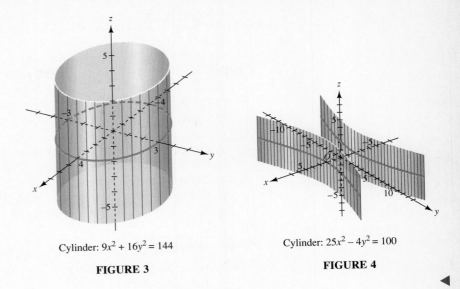

Cylinder: $9x^2 + 16y^2 = 144$

FIGURE 3

Cylinder: $25x^2 - 4y^2 = 100$

FIGURE 4

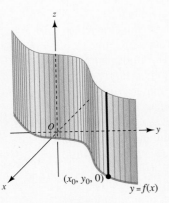

FIGURE 5

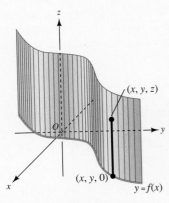

FIGURE 6

Consider the problem of finding an equation of a cylinder having a directrix in a coordinate plane and rulings parallel to the coordinate axis not in that plane. To be specific, take the directrix in the xy plane and the rulings parallel to the z axis. Refer to Figure 5. Suppose that an equation of the directrix in the xy plane is $y = f(x)$. If the point $(x_0, y_0, 0)$ in the xy plane satisfies this equation, any point (x_0, y_0, z) in three-dimensional space, where z is any real number, will satisfy the same equation because z does not appear in the equation. The points having representations (x_0, y_0, z) all lie on the line parallel to the z axis through the point $(x_0, y_0, 0)$. This line is a ruling of the cylinder. Hence any point whose x and y coordinates satisfy the equation $y = f(x)$ lies on the cylinder. Conversely, if the point $P(x, y, z)$ lies on the cylinder (see Figure 6), then the point $(x, y, 0)$ lies on the directrix of the cylinder in the xy plane, and hence the x and y coordinates of P satisfy the equation $y = f(x)$. Therefore, if $y = f(x)$ is considered as an equation of a graph in three-dimensional space, the graph is a cylinder whose rulings are parallel to the z axis and which has as a directrix the curve $y = f(x)$ in the plane $z = 0$. A similar discussion pertains when the directrix is in either of the other coordinate planes. The results are summarized in the following theorem.

10.6.2 Theorem

In three-dimensional space, the graph of an equation in two of the three variables x, y, and z is a cylinder whose rulings are parallel to the axis associated with the missing variable and whose directrix is a curve in the plane associated with the two variables appearing in the equation.

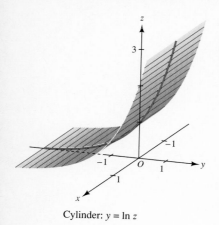

Cylinder: $y = \ln z$

FIGURE 7

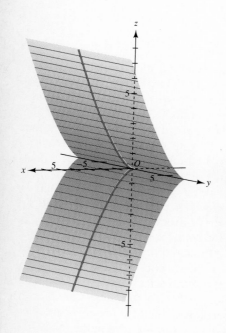

Cylinder: $z^2 = x^3$

FIGURE 8

▷ **ILLUSTRATION 2**   From Theorem 10.6.2, an equation of the right-circular cylinder in Figure 1 is $x^2 + y^2 = 4$, considered as an equation in R^3. Similarly, an equation of the parabolic cylinder of Figure 2 is $y^2 = 8x$, considered as an equation in R^3. The equations of the elliptic cylinder of Figure 3 and the hyperbolic cylinder of Figure 4 are, respectively, $9x^2 + 16y^2 = 144$ and $25x^2 - 4y^2 = 100$ both considered as equations in R^3.   ◀

A **cross section** of a surface in a plane is the set of all points of the surface that lie in the given plane. If a plane is parallel to the plane of the directrix of a cylinder, the cross section of the cylinder is congruent to the directrix. For example, the cross section of the elliptic cylinder of Figure 3 in any plane parallel to the xy plane is an ellipse.

▶ **EXAMPLE 1**   Sketch the graph of each of the following equations:
(a) $y = \ln z$; **(b)** $z^2 = x^3$.

Solution

(a) The graph is a cylinder whose directrix lying in the yz plane is the curve $y = \ln z$ and whose rulings are parallel to the x axis. The graph is sketched in Figure 7.

(b) The graph is a cylinder whose directrix lies in the xz plane and whose rulings are parallel to the y axis. An equation of the directrix is $z^2 = x^3$. Figure 8 shows the graph.

10.6.3 Definition of a Surface of Revolution

If a plane curve is revolved about a fixed line lying in the plane of the curve, the surface generated is called a **surface of revolution.** The fixed line is called the **axis** of the surface of revolution, and the plane curve is called the **generating curve.**

Figure 9 shows a surface of revolution whose generating curve is the curve C in the yz plane and whose axis is the z axis. A sphere is a particular example of a surface of revolution because a sphere can be generated by revolving a semicircle about a diameter. Another example of a surface of revolution is a right-circular cylinder for which the generating curve and the axis are parallel lines.

▷ **ILLUSTRATION 3**   A sphere generated by revolving the semicircle $y^2 + z^2 = r^2$, $z \geq 0$, about the y axis appears in Figure 10. Figure 11 shows the right-circular cylinder for which the generating curve is the line $z = k$ in the xz plane and the axis is the x axis.   ◀

We now find an equation of the surface generated by revolving about the y axis the curve in the yz plane having the two-dimensional equation

$$z = f(y) \tag{1}$$

Refer to Figure 12. Let $P(x, y, z)$ be any point on the surface of revolution. Through P, we pass a plane perpendicular to the y axis, and denote the point

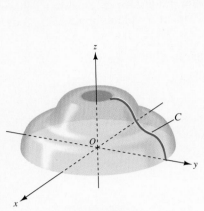

FIGURE 9

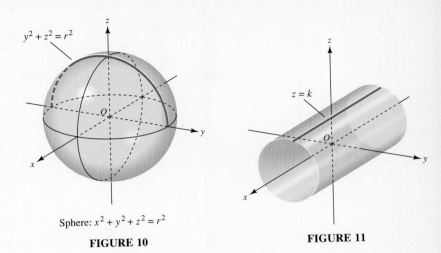

Sphere: $x^2 + y^2 + z^2 = r^2$

FIGURE 10

FIGURE 11

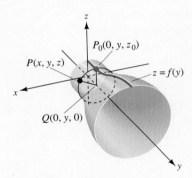

FIGURE 12

of intersection of this plane with the y axis by $Q(0, y, 0)$. We let $P_0(0, y, z_0)$ be the point of intersection of the plane with the generating curve. Because the cross section of the surface with the plane through P is a circle, P is on the surface if and only if

$$|\overline{QP}|^2 = |\overline{QP_0}|^2$$

Because $|\overline{QP}| = \sqrt{x^2 + z^2}$ and $|\overline{QP_0}| = z_0$, we obtain from this equation

$$x^2 + z^2 = z_0^2 \qquad (2)$$

The point P_0 is on the generating curve; so its coordinates must satisfy (1). Therefore

$$z_0 = f(y)$$

From this equation and (2), the point P is on the surface of revolution if and only if

$$x^2 + z^2 = [f(y)]^2 \qquad (3)$$

This is the desired equation of the surface of revolution. Because (3) is equivalent to

$$\pm\sqrt{x^2 + z^2} = f(y)$$

we can obtain (3) by replacing z in (1) by $\pm\sqrt{x^2 + z^2}$.

In a similar manner we can show that if the curve in the yz plane having the two-dimensional equation

$$y = g(z) \qquad (4)$$

is revolved about the z axis, an equation of the surface of revolution generated is obtained by replacing y in (4) by $\pm\sqrt{x^2 + y^2}$. Analogous remarks hold when a curve in any coordinate plane is revolved about either one of the coordinate axes in that plane. In summary, the graphs of the following equations are surfaces of revolution having the indicated axis: $x^2 + y^2 = [F(z)]^2$—z axis; $x^2 + z^2 = [F(y)]^2$—y axis; $y^2 + z^2 = [F(x)]^2$—x axis. In each case, cross sections of the surface in planes perpendicular to the axis are circles having centers on the axis.

▶ **EXAMPLE 2**   Find an equation of the surface of revolution generated by revolving the parabola $y^2 = 4x$ in the xy plane about the x axis. Sketch the surface.

Solution   In the equation of the parabola we replace y by $\pm\sqrt{y^2 + z^2}$ and obtain

$$y^2 + z^2 = 4x$$

The surface is sketched in Figure 13. The same surface is generated if the parabola $z^2 = 4x$ in the xz plane is revolved about the x axis.   ◀

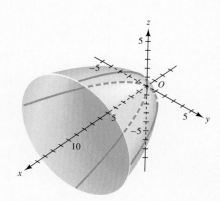

Paraboloid of revolution: $y^2 + z^2 = 4x$

FIGURE 13

The surface in Example 2 is called a **paraboloid of revolution.** If an ellipse is revolved about one of its axes, the surface generated is called an **ellipsoid of revolution.** A **hyperboloid of revolution** is obtained when a hyperbola is revolved about an axis. The surface in the next example is called a **right-circular cone.**

▶ **EXAMPLE 3**   Sketch the surface $x^2 + z^2 - 4y^2 = 0$, $y \geq 0$.

Solution   The given equation is of the form $x^2 + z^2 = [F(y)]^2$; so its graph is a surface of revolution having the y axis as axis. Solving the given equation for y, we obtain

$$2y = \pm\sqrt{x^2 + z^2}$$

Hence the generating curve can be either the line $2y = x$ in the xy plane or the line $2y = z$ in the yz plane. By sketching the two possible generating curves and using the fact that cross sections of the surface in planes perpendicular to the y axis are circles having centers on the y axis, we obtain the surface shown in Figure 14. Note that because $y \geq 0$, the cone has only one nappe.   ◀

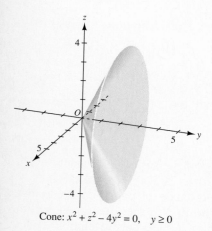

Cone: $x^2 + z^2 - 4y^2 = 0$, $y \geq 0$

FIGURE 14

You may have learned in a precalculus course (otherwise see Appendix Section A.10) that the graph of a second-degree equation in two variables x and y,

$$Ax^2 + Bxy + Cy^2 + Dx + Ey + F = 0$$

is a conic section. The graph of a second-degree equation in three variables x, y, and z,

$$Ax^2 + By^2 + Cz^2 + Dxy + Exz + Fyz + Gx + Hy + Iz + J = 0 \qquad \textbf{(5)}$$

is called a **quadric surface.** The simplest types of quadric surfaces are the parabolic, elliptic, and hyperbolic cylinders that we have already discussed. We now consider six other types of quadric surfaces. In the discussion of each of these surfaces, we choose the coordinate axes so that the equations are in simplest form and we refer to the cross sections of the surfaces in planes parallel to the coordinate planes. These cross sections help to visualize the surface.

The ellipsoid

$$\frac{x^2}{a^2} + \frac{y^2}{b^2} + \frac{z^2}{c^2} = 1 \qquad\qquad \textbf{(6)}$$

where a, b, and c are positive. See Figure 15.

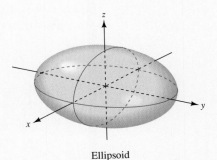

Ellipsoid

FIGURE 15

If in (6) z is replaced by zero, we obtain the cross section of the ellipsoid in the xy plane, which is the ellipse

$$\frac{x^2}{a^2} + \frac{y^2}{b^2} = 1$$

To obtain the cross sections of the surface with the planes $z = k$, we replace z by k in the equation of the ellipsoid and get

$$\frac{x^2}{a^2} + \frac{y^2}{b^2} = 1 - \frac{k^2}{c^2}$$

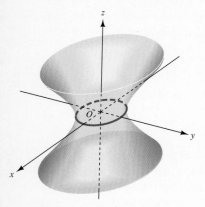

Elliptic hyperboloid of one sheet

FIGURE 16

If $|k| < c$, the cross section is an ellipse and the lengths of the semiaxes decrease to zero as $|k|$ increases to the value c. If $|k| = c$, the intersection of a plane $z = k$ with the ellipsoid is the single point $(0, 0, k)$. If $|k| > c$, there is no intersection. The discussion is similar if we consider cross sections formed by planes parallel to either of the other coordinate planes.

The numbers a, b, and c are the lengths of the semiaxes of the ellipsoid. If any two of these three numbers are equal, we have an ellipsoid of revolution, also called a **spheroid**. A spheroid for which the third number is greater than the two equal numbers is said to be **prolate**. A prolate spheroid is shaped like a football. An **oblate** spheroid is obtained if the third number is less than the two equal numbers. If all three numbers, a, b, and c in the equation of an ellipsoid are equal, the ellipsoid is a **sphere**.

The elliptic hyperboloid of one sheet

$$\frac{x^2}{a^2} + \frac{y^2}{b^2} - \frac{z^2}{c^2} = 1 \qquad (7)$$

where a, b, and c are positive. See Figure 16.

The cross sections in the planes $z = k$ are the ellipses

$$\frac{x^2}{a^2} + \frac{y^2}{b^2} = 1 + \frac{k^2}{c^2}$$

When $k = 0$, the lengths of the semiaxes of the ellipse are smallest, and these lengths increase as $|k|$ increases. The cross sections in the planes $x = k$ are the hyperbolas

$$\frac{y^2}{b^2} - \frac{z^2}{c^2} = 1 - \frac{k^2}{a^2}$$

If $|k| < a$, the transverse axis of the hyperbola is parallel to the y axis, and if $|k| > a$, the transverse axis is parallel to the z axis. If $k = a$, the hyperbola degenerates into two lines:

$$\frac{y}{b} - \frac{z}{c} = 0 \quad \text{and} \quad \frac{y}{b} + \frac{z}{c} = 0$$

In an analogous manner, the cross sections in the planes $y = k$ are also hyperbolas. The axis of this hyperboloid is the z axis.

If $a = b$, the surface is a hyperboloid of revolution for which the axis is the line containing the conjugate axis.

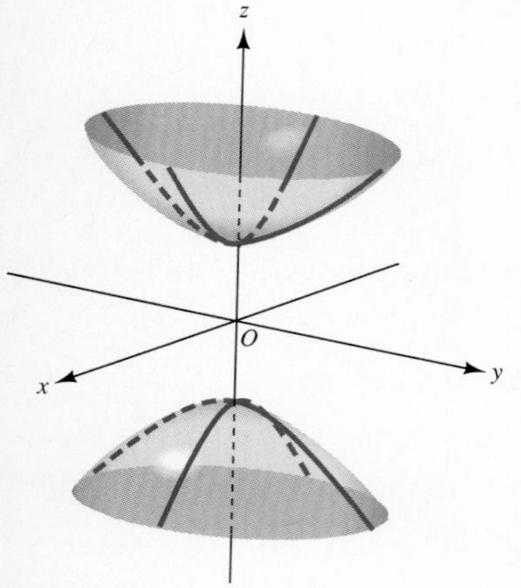

The elliptic hyperboloid of two sheets

$$-\frac{x^2}{a^2} - \frac{y^2}{b^2} + \frac{z^2}{c^2} = 1 \qquad (8)$$

where a, b, and c are positive. See Figure 17.

Replacing z by k in (8) we obtain

$$\frac{x^2}{a^2} + \frac{y^2}{b^2} = \frac{k^2}{c^2} - 1$$

Elliptic hyperboloid of two sheets

FIGURE 17

If $|k| < c$, the plane $z = k$ does not intersect the surface; hence there are no points of the surface between the planes $z = -c$ and $z = c$. If $|k| = c$, the intersection of the plane $z = k$ with the surface is the single point $(0, 0, k)$. When $|k| > c$, the cross section of the surface in the plane $z = k$ is an ellipse, and the lengths of the semiaxes of the ellipse increase as $|k|$ increases.

The cross sections of the surface in the planes $x = k$ are the hyperbolas

$$\frac{z^2}{c^2} - \frac{y^2}{b^2} = 1 + \frac{k^2}{a^2}$$

whose transverse axes are parallel to the z axis. In a similar fashion, the cross sections in the planes $y = k$ are the hyperbolas

$$\frac{z^2}{c^2} - \frac{x^2}{a^2} = 1 + \frac{k^2}{b^2}$$

for which the transverse axes are also parallel to the z axis.

If $a = b$, the surface is a hyperboloid of revolution in which the axis is the line containing the transverse axis of the hyperbola.

Each of the above three quadric surfaces is symmetric with respect to each of the coordinate planes and symmetric with respect to the origin. Their graphs are called **central quadrics** and their center is at the origin. The graph of any equation of the form

$$\pm \frac{x^2}{a^2} \pm \frac{y^2}{b^2} \pm \frac{z^2}{c^2} = 1$$

where a, b, and c are positive, is a central quadric.

▶ **EXAMPLE 4**   Sketch the graph of the equation

$$4x^2 - y^2 + 25z^2 = 100$$

and name the surface.

Solution   We divide both sides of the equation by 100 and obtain

$$\frac{x^2}{25} - \frac{y^2}{100} + \frac{z^2}{4} = 1$$

which is of the form of (7) with y and z interchanged. Hence the surface is an elliptic hyperboloid of one sheet whose axis is the y axis. The cross sections in the planes $y = k$ are the ellipses

$$\frac{x^2}{25} + \frac{z^2}{4} = 1 + \frac{k^2}{100}$$

The cross sections in the planes $x = k$ are the hyperbolas

$$\frac{z^2}{4} - \frac{y^2}{100} = 1 - \frac{k^2}{25}$$

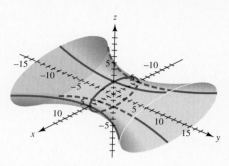

Elliptic hyperboloid of one sheet

$$\frac{x^2}{25} - \frac{y^2}{100} + \frac{z^2}{4} = 1$$

FIGURE 18

and the cross sections in the planes $z = k$ are the hyperbolas

$$\frac{x^2}{25} - \frac{y^2}{100} = 1 - \frac{k^2}{4}$$

The surface is sketched in Figure 18.   ◄

▶ **EXAMPLE 5**   Sketch the graph of the equation

$$4x^2 - 25y^2 - z^2 = 100$$

and name the surface.

Solution   By dividing on both sides by 100 we can write the given equation as

$$\frac{x^2}{25} - \frac{y^2}{4} - \frac{z^2}{100} = 1$$

which is of the form of (8) with x and z interchanged; thus the surface is an elliptic hyperboloid of two sheets whose axis is the x axis. The cross sections in the planes $x = k$, where $|k| > 5$, are the ellipses

$$\frac{y^2}{4} + \frac{z^2}{100} = \frac{k^2}{25} - 1$$

The planes $x = k$, where $|k| < 5$, do not intersect the surface. The cross sections in the planes $y = k$ are the hyperbolas

$$\frac{x^2}{25} - \frac{z^2}{100} = 1 + \frac{k^2}{4}$$

and the cross sections in the planes $z = k$ are the hyperbolas

$$\frac{x^2}{25} - \frac{y^2}{4} = 1 + \frac{k^2}{100}$$

The required surface appears in Figure 19.   ◄

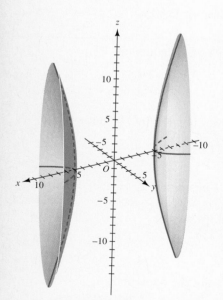

Elliptic hyperboloid of two sheets

$$\frac{x^2}{25} - \frac{y^2}{4} - \frac{z^2}{100} = 1$$

FIGURE 19

The next two surfaces are called noncentral quadrics.

The elliptic paraboloid

$$\frac{x^2}{a^2} + \frac{y^2}{b^2} = \frac{z}{c} \tag{9}$$

where a and b are positive and $c \neq 0$. Figure 20 shows the surface if $c > 0$.

Substituting k for z in (9) we obtain

$$\frac{x^2}{a^2} + \frac{y^2}{b^2} = \frac{k}{c}$$

When $k = 0$, this equation becomes $b^2x^2 + a^2y^2 = 0$, which represents a single point, the origin. If $k \neq 0$ and k and c have the same sign, the equation is that of an ellipse. So we conclude that cross sections of the surface in the planes $z = k$, where k and c have the same sign, are ellipses and the lengths of the semiaxes increase as $|k|$ increases. If k and c have opposite signs, the planes $z = k$ do not intersect the surface. The cross sections of the surface with the planes $x = k$ and $y = k$ are parabolas. When $c > 0$, the parabolas open upward, as shown in Figure 20; when $c < 0$, the parabolas open downward.

If $a = b$, the surface is a paraboloid of revolution.

The hyperbolic paraboloid

$$\frac{y^2}{b^2} - \frac{x^2}{a^2} = \frac{z}{c} \tag{10}$$

where a and b are positive and $c \neq 0$. The surface appears in Figure 21 for $c > 0$.

The cross sections of the surface in the planes $z = k$, where $k \neq 0$, are hyperbolas having their transverse axes parallel to the y axis if k and c have the same sign and parallel to the x axis if k and c have opposite signs. The cross section of the surface in the plane $z = 0$ consists of two straight lines

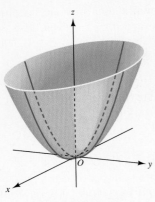

Elliptic paraboloid

FIGURE 20

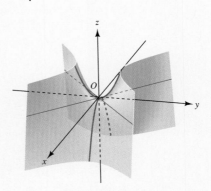

Hyperbolic paraboloid

FIGURE 21

through the origin. The cross sections in the planes $x = k$ are parabolas opening upward if $c > 0$ and opening downward if $c < 0$. The cross sections in the planes $y = k$ are parabolas opening downward if $c > 0$ and opening upward if $c < 0$.

▶ **EXAMPLE 6**   Sketch the graph of the equation

$$3y^2 + 12z^2 = 16x$$

and name the surface.

Solution   The given equation can be written as

$$\frac{y^2}{16} + \frac{z^2}{4} = \frac{x}{3}$$

which is of the form of (9) with x and z interchanged. Hence the graph of the equation is an elliptic paraboloid whose axis is the x axis. The cross sections in the planes $x = k$, where $k > 0$, are the ellipses

$$\frac{y^2}{16} + \frac{z^2}{4} = \frac{k}{3}$$

The planes $x = k$, where $k < 0$, do not intersect the surface. The cross sections in the planes $y = k$ are the parabolas $12z^2 = 16x - 3k^2$, and the cross sections in the planes $z = k$ are the parabolas $3y^2 = 16x - 12k^2$. Figure 22 shows the elliptic paraboloid.   ◀

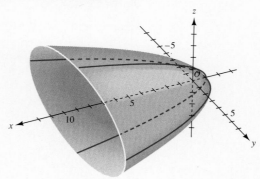

Elliptic paraboloid
$$\frac{y^2}{16} + \frac{z^2}{4} = \frac{x}{3}$$

FIGURE 22

▶ **EXAMPLE 7**   Sketch the graph of the equation

$$3y^2 - 12z^2 = 16x$$

and name the surface.

Solution   The given equation written as

$$\frac{y^2}{16} - \frac{z^2}{4} = \frac{x}{3}$$

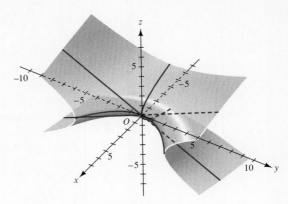

Hyperbolic paraboloid

$$\frac{y^2}{16} - \frac{z^2}{4} = \frac{x}{3}$$

FIGURE 23

is of the form of (10) with x and z interchanged. The surface is therefore a hyperbolic paraboloid. The cross sections in the planes $x = k$, where $k \neq 0$, are the hyperbolas

$$\frac{y^2}{16} - \frac{z^2}{4} = \frac{k}{3}$$

The cross section in the yz plane consists of the two lines $y = 2z$ and $y = -2z$. In the planes $z = k$ the cross sections are the parabolas $3y^2 = 16x + 12k^2$; in the planes $y = k$ the cross sections are the parabolas $12z^2 = 3k^2 - 16x$. The hyperbolic paraboloid appears in Figure 23. ◀

The elliptic cone

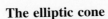

$$\frac{x^2}{a^2} + \frac{y^2}{b^2} - \frac{z^2}{c^2} = 0 \qquad (11)$$

where a, b, and c are positive. See Figure 24.

The intersection of the plane $z = 0$ with the surface is a point, the origin. The cross sections of the surface in the planes $z = k$, where $k \neq 0$, are ellipses, and the lengths of the semiaxes increase as k increases. Cross sections in the planes $x = 0$ and $y = 0$ are pairs of intersecting lines. In the planes $x = k$ and $y = k$, where $k \neq 0$, cross sections are hyperbolas.

Elliptic cone

FIGURE 24

▶ **EXAMPLE 8**   Sketch the graph of the equation

$$4x^2 - y^2 + 25z^2 = 0$$

and name the surface.

Solution   We can write the given equation as

$$\frac{x^2}{25} - \frac{y^2}{100} + \frac{z^2}{4} = 0$$

which is of the form of (11) with y and z interchanged. Therefore the surface is an elliptic cone having the y axis as its axis. The surface intersects the plane $y = 0$ at the origin only. The intersection of the surface with the plane $x = 0$ is the pair of intersecting lines $y = \pm 5z$, and the intersection with the plane $z = 0$ is the pair of intersecting lines $y = \pm 2x$. The cross sections in the planes $y = k$, where $k \neq 0$, are the ellipses

$$\frac{x^2}{25} + \frac{z^2}{4} = \frac{k^2}{100}$$

In the planes $x = k$ and $z = k$, where $k \neq 0$, the cross sections are, respectively, the hyperbolas

$$\frac{y^2}{100} - \frac{z^2}{4} = \frac{k^2}{25} \quad \text{and} \quad \frac{y^2}{100} - \frac{x^2}{25} = \frac{k^2}{4}$$

The surface is sketched in Figure 25.   ◀

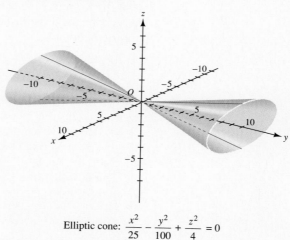

Elliptic cone: $\dfrac{x^2}{25} - \dfrac{y^2}{100} + \dfrac{z^2}{4} = 0$

FIGURE 25

Table 1 summarizes our discussion of the six basic types of quadric surfaces. Two graphs appear in the table for each surface. One graph was sketched, and the other was plotted by a computer program used to generate surfaces. Many computer-generated plots, usually involving numerous numerical computations, are available. The programs are called **computer graphics,** discussed in more detail in Section 12.1 where we demonstrate the diverse and intricate surfaces that can be plotted.

Equation (5) is the general equation of the second degree in x, y, and z. It can be shown that by translation and rotation of the three-dimensional coordinate axes (the study of which is beyond the scope of this book) this equation can be reduced to one of the following two forms:

$$Ax^2 + By^2 + Cz^2 + J = 0 \qquad \qquad \textbf{(12)}$$
$$Ax^2 + By^2 + Iz = 0 \qquad \qquad \textbf{(13)}$$

Quadric Surface	Traces in Indicated Plane	Sketch	Plotted by Mathematica
Ellipsoid $$\frac{x^2}{a^2} + \frac{y^2}{b^2} + \frac{z^2}{c^2} = 1$$	xy plane: Ellipse $z = \lvert k \rvert < c$: Ellipse yz plane: Ellipse $x = \lvert k \rvert < c$: Ellipse xz plane: Ellipse $y = \lvert k \rvert < c$: Ellipse		
Elliptic Hyperboloid of One Sheet $$\frac{x^2}{a^2} + \frac{y^2}{b^2} - \frac{z^2}{c^2} = 1$$	xy plane: Ellipse $z = k$: Ellipse yz plane: Hyperbola $x = k$: Hyperbola xz plane: Hyperbola $y = k$: Hyperbola		
Elliptic Hyperboloid of Two Sheets $$\frac{z^2}{c^2} - \frac{x^2}{a^2} - \frac{y^2}{b^2} = 1$$	xy plane: None $z = \lvert k \rvert < c$: None $z = \lvert k \rvert > c$: Ellipse yz plane: Hyperbola $x = k$: Hyperbola xz plane: Hyperbola $y = k$: Hyperbola		
Elliptic Paraboloid $$\frac{x^2}{a^2} + \frac{y^2}{b^2} = \frac{z}{c}$$ $$c > 0$$	xy plane: Point (origin) $z = k > 0$: Ellipse $z = k < 0$: None yz plane: Parabola $x = k$: Parabola xz plane: Parabola $y = k$: Parabola		
Hyperbolic Paraboloid $$\frac{y^2}{b^2} - \frac{x^2}{a^2} = \frac{z}{c}$$ $$c > 0$$	xy plane: Two intersecting lines (at origin) $z = k \neq 0$: Hyperbola yz plane: Parabola $x = k$: Parabola xz plane: Parabola $y = k$: Parabola		
Elliptic Cone $$\frac{x^2}{a^2} + \frac{y^2}{b^2} - \frac{z^2}{c^2} = 0$$	xy plane: Point (origin) $z = k \neq 0$: Ellipse yz plane: Two intersecting lines (at origin) $x = k \neq 0$: Hyperbola xz plane: Two intersecting lines (at origin) $y = k \neq 0$: Hyperbola		

Table 1

Graphs of the equations of the second degree will either be one of the above six types of quadrics or else will degenerate into a cylinder, plane, line, point, or the empty set.

The nondegenerate surfaces associated with equations of the form (12) are the central quadrics and the elliptic cone, whereas those associated with equations of the form (13) are the noncentral quadrics. Following are examples of some degenerate cases:

$$x^2 - y^2 = 0; \text{ two planes, } x - y = 0 \text{ and } x + y = 0$$
$$z^2 = 0; \text{ one plane, the } xy \text{ plane}$$
$$x^2 + y^2 = 0; \text{ one line, the } z \text{ axis}$$
$$x^2 + y^2 + z^2 = 0; \text{ a point, the origin}$$
$$x^2 + y^2 + z^2 + 1 = 0; \text{ the empty set}$$

EXERCISES 10.6

In Exercises 1 through 4, sketch the cross section of the given cylinder in the indicated plane.

1. $4x^2 + y^2 = 16$; xy plane

2. $4z^2 - y^2 = 4$; yz plane

3. $z = e^x$; xz plane　　**4.** $x = |y|$; xy plane

In Exercises 5 through 12, sketch the cylinder having the given equation.

5. $4x^2 + 9y^2 = 36$　　　　**6.** $z = \sin y$

7. $y = |z|$　　　　　　　　**8.** $x^2 - z^2 = 4$

9. $z = 2x^2$　　　　　　　**10.** $z^2 = 4y^2$

11. $y = \cosh x$　　　　　**12.** $x^2 = y^3$

In Exercises 13 through 20, find an equation of the surface of revolution generated by revolving the plane curve about the indicated axis. Sketch the surface.

13. $x^2 = 4y$ in the xy plane, about the y axis

14. $x^2 + 4z^2 = 16$ in the xz plane, about the z axis

15. $x^2 + 4z^2 = 16$ in the xz plane, about the x axis

16. $x^2 = 4y$ in the xy plane, about the x axis

17. $y = 3z$ in the yz plane, about the y axis

18. $9y^2 - 4z^2 = 144$ in the yz plane, about the z axis

19. $y = \sin x$ in the xy plane, about the x axis

20. $y^2 = z^3$ in the yz plane, about the z axis

In Exercises 21 through 28, find a generating curve and the axis for the surface of revolution. Sketch the surface.

21. $x^2 + y^2 + z^2 = 16$　　**22.** $x^2 + z^2 = y$

23. $x^2 + y^2 - z^2 = 4$　　**24.** $y^2 + z^2 = e^{2x}$

25. $x^2 + z^2 = |y|$

26. $4x^2 + 9y^2 + 4z^2 = 36$

27. $9x^2 - y^2 + 9z^2 = 0$　　**28.** $4x^2 + 4y^2 - z = 9$

29. In (a)–(f), match the equation with one of the computer-generated surfaces (i)–(vi) and name the surface.

(a) $9x^2 - 4y^2 + 36z^2 = 36$

(b) $5x^2 - 2z^2 = 3y$

(c) $9x^2 - 4y^2 + 36z^2 = 0$

(d) $5x^2 + 2z^2 = 3y$

(e) $9x^2 + 4y^2 + 36z^2 = 36$

(f) $9x^2 - 4y^2 - 36z^2 = 36$

(i)

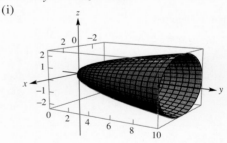

(ii)

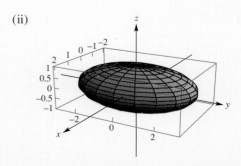

(iii)

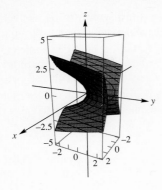

(iv)

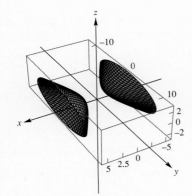

(v)

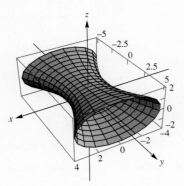

(vi)

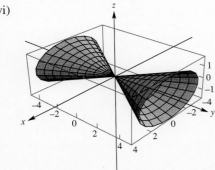

30. In (a)–(f), match the equation with one of the computer-generated surfaces (i)-(vi) and name the surface.

(a) $4x^2 - 16y^2 + 9z^2 = 0$

(b) $3y^2 + 7z^2 = 6x$

(c) $25x^2 = 4y^2 + z^2 + 100$

(d) $3y^2 - 7z^2 = 6x$

(e) $25x^2 = 4y^2 - z^2 + 100$

(f) $25x^2 = 100 - 4y^2 - z^2$

(i)

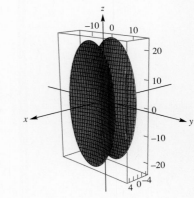

(ii)

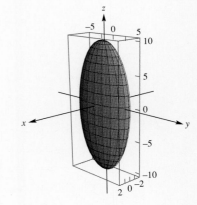

(iii)

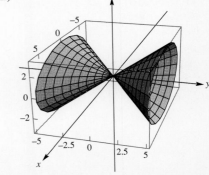

(iv)

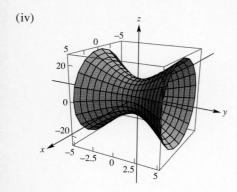

(v)

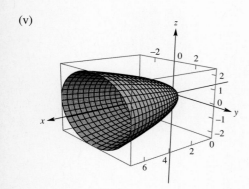

(vi)

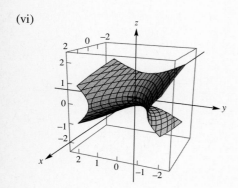

In Exercises 31 through 42, sketch the graph of the equation and name the surface.

31. $4x^2 + 9y^2 + z^2 = 36$ **32.** $4x^2 - 9y^2 - z^2 = 36$

33. $4x^2 + 9y^2 - z^2 = 36$ **34.** $4x^2 - 9y^2 + z^2 = 36$

35. $x^2 = y^2 - z^2$ **36.** $x^2 = y^2 + z^2$

37. $\dfrac{x^2}{36} + \dfrac{z^2}{25} = 4y$ **38.** $\dfrac{y^2}{25} + \dfrac{x^2}{36} = 4z$

39. $\dfrac{x^2}{36} - \dfrac{z^2}{25} = 9y$ **40.** $x^2 = 2y + 4z$

41. $x^2 + 16z^2 = 4y^2 - 16$ **42.** $9y^2 - 4z^2 + 18x = 0$

43. Find the values of k for which the intersection of the plane $x + ky = 1$ and the elliptic hyperboloid of two sheets $y^2 - x^2 - z^2 = 1$ is **(a)** an ellipse and **(b)** a hyperbola.

44. Find the vertex and focus of the parabola that is the intersection of the plane $y = 2$ with the hyperbolic paraboloid $\dfrac{y^2}{16} - \dfrac{x^2}{4} = \dfrac{z}{9}$.

45. Find the vertex and focus of the parabola that is the intersection of the plane $x = 1$ with the hyperbolic paraboloid $\dfrac{z^2}{4} - \dfrac{x^2}{9} = \dfrac{y}{3}$.

46. Find the area of the plane section formed by the intersection of the plane $y = 3$ with the solid bounded by the ellipsoid $\dfrac{x^2}{9} + \dfrac{y^2}{25} + \dfrac{z^2}{4} = 1$.

47. Show that the intersection of the surface $x^2 - 4y^2 - 9z^2 = 36$ and the plane $x + z = 9$ is a circle.

48. Show that the intersection of the hyperbolic paraboloid $\dfrac{y^2}{b^2} - \dfrac{x^2}{a^2} = \dfrac{z}{c}$ and the plane $z = bx + ay$ consists of two intersecting lines.

In Exercises 49 through 51, use the method of slicing to find the volume of the solid. The measure of the area of the region enclosed by the ellipse having semiaxes a and b is πab.

49. The solid bounded by the ellipsoid $36x^2 + 9y^2 + 4z^2 = 36$.

50. The solid bounded by the ellipsoid $\dfrac{x^2}{a^2} + \dfrac{y^2}{b^2} + \dfrac{z^2}{c^2} = 1$.

51. The solid bounded by the plane $z = h$, where $h > 0$, and the elliptic paraboloid $\dfrac{x^2}{a^2} + \dfrac{y^2}{b^2} = \dfrac{z}{c}$, where $c > 0$.

52. Sketch the surface of revolution generated by revolving the tractrix
$$x = 3 \ln\left(\frac{3 + \sqrt{9 - y^2}}{y}\right) - \sqrt{9 - y^2}$$
about the x axis.

53. Describe how you would sketch the cylindrical surface generated by revolving the curve $x = f(y)$ in the xy plane about the y axis. In your description make up an example of a particular curve $x = f(y)$ and include the equation of the cylindrical surface obtained.

CHAPTER 10 REVIEW

▶ *SUGGESTIONS FOR REVIEW OF CHAPTER 10*

1. Define a vector **(i)** in the plane and **(ii)** in three-dimensional space.

2. How are vectors represented geometrically? How do you determine when two representations are for the same vector?

3. How do you find the magnitude and direction of a vector in **(i)** V_2 and **(ii)** V_3? Make up examples.

4. How do you find the sum and difference of two vectors in **(i)** V_2 and **(ii)** V_3? Make up examples.

5. Interpret the sum and difference of two vectors geometrically.

6. Define the product of a scalar c and a vector **A** in **(i)** V_2 and **(ii)** V_3. Make up examples.

7. What is the relationship between c**A** and **A** if **(i)** $c > 0$ and **(ii)** $c < 0$? Make up examples.

8. What algebraic laws are satisfied by the operations of vector addition and scalar multiplication of any vectors in V_2 and V_3?

9. How do you express any vector **(i)** in V_2 in terms of the unit vectors **i** and **j** and **(ii)** in V_3 in terms of the unit vectors **i**, **j**, and **k**? Make up examples.

10. Why do **i** and **j** form a basis for the vector space V_2 and **i**, **j**, and **k** for the vector space V_3?

11. How do you express a vector **(i)** in V_2 in terms of its magnitude and direction angle and **(ii)** in V_3 in terms of its magnitude and direction cosines? Make up examples.

12. Write an equation giving the relationship satisfied by the direction cosines of any vector in V_3.

13. What is the formula for the undirected distance between two points in R^3? Make up an example.

14. What are the formulas for the coordinates of the midpoint of the line segment between two points in R^3? Make up an example.

15. Define a sphere. What is the center-radius form of an equation of the sphere of radius r and center at (h, k, l)? What is the general form? Make up an example.

16. Define the dot product of two vectors **(i)** in V_2 and **(ii)** in V_3. Make up examples.

17. Which algebraic laws are satisfied by the dot product of two vectors?

18. Define an angle between two vectors.

19. How is the dot product used to find the angle between two vectors? Make up an example.

20. How is the dot product used to determine if two vectors are orthogonal? Make up an example.

21. Define the scalar projection of one vector onto another. What is the formula for determining the scalar projection of the vector **B** onto the vector **A**? Make up an example.

22. What is the formula for determining the vector projection of the vector **B** onto the vector **A**? Make up an example.

23. Make up an example showing how vectors can be used to find the distance from a point P to a line through points A and B in R^3.

24. Make up an example showing how to find the work done by a force **F** in moving an object from point A to point B if the direction of **F** is not along the line of motion from A to B.

25. Define the plane through the point $P_0(x_0, y_0, z_0)$ and having **N** as a normal vector. Write an equation of this plane if **N** is $\langle a, b, c \rangle$. Make up an example.

26. Define an angle between two planes. Make up an example.

27. Make up an example of **(i)** two parallel planes and **(ii)** two perpendicular planes.

28. Make up an example showing how vectors can be used to find the distance from a point to a plane.

29. Write parametric equations of the line through the point $P_0(x_0, y_0, z_0)$ and parallel to representations of the vector $\langle a, b, c \rangle$. Write symmetric equations of this line.

30. Make up an example showing how to find symmetric equations of a line through two points in R^3.

31. Define the cross product of two vectors. Write the symbolic determinant notation used as a mnemonic device to remember the cross-product formula. Make up an example.

32. Which algebraic laws are satisfied by the cross product of two vectors, and which are not?

33. Write three cross products involving the vector **A** which yield the zero vector.

34. What is the triple scalar product of the three vectors **A**, **B**, and **C**? Make up an example.

35. What is the triple vector product of the three vectors **A**, **B**, and **C**? Make up an example.

36. Write the formula expressing $\|\mathbf{A} \times \mathbf{B}\|$ in terms of $\|\mathbf{A}\|$, $\|\mathbf{B}\|$, and the angle between **A** and **B**.

37. Give the geometric interpretation of $\|\mathbf{A} \times \mathbf{B}\|$. Make up an example.

38. How can the cross product be used to determine if two vectors are parallel? Make up an example.

39. Make up an example showing how the cross product can be used to find an equation of the plane through three points in R^3.

40. What is the geometric interpretation of the triple scalar product? Make up an example.

41. Define a cylinder.

42. Make up an example of an equation of a cylinder whose rulings are parallel to **(i)** the x axis, **(ii)** the y axis, and **(iii)** the z axis. Sketch the surface.

43. Make up an example of an equation of a surface of revolution whose generating curve is in the xy plane and whose axis is **(i)** the x axis and **(ii)** the y axis. Sketch the surface.

44. Make up an example of an equation of an ellipsoid and sketch the surface.

45. Make up an example of an equation of an elliptic hyperboloid of one sheet and sketch the surface.

46. Make up an example of an equation of an elliptic hyperboloid of two sheets and sketch the surface.

47. Make up an example of an equation of an elliptic paraboloid and sketch the surface.

48. Make up an example of an equation of a hyperbolic paraboloid and sketch the surface.

49. Make up an example of an equation of an elliptic cone and sketch the surface.

▶ **MISCELLANEOUS EXERCISES FOR CHAPTER 10**

In Exercises 1 through 18, $\mathbf{A} = 4\mathbf{i} - 6\mathbf{j}$, $\mathbf{B} = \mathbf{i} + 7\mathbf{j}$, *and* $\mathbf{C} = 9\mathbf{i} - 5\mathbf{j}$.

1. Find $3\mathbf{B} - 7\mathbf{A}$.
2. Find $5\mathbf{B} - 3\mathbf{C}$.
3. Find $\| 3\mathbf{B} - 7\mathbf{A} \|$.
4. Find $\| 5\mathbf{B} - 3\mathbf{C} \|$.
5. Find $\| 3\mathbf{B} \| - \| 7\mathbf{A} \|$.
6. Find $\| 5\mathbf{B} \| - \| 3\mathbf{C} \|$.
7. Find $(\mathbf{A} - \mathbf{B}) \cdot \mathbf{C}$.
8. Find $(\mathbf{A} \cdot \mathbf{B})\mathbf{C}$.
9. Find a unit vector having the same direction as $2\mathbf{A} + \mathbf{B}$.
10. Find the unit vectors orthogonal to $\mathbf{B}$.
11. Find scalars h and k such that $\mathbf{A} = h\mathbf{B} + k\mathbf{C}$.
12. Find scalars h and k such that $h\mathbf{A} + k\mathbf{B} = -\mathbf{C}$.
13. Find the scalar projection of $\mathbf{A}$ onto $\mathbf{B}$.
14. Find the scalar projection of $\mathbf{C}$ onto $\mathbf{A}$.
15. Find the vector projection of $\mathbf{A}$ onto $\mathbf{B}$.
16. Find the vector projection of $\mathbf{C}$ onto $\mathbf{A}$.
17. Find the component of $\mathbf{B}$ in the direction of $\mathbf{A}$.
18. Find $\cos \alpha$ if α is the angle between $\mathbf{A}$ and $\mathbf{C}$.

In Exercises 19 and 20, $\mathbf{A} = -2\mathbf{i} + 5\mathbf{j}$ *and* $\mathbf{B} = h\mathbf{i} - 2\mathbf{j}$.

19. Determine h so that the angle between $\mathbf{A}$ and $\mathbf{B}$ is $\frac{2}{3}\pi$.

20. Show that no h exists such that the angle between $\mathbf{A}$ and $\mathbf{B}$ is $\frac{1}{3}\pi$.

In Exercises 21 through 30, $\mathbf{A} = -\mathbf{i} + 3\mathbf{j} + 2\mathbf{k}$, $\mathbf{B} = 2\mathbf{i} + \mathbf{j} - 4\mathbf{k}$, $\mathbf{C} = \mathbf{i} + 2\mathbf{j} - 2\mathbf{k}$, $\mathbf{D} = 3\mathbf{j} - \mathbf{k}$, *and* $\mathbf{E} = 5\mathbf{i} - 2\mathbf{j}$.

21. Find $6\mathbf{C} + 4\mathbf{D} - \mathbf{E}$.
22. Find $3\mathbf{A} - 2\mathbf{B} + \mathbf{C}$.
23. Find $\mathbf{D} \cdot \mathbf{B} \times \mathbf{C}$.
24. Find $(\mathbf{A} \times \mathbf{C}) - (\mathbf{D} \times \mathbf{E})$.
25. Find $\| \mathbf{A} \times \mathbf{B} \| \| \mathbf{D} \times \mathbf{E} \|$.
26. Find $2\mathbf{B} \cdot \mathbf{C} + 3\mathbf{D} \cdot \mathbf{E}$.
27. Find the scalar projection of $\mathbf{A}$ onto $\mathbf{B}$.
28. Find the scalar projection of $\mathbf{C}$ onto $\mathbf{D}$.
29. Find the vector projection of $\mathbf{E}$ onto $\mathbf{C}$.
30. Find the vector projection of $\mathbf{D}$ onto $\mathbf{E}$.

In Exercises 31 through 36, there is only one way that a meaningful expression can be obtained by inserting parentheses. Insert the parentheses and find the indicated vector or scalar if $\mathbf{A} = \langle 3, -2, 4 \rangle$, $\mathbf{B} = \langle -5, 7, 2 \rangle$, *and* $\mathbf{C} = \langle 4, 6, -1 \rangle$.

31. $\mathbf{A}\mathbf{B} \cdot \mathbf{C}$
32. $\mathbf{A} \cdot \mathbf{B}\mathbf{C}$
33. $\mathbf{A} + \mathbf{B} \cdot \mathbf{C}$
34. $\mathbf{B} \cdot \mathbf{A} - \mathbf{C}$
35. $\mathbf{A} \times \mathbf{B} \cdot \mathbf{A} + \mathbf{B} - \mathbf{C}$
36. $\mathbf{A} \times \mathbf{B} \cdot \mathbf{C} \times \mathbf{A}$

37. Sketch the graph of $x = 3$ in R, R^2, and R^3.

38. Sketch the set of points satisfying the simultaneous equations $x = 6$ and $y = 3$ in R^2 and R^3.

In Exercises 39 through 48, describe in words the set of points in R^3 *satisfying the equation or the pair of equations. Sketch the graph.*

39. $\begin{cases} y = 0 \\ z = 0 \end{cases}$
40. $\begin{cases} x = z \\ y = z \end{cases}$
41. $\begin{cases} x^2 + z^2 = 4 \\ y = 0 \end{cases}$
42. $y^2 - z^2 = 0$
43. $x = y$
44. $x^2 + y^2 + z^2 = 25$
45. $x^2 + y^2 = 9z$
46. $x^2 + y^2 = z^2$
47. $x^2 - y^2 = z^2$
48. $x^2 + z^2 = 4$

49. Two forces of magnitudes 50 lb and 70 lb make an angle of 60° with each other and are applied to an object at the same point. Find **(a)** the magnitude of the resultant force and **(b)** to the nearest degree the angle it makes with the force of 50 lb.

50. Determine the angle between two forces of 112 lb and 136 lb applied to an object at the same point if the resultant force has a magnitude of 168 lb.

51. A force is represented by a vector $\mathbf{F}$ having a magnitude of 30 lb and a direction angle of radian measure $\frac{3}{4}\pi$. If distance is measured in feet find the work done by the force in moving a particle along a line from the point $(3, 6)$ to the point $(-2, 7)$.

52. The compass heading of an airplane is 107°and its air speed is 210 mi/hr. If a wind is blowing from the west at 36 mi/hr, what are **(a)** the plane's ground speed and **(b)** its course?

53. A line is drawn through the point $(-3, 5, 1)$ perpendicular to the xz plane. Find the coordinates of the points on this line at a distance of 13 units from $(-2, 0, 0)$.

54. Find an equation of the sphere having as a diameter the line segment with endpoints $(3, 5, -4)$ and $(-1, 7, 4)$.

55. Find an equation of the sphere concentric with the sphere $x^2 + y^2 + z^2 + 4x + 2y - 6z + 10 = 0$ and containing the point $(-4, 2, 5)$.

56. Prove that the points $(4, 1, -1)$ $(2, 0, 1)$, and $(4, 3, 0)$ are the vertices of a right triangle, and find the area of the triangle.

57. Find a generating curve and the axis for the surface of revolution having the equation $x^2 + z^2 = e^{4y}$.

58. Find an equation of the surface of revolution generated by revolving the ellipse $9x^2 + 4z^2 = 36$ in the xz plane about the x axis. Sketch the surface.

59. Determine the value of c such that the vectors $3\mathbf{i} + c\mathbf{j} - 3\mathbf{k}$ and $5\mathbf{i} - 4\mathbf{j} + \mathbf{k}$ are orthogonal.

60. Show that there are representations of the three vectors $\mathbf{A} = 5\mathbf{i} + \mathbf{j} - 3\mathbf{k}$, $\mathbf{B} = \mathbf{i} + 3\mathbf{j} - 2\mathbf{k}$, and $\mathbf{C} = -4\mathbf{i} + 2\mathbf{j} + \mathbf{k}$ which form a triangle.

61. Given the points $A(5, 9, -3)$ and $B(-2, 4, -5)$, find **(a)** the direction cosines of $\mathbf{V}(\vec{AB})$ and **(b)** the unit vector having the same direction as $\mathbf{V}(\vec{AB})$.

62. If $\mathbf{A} = \mathbf{i} + \mathbf{j} - \mathbf{k}$, $\mathbf{B} = 2\mathbf{i} - \mathbf{j} + \mathbf{k}$, $\mathbf{C} = 3\mathbf{i} - 2\mathbf{j} + 4\mathbf{k}$, and $\mathbf{D} = 5\mathbf{i} + 6\mathbf{j} - 8\mathbf{k}$, find scalars a, b, and c such that $a\mathbf{A} + b\mathbf{B} + c\mathbf{C} = \mathbf{D}$.

63. If $\mathbf{A} = \langle 7, -1, 5 \rangle$ and $\mathbf{B} = \langle -2, 3, 1 \rangle$, find **(a)** the scalar projection of $\mathbf{B}$ onto $\mathbf{A}$ and **(b)** the vector projection of $\mathbf{B}$ onto $\mathbf{A}$.

64. Find an equation of the plane containing the points $(1, 7, -3)$ and $(3, 1, 2)$ and which does not intersect the x axis.

65. Find an equation of the plane through the three points $(-1, 2, 1)$, $(1, 4, 0)$, and $(1, -1, 3)$ by two methods: **(a)** using the cross product; **(b)** without using the cross product.

66. Find an equation of the plane that contains the point $(7, -2, -5)$ and is perpendicular to the line through

the points $(-3, 0, 4)$ and $(3, 2, 1)$.

67. Find the distance from the origin to the plane through the point $(-6, 3, -2)$ and having $5\mathbf{i} - 3\mathbf{j} + 4\mathbf{k}$ as a normal vector.

68. Find two unit vectors orthogonal to $\mathbf{i} - 3\mathbf{j} + 4\mathbf{k}$ and whose representations are parallel to the yz plane.

69. Find the distance from the point $P(4, 6, -4)$ to the line through the two points $A(2, 2, 1)$ and $B(4, 3, -1)$.

70. Find the distance from the plane $9x - 2y + 6z + 44 = 0$ to the point $(-3, 2, 0)$.

71. If θ is the angle between the vectors $\mathbf{A} = 2\mathbf{i} + \mathbf{j} + \mathbf{k}$ and $\mathbf{B} = 4\mathbf{i} - 3\mathbf{j} + 5\mathbf{k}$, find $\cos \theta$ in two ways: **(a)** by using the dot product; **(b)** by using the cross product and a trigonometric identity.

72. Prove that the lines $\dfrac{x-1}{1} = \dfrac{y+2}{2} = \dfrac{z-2}{2}$ and $\dfrac{x-2}{2} = \dfrac{y-5}{3} = \dfrac{z-5}{1}$ are skew lines, and find the distance between them.

73. Find symmetric and parametric equations of the line through the origin and perpendicular to each of the lines of Exercise 72.

74. Find symmetric and parametric equations of the line through the two points $(-3, 5, 2)$ and $(1, -3, 4)$.

75. Show that the lines $\dfrac{x-2}{3} = \dfrac{y+3}{-1} = \dfrac{z-5}{4}$ and $\dfrac{x+1}{-6} = \dfrac{y+2}{2} = \dfrac{z-1}{-8}$ are coincident.

76. Find an equation of the plane containing the line $\frac{1}{2}(x - 3) = -(y + 5) = \frac{1}{3}(z + 2)$ and the point $(5, 0, -4)$.

77. Find the area of the cross section of the ellipsoid $$\frac{x^2}{4} + \frac{y^2}{9} + \frac{z^2}{25} = 1$$ in the plane $z = 4$.

78. Find the area of the parallelogram two of whose sides are the position representations of the vectors $2\mathbf{j} - 3\mathbf{k}$ and $5\mathbf{i} + 4\mathbf{k}$.

79. Find the volume of the parallelepiped having vertices at $(1, 3, 0)$, $(2, -1, 3)$, $(-2, 2, -1)$, and $(-1, 1, 2)$.

80. Prove by vector analysis that the diagonals of a parallelogram bisect each other.

In Exercises 81 and 82, let

$$\mathbf{A} = \cos \alpha \mathbf{i} + \sin \alpha \mathbf{j} \quad and \quad \mathbf{B} = \cos \beta \mathbf{i} + \sin \beta \mathbf{j}$$

See the accompanying figure.

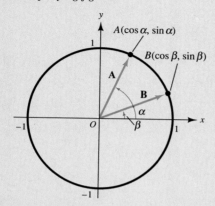

81. Use the dot product of $\mathbf{A}$ and $\mathbf{B}$ to prove that

$$\cos(\alpha - \beta) = \cos \alpha \cos \beta + \sin \alpha \sin \beta$$

82. Use the cross product of $\mathbf{A}$ and $\mathbf{B}$, with 0 as the $\mathbf{k}$ component of each vector, to prove that

$$|\sin(\alpha - \beta)| = |\sin \alpha \cos \beta - \cos \alpha \sin \beta|$$

83. If $\mathbf{A}$ is any vector in V_3, prove that

$$\mathbf{A} = (\mathbf{A} \cdot \mathbf{i})\mathbf{i} + (\mathbf{A} \cdot \mathbf{j})\mathbf{j} + (\mathbf{A} \cdot \mathbf{k})\mathbf{k}$$

84. Let $\mathbf{A}$ and $\mathbf{B}$ be vectors in V_3, c_1, c_2, and c_3 be direction cosines of $\mathbf{A}$, and d_1, d_2, and d_3 be direction cosines of $\mathbf{B}$. If

$$\frac{c_1}{d_1} = \frac{c_2}{d_2} = \frac{c_3}{d_3}$$

prove that $\mathbf{A}$ and $\mathbf{B}$ are parallel.

85. If $\mathbf{A}$, $\mathbf{B}$, $\mathbf{C}$, and $\mathbf{D}$ are vectors in V_3, prove **Lagrange's identity**

$$(\mathbf{A} \times \mathbf{B}) \cdot (\mathbf{C} \times \mathbf{D}) = \begin{vmatrix} \mathbf{A} \cdot \mathbf{C} & \mathbf{A} \cdot \mathbf{D} \\ \mathbf{B} \cdot \mathbf{C} & \mathbf{B} \cdot \mathbf{D} \end{vmatrix}$$

86. Given triangle ABC, points D, E, and F are on the sides AB, BC, and AC, respectively, and

$$\mathbf{V}(\overrightarrow{AD}) = \tfrac{1}{3}\mathbf{V}(\overrightarrow{AB}) \qquad \mathbf{V}(\overrightarrow{BE}) = \tfrac{1}{3}\mathbf{V}(\overrightarrow{BC})$$
$$\mathbf{V}(\overrightarrow{CF}) = \tfrac{1}{3}\mathbf{V}(\overrightarrow{CA})$$

Prove $\mathbf{V}(\overrightarrow{AE}) + \mathbf{V}(\overrightarrow{BF}) + \mathbf{V}(\overrightarrow{CD}) = \mathbf{0}$.

VECTOR-VALUED FUNCTIONS

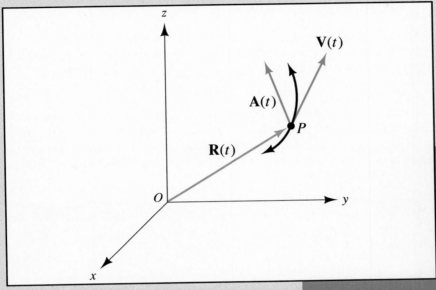

Vector-valued functions are those whose domain is a set of real numbers and whose range is a set of vectors. These functions are introduced in Section 11.1, where we also discuss graphs of vector-valued functions. The graphs are curves, which can also be represented by parametric equations. The calculus of vector-valued functions, presented in Section 11.2, pertains to derivatives and indefinite integrals of these functions, and you will learn that the definitions and theorems are similar to those for the calculus of real-valued functions.

The remaining sections of the chapter pertain to applications of vectors to geometry, physics, and engineering. The geometrical applications include *arc length, tangent and normal vectors* to curves, and *curvature*. For applications in physics and engineering, we use vectors to discuss motion of a particle along a curve, which is called *curvilinear motion*.

11.1 VECTOR-VALUED FUNCTIONS AND CURVES IN R^3

In Section 9.1, we introduced parametric equations by considering a particle moving in a plane so that the coordinates (x, y) of its position at any time t are given by the equations

$$x = f(t) \quad \text{and} \quad y = g(t) \tag{1}$$

We can extend this idea to three-dimensional space, in which case the coordinates (x, y, z) of the particle's position at any time t are given by the three parametric equations

$$x = f(t) \qquad y = g(t) \qquad z = h(t) \tag{2}$$

A vector exists for any position of the particle, and the endpoints of the position representations of these vectors trace a curve traveled by the particle. This concept leads us to consider a function whose domain is a set of real numbers and whose range is a set of vectors. Such a function is called a *vector-valued function.*

11.1.1 Definition of a Vector-Valued Function

Let f, g, and h be real-valued functions of a real variable t. Then there is a **vector-valued function R**, defined by

$$\mathbf{R}(t) = f(t)\mathbf{i} + g(t)\mathbf{j} + h(t)\mathbf{k}$$

where t is any number in the domain common to f, g, and h. In the plane, a **vector-valued function R** is defined by

$$\mathbf{R}(t) = f(t)\mathbf{i} + g(t)\mathbf{j}$$

where t is in the domain common to f and g.

▷ **ILLUSTRATION 1** Let **R** be the vector-valued function defined by

$$\mathbf{R}(t) = \sqrt{t - 2}\,\mathbf{i} + (t - 3)^{-1}\mathbf{j} + \ln t\,\mathbf{k}$$

If $f(t) = \sqrt{t - 2}$, $g(t) = (t - 3)^{-1}$, and $h(t) = \ln t$, the domain of **R** is the set of values of t for which $f(t)$, $g(t)$, and $h(t)$ are all defined. Because $f(t)$ is defined for $t \geq 2$, $g(t)$ is defined for all real numbers except 3, and $h(t)$ is defined for all positive numbers, the domain of **R** is $\{t \mid t \geq 2, t \neq 3\}$. ◄

The equation

$$\mathbf{R}(t) = f(t)\mathbf{i} + g(t)\mathbf{j} + h(t)\mathbf{k} \tag{3}$$

is called a **vector equation** which traces the curve C defined by the corresponding parametric equations (2); that is, a curve can be defined by either a vector equation or a set of parametric equations. If in (3), $h(t) = 0$ for all t in the domain of R, the curve C lies in the xy plane and is defined by the corresponding parametric equations (1). We discussed such curves in Section 9.1.

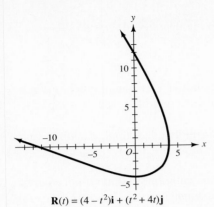

$$\mathbf{R}(t) = (4 - t^2)\mathbf{i} + (t^2 + 4t)\mathbf{j}$$

FIGURE 1

Table 1

t	x	y	z
0	2	0	0
$\frac{1}{2}\pi$	0	2	$\frac{1}{2}\pi$
π	-2	0	π
$\frac{3}{2}\pi$	0	-2	$\frac{3}{2}\pi$
2π	2	0	2π
$\frac{5}{2}\pi$	0	2	$\frac{5}{2}\pi$
3π	-2	0	3π
$\frac{7}{2}\pi$	0	-2	$\frac{7}{2}\pi$
4π	2	0	4π

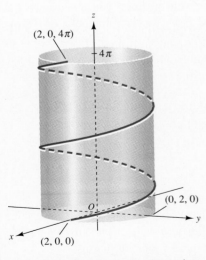

$\mathbf{R}(t) = 2\cos t\,\mathbf{i} + 2\sin t\,\mathbf{j} + t\,\mathbf{k}$ $0 \le t \le 4\pi$

FIGURE 2

▷ **ILLUSTRATION 2**   The plane curve defined by the vector equation

$$\mathbf{R}(t) = (4 - t^2)\mathbf{i} + (t^2 + 4t)\mathbf{j}$$

is also defined by the parametric equations

$$x = 4 - t^2 \quad \text{and} \quad y = t^2 + 4t$$

In Example 5 of Section 9.1 we sketched this curve and obtained the graph shown here in Figure 1. ◀

A vector equation of a curve gives the curve a direction at each point. That is, if we think of the curve as being traced by a particle, we can consider the positive direction along a curve as the direction in which the particle moves as the parameter t increases. In such a case as this, t may be a measure of time, and the vector $\mathbf{R}(t)$ is called the **position vector.**

By eliminating t from parametric equations (2) we obtain two equations in x, y, and z, called **cartesian equations** of the curve C. The graph of each cartesian equation is a surface, and curve C is the intersection of the two surfaces. The equations of any two surfaces containing C may be taken as cartesian equations defining C.

▶ **EXAMPLE 1**   Sketch the curve having the vector equation

$$\mathbf{R}(t) = 2\cos t\,\mathbf{i} + 2\sin t\,\mathbf{j} + t\,\mathbf{k} \qquad 0 \le t \le 4\pi$$

Solution   Parametric equations of the curve are

$$x = 2\cos t \qquad y = 2\sin t \qquad z = t$$

We eliminate t from the first two equations by squaring on both sides and adding corresponding members to obtain

$$x^2 + y^2 = 4\cos^2 t + 4\sin^2 t$$
$$x^2 + y^2 = 4$$

The curve, therefore, lies entirely on the right-circular cylinder whose directrix is the circle $x^2 + y^2 = 4$ in the xy plane and whose rulings are parallel to the z axis. Table 1 gives sets of values of x, y, and z for specific values of t. Figure 2 shows the curve. ◀

The curve of Example 1 is called a **circular helix.** A more general **helix** has the vector equation

$$\mathbf{R}(t) = a\cos t\,\mathbf{i} + b\sin t\,\mathbf{j} + ct\,\mathbf{k} \tag{4}$$

and parametric equations

$$x = a\cos t \qquad y = b\sin t \qquad z = ct$$

where a, b, and c are nonzero constants. When $a = b$, the curve is a circular helix. To eliminate t from the first two parametric equations we write them as

$$\frac{x^2}{a^2} = \cos^2 t \quad \text{and} \quad \frac{y^2}{b^2} = \sin^2 t$$

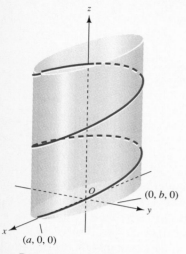

$$\mathbf{R}(t) = a \cos t\, \mathbf{i} + b \sin t\, \mathbf{j} + ct\, \mathbf{k}$$

FIGURE 3

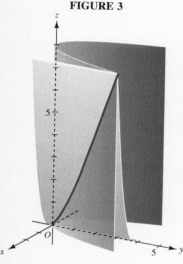

$$\mathbf{R}(t) = t\mathbf{i} + t^2\mathbf{j} + t^3\mathbf{k},\ 0 \le t \le 2$$

FIGURE 4

Adding corresponding members of these two equations we obtain

$$\frac{x^2}{a^2} + \frac{y^2}{b^2} = 1$$

The curve defined by (4), therefore, lies entirely on the elliptical cylinder whose directrix is an ellipse in the xy plane and whose rulings are parallel to the z axis as shown in Figure 3.

A curve having the vector equation

$$\mathbf{R}(t) = at\mathbf{i} + bt^2\mathbf{j} + ct^3\mathbf{k}$$

where a, b, and c are nonzero constants, is called a **twisted cubic**, a particular case of which appears in the next example.

▶ **EXAMPLE 2** Sketch the twisted cubic having the vector equation

$$\mathbf{R}(t) = t\mathbf{i} + t^2\mathbf{j} + t^3\mathbf{k} \qquad 0 \le t \le 2$$

Solution Parametric equations of this twisted cubic are

$$x = t \qquad y = t^2 \qquad z = t^3$$

Eliminating t from the first two of these equations yields $y = x^2$, an equation of a cylinder whose directrix in the xy plane is a parabola and whose rulings are parallel to the z axis. Eliminating t from the first and third equations gives $z = x^3$, an equation of a cylinder with rulings parallel to the y axis and whose directrix is in the xz plane. The twisted cubic is the intersection of the two cylinders. Figure 4 shows the two cylinders and the twisted cubic from $t = 0$ to $t = 2$. ◀

The helix and twisted cubic in the above two examples were sketched in a fairly straight-forward manner. Sketching most three-dimensional curves, however, is much more complicated. Fortunately in this age of technology we can resort to computer graphics to plot these curves. Often the software allows a choice of the viewer's location that permits you to observe the curve from various perspectives. Figures 5(a)–(c) show the helix of Example 1 generated by Mathematica as viewed from three different points in

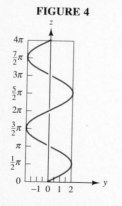

$\mathbf{R}(t) = 2 \cos t\mathbf{i} + 2 \sin t\mathbf{j} + t\mathbf{k}$ $0 \le t \le 4\pi$
viewed from $(16, 0, 0)$

FIGURE 5a

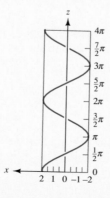

$\mathbf{R}(t) = 2 \cos t\mathbf{i} + 2 \sin t\mathbf{j} + t\mathbf{k}$ $0 \le t \le 4\pi$
viewed from $(0, 16, 0)$

FIGURE 5b

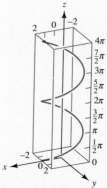

$\mathbf{R}(t) = 2 \cos t\mathbf{i} + 2 \sin t\mathbf{j} + t\mathbf{k}$ $0 \le t \le 4\pi$
viewed from $(8, 16, 8)$

FIGURE 5c

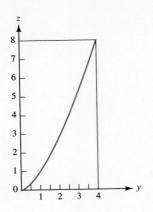

$\mathbf{R}(t) = t\mathbf{i} + t^2\mathbf{j} + t^3\mathbf{k} \quad 0 \le t \le 2\pi$

viewed from (16, 0, 0)

FIGURE 6a

$\mathbf{R}(t) = t\mathbf{i} + t^2\mathbf{j} + t^3\mathbf{k} \quad 0 \le t \le 2$

viewed from (0, 16, 0)

FIGURE 6b

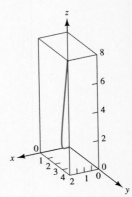

$\mathbf{R}(t) = t\mathbf{i} + t^2\mathbf{j} + t^3\mathbf{k} \quad 0 \le t \le 2$

viewed from (8, 16, 8)

FIGURE 6c

space. Figures 6(a)–(c) show the twisted cubic of Example 2 also generated by Mathematica as viewed from the same three points.

We can perform vector operations on vector-valued functions by applying the procedures you learned in Chapter 10 as indicated in the following definition of these operations.

11.1.2 Definition of Operations on Vector-Valued Functions

Given the vector-valued functions **F** and **G** and the real-valued functions f and g:

(i) the **sum** of F and G, denoted by $\mathbf{F} + \mathbf{G}$, is the vector-valued function defined by

$$(\mathbf{F} + \mathbf{G})(t) = \mathbf{F}(t) + \mathbf{G}(t)$$

(ii) the **difference** of F and G, denoted by $\mathbf{F} - \mathbf{G}$, is the vector-valued function defined by

$$(\mathbf{F} - \mathbf{G})(t) = \mathbf{F}(t) - \mathbf{G}(t)$$

(iii) the **dot product** of F and G, denoted by $\mathbf{F} \cdot \mathbf{G}$, is the real-valued function defined by

$$(\mathbf{F} \cdot \mathbf{G})(t) = \mathbf{F}(t) \cdot \mathbf{G}(t)$$

(iv) the **cross product** of F and G, denoted by $\mathbf{F} \times \mathbf{G}$, is the vector-valued function defined by

$$(\mathbf{F} \times \mathbf{G})(t) = \mathbf{F}(t) \times \mathbf{G}(t)$$

(v) the **product** of $f(t)$ and $\mathbf{F}(t)$, denoted by $f\mathbf{F}$, is the vector-valued function defined by

$$(f\mathbf{F})(t) = f(t)\mathbf{F}(t)$$

(vi) the **composite function,** denoted by $\mathbf{F} \circ g$, is the vector-valued function defined by

$$(\mathbf{F} \circ g)(t) = \mathbf{F}(g(t))$$

▶ **EXAMPLE 3** Given $\mathbf{F}(t) = \sin 2t\mathbf{i} + \cos 2t\mathbf{j} + \sqrt{t}\mathbf{k}$, $\mathbf{G}(t) = -\cos 2t\mathbf{i} + \sin 2t\mathbf{j} + \sqrt{t}\mathbf{k}$, and $f(t) = t^{3/2}$, find: (a) $(\mathbf{F} + \mathbf{G})(t)$; (b) $(\mathbf{F} - \mathbf{G})(t)$; (c) $(\mathbf{F} \cdot \mathbf{G})(t)$; (d) $(\mathbf{F} \times \mathbf{G})(t)$; (e) $(f\mathbf{F})(t)$; (f) $(\mathbf{G} \circ f)(t)$.

Solution

(a) $(\mathbf{F} + \mathbf{G})(t) = (\sin 2t - \cos 2t)\mathbf{i} + (\cos 2t + \sin 2t)\mathbf{j} + 2\sqrt{t}\mathbf{k}$

(b) $(\mathbf{F} - \mathbf{G})(t) = (\sin 2t + \cos 2t)\mathbf{i} + (\cos 2t - \sin 2t)\mathbf{j}$

(c) $(\mathbf{F} \cdot \mathbf{G})(t) = -\sin 2t \cos 2t + \sin 2t \cos 2t + \sqrt{t^2}$

$$= t \qquad \text{(because } t \geq 0)$$

(d) $(\mathbf{F} \times \mathbf{G})(t) = \sqrt{t} \cos 2t\mathbf{i} - \sqrt{t} \cos 2t\mathbf{j} + \sin^2 2t\mathbf{k} + \cos^2 2t\mathbf{k} - \sqrt{t} \sin 2t\mathbf{i} - \sqrt{t} \sin 2t\mathbf{j}$

$$= \sqrt{t}(\cos 2t - \sin 2t)\mathbf{i} - \sqrt{t}(\cos 2t + \sin 2t)\mathbf{j} + \mathbf{k}$$

(e) $(f\mathbf{F})(t) = t^{3/2} \sin 2t\mathbf{i} + t^{3/2} \cos 2t\mathbf{j} + t^2\mathbf{k}$

(f) $(\mathbf{G} \circ f)(t) = \mathbf{G}(f(t))$

$$= -\cos 2t^{3/2}\mathbf{i} + \sin 2t^{3/2}\mathbf{j} + t^{3/4}\mathbf{k}$$ ◀

The limit of a vector-valued function is defined in terms of the limits of its real-valued components.

11.1.3 Definition of the Limit of a Vector-Valued Function

Let $\mathbf{R}$ be a vector-valued function whose function values are given by

$$\mathbf{R}(t) = f(t)\mathbf{i} + g(t)\mathbf{j} + h(t)\mathbf{k}$$

Then the limit of $\mathbf{R}(t)$ as t approaches a is defined by

$$\lim_{t \to a} \mathbf{R}(t) = [\lim_{t \to a} f(t)]\mathbf{i} + [\lim_{t \to a} g(t)]\mathbf{j} + [\lim_{t \to a} h(t)]\mathbf{k}$$

if $\lim_{t \to a} f(t)$, $\lim_{t \to a} g(t)$, and $\lim_{t \to a} h(t)$ all exist.

Of course, this definition also applies to vector-valued functions in the plane by taking the $\mathbf{k}$ component as zero.

▷ **ILLUSTRATION 3** If $\mathbf{R}(t) = \cos t\mathbf{i} + 2e^t\mathbf{j} + 3\mathbf{k}$

$$\lim_{t \to 0} \mathbf{R}(t) = (\lim_{t \to 0} \cos t)\mathbf{i} + (\lim_{t \to 0} 2e^t)\mathbf{j} + (\lim_{t \to 0} 3)\mathbf{k}$$

$$= \mathbf{i} + 2\mathbf{j} + 3\mathbf{k}$$ ◀

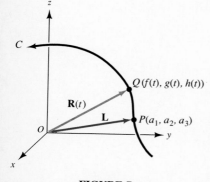

FIGURE 7

For the geometric interpretation of Definition 11.1.3, see Figure 7 with $\mathbf{R}(t) = f(t)\mathbf{i} + g(t)\mathbf{j} + h(t)\mathbf{k}$, $\lim_{t \to a} f(t) = a_1$, $\lim_{t \to a} g(t) = a_2$, $\lim_{t \to a} h(t) = a_3$, and $\mathbf{L} = a_1\mathbf{i} + a_2\mathbf{j} + a_3\mathbf{k}$. The vector-valued function $\mathbf{R}$ defines curve C containing the points $Q(f(t), g(t), h(t))$ and $P(a_1, a_2, a_3)$. The position representations of vectors $\mathbf{R}$ and $\mathbf{L}$ are, respectively, $\overrightarrow{OQ}$ and $\overrightarrow{OP}$. As t approaches a, $\mathbf{R}(t)$ approaches $\mathbf{L}$, so that point Q approaches the point P along C.

Limit theorems for vector-valued functions that correspond to the limit theorems for real-valued functions that you learned in Chapter 1 can be proved from Definition 11.1.3. You are asked to prove some of these limit theorems in the exercises.

11.1.4 Definition of Continuity of a Vector-Valued Function

The vector-valued function $\mathbf{R}$ is continuous at the number a if and only if the following three conditions are satisfied:

(i) $\mathbf{R}(a)$ exists;

(ii) $\lim\limits_{t \to a} \mathbf{R}(t)$ exists;

(iii) $\lim\limits_{t \to a} \mathbf{R}(t) = \mathbf{R}(a)$

From this definition, a vector-valued function is continuous at the number a if and only if its real-valued components are continuous at a.

▶ **EXAMPLE 4**   Determine the numbers at which the following vector-valued function is continuous:

$$\mathbf{R}(t) = \sin t\mathbf{i} + \ln t\mathbf{j} + \frac{t^2 - 1}{t - 1}\mathbf{k}$$

Solution   Because $\sin t$ is defined for all real numbers, $\ln t$ is defined only when $t > 0$, and $(t^2 - 1)/(t - 1)$ is defined at all real numbers except 1, the domain of $\mathbf{R}$ is $\{t \mid t > 0 \text{ and } t \neq 1\}$. If a is any number in the domain of $\mathbf{R}$,

$$\mathbf{R}(a) = \sin a\mathbf{i} + \ln a\mathbf{j} + (a + 1)\mathbf{k}$$

$$\lim_{t \to a} \mathbf{R}(t) = \lim_{t \to a} \sin t\mathbf{i} + \lim_{t \to a} \ln t\mathbf{j} + \lim_{t \to a} \frac{t^2 - 1}{t - 1}\mathbf{k}$$

$$= \sin a\mathbf{i} + \ln a\mathbf{j} + (a + 1)\mathbf{k}$$

Thus, $\lim\limits_{t \to a} \mathbf{R}(t) = \mathbf{R}(a)$, and $\mathbf{R}$ is continuous at a.

The vector-valued function $\mathbf{R}$ is, therefore, continuous at every number in its domain.   ◀

EXERCISES 11.1

In Exercises 1 through 8, find the domain of the vector-valued function.

1. $\mathbf{R}(t) = \dfrac{1}{t}\mathbf{i} + \sqrt{4 - t}\,\mathbf{j}$

2. $\mathbf{R}(t) = (t^2 + 3)\mathbf{i} + \dfrac{1}{t - 1}\mathbf{j}$

3. $\mathbf{R}(t) = (\sin^{-1} t)\mathbf{i} + \ln(t + 1)\mathbf{j}$

4. $\mathbf{R}(t) = (\cos^{-1} t)\mathbf{i} + (\sec^{-1} t)\mathbf{j}$

5. $\mathbf{R}(t) = \sqrt{t + 2}\,\mathbf{i} + \sqrt{4 - t}\,\mathbf{j} + \cot t\mathbf{k}$

6. $\mathbf{R}(t) = \sqrt{t^2 - 9}\,\mathbf{i} + \ln|t - 3|\mathbf{j} + (t^2 + 2t - 8)\mathbf{k}$

7. $\mathbf{R}(t) = \ln|\sin t|\mathbf{i} + \sqrt{16 - t^2}\,\mathbf{j} + \ln|t + 4|\mathbf{k}$

8. $\mathbf{R}(t) = \tan t\mathbf{i} + \sqrt{4 - t^2}\,\mathbf{j} + \dfrac{1}{2 + t}\mathbf{k}$

In Exercises 9 through 12, find: (a) $(\mathbf{F} + \mathbf{G})(t)$*; (b)* $(\mathbf{F} - \mathbf{G})(t)$*; (c)* $(\mathbf{F} \cdot \mathbf{G})(t)$*; (d)* $(\mathbf{F} \times \mathbf{G})(t)$*.*

9. $\mathbf{F}(t) = (t + 1)\mathbf{i} + (t^2 - 1)\mathbf{j} + (t - 1)\mathbf{k}$;
   $\mathbf{G}(t) = (t - 1)\mathbf{i} + \mathbf{j} + (t + 1)\mathbf{k}$

10. $\mathbf{F}(t) = (4 - t^2)\mathbf{i} + 4\mathbf{j} - (4 - t^2)\mathbf{k}$;
    $\mathbf{G}(t) = t^2\mathbf{i} + (t^2 - 4)\mathbf{j} - 4\mathbf{k}$

11. $\mathbf{F}(t) = \cos t\mathbf{i} - \sin t\mathbf{j} + t\mathbf{k}$;
    $\mathbf{G}(t) = \sin t\mathbf{i} + \cos t\mathbf{j} - t\mathbf{k}$

12. $\mathbf{F}(t) = \sec t\mathbf{i} + \tan t\mathbf{j} - 2\mathbf{k}$;
    $\mathbf{G}(t) = \sec t\mathbf{i} - \tan t\mathbf{j} + t\mathbf{k}$

In Exercises 13 through 16, find: (a) $(f\mathbf{F})(t)$; (b) $(f\mathbf{G})(t)$; (c) $(\mathbf{F} \circ g)(t)$; (d) $(\mathbf{G} \circ g)(t)$.

13. **F** and **G** are the functions of Exercise 9;
    $f(t) = t - 1$; $g(t) = t + 1$

14. **F** and **G** are the functions of Exercise 10;
    $f(t) = 1/(2 - t)$; $g(t) = 2 - t$

15. **F** and **G** are the functions of Exercise 11;
    $f(t) = \sin t$; $g(t) = \sin^{-1} t$

16. **F** and **G** are the functions of Exercise 12;
    $f(t) = \cos t$; $g(t) = \cos^{-1} t$

In Exercises 17 through 24, find the indicated limit, if it exists.

17. $\mathbf{R}(t) = (t - 2)\mathbf{i} + \dfrac{t^2 - 4}{t - 2}\mathbf{j} + t\mathbf{k}$; $\lim\limits_{t \to 2} \mathbf{R}(t)$

18. $\mathbf{R}(t) = \dfrac{t^2 - 1}{t + 1}\mathbf{i} + \dfrac{t + 1}{t - 1}\mathbf{j} + |t + 1|\mathbf{k}$; $\lim\limits_{t \to -1} \mathbf{R}(t)$

19. $\mathbf{R}(t) = \sin t\mathbf{i} + \cos t\mathbf{j} + \dfrac{\sin t}{t}\mathbf{k}$; $\lim\limits_{t \to 0} \mathbf{R}(t)$

20. $\mathbf{R}(t) = \dfrac{1 - \cos t}{t}\mathbf{i} + e^t\mathbf{j} + e^{-t}\mathbf{k}$; $\lim\limits_{t \to 0} \mathbf{R}(t)$

21. $\mathbf{R}(t) = \dfrac{|t - 2|}{t - 2}\mathbf{i} + \dfrac{\sin \pi t}{t^2 - 1}\mathbf{j} + \dfrac{\tan \pi t}{t - 1}\mathbf{k}$; $\lim\limits_{t \to 1} \mathbf{R}(t)$

22. $\mathbf{R}(t) = \dfrac{1 + \cos t}{1 - \sin t}\mathbf{i} + \dfrac{1 - \cos^2 t}{1 - \cos t}\mathbf{j} + \dfrac{t^2}{\sin t}\mathbf{k}$; $\lim\limits_{t \to 0} \mathbf{R}(t)$

23. $\mathbf{R}(t) = e^{t+1}\mathbf{i} + e^{1-t}\mathbf{j} + (1 + t)^{1/t}\mathbf{k}$; $\lim\limits_{t \to 0} \mathbf{R}(t)$

24. $\mathbf{R}(t) = \dfrac{\ln(t + 1)}{t}\mathbf{i} + \sinh t\mathbf{j} + \cosh t\mathbf{k}$; $\lim\limits_{t \to 0} \mathbf{R}(t)$

In Exercises 25 through 30, determine the numbers at which the vector-valued function is continuous.

25. $\mathbf{R}(t) = t^2\mathbf{i} + \ln(t - 1)\mathbf{j} + \dfrac{1}{t - 2}\mathbf{k}$

26. $\mathbf{R}(t) = (t - 1)\mathbf{i} + \dfrac{1}{e^t - 1}\mathbf{j} + \dfrac{|t - 1|}{t - 1}\mathbf{k}$

27. $\mathbf{R}(t) = \cos t\mathbf{i} + \sec t\mathbf{j} + \tan t\mathbf{k}$

28. $\mathbf{R}(t) = \sin \pi t\mathbf{i} - \tan \pi t\mathbf{j} + \cot \pi t\mathbf{k}$

29. $\mathbf{R}(t) = \begin{cases} e^{-1/t^2}\,\mathbf{i} + t^2\mathbf{j} + t\mathbf{k} & \text{if } t \neq 0 \\ 0 & \text{if } t = 0 \end{cases}$

30. $\mathbf{R}(t) = \begin{cases} \dfrac{\sin t}{t}\mathbf{i} + \dfrac{1 - \cos t}{t}\mathbf{j} + \dfrac{1 - e^t}{t}\mathbf{k} & \text{if } t \neq 0 \\ \mathbf{i} - \mathbf{k} & \text{if } t = 0 \end{cases}$

In Exercises 31 through 42, sketch the graph of the vector-valued function.

31. $\mathbf{R}(t) = t^2\mathbf{i} + (t + 1)\mathbf{j}$ 32. $\mathbf{R}(t) = \dfrac{4}{t^2}\mathbf{i} + \dfrac{4}{t}\mathbf{j}$

33. $\mathbf{R}(t) = (t - 2)\mathbf{i} + (t^2 + 4)\mathbf{j}$

34. $\mathbf{R}(t) = 3 \cosh t\mathbf{i} + 5 \sinh t\mathbf{j}$

35. $\mathbf{R}(t) = t\mathbf{i} + (6 - 4t)\mathbf{j} + (5 - 2t)\mathbf{k}$

36. $\mathbf{R}(t) = (t + 1)\mathbf{i} + (2t - 3)\mathbf{j} + (2t + 3)\mathbf{k}$

37. $\mathbf{R}(t) = \cos t\mathbf{i} + \sin t\mathbf{j} + t\mathbf{k}$, $0 \leq t \leq 2\pi$

38. $\mathbf{R}(t) = 3 \cos t\mathbf{i} + 3 \sin t\mathbf{j} + 2t\mathbf{k}$, $0 \leq t \leq 4\pi$

39. $\mathbf{R}(t) = 2 \cos t\mathbf{i} + 3 \sin t\mathbf{j} + 4t\mathbf{k}$, $0 \leq t \leq 4\pi$

40. $\mathbf{R}(t) = 4 \cos t\mathbf{i} + \sin t\mathbf{j} + \tfrac{1}{2}t\mathbf{k}$, $0 \leq t \leq 2\pi$

41. $\mathbf{R}(t) = 3t\mathbf{i} + 2t^2\mathbf{j} + t\mathbf{k}$, $0 \leq t \leq 2$

42. $\mathbf{R}(t) = t\mathbf{i} + t^2\mathbf{j} + \tfrac{3}{2}t^3\mathbf{k}$, $0 \leq t \leq 2$

In Exercises 43 through 46, Figures (a)–(c) are computer-generated graphs of the curve in the indicated exercise viewed from three different points in space. Match the graph with one of the given viewing points.

43. Exercise 37; $(0, 0, 8)$, $(0, 8, 0)$, and $(4, 8, 4)$

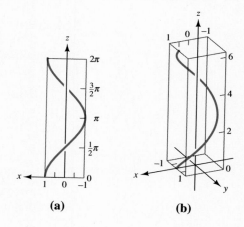

(a)   (b)

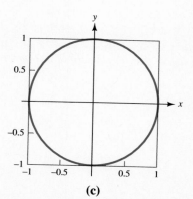

(c)

44. Exercise 38; (0, 0, 28), (0, 28, 0), and (14, 28, 14)

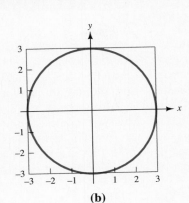

(a)   (b)

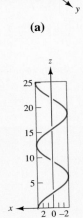

(c)

45. Exercise 41; (10, 0, 0), (−10, 0, 0), and (0, 0, 10)

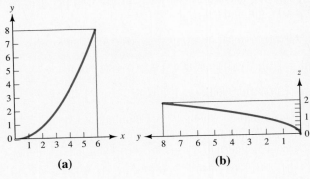

(a)   (b)

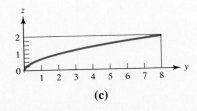

(c)

46. Exercise 42; (15, 0, 0), (−15, 0, 0), and (0, 0, 15)

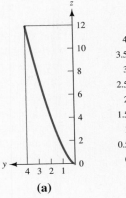   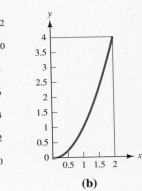

(a)   (b)

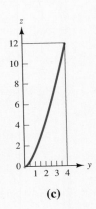

(c)

In Exercises 47 through 49, prove the limit theorem if $\mathbf{U}(t)$ *and* $\mathbf{V}(t)$ *are vector-valued functions such that* $\lim_{t \to a} \mathbf{U}(t)$ *and* $\lim_{t \to a} \mathbf{V}(t)$ *exist.*

47. $\lim_{t \to a}[\mathbf{U}(t) + \mathbf{V}(t)] = \lim_{t \to a} \mathbf{U}(t) + \lim_{t \to a} \mathbf{V}(t)$

48. $\lim_{t \to a}[\mathbf{U}(t) \cdot \mathbf{V}(t)] = \lim_{t \to a} \mathbf{U}(t) \cdot \lim_{t \to a} \mathbf{V}(t)$

49. $\lim_{t \to a}[\mathbf{U}(t) \times \mathbf{V}(t)] = \lim_{t \to a} \mathbf{U}(t) \times \lim_{t \to a} \mathbf{V}(t)$

50. If f is a real-valued function such that $\lim_{t \to a} f(t)$ exists and $\mathbf{V}$ is a vector-valued function such that $\lim_{t \to a} \mathbf{V}(t)$ exists, prove that
$$\lim_{t \to a} f(t)\mathbf{V}(t) = [\lim_{t \to a} f(t)][\lim_{t \to a} \mathbf{V}(t)].$$

51. Prove that if the vector-valued function $\mathbf{V}$ is continuous at the number a then $\|\mathbf{V}(t)\|$ is continuous at a.

52. Instead of Definition 11.1.3, the limit of a vector-valued function can be defined as follows: The limit of $\mathbf{R}(t)$ as t approaches a is the vector $\mathbf{L}$ if for any $\epsilon > 0$ there exists a $\delta > 0$ such that

  if $0 < |t - a| < \delta$ then $\|\mathbf{R}(t) - \mathbf{L}\| < \epsilon$

Without using the words *limit* or *approaches* and without using symbols such as ϵ and δ, state in words what this means.

11.2 CALCULUS OF VECTOR-VALUED FUNCTIONS

The study of curves and surfaces by means of calculus provides the subject matter of a course in *differential geometry,* a short introduction of which is presented in Sections 11.3 and 11.4. Then in Section 11.5, we apply calculus to *curvilinear motion,* the motion of a particle along a curve. This section lays the groundwork for those topics.

The definitions of derivatives and indefinite integrals of vector-valued functions involve the corresponding definitions for real-valued functions just as you learned in Section 11.1 was the situation for limits and continuity of these functions. In the following definition of the derivative, the expression

$$\frac{\mathbf{R}(t + \Delta t) - \mathbf{R}(t)}{\Delta t}$$

is used to indicate the division of a vector by a scalar and it means

$$\frac{1}{\Delta t}[\mathbf{R}(t + \Delta t) - \mathbf{R}(t)]$$

11.2.1 Definition of the Derivative of a Vector-Valued Function

If $\mathbf{R}$ is a vector-valued function, then the **derivative** of $\mathbf{R}$ is a vector-valued function, denoted by $\mathbf{R}'$ and defined by

$$\mathbf{R}'(t) = \lim_{\Delta t \to 0} \frac{\mathbf{R}(t + \Delta t) - \mathbf{R}(t)}{\Delta t}$$

if this limit exists.

The notation $D_t\mathbf{R}(t)$ is sometimes used in place of $\mathbf{R}'(t)$.

The next theorem follows from Definition 11.2.1 and the definition of the derivative of a real-valued function.

11.2.2 Theorem

If $\mathbf{R}$ is a vector-valued function defined by

$$\mathbf{R}(t) = f(t)\mathbf{i} + g(t)\mathbf{j} + h(t)\mathbf{k}$$

then

$$\mathbf{R}'(t) = f'(t)\mathbf{i} + g'(t)\mathbf{j} + h'(t)\mathbf{k}$$

if $f'(t)$, $g'(t)$, and $h'(t)$ exist.

Proof   From Definition 11.2.1

$$\mathbf{R}'(t) = \lim_{\Delta t \to 0} \frac{\mathbf{R}(t + \Delta t) - \mathbf{R}(t)}{\Delta t}$$

$$= \lim_{\Delta t \to 0} \frac{[f(t + \Delta t)\mathbf{i} + g(t + \Delta t)\mathbf{j} + h(t + \Delta t)\mathbf{k}] - [f(t)\mathbf{i} + g(t)\mathbf{j} + h(t)\mathbf{k}]}{\Delta t}$$

$$= \lim_{\Delta t \to 0} \frac{f(t + \Delta t) - f(t)}{\Delta t}\mathbf{i} + \lim_{\Delta t \to 0} \frac{g(t + \Delta t) - g(t)}{\Delta t}\mathbf{j} + \lim_{\Delta t \to 0} \frac{h(t + \Delta t) - h(t)}{\Delta t}\mathbf{k}$$

$$= f'(t)\mathbf{i} + g'(t)\mathbf{j} + h'(t)\mathbf{k} \qquad\blacksquare$$

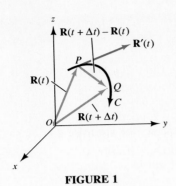

FIGURE 1

▷ **ILLUSTRATION 1** If $\mathbf{R}(t) = (2 + \sin t)\mathbf{i} + \cos t\mathbf{j} - t^2\mathbf{k}$, then

$$\mathbf{R}'(t) = \cos t\mathbf{i} - \sin t\mathbf{j} - 2t\mathbf{k} \qquad ◀$$

A geometric interpretation of Definition 11.2.1 is obtained by considering representations of the vectors $\mathbf{R}(t)$, $\mathbf{R}(t + \Delta t)$, and $\mathbf{R}'(t)$. Refer to Figure 1. The curve C is traced by the endpoint of the position representation of $\mathbf{R}(t)$ as t assumes all values in the domain of $\mathbf{R}$. Let $\overrightarrow{OP}$ be the position representation of $\mathbf{R}(t)$ and $\overrightarrow{OQ}$ be the position representation of $\mathbf{R}(t + \Delta t)$. Then $\mathbf{R}(t + \Delta t) - \mathbf{R}(t)$ is a vector for which $\overrightarrow{PQ}$ is a representation. If the vector $\mathbf{R}(t + \Delta t) - \mathbf{R}(t)$ is multiplied by the scalar $1/\Delta t$, we obtain a vector having the same direction and whose magnitude is $1/|\Delta t|$ times the magnitude of $\mathbf{R}(t + \Delta t) - \mathbf{R}(t)$. As Δt approaches zero, point Q approaches point P along C, and the vector $[\mathbf{R}(t + \Delta t) - \mathbf{R}(t)]/\Delta t$ approaches a vector having one of its representations tangent to curve C at the point P.

Observe that for vectors in the plane where

$$\mathbf{R}(t) = f(t)\mathbf{i} + g(t)\mathbf{j}$$

the direction of $\mathbf{R}'(t)$ is given by θ $(0 \leq \theta < 2\pi)$ where $\tan \theta = g'(t)/f'(t)$; that is, with $x = f(t)$ and $y = g(t)$

$$\tan \theta = \frac{\dfrac{dy}{dt}}{\dfrac{dx}{dt}}$$

Higher-order derivatives of vector-valued functions are defined as for higher-order derivatives of real-valued functions. So if $\mathbf{R}$ is a vector-valued function, the second derivative of $\mathbf{R}$, denoted by $\mathbf{R}''(t)$, is given by

$$\mathbf{R}''(t) = D_t[\mathbf{R}'(t)]$$

The notation $D_t^2\,\mathbf{R}(t)$ can be used in place of $\mathbf{R}''(t)$. By applying Theorem 11.2.2 to $\mathbf{R}'(t)$,

$$\mathbf{R}''(t) = f''(t)\mathbf{i} + g''(t)\mathbf{j} + h''(t)\mathbf{k}$$

if $f''(t)$, $g''(t)$, and $h''(t)$ exist.

▷ **ILLUSTRATION 2** If $\mathbf{R}(t) = (\ln t)\mathbf{i} + \dfrac{1}{t}\mathbf{j} - \dfrac{1}{t^2}\mathbf{k}$, then

$$\mathbf{R}'(t) = \frac{1}{t}\mathbf{i} - \frac{1}{t^2}\mathbf{j} + \frac{2}{t^3}\mathbf{k} \qquad \mathbf{R}''(t) = -\frac{1}{t^2}\mathbf{i} + \frac{2}{t^3}\mathbf{j} - \frac{6}{t^4}\mathbf{k} \qquad ◀$$

11.2.3 Definition of a Vector-Valued Function Differentiable on an Interval

A vector-valued function $\mathbf{R}$ is said to be **differentiable on an interval** if $\mathbf{R}'(t)$ exists for all values of t in the interval.

The following theorems give differentiation formulas for vector-valued functions. The proofs are based on Theorem 11.2.2 and theorems on differentiation of real-valued functions.

> **11.2.4 Theorem   The Derivative of the Sum of Two Vector-Valued Functions**
>
> If $\mathbf{R}$ and $\mathbf{Q}$ are differentiable vector-valued functions on an interval, then $\mathbf{R} + \mathbf{Q}$ is differentiable on the interval, and
>
> $$D_t[\mathbf{R}(t) + \mathbf{Q}(t)] = D_t\mathbf{R}(t) + D_t\mathbf{Q}(t)$$

The proof of this theorem is left as an exercise (see Exercise 29).

▶ **EXAMPLE 1**   Verify Theorem 11.2.4 if

$$\mathbf{R}(t) = t^2\mathbf{i} + (t - 1)\mathbf{j} \quad \text{and} \quad \mathbf{Q}(t) = \sin t\mathbf{i} + \cos t\mathbf{j}$$

Solution

$$
\begin{aligned}
D_t[\mathbf{R}(t) + \mathbf{Q}(t)] &= D_t([t^2\mathbf{i} + (t - 1)\mathbf{j}] + [\sin t\mathbf{i} + \cos t\mathbf{j}]) \\
&= D_t[(t^2 + \sin t)\mathbf{i} + (t - 1 + \cos t)\mathbf{j}] \\
&= (2t + \cos t)\mathbf{i} + (1 - \sin t)\mathbf{j} \\
D_t\mathbf{R}(t) + D_t\mathbf{Q}(t) &= D_t[t^2\mathbf{i} + (t - 1)\mathbf{j}] + D_t(\sin t\mathbf{i} + \cos t\mathbf{j}) \\
&= (2t\mathbf{i} + \mathbf{j}) + (\cos t\mathbf{i} - \sin t\mathbf{j}) \\
&= (2t + \cos t)\mathbf{i} + (1 - \sin t)\mathbf{j}
\end{aligned}
$$

Hence $D_t[\mathbf{R}(t) + \mathbf{Q}(t)] = D_t\mathbf{R}(t) + D_t\mathbf{Q}(t)$. ◀

> **11.2.5 Theorem   The Derivative of the Dot Product of Two Vector-Valued Functions**
>
> If $\mathbf{R}$ and $\mathbf{Q}$ are differentiable vector-valued functions on an interval, then $\mathbf{R} \cdot \mathbf{Q}$ is differentiable on the interval, and
>
> $$D_t[\mathbf{R}(t) \cdot \mathbf{Q}(t)] = [D_t\mathbf{R}(t)] \cdot \mathbf{Q}(t) + \mathbf{R}(t) \cdot [D_t\mathbf{Q}(t)]$$

Proof   We prove the theorem for vectors in V_2. The proof for vectors in V_3 is, of course, similar. Let

$$\mathbf{R}(t) = f_1(t)\mathbf{i} + g_1(t)\mathbf{j} \qquad \mathbf{Q}(t) = f_2(t)\mathbf{i} + g_2(t)\mathbf{j}$$

Then by Theorem 11.2.2,

$$D_t\mathbf{R}(t) = f_1'(t)\mathbf{i} + g_1'(t)\mathbf{j} \qquad D_t\mathbf{Q}(t) = f_2'(t)\mathbf{i} + g_2'(t)\mathbf{j}$$
$$\mathbf{R}(t) \cdot \mathbf{Q}(t) = [f_1(t)][f_2(t)] + [g_1(t)][g_2(t)]$$

Therefore

$$
\begin{aligned}
&D_t[\mathbf{R}(t) \cdot \mathbf{Q}(t)] \\
&= [f_1'(t)][f_2(t)] + [f_1(t)][f_2'(t)] + [g_1'(t)][g_2(t)] + [g_1(t)][g_2'(t)] \\
&= \{[f_1'(t)][f_2(t)] + [g_1'(t)][g_2(t)]\} + \{[f_1(t)][f_2'(t)] + [g_1(t)][g_2'(t)]\} \\
&= [D_t\mathbf{R}(t)] \cdot \mathbf{Q}(t) + \mathbf{R}(t) \cdot [D_t\mathbf{Q}(t)]
\end{aligned}
$$
∎

▶ **EXAMPLE 2**   Verify Theorem 11.2.5 for the vectors of Example 1.

Solution   The vectors are

$$\mathbf{R}(t) = t^2\mathbf{i} + (t - 1)\mathbf{j} \qquad \mathbf{Q}(t) = \sin t\mathbf{i} + \cos t\mathbf{j}$$

Thus $\mathbf{R}(t) \cdot \mathbf{Q}(t) = t^2 \sin t + (t - 1) \cos t$. Therefore

$$D_t[\mathbf{R}(t) \cdot \mathbf{Q}(t)] = 2t \sin t + t^2 \cos t + \cos t + (t - 1)(-\sin t)$$
$$= (t + 1) \sin t + (t^2 + 1) \cos t \qquad \textbf{(1)}$$

Because $D_t\mathbf{R}(t) = 2t\mathbf{i} + \mathbf{j}$ and $D_t\mathbf{Q}(t) = \cos t\mathbf{i} - \sin t\mathbf{j}$, we have

$$[D_t\mathbf{R}(t)] \cdot \mathbf{Q}(t) + \mathbf{R}(t) \cdot [D_t\mathbf{Q}(t)]$$
$$= (2t\mathbf{i} + \mathbf{j}) \cdot (\sin t\mathbf{i} + \cos t\mathbf{j}) + [t^2\mathbf{i} + (t - 1)\mathbf{j}] \cdot (\cos t\mathbf{i} - \sin t\mathbf{j})$$
$$= (2t \sin t + \cos t) + [t^2 \cos t - (t - 1) \sin t]$$
$$= (t + 1) \sin t + (t^2 + 1) \cos t \qquad \textbf{(2)}$$

Comparing (1) and (2), we see that Theorem 11.2.5 holds for these vectors. ◄

11.2.6 Theorem The Derivative of the Product of a Real-Valued Function and a Vector-Valued Function

If $\mathbf{R}$ is a differentiable vector-valued function on an interval and f is a differentiable real-valued function on the interval, then

$$D_t\{[f(t)][\mathbf{R}(t)]\} = [D_t f(t)]\mathbf{R}(t) + f(t) \, D_t\mathbf{R}(t)$$

The proof is left as an exercise (see Exercise 30).

The next theorem regarding the derivative of the cross product of two vector-valued functions is similar to the corresponding formula for the derivative of the product of real-valued functions; it is important, however, to maintain the correct order of the vector-valued functions because the cross product is not commutative.

11.2.7 Theorem The Derivative of the Cross Product of Two Vector-Valued Functions

If $\mathbf{R}$ and $\mathbf{Q}$ are vector-valued functions, then

$$D_t[\mathbf{R}(t) \times \mathbf{Q}(t)] = \mathbf{R}'(t) \times \mathbf{Q}(t) + \mathbf{R}(t) \times \mathbf{Q}'(t)$$

for all values of t for which $\mathbf{R}'(t)$ and $\mathbf{Q}'(t)$ exist.

The proof is left as an exercise (see Exercise 31).

11.2.8 Theorem The Chain Rule for Vector-Valued Functions

Suppose that $\mathbf{F}$ is a vector-valued function, h is a real-valued function, and $\mathbf{G}$ is the vector-valued function defined by $\mathbf{G}(t) = \mathbf{F}(h(t))$. If $\phi = h(t)$ and both $\dfrac{d\phi}{dt}$ and $D_\phi \mathbf{G}(t)$ exist, then $D_t\mathbf{G}(t)$ exists and is given by

$$D_t\mathbf{G}(t) = [D_\phi\mathbf{G}(t)]\frac{d\phi}{dt}$$

The proof, left as an exercise (see Exercise 32), is based on Theorem 11.2.2 and the chain rule for real-valued functions.

▶ **EXAMPLE 3** Verify Theorem 11.2.8 if the functions $\mathbf{F}$ and h are defined by

$$\mathbf{F}(\phi) = \phi^2\mathbf{i} + e^\phi\mathbf{j} + \ln\phi\mathbf{k} \quad \text{and} \quad h(t) = \sin t$$

Solution With $\phi = h(t)$ and $\mathbf{G}(t) = \mathbf{F}(h(t))$

$$\phi = \sin t \quad \text{and} \quad \mathbf{G}(t) = \sin^2 t\,\mathbf{i} + e^{\sin t}\,\mathbf{j} + \ln\sin t\,\mathbf{k}$$

Computing $D_t\mathbf{G}(t)$ by Theorem 11.2.2, we have

$$D_t\mathbf{G}(t) = 2\sin t\cos t\,\mathbf{i} + e^{\sin t}\cos t\,\mathbf{j} + \cot t\,\mathbf{k} \qquad (3)$$

We now compute the right-hand side of the equation of Theorem 11.2.8. Because $\mathbf{G}(t)$ can also be written as $\phi^2\mathbf{i} + e^\phi\mathbf{j} + \ln\phi\mathbf{k}$, we have

$$D_\phi[\mathbf{G}(t)]\frac{d\phi}{dt} = \left(2\phi\mathbf{i} + e^\phi\mathbf{j} + \frac{1}{\phi}\mathbf{k}\right)\frac{d\phi}{dt}$$

But $\phi = \sin t$; thus

$$D_\phi[\mathbf{G}(t)]\frac{d\phi}{dt} = \left(2\sin t\,\mathbf{i} + e^{\sin t}\,\mathbf{j} + \frac{1}{\sin t}\mathbf{k}\right)\cos t$$

$$= 2\sin t\cos t\,\mathbf{i} + e^{\sin t}\cos t\,\mathbf{j} + \cot t\,\mathbf{k}$$

From (3), the right-hand side of this equation is $D_t\mathbf{G}(t)$. Thus

$$D_\phi[\mathbf{G}(t)]\frac{d\phi}{dt} = D_t\mathbf{G}(t)$$

which verifies Theorem 11.2.8 for these functions. ◀

The next theorem will be useful later.

11.2.9 Theorem

If $\mathbf{R}$ is a differentiable vector-valued function on an interval and $\|\mathbf{R}(t)\|$ is constant for all t in the interval, then the vectors $\mathbf{R}(t)$ and $D_t\mathbf{R}(t)$ are orthogonal.

Proof Let $\|\mathbf{R}(t)\| = k$. Then by Theorem 10.3.3 (iii),

$$\mathbf{R}(t) \cdot \mathbf{R}(t) = k^2$$

Differentiating on both sides with respect to t and applying Theorem 11.2.5 we obtain

$$[D_t\mathbf{R}(t)] \cdot \mathbf{R}(t) + \mathbf{R}(t) \cdot [D_t\mathbf{R}(t)] = 0$$
$$2\mathbf{R}(t) \cdot D_t\mathbf{R}(t) = 0$$

Because the dot product of $\mathbf{R}(t)$ and $D_t\mathbf{R}(t)$ is zero, it follows from Definition 10.3.7 that $\mathbf{R}(t)$ and $D_t\mathbf{R}(t)$ are orthogonal. ■

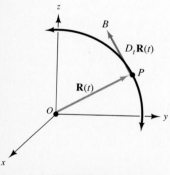

FIGURE 2

See Figure 2 for the geometric interpretation of Theorem 11.2.9. Because the vector $\mathbf{R}(t)$ has constant magnitude k, the position representation

$\overrightarrow{OP}$ of $\mathbf{R}(t)$ has its terminal point P on the circle with center at the origin and radius k. So the graph of $\mathbf{R}$ is this circle, a quarter of which appears in Figure 2 along with $\overrightarrow{OP}$ and the representation $\overrightarrow{PB}$ of $D_t\mathbf{R}(t)$. Because $D_t\mathbf{R}(t)$ and $\mathbf{R}(t)$ are orthogonal, $\overrightarrow{OP}$ is perpendicular to $\overrightarrow{PB}$.

We now define an indefinite integral (or antiderivative) of a vector-valued function.

> **11.2.10 Definition of an Indefinite Integral of a Vector-Valued Function**
>
> If $\mathbf{Q}$ is the vector-valued function given by
> $$\mathbf{Q}(t) = f(t)\mathbf{i} + g(t)\mathbf{j} + h(t)\mathbf{k}$$
> then the **indefinite integral** of $\mathbf{Q}(t)$ is defined by
> $$\int \mathbf{Q}(t)\,dt = \mathbf{i}\int f(t)\,dt + \mathbf{j}\int g(t)\,dt + \mathbf{k}\int h(t)\,dt \qquad (4)$$

This definition is consistent with the definition of an indefinite integral of a real-valued function because if we take the derivative on both sides of (4) with respect to t,

$$D_t\int \mathbf{Q}(t)\,dt = \mathbf{i}D_t\int f(t)\,dt + \mathbf{j}D_t\int g(t)\,dt + \mathbf{k}D_t\int h(t)\,dt$$
$$= \mathbf{i}f(t) + \mathbf{j}g(t) + \mathbf{k}h(t)$$

An arbitrary scalar constant arises from each of the indefinite integrals on the right-hand side of (4). When each of these scalars is multiplied by $\mathbf{i}$, $\mathbf{j}$, or $\mathbf{k}$, an arbitrary constant vector occurs in the sum. Thus

$$\int \mathbf{Q}(t)\,dt = \mathbf{R}(t) + \mathbf{C}$$

where $D_t\mathbf{R}(t) = \mathbf{Q}(t)$ and $\mathbf{C}$ is an arbitrary constant vector.

▶ **EXAMPLE 4**   Find the most general vector-valued function whose derivative is
$$\mathbf{Q}(t) = \sin t\mathbf{i} - 3\cos t\mathbf{j} + 2t\mathbf{k}$$

Solution   If $D_t\mathbf{R}(t) = \mathbf{Q}(t)$, then $\mathbf{R}(t) = \int \mathbf{Q}(t)\,dt$; that is

$$\mathbf{R}(t) = \mathbf{i}\int \sin t\,dt - 3\mathbf{j}\int \cos t\,dt + \mathbf{k}\int 2t\,dt$$
$$= \mathbf{i}(-\cos t + C_1) - 3\mathbf{j}(\sin t + C_2) + \mathbf{k}(t^2 + C_3)$$
$$= -\cos t\mathbf{i} - 3\sin t\mathbf{j} + t^2\mathbf{k} + (C_1\mathbf{i} - 3C_2\mathbf{j} + C_3\mathbf{k})$$
$$= -\cos t\mathbf{i} - 3\sin t\mathbf{j} + t^2\mathbf{k} + \mathbf{C}$$ ◀

▶ **EXAMPLE 5**   Find the vector $\mathbf{R}(t)$ for which
$$D_t\mathbf{R}(t) = e^{-t}\mathbf{i} + e^t\mathbf{j} + 3\mathbf{k} \quad \text{and} \quad \mathbf{R}(0) = \mathbf{i} + \mathbf{j} + 5\mathbf{k}$$

Solution

$$\mathbf{R}(t) = \mathbf{i} \int e^{-t}\, dt + \mathbf{j} \int e^{t}\, dt + \mathbf{k} \int 3\, dt$$

$$= \mathbf{i}(-e^{-t} + C_1) + \mathbf{j}(e^{t} + C_2) + \mathbf{k}(3t + C_3)$$

Because $\mathbf{R}(0) = \mathbf{i} + \mathbf{j} + 5\mathbf{k}$

$$\mathbf{i} + \mathbf{j} + 5\mathbf{k} = \mathbf{i}(-1 + C_1) + \mathbf{j}(1 + C_2) + \mathbf{k}(C_3)$$

Therefore

$$C_1 - 1 = 1 \qquad C_2 + 1 = 1 \qquad C_3 = 5$$
$$C_1 = 2 \qquad\qquad C_2 = 0$$

Hence

$$\mathbf{R}(t) = (-e^{-t} + 2)\mathbf{i} + e^{t}\mathbf{j} + (3t + 5)\mathbf{k} \qquad\blacktriangleleft$$

In Section 9.2 you learned from Theorem 9.2.3 that if C is a plane curve having parametric equations $x = f(t)$ and $y = g(t)$ where f' and g' are continuous on the closed interval $[a, b]$ and if L units is the length of arc of C from the point $(f(a), g(a))$ to the point $(f(b), g(b))$,

$$L = \int_a^b \sqrt{[f'(t)]^2 + [g'(t)]^2}\, dt$$

Because a vector equation of C is $\mathbf{R}(t) = f(t)\mathbf{i} + g(t)\mathbf{j}$, this formula can be written as

$$L = \int_a^b \| \mathbf{R}'(t) \|\, dt \qquad (5)$$

▶ **EXAMPLE 6**   Find the length of arc traced by the terminal point of the position representation of $\mathbf{R}(t)$ as t increases from 1 to 4 if

$$\mathbf{R}(t) = e^{t} \sin t\, \mathbf{i} + e^{t} \cos t\, \mathbf{j}$$

Solution

$$\mathbf{R}'(t) = (e^{t} \sin t + e^{t} \cos t)\mathbf{i} + (e^{t} \cos t - e^{t} \sin t)\mathbf{j}$$
$$\| \mathbf{R}'(t) \| = \sqrt{(e^{t} \sin t + e^{t} \cos t)^2 + (e^{t} \cos t - e^{t} \sin t)^2}$$
$$= \sqrt{e^{2t}} \sqrt{\sin^2 t + 2 \sin t \cos t + \cos^2 t + \cos^2 t - 2 \sin t \cos t + \sin^2 t}$$
$$= e^{t}\sqrt{2}$$

From formula (5),

$$L = \int_1^4 \sqrt{2}\, e^{t}\, dt$$
$$= \sqrt{2}e^{t} \Big]_1^4$$
$$= \sqrt{2}(e^4 - e) \qquad\blacktriangleleft$$

The length of arc of a curve in three-dimensional space can be defined exactly as we defined the length of arc of a plane curve in Definition 9.2.1.

Furthermore, if C is the curve having parametric equations $x = f(t)$, $y = g(t)$, $z = h(t)$ or, equivalently, the vector equation

$$\mathbf{R}(t) = f(t)\mathbf{i} + g(t)\mathbf{j} + h(t)\mathbf{k}$$

then we can prove, in the same way as we proved Theorem 9.2.3, the following theorem.

11.2.11 Theorem

Let curve C have the vector equation $\mathbf{R}(t) = f(t)\mathbf{i} + g(t)\mathbf{j} + h(t)\mathbf{k}$, and suppose f', g', and h' are continuous on the closed interval $[a, b]$. Then if L is the length of arc of C from the point $(f(a), g(a), h(a))$ to the point $(f(b), g(b), h(b))$,

$$L = \int_a^b \| \mathbf{R}'(t) \| \, dt$$

▶ **EXAMPLE 7**   Find the length of arc of the circular helix of Example 1 in Section 11.1:

$$\mathbf{R}(t) = 2 \cos t\mathbf{i} + 2 \sin t\mathbf{j} + t\mathbf{k}$$

from $t = 0$ to $t = 4\pi$.

Solution   In Section 11.1 we sketched the helix which appears here in Figure 3. From the given vector equation,

$$\mathbf{R}'(t) = -2 \sin t\mathbf{i} + 2 \cos t\mathbf{j} + \mathbf{k}$$

Thus from Theorem 11.2.11,

$$
\begin{aligned}
L &= \int_0^{4\pi} \sqrt{(-2 \sin t)^2 + (2 \cos t)^2 + 1} \, dt \\
&= \int_0^{4\pi} \sqrt{4 \sin^2 t + 4 \cos^2 t + 1} \, dt \\
&= \int_0^{4\pi} \sqrt{5} \, dt \\
&= 4\pi \sqrt{5} \\
&\approx 28.10
\end{aligned}
$$

◀

The definite integral in the above example was easy to evaluate, but as you learned in our previous discussions of length of arc, most of the time we can only approximate the value. This situation arises in Exercises 53 through 56 where you are asked to use the NINT capability of your graphics calculator to obtain an approximation of the length of an arc.

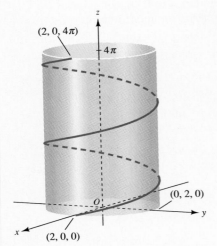

(2, 0, 4π)

(0, 2, 0)

(2, 0, 0)

$\mathbf{R}(t) = 2 \cos t\,\mathbf{i} + 2 \sin t\,\mathbf{j} + t\,\mathbf{k}$ $0 \le t \le 4\pi$

FIGURE 3

EXERCISES 11.2

In Exercises 1 through 10, find $\mathbf{R}'(t)$ and $\mathbf{R}''(t)$.

1. $\mathbf{R}(t) = t\mathbf{i} + \dfrac{1}{t}\mathbf{j}$

2. $\mathbf{R}(t) = (t^2 - 3)\mathbf{i} + (2t + 1)\mathbf{j}$

3. $\mathbf{R}(t) = \dfrac{t - 1}{t + 1}\mathbf{i} + \dfrac{t - 2}{t}\mathbf{j}$

4. $\mathbf{R}(t) = (t^2 + 4)^{-1}\mathbf{i} + \sqrt{1 - 5t}\,\mathbf{j}$

5. $\mathbf{R}(t) = e^{2t}\mathbf{i} + \ln t\mathbf{j} + t^2\mathbf{k}$

6. $\mathbf{R}(t) = \cos 2t\mathbf{i} + \tan t\mathbf{j} + t\mathbf{k}$
7. $\mathbf{R}(t) = \tan^{-1} t\mathbf{i} + \sin^{-1} t\mathbf{j} + \cos^{-1} t\mathbf{k}$
8. $\mathbf{R}(t) = (e^{3t} + 2)\mathbf{i} + 2e^{3t}\mathbf{j} + 3 \cdot 2^t\mathbf{k}$
9. $\mathbf{R}(t) = 5 \sin 2t\mathbf{i} - \sec 4t\mathbf{j} + 4 \cos 2t\mathbf{k}$
10. $\mathbf{R}(t) = \tan 3t\mathbf{i} + \ln \sin t\mathbf{j} - \dfrac{1}{t}\mathbf{k}$

In Exercises 11 through 14, find $D_t \| \mathbf{R}(t) \|$.

11. $\mathbf{R}(t) = (t - 1)\mathbf{i} + (2 - t)\mathbf{j}$
12. $\mathbf{R}(t) = (e^t + 1)\mathbf{i} + (e^t - 1)\mathbf{j}$
13. $\mathbf{R}(t) = \sin 3t\mathbf{i} + \cos 3t\mathbf{j} + 2e^{3t}\mathbf{k}$
14. $\mathbf{R}(t) = \sqrt{t^2 + 1}\mathbf{i} + \sqrt{t^2 - 1}\mathbf{j} + t\mathbf{k}$

In Exercises 15 through 18, verify Theorem 11.2.4 for the given vector-valued functions.

15. $\mathbf{R}(t) = (t^2 + e^t)\mathbf{i} + (t - e^{2t})\mathbf{j}$;
$\mathbf{Q}(t) = (t^3 + 2e^t)\mathbf{i} - (3t + e^{2t})\mathbf{j}$
16. $\mathbf{R}(t) = \cos 2t\mathbf{i} - \sin 2t\mathbf{j}$; $\mathbf{Q}(t) = \sin^2 t\mathbf{i} + \cos 2t\mathbf{j}$
17. $\mathbf{R}(t) = 2 \sin t\mathbf{i} + \cos t\mathbf{j} - \sin 2t\mathbf{k}$;
$\mathbf{Q}(t) = \cos t\mathbf{i} + 2 \sin t\mathbf{j} + \mathbf{k}$
18. $\mathbf{R}(t) = e^{3t}\mathbf{i} - 4e^{3t}\mathbf{j} - 2\mathbf{k}$; $\mathbf{Q}(t) = e^t\mathbf{i} - e^t\mathbf{j} - 2e^{4t}\mathbf{k}$

In Exercises 19 through 22, verify Theorem 11.2.5 for the vector-valued functions of the indicated exercise.

19. Exercise 15 20. Exercise 16
21. Exercise 17 22. Exercise 18

In Exercises 23 and 24, verify Theorem 11.2.6 for the given functions.

23. $f(t) = \cos 2t$; $\mathbf{R}$ is the function of Exercise 9.
24. $f(t) = e^t$; $\mathbf{R}$ is the function of Exercise 8.

In Exercises 25 and 26, verify Theorem 11.2.7 for the vector-valued functions of the indicated exercise.

25. Exercise 17 26. Exercise 18

In Exercises 27 and 28, verify Theorem 11.2.8 for the given functions.

27. $\mathbf{F}(\phi) = \phi\mathbf{i} + \phi^2\mathbf{j} + \ln \phi\mathbf{k}$ and $h(t) = e^t$
28. $\mathbf{F}(\phi) = \sin \phi\mathbf{i} + \cos \phi\mathbf{j} + \phi\mathbf{k}$ and $h(t) = \sin^{-1} t$
29. Prove Theorem 11.2.4. 30. Prove Theorem 11.2.6.
31. Prove Theorem 11.2.7. 32. Prove Theorem 11.2.8.

In Exercises 33 through 40, find the most general vector-valued function whose derivative has the given function value.

33. $\tan t\mathbf{i} - \dfrac{1}{t}\mathbf{j}$

34. $(t^2 - 9)\mathbf{i} + (2t - 5)\mathbf{j}$

35. $\ln t\mathbf{i} + t^2\mathbf{j}$

36. $\dfrac{1}{4 + t^2}\mathbf{i} - \dfrac{4}{1 - t^2}\mathbf{j}$

37. $e^{3t}\mathbf{i} + e^{-3t}\mathbf{j} - te^{3t}\mathbf{k}$ 38. $3^t\mathbf{i} - 2^t\mathbf{j} + e^t\mathbf{k}$

39. $\tan t\mathbf{i} + \sec t\mathbf{j} + \dfrac{1}{t}\mathbf{k}$ 40. $t \sin t\mathbf{i} - t \cos t\mathbf{j} + t\mathbf{k}$

41. If $\mathbf{R}'(t) = t^2\mathbf{i} + \dfrac{1}{t - 2}\mathbf{j}$ and $\mathbf{R}(3) = 2\mathbf{i} - 5\mathbf{j}$,
find $\mathbf{R}(t)$.
42. If $\mathbf{R}'(t) = \sin^2 t\mathbf{i} + 2 \cos^2 t\mathbf{j}$ and $\mathbf{R}(\pi) = \mathbf{0}$,
find $\mathbf{R}(t)$.
43. If $\mathbf{R}'(t) = e^t \sin t\mathbf{i} + \cos t\mathbf{j} - e^t\mathbf{k}$ and
$R(0) = \mathbf{i} - \mathbf{j} + \mathbf{k}$, find $\mathbf{R}(t)$.
44. If $R'(t) = \dfrac{1}{t + 1}\mathbf{i} - \tan t\mathbf{j} + \dfrac{t}{t^2 - 1}\mathbf{k}$ and
$\mathbf{R}(0) = 4\mathbf{i} - 3\mathbf{j} + 5\mathbf{k}$, find $\mathbf{R}(t)$.

In Exercises 45 and 46, do the following: (a) Find a cartesian equation of the curve traced by the endpoint of the position representation of $\mathbf{R}'(t)$; (b) compute $\mathbf{R}(t) \cdot \mathbf{R}'(t)$ and interpret the result geometrically.

45. $\mathbf{R}(t) = \cos t\mathbf{i} + \sin t\mathbf{j}$
46. $\mathbf{R}(t) = \cosh t\mathbf{i} - \sinh t\mathbf{j}$

In Exercises 47 and 48, if $\alpha(t)$ is the radian measure of the angle between $\mathbf{R}(t)$ and $\mathbf{Q}(t)$, find $D_t\alpha(t)$.

47. $\mathbf{R}(t) = 3e^{2t}\mathbf{i} - 4e^{2t}\mathbf{j}$ and $\mathbf{Q}(t) = 6e^{3t}\mathbf{j}$
48. $\mathbf{R}(t) = 2t\mathbf{i} + (t^2 - 1)\mathbf{j}$ and $\mathbf{Q}(t) = 3t\mathbf{i}$

In Exercises 49 through 52, find the exact length of arc from t_1 to t_2 of the curve having the given vector equation.

49. $\mathbf{R}(t) = (t + 1)\mathbf{i} - t^2\mathbf{j} + (1 - 2t)\mathbf{k}$; $t_1 = -1$; $t_2 = 2$
50. $\mathbf{R}(t) = \sin 2t\mathbf{i} + \cos 2t\mathbf{j} + 2t^{3/2}\mathbf{k}$; $t_1 = 0$; $t_2 = 1$
51. $\mathbf{R}(t) = 4t^{3/2}\mathbf{i} - 3 \sin t\mathbf{j} + 3 \cos t\mathbf{k}$; $t_1 = 0$; $t_2 = 2$
52. $\mathbf{R}(t) = t^2\mathbf{i} + (t + \frac{1}{3}t^3)\mathbf{j} + (t - \frac{1}{3}t^3)\mathbf{k}$; $t_1 = 0$; $t_2 = 1$

In Exercises 53 through 56, use the NINT capability of your graphics calculator to find an approximate value to four significant digits of the length of arc from t_1 to t_2 of the curve having the given vector equation.

53. The twisted cubic $\mathbf{R}(t) = t\mathbf{i} + t^2\mathbf{j} + t^3\mathbf{k}$; $t_1 = 0$;
$t_2 = 2$
54. $\mathbf{R}(t) = e^t\mathbf{i} + e^t\mathbf{j} + \ln t\mathbf{k}$; $t_1 = 1$; $t_2 = 2$
55. $\mathbf{R}(t) = \cos t\mathbf{i} + \sin t\mathbf{j} + t^3\mathbf{k}$; $t_1 = -1$; $t_2 = 1$
56. $\mathbf{R}(t) = \sin 2t\mathbf{i} + \cos 2t\mathbf{j} + t^{1/2}\mathbf{k}$; $t_1 = 0$; $t_2 = 4$
57. Suppose that $\mathbf{R}$ and $\mathbf{R}'$ are vector-valued functions defined on an interval and $\mathbf{R}'$ is differentiable on the interval. Prove

$$D_t[\mathbf{R}'(t) \cdot \mathbf{R}(t)] = \| \mathbf{R}'(t) \|^2 + \mathbf{R}(t) \cdot \mathbf{R}''(t)$$

58. If $\| \mathbf{R}(t) \| = h(t)$, prove that
$$\mathbf{R}(t) \cdot \mathbf{R}'(t) = [h(t)][(h'(t)]$$

59. If the vector-valued function $\mathbf{R}$ and the real-valued function f are both differentiable on an interval and $f(t) \neq 0$ on the interval, prove that $\mathbf{R}/f$ is also differentiable on the interval and

$$D_t \left[\frac{\mathbf{R}(t)}{f(t)} \right] = \frac{f(t)\mathbf{R}'(t) - f'(t)\mathbf{R}(t)}{[f(t)]^2}$$

60. Prove that if $\mathbf{A}$ and $\mathbf{B}$ are constant vectors and f and g are integrable functions, then

$$\int [\mathbf{A}f(t) + \mathbf{B}g(t)] \, dt = \mathbf{A} \int f(t) \, dt + \mathbf{B} \int g(t) \, dt$$

Hint: Express $\mathbf{A}$ and $\mathbf{B}$ in terms of $\mathbf{i}$, $\mathbf{j}$, and $\mathbf{k}$.

61. Use Theorem 4.1.2 for real-valued functions to prove the following corresponding theorem for vector-valued functions: If $\mathbf{R}$ and $\mathbf{Q}$ are two vector-valued functions such that $\mathbf{R}'(t) = \mathbf{Q}'(t)$ for all t on an interval I, then there is a constant vector $\mathbf{K}$ such that $\mathbf{R}(t) = \mathbf{Q}(t) + \mathbf{K}$ for all t in I.

62. Use the theorem in Exercise 61 to prove the following theorem that corresponds to Theorem 4.1.3 for real-valued functions: If $\mathbf{F}(t)$ is a particular antiderivative of $\mathbf{R}$ on an interval I, then every antiderivative of $\mathbf{R}$ on I is given by $\mathbf{F}(t) + \mathbf{C}$, where $\mathbf{C}$ is an arbitrary constant vector.

63. Define a definite integral of a vector-valued function in a way similar to that of an indefinite integral. Then use the first fundamental theorem of the calculus (4.7.1) to prove the following corresponding theorem for vector-valued functions: If the function $\mathbf{R}$ is continuous on the closed interval $[a, b]$ and t is any number in $[a, b]$, then

$$D_t \int_a^t \mathbf{R}(u) \, du = \mathbf{R}(t)$$

64. Use the theorems of Exercises 62 and 63 to prove the following theorem that corresponds to the second fundamental theorem of the calculus (4.7.2): If the function $\mathbf{R}$ is continuous on the closed interval $[a, b]$ and if $\mathbf{F}(t)$ is any antiderivative of $\mathbf{R}$ on $[a, b]$, then

$$\int_a^b \mathbf{R}(t) \, dt = \mathbf{F}(b) - \mathbf{F}(a)$$

11.3 THE UNIT TANGENT AND UNIT NORMAL VECTORS AND ARC LENGTH AS PARAMETER

With each point on a curve we now associate two unit vectors, the *unit tangent vector* and the *unit normal vector*. These vectors occur in many applications of vector-valued functions, some of which you will encounter in the next two sections. In this section and the following sections of this chapter, we assume that a curve has a direction (or orientation) implied by increasing values of the parameter.

11.3.1 Definition of the Unit Tangent Vector

If $\mathbf{R}(t)$ is the position vector of curve C at a point P on C, the **unit tangent vector** of C at P, denoted by $\mathbf{T}(t)$, is the unit vector in the direction of $D_t \mathbf{R}(t)$ if $D_t \mathbf{R}(t) \neq \mathbf{0}$.

Because the unit vector in the direction of $D_t \mathbf{R}(t)$ is given by $D_t \mathbf{R}(t)/\| D_t \mathbf{R}(t) \|$,

$$\mathbf{T}(t) = \frac{D_t \mathbf{R}(t)}{\| D_t \mathbf{R}(t) \|} \tag{1}$$

From Theorem 11.2.9, because $\mathbf{T}(t)$ is a unit vector, $D_t \mathbf{T}(t)$ must be orthogonal to $\mathbf{T}(t)$. While $D_t \mathbf{T}(t)$ is not necessarily a unit vector, the vector $D_t \mathbf{T}(t)/\| D_t \mathbf{T}(t) \|$ is of unit magnitude and has the same direction as $D_t \mathbf{T}(t)$. Therefore $D_t \mathbf{T}(t)/\| D_t \mathbf{T}(t) \|$ is a unit vector orthogonal to $\mathbf{T}(t)$, and it is called the *unit normal vector*.

11.3.2 Definition of the Unit Normal Vector

If $\mathbf{T}(t)$ is the unit tangent vector of curve C at a point P on C, the **unit normal vector,** denoted by $\mathbf{N}(t)$, is the unit vector in the direction of $D_t\mathbf{T}(t)$.

From this definition and the discussion preceding it,

$$\mathbf{N}(t) = \frac{D_t\mathbf{T}(t)}{\|D_t\mathbf{T}(t)\|} \qquad\qquad (2)$$

▶ **EXAMPLE 1**   Find $\mathbf{T}(t)$ and $\mathbf{N}(t)$ for the curve having the vector equation

$$\mathbf{R}(t) = (t^3 - 3t)\mathbf{i} + 3t^2\mathbf{j}$$

Sketch a portion of the curve at $t = 2$ and draw the representations of $\mathbf{T}(2)$ and $\mathbf{N}(2)$ having their initial point at $t = 2$.

Solution

$$D_t\mathbf{R}(t) = (3t^2 - 3)\mathbf{i} + 6t\mathbf{j} \qquad \|D_t\mathbf{R}(t)\| = \sqrt{(3t^2 - 3)^2 + 36t^2}$$
$$= \sqrt{9(t^4 + 2t^2 + 1)}$$
$$= 3(t^2 + 1)$$

From (1),

$$\mathbf{T}(t) = \frac{D_t\mathbf{R}(t)}{\|D_t\mathbf{R}(t)\|}$$
$$= \frac{t^2 - 1}{t^2 + 1}\mathbf{i} + \frac{2t}{t^2 + 1}\mathbf{j}$$

Differentiating $\mathbf{T}(t)$ with respect to t we obtain

$$D_t\mathbf{T}(t) = \frac{4t}{(t^2 + 1)^2}\mathbf{i} + \frac{2 - 2t^2}{(t^2 + 1)^2}\mathbf{j}$$

Therefore

$$\|D_t\mathbf{T}(t)\| = \sqrt{\frac{16t^2}{(t^2 + 1)^4} + \frac{4 - 8t^2 + 4t^4}{(t^2 + 1)^4}}$$
$$= \sqrt{\frac{4 + 8t^2 + 4t^4}{(t^2 + 1)^4}}$$
$$= \sqrt{\frac{4(t^2 + 1)^2}{(t^2 + 1)^4}}$$
$$= \frac{2}{t^2 + 1}$$

From (2),

$$\mathbf{N}(t) = \frac{D_t\mathbf{T}(t)}{\|D_t\mathbf{T}(t)\|}$$
$$= \frac{2t}{t^2 + 1}\mathbf{i} + \frac{1 - t^2}{t^2 + 1}\mathbf{j}$$

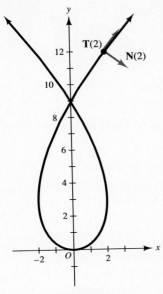

FIGURE 1

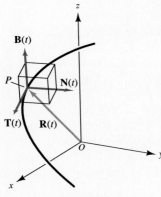

FIGURE 2

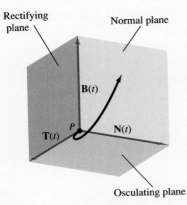

FIGURE 3

We find $\mathbf{R}(t)$, $\mathbf{T}(t)$, and $\mathbf{N}(t)$ when $t = 2$.

$$\mathbf{R}(2) = 2\mathbf{i} + 12\mathbf{j} \qquad \mathbf{T}(2) = \tfrac{3}{5}\mathbf{i} + \tfrac{4}{5}\mathbf{j} \qquad \mathbf{N}(2) = \tfrac{4}{5}\mathbf{i} - \tfrac{3}{5}\mathbf{j}$$

The required curve and vectors appear in Figure 1. ◀

Because the unit tangent and unit normal vectors are orthogonal, the angle between them is $\tfrac{1}{2}\pi$. So from Theorem 10.5.8,

$$\|\mathbf{T}(t) \times \mathbf{N}(t)\| = \|\mathbf{T}(t)\|\|\mathbf{N}(t)\| \sin \tfrac{1}{2}\pi$$
$$= 1$$

The cross product of $\mathbf{T}(t)$ and $\mathbf{N}(t)$ is, therefore, a unit vector, and by Theorem 10.5.10 is orthogonal to both $\mathbf{T}(t)$ and $\mathbf{N}(t)$. This vector, called the **unit binormal vector,** and denoted by $\mathbf{B}(t)$, is defined by

$$\mathbf{B}(t) = \mathbf{T}(t) \times \mathbf{N}(t) \tag{3}$$

The three mutually orthogonal unit vectors $\mathbf{T}(t)$, $\mathbf{N}(t)$, and $\mathbf{B}(t)$ of a curve C are called the **moving trihedral** of C, which is important in space travel. See Figure 2. The moving trihedral is also referred to as the **Frenet frame,** named for Jean-Frederic Frenet (1816–1900). The planes determined by representations of the three vectors at a point in space have specific names. As indicated in Figure 3, the representations of $\mathbf{T}(t)$ and $\mathbf{N}(t)$ at point P form the **osculating plane,** the representations of $\mathbf{T}(t)$ and $\mathbf{B}(t)$ form the **rectifying plane,** and the representations of $\mathbf{N}(t)$ and $\mathbf{B}(t)$ form the **normal plane.**

▶ **EXAMPLE 2** Find the moving trihedral at any point of the circular helix

$$\mathbf{R}(t) = a \cos t\mathbf{i} + a \sin t\mathbf{j} + t\mathbf{k} \qquad a > 0$$

Solution With

$$D_t\mathbf{R}(t) = -a \sin t\mathbf{i} + a \cos t\mathbf{j} + \mathbf{k} \quad \text{and} \quad \|D_t\mathbf{R}(t)\| = \sqrt{a^2 + 1}$$

we obtain from (1)

$$\mathbf{T}(t) = \frac{1}{\sqrt{a^2 + 1}}(-a \sin t\mathbf{i} + a \cos t\mathbf{j} + \mathbf{k})$$

With

$$D_t\mathbf{T}(t) = \frac{1}{\sqrt{a^2 + 1}}(-a \cos t\mathbf{i} - a \sin t\mathbf{j}) \quad \text{and} \quad \|D_t\mathbf{T}(t)\| = \frac{a}{\sqrt{a^2 + 1}}$$

we obtain from (2)

$$\mathbf{N}(t) = \frac{\dfrac{1}{\sqrt{a^2 + 1}}(-a \cos t\mathbf{i} - a \sin t\mathbf{j})}{\dfrac{a}{\sqrt{a^2 + 1}}}$$

$$= -\cos t\mathbf{i} - \sin t\mathbf{j}$$

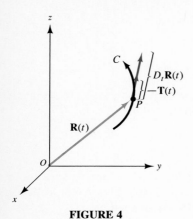

FIGURE 4

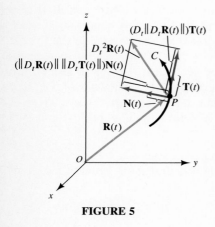

FIGURE 5

Applying (3) we get

$$\mathbf{B}(t) = \frac{1}{\sqrt{a^2 + 1}}(-a \sin t\mathbf{i} + a \cos t\mathbf{j} + \mathbf{k}) \times (-\cos t\mathbf{i} - \sin t\mathbf{j})$$

$$= \frac{1}{\sqrt{a^2 + 1}}(\sin t\mathbf{i} - \cos t\mathbf{j} + a\mathbf{k}) \qquad \blacktriangleleft$$

From Equation (1), the vector $D_t\mathbf{R}(t)$ can be expressed as a scalar times the unit tangent vector as follows:

$$D_t\mathbf{R}(t) = \| D_t\mathbf{R}(t) \|\mathbf{T}(t) \tag{4}$$

Figure 4 shows a portion of a curve C with the position representation of $\mathbf{R}(t)$ and the representations of $\mathbf{T}(t)$ and $D_t\mathbf{R}(t)$ whose initial points are at the point P on C.

We now use (4) to compute $D_t{}^2\mathbf{R}(t)$ by applying Theorem 11.2.6.

$$D_t{}^2\mathbf{R}(t) = (D_t\| D_t\mathbf{R}(t) \|)\mathbf{T}(t) + \| D_t\mathbf{R}(t) \|(D_t\mathbf{T}(t)) \tag{5}$$

From (2),

$$D_t\mathbf{T}(t) = \| D_t\mathbf{T}(t) \|\mathbf{N}(t)$$

Substituting from this equation into (5) we get

$$D_t{}^2\mathbf{R}(t) = (D_t\| D_t\mathbf{R}(t) \|)\mathbf{T}(t) + (\| D_t\mathbf{R}(t) \| \| D_t\mathbf{T}(t) \|)\mathbf{N}(t)$$

This equation expresses the vector $D_t{}^2\mathbf{R}(t)$ as a scalar times the unit tangent vector plus a scalar times the unit normal vector. The coefficient of $\mathbf{T}(t)$ on the right side of (6) is the component of the vector $D_t{}^2\mathbf{R}(t)$ in the direction of the unit tangent vector, while the coefficient of $\mathbf{N}(t)$ is the component of $D_t{}^2\mathbf{R}(t)$ in the direction of the unit normal vector.

Figure 5 shows the position representation of $\mathbf{R}(t)$ and the same portion of the curve C as in Figure 4. Also shown in Figure 5 are the representations of the following vectors, all of whose initial points are at the point P on C:

$$D_t{}^2\mathbf{R}(t) \qquad \mathbf{T}(t) \qquad (D_t\| D_t\mathbf{R}(t) \|)\mathbf{T}(t) \qquad \mathbf{N}(t) \qquad (\| D_t\mathbf{R}(t) \| \| D_t\mathbf{T}(t) \|)\mathbf{N}(t)$$

Observe that the representation of the unit normal vector $\mathbf{N}(t)$ is on the concave side of the curve.

Sometimes, as in the next section when computing *curvature,* it is convenient for the parameter in the vector equation of a curve to represent arc length. For instance, if a vector equation of curve C is

$$\mathbf{R}(t) = f(t)\mathbf{i} + g(t)\mathbf{j} + h(t)\mathbf{k}$$

then instead of parameter t, we may wish to use as a parameter the number of units of arc length s from an arbitrarily chosen point $P_0(f(t_0), g(t_0), h(t_0))$ on C to the point $P(f(t), g(t), h(t))$ on C. Let s increase as t increases so that s is positive if the arc length is measured in the direction of increasing t and negative if measured in the opposite direction. Therefore s is a directed distance. A unique point P on C corresponds to each value of s. Consequently, the coordinates of P are functions of s and s is a function of t, which from Theorem 11.2.11 is given by

$$s = \int_{t_0}^{t} \| D_u \mathbf{R}(u) \| \, du$$

From the first fundamental theorem of the calculus

$$\frac{ds}{dt} = \| D_t \mathbf{R}(t) \| \qquad (7)$$

Substituting from (7) into (4) we get

$$D_t \mathbf{R}(t) = \frac{ds}{dt} \mathbf{T}(t) \qquad (8)$$

If the parameter in the vector equation of C is s instead of t, we obtain from this equation, by taking $t = s$ and noting that $ds/ds = 1$,

$$D_s \mathbf{R}(s) = \mathbf{T}(s)$$

We state this result as a theorem.

11.3.3 Theorem

If the vector equation of a curve C is

$$\mathbf{R}(s) = f(s)\mathbf{i} + g(s)\mathbf{j} + h(s)\mathbf{k}$$

where s units is the length of arc measured from a particular point P_0 on C to the point P, then the unit tangent vector of C at P is given by

$$\mathbf{T}(s) = D_s \mathbf{R}(s)$$

if it exists.

As you learned in Sections 9.2 and 11.2, most of the time the formula for computing the length of arc leads to a definite integral for which the corresponding indefinite integral cannot be evaluated in closed form, which meant we could only approximate the length of arc by numerical techniques or using the NINT capability of a graphics calculator. Similar problems arise when we are given a vector equation of a curve involving a parameter t and we wish to find a vector equation of the curve with arc length s as parameter. That is, generally we cannot express s in terms of t. We can, however, generally compute ds/dt from Equation (7), which often satisfies our purposes.

▶ **EXAMPLE 3**   Given curve C having the vector equation

$$\mathbf{R}(t) = t^3 \mathbf{i} + t^2 \mathbf{j} + t \mathbf{k}$$

find ds/dt.

Solution   From (7)

$$\frac{ds}{dt} = \| D_t\mathbf{R}(t) \|$$

$$= \| 3t^2\mathbf{i} + 2t\mathbf{j} + \mathbf{k} \|$$
$$= \sqrt{(3t^2)^2 + (2t)^2 + 1}$$
$$= \sqrt{9t^4 + 4t^2 + 1} \qquad \blacktriangleleft$$

Observe that for the curve in the above example, if you wished to express s in terms of t from the equation

$$\frac{ds}{dt} = \sqrt{9t^4 + 4t^2 + 1}$$

you would need to evaluate the integral $\int \sqrt{9t^4 + 4t^2 + 1} \, dt$.

Once in a great while you can express s in terms of t, as in the following example, where the $\mathbf{i}$ and $\mathbf{j}$ components are the same as in Example 3 but the $\mathbf{k}$ component is 2 instead of t.

▶ **EXAMPLE 4**   Given that a vector equation of C is

$$\mathbf{R}(t) = t^3\mathbf{i} + t^2\mathbf{j} + 2\mathbf{k} \qquad t \geq 0$$

Find a vector equation of C having s as a parameter, where s units is the arc length measured from the point where $t = 0$.

Solution

$$D_t\mathbf{R}(t) = 3t^2\mathbf{i} + 2t\mathbf{j}$$
$$\| D_t\mathbf{R}(t) \| = \sqrt{9t^4 + 4t^2}$$
$$= \sqrt{t^2} \sqrt{9t^2 + 4}$$
$$= t\sqrt{9t^2 + 4} \qquad \text{(because } t \geq 0\text{)}$$

Therefore

$$\frac{ds}{dt} = t\sqrt{9t^2 + 4}$$

$$s = \int t\sqrt{9t^2 + 4} \, dt$$

$$= \frac{1}{18} \int \sqrt{9t^2 + 4}(18t \, dt)$$

$$= \tfrac{1}{27}(9t^2 + 4)^{3/2} + C$$

Because $s = 0$ when $t = 0$, we obtain $C = -\tfrac{8}{27}$. Therefore

$$s = \tfrac{1}{27}(9t^2 + 4)^{3/2} - \tfrac{8}{27}$$

Solving this equation for t in terms of s we have

$$(9t^2 + 4)^{3/2} = 27s + 8$$
$$9t^2 + 4 = (27s + 8)^{2/3}$$

Because $t \geq 0$,

$$t = \tfrac{1}{3}\sqrt{(27s + 8)^{2/3} - 4}$$

Substituting this value of t into the given vector equation of C we obtain

$$\mathbf{R}(s) = \tfrac{1}{27}[(27s + 8)^{2/3} - 4]^{3/2}\mathbf{i} + \tfrac{1}{9}[(27s + 8)^{2/3} - 4]\mathbf{j} + 2\mathbf{k} \quad \blacktriangleleft$$

Because $D_s\mathbf{R}(s) = \mathbf{T}(s)$, then if $\mathbf{R}(s) = f(s)\mathbf{i} + g(s)\mathbf{j} + h(s)\mathbf{k}$,

$$\mathbf{T}(s) = f'(s)\mathbf{i} + g'(s)\mathbf{j} + h'(s)\mathbf{k}$$

Thus, because $\mathbf{T}(s)$ is a unit vector,

$$[f'(s)]^2 + [g'(s)]^2 + [h'(s)]^2 = 1 \tag{9}$$

In Exercise 30 you are asked to use this equation to check the answer in Example 4.

EXERCISES 11.3

In Exercises 1 through 6, find $\mathbf{T}(t)$ *and* $\mathbf{N}(t)$, *and at* $t = t_1$, *sketch a portion of the curve and draw the representations of* $\mathbf{T}(t_1)$ *and* $\mathbf{N}(t_1)$ *having initial point at* $t = t_1$.

1. $\mathbf{R}(t) = 3 \cos t\mathbf{i} + 3 \sin t\mathbf{j}$; $t_1 = \tfrac{1}{2}\pi$
2. $\mathbf{R}(t) = \cos 3t\mathbf{i} + \sin 3t\mathbf{j}$; $t_1 = \tfrac{1}{3}\pi$
3. $\mathbf{R}(t) = \ln \sin t\mathbf{i} + t\mathbf{j}$, $0 < t < \pi$; $t_1 = \tfrac{1}{2}\pi$
4. $\mathbf{R}(t) = t\mathbf{i} - \ln \cos t\mathbf{j}$, $-\tfrac{1}{2}\pi < t < \tfrac{1}{2}\pi$; $t_1 = 0$
5. $\mathbf{R}(t) = (\tfrac{1}{3}t^3 - t)\mathbf{i} + t^2\mathbf{j}$; $t_1 = 2$
6. $\mathbf{R}(t) = \tfrac{1}{2}t^2\mathbf{i} + \tfrac{1}{3}t^3\mathbf{j}$; $t_1 = 1$

In Exercises 7 through 10, find $\mathbf{T}(t)$ *and* $\mathbf{N}(t)$.

7. $\mathbf{R}(t) = (\sin t - t \cos t)\mathbf{i} + (\cos t + t \sin t)\mathbf{j} + 2\mathbf{k}$
8. $\mathbf{R}(t) = \sin 3t\mathbf{i} - \cos 3t\mathbf{j} + 4t\mathbf{k}$
9. $\mathbf{R}(t) = \mathbf{i} + \tfrac{1}{2}t^2\mathbf{j} + \tfrac{1}{3}t^3\mathbf{k}$, $t > 0$
10. $\mathbf{R}(t) = e^t \cos t\mathbf{i} + e^t \sin t\mathbf{j} + e^t\mathbf{k}$

In Exercises 11 through 14, find the moving trihedral of the curve at $t = t_1$.

11. The curve of Exercise 7; $t_1 = \tfrac{1}{2}\pi$
12. The curve of Exercise 8; $t_1 = \tfrac{1}{3}\pi$
13. The curve of Exercise 9; $t_1 = 1$
14. The curve of Exercise 10; $t_1 = 0$

In Exercises 15 and 16, find the moving trihedral at any point of the curve.

15. $\mathbf{R}(t) = \cos^3 t\mathbf{i} + \sin^3 t\mathbf{j} + 2\mathbf{k}$, $0 \le t \le \tfrac{1}{2}\pi$
16. $\mathbf{R}(t) = \cosh t\mathbf{i} + \sinh t\mathbf{j} + t\mathbf{k}$

In Exercises 17 through 22, find equations of the osculating, rectifying, and normal planes for the curve at $t = t_1$.

17. The curve of Exercises 7 and 11; $t_1 = \tfrac{1}{2}\pi$
18. The curve of Exercises 10 and 14; $t_1 = 0$
19. The curve of Exercises 9 and 13; $t_1 = 1$

20. The curve of Exercises 8 and 12; $t_1 = \tfrac{1}{3}\pi$
21. The curve of Exercise 15; $t_1 = \tfrac{1}{4}\pi$
22. The curve of Exercise 16; $t_1 = 0$
23. Use the results of Example 2 to determine the moving trihedral of the circular helix

    $$\mathbf{R}(t) = 2 \cos t\mathbf{i} + 2 \sin t\mathbf{j} + t\mathbf{k}$$

    at the point where $t = \tfrac{1}{2}\pi$. Then find equations of the osculating, rectifying, and normal planes at that point.
24. Find the cosine of the angle between the vectors $\mathbf{R}(2)$ and $\mathbf{T}(2)$ for the curve $\mathbf{R}(t) = 3t^2\mathbf{i} + (t^3 - 3t)\mathbf{j}$.
25. Find the cosine of the angle between the vectors $\mathbf{R}(\tfrac{1}{6}\pi)$ and $\mathbf{T}(\tfrac{1}{6}\pi)$ for the curve

    $$\mathbf{R}(t) = 2 \sin t\mathbf{i} + \sin 2t\mathbf{j} + \cos 3t\mathbf{k}$$
26. Find at the point where $t = \pi$ the cosine of the angle between the vector $\mathbf{j}$ and the unit tangent vector of the curve $\mathbf{R}(t) = \cos 2t\mathbf{i} - 3t\mathbf{j} + 2 \sin 2t\mathbf{k}$.
27. Find the radian measure of the angle between the vectors $\mathbf{N}(1)$ and $D_t^2\mathbf{R}(1)$ for the curve $\mathbf{R}(t) = (4 - 3t^2)\mathbf{i} + (t^3 - 3t)\mathbf{j}$.

In Exercises 28 and 29, for the given curve, express the arc length s as a function of t, where s is measured from the point where $t = 0$.

28. The cycloid $\mathbf{R}(t) = 2(t - \sin t)\mathbf{i} + 2(1 - \cos t)\mathbf{j}$.
29. $\mathbf{R}(t) = t\mathbf{i} + t^{3/2}\mathbf{j}$
30. Check the answer in Example 4 by using Equation (9).

In Exercises 31 through 36, find a vector equation of the curve having arc length s as a parameter, where s is measured from the point where $t = 0$. *Check your answer by using Equation (9).*

31. The curve of Exercise 7
32. The curve of Exercise 8

33. The curve of Exercise 9
34. The curve of Exercise 10
35. The curve of Exercise 15
36. The curve of Exercise 16

37. Prove that the unit tangent vector of the circular helix of Example 2 makes an angle of constant radian measure with the unit vector **k**.

38. Prove that if a particle is moving on a line, the unit normal vector is undefined.

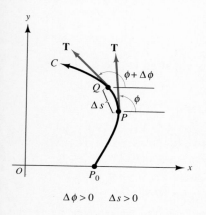

$\Delta\phi > 0 \quad \Delta s > 0$

FIGURE 1

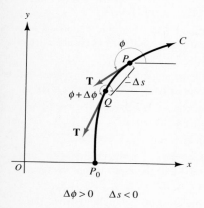

$\Delta\phi > 0 \quad \Delta s < 0$

FIGURE 2

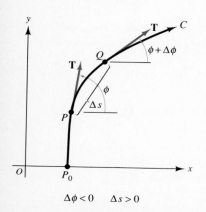

$\Delta\phi < 0 \quad \Delta s > 0$

FIGURE 3

11.4 CURVATURE

An important concept in the study of both differential geometry and curvilinear motion is *curvature,* which gives the rate of change of the direction of a curve with respect to a change in its length.

We begin with a plane curve C, and we let ϕ be the radian measure of the angle from the direction of the positive x axis counterclockwise to the direction of the unit tangent vector $\mathbf{T}(t)$ at point P on C. Refer to Figure 1 showing ϕ and $\mathbf{T}(t)$, where s units is the arc length from a point P_0 on C to P. At point Q on C, the radian measure of the angle giving the direction of $\mathbf{T}(t + \Delta t)$ is $\phi + \Delta\phi$, and $s + \Delta s$ units is the arc length from P_0 to Q. In Figure 1, both $\Delta\phi$ and Δs are positive numbers. Figures 2, 3, and 4 show the situation when at least one of these numbers is negative. In all four figures, the arc length from P to Q is $|\Delta s|$ units, and the ratio $|\Delta\phi/\Delta s|$ seems like a good measure of what we would intuitively think of as the *average curvature* along arc PQ. Thus a suitable definition for the curvature of a plane curve would be the number $|d\phi/ds|$, which is the absolute value of the rate of change of ϕ with respect to the measure of arc length along the curve. While this number is consistent with our intuitive notion of curvature for a plane curve, such a definition would not be possible for the curvature of a curve in three-dimensional space because no single angle ϕ is associated with the unit tangent vector. To arrive at a definition that applies to curves in both R^2 and R^3, we proceed to obtain an equivalent expression for $|d\phi/ds|$ in R^2 that also has meaning in R^3.

See Figure 5 where C is a curve in R^2. We first express $\mathbf{T}(t)$ in terms of ϕ. Because $\|\mathbf{T}(t)\| = 1$, we have from Equation (5) in Section 10.1

$$\mathbf{T}(t) = \cos\phi\mathbf{i} + \sin\phi\mathbf{j}$$

Differentiating with respect to ϕ, we obtain

$$D_\phi\mathbf{T}(t) = -\sin\phi\mathbf{i} + \cos\phi\mathbf{j} \tag{1}$$

Thus

$$\|D_\phi\mathbf{T}(t)\| = 1 \tag{2}$$

so that $D_\phi\mathbf{T}(t)$ is a unit vector.

Let us now obtain an expression for $D_s\mathbf{T}(t)$, where s units is the arc length measured from an arbitrarily chosen point on C to point P and s increases as t increases. From the chain rule (Theorem 11.2.8),

$$D_s\mathbf{T}(t) = D_\phi\mathbf{T}(t)\frac{d\phi}{ds}$$

$$\|D_s\mathbf{T}(t)\| = \left\|D_\phi\mathbf{T}(t)\frac{d\phi}{ds}\right\|$$

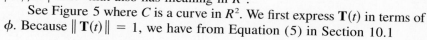

$$= \|D_\phi\mathbf{T}(t)\|\left|\frac{d\phi}{ds}\right|$$

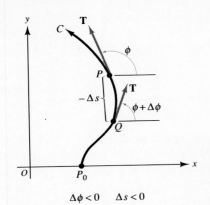

$\Delta\phi < 0 \qquad \Delta s < 0$

FIGURE 4

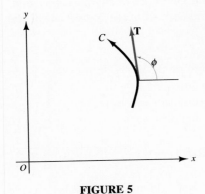

FIGURE 5

Replacing $\| D_\phi \mathbf{T}(t) \|$ by 1 from (2), we obtain

$$\| D_s \mathbf{T}(t) \| = \left| \frac{d\phi}{ds} \right| \qquad (3)$$

Because $\| D_s \mathbf{T}(t) \|$ has meaning for curves in R^3 as well as in R^2 we define it to be the *curvature* of a curve at a point, and we define the corresponding vector to be the *curvature vector*.

11.4.1 Definition of the Curvature Vector and Curvature

If $\mathbf{T}(t)$ is the unit tangent vector to a curve C at a point P, s is the arc length measured from an arbitrarily chosen point on C to P, and s increases as t increases, then the **curvature vector** of C at P, denoted by $\mathbf{K}(t)$, is given by

$$\mathbf{K}(t) = D_s \mathbf{T}(t)$$

The **curvature** of C at P, denoted by $K(t)$, is the magnitude of the curvature vector; that is,

$$K(t) = \| D_s \mathbf{T}(t) \|$$

To compute the curvature vector and curvature for a particular curve it is convenient to have a formula expressing the curvature vector in terms of derivatives with respect to t. From the chain rule,

$$D_t \mathbf{T}(t) = D_s \mathbf{T}(t) \frac{ds}{dt}$$

From Equation (7) in Section 11.3, $\dfrac{ds}{dt} = \| D_t \mathbf{R}(t) \|$. Thus

$$D_t \mathbf{T}(t) = [D_s \mathbf{T}(t)] \| D_t \mathbf{R}(t) \|$$
$$D_s \mathbf{T}(t) = \frac{D_t \mathbf{T}(t)}{\| D_t \mathbf{R}(t) \|}$$

Substituting from this equation in the formula for $\mathbf{K}(t)$ in Definition 11.4.1, we obtain

$$\mathbf{K}(t) = \frac{D_t \mathbf{T}(t)}{\| D_t \mathbf{R}(t) \|} \qquad (4)$$

Because $K(t) = \| \mathbf{K}(t) \|$, the curvature is given by

$$K(t) = \frac{\| D_t \mathbf{T}(t) \|}{\| D_t \mathbf{R}(t) \|} \qquad (5)$$

▶ **EXAMPLE 1** Given the circle with radius a:

$$\mathbf{R}(t) = a \cos t\mathbf{i} + a \sin t\mathbf{j} \qquad a > 0$$

find the curvature vector and the curvature at any t.

Solution

$$D_t \mathbf{R}(t) = -a \sin t\mathbf{i} + a \cos t\mathbf{j} \qquad \| D_t \mathbf{R}(t) \| = \sqrt{(-a \sin t)^2 + (a \cos t)^2}$$
$$= a$$

Therefore

$$\mathbf{T}(t) = \frac{D_t\mathbf{R}(t)}{\|D_t\mathbf{R}(t)\|} \qquad\qquad D_t\mathbf{T}(t) = -\cos t\mathbf{i} - \sin t\mathbf{j}$$

$$= -\sin t\mathbf{i} + \cos t\mathbf{j}$$

$$\frac{D_t\mathbf{T}(t)}{\|D_t\mathbf{R}(t)\|} = -\frac{\cos t}{a}\mathbf{i} - \frac{\sin t}{a}\mathbf{j}$$

Hence the curvature vector and the curvature are given by

$$\mathbf{K}(t) = -\frac{1}{a}\cos t\mathbf{i} - \frac{1}{a}\sin t\mathbf{j} \qquad\qquad K(t) = \|\mathbf{K}(t)\|$$

$$= \frac{1}{a} \qquad \blacktriangleleft$$

The result of Example 1 states that the curvature of a circle is constant, which is what you would expect. Furthermore, it is the reciprocal of the radius.

▶ **EXAMPLE 2** Find the curvature of the curve having the vector equation

$$\mathbf{R}(t) = t^{-1}\mathbf{i} + 2 \ln t\mathbf{j} + 2t\mathbf{k}$$

Solution

$$D_t\mathbf{R}(t) = -t^{-2}\mathbf{i} + 2t^{-1}\mathbf{j} + 2\mathbf{k} \qquad \|D_t\mathbf{R}(t)\| = \sqrt{(-t^{-2})^2 + (2t^{-1})^2 + 2^2}$$

$$= \sqrt{t^{-4} + 4t^{-2} + 4}$$

$$= t^{-2} + 2$$

$$\mathbf{T}(t) = \frac{D_t\mathbf{R}(t)}{\|D_t\mathbf{R}(t)\|}$$

$$= \frac{-t^{-2}\mathbf{i} + 2t^{-1}\mathbf{j} + 2\mathbf{k}}{t^{-2} + 2}$$

$$= \frac{-\mathbf{i} + 2t\mathbf{j} + 2t^2\mathbf{k}}{1 + 2t^2}$$

$$D_t\mathbf{T}(t) = \frac{(1 + 2t^2)(2\mathbf{j} + 4t\mathbf{k}) - 4t(-\mathbf{i} + 2t\mathbf{j} + 2t^2\mathbf{k})}{(1 + 2t^2)^2}$$

$$= \frac{4t\mathbf{i} + (2 - 4t^2)\mathbf{j} + 4t\mathbf{k}}{(1 + 2t^2)^2}$$

$$\|D_t\mathbf{T}(t)\| = \frac{\sqrt{(4t)^2 + (2 - 4t^2)^2 + (4t)^2}}{(1 + 2t^2)^2}$$

$$= \frac{\sqrt{4 + 16t^2 + 16t^4}}{(1 + 2t^2)^2}$$

$$= \frac{2\sqrt{(1 + 2t^2)^2}}{(1 + 2t^2)^2}$$

$$= \frac{2}{1 + 2t^2}$$

$$K(t) = \frac{\| D_t \mathbf{T}(t) \|}{\| D_t \mathbf{R}(t) \|}$$

$$= \frac{\dfrac{2}{1 + 2t^2}}{t^{-2} + 2}$$

$$= \frac{2t^2}{(1 + 2t^2)^2} \qquad \blacktriangleleft$$

As you can see from the above example, finding curvature from formulas (4) and (5) can be lengthy and tedious. The following theorem gives a more practical formula for computing curvature that is easier to apply than the procedure of Example 2.

11.4.2 Theorem

If $\mathbf{R}(t)$ is the position vector of a curve C, then the curvature $K(t)$ of C is given by

$$K(t) = \frac{\| D_t \mathbf{R}(t) \times D_t^2 \mathbf{R}(t) \|}{\| D_t \mathbf{R}(t) \|^3}$$

The proof of this theorem is left as an exercise (see Exercise 56). Even though the cross product is not defined for two-dimensional vectors, the formula in the theorem can also be applied to curves in R^2 by taking the $\mathbf{k}$ component as 0.

▶ **EXAMPLE 3**   Apply the formula in Theorem 11.4.2 to compute the curvature of the curve in Example 2.

Solution   A vector equation of the curve is

$$\mathbf{R}(t) = t^{-1}\mathbf{i} + 2 \ln t\,\mathbf{j} + 2t\mathbf{k}$$

$$D_t\mathbf{R}(t) = -t^{-2}\mathbf{i} + 2t^{-1}\mathbf{j} + 2\mathbf{k} \qquad \| D_t\mathbf{R}(t) \| = t^{-2} + 2$$

$$D_t^2\mathbf{R}(t) = 2t^{-3}\mathbf{i} - 2t^{-2}\mathbf{j}$$

$$D_t\mathbf{R}(t) \times D_t^2\mathbf{R}(t) = \begin{vmatrix} \mathbf{i} & \mathbf{j} & \mathbf{k} \\ -t^{-2} & 2t^{-1} & 2 \\ 2t^{-3} & -2t^{-2} & 0 \end{vmatrix}$$

$$= 4t^{-3}\mathbf{j} + 2t^{-4}\mathbf{k} - 4t^{-4}\mathbf{k} + 4t^{-2}\mathbf{i}$$

$$= 4t^{-2}\mathbf{i} + 4t^{-3}\mathbf{j} - 2t^{-4}\mathbf{k}$$

$$\| D_t\mathbf{R}(t) \times D_t^2\mathbf{R}(t) \| = \sqrt{16t^{-4} + 16t^{-6} + 4t^{-8}}$$

$$= 2t^{-2}\sqrt{4 + 4t^{-2} + t^{-4}}$$

$$= 2t^{-2}(2 + t^{-2})$$

From the formula of Theorem 11.4.2,

$$K(t) = \frac{2t^{-2}(2 + t^{-2})}{(t^{-2} + 2)^3}$$

$$= \frac{2t^{-2}}{(t^{-2} + 2)^2}$$

$$= \frac{2t^2}{(1 + 2t^2)^2}$$

◀

Compare the solution in the above example with that in Example 2, which should convince you of the advantage of using Theorem 11.4.2.

Suppose now we are given a plane curve C having the vector equation $\mathbf{R}(t) = f(t)\mathbf{i} + g(t)\mathbf{j}$ and at a particular point $P_0(f(t_0), g(t_0))$ the curvature is $K(t_0) \neq 0$. Consider the circle having the constant curvature $K(t_0)$, whose center is on the concave side of C, and that is tangent to curve C at P_0. From Example 1, the radius of the circle is $1/K(t_0)$. This circle is called the **circle of curvature** (or **osculating circle**) of C at P_0, and its radius is the *radius of curvature*, which we now formally define.

11.4.3 Definition of Radius of Curvature

If $K(t_0)$ is the curvature of a plane curve C at point P_0, where $t = t_0$, and $K(t_0) \neq 0$, then the radius of curvature of C at P_0, denoted by $\rho(t_0)$, is defined by

$$\rho(t_0) = \frac{1}{K(t_0)}$$

▶ **EXAMPLE 4**   For the curve having the vector equation

$$\mathbf{R}(t) = 2t\mathbf{i} + (t^2 - 1)\mathbf{j}$$

find the following at $t = 1$: **(a)** the unit tangent vector; **(b)** the curvature; **(c)** the radius of curvature. Sketch a portion of the curve, the unit tangent vector, and the circle of curvature at $t = 1$.

Solution

$$D_t\mathbf{R}(t) = 2\mathbf{i} + 2t\mathbf{j} \qquad \|D_t\mathbf{R}(t)\| = 2\sqrt{1 + t^2}$$

$$\mathbf{T}(t) = \frac{D_t\mathbf{R}(t)}{\|D_t\mathbf{R}(t)\|}$$

$$= \frac{1}{\sqrt{1 + t^2}}\mathbf{i} + \frac{t}{\sqrt{1 + t^2}}\mathbf{j}$$

$$D_t\mathbf{T}(t) = -\frac{t}{(1 + t^2)^{3/2}}\mathbf{i} + \frac{1}{(1 + t^2)^{3/2}}\mathbf{j}$$

$$\mathbf{K}(t) = \frac{D_t\mathbf{T}(t)}{\|D_t\mathbf{R}(t)\|}$$

$$= -\frac{t}{2(1 + t^2)^2}\mathbf{i} + \frac{1}{2(1 + t^2)^2}\mathbf{j}$$

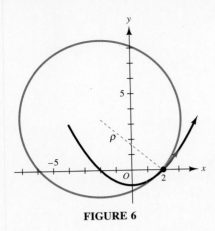

FIGURE 6

Table 1

t	x	y
-2	-4	3
-1	-2	0
0	0	-1
1	2	0
2	4	3

$$K(t) = \| \mathbf{K}(t) \|$$

$$= \sqrt{\frac{t^2}{4(1 + t^2)^4} + \frac{1}{4(1 + t^2)^4}}$$

$$= \frac{1}{2(1 + t^2)^{3/2}}$$

(a) $\mathbf{T}(1) = \frac{1}{\sqrt{2}}\mathbf{i} + \frac{1}{\sqrt{2}}\mathbf{j}$ **(b)** $K(1) = \frac{1}{4\sqrt{2}}$ **(c)** $\rho(1) = 4\sqrt{2}$

Figure 6 shows a portion of the curve, the unit tangent vector, and the circle of curvature at $t = 1$. To sketch the curve we located points from values of x and y given in Table 1 when t is $-2, -1, 0, 1$, and 2. We also noted that the curve has a horizontal tangent line at $t = 0$. ◀

We now derive a formula for computing the curvature of a plane curve from parametric equations of the curve:

$$x = f(t) \quad \text{and} \quad y = g(t)$$

Because $K(t) = |d\phi/ds|$, we first compute $d\phi/ds$.

$$\frac{d\phi}{ds} = \frac{\dfrac{d\phi}{dt}}{\dfrac{ds}{dt}}$$

With the assumption that s and t increase together, $\dfrac{ds}{dt} > 0$. Thus

$$\frac{d\phi}{ds} = \frac{\dfrac{d\phi}{dt}}{\sqrt{\left(\dfrac{dx}{dt}\right)^2 + \left(\dfrac{dy}{dt}\right)^2}} \tag{6}$$

To find $\dfrac{d\phi}{dt}$ we observe that because ϕ is the radian measure of the angle giving the direction of the unit tangent vector,

$$\tan \phi = \frac{\dfrac{dy}{dt}}{\dfrac{dx}{dt}}$$

Differentiating implicitly with respect to t the left and right members of this equation, we obtain

$$\sec^2 \phi \frac{d\phi}{dt} = \frac{\left(\dfrac{dx}{dt}\right)\left(\dfrac{d^2y}{dt^2}\right) - \left(\dfrac{dy}{dt}\right)\left(\dfrac{d^2x}{dt^2}\right)}{\left(\dfrac{dx}{dt}\right)^2}$$

$$\frac{d\phi}{dt} = \frac{\left(\dfrac{dx}{dt}\right)\left(\dfrac{d^2y}{dt^2}\right) - \left(\dfrac{dy}{dt}\right)\left(\dfrac{d^2x}{dt^2}\right)}{\sec^2 \phi \left(\dfrac{dx}{dt}\right)^2} \tag{7}$$

Because $\sec^2 \phi = 1 + \tan^2 \phi$, we have

$$\sec^2 \phi = 1 + \frac{\left(\dfrac{dy}{dt}\right)^2}{\left(\dfrac{dx}{dt}\right)^2}$$

Substituting this expression for $\sec^2 \phi$ in (7) we get

$$\frac{d\phi}{dt} = \frac{\left(\dfrac{dx}{dt}\right)\left(\dfrac{d^2y}{dt^2}\right) - \left(\dfrac{dy}{dt}\right)\left(\dfrac{d^2x}{dt^2}\right)}{\left(\dfrac{dx}{dt}\right)^2 + \left(\dfrac{dy}{dt}\right)^2}$$

Substituting from this equation into (6), and because $K(t) = \left| \dfrac{d\phi}{ds} \right|$, we have

$$K(t) = \frac{\left| \left(\dfrac{dx}{dt}\right)\left(\dfrac{d^2y}{dt^2}\right) - \left(\dfrac{dy}{dt}\right)\left(\dfrac{d^2x}{dt^2}\right) \right|}{\left[\left(\dfrac{dx}{dt}\right)^2 + \left(\dfrac{dy}{dt}\right)^2 \right]^{3/2}} \tag{8}$$

▶ **EXAMPLE 5**   Find the curvature of the curve in Example 4 by using formula (8).

Solution   Parametric equations of C are $x = 2t$ and $y = t^2 - 1$. Hence

$$\frac{dx}{dt} = 2 \qquad \frac{d^2x}{dt^2} = 0 \qquad \frac{dy}{dt} = 2t \qquad \frac{d^2y}{dt^2} = 2$$

Therefore, from (8),

$$K(t) = \frac{|2(2) - 2t(0)|}{[(2)^2 + (2t)^2]^{3/2}}$$

$$= \frac{4}{(4 + 4t^2)^{3/2}}$$

$$= \frac{1}{2(1 + t^2)^{3/2}} \qquad\qquad ◀$$

Suppose a cartesian equation of a curve is given in either of the forms $y = F(x)$ or $x = G(y)$. Special cases of formula (8) can be used to find the curvature of a curve in such situations.

If $y = F(x)$ is an equation of a curve C, a set of parametric equations of C is $x = t$ and $y = F(t)$. Then

$$\frac{dx}{dt} = 1 \qquad \frac{d^2x}{dt^2} = 0 \qquad \frac{dy}{dt} = \frac{dy}{dx} \qquad \frac{d^2y}{dt^2} = \frac{d^2y}{dx^2}$$

Substituting into (8) we obtain

$$K = \frac{\left|\dfrac{d^2y}{dx^2}\right|}{\left[1 + \left(\dfrac{dy}{dx}\right)^2\right]^{3/2}} \qquad (9)$$

Similarly, if an equation of a curve C is $x = G(y)$,

$$K = \frac{\left|\dfrac{d^2x}{dy^2}\right|}{\left[1 + \left(\dfrac{dx}{dy}\right)^2\right]^{3/2}}$$

▶ **EXAMPLE 6** If an equation of curve C is

$$y = \frac{1}{x}$$

find the radius of curvature of C at the point $(1, 1)$, and sketch the curve and the circle of curvature at $(1, 1)$.

Solution

$$\frac{dy}{dx} = -\frac{1}{x^2} \qquad \frac{d^2y}{dx^2} = \frac{2}{x^3}$$

We compute K from (9) and then $\rho = 1/K$.

$$K = \frac{\left|\dfrac{2}{x^3}\right|}{\left[1 + \dfrac{1}{x^4}\right]^{3/2}} \qquad \rho = \frac{(x^4 + 1)^{3/2}}{2|x^3|}$$

$$= \frac{2|x^3|}{(x^4 + 1)^{3/2}}$$

Therefore at $(1, 1)$, $\rho = \sqrt{2}$. The curve and circle of curvature appear in Figure 7. ◀

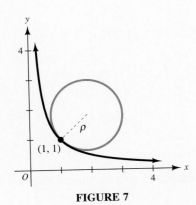

FIGURE 7

EXERCISES 11.4

In Exercises 1 through 6, for the curve and t_1 in the indicated exercise of Exercises 11.3, find the curvature K and the radius of curvature ρ at the point where $t = t_1$. Use formula (5) to find K. Sketch a portion of the curve, the unit tangent vector, and the circle of curvature at $t = t_1$.

1. Exercise 1   **2.** Exercise 2   **3.** Exercise 3

4. Exercise 4   **5.** Exercise 5   **6.** Exercise 6

In Exercises 7 through 10, for the curve in the indicated exercise of Exercises 11.3, find the curvature K by applying formula (5).

7. Exercise 7   **8.** Exercise 8   **9.** Exercise 9

10. Exercise 10

In Exercises 11 through 14, apply the formula in Theorem 11.4.2 to compute the curvature of the curve in the indicated exercise of this section.

11. Exercise 7   **12.** Exercise 8   **13.** Exercise 9
14. Exercise 10

In Exercises 15 and 16, apply the formula in Theorem 11.4.2 to compute the curvature of the curve at the indicated point.

15. The twisted cubic $\mathbf{R}(t) = t\mathbf{i} + t^2\mathbf{j} + t^3\mathbf{k}$; the origin
16. $\mathbf{R}(t) = e^t\mathbf{i} + e^{-t}\mathbf{j} + t\mathbf{k}$; $t = 0$

In Exercises 17 and 18, find the curvature K by applying formula (8). Then find K and ρ at the point where $t = t_1$, and sketch a portion of the curve, the unit tangent vector, and the circle of curvature at $t = t_1$.

17. $x = \dfrac{1}{1+t}$, $y = \dfrac{1}{1-t}$; $t_1 = 0$
18. $x = e^t + e^{-t}$, $y = e^t - e^{-t}$; $t_1 = 0$

In Exercises 19 through 26, find the curvature K and the radius of curvature ρ at the given point. Sketch a portion of the curve, a piece of the tangent line, and the circle of curvature at the given point.

19. $y = 2\sqrt{x}$; $(0, 0)$ **20.** $y^2 = x^3$; $(\frac{1}{4}, \frac{1}{8})$
21. $y = e^x$; $(0, 1)$ **22.** $y = \ln x$; $(e, 1)$
23. $x = \sin y$; $(\frac{1}{2}, \frac{1}{6}\pi)$ **24.** $4x^2 + 9y^2 = 36$; $(0, 2)$
25. $x = \sqrt{y - 1}$; $(2, 5)$ **26.** $x = \tan y$; $(1, \frac{1}{4}\pi)$

In Exercises 27 through 34, find the radius of curvature at any point on the given curve.

27. $y = \sin^{-1} x$ **28.** $y = \ln \sec x$
29. $4x^2 - 9y^2 = 16$ **30.** $x = \tan^{-1} y$
31. $x^{1/2} + y^{1/2} = a^{1/2}$
32. $\mathbf{R}(t) = e^t \sin t\mathbf{i} + e^t \cos t\mathbf{j}$
33. The cycloid $x = a(t - \sin t)$, $y = a(1 - \cos t)$
34. The tractrix $x = t - a \tanh \dfrac{t}{a}$, $y = a \operatorname{sech} \dfrac{t}{a}$

In Exercises 35 through 38, find a point on the given curve at which the curvature is an absolute maximum.

35. $y = e^x$ **36.** $y = x^2 - 2x + 3$
37. $\mathbf{R}(t) = (2t - 3)\mathbf{i} + (t^2 - 1)\mathbf{j}$ **38.** $y = \sin x$

39. The center of the circle of curvature of a curve C at a point P is called the **center of curvature** at P. Prove that the coordinates of the center of curvature of C at $P(x, y)$ are given by

$$\bar{x}_c = x - \frac{\left(\dfrac{dy}{dx}\right)\left[1 + \left(\dfrac{dy}{dx}\right)^2\right]}{\dfrac{d^2y}{dx^2}}$$

$$y_c = y + \frac{\left(\dfrac{dy}{dx}\right)^2 + 1}{\dfrac{d^2y}{dx^2}}$$

In Exercises 40 through 42, find the curvature K, the radius of curvature ρ, and the center of curvature at the given point. Sketch the curve and the circle of curvature.

40. $y = \ln x$; $(1, 0)$ **41.** $y = x^4 - x^2$; $(0, 0)$
42. $y = \cos x$; $(\frac{1}{3}\pi, \frac{1}{2})$

In Exercises 43 through 46, find the coordinates of the center of curvature at any point.

43. $y^2 = 4px$ **44.** $y^3 = a^2x$
45. $\mathbf{R}(t) = a \cos t\mathbf{i} + b \sin t\mathbf{j}$
46. $\mathbf{R}(t) = a \cos^3 t\mathbf{i} + a \sin^3 t\mathbf{j}$

47. The figure below shows a curved exit ramp from a straight roadway and a rectangular cartesian coordinate system placed so that the exit ramp begins at the origin and the roadway is on the x axis. The exit curve is along the graph of $y = \frac{1}{81} x^4$ from the origin to the point $P(3, 1)$ and then along the circle of curvature of this graph at P. Find the center and radius of the circle.

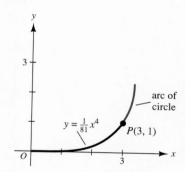

48. Show that the curvature of a line is zero at every point.

49. Find an equation of the circle of curvature of the curve $y = e^x$ at the point $(0, 1)$.

50. If a polar equation of a curve is $r = F(\theta)$, prove that the curvature K is given by the formula

$$K = \frac{\left| r^2 + 2\left(\dfrac{dr}{d\theta}\right)^2 - r\left(\dfrac{d^2r}{d\theta^2}\right) \right|}{\left[r^2 + \left(\dfrac{dr}{d\theta}\right)^2 \right]^{3/2}}$$

In Exercises 51 through 54, find the curvature K and the radius of curvature ρ at the indicated point. Use the formula of Exercise 50 to find K.

51. $r = 4 \cos 2\theta$; $\theta = \frac{1}{12}\pi$ **52.** $r = 1 - \sin\theta$; $\theta = 0$

53. $r = a \sec^2 \frac{1}{2}\theta$; $\theta = \frac{2}{3}\pi$ **54.** $r = a\theta$; $\theta = 1$

55. Prove that if $\mathbf{R}(t)$ is the position vector of a curve C, $K(t)$ is the curvature of C at a point P, and s units is the arc length measured from an arbitrarily chosen point on C to P, then

$$D_s \mathbf{R}(t) \cdot D_s^3 \mathbf{R}(t) = -[K(t)]^2$$

56. Prove Theorem 11.4.2.

57. Show that the curvature of the catenary $y = a \cosh(x/a)$ at any point (x, y) on the curve is a/y^2. Draw the circle of curvature at the point $(0, a)$.

Explain why the curvature K is an absolute maximum at $(0, a)$ without referring to $K'(x)$.

58. Show that the curvature of the circular helix

$$\mathbf{R}(t) = a \cos t\mathbf{i} + a \sin t\mathbf{j} + bt\mathbf{k} \qquad a > 0, b > 0$$

is $a/(a^2 + b^2)$. *Hint:* Use the formula in Theorem 11.4.2.

59. From the result of Exercise 58, determine the maximum curvature for the helix of that exercise for a fixed value of b.

60. From the result of Exercise 58, explain the effect on the curvature of the helix if (i) b is increased for a fixed value of a and (ii) if a is decreased for a fixed value of b.

11.5 CURVILINEAR MOTION

Our previous discussions of the motion of a particle were confined to rectilinear motion. We now consider the motion of a particle along a curve, called **curvilinear motion.**

Suppose that C is the curve having the vector equation

$$\mathbf{R}(t) = f(t)\mathbf{i} + g(t)\mathbf{j} + h(t)\mathbf{k}$$

where t denotes time. As t varies the endpoint P of $\overrightarrow{OP}$ traces the curve C, so that the position at time t units of a particle moving along C is the point $P(f(t), g(t), h(t))$. We now define the *velocity and acceleration vectors.*

> **11.5.1 Definition of Velocity and Acceleration in Curvilinear Motion**
>
> Let C be the curve having the vector equation
>
> $$\mathbf{R}(t) = f(t)\mathbf{i} + g(t)\mathbf{j} + h(t)\mathbf{k}$$
>
> If a particle is moving along C so that its position at any time t units is the point $P(f(t), g(t), h(t))$, then the velocity vector $\mathbf{V}(t)$ and the acceleration vector $\mathbf{A}(t)$ at the point P are defined by
>
> $$\mathbf{V}(t) = \mathbf{R}'(t) \iff \mathbf{V}(t) = f'(t)\mathbf{i} + g'(t)\mathbf{j} + h'(t)\mathbf{k}$$
> $$\mathbf{A}(t) = \mathbf{R}''(t) \iff \mathbf{A}(t) = f''(t)\mathbf{i} + g''(t)\mathbf{j} + h''(t)\mathbf{k} \iff \mathbf{A}(t) = \mathbf{V}'(t)$$
>
> where $\mathbf{R}''(t)$ exists.

Because the direction of $\mathbf{R}'(t)$ at the point P is along the tangent line to the curve at P, the velocity vector $\mathbf{V}(t)$ has this direction at P.

The magnitude of the velocity vector, $\|\mathbf{V}(t)\|$, is a measure of the **speed** of the particle.

Figure 1 shows the representations of the velocity and acceleration vectors at point P on C.

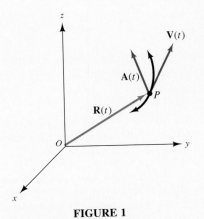

FIGURE 1

▶ **EXAMPLE 1**   A particle is moving along the plane curve having the vector equation

$$\mathbf{R}(t) = 4 \cos \tfrac{1}{2}t\mathbf{i} + 4 \sin \tfrac{1}{2}t\mathbf{j}$$

Find the particle's speed and the magnitude of the particle's acceleration vector at t seconds if distance is measured in centimeters. Sketch the particle's path and draw the representations of the velocity and acceleration vectors at the point where $t = \tfrac{1}{3}\pi$.

Solution

$$\mathbf{V}(t) = \mathbf{R}'(t)$$
$$= -2 \sin \tfrac{1}{2}t\mathbf{i} + 2 \cos \tfrac{1}{2}t\mathbf{j}$$
$$\|\mathbf{V}(t)\| = \sqrt{(-2 \sin \tfrac{1}{2}t)^2 + (2 \cos \tfrac{1}{2}t)^2}$$
$$= \sqrt{4 \sin^2 \tfrac{1}{2}t + 4 \cos^2 \tfrac{1}{2}t}$$
$$= 2$$

$$\mathbf{A}(t) = \mathbf{V}'(t)$$
$$= -\cos \tfrac{1}{2}t\mathbf{i} - \sin \tfrac{1}{2}t\mathbf{j}$$
$$\|\mathbf{A}(t)\| = \sqrt{(-\cos \tfrac{1}{2}t)^2 + (-\sin \tfrac{1}{2}t)^2}$$
$$= 1$$

Therefore, the speed of the particle is constant and is 2 cm/sec. The magnitude of the acceleration vector is also constant and is 1 cm/sec².
Parametric equations of C are

$$x = 4 \cos \tfrac{1}{2}t \qquad \text{and} \qquad y = 4 \sin \tfrac{1}{2}t \qquad 0 \le t \le 4\pi$$

Eliminating t between these equations, we obtain the cartesian equation

$$x^2 + y^2 = 16$$

which is a circle with its center at the origin and radius 4. We now find the velocity and acceleration vectors at $t = \tfrac{1}{3}\pi$.

$$\mathbf{V}(\tfrac{1}{3}\pi) = -2 \sin \tfrac{1}{6}\pi\mathbf{i} + 2 \cos \tfrac{1}{6}\pi\mathbf{j} \qquad \mathbf{A}(\tfrac{1}{3}\pi) = -\cos \tfrac{1}{6}\pi\mathbf{i} - \sin \tfrac{1}{6}\pi\mathbf{j}$$
$$= -\mathbf{i} + \sqrt{3}\mathbf{j} \qquad\qquad\qquad\qquad = -\tfrac{1}{2}\sqrt{3}\mathbf{i} - \tfrac{1}{2}\mathbf{j}$$

The direction of $\mathbf{V}(\tfrac{1}{3}\pi)$ is given by

$$\tan \theta_1 = -\sqrt{3} \qquad \tfrac{1}{2}\pi < \theta_1 < \pi$$

and the direction of $\mathbf{A}(\tfrac{1}{3}\pi)$ is given by

$$\tan \theta_2 = \frac{1}{\sqrt{3}} \qquad \pi < \theta_2 < \tfrac{3}{2}\pi$$

Thus $\theta_1 = \tfrac{2}{3}\pi$ and $\theta_2 = \tfrac{7}{6}\pi$. Figure 2 shows the particle's path and representations of the velocity and acceleration vectors having initial point where $t = \tfrac{1}{3}\pi$.   ◀

Just as with rectilinear motion, you can simulate curvilinear motion in the plane on a graphics calculator as demonstrated in the following illustration.

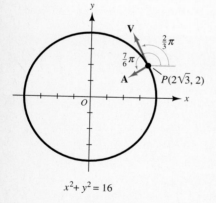

$x^2 + y^2 = 16$

FIGURE 2

▷ **ILLUSTRATION 1**   To observe the particle move on the circle in Example 1, set the calculator in parametric mode and enter the parametric equations of the circle. In the approximately square window $[-7.5, 7.5]$ by $[-5, 5]$, let $t_{\min} = 0$, $t_{\max} = 4\pi$ and $t_{\text{step}} = 0.1$. Press the $\boxed{\text{TRACE}}$ key and then press the left-arrow key and hold it down until the cursor is at $t = 0$. Now

Table 1

t	x	y
0	1	0
0.5	2.25	0.125
1	4	1
1.5	6.25	3.375
2	9	8

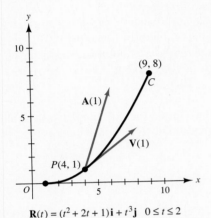

$R(t) = (t^2 + 2t + 1)\mathbf{i} + t^3\mathbf{j} \quad 0 \le t \le 2$

FIGURE 3

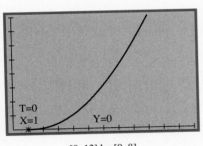

[0, 12] by [0, 8]

$x = t^2 + 2t + 1 \quad \text{and} \quad y = t^3$

FIGURE 4

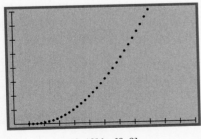

[0, 12] by [0, 8]

$x = t^2 + 2t + 1 \quad \text{and} \quad y = t^3$

FIGURE 5

press the right-arrow key and hold it down. The cursor represents the particle moving along the circle. ◀

▶ **EXAMPLE 2**   The position of a particle moving in the plane at time t units is given by the vector equation

$$\mathbf{R}(t) = (t^2 + 2t + 1)\mathbf{i} + t^3\mathbf{j} \qquad 0 \le t \le 2$$

(a) Find $\mathbf{V}(t)$, $\mathbf{A}(t)$, $\|\mathbf{V}(t)\|$, and $\|\mathbf{A}(t)\|$. **(b)** Find the velocity and acceleration vectors at $t = 1$. **(c)** Sketch the path of the particle and draw representations of the velocity and acceleration vectors at $t = 1$. **(d)** Simulate the motion of the particle on a graphics calculator. **(e)** Plot the path of the particle on a graphics calculator in dot mode.

Solution

(a) $\mathbf{V}(t) = \mathbf{R}'(t)$ $\mathbf{A}(t) = \mathbf{V}'(t)$
             $= (2t + 2)\mathbf{i} + 3t^2\mathbf{j}$ $= 2\mathbf{i} + 6t\mathbf{j}$
   $\|\mathbf{V}(t)\| = \sqrt{(2t + 2)^2 + (3t^2)^2}$ $\|\mathbf{A}(t)\| = \sqrt{4 + 36t^2}$
             $= \sqrt{9t^4 + 4t^2 + 8t + 4}$

(b) $\|\mathbf{V}(1)\| = 5$ $\|\mathbf{A}(1)\| = \sqrt{40}$
                                      ≈ 6.32

(c) Parametric equations of the path of the particle are

$$x = t^2 + 2t + 1 \quad \text{and} \quad y = t^3$$

We locate points (x, y) on the path from values in Table 1. From these points and the continuity of the components of $\mathbf{R}(t)$ we sketch the path shown in Figure 3. The figure also shows representations of $\mathbf{V}(1)$ and $\mathbf{A}(1)$.

(d) To simulate the motion on our graphics calculator, we set the calculator in parametric mode and enter the parametric equations in part (c). In the window [0, 12] by [0, 8], we let $t_{\min} = 0$, $t_{\max} = 2$, and $t_{\text{step}} = 0.05$. We now press the $\boxed{\text{TRACE}}$ key and then press the left-arrow key and hold it down until the cursor is at $t = 0$. Figure 4 shows the calculator screen as it now appears. We press the right-arrow key and observe the particle, represented by the cursor, moving along the curve.

(e) Figure 5 shows the calculator screen with our calculator in parametric and dot mode and with the same window and same values of t and t_{step} as in part (c). Notice that the distance between successive plotted points gets larger as t increases, which indicates that the speed of the particle is increasing as t increases. ◀

▶ **EXAMPLE 3**   A particle is moving along the curve having the vector equation

$$\mathbf{R}(t) = 3t\mathbf{i} + t^2\mathbf{j} + \tfrac{2}{3}t^3\mathbf{k} \qquad t \ge 0$$

Find the velocity and acceleration vectors and the speed of the particle at $t = 1$. Sketch a portion of the curve at $t = 1$, and draw representations of the velocity and acceleration vectors there.

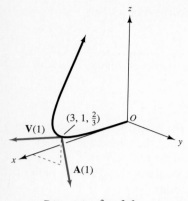

$\mathbf{R}(t) = 3t\mathbf{i} + t^2\mathbf{j} + \frac{2}{3}t^3\mathbf{k} \quad t \geq 0$

FIGURE 6

Solution

$$\mathbf{V}(t) = D_t\mathbf{R}(t) \qquad\qquad \mathbf{A}(t) = D_t\mathbf{V}(t)$$
$$= 3\mathbf{i} + 2t\mathbf{j} + 2t^2\mathbf{k} \qquad\qquad = 2\mathbf{j} + 4t\mathbf{k}$$
$$\|\mathbf{V}(t)\| = \sqrt{9 + 4t^2 + 4t^4}$$

Thus

$$\mathbf{V}(1) = 3\mathbf{i} + 2\mathbf{j} + 2\mathbf{k} \qquad \mathbf{A}(1) = 2\mathbf{j} + 4\mathbf{k} \qquad \|\mathbf{V}(1)\| = \sqrt{17}$$

Parametric equations of the given curve are

$$x = 3t \qquad y = t^2 \qquad z = \tfrac{2}{3}t^3$$

Because $t \geq 0$, the particle starts at the origin and moves upward in the first octant as t increases. The portion of the curve at $t = 1$ and representations of $\mathbf{V}(1)$ and $\mathbf{A}(1)$ appear in Figure 6. ◀

From Equation (8) in Section 11.3, if $\mathbf{T}(t)$ is the unit tangent vector at P, s is the length of arc of C from a fixed point to P, and s increases as t increases,

$$D_t\mathbf{R}(t) = \frac{ds}{dt}\mathbf{T}(t)$$

Because the left-hand side of this equation is the velocity vector, we have

$$\mathbf{V}(t) = \frac{ds}{dt}\mathbf{T}(t) \tag{1}$$

and therefore,

$$\|\mathbf{V}(t)\| = \frac{ds}{dt} \tag{2}$$

that is, the speed of a particle is the rate of change of s with respect to t. From (1) and (2),

$$\mathbf{T}(t) = \frac{\mathbf{V}(t)}{\|\mathbf{V}(t)\|}$$

Equation (1) expresses the velocity vector as a scalar times the unit tangent vector. The coefficient of $\mathbf{T}(t)$, ds/dt, is called the **tangential component of the velocity vector.** We now proceed to express the acceleration vector in terms of a vector tangent to the direction of motion and a vector normal to the direction of motion.

From Equation (6) in Section 11.3 with $D_t{}^2\mathbf{R}(t)$ replaced by $\mathbf{A}(t)$,

$$\mathbf{A}(t) = (D_t\|D_t\mathbf{R}(t)\|)\,\mathbf{T}(t) + (\|D_t\mathbf{R}(t)\|\,\|D_t\mathbf{T}(t)\|)\mathbf{N}(t)$$

From Equation (5) in Section 11.4, $\|D_t\mathbf{T}(t)\| = \|D_t\mathbf{R}(t)\|K(t)$. Making this substitution, as well as replacing $\|D_t\mathbf{R}(t)\|$ by ds/dt, in the above equation, we have

$$\mathbf{A}(t) = \frac{d^2s}{dt^2}\mathbf{T}(t) + \left(\frac{ds}{dt}\right)^2 K(t)\mathbf{N}(t) \tag{3}$$

Equation (3) expresses the acceleration vector as the sum of a scalar times the unit tangent vector and a scalar times the unit normal vector; that is, it converts $\mathbf{A}(t)$ into the sum of a vector tangent to the direction of motion and a vector normal to the direction of motion. The coefficient of $\mathbf{T}(t)$ is called the **tangential component of the acceleration vector** and is denoted by $A_T(t)$, whereas the coefficient of $\mathbf{N}(t)$ is called the **normal component of the acceleration vector** and is denoted by $A_N(t)$. Thus

$$\mathbf{A}(t) = A_T(t)\mathbf{T}(t) + A_N(t)\mathbf{N}(t) \tag{4}$$

where

$$A_T(t) = \frac{d^2s}{dt^2} \tag{5}$$

and

$$A_N(t) = \left(\frac{ds}{dt}\right)^2 K(t) \quad \Leftrightarrow \quad A_N(t) = \frac{\left(\frac{ds}{dt}\right)^2}{\rho(t)} \tag{6}$$

A change in the velocity vector, $\mathbf{V}(t)$, of a particle can be caused by a change in either its magnitude or direction. Because $\mathbf{A}(t) = D_t\mathbf{V}(t)$, the rate of change of $\mathbf{V}(t)$ is $\mathbf{A}(t)$. Observe from Equation (5) that $A_T(t)$ is the rate of change of the particle's speed; that is $A_T(t)$ is related to the change in the magnitude of $\mathbf{V}(t)$. Because $A_N(t)$ involves the curvature $K(t)$, $A_N(t)$ is related to the change in the direction of $\mathbf{V}(t)$. These results are important in mechanics.

Newton's second law of motion is

$$\mathbf{F} = m\mathbf{A} \tag{7}$$

where $\mathbf{F}$ is the force vector applied to a moving object, m is the constant measure of the mass of the object, and $\mathbf{A}$ is the acceleration vector of the object. Substituting from (3) in (7) and letting $v = ds/dt$, we have

$$\mathbf{F}(t) = m\frac{dv}{dt}\mathbf{T}(t) + mv^2 K(t)\mathbf{N}(t)$$

Thus in curvilinear motion, the normal component of $\mathbf{F}$ is

$$mv^2 K(t) \quad \Leftrightarrow \quad \frac{mv^2}{\rho(t)}$$

which is the magnitude of the force normal to the curve necessary to keep the object on the curve. For example, if an automobile is going around a curve at a high speed, then the normal force exerted by the roadway must have a large magnitude to keep the car on the road. Also, if the curve is sharp, the radius of curvature is a small number; so again the magnitude of the normal force must be a large number. In the construction of an automobile racetrack, for example, the track is inclined to increase the magnitude of the normal force.

From Equation (4)

$$\|\mathbf{A}(t)\| = \sqrt{[A_T(t)]^2 + [A_N(t)]^2}$$

Solving this equation for $A_N(t)$, and noting from (6) that $A_N(t)$ is nonnegative, we have

$$A_N(t) = \sqrt{\|\mathbf{A}(t)\|^2 - [A_T(t)]^2}$$

which is a convenient formula for computing $A_N(t)$.

▶ **EXAMPLE 4**   A particle is moving along the curve having the vector equation

$$\mathbf{R}(t) = (t^2 - 1)\mathbf{i} + (\tfrac{1}{3}t^3 - t)\mathbf{j} \qquad t \geq 0$$

Find each of the following vectors: $\mathbf{V}(t)$, $\mathbf{A}(t)$, $\mathbf{T}(t)$, and $\mathbf{N}(t)$. Also find the following scalars: $\|\mathbf{V}(t)\|$, $A_T(t)$, $A_N(t)$, and $K(t)$. Find the particular values when $t = 2$. Sketch a portion of the curve at the point where $t = 2$, and representations of $\mathbf{V}(2)$, $\mathbf{A}(2)$, $A_T(2)\mathbf{T}(2)$, and $A_N(2)\mathbf{N}(2)$, having their initial point at $t = 2$.

Solution   Because $\mathbf{V}(t) = D_t\mathbf{R}(t)$ and $\mathbf{A}(t) = D_t\mathbf{V}(t)$,

$$\mathbf{V}(t) = 2t\mathbf{i} + (t^2 - 1)\mathbf{j} \qquad\qquad \mathbf{A}(t) = 2\mathbf{i} + 2t\mathbf{j}$$
$$\|\mathbf{V}(t)\| = \sqrt{4t^2 + (t^2 - 1)^2} \qquad \|\mathbf{A}(t)\| = \sqrt{4 + 4t^2}$$
$$= \sqrt{t^4 + 2t^2 + 1} \qquad\qquad\quad = 2\sqrt{1 + t^2}$$
$$= t^2 + 1$$

Therefore, $\dfrac{ds}{dt} = t^2 + 1$. Hence

$$A_T(t) = \frac{d^2s}{dt^2} \qquad\qquad A_N(t) = \sqrt{\|\mathbf{A}(t)\|^2 - [A_T(t)]^2}$$
$$= 2t \qquad\qquad\qquad\quad = \sqrt{4 + 4t^2 - 4t^2}$$
$$= 2$$

$$\mathbf{T}(t) = \frac{\mathbf{V}(t)}{\|\mathbf{V}(t)\|}$$
$$= \frac{2t}{t^2 + 1}\mathbf{i} + \frac{t^2 - 1}{t^2 + 1}\mathbf{j}$$

To compute $\mathbf{N}(t)$ we use the following formula that comes from (3):

$$\mathbf{N}(t) = \frac{1}{(D_t s)^2 K(t)}[\mathbf{A}(t) - (D_t^2 s)\mathbf{T}(t)] \tag{8}$$

$$\mathbf{A}(t) - (D_t^2 s)\mathbf{T}(t) = 2\mathbf{i} + 2t\mathbf{j} - 2t\left(\frac{2t}{t^2 + 1}\mathbf{i} + \frac{t^2 - 1}{t^2 + 1}\mathbf{j}\right)$$

$$\mathbf{A}(t) - (D_t^2 s)\mathbf{T}(t) = \frac{2}{t^2 + 1}[(1 - t^2)\mathbf{i} + 2t\mathbf{j}] \tag{9}$$

From (8), $\mathbf{N}(t)$ is a scalar times the vector in (9). Because $\mathbf{N}(t)$ is a unit vector, $\mathbf{N}(t)$ can be obtained by dividing the vector in (9) by its magnitude. Thus

$$\mathbf{N}(t) = \frac{(1 - t^2)\mathbf{i} + 2t\mathbf{j}}{\sqrt{(1 - t^2)^2 + (2t)^2}}$$
$$= \frac{1 - t^2}{1 + t^2}\mathbf{i} + \frac{2t}{1 + t^2}\mathbf{j}$$

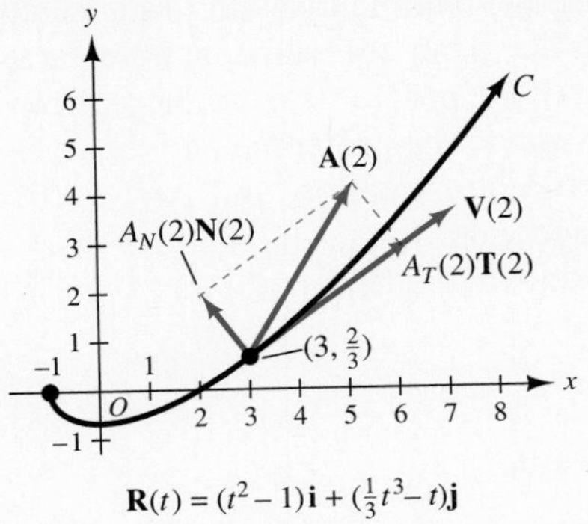

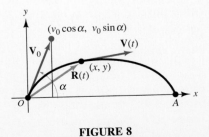

$$\mathbf{R}(t) = (t^2 - 1)\mathbf{i} + (\tfrac{1}{3}t^3 - t)\mathbf{j}$$

FIGURE 7

We compute the curvature $K(t)$ from the first equation in (6). With $A_N(t) = 2$ and $D_t s = t^2 + 1$, we get

$$K(t) = \frac{2}{(t^2 + 1)^2}$$

The required vectors and scalars at $t = 2$ are as follows:

$$\mathbf{V}(2) = 4\mathbf{i} + 3\mathbf{j} \qquad\qquad \mathbf{A}(2) = 2\mathbf{i} + 4\mathbf{j}$$

$$\|\mathbf{V}(2)\| = 5 \qquad\qquad A_T(2) = 4$$

$$\mathbf{T}(2) = \tfrac{4}{5}\mathbf{i} + \tfrac{3}{5}\mathbf{j} \qquad\qquad \mathbf{N}(2) = -\tfrac{3}{5}\mathbf{i} + \tfrac{4}{5}\mathbf{j}$$

$$A_N(2) = 2 \qquad\qquad K(2) = \tfrac{2}{25}$$

The required curve and representations of vectors appear in Figure 7. ◀

▶ **EXAMPLE 5**   A particle is moving along the curve having the vector equation

$$\mathbf{R}(t) = t\mathbf{i} + e^t\mathbf{j} + t\mathbf{k}$$

Find the tangential and normal components of the acceleration vector.

Solution

$$\mathbf{V}(t) = D_t\mathbf{R}(t) \qquad\qquad \mathbf{A}(t) = D_t\mathbf{V}(t)$$
$$= \mathbf{i} + e^t\mathbf{j} + \mathbf{k} \qquad\qquad\qquad = e^t\mathbf{j}$$
$$\|\mathbf{V}(t)\| = \sqrt{2 + e^{2t}} \qquad\qquad \|\mathbf{A}(t)\| = e^t$$
$$\frac{ds}{dt} = \sqrt{2 + e^{2t}} \quad \text{and} \quad \frac{d^2s}{dt^2} = \frac{e^{2t}}{\sqrt{2 + e^{2t}}}$$

Therefore

$$A_T(t) = \frac{e^{2t}}{\sqrt{2 + e^{2t}}} \qquad\qquad A_N(t) = \sqrt{\|\mathbf{A}(t)\|^2 - [A_T(t)]^2}$$

$$= \sqrt{e^{2t} - \frac{e^{4t}}{2 + e^{2t}}}$$

$$= \frac{\sqrt{2}\,e^t}{\sqrt{2 + e^{2t}}} \qquad ◀$$

We conclude this treatment of curvilinear motion by discussing the motion of a projectile. Assume that the projectile is moving in a vertical plane and that the only force acting on the projectile is its weight, directed downward with a magnitude of mg pounds where m slugs is its mass and g feet per second squared is the constant acceleration caused by gravity. We are neglecting the force attributed to air resistance, which for dense bodies traveling at small speeds has no noticeable effect. Let the positive direction be vertically upward and horizontally to the right.

Suppose that a projectile is shot from a gun having an angle of elevation of radian measure α. Let the number of feet per second in the initial speed, or *muzzle speed*, be denoted by v_0. The coordinate axes are set up so that the gun is located at the origin. Refer to Figure 8. The initial velocity vector, $\mathbf{V}_0$, of the projectile is given by

$$\mathbf{V}_0 = v_0 \cos \alpha \mathbf{i} + v_0 \sin \alpha \mathbf{j} \qquad\qquad \textbf{(10)}$$

FIGURE 8

Let t seconds be the time that has elapsed since the gun was fired, x feet be the horizontal distance of the projectile from the starting point at t seconds and y feet be the vertical distance of the projectile from the starting point at t seconds. $\mathbf{R}(t)$ is the position vector of the projectile at t seconds, $\mathbf{V}(t)$ is the velocity vector of the projectile at t seconds, and $\mathbf{A}(t)$ is the acceleration vector of the projectile at t seconds.

Because x and y are functions of t, we write the horizontal and vertical components of $\mathbf{R}(t)$ as $x(t)$ and $y(t)$; thus

$$\mathbf{R}(t) = x(t)\mathbf{i} + y(t)\mathbf{j}$$

If $\mathbf{F}$ denotes the force acting on the projectile

$$\mathbf{F} = -mg\mathbf{j}$$

From this equation and Equation (7) (Newton's second law of motion),

$$mA(t) = -mg\mathbf{j}$$
$$\mathbf{A}(t) = -g\mathbf{j} \quad \Leftrightarrow \quad \mathbf{V}'(t) = -g\mathbf{j}$$

Integrating on both sides of this equation with respect to t, we obtain

$$\mathbf{V}(t) = -gt\mathbf{j} + \mathbf{C}_1$$

Because $\mathbf{V}(0) = \mathbf{V}_0$, then $\mathbf{C}_1 = \mathbf{V}_0$. Therefore

$$\mathbf{V}(t) = -gt\mathbf{j} + \mathbf{V}_0 \quad \Leftrightarrow \quad \mathbf{R}'(t) = -gt\mathbf{j} + \mathbf{V}_0$$

Integrating again, we get

$$\mathbf{R}(t) = -\tfrac{1}{2}gt^2\mathbf{j} + \mathbf{V}_0 t + \mathbf{C}_2$$

Because the projectile starts at the origin, $\mathbf{R}(0) = \mathbf{0}$; so $\mathbf{C}_2 = \mathbf{0}$. Thus

$$\mathbf{R}(t) = -\tfrac{1}{2}gt^2\mathbf{j} + \mathbf{V}_0 t$$

With the value of $\mathbf{V}_0$ from (10), this equation becomes

$$\mathbf{R}(t) = -\tfrac{1}{2}gt^2\mathbf{j} + (v_0 \cos \alpha \mathbf{i} + v_0 \sin \alpha \mathbf{j})t$$
$$\mathbf{R}(t) = tv_0 \cos \alpha \mathbf{i} + (tv_0 \sin \alpha - \tfrac{1}{2}gt^2)\mathbf{j} \tag{11}$$

Equation (11) gives the position vector of the projectile at time t seconds. From this equation we can discuss the motion of the projectile. We are usually concerned with the following questions:

1. What is the range of the projectile? The range is the distance $|OA|$ along the x axis (see Figure 8).
2. What is the total time of flight, that is, the time it takes the projectile to go from O to A?
3. What is the maximum height of the projectile?
4. What is a cartesian equation of the curve traveled by the projectile?
5. What is the velocity vector of the projectile at impact?

These questions are answered in the following example.

▶ **EXAMPLE 6**   A projectile is shot from a gun at an angle of elevation of radian measure $\tfrac{1}{6}\pi$, and its muzzle speed is 480 ft/sec. Find: **(a)** the initial velocity vector; **(b)** the position vector $\mathbf{R}(t)$ and parametric equations of the path of the projectile; **(c)** the time of flight; **(d)** the range; **(e)** the maximum height; **(f)** the velocity vector and the speed at impact; **(g)** the position vector, the velocity vector, and the speed at 2 sec; and **(h)** a cartesian equation of the path of the projectile.

Solution

(a) From (10) with $v_0 = 480$ and $\alpha = \frac{1}{6}\pi$, the initial velocity vector is

$$\mathbf{V}_0 = 480 \cos \tfrac{1}{6}\pi\mathbf{i} + 480 \sin \tfrac{1}{6}\pi\mathbf{j}$$
$$= 240\sqrt{3}\mathbf{i} + 240\mathbf{j}$$

(b) We can obtain the position vector at t seconds by applying (11); we get

$$\mathbf{R}(t) = 240\sqrt{3}t\mathbf{i} + (240t - \tfrac{1}{2}gt^2)\mathbf{j}$$

By letting $g = 32$ we have

$$\mathbf{R}(t) = 240\sqrt{3}t\mathbf{i} + (240t - 16t^2)\mathbf{j} \tag{12}$$

If $(x(t), y(t))$ is the projectile's position at t seconds,

$$x(t) = 240\sqrt{3}t \quad \text{and} \quad y(t) = 240t - 16t^2 \tag{13}$$

(c) To determine the time of flight, we must find t when $y(t) = 0$. We set $y(t) = 0$ in the second equation of (13):

$$240t - 16t^2 = 0$$
$$t(240 - 16t) = 0$$
$$t = 0 \qquad t = 15$$

The 0 value for t occurs when the projectile is fired. Because $y(15) = 0$, the time of flight is 15 sec.

(d) To find the range, we compute $x(15)$. From the first equation of (13), $x(15) = 3600\sqrt{3}$. Hence the range is $3600\sqrt{3}$ ft ≈ 6200 ft.

(e) The maximum height is attained when the vertical component of the velocity vector is 0, that is, when $y'(t) = 0$. We compute $y'(t)$ from the second equation of (13) and get

$$y'(t) = 240 - 32t$$

Setting $y'(t) = 0$, we obtain $t = 7.5$, which is half the total time of flight. Because $y(7.5) = 900$, the maximum height is 900 ft.

(f) Because the time of flight is 15 sec, the velocity vector at impact is $\mathbf{V}(15)$. With $\mathbf{V}(t) = \mathbf{R}'(t)$, we get from (12)

$$\mathbf{V}(t) = 240\sqrt{3}\mathbf{i} + (240 - 32t)\mathbf{j} \tag{14}$$

Thus

$$\mathbf{V}(15) = 240\sqrt{3}\mathbf{i} - 240\mathbf{j}$$

Because $\|\mathbf{V}(15)\| = 480$, the speed at impact is 480 ft/sec.

(g) From (12) and (14),

$$\mathbf{R}(2) = 480\sqrt{3}\mathbf{i} + 416\mathbf{j} \qquad \mathbf{V}(2) = 240\sqrt{3}\mathbf{i} + 176\mathbf{j}$$
$$\|\mathbf{V}(2)\| = \sqrt{(240\sqrt{3})^2 + (176)^2}$$
$$= 32\sqrt{199}$$

At 2 sec, therefore, the speed is $32\sqrt{199}$ ft/sec ≈ 450 ft/sec.

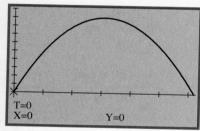

[0, 6300] by [−300, 1000]

$x(t) = 240\sqrt{3}t$ and $y(t) = 240t - 16t^2$

FIGURE 9

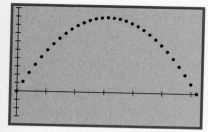

[0, 6300] by [−300, 1000]

$x(t) = 240\sqrt{3}t$ and $y(t) = 240t - 16t^2$

FIGURE 10

(h) To find a cartesian equation of the path of the projectile, we eliminate t between parametric equations (13). Substituting the value of t from the first equation into the second, we have

$$y = 240\left(\frac{x}{240\sqrt{3}}\right) - 16\left(\frac{x}{240\sqrt{3}}\right)^2$$

$$y = \frac{1}{\sqrt{3}}x - \frac{1}{10,800}x^2$$

which is an equation of a parabola.   ◀

▶ **EXAMPLE 7**   **(a)** From the answers in parts (b)–(e) of Example 6, plot the path of the projectile on a graphics calculator and simulate the motion of the projectile. **(b)** Plot the path of the projectile in dot mode.

Solution   **(a)** With our calculator in parametric mode, we enter the parametric equations

$$x(t) = 240\sqrt{3}t \text{ and } y(t) = 240t - 16t^2$$

In the window [0, 6300] by [−300, 1000], we let $t_{min} = 0$, $t_{max} = 15$, and $t_{step} = 0.5$. We press the TRACE key and then the left-arrow key and hold it down until the cursor is at $t = 0$. Figure 9 shows the calculator screen as it now appears. By pressing the right-arrow key, we observe the particle, represented by the cursor, moving along the curve.

(b) Figure 10 shows the calculator screen with our calculator in parametric and dot mode and with the same window and same values of t and t_{step} as in part (a). Observe that the distance between successive plotted points gets smaller as t increases from 0 to 7.5, when the projectile reaches its maximum height. Then as t increases from 7.5 to 15, the distance between successive plotted points gets larger. These observations indicate that the speed of the projectile decreases as it rises from its initial position to its maximum height, when the speed is zero; then as the projectile falls its speed increases until it strikes the ground.   ◀

EXERCISES 11.5

In Exercises 1 through 10, the position of a particle moving in the xy plane at time t units is given by the vector equation. (a) Find $\mathbf{V}(t)$, $\mathbf{A}(t)$, $\|\mathbf{V}(t)\|$, and $\|\mathbf{A}(t)\|$.
(b) Find the velocity and acceleration vectors at $t = t_1$.
(c) Sketch the path of the particle and draw representations of the velocity and acceleration vectors at $t = t_1$.
(d) Simulate the motion of the particle on your graphics calculator. (e) Plot the path of the particle on your graphics calculator in dot mode.

1. $\mathbf{R}(t) = (t^2 + 4)\mathbf{i} + (t - 2)\mathbf{j}$; $t_1 = 3$
2. $\mathbf{R}(t) = (1 + t)\mathbf{i} + (t^2 - 1)\mathbf{j}$; $t_1 = 1$

3. $\mathbf{R}(t) = 5 \cos 2t\mathbf{i} + 3 \sin 2t\mathbf{j}$; $t_1 = \frac{1}{4}\pi$
4. $\mathbf{R}(t) = \frac{2}{t}\mathbf{i} - \frac{1}{4}t\mathbf{j}$; $t_1 = 4$
5. $\mathbf{R}(t) = e^t\mathbf{i} + e^{2t}\mathbf{j}$; $t_1 = \ln 2$
6. $\mathbf{R}(t) = e^{2t}\mathbf{i} + e^{3t}\mathbf{j}$; $t_1 = 0$
7. $\mathbf{R}(t) = t\mathbf{i} + \ln \sec t\mathbf{j}$; $t_1 = \frac{1}{4}\pi$
8. $\mathbf{R}(t) = 2(1 - \cos t)\mathbf{i} + 2(1 - \sin t)\mathbf{j}$; $t_1 = \frac{5}{6}\pi$
9. $\mathbf{R}(t) = (t^2 + 3t)\mathbf{i} + (1 - 3t^2)\mathbf{j}$; $t_1 = \frac{1}{2}$
10. $\mathbf{R}(t) = \ln(t + 2)\mathbf{i} + \frac{1}{3}t^2\mathbf{j}$; $t_1 = 1$

In Exercises 11 through 16, the position of a particle moving in three-dimensional space at time t units is given by the vector equation. Find the velocity and acceleration vectors and the speed of the particle at $t = t_1$. Sketch a portion of the curve at $t = t_1$, and draw representations of the velocity and acceleration vectors there.

11. $\mathbf{R}(t) = 2 \cos t\mathbf{i} + 2 \sin t\mathbf{j} + t\mathbf{k}$; $t_1 = \frac{1}{2}\pi$

12. $\mathbf{R}(t) = t\mathbf{i} + \frac{1}{2}t^2\mathbf{j} + \frac{1}{3}t^3\mathbf{k}$; $t_1 = 2$

13. $\mathbf{R}(t) = t\mathbf{i} + (t^2 - 2t)\mathbf{j} + 2(t - 1)\mathbf{k}$; $t_1 = 2$

14. $\mathbf{R}(t) = 3 \cos t\mathbf{i} + 4 \sin t\mathbf{j} + 2t\mathbf{k}$; $t_1 = \frac{1}{2}\pi$

15. $\mathbf{R}(t) = e^t \cos t\mathbf{i} + e^t \sin t\mathbf{j} + e^t\mathbf{k}$; $t_1 = 0$

16. $\mathbf{R}(t) = \frac{1}{2}(t^2 + 1)^{-1}\mathbf{i} + \ln(1 + t^2)\mathbf{j} + \tan^{-1} t\mathbf{k}$; $t_1 = 1$

In Exercises 17 through 20, a particle is moving in the xy plane so that the given equation and initial conditions are satisfied. Find a vector equation of the path of the particle.

17. $\mathbf{V}(t) = \dfrac{1}{(t - 1)^2}\mathbf{i} - (t + 1)\mathbf{j}$ and $\mathbf{R}(0) = 3\mathbf{i} + 2\mathbf{j}$

18. $\mathbf{V}(t) = (2t - 1)\mathbf{i} + 3t^{-2}\mathbf{j}$ and $\mathbf{R}(1) = 4\mathbf{i} - 3\mathbf{j}$

19. $\mathbf{A}(t) = e^{-t}\mathbf{i} + 2e^{2t}\mathbf{j}$, $\mathbf{V}(0) = 2\mathbf{i} + \mathbf{j}$, and $\mathbf{R}(0) = 3\mathbf{j}$

20. $\mathbf{A}(t) = 2 \cos 2t\mathbf{i} + 2 \sin 2t\mathbf{j}$, $\mathbf{V}(0) = \mathbf{i} + \mathbf{j}$, and $\mathbf{R}(0) = \frac{1}{2}\mathbf{i} - \frac{1}{2}\mathbf{j}$

In Exercises 21 through 24, a particle is moving in three-dimensional space so that the given equation and initial conditions are satisfied. Find a vector equation of the path of the particle.

21. $\mathbf{V}(t) = \mathbf{i} + \mathbf{j} - 32t\mathbf{k}$ and $\mathbf{R}(0) = \mathbf{i} + 2\mathbf{j}$

22. $\mathbf{V}(t) = (t^2 + 2t)\mathbf{i} + 2t\mathbf{j} + 3t^2\mathbf{k}$, and $\mathbf{R}(0) = 2\mathbf{j} + \mathbf{k}$

23. $\mathbf{A}(t) = 6t\mathbf{i} + 12t^2\mathbf{j} + \mathbf{k}$, $\mathbf{V}(0) = 2\mathbf{i} + 3\mathbf{j}$, and $\mathbf{R}(0) = 4\mathbf{k}$

24. $\mathbf{A}(t) = -32\mathbf{k}$, $\mathbf{V}(0) = 4\mathbf{i} + 4\mathbf{j}$, and $\mathbf{R}(0) = 60\mathbf{k}$

In Exercises 25 through 30, a particle is moving along the curve having the vector equation. In each exercise, find the vectors $\mathbf{V}(t)$, $\mathbf{A}(t)$, $\mathbf{T}(t)$, and $\mathbf{N}(t)$, and the following scalars for an arbitrary value of t: $\|\mathbf{V}(t)\|$, $A_T(t)$, $A_N(t)$, and $K(t)$. Also find the particular values when $t = t_1$. At $t = t_1$, sketch a portion of the curve and draw representations of the vectors $\mathbf{V}(t_1)$, $\mathbf{A}(t_1)$, $A_T(t_1)\,\mathbf{T}(t_1)$, and $A_N(t_1)\,\mathbf{N}(t_1)$.

25. $\mathbf{R}(t) = (2t + 3)\mathbf{i} + (t^2 - 1)\mathbf{j}$; $t_1 = 2$

26. $\mathbf{R}(t) = (t - 1)\mathbf{i} + t^2\mathbf{j}$; $t_1 = 1$

27. $\mathbf{R}(t) = 5 \cos 3t\mathbf{i} + 5 \sin 3t\mathbf{j}$; $t_1 = \frac{1}{3}\pi$

28. $\mathbf{R}(t) = 3t^2\mathbf{i} + 2t^3\mathbf{j}$; $t_1 = 1$

29. $\mathbf{R}(t) = e^t\mathbf{i} + e^{-t}\mathbf{j}$; $t_1 = 0$

30. $\mathbf{R}(t) = \cos t^2\mathbf{i} + \sin t^2\mathbf{j}$; $t_1 = \frac{1}{2}\sqrt{\pi}$

In Exercises 31 through 36, a particle is moving along the curve having the given vector equation. Find the tangential and normal components of the acceleration vector and use them to write $\mathbf{A}(t) = A_T(t)\mathbf{T}(t) + A_N(t)\mathbf{N}(t)$ without computing $\mathbf{T}(t)$ and $\mathbf{N}(t)$.

31. $\mathbf{R}(t) = t\mathbf{i} + t^2\mathbf{j} + t\mathbf{k}$

32. $\mathbf{R}(t) = e^{-t}\mathbf{i} + e^t\mathbf{j} + \sqrt{2}t\mathbf{k}$

33. $\mathbf{R}(t) = (\cos t + t \sin t)\mathbf{i} + (\sin t - t \cos t)\mathbf{j} + 2\mathbf{k}$, $t \geq 0$

34. $\mathbf{R}(t) = 2t^2\mathbf{i} + t^2\mathbf{j} + 4t\mathbf{k}$

35. $\mathbf{R}(t) = t^2\mathbf{i} + (\frac{1}{3}t^3 + t)\mathbf{j} + (\frac{1}{3}t^3 - t)\mathbf{k}$

36. $\mathbf{R}(t) = t \cos t\mathbf{i} + t \sin t\mathbf{j} + t\mathbf{k}$

37. Prove that if the speed of a moving particle is constant, its acceleration vector is always orthogonal to its velocity vector.

38. A particle is moving along the curve having the vector equation $\mathbf{R}(t) = \tan t\mathbf{i} + \sinh 2t\mathbf{j} + \operatorname{sech} t\mathbf{k}$. Prove that the velocity and acceleration vectors are orthogonal at $t = 0$.

39. A particle is moving along the twisted cubic

$$\mathbf{R}(t) = t\mathbf{i} + t^2\mathbf{j} + t^3\mathbf{k}$$

Find an equation of the plane determined by the unit tangent and unit normal vectors at the point on the curve where $t = 1$.

40. Prove that for the twisted cubic of Exercise 39, if $t \neq 0$, no two of the vectors $\mathbf{R}(t)$, $\mathbf{V}(t)$, and $\mathbf{A}(t)$ are orthogonal.

In Exercises 41 and 42, a projectile is shot from a gun at an angle of elevation of radian measure α, and its muzzle speed is v_0 ft/sec. Find: (a) the initial velocity vector; (b) the position vector $\mathbf{R}(t)$ and parametric equations of the path of the projectile; (c) the time of flight; (d) the range; (e) the maximum height; (f) the velocity vector and the speed at impact; (g) the position vector, the velocity vector, and the speed at t_1 sec; and (h) a cartesian equation of the path of the projectile.

41. $\alpha = \frac{1}{4}\pi$; $v_0 = 320$; $t_1 = 6$

42. $\alpha = \frac{1}{3}\pi$; $v_0 = 160$; $t_1 = 4$

In Exercises 43 and 44 do the following: (a) From the answers in parts (b)–(e) of the indicated exercise, plot the path of the projectile on your graphics calculator and simulate the motion of the projectile; (b) plot the path of the projectile in dot mode; (c) sketch what you see on the screen of your graphics calculator in part (b); (d) describe what your calculator screen in part (b) tells you about the speed of the projectile.

43. Exercise 41

44. Exercise 42

45. A projectile is shot from the top of a building 96 ft high from a gun at an angle of 30° with the horizontal. If the muzzle speed is 1600 ft/sec, find the time of flight and the distance from the base of the building to the point where the projectile lands.

46. The muzzle speed of a gun is 160 ft/sec. At what angle of elevation should the gun be fired so that a projectile will hit an object on the same level as the gun and at a distance of 400 ft from it?

47. What is the muzzle speed of a gun if a projectile fired from it has a range of 2000 ft and reaches a maximum height of 1000 ft?

48. A ball is thrown horizontally from the top of a cliff 256 ft high with an initial speed of 50 ft/sec. Find the time of flight of the ball and the distance from the base of the cliff to the point where the ball lands.

49. As a ship is pulling away from a dock, a girl standing on the ship's deck, 55 ft above the dock, throws to a friend, standing on the dock, a note attached to a stone. The ship is 28 ft away from the dock at the instant the girl tosses the stone from her hand, 5 ft above the deck, toward the dock at an initial speed of 15 ft/sec and at an angle of 45° with the horizontal. Will the stone reach the dock so that her friend can retrieve the note or will it land in the water and sink? Justify your answer.

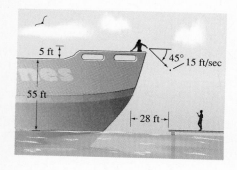

50. Answer the question of Exercise 49 if the girl tosses the stone horizontally with an initial speed of 15 ft/sec.

51. A boy bets his friend that he can throw a ball to hit a billboard 25 ft away from him. The billboard is 10 ft high and its base is 35 ft above the ground. The boy throws the ball with an initial speed of 60 ft/sec toward the billboard at an angle of elevation of 60°. If

the boy's hand is 5 ft above the ground, show that the boy wins the bet and determine the direction of the ball at the moment of impact.

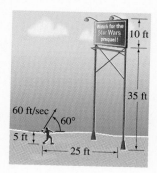

52. A basketball player is given a free toss at the basket whose hoop is 10 ft above the gymnasium floor. If the player is at a horizontal distance of 11 ft from the center of the basket, determine the angle at which she should throw the ball at an initial speed of 25 ft/sec if her hands are 6 ft above the floor at the moment of toss.

53. A tree, 45 ft tall, stands directly between the pin and a golf ball, which is 225 ft from the pin. The tree is 100 ft from the ball. A golfer hits the ball toward the pin with a speed of 80 ft/sec and at an angle of 45°. Show that the ball avoids hitting the tree, and determine how far from the pin the ball lands.

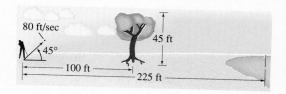

54. Determine the angle of elevation at which a gun should be fired to obtain the maximum range for a given muzzle speed.

55. A particle starts at point $(r, 0)$ on the circle with center at the origin and radius r and moves on the circle at a constant angular speed of ω radians per second. An equation of its path is

$$\mathbf{R}(t) = \mathbf{i}r \cos \omega t + \mathbf{j}r \sin \omega t$$

This equation describes **uniform circular motion.**
(a) Show that the speed of the particle is given by $r\omega$.
(b) Show that if $\mathbf{A}(t)$ is the acceleration vector, the direction of $\mathbf{A}(t)$ is opposite that of $\mathbf{R}(t)$ and $\|\mathbf{A}(t)\| = r\omega^2$. **(c)** Find $\mathbf{T}(t)$, $\mathbf{N}(t)$, $A_T(t)$, and $A_N(t)$.
(d) What is the effect on $A_N(t)$ if the angular speed is doubled?

CHAPTER 11 REVIEW

▶ *SUGGESTIONS FOR REVIEW OF CHAPTER 11*

1. What is a vector-valued function and how does it differ from a real-valued function?

2. How are properties of real-valued functions used in the study of vector-valued functions?

3. How do the definitions of the limit and continuity of a vector-valued function depend on the corresponding definitions for a real-valued function?

4. How do you obtain cartesian equations of a curve in three-dimensional space from its vector equation? Make up an example to illustrate your answer.

5. How do the definitions of the derivative and indefinite integral of a vector-valued function compare with the corresponding definitions for a real-valued function?

6. What is a geometric interpretation of the derivative of a vector-valued function?

7. How do the theorems of the derivative of the sum, dot product, and cross product of two vector-valued functions compare with the corresponding theorems for real-valued functions? Make up examples to illustrate your answer.

8. What is the chain rule for vector-valued functions? Make up an example showing its application.

9. What can you conclude about a vector-valued function and its derivative if the magnitude of the vector-valued function is constant?

10. What is the formula in three-dimensional space for the length of arc of a curve defined by a vector equation?

11. What is the unit tangent vector $\mathbf{T}(t)$ of a curve C at a point P on C if $\mathbf{R}(t)$ is the position vector? State a formula for computing $\mathbf{T}(t)$ from $\mathbf{R}(t)$.

12. What is the unit normal vector $\mathbf{N}(t)$ of a curve C at a point P on C if $\mathbf{T}(t)$ is the unit tangent vector? State a formula for computing $\mathbf{N}(t)$ from $\mathbf{T}(t)$.

13. Express the unit binormal vector of a curve C at a point P on C in terms of the unit tangent vector and unit normal vector.

14. What are the osculating, rectifying, and normal planes of a curve C at a point P on C? How do you find equations of these planes?

15. If $\mathbf{R}(t) = f(t)\mathbf{i} + g(t)\mathbf{j} + h(t)\mathbf{k}$ is a vector equation of a curve C, how do you obtain an equation involving t and the number of units of arc length s from an arbitrary point on C to the point $P(f(t), g(t), h(t))$? Why can you generally not solve this equation for s in terms of t? Make up an example.

16. If $\mathbf{R}(t)$ is the position vector of a curve C in three-dimensional space, define the curvature $K(t)$ of C at a point on the curve.

17. Give two formulas for computing the curvature $K(t)$: (i) one in terms of $D_t\mathbf{R}(t)$ and $D_t\mathbf{T}(t)$; (ii) one in terms of $D_t\mathbf{R}(t)$ and $D_{t^2}\mathbf{R}(t)$. Which of these formulas is usually easier to apply?

18. Define the radius of curvature and circle of curvature for curves in the xy plane.

19. State a formula for computing the curvature of a plane curve defined by an equation of the form $y = f(x)$.

20. If a particle is moving along the curve C having the vector equation $\mathbf{R}(t) = f(t)\mathbf{i} + g(t)\mathbf{j} + h(t)\mathbf{k}$, define the velocity and acceleration vectors at a point P on C. What is the speed of the particle at P? Make up an example.

21. State a formula expressing the acceleration vector as the sum of a vector tangent to the direction of motion and a vector normal to the direction of motion.

22. State the formulas giving the tangential and normal components of acceleration.

23. What is the position vector of a projectile shot from a gun having an angle of elevation of α and at a muzzle speed of v_0 feet per second? How do you find the maximum height, time of flight, and range of the projectile from this vector? Make up an example.

▶ MISCELLANEOUS EXERCISES FOR CHAPTER 11

In Exercises 1 through 4, find the domain of the vector-valued function.

1. $\mathbf{R}(t) = \dfrac{1}{t-3}\mathbf{i} + \sqrt{t}\,\mathbf{j}$ **2.** $\mathbf{R}(t) = \ln(t+1)\mathbf{i} + e^{1/t}\mathbf{j}$

3. $\mathbf{R}(t) = \ln|\cos t|\,\mathbf{i} + \sqrt{4t^2 - 1}\,\mathbf{j} + \sqrt{4 - t^2}\,\mathbf{k}$

4. $\mathbf{R}(t) = \sqrt{9 - t^2}\,\mathbf{i} + \tan t\mathbf{j} + \dfrac{t}{t-1}\mathbf{k}$

In Exercises 5 through 8, find the indicated limit, if it exists.

5. $\lim\limits_{t \to 1}\left(\dfrac{1}{t+1}\mathbf{i} + \dfrac{\sqrt{t}-1}{t-1}\mathbf{j}\right)$

6. $\lim\limits_{t \to 0}\left(\cos t\mathbf{i} + \dfrac{\sin t}{t}\mathbf{j}\right)$

7. $\lim\limits_{t \to 0^+}\left(e^{-1/t}\mathbf{i} + \dfrac{1 - \cos t}{t}\mathbf{j} + \dfrac{\sin^{-1}t}{t}\mathbf{k}\right)$

8. $\lim\limits_{t \to 4}\left(\dfrac{t^2 - 16}{t-4}\mathbf{i} + \dfrac{\tan^{-1}(t-4)}{t-4}\mathbf{j} + |t-4|\mathbf{k}\right)$

In Exercises 9 through 12, determine the numbers at which the vector-valued function is continuous.

9. $\mathbf{R}(t) = e^{-t}\mathbf{i} + \ln t\mathbf{j} + \dfrac{1}{\sqrt{4-t}}\mathbf{k}$

10. $\mathbf{R}(t) = \ln|\cos t|\mathbf{i} + \dfrac{1}{|t|-1}\mathbf{j} + \sqrt{1 - t^2}\mathbf{k}$

11. $\mathbf{R}(t) = \begin{cases} \dfrac{\sin(t-1)}{t-1}\mathbf{i} + \dfrac{t^2-1}{2(t-1)}\mathbf{j} \\ \qquad\qquad + (t-1)\ln|t-1|\mathbf{k} & \text{if } t \neq 1 \\ \mathbf{i} + \mathbf{j} & \text{if } t = 1 \end{cases}$

12. $\mathbf{R}(t) = \begin{cases} (1+t)^{1/t}\mathbf{i} + e^{1+t}\mathbf{j} + \dfrac{e^{1-t}}{1-t}\mathbf{k} & \text{if } t \neq 0 \\ e(\mathbf{i} + \mathbf{j} + \mathbf{k}) & \text{if } t = 0 \end{cases}$

In Exercises 13 through 16, sketch the graph of the vector-valued function.

13. $\mathbf{R}(t) = 2\sec t\mathbf{i} + 2\tan t\mathbf{j}$
14. $\mathbf{R}(t) = 2\sqrt{t}\mathbf{i} + (t+1)\mathbf{j}$
15. $\mathbf{R}(t) = t\mathbf{i} + t^2\mathbf{j} + 2t^3\mathbf{k},\ 0 \le t \le 2$
16. $\mathbf{R}(t) = 3\cos t\mathbf{i} + 3\sin t\mathbf{j} + 3t\mathbf{k},\ 0 \le t \le 2\pi$

In Exercises 17 and 18, find $\mathbf{R}'(t)$ and $\mathbf{R}''(t)$.

17. $\mathbf{R}(t) = \dfrac{1}{t^2+9}\mathbf{i} + \dfrac{1}{t}\mathbf{j} - \ln t\mathbf{k}$

18. $\mathbf{R}(t) = \dfrac{t}{t-1}\mathbf{i} - \dfrac{t+1}{t}\mathbf{j} + \dfrac{t+1}{t-1}\mathbf{k}$

In Exercises 19 and 20, find $D_t\|\mathbf{R}(t)\|$ and $\|D_t\mathbf{R}(t)\|$.
19. $\mathbf{R}(t) = 2(e^t - 1)\mathbf{i} + 2(e^t + 1)\mathbf{j} + e^t\mathbf{k}$
20. $\mathbf{R}(t) = \cos 2t\mathbf{i} + \sin 2t\mathbf{j} + 2t^2\mathbf{k}$

21. If $\mathbf{R}'(t) = \dfrac{1}{t+2}\mathbf{i} + \dfrac{1}{t^2+1}\mathbf{j}$ and $\mathbf{R}(0) = \mathbf{j}$, find $\mathbf{R}(t)$.

22. If $\mathbf{R}'(t) = \dfrac{1}{t}\mathbf{i} + \dfrac{2\ln t}{t}\mathbf{j}$ and $\mathbf{R}(1) = 3\mathbf{i} - 2\mathbf{j}$, find $\mathbf{R}(t)$.

23. If $\mathbf{R}'(t) = 2e^{t/2}\mathbf{i} - 2e^{-t/2}\mathbf{j} + 2\cosh\dfrac{t}{2}\mathbf{k}$ and $\mathbf{R}(2) = 2e\mathbf{i} - 2e^{-1}\mathbf{j} + \mathbf{k}$, find $\mathbf{R}(t)$.

24. If $\mathbf{R}'(t) = \cos^2 t\mathbf{i} + \cos 2t\mathbf{j} - 2\sin 2t\mathbf{k}$ and $\mathbf{R}(0) = \mathbf{i}$, find $\mathbf{R}(t)$.

In Exercises 25 and 26, find the exact length of arc from t_1 to t_2 of the curve having the given vector equation.
25. $\mathbf{R}(t) = t\cos t\mathbf{i} + t\sin t\mathbf{j} + t\mathbf{k};\ t_1 = 0;\ t_2 = \frac{1}{2}\pi$.
26. $\mathbf{R}(t) = (2 - 3t)\mathbf{i} + (4t - 1)\mathbf{j} + t^2\mathbf{k};\ t_1 = 0;\ t_2 = \frac{5}{2}$.

In Exercises 27 and 28, use the NINT capability of your graphics calculator to find an approximate value to four significant digits of the length of arc from t_1 to t_2 of the curve having the given vector equation.

27. $\mathbf{R}(t) = \ln t\mathbf{i} + \dfrac{1}{t}\mathbf{j} - \dfrac{1}{t}\mathbf{k};\ t_1 = 1;\ t_2 = 2$

28. $\mathbf{R}(t) = \cos t\mathbf{i} + \sin t\mathbf{j} + e^{2t}\mathbf{k};\ t_1 = 0;\ t_2 = \frac{1}{2}\pi$

In Exercises 29 and 30, find $\mathbf{T}(t)$ and $\mathbf{N}(t)$, and at $t = t_1$ sketch a portion of the curve and draw the representations of $\mathbf{T}(t_1)$ and $\mathbf{N}(t_1)$ having initial point at $t = t_1$.
29. $\mathbf{R}(t) = \frac{1}{2}e^{2t}\mathbf{i} + t\mathbf{j};\ t_1 = \ln 2$
30. $\mathbf{R}(t) = t^2\mathbf{i} + \frac{1}{3}t^3\mathbf{j};\ t_1 = 1$

In Exercises 31 through 34, find $\mathbf{T}(t)$ and $\mathbf{N}(t)$.
31. $\mathbf{R}(t) = \frac{1}{3}t^3\mathbf{i} + t^2\mathbf{j} + 2t\mathbf{k}$
32. $\mathbf{R}(t) = e^t\mathbf{i} + 2e^{-t}\mathbf{j} + 2t\mathbf{k}$
33. $\mathbf{R}(t) = 3\sin 2t\mathbf{i} + 4t\mathbf{j} + 3\cos 2t\mathbf{k}$
34. $\mathbf{R}(t) = 3(\cos t + t\sin t)\mathbf{i} + 3(\sin t - t\cos t)\mathbf{j} + 3\mathbf{k}$

In Exercises 35 through 38, find the moving trihedral and equations of the osculating, rectifying, and normal planes for the curve at $t = t_1$.

35. The curve of Exercise 31; $t_1 = 1$
36. The curve of Exercise 32; $t_1 = 0$
37. The curve of Exercise 33; $t_1 = 0$
38. The curve of Exercise 34; $t_1 = \frac{1}{2}\pi$

In Exercises 39 and 40, for the given curve, express the arc length s as a function of t, where s is measured from the point where t = 0.

39. The curve of Exercise 31

40. The curve of Exercise 32

In Exercises 41 through 44, find a vector equation of the curve having arc length s as a parameter, where s is measured from the point where t = 0. Check your answer by using Equation (9) of Section 11.3.

41. $\mathbf{R}(t) = 4t\mathbf{i} + \frac{1}{3}(2t + 1)^{3/2}\mathbf{j}$

42. The curve of Exercise 30

43. The curve of Exercise 33

44. The curve of Exercise 34

In Exercises 45 and 46, for the curve and t_1 in the indicated exercise, find the curvature K and the radius of curvature ρ at the point where $t = t_1$. Sketch a portion of the curve, the unit tangent vector, and the circle of curvature at $t = t_1$.

45. Exercise 29   **46.** Exercise 30

In Exercises 47 through 50, for the curve in the indicated exercise, find the curvature K.

47. Exercise 31   **48.** Exercise 32

49. Exercise 33   **50.** Exercise 34

51. Show that the curvature of the curve $y = \ln x$ at any point (x, y) is $x/(x^2 + 1)^{3/2}$. Also show that the absolute maximum curvature is $\frac{2}{9}\sqrt{3}$, which occurs at the point $(\frac{1}{2}\sqrt{2}, -\frac{1}{2}\ln 2)$.

52. Find the curvature at any point on the branch of the hyperbola defined by the parametric equations $x = a \cosh t$ and $y = b \sinh t$.

53. Find the curvature and radius of curvature of the curve having parametric equations $x = 3t^2$ and $y = t^3 - 3t$ at the point where $t = 2$.

54. Find the curvature and radius of curvature of the curve $y = e^{-x}$ at the point $(0, 1)$.

55. Find the center of curvature for the curve of Exercise 53 at the point where $t = 2$, and sketch a portion of the curve and the circle of curvature at that point.

56. Find the center of curvature for the curve of Exercise 54 at the point $(0, 1)$, and sketch a portion of the curve and the circle of curvature at that point.

In Exercises 57 and 58, the position of a particle moving in the xy plane at time t units is given by the vector equation. (a) Find $\mathbf{V}(t)$, $\mathbf{A}(t)$, $\|\mathbf{V}(t)\|$, and $\|\mathbf{A}(t)\|$. (b) Find the velocity and acceleration vectors at t = 1. (c) Sketch the path of the particle and draw representations of the velocity and acceleration vectors at t = 1. (d) Simulate the motion of the particle on your graphics calculator.

(e) Plot the path of the particle on your graphics calculator in dot mode.

57. $\mathbf{R}(t) = 3t\mathbf{i} + (4t - t^2)\mathbf{j}$ **58.** $\mathbf{R}(t) = 2e^t\mathbf{i} + 3e^{-t}\mathbf{j}$

In Exercises 59 and 60, a particle is moving along the given curve. Find the velocity and acceleration vectors and the speed at the indicated point. Sketch a portion of the curve at that point and draw the representations of the velocity and acceleration vectors there.

59. The curve of Exercise 25 at $t = \frac{1}{2}\pi$

60. The curve of Exercise 26 at $t = \frac{1}{2}$

In Exercises 61 and 62, a particle is moving in the xy plane so that the given equation and initial conditions are satisfied. Find a vector equation of the path of the particle.

61. $\mathbf{V}(t) = e^{2t}\mathbf{i} + e^{-t}\mathbf{j}$ and $\mathbf{R}(0) = 2\mathbf{i} - \mathbf{j}$

62. $\mathbf{A}(t) = t^2\mathbf{i} - t^{-2}\mathbf{j}$, $\mathbf{V}(1) = \mathbf{j}$, and $R(1) = \frac{1}{4}\mathbf{i} + \frac{1}{2}\mathbf{j}$

In Exercises 63 through 66, a particle is moving in three-dimensional space so that the given equation and initial conditions are satisfied. Find a vector equation of the path of the particle.

63. $\mathbf{V}(t) = -2 \sin t\mathbf{i} + 2 \cos t\mathbf{i} + \mathbf{k}$, $\mathbf{R}(0) = 2\mathbf{i} + 2\mathbf{j}$

64. $\mathbf{V}(t) = e^t\mathbf{i} - e^t\mathbf{j} - 8e^{4t}\mathbf{k}$, $\mathbf{R}(0) = 2\mathbf{i} - \mathbf{j} - \mathbf{k}$

65. $\mathbf{A}(t) = 3\mathbf{j} - 2\mathbf{k}$, $\mathbf{V}(1) = \mathbf{i} + \mathbf{k}$, $\mathbf{R}(1) = 2\mathbf{i} + 4\mathbf{j}$

66. $\mathbf{A}(t) = 4\mathbf{i} + 12t^2\mathbf{j}$, $\mathbf{V}(\frac{1}{2}) = 2\mathbf{i} + \frac{1}{2}\mathbf{j} + \mathbf{k}$,
$\mathbf{R}(\frac{1}{2}) = \mathbf{i} + \frac{1}{16}\mathbf{j} + \mathbf{k}$

In Exercises 67 and 68, a particle is moving along the curve of the indicated exercise. In each exercise, find the vectors $\mathbf{V}(t)$, $\mathbf{A}(t)$, $\mathbf{T}(t)$, and $\mathbf{N}(t)$, and the following scalars for an arbitrary value of t: $\|\mathbf{V}(t)\|$, $A_T(t)$, $A_N(t)$, and K(t). Also find the particular values when t = 1. At t = 1, sketch a portion of the curve and draw representations of the vectors $\mathbf{V}(1)$, $\mathbf{A}(1)$, $A_T(1)\mathbf{T}(1)$, and $A_N(1)\mathbf{N}(1)$.

67. Exercise 57   **68.** Exercise 58

In Exercises 69 and 70, a particle is moving along the curve having the given vector equation. Find the tangential and normal components of the acceleration vector and use them to write $\mathbf{A}(t) = A_T(t)\mathbf{T}(t) + A_N(t)\mathbf{N}(t)$ without computing $\mathbf{T}(t)$ and $\mathbf{N}(t)$.

69. $\mathbf{R}(t) = 2t\mathbf{i} + e^t\mathbf{j} + e^{-t}\mathbf{k}$

70. $\mathbf{R}(t) = t^2\mathbf{i} + 2t\mathbf{j} + 2\mathbf{k}$

In Exercises 71 and 72, find (a) the velocity and acceleration vectors, (b) the speed, and (c) the tangential and normal components of acceleration.

71. $\mathbf{R}(t) = \cosh 2t\mathbf{i} + \sinh 2t\mathbf{j} + \mathbf{k}$

72. $\mathbf{R}(t) = (2 \tan^{-1}t - t)\mathbf{i} + \ln(1 + t^2)\mathbf{j} + 2\mathbf{k}$

73. A projectile is shot from a gun at an angle of elevation of 30° and a muzzle speed of 150 ft/sec. Find: (a) the position vector $\mathbf{R}(t)$; (b) the range of the projectile; (c) the maximum height; (d) the speed at impact.

74. For the projectile of Exercise 73, (a) plot the path of the projectile on your graphics calculator and simulate the motion of the projectile; (b) plot the path of the projectile in dot mode; (c) sketch what you see on your graphics calculator in part (b); (d) describe what your calculator screen in part (b) tells you about the speed of the projectile.

75. If a projectile is shot at an angle of elevation of 40°, determine the minimum muzzle speed that will yield a range of at least 300 ft.

76. Find a formula for obtaining the maximum height reached by a projectile fired from a gun having a given muzzle speed of v_0 feet per second and an angle of elevation of radian measure α.

77. A spectator, seated in the stands 20 ft above the field at a baseball game, retrieves a ball hit into the stands. She throws the ball from her seat back to the field at an angle of depression of 25° at an initial speed of 24 ft/sec.
(a) How long does it take the ball to strike the ground?

(b) What is the distance from the point on the ground directly below her seat to the point on the field where the ball lands?

78. Answer the questions of Exercise 77 if the spectator throws the ball horizontally with an initial speed of 24 ft/sec.

79. If a particle is moving in the xy plane so that its velocity vector is always orthogonal to its position vector, prove that the path of the particle is a circle with its center at the origin.

80. If a particle is moving along a curve, under what conditions will the acceleration vector and the unit tangent vector have the same or opposite directions?

81. The vectors $\mathbf{V}$, $\mathbf{A}$, and $\mathbf{N}$ are, respectively, the velocity, acceleration, and unit normal vectors for the curvilinear motion of a particle. Prove that if $\|(\mathbf{V} \cdot \mathbf{V})\mathbf{A} - (\mathbf{V} \cdot \mathbf{A})\mathbf{V}\| \neq 0$,

$$\mathbf{N} = \frac{(\mathbf{V} \cdot \mathbf{V})\mathbf{A} - (\mathbf{V} \cdot \mathbf{A})\mathbf{V}}{\|(\mathbf{V} \cdot \mathbf{V})\mathbf{A} - (\mathbf{V} \cdot \mathbf{A})\mathbf{V}\|}$$

82. If $\mathbf{R}$, $\mathbf{Q}$, and $\mathbf{W}$ are three vector-valued functions whose derivatives with respect to t exist, prove that

$$D_t[\mathbf{R}(t) \cdot \mathbf{Q}(t) \times \mathbf{W}(t)] = D_t\mathbf{R}(t) \cdot \mathbf{Q}(t) \times \mathbf{W}(t)$$
$$+ \mathbf{R}(t) \cdot D_t\mathbf{Q}(t) \times \mathbf{W}(t) + \mathbf{R}(t) \cdot \mathbf{Q}(t) \times D_t\mathbf{W}(t)$$

DIFFERENTIAL CALCULUS OF FUNCTIONS OF MORE THAN ONE VARIABLE

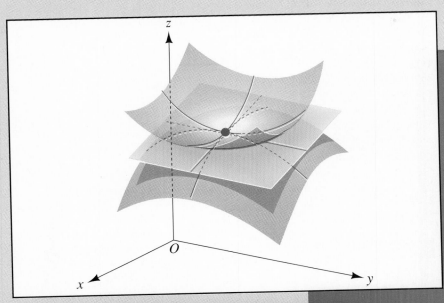

In Section 12.1, the concept of a function of a real variable is extended to a *function of several real variables*, and in the next section, the concepts of *limit* and *continuity* are extended for functions of several variables. Most of the discussion in these two sections is confined to functions of two and three variables; however, we make the definitions for functions of n variables and then show the applications of these definitions to functions of two and three variables. We also show that when each of these definitions is applied to a function of one variable, the definition previously given is obtained.

The treatment of differentiation of functions of several variables begins in Section 12.3, where the *partial derivatives* of such functions are defined. Then in Section 12.4, we discuss *differentiability* of these functions as well as the *total differential*. The several-variable version of the *chain rule* is presented in Section 12.5. The applications of differentiation in Sections 12.3 through 12.5 are to find rates of change and to compute approximations.

While the partial derivatives of a function with respect to x and y measure rates of change of the function values in the direction of the x and y axes, respectively, the *directional derivatives*, introduced in Section 12.6, give rates of change of these function values in any direction. The *gradient*, also introduced in Section 12.6, gives the direction in which the function has its greatest rate of change. This concept is applied in Section 12.7 to a discussion of *tangent planes* and *normals to surfaces*.

Just as first and second derivatives are used to determine maxima and minima of functions of a single variable, we show in Section 12.8 how partial derivatives enable us to find extreme values of functions of two variables. The applications in this section include the *method of least squares* to obtain a linear mathematical model for a given set of data. In Section 12.9, *Lagrange multipliers* are introduced to compute extrema of a function subject to a constraint.

12.1 FUNCTIONS OF MORE THAN ONE VARIABLE

We now generalize the notion of a function to functions of more than one independent variable. Such functions often occur in practical situations. For example, a person's approximate body surface area depends on the person's weight and height. The volume of a right-circular cylinder depends on its radius and altitude. According to the ideal gas law, the volume occupied by a confined gas is directly proportional to its temperature and inversely proportional to its pressure. The selling price of a particular product may be dependent upon the cost of labor, the cost of materials, and overhead expenses.

To extend the concept of a function to functions of any number of variables we must first consider points in n-dimensional number space. Just as we denoted a point in R by a real number x, a point in R^2 by an ordered pair of real numbers (x, y), and a point in R^3 by an ordered triple of real numbers (x, y, z), a point in n-dimensional number space, R^n, is represented by an ordered n-tuple of real numbers customarily denoted by $P = (x_1, x_2, \ldots, x_n)$. In particular, if $n = 1$, let $P = x$; if $n = 2$, $P = (x, y)$; if $n = 3$, $P = (x, y, z)$; if $n = 6$, $P = (x_1, x_2, x_3, x_4, x_5, x_6)$.

12.1.1 Definition of the *n*-Dimensional Number Space

The set of all ordered n-tuples of real numbers is called the **n-dimensional number space** and is denoted by R^n. Each ordered n-tuple $(x_1, x_2, \ldots, x_n)$ is called a **point** in the n-dimensional number space.

12.1.2 Definition of a Function of *n* Variables

A **function of n variables** is a set of ordered pairs of the form (P, w) in which no two distinct ordered pairs have the same first element. P is a point in n-dimensional number space and w is a real number. The set of all admissible points P is called the **domain** of the function, and the set of all resulting values of w is called the **range** of the function.

From this definition, the domain of a function of n variables is a set of points in R^n and the range is a set of real numbers in R. When $n = 1$, we have a function of one variable; thus the domain is a set of points in R or, equivalently, a set of real numbers. Hence Definition 1.1.1 is a special case of Definition 12.1.2. If $n = 2$, we have a function of two variables, and the domain is a set of points in R^2 or, equivalently, a set of ordered pairs of real numbers (x, y).

▷ **ILLUSTRATION 1**   Let the function f of two variables x and y be the set of all ordered pairs of the form (P, z) such that

$$z = \sqrt{25 - x^2 - y^2}$$

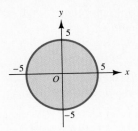

FIGURE 1

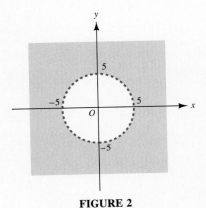

FIGURE 2

The domain of f is the set $\{(x, y) \mid x^2 + y^2 \le 25\}$. This is the set of points in the xy plane on the circle $x^2 + y^2 = 25$ and in the interior region bounded by the circle. Figure 1 shows as a shaded region in R^2 the set of points in the domain of f.

Because $z = \sqrt{25 - (x^2 + y^2)}$, then $0 \le z \le 5$; therefore the range of f is the set of all real numbers in the closed interval $[0, 5]$.   ◄

▷ **ILLUSTRATION 2**   The function g of two variables x and y is the set of all ordered pairs of the form (P, z) such that

$$z = \frac{1}{\sqrt{x^2 + y^2 - 25}}$$

The domain of g is the set $\{(x, y) \mid x^2 + y^2 > 25\}$. This is the set of points in the exterior region bounded by the circle $x^2 + y^2 = 25$. Figure 2 shows as a shaded region in R^2 the set of points in the domain of g.   ◄

If f is a function of n variables, then according to Definition 12.1.2, f is a set of ordered pairs of the form (P, w), where $P = (x_1, x_2, \ldots, x_n)$ is a point in R^n and w is a real number. The particular value of w that corresponds to a point P is denoted by the symbol $f(P)$ or $f(x_1, x_2, \ldots, x_n)$. In particular, if $n = 2$ and $P = (x, y)$, we can represent the function value by either $f(P)$ or $f(x, y)$. Similarly, if $n = 3$ and $P = (x, y, z)$, we denote the function value by either $f(P)$ or $f(x, y, z)$. Note that if $n = 1$, $P = x$; hence if f is a function of one variable, $f(P) = f(x)$. Therefore this notation is consistent with the notation for function values of one variable.

A function f of n variables can be defined by the equation

$$w = f(x_1, x_2, \ldots, x_n)$$

The variables $x_1, x_2, \ldots, x_n$ are called the *independent variables*, and w is called the *dependent variable*.

▷ **ILLUSTRATION 3**   Let f be the function of Illustration 1; that is,
$$f(x, y) = \sqrt{25 - x^2 - y^2}$$

Then

$$f(3, -4) = \sqrt{25 - 3^2 - (-4)^2} \qquad f(-2, 1) = \sqrt{25 - (-2)^2 - 1^2}$$
$$= \sqrt{25 - 9 - 16} \qquad\qquad\quad = \sqrt{25 - 4 - 1}$$
$$= 0 \qquad\qquad\qquad\qquad\qquad = 2\sqrt{5}$$
$$f(u, 3v) = \sqrt{25 - u^2 - (3v)^2}$$
$$= \sqrt{25 - u^2 - 9v^2} \qquad\qquad\qquad\qquad\qquad\qquad ◄$$

► **EXAMPLE 1**   The function g is defined by
$$g(x, y, z) = x^3 - 4yz^2$$
Find: **(a)** $g(1, 3, -2)$; **(b)** $g(2a, -4b, 3c)$; **(c)** $g(x^2, y^2, z^2)$; **(d)** $g(y, z, -x)$.

Solution

(a) $g(1, 3, -2) = 1^3 - 4(3)(-2)^2$
$$= 1 - 48$$
$$= -47$$

(b) $g(2a, -4b, 3c) = (2a)^3 - 4(-4b)(3c)^2$
$$= 8a^3 + 144bc^2$$

(c) $g(x^2, y^2, z^2) = (x^2)^3 - 4y^2(z^2)^2$
$$= x^6 - 4y^2z^4$$

(d) $g(y, z, -x) = y^3 - 4z(-x)^2$
$$= y^3 - 4x^2z$$ ◀

12.1.3 Definition of a Composite Function of Two Variables

If f is a function of a single variable and g is a function of two variables, then the **composite function** $f \circ g$ is the function of two variables defined by

$$(f \circ g)(x, y) = f(g(x, y))$$

and the domain of $f \circ g$ is the set of all points (x, y) in the domain of g such that $g(x, y)$ is in the domain of f.

▶ **EXAMPLE 2** Given $f(t) = \ln t$ and $g(x, y) = x^2 + y$, find $h(x, y)$ if $h = f \circ g$, and determine the domain of h.

Solution

$$h(x, y) = (f \circ g)(x, y)$$
$$= f(g(x, y))$$
$$= f(x^2 + y)$$
$$= \ln(x^2 + y)$$

The domain of g is the set of all points in R^2, and the domain of f is $(0, +\infty)$. Therefore the domain of h is the set $\{(x, y) \mid x^2 + y > 0\}$. ◀

Definition 12.1.3 can be extended to a composite function of n variables as follows.

12.1.4 Definition of the Composite Function of n Variables

If f is a function of a single variable and g is a function of n variables, then the **composite function** $f \circ g$ is the function of n variables defined by

$$(f \circ g)(x_1, x_2, \ldots, x_n) = f(g(x_1, x_2, \ldots, x_n))$$

and the domain of $f \circ g$ is the set of all points $(x_1, x_2, \ldots, x_n)$ in the domain of g such that $g(x_1, x_2, \ldots, x_n)$ is in the domain of f.

▶ **EXAMPLE 3** Given $F(x) = \sin^{-1} x$ and

$$G(x, y, z) = \sqrt{x^2 + y^2 + z^2 - 4}$$

find the function $F \circ G$ and its domain.

Solution

$$(F \circ G)(x, y, z) = F(G(x, y, z))$$
$$= F(\sqrt{x^2 + y^2 + z^2 - 4})$$
$$= \sin^{-1}\sqrt{x^2 + y^2 + z^2 - 4}$$

The domain of G is the set $\{(x, y, z) \mid x^2 + y^2 + z^2 - 4 \geq 0\}$, and the domain of F is $[-1, 1]$. So the domain of $F \circ G$ is the set of all points (x, y, z) in R^3 such that $0 \leq x^2 + y^2 + z^2 - 4 \leq 1$ or, equivalently, $4 \leq x^2 + y^2 + z^2 \leq 5$. ◀

A **polynomial function** of two variables x and y is a function f such that $f(x, y)$ is the sum of terms of the form $cx^n y^m$, where c is a real number and n and m are nonnegative integers. The **degree** of the polynomial function is determined by the largest sum of the exponents of x and y appearing in any one term.

▷ **ILLUSTRATION 4**

(a) The function f defined by

$$f(x, y) = x^3 + 2x^2 y^2 - y^3$$

is a polynomial function of degree 4 because the term of highest degree is $2x^2 y^2$.

(b) If

$$g(x, y) = 6x^3 y^2 - 5xy^3 + 7x^2 y - 2x^2 + y + 4$$

g is a polynomial function of degree 5. ◀

The graph of a function f of a single variable consists of the set of points (x, y) in R^2 for which $y = f(x)$. Similarly, the graph of a function of two variables is a set of points in R^3.

12.1.5 Definition of the Graph of a Function of Two Variables

If f is a function of two variables, then the **graph** of f is the set of all points (x, y, z) in R^3 for which (x, y) is a point in the domain of f and $z = f(x, y)$.

Hence the graph of a function f of two variables is a surface that is the set of all points in three-dimensional space whose cartesian coordinates are given by the ordered triples of real numbers (x, y, z). Because the domain of f is a set of points in the xy plane, and because for each ordered pair (x, y) in the domain of f there corresponds a unique value of z, no line perpendicular to the xy plane can intersect the graph of f in more than one point.

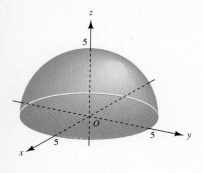

$$z = \sqrt{25 - x^2 - y^2}$$

FIGURE 3

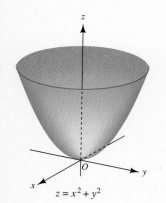

$$z = x^2 + y^2$$

FIGURE 4

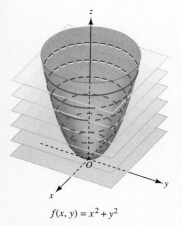

$$f(x, y) = x^2 + y^2$$

FIGURE 5

▷ **ILLUSTRATION 5**   The function f of Illustration 1 is the set of all ordered pairs of the form (P, z) such that

$$z = \sqrt{25 - x^2 - y^2}$$

The graph of f is, therefore, the hemisphere on and above the xy plane having its center at the origin and a radius of 5. This hemisphere appears in Figure 3.   ◀

▶ **EXAMPLE 4**   Sketch the graph of the function having function values

$$f(x, y) = x^2 + y^2$$

Solution   The graph of f is the surface having the equation $z = x^2 + y^2$. The trace of the surface in the xy plane is found by using the equation $z = 0$ simultaneously with the equation of the surface. We obtain $x^2 + y^2 = 0$, which is the origin. The traces in the xz and yz planes are found by using the equations $y = 0$ and $x = 0$, respectively, with the equation $z = x^2 + y^2$. These traces are the parabolas $z = x^2$ and $z = y^2$. The cross section of the surface in a plane $z = k$, parallel to the xy plane, is a circle with its center on the z axis and radius $\sqrt{k}$. With this information we have the required graph shown in Figure 4, which is a circular paraboloid.   ◀

Another useful method of representing a function of two variables geometrically is similar to that of representing a three-dimensional landscape by a two-dimensional topographical map. Suppose that the surface $z = f(x, y)$ is intersected by the plane $z = k$, and the curve of intersection is projected onto the xy plane. This projected curve has $f(x, y) = k$ as an equation, and the curve is called the **level curve** (or **contour curve**) of the function f at k. Each point on the level curve corresponds to the unique point on the surface that is k units above it if k is positive, or k units below it if k is negative. By considering different values for the constant k we obtain a set of level curves called a **contour map**. The set of all possible values of k is the range of the function f, and each level curve, $f(x, y) = k$, in the contour map consists of the points (x, y) in the domain of f having equal function values of k.

▷ **ILLUSTRATION 6**   Figure 5 shows the graph of the function of Example 4 defined by

$$f(x, y) = x^2 + y^2$$

along with the curves of intersection of this surface with the planes $z = k$ where k equals 1, 2, 3, 4, 5, and 6. These curves are circles with center on the z axis and radius $\sqrt{k}$. Figure 6 shows the curves projected onto the xy plane. The projected circles, which are level curves of function f, represent the view of the circles of Figure 5 obtained from looking down on the surface from a point on the z axis.   ◀

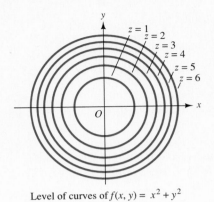

Level of curves of $f(x, y) = x^2 + y^2$

FIGURE 6

A contour map of $z = f(x, y)$ shows the variation of z with x and y in the xy plane by considering the level curves. The values of z are changing more rapidly when the level curves are close together than when they are far apart; that is, when the level curves are close together the surface is steep, and when the level curves are far apart the elevation of the surface relative to the xy plane is changing slowly. Notice this situation in Figure 6 for the level curves of the surface of Figure 5.

On a two-dimensional topographical map of a landscape, a general notion of its steepness is obtained by considering the spacing of its level curves. Also on a topographical map if the path of a level curve is followed, the elevation remains constant.

▶ **EXAMPLE 5**   Let function f be defined by

$$f(x, y) = 8 - x^2 - 2y$$

Sketch the graph of f and a contour map of f showing the level curves at constant intervals of 2 units from 8 down to -8.

Solution   The graph of f, sketched in Figure 7, is the surface

$$z = 8 - x^2 - 2y$$

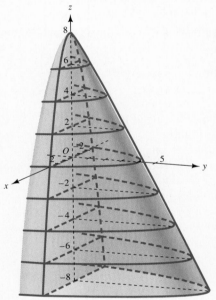

$f(x, y) = 8 - x^2 - 2y$

FIGURE 7

The trace in the xy plane is obtained by setting $z = 0$, which gives the parabola $x^2 = -2(y - 4)$. Setting $y = 0$ and $x = 0$, we obtain the traces in the xz and yz planes, which are, respectively, the parabola $x^2 = -(z - 8)$ and the line $2y + z = 8$. The cross section of the surface made by the plane $z = k$ is a parabola having its vertex on the line $2y + z = 8$ in the yz plane and opening to the left. The cross sections for z equals 8, 6, 4, 2, 0, -2, -4, -6, and -8 are shown in the figure.

The level curves of f are the parabolas $x^2 = -2(y - 4 + \frac{1}{2}k)$. The contour map of f with sketches of the required level curves appears in Figure 8.   ◀

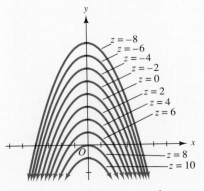

Level of curves of $f(x, y) = 8 - x^2 - 2y$

FIGURE 8

To illustrate a use of level curves, suppose that the temperature at any point of a flat metal plate is given by the function f; that is, if T degrees is the temperature, then at the point (x, y), $T = f(x, y)$. Then the curves having equations of the form $f(x, y) = k$, where k is a constant, are curves on which the temperature is constant. These level curves are called **isotherms.** Furthermore, if V volts gives the electric potential at any point (x, y) of the xy plane, and $V = f(x, y)$, then the level curves are called **equipotential curves** because the electric potential at each point of such a curve is the same.

For an application of level curves in economics, consider the productivity (or output) of an industry dependent on several inputs. Among the inputs may be the number of machines used in production, the number of person-hours available, the amount of working capital, the quantity of material used, and the amount of land available. Suppose the amounts of the inputs are given by x and y, the amount of the output is given by z, and $z = f(x, y)$. Such a function is called a **production function,** and the level curves having equations of the form $f(x, y) = k$, where k is a constant, are called **constant product curves.**

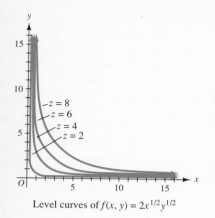

Level curves of $f(x, y) = 2x^{1/2}y^{1/2}$

FIGURE 9

 EXAMPLE 6 Let f be the production function for which

$$f(x, y) = 2x^{1/2}y^{1/2}$$

Draw a contour map of f showing the constant product curves at 8, 6, 4, and 2.

Solution The contour map consists of the curves of intersection of the surface

$$z = 2x^{1/2}y^{1/2} \tag{1}$$

with the planes $z = k$, where k equals 8, 6, 4, and 2. Substituting $z = 8$ in (1) we obtain $4 = x^{1/2}y^{1/2}$ or, equivalently,

$$xy = 16 \qquad x > 0 \quad \text{and} \quad y > 0 \tag{2}$$

The curve in the xy plane represented by (2) is a branch of a hyperbola lying in the first quadrant. With each of the numbers 6, 4, and 2 we also obtain a branch of a hyperbola in the first quadrant. These are the constant product curves shown in Figure 9. ◀

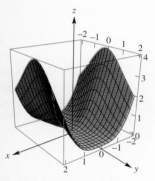

$[-2, 2]$ by $[-2, 2]$ by $[0, 4]$

$$f(x, y) = \frac{x^4}{x^2 + y^2}$$

FIGURE 10a

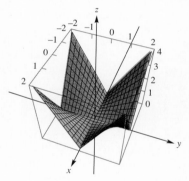

$[-2, 2]$ by $[-2, 2]$ by $[0, 4]$

$$f(x, y) = |xy|$$

FIGURE 11a

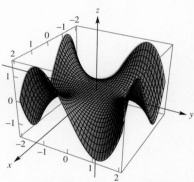

$[-2, 2]$ by $[-2, 2]$ by $[-1.5, 1.5]$

$$f(x, y) = \tfrac{1}{4}xy(y^2 - x^2)$$

FIGURE 12a

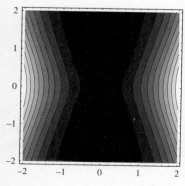

Level curves of $f(x, y) = \dfrac{x^4}{x^2 + y^2}$

FIGURE 10b

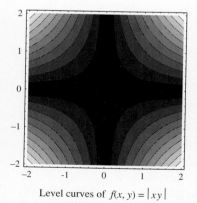

Level curves of $f(x, y) = |xy|$

FIGURE 11b

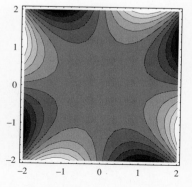

Level curves of $f(x, y) = \tfrac{1}{4}xy(y^2 - x^2)$

FIGURE 12b

In the above examples and illustrations, we used functions whose graphs and level curves were relatively easy to sketch. **Computer graphics** can be applied to plot more complicated surfaces. These computer programs usually show traces of the surface in planes parallel to the coordinate planes. They often allow a choice of the viewer's location that permits you to observe the surface from various perspectives. Normally the programs require that a **viewing box** be stipulated. This viewing box corresponds to the *window* (or *viewing rectangle*) selected when plotting two-dimensional curves on a graphics calculator. The viewing box, denoted by $[x_{\min}, x_{\max}]$ by $[y_{\min}, y_{\max}]$ by $[z_{\min}, z_{\max}]$, is the set of points in R^3 for which $x_{\min} \le x \le x_{\max}$, $y_{\min} \le y \le y_{\max}$, and $z_{\min} \le z \le z_{\max}$.

The computer graphics in this text were generated by *Mathematica*. The figures representing these graphics show the surface in the viewing box designated below the figure. Most of the graphics place the viewer in the first octant of a right-handed coordinate system. Color has been added to enhance the three-dimensional appearance. Parts (a) of Figures 10 through 15 show computer graphics of surfaces defined by some particular functions of two variables; parts (b) of Figures 10 through 15 show computer graphics of some of the corresponding level curves. More computer graphics appear in Exercises 51 through 54, where you are asked to match a function with a surface and a set of level curves.

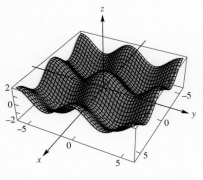

[−6, 6] by [−6, 6] by [−2, 2]

$f(x, y) = \cos x + \cos y$

FIGURE 13a

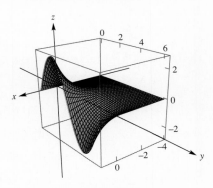

[−4, 1] by [0, 6.5] by [−3, 3]

$f(x, y) = e^x \sin y$

FIGURE 14a

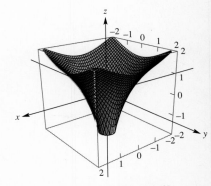

[−2, 2] by [−2, 2] by [−2, 2]

$f(x, y) = \ln(x^2 + y^2)$

FIGURE 15a

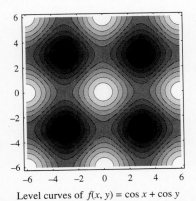

Level curves of $f(x, y) = \cos x + \cos y$

FIGURE 13b

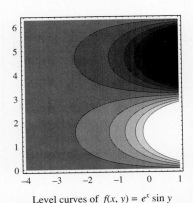

Level curves of $f(x, y) = e^x \sin y$

FIGURE 14b

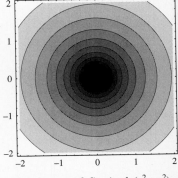

Level curves of $f(x, y) = \ln(x^2 + y^2)$

FIGURE 15b

The following definition extends the notion of the graph of a function to a function of n variables.

12.1.6 Definition of the Graph of a Function of n Variables

If f is a function of n variables, then the **graph** of f is the set of all points $(x_1, x_2, \ldots, x_n, w)$ in R^{n+1} for which $(x_1, x_2, \ldots, x_n)$ is a point in the domain of f and $w = f(x_1, x_2, \ldots, x_n)$.

Functions of three variables have *level surfaces,* a concept analogous to level curves for functions of two variables. If f is a function whose domain is a set of points in R^3, then if k is a number in the range of f, the graph of the equation

$$f(x, y, z) = k$$

is a **level surface** of f at k. Every surface in three-dimensional space can be considered as a level surface of some function of three variables.

▷ **ILLUSTRATION 7**   If the function g is defined by

$$g(x, y, z) = x^2 + y^2 - z$$

then the circular paraboloid $z = x^2 + y^2$, shown in Figure 4, is the level surface of g at 0. The level surface of g at the number k has the equation $z + k = x^2 + y^2$, a circular paraboloid whose vertex is the point $(0, 0, -k)$ on the z axis. Figure 16 shows the level surfaces for k equals -4, -2, 0, 2, and 4. ◀

▶ **EXAMPLE 7**   The function f is defined by

$$f(x, y, z) = x + 2y + 4z$$

Sketch the level surfaces of f for the following values of k: 16, 12, 8, 4, 2.

Solution   An equation of the level surface of f at k is

$$x + 2y + 4z = k$$

whose graph is a plane. For the given values of k we have the following parallel planes:

$$x + 2y + 4z = 16$$
$$x + 2y + 4z = 12$$
$$x + 2y + 4z = 8$$
$$x + 2y + 4z = 4$$
$$x + 2y + 4z = 2$$

These planes are sketched in Figure 17. ◀

▶ **EXAMPLE 8**   The function f is defined by

$$f(x, y, z) = x^2 + y^2 - z^2$$

Describe the level surfaces of f for **(a)** $k = 4$, **(b)** $k = -4$, and **(c)** $k = 0$.

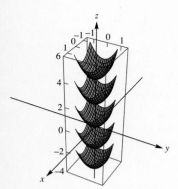

[−1.5, 1.5] by [−1.5, 1.5] by [−4, 6]

Level surfaces of $g(x, y, z) = x^2 + y^2 - z$

FIGURE 16

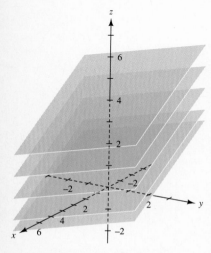

Level surfaces of $f(x, y, z) = x + 2y + 4z$

FIGURE 17

Solution

(a) The level surface for $k = 4$ has the equation

$$x^2 + y^2 - z^2 = 4$$

This surface, a hyperboloid of one sheet whose axis is the z axis, is sketched in Figure 18.

(b) The level surface for $k = -4$ has the equation

$$x^2 + y^2 - z^2 = -4 \iff -x^2 - y^2 + z^2 = 4$$

This surface is a hyperboloid of two sheets whose axis is the z axis, and is sketched in Figure 19.

(c) The level surface for $k = 0$ has the equation

$$x^2 + y^2 - z^2 = 0$$

This surface, a cone whose axis is the z axis, is sketched in Figure 20. ◄

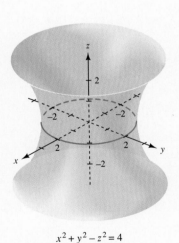

$x^2 + y^2 - z^2 = 4$

FIGURE 18

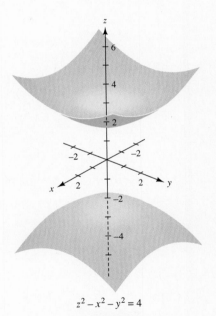

$z^2 - x^2 - y^2 = 4$

FIGURE 19

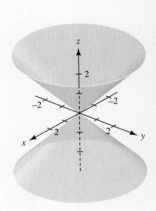

$x^2 + y^2 - z^2 = 0$

FIGURE 20

EXERCISES 12.1

1. Let the function f of two variables x and y be the set of all ordered pairs of the form (P, z) such that

$$z = \frac{x + y}{x - y} \iff f(x, y) = \frac{x + y}{x - y}$$

Find: **(a)** $f(-3, 4)$; **(b)** $f(\frac{1}{2}, \frac{1}{3})$;
(c) $f(x + 1, y - 1)$; **(d)** $f(-x, y) - f(x, -y)$.

2. Let the function g of two variables x and y be the set of all ordered pairs of the form (P, z) such that

$$z = \sqrt{x^2 - y} \iff g(x, y) = \sqrt{x^2 - y}$$

Find: **(a)** $g(3, 5)$; **(b)** $g(-4, -9)$;
(c) $g(x + 2, 4x + 4)$; **(d)** $g\left(\frac{1}{x}, \frac{-3}{x^2}\right)$.

3. Let the function g of three variables x, y, and z be the set of all ordered pairs of the form (P, w) such that
$$w = \sqrt{4 - x^2 - y^2 - z^2}$$
$$\Leftrightarrow \quad g(x, y, z) = \sqrt{4 - x^2 - y^2 - z^2}$$
Find: **(a)** $g(1, -1, -1)$; **(b)** $g(-1, \frac{1}{2}, \frac{3}{2})$;
(c) $g(\frac{1}{2}x, \frac{1}{2}y, \frac{1}{2}z)$;
(d) $[g(x, y, z)]^2 - [g(x + 2, y + 2, z)]^2$.

4. Let the function f of three variables x, y, and z be the set of all ordered pairs of the form (P, w) such that
$$w = \frac{4}{x^2 + y^2 + z^2 - 9}$$
$$\Leftrightarrow \quad f(x, y, z) = \frac{4}{x^2 + y^2 + z^2 - 9}$$
Find: **(a)** $f(1, 2, 3)$; **(b)** $f(2, -\frac{1}{2}, \frac{3}{2})$;
(c) $f\left(-\frac{2}{x}, \frac{2}{x}, -\frac{1}{x}\right)$; **(d)** $f(x + 2, 1, x - 2)$.

In Exercises 5 through 20, determine the domain of f and sketch as a region in R^2 the set of points in the domain. Use dashed curves to indicate any part of the boundary not in the domain and solid curves to indicate parts of the boundary in the domain.

5. $f(x, y) = \dfrac{1}{x^2 + y^2 - 1}$ 6. $f(x, y) = \dfrac{4}{4 - x^2 - y^2}$

7. $f(x, y) = \sqrt{1 - x^2 - y^2}$

8. $f(x, y) = \sqrt{16 - x^2 - 4y^2}$

9. $f(x, y) = \sqrt{x^2 - y^2 - 1}$

10. $f(x, y) = \sqrt{x^2 - 4y^2 + 16}$

11. $f(x, y) = \sqrt{x^2 + y^2 - 1}$

12. $f(x, y) = \sqrt{x^2 + 4y^2 - 16}$

13. $f(x, y) = \dfrac{1}{\sqrt{1 - x^2 - y^2}}$

14. $f(x, y) = \dfrac{1}{\sqrt{16 - x^2 - 4y^2}}$

15. $f(x, y) = \dfrac{x^4 - y^4}{x^2 - y^2}$ 16. $f(x, y) = \dfrac{x - y}{x + y}$

17. $f(x, y) = \cos^{-1}(x - y)$ 18. $f(x, y) = \ln(x^2 + y)$

19. $f(x, y) = \ln(xy - 1)$ 20. $f(x, y) = \sin^{-1}(x + y)$

In Exercises 21 through 28, determine the domain of f and describe as a region in R^3 the set of points in the domain.

21. $f(x, y, z) = \dfrac{x + y + z}{x - y - z}$ 22. $f(x, y, z) = \dfrac{z}{x^2 - y}$

23. $f(x, y, z) = \sqrt{16 - x^2 - 4y^2 - z^2}$

24. $f(x, y, z) = \sqrt{9 - x^2 - y^2 - z^2}$

25. $f(x, y, z) = \sin^{-1} x + \sin^{-1} y + \sin^{-1} z$

26. $f(x, y, z) = \ln x + \ln y + \ln z$

27. $f(x, y, z) = \ln(4 - x^2 - y^2) + |z|$

28. $f(x, y, z) = xz \cos^{-1}(y^2 - 1)$

In Exercises 29 through 36, determine the domain of f and sketch the graph of f.

29. $f(x, y) = \sqrt{16 - x^2 - y^2}$

30. $f(x, y) = 6 - 2x + 2y$

31. $f(x, y) = 16 - x^2 - y^2$

32. $f(x, y) = \sqrt{100 - 25x^2 - 4y^2}$

33. $f(x, y) = x^2 - y^2$ 34. $f(x, y) = 144 - 9x^2 - 16y^2$

35. $f(x, y) = 4x^2 + 9y^2$ 36. $f(x, y) = \sqrt{x + y}$

In Exercises 37 through 46, sketch a contour map of f showing the level curves at the given numbers.

37. The function of Exercise 29 at 0, 1, 2, 3, and 4

38. The function of Exercise 30 at 10, 6, 2, 0, -2, -6, and -10

39. The function of Exercise 31 at 16, 12, 7, 0, -9, and -20

40. The function of Exercise 32 at 0, 2, 4, 6, 8, and 10

41. The function of Exercise 33 at 16, 9, 4, 0, -4, -9, and -16

42. The function of Exercise 36 at 10, 8, 6, 5, and 0

43. $f(x, y) = \frac{1}{2}(x^2 + y^2)$ at 8, 6, 4, 2, and 0

44. $f(x, y) = (x - 3)/(y + 2)$ at 4, 2, 1, $\frac{1}{2}$, $\frac{1}{4}$, 0, $-\frac{1}{4}$, $-\frac{1}{2}$, -1, -2, and -4

45. $f(x, y) = e^{xy}$ at 1, 2, e, 4, $\frac{1}{2}$, e^{-1}, and $\frac{1}{4}$

46. $f(x, y) = \ln xy$ at 0, 1, 2, 4, -1, -2, and -4

47. Given $f(x, y) = x - y$, $g(t) = \sqrt{t}$, $h(s) = s^2$. Find
(a) $(g \circ f)(5, 1)$; **(b)** $f(h(3), g(9))$; **(c)** $f(g(x), h(y))$;
(d) $g((h \circ f)(x, y))$; **(e)** $(g \circ h)(f(x, y))$.

48. Given $f(x, y) = x/y^2$, $g(x) = x^2$, $h(x) = \sqrt{x}$. Find
(a) $(h \circ f)(2, 1)$; **(b)** $f(g(2), h(4))$;
(c) $f(g(\sqrt{x}), h(x^2))$; **(d)** $h((g \circ f)(x, y))$;
(e) $(h \circ g)(f(x, y))$.

In Exercises 49 and 50, find $h(x, y)$ if $h = f \circ g$; also find the domain of h.

49. $f(t) = \sin^{-1} t$; $g(x, y) = \sqrt{1 - x^2 - y^2}$

50. $f(t) = e^t$; $g(x, y) = y \ln x$

In Exercises 51 through 54, match the function with one of the surfaces in (a)–(d) and with one of the contour maps in (i)–(iv). On the contour maps, the x axis is horizontal, the y axis is vertical, black represents the smallest function value, and white represents the largest function value.

51. $f(x, y) = \dfrac{x^2}{x^2 + y^2}$

52. $f(x, y) = \ln|x + y|$

53. $f(x, y) = e^y \cos x$

54. $f(x, y) = \sin x + \cos y$

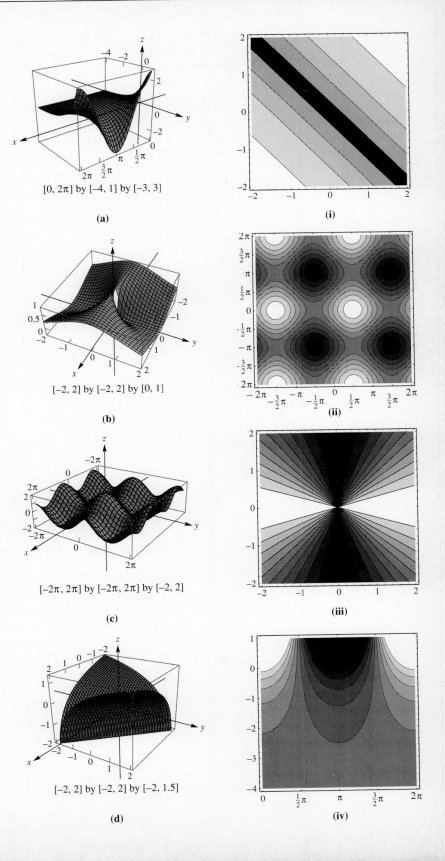

$[0, 2\pi]$ by $[-4, 1]$ by $[-3, 3]$

(a)

(i)

$[-2, 2]$ by $[-2, 2]$ by $[0, 1]$

(b)

(ii)

$[-2\pi, 2\pi]$ by $[-2\pi, 2\pi]$ by $[-2, 2]$

(c)

(iii)

$[-2, 2]$ by $[-2, 2]$ by $[-2, 1.5]$

(d)

(iv)

55. A closed rectangular box to contain 16 ft^3 is to be made of three kinds of materials. The material for the top and bottom costs \$0.18 per square foot, the material for the front and back costs \$0.16 per square foot, and the material for the other two sides costs \$0.12 per square foot. **(a)** Find a mathematical model expressing the total cost of the material as a function of the dimensions of the front and back. State the domain of the function. **(b)** What is the cost of the material if the dimensions of the front and back are 2 ft and 4 ft, where 4 ft is the height of the box?

56. A rectangular box without a top is to be made at a cost of \$10 for the material. The material for the bottom costs \$0.15 per square foot and the material for the sides costs \$0.30 per square foot. **(a)** Find a mathematical model expressing the volume of the box as a function of the dimensions of the bottom. State the domain of the function. **(b)** What is the volume of the box if the bottom is a square of side 3 ft?

57. A rectangular solid in the first octant with three sides in the coordinate planes has a vertex at the origin and the opposite vertex at the point (x, y, z) in the plane $x + 3y + 2z = 6$. **(a)** Find a mathematical model expressing the volume of the solid as a function of the dimensions of the base. State the domain of the function. **(b)** What is the volume if the base is a square of side 1.25 units?

58. (a) Find a mathematical model expressing the total surface area of the solid in Exercise 57 as a function of the dimensions of the base. State the domain of the function. **(b)** What is the total surface area if the base is a square of side 1.25 units?

59. The electric potential at a point (x, y) is $V(x, y)$ volts and $V(x, y) = 4/\sqrt{9 - x^2 - y^2}$. Draw the equipotential curves for V at 16, 12, 8, and 4.

60. The production function f for a certain commodity has function values $f(x, y) = 4x^{1/3}y^{2/3}$, where x and y give the amounts of two inputs. Draw a contour map of f showing the constant product curves at 16, 12, 8, 4, and 2.

61. Suppose f is the production function of a certain commodity, where $f(x, y)$ units are produced when x machines are used and y person-hours are available. If $f(x, y) = 6xy$, draw a contour map of f showing the constant product curves at 30, 24, 18, 12, and 6.

62. $T(x, y)$ degrees is the temperature at a point (x, y) of a flat metal plate where $T(x, y) = 4x^2 + 2y^2$. Draw a contour map of T showing the isotherms at 12, 18, 4, 1, and 0.

63. The pressure of a gas at the point (x, y, z) in three-dimensional space is $P(x, y, z)$ atmospheres where

$$P(x, y, z) = 4e^{-(x^2+y^2+z^2)}$$

Describe the level surfaces, called *isobaric surfaces,* of P at 4, 2, 1, and $\frac{1}{2}$.

64. The electric potential at a point (x, y, z) in three-dimensional space is $V(x, y, z)$ volts where

$$V(x, y, z) = \frac{8}{\sqrt{16x^2 + 4y^2 + z^2}}$$

The level surfaces of V are called *equipotential surfaces.* Describe these surfaces at 4, 2, 1, and $\frac{1}{2}$.

12.2 LIMITS AND CONTINUITY OF FUNCTIONS OF MORE THAN ONE VARIABLE

The definition of the limit of a function of one variable involved the distance between two points on the real-number line. The limit of a function of more than one variable also involves the distance between two points; so we begin our discussion by defining the distance between two points in R^n.

In R the distance between two points is the absolute value of the difference of two real numbers. That is, $|x - a|$ is the distance between the points x and a on the real-number line. In R^2 the distance between the two points $P(x, y)$ and $P_0(x_0, y_0)$ is given by $\sqrt{(x - x_0)^2 + (y - y_0)^2}$. In R^3 the distance between the two points $P(x, y, z)$ and $P_0(x_0, y_0, z_0)$ is given by $\sqrt{(x - x_0)^2 + (y - y_0)^2 + (z - z_0)^2}$. In R^n the distance between two points is defined analogously.

12.2.1 Definition of the Distance Between Two Points in R^n

If $P(x_1, x_2, \ldots, x_n)$ and $A(a_1, a_2, \ldots, a_n)$ are two points in R^n, then the **distance between P and A,** denoted by $\| P - A \|$, is given by

$$\| P - A \| = \sqrt{(x_1 - a_1)^2 + (x_2 - a_2)^2 + \ldots + (x_n - a_n)^2}$$

The symbol $\| P - A \|$ represents a nonnegative number and is read as "the distance between P and A."

In R, R^2, and R^3, the formula in Definition 12.2.1 becomes, respectively,

$$\| x - a \| = | x - a |$$
$$\|(x, y) - (x_0, y_0)\| = \sqrt{(x - x_0)^2 + (y - y_0)^2}$$
$$\|(x, y, z) - (x_0, y_0, z_0)\| = \sqrt{(x - x_0)^2 + (y - y_0)^2 + (z - z_0)^2}$$

12.2.2 Definition of an Open Ball in R^n

If A is a point in R^n and r is a positive number, then the **open ball** $B(A; r)$ is the set of all points P in R^n such that $\| P - A \| < r$.

12.2.3 Definition of a Closed Ball in R^n

If A is a point in R^n and r is a positive number, then the **closed ball** $B[A; r]$ is the set of all points P in R^n such that $\| P - A \| \leq r$.

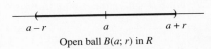

Open ball $B(a; r)$ in R

FIGURE 1

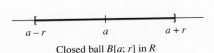

Closed ball $B[a; r]$ in R

FIGURE 2

Open ball $B((x_0, y_0); r)$ in R^2

FIGURE 3

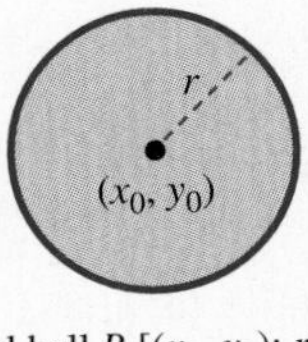

Closed ball $B[(x_0, y_0); r]$ in R^2

FIGURE 4

To illustrate these definitions, we show what they mean in R, R^2, and R^3. First of all, if a is a point in R, then the open ball $B(a; r)$ is the set of all points x in R such that

$$| x - a | < r$$

The set of all points x satisfying this inequality is the set of all points in the open interval $(a - r, a + r)$; so the open ball $B(a; r)$ in R (see Figure 1) is simply an open interval having its midpoint at a and endpoints at $a - r$ and $a + r$. The closed ball $B[a; r]$ in R (Figure 2) is the closed interval $[a - r, a + r]$.

If (x_0, y_0) is a point in R^2, then the open ball $B((x_0, y_0); r)$ is the set of all points (x, y) in R^2 such that

$$\sqrt{(x - x_0)^2 + (y - y_0)^2} < r$$

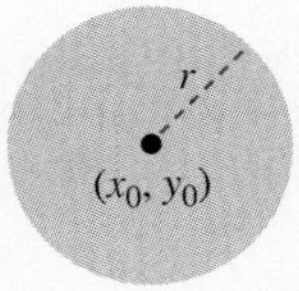

So the open ball $B((x_0, y_0); r)$ in R^2 (Figure 3) consists of all points in the interior region bounded by the circle having its center at (x_0, y_0) and radius r. An open ball in R^2 is sometimes called an *open disk*. The closed ball, or closed disk, $B[(x_0, y_0); r]$ in R^2 (Figure 4) is the set of all points in the open ball $B((x_0, y_0); r)$ and on the circle having its center at (x_0, y_0) and radius r.

If (x_0, y_0, z_0) is a point in R^3, then the open ball $B((x_0, y_0, z_0); r)$ is the set of all points (x, y, z) in R^3 such that

$$\sqrt{(x - x_0)^2 + (y - y_0)^2 + (z - z_0)^2} < r$$

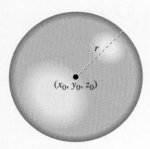

Open ball $B((x_0, y_0, z_0); r)$ in R^3

FIGURE 5

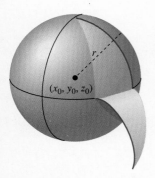

Closed ball $B[(x_0, y_0, z_0); r]$ in R^3

FIGURE 6

Therefore the open ball $B((x_0, y_0, z_0); r)$ in R^3 (Figure 5) consists of all points in the interior region bounded by the sphere having its center at (x_0, y_0, z_0) and radius r. Similarly, the closed ball $B[(x_0, y_0, z_0); r]$ in R^3 (Figure 6) consists of all points in the open ball $B((x_0, y_0, z_0); r)$ and on the sphere having its center at (x_0, y_0, z_0) and radius r.

12.2.4 Definition of the Limit of a Function of n Variables

Let f be a function of n variables defined on some open ball $B(A; r)$, except possibly at the point A itself. Then the **limit of $f(P)$ as P approaches A is L,** written as

$$\lim_{P \to A} f(P) = L$$

if for any $\epsilon > 0$, however small, there exists a $\delta > 0$ such that

$$\text{if} \quad 0 < \| P - A \| < \delta \quad \text{then} \quad |f(P) - L| < \epsilon$$

If in the above definition, f is a function of one variable, $A = a$ in R, and $P = x$, then the definition states: if f is defined on some open interval centered at a, except possibly at a itself,

$$\lim_{x \to a} f(x) = L$$

if for any $\epsilon > 0$, however small, there exists a $\delta > 0$ such that

$$\text{if} \quad 0 < |x - a| < \delta \quad \text{then} \quad |f(x) - L| < \epsilon$$

So the definition (1.5.1) of the limit of a function of one variable is a special case of Definition 12.2.4.

The definition of the limit of a function of two variables is the special case of Definition 12.2.4 where A is the point (x_0, y_0) and P is the point (x, y).

12.2.5 Definition of the Limit of a Function of Two Variables

Let f be a function of two variables defined on some open disk $B((x_0, y_0); r)$, except possibly at the point (x_0, y_0) itself. Then the **limit of $f(x, y)$ as (x, y) approaches (x_0, y_0) is L,** written as

$$\lim_{(x,y) \to (x_0, y_0)} f(x, y) = L$$

if for any $\epsilon > 0$, however small, there exists a $\delta > 0$ such that

$$\text{if} \quad 0 < \sqrt{(x - x_0)^2 + (y - y_0)^2} < \delta \quad \text{then} \quad |f(x, y) - L| < \epsilon$$

In words, this definition states that the function values $f(x, y)$ approach a limit L as the point (x, y) approaches the point (x_0, y_0) if the absolute value of the difference between $f(x, y)$ and L can be made arbitrarily small by taking the point (x, y) sufficiently close to (x_0, y_0) but not equal to (x_0, y_0). In the definition nothing is said about the function value at the point (x_0, y_0); that is, it is not necessary that the function be defined at (x_0, y_0) for $\lim_{(x,y) \to (x_0, y_0)} f(x, y)$ to exist.

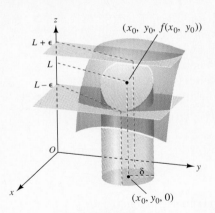

FIGURE 7

A geometric interpretation of Definition 12.2.5 is illustrated in Figure 7. The portion above the open disk $B((x_0, y_0); \delta)$ of the surface having equation $z = f(x, y)$ is shown. We see that $f(x, y)$ on the z axis will lie between $L - \epsilon$ and $L + \epsilon$ whenever the point (x, y) in the xy plane is in the open disk $B((x_0, y_0); \delta)$. Another way of stating this is that $f(x, y)$ on the z axis can be restricted to lie between $L - \epsilon$ and $L + \epsilon$ by restricting the point (x, y) in the xy plane to be in the open disk $B((x_0, y_0); \delta)$.

▶ **EXAMPLE 1**   Use Definition 12.2.5 to prove

$$\lim_{(x,y)\to(1,3)} (2x + 3y) = 11$$

Solution   The first requirement of the definition is that $2x + 3y$ must be defined on some open disk having its center at the point $(1, 3)$, except possibly at $(1, 3)$. Because $2x + 3y$ is defined at every point (x, y), any open disk having its center at $(1, 3)$ will satisfy this requirement. Now, we must show that for any $\epsilon > 0$ there exits a $\delta > 0$ such that

$$\text{if}\quad 0 < \sqrt{(x - 1)^2 + (y - 3)^2} < \delta \quad \text{then}\quad |(2x + 3y) - 11| < \epsilon \qquad \textbf{(1)}$$

From the triangle inequality,

$$|2x + 3y - 11| = |2x - 2 + 3y - 9|$$
$$\leq 2|x - 1| + 3|y - 3|$$

Because

$$|x - 1| \leq \sqrt{(x - 1)^2 + (y - 3)^2} \quad \text{and}\quad |y - 3| \leq \sqrt{(x - 1)^2 + (y - 3)^2}$$

it follows that

$$\text{if}\quad 0 < \sqrt{(x - 1)^2 + (y - 3)^2} < \delta \quad \text{then}\quad 2|x - 1| + 3|y - 3| < 2\delta + 3\delta$$

This statement indicates that a suitable choice for δ is $5\delta = \epsilon$, that is, $\delta = \frac{1}{5}\epsilon$. With this δ we have the following argument:

$$0 < \sqrt{(x - 1)^2 + (y - 3)^2} < \delta$$
$$\Rightarrow |x - 1| < \delta \quad \text{and}\quad |y - 3| < \delta$$
$$\Rightarrow 2|x - 1| + 3|y - 3| < 5\delta$$
$$\Rightarrow |2(x - 1) + 3(y - 3)| < 5(\tfrac{1}{5}\epsilon)$$
$$\Rightarrow \qquad |2x + 3y - 11| < \epsilon$$

We have demonstrated that for any $\epsilon > 0$ choose $\delta = \frac{1}{5}\epsilon$ and statement (1) is true. This proves that $\lim_{(x,y)\to(1,3)} (2x + 3y) = 11$.   ◀

The limit theorems of Section 1.5 and their proofs, with minor modifications, apply to functions of more than one variable. For example, corresponding to Limit Theorem 1 in Section 1.5 we have

$$\lim_{(x,y)\to(a,b)} (mx + ny + d) = ma + nb + d$$

and the proof is a generalization of the proof in Example 1. We use the limit theorems without restating them and their proofs.

▷ **ILLUSTRATION 1**   By applying the limit theorems on sums and products,

$$\lim_{(x,y)\to(-2,1)} (x^3 + 2x^2y - y^2 + 2) = (-2)^3 + 2(-2)^2(1) - (1)^2 + 2$$
$$= 1 \quad \blacktriangleleft$$

▶ **EXAMPLE 2**   Find $\lim_{(x,y)\to(0,0)} f(x, y)$ if

$$f(x, y) = \frac{y^4 - x^4}{y^2 + x^2}$$

Solution

$$\lim_{(x,y)\to(0,0)} \frac{y^4 - x^4}{y^2 + x^2} = \lim_{(x,y)\to(0,0)} \frac{(y^2 - x^2)(y^2 + x^2)}{y^2 + x^2}$$
$$= \lim_{(x,y)\to(0,0)} (y^2 - x^2)$$
$$= 0$$

The graph of f, shown in Figure 8, is the hyperbolic paraboloid

$$z = y^2 - x^2$$

with the origin deleted. The graph supports our answer. ◀

The next theorem regarding the limit of a composite function of two variables is analogous to Theorem 1.9.1 for functions of a single variable, and its proof is similar.

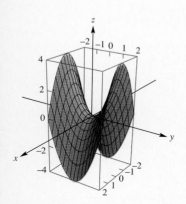

[-2, 2] by [-2, 2] by [-4, 4]

$$f(x, y) = \frac{y^4 - x^4}{y^2 + x^2}$$

FIGURE 8

12.2.6 Theorem

If g is a function of two variables and $\lim\limits_{(x,y)\to(x_0,y_0)} g(x, y) = b$, and f is a function of a single variable continuous at b, then

$$\lim_{(x,y)\to(x_0,y_0)} (f \circ g)(x, y) = f(b)$$

$$\Leftrightarrow \quad \lim_{(x,y)\to(x_0,y_0)} f(g(x, y)) = f\left(\lim_{(x,y)\to(x_0,y_0)} g(x, y)\right)$$

▶ **EXAMPLE 3**   Use Theorem 12.2.6 to find $\lim\limits_{(x,y)\to(2,1)} \ln(xy - 1)$.

Solution   Let g be the function such that $g(x, y) = xy - 1$, and let f be the function such that $f(t) = \ln t$.

$$\lim_{(x,y)\to(2,1)} (xy - 1) = 1$$

and because f is continuous at 1, from Theorem 12.2.6,

$$\lim_{(x,y)\to(2,1)} \ln(xy - 1) = \ln\left(\lim_{(x,y)\to(2,1)} (xy - 1)\right)$$
$$= \ln 1$$
$$= 0 \quad \blacktriangleleft$$

We now introduce the concept of an *accumulation point,* which is needed to continue the discussion of limits of functions of two variables.

12.2.7 Definition of an Accumulation Point

A point P_0 is an **accumulation point** of a set S of points in R^n if every open ball $B(P_0; r)$ contains infinitely many points of S.

▷ **ILLUSTRATION 2**   If S is the set of all points in R^2 on the positive side of the x axis, the origin will be an accumulation point of S because no matter how small we take the value of r, every open disk having its center at the origin and radius r will contain infinitely many points of S. This is an example of a set having an accumulation point for which the accumulation point is not a point of the set. Any point of this set S also will be an accumulation point of S.   ◀

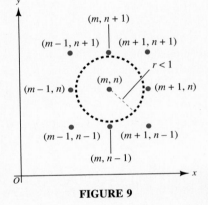

FIGURE 9

▷ **ILLUSTRATION 3**   If S is the set of all points in R^2 for which the cartesian coordinates are positive integers, then this set has no accumulation point. This can be seen by considering the point (m, n), where m and n are positive integers. Then an open disk having its center at (m, n) and radius less than 1 will contain no points of S other than (m, n); therefore Definition 12.2.7 will not be satisfied (see Figure 9).   ◀

We now consider the limit of a function of two variables as a point (x, y) approaches a point (x_0, y_0), where (x, y) is restricted to a specific set of points.

12.2.8 Definition of the Limit of a Function of Two Variables Through a Specific Set

Let f be a function defined on a set of points S in R^2, and let (x_0, y_0) be an accumulation point of S. Then the **limit of $f(x, y)$ as (x, y) approaches (x_0, y_0) in S is L**, written as

$$\lim_{\substack{(x,y)\to(x_0,y_0)\\(P\,\text{in}\,S)}} f(x, y) = L$$

if for any $\epsilon > 0$, however small, there exits a $\delta > 0$ such that

$$\text{if}\quad 0 < \|(x, y) - (x_0, y_0)\| < \delta \quad\text{then}\quad |f(x, y) - L| < \epsilon$$

where (x, y) is in S.

In some cases the limit in the above definition becomes the limit of a function of one variable. For example, consider $\lim\limits_{(x,y)\to(0,0)} f(x, y)$. Then if S_1 is the set of all points on the positive side of the x axis,

$$\lim_{\substack{(x,y)\to(0,0)\\(P\,\text{in}\,S_1)}} f(x, y) = \lim_{x\to 0^+} f(x, 0)$$

If S_2 is the set of all points on the negative side of the y axis,

$$\lim_{\substack{(x,y)\to(0,0)\\(P\,\text{in}\,S_2)}} f(x, y) = \lim_{y\to 0^-} f(0, y)$$

If S_3 is the set of all points on the x axis,

$$\lim_{\substack{(x, y) \to (0, 0) \\ (P \text{ in } S_3)}} f(x, y) = \lim_{x \to 0} f(x, 0)$$

If S_4 is the set of all points on the parabola $y = x^2$,

$$\lim_{\substack{(x,y) \to (0,0) \\ (P \text{ in } S_4)}} f(x, y) = \lim_{x \to 0} f(x, x^2)$$

12.2.9 Theorem

Suppose that the function f is defined for all points on an open disk having its center at (x_0, y_0), except possibly at (x_0, y_0) itself, and

$$\lim_{(x,y) \to (x_0,y_0)} f(x, y) = L$$

Then if S is any set of points in R^2 having (x_0, y_0) as an accumulation point,

$$\lim_{\substack{(x,y) \to (x_0,y_0) \\ (P \text{ in } S)}} f(x, y)$$

exists and always has the value L.

Proof Because $\lim_{(x,y) \to (x_0,y_0)} f(x, y) = L$, then by Definition 12.2.5, for any $\epsilon > 0$ there exists a $\delta > 0$ such that

$$\text{if} \quad 0 < \|(x, y) - (x_0, y_0)\| < \delta \quad \text{then} \quad |f(x, y) - L| < \epsilon$$

The above will be true if we further restrict (x, y) by the requirement that (x, y) be in a set S, where S is any set of points having (x_0, y_0) as an accumulation point. Therefore, by Definition 12.2.8,

$$\lim_{\substack{(x,y) \to (x_0,y_0) \\ (P \text{ in } S)}} f(x, y) = L$$

and L does not depend on the set S through which (x, y) is approaching (x_0, y_0). This proves the theorem. ∎

The next theorem is an immediate consequence of Theorem 12.2.9.

12.2.10 Theorem

If the function f has different limits as (x, y) approaches (x_0, y_0) through two distinct sets of points having (x_0, y_0) as an accumulation point, then $\lim_{(x,y) \to (x_0,y_0)} f(x, y)$ does not exist.

Proof Suppose S_1 and S_2 are two distinct sets of points in R^2 having (x_0, y_0) as an accumulation point, and let

$$\lim_{\substack{(x,y) \to (x_0,y_0) \\ (P \text{ in } S_1)}} f(x, y) = L_1 \quad \text{and} \quad \lim_{\substack{(x,y) \to (x_0,y_0) \\ (P \text{ in } S_2)}} f(x, y) = L_2$$

Now assume that $\lim_{(x,y) \to (x_0,y_0)} f(x,y)$ exists. Then by Theorem 12.2.9 L_1 must equal L_2; but by hypothesis $L_1 \neq L_2$, and so we have a contradiction. Therefore $\lim_{(x,y) \to (x_0,y_0)} f(x, y)$ does not exist. ∎

▶ **EXAMPLE 4**   Given

$$f(x, y) = \frac{x^2 - y^2}{x^2 + y^2}$$

Use Theorem 12.2.10 to prove that $\lim\limits_{(x,y)\to(0,0)} f(x, y)$ does not exist.

Solution   The function f is defined at all points in R^2 except $(0, 0)$. Let S_1 be the set of all points on the x axis and S_2 be the set of all points on the y axis. Then

$$\lim_{\substack{(x,y)\to(0,0)\\(P\,\text{in}\,S_1)}} f(x, y) = \lim_{x\to0} f(x, 0) \qquad \lim_{\substack{(x,y)\to(0,0)\\(P\,\text{in}\,S_2)}} f(x, y) = \lim_{y\to0} f(0, y)$$

$$= \lim_{x\to0} \frac{x^2}{x^2} \qquad\qquad\qquad = \lim_{y\to0} \frac{-y^2}{y^2}$$

$$= \lim_{x\to0} 1 \qquad\qquad\qquad = \lim_{y\to0} (-1)$$

$$= 1 \qquad\qquad\qquad\qquad = -1$$

Because

$$\lim_{\substack{(x,y)\to(0,0)\\(P\,\text{in}\,S_1)}} f(x, y) \neq \lim_{\substack{(x,y)\to(0,0)\\(P\,\text{in}\,S_2)}} f(x, y)$$

we conclude from Theorem 12.2.10 that $\lim\limits_{(x,y)\to(0,0)} f(x, y)$ does not exist.

Figure 10 shows the graph of f. Observe from the figure that as (x, y) approaches $(0, 0)$ along the x axis, $f(x, y)$ appears to be approaching 1 and as (x, y) approaches $(0, 0)$ along the y axis, $f(x, y)$ appears to be approaching -1. These observations support our results.   ◀

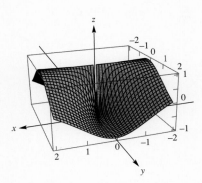

$[-2, 2]$ by $[-2, 2]$ by $[-1, 1]$

$$f(x, y) = \frac{x^2 - y^2}{x^2 + y^2}$$

FIGURE 10

▶ **EXAMPLE 5**   Prove that the following limit does not exist:

$$\lim_{(x,y)\to(0,0)} \frac{x}{x^2 + y^2}$$

Solution   The expression $x/(x^2 + y^2)$ is defined at all points in R^2 except $(0, 0)$. Let S be the set of points on the positive x axis. Then

$$\lim_{\substack{(x,y)\to(0,0)\\(P\,\text{in}\,S)}} \frac{x}{x^2 + y^2} = \lim_{x\to0^+} \frac{x}{x^2}$$

$$= \lim_{x\to0^+} \frac{1}{x}$$

$$= +\infty$$

Therefore, the limit does not exist.

Figure 11 shows the graph of the function having values $x/(x^2 + y^2)$. Observe that as (x, y) approaches the origin along the positive x axis, the function values appear to increase without bound, which supports our answer.   ◀

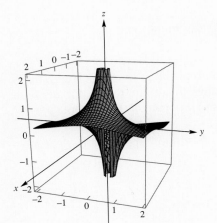

$[-2, 2]$ by $[-2, 2]$ by $[-2.2, 2.2]$

$$f(x, y) = \frac{x}{x^2 + y^2}$$

FIGURE 11

▶ **EXAMPLE 6** Given

$$f(x, y) = \frac{xy}{x^2 + y^2}$$

find $\displaystyle\lim_{(x,y)\to(0,0)} f(x, y)$ if it exists.

Solution The function is defined at all points in R^2 except $(0, 0)$. Let S_1 be the set of all points on the x axis, and S_2 be the set of all points on the line $y = x$. Then

$$\lim_{\substack{(x,y)\to(0,0)\\(P \text{ in } S_1)}} f(x, y) = \lim_{x\to 0} f(x, 0) \qquad \lim_{\substack{(x,y)\to(0,0)\\(P \text{ in } S_2)}} f(x, y) = \lim_{x\to 0} f(x, x)$$

$$= \lim_{x\to 0} \frac{0}{x^2 + 0} \qquad\qquad\qquad = \lim_{x\to 0} \frac{x^2}{x^2 + x^2}$$

$$= \lim_{x\to 0} 0 \qquad\qquad\qquad\qquad = \lim_{x\to 0} \tfrac{1}{2}$$

$$= 0 \qquad\qquad\qquad\qquad\qquad = \tfrac{1}{2}$$

Because

$$\lim_{\substack{(x,y)\to(0,0)\\(P \text{ in } S_1)}} f(x, y) \neq \lim_{\substack{(x,y)\to(0,0)\\(P \text{ in } S_2)}} f(x, y)$$

then from Theorem 12.2.10 $\displaystyle\lim_{(x,y)\to(0,0)} f(x, y)$ does not exist.

Figure 12 shows the graph of f which supports the fact that $\displaystyle\lim_{(x,y)\to(0,0)} f(x, y)$ does not exist. ◀

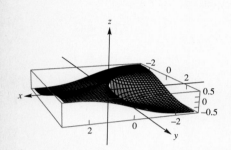

[−2.6, 2.6] by [−2.6, 2.6] by [−0.5, 0.5]

$$f(x, y) = \frac{xy}{x^2 + y^2}$$

FIGURE 12

▶ **EXAMPLE 7** Given

$$f(x, y) = \frac{2x^2 y}{x^4 + y^2}$$

find $\displaystyle\lim_{(x,y)\to(0,0)} f(x, y)$ if it exists.

Solution The function is defined at all points in R^2 except $(0, 0)$. Let S_1 be the set of all points on any line through the origin; that is, for any point (x, y) in S_1, $y = mx$. Let S_2 be the set of all points on the parabola $y = x^2$. Then

$$\lim_{\substack{(x,y)\to(0,0)\\(P \text{ in } S_1)}} f(x, y) = \lim_{x\to 0} f(x, mx) \qquad \lim_{\substack{(x,y)\to(0,0)\\(P \text{ in } S_2)}} f(x, y) = \lim_{x\to 0} f(x, x^2)$$

$$= \lim_{x\to 0} \frac{2mx^3}{x^4 + m^2 x^2} \qquad\qquad = \lim_{x\to 0} \frac{2x^4}{x^4 + x^4}$$

$$= \lim_{x\to 0} \frac{2mx}{x^2 + m^2} \qquad\qquad\quad = \lim_{x\to 0} 1$$

$$= 0 \qquad\qquad\qquad\qquad\qquad = 1$$

Because

$$\lim_{\substack{(x,y)\to(0,0)\\(P \text{ in } S_2)}} f(x, y) \neq \lim_{\substack{(x,y)\to(0,0)\\(P \text{ in } S_1)}} f(x, y)$$

then $\displaystyle\lim_{(x,y)\to(0,0)} f(x, y)$ does not exist.

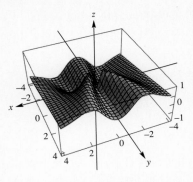

[−4, 4] by [−4, 4] by [−1, 1]

$$f(x, y) = \frac{2x^2 y}{x^4 + y^2}$$

FIGURE 13

Figure 13, showing the graph of f, supports the fact that $\lim\limits_{(x,y)\to(0,0)} f(x, y)$ does not exist. ◀

▶ **EXAMPLE 8**   Given

$$f(x, y) = \frac{x^4 + 2x^2 + 2y^2 + y^4}{x^2 + y^2}$$

Find $\lim\limits_{(x,y)\to(0,0)} f(x, y)$ if it exists.

Solution   The function is defined at all points in R^2 except $(0, 0)$. Let S_1 be the set of all points on any line through the origin; so if (x, y) is a point in S_1, $y = mx$. Let S_2 be the set of all points on the parabola $y = x^2$. Then

$$\lim_{\substack{(x,y)\to(0,0) \\ (P \text{ in } S_1)}} f(x, y) = \lim_{x\to 0} \frac{x^4 + 2x^2 + 2m^2x^2 + m^4x^4}{x^2 + m^2x^2}$$

$$= \lim_{x\to 0} \frac{x^4(1 + m^4) + 2x^2(1 + m^2)}{x^2(1 + m^2)}$$

$$= \lim_{x\to 0} \frac{x^2(1 + m^4) + 2(1 + m^2)}{1 + m^2}$$

$$= 2$$

$$\lim_{\substack{(x,y)\to(0,0) \\ (P \text{ in } S_2)}} f(x, y) = \lim_{x\to 0} \frac{x^4 + 2x^2 + 2x^4 + x^8}{x^2 + x^4}$$

$$= \lim_{x\to 0} \frac{x^8 + 3x^4 + 2x^2}{x^2 + x^4}$$

$$= \lim_{x\to 0} \frac{x^6 + 3x^2 + 2}{1 + x^2}$$

$$= 2$$

Even though the same limit of 2 is obtained if (x, y) approaches $(0, 0)$ through a set of points on any line through the origin as well as on the parabola $y = x^2$, we cannot conclude that the limit exists and is 2, even though we may expect that is the case. So, let us attempt to prove that the limit is 2. Any open disk having its center at the origin will satisfy the first requirement of Definition 12.2.5. If we can show that for any $\epsilon > 0$ there exists a $\delta > 0$ such that

$$\text{if}\quad 0 < \sqrt{x^2 + y^2} < \delta \quad \text{then} \quad \left| \frac{x^4 + 2x^2 + 2y^2 + y^4}{x^2 + y^2} - 2 \right| < \epsilon$$

$$\Leftrightarrow \quad \text{if}\quad 0 < \sqrt{x^2 + y^2} < \delta \quad \text{then} \quad \left| \frac{x^4 + y^4}{x^2 + y^2} \right| < \epsilon \qquad \text{(2)}$$

then we have proved that $\lim\limits_{(x,y)\to(0,0)} f(x, y) = 2$.

Because $x^2 \le x^2 + y^2$ and $y^2 \le x^2 + y^2$,

$$\left| \frac{x^4 + y^4}{x^2 + y^2} \right| \le \frac{(x^2 + y^2)^2 + (x^2 + y^2)^2}{x^2 + y^2} = 2(x^2 + y^2)$$

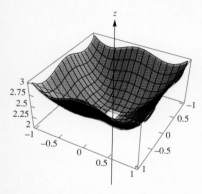

[−1, 1] by [−1, 1] by [2, 3]

$$f(x, y) = \frac{x^4 + 2x^2 + 2y^2 + y^4}{x^2 + y^2}$$

FIGURE 14

Thus a suitable choice for δ is found by solving $2\delta^2 = \epsilon$; that is $\delta = \sqrt{\epsilon/2}$. With this δ we have the following argument:

$$0 < \sqrt{x^2 + y^2} < \delta$$

$$\Rightarrow 2(x^2 + y^2) < 2\delta^2$$

$$\Rightarrow \frac{2(x^2 + y^2)^2}{x^2 + y^2} < 2\delta^2$$

$$\Rightarrow \frac{(x^2 + y^2)^2 + (x^2 + y^2)^2}{x^2 + y^2} < 2 \cdot \frac{\epsilon}{2}$$

$$\Rightarrow \left| \frac{x^4 + y^4}{x^2 + y^2} \right| < \epsilon$$

Thus if $\delta = \sqrt{\epsilon/2}$, statement (2) holds and we have proved that

$$\lim_{(x,y) \to (0,0)} f(x, y) = 2.$$

Figure 14 shows the graph of f, which supports the fact that the limit is 2. ◀

We now define continuity of a function of n variables at a point in R^n. Observe that Definition 1.8.1 of continuity of a function of a single variable at a number a is a special case of this definition.

12.2.11 Definition of Continuity of a Function of n Variables

Suppose that f is a function of n variables and A is a point in R^n. Then f is said to be **continuous** at the point A if and only if the following three conditions are satisfied:

(i) $f(A)$ exists;
(ii) $\lim\limits_{P \to A} f(P)$ exists;
(iii) $\lim\limits_{P \to A} f(P) = f(A)$.

If one or more of these three conditions fails to hold at the point A, then f is said to be **discontinuous** at A.

If f is a function of two variables, A is the point (x_0, y_0), and P is a point (x, y), then Definition 12.2.11 becomes the following.

12.2.12 Definition of Continuity of a Function of Two Variables

The function f of two variables x and y is said to be **continuous** at the point (x_0, y_0) if and only if the following three conditions are satisfied:

(i) $f(x_0, y_0)$ exists;
(ii) $\lim\limits_{(x,y) \to (x_0, y_0)} f(x, y)$ exists;
(iii) $\lim\limits_{(x,y) \to (x_0, y_0)} f(x, y) = f(x_0, y_0)$.

▶ **EXAMPLE 9**   Determine whether g is continuous at $(0, 0)$ if

$$g(x, y) = \begin{cases} \dfrac{x^4 + 2x^2 + 2y^2 + y^4}{x^2 + y^2} & \text{if } (x, y) \neq (0, 0) \\ 2 & \text{if } (x, y) = (0, 0) \end{cases}$$

Solution   We check the three conditions of Definition 12.2.12 at the point $(0, 0)$.

(i) $g(0, 0) = 2$. Therefore condition (i) holds.

(ii) $\displaystyle\lim_{(x,y)\to(0,0)} g(x, y) = \lim_{(x,y)\to(0,0)} \dfrac{x^4 + 2x^2 + 2y^2 + y^4}{x^2 + y^2}$

$\qquad\qquad = 2$

This fact was proved in Example 8.

(iii) $\displaystyle\lim_{(x,y)\to(0,0)} g(x, y) = g(0, 0)$

Therefore g is continuous at $(0, 0)$.   ◀

▶ **EXAMPLE 10**   Determine whether h is continuous at $(0, 0)$ if

$$h(x, y) = \begin{cases} \dfrac{xy}{x^2 + y^2} & \text{if } (x, y) \neq (0, 0) \\ 0 & \text{if } (x, y) = (0, 0) \end{cases}$$

Solution   Checking the conditions of Definition 12.2.12, we have:

(i) $h(0, 0) = 0$. Therefore condition (i) holds.

(ii) When $(x, y) \neq (0, 0)$, $h(x, y) = xy/(x^2 + y^2)$. In Example 6, we showed that $\displaystyle\lim_{(x,y)\to(0,0)} xy/(x^2 + y^2)$ does not exist; so $\displaystyle\lim_{(x,y)\to(0,0)} h(x, y)$ does not exist. Therefore condition (ii) fails to hold.

Thus h is discontinuous at $(0, 0)$.   ◀

If a function f of two variables is discontinuous at the point (x_0, y_0) but $\displaystyle\lim_{(x,y)\to(x_0,y_0)} f(x, y)$ exists, then f is said to have a **removable discontinuity** at (x_0, y_0) because if f is redefined at (x_0, y_0) so that

$$f(x_0, y_0) = \lim_{(x,y)\to(x_0,y_0)} f(x, y)$$

then the new function is continuous at (x_0, y_0). If the discontinuity is not removable, it is called an **essential discontinuity.**

▷ **ILLUSTRATION 4**

(a) If $f(x, y) = (x^4 + 2x^2 + 2y^2 + y^4)/(x^2 + y^2)$, then f is discontinuous at $(0, 0)$ because $f(0, 0)$ is not defined. However, in Example 8, we showed that $\displaystyle\lim_{(x,y)\to(0,0)} f(x, y) = 2$. Therefore, the discontinuity is removable by redefining $f(0, 0)$ to be 2. Refer to Example 9.

(b) Let $f(x, y) = xy/(x^2 + y^2)$. Then f is discontinuous at $(0, 0)$ because $f(0, 0)$ is not defined. In Example 6, we showed that $\displaystyle\lim_{(x, y)\to(0, 0)} f(x, y)$ does not exist. Therefore, the discontinuity is essential.   ◀

The theorems about continuity for functions of a single variable can be extended to functions of two variables.

12.2.13 Theorem

If f and g are two functions continuous at the point (x_0, y_0), then

    (i) $f + g$ is continuous at (x_0, y_0);
    (ii) $f - g$ is continuous at (x_0, y_0);
    (iii) fg is continuous at (x_0, y_0);
    (iv) f/g is continuous at (x_0, y_0), provided that $g(x_0, y_0) \neq 0$.

The proof of this theorem is analogous to the proof of the corresponding theorem (1.8.2) for functions of a single variable.

12.2.14 Theorem

A polynomial function of two variables is continuous at every point in R^2.

Proof   Every polynomial function is the sum of products of the functions defined by $f(x, y) = x$, $g(x, y) = y$, and $h(x, y) = c$, where c is a real number. Because f, g, and h are continuous at every point in R^2, the theorem follows by repeated applications of Theorem 12.2.13 parts (i) and (iii). ∎

12.2.15 Theorem

A rational function of two variables is continuous at every point in its domain.

Proof   A rational function is the quotient of two polynomial functions f and g that are continuous at every point in R^2, by Theorem 12.2.14. If (x_0, y_0) is any point in the domain of f/g, then $g(x_0, y_0) \neq 0$; so by Theorem 12.2.13 (iv) f/g is continuous there. ∎

▶ **EXAMPLE 11**   Determine all points at which f is continuous if

$$f(x, y) = \begin{cases} x^2 + y^2 & \text{if } x^2 + y^2 \leq 1 \\ 0 & \text{if } x^2 + y^2 > 1 \end{cases}$$

Solution   The function f is defined at all points in R^2. Therefore condition (i) of Definition 12.2.12 holds for every point (x_0, y_0).
    Consider the points (x_0, y_0) if $x_0{}^2 + y_0{}^2 \neq 1$.

If $x_0{}^2 + y_0{}^2 < 1$,

$$\lim_{(x,y)\to(x_0,y_0)} f(x, y) = \lim_{(x,y)\to(x_0,y_0)} (x^2 + y^2)$$
$$= x_0{}^2 + y_0{}^2$$
$$= f(x_0, y_0)$$

If $x_0{}^2 + y_0{}^2 > 1$,

$$\lim_{(x,y)\to(x_0,y_0)} f(x, y) = \lim_{(x,y)\to(x_0,y_0)} 0$$
$$= 0$$
$$= f(x_0, y_0)$$

Thus f is continuous at all points (x_0, y_0) for which $x_0{}^2 + y_0{}^2 \neq 1$.
    To determine the continuity of f at points (x_0, y_0) for which $x_0{}^2 + y_0{}^2 = 1$, we consider $\lim_{(x,y)\to(x_0,y_0)} f(x, y)$ for these points.

Let S_1 be the set of all points (x, y) such that $x^2 + y^2 \leq 1$, and S_2 be the set of all points (x, y) such that $x^2 + y^2 > 1$. Then

$$\lim_{\substack{(x,y) \to (x_0,y_0) \\ (P \text{ in } S_1)}} f(x, y) = \lim_{\substack{(x,y) \to (x_0,y_0) \\ (P \text{ in } S_1)}} (x^2 + y^2) \qquad \lim_{\substack{(x,y) \to (x_0,y_0) \\ (P \text{ in } S_2)}} f(x, y) = \lim_{\substack{(x,y) \to (x_0,y_0) \\ (P \text{ in } S_2)}} 0$$

$$= x_0^2 + y_0^2 \qquad\qquad\qquad = 0$$

$$= 1$$

Because

$$\lim_{\substack{(x,y) \to (x_0,y_0) \\ (P \text{ in } S_1)}} f(x, y) \neq \lim_{\substack{(x,y) \to (x_0,y_0) \\ (P \text{ in } S_2)}} f(x, y)$$

we conclude that $\displaystyle\lim_{(x,y) \to (x_0,y_0)} f(x, y)$ does not exist. Hence f is discontinuous at all points (x_0, y_0) for which $x_0^2 + y_0^2 = 1$.

We have proved that f is continuous at all points in R^2 except those on the circle $x^2 + y^2 = 1$.   ◀

12.2.16 Definition of Continuity on an Open Ball

The function f of n variables is continuous on an open ball if it is continuous at every point in the open ball.

▷   **ILLUSTRATION 5**   From the results of Example 11, the function of that example is continuous on every open disk that does not contain a point of the circle $x^2 + y^2 = 1$.   ◀

The next theorem, analogous to Theorem 1.9.2, states that a continuous function of a continuous function is continuous.

12.2.17 Theorem

Suppose that f is a function of a single variable and g is a function of two variables such that g is continuous at (x_0, y_0) and f is continuous at $g(x_0, y_0)$. Then the composite function $f \circ g$ is continuous at (x_0, y_0).

The proof of this theorem is similar to that of Theorem 1.9.2.

▷   **ILLUSTRATION 6**   Let h be the function of Example 3:

$$h(x, y) = \ln(xy - 1)$$

If $g(x, y) = xy - 1$, g is continuous at all points in R^2. The natural logarithmic function is continuous on its entire domain, which is the set of all positive numbers. So if f is the function defined by $f(t) = \ln t$, f is continuous for all $t > 0$. Then the function h is the composite function $f \circ g$ and, by Theorem 12.2.17, is continuous at all points (x, y) in R^2 for which $xy - 1 > 0$.   ◀

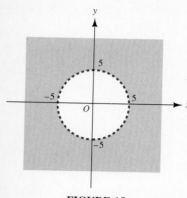

FIGURE 15

▶ **EXAMPLE 12**   Determine all points at which f is continuous if

$$f(x, y) = \frac{1}{\sqrt{x^2 + y^2 - 25}}$$

Solution   The domain of f is the set of all points (x, y) in R^2 for which $x^2 + y^2 - 25 > 0$. These are the points in the exterior region bounded by the circle $x^2 + y^2 = 25$ as shown in Figure 15. The function f is the quotient of the functions g and h for which

$$g(x, y) = 1 \qquad h(x, y) = \sqrt{x^2 + y^2 - 25}$$

Because g is a constant function, it is continuous everywhere. From Theorem 12.2.17, h is continuous at all points in R^2 for which $x^2 + y^2 > 25$. Therefore, by Theorem 12.2.13(iv), f is continuous at all points in its domain.   ◀

EXERCISES 12.2

In Exercises 1 through 6, evaluate the limit by limit theorems.

1. $\displaystyle\lim_{(x,y)\to(2,3)} (3x^2 + xy - 2y^2)$

2. $\displaystyle\lim_{(x,y)\to(-1,4)} (5x^2 - 2xy + y^2)$

3. $\displaystyle\lim_{(x,y)\to(2,-1)} \frac{3x - 2y}{x + 4y}$

4. $\displaystyle\lim_{(x,y)\to(-2,4)} y\sqrt[3]{x^3 + 2y}$

5. $\displaystyle\lim_{(x,y)\to(0,1)} \frac{x^4 - (y - 1)^4}{x^2 + (y - 1)^2}$

6. $\displaystyle\lim_{(x,y)\to(1,1)} \frac{(x - 1)^{4/3} - (y - 1)^{4/3}}{(x - 1)^{2/3} + (y - 1)^{2/3}}$

In Exercises 7 through 10, establish the limit by finding a $\delta > 0$ for any $\epsilon > 0$ such that Definition 12.2.5 holds.

7. $\displaystyle\lim_{(x,y)\to(3,2)} (3x - 4y) = 1$

8. $\displaystyle\lim_{(x,y)\to(-2,1)} (5x + 4y) = -6$

9. $\displaystyle\lim_{(x,y)\to(-1,3)} (3x - 2y) = -9$

10. $\displaystyle\lim_{(x,y)\to(2,4)} (5x - 3y) = -2$

In Exercises 11 through 16, prove that $\displaystyle\lim_{(x, y)\to(0, 0)} f(x, y)$ does not exist.

11. $f(x, y) = \dfrac{x^2 - y^2}{x^2 + y^2}$

12. $f(x, y) = \dfrac{x^2}{x^2 + y^2}$

13. $f(x, y) = \dfrac{x^4 y^4}{(x^2 + y^4)^3}$

14. $f(x, y) = \dfrac{x^4 + 3x^2 y^2 + 2xy^3}{(x^2 + y^2)^2}$

15. $f(x, y) = \dfrac{x^9 y}{(x^6 + y^2)^2}$

16. $f(x, y) = \dfrac{x^2 y^2}{x^4 + y^4}$

In Exercises 17 through 20, prove that $\displaystyle\lim_{(x,y)\to(0,0)} f(x, y)$ exists.

17. $f(x, y) = \dfrac{x^2 y + xy^2}{x^2 + y^2}$

18. $f(x, y) = \dfrac{x^3 + y^3}{x^2 + y^2}$

19. $f(x, y) = \dfrac{xy}{\sqrt{x^2 + y^2}}$

20. $f(x, y) = \dfrac{x^2 + 2xy}{\sqrt{x^2 + y^2}}$

In Exercises 21 through 24, determine if the limit exists.

21. $\displaystyle\lim_{(x,y)\to(0,0)} \frac{x^2 y^2}{x^2 + y^2}$

22. $\displaystyle\lim_{(x,y)\to(0,0)} \frac{x^2 y^4}{x^4 + y^4}$

23. $\displaystyle\lim_{(x,y)\to(0,0)} \frac{x^2 + y}{x^2 + y^2}$

24. $\displaystyle\lim_{(x,y)\to(0,0)} \frac{x^2 y^2}{x^3 + y^3}$

In Exercises 25 through 28, show the application of Theorem 12.2.6 to find the limit.

25. $\displaystyle\lim_{(x,y)\to(2,2)} \tan^{-1} \frac{y}{x}$

26. $\displaystyle\lim_{(x,y)\to(\ln 3, \ln 2)} e^{x-y}$

27. $\displaystyle\lim_{(x,y)\to(4,2)} \sqrt{\frac{1}{3x - 4y}}$

28. $\displaystyle\lim_{(x,y)\to(-2,3)} [\![5x + \tfrac{1}{2}y^2]\!]$

In Exercises 29 through 52, determine all points at which the function is continuous.

29. $f(x, y) = \dfrac{x^2}{y - 1}$

30. $F(x, y) = \dfrac{1}{x - y}$

31. $h(x, y) = \sin \dfrac{y}{x}$

32. $f(x, y) = \ln xy^2$

33. $f(x, y) = \dfrac{4x^2 y + 3y^2}{2x - y}$

34. $g(x, y) = \dfrac{5xy^2 + 2y}{16 - x^2 - 4y^2}$

35. $g(x, y) = \ln(25 - x^2 - y^2)$

36. $f(x, y) = \cos^{-1}(x + y)$

37. $f(x, y) = \begin{cases} \dfrac{xy}{\sqrt{x^2 + y^2}} & \text{if } (x, y) \neq (0, 0) \\ 0 & \text{if } (x, y) = (0, 0) \end{cases}$

Hint: See Exercise 19.

38. $h(x, y) = \begin{cases} \dfrac{2x^2 y}{x^4 + y^2} & \text{if } (x, y) \neq (0, 0) \\ 0 & \text{if } (x, y) = (0, 0) \end{cases}$

Hint: See Example 7.

39. $f(x, y) = \begin{cases} \dfrac{x + y}{x^2 + y^2} & \text{if } (x, y) \neq (0, 0) \\ 0 & \text{if } (x, y) = (0, 0) \end{cases}$

40. $f(x, y) = \begin{cases} \dfrac{x^3 + y^3}{x^2 + y^2} & \text{if } (x, y) \neq (0, 0) \\ 0 & \text{if } (x, y) = (0, 0) \end{cases}$

41. $G(x, y) = \begin{cases} \dfrac{xy}{|x| + |y|} & \text{if } (x, y) \neq (0, 0) \\ 0 & \text{if } (x, y) = (0, 0) \end{cases}$

42. $F(x, y) = \begin{cases} \dfrac{x^2 y^2}{|x^3| + |y^3|} & \text{if } (x, y) \neq (0, 0) \\ 0 & \text{if } (x, y) = (0, 0) \end{cases}$

43. $f(x, y) = \dfrac{xy}{\sqrt{16 - x^2 - y^2}}$

44. $f(x, y) = \dfrac{y}{\sqrt{x^2 - y^2 - 4}}$

45. $f(x, y) = \dfrac{x}{\sqrt{4x^2 + 9y^2 - 36}}$

46. $f(x, y) = \dfrac{x^2 + y^2}{\sqrt{9 - x^2 - y^2}}$

47. $f(x, y) = \sec^{-1}(xy)$

48. $f(x, y) = \ln(x^2 + y^2 - 9) - \ln(1 - x^2 - y^2)$

49. $f(x, y) = \sin^{-1}(x + y) + \ln(xy)$

50. $f(x, y) = \sin^{-1}(xy)$

51. $f(x, y) = \begin{cases} \dfrac{\sin(x + y)}{x + y} & \text{if } x + y \neq 0 \\ 1 & \text{if } x + y = 0 \end{cases}$

52. $f(x, y) = \begin{cases} \dfrac{x^2 - y^2}{x - y} & \text{if } x \neq y \\ x - y & \text{if } x = y \end{cases}$

In Exercises 53 through 59, the function is discontinuous at the origin because $f(0, 0)$ does not exist. Determine if the discontinuity is removable or essential. If the discontinuity is removable, redefine $f(0, 0)$ so that the new function is continuous at $(0, 0)$.

53. $f(x, y) = \dfrac{xy}{x^2 + xy + y^2}$ **54.** $f(x, y) = \dfrac{x}{x^2 + y^2}$

55. $f(x, y) = (x + y) \sin \dfrac{x}{x^2 + y^2}$

56. $f(x, y) = \dfrac{x^2 y^2}{x^2 + y^2}$ **57.** $f(x, y) = \dfrac{x^3 y^2}{x^6 + y^4}$

58. $f(x, y) = \dfrac{2y^2 - 3xy}{\sqrt{x^2 + y^2}}$ **59.** $f(x, y) = \dfrac{x^3 - 4xy^2}{x^2 + y^2}$

60. (a) Give a definition, similar to Definition 12.2.5 of the limit of a function of three variables as a point (x, y, z) approaches a point (x_0, y_0, z_0). **(b)** Give a definition, similar to Definition 12.2.8, of the limit of a function of three variables as a point (x, y, z) approaches a point (x_0, y_0, z_0) in a specific set of points S in R^3.

61. (a) State a theorem similar to Theorem 12.2.9 for a function f of three variables. **(b)** State a theorem similar to Theorem 12.2.10 for a function f of three variables.

In Exercises 62 through 65, use the definitions and theorems of Exercises 60 and 61 to prove that
$$\lim_{(x,y,z) \to (0,0,0)} f(x, y, z) \text{ does not exist.}$$

62. $f(x, y, z) = \dfrac{x^3 + yz^2}{x^4 + y^2 + z^4}$

63. $f(x, y, z) = \dfrac{x^2 + y^2 - z^2}{x^2 + y^2 + z^2}$

64. $f(x, y, z) = \dfrac{x^4 + yx^3 + z^2 x^2}{x^4 + y^4 + z^4}$

65. $f(x, y, z) = \dfrac{x^2 y^2 z^2}{x^6 + y^6 + z^6}$

In Exercises 66 and 67, use the definition in Exercise 60(a) to prove that $\lim\limits_{(x,y,z) \to (0,0,0)} f(x, y, z)$ exists.

66. $f(x, y, z) = \dfrac{y^3 + xz^2}{x^2 + y^2 + z^2}$

67. $f(x, y, z) = \dfrac{xy + xz + yz}{\sqrt{x^2 + y^2 + z^2}}$

68. (a) Given a definition of continuity at a point for a function of three variables, similar to Definition 12.2.12. **(b)** State theorems for functions of three variables similar to Theorems 12.2.13 and 12.2.17.

In Exercises 69 through 72, use the definitions and theorems of Exercise 68 to determine all points at which the function is continuous.

69. $f(x, y, z) = \dfrac{xz}{\sqrt{x^2 + y^2 + z^2 - 1}}$

70. $f(x, y, z) = \ln(36 - 4x^2 - y^2 - 9z^2)$

71. $f(x, y, z) = \begin{cases} \dfrac{3xyz}{x^2 + y^2 + z^2} & \text{if } (x, y, z) \neq (0, 0, 0) \\ 0 & \text{if } (x, y, z) = (0, 0, 0) \end{cases}$

72. $f(x, y, z) = \begin{cases} \dfrac{xz - y^2}{x^2 + y^2 + z^2} & \text{if } (x, y, z) \neq (0, 0, 0) \\ 0 & \text{if } (x, y, z) = (0, 0, 0) \end{cases}$

73. The function G is defined by

$$G(x, y) = \begin{cases} x^2 + 4y^2 & \text{if } x^2 + 4y^2 \leq 5 \\ 3 & \text{if } x^2 + 4y^2 > 5 \end{cases}$$

Show that G is continuous at all points (x, y) in R^2 except those on the ellipse $x^2 + 4y^2 = 5$.

74. The function F is defined by

$$F(x, y) = \begin{cases} x^2 - 3y^2 & \text{if } x^2 - 3y^2 \leq 1 \\ 2 & \text{if } x^2 - 3y^2 > 1 \end{cases}$$

Show that F is continuous at all points (x, y) in R^2 except those on the hyperbola $x^2 - 3y^2 = 1$.

75. Suppose that f and g are functions of two variables satisfying the following conditions:
(i) $f(tx, ty) = t^n f(x, y)$; $g(tx, ty) = t^n g(x, y)$ for some n and for all t;
(ii) $g(1, 1) \neq 0$ and $g(1, 0) \neq 0$;
(iii) $g(1, 1) \cdot f(1, 0) \neq g(1, 0) \cdot f(1, 1)$.

Show that $\displaystyle\lim_{(x,y)\to(0,0)} \frac{f(x, y)}{g(x, y)}$ does not exist.

12.3 PARTIAL DERIVATIVES

Differentiation of real-valued functions of n variables is reduced to the one-dimensional case by treating a function of n variables as a function of one variable at a time and holding the others fixed. This leads to the concept of a *partial derivative*. We begin with functions of two variables.

12.3.1 Definition of a Partial Derivative of a Function of Two Variables

Let f be a function of two variables, x and y. The **partial derivative of f with respect to x** is that function, denoted by $D_1 f$, such that its function value at any point (x, y) in the domain of f is given by

$$D_1 f(x, y) = \lim_{\Delta x \to 0} \frac{f(x + \Delta x, y) - f(x, y)}{\Delta x}$$

if this limit exists. Similarly, the **partial derivative of f with respect to y** is that function denoted by $D_2 f$, such that its function value at any point (x, y) in the domain of f is given by

$$D_2 f(x, y) = \lim_{\Delta y \to 0} \frac{f(x, y + \Delta y) - f(x, y)}{\Delta y}$$

if this limit exists.

The process of computing a partial derivative is called **partial differentiation.**

$D_1 f$ is read as "D sub 1 of f," and this denotes the function that is the partial derivative of f with respect to the first variable. $D_1 f(x, y)$ is read as

"D sub 1 of f of x and y," and this denotes the function value of D_1f at the point (x, y). Other notations for D_1f are f_1, f_x, and $\dfrac{\partial f}{\partial x}$. Other notations for $D_1f(x, y)$ are $f_1(x, y)$, $f_x(x, y)$, and $\dfrac{\partial f(x, y)}{\partial x}$. Similarly, other notations for D_2f are f_2, f_y, and $\dfrac{\partial f}{\partial y}$; other notations for $D_2f(x, y)$ are $f_2(x, y)$, $f_y(x, y)$, and $\dfrac{\partial f(x, y)}{\partial y}$. If $z = f(x, y)$, we can write $\dfrac{\partial z}{\partial x}$ for $D_1f(x, y)$. A partial derivative cannot be thought of as a ratio of ∂z and ∂x because neither of these symbols has a separate meaning. You learned that the notation $\dfrac{dy}{dx}$ can be regarded as the quotient of two differentials when y is a function of the single variable x, but there is no similar interpretation for $\dfrac{\partial z}{\partial x}$.

▶ **EXAMPLE 1** Apply the definition of a partial derivative to compute $D_1f(x, y)$ and $D_2f(x, y)$ if

$$f(x, y) = 3x^2 - 2xy + y^2$$

Solution

$$
\begin{aligned}
D_1 f(x, y) &= \lim_{\Delta x \to 0} \frac{f(x + \Delta x, y) - f(x, y)}{\Delta x} \\
&= \lim_{\Delta x \to 0} \frac{3(x + \Delta x)^2 - 2(x + \Delta x)y + y^2 - (3x^2 - 2xy + y^2)}{\Delta x} \\
&= \lim_{\Delta x \to 0} \frac{3x^2 + 6x\,\Delta x + 3(\Delta x)^2 - 2xy - 2y\,\Delta x + y^2 - 3x^2 + 2xy - y^2}{\Delta x} \\
&= \lim_{\Delta x \to 0} \frac{6x\,\Delta x + 3(\Delta x)^2 - 2y\,\Delta x}{\Delta x} \\
&= \lim_{\Delta x \to 0} (6x + 3\,\Delta x - 2y) \\
&= 6x - 2y
\end{aligned}
$$

$$
\begin{aligned}
D_2 f(x, y) &= \lim_{\Delta y \to 0} \frac{f(x, y + \Delta y) - f(x, y)}{\Delta y} \\
&= \lim_{\Delta y \to 0} \frac{3x^2 - 2x(y + \Delta y) + (y + \Delta y)^2 - (3x^2 - 2xy + y^2)}{\Delta y} \\
&= \lim_{\Delta y \to 0} \frac{3x^2 - 2xy - 2x\,\Delta y + y^2 + 2y\,\Delta y + (\Delta y)^2 - 3x^2 + 2xy - y^2}{\Delta y} \\
&= \lim_{\Delta y \to 0} \frac{-2x\,\Delta y + 2y\,\Delta y + (\Delta y)^2}{\Delta y} \\
&= \lim_{\Delta y \to 0} (-2x + 2y + \Delta y) \\
&= -2x + 2y
\end{aligned}
$$

◀

If (x_0, y_0) is a particular point in the domain of f, then

$$D_1 f(x_0, y_0) = \lim_{\Delta x \to 0} \frac{f(x_0 + \Delta x, y_0) - f(x_0, y_0)}{\Delta x} \tag{1}$$

if this limit exists, and

$$D_2 f(x_0, y_0) = \lim_{\Delta y \to 0} \frac{f(x_0, y_0 + \Delta y) - f(x_0, y_0)}{\Delta y} \tag{2}$$

if this limit exists.

▷ **ILLUSTRATION 1**   We apply formula (1) to find $D_1 f(3, -2)$ for the function f of Example 1.

$$
\begin{aligned}
D_1 f(3, -2) &= \lim_{\Delta x \to 0} \frac{f(3 + \Delta x, -2) - f(3, -2)}{\Delta x} \\
&= \lim_{\Delta x \to 0} \frac{3(3 + \Delta x)^2 - 2(3 + \Delta x)(-2) + (-2)^2 - (27 + 12 + 4)}{\Delta x} \\
&= \lim_{\Delta x \to 0} \frac{27 + 18\,\Delta x + 3(\Delta x)^2 + 12 + 4\,\Delta x + 4 - 43}{\Delta x} \\
&= \lim_{\Delta x \to 0} (18 + 3\,\Delta x + 4) \\
&= 22
\end{aligned}
$$

◀

Alternate formulas to (1) and (2) for $D_1 f(x_0, y_0)$ and $D_2 f(x_0, y_0)$ are given by

$$D_1 f(x_0, y_0) = \lim_{x \to x_0} \frac{f(x, y_0) - f(x_0, y_0)}{x - x_0} \tag{3}$$

if this limit exists, and

$$D_2 f(x_0, y_0) = \lim_{y \to y_0} \frac{f(x_0, y) - f(x_0, y_0)}{y - y_0} \tag{4}$$

if this limit exists.

▷ **ILLUSTRATION 2**   We apply formula (3) to find $D_1 f(3, -2)$ for the function f of Example 1.

$$
\begin{aligned}
D_1 f(3, -2) &= \lim_{x \to 3} \frac{f(x, -2) - f(3, -2)}{x - 3} \\
&= \lim_{x \to 3} \frac{3x^2 + 4x + 4 - 43}{x - 3} \\
&= \lim_{x \to 3} \frac{3x^2 + 4x - 39}{x - 3} \\
&= \lim_{x \to 3} \frac{(3x + 13)(x - 3)}{x - 3} \\
&= \lim_{x \to 3} (3x + 13) \\
&= 22
\end{aligned}
$$

◀

▷ **ILLUSTRATION 3**   In Example 1 we showed that

$$D_1 f(x, y) = 6x - 2y$$

Therefore

$$D_1 f(3, -2) = 18 + 4$$
$$= 22$$

This result agrees with those of Illustrations 1 and 2.   ◄

Comparing the definition of a partial derivative (12.3.1) with the definition of an ordinary derivative (2.1.3), we see that $D_1 f(x, y)$ is the ordinary derivative of f if f is considered as a function of one variable x (i.e., y is held constant), and $D_2 f(x, y)$ is the ordinary derivative of f if f is considered as a function of one variable y (and x is held constant). So the results in Example 1 can be obtained more easily by applying the theorems for ordinary differentiation if y is considered constant when finding $D_1 f(x, y)$ and if x is considered constant when finding $D_2 f(x, y)$. The following example illustrates this.

▶ **EXAMPLE 2**   Find $f_x(x, y)$ and $f_y(x, y)$ if

$$f(x, y) = 3x^3 - 4x^2 y + 3xy^2 + \sin xy^2$$

Solution   Treating f as a function of x and holding y constant we have

$$f_x(x, y) = 9x^2 - 8xy + 3y^2 + y^2 \cos xy^2$$

Considering f as a function of y and holding x constant we have

$$f_y(x, y) = -4x^2 + 6xy + 2xy \cos xy^2$$ ◄

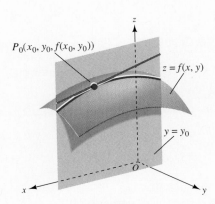

$P_0(x_0, y_0, f(x_0, y_0))$

$z = f(x, y)$

$y = y_0$

FIGURE 1

Geometric interpretations of the partial derivatives of a function of two variables are similar to those of a function of one variable. The graph of a function f of two variables is a surface having equation $z = f(x, y)$. If y is held constant (say, $y = y_0$), then $z = f(x, y_0)$ is an equation of the trace of this surface in the plane $y = y_0$. The curve can be represented by the two equations

$$y = y_0 \quad \text{and} \quad z = f(x, y) \tag{5}$$

because the curve is the intersection of these two surfaces.

Then $D_1 f(x_0, y_0)$ is the slope of the tangent line to the curve given by (5) at the point $P_0(x_0, y_0, f(x_0, y_0))$ in the plane $y = y_0$. In an analogous fashion, $D_2 f(x_0, y_0)$ represents the slope of the tangent line to the curve having equations

$$x = x_0 \quad \text{and} \quad z = f(x, y)$$

at the point P_0 in the plane $x = x_0$. Figures 1 and 2 show a portion of the curve and the tangent line.

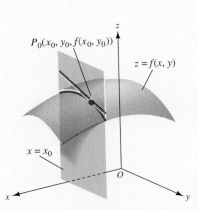

$P_0(x_0, y_0, f(x_0, y_0))$

$z = f(x, y)$

$x = x_0$

FIGURE 2

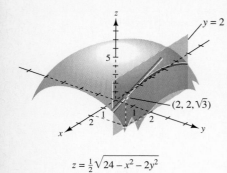

$$z = \tfrac{1}{2}\sqrt{24 - x^2 - 2y^2}$$

FIGURE 3

▶ **EXAMPLE 3**   Find the slope of the tangent line to the curve of intersection of the surface

$$z = \tfrac{1}{2}\sqrt{24 - x^2 - 2y^2}$$

with the plane $y = 2$ at the point $(2, 2, \sqrt{3})$.

Solution   Figure 3 shows the curve of intersection of the surface and the plane, and the tangent line. The required slope is the value of $\dfrac{\partial z}{\partial x}$ at the point $(2, 2, \sqrt{3})$.

$$\frac{\partial z}{\partial x} = \frac{-x}{2\sqrt{24 - x^2 - 2y^2}}$$

So at $(2, 2, \sqrt{3})$,

$$\frac{\partial z}{\partial x} = \frac{-2}{2\sqrt{12}}$$

$$= -\frac{1}{2\sqrt{3}} \qquad \blacktriangleleft$$

When computing a partial derivative at a particular point, it is sometimes necessary to apply formulas (1) through (4) as in the following example.

▶ **EXAMPLE 4**   Given

$$f(x, y) = \begin{cases} \dfrac{xy(x^2 - y^2)}{x^2 + y^2} & \text{if } (x, y) \neq (0, 0) \\ 0 & \text{if } (x, y) = (0, 0) \end{cases}$$

Show that $f_1(0, 0) = 0$ and $f_2(0, 0) = 0$.

Solution   We compute $f_1(0, 0)$ from (3) with $y_0 = 0$ and $f_2(0, 0)$ from (4) with $x_0 = 0$.

$$f_1(0, 0) = \lim_{x \to 0} \frac{f(x, 0) - f(0, 0)}{x - 0} \qquad f_2(0, 0) = \lim_{y \to 0} \frac{f(0, y) - f(0, 0)}{y - 0}$$

$$= \lim_{x \to 0} \frac{0 - 0}{x} \qquad\qquad\qquad = \lim_{y \to 0} \frac{0 - 0}{y}$$

$$= \lim_{x \to 0} 0 \qquad\qquad\qquad\quad = \lim_{y \to 0} 0$$

$$= 0 \qquad\qquad\qquad\qquad = 0 \qquad \blacktriangleleft$$

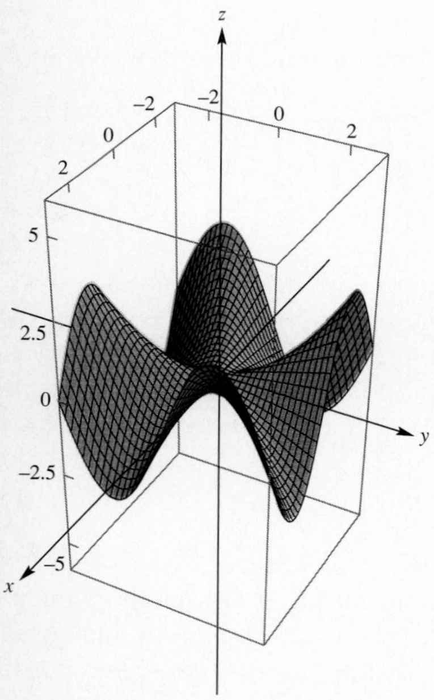

$$[-2.5, 2.5] \text{ by } [-2.5, 2.5] \text{ by } [-6, 6]$$

$$f(x, y) = \begin{cases} \dfrac{xy(x^2 - y^2)}{x^2 + y^2} & \text{if } (x, y) \neq (0, 0) \\ 0 & \text{if } (x, y) = (0, 0) \end{cases}$$

FIGURE 4

Figure 4, showing the surface defined by the function of Example 4, supports the fact that both $f_1(0, 0)$ and $f_2(0, 0)$ are zero. The intersection of the plane $y = 0$ and the surface is the x axis, and $f_1(0, 0)$ is the slope of the x axis in the xz plane, which of course is zero. Similarly, $f_2(0, 0)$ is the slope of the y axis in the yz plane, which is also zero.

▶ **EXAMPLE 5** For the function of Example 4, show:
(a) $f_1(0, y) = -y$ for all y; (b) $f_2(x, 0) = x$ for all x.

Solution

(a) If $y \neq 0$, from (3),

$$f_1(0, y) = \lim_{x \to 0} \frac{f(x, y) - f(0, y)}{x - 0}$$

$$= \lim_{x \to 0} \frac{\dfrac{xy(x^2 - y^2)}{x^2 + y^2} - 0}{x}$$

$$= \lim_{x \to 0} \frac{y(x^2 - y^2)}{x^2 + y^2}$$

$$= -\frac{y^3}{y^2}$$

$$= -y$$

(b) If $x \neq 0$, from (4),

$$f_2(x, 0) = \lim_{y \to 0} \frac{f(x, y) - f(x, 0)}{y - 0}$$

$$= \lim_{y \to 0} \frac{\dfrac{xy(x^2 - y^2)}{x^2 + y^2} - 0}{y}$$

$$= \lim_{y \to 0} \frac{x(x^2 - y^2)}{x^2 + y^2}$$

$$= \frac{x^3}{x^2}$$

$$= x$$

(a) Because $f_1(0, y) = -y$ if $y \neq 0$ and, from Example 4, $f_1(0, 0) = 0$, we can conclude that $f_1(0, y) = -y$ for all y.

(b) Because $f_2(x, 0) = x$ if $x \neq 0$ and, from Example 4, $f_2(x, 0) = 0$, then $f_2(x, 0) = x$ for all x. ◀

Because every derivative is a measure of a rate of change, a partial derivative can be so interpreted. If f is a function of two variables x and y, the partial derivative of f with respect to x at the point $P_0(x_0, y_0)$ gives the instantaneous rate of change, at P_0, of $f(x, y)$ per unit change in x (x alone varies and y is held fixed at y_0). Similarly, the partial derivative of f with respect to y at P_0 gives the instantaneous rate of change, at P_0, of $f(x, y)$ per unit change in y.

▶ **EXAMPLE 6** According to the *ideal gas law* for a confined gas, if P atmospheres is the pressure, V liters is the volume, and T degrees is the absolute temperature on the Kelvin scale, we have the formula

$$PV = kT \qquad (6)$$

where k is a constant of proportionality. Suppose that the volume of a gas in a certain container is 12 liters and the temperature is 290°K with $k = 0.6$. (a) Find the instantaneous rate of change of P per unit change in T if V remains fixed at 12. (b) Use the result of part (a) to approximate the change in the pressure if the temperature is increased to 295°K. (c) Find the instantaneous rate of change of V per unit change in P if T remains fixed at 290. (d) Suppose that the temperature is held constant. Use the result of part (c) to find the approximate change in the volume necessary to produce the same change in the pressure as obtained in part (b).

Solution   Substituting $V = 12$, $T = 290$, and $k = 0.6$ in (6), we obtain $P = 14.5$.

(a) Solving (6) for P when $k = 0.6$ we get

$$P = \frac{0.6T}{V}$$

The instantaneous rate of change of P per unit change in T if V remains constant is $\dfrac{\partial P}{\partial T}$, and

$$\frac{\partial P}{\partial T} = \frac{0.6}{V}$$

When $T = 290$ and $V = 12$, $\dfrac{\partial P}{\partial T} = 0.05$, which is the answer required.

(b) From the result of part (a) when T is increased by 5(290 to 295) and V remains fixed, an approximate increase in P is $5(0.05) = 0.25$.

<u>Conclusion:</u>   If the temperature is increased from 290°K to 295°K the increase in the pressure is approximately 0.25 atm.

(c) Solving (6) for V when $k = 0.6$, we obtain

$$V = \frac{0.6T}{P}$$

The instantaneous rate of change of V per unit change in P if T remains fixed is $\dfrac{\partial V}{\partial P}$, and

$$\frac{\partial V}{\partial P} = -\frac{0.6T}{P^2}$$

When $T = 290$ and $P = 14.5$,

$$\frac{\partial V}{\partial P} = -\frac{0.6(290)}{(14.5)^2}$$
$$= -0.83$$

which is the instantaneous rate of change of V per unit change in P when $T = 290$ and $P = 14.5$ if T remains fixed at 290.

(d) If P is to be increased by 0.25 and T is held fixed, then from the result of part (c) the change in V should be approximately

$$(0.25)(-0.83) = -0.21$$

<u>Conclusion:</u>   The volume should be decreased by approximately 0.21 liter if the pressure is to be increased from 14.5 atm to 14.75 atm.   ◄

We now extend the concept of partial derivative to functions of n variables.

12.3.2 Definition of the Partial Derivative of a Function of n Variables

Let $P(x_1, x_2, \ldots, x_n)$ be a point in R^n, and let f be a function of the n variables $x_1, x_2, \ldots x_n$. Then the partial derivative of f with respect to x_k is that function, denoted by $D_k f$, such that its function value at any point P in the domain of f is given by

$$D_k f(x_1, x_2, \ldots, x_n)$$
$$= \lim_{\Delta x_k \to 0} \frac{f(x_1, x_2, \ldots, x_k + \Delta x_k, \ldots, x_n) - f(x_1, x_2, \ldots, x_n)}{\Delta x_k}$$

if this limit exists.

In particular, if f is a function of the three variables x, y, and z, then the partial derivatives of f are given by

$$D_1 f(x, y, z) = \lim_{\Delta x \to 0} \frac{f(x + \Delta x, y, z) - f(x, y, z)}{\Delta x}$$

$$D_2 f(x, y, z) = \lim_{\Delta y \to 0} \frac{f(x, y + \Delta y, z) - f(x, y, z)}{\Delta y}$$

$$D_3 f(x, y, z) = \lim_{\Delta z \to 0} \frac{f(x, y, z + \Delta z) - f(x, y, z)}{\Delta z}$$

if these limits exist.

▶ **EXAMPLE 7** Given $f(x, y, z) = x^2 y + y z^2 + z^3$, verify that

$$x f_1(x, y, z) + y f_2(x, y, z) + z f_3(x, y, z) = 3 f(x, y, z)$$

Solution Holding y and z constant we get

$$f_1(x, y, z) = 2xy$$

Holding x and z constant we obtain

$$f_2(x, y, z) = x^2 + z^2$$

Holding x and y constant we get

$$f_3(x, y, z) = 2yz + 3z^2$$

Therefore

$$
\begin{aligned}
x f_1(x, y, z) + y f_2(x, y, z) + z f_3(x, y, z) &= x(2xy) + y(x^2 + z^2) + z(2yz + 3z^2) \\
&= 2x^2 y + x^2 y + yz^2 + 2yz^2 + 3z^3 \\
&= 3(x^2 y + yz^2 + z^3) \\
&= 3 f(x, y, z) \quad \blacktriangleleft
\end{aligned}
$$

If f is a function of two variables, then in general $D_1 f$ and $D_2 f$ are also functions of two variables. And if the partial derivatives of these functions exist, they are called second partial derivatives of f. In contrast, $D_1 f$ and $D_2 f$ are called first partial derivatives of f. There are four second partial derivatives of a function of two variables. If f is a function of the two variables x and y, the notations

$$D_2(D_1 f) \qquad D_{12} f \qquad f_{12} \qquad f_{xy} \qquad \frac{\partial^2 f}{\partial y\, \partial x}$$

all denote the second partial derivative of f that is obtained by first partial-differentiating f with respect to x and then partial-differentiating the result with respect to y. This second partial derivative is defined by

$$f_{12}(x, y) = \lim_{\Delta y \to 0} \frac{f_1(x, y + \Delta y) - f_1(x, y)}{\Delta y} \qquad (7)$$

if this limit exists. The notations

$$D_1(D_1 f) \qquad D_{11} f \qquad f_{11} \qquad f_{xx} \qquad \frac{\partial^2 f}{\partial x^2}$$

all denote the second partial derivative of f that is obtained by partial-differentiating twice with respect to x. We have the definition

$$f_{11}(x, y) = \lim_{\Delta x \to 0} \frac{f_1(x + \Delta x, y) - f_1(x, y)}{\Delta x} \qquad (8)$$

if this limit exists. The other two second partial derivatives are defined in an analogous way.

$$f_{21}(x, y) = \lim_{\Delta x \to 0} \frac{f_2(x + \Delta x, y) - f_2(x, y)}{\Delta x} \qquad (9)$$

$$f_{22}(x, y) = \lim_{\Delta y \to 0} \frac{f_2(x, y + \Delta y) - f_2(x, y)}{\Delta y} \qquad (10)$$

if these limits exist.

The definitions of higher-order partial derivatives are similar. Again there are various notations for a specific derivative. For example,

$$D_{112} f \qquad f_{112} \qquad f_{xxy} \qquad \frac{\partial^3 f}{\partial y\, \partial x\, \partial x} \qquad \frac{\partial^3 f}{\partial y\, \partial x^2}$$

all stand for the third partial derivative of f that is obtained by partial-differentiating twice with respect to x and then once with respect to y. In the subscript notation, the order of partial differentiation is from left to right; in the notation $\dfrac{\partial^3 f}{\partial y\, \partial x\, \partial x}$, the order is from right to left.

▶ **EXAMPLE 8**   Given

$$f(x, y) = e^x \sin y + \ln xy$$

Find: **(a)** $D_{11} f(x, y)$; **(b)** $D_{12} f(x, y)$; **(c)** $\dfrac{\partial^3 f}{\partial x\, \partial y^2}$

Solution

$$D_1 f(x, y) = e^x \sin y + \frac{1}{xy}(y)$$

$$= e^x \sin y + \frac{1}{x}$$

(a) $D_{11} f(x, y) = e^x \sin y - \dfrac{1}{x^2}$ **(b)** $D_{12} f(x, y) = e^x \cos y$

(c) To find $\dfrac{\partial^3 f}{\partial x \, \partial y^2}$ we partial-differentiate twice with respect to y and then once with respect to x. We have, then,

$$\frac{\partial f}{\partial y} = e^x \cos y + \frac{1}{y} \qquad \frac{\partial^2 f}{\partial y^2} = -e^x \sin y - \frac{1}{y^2} \qquad \frac{\partial^3 f}{\partial x \, \partial y^2} = -e^x \sin y \quad \blacktriangleleft$$

Higher-order partial derivatives of a function of n variables have definitions that are analogous to the definitions of higher-order partial derivatives of a function of two variables. If f is a function of n variables, there may be n^2 second partial derivatives of f at a particular point. That is, for a function of three variables, if all the second-order partial derivatives exist, there are nine of them: $f_{11}, f_{12}, f_{13}, f_{21}, f_{22}, f_{23}, f_{31}, f_{32},$ and f_{33}.

▶ **EXAMPLE 9**   Find $D_{132} f(x, y, z)$ if

$$f(x, y, z) = \sin(xy + 2z)$$

Solution

$$D_1 f(x, y, z) = y \cos(xy + 2z)$$
$$D_{13} f(x, y, z) = -2y \sin(xy + 2z)$$
$$D_{132} f(x, y, z) = -2 \sin(xy + 2z) - 2xy \cos(xy + 2z) \quad \blacktriangleleft$$

▶ **EXAMPLE 10**   Given

$$f(x, y) = x^3 y - y \cosh xy$$

Find: **(a)** $f_{xy}(x, y)$; **(b)** $f_{yx}(x, y)$.

Solution

(a) $f_x(x, y) = 3x^2 y - y^2 \sinh xy$
    $f_{xy}(x, y) = 3x^2 - 2y \sinh xy - xy^2 \cosh xy$

(b) $f_y(x, y) = x^3 - \cosh xy - xy \sinh xy$
    $f_{yx}(x, y) = 3x^2 - y \sinh xy - y \sinh xy - xy^2 \cosh xy$
    $\qquad\quad = 3x^2 - 2y \sinh xy - xy^2 \cosh xy \quad \blacktriangleleft$

Observe in Example 10 the "mixed" partial derivatives $f_{xy}(x, y)$ and $f_{yx}(x, y)$ are equal. So for this particular function, when finding the second partial derivative with respect to x and then y, the order of differentiation is immaterial. This condition holds for many functions. However, the following example shows that it is not always true.

▶ **EXAMPLE 11** Find $f_{12}(0, 0)$ and $f_{21}(0, 0)$ if

$$f(x, y) = \begin{cases} (xy)\dfrac{x^2 - y^2}{x^2 + y^2} & \text{if } (x, y) \neq (0, 0) \\ 0 & \text{if } (x, y) = (0, 0) \end{cases}$$

Solution In Example 5, we showed that for this function

$$f_1(0, y) = -y \qquad \text{for all } y \tag{11}$$

and

$$f_2(x, 0) = x \qquad \text{for all } x \tag{12}$$

From (7),

$$f_{12}(0, 0) = \lim_{\Delta y \to 0} \frac{f_1(0, 0 + \Delta y) - f_1(0, 0)}{\Delta y}$$

But from (11), $f_1(0, \Delta y) = -\Delta y$ and $f_1(0, 0) = 0$; so

$$\begin{aligned} f_{12}(0, 0) &= \lim_{\Delta y \to 0} \frac{-\Delta y - 0}{\Delta y} \\ &= \lim_{\Delta y \to 0} (-1) \\ &= -1 \end{aligned}$$

From (9),

$$f_{21}(0, 0) = \lim_{\Delta x \to 0} \frac{f_2(0 + \Delta x, 0) - f_2(0, 0)}{\Delta x}$$

From (12), $f_2(\Delta x, 0) = \Delta x$ and $f_2(0, 0) = 0$. Therefore

$$\begin{aligned} f_{21}(0, 0) &= \lim_{\Delta x \to 0} \frac{\Delta x - 0}{\Delta x} \\ &= \lim_{\Delta x \to 0} 1 \\ &= 1 \end{aligned}$$

◀

For the function in Example 11 the mixed partial derivatives $f_{12}(x, y)$ and $f_{21}(x, y)$ are not equal at $(0, 0)$. A set of conditions for which $f_{12}(x_0, y_0)$ and $f_{21}(x_0, y_0)$ are equal is given by Theorem 12.3.3, which follows. The function of Example 11 does not satisfy the hypothesis of this theorem because both f_{12} and f_{21} are discontinuous at $(0, 0)$. It is left as an exercise to show this (see Exercise 64).

12.3.3 Theorem

Suppose that f is a function of two variables x and y defined on an open disk $B((x_0, y_0); r)$ and f_x, f_y, f_{xy}, and f_{yx} also are defined on B. Furthermore, suppose that f_{xy} and f_{yx} are continuous on B. Then

$$f_{xy}(x_0, y_0) = f_{yx}(x_0, y_0)$$

The proof of this theorem appears in the supplement of this section.

As a result of Theorem 12.3.3, if the function f of two variables has continuous partial derivatives on some open disk, then the order of partial differentiation can be changed without affecting the result; that is,

$$D_{112}f = D_{121}f = D_{211}f$$

$$D_{1122}f = D_{1212}f = D_{1221}f = D_{2112}f = D_{2121}f = D_{2211}f$$

and so forth. In particular, assuming that all of the partial derivatives are continuous on some open disk, we can prove that $D_{211}f = D_{112}f$ by applying Theorem 12.3.3 repeatedly. Doing this we have

$$D_{211}f = D_1(D_{21}f) = D_1(D_{12}f) = D_1[D_2(D_1f)] = D_2[D_1(D_1f)]$$
$$= D_2(D_{11}f) = D_{112}f$$

EXERCISES 12.3

In Exercises 1 through 6, apply Definition 12.3.1 to find the partial derivative.

1. $f(x, y) = 6x + 3y - 7$; $D_1f(x, y)$

2. $f(x, y) = 4x^2 - 3xy$; $D_1f(x, y)$

3. $f(x, y) = 3xy + 6x - y^2$; $D_2f(x, y)$

4. $f(x, y) = xy^2 - 5y + 6$; $D_2f(x, y)$

5. $f(x, y) = \sqrt{x^2 + y^2}$; $f_x(x, y)$

6. $f(x, y) = \dfrac{x + 2y}{x^2 - y}$; $f_y(x, y)$

In Exercises 7 through 10, apply Definition 12.3.2 to find the partial derivative.

7. $f(x, y, z) = x^2y - 3xy^2 + 2yz$; $D_2f(x, y, z)$

8. $f(x, y, z) = x^2 + 4y^2 + 9z^2$; $D_1f(x, y, z)$

9. $f(x, y, z, r, t) = xyr + yzt + yrt + zrt$; $f_r(x, y, z, r, t)$

10. $f(r, s, t, u, v, w) = 3r^2st + st^2v - 2tuv^2 - tvw + 3uw^2$; $f_v(r, s, t, u, v, w)$

11. Given $f(x, y) = x^2 - 9y^2$. Find $D_1f(2, 1)$ by (a) applying formula (1); (b) applying formula (3); (c) applying Definition 12.3.1 and then replacing x and y by 2 and 1, respectively.

12. For the function in Exercise 11, find $D_2f(2, 1)$ by (a) applying formula (2); (b) applying formula (4); (c) applying Definition 12.3.1 and then replacing x and y by 2 and 1, respectively.

In Exercises 13 through 24, find the partial derivative by holding all but one of the variables constant and applying theorems for ordinary differentiation.

13. $f(x, y) = 4y^3 + \sqrt{x^2 + y^2}$; $D_1f(x, y)$

14. $f(x, y) = \dfrac{x + y}{\sqrt{y^2 - x^2}}$; $D_2f(x, y)$

15. $f(\theta, \phi) = \sin 3\theta \cos 2\phi$; $f_\phi(\theta, \phi)$

16. $f(r, \theta) = r^2 \cos \theta - 2r \tan \theta$; $f_\theta(r, \theta)$

17. $z = e^{y/x} \ln \dfrac{x^2}{y}$; $\dfrac{\partial z}{\partial y}$

18. $r = e^{-\theta} \cos(\theta + \phi)$; $\dfrac{\partial r}{\partial \theta}$

19. $u = (x^2 + y^2 + z^2)^{-1/2}$; $\dfrac{\partial u}{\partial z}$

20. $u = \tan^{-1}(xyzw)$; $\dfrac{\partial u}{\partial w}$

21. $f(x, y, z) = 4xyz + \ln(2xyz)$; $f_3(x, y, z)$

22. $f(x, y, z) = e^{xy} \sinh 2z - e^{xy} \cosh 2z$; $f_z(x, y, z)$

23. $f(x, y, z) = e^{xyz} + \tan^{-1} \dfrac{3xy}{z^2}$; $f_y(x, y, z)$

24. $f(r, \theta, \phi) = 4r^2 \sin \theta + 5e^r \cos \theta \sin \phi - 2 \cos \phi$; $f_2(r, \theta, \phi)$

25. If $f(r, \theta) = r \tan \theta - r^2 \sin \theta$, find (a) $f_1(\sqrt{2}, \frac{1}{4}\pi)$; (b) $f_2(3, \pi)$.

26. If $f(x, y, z) = e^{xy^2} + \ln(y + z)$, find (a) $f_1(3, 0, 17)$; (b) $f_2(1, 0, 2)$; (c) $f_3(0, 0, 1)$.

In Exercises 27 and 28, find $f_x(x, y)$ and $f_y(x, y)$.

27. $f(x, y) = \displaystyle\int_x^y \ln \sin t \, dt$

28. $f(x, y) = \displaystyle\int_x^y e^{\cos t} \, dt$

In Exercises 29 through 38, do each of the following: (a) Find $D_{11}f(x, y)$; (b) find $D_{22}f(x, y)$; (c) show that $D_{12}f(x, y)$ and $D_{21}f(x, y)$ are equal.

29. $f(x, y) = \dfrac{x^2}{y} - \dfrac{y}{x^2}$

30. $f(x, y) = 2x^3 - 3x^2y + xy^2$

31. $f(x, y) = e^{2x} \sin y$

32. $f(x, y) = e^{-x/y} + \ln \dfrac{y}{x}$

33. $f(x, y) = (x^2 + y^2)\tan^{-1} \dfrac{y}{x}$

34. $f(x, y) = \sin^{-1} \dfrac{3y}{x^2}$

35. $f(x, y) = 4x \sinh y + 3y \cosh x$

36. $f(x, y) = x \cos y - y e^x$

37. $f(x, y) = e^x \cos y + \tan^{-1} x \cdot \ln y$

38. $f(x, y) = 3x \cosh y - y \sin^{-1} e^x$

In Exercises 39 through 46, find the indicated partial derivatives.

39. $f(x, y) = 2x^3y + 5x^2y^2 - 3xy^2$;   **(a)** $f_{121}(x, y)$;   **(b)** $f_{211}(x, y)$

40. $G(x, y) = 3x^3y^2 + 5x^2y^3 + 2x$;   **(a)** $G_{yyx}(x, y)$;   **(b)** $G_{yxy}(x, y)$

41. $f(x, y, z) = ye^x + ze^y + e^z$;   **(a)** $f_{xz}(x, y, z)$;   **(b)** $f_{yz}(x, y, z)$

42. $g(x, y, z) = \sin(xyz)$;   **(a)** $g_{23}(x, y, z)$;   **(b)** $g_{12}(x, y, z)$

43. $f(w, z) = w^2 \cos e^z$;   **(a)** $f_{121}(w, z)$;   **(b)** $f_{212}(w, z)$

44. $f(u, v) = \ln \cos(u - v)$;   **(a)** $f_{uuv}(u, v)$;   **(b)** $f_{vuv}(u, v)$

45. $g(r, s, t) = \ln(r^2 + 4s^2 - 5t^2)$;   **(a)** $g_{132}(r, s, t)$;   **(b)** $g_{122}(r, s, t)$

46. $f(x, y, z) = \tan^{-1}(3xyz)$;   **(a)** $f_{113}(x, y, z)$;   **(b)** $f_{123}(x, y, z)$

47. Given $u = \sin \dfrac{r}{t} + \ln \dfrac{t}{r}$. Verify $t\dfrac{\partial u}{\partial t} + r\dfrac{\partial u}{\partial r} = 0$.

48. Given $w = x^2y + y^2z + z^2x$. Verify

$$\frac{\partial w}{\partial x} + \frac{\partial w}{\partial y} + \frac{\partial w}{\partial z} = (x + y + z)^2$$

In Exercises 49 through 52, show that $u(x, y)$ satisfies the equation $\dfrac{\partial^2 u}{\partial x^2} + \dfrac{\partial^2 u}{\partial y^2} = 0$, which is known as Laplace's *equation in R^2.*

49. $u(x, y) = \ln(x^2 + y^2)$

50. $u(x, y) = \tan^{-1} \dfrac{2xy}{x^2 - y^2}$

51. $u(x, y) = \tan^{-1} \dfrac{y}{x} + \dfrac{x}{x^2 + y^2}$

52. $u(x, y) = e^x \sin y + e^y \cos x$

53. Laplace's equation in R^3 is

$$\frac{\partial^2 u}{\partial x^2} + \frac{\partial^2 u}{\partial y^2} + \frac{\partial^2 u}{\partial z^2} = 0$$

Show that $u(x, y, z) = (x^2 + y^2 + z^2)^{-1/2}$ satisfies this equation.

54. Find the slope of the tangent line to the curve of intersection of the surface

$$36x^2 - 9y^2 + 4z^2 + 36 = 0$$

with the plane $x = 1$ at the point $(1, \sqrt{12}, -3)$. Interpret this slope as a partial derivative.

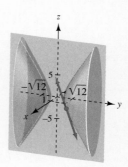

55. Find the slope of the tangent line to the curve of intersection of the surface $z = x^2 + y^2$ with the plane $y = 1$ at the point $(2, 1, 5)$. Sketch the curve. Interpret this slope as a partial derivative.

56. Find equations of the tangent line to the curve of intersection of the surface $x^2 + y^2 + z^2 = 9$ with the plane $y = 2$ at the point $(1, 2, 2)$.

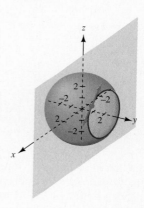

57. The temperature at any point (x, y) of a flat plate is T degrees and $T = 54 - \frac{2}{3}x^2 - 4y^2$. If distance is measured in centimeters, find the rate of change of the temperature with respect to the distance moved along the plate in the directions of the positive x and y axes, respectively, at the point $(3, 1)$.

58. Use the ideal gas law for a confined gas (see Example 6) to show that

$$\frac{\partial V}{\partial T} \cdot \frac{\partial T}{\partial P} \cdot \frac{\partial P}{\partial V} = -1$$

59. If V dollars is the present value of an ordinary annuity of equal payments of $100 per year for t years at an interest rate of $100i$ percent per year, then

$$V = 100 \left[\frac{1 - (1 + i)^{-t}}{i} \right]$$

   (a) Find the instantaneous rate of change of V per unit change in i if t remains fixed at 8. **(b)** Use the result of part (a) to find the approximate change in the present value if the interest rate changes from 6 percent to 7 percent and the time remains fixed at 8 years. **(c)** Find the instantaneous rate of change of V per unit change in t if i remains fixed at 0.06. **(d)** Use the result of part (c) to find the approximate change in the present value if the time is decreased from 8 to 7 years and the interest rate remains fixed at 6 percent.

60. Suppose that $10,000x$ dollars is the inventory carried in a store employing y clerks, P dollars is the weekly profit of the store, and

$$P = 3000 + 240y + 20y(x - 2y) - 10(x - 12)^2$$

   where $15 \leq x \leq 25$ and $5 \leq y \leq 12$. At present the inventory is $180,000 and there are 8 clerks. **(a)** Find the instantaneous rate of change of P per unit change in x if y remains fixed at 8. **(b)** Use the result of part (a) to find the approximate change in the weekly profit if the inventory changes from $180,000 to $200,000 and the number of clerks remains fixed at 8. **(c)** Find the instantaneous rate of change of P per unit change in y if x remains fixed at 18. **(d)** Use the result of part (c) to find the approximate change in the weekly profit if the number of

clerks is increased from 8 to 10 and the inventory remains fixed at $180,000.

61. Given $f(x, y) = \begin{cases} \dfrac{x^3 + y^3}{x^2 + y^2} & \text{if } (x, y) \neq (0, 0) \\ 0 & \text{if } (x, y) = (0, 0) \end{cases}$

   Find **(a)** $f_1(0, 0)$; **(b)** $f_2(0, 0)$.

62. Given $f(x, y) = \begin{cases} \dfrac{x^2 - xy}{x + y} & \text{if } (x, y) \neq (0, 0) \\ 0 & \text{if } (x, y) = (0, 0) \end{cases}$

   Find **(a)** $f_1(0, y)$ if $y \neq 0$; **(b)** $f_1(0, 0)$.

63. For the function of Exercise 62 find **(a)** $f_2(x, 0)$ if $x \neq 0$; **(b)** $f_2(0, 0)$.

64. For the function of Example 11, show that f_{12} is discontinuous at $(0, 0)$ and hence that the hypothesis of Theorem 12.3.3 is not satisfied if $(x_0, y_0) = (0, 0)$.

In Exercises 65 through 67, find $f_{12}(0, 0)$ and $f_{21}(0, 0)$, if they exist.

65. $f(x, y) = \begin{cases} \dfrac{2xy}{x^2 + y^2} & \text{if } (x, y) \neq (0, 0) \\ 0 & \text{if } (x, y) = (0, 0) \end{cases}$

66. $f(x, y) = \begin{cases} \dfrac{x^2 y^2}{x^4 + y^4} & \text{if } (x, y) \neq (0, 0) \\ 0 & \text{if } (x, y) = (0, 0) \end{cases}$

67. $f(x, y) = \begin{cases} x^2 \tan^{-1} \dfrac{y}{x} - y^2 \tan^{-1} \dfrac{x}{y} & \text{if } xy \neq 0 \\ 0 & \text{if } xy = 0 \end{cases}$

68. Prove that if f is a function of two variables and all the partial derivatives of f up to the fourth order are continuous on some open disk, then

$$D_{1122}f = D_{2121}f$$

69. If S square meters is a person's body surface area, then a formula giving an approximate value of S is

$$S = 2W^{0.4}H^{0.7}$$

   where W kilograms is the person's weight and H meters is the person's height. When $W = 70$ and $H = 1.8$, find $\dfrac{\partial S}{\partial W}$ and $\dfrac{\partial S}{\partial H}$, and interpret the results.

12.4 DIFFERENTIABILITY AND THE TOTAL DIFFERENTIAL

We shall define *differentiability* of functions of more than one variable by means of an equation involving the increment of a function. To motivate this definition we first obtain a representation for the increment of a function of a single variable that is similar to what will appear in our definition (12.4.2) of differentiability.

Recall from Section 2.1 that if f is a differentiable function of x and $y = f(x)$, then

$$f'(x) = \lim_{\Delta x \to 0} \frac{\Delta y}{\Delta x}$$

where Δx and Δy are increments of x and y and

$$\Delta y = f(x + \Delta x) - f(x)$$

When $|\Delta x|$ is small and $\Delta x \neq 0$, $\Delta y / \Delta x$ differs from $f'(x)$ by a small number that depends on Δx, which we shall denote by ϵ. Thus

$$\epsilon = \frac{\Delta y}{\Delta x} - f'(x) \qquad \text{if } \Delta x \neq 0$$

where ϵ is a function of Δx. From this equation we obtain

$$\Delta y = f'(x)\,\Delta x + \epsilon\,\Delta x$$

where ϵ is a function of Δx and $\epsilon \to 0$ as $\Delta x \to 0$.

From the above it follows that if the function f is differentiable at x_0, the increment of f at x_0, denoted by $\Delta f(x_0)$, is given by

$$\Delta f(x_0) = f'(x_0)\,\Delta x + \epsilon\,\Delta x \qquad \text{where } \lim_{\Delta x \to 0} \epsilon = 0$$

For functions of two or more variables an equation corresponding to this one is used to define differentiability. And from the definition we determine criteria for a function to be differentiable at a point. We give the details for a function of two variables and begin by defining the *increment* of such a function.

12.4.1 Definition of an Increment of a Function of Two Variables

If f is a function of two variables x and y, then the **increment of f** at the point (x_0, y_0), denoted by $\Delta f(x_0, y_0)$, is given by

$$\Delta f(x_0, y_0) = f(x_0 + \Delta x, y_0 + \Delta y) - f(x_0, y_0)$$

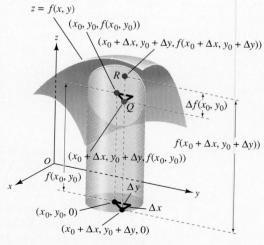

FIGURE 1

Figure 1 illustrates this definition for a function continuous on an open disk containing the points (x_0, y_0) and $(x_0 + \Delta x, y_0 + \Delta y)$. The figure shows a portion of the surface $z = f(x, y)$. $\Delta f(x_0, y_0) = \overline{QR}$, where Q is the point $(x_0 + \Delta x, y_0 + \Delta y, f(x_0, y_0))$ and R is the point having coordinates $(x_0 + \Delta x, y_0 + \Delta y, f(x_0 + \Delta x, y_0 + \Delta y))$.

▷ **ILLUSTRATION 1**   For the function f defined by

$$f(x, y) = 3x - xy^2$$

we find the increment of f at any point (x_0, y_0).

$$\Delta f(x_0, y_0) = f(x_0 + \Delta x, y_0 + \Delta y) - f(x_0, y_0)$$
$$= 3(x_0 + \Delta x) - (x_0 + \Delta x)(y_0 + \Delta y)^2 - (3x_0 - x_0 y_0^2)$$
$$= 3x_0 + 3\,\Delta x - x_0 y_0^2 - y_0^2\,\Delta x - 2x_0 y_0\,\Delta y - 2y_0\,\Delta x\,\Delta y$$
$$\qquad\qquad\qquad - x_0(\Delta y)^2 - \Delta x(\Delta y)^2 - 3x_0 + x_0 y_0^2$$
$$= 3\,\Delta x - y_0^2\,\Delta x - 2x_0 y_0\,\Delta y - 2y_0\,\Delta x\,\Delta y - x_0(\Delta y)^2 - \Delta x(\Delta y)^2 \quad ◀$$

12.4.2 Definition of a Differentiable Function of Two Variables

If f is a function of two variables x and y and the increment of f at (x_0, y_0) can be written as

$$\Delta f(x_0, y_0) = D_1 f(x_0, y_0)\,\Delta x + D_2 f(x_0, y_0)\,\Delta y + \epsilon_1\,\Delta x + \epsilon_2\,\Delta y$$

where ϵ_1 and ϵ_2 are functions of Δx and Δy such that $\epsilon_1 \to 0$ and $\epsilon_2 \to 0$ as $(\Delta x, \Delta y) \to (0, 0)$, then f is **differentiable** at (x_0, y_0).

▷ **ILLUSTRATION 2**   We use Definition 12.4.2 to prove that the function of Illustration 1 is differentiable at all points in R^2. We must show that for all points (x_0, y_0) in R^2 we can find an ϵ_1 and an ϵ_2 such that

$$\Delta f(x_0, y_0) - D_1 f(x_0, y_0)\,\Delta x - D_2 f(x_0, y_0)\,\Delta y = \epsilon_1\,\Delta x + \epsilon_2\,\Delta y$$

and $\epsilon_1 \to 0$ and $\epsilon_2 \to 0$ as $(\Delta x, \Delta y) \to (0, 0)$.

Because $f(x, y) = 3x - xy^2$,

$$D_1 f(x_0, y_0) = 3 - y_0^2 \quad \text{and} \quad D_2 f(x_0, y_0) = -2x_0 y_0$$

With these values and the value of $\Delta f(x_0, y_0)$ from Illustration 1,

$$\Delta f(x_0, y_0) - D_1 f(x_0, y_0)\,\Delta x - D_2 f(x_0, y_0)\,\Delta y = -x_0(\Delta y)^2 - 2y_0\,\Delta x\,\Delta y - \Delta x\,(\Delta y)^2$$

The right side of the above equation can be written in the following ways:

$$[-2y_0\,\Delta y - (\Delta y)^2]\,\Delta x + (-x_0\,\Delta y)\,\Delta y$$
$$(-2y_0\,\Delta y)\,\Delta x + (-\Delta x\,\Delta y - x_0\,\Delta y)\,\Delta y$$
$$[-(\Delta y)^2]\,\Delta x + (-2y_0\,\Delta x - x_0\,\Delta y)\,\Delta y$$
$$0 \cdot \Delta x + [-2y_0\,\Delta x - \Delta x\,\Delta y - x_0\,\Delta y]\,\Delta y$$

So there are at least four possible pairs of values for ϵ_1 and ϵ_2:

$$\epsilon_1 = -2y_0\,\Delta y - (\Delta y)^2 \quad \text{and} \quad \epsilon_2 = -x_0\,\Delta y$$
$$\epsilon_1 = -2y_0\,\Delta y \qquad\qquad \text{and} \quad \epsilon_2 = -\Delta x\,\Delta y - x_0\,\Delta y$$
$$\epsilon_1 = -(\Delta y)^2 \qquad\qquad \text{and} \quad \epsilon_2 = -2y_0\,\Delta x - x_0\,\Delta y$$
$$\epsilon_1 = 0 \qquad\qquad\qquad \text{and} \quad \epsilon_2 = -2y_0\,\Delta x - \Delta x\,\Delta y - x_0\,\Delta y$$

For each pair,

$$\lim_{(\Delta x, \Delta y) \to (0,0)} \epsilon_1 = 0 \quad \text{and} \quad \lim_{(\Delta x, \Delta y) \to (0,0)} \epsilon_2 = 0$$

Note that it is only necessary to find one pair of values for ϵ_1 and ϵ_2.   ◀

The next theorem states that for a function of two variables, differentiability implies continuity, just as was the case for a function of a single variable.

12.4.3 Theorem

If a function f of two variables is differentiable at a point, it is continuous at that point.

Proof   If f is differentiable at the point (x_0, y_0), then from Definition 12.4.2

$$f(x_0 + \Delta x, y_0 + \Delta y) - f(x_0, y_0)$$
$$= D_1 f(x_0, y_0)\,\Delta x + D_2 f(x_0, y_0)\,\Delta y + \epsilon_1\,\Delta x + \epsilon_2\,\Delta y$$

where $\epsilon_1 \to 0$ and $\epsilon_2 \to 0$ as $(\Delta x, \Delta y) \to (0, 0)$. Therefore

$$f(x_0 + \Delta x, y_0 + \Delta y)$$
$$= f(x_0, y_0) + D_1 f(x_0, y_0)\,\Delta x + D_2 f(x_0, y_0)\,\Delta y + \epsilon_1\,\Delta x + \epsilon_2\,\Delta y$$

Taking the limit on both sides of the above as $(\Delta x, \Delta y) \to (0, 0)$ we obtain

$$\lim_{(\Delta x, \Delta y) \to (0,0)} f(x_0 + \Delta x, y_0 + \Delta y) = f(x_0, y_0) \tag{1}$$

If we let $x_0 + \Delta x = x$ and $y_0 + \Delta y = y$, then "$(\Delta x, \Delta y) \to (0, 0)$" is equivalent to "$(x, y) \to (x_0, y_0)$." Thus, from (1),

$$\lim_{(x,y) \to (x_0, y_0)} f(x, y) = f(x_0, y_0)$$

which proves that f is continuous at (x_0, y_0).   ■

You learned that for a function f of a single variable, the existence of the derivative of f at a number implies differentiability and, therefore, continuity at that number. However, as the following example shows, for a function of two variables the existence of the partial derivatives at a point does not imply differentiability at that point.

▶ **EXAMPLE 1**   Given

$$f(x, y) = \begin{cases} \dfrac{xy}{x^2 + y^2} & \text{if } (x, y) \neq (0, 0) \\ 0 & \text{if } (x, y) = (0, 0) \end{cases}$$

prove that $D_1f(0, 0)$ and $D_2f(0, 0)$ exist but that f is not differentiable at $(0, 0)$.

Solution

$$D_1f(0, 0) = \lim_{x \to 0} \frac{f(x, 0) - f(0, 0)}{x - 0} \qquad D_2f(0, 0) = \lim_{y \to 0} \frac{f(0, y) - f(0, 0)}{y - 0}$$

$$= \lim_{x \to 0} \frac{0 - 0}{x} \qquad\qquad\qquad = \lim_{y \to 0} \frac{0 - 0}{y}$$

$$= \lim_{x \to 0} 0 \qquad\qquad\qquad\qquad = \lim_{y \to 0} 0$$

$$= 0 \qquad\qquad\qquad\qquad\qquad = 0$$

Therefore both $D_1f(0, 0)$ and $D_2f(0, 0)$ exist.

In Example 6 of Section 12.2 we demonstrated that for this function $\lim_{(x,y) \to (0,0)} f(x, y)$ does not exist; hence f is not continuous at $(0, 0)$. Because f is not continuous at $(0, 0)$, then from Theorem 12.4.3 f is not differentiable there.

A graph of this function appears in Figure 2. The partial derivatives at the origin exist even though the function is not continuous at the origin because $D_1f(0, 0)$ and $D_2f(0, 0)$ depend only on the behavior of $f(x, y)$ on the x and y axes whereas the continuity of f at $(0, 0)$ depends on the behavior of f on an open disk having its center at the origin. ◀

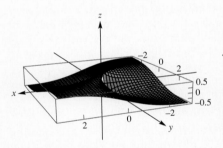

[−2.6, 2.6] by [−2.6, 2.6] by [−0.5, 0.5]

$$f(x, y) = \begin{cases} \dfrac{xy}{x^2 + y^2} & \text{if } (x, y) \neq (0, 0) \\ 0 & \text{if } (x, y) = (0, 0) \end{cases}$$

FIGURE 2

While the mere existence of the partial derivatives of a function of two variables at a point does not guarantee differentiability at that point, there are additional conditions required of the function that provide such a guarantee. These conditions are given in the following theorem, whose proof appears in the supplement of this section.

12.4.4 Theorem

Let f be a function of x and y such that D_1f and D_2f exist on an open disk $B(P_0; r)$, where P_0 is the point (x_0, y_0). Then if D_1f and D_2f are continuous at P_0, f is differentiable at P_0.

This theorem is much easier to apply than Definition 12.4.2 to prove differentiability of a function of two variables. For instance, because the partial derivatives of any polynomial function are also polynomials, and polynomial functions are continuous everywhere, Theorem 12.4.4 tells us that polynomial functions are differentiable everywhere.

▶ **EXAMPLE 2**   Use Theorem 12.4.4 to prove that the function defined by

$$f(x, y) = xe^y - y \ln x$$

is differentiable at all points in its domain.

Solution   The domain of f is the set of all points (x, y) in R^2 for which $x > 0$. We compute the partial derivatives:

$$D_1 f(x, y) = e^y - \frac{y}{x} \qquad D_2 f(x, y) = xe^y - \ln x$$

Because $D_1 f$ and $D_2 f$ are continuous at all points in R^2 for which $x > 0$, then from Theorem 12.4.4, f is differentiable at all points in its domain.   ◀

In Example 5 at the end of this section, we show how Theorem 12.4.4 can be applied to prove that a particular piecewise-defined function is differentiable.

A function satisfying the hypothesis of Theorem 12.4.4 at a point is said to be **continuously differentiable** at the point. Whereas continuous differentiability at a point is a sufficient condition to prove that a function is differentiable at the point, it is not a necessary one. That is, it is possible for a function to be differentiable at a point even if its partial derivatives are not continuous there. An example of such a function appears in Exercises 42 through 45.

The equation in Definition 12.4.2 is

$$\Delta f(x_0, y_0) = D_1 f(x_0, y_0) \, \Delta x + D_2 f(x_0, y_0) \, \Delta y + \epsilon_1 \, \Delta x + \epsilon_2 \, \Delta y \quad (2)$$

The expression involving the first two terms on the right side of this equation is called the *principal part* of $\Delta f(x_0, y_0)$ or the *total differential* of f at (x_0, y_0).

12.4.5 Definition of the Total Differential of a Function of Two Variables

If f is a function of two variables x and y, and f is differentiable at (x, y), then the **total differential** of f is the function df having function values given by

$$df(x, y, \Delta x, \Delta y) = D_1 f(x, y) \, \Delta x + D_2 f(x, y) \, \Delta y$$

Note that df is a function of the four variables x, y, Δx, and Δy. If $z = f(x, y)$, we sometimes use dz in place of $df(x, y, \Delta x, \Delta y)$, and write

$$dz = D_1 f(x, y) \, \Delta x + D_2 f(x, y) \, \Delta y \qquad\qquad (3)$$

If in (3), $f(x, y) = x$, then $z = x$, $D_1 f(x, y) = 1$, and $D_2 f(x, y) = 0$; so (3) gives $dz = \Delta x$. Because $z = x$, for this function $dx = \Delta x$. In a similar fashion, if we take $f(x, y) = y$, then $z = y$, $D_1 f(x, y) = 0$, and $D_2 f(x, y) = 1$; thus (3) gives $dz = \Delta y$. Because $z = y$, then for this function $dy = \Delta y$. Hence we define the differentials of the independent variables as $dx = \Delta x$ and $dy = \Delta y$. Then (3) can be written as

$$dz = D_1 f(x, y) \, dx + D_2 f(x, y) \, dy \qquad (4)$$

and at the point (x_0, y_0),

$$dz = D_1 f(x_0, y_0) \, dx + D_2 f(x_0, y_0) \, dy \qquad (5)$$

In (2) let $\Delta z = \Delta f(x_0, y_0)$, $dx = \Delta x$, and $dy = \Delta y$. Then

$$\Delta z = D_1 f(x_0, y_0) \, dx + D_2 f(x_0, y_0) \, dy + \epsilon_1 \, dx + \epsilon_2 \, dy$$

By comparing this equation and (5), observe that when dx (i.e., Δx) and dy (i.e., Δy) are close to zero, and because then ϵ_1 and ϵ_2 also will be close to zero, dz is an approximation to Δz.

Equation (4) with the notation $\partial z/\partial x$ and $\partial z/\partial y$ becomes

$$dz = \frac{\partial z}{\partial x} \, dx + \frac{\partial z}{\partial y} \, dy \qquad (6)$$

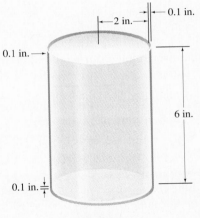

FIGURE 3

▶ **EXAMPLE 3**   A closed metal container in the shape of a right-circular cylinder has an inside height of 6 in., an inside radius of 2 in., and a thickness of 0.1 in. If the cost of the metal is 40 cents per cubic inch, approximate by differentials the total cost of the metal used in the manufacture of the container.

Solution   Figure 3 shows the container. If V cubic inches is the volume of a right-circular cylinder of radius r inches and height h inches, then

$$V = \pi r^2 h$$

The exact volume of metal in the container is the difference between the volumes of two right-circular cylinders for which $r = 2.1$, $h = 6.2$, and $r = 2$, $h = 6$, respectively. The increment ΔV gives the exact volume of metal, but because only an approximate value is wanted, we find dV instead. From (6)

$$dV = \frac{\partial V}{\partial r} \, dr + \frac{\partial V}{\partial h} \, dh$$

$$= 2\pi r h \, dr + \pi r^2 \, dh$$

With $r = 2$, $h = 6$, $dr = 0.1$, and $dh = 0.2$,

$$dV = 2\pi(2)(6)(0.1) + \pi(2)^2 (0.2)$$

$$= 3.2\pi$$

Thus $\Delta V \approx 3.2\pi$, so that the volume of metal in the container is approximately 3.2π in³. Because the cost of the metal is 40 cents per cubic inch, the number of cents in the approximate cost of the metal is, therefore, $128\pi \approx 402$.

Conclusion: The approximate cost of the metal is $4.02. ◀

We now extend the concepts of differentiability and the total differential to functions of n variables.

12.4.6 Definition of an Increment of a Function of n Variables

If f is a function of the n variables $x_1, x_2, \ldots, x_n$, and $\overline{P}$ is the point $(\overline{x}_1, \overline{x}_2, \ldots, \overline{x}_n)$, then the **increment of** f at $\overline{P}$ is given by

$$\Delta f(\overline{P}) = f(\overline{x}_1 + \Delta x_1, \overline{x}_2 + \Delta x_2, \ldots, \overline{x}_n + \Delta x_n) - f(\overline{P})$$

12.4.7 Definition of a Differentiable Function of n Variables

If f is a function of the n variables $x_1, x_2, \ldots, x_n$, and the increment of f at the point $\overline{P}$ can be written as

$$\Delta f(\overline{P}) = D_1 f(\overline{P}) \, \Delta x_1 + D_2 f(\overline{P}) \, \Delta x_2 + \ldots + D_n f(\overline{P}) \, \Delta x_n$$
$$+ \epsilon_1 \, \Delta x_1 + \epsilon_2 \, \Delta x_2 + \ldots + \epsilon_n \, \Delta x_n$$

where $\epsilon_1 \to 0$, $\epsilon_2 \to 0$, $\ldots$, $\epsilon_n \to 0$, as

$$(\Delta x_1, \Delta x_2, \ldots, \Delta x_n) \to (0, 0, \ldots, 0),$$

then f is said to be **differentiable** at $\overline{P}$.

Analogous to Theorem 12.4.4, we can prove that sufficient conditions for a function f of n variables to be differentiable at a point $\overline{P}$ are that $D_1 f$, $D_2 f, \ldots, D_n f$ all exist on an open ball $B(\overline{P}; r)$ and that $D_1 f, D_2 f, \ldots, D_n f$ are all continuous at $\overline{P}$. As was the case for functions of two variables, for functions of n variables differentiability implies continuity. However, the existence of the partial derivatives $D_1 f, D_2 f, \ldots, D_n f$ at a point does not imply differentiability of the function at the point.

12.4.8 Definition of the Total Differential of a Function of n Variables

If f is a function of the n variables $x_1, x_2, \ldots x_n$ and f is differentiable at P, then the **total differential** of f is the function df having function values given by

$$df(P, \Delta x_1, \Delta x_2, \ldots, \Delta x_n)$$
$$= D_1 f(P) \, \Delta x_1 + D_2 f(P) \, \Delta x_2 + \ldots + D_n f(P) \, \Delta x_n$$

Letting $w = f(x_1, x_2, \ldots, x_n)$, defining $dx_1 = \Delta x_1$, $dx_2 = \Delta x_2, \ldots,$ $dx_n = \Delta x_n$, and using the notation $\dfrac{\partial w}{\partial x_i}$ instead of $D_i f(P)$, we can write the equation of Definition 12.4.8 as

$$dw = \frac{\partial w}{\partial x_1} dx_1 + \frac{\partial w}{\partial x_2} dx_2 + \ldots + \frac{\partial w}{\partial x_n} dx_n \tag{7}$$

▶ **EXAMPLE 4**   Measurements of the dimensions of a box are 10 cm, 12 cm, and 15 cm, each correct to 0.02 cm. **(a)** Approximate by differentials the greatest error if the volume of the box is computed from these measurements. **(b)** Approximate the percent error.

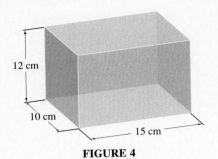

12 cm

10 cm

15 cm

FIGURE 4

Solution   Figure 4 shows the box.

(a) If V cubic centimeters is the volume of the box whose dimensions are x, y, and z centimeters,

$$V = xyz$$

The exact value of the error is found from ΔV; however, we use dV as an approximation to ΔV. From (7) for three independent variables,

$$dV = \frac{\partial V}{\partial x}\, dx + \frac{\partial V}{\partial y}\, dy + \frac{\partial V}{\partial z}\, dz$$

$$= yz\, dx + xz\, dy + xy\, dz$$

From the given facts $|\Delta x| \le 0.02$, $|\Delta y| \le 0.02$, and $|\Delta z| \le 0.02$. To find the greatest error in the volume we take the greatest error in the measurements of the three dimensions. So taking $dx = 0.02$, $dy = 0.02$, $dz = 0.02$, and $x = 10$, $y = 12$, $z = 15$, we have

$$dV = (12)(15)(0.02) + (10)(15)(0.02) + (10)(12)(0.02)$$

$$= 9$$

Thus $\Delta V \approx 9$.

Conclusion: The greatest possible error in the calculation of the volume from the given measurements is approximately 9 cm^3.

(b) The relative error is found by dividing the error by the actual value. Therefore, the relative error in computing the volume from the given measurements is $\Delta V/V \approx dV/V$. Because $dV/V = 9/1800$,

$$\frac{\Delta V}{V} \approx 0.005$$

Conclusion: The approximate percent error is 0.5 percent.   ◄

▶ **EXAMPLE 5**   Given

$$f(x, y) = \begin{cases} \dfrac{x^2 y^2}{x^2 + y^2} & \text{if } (x, y) \ne (0, 0) \\ 0 & \text{if } (x, y) = (0, 0) \end{cases}$$

use Theorem 12.4.4 to prove that f is differentiable at $(0, 0)$.

Solution   To find $D_1 f$, we consider two cases: $(x, y) = (0, 0)$ and $(x, y) \ne (0, 0)$. If $(x, y) = (0, 0)$, we have

$$D_1 f(0, 0) = \lim_{x \to 0} \frac{f(x, 0) - f(0, 0)}{x - 0}$$

$$= \lim_{x \to 0} \frac{0 - 0}{x}$$

$$= 0$$

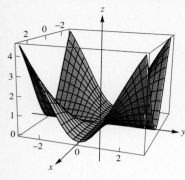

$[-3, 3]$ by $[-3, 3]$ by $[0, 4.3]$

$$f(x, y) = \begin{cases} \dfrac{x^2 y^2}{x^2 + y^2} & \text{if } (x, y) \neq (0, 0) \\ 0 & \text{if } (x, y) = (0, 0) \end{cases}$$

FIGURE 5

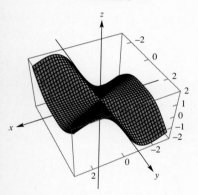

$[-3, 3]$ by $[-3, 3]$ by $[-2, 2]$

$$D_1 f(x, y) = \begin{cases} \dfrac{2xy^4}{(x^2 + y^2)^2} & \text{if } (x, y) \neq (0, 0) \\ 0 & \text{if } (x, y) = (0, 0) \end{cases}$$

FIGURE 6

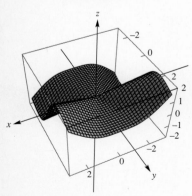

$[-3, 3]$ by $[-3, 3]$ by $[-2, 2]$

$$D_2 f(x, y) = \begin{cases} \dfrac{2x^4 y}{(x^2 + y^2)^2} & \text{if } (x, y) \neq (0, 0) \\ 0 & \text{if } (x, y) = (0, 0) \end{cases}$$

FIGURE 7

If $(x, y) \neq (0, 0)$, $f(x, y) = x^2 y^2 / (x^2 + y^2)$. To find $D_1 f(x, y)$ we use the theorem for the ordinary derivative of a quotient and consider y as a constant.

$$D_1 f(x, y) = \frac{2xy^2(x^2 + y^2) - 2x(x^2 y^2)}{(x^2 + y^2)^2}$$

$$= \frac{2xy^4}{(x^2 + y^2)^2}$$

The function $D_1 f$ is therefore defined by

$$D_1 f(x, y) = \begin{cases} \dfrac{2xy^4}{(x^2 + y^2)^2} & \text{if } (x, y) \neq (0, 0) \\ 0 & \text{if } (x, y) = (0, 0) \end{cases}$$

In the same manner we obtain the function $D_2 f$ defined by

$$D_2 f(x, y) = \begin{cases} \dfrac{2x^4 y}{(x^2 + y^2)^2} & \text{if } (x, y) \neq (0, 0) \\ 0 & \text{if } (x, y) = (0, 0) \end{cases}$$

Both $D_1 f$ and $D_2 f$ exist on every open disk having its center at the origin. It remains to show that $D_1 f$ and $D_2 f$ are continuous at $(0, 0)$.

Because $D_1 f(0, 0) = 0$, $D_1 f$ will be continuous at $(0, 0)$ if

$$\lim_{(x,y)\to(0,0)} D_1 f(x, y) = 0$$

Therefore we must show that for any $\epsilon > 0$ there exists a $\delta > 0$ such that

$$\text{if} \quad 0 < \sqrt{x^2 + y^2} < \delta \quad \text{then} \quad \left| \frac{2xy^4}{(x^2 + y^2)^2} \right| < \epsilon \qquad (8)$$

$$\left| \frac{2xy^4}{(x^2 + y^2)^2} \right| = \frac{2|x| y^4}{(x^2 + y^2)^2}$$

$$\leq \frac{2\sqrt{x^2 + y^2}\, (\sqrt{x^2 + y^2})^4}{(x^2 + y^2)^2}$$

$$= 2\sqrt{x^2 + y^2}$$

Thus a suitable choice for δ is $2\delta = \epsilon$, that is, $\delta = \frac{1}{2}\epsilon$. With this δ we have the following argument:

$$0 < \sqrt{x^2 + y^2} < \delta \quad \text{and} \quad \delta = \tfrac{1}{2}\epsilon$$

$$\Rightarrow \qquad 2\sqrt{x^2 + y^2} < 2(\tfrac{1}{2}\epsilon)$$

$$\Rightarrow \quad \frac{2\sqrt{x^2 + y^2}\, (\sqrt{x^2 + y^2})^4}{(x^2 + y^2)^2} < \epsilon$$

$$\Rightarrow \qquad \frac{2|x| y^4}{(x^2 + y^2)^2} < \epsilon$$

$$\Rightarrow \qquad \left| \frac{2xy^4}{(x^2 + y^2)^2} \right| < \epsilon$$

We have therefore shown that (8) holds. Hence $D_1 f$ is continuous at $(0, 0)$. In the same way we can show that $D_2 f$ is continuous at $(0, 0)$. Hence from Theorem 12.4.4, f is differentiable at $(0, 0)$.

Figures 5, 6, and 7 show computer-generated graphs of f, $D_1 f$ and $D_2 f$, which support the results of this example. ◀

EXERCISES 12.4

1. If $f(x, y) = 3x^2 + 2xy - y^2$, find:
(a) $\Delta f(1, 4)$, the increment of f at $(1, 4)$;
(b) $\Delta f(1, 4)$ when $\Delta x = 0.03$ and $\Delta y = -0.02$;
(c) $df(1, 4, \Delta x, \Delta y)$, the total differential of f at $(1, 4)$;
(d) $df(1, 4. 0.03, -0.02)$.

2. If $f(x, y) = 2x^2 + 5xy + 4y^2$, find:
(a) $\Delta f(2, -1)$, the increment of f at $(2, -1)$;
(b) $\Delta f(2, -1)$ when $\Delta x = -0.01$ and $\Delta y = 0.02$;
(c) $df(2, -1, \Delta x, \Delta y)$, the total differential of f at $(2, -1)$; (d) $df(2, -1, -0.01, 0.02)$.

3. If $g(x, y) = xye^{xy}$, find:
(a) $\Delta g(2, -4)$, the increment of g at $(2, -4)$;
(b) $\Delta g(2, -4)$ when $\Delta x = -0.1$ and $\Delta y = 0.2$;
(c) $dg(2, -4, \Delta x, \Delta y)$, the total differential of g at $(2, -4)$; (d) $dg(2, -4, -0.1, 0.2)$.

4. If $h(x, y) = (x + y)/(x - y)$, find:
(a) $\Delta h(3, 0)$, the increment of h at $(3, 0)$; (b) $\Delta h(3, 0)$ when $\Delta x = 0.04$ and $\Delta y = 0.03$;
(c) $dh(3, 0, \Delta x, \Delta y)$, the total differential of h at $(3, 0)$;
(d) $dh(3, 0, 0.04, 0.03)$.

5. If $F(x, y, z) = xy + \ln(yz)$, find:
(a) $\Delta F(4, 1, 5)$, the increment of F at $(4, 1, 5)$;
(b) $\Delta F(4, 1, 5)$ when $\Delta x = 0.02$, $\Delta y = 0.04$, and $\Delta z = -0.03$; (c) $dF(4, 1, 5, \Delta x, \Delta y, \Delta z)$, the total differential of F at $(4, 1, 5)$;
(d) $dF(4, 1, 5, 0.02, 0.04, -0.03)$.

6. If $G(x, y, z) = x^2y + 2xyz - z^3$, find:
(a) $\Delta G(-3, 0, 2)$, the increment of G at $(-3, 0, 2)$;
(b) $\Delta G(-3, 0, 2)$ when $\Delta x = 0.01$, $\Delta y = 0.03$, $\Delta z = -0.01$; (c) $dG(-3, 0, 2, \Delta x, \Delta y, \Delta z)$, the total differential of G at $(-3, 0, 2)$;
(d) $dG(-3, 0, 2, 0.01, 0.03, -0.01)$.

In Exercises 7 through 14, find the total differential dw.

7. $w = 4x^3 - xy^2 + 3y - 7$

8. $w = y \tan x^2 - 2xy$

9. $w = x \cos y - y \sin x$ **10.** $w = xe^{2y} + e^{-y}$

11. $w = \ln(x^2 + y^2 + z^2)$ **12.** $w = \dfrac{xyz}{x + y + z}$

13. $w = x \tan^{-1} z - \dfrac{y^2}{z}$ **14.** $w = e^{yz} - \cos xz$

In Exercises 15 through 18, prove that f is differentiable at all points in its domain by doing each of the following: (a) Find $\Delta f(x_0, y_0)$; (b) find an ϵ_1 and an ϵ_2 so that Equation (2) holds; (c) show that the ϵ_1 and ϵ_2 found in part (b) both approach zero as $(\Delta x, \Delta y) \to (0, 0)$.

15. $f(x, y) = x^2y - 2xy$ **16.** $f(x, y) = 2x^2 + 3y^2$

17. $f(x, y) = \dfrac{x^2}{y}$ **18.** $f(x, y) = \dfrac{y}{x}$

In Exercises 19 through 26, use Theorem 12.4.4 to prove that the function is differentiable at all points in its domain.

19. $g(x, y) = 2x^4 - 3x^2y^2 + x^{-2}y^{-2}$

20. $f(x, y) = \dfrac{3x - 4y}{x^2 + 8y}$

21. $f(x, y) = 3 \ln xy + 5 \sin x$

22. $f(x, y) = \sin \dfrac{y}{x} + \cos \dfrac{x}{y}$

23. $h(x, y) = \tan^{-1}(x + y) + \dfrac{1}{x - y}$

24. $g(x, y) = y \ln x - \dfrac{x}{y}$

25. $f(x, y) = ye^{3x} - xe^{-3y}$

26. $f(x, y) = e^{2x} \sin y + e^{-2x} \cos y$

27. Given $f(x, y) = \begin{cases} x + y - 2 & \text{if } x = 1 \text{ or } y = 1 \\ 2 & \text{if } x \neq 1 \text{ and } y \neq 1 \end{cases}$
Prove that $D_1f(1, 1)$ and $D_2f(1, 1)$ exist but f is not differentiable at $(1, 1)$.

28. Given $f(x, y) = \begin{cases} \dfrac{3x^2y}{x^2 + y^2} & \text{if } (x, y) \neq (0, 0) \\ 0 & \text{if } (x, y) = (0, 0) \end{cases}$
Prove that $D_1f(0, 0)$ and $D_2f(0, 0)$ exist but D_1f and D_2f are not continuous at $(0, 0)$.

In Exercises 29 and 30, prove that $D_1f(0, 0)$ and $D_2f(0, 0)$ exist but f is not differentiable at $(0, 0)$.

29. $f(x, y) = \begin{cases} \dfrac{2x^2y^2}{x^4 + y^4} & \text{if } (x, y) \neq (0, 0) \\ 0 & \text{if } (x, y) = (0, 0) \end{cases}$

30. $f(x, y) = \begin{cases} \dfrac{xy^2}{x^2 + y^4} & \text{if } (x, y) \neq (0, 0) \\ 0 & \text{if } (x, y) = (0, 0) \end{cases}$

In Exercises 31 and 32, prove that f is differentiable at all points in R^3 by doing each of the following: (a) Find $\Delta f(x_0, y_0, z_0)$; (b) find an ϵ_1, ϵ_2, and ϵ_3 such that the equation of Definition 12.4.7 holds; (c) show that the ϵ_1, ϵ_2, and ϵ_3 found in (b) all approach zero as $(\Delta x, \Delta y, \Delta z)$ approaches $(0, 0, 0)$.

31. $f(x, y, z) = xy - xz + z^2$

32. $f(x, y, z) = 2x^2z - 3yz^2$

In Exercises 33 and 34, prove that $D_1 f(0, 0, 0)$, $D_2 f(0, 0, 0)$, and $D_3 f(0, 0, 0)$ exist but that f is not differentiable at (0, 0, 0).

33. $f(x, y, z) = \begin{cases} \dfrac{xy^2z}{x^4 + y^4 + z^4} & \text{if } (x, y, z) \neq (0, 0, 0) \\ 0 & \text{if } (x, y, z) = (0, 0, 0) \end{cases}$

34. $f(x, y, z) = \begin{cases} \dfrac{3yz}{x^4 + y^2 + z^2} & \text{if } (x, y, z) \neq (0, 0, 0) \\ 0 & \text{if } (x, y, z) = (0, 0, 0) \end{cases}$

35. A closed container in the shape of a rectangular solid is to have an inside length of 8 m, an inside width of 5 m, an inside height of 4 m, and a thickness of 4 cm. Use differentials to approximate the amount of material needed to construct the container.

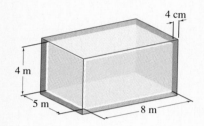

36. Use the total differential to find approximately the greatest error in calculating the area of a right triangle from the lengths of the legs if they are measured to be 6 cm and 8 cm, respectively, with a possible error of 0.1 cm for each measurement. Also find the approximate percent error.

37. Find approximately, by using the total differential, the greatest error in calculating the length of the hypotenuse of the right triangle from the measurements of Exercise 36. Also find the approximate percent error.

38. If the ideal gas law (see Example 6, Section 12.3) is used to find P when T and V are given, but there is an error of 0.3 percent in measuring T and an error of 0.8 percent in measuring V, find approximately the greatest percent error in P.

39. The specific gravity s of an object is given by the formula

$$s = \frac{A}{A - W}$$

where A pounds is the weight of the object in air and W pounds is the weight of the object in water. If the weight of an object in air is read as 20 lb with a pos-

sible error of 0.01 lb and its weight in water is read as 12 lb with a possible error of 0.02 lb, find approximately the largest possible error in calculating s from these measurements. Also find the largest possible relative error.

40. A wooden box is to be made of lumber that is $\frac{2}{3}$ in. thick. The inside length is to be 6 ft, the inside width is to be 3 ft, the inside depth is to be 4 ft, and the box is to have no top. Use the total differential to find the approximate amount of lumber to be used in the box.

41. A company has contracted to manufacture 10,000 closed wooden crates having dimensions 3 m, 4 m, and 5 m. The cost of the wood to be used is $3 per square meter. If the machines that are used to cut the pieces of wood have a possible error of 0.5 cm in each dimension, find approximately, by using the total differential, the greatest possible error in the estimate of the cost of the wood.

Exercises 42 through 45 show that a function may be differentiable at a point even though it is not continuously differentiable there. Hence the conditions of Theorem 12.4.4 are sufficient but not necessary for differentiability. The function f in these exercises is defined by

$$f(x, y) = \begin{cases} (x^2 + y^2) \sin \dfrac{1}{\sqrt{x^2 + y^2}} & \text{if } (x, y) \neq (0, 0) \\ 0 & \text{if } (x, y) = (0, 0) \end{cases}$$

42. Find $\Delta f(0, 0)$.

43. Find $D_1 f(x, y)$ and $D_2 f(x, y)$.

44. Prove that f is differentiable at (0, 0) by using Definition 12.4.2 and the results of Exercises 42 and 43.

45. Prove that $D_1 f$ and $D_2 f$ are not continuous at (0, 0).

46. Given

$$f(x, y) = \begin{cases} \dfrac{xy(x^2 - y^2)}{x^2 + y^2} & \text{if } (x, y) \neq (0, 0) \\ 0 & \text{if } (x, y) = (0, 0) \end{cases}$$

The graph of this function appears in Figure 4 in Section 12.3. Prove that f is differentiable at (0, 0) by using Theorem 12.4.4.

47. Given

$$f(x, y, z) = \begin{cases} \dfrac{xyz^2}{x^2 + y^2 + z^2} & \text{if } (x, y, z) \neq (0, 0, 0) \\ 0 & \text{if } (x, y, z) = (0, 0, 0) \end{cases}$$

Prove that f is differentiable at (0, 0, 0).

12.5 THE CHAIN RULE FOR FUNCTIONS OF MORE THAN ONE VARIABLE

Recall that with Leibniz notation the chain rule for a function of a single variable is as follows: If y is a function of u and $\dfrac{dy}{du}$ exists, and u is a function of x and $\dfrac{du}{dx}$ exists, then y is a function of x and $\dfrac{dy}{dx}$ exists and is given by

$$\frac{dy}{dx} = \frac{dy}{du} \cdot \frac{du}{dx}$$

We now consider the chain rule for a function of two variables, where each of these variables is also a function of two variables.

12.5.1 Theorem   The Chain Rule

If u is a differentiable function of x and y, defined by $u = f(x, y)$, where $x = F(r, s)$, $y = G(r, s)$, and $\dfrac{\partial x}{\partial r}, \dfrac{\partial x}{\partial s}, \dfrac{\partial y}{\partial r}$, and $\dfrac{\partial y}{\partial s}$ all exist, then u is a function of r and s and

$$\frac{\partial u}{\partial r} = \frac{\partial u}{\partial x}\frac{\partial x}{\partial r} + \frac{\partial u}{\partial y}\frac{\partial y}{\partial r}$$

$$\frac{\partial u}{\partial s} = \frac{\partial u}{\partial x}\frac{\partial x}{\partial s} + \frac{\partial u}{\partial y}\frac{\partial y}{\partial s}$$

We defer the proof of this theorem to the end of the section so that first you can become familiar with the statement of the chain rule through illustrations and examples.

The chain rule for functions of a single variable is easily remembered by thinking of an ordinary derivative as the quotient of two differentials, but there is no similar interpretation for partial derivatives. A convenient mnemonic device for remembering the chain rule consists of a tree diagram with branches from one variable to another as shown in Figure 1. Because u is a function of x and y, place u at the top of the tree and draw branches to x and y. Then since x is a function of r and s, draw branches from x to r and s. In a similar fashion draw branches from y to r and s. Note that each variable depends on the variables below it. Along the sides of the branches write the partial derivative corresponding to the specific variables.

To obtain the equation for $\partial u/\partial r$, consider the paths along the branches from u to r. There are two such paths with each path consisting of a pair of branches. Add the products of the partial derivatives associated with the branches of each path, so that

$$\frac{\partial u}{\partial r} = \frac{\partial u}{\partial x}\frac{\partial x}{\partial r} + \frac{\partial u}{\partial y}\frac{\partial y}{\partial r}$$

which is the first equation of Theorem 12.5.1. The second equation of the theorem can be obtained the same way by considering the two paths along the branches from u to s.

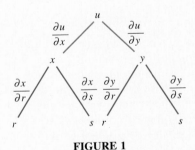

FIGURE 1

▶ **EXAMPLE 1**   Given

$$u = x^2 + y^3 \qquad x = re^s \qquad y = re^{-s}$$

Apply the chain rule to find $\dfrac{\partial u}{\partial r}$ and $\dfrac{\partial u}{\partial s}$.

Solution

$$\frac{\partial u}{\partial r} = \frac{\partial u}{\partial x}\frac{\partial x}{\partial r} + \frac{\partial u}{\partial y}\frac{\partial y}{\partial r} \qquad\qquad \frac{\partial u}{\partial s} = \frac{\partial u}{\partial x}\frac{\partial x}{\partial s} + \frac{\partial u}{\partial y}\frac{\partial y}{\partial s}$$

$$= 2x(e^s) + 3y^2(e^{-s}) \qquad\qquad = 2x(re^s) + 3y^2(-re^{-s})$$

$$= 2(re^s)(e^s) + 3(re^{-s})^2(e^{-s}) \qquad = 2(re^s)(re^s) + 3(re^{-s})^2(-re^{-s})$$

$$= 2re^{2s} + 3r^2e^{-3s} \qquad\qquad = 2r^2e^{2s} - 3r^3e^{-3s} \qquad ◀$$

A particular notational problem arises when considering u as a function of x and y and then as a function of r and s. If $u = f(x, y)$, $x = F(r, s)$, and $y = G(r, s)$, then $u = f(F(r, s), G(r, s))$. Note that $u \neq f(r, s)$.

▷ **ILLUSTRATION 1**   In Example 1

$$u = f(x, y) \qquad x = F(r, s) \qquad y = G(r, s)$$
$$= x^2 + y^3 \qquad\quad = re^s \qquad\qquad = re^{-s}$$

Thus

$$u = f(F(r, s), G(r, s)) \qquad \text{and} \qquad f(r, s) = r^2 + s^3$$
$$= r^2e^{2s} + r^3e^{-3s}$$

That is, $u \neq f(r, s)$.   ◀

The purpose of Example 1 is to demonstrate the application of the chain rule. We could have obtained the partial derivatives in a simpler fashion by substituting the expressions for x and y into the expression for u before differentiating as shown in the following illustration.

▷ **ILLUSTRATION 2**   From Example 1, as shown in Illustration 2, $u = r^2e^{2s} + r^3e^{-3s}$. Computing the partial derivatives from this expression, we have

$$\frac{\partial u}{\partial r} = 2re^{2s} + 3r^2e^{-3s} \qquad \frac{\partial u}{\partial s} = r^2(2e^{2s}) + r^3(-3e^{-3s})$$

$$= 2r^2e^{2s} - 3r^3e^{-3s}$$

which agree with the results in Example 1.   ◀

Now suppose that u is a differentiable function of the two variables x and y, and both x and y are differentiable functions of the single variable t.

Then u is also a function of the single variable t. So the formula for the chain rule, with ordinary derivatives instead of partial derivatives, becomes

$$\frac{du}{dt} = \frac{\partial u}{\partial x}\frac{dx}{dt} + \frac{\partial u}{\partial y}\frac{dy}{dt}$$

The ordinary derivative du/dt given by this formula is called the **total derivative** of u with respect to t.

▶ **EXAMPLE 2**   Given

$$y = 2wz + z^2 \qquad w = e^x \qquad z = \cos x$$

Find the total derivative $\dfrac{dy}{dx}$ by applying the chain rule.

Solution   From the chain rule, using the tree diagram in Figure 2,

$$\begin{aligned}
\frac{dy}{dx} &= \frac{\partial y}{\partial w}\frac{dw}{dx} + \frac{\partial y}{\partial z}\frac{dz}{dx} \\
&= 2z(e^x) + (2w + 2z)(-\sin x) \\
&= 2(\cos x)(e^x) + (2e^x + 2\cos x)(-\sin x) \\
&= 2e^x \cos x - 2e^x \sin x - 2\sin x \cos x
\end{aligned}$$

◀

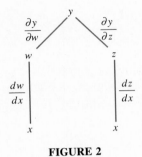

FIGURE 2

In the statement of Theorem 12.5.1, u is the dependent variable, r and s are the independent variables, and x and y are called the **intermediate variables.** We now extend the chain rule to n intermediate variables and m independent variables.

12.5.2 Theorem   The General Chain Rule

Suppose that u is a differentiable function of the n variables $x_1, x_2, \ldots, x_n$, and each of these variables is in turn a function of the m variables $y_1, y_2, \ldots, y_m$. Suppose further that each of the partial derivatives $\dfrac{\partial x_i}{\partial y_j}$ $(i = 1, 2, \ldots, n; j = 1, 2, \ldots, m)$ exists. Then u is a function of $y_1, y_2, \ldots, y_m$, and

$$\frac{\partial u}{\partial y_1} = \frac{\partial u}{\partial x_1}\frac{\partial x_1}{\partial y_1} + \frac{\partial u}{\partial x_2}\frac{\partial x_2}{\partial y_1} + \ldots + \frac{\partial u}{\partial x_n}\frac{\partial x_n}{\partial y_1}$$

$$\frac{\partial u}{\partial y_2} = \frac{\partial u}{\partial x_1}\frac{\partial x_1}{\partial y_2} + \frac{\partial u}{\partial x_2}\frac{\partial x_2}{\partial y_2} + \ldots + \frac{\partial u}{\partial x_n}\frac{\partial x_n}{\partial y_2}$$

$$\vdots$$

$$\frac{\partial u}{\partial y_m} = \frac{\partial u}{\partial x_1}\frac{\partial x_1}{\partial y_m} + \frac{\partial u}{\partial x_2}\frac{\partial x_2}{\partial y_m} + \ldots + \frac{\partial u}{\partial x_n}\frac{\partial x_n}{\partial y_m}$$

The proof is an extension of the proof of Theorem 12.5.1.

Observe that in the general chain rule there are as many terms on the right side of each equation as there are intermediate variables.

If u is a differentiable function of the n variables $x_1, x_2, \ldots, x_n$ and each x_i is a differentiable function of the single variable t, then u is a function of t and the total derivative of u with respect to t is given by

$$\frac{du}{dt} = \frac{\partial u}{\partial x_1}\frac{dx_1}{dt} + \frac{\partial u}{\partial x_2}\frac{dx_2}{dt} + \ldots + \frac{\partial u}{\partial x_n}\frac{dx_n}{dt}$$

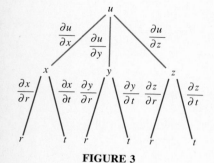

FIGURE 3

EXAMPLE 3 Given

$$u = x^2 + yz \qquad x = r\sin t \qquad y = r\cos t \qquad z = r\sin^2 t$$

Find $\frac{\partial u}{\partial r}$ and $\frac{\partial u}{\partial t}$ by applying the chain rule.

Solution From the chain rule, using the tree diagram in Figure 3,

$$\begin{aligned}
\frac{\partial u}{\partial r} &= \frac{\partial u}{\partial x}\frac{\partial x}{\partial r} + \frac{\partial u}{\partial y}\frac{\partial y}{\partial r} + \frac{\partial u}{\partial z}\frac{\partial z}{\partial r}\\
&= 2x(\sin t) + z(\cos t) + y(\sin^2 t)\\
&= 2(r\sin t)(\sin t) + (r\sin^2 t)(\cos t) + (r\cos t)(\sin^2 t)\\
&= 2r\sin^2 t + r\sin^2 t\cos t + r\sin^2 t\cos t\\
&= 2r\sin^2 t + 2r\sin^2 t\cos t\\
&= 2r\sin^2 t(1 + \cos t)
\end{aligned}$$

$$\begin{aligned}
\frac{\partial u}{\partial t} &= \frac{\partial u}{\partial x}\frac{\partial x}{\partial t} + \frac{\partial u}{\partial y}\frac{\partial y}{\partial t} + \frac{\partial u}{\partial z}\frac{\partial z}{\partial t}\\
&= 2x(r\cos t) + z(-r\sin t) + y(2r\sin t\cos t)\\
&= 2(r\sin t)(r\cos t) + (r\sin^2 t)(-r\sin t) + (r\cos t)(2r\sin t\cos t)\\
&= 2r^2\sin t\cos t - r^2\sin^3 t + 2r^2\sin t\cos^2 t\\
&= r^2\sin t(2\cos t + 2\cos^2 t - \sin^2 t)
\end{aligned}$$

◀

FIGURE 4

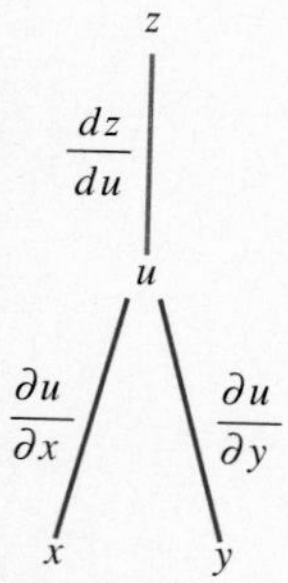

EXAMPLE 4 If f is a differentiable function and a and b are constants, show that $z = f(\frac{1}{2}bx^2 - \frac{1}{3}ay^3)$ satisfies the partial differential equation

$$ay^2\frac{\partial z}{\partial x} + bx\frac{\partial z}{\partial y} = 0$$

Solution Let $u = \frac{1}{2}bx^2 - \frac{1}{3}ay^3$. We wish to show that $z = f(u)$ satisfies the given equation. From the chain rule, using the tree diagram in Figure 4,

$$\begin{aligned}
\frac{\partial z}{\partial x} &= \frac{dz}{du}\frac{\partial u}{\partial x} & \qquad \frac{\partial z}{\partial y} &= \frac{dz}{du}\frac{\partial u}{\partial y}\\
&= f'(u)(bx) & &= f'(u)(-ay^2)
\end{aligned}$$

Therefore

$$\begin{aligned}
ay^2\frac{\partial z}{\partial x} + bx\frac{\partial z}{\partial y} &= ay^2[f'(u)(bx)] + bx[f'(u)(-ay^2)]\\
&= 0
\end{aligned}$$

which we wished to prove.

◀

In the following example we apply the chain rule in an application involving related rates.

▶ **EXAMPLE 5**   Use the ideal gas law (see Example 6, Section 12.3) with $k = 0.8$ to find the rate at which the temperature is changing at the instant when the volume of the gas is 15 liters and the gas is under a pressure of 12 atm if the volume is increasing at the rate of 0.1 liter/min and the pressure is decreasing at the rate of 0.2 atm/min.

Solution   Let t minutes be the time that has elapsed since the volume of the gas started to increase. At t minutes let the Kelvin temperature be T degrees, the pressure be P atmospheres, and the volume be V liters. From the ideal gas law

$$PV = 0.8T$$
$$T = 1.25\,PV$$

At the given instant, $P = 12$, $V = 15$, $\dfrac{dP}{dt} = -0.2$, and $\dfrac{dV}{dt} = 0.1$. From the chain rule

$$\frac{dT}{dt} = \frac{\partial T}{\partial P}\frac{dP}{dt} + \frac{\partial T}{\partial V}\frac{dV}{dt}$$
$$= 1.25V\frac{dP}{dt} + 1.25P\frac{dV}{dt}$$
$$= 1.25(15)(-0.2) + 1.25(12)(0.1)$$
$$= -2.25$$

Conclusion: The temperature is decreasing at the rate of 2.25° K/min. at the given instant.   ◄

We now apply the chain rule to prove a theorem that gives a formula for computing the derivative of a function defined implicitly.

12.5.3 Theorem

If f is a differentiable function of the single variable x such that $y = f(x)$, and f is defined implicitly by the equation $F(x, y) = 0$, then if F is differentiable and $F_y(x, y) \neq 0$

$$\frac{dy}{dx} = -\frac{F_x(x, y)}{F_y(x, y)}$$

Proof   Let

$$w = F(x, y) \qquad \text{where} \qquad y = f(x)$$

From the chain rule

$$\frac{dw}{dx} = F_x(x, y)\frac{dx}{dx} + F_y(x, y)\frac{dy}{dx} \tag{1}$$

Because $w = F(x, f(x))$ for all x in the domain of f and by hypothesis $F(x, f(x)) = 0$, then $dw/dx = 0$. Furthermore, $dx/dx = 1$. Therefore, from (1)

$$0 = F_x(x, y)(1) + F_y(x, y)\frac{dy}{dx}$$

Because $F_y(x, y) \neq 0$, we solve this equation for dy/dx and obtain

$$\frac{dy}{dx} = -\frac{F_x(x, y)}{F_y(x, y)}$$

■

▶ **EXAMPLE 6**   Find dy/dx if

$$x \cos y + y \cos x - 1 = 0$$

Solution   Let $F(x, y) = x \cos y + y \cos x - 1$. Then

$$F_x(x, y) = \cos y - y \sin x \qquad F_y(x, y) = -x \sin y + \cos x$$

From Theorem 12.5.3

$$\frac{dy}{dx} = -\frac{\cos y - y \sin x}{-x \sin y + \cos x}$$

$$= \frac{y \sin x - \cos y}{\cos x - x \sin y}$$

◀

Compare the solution of the above example with that of Example 4 in Section 2.9 where we obtained the same expression for dy/dx by implicit differentiation.

Consider now an equation in three variables x, y, and z and assume that the equation defines z implicitly as one or more differentiable functions of x and y. By the following theorem, analogous to Theorem 12.5.3, we can compute $\partial z/\partial x$ and $\partial z/\partial y$ without solving the equation for z.

12.5.4 Theorem

If f is a differentiable function of x and y such that $z = f(x, y)$ and f is defined implicitly by the equation $F(x, y, z) = 0$, then if F is differentiable and $F_z(x, y, z) \neq 0$

$$\frac{\partial z}{\partial x} = -\frac{F_x(x, y, z)}{F_z(x, y, z)} \qquad \text{and} \qquad \frac{\partial z}{\partial y} = -\frac{F_y(x, y, z)}{F_z(x, y, z)}$$

Proof   Let

$$w = F(x, y, z) \qquad \text{where} \qquad z = f(x, y)$$

From the chain rule,

$$\frac{\partial w}{\partial x} = F_x(x, y, z)\frac{\partial x}{\partial x} + F_y(x, y, z)\frac{\partial y}{\partial x} + F_z(x, y, z)\frac{\partial z}{\partial x} \tag{2}$$

Because $w = F(x, y, f(x, y))$ for all points (x, y) in the domain of F, and by hypothesis, $F(x, y, f(x, y)) = 0$, then $\partial w/\partial x = 0$. Because y is constant when computing the partial derivative with respect to x, $\partial y/\partial x = 0$. Furthermore, $\partial x/\partial x = 1$. Therefore, from (2)

$$0 = F_x(x, y, z)(1) + F_y(x, y, z)(0) + F_z(x, y, z)\frac{\partial z}{\partial x}$$

Because $F_z(x, y, z) \neq 0$, we solve this equation for $\partial z/\partial x$ and obtain

$$\frac{\partial z}{\partial x} = -\frac{F_x(x, y, z)}{F_z(x, y, z)}$$

The formula for $\partial z/\partial y$ is obtained in the same manner by computing $\partial w/\partial y$ by the chain rule. ∎

▶ **EXAMPLE 7**   Find $\partial z/\partial x$ and $\partial z/\partial y$ if

$$4z^3 + 3xz^2 - xyz - 2xy^2 + 7 = 0$$

Solution   Let $F(x, y, z) = 4z^3 + 3xz^2 - xyz - 2xy^2 + 7 = 0$. Then

$$F_x(x, y, z) = 3z^2 - yz - 2y^2 \qquad F_y(x, y, z) = -xz - 4xy$$
$$F_z(x, y, z) = 12z^2 + 6xz - xy$$

From Theorem 12.5.4,

$$\frac{\partial z}{\partial x} = -\frac{3z^2 - yz - 2y}{12z^2 + 6xz - xy} \quad \text{and} \quad \frac{\partial z}{\partial y} = -\frac{-xz - 4xy}{12z^2 + 6xz - xy} \qquad ◀$$

We conclude this section with the proof of the chain rule as stated in Theorem 12.5.1.

Proof of Theorem 12.5.1.   We prove the theorem for $\partial u/\partial r$. The proof for $\partial u/\partial s$ is similar.

If s is held fixed and r is changed by an amount Δr, then x is changed by an amount Δx and y is changed by an amount Δy. Thus

$$\Delta x = F(r + \Delta r, s) - F(r, s) \tag{3}$$

and

$$\Delta y = G(r + \Delta r, s) - G(r, s) \tag{4}$$

Because f is differentiable,

$$\Delta f(x, y) = D_1 f(x, y)\, \Delta x + D_2 f(x, y)\, \Delta y + \epsilon_1\, \Delta x + \epsilon_2\, \Delta y \tag{5}$$

where ϵ_1 and ϵ_2 both approach zero as $(\Delta x, \Delta y)$ approaches $(0, 0)$. Furthermore, we require that $\epsilon_1 = 0$ and $\epsilon_2 = 0$ when $(\Delta x, \Delta y) = (0, 0)$. We make this requirement so that ϵ_1 and ϵ_2, which are functions of Δx and Δy, will be continuous at $(\Delta x, \Delta y) = (0, 0)$.

If in (5) we replace $\Delta f(x, y)$ by Δu, $D_1 f(x, y)$ by $\dfrac{\partial u}{\partial x}$, and $D_2 f(x, y)$ by $\dfrac{\partial u}{\partial y}$ and divide on both sides by Δr ($\Delta r \neq 0$), we obtain

$$\frac{\Delta u}{\Delta r} = \frac{\partial u}{\partial x}\frac{\Delta x}{\Delta r} + \frac{\partial u}{\partial y}\frac{\Delta y}{\Delta r} + \epsilon_1\frac{\Delta x}{\Delta r} + \epsilon_2\frac{\Delta y}{\Delta r}$$

Taking the limit on both sides of the above as Δr approaches zero we get

$$\lim_{\Delta r \to 0} \frac{\Delta u}{\Delta r} = \frac{\partial u}{\partial x} \lim_{\Delta r \to 0} \frac{\Delta x}{\Delta r} + \frac{\partial u}{\partial y} \lim_{\Delta r \to 0} \frac{\Delta y}{\Delta r} + \left(\lim_{\Delta r \to 0} \epsilon_1\right)\lim_{\Delta r \to 0} \frac{\Delta x}{\Delta r} + \left(\lim_{\Delta r \to 0} \epsilon_2\right) \lim_{\Delta r \to 0} \frac{\Delta y}{\Delta r} \quad (6)$$

Because u is a function of x and y and both x and y are functions of r and s, u is a function of r and s. Because s is held fixed and r is changed by an amount Δr,

$$\lim_{\Delta r \to 0} \frac{\Delta u}{\Delta r} = \lim_{\Delta r \to 0} \frac{u(r + \Delta r, s) - u(r, s)}{\Delta r}$$

$$= \frac{\partial u}{\partial r} \quad (7)$$

Also

$$\lim_{\Delta r \to 0} \frac{\Delta x}{\Delta r} = \frac{\partial x}{\partial r} \quad \text{and} \quad \lim_{\Delta r \to 0} \frac{\Delta y}{\Delta r} = \frac{\partial y}{\partial r} \quad (8)$$

Because $\dfrac{\partial x}{\partial r}$ and $\dfrac{\partial y}{\partial r}$ exist, F and G are each continuous with respect to the variable r. (*Note:* The existence of the partial derivatives of a function does not imply continuity with respect to all of the variables simultaneously, as we saw in the preceding section, but as with functions of a single variable it does imply continuity of the function with respect to each variable separately.) Hence, from (3),

$$\lim_{\Delta r \to 0} \Delta x = \lim_{\Delta r \to 0} [F(r + \Delta r, s) - F(r, s)]$$

$$= F(r, s) - F(r, s)$$

$$= 0$$

and from (4),

$$\lim_{\Delta r \to 0} \Delta y = \lim_{\Delta r \to 0} [G(r + \Delta r, s) - G(r, s)]$$

$$= G(r, s) - G(r, s)$$

$$= 0$$

Therefore, as Δr approaches zero, both Δx and Δy approach zero. And because both ϵ_1 and ϵ_2 approach zero as $(\Delta x, \Delta y)$ approaches $(0, 0)$, we can conclude that

$$\lim_{\Delta r \to 0} \epsilon_1 = 0 \quad \text{and} \quad \lim_{\Delta r \to 0} \epsilon_2 = 0 \quad (9)$$

Now, it is possible that for certain values of Δr, $\Delta x = 0$ and $\Delta y = 0$. Because we required in such a case that $\epsilon_1 = 0$ and $\epsilon_2 = 0$, the limits in (9) are still zero. Substituting from (7), (8), and (9) into (6) we obtain

$$\frac{\partial u}{\partial r} = \frac{\partial u}{\partial x} \frac{\partial x}{\partial r} + \frac{\partial u}{\partial y} \frac{\partial y}{\partial r}$$

which we wished to prove. ∎

EXERCISES 12.5

In Exercises 1 through 6, find the indicated partial derivative by two methods: (a) Use the chain rule; (b) make the substitutions for x and y before differentiating.

1. $u = x^2 - y^2$; $x = 3r - s$: $y = r + 2s$; $\dfrac{\partial u}{\partial r}$; $\dfrac{\partial u}{\partial s}$

2. $u = 3x - 4y^2$; $x = 5pq$; $y = 3p^2 - 2q$; $\dfrac{\partial u}{\partial p}$; $\dfrac{\partial u}{\partial q}$

3. $u = 3x^2 + xy - 2y^2 + 3x - y$; $x = 2r - 3s$; $y = r + s$; $\dfrac{\partial u}{\partial r}$; $\dfrac{\partial u}{\partial s}$

4. $u = x^2 + y^2$; $x = \cosh r \cos t$; $y = \sinh r \sin t$; $\dfrac{\partial u}{\partial r}$; $\dfrac{\partial u}{\partial t}$

5. $u = e^{y/x}$; $x = 2r \cos t$; $y = 4r \sin t$: $\dfrac{\partial u}{\partial r}$; $\dfrac{\partial u}{\partial t}$

6. $V = \pi x^2 y$; $x = \cos z \sin t$; $y = z^2 e^t$; $\dfrac{\partial V}{\partial z}$; $\dfrac{\partial V}{\partial t}$

In Exercises 7 through 14, find the indicated partial derivative by using the chain rule.

7. $u = x^2 + xy$; $x = r^2 + s^2$; $y = 3r - 2s$; $\dfrac{\partial u}{\partial r}$; $\dfrac{\partial u}{\partial s}$

8. $u = xy + xz + yz$; $x = rs$; $y = r^2 - s^2$; $z = (r - s)^2$; $\dfrac{\partial u}{\partial r}$; $\dfrac{\partial u}{\partial s}$

9. $u = \sin^{-1}(3x + y)$; $x = r^2 e^s$; $y = \sin rs$; $\dfrac{\partial u}{\partial r}$; $\dfrac{\partial u}{\partial s}$

10. $u = \sin(xy)$; $x = 2ze^t$; $y = t^2 e^{-z}$; $\dfrac{\partial u}{\partial t}$; $\dfrac{\partial u}{\partial z}$

11. $u = \cosh \dfrac{y}{x}$; $x = 3r^2 s$; $y = 6se^r$; $\dfrac{\partial u}{\partial r}$; $\dfrac{\partial u}{\partial s}$

12. $u = xe^{-y}$; $x = \tan^{-1}(rst)$; $y = \ln(3rs + 5st)$; $\dfrac{\partial u}{\partial r}$; $\dfrac{\partial u}{\partial s}$; $\dfrac{\partial u}{\partial t}$

13. $u = x^2 + y^2 + z^2$; $x = r \sin \phi \cos \theta$; $y = r \sin \phi \sin \theta$; $z = r \cos \phi$; $\dfrac{\partial u}{\partial r}$; $\dfrac{\partial u}{\partial \phi}$; $\dfrac{\partial u}{\partial \theta}$

14. $u = x^2 yz$; $x = \dfrac{r}{s}$; $y = re^s$; $z = re^{-s}$; $\dfrac{\partial u}{\partial r}$; $\dfrac{\partial u}{\partial s}$

In Exercises 15 through 18, find the total derivative $\dfrac{du}{dt}$ by two methods: (a) Use the chain rule; (b) make the substitutions for x and y or for x, y, and z before differentiating.

15. $u = ye^x + xe^y$; $x = \cos t$; $y = \sin t$

16. $u = \ln xy + y^2$; $x = e^t$; $y = e^{-t}$

17. $u = \sqrt{x^2 + y^2 + z^2}$; $x = \tan t$; $y = \cos t$; $z = \sin t$; $0 < t < \frac{1}{2}\pi$

18. $u = \dfrac{t + e^x}{y - e^t}$; $x = 3 \sin t$; $y = \ln t$

In Exercises 19 through 22, find the total derivative $\dfrac{du}{dt}$ by using the chain rule; do not express u as a function of t before differentiating.

19. $u = \tan^{-1}\left(\dfrac{y}{x}\right)$; $x = \ln t$; $y = e^t$

20. $u = xy + xz + yz$; $x = t \cos t$; $y = t \sin t$; $z = t$

21. $u = \dfrac{x + t}{y + t}$; $x = \ln t$; $y = \ln \dfrac{1}{t}$

22. $u = \ln(x^2 + y^2 + t^2)$; $x = t \sin t$; $y = \cos t$

In Exercises 23 through 26, find $\dfrac{dy}{dx}$ by Theorem 12.5.3. Compare your solution with that of the indicated exercise in Exercises 2.9.

23. $x^3 + y^3 = 8xy$; Exercise 19

24. $2x^3 y + 3xy^3 = 5$; Exercise 24

25. $x \sin y + y \cos x = 1$; Exercise 31

26. $\cos(x + y) = y \sin x$; Exercise 32

In Exercises 27 through 30, assume that the equation defines z as a differentiable function of x and y. Find $\dfrac{\partial z}{\partial x}$ and $\dfrac{\partial z}{\partial y}$ by two methods: (a) Use Theorem 12.5.4; (b) differentiate implicitly.

27. $3x^2 + y^2 + z^2 - 3xy + 4xz - 15 = 0$

28. $z = (x^2 + y^2) \sin xz$ **29.** $ye^{xyz} \cos 3xz = 5$

30. $ze^{yz} + 2xe^{xz} - 4e^{xy} = 3$

31. If f is a differentiable function of the variable u, let $u = bx - ay$ and prove that $z = f(bx - ay)$ satisfies the equation $a\left(\dfrac{\partial z}{\partial x}\right) + b\left(\dfrac{\partial z}{\partial y}\right) = 0$, where a and b are constants.

32. If f is a differentiable function of two variables u and v, let $u = x - y$ and $v = y - x$; prove that $z = f(x - y, y - x)$ satisfies the equation $\dfrac{\partial z}{\partial x} + \dfrac{\partial z}{\partial y} = 0$.

33. Suppose that f is a differentiable function of x and y, and $u = f(x, y)$. Then if $x = \cosh v \cos w$ and $y = \sinh v \sin w$, express $\dfrac{\partial u}{\partial v}$ and $\dfrac{\partial u}{\partial w}$ in terms of $\dfrac{\partial u}{\partial x}$ and $\dfrac{\partial u}{\partial y}$.

34. Given $u = e^y \cos x$, $x = 2t$, $y = t^2$. Find $\dfrac{d^2u}{dt^2}$ in two ways: **(a)** first express u in terms of t; **(b)** use the chain rule.

35. Given $u = 3xy - 4y^2$, $x = 2se^r$, $y = re^{-s}$. Find $\dfrac{\partial^2 u}{\partial r^2}$ in two ways: **(a)** first express u in terms of r and s; **(b)** use the chain rule.

36. For u, x, and y as given in Exercise 35, find $\dfrac{\partial^2 u}{\partial s\, \partial r}$ in two ways: **(a)** first express u in terms of r and s; **(b)** use the chain rule.

37. Given $u = 9x^2 + 4y^2$, $x = r \cos \theta$, $y = r \sin \theta$. Find $\dfrac{\partial^2 u}{\partial r^2}$ in two ways: **(a)** first express u in terms of r and θ; **(b)** use the chain rule.

38. For u, x, and y as given in Exercise 37, find $\dfrac{\partial^2 u}{\partial \theta^2}$ in two ways: **(a)** first express u in terms of r and θ; **(b)** use the chain rule.

39. For u, x, and y as given in Exercise 37, find $\dfrac{\partial^2 u}{\partial r\, \partial \theta}$ in two ways: **(a)** first express u in terms of r and θ; **(b)** use the chain rule.

40. Suppose that f is a differentiable function of x, y, and z, and $u = f(x, y, z)$. Then if $x = r \sin \phi \cos \theta$, $y = r \sin \phi \sin \theta$, and $z = r \cos \phi$, express $\dfrac{\partial u}{\partial r}$, $\dfrac{\partial u}{\partial \phi}$, and $\dfrac{\partial u}{\partial \theta}$ in terms of $\dfrac{\partial u}{\partial x}$, $\dfrac{\partial u}{\partial y}$, and $\dfrac{\partial u}{\partial z}$.

41. If $u = f(x, y)$ and $v = g(x, y)$, then the equations

$$\frac{\partial u}{\partial x} = \frac{\partial v}{\partial y} \quad \text{and} \quad \frac{\partial v}{\partial x} = -\frac{\partial u}{\partial y}$$

are called the *Cauchy-Riemann* equations. Show that the Cauchy-Riemann equations are satisfied if

$$u = \tfrac{1}{2} \ln(x^2 + y^2) \text{ and } v = \tan^{-1} \frac{y}{x}.$$

42. Suppose that f and g are differentiable functions of x and y, and $u = f(x, y)$ and $v = g(x, y)$. Show that if the Cauchy-Riemann equations (see Exercise 41) hold and if $x = r \cos \theta$ and $y = r \sin \theta$, then

$$\frac{\partial u}{\partial r} = \frac{1}{r} \frac{\partial v}{\partial \theta} \quad \text{and} \quad \frac{\partial v}{\partial r} = -\frac{1}{r} \frac{\partial u}{\partial \theta}$$

43. At a given instant, the length of one leg of a right triangle is 10 cm and it is increasing at the rate of 1 cm/min, and the length of the other leg is 12 cm and it is decreasing at the rate of 2 cm/min. Find the rate of change of the measure of the acute angle opposite the leg of length 12 cm at the given instant.

44. Water is flowing into a tank in the form of a right-circular cylinder at the rate of $\tfrac{4}{5}\pi$ m³/min. The tank is stretching in such a way that even though it remains cylindrical, its radius is increasing at the rate of 0.2 cm/min. How fast is the surface of the water rising when the radius is 2 m and the volume of water in the tank is 20π m³?

45. The height of a right-circular cylinder is decreasing at the rate of 10 cm/min and the radius is increasing at the rate of 4 cm/min. Find the rate of change of the volume at the instant when the height is 50 cm and the radius is 16 cm.

46. The height of a right-circular cone is increasing at the rate of 40 cm/min and the radius is decreasing at the rate of 15 cm/min. Find the rate of change of the volume at the instant when the height is 200 cm and the radius is 60 cm.

47. A quantity of gas obeys the ideal gas law (see Example 6, Section 12.3) with $k = 1.2$, and the gas is in a container that is being heated at a rate of 3°K/min. If at the instant when the temperature is 300°K, the pressure is 6 atm and is decreasing at the rate of 0.1 atm/min, find the rate of change of the volume at that instant.

48. A retaining wall makes an angle of radian measure $\tfrac{2}{3}\pi$ with the ground. A ladder of length 20 ft is leaning against the wall and its top is sliding down the wall at the rate of 3 ft/sec. How fast is the area of the triangle formed by the ladder, the wall, and the ground changing when the ladder makes an angle of $\tfrac{1}{6}\pi$ radians with the ground?

49. One kilomole of a real gas obeys Van der Waals' equation: If P, V, and T are, respectively, the measures of the pressure, volume, and absolute temperature, then

$$\left(P + \frac{a}{V^2} \right)(V - b) = RT$$

where R is the universal gas constant, and a and b are constants that depend on the particular gas. If β is the coefficient of volume expansion and κ is the coefficient of compressibility, then

$$\beta = \frac{1}{V}\left(\frac{\partial V}{\partial T} \right) \quad \text{and} \quad \kappa = -\frac{1}{V}\left(\frac{\partial V}{\partial P} \right)$$

Show that $\dfrac{\partial \beta}{\partial P} = -\dfrac{\partial \kappa}{\partial T}$.

50. From Van der Waals' equation and β and κ as given in Exercise 49, show that

$$\beta = \frac{RV^2(V - b)}{RTV^3 - 2a(V - b)^2} \quad \kappa = \frac{V^2(V - b)^2}{RTV^3 - 2a(V - b)^2}$$

For an ideal gas, $a = 0$ and $b = 0$. What are the expressions for β and κ for an ideal gas?

51. If f is a differentiable function of x and y, and $u = f(x, y)$, $x = r \cos \theta$, and $y = r \sin \theta$, show that

$$\frac{\partial u}{\partial x} = \frac{\partial u}{\partial r} \cos \theta - \frac{\partial u}{\partial \theta} \frac{\sin \theta}{r}$$

$$\frac{\partial u}{\partial y} = \frac{\partial u}{\partial r} \sin \theta + \frac{\partial u}{\partial \theta} \frac{\cos \theta}{r}$$

52. Suppose that $u = f(x, y)$ and $v = g(x, y)$, and that f and g and their first and second partial derivatives are continuous. Prove that if u and v satisfy the Cauchy-Riemann equations (see Exercise 41), they also satisfy Laplace's equation (see Exercises 49 through 52 in Exercises 12.3).

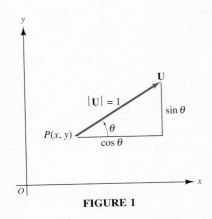

FIGURE 1

12.6 DIRECTIONAL DERIVATIVES AND GRADIENTS

You have seen how the partial derivatives of a function characterize the rate of change of a function along lines parallel to the coordinate axes. That is, if f is a function of the two variables x and y, the partial derivative $f_x(x, y)$ describes the rate of change of f in the direction of the x axis, and $f_y(x, y)$ describes the rate of change of f in the direction of the y axis. We now generalize the definition of a partial derivative to obtain the rate of change of a function with respect to any direction. This leads to the notion of a *directional derivative.*

To indicate a direction, we use the concept of a unit vector $\mathbf{U}$ making an angle of radian measure θ with the positive side of the x axis, so that

$$\mathbf{U} = \cos \theta \mathbf{i} + \sin \theta \mathbf{j}$$

Figure 1 shows the representation of $\mathbf{U}$ having its initial point at $P(x, y)$ in the xy plane. If f is a function of x and y, the rate of change of the function values $f(x, y)$ with respect to the direction of the unit vector $\mathbf{U}$ is given by the directional derivative.

> **12.6.1 Definition of a Directional Derivative of a Function of Two Variables**
>
> Let f be a function of two variables x and y. If $\mathbf{U}$ is the unit vector $\cos \theta \mathbf{i} + \sin \theta \mathbf{j}$, then the **directional derivative** of f in the direction of $\mathbf{U}$, denoted by $D_{\mathbf{U}}f$, is given by
>
> $$D_{\mathbf{U}}f(x, y) = \lim_{h \to 0} \frac{f(x + h \cos \theta, y + h \sin \theta) - f(x, y)}{h}$$
>
> if this limit exists.

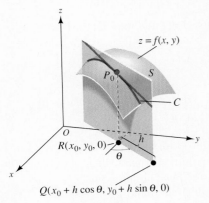

FIGURE 2

The geometric interpretation of the directional derivative is illustrated in Figure 2. An equation of the surface S in the figure is $z = f(x, y)$. Point $P_0(x_0, y_0, z_0)$ is on the surface, and points $R(x_0, y_0, 0)$ and $Q(x_0 + h \cos \theta, y_0 + h \sin \theta, 0)$ are in the xy plane. The plane through R and Q, parallel to the z axis, makes an angle of θ radians with the positive direction on the x axis. This plane intersects the surface S in the curve C. The directional derivative $D_{\mathbf{U}}f$, evaluated at P_0, is the slope of the tangent line to the curve C at P_0 in the plane of R, Q, and P_0.

If $\mathbf{U} = \mathbf{i}$, then $\cos \theta = 1$ and $\sin \theta = 0$, and from Definition 12.6.1,

$$D_{\mathbf{i}} f(x, y) = \lim_{h \to 0} \frac{f(x + h, y) - f(x, y)}{h}$$

which is the partial derivative of f with respect to x.

If $\mathbf{U} = \mathbf{j}$, then $\cos \theta = 0$ and $\sin \theta = 1$, and

$$D_{\mathbf{j}} f(x, y) = \lim_{h \to 0} \frac{f(x, y + h) - f(x, y)}{h}$$

which is the partial derivative of f with respect to y.

So f_x and f_y are special cases of the directional derivative in the directions of the unit vectors $\mathbf{i}$ and $\mathbf{j}$, respectively.

▶ **EXAMPLE 1**   Apply Definition 12.6.1 to find $D_{\mathbf{U}} f(x, y)$ if

$$f(x, y) = 12 - x^2 - 4y^2$$

and $\mathbf{U}$ is the unit vector in the direction $\frac{1}{6}\pi$.

Solution   Because $\mathbf{U} = \cos \frac{1}{6}\pi \mathbf{i} + \sin \frac{1}{6}\pi \mathbf{j}$, $\mathbf{U} = \frac{1}{2}\sqrt{3}\mathbf{i} + \frac{1}{2}\mathbf{j}$.

$$
\begin{aligned}
D_{\mathbf{U}} f(x, y) &= \lim_{h \to 0} \frac{f(x + \frac{1}{2}\sqrt{3}h, \, y + \frac{1}{2}h) - f(x, y)}{h} \\
&= \lim_{h \to 0} \frac{12 - (x + \frac{1}{2}\sqrt{3}h)^2 - 4(y + \frac{1}{2}h)^2 - (12 - x^2 - 4y^2)}{h} \\
&= \lim_{h \to 0} \frac{12 - x^2 - \sqrt{3}hx - \frac{3}{4}h^2 - 4y^2 - 4hy - h^2 - 12 + x^2 + 4y^2}{h} \\
&= \lim_{h \to 0} \frac{-\sqrt{3}hx - \frac{7}{4}h^2 - 4hy}{h} \\
&= \lim_{h \to 0} (-\sqrt{3}x - \tfrac{7}{4}h - 4y) \\
&= -\sqrt{3}x - 4y
\end{aligned}
$$

◀

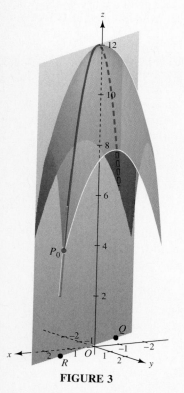

FIGURE 3

▷ **ILLUSTRATION 1**   For the function f and unit vector $\mathbf{U}$ of Example 1,

$$
\begin{aligned}
D_{\mathbf{U}} f(2, 1) &= -2\sqrt{3} - 4 \\
&\approx -7.464
\end{aligned}
$$

Figure 3 shows the geometric interpretation of this directional derivative. The curve C is the intersection of the surface

$$z = 12 - x^2 - 4y^2$$

with the plane of $R(2, 1, 0)$, $Q(2 + \frac{1}{2}\sqrt{3}h, 1 + \frac{1}{2}h, 0)$, and $P_0(2, 1, 4)$. The directional derivative -7.464 is the slope of the tangent line to the curve C at P_0 in the plane of R, Q, and P_0.   ◀

We now proceed to obtain a formula that will enable us to calculate a directional derivative in a shorter way than using the definition. Let g be the function of the single variable t, with x, y, and θ fixed, such that

$$g(t) = f(x + t \cos \theta, y + t \sin \theta) \tag{1}$$

and let $\mathbf{U} = \cos \theta \mathbf{i} + \sin \theta \mathbf{j}$. Then by the definition of an ordinary derivative,

$$g'(0) = \lim_{h \to 0} \frac{f(x + (0 + h)\cos \theta, y + (0 + h)\sin \theta) - f(x + 0 \cos \theta, y + 0 \sin \theta)}{h}$$

$$g'(0) = \lim_{h \to 0} \frac{f(x + h \cos \theta, y + h \sin \theta) - f(x, y)}{h}$$

Because the right side of the above is $D_{\mathbf{U}}f(x, y)$,

$$g'(0) = D_{\mathbf{U}}f(x, y) \tag{2}$$

We now find $g'(t)$ by applying the chain rule to the right side of (1), which gives

$$g'(t) = f_1(x + t \cos \theta, y + t \sin \theta)\frac{\partial(x + t \cos \theta)}{\partial t} + f_2(x + t \cos \theta, y + t \sin \theta)\frac{\partial(y + t \sin \theta)}{\partial t}$$

$$= f_1(x + t \cos \theta, y + t \sin \theta)\cos \theta + f_2(x + t \cos \theta, y + t \sin \theta)\sin \theta$$

Therefore

$$g'(0) = f_x(x, y)\cos \theta + f_y(x, y)\sin \theta$$

From this equation and (2) we have the following theorem.

> **12.6.2 Theorem**
>
> If f is a differentiable function of x and y, and $\mathbf{U} = \cos \theta \mathbf{i} + \sin \theta \mathbf{j}$,
>
> $$D_{\mathbf{U}}f(x, y) = f_x(x, y)\cos \theta + f_y(x, y)\sin \theta$$

▷ **ILLUSTRATION 2**   We apply Theorem 12.6.2 to compute $D_{\mathbf{U}}f$ for the function and unit vector of Example 1.

$$f(x, y) = 12 - x^2 - 4y^2 \qquad \mathbf{U} = \cos \tfrac{1}{6}\pi \mathbf{i} + \sin \tfrac{1}{6}\pi \mathbf{j}$$

$$D_{\mathbf{U}}f(x, y) = f_x(x, y) \cos \tfrac{1}{6}\pi + f_y(x, y) \sin \tfrac{1}{6}\pi$$

$$= -2x(\tfrac{1}{2}\sqrt{3}) - 8y(\tfrac{1}{2})$$

$$= -\sqrt{3}x - 4y$$

which agrees with the result in Example 1.   ◀

The directional derivative can be written as the dot product of two vectors. Because

$$f_x(x, y)\cos \theta + f_y(x, y) \sin \theta = (\cos \theta \mathbf{i} + \sin \theta \mathbf{j}) \cdot [f_x(x, y)\mathbf{i} + f_y(x, y)\mathbf{j}]$$

then from Theorem 12.6.2

$$D_{\mathbf{U}}f(x, y) = (\cos \theta \mathbf{i} + \sin \theta \mathbf{j}) \cdot [f_x(x, y)\mathbf{i} + f_y(x, y)\mathbf{j}] \tag{3}$$

The vector-valued function on the right side of (3) is an important one, and it is called the *gradient* of the function f of the two variables x and y. The symbol used for the gradient of f is ∇f, where ∇ is an inverted capital delta and is read "del." Sometimes the abbreviation *grad f* is used.

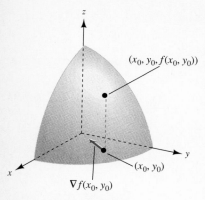

FIGURE 4

12.6.3 Definition of the Gradient of a Function of Two Variables

If f is a function of two variables x and y, and f_x and f_y exist, then the **gradient** of f, denoted by ∇f (read "del f"), is defined by

$$\nabla f(x, y) = f_x(x, y)\mathbf{i} + f_y(x, y)\mathbf{j}$$

To represent the gradient vector $\nabla f(x_0, y_0)$ in the xy plane, we take the initial point at (x_0, y_0). See Figure 4.

From Definition 12.6.3, Equation (3) can be written as

$$D_{\mathbf{U}}f(x, y) = \mathbf{U} \cdot \nabla f(x, y) \tag{4}$$

Therefore any directional derivative of a differentiable function can be obtained by dot-multiplying the gradient by a unit vector in the desired direction. This formula is the most convenient one to use to compute a directional derivative.

▶ **EXAMPLE 2**   If

$$f(x, y) = \frac{x^2}{16} + \frac{y^2}{9}$$

(a) Find the gradient of f at $R(4, 3)$.   **(b)** Use the gradient to compute the directional derivative of f at R in the direction from R to $Q(5, 6)$. **(c)** Sketch the representations of vectors $\nabla f(4, 3)$ and $\mathbf{V}(\overrightarrow{RQ})$ having their initial point at R.

Solution

(a) Because $f_x(x, y) = x/8$ and $f_y(x, y) = 2y/9$,

$$\nabla f(x, y) = \frac{x}{8}\mathbf{i} + \frac{2y}{9}\mathbf{j} \qquad \nabla f(4, 3) = \frac{1}{2}\mathbf{i} + \frac{2}{3}\mathbf{j}$$

(b) The vector in the direction from $R(4, 3)$ to $Q(5, 6)$ is

$$\mathbf{V}(\overrightarrow{RQ}) = (5 - 4)\mathbf{i} + (6 - 3)\mathbf{j}$$
$$= \mathbf{i} + 3\mathbf{j}$$

The unit vector $\mathbf{U}$ in the same direction is $\mathbf{V}(\overrightarrow{RQ})/\|\mathbf{V}(\overrightarrow{RQ})\|$:

$$\mathbf{U} = \frac{1}{\sqrt{10}}\mathbf{i} + \frac{3}{\sqrt{10}}\mathbf{j}$$

We compute $D_{\mathbf{U}}f(4, 3)$ by dot-multiplying $\mathbf{U}$ by $\nabla f(4, 3)$:

$$D_{\mathbf{U}}f(4, 3) = \left(\frac{1}{\sqrt{10}}\mathbf{i} + \frac{3}{\sqrt{10}}\mathbf{j}\right) \cdot \left(\frac{1}{2}\mathbf{i} + \frac{2}{3}\mathbf{j}\right)$$

$$= \frac{1}{2\sqrt{10}} + \frac{2}{\sqrt{10}}$$

$$= \frac{5}{2\sqrt{10}} \approx 0.79$$

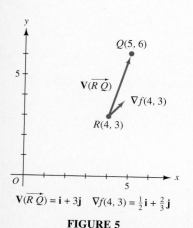

$\mathbf{V}(\overrightarrow{RQ}) = \mathbf{i} + 3\mathbf{j}$ $\nabla f(4, 3) = \frac{1}{2}\mathbf{i} + \frac{2}{3}\mathbf{j}$

FIGURE 5

(c) The representations of $\nabla f(4, 3)$ and $\mathbf{V}(\overrightarrow{RQ})$ appear in Figure 5.   ◀

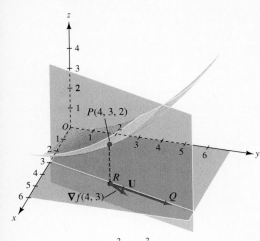

$$f(x, y) = \frac{x^2}{16} + \frac{y^2}{9}$$

FIGURE 6

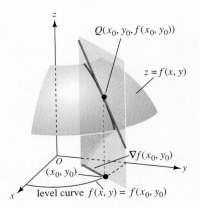

FIGURE 7

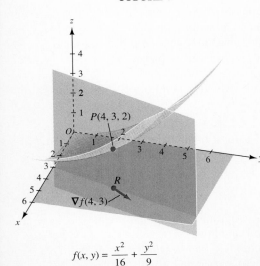

$$f(x, y) = \frac{x^2}{16} + \frac{y^2}{9}$$

FIGURE 8

The graph of the function f of Example 2 is an elliptic paraboloid. Figure 6 shows this surface, the gradient of f at R, the unit vector $\mathbf{U}$ in the same direction as $\mathbf{V}(\overrightarrow{RQ})$, and the plane through R, Q, and the point $P(4, 3, 2)$ on the paraboloid. $D_{\mathbf{U}}f(4, 3)$ is the slope of the tangent line at P to the curve of intersection of the plane with the paraboloid.

From (4), we can conclude that if $\nabla f(x_0, y_0) = \mathbf{0}$, then $D_{\mathbf{U}}f(x_0, y_0) = 0$ for any $\mathbf{U}$. If $\nabla f(x_0, y_0) \neq \mathbf{0}$, then from (4) and Theorem 10.3.5 if α is the radian measure of the angle between the two vectors $\mathbf{U}$ and $\nabla f(x_0, y_0)$,

$$\begin{aligned}
D_{\mathbf{U}}f(x_0, y_0) &= \mathbf{U} \cdot \nabla f(x_0, y_0) \\
&= \|\mathbf{U}\| \|\nabla f(x_0, y_0)\| \cos \alpha \\
&= \|\nabla f(x_0, y_0)\| \cos \alpha
\end{aligned}$$

From this equation, the maximum value of $D_{\mathbf{U}}f(x_0, y_0)$ occurs when $\cos \alpha = 1$; that is, when $\alpha = 0$ or, equivalently, when $\mathbf{U}$ is in the direction of $\nabla f(x_0, y_0)$. The maximum value of $D_{\mathbf{U}}f(x_0, y_0)$ is $\|\nabla f(x_0, y_0)\|$. In a similar manner, the minimum value of $D_{\mathbf{U}}f(x_0, y_0)$ occurs when $\cos \alpha = -1$; that is, when $\alpha = \pi$ or, equivalently, when the direction of $\mathbf{U}$ is opposite that of $\nabla f(x_0, y_0)$. The minimum value of $D_{\mathbf{U}}f(x_0, y_0)$ is $-\|\nabla f(x_0, y_0)\|$. The following theorem summarizes these results.

12.6.4 Theorem

Let f be a function of two variables and differentiable at (x_0, y_0), where $\nabla f(x_0, y_0) \neq \mathbf{0}$. Let $\mathbf{U}$ be any unit vector, so that $D_{\mathbf{U}}f(x_0, y_0)$ is a function of $\mathbf{U}$.

(i) The maximum value of $D_{\mathbf{U}}f(x_0, y_0)$ is $\|\nabla f(x_0, y_0)\|$. This maximum value is attained when the direction of $\mathbf{U}$ is the same as the direction of $\nabla f(x_0, y_0)$.

(ii) The minimum value of $D_{\mathbf{U}}f(x_0, y_0)$ is $-\|\nabla f(x_0, y_0)\|$. This minimum value is attained when the direction of $\mathbf{U}$ is opposite the direction of $\nabla f(x_0, y_0)$.

Part (i) of this theorem states that if $z = f(x, y)$, then the maximum rate of increase of z at (x_0, y_0) occurs in the direction of $\nabla f(x_0, y_0)$, as indicated in Figure 7. Thus $\nabla f(x_0, y_0)$ points in the direction of *steepest ascent*. This fact accounts for the name *gradient;* that is, the grade is steepest in the direction of the gradient.

The following illustration interprets the theorem in terms of geometry for a particular function.

▷ **ILLUSTRATION 3** Refer to Figure 8 showing the elliptic paraboloid defined by the function f of Example 2, so that

$$z = \frac{x^2}{16} + \frac{y^2}{9}$$

The figure also shows the point $R(4, 3)$ in the xy plane, the point $P(4, 3, 2)$ on the paraboloid, and the gradient vector $\nabla f(4, 3)$ in the xy plane. From point P the maximum rate of increase of z occurs in the direction $\nabla f(4, 3)$. Similarly, the minimum rate of increase or, equivalently, the maximum rate of decrease of z occurs in the direction of $-\nabla f(4, 3)$. ◀

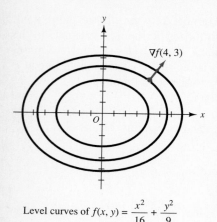

Level curves of $f(x, y) = \dfrac{x^2}{16} + \dfrac{y^2}{9}$

FIGURE 9

▷ **ILLUSTRATION 4**   A contour map, showing the level curves of the function of Example 2 and Illustration 3 at 1, 2, and 3, appears in Figure 9. These level curves are ellipses. The figure also shows the representation of $\nabla f(4, 3)$ having its initial point at $(4, 3)$ and pointing in the direction of steepest ascent.   ◀

▶ **EXAMPLE 3**   Given

$$f(x, y) = 2x^2 - y^2 + 3x - y$$

find the maximum value of $D_{\mathbf{U}} f$ at the point where $x = 1$ and $y = -2$.

Solution   Because $f_x(x, y) = 4x + 3$ and $f_y(x, y) = -2y - 1$,

$$\nabla f(x, y) = (4x + 3)\mathbf{i} + (-2y - 1)\mathbf{j} \qquad \nabla f(1, -2) = 7\mathbf{i} + 3\mathbf{j}$$

Thus the maximum value of $D_{\mathbf{U}} f$ at $(1, -2)$ is

$$\begin{aligned} \| \nabla f(1, -2) \| &= \sqrt{49 + 9} \\ &= \sqrt{58} \end{aligned}$$

This result indicates that the graph of f is very steep at the point $(1, -2, 3)$ on the surface.   ◀

▶ **EXAMPLE 4**   The temperature at any point (x, y) of a rectangular plate lying in the xy plane is determined by

$$T(x, y) = x^2 + y^2$$

(a) Find the rate of change of the temperature at the point $(3, 4)$ in the direction making an angle of $\frac{1}{3}\pi$ radians with the positive x axis. **(b)** Find the angle giving the direction for which the rate of change of the temperature at the point $(-3, 1)$ is a maximum.

Solution

(a) We wish to find $D_{\mathbf{U}} T(x, y)$, where

$$\begin{aligned} \mathbf{U} &= \cos \tfrac{1}{3}\pi \mathbf{i} + \sin \tfrac{1}{3}\pi \mathbf{j} \quad \text{and} \quad \nabla T(x, y) = T_x(x, y)\mathbf{i} + T_y(x, y)\mathbf{j} \\ &= \tfrac{1}{2}\mathbf{i} + \tfrac{1}{2}\sqrt{3}\mathbf{j} \qquad\qquad\qquad\qquad\quad = 2x\mathbf{i} + 2y\mathbf{j} \end{aligned}$$

Therefore

$$\begin{aligned} D_{\mathbf{U}} T(x, y) &= \mathbf{U} \cdot \nabla T(x, y) \\ &= (\tfrac{1}{2}\mathbf{i} + \tfrac{1}{2}\sqrt{3}\mathbf{j}) \cdot (2x\mathbf{i} + 2y\mathbf{j}) \\ &= x + \sqrt{3}y \end{aligned}$$

Thus

$$\begin{aligned} D_{\mathbf{U}} T(3, 4) &= 3 + 4\sqrt{3} \\ &\approx 9.93 \end{aligned}$$

Conclusion: At $(3, 4)$ the temperature is increasing at the rate of approximately 9.93 units per unit change in the distance measured in the direction of **U**.

(b) $D_U T(-3, 1)$ is a maximum when **U** is in the direction of $\nabla T(-3, 1)$. Because $\nabla T(-3, 1) = -6\mathbf{i} + 2\mathbf{j}$, the radian measure of the angle giving the direction of $\nabla T(-3, 1)$ is θ, where $\tan \theta = -\frac{1}{3}$. Thus $\theta = \pi - \tan^{-1} \frac{1}{3} \approx 2.82$.

Conclusion: The rate of change of the temperature at the point $(-3, 1)$ is a maximum in the direction making an angle of approximately 2.82 radians with the positive side of the x axis. ◀

The next definition extends the concept of a directional derivative to a function of three variables, so that it gives the rate of change of the function values $f(x, y, z)$ with respect to distance in three-dimensional space measured in the direction of a unit vector $\mathbf{U} = \cos \alpha \mathbf{i} + \cos \beta \mathbf{j} + \cos \gamma \mathbf{k}$.

12.6.5 Definition of a Directional Derivative of a Function of Three Variables

Suppose that f is a function of three variables x, y, and z. If **U** is the unit vector $\cos \alpha \mathbf{i} + \cos \beta \mathbf{j} + \cos \gamma \mathbf{k}$, then the **directional derivative** of f in the direction of **U**, denoted by $D_U f$, is given by

$$D_U f(x, y, z)$$
$$= \lim_{h \to 0} \frac{f(x + h \cos \alpha, y + h \cos \beta, z + h \cos \gamma) - f(x, y, z)}{h}$$

if this limit exists.

The following theorem, which provides a method for calculating a directional derivative for a function of three variables, is proved in a manner similar to the proof of Theorem 12.6.2, the corresponding one for two-variable functions.

12.6.6 Theorem

If f is a differentiable function of x, y, and z and

$$\mathbf{U} = \cos \alpha \mathbf{i} + \cos \beta \mathbf{j} + \cos \gamma \mathbf{k}$$

then

$$D_U f(x, y, z) = f_x(x, y, z)\cos \alpha + f_y(x, y, z)\cos \beta + f_z(x, y, z)\cos \gamma$$

▶ **EXAMPLE 5**   Given

$$f(x, y, z) = 3x^2 + xy - 2y^2 - yz + z^2$$

find the rate of change of $f(x, y, z)$ at $(1, -2, -1)$ in the direction of the vector $2\mathbf{i} - 2\mathbf{j} - \mathbf{k}$.

Solution The unit vector in the direction of $2\mathbf{i} - 2\mathbf{j} - \mathbf{k}$ is

$$\mathbf{U} = \tfrac{2}{3}\mathbf{i} - \tfrac{2}{3}\mathbf{j} - \tfrac{1}{3}\mathbf{k}$$

So from Theorem 12.6.6,

$$D_{\mathbf{U}}f(x, y, z) = \tfrac{2}{3}(6x + y) - \tfrac{2}{3}(x - 4y - z) - \tfrac{1}{3}(-y + 2z)$$

Therefore the rate of change of $f(x, y, z)$ at $(1, -2, -1)$ in the direction of $\mathbf{U}$ is given by

$$D_{\mathbf{U}}f(1, -2, -1) = \tfrac{2}{3}(4) - \tfrac{2}{3}(10) - \tfrac{1}{3}(0)$$
$$= -4 \qquad \blacktriangleleft$$

12.6.7 Definition of the Gradient of a Function of Three Variables

If f is a function of three variables x, y, and z and the first partial derivatives f_x, f_y, and f_z exist, then the **gradient** of f, denoted by ∇f, is defined by

$$\nabla f(x, y, z) = f_x(x, y, z)\mathbf{i} + f_y(x, y, z)\mathbf{j} + f_z(x, y, z)\mathbf{k}$$

As for functions of two variables, if $\mathbf{U}$ is a unit vector, then from the above definition and Theorem 12.6.6

$$D_{\mathbf{U}}f(x, y, z) = \mathbf{U} \cdot \nabla f(x, y, z)$$

Theorem 12.6.4(i) can be extended to functions of three variables, so that the directional derivative is a maximum when $\mathbf{U}$ is in the direction of the gradient, and the maximum directional derivative is the magnitude of the gradient. A similar comment holds for part (ii) of Theorem 12.6.4.

Applications of the gradient occur in physics in problems involving heat conduction and electricity. Suppose, for instance, that the function f is defined by the equation $w = f(x, y, z)$. The level surface of f at the constant k is given by the equation

$$f(x, y, z) = k$$

If w degrees is the temperature at point (x, y, z), then all points on this level surface have the same temperature of k degrees, and the surface is called an **isothermal surface.** If w volts is the electric potential at point (x, y, z), then all points on the surface are at the same potential, and the surface is called an **equipotential surface.** For an isothermal surface, the gradient gives the direction of the greatest rate of change of temperature, and for an equipotential surface, the gradient gives the direction of the greatest rate of change of potential.

▶ **EXAMPLE 6** Suppose $V(x, y, z)$ volts is the electric potential at any point (x, y, z) in three-dimensional space and

$$V(x, y, z) = \frac{1}{\sqrt{x^2 + y^2 + z^2}}$$

(a) Find the rate of change of V at the point $(2, 2, -1)$ in the direction of the vector $2\mathbf{i} - 3\mathbf{j} + 6\mathbf{k}$. **(b)** Determine the direction of the greatest rate of change of V at $(2, 2, -1)$.

Solution

(a) A unit vector in the direction of $2\mathbf{i} - 3\mathbf{j} + 6\mathbf{k}$ is

$$\mathbf{U} = \tfrac{2}{7}\mathbf{i} - \tfrac{3}{7}\mathbf{j} + \tfrac{6}{7}\mathbf{k}$$

We wish to find $D_{\mathbf{U}}V(2, 2, -1)$.

$$\nabla V(x, y, z) = V_x(x, y, z)\mathbf{i} + V_y(x, y, z)\mathbf{j} + V_z(x, y, z)\mathbf{k}$$

$$= \frac{-x}{(x^2 + y^2 + z^2)^{3/2}}\mathbf{i} + \frac{-y}{(x^2 + y^2 + z^2)^{3/2}}\mathbf{j} + \frac{-z}{(x^2 + y^2 + z^2)^{3/2}}\mathbf{k}$$

Then

$$D_{\mathbf{U}}V(2, 2, -1) = \mathbf{U} \cdot \nabla V(2, 2, -1)$$

$$= (\tfrac{2}{7}\mathbf{i} - \tfrac{3}{7}\mathbf{j} + \tfrac{6}{7}\mathbf{k}) \cdot (-\tfrac{2}{27}\mathbf{i} - \tfrac{2}{27}\mathbf{j} + \tfrac{1}{27}\mathbf{k})$$

$$= -\tfrac{4}{189} + \tfrac{6}{189} + \tfrac{6}{189}$$

$$= \tfrac{8}{189}$$

$$\approx 0.042$$

Conclusion: At $(2, 2, -1)$, the potential is increasing at the rate of approximately 0.042 volt per unit change in the distance measured in the direction of $\mathbf{U}$.

(b) $\nabla V(2, 2, -1) = -\tfrac{2}{27}\mathbf{i} - \tfrac{2}{27}\mathbf{j} + \tfrac{1}{27}\mathbf{k}$. A unit vector in the direction of $\nabla V(2, 2, -1)$ is

$$\frac{\nabla V(2, 2, -1)}{\|\nabla V(2, 2, -1)\|} = \frac{-\tfrac{2}{27}\mathbf{i} - \tfrac{2}{27}\mathbf{j} + \tfrac{1}{27}\mathbf{k}}{\tfrac{3}{27}}$$

$$= -\tfrac{2}{3}\mathbf{i} - \tfrac{2}{3}\mathbf{j} + \tfrac{1}{3}\mathbf{k}$$

The direction cosines of this vector are $-\tfrac{2}{3}$, $-\tfrac{2}{3}$, and $\tfrac{1}{3}$, which give the direction of the greatest rate of change of V at $(2, 2, -1)$. ◀

EXERCISES 12.6

In Exercises 1 through 6, find the directional derivative of the function in the direction of the unit vector $\mathbf{U}$ by using either Definition 12.6.1 or Definition 12.6.5, and then verify your result by applying either Theorem 12.6.2 or Theorem 12.6.6, whichever one applies.

1. $f(x, y) = 2x^2 + 5y^2$; $\mathbf{U} = \cos\tfrac{1}{4}\pi\mathbf{i} + \sin\tfrac{1}{4}\pi\mathbf{j}$

2. $g(x, y) = 3x^2 - 4y^2$; $\mathbf{U} = \cos\tfrac{1}{3}\pi\mathbf{i} + \sin\tfrac{1}{3}\pi\mathbf{j}$

3. $g(x, y, z) = 3x^2 + y^2 - 4z^2$;
$\mathbf{U} = \cos\tfrac{1}{3}\pi\mathbf{i} + \cos\tfrac{1}{4}\pi\mathbf{j} + \cos\tfrac{2}{3}\pi\mathbf{k}$

4. $f(x, y, z) = 6x^2 - 2xy + yz$; $\mathbf{U} = \tfrac{3}{7}\mathbf{i} + \tfrac{2}{7}\mathbf{j} + \tfrac{6}{7}\mathbf{k}$

5. $g(x, y) = \dfrac{1}{x - y}$; $\mathbf{U} = -\tfrac{12}{13}\mathbf{i} + \tfrac{5}{13}\mathbf{j}$

6. $f(x, y) = \dfrac{1}{x^2 + y^2}$; $\mathbf{U} = \tfrac{3}{5}\mathbf{i} - \tfrac{4}{5}\mathbf{j}$

In Exercises 7 through 14, find the gradient of the function.

7. $f(x, y) = 4x^2 - 3xy + y^2$

8. $g(x, y) = \dfrac{xy}{x^2 + y^2}$

9. $g(x, y) = \ln\sqrt{x^2 + y^2}$

10. $f(x, y) = e^y \tan 2x$

11. $f(x, y, z) = \dfrac{x - y}{x + z}$

12. $f(x, y, z) = 3z\ln(x + y)$

13. $g(x, y, z) = xe^{-2y}\sec z$

14. $g(x, y, z) = e^{2z}(\sin x - \cos y)$

In Exercises 15 through 22, find the value of the directional derivative at the point P_0 for the function in the direction of $\mathbf{U}$.

15. $f(x, y) = x^2 - 2xy^2$; $\mathbf{U} = \cos \pi \mathbf{i} + \sin \pi \mathbf{j}$; $P_0 = (1, -2)$

16. $g(x, y) = 3x^3y + 4y^2 - xy$; $\mathbf{U} = \cos \frac{1}{4}\pi \mathbf{i} + \sin \frac{1}{4}\pi \mathbf{j}$; $P_0 = (0, 3)$

17. $g(x, y) = y^2 \tan^2 x$; $\mathbf{U} = -\frac{1}{2}\sqrt{3}\mathbf{i} + \frac{1}{2}\mathbf{j}$; $P_0 = (\frac{1}{3}\pi, 2)$

18. $f(x, y) = xe^{2y}$; $\mathbf{U} = \frac{1}{2}\mathbf{i} + \frac{1}{2}\sqrt{3}\mathbf{j}$; $P_0 = (2, 0)$

19. $h(x, y, z) = \cos(xy) + \sin(yz)$; $\mathbf{U} = -\frac{1}{3}\mathbf{i} + \frac{2}{3}\mathbf{j} + \frac{2}{3}\mathbf{k}$; $P_0 = (2, 0, -3)$

20. $f(x, y, z) = \ln(x^2 + y^2 + z^2)$; $\mathbf{U} = \frac{1}{\sqrt{3}}\mathbf{i} - \frac{1}{\sqrt{3}}\mathbf{j} - \frac{1}{\sqrt{3}}\mathbf{k}$; $P_0 = (1, 3, 2)$

21. $f(x, y) = e^{-3x} \cos 3y$; $\mathbf{U} = \cos(-\frac{1}{12}\pi)\mathbf{i} + \sin(-\frac{1}{12}\pi)\mathbf{j}$; $P_0 = (-\frac{1}{12}\pi, 0)$

22. $g(x, y, z) = \cos 2x \cos 3y \sinh 4z$; $\mathbf{U} = \frac{1}{\sqrt{3}}\mathbf{i} - \frac{1}{\sqrt{3}}\mathbf{j} + \frac{1}{\sqrt{3}}\mathbf{k}$; $P_0 = (\frac{1}{2}\pi, 0, 0)$

In Exercises 23 through 26, find (a) the gradient of f at P and (b) the rate of change of the function value in the direction of $\mathbf{U}$ at P.

23. $f(x, y) = x^2 - 4y$; $P = (-2, 2)$; $\mathbf{U} = \cos \frac{1}{3}\pi \mathbf{i} + \sin \frac{1}{3}\pi \mathbf{j}$

24. $f(x, y) = e^{2xy}$; $P = (2, 1)$; $\mathbf{U} = \frac{4}{5}\mathbf{i} - \frac{3}{5}\mathbf{j}$

25. $f(x, y, z) = y^2 + z^2 - 4xz$; $P = (-2, 1, 3)$; $\mathbf{U} = \frac{2}{7}\mathbf{i} - \frac{6}{7}\mathbf{j} + \frac{3}{7}\mathbf{k}$

26. $f(x, y, z) = 2x^3 + xy^2 + xz^2$; $P = (1, 1, 1)$; $\mathbf{U} = \frac{1}{7}\sqrt{21}\,\mathbf{j} - \frac{2}{7}\sqrt{7}\mathbf{k}$

27. Draw a contour map showing the level curves of the function of Exercise 23 at 8, 4, 0, −4, and −8. Also show the representation of $\nabla f(-2, 2)$ having its initial point at $(-2, 2)$.

28. Draw a contour map showing the level curves of the function of Exercise 24, at e^8, e^4, 1, e^{-4}, and e^{-8}. Also show the representation of $\nabla f(2, 1)$ having its initial point at $(2, 1)$.

In Exercises 29 through 32, find $D_{\mathbf{U}}f$ at the point P for which $\mathbf{U}$ is a unit vector in the direction of $\overrightarrow{PQ}$. Also at P find $D_{\mathbf{U}}f$, if $\mathbf{U}$ is a unit vector for which $D_{\mathbf{U}}f$ is a maximum.

29. $f(x, y) = e^x \tan^{-1} y$; $P(0, 1)$, $Q(3, 5)$

30. $f(x, y) = e^x \cos y + e^y \sin x$; $P(1, 0)$, $Q(-3, 3)$

31. $f(x, y, z) = x - 2y + z^2$; $P(3, 1, -2)$, $Q(10, 7, 4)$

32. $f(x, y, z) = x^2 + y^2 - 4xz$; $P(3, 1, -2)$, $Q(-6, 3, 4)$

33. Find the direction from the point $(1, 3)$ for which the value of f does not change if $f(x, y) = e^{2y} \tan^{-1} \frac{y}{3x}$.

34. The density is $\rho(x, y)$ kilograms per square meter at any point of a rectangular plate in the xy plane and

$$\rho(x, y) = \frac{1}{\sqrt{x^2 + y^2 + 3}}$$

(a) Find the rate of change of the density at the point $(3, 2)$ in the direction of the unit vector $\cos \frac{2}{3}\pi \mathbf{i} + \sin \frac{2}{3}\pi \mathbf{j}$. **(b)** Find the direction and magnitude of the greatest rate of change of ρ at $(3, 2)$.

35. The temperature is $T(x, y)$ degrees at any point of a rectangular plate lying in the xy plane, and $T(x, y) = 3x^2 + 2xy$. Distance is measured in meters. **(a)** Find the maximum rate of change of the temperature at the point $(3, -6)$ on the plate. **(b)** Find the direction for which this maximum rate of change at $(3, -6)$ occurs.

36. The temperature is $T(x, y, z)$ degrees at any point of a solid in three-dimensional space, and

$$T(x, y, z) = \frac{60}{x^2 + y^2 + z^2 + 3}$$

Distance is measured in inches. **(a)** Find the rate of change of the temperature at the point $(3, -2, 2)$ in the direction of the vector $-2\mathbf{i} + 3\mathbf{j} - 6\mathbf{k}$. **(b)** Find the direction and magnitude of the greatest rate of change of T at $(3, -2, 2)$.

37. The electric potential is $V(x, y)$ volts at any point in the xy plane, and $V(x, y) = e^{-2x} \cos 2y$. Distance is measured in feet. **(a)** Find the rate of change of the potential at the point $(0, \frac{1}{4}\pi)$ in the direction of the unit vector $\cos \frac{1}{6}\pi \mathbf{i} + \sin \frac{1}{6}\pi \mathbf{j}$. **(b)** Find the direction and magnitude of the greatest rate of change of V at $(0, \frac{1}{4}\pi)$.

38. An equation of the surface of a mountain is

$$z = 1200 - 3x^2 - 2y^2$$

where distance is measured in meters, the x axis points to the east, and the y axis points to the north. A mountain climber is at the point corresponding to $(-10, 5, 850)$. **(a)** What is the direction of steepest ascent? **(b)** If the climber moves in the east direction, is she ascending or descending, and what is her rate. **(c)** If the climber moves in the southwest direction, is she ascending or descending, and what is her rate? **(d)** In what direction is she traveling a level path?

12.7 TANGENT PLANES AND NORMALS TO SURFACES

We now show how the gradient vector is employed to study tangent planes and normal lines to surfaces in three-dimensional space. Consider the equation

$$F(x, y, z) = 0 \tag{1}$$

where F is differentiable and F_x, F_y, and F_z are not all zero. A theorem from advanced calculus, known as the *implicit function theorem,* guarantees that one of the three variables x, y, or z is a function of the other two. Therefore, we can refer to the graph of Equation (1) as a surface S.

Suppose that P_0 is a point (x_0, y_0, z_0) on S, so that $F(x_0, y_0, z_0) = 0$. Suppose further that C is a curve on S through P_0 and that a set of parametric equations of C is

$$x = f(t) \qquad y = g(t) \qquad z = h(t) \tag{2}$$

where the value of the parameter t at P_0 is t_0. A vector equation of C is

$$\mathbf{R}(t) = f(t)\mathbf{i} + g(t)\mathbf{j} + h(t)\mathbf{k}$$

Because curve C is on surface S, we have, upon substituting from (2) in (1),

$$F(f(t), g(t), h(t)) = 0 \tag{3}$$

Let $G(t) = F(f(t), g(t), h(t))$. If F is differentiable and F_x, F_y, and F_z are not all zero at P_0, and if $f'(t_0)$, $g'(t_0)$, and $h'(t_0)$ exist, then the total derivative of F with respect to t at P_0 is given by

$$G'(t_0) = F_x(x_0, y_0, z_0)f'(t_0) + F_y(x_0, y_0, z_0)g'(t_0) + F_z(x_0, y_0, z_0)h'(t_0)$$

The right side of this equation can be written as

$$[F_x(x_0, y_0, z_0)\mathbf{i} + F_y(x_0, y_0, z_0)\mathbf{j} + F_z(x_0, y_0, z_0)\mathbf{k}] \cdot [f'(t_0)\mathbf{i} + g'(t_0)\mathbf{j} + h'(t_0)\mathbf{k}]$$

Thus

$$G'(t_0) = \nabla F(x_0, y_0, z_0) \cdot D_t\mathbf{R}(t_0)$$

Since $G'(t) = 0$ for all t under consideration (because of (3)), $G'(t_0) = 0$; so from the above

$$\nabla F(x_0, y_0, z_0) \cdot D_t\mathbf{R}(t_0) = 0 \tag{4}$$

From Section 11.3 we know that $D_t\mathbf{R}(t_0)$ has the same direction as a tangent vector to curve C at P_0. Therefore, from (4) we can conclude that the gradient vector of F at P_0 is orthogonal to a tangent vector of every curve C on S through the point P_0. We have proved the next theorem which utilizes the terminology *normal vector,* which we define first.

12.7.1 Definition of a Normal Vector

A vector orthogonal to a tangent vector of every curve C through a point P_0 on a surface S is called a **normal vector** to S at P_0.

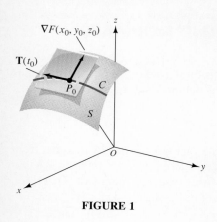

FIGURE 1

12.7.2 Theorem

If an equation of a surface S is $F(x, y, z) = 0$, and F is differentiable and F_x, F_y, and F_z are not all zero at the point $P_0(x_0, y_0, z_0)$ on S, then $\nabla F(x_0, y_0, z_0)$ is a normal vector to S at P_0.

The concept of a normal vector is used to define the *tangent plane* to a surface at a point.

12.7.3 Definition of a Tangent Plane

If an equation of a surface S is $F(x, y, z) = 0$ and F satisfies the hypothesis of Theorem 12.7.2, then the **tangent plane** of S at a point $P_0(x_0, y_0, z_0)$ is the plane through P_0 having $\nabla F(x_0, y_0, z_0)$ as a normal vector.

An equation of the tangent plane of the above definition is

$$F_x(x_0, y_0, z_0)(x - x_0) + F_y(x_0, y_0, z_0)(y - y_0) + F_z(x_0, y_0, z_0)(z - z_0) = 0 \quad \textbf{(5)}$$

Refer to Figure 1, which shows the tangent plane to the surface S at P_0 and the representation of the gradient vector having its initial point at P_0. A vector equation of the tangent plane given by (5) is

$$\nabla F(x_0, y_0, z_0) \cdot [(x - x_0)\mathbf{i} + (y - y_0)\mathbf{j} + (z - z_0)\mathbf{k}] = 0 \quad \textbf{(6)}$$

▶ **EXAMPLE 1**   Find an equation of the tangent plane to the elliptic paraboloid

$$4x^2 + y^2 - 16z = 0$$

at the point $(2, 4, 2)$.

Solution   Let $F(x, y, z) = 4x^2 + y^2 - 16z$. Then

$$\nabla F(x, y, z) = 8x\mathbf{i} + 2y\mathbf{j} - 16\mathbf{k} \qquad \nabla F(2, 4, 2) = 16\mathbf{i} + 8\mathbf{j} - 16\mathbf{k}$$

From (6) it follows that an equation of the tangent plane is

$$16(x - 2) + 8(y - 4) - 16(z - 2) = 0$$
$$2x + y - 2z - 4 = 0$$

Figure 2 shows the elliptic paraboloid along with the tangent plane and the representation of the normal vector at $(2, 4, 2)$.   ◀

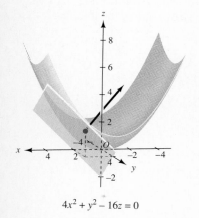

$4x^2 + y^2 - 16z = 0$

FIGURE 2

The following definition of the *normal line* to a surface at a point is motivated by the requirement that the representation of the normal vector at that point should lie on the normal line.

12.7.4 Definition of a Normal Line to a Surface

The **normal line** to a surface S at a point P_0 on S is the line through P_0 having as a set of direction numbers the components of any normal vector to S at P_0.

From this definition, if an equation of a surface S is $F(x, y, z) = 0$, then symmetric equations of the normal line to S at (x_0, y_0, z_0) are

$$\frac{x - x_0}{F_x(x_0, y_0, z_0)} = \frac{y - y_0}{F_y(x_0, y_0, z_0)} = \frac{z - z_0}{F_z(x_0, y_0, z_0)}$$

because the denominators are components of $\nabla F(x_0, y_0, z_0)$, which is a normal vector to S at (x_0, y_0, z_0).

▶ **EXAMPLE 2**   Find symmetric equations of the normal line to the surface of Example 1 at $(2, 4, 2)$.

Solution   Because $\nabla F(2, 4, 2) = 16\mathbf{i} + 8\mathbf{j} - 16\mathbf{k}$, symmetric equations of the normal line are

$$\frac{x - 2}{2} = \frac{y - 4}{1} = \frac{z - 2}{-2} \qquad \blacktriangleleft$$

12.7.5 Definition of the Tangent Line to a Curve in Three-Dimensional Space

The **tangent line** to a curve C at the point P_0 is the line through P_0 having as direction numbers the components of the unit tangent vector to C at P_0.

From this definition and Definition 12.7.3, all the tangent lines at the point P_0 to the curves lying on a given surface lie in the tangent plane to the surface at P_0. Refer to Figure 3, showing sketches of a surface and the tangent plane at P_0. The figure also shows sketches of some of the curves through P_0 and their tangent lines.

Consider now the curve C of intersection of two surfaces having equations

$$F(x, y, z) = 0 \quad \text{and} \quad G(x, y, z) = 0$$

respectively. We shall show how to obtain equations of the tangent line to C at a point $P_0(x_0, y_0, z_0)$. Because this tangent line lies in each of the tangent planes to the given surfaces at P_0, it is the line of intersection of the two tangent planes. Let $\mathbf{N}_1$ be a normal vector at P_0 to the surface having the equation $F(x, y, z) = 0$, and let $\mathbf{N}_2$ be a normal vector at P_0 to the surface having the equation $G(x, y, z) = 0$. Then

$$\mathbf{N}_1 = \nabla F(x_0, y_0, z_0) \quad \text{and} \quad \mathbf{N}_2 = \nabla G(x_0, y_0, z_0)$$

Both $\mathbf{N}_1$ and $\mathbf{N}_2$ are orthogonal to the unit tangent vector to C at P_0. Thus if $\mathbf{N}_1$ and $\mathbf{N}_2$ are not parallel, then from Theorem 10.5.10 the unit tangent vector has a direction the same as, or opposite to, the direction of $\mathbf{N}_1 \times \mathbf{N}_2$. Therefore the components of $\mathbf{N}_1 \times \mathbf{N}_2$ serve as a set of direction numbers of the tangent line. From this set of direction numbers and the coordinates of P_0 we can obtain symmetric equations of the required tangent line, as illustrated in the following example.

P_0

FIGURE 3

▶ **EXAMPLE 3**   Find symmetric equations of the tangent line to the curve of intersection of the surfaces

$$3x^2 + 2y^2 + z^2 = 49 \quad \text{and} \quad x^2 + y^2 - 2z^2 = 10$$

at the point $(3, -3, 2)$.

Solution   Let

$$F(x, y, z) = 3x^2 + 2y^2 + z^2 - 49 \quad \text{and} \quad G(x, y, z) = x^2 + y^2 - 2z^2 - 10$$
$$\nabla F(x, y, z) = 6x\mathbf{i} + 4y\mathbf{j} + 2z\mathbf{k} \qquad \nabla G(x, y, z) = 2x\mathbf{i} + 2y\mathbf{j} - 4z\mathbf{k}$$

Therefore

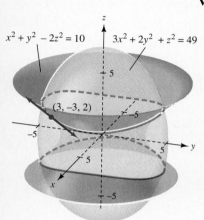

$x^2 + y^2 - 2z^2 = 10$ $3x^2 + 2y^2 + z^2 = 49$

$(3, -3, 2)$

FIGURE 4

$$\begin{aligned}
\mathbf{N}_1 &= \nabla F(3, -3, 2) & \mathbf{N}_2 &= \nabla G(3, -3, 2) \\
&= 18\mathbf{i} - 12\mathbf{j} + 4\mathbf{k} & &= 6\mathbf{i} - 6\mathbf{j} - 8\mathbf{k} \\
&= 2(9\mathbf{i} - 6\mathbf{j} + 2\mathbf{k}) & &= 2(3\mathbf{i} - 3\mathbf{j} - 4\mathbf{k})
\end{aligned}$$

$$\begin{aligned}
\mathbf{N}_1 \times \mathbf{N}_2 &= 4(9\mathbf{i} - 6\mathbf{j} + 2\mathbf{k}) \times (3\mathbf{i} - 3\mathbf{j} - 4\mathbf{k}) \\
&= 4(30\mathbf{i} + 42\mathbf{j} - 9\mathbf{k}) \\
&= 12(10\mathbf{i} + 14\mathbf{j} - 3\mathbf{k})
\end{aligned}$$

Therefore a set of direction numbers of the tangent line is $[10, 14, -3]$. Symmetric equations of the line are, then,

$$\frac{x - 3}{10} = \frac{y + 3}{14} = \frac{z - 2}{-3}$$

Figure 4 shows sketches of the two surfaces, the curve of intersection, and the tangent line at $(3, -3, 2)$.   ◀

If two surfaces have a common tangent plane at a point, the two surfaces are said to be **tangent** at that point. See Figure 5. From Definition 12.7.3, two surfaces, whose equations are $F(x, y, z) = 0$ and $G(x, y, z) = 0$, are tangent at the point (x_0, y_0, z_0) if for some constant k

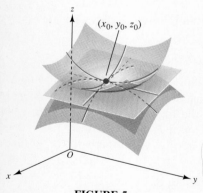

(x_0, y_0, z_0)

FIGURE 5

$$\nabla F(x_0, y_0, z_0) = k \nabla G(x_0, y_0, z_0)$$

▶ **EXAMPLE 4**   Prove that the spheres

$$x^2 + y^2 + z^2 = 4 \quad \text{and} \quad (x - 1)^2 + y^2 + z^2 = 1$$

are tangent at the point $(2, 0, 0)$.

Solution   Let

$$F(x, y, z) = x^2 + y^2 + z^2 - 4 \quad \text{and} \quad G(x, y, z) = (x - 1)^2 + y^2 + z^2 - 1$$
$$\nabla F(x, y, z) = 2x\mathbf{i} + 2y\mathbf{j} + 2z\mathbf{k} \qquad \nabla G(x, y, z) = 2(x - 1)\mathbf{i} + 2y\mathbf{j} + 2z\mathbf{k}$$
$$\begin{aligned}
\mathbf{N}_1 &= \nabla F(2, 0, 0) & \mathbf{N}_2 &= \nabla G(2, 0, 0) \\
&= 4\mathbf{i} & &= 2\mathbf{i}
\end{aligned}$$

Because $\mathbf{N}_1 = 2\mathbf{N}_2$ or, equivalently, $\nabla F(2, 0, 0) = 2 \nabla G(2, 0, 0)$, the spheres are tangent at $(2, 0, 0)$. See Figure 6.   ◀

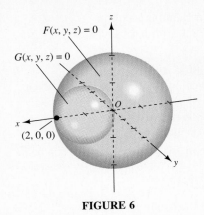

$F(x, y, z) = 0$

$G(x, y, z) = 0$

$(2, 0, 0)$

FIGURE 6

The following theorem for functions of two variables is analogous to Theorem 12.7.2 and the proof is similar.

If an equation of a curve C is $F(x, y) = 0$ and F is differentiable and F_x and F_y are not both zero at the point $P_0(x_0, y_0)$ on C, then $\nabla F(x_0, y_0)$ is a normal vector to C at P_0.

Analogous to Equations (5) and (6) for a tangent plane, we have the following equations for a tangent line at the point $P_0(x_0, y_0)$ on the curve in the xy plane whose equation is $F(x, y) = 0$:

$$F_x(x_0, y_0)(x - x_0) + F_y(x_0, y_0)(y - y_0) = 0$$

or, equivalently,

$$\nabla F(x_0, y_0) \cdot [(x - x_0)\mathbf{i} + (y - y_0)\mathbf{k}] = 0$$

▶ **EXAMPLE 5**   Use the gradient to find an equation of the line tangent to the curve $x^3 + y^3 = 9$ at the point $(1, 2)$.

Solution   Let $F(x, y) = x^3 + y^3 - 9$. The gradient of F is

$$\nabla F(x, y) = 3x^2\mathbf{i} + 3y^2\mathbf{j}$$

At the point $(1, 2)$ on the curve, a normal vector is

$$\nabla F(1, 2) = 3\mathbf{i} + 12\mathbf{j}$$

Therefore, an equation of the tangent line at $(1, 2)$ is

$$\nabla F(1, 2) \cdot [(x - 1)\mathbf{i} + (y - 2)\mathbf{j}] = 0$$
$$(3\mathbf{i} + 12\mathbf{j}) \cdot [(x - 1)\mathbf{i} + (y - 2)\mathbf{j}] = 0$$
$$3(x - 1) + 12(y - 2) = 0$$
$$x + 4y - 9 = 0$$

Figure 7 shows sketches of the curve, and the normal vector and tangent line at $(1, 2)$.   ◀

Compare the solution of Example 5 with the solution of Example 3 in Section 2.9 for the same problem.

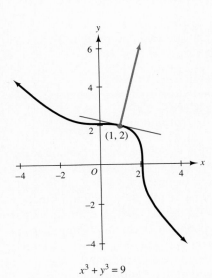

$(1, 2)$

$x^3 + y^3 = 9$

FIGURE 7

EXERCISES 12.7

In Exercises 1 through 12, find an equation of the tangent plane and equations of the normal line to the surface at the indicated point.

1. $x^2 + y^2 + z^2 = 17$; $(2, -2, 3)$

2. $4x^2 + y^2 + 2z^2 = 26$; $(1, -2, 3)$

3. $x^2 + y^2 - 3z = 2$; $(-2, -4, 6)$

4. $x^2 + y^2 - z^2 = 6$; $(3, -1, 2)$

5. $y = e^x \cos z$; $(1, e, 0)$

6. $z = e^{3x} \sin 3y$; $(0, \frac{1}{6}\pi, 1)$

7. $x^2 = 12y$; $(6, 3, 3)$

8. $z = x^{1/2} + y^{1/2}$; $(1, 1, 2)$

9. $x^{1/2} + y^{1/2} + z^{1/2} = 4$; $(4, 1, 1)$

10. $zx^2 - xy^2 - yz^2 = 18$; $(0, -2, 3)$

11. $x^{2/3} + y^{2/3} + z^{2/3} = 14$; $(-8, 27, 1)$

12. $x^{1/2} + z^{1/2} = 8$; $(25, 2, 9)$

In Exercises 13 through 20, if the two surfaces intersect in a curve, find equations of the tangent line to the curve of intersection at the given point; if the two surfaces are tangent at the given point, prove it.

13. $x^2 + y^2 - z = 8$, $x - y^2 + z^2 = -2$; $(2, -2, 0)$

14. $x^2 + y^2 - 2z + 1 = 0$, $x^2 + y^2 - z^2 = 0$; $(0, 1, 1)$

15. $y = x^2$, $y = 16 - z^2$; $(4, 16, 0)$

16. $x = 2 + \cos \pi yz$, $y = 1 + \sin \pi xz$; $(3, 1, 2)$

17. $y = e^x \sin 2\pi z + 2$, $z = y^2 - \ln(x + 1) - 3$; $(0, 2, 1)$

18. $x^2 - 3xy + y^2 = z$, $2x^2 + y^2 - 3z + 27 = 0$; $(1, -2, 11)$

19. $x^2 + z^2 + 4y = 0$, $x^2 + y^2 + z^2 - 6z + 7 = 0$; $(0, -1, 2)$

20. $x^2 + y^2 + z^2 = 8$, $yz = 4$; $(0, 2, 2)$

In Exercises 21 through 24, use the gradient to find an equation of the tangent line to the given curve at the indicated point.

21. $9x^3 - y^3 = 1$; $(1, 2)$

22. $16x^4 + y^4 = 32$; $(1, 2)$

23. $2x^3 + 2y^3 - 9xy = 0$; $(1, 2)$

24. $x^4 + 2xy - y^2 = 4$; $(2, -2)$

25. Show that the spheres $x^2 + y^2 + z^2 = a^2$ and $(x - b)^2 + y^2 + z^2 = (b - a)^2$ are tangent at the point $(a, 0, 0)$.

26. Show that the surfaces $4x^2 + y^2 + 9z^2 = 108$ and $xyz = 36$ are tangent at the point $(3, 6, 2)$.

27. Two surfaces are said to be *perpendicular* at a point P_0 of intersection if the normal vectors to the surfaces at P_0 are orthogonal. Show that at the point $(1, -1, 2)$ the surface $x^2 - 2yz + y^3 = 4$ is perpendicular to every member of the family of surfaces $x^2 + (4c - 2)y^2 - cz^2 + 1 = 0$.

28. Prove that every normal line to the sphere $x^2 + y^2 + z^2 = a^2$ passes through the center of the sphere.

12.8 EXTREMA OF FUNCTIONS OF TWO VARIABLES

You learned in Chapter 3 that an important use of the derivative of a single variable entailed extreme values of a function, which led to a variety of applications. In that discussion we proved theorems involving the first and second derivatives, from which relative maximum and minimum function values were determined. We then showed that the relative extreme values were included in the possibilities for absolute extrema. In extending the theory to functions of two variables, you will see that the procedure is similar to the one-variable case; however, more complications arise.

We begin by defining both *absolute* and *relative extrema* of functions of two variables.

12.8.1 Definition of Absolute Extrema of Functions of Two Variables

(i) The function f of two variables is said to have an **absolute maximum value** on its domain D in the xy plane if there is some point (x_0, y_0) in D such that $f(x_0, y_0) \geq f(x, y)$ for all points (x, y) in D. In such a case, $f(x_0, y_0)$ is the absolute maximum value of f on D.

(ii) The function f of two variables is said to have an **absolute minimum value** on its domain D in the xy plane if there is some point (x_0, y_0) in D such that $f(x_0, y_0) \leq f(x, y)$ for all (x, y) in D. In such a case, $f(x_0, y_0)$ is the absolute minimum value of f on D.

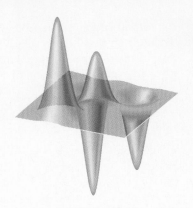

FIGURE 1

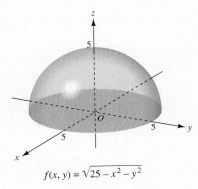

$f(x, y) = \sqrt{25 - x^2 - y^2}$

FIGURE 2

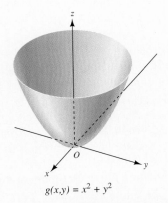

$g(x,y) = x^2 + y^2$

FIGURE 3

12.8.2 Definition of Relative Extrema of Functions of Two Variables

(i) The function f of two variables is said to have a **relative maximum value** at the point (x_0, y_0) if there exists an open disk $B((x_0, y_0); r)$ such that $f(x_0, y_0) \geq f(x, y)$ for all (x, y) in B.

(ii) The function f of two variables is said to have a **relative minimum value** at the point (x_0, y_0) if there exists an open disk $B((x_0, y_0); r)$ such that $f(x_0, y_0) \leq f(x, y)$ for all (x, y) in B.

Refer to Figure 1 showing the graph of a function f whose domain is the xy plane. The function has four relative extrema, one of which is an absolute maximum and one of which is an absolute minimum. If the domain of a function is either an open disk or the entire xy plane, as in Figure 1, an absolute extremum must be a relative extremum.

▷ **ILLUSTRATION 1** Figure 2 shows the graph of the function defined by

$$f(x, y) = \sqrt{25 - x^2 - y^2}$$

Let B be any open disk $((0, 0); r)$ for which $r < 5$. From Definition 12.8.2(i), f has a relative maximum value of 5 at the point where $x = 0$ and $y = 0$. From Definition 12.8.1(i), 5 is also the absolute maximum value of f. ◀

▷ **ILLUSTRATION 2** Figure 3 shows the graph of the function defined by

$$g(x, y) = x^2 + y^2$$

The domain of g is the entire xy plane. Let B be any open disk $((0, 0); r)$. From Definition 12.8.2(ii), g has a relative minimum value of 0 at the origin. From Definition 12.8.1(ii), 0 is also the absolute minimum value of g. ◀

Theorem 3.1.3 stated: If $f(x)$ exists for all values of x in the open interval (a, b), and if f has a relative extremum at c, where $a < c < b$, and if $f'(c)$ exists, then $f'(c) = 0$. The following theorem for functions of two variables is analogous.

12.8.3 Theorem

If $f(x, y)$ exists at all points in some open disk $B((x_0, y_0); r)$ and if f has a relative extremum at (x_0, y_0), then if $f_x(x_0, y_0)$ and $f_y(x_0, y_0)$ exist,

$$f_x(x_0, y_0) = 0 \quad \text{and} \quad f_y(x_0, y_0) = 0$$

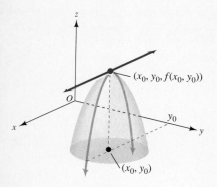

FIGURE 4

Before proving this theorem, we give an informal geometric argument. Let f be a function, satisfying the hypothesis and such that f has a relative maximum value at (x_0, y_0). Consider the curve of intersection of the plane $y = y_0$ with the surface $z = f(x, y)$, as shown in Figure 4. This curve is represented by the equations

$$y = y_0 \quad \text{and} \quad z = f(x, y)$$

Because f has a relative maximum value at the point where $x = x_0$ and $y = y_0$, this curve has a horizontal tangent line in the plane $y = y_0$ at $(x_0, y_0, f(x_0, y_0))$. The slope of this tangent line is $f_x(x_0, y_0)$; so $f_x(x_0, y_0) = 0$. In a similar way we can consider the curve of intersection of the plane $x = x_0$ with the surface $z = f(x, y)$ and obtain $f_y(x_0, y_0) = 0$. A similar discussion can be given if f has a relative minimum value at (x_0, y_0). Following is the formal proof, which utilizes Theorem 3.1.3.

Proof of Theorem 12.8.3 Consider the two functions g and h of a single variable defined by

$$g(x) = f(x, y_0) \quad \text{and} \quad h(y) = f(x_0, y)$$

Then

$$g'(x_0) = f_x(x_0, y_0) \quad \text{and} \quad h'(y_0) = f_y(x_0, y_0)$$

Because $f_x(x_0, y_0)$ and $f_y(x_0, y_0)$ exist, $g'(x_0)$ and $h'(y_0)$ exist. Because f has a relative extremum at (x_0, y_0), g has a relative extremum at x_0 and h has a relative extremum at y_0. Thus by Theorem 3.1.3,

$$g'(x_0) = 0 \quad \text{and} \quad h'(y_0) = 0$$

Therefore

$$f_x(x_0, y_0) = 0 \quad \text{and} \quad f_y(x_0, y_0) = 0 \qquad \blacksquare$$

Observe that the condition that both $f_x(x_0, y_0)$ and $f_y(x_0, y_0)$ are zero is equivalent to the condition that the gradient vector $\nabla f(x_0, y_0)$ is zero. Furthermore, this condition implies that the graph of f has a horizontal tangent plane at the point $(x_0, y_0, f(x_0, y_0))$. You are asked to prove this in Exercise 51.

From Theorem 12.8.3, a necessary condition for a function of two variables to have a relative extremum at a point is that either its first partial derivatives are both zero at the point or at least one of the partial derivatives does not exist at the point. Such a point is called a *critical point* of the function.

12.8.4 Definition of a Critical Point

If $f(x, y)$ exists at all points in some open disk $B((x_0, y_0); r)$, the point (x_0, y_0) is a critical point of f if one of the following conditions holds:

(i) $f_x(x_0, y_0) = 0$ and $f_y(x_0, y_0) = 0$;
(ii) $f_x(x_0, y_0)$ or $f_y(x_0, y_0)$ does not exist.

When examining a function for relative extrema, we first locate any critical points. We must then apply other criteria to determine if a relative extremum occurs at a particular critical point.

▶ **EXAMPLE 1** Find any relative extrema of the function defined by

$$f(x, y) = 6x - 4y - x^2 - 2y^2$$

Solution We begin by finding any critical points of f. Differentiating we obtain

$$f_x(x, y) = 6 - 2x \quad \text{and} \quad f_y(x, y) = -4 - 4y$$

Both partial derivatives exist everywhere. Setting $f_x(x, y)$ and $f_y(x, y)$ equal to zero, we get $x = 3$ and $y = -1$. Therefore, the only critical point is $(3, -1)$, and $f(3, -1) = 11$. To test for a relative extremum at $(3, -1)$ we complete the squares in the expression for $f(x, y)$:

$$f(x, y) = -(x^2 - 6x + 9) - 2(y^2 + 2y + 1) + 9 + 2$$
$$= -(x - 3)^2 - 2(y + 1)^2 + 11$$

Thus, if $(x, y) \neq (3, -1)$, $f(x, y) < 11$. Therefore, by Definition 12.8.2(i), $f(3, -1) = 11$ is a relative maximum value. By Definition 12.8.1(i), this is also an absolute maximum value.

See Figure 5 for the graph of f, which is a paraboloid opening downward with its vertex at $(3, -1, 11)$. The graph supports our answer. ◀

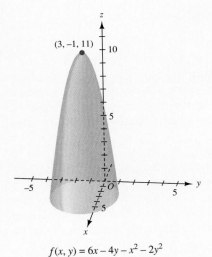

$f(x, y) = 6x - 4y - x^2 - 2y^2$

FIGURE 5

▶ **EXAMPLE 2** Find any relative extrema of the function defined by

$$g(x, y) = 4 - \sqrt{x^2 + y^2}$$

Solution We compute the partial derivatives of g:

$$g_x(x, y) = -\frac{x}{\sqrt{x^2 + y^2}} \quad \text{and} \quad g_y(x, y) = -\frac{y}{\sqrt{x^2 + y^2}}$$

The domain of g is the set of all points in R^2 and g_x and g_y exist at all points except $(0, 0)$. Furthermore, $g_x(x, y) = 0$ only when $x = 0$, but then $g_y(x, y) \neq 0$; and $g_y(x, y) = 0$ only when $y = 0$, but then $g_x(x, y) \neq 0$.

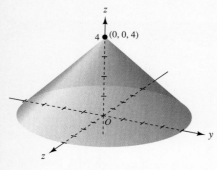

$$g(x, y) = 4 - \sqrt{x^2 + y^2}$$

FIGURE 6

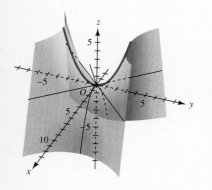

$$f(x,y) = y^2 - x^2$$

FIGURE 7

Therefore, the only critical point of g is $(0, 0)$. Because $g(0, 0) = 4$ and if $(x, y) \neq (0, 0)$

$$g(x, y) = 4 - \sqrt{x^2 + y^2} < 4$$

g has a relative maximum value of 4 at $(0, 0)$, which is also an absolute maximum value. Figure 6 shows the graph of g having its highest point at $(0, 0, 4)$, which supports our answer. ◀

A critical point of a function does not necessarily yield a relative extremum for the function, as demonstrated in the following illustration.

▷ **ILLUSTRATION 3**   Let the function f be defined by

$$f(x, y) = y^2 - x^2$$

Then

$$f_x(x, y) = -2x \qquad f_y(x, y) = 2y$$

Both $f_x(0, 0)$ and $f_y(0, 0)$ equal zero. The graph of f appearing in Figure 7 is saddle-shaped at points close to the origin. At points in the xz plane, where $y = 0$ and $x \neq 0$, the function values are negative, and at points in the yz plane, where $x = 0$ and $y \neq 0$, the function values are positive. The function f, therefore, does not satisfy Definition 12.8.1 when $(x_0, y_0) = (0, 0)$. ◀

A critical point at which there is no relative extremum, such as the point $(0, 0, 0)$ in Illustration 3, is called a **saddle point** of the function f.

The basic test for determining relative extrema for functions of two variables is the following *second-derivative test*, which gives conditions guaranteeing that a function has a relative extremum at a point where the first partial derivatives are zero.

12.8.5 Theorem   Second-Derivative Test

Let f be a function of two variables such that f and its first- and second-order partial derivatives are continuous on some open disk $B((a, b); r)$. Suppose further that $f_x(a, b) = 0$ and $f_y(a, b) = 0$. Let

$$D(a, b) = f_{xx}(a, b) f_{yy}(a, b) - [f_{xy}(a, b)]^2$$

(i) f has a relative minimum value at (a, b) if

$$D(a, b) > 0 \quad \text{and} \quad f_{xx}(a, b) > 0 \quad (\text{or } f_{yy}(a, b) > 0)$$

(ii) f has a relative maximum value at (a, b) if

$$D(a, b) > 0 \quad \text{and} \quad f_{xx}(a, b) < 0 \quad (\text{or } f_{yy}(a, b) < 0)$$

(iii) $f(a, b)$ is not a relative extremum, but f has a saddle point at $(a, b, f(a, b))$ if

$$D(a, b) < 0$$

(iv) No conclusion regarding relative extrema can be made if

$$D(a, b) = 0$$

The proof of part (i) of the second-derivative test appears in the supplement of this section. The proofs of parts (ii) and (iii) are left as Supplementary Exercises 1 and 2. Part (iv) is included to cover all possible cases.

If $f_{xy}(a, b) = f_{yx}(a, b)$ the expression for $D(a, b)$ in the statement of the second-derivative test is the value of the determinant

$$\begin{vmatrix} f_{xx}(a, b) & f_{xy}(a, b) \\ f_{yx}(a, b) & f_{yy}(a, b) \end{vmatrix}$$

This determinant, called the **Hessian** (or **discriminant**) of the function f, provides a convenient method for remembering $D(a, b)$.

▶ *EXAMPLE 3*   Given

$$f(x, y) = 2x^4 + y^2 - x^2 - 2y$$

determine the relative extrema of f if there are any.

Solution   To apply the second-derivative test, we find the first and second partial derivatives of f.

$$f_x(x, y) = 8x^3 - 2x \qquad f_y(x, y) = 2y - 2$$
$$f_{xx}(x, y) = 24x^2 - 2 \qquad f_{yy}(x, y) = 2 \qquad f_{xy}(x, y) = 0$$

Setting $f_x(x, y) = 0$ we get $x = -\frac{1}{2}$, $x = 0$, or $x = \frac{1}{2}$. Setting $f_y(x, y) = 0$ we obtain $y = 1$. Therefore f_x and f_y are both 0 at the points $(-\frac{1}{2}, 1)$, $(0, 1)$, and $(\frac{1}{2}, 1)$, and these are the critical points of f. The results of applying the second-derivative test at these points are summarized in Table 1.

Table 1

Critical Point (a, b)	$f_{xx}(a, b)$	$f_{yy}(a, b)$	$f_{xy}(a, b)$	$D(a, b)$	Conclusion
$(-\frac{1}{2}, 1)$	4	2	0	8	f has a relative minimum value
$(0, 1)$	-2	2	0	-4	f does not have a relative extremum
$(\frac{1}{2}, 1)$	4	2	0	8	f has a relative minimum value

At the critical points $(-\frac{1}{2}, 1)$ and $(\frac{1}{2}, 1)$, f has a relative minimum value from part (i) of the second-derivative test. At the critical point $(0, 1)$, from part (iii) of the test, f does not have a relative extremum.

Because $f(-\frac{1}{2}, 1) = -\frac{9}{8}$ and $f(\frac{1}{2}, 1) = -\frac{9}{8}$, we conclude that f has a relative minimum value of $-\frac{9}{8}$ at the two critical points $(-\frac{1}{2}, 1)$ and $(\frac{1}{2}, 1)$.

Figure 8 showing the graph of f with low points at $(-\frac{1}{2}, 1, -\frac{9}{8})$ and $(\frac{1}{2}, 1, -\frac{9}{8})$ and a saddle point at $(0, 1, -1)$ supports our results.   ◀

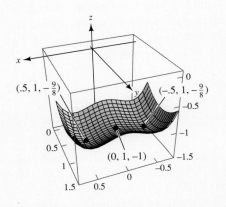

FIGURE 8

▶ *EXAMPLE 4*   Determine the relative dimensions of a rectangular box, without a top and having a specific volume, if the least amount of material is to be used in its manufacture.

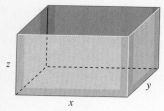

FIGURE 9

Solution Figure 9 shows the box where x units is the length of the base, y units is the width of the base, and z units is the depth. Let S square units be the surface area of the box. If V cubic units is the volume of the box, V is a constant because the box has a specific volume.

Each of the variables x, y, and z is in the interval $(0, +\infty)$. From the formulas for surface area and volume,

$$S = xy + 2xz + 2yz \quad \text{and} \quad V = xyz$$

Solving the second equation for z in terms of x, y, and the constant V, we get $z = \dfrac{V}{xy}$, and substituting this into the first equation gives

$$S = xy + \frac{2V}{y} + \frac{2V}{x} \tag{1}$$

Differentiating we get

$$\frac{\partial S}{\partial x} = y - \frac{2V}{x^2} \qquad\qquad \frac{\partial S}{\partial y} = x - \frac{2V}{y^2}$$

$$\frac{\partial^2 S}{\partial x^2} = \frac{4V}{x^3} \qquad\qquad \frac{\partial^2 S}{\partial y\, \partial x} = 1 \qquad\qquad \frac{\partial^2 S}{\partial y^2} = \frac{4V}{y^3}$$

Setting $\dfrac{\partial S}{\partial x} = 0$ and $\dfrac{\partial S}{\partial y} = 0$ we have

$$x^2 y - 2V = 0$$
$$xy^2 - 2V = 0$$

Solving these two equations simultaneously, we obtain $x = \sqrt[3]{2V}$ and $y = \sqrt[3]{2V}$. For these values of x and y,

$$\frac{\partial^2 S}{\partial x^2} = \frac{4V}{(\sqrt[3]{2V})^3} \qquad \frac{\partial^2 S}{\partial x^2} \cdot \frac{\partial^2 S}{\partial y^2} - \left(\frac{\partial^2 S}{\partial y\, \partial x}\right)^2 = \frac{4V}{(\sqrt[3]{2V})^3} \cdot \frac{4V}{(\sqrt[3]{2V})^3} - 1$$

$$= 2 > 0 \qquad\qquad\qquad\qquad\qquad = 3 > 0$$

From part (i) of the second-derivative test, S has a relative minimum value when $x = \sqrt[3]{2V}$ and $y = \sqrt[3]{2V}$. Recall that x and y are both in the interval $(0, +\infty)$, and notice from Equation (1) that S is very large when x and y are either close to zero or very large. We therefore conclude that the relative minimum value of S is an absolute minimum value of S.

Because $z = V/(xy)$, then when $x = \sqrt[3]{2V}$ and $y = \sqrt[3]{2V}$,

$$z = \frac{V}{\sqrt[3]{4V^2}}$$

$$= \frac{\sqrt[3]{2V}}{2}$$

<u>Conclusion:</u> The box should have a square base and a depth one-half the length of a side of the base. ◀

Recall the extreme-value theorem for functions of a single variable: If the function f is continuous on a closed interval, then f has an absolute

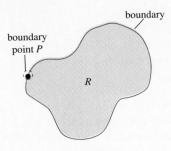

FIGURE 10

FIGURE 11

FIGURE 12

FIGURE 13

maximum value and an absolute minimum value on that closed interval. You learned that an absolute extremum of a function continuous on a closed interval must be either a relative extremum or a function value at an endpoint of the interval. A corresponding situation, involving an extreme-value theorem, occurs for functions of two variables.

The terminology *closed bounded region* is used in the statement of the extreme-value theorem for functions of two variables. A region R is **bounded** if it is a subregion of a closed disk. The **boundary** of a region R is the set of all points P for which every open disk having its center at P contains a point in R and a point not in R. A **closed region** is one that contains its boundary.

See Figure 10 showing a closed bounded region R, the boundary of R, and a point P on the boundary. The following illustration gives some closed bounded regions, and the boundary of each region is identified.

▷ **ILLUSTRATION 4**

(a) A closed disk is a closed bounded region. The boundary is the circumference of the disk. See Figure 11.
(b) The sides of a triangle together with the region enclosed by the triangle is a closed bounded region. The boundary consists of the sides of the triangle. See Figure 12.
(c) The edges of a rectangle together with the region enclosed by the rectangle is a closed bounded region. Tbe boundary consists of the edges of the rectangle. See Figure 13.   ◀

12.8.6 The Extreme-Value Theorem for Functions of Two Variables

Let R be a closed bounded region in the xy plane, and let f be a continuous function on R. Then f has an absolute maximum value and an absolute minimum value on R.

The proof of this theorem is beyond the scope of this book and is omitted.

If f is a function of two variables satisfying the extreme-value theorem, then an absolute extremum of f is either a relative extremum or a function value at a point on the boundary of the region R. The absolute extrema in such a situation can then be determined by the following procedure:

1. Find the function values at the critical points of f in the interior of region R.
2. Find any possible extreme values of f on the boundary of region R.
3. The largest of the values from steps 1 and 2 is the absolute maximum value, and the smallest of the values is the absolute minimum value.

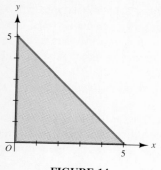

FIGURE 14

▶ **EXAMPLE 5**   Find the absolute extrema of the function defined by

$$f(x, y) = x^2 + y^2 - 4x - 2y + 7$$

if the domain of f is the closed triangular region whose sides are on the x axis, the y axis, and the line $x + y = 5$.

Solution   Figure 14 shows the given closed triangular region R. The polynomial function f is continuous on R, so the extreme-value theorem applies. To find the critical points of f we compute the first partial derivatives:

$$f_x(x, y) = 2x - 4   \text{and}   f_y(x, y) = 2y - 2$$

The partial derivatives exist everywhere. Setting $f_x(x, y)$ and $f_y(x, y)$ equal to 0, we obtain $x = 2$ and $y = 1$. The only critical point of f is, therefore, $(2, 1)$.

We now consider function values on the boundary of R. We examine each side of the triangle separately.

On the x axis, where $y = 0$ and $0 \leq x \leq 5$, we have $f(x, 0) = x^2 - 4x + 7$, a quadratic function of a single variable. Let $\alpha(x) = f(x, 0)$, so that

$$\alpha(x) = x^2 - 4x + 7   0 \leq x \leq 5$$

The function α will have extreme values either where $\alpha'(x) = 0$ or at the endpoints of the interval $[0, 5]$.

$$\alpha'(x) = 2x - 4$$

Setting $\alpha'(x) = 0$, we get $x = 2$. Thus on the x axis, we must consider function values at $(2, 0)$, $(0, 0)$, and $(5, 0)$.

On the y axis, $x = 0$ and $0 \leq y \leq 5$, and $f(0, y) = y^2 - 2y + 7$. Let $\beta(y) = f(0, y)$, so that

$$\beta(y) = y^2 - 2y + 7   0 \leq y \leq 5$$
$$\beta'(y) = 2y - 2$$

Setting $\beta'(y) = 0$, we get $y = 1$. Therefore on the y axis, we must consider function values at $(0, 1)$ $(0, 0)$, and $(0, 5)$.

On the line $x + y = 5$: $y = 5 - x$; $0 \leq x \leq 5$; and $0 \leq y \leq 5$.

$$f(x, 5 - x) = x^2 + (5 - x)^2 - 4x - 2(5 - x) + 7$$
$$= 2x^2 - 12x + 22   0 \leq x \leq 5$$

Let $\gamma(x) = f(x, 5 - x)$, so that

$$\gamma(x) = 2x^2 - 12x + 22   0 \leq x \leq 5$$
$$\gamma'(x) = 4x - 12$$

Setting $\gamma'(x) = 0$, we get $x = 3$. Thus on the line $x + y = 5$, we must consider function values at $(3, 2)$, $(5, 0)$, and $(0, 5)$.

So in summary, the possible points (x, y) for absolute extrema are $(2, 1)$, $(2, 0)$, $(0, 1)$, $(3, 2)$, $(0, 0)$, $(5, 0)$, and $(0, 5)$. The function values at these points are listed in Table 2. The absolute maximum value is $f(0, 5) = 22$ and the absolute minimum value is $f(2, 1) = 2$.

Table 2

(x, y)	$f(x, y)$
$(2, 1)$	2
$(2, 0)$	3
$(0, 1)$	6
$(3, 2)$	4
$(0, 0)$	7
$(5, 0)$	12
$(0, 5)$	22

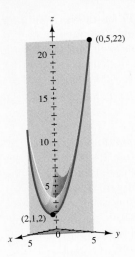

FIGURE 15

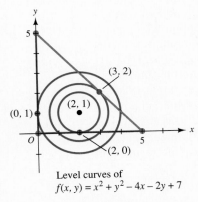

Level curves of
$f(x, y) = x^2 + y^2 - 4x - 2y + 7$

FIGURE 16

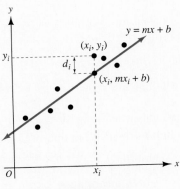

FIGURE 17

Figure 15 shows the graph of f: the portion of a paraboloid above the given triangular region in the xy plane. The graph supports our results.

Figure 16 shows the triangular region R and three level curves of f, circles in the xy plane with centers at $(2, 1)$. Observe that the boundary points in Table 2 are the vertices of the triangle, the center of the circles, and the points on the sides of the triangle where the side is tangent to a level curve. ◀

Throughout this book, you have seen how mathematical models are utilized in many applications. Often these models were in the form of equations containing the variables in the situation. Various methods are used to obtain such models, one of which involves a *regression line* that *best fits* a set of data points. The procedure for finding a regression line requires locating an absolute minimum value of a function of two variables.

Suppose, for instance, we wish to find a mathematical model for some data given by a set of points $(x_1, y_1), (x_2, y_2), \ldots, (x_n, y_n)$. In particular, y_i may be the number of dollars in a manufacturer's weekly profit when x_i is the number of units sold in a week, or y_i could be a company's total annual sales when x_i years have elapsed since the start of the company. The number of new cases of a certain disease could be y_i when x_i is the number of days since the outbreak of an epidemic of the disease. The desired model is a relationship involving x and y that can be used to make future predictions. Such a relationship is afforded by a line that "fits" the data.

To arrive at a suitable definition for the line of best fit we first indicate how well a particular line fits a set of data points by measuring the vertical distances from the points to the line. For instance, Figure 17 shows n data points, and the line $y = mx + b$. The point (x_i, y_i) is the ith data point, and corresponding to it on the line is the point $(x_i, mx_i + b)$. The **deviation** (or **error**) between the ith data point and the line is defined to be d_i, where

$$d_i = y_i - (mx_i + b)$$

The sum of the squares of the deviations is

$$\sum_{i=1}^{n} d_i^2 = \sum_{i=1}^{n} [y_i - (mx_i + b)]^2$$

which is never negative and is zero only if each d_i is zero, in which case all the data points lie on the line. We shall take as the line of best fit the one for which $\sum_{i=1}^{n} d_i^2$ is an absolute minimum. This line is called the **regression line** of y on x, and the process for finding it is called the **method of least squares.**

We now give the procedure for using the method of least squares to find the regression line $y = mx + b$ for a set of n data points. Because x_i and y_i are constants and m and b are variables, $\sum_{i=1}^{n} d_i^2$ is a function of m and b. Denote this function by f, so that

$$f(m, b) = \sum_{i=1}^{n} (y_i - mx_i - b)^2$$

To find the values of m and b that make $f(m, b)$ an absolute minimum, we first compute the partial derivatives $f_m(m, b)$ and $f_b(m, b)$.

$$f_m(m, b) = \sum_{i=1}^{n} \frac{\partial}{\partial m}[(y_i - mx_i - b)^2]$$

$$= \sum_{i=1}^{n} 2(y_i - mx_i - b)(-x_i)$$

$$= 2\sum_{i=1}^{n} (-x_i y_i + mx_i^2 + bx_i)$$

$$= 2\left[-\sum_{i=1}^{n} x_i y_i + m\sum_{i=1}^{n} x_i^2 + b\sum_{i=1}^{n} x_i\right]$$

$$f_b(m, b) = \sum_{i=1}^{n} \frac{\partial}{\partial b}[(y_i - mx_i - b)^2]$$

$$= \sum_{i=1}^{n} 2(y_i - mx_i - b)(-1)$$

$$= 2\sum_{i=1}^{n} (-y_i + mx_i + b)$$

$$= 2\left(-\sum_{i=1}^{n} y_i + m\sum_{i=1}^{n} x_i + nb\right)$$

Setting $f_m(m, b) = 0$ and $f_b(m, b) = 0$ we obtain two simultaneous equations in m and b:

$$\left(\sum_{i=1}^{n} x_i^2\right)m + \left(\sum_{i=1}^{n} x_i\right)b = \sum_{i=1}^{n} x_i y_i \qquad (2)$$

and

$$\left(\sum_{i=1}^{n} x_i\right)m + nb = \sum_{i=1}^{n} y_i$$

Solving the second equation for b gives

$$b = \frac{1}{n}\left(\sum_{i=1}^{n} y_i - m\sum_{i=1}^{n} x_i\right) \qquad (3)$$

Substituting this value of b in (2) we get

$$m = \frac{n\sum_{i=1}^{n} x_i y_i - \sum_{i=1}^{n} x_i \sum_{i=1}^{n} y_i}{n\sum_{i=1}^{n} x_i^2 - \left(\sum_{i=1}^{n} x_i\right)^2} \qquad (4)$$

In Exercise 52 you are asked to supply the details involved to obtain Equation (4) from (2) and (3). In Exercise 53 you are asked to use the second-derivative test to show that f has a relative minimum value for the values of m and b in (3) and (4). You will see that there is only one relative extremum for f. Also, m and b are both in the interval $(-\infty, +\infty)$ and $f(m, b)$ is large when either the absolute value of m or the absolute value of b is large. Thus we can conclude that the relative minimum value of f is an absolute minimum value.

Observe that four distinct summations appear in formulas (3) and (4). These formulas can be evaluated on a computer or many calculators. When a small amount of data is involved, a convenient way of computing the summations is shown in the following examples.

▶ **EXAMPLE 6**   A rare antique was purchased in 1975 for $1200. Its value was $1800 in 1980, $2500 in 1985, and $3100 in 1990. If the value of the antique were to appreciate according to the same pattern through 2000, use the method of least squares to estimate the value of the antique in the year 2000.

Solution   To find a regression line $y = mx + b$, we let x be the number of 5-year periods since 1975 and let y dollars be the value of the antique $5x$ years since 1975. Thus we have the data points given in Table 3.

Table 4 shows the computation of the four summations appearing in Equations (3) and (4). From the table,

$$\sum_{i=1}^{4} x_i = 6 \qquad \sum_{i=1}^{4} y_i = 8600 \qquad \sum_{i=1}^{4} x_i^2 = 14 \qquad \sum_{i=1}^{4} x_i y_i = 16{,}100$$

With these values and $n = 4$ we obtain, from (4) and (3),

$$m = \frac{4(16{,}100) - 6(8600)}{4(14) - 6(6)} \qquad b = \tfrac{1}{4}[8600 - 640(6)]$$
$$= 640 \qquad\qquad = 1190$$

An equation of the regression line is, therefore,

$$y = 640x + 1190$$

For the year 2000, $x = 5$, and for this value of x

$$y = 640(5) + 1190$$
$$= 4390$$

Conclusion: The value of the antique is estimated to be $4390 in the year 2000.   ◀

▶ **EXAMPLE 7**   In Table 5, x days have elapsed since the outbreak of a particular disease, and y is the number of new cases of the disease on the xth day. **(a)** Find the regression line for the data points (x_i, y_i). **(b)** Use the regression line to estimate the number of new cases of the disease on the sixth day.

Solution

(a) The required line has the equation $y = mx + b$. To determine m and b we first find the summations in Equations (3) and (4) from the computation in Table 6. From the table,

$$\sum_{i=1}^{5} x_i = 15 \qquad \sum_{i=1}^{5} y_i = 151 \qquad \sum_{i=1}^{5} x_i^2 = 55 \qquad \sum_{i=1}^{5} x_i y_i = 508$$

Table 3

x	0	1	2	3
y	1200	1800	2500	3100

Table 4

x_i	y_i	x_i^2	$x_i y_i$
0	1200	0	0
1	1800	1	1800
2	2500	4	5000
3	3100	9	9300
$\sum$ 6	8600	14	16,100

Table 5

x	1	2	3	4	5
y	20	24	30	35	42

Table 6

x_i	y_i	x_i^2	$x_i y_i$
1	20	1	20
2	24	4	48
3	30	9	90
4	35	16	140
5	42	25	210
$\sum$ 15	151	55	508

From (4) and (3) with these values and $n = 5$ we obtain

$$m = \frac{5(508) - (15)(151)}{5(55) - (15)(15)} \qquad b = \frac{1}{5}[151 - 5.5(15)]$$
$$= 5.5 \qquad\qquad = 13.7$$

Therefore the regression line has the equation

$$y = 5.5x + 13.7$$

(b) With $x = 6$ in the equation of the regression line,

$$y = 5.5(6) + 13.7$$
$$= 46.7$$

Conclusion: On the sixth day of the epidemic, 47 new cases are estimated.

◀

Many calculators have built-in programs for obtaining a linear regression model by a least-squares fit. If your calculator has this capability, use it to support the results of Examples 6 and 7. Other built-in programs can produce quadratic, cubic, quartic, logarithmic, and exponential regression models. Refer to your users manual for the key strokes for your particular calculator if it has these capabilities.

EXERCISES 12.8

In Exercises 1 through 6, find any relative extrema of the function by first finding the critical points and then applying Definition 12.8.2. Determine if any relative extremum is an absolute extremum.

1. $f(x, y) = \sqrt{16 - x^2 - y^2}$

2. $f(x, y) = \sqrt{x^2 + y^2 + 9}$

3. $f(x, y) = x^2 + y^2 - 4x - 8y + 16$

4. $f(x, y) = 2 + 2x + 6y - x^2 - y^2$

5. $f(x, y) = 9 - \sqrt{x^2 + y^2 - 2x + 1}$

6. $f(x, y) = \sqrt{x^2 + y^2} + 1$

In Exercises 7 through 18, determine the relative extrema of f, if there are any, and locate any saddle points.

7. $f(x, y) = x^3 + y^2 - 6x^2 + y - 1$

8. $f(x, y) = 18x^2 - 32y^2 - 36x - 128y - 110$

9. $f(x, y) = y^2 - x^2 + 2x - 4y + 3$

10. $f(x, y) = x^2 - y^2 + 6x - 8y + 25$

11. $f(x, y) = \dfrac{1}{x} - \dfrac{64}{y} + xy$

12. $f(x, y) = x^2 - 4xy + y^3 + 4y$

13. $f(x, y) = 4xy^2 - 2x^2y - x$

14. $f(x, y) = y^4 - 4y^3 + 2x^2 + 8xy$

15. $f(x, y) = x^3 + y^3 + 3y^2 - 3x - 9y + 2$

16. $f(x, y) = e^x \sin y$ **17.** $f(x, y) = e^{xy}$

18. $f(x, y) = x^3 + y^3 - 18xy$

In Exercises 19 through 24, find the absolute extrema of the function whose domain is the closed bounded region R in the xy plane.

19. The function of Exercise 3; R is the triangular region having vertices at $(0, 0)$, $(4, 0)$, and $(0, 8)$

20. The function of Exercise 4; R is the triangular region whose sides are the x axis, the y axis, and the line $x + y = 5$

21. $f(x, y) = 3x^2 + xy$; R is the region bounded by the parabola $y = x^2$ and the line $y = 4$

22. $f(x, y) = x^2 - 2xy + 2y$; R is the region bounded by the parabola $y = 4 - x^2$ and the x axis.

23. $f(x, y) = y^3 + x^2 - 3y$; R is the region bounded by the circle $x^2 + (y - 1)^2 = 1$

24. $f(x, y) = \sin x + \sin y$; R is the region bounded by the square having vertices at $(0, 0)$, $(\pi, 0)$, $(0, \pi)$, and (π, π)

25. Find the three positive numbers whose sum is 24 such that their product is as great as possible.

26. Find the three positive numbers whose product is 24 such that their sum is as small as possible.

27. Find the point in the plane $3x + 2y - z = 5$ that is closest to the point $(1, -2, 3)$, and find the minimum distance.

28. Find the points on the surface $y^2 - xz = 4$ that are closest to the origin, and find the minimum distance.

29. Find the points on the curve of intersection of the ellipsoid $x^2 + 4y^2 + 4z^2 = 4$ and the plane $x - 4y - z = 0$ that are closest to the origin, and find the minimum distance.

30. A manufacturing plant has two classifications for its workers, A and B. Class A workers earn \$14 per run, and class B workers earn \$13 per run. For a certain production run it is determined that in addition to the salaries of the workers, if x class A workers and y class B workers are used, the number of dollars in the cost of the run is $y^3 + x^2 - 8xy + 600$. How many workers of each class should be used so that the cost of the run is a minimum if at least three workers of each class are required for a run?

31. An injection of x milligrams of drug A and y milligrams of drug B causes a response of R units, and $R = x^2y^3(c - x - y)$, where c is a positive constant. What quantity of each drug will cause the maximum response?

32. Suppose that t hours after the injection of x milligrams of adrenalin the response is R units, and $R = te^{-t}(c - x)x$, where c is a positive constant. What values of x and t will cause the maximum response?

33. Find the volume of the largest rectangular parallelepiped that can be inscribed in the ellipsoid $36x^2 + 9y^2 + 4z^2 = 36$ if the edges are parallel to the coordinate axes.

34. A rectangular box without a top is to be made at a cost of \$10 for the material. If the material for the bottom of the box costs \$0.15 per square foot and the material for the sides costs \$0.30 per square foot, find the dimensions of the box of greatest volume that can be made.

35. A closed rectangular box to contain 16 ft³ is to be made of three kinds of materials. The cost of the material for the top and the bottom is \$0.18 per square foot, the cost of the material for the front and the back is \$0.16 per square foot, and the cost of the material for the other two sides is \$0.12 per square foot. Find the dimensions of the box such that the cost of the materials is a minimum.

36. Suppose that T degrees is the temperature at any point (x, y, z) on the sphere $x^2 + y^2 + z^2 = 4$, and $T = 100xy^2z$. Find the points on the sphere where the temperature is the greatest and also the points where the temperature is the least. Also find the temperature at these points.

37. Suppose that when the production of a particular commodity requires x machine-hours and y person-hours, the cost of production is given by $f(x, y)$, where

$$f(x, y) = 2x^3 - 6xy + y^2 + 500$$

Determine the number of machine-hours and the number of person-hours needed to produce the commodity at the least cost.

38. A clothing store sells two kinds of shirts that are similar but are made by different manufacturers. The cost to the store of the first kind is \$40 and the cost of the second kind is \$50. It has been determined by experience that if the selling price of the first kind is x dollars and the selling price of the second kind is y dollars, then the number sold monthly of the first kind is $3200 - 50x + 25y$, and the number sold monthly of the second kind is $25x - 25y$. What should be the selling price of each kind of shirt for the greatest gross profit?

39. An early abstract painting was sold by the artist in 1921 for \$100. Because of its historical importance its value has increased over the years. Its value was \$4600 in 1941, \$11,000 in 1961, and \$20,000 in 1981. With the assumption that the value of the painting will appreciate according to the same pattern through 2001, use the method of least squares to estimate its value in 2001.

40. A 1991 model car was sold as a used car in 1992 for \$6800. Its value was \$6200 in 1993, \$5700 in 1994, and \$4800 in 1996. Use the method of least squares to estimate what its value was in 1995.

41. A motion picture has been playing at Cinema One for 5 weeks, and the weekly attendance (to the nearest 100) for each week is given in the following table.

Week Number	1	2	3	4	5
Attendance	5000	4500	4100	3900	3500

Assume that the weekly attendance will continue to decline according to the same pattern until it reaches 1500. (a) Use the regression line for the data in the table to determine the expected attendance for the sixth week. **(b)** The film will move over to the smaller Cinema Two when the weekly attendance drops below 2250. How many weeks is the film expected to play in Cinema One?

42. Five trees had their sap analyzed for the amount of a plant hormone that causes the detachment of leaves. For the trees in the following table, when x micrograms (μg) of plant hormone were released, y leaves were detached.

	Oak Tree	Maple Tree	Birch Tree	Pine Tree	Locust Tree
x	28	57	38	75	82
y	208	350	300	620	719

(a) Find an equation of the regression line for the data in the table. **(b)** Use the regression line to estimate the number of leaves detached from another kind of tree when 100 μg of plant hormone are released.

43. Five joggers were given examinations to determine their maximum oxygen uptake, a measure used to denote a person's cardiovascular fitness. The results are given in the following table, where x seconds is the jogger's best time for a mile run and y milliliters per minute per kilogram of body weight is the jogger's maximum oxygen uptake.

	Jogger A	Jogger B	Jogger C	Jogger D	Jogger E
x	300.5	350.6	407.3	326.2	512.8
y	418.5	375.6	350.2	400.2	325.8

(a) Find an equation of the regression line for the data in the table. **(b)** Use the regression line to estimate a jogger's maximum oxygen uptake if the jogger's best time for a mile run is 340.4 sec.

44. The score on a student's entrance examination was used to predict the student's grade-point average at the end of the freshman year. The following table gives the data for six students, where x is the test score and y is the grade-point average.

	Student A	Student B	Student C	Student D	Student E	Student F
x	92	81	73	98	79	85
y	3.4	2.7	3.1	3.8	2.2	3.0

(a) Find an equation of the regression line for the data in the table. **(b)** Use the regression line to esti-

mate a student's grade-point average at the end of the freshman year if the student had a score of 88 on the college entrance examination.

45. The following table gives a manufacturer's monthly production and profit for the first 5 months of the year, where x thousands of units were produced and y thousands of dollars was the profit.

	Jan.	Feb.	Mar.	April	May
x	65	72	82	90	100
y	30	35	42	48	60

If the production for June is to be 105,000 units, use the regression line for the data in the table to estimate that month's profit.

46. In the following table, for five healthy children, w kg is the body weight and y mm of mercury is the mean arterial pressure (average of systolic and diastolic blood pressures).

	Child A	Child B	Child C	Child D	Child E
w	20	30	35	40	50
y	70	85	90	96	100

(a) An equation that "fits" the data in this table is $y = m(\ln w) + b$. To find such an equation let $x = \ln w$, and use the method of least squares for the points (x_i, y_i). **(b)** Use the result of part (a) to estimate the mean arterial pressure of a healthy child of weight 45 kg.

47. A decorator, who is a monopolist, makes two types of specialty picture frames. From experience, the decorator has determined that if x frames of the first type and y frames of the second type are made and put on sale in a showroom, they can be sold for $(100 - 2x)$ dollars and $(120 - 3y)$ dollars each, respectively. The total cost of constructing these frames is $(12x + 12y + 4xy)$ dollars. How many frames of each type should be produced to realize the greatest profit, and what is the greatest profit?

48. Prove that the rectangular box having the largest volume that can be placed inside a sphere has the shape of a cube.

49. Determine the relative dimensions of a rectangular box, without a top, to be made from a given amount of material for the box to have the greatest possible volume.

50. A monopolist produces staplers and staples having demand equations $x = 11 - 2p - 2q$ and $y = 19 - 2p - 3q$, where $1000x$ staplers are demanded if the price is p dollars per stapler and $1000y$ boxes of staples are demanded if the price per box of staples is q dollars. It costs \$2 to produce each stapler and \$1 to produce each box of staples. Show that to have the greatest total profit, the staplers should be free and the staples should be expensive.

51. If f is a differentiable function for which $\nabla f(x_0, y_0) = \mathbf{0}$, prove that the graph of f has a horizontal tangent plane at the point $(x_0, y_0, f(x_0, y_0))$.

52. Obtain Equation (4) by substituting from (3) in (2).

53. If $f(m, b) = \sum_{i=1}^{n} (y_i - mx_i - b)^2$, use the second-derivative test to prove that the values of m and b in (3) and (4) give a relative minimum value of f. *Hint:* First show that $f_{mm}(m, b) > 0$. To show that $D(m, b) > 0$, you must prove that $\sum_{i=1}^{n} x_i^2 > \left(\sum_{i=1}^{n} x_i\right)^2$. To prove this, let $\bar{x} = \frac{1}{n} \sum_{i=1}^{n} x_i$ and apply properties of the sigma notation to the inequality $\sum_{i=1}^{n} (\bar{x} - x_i)^2 > 0$.

12.9 LAGRANGE MULTIPLIERS

In the solution of Example 4 of Section 12.8 we minimized the function having function values $xy + 2xz + 2yz$, subject to the condition that x, y, and z satisfy the equation $xyz = V$. Compare this with Example 3 of Section 12.8 in which we found the relative extrema of f for which $f(x, y) = 2x^4 + y^2 - x^2 - 2y$. These are essentially two different kinds of problems because in Example 4 we had an additional condition, called a *constraint* (or *side condition*). Such a problem is called one in *constrained extrema*, whereas that of Example 3 is called a problem in *free extrema*.

▷ **ILLUSTRATION 1** In Illustration 1 of Section 12.8, we showed that the function defined by

$$f(x, y) = \sqrt{25 - x^2 - y^2} \tag{1}$$

has a relative maximum value of 5 when $x = 0$ and $y = 0$. The number 5 is a free maximum of f.

Suppose, in addition to satisfying Equation (1), we impose the condition that x and y must satisfy the equation

$$x + y = 2 \tag{2}$$

We are now looking for a constrained maximum. The point corresponding to the constrained maximum will lie on the hemisphere defined by Equation (1) and the plane defined by Equation (2); that is, it will lie on the curve of intersection of the hemisphere and the plane. See Figure 1. You can determine that the constrained maximum value is $\sqrt{23}$ when $x = 1$ and $y = 1$ by the techniques you learned in Chapter 2: substitute the value of y in terms of x from (2) into (1), and find the relative maximum value of the resulting function of a single variable. ◀

$z = \sqrt{25 - x^2 - y^2}$ and $x + y = 2$

FIGURE 1

Because it is not always feasible to solve the constraint for one of the variables in terms of the others, as outlined in Illustration 1, another approach can be followed to find the critical points to solve a problem in constrained extrema. The procedure is called the method of **Lagrange**

multipliers, named for its discoverer Joseph L. Lagrange, the French mathematician we have mentioned a number of times in this book. The method is based on the following theorem.

12.9.1 Theorem

Suppose f and g are functions of two variables with continuous first partial derivatives. If f has a relative extremum at the point $(x_0, y_0, f(x_0,y_0))$ subject to the constraint $g(x, y) = 0$, and $\nabla g(x_0, y_0) \neq \mathbf{0}$, then there is a constant λ such that

$$\nabla f(x_0, y_0) + \lambda \nabla g(x_0, y_0) = \mathbf{0} \tag{3}$$

Proof If $\nabla f(x_0, y_0) = \mathbf{0}$, then (3) holds if $\lambda = 0$. We will now prove (3) with the assumption that $\nabla f(x_0, y_0) \neq \mathbf{0}$. From the given conditions, the implicit function theorem proved in advanced calculus permits us to represent the curve C having the equation $g(x, y) = 0$ by the vector equation

$$\mathbf{R}(t) = \alpha(t)\mathbf{i} + \beta(t)\mathbf{j}$$

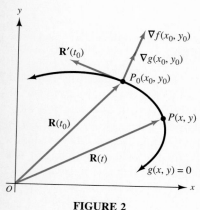

for t in some interval for which $\mathbf{R}'(t) \neq \mathbf{0}$. See Figure 2. Let t_0 be the value of t corresponding to the point $(x_0, y_0, f(x_0, y_0))$ where f has a relative extremum. As t varies along C, we obtain other function values of f, of which the corresponding points $(x, y, f(x, y))$ are on the surface defined by f and subject to the constraint $g(x, y) = 0$.

Let ϕ be the function of the single variable t defined by

$$\phi(t) = f(\alpha(t), \beta(t))$$

Because f has a relative extremum at $(x_0, y_0, f(x_0, y_0))$ ϕ has a relative extremum at t_0. Therefore, $\phi'(t_0) = 0$. We now compute $\phi'(t)$ by the chain rule:

$$\phi'(t) = f_x(x, y)\alpha'(t) + f_y(x, y)\beta'(t)$$
$$\phi'(t_0) = f_x(x_0, y_0)\alpha'(t_0) + f_y(x_0, y_0)\beta'(t_0)$$

Because $\phi'(t_0) = 0$, we have from this equation

$$f_x(x_0, y_0)\alpha'(t_0) + f_y(x_0, y_0)\beta'(t_0) = 0$$
$$\Leftrightarrow \qquad \nabla f(x_0, y_0) \cdot \mathbf{R}'(t_0) = 0$$

Because neither $\nabla f(x_0, y_0)$ nor $\mathbf{R}'(t_0)$ is the zero vector, we can conclude from this equation that $\nabla f(x_0, y_0)$ is orthogonal to $\mathbf{R}'(t_0)$. However, from Theorem 12.7.6 $\nabla g(x_0, y_0)$ is also orthogonal to $\mathbf{R}'(t_0)$. Figure 2 illustrates these concepts. Because $\nabla f(x_0, y_0)$ and $\nabla g(x_0, y_0)$ are orthogonal to the same vector, they are parallel, so that Equation (3) holds. ∎

We now show how to apply Theorem 12.9.1 to find the relative extrema of a function f of the two variables x and y subject to the constraint $g(x, y) = 0$.

Introduce a new variable λ, called a Lagrange multiplier, and form the auxiliary function F of the three variables x, y, and λ for which

$$F(x, y, \lambda) = f(x, y) + \lambda g(x, y)$$

FIGURE 2

The problem then becomes one of finding the critical points of F at which the three first partial derivatives of F are zero:

$$F_x(x, y, \lambda) = 0 \qquad F_y(x, y, \lambda) = 0 \qquad F_\lambda(x, y, \lambda) = 0 \qquad \textbf{(4)}$$

Observe that the first two equations in (4) are equivalent to

$$f_x(x, y) + \lambda g_x(x, y) = 0 \quad \text{and} \quad f_y(x, y) + \lambda g_y(x, y) = 0$$

and these two equations are equivalent to the vector equation

$$\nabla f(x, y) + \lambda \nabla g(x, y) = \mathbf{0}$$

which is Equation (3) of Theorem 12.9.1. Furthermore, the third equation in (4) is $g(x, y) = 0$, which is the constraint.

The following procedure summarizes this discussion.

> To apply the method of Lagrange multipliers to find relative extrema of a function f of two variables x and y subject to the constraint $g(x, y) = 0$:
>
> 1. Create the auxiliary function F of three variables x, y, and λ for which
>
> $$F(x, y, \lambda) = f(x, y) + \lambda g(x, y)$$
>
> 2. Establish the system of equations obtained by setting the three first partial derivatives of F equal to zero.
>
> $$\begin{cases} F_x(x, y, \lambda) = 0 \\ F_y(x, y, \lambda) = 0 \\ F_\lambda(x, y, \lambda) = 0 \end{cases}$$
>
> 3. Solve the system of equations in step 2 to determine critical points of F.
> 4. Among the first two coordinates of the critical points of F found in step 3 are values of x and y that give the desired relative extrema.

Note that relative extrema of f subject to the constraint may occur at a point where both $g_x(x, y)$ and $g_y(x, y)$ are zero. These points may not be revealed by the method of Lagrange multipliers and may have to be examined separately.

▶ **EXAMPLE 1**   Use the method of Lagrange multipliers to find the relative extrema of the function f for which

$$f(x, y) = 3x + 4y - 3$$

if the point (x, y) is on the circle $(x - 1)^2 + y^2 = 25$.

Solution   We write the given equation of the circle in the form

$$x^2 + y^2 - 2x - 24 = 0$$

To find the relative extrema of f subject to this constraint, we create the function F:

$$F(x, y, \lambda) = 3x + 4y - 3 + \lambda(x^2 + y^2 - 2x - 24)$$

We compute the partial derivatives F_x, F_y, and F_λ, and set the resulting function values equal to zero.

$$F_x: \qquad 3 + 2\lambda(x - 1) = 0 \tag{5}$$
$$F_y: \qquad 4 + 2\lambda y = 0 \tag{6}$$
$$F_\lambda: \qquad x^2 + y^2 - 2x - 24 = 0 \tag{7}$$

Observe from Equations (5) and (6) that $x \neq 1$ and $y \neq 0$. Solving these equations for λ, we have

$$\lambda = -\frac{3}{2(x - 1)} \quad \text{and} \quad \lambda = -\frac{2}{y} \tag{8}$$

Equating these two values of λ, we obtain

$$3y = 4(x - 1)$$
$$y = \frac{4}{3}(x - 1) \tag{9}$$

We substitute this value of y in Equation (7) and solve for x:

$$x^2 + \tfrac{16}{9}(x^2 - 2x + 1) - 2x - 24 = 0$$
$$9x^2 + 16x^2 - 32x + 16 - 18x - 216 = 0$$
$$25x^2 - 50x - 200 = 0$$
$$x^2 - 2x - 8 = 0$$
$$(x + 2)(x - 4) = 0$$
$$x = -2 \qquad x = 4$$

From Equations (9) and (8): when $x = -2$, then $y = -4$ and $\lambda = \frac{1}{2}$; and when $x = 4$, then $y = 4$ and $\lambda = -\frac{1}{2}$. The points $(-2, -4, \frac{1}{2})$ and $(4, 4, -\frac{1}{2})$ are, therefore, critical points of F. Thus $(-2, -4)$ and $(4, 4)$ are the only possible points for which f has a relative extremum. Because

$$f(-2, -4) = 3(-2) + 4(-4) \quad \text{and} \quad f(4, 4) = (3)(4) + 4(4) - 3$$
$$= -25 \qquad\qquad\qquad\qquad\qquad = 25$$

a relative minimum value of f is -25 and a relative maximum value is 25.   ◀

▷ **ILLUSTRATION 2**   The function f of Example 1 is continuous on the closed disk defined by

$$(x - 1)^2 + y^2 \leq 25$$

Therefore, by the extreme-value theorem, f has an absolute maximum value and an absolute minimum value on the disk. Because

$$f_x(x, y) = 3 \quad \text{and} \quad f_y(x, y) = 4$$

and these values are never zero, f has no relative extrema within the circle.

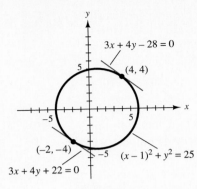

FIGURE 3

Thus the absolute extrema must occur on the circumference. From the result of Example 1, we can, therefore, conclude that 25 is an absolute maximum value and -25 is an absolute minimum value on the closed disk.

Refer to Figure 3. The lines

$$3x + 4y - 3 = 25 \quad \Leftrightarrow \quad 3x + 4y - 28 = 0$$
$$3x + 4y - 3 = -25 \quad \Leftrightarrow \quad 3x + 4y + 22 = 0$$

are level curves of f tangent to the constraint circle at the points $(4, 4)$ and $(-2, -4)$, respectively. ◀

The method of Lagrange multipliers can be extended to functions of three variables. The following theorem is similar to Theorem 12.9.1.

12.9.2 Theorem

Suppose f and g are functions of three variables with continuous first partial derivatives. If f has a relative extremum where $x = x_0$, $y = y_0$, and $z = z_0$, subject to the constraint $g(x, y, z) = 0$ and $\nabla g(x_0, y_0, z_0) \neq \mathbf{0}$, then there is a constant λ such that

$$\nabla f(x_0, y_0, z_0) + \lambda \nabla g(x_0, y_0, z_0) = \mathbf{0} \qquad (10)$$

The proof of this theorem, similar to that of Theorem 12.9.1, involves showing that when neither $\nabla f(x_0, y_0, z_0)$ nor $\nabla g(x_0, y_0, z_0)$ is the zero vector, they are both orthogonal to the surface $g(x, y, z) = 0$, which implies that $\nabla f(x_0, y_0, z_0)$ and $\nabla g(x_0, y_0, z_0)$ are parallel. This fact yields Equation (10).

As Theorem 12.9.1 did for functions of two variables, Theorem 12.9.2 provides the following procedure for functions of three variables.

To apply the method of Lagrange multipliers to find relative extrema of a function f of three variables x, y, and z subject to the constraint $g(x, y, z) = 0$:

1. Create the auxiliary function F of four variables x, y, z, and λ for which

$$F(x, y, z, \lambda) = f(x, y, z) + \lambda g(x, y, z)$$

2. Establish the system of equations obtained by setting the four first partial derivatives of F equal to zero.

$$\begin{cases} F_x(x, y, z, \lambda) = 0 \\ F_y(x, y, z, \lambda) = 0 \\ F_\lambda(x, y, z, \lambda) = 0 \\ F_z(x, y, z, \lambda) = 0 \end{cases}$$

3. Solve the system of equations in step 2 to determine critical points of F.

4. Among the first three coordinates of the critical points of F found in step 3 are values of x, y, and z that give the desired relative extrema.

▶ **EXAMPLE 2** Solve Example 4 of Section 12.8 by the method of Lagrange multipliers.

Solution Define the variables x, y, and z and the constant V as in the solution in Section 12.8. Let

$$S = f(x, y, z) \qquad \text{and} \quad g(x, y, z) = xyz - V$$
$$= xy + 2xz + 2yz$$

We wish to minimize the function f subject to the constraint that

$$g(x, y, z) = 0$$

We form the function F for which

$$F(x, y, z, \lambda) = f(x, y, z) + \lambda g(x, y, z)$$
$$= xy + 2xz + 2yz + \lambda(xyz - V)$$

To find the critical points of F we compute the four partial derivatives F_x, F_y, F_z, and F_λ and set the function values equal to zero.

$$\begin{aligned} F_x: & \quad y + 2z + \lambda yz = 0 & \qquad \textbf{(11)}\\ F_y: & \quad x + 2z + \lambda xz = 0 & \qquad \textbf{(12)}\\ F_z: & \quad 2x + 2y + \lambda xy = 0 & \qquad \textbf{(13)}\\ F_\lambda: & \quad xyz - V = 0 & \qquad \textbf{(14)} \end{aligned}$$

Subtracting corresponding members of (12) from those of (11) we obtain

$$y - x + \lambda z(y - x) = 0$$
$$(y - x)(1 + \lambda z) = 0$$

giving the two equations

$$y = x \qquad\qquad \textbf{(15)}$$

and because $z \neq 0$,

$$\lambda = -\frac{1}{z}$$

Substituting $\lambda = -1/z$ into (12) we get $x + 2z - x = 0$, giving $z = 0$, which is impossible because z is in the interval $(0, +\infty)$. Substituting from (15) into (13) gives

$$2x + 2x + \lambda x^2 = 0$$
$$x(4 + \lambda x) = 0$$
$$\lambda = -\frac{4}{x} \qquad (\text{because } x \neq 0)$$

If in (12), $\lambda = -4/x$, then

$$x + 2z - \frac{4}{x}(xz) = 0$$
$$x + 2z - 4z = 0$$
$$z = \frac{x}{2} \qquad\qquad \textbf{(16)}$$

Substituting from (15) and (16) into (14) we obtain $\frac{1}{2}x^3 - V = 0$, from which $x = \sqrt[3]{2V}$. With this value in (15) and (16), $y = \sqrt[3]{2V}$ and $z = \frac{1}{2}\sqrt[3]{2V}$. The point $(\sqrt[3]{2V}, \sqrt[3]{2V}, \frac{1}{2}\sqrt[3]{2V}, \lambda)$ is, therefore a critical point of F, and, as shown in Section 12.8, f has a minimum value where $x = \sqrt[3]{2V}$, $y = \sqrt[3]{2V}$, and $z = \frac{1}{2}\sqrt[3]{2V}$. ◀

The next example pertains to an economic situation involving a **utility function** that measures the satisfaction from quantities of various commodities. A value of a utility function is called a **utility index,** which describes numerically an individual's preference for the commodities.

▶ **EXAMPLE 3** Suppose that U is a utility function for which

$$U(x, y, z) = xyz$$

where x, y, and z represent the number of units of commodities A, B, and C, respectively, that are consumed weekly by a particular person. Assume that \$2, \$3, and \$4 are the unit prices of A, B, and C, respectively, and that the total weekly expense for the commodities is budgeted at \$90. How many units of each commodity should be purchased per week to maximize the consumer's utility index?

Solution We wish to determine the values of x, y, and z, each in the interval $[0, +\infty)$, that maximize $U(x, y, z)$ subject to the budget constraint $2x + 3y + 4z = 90$. Let

$$g(x, y, z) = 2x + 3y + 4z - 90$$

and

$$F(x, y, z, \lambda) = xyz + \lambda(2x + 3y + 4z - 90)$$

We compute the partial derivatives and set the function values equal to zero.

$$F_x: \qquad yz + 2\lambda = 0 \tag{17}$$
$$F_y: \qquad xz + 3\lambda = 0 \tag{18}$$
$$F_z: \qquad xy + 4\lambda = 0 \tag{19}$$
$$F_\lambda: \qquad 2x + 3y + 4z - 90 = 0 \tag{20}$$

From (17) and (18), and then from (17) and (19)

$$y = \tfrac{2}{3}x \quad \text{and} \quad z = \tfrac{1}{2}x \tag{21}$$

Substituting from these equations into (20), we obtain

$$2x + 3(\tfrac{2}{3}x) + 4(\tfrac{1}{2}x) - 90 = 0$$
$$x = 15$$

With this value of x in Equations (21), $y = 10$ and $z = 7.5$. We therefore compute

$$U(15, 10, 7.5) = (15)\,(10)\,(7.5)$$
$$= 1125$$

Because x, y, and z are in the interval $[0, +\infty)$, it is apparent that this value cannot be a minimum because there are many values of U subject to the given constraint that are less than 1125. This value, therefore, maximizes U subject to the given constraint.

Conclusion: To maximize the consumer's utility index, the consumer should purchase 15, 10, and 7.5 units of commodities A, B, and C, respectively, per week. ◀

▶ **EXAMPLE 4** Use Lagrange multipliers to find the shortest distance from the origin to the plane $Ax + By + Cz = D$.

Solution Let w units be the distance from the origin to a point (x, y, z) in the plane. Then

$$w = \sqrt{x^2 + y^2 + z^2}$$

Because w will be a minimum when w^2 is a minimum, we form the function f for which

$$f(x, y, z) = x^2 + y^2 + z^2$$

We wish to find the minimum value of f subject to the constraint

$$Ax + By + Cz - D = 0$$

With the assumption that there is such a minimum value it will occur at a critical point of the function F such that

$$F(x, y, z, \lambda) = x^2 + y^2 + z^2 + \lambda(Ax + By + Cz - D)$$

To find the critical points of F we compute the partial derivatives of F and set them equal to zero.

$$
\begin{aligned}
F_x: & \quad 2x + \lambda A = 0 \\
F_y: & \quad 2y + \lambda B = 0 \\
F_z: & \quad 2z + \lambda C = 0 \\
F_\lambda: & \quad Ax + By + Cz - D = 0
\end{aligned}
\tag{22}
$$

From the first three of these equations

$$x = -\tfrac{1}{2}\lambda A \qquad y = -\tfrac{1}{2}\lambda B \qquad z = -\tfrac{1}{2}\lambda C \tag{23}$$

Substituting these values of x, y, and z into (22) we get

$$-\tfrac{1}{2}\lambda(A^2 + B^2 + C^2) = D$$

$$-\tfrac{1}{2}\lambda = \frac{D}{A^2 + B^2 + C^2}$$

We replace $-\tfrac{1}{2}\lambda$ by this value in Equations (23) and obtain

$$x = \frac{AD}{A^2 + B^2 + C^2} \qquad y = \frac{BD}{A^2 + B^2 + C^2} \qquad z = \frac{CD}{A^2 + B^2 + C^2} \tag{24}$$

The point having these coordinates is the one and only critical point of F.

Therefore the minimum distance from the origin to the plane is the distance from the origin to the point (x_0, y_0, z_0), where x_0, y_0, and z_0 are the values of x, y, and z in Equations (24). The minimum distance then is

$$\sqrt{x_0{}^2 + y_0{}^2 + z_0{}^2} = \sqrt{\frac{A^2 D^2}{(A^2 + B^2 + C^2)^2} + \frac{B^2 D^2}{(A^2 + B^2 + C^2)^2} + \frac{C^2 D^2}{(A^2 + B^2 + C^2)^2}}$$

$$= \frac{|D|}{\sqrt{A^2 + B^2 + C^2}} \qquad \blacktriangleleft$$

If several constraints are imposed, the method of Lagrange multipliers can be extended by using several multipliers. In particular, if we wish to find critical points of the function having values $f(x, y, z)$ subject to the two side conditions $g(x, y, z) = 0$ and $h(x, y, z) = 0$, we find the critical points of the function F of the five variables x, y, z, λ, and μ for which

$$F(x, y, z, \lambda, \mu) = f(x, y, z) + \lambda g(x, y, z) + \mu h(x, y, z)$$

The following example illustrates the method.

▶ **EXAMPLE 5**   Find the relative extrema of the function f if

$$f(x, y, z) = xz + yz$$

and the point (x, y, z) lies on the intersection of the surfaces $x^2 + z^2 = 2$ and $yz = 2$.

Solution   We form the function F for which

$$F(x, y, z, \lambda, \mu) = xz + yz + \lambda(x^2 + z^2 - 2) + \mu(yz - 2)$$

Finding the five partial derivatives and setting them equal to zero we have

$$F_x: \qquad z + 2\lambda x = 0 \qquad\qquad\qquad (25)$$
$$F_y: \qquad z + \mu z = 0 \qquad\qquad\qquad\quad (26)$$
$$F_z: \qquad x + y + 2\lambda z + \mu y = 0 \qquad (27)$$
$$F_\lambda: \qquad x^2 + z^2 - 2 = 0 \qquad\qquad\quad (28)$$
$$F_\mu: \qquad yz - 2 = 0 \qquad\qquad\qquad\quad (29)$$

From (26) we obtain $\mu = -1$ and $z = 0$. We reject $z = 0$ because this contradicts (29). From (25) we obtain, if $x \neq 0$,

$$\lambda = -\frac{z}{2x}$$

Substituting this value of λ and $\mu = -1$ into (27) we get

$$x + y - \frac{z^2}{x} - y = 0$$
$$x^2 = z^2 \qquad\qquad\qquad (30)$$

Substituting from (30) into (28) we have $2x^2 - 2 = 0$, or $x^2 = 1$. This gives two values for x, namely 1 and -1; and for each of these values of x we get, from (30), the two values 1 and -1 for z. Obtaining the corresponding values for y from (29) we have four sets of solutions for the five Equations (25) through (29). These solutions are

$$x = 1 \qquad y = 2 \qquad z = 1 \qquad \lambda = -\tfrac{1}{2} \qquad \mu = -1$$
$$x = 1 \qquad y = -2 \qquad z = -1 \qquad \lambda = \tfrac{1}{2} \qquad \mu = -1$$
$$x = -1 \qquad y = 2 \qquad z = 1 \qquad \lambda = \tfrac{1}{2} \qquad \mu = -1$$
$$x = -1 \qquad y = -2 \qquad z = -1 \qquad \lambda = -\tfrac{1}{2} \qquad \mu = -1$$

The first and fourth sets of solutions give $f(x, y, z) = 3$, and the second and third sets of solutions give $f(x, y, z) = 1$. Hence f has a relative maximum function value of 3 and a relative minimum function value of 1. ◀

EXERCISES 12.9

In Exercises 1 through 4, use Lagrange multipliers to find the critical points of the function subject to the constraint.

1. $f(x, y) = 25 - x^2 - y^2$ with constraint $x^2 + y^2 - 4y = 0$

2. $f(x, y) = 4x^2 + 2y^2 + 5$ with constraint $x^2 + y^2 - 2y = 0$

3. $f(x, y, z) = x^2 + y^2 + z^2$ with constraint $3x - 2y + z - 4 = 0$

4. $f(x, y, z) = x^2 + y^2 + z^2$ with constraint $y^2 - x^2 = 1$

In Exercises 5 through 8, use Lagrange multipliers to find the absolute extrema of f subject to the constraint. Also find the points at which the extrema occur.

5. $f(x, y) = x^2 + y$ with constraint $x^2 + y^2 = 9$

6. $f(x, y) = x^2y$ with constraint $x^2 + 8y^2 = 24$

7. $f(x, y, z) = xyz$ with constraint $x^2 + 2y^2 + 4z^2 = 4$

8. $f(x, y, z) = y^3 + xz^2$ with constraint $x^2 + y^2 + z^2 = 1$

In Exercises 9 through 12, find the absolute maximum and absolute minimum values of f in the given region. Use your answers in Exercises 5 through 8 for the extrema on the boundary.

9. The function of Exercise 5; $x^2 + y^2 \leq 9$

10. The function of Exercise 6; $x^2 + 8y^2 \leq 24$

11. The function of Exercise 7; $x^2 + 2y^2 + 4z^2 \leq 4$

12. The function of Exercise 8; $x^2 + y^2 + z^2 \leq 1$

In Exercises 13 and 14, find the absolute minimum value of f subject to the constraint.

13. $f(x, y, z) = x^2 + y^2 + z^2$ with constraint $xyz = 1$

14. $f(x, y, z) = xyz$ with constraint $x^2 + y^2 + z^2 = 1$

In Exercises 15 and 16, find the absolute maximum value of f subject to the constraint.

15. $f(x, y, z) = x + y + z$ with constraint $x^2 + y^2 + z^2 = 9$

16. $f(x, y, z) = xyz$, $x \geq 0$, $y \geq 0$, and $z \geq 0$ with constraint $2xy + 3xz + yz = 72$

17. Find a relative minimum value of the function f for which $f(x, y, z) = x^2 + 4y^2 + 16z^2$ with the constraint **(a)** $xyz = 1$; **(b)** $xy = 1$; **(c)** $x = 1$.

18. Use Lagrange multipliers to find the shortest distance from the point $(1, 3, 0)$ to the plane $4x + 2y - z = 5$.

19. Use Lagrange multipliers to find the shortest distance from the point $(1, -1, -1)$ to the plane $x + 4y + 3z = 2$.

20. Find the least and greatest distances from the origin to a point on the ellipse $x^2 + 4y^2 = 16$.

21. Find the least and greatest distances from the origin to a point on the ellipsoid $9x^2 + 4y^2 + z^2 = 36$.

22. If $f(x, y, z) = 2x^2 + 3y^2 + z^2$, use Lagrange multipliers to find the point in the plane $x + y + z = 5$ at which $f(x, y, z)$ is least.

23. Use Lagrange multipliers to find the absolute minimum function value of f if $f(x, y, z) = x^2 + y^2 + z^2$ with the two constraints $x + 2y + 3z = 6$ and $x - y - z = -1$.

24. Use Lagrange multipliers to find the absolute minimum function value of f if $f(x, y, z) = x^2 + y^2 + z^2$ with the two constraints $x + y + 2z = 1$ and $3x - 2y + z = -4$.

25. Use Lagrange multipliers to find a relative maximum function value of f if $f(x, y, z) = xyz$ with the two constraints $x + y + z = 4$ and $x - y - z = 3$.

26. Use Lagrange multipliers to find the absolute minimum function value of f if $f(x, y, z) = x^3 + y^3 + z^3$

with the two constraints $x + y + z = 1$ and $x + y - z = 0$.

In Exercises 27 through 36, use Lagrange multipliers to solve the indicated exercise of Exercises 12.8.

27. Exercise 25 **28.** Exercise 26 **29.** Exercise 27

30. Exercise 28 **31.** Exercise 29 **32.** Exercise 34

33. Exercise 35 **34.** Exercise 36 **35.** Exercise 49

36. Exercise 48

37. Solve Example 3 if $U(x, y, z) = e^{x^2yz}$.

38. Solve Example 3 if $U(x, y, z) = x^2y^3z$.

39. If $T(x, y)$ degrees is the temperature at any point (x, y) of the circular disk bounded by the circle $x^2 + y^2 = 1$ and

$$T(x, y) = 2x^2 + y^2 - y$$

find the hottest and coldest points on the disk and the temperature at those points.

40. In Exercise 39 suppose the region is the top half of the circular disk, so that the region is defined by $x^2 + y^2 \leq 1$ and $y \geq 0$. Find the hottest and coldest points in the region if

$$T(x, y) = 2x^2 - 3xy + 5y^2$$

and the temperature at those points.

41. In Example 3, suppose that the utility function involves five commodities A, B, C, D, and E. Further-

more, suppose that x units of A, y units of B, z units of C, s units of D, and t units of E are consumed weekly, and the unit prices of A, B, C, D, and E are, respectively, \$2, \$3, \$4, \$1, and \$5. If

$$U(x, y, z, s, t) = xyzst$$

and the total weekly expense for the commodities is to be \$150, how many units of each commodity should be purchased per week to maximize the consumer's utility index?

42. A company has three factories, each manufacturing the same product. If factory A produces x units, factory B produces y units, and factory C produces z units, their respective manufacturing costs are $(3x^2 + 200)$ dollars, $(y^2 + 400)$ dollars, and $(2z^2 + 300)$ dollars. If an order for 1100 units is to be filled, use Lagrange mutlipliers to determine how the production should be distributed among the three factories to minimize the total manufacturing cost.

43. (a) Show that if $f(x, y, z) = x^2y^2z^2$, the maximum value of f subject to the constraint

$$x^2 + y^2 + z^2 = R^2$$

is $(\frac{1}{3}R^2)^3$. (b) Use the result of part (a) to prove that

$$(x^2y^2z^2)^{1/3} \leq \frac{x^2 + y^2 + z^2}{3}$$

for all values of x, y, and z.

CHAPTER 12 REVIEW

▶ SUGGESTIONS FOR REVIEW OF CHAPTER 12

1. Define a function of two variables and include in your definition the meaning of domain and range.

2. Do Suggestion 1 for a function of three variables.

3. Define the composite function $f \circ g$, where f is a function of a single variable and g is a function of two variables. State how the domain of $f \circ g$ is related to the domains of f and g.

4. Define the graph of a function of two variables.

5. What is a level curve of a function of two variables? Make up an example.

6. What is a level surface of a function of three variables? Make up an example.

7. Write a formula for the distance between two points in each of R, R^2, and R^3.

8. Define: $\lim_{(x,y) \to (x_0,y_0)} f(x, y) = L$

9. State a theorem that can be used to show that $\lim_{(x,y) \to (x_0,y_0)} f(x, y)$ does not exist. Make up an example illustrating the application of the theorem.

10. State the definition of continuity of a function of two variables.

11. Make up an example of a function of two variables that has a removable discontinuity at the origin.

12. Make up an example of a function of two variables that has an essential discontinuity at the origin.

13. If f is a function of the two variables x and y, define: (a) the partial derivative of f with respect to x, and (b) the partial derivative of f with respect to y.

14. Give the geometric interpretation of the partial derivatives in Suggestion 13.

15. Interpret the partial derivatives in Suggestion 13 as rates of change.

16. How are the partial derivatives in Suggestion 13 calculated without using the definition?

17. Make up an example of a polynomial function of two variables and calculate the two partial derivatives.

18. Do Suggestion 17 for a non-polynomial function.

19. Compute the four second-order partial derivatives for your function in (a) Suggestion 17 and (b) Suggestion 18.

20. State the theorem guaranteeing that the two mixed partial derivatives of a function of two variables are equal.

21. Define a differentiable function of two variables.

22. State a theorem guaranteeing the differentiability of a function of two variables.

23. Define the total differential of a function of two variables. Make up an example.

24. How is the total differential applied to approximate a function value? Make up an example.

25. State the chain rule that gives the formulas for the partial derivative of u with respect to r and the partial derivative of u with respect to s if $u = f(x, y)$ where $x = F(r, s)$ and $y = G(r, s)$.

26. Make up an example applying the formulas in Suggestion 25 where f, F, and G are polynomial functions.

27. Make up an example applying the formulas in Suggestion 25 where f is a polynomial function, F is a trigonometric function, and G is an exponential function.

28. State a formula that gives the derivative of a function of a single variable defined implicitly. Make up an example.

29. State formulas that give the partial derivatives of a function of two variables defined implicitly. Make up an example.

30. Define the directional derivative of a function of two variables in the direction of a given unit vector. State a formula for computing a directional derivative in a shorter way than using the definition. Make up an example.

31. Do Suggestion 30 for a function of three variables.

32. Define the gradient of a function of two variables. How is the gradient applied to compute a directional derivative? Make up an example.

33. Do Suggestion 32 for a function of three variables.

34. How is the gradient applied to determine the direction of the maximum value of the directional derivative at a point? Make up an example.

35. How is the gradient applied to find the normal vector and the tangent plane to a surface at a particular point? Make up an example.

36. Make up an example showing how to apply the gradient to find an equation of the tangent line at a particular point of a curve in the xy plane defined by an equation of the form $F(x, y) = 0$.

37. What is a critical point of a function of two variables? Make up an example of a function having a critical point where (a) both partial derivatives are zero and (b) where at least one of the partial derivatives does not exist.

38. How are critical points used to determine relative extrema of a function of two variables? Make up an example.

39. Make up an example of a function having a critical point where the function does not have a relative extremum.

40. State the second-derivative test for determining relative extrema of a function of two variables.

41. Make up an example showing the application of the second-derivative test.

42. State the extreme-value theorem for functions of two variables.

43. Outline the procedure used to determine the absolute extrema of a function of two variables that satisfies the extreme-value theorem. Make up an example.

44. How is the method of least squares used to find a mathematical model that best fits a set of data points? Make up an example.

45. How is the method of Lagrange multipliers used to find relative extrema of a function of two variables subject to a given constraint? Make up an example.

46. Do Suggestion 45 for a function of three variables.

▶ MISCELLANEOUS EXERCISES FOR CHAPTER 12

In Exercises 1 through 4, determine the domain of f and sketch as a region in R^2 the set of points in the domain.

1. $f(x, y) = \sqrt{x^2 + 4y^2 - 16}$

2. $f(x, y) = \dfrac{6}{\sqrt{36 - x^2 - y^2}}$

3. $f(x, y) = \ln(y - x^2)$

4. $f(x, y) = \sin^{-1}(5 - x^2 - y^2)$

In Exercises 5 and 6, determine the domain of f and describe the region in R^3 that is the set of points in the domain.

5. $f(x, y, z) = \dfrac{x}{|y| - |z|}$

6. $f(x, y, z) = \ln(x^2 + y^2 + z^2 - 4)$

In Exercises 7 and 8, determine the domain of f and sketch the graph of f.

7. $f(x, y) = \sqrt{36 - 4x^2 - 9y^2}$

8. $f(x, y) = 16x^2 - y^2$

9. The production function for a certain commodity is f, where $f(x, y) = 4x^{1/2}y$, and x and y give the amounts of two inputs. Draw a contour map of f showing the constant product curves at 16, 8, 4, and 2.

10. The temperature at a point (x, y) of a flat metal plate is $t(x, y)$ degrees, and $t(x, y) = x^2 + 2y$. Draw the isothermals for t at 0, 2, 4, 6, and 8.

In Exercises 11 through 24, find the indicated partial derivatives.

11. $f(x, y) = 2x^2y - 3xy^2 + 4x - 2y$; **(a)** $D_1f(x, y)$; **(b)** $D_2f(x, y)$; **(c)** $D_{11}f(x, y)$; **(d)** $D_{22}f(x, y)$; **(e)** $D_{12}f(x, y)$; **(f)** $D_{21}f(x, y)$

12. $f(x, y) = (4x^2 - 2y)^3$; **(a)** $f_1(x, y)$; **(b)** $f_2(x, y)$; **(c)** $f_{11}(x, y)$; **(d)** $f_{22}(x, y)$; **(e)** $f_{12}(x, y)$; **(f)** $f_{21}(x, y)$

13. $f(x, y) = \dfrac{x^2 - y}{3y^2}$; **(a)** $f_x(x, y)$; **(b)** $f_y(x, y)$; **(c)** $f_{xy}(x, y)$; **(d)** $f_{yx}(x, y)$

14. $f(r, s) = re^{2rs}$; **(a)** $D_rf(r, s)$; **(b)** $D_sf(r, s)$; **(c)** $D_{rs}f(r, s)$; **(d)** $D_{sr}f(r, s)$

15. $g(s, t) = \sin(st^2) + te^s$; **(a)** $D_sg(s, t)$; **(b)** $D_tg(s, t)$; **(c)** $D_{st}g(s, t)$; **(d)** $D_{ts}g(s, t)$

16. $h(x, y) = \tan^{-1}\dfrac{x^3}{y^2}$; **(a)** $D_1h(x, y)$; **(b)** $D_2h(x, y)$; **(c)** $D_{11}h(x, y)$; **(d)** $D_{22}h(x, y)$

17. $f(x, y) = e^{x/y} + \ln\dfrac{x}{y}$; **(a)** $f_x(x, y)$; **(b)** $f_y(x, y)$; **(c)** $f_{xx}(x, y)$; **(d)** $f_{yy}(x, y)$

18. $f(x, y) = \ln\sqrt{x^2 + y^2}$; **(a)** $f_1(x, y)$; **(b)** $f_{11}(x, y)$; **(c)** $f_{12}(x, y)$; **(d)** $f_{121}(x, y)$

19. $f(x, y, z) = \dfrac{x}{x^2 + y^2 + z^2}$; **(a)** $D_1f(x, y, z)$; **(b)** $D_2f(x, y, z)$; **(c)** $D_3f(x, y, z)$

20. $f(x, y, z) = \sqrt{x^2 + 3yz - z^2}$; **(a)** $f_x(x, y, z)$; **(b)** $f_y(x, y, z)$; **(c)** $f_z(x, y, z)$

21. $f(u, v, w) = \ln(u^2 + 4v^2 - 5w^2)$; **(a)** $f_{uvw}(u, v, w)$; **(b)** $f_{uvv}(u, v, w)$.

22. $f(r, s, t) = t^2e^{4rst}$; **(a)** $f_r(r, s, t)$; **(b)** $f_{rt}(r, s, t)$; **(c)** $f_{rts}(r, s, t)$

23. $f(r, s, t) = \dfrac{\ln 4rs}{t^2}$; **(a)** $D_1f(r, s, t)$; **(b)** $D_{13}f(r, s, t)$; **(c)** $D_{131}f(r, s, t)$

24. $f(u, v, w) = w\cos 2v + 3v\sin u - 2uv\tan w$; **(a)** $D_2f(u, v, w)$; **(b)** $D_1f(u, v, w)$; **(c)** $D_{131}f(u, v, w)$

25. If $w = x^2y - y^2x + y^2z - z^2y + z^2x - x^2z$, show that
$$\frac{\partial w}{\partial x} + \frac{\partial w}{\partial y} + \frac{\partial w}{\partial z} = 0$$

26. If $u = (x^2 + y^2 + z^2)^{-1/2}$, show that
$$\frac{\partial^2 u}{\partial x^2} + \frac{\partial^2 u}{\partial y^2} + \frac{\partial^2 u}{\partial z^2} = 0$$

In Exercises 27 and 28, find $\dfrac{\partial u}{\partial t}$ and $\dfrac{\partial u}{\partial s}$ by two methods.

27. $u = y\ln(x^2 + y^2)$, $x = 2s + 3t$, $y = 3t - 2s$

28. $u = e^{2x+y}\cos(2y - x)$, $x = 2s^2 - t^2$, $y = s^2 + 2t^2$

29. If $u = 3x^2y + 2xy - 3yz - 2z^2$, $x = e^{3rs}$, $y = r^3s^2$, and $z = \ln 4$, find $\dfrac{\partial u}{\partial r}$ by two methods:
(a) Use the chain rule; **(b)** make the substitutions for x, y, and z before differentiating.

30. If $u = e^{x^2+y^2} - \dfrac{3x}{y} + 3z$, $x = \sin\theta$, $y = \cos\theta$, and $z = \tan\theta$, find the total derivative $du/d\theta$ by two methods: **(a)** Do not express u in terms of θ before differentiating; **(b)** express u in terms of θ before differentiating.

31. If $u = xy + x^2$, $x = 4\cos t$, and $y = 3\sin t$, find the value of the total derivative du/dt at $t = \frac{1}{4}\pi$ by two methods: **(a)** Do not express u in terms of t before differentiating; **(b)** express u in terms of t before differentiating.

32. If $f(x, y) = x^2 + ye^2$, find: **(a)** $\Delta f(0, 2)$, the increment of f at $(0, 2)$; **(b)** $\Delta f(0, 2)$ when $\Delta x = -0.1$ and $\Delta y = 0.2$; **(c)** $df(0, 2, \Delta x, \Delta y)$, the total differential of f at $(0, 2)$; **(d)** $df(0, 2, -0.1, 0.2)$.

33. If $f(x, y, z) = 3xy^2 - 5xz^2 - 2xyz$, find:
(a) $\Delta f(-1, 3, 2)$, the increment of f at $(-1, 3, 2)$;
(b) $\Delta f(-1, 3, 2)$ when $\Delta x = 0.02$, $\Delta y = -0.01$, and $\Delta z = -0.02$; **(c)** $df(-1, 3, 2, \Delta x, \Delta y, \Delta z)$, the total differential of f at $(-1, 3, 2)$;
(d) $df(-1, 3, 2, 0.02, -0.01, -0,02)$.

34. Given $f(x) = x^2 + 1$, $g(x, y) = \dfrac{2x}{3y}$, and $h(x) = \dfrac{1}{x}$, find: **(a)** $(h \circ g)(-3, 4)$; **(b)** $g(f(3), h(\frac{1}{4}))$; **(c)** $g(f(x), h(y))$; **(d)** $f((h \circ g)(x, y))$.

In Exercises 35 through 37, evaluate the limit by the use of limit theorems.

35. $\displaystyle\lim_{(x,y)\to(e,0)} \ln\left(\frac{x^2}{y + 1}\right)$

36. $\displaystyle\lim_{(x,y)\to(0,\pi/2)} \frac{xy^2 + e^x}{\cos x + \sin y}$

37. $\displaystyle\lim_{(x,y)\to(1,3)} \sin^{-1}\left(\frac{3x}{2y}\right)$

In Exercises 38 through 40, establish the limit by finding a $\delta > 0$ for any $\epsilon > 0$ such that Definition 12.2.5 holds.

38. $\lim\limits_{(x,y)\to(4,-1)} (4x - 5y) = 21$

39. $\lim\limits_{(x,y)\to(2,-2)} (3x^2 - 4y^2) = -4$

40. $\lim\limits_{(x,y)\to(3,1)} (x^2 - y^2 + 2x - 4y) = 10$

In Exercises 41 through 44, determine if the limit exists.

41. $\lim\limits_{(x,y)\to(0,0)} \dfrac{x^3 y^3}{x^2 + y^2}$

42. $\lim\limits_{(x,y)\to(0,0)} \dfrac{x^4 - y^4}{x^4 + y^4}$

43. $\lim\limits_{(x,y)\to(0,0)} \dfrac{x^9 y}{(x^6 + y^2)^2}$

44. $\lim\limits_{(x,y)\to(0,0)} \dfrac{2x^3 + 4x^2 y}{x^2 + y^2}$

In Exercises 45 through 48, determine all points at which f is continuous.

45. $f(x, y) = \dfrac{x^2 + 4y^2}{x^2 - 4y^2}$

46. $f(x, y) = \dfrac{1}{\cos^2 \frac{1}{2}\pi x + \cos^2 \frac{1}{2}\pi y}$

47. $f(x, y) = \begin{cases} \dfrac{x^3 y^3}{x^2 + y^2} & \text{if } (x, y) \neq (0, 0) \\ 0 & \text{if } (x, y) = (0, 0) \end{cases}$

Hint: See Exercise 41.

48. $f(x, y) = \begin{cases} \dfrac{x^4 - y^4}{x^4 + y^4} & \text{if } (x, y) \neq (0, 0) \\ 0 & \text{if } (x, y) = (0, 0) \end{cases}$

Hint: See Exercise 42.

In Exercises 49 through 53, find the value of the directional derivative at the point P_0 for the function in the direction of U.

49. $f(x, y) = 3x^2 - 2xy + 1$; $\mathbf{U} = \frac{3}{5}\mathbf{i} - \frac{4}{5}\mathbf{j}$; $P_0 = (5, 10)$

50. $g(x, y) = \tan^{-1} \dfrac{y}{x}$; $\mathbf{U} = \dfrac{2}{\sqrt{13}}\mathbf{i} - \dfrac{3}{\sqrt{13}}\mathbf{j}$; $P_0 = (4, -4)$

51. $h(x, y) = e^x + y^2 \cos x$; $\mathbf{U} = \frac{1}{2}\sqrt{2}\mathbf{i} - \frac{1}{2}\sqrt{2}\mathbf{j}$; $P_0 = (0, 3)$

52. $f(x, y) = x^2 - 2x^2 y + \ln x$; $\mathbf{U} = \cos \pi \mathbf{i} + \sin \pi \mathbf{j}$; $P_0 = (1, -2)$

53. $f(x, y, z) = xy^2 z - 3xyz + 2xz^2$; $\mathbf{U} = -\dfrac{2}{3}\mathbf{i} + \dfrac{2}{3}\mathbf{j} - \dfrac{1}{3}\mathbf{k}$; $P_0 = (2, 1, 1)$

In Exercises 54 through 57, find (a) the gradient of f at P_0; (b) the rate of change of the function value in the direction of U at P_0.

54. $f(x, y) = 3x^2 - 2xy^3$; $\mathbf{U} = \cos \frac{1}{6}\pi \mathbf{i} + \sin \frac{1}{6}\pi \mathbf{j}$; $P_0 = (-3, 1)$

55. $f(x, y) = \frac{1}{2}\ln(x^2 + y^2)$; $\mathbf{U} = \frac{1}{2}\mathbf{i} + \frac{1}{2}\sqrt{3}\mathbf{j}$; $P_0 = (1, 1)$

56. $f(x, y, z) = yz - y^2 - xz$; $\mathbf{U} = \frac{6}{7}\mathbf{i} + \frac{3}{7}\mathbf{j} + \frac{2}{7}\mathbf{k}$; $P_0 = (1, 2, 3)$

57. $f(x, y, z) = x^3 + y^3 + 2xyz$; $\mathbf{U} = \dfrac{3}{\sqrt{14}}\mathbf{i} - \dfrac{2}{\sqrt{14}}\mathbf{j} + \dfrac{1}{\sqrt{14}}\mathbf{k}$; $P_0 = (2, -1, 0)$

In Exercises 58 and 59, determine the relative extrema of f, if there are any.

58. $f(x, y) = 2x^2 - 3xy + 2y^2 + 10x - 11y$

59. $f(x, y) = x^3 + y^3 + 3xy$

In Exercises 60 and 61, prove that f is differentiable at all points in its domain by showing that Definition 12.4.2 holds.

60. $f(x, y) = 3xy^2 - 4x^2 + y^2$ **61.** $f(x, y) = \dfrac{2x + y}{y^2}$

62. Suppose α is the radian measure of an acute angle of a right triangle and $\sin \alpha$ is determined by a/c, where a centimeters is the length of the side opposite the angle and c centimeters is the length of the hypotenuse. If by measurement a is found to be 3.52 and c is found to be 7.14, and there is a possible error of 0.01 in each, find the possible error in the computation of $\sin \alpha$ from these measurements.

63. A painting contractor charges \$4 per square meter for painting the four walls and ceiling of a room. If the dimensions of the ceiling are measured to be 4 m and 5 m, the height of the room is measured to be 3 m, and these measurements are correct to 0.5 cm, find approximately, by using the total differential, the greatest error in estimating the cost of the job from these measurements.

64. At a given instant, the length of one side of a rectangle is 6 cm and it is increasing at the rate of 1 cm/sec, and the length of another side of the rectangle is 10 cm and it is decreasing at the rate of 2 cm/sec. Find the rate of change of the area of the rectangle at the given instant.

65. The radius of a right-circular cylinder is decreasing at the rate of 5 cm/min and the height is increasing at the rate of 12 cm/min. Find the rate of change of the volume at the instant when the radius is 20 cm and the height is 40 cm.

66. Find the slope of the tangent line to the curve of intersection of the surface $25x^2 - 16y^2 + 9z^2 - 4 = 0$ with the plane $x = 4$ at the point $(4, 9, 10)$.

67. Use the ideal gas law (see Example 6, Section 12.3) with $k = 1.4$ to find the rate of change of the pressure at the instant when the Kelvin temperature is 75° and the volume of the gas is 20 liters if the temperature is increasing at the rate of 0.5°K/min and the volume is increasing at the rate of 0.3 liter/min.

In Exercises 68 through 70, find an equation of the tangent plane and equations of the normal line to the surface at the indicated point.

68. $z = x^2 + 2xy$; $(1, 3, 7)$

69. $x^2 + 2y + z = 8$; $(2, 1, 2)$

70. $3x^2 + 2xy - y^2 = 15$; $(2, 3, 4)$

71. Find symmetric equations of the tangent line to the curve of intersection of the surfaces $x^2 - 3xy + y^2 - z = 0$ and $2x^2 + y^2 - 3z + 27 = 0$ at the point $(1, -2, 11)$.

72. Find equations of the tangent line to the curve of intersection of the surface $z = 3x^2 + y^2 + 1$ with the plane $x = 2$ at the point $(2, -1, 14)$.

73. An equation of the surface of a mountain is $z = 900 - 3xy$, where distance is measured in meters, the x axis points to the west, and the y axis points to the south. A mountain climber is at the point corresponding to $(50, 4, 300)$.
(a) What is the direction of steepest ascent?
(b) Is the climber ascending or descending when moving in the north direction?
(c) In what direction is the climber traveling a level path?

74. If $f(x, y)$ units are produced by x workers and y machines, then $D_x f(x, y)$ is called the *marginal productivity of labor* and $D_y f(x, y)$ is called the *marginal productivity of machines*. Suppose that

$$f(x, y) = x^2 + 6xy + 3y^2$$

where $5 \leq x \leq 30$ and $4 \leq y \leq 12$.
(a) Find the number of units produced in a day when the labor force for that day consists of 15 workers, and 8 machines are used.
(b) Use the marginal productivity of labor to determine the approximate number of additional units that can be produced in 1 day if the labor force is increased from 15 to 16 and the number of machines remains fixed at 8.
(c) Use the marginal productivity of machines to determine the approximate number of additional units that can be produced in 1 day if the number of machines is increased from 8 to 9 and the number of workers remains fixed at 15.

In Exercises 75 through 78, use Lagrange multipliers to find the critical point(s) of the function subject to the constraint. Determine if the function has a relative maximum or a relative minimum value at any critical point.

75. $f(x, y) = 5 + x^2 - y^2$ with constraint $x^2 - 2y^2 = 5$

76. $f(x, y, z) = x^2 + y^2 + z^2$ with constraint $x^2 - y^2 = 1$

77. $f(x, y, z) = y + xz - 2x^2 - y^2 - z^2$ with constraint $z = 35 - x - y$

78. $f(x, y, z) = xz^2 + y^3$ with constraint $x^2 + y^2 + z^2 = 1$

79. Use Lagrange multipliers to find the shortest distance from the point $(4, 1, 2)$ to the plane $x - y + 2z = 0$.

80. Use Lagrange multipliers to find the point on the surface $z = x^2 - y^2 + 2$ that is closest to the origin.

81. Find three numbers whose sum is 100 and the sum of whose squares is least.

82. A manufacturer produces daily x units of commodity A and y units of commodity B. If $P(x, y)$ dollars is the daily profit from their sale, and $P(x, y) = 33x + 66y + xy - x^2 - 3y^2$, how many units of each commodity should be produced daily for the manufacturer to receive the greatest profit?

83. Find the dimensions of the rectangular parallelepiped of greatest volume that can be inscribed in the ellipsoid $x^2 + 9y^2 + z^2 = 9$. Assume that the edges are parallel to the coordinate axes.

84. The temperature is T degrees at any point (x, y) of the curve $4x^2 + 12y^2 = 1$, and

$$T = 4x^2 + 24y^2 - 2x$$

Find the points on the curve where the temperature is the greatest and where it is the least. Also find the temperature at these points.

85. The temperature is T degrees at any point (x, y) on a heated circular plate and

$$T = \frac{44}{x^2 + y^2 + 9}$$

where distance is measured in centimeters from the origin at the center of the plate.
(a) Find the rate of change of the temperature at the point $(3, 2)$ in the direction of the vector $\cos \frac{1}{6}\pi \mathbf{i} + \sin \frac{1}{6}\pi \mathbf{j}$.
(b) Find the direction and magnitude of the greatest rate of change of T at the point $(3, 2)$.

86. A rectangular crate without a top is to have a surface area of 216 ft^2. What are the dimensions for a crate of greatest volume?

87. For the crate of Exercise 86, suppose instead of a surface area of 216 ft^2, the sum of the lengths of the edges is 216 ft. What then are the dimensions for a crate of greatest volume?

88. A piece of wire L units long is cut into three pieces. One piece is bent into the shape of a circle, a second piece is bent into the shape of a square, and the third piece is bent into the shape of an equilateral triangle. How should the wire be cut so that **(a)** the combined area of the three figures is as small as possible and **(b)** the combined area of the three figures is as large as possible?

89. Determine the relative dimensions of a rectangular box, without a top and having a specific surface area, if the volume is to be a maximum.

90. Find the greatest and least distances from the origin to the curve of intersection of the surfaces $x^2 + 3y^2 + 2z^2 = 30$ and $x^2 = 2yz$.

91. The following table gives data for five patients having a particular surgical operation at a certain hospital, where x years is the patient's age and y days is the length of time the patient remained in the hospital while recuperating after the surgery.

	Patient A	Patient B	Patient C	Patient D	Patient E
x	54	46	40	36	30
y	15	12	9	10	8

(a) Find an equation of the regression line for the data in the table.
(b) Use the regression line to estimate the length of stay in the hospital for a 42-year-old person having the surgery.

92. In the following table, a patient's systolic blood pressure and corresponding heart rate are given, where x millimeters of mercury is the systolic blood pressure and y beats per minute is the heart rate.

	Patient A	Patient B	Patient C	Patient D	Patient E	Patient F
x	110	117	133	146	115	127
y	70	74	80	85	60	77

(a) Find an equation of the regression line for the data in the table.
(b) Use the regression line to estimate a patient's heart rate if the systolic blood pressure is 85 mm of mercury.

93. In deserts, water is a factor that sharply limits plant activity. In the following table x is the number of millimeters of precipitation per year for six different regions, and y is the number of kilograms per hectare in the net photosynthate produced.

	Region A	Region B	Region C	Region D	Region E	Region F
x	100	200	400	500	600	650
y	1000	1900	3200	4400	5800	6400

(a) Find an equation of the regression line for the data in the table.
(b) Use the regression line to estimate the net photosynthate produced in a region having an annual precipitation of 300 mm.

94. A breakfast cereal was test-sold in four cities of the same size at different prices; the results are shown in the table, where x cents was the price per box and y thousands of cases were sold per week.

	City A	City B	City C	City D
x	130	140	150	160
y	100	85	75	63

(a) Find an equation of the regression line for the data in the table. Use the regression line in part (a) as the demand curve to estimate the weekly sales if the price per box is **(b)** \$1.20 and **(c)** \$1.70.

95. Find **(a)** $f_2(x, 0)$ if $x \neq 0$ and **(b)** $f_2(0, 0)$ if

$$f(x, y) = \begin{cases} \dfrac{12x^2y - 3y^2}{x^2 + y} & \text{if } (x, y) \neq (0, 0) \\ 0 & \text{if } (x, y) = (0, 0) \end{cases}$$

96. Verify that $u(x, y) = (\sinh x)(\sin y)$ satisfies Laplace's equation in R^2:

$$\frac{\partial^2 u}{\partial x^2} + \frac{\partial^2 u}{\partial y^2} = 0$$

97. If f is a differentiable function of u, let $u = x^2 + y^2$ and prove that $z = xy + f(x^2 + y^2)$ satisfies the equation

$$y \frac{\partial z}{\partial x} - x \frac{\partial z}{\partial y} = y^2 - x^2$$

98. Laplace's equation in polar coordinates is

$$r^2 \frac{\partial^2 u}{\partial r^2} + r \frac{\partial u}{\partial r} + \frac{\partial^2 u}{\partial \theta^2} = 0$$

Verify that $u(r, \theta) = r^n \sin n\theta$, where n is a constant, satisfies this equation.

99. Verify that $u(x, y, z) = e^{3x+4y} \sin 5z$ satisfies Laplace's equation in R^3:

$$\frac{\partial^2 u}{\partial x^2} + \frac{\partial^2 u}{\partial y^2} + \frac{\partial^2 u}{\partial z^2} = 0$$

100. Verify that $u(x, t) = A \cos(kat) \sin(kx)$, where A and k are arbitrary constants, satisfies the partial differential equation for a vibrating string:

$$\frac{\partial^2 u}{\partial t^2} = a^2 \frac{\partial^2 u}{\partial x^2}$$

101. Verify that

$$u(x, t) = \sin \frac{n\pi x}{L} e^{(-n^2\pi^2 k^2/L^2)t}$$

satisfies the one-dimensional heat-conduction partial differential equation:

$$\frac{\partial u}{\partial t} = k^2 \frac{\partial^2 u}{\partial x^2}$$

102. Given

$$f(x, y) = \begin{cases} \dfrac{2x^2 y}{x^4 + y^2} & \text{if } (x, y) \neq (0, 0) \\ 0 & \text{if } (x, y) = (0, 0) \end{cases}$$

Prove that $D_1 f(0, 0)$ and $D_2 f(0, 0)$ exist but that f is not differentiable at $(0, 0)$. *Hint:* See Example 7, Section 12.2 and Exercise 38 in Exercises 12.2.

103. Given

$$f(x, y, z) = \begin{cases} \dfrac{x^2 y^2 z^2}{(x^2 + y^2 + z^2)^2} & \text{if } (x, y, z) \neq (0, 0, 0) \\ 0 & \text{if } (x, y, z) = (0, 0, 0) \end{cases}$$

Prove that f is differentiable at $(0, 0, 0)$.

104. Let f be the function defined by

$$f(x, y) = \begin{cases} \dfrac{e^{-1/x^2} y}{e^{-2/x^2} + y^2} & \text{if } x \neq 0 \\ 0 & \text{if } x = 0 \end{cases}$$

Prove that f is discontinuous at the origin.

105. For the function of Exercise 104, prove that $D_1 f(0, 0)$ and $D_2 f(0, 0)$ both exist.

106. If f is a differentiable function of x and y and $u = f(x, y)$, $x = r \cos \theta$, and $y = r \sin \theta$, show that

$$\left(\frac{\partial u}{\partial r}\right)^2 + \frac{1}{r^2}\left(\frac{\partial u}{\partial \theta}\right)^2 = \left(\frac{\partial u}{\partial x}\right)^2 + \left(\frac{\partial u}{\partial y}\right)^2$$

107. The one-dimensional heat-conduction partial differential equation is given in Exercise 101. Show that if f is a function of x satisfying the equation

$$\frac{d^2 f}{dx^2} + \lambda^2 f(x) = 0$$

and g is a function of t satisfying the equation

$$\frac{dg}{dt} + k^2 \lambda^2 g(t) = 0,$$

then if $u = f(x)g(t)$ and k and λ are constants, the partial differential equation is satisfied.

108. The partial differential equation for a vibrating string is given in Exercise 100. Show that if f is a

function of x satisfying the equation

$$\frac{d^2 f}{dx^2} + \lambda^2 f(x) = 0 \text{ and } g \text{ is a function of } t \text{ satisfying}$$

the equation $\dfrac{d^2 g}{dt^2} + a^2 \lambda^2 g(t) = 0$, then if

$u = f(x)g(t)$ and a and λ are constants, the partial differential equation is satisfied.

109. Prove that if f and g are two arbitrary functions of a real variable having continuous second derivatives and

$$u = f(x + at) + g(x - at)$$

then u satisfies the partial differential equation of the vibrating string given in Exercise 100. *Hint:* Let $v = x + at$ and $w = x - at$; then u is a function of v and w, and v and w are in turn functions of x and t.

110. A nonhomogeneous electromagnetic wave equation for a scalar potential $V(r, t)$ that assumes *spherical symmetry* r units from the origin is

$$\frac{1}{r^2} \frac{\partial}{\partial r}\left(r^2 \frac{\partial V}{\partial r}\right) - \mu\epsilon \frac{\partial^2 V}{\partial t^2} = 0$$

where μ is the constant permeability of free space and ϵ is the constant permitivity of free space.
(a) Suppose $V(r, t) = \phi(r, t)/r$ where the second partial derivatives of ϕ with respect to r and t both exist. Show that the nonhomogeneous wave equation may be written as

$$\frac{\partial^2 \phi}{\partial r^2} - \mu\epsilon \frac{\partial^2 \phi}{\partial t^2} = 0$$

which is the one-dimensional homogeneous wave equation. **(b)** Let f be a function of one variable whose second derivative exists. Show by direct substitution that $\phi = f(t - r\sqrt{\mu\epsilon})$ is a solution of the one-dimensional homogeneous wave equation.

111. The two-dimensional equation for transverse electric waves is

$$\frac{\partial^2 h}{\partial x^2} + \frac{\partial^2 h}{\partial y^2} + K^2 h = 0$$

where $K^2 = \left(\dfrac{m\pi}{a}\right)^2 + \left(\dfrac{n\pi}{b}\right)^2$ and K, m, n, a, and b

are constants. Show that a solution of this equation is

$$h = H \cos\left(\frac{m\pi}{a} x\right) \cos\left(\frac{n\pi}{b} y\right)$$

where H is a constant.

MULTIPLE INTEGRATION

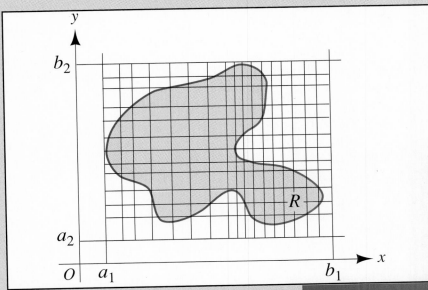

Cylindrical and spherical coordinates are generalizations of polar coordinates to three-dimensional space. They are discussed in the first section so that they will be available later for applications.

The main purpose of this chapter is to extend the definite integral of a function of a single variable to a function of several variables. We begin in Section 13.2 by defining the *double integral* of a function of two variables on a closed rectangular region in R^2. We then extend the concept to consider the double integral of a function on a more general plane region. We also show in Section 13.2 how *iterated integrals* are used to evaluate double integrals. We apply double integrals in Section 13.2 to find volumes of solids and in Section 13.3 to calculate mass, center of mass, moments of inertia, and areas of surfaces. Then in Section 13.4, we demonstrate how polar coordinates can be used to evaluate certain double integrals.

We consider the *triple integral* in Section 13.5 by first defining it on a rectangular parallelepiped and then on a more general region in R^3. We show in Section 13.6 that when the region has an axis of symmetry, cylindrical coordinates are used to evaluate a triple integral and when there is symmetry with respect to a point, spherical coordinates are used.

The treatment here is less formal and more intuitive than in previous chapters because the proofs of most theorems in this chapter belong to a course in advanced calculus.

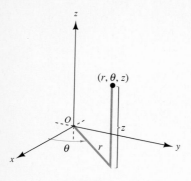

FIGURE 1

13.1 CYLINDRICAL AND SPHERICAL COORDINATES

Prior to our treatment of multiple integrals and their applications, we introduce two new systems of coordinates for three-dimensional space: *cylindrical* and *spherical coordinates*. These coordinate systems will simplify our work in a number of cases in this chapter.

The cylindrical coordinate system is an extension of polar coordinates to three dimensions. The **cylindrical coordinate** representation of a point P is (r, θ, z), where r and θ are the polar coordinates of the projection of P on a polar plane and z is the directed distance from this polar plane to P. See Figure 1.

▶ **EXAMPLE 1**   Sketch the graph of each of the following equations, expressed in cylindrical coordinates, where c is a constant: **(a)** $r = c$; **(b)** $\theta = c$; **(c)** $z = c$.

Solution

(a) For a point $P(r, \theta, z)$ on the graph of $r = c$, θ and z can have any values and r is constant. The graph is a right-circular cylinder having radius $|c|$ and the z axis as its axis. The graph appears in Figure 2.

(b) For all points $P(r, \theta, z)$ on the graph of $\theta = c$, r and z can assume any value while θ remains constant. The graph is a plane through the z axis. See Figure 3 for the graph, where $0 < c < \frac{1}{2}\pi$.

(c) The graph of $z = c$ is a plane parallel to the polar plane at a directed distance of c units from it. Figure 4 shows the graph for $c > 0$.   ◀

The name "cylindrical coordinates" comes from the fact that the graph of $r = c$ is a right-circular cylinder as in Example 1(a). Cylindrical coordinates are often used in a physical problem when there is an axis of symmetry.

Suppose that a cartesian coordinate system and a cylindrical coordinate system are placed so the xy plane is the polar plane of the cylindrical

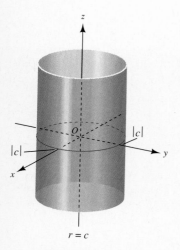

$r = c$

FIGURE 2

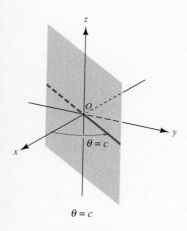

$\theta = c$

FIGURE 3

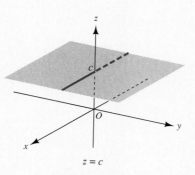

$z = c$

FIGURE 4

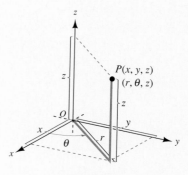

FIGURE 5

coordinate system and the positive side of the x axis is the polar axis as shown in Figure 5. Then the point P has (x, y, z) and (r, θ, z) as two sets of coordinates that are related by the equations.

$$x = r \cos \theta \qquad y = r \sin \theta \qquad z = z \tag{1}$$

$$r^2 = x^2 + y^2 \qquad \tan \theta = \frac{y}{x} \text{ if } x \neq 0 \qquad z = z \tag{2}$$

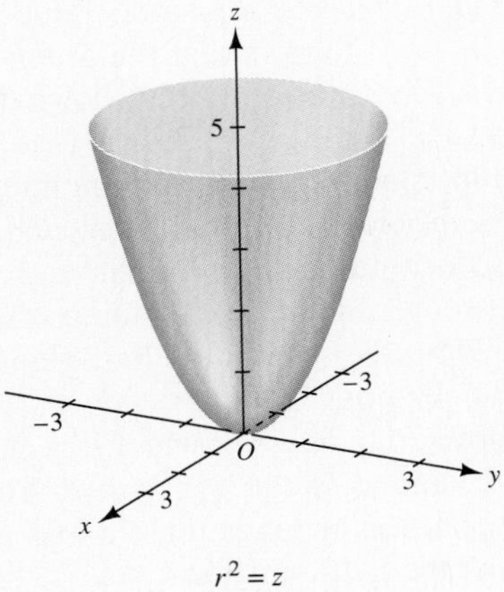

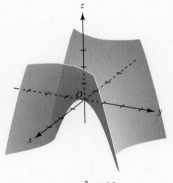

$r^2 = z$

FIGURE 6

▶ **EXAMPLE 2** Find an equation in cartesian coordinates of the following surfaces whose equations are expressed in cylindrical coordinates, and identify the surface: **(a)** $r = 6 \sin \theta$; **(b)** $r(3 \cos \theta + 2 \sin \theta) + 6z = 0$.

Solution

(a) Multiplying on both sides of the equation by r we get $r^2 = 6r \sin \theta$. Because $r^2 = x^2 + y^2$ and $r \sin \theta = y$, then $x^2 + y^2 = 6y$. This equation can be written in the form $x^2 + (y - 3)^2 = 9$, which shows that its graph is a right-circular cylinder whose cross section in the xy plane is the circle with its center at $(0, 3)$ and radius 3.

(b) Replacing $r \cos \theta$ with x and $r \sin \theta$ with y we obtain the equation $3x + 2y + 6z = 0$. Hence the graph is a plane through the origin and has $\langle 3, 2, 6 \rangle$ as a normal vector. ◀

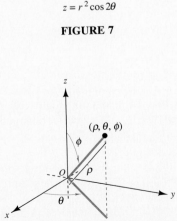

$z = r^2 \cos 2\theta$

FIGURE 7

▶ **EXAMPLE 3** Find an equation in cylindrical coordinates for each of the following surfaces whose equations are given in cartesian coordinates, and identify the surface: **(a)** $x^2 + y^2 = z$; **(b)** $x^2 - y^2 = z$.

Solution

(a) The equation is similar to Equation 9 of Section 10.6; so the graph is an elliptic paraboloid. The elliptic paraboloid appears in Figure 6. If $x^2 + y^2$ is replaced by r^2, the equation becomes $r^2 = z$.

(b) The equation is similar to Equation 10 of Section 10.6 with x and y interchanged. The graph is therefore a hyperbolic paraboloid having the z axis as its axis. When x is replaced by $r \cos \theta$ and y is replaced by $r \sin \theta$, we get the equation $r^2 \cos^2 \theta - r^2 \sin^2 \theta = z$; because $\cos^2 \theta - \sin^2 \theta = \cos 2\theta$, we can write this as $z = r^2 \cos 2\theta$. Figure 7 shows the hyperbolic paraboloid. ◀

In a spherical coordinate system there is a polar plane and an axis perpendicular to the polar plane, with the origin of the z axis at the pole of the polar plane. A point is located by three numbers, and the **spherical coordinate** representation of a point P is (ρ, θ, ϕ), where $\rho = |\overline{OP}|$, θ is the radian measure of the polar angle of the projection of P on the polar plane, and ϕ is the nonnegative radian measure of the smallest angle measured from the positive side of the z axis to the line OP. See Figure 8. The origin has the spherical coordinate representation $(0, \theta, \phi)$, where θ and ϕ may have any values. If the point $P(\rho, \theta, \phi)$ is not the origin, then $\rho > 0$ and $0 \leq \phi \leq \pi$, where $\phi = 0$ if P is on the positive side of the z axis and $\phi = \pi$ if P is on the negative side of the z axis.

(ρ, θ, ϕ)

FIGURE 8

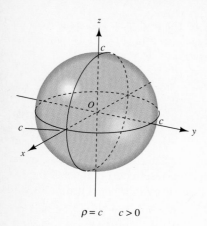

$\rho = c \quad c > 0$

FIGURE 9

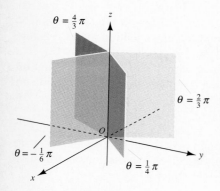

FIGURE 10

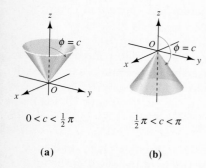

(a) $0 < c < \frac{1}{2}\pi$ (b) $\frac{1}{2}\pi < c < \pi$

FIGURE 11

▶ **EXAMPLE 4** Sketch the graph of each of the following equations, expressed in spherical coordinates, where c is a constant: **(a)** $\rho = c$, and $c > 0$; **(b)** $\theta = c$; **(c)** $\phi = c$, and $0 < c < \pi$.

Solution

(a) Every point $P(\rho, \theta, \phi)$ on the graph of $\rho = c$ has the same value of ρ, θ may be any number, and $0 \le \phi \le \pi$. It follows that the graph is a sphere of radius c and has its center at the pole. Figure 9 shows the sphere.

(b) For any point $P(\rho, \theta, \phi)$ on the graph of $\theta = c$, ρ may be any nonnegative number, ϕ may be any number in the closed interval $[0, \pi]$ and θ is constant. The graph is a half plane containing the z axis and is obtained by rotating about the z axis through an angle of c radians that half of the xz plane for which $x \ge 0$. Figure 10 shows the half planes for $\theta = \frac{1}{4}\pi$, $\theta = \frac{2}{3}\pi$, $\theta = \frac{4}{3}\pi$, and $\theta = -\frac{1}{6}\pi$.

(c) The graph of $\phi = c$ contains all the points $P(\rho, \theta, \phi)$ for which ρ is any nonnegative number, θ is any number, and ϕ is the constant c. The graph is half of a cone having its vertex at the origin and the z axis as its axis. Figures 11(a) and (b) each show the half cone for $0 < c < \frac{1}{2}\pi$ and $\frac{1}{2}\pi < c < \pi$, respectively. ◀

Because the graph of $\rho = c$ is a sphere as seen in Example 4(a), we have the name "spherical coordinates." In a physical problem when a point is a center of symmetry, spherical coordinates are often used.

By placing a spherical coordinate system and a cartesian coordinate system together as shown in Figure 12, we obtain relationships between the spherical and cartesian coordinates of a point P from

$$x = |\overline{OQ}| \cos \theta \qquad y = |\overline{OQ}| \sin \theta \qquad z = |\overline{QP}|$$

Because $|\overline{OQ}| = \rho \sin \phi$ and $|\overline{QP}| = \rho \cos \phi$, these equations become

$$x = \rho \sin \phi \cos \theta \qquad y = \rho \sin \phi \sin \theta \qquad z = \rho \cos \phi \qquad (3)$$

By squaring each of the equations in (3) and adding,

$$x^2 + y^2 + z^2 = \rho^2 \sin^2 \phi \cos^2 \theta + \rho^2 \sin^2 \phi \sin^2 \theta + \rho^2 \cos^2 \phi$$
$$x^2 + y^2 + z^2 = \rho^2 \sin^2 \phi (\cos^2 \theta + \sin^2 \theta) + \rho^2 \cos^2 \phi$$
$$x^2 + y^2 + z^2 = \rho^2 (\sin^2 \phi + \cos^2 \phi)$$
$$x^2 + y^2 + z^2 = \rho^2$$

▶ **EXAMPLE 5** Find an equation in cartesian coordinates of the following surfaces whose equations are expressed in spherical coordinates, and identify the surface **(a)** $\rho \cos \phi = 4$; **(b)** $\rho \sin \phi = 4$.

Solution

(a) Because $z = \rho \cos \phi$, the equation becomes $z = 4$. Hence the graph is a plane parallel to the xy plane and 4 units above it.

(b) For spherical coordinates $\rho \ge 0$ and $\sin \phi \ge 0$ (because $0 \le \phi \le \pi$); therefore, by squaring on both sides of the given equation we obtain the

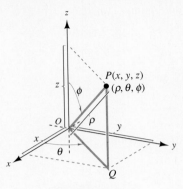

FIGURE 12

equivalent equation $\rho^2 \sin^2 \phi = 16$, which in turn is equivalent to

$$\rho^2(1 - \cos^2 \phi) = 16$$
$$\rho^2 - \rho^2 \cos^2 \phi = 16$$

Replacing ρ^2 by $x^2 + y^2 + z^2$ and $\rho \cos \phi$ by z we get

$$x^2 + y^2 + z^2 - z^2 = 16$$
$$x^2 + y^2 = 16$$

Therefore the graph is the right-circular cylinder having the z axis as its axis and radius 4. ◄

▶ **EXAMPLE 6**   Find an equation in spherical coordinates for **(a)** the elliptic paraboloid of Example 3(a); **(b)** the plane of Example 2(b).

Solution

(a) A cartesian equation of the elliptic paraboloid of Example 3(a) is $x^2 + y^2 = z$. Replacing x by $\rho \sin \phi \cos \theta$, y by $\rho \sin \phi \sin \theta$, and z by $\rho \cos \phi$ we get

$$\rho^2 \sin^2 \phi \cos^2 \theta + \rho^2 \sin^2 \phi \sin^2 \theta = \rho \cos \phi$$
$$\rho^2 \sin^2 \phi(\cos^2 \theta + \sin^2 \theta) = \rho \cos \phi$$

which is equivalent to the two equations

$$\rho = 0 \quad \text{and} \quad \rho \sin^2 \phi = \cos \phi$$

The origin is the only point whose coordinates satisfy $\rho = 0$. Because the origin $(0, \theta, \frac{1}{2}\pi)$ lies on $\rho \sin^2 \phi = \cos \phi$, we can disregard the equation $\rho = 0$. Furthermore, $\sin \phi \neq 0$ because there is no value of ϕ for which both $\sin \phi$ and $\cos \phi$ are 0. Therefore the equation $\rho \sin^2 \phi = \cos \phi$ can be written as $\rho = \csc^2 \phi \cos \phi$, or, equivalently, $\rho = \csc \phi \cot \phi$.

(b) A cartesian equation of the plane of Example 2(b) is $3x + 2y + 6z = 0$. By using Equations (3) this equation becomes

$$3\rho \sin \phi \cos \theta + 2\rho \sin \phi \sin \theta + 6\rho \cos \phi = 0 \qquad ◄$$

EXERCISES 13.1

1. Find the cartesian coordinates of the point having the given cylindrical coordinates: **(a)** $(3, \frac{1}{2}\pi, 5)$; **(b)** $(7, \frac{2}{3}\pi, -4)$; **(c)** $(1, 1, 1)$.

2. Find a set of cylindrical coordinates of the point having the given cartesian coordinates: **(a)** $(4, 4, -2)$; **(b)** $(-3\sqrt{3}, 3, 6)$; **(c)** $(1, 1, 1)$.

3. Find the cartesian coordinates of the point having the given spherical coordinates: **(a)** $(4, \frac{1}{6}\pi, \frac{1}{4}\pi)$; **(b)** $(4, \frac{1}{2}\pi, \frac{1}{3}\pi)$; **(c)** $(\sqrt{6}, \frac{1}{3}\pi, \frac{3}{4}\pi)$.

4. Find a set of spherical coordinates of the point having the given cartesian coordinates: **(a)** $(1, -1, -\sqrt{2})$; **(b)** $(-1, \sqrt{3}, 2,)$; **(c)** $(2, 2, 2)$.

5. Find a set of cylindrical coordinates of the point having the given spherical coordinates: **(a)** $(4, \frac{2}{3}\pi, \frac{5}{6}\pi)$; **(b)** $(\sqrt{2}, \frac{3}{4}\pi, \pi)$; **(c)** $(2\sqrt{3}, \frac{1}{3}\pi, \frac{1}{4}\pi)$.

6. Find a set of spherical coordinates of the point having the given cylindrical coordinates: **(a)** $(3, \frac{1}{6}\pi, 3)$; **(b)** $(3, \frac{1}{2}\pi, 2)$; **(c)** $(2, \frac{5}{6}\pi, -4)$.

In Exercises 7 through 12, find an equation in cylindrical coordinates of the surface, and identify the surface.

7. $x^2 + y^2 + 4z^2 = 16$ 8. $x^2 - y^2 = 9$

9. $x^2 + y^2 = 3z$ 10. $9x^2 + 4y^2 = 36$

11. $x^2 - y^2 = 3z^2$ 12. $x^2 + y^2 = z^2$

In Exercises 13 through 17, find an equation in spherical coordinates of the surface, and identify the surface.

13. $x^2 + y^2 + z^2 - 9z = 0$ **14.** $x^2 + y^2 = z^2$

15. $x^2 + y^2 = 9$ **16.** $x^2 + y^2 = 2z$

17. $x^2 + y^2 + z^2 - 8x = 0$

In Exercises 18 through 22, find an equation in cartesian coordinates for the surface whose equation is given in cylindrical coordinates. In Exercises 18 and 19, identify the surface.

18. $r = 3 \cos \theta$ **19. (a)** $r = 4$; **(b)** $\theta = \frac{1}{4} \pi$

20. $r = 3 + 2 \cos \theta$ **21.** $r^2 \cos 2\theta = z^3$

22. $z^2 \sin^3 \theta = r^3$

In Exercises 23 through 28, find an equation in cartesian coordinates for the surface whose equation is given in spherical coordinates. In Exercises 23 through 25, identify the surface.

23. (a) $\rho = 9$; **(b)** $\theta = \frac{1}{4} \pi$; **(c)** $\phi = \frac{1}{4} \pi$

24. $\rho = 9 \sec \phi$ **25.** $\rho = 6 \csc \phi$

26. $\rho = 3 \cos \phi$ **27.** $\rho = 2 \tan \theta$

28. $\rho = 6 \sin \phi \sin \theta + 3 \cos \phi$

In Exercises 29 through 32, match the equation, which is in either cylindrical or spherical coordinates, with one of the surfaces shown in (i)–(x).

29. (a) $r = 4$; **(b)** $\rho = 4$; **(c)** $r = 2 \sin \theta$

30. (a) $\theta = \frac{1}{3} \pi$; **(b)** $\phi = \frac{1}{3} \pi$; **(c)** $r = 2 \cos \theta$

31. (a) $\rho \sin \phi = 2$; **(b)** $r^2 = 4z$

32. (a) $\rho \cos \phi = 2$; **(b)** $z^2 + r^2 = 4$

ii.

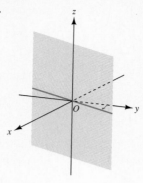

iii.

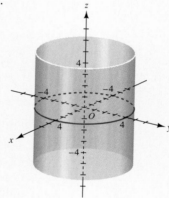

i.

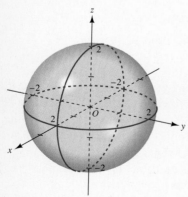

iv.

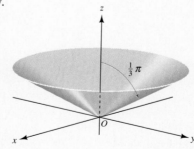

v.

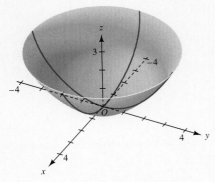

vi.

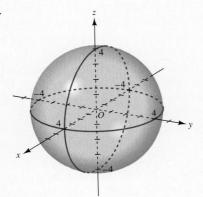

vii.

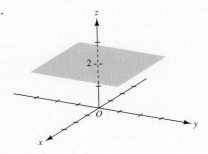

viii.

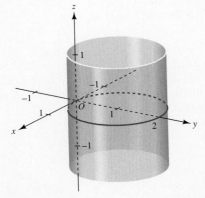

ix.

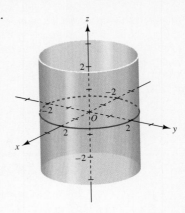

x.

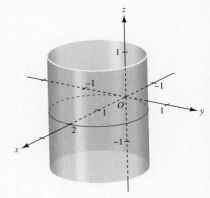

33. A curve C in R^3 has the following parametric equations in cylindrical coordinates: $r = F_1(t)$, $\theta = F_2(t)$, $z = F_3(t)$. Use the formula of Theorem 11.2.11 and formulas (1) of this section to prove that if L units is the length of arc of C from the point where $t = a$ to the point where $t = b$, then

$$L = \int_a^b \sqrt{\left(\frac{dr}{dt}\right)^2 + r^2\left(\frac{d\theta}{dt}\right)^2 + \left(\frac{dz}{dt}\right)^2}\, dt$$

34. A curve C in R^3 has the following parametric equations in spherical coordinates: $\rho = G_1(t)$, $\theta = G_2(t)$, $\phi = G_3(t)$. Use the formula of Theorem 11.2.11 and formulas (3) of this section to prove that if L units is the length of arc of C from the point where $t = a$ to the point where $t = b$, then

$$L = \int_a^b \sqrt{\left(\frac{d\rho}{dt}\right)^2 + \rho^2 \sin^2\phi\left(\frac{d\theta}{dt}\right)^2 + \rho^2\left(\frac{d\theta}{dt}\right)^2}\, dt$$

35. **(a)** Show that parametric equations for the circular helix of Example 7, Section 11.2 are $r = 2$, $\theta = t$, $z = t$. **(b)** Use the formula of Exercise 33 to find the length of arc of the circular helix of part (a) from $t = 0$ to $t = 4\pi$. Check your result with that of Example 7, Section 11.2.

36. A *conical helix* winds around a cone in a way similar to that in which a circular helix winds around a cylinder. Use the formula of Exercise 34 to find the length of arc from $t = 0$ to $t = 2\pi$ of the conical helix having parametric equations $\rho = t$, $\theta = t$, $\phi = \frac{1}{4}\pi$.

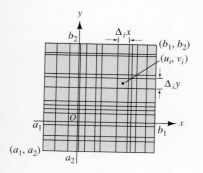

FIGURE 1

13.2 DOUBLE INTEGRALS

In our treatment of *multiple integrals,* which involve a function of several variables, we shall refer to an integral of a function of a single variable as a **single integral**. Recall that in the discussion of a single integral we required that the function be defined on a closed interval in the set of real numbers. For the *double integral* of a function of two variables, we shall require that the function be defined on a closed region in R^2. In this chapter, when we refer to a region, we assume it is closed.

The simplest kind of closed region in R^2 is a *closed rectangular region*, which we now proceed to define. Two distinct points $A(a_1, a_2)$ and $B(b_1, b_2)$, such that $a_1 \leq b_1$ and $a_2 \leq b_2$, determine a rectangle having sides parallel to the coordinate axes. Refer to Figure 1. The two points, together with the points (b_1, a_2) and (a_1, b_2), are called the *vertices* of the rectangle. The line segments joining consecutive vertices are called the *edges* of the rectangle. The set of all points interior to the rectangle is called an *open rectangular region*, and the set of all points in the open rectangle, together with the points on the edges, is called a **closed rectangular region.**

Let the closed rectangular region of Figure 1 be denoted by R, and let f be a function defined on R. The region R can be considered as a **region of integration.** The first step is to define a **partition,** Δ, of R. We draw lines parallel to the coordinate axes and obtain a network of rectangular subregions that cover R. The **norm** of this partition, denoted by $\|\Delta\|$, is determined by the length of the longest diagonal of a rectangular subregion of the partition. The length of the diagonal is chosen because it represents the greatest distance between any two points in a rectangular subregion. Number the subregions in some arbitrary way and let the total be n. Denote the width of the ith subregion by $\Delta_i x$ units and its height by $\Delta_i y$ units. Then if $\Delta_i A$ square units is the area of the ith rectangular subregion,

$$\Delta_i A = \Delta_i x \, \Delta_i y$$

Let (u_i, v_i) be an arbitrary point in the ith subregion and let $f(u_i, v_i)$ be the function value there. Consider the product $f(u_i, v_i) \, \Delta_i A$. Associated with each of the n subregions is such a product, and their sum is

$$\sum_{i=1}^{n} f(u_i, v_i) \, \Delta_i A \tag{1}$$

called a **Riemann sum** of a function of two variables. There are many Riemann sums associated with a particular function because the norm of the partition can be any positive number and each point (u_1, v_1) can be any point in the ith subregion. If all such Riemann sums can be made arbitrarily close to one number L by taking partitions with sufficiently small norms, then L is defined to be the *limit* of these sums as the norm of the partition of R approaches zero. This discussion leads to the following definition.

13.2.1 Definition of the Limit of a Riemann Sum of a Function of Two Variables

Let f be a function defined on a closed rectangular region R. The number L is the **limit** of sums of the form $\sum_{i=1}^{n} f(u_i, v_i) \, \Delta_i A$ if L satisfies the property that for any $\epsilon > 0$ there exists a $\delta > 0$ such that for every partition Δ for which $\| \Delta \| < \delta$ and for all possible selections of the point (u_i, v_i) in the ith rectangle, $i = 1, 2, \ldots, n$.

$$\left| \sum_{i=1}^{n} f(u_i, v_i) \, \Delta_i A - L \right| < \epsilon$$

If such a number L exists, we write

$$\lim_{\| \Delta \| \to 0} \sum_{i=1}^{n} (u_i, v_i) \, \Delta_i A = L$$

A number L satisfying this definition can be shown to be unique. The proof is similar to the proof of Theorem 1.5.16 regarding the uniqueness of the limit of a function of a single variable.

13.2.2 Definition of a Double Integral

Let f be a function of two variables defined on a closed rectangular region R. The **double integral** of f on R, denoted by $\iint\limits_{R} f(x, y) \, dA$, is defined by

$$\iint\limits_{R} f(x, y) \, dA = \lim_{\| \Delta \| \to 0} \sum_{i=1}^{n} f(u_1, v_i) \, \Delta_i A$$

if this limit exists.

If the double integral of f on R exists, f is said to be **integrable** on R. The following theorem, stated without proof, gives a sufficient condition for which a function of two variables is integrable.

13.2.3 Theorem

If a function of two variables is continuous on a closed rectangular region R, then it is integrable on R.

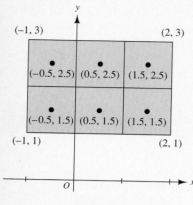

FIGURE 2

▶ **EXAMPLE 1**   Find an approximate value of the double integral

$$\iint\limits_{R} (3y - 2x^2)\, dA$$

where R is the rectangular region having vertices $(-1, 1)$ and $(2, 3)$. Take a partition of R formed by the lines $x = 0$, $x = 1$, and $y = 2$, and take (u_i, v_i) at the center of the ith subregion.

Solution   Refer to Figure 2, which shows the region R partitioned into six subregions that are squares having sides one unit in length. So for each i, $\Delta_i A = 1$. In each of the subregions the point (u_i, v_i) is at the center of the square. With $f(x, y) = 3y - 2x^2$, an approximation to the given double integral is given by

$$
\begin{aligned}
\iint\limits_{R} (3y - 2x^2)\, dA \approx\ & f(-0.5, 1.5) \cdot 1 + f(0.5, 1.5) \cdot 1 + f(1.5, 1.5) \cdot 1 \\
& + f(1.5, 2.5) \cdot 1 + f(0.5, 2.5) \cdot 1 + f(-0.5, 2.5) \cdot 1 \\
=\ & 4 \cdot 1 + 4 \cdot 1 + 0 \cdot 1 + 3 \cdot 1 + 7 \cdot 1 + 7 \cdot 1 \\
=\ & 25
\end{aligned}
$$

◀

The exact value of the double integral in Example 1 is 24, as we will show in Example 3.

We now consider the double integral of a function over a more general region. Recall that a smooth curve is the graph of a smooth function, one that has a continuous derivative. Let R be a closed region whose boundary consists of a finite number of arcs of smooth curves joined together to form a simple closed curve. As with a rectangular region, we draw lines parallel to the coordinate axes, which yields a rectangular partition of R. By discarding the subregions that contain points not in R, we consider only those lying entirely in R. The number of these subregions, shaded in Figure 3, is n. By proceeding in a manner analogous to that used for a rectangular region, Definitions 13.2.1 and 13.2.2 apply for this more general region R. As the norm of the partition approaches zero, n increases without bound, and the area of the omitted region (i.e., the discarded rectangles) approaches zero. If a function is integrable on a region R, it can be proved that the limit of the approximating Riemann sums is the same no matter how R is subdivided as long as each subregion has a shape to which an area can be assigned.

Just as the integral of a function of a single variable is interpreted geometrically in terms of the area of a plane region, the double integral can be interpreted geometrically in terms of the volume of a three-dimensional solid. Suppose that the function f is continuous on a closed region R in R^2. Furthermore, for simplicity in this discussion, assume that $f(x, y)$ is nonnegative on R. The graph of the equation $z = f(x, y)$ is a surface lying above

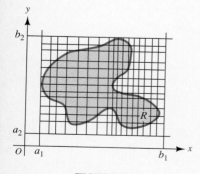

FIGURE 3

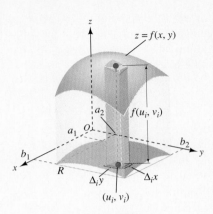

FIGURE 4

the xy plane, as shown in Figure 4. The figure shows a particular rectangular subregion of R, having dimensions of measures $\Delta_i x$ and $\Delta_i y$. The figure also shows a rectangular solid having this subregion as a base and $f(u_i, v_i)$ as the measure of the altitude, where $f(u_i, v_i)$ is a point in the ith subregion. The volume of the rectangular solid is determined by

$$\Delta_i V = f(u_i, v_i) \Delta_i A$$
$$= f(u_i, v_i) \Delta_i x \, \Delta_i y$$

The number $\Delta_i V$ is the measure of the volume of the thin rectangular solid shown in Figure 4; thus the sum given in (1) is the sum of the measures of the volumes of n such solids. This sum approximates the measure of the volume of the three-dimensional solid appearing in Figure 4. The solid is bounded above by the graph of f and below by the region R in the xy plane. The sum in (1) also approximates the number given by the double integral

$$\iint_R f(x, y) \, dA$$

and the volume of the three-dimensional solid of Figure 4 is the value of the double integral. This fact is stated in the following theorem, for which a formal proof is omitted.

13.2.4 Theorem

Let f be a function of two variables continuous on a closed region R in the xy plane and $f(x, y) \geq 0$ for all (x, y) in R. If V cubic units is the volume of the solid S having the region R as its base and having an altitude of $f(x, y)$ units at the point (x, y) in R, then

$$V = \lim_{\|\Delta\| \to 0} \sum_{i=1}^{n} f(u_i, v_i) \, \Delta_i A$$

$$= \iint_R f(x, y) \, dA$$

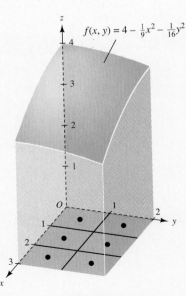

FIGURE 5

▶ **EXAMPLE 2** Express the volume of the solid bounded by the surface

$$f(x, y) = 4 - \tfrac{1}{9}x^2 - \tfrac{1}{16}y^2$$

the planes $x = 3$ and $y = 2$, and the three coordinate planes as a double integral. To find an approximate value of the double integral take a partition of the region in the xy plane by drawing the lines $x = 1$, $x = 2$, and $y = 1$, and take (u_i, v_i) at the center of the ith subregion.

Solution The solid is shown in Figure 5. The rectangular region R is the rectangle in the xy plane bounded by the coordinate axes and the lines $x = 3$ and $y = 2$. From Theorem 13.2.4, if V cubic units is the volume of the solid,

$$V = \iint_R (4 - \tfrac{1}{9}x^2 - \tfrac{1}{16}y^2) \, dA$$

Figure 5 shows R partitioned into six subregions that are squares having sides of length one unit. Therefore, for each i, $\Delta_i A = 1$. The point (u_i, v_i) in each subregion is at the center of the square. Then an approximation of V is given by an approximation of the double integral. Therefore

$$V \approx f(0.5, 0.5) \cdot 1 + f(1.5, 0.5) \cdot 1 + f(2.5, 0.5) \cdot 1$$
$$+ f(0.5, 1.5) \cdot 1 + f(1.5, 1.5) \cdot 1 + f(2.5, 1.5) \cdot 1$$

Using a calculator to compute the function values, we obtain

$$V \approx 3.957 + 3.734 + 3.290 + 3.832 + 3.609 + 3.165$$
$$\approx 21.59$$

Conclusion: The volume is approximately 21.59 cubic units.   ◄

The exact volume in the above example is 21.5 cubic units. as we show in Example 4.

Several properties of the double integral are analogous to properties of the definite integral of a function of a single variable. The most important ones are given in the following five theorems.

13.2.5 Theorem

If c is a constant and the function f is integrable on a closed region R, then cf is integrable on R and

$$\iint\limits_R cf(x, y)\, dA = c \iint\limits_R f(x, y)\, dA$$

The proof of this theorem and that of the next one follow from the definition of a double integral.

13.2.6 Theorem

If the functions f and g are integrable on a closed region R, then the function $f + g$ is integrable on R and

$$\iint\limits_R [f(x, y) + g(x, y)]\, dA = \iint\limits_R f(x, y)\, dA + \iint\limits_R g(x, y)\, dA$$

The result of this theorem can be extended to any finite number of integrable functions.

13.2.7 Theorem

If the functions f and g are integrable on the closed region R and furthermore $f(x, y) \geq g(x, y)$ for all (x, y) in R, then

$$\iint\limits_R f(x, y)\, dA \geq \iint\limits_R g(x, y)\, dA$$

This theorem is analogous to Theorem 4.6.1, and the next one is analogous to Theorem 4.6.2. Their proofs are similar to the corresponding ones in Section 4.6.

13.2.8 Theorem

Let the function f be integrable on a closed region R, and suppose that m and M are two numbers such that $m \leq f(x, y) \leq M$ for all (x, y) in R. Then if A is the measure of the area of region R,

$$mA \leq \iint\limits_{R} f(x, y)\, dA \leq MA$$

13.2.9 Theorem

Suppose that the function f is continuous on the closed region R and that region R is composed of the two subregions R_1 and R_2 that have no points in common except for points on parts of their boundaries. Then

$$\iint\limits_{R} f(x, y)\, dA = \iint\limits_{R_1} f(x, y)\, dA + \iint\limits_{R_2} f(x, y)\, dA$$

The proof of this theorem depends on the definition of a double integral and limit theorems.

For functions of a single variable, the second fundamental theorem of the calculus provides a method for evaluating a definite integral by finding an antiderivative, or indefinite integral, of the integrand. A corresponding method for evaluating a double integral involves performing successive single indefinite integrations. A rigorous development of this procedure belongs to a course in advanced calculus. Our treatment here is an intuitive one, and we use the geometric interpretation of the double integral as the measure of a volume. We first develop the method for the double integral on a rectangular region.

Let f be a function integrable on a closed rectangular region R in the xy plane bounded by the lines $x = a_1$, $x = b_1$, $y = a_2$, and $y = b_2$. Assume that $f(x, y) \geq 0$ for all (x, y) in R. Refer to Figure 6, showing a graph of the equation $z = f(x, y)$ when (x, y) is in R. The number that represents the value of the double integral

$$\iint\limits_{R} f(x, y)\, dA$$

is the measure of the volume of the solid between the surface and the region R. This number can be found by slicing as we now do.

Let y be a number in $[a_2, b_2]$. Consider the plane parallel to the xz plane through the point $(0, y, 0)$. Let $A(y)$ square units be the area of the plane

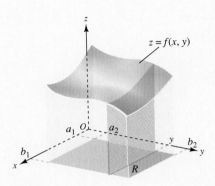

FIGURE 6

region of intersection of this plane with the solid. The measure of the volume of the solid is expressed by

$$\int_{a_2}^{b_2} A(y) \, dy$$

Because the volume of the solid also is determined by the double integral,

$$\iint_R f(x, y) \, dA = \int_{a_2}^{b_2} A(y) \, dy \tag{2}$$

Thus we can find the value of the double integral of the function f on R by evaluating a single integral of $A(y)$. We now must find $A(y)$ when y is given. Because $A(y)$ square units is the area of a plane region, we can find it by integration. In Figure 6, notice that the upper boundary of the plane region is the graph of the equation $z = f(x, y)$ when x is in $[a_1, b_1]$. Therefore $A(y) = \int_{a_1}^{b_1} f(x, y) \, dx$. Substituting from this equation into (1) we obtain

$$\iint_R f(x,y) \, dA = \int_{a_2}^{b_2} \left[\int_{a_1}^{b_1} f(x, y) \, dx \right] dy \tag{3}$$

The integral on the right side of (3) is called an **iterated integral.** Because the brackets are usually omitted when writing an iterated integral, (3) can be written as

$$\iint_R (x, y) \, dA = \int_{a_2}^{b_2} \int_{a_1}^{b_1} f(x, y) \, dx \, dy \tag{4}$$

When evaluating the "inner integral" in (4), remember that x is the variable of integration and y is considered a constant. This is comparable to considering y as a constant when finding the partial derivative of $f(x, y)$ with respect to x.

By considering plane sections parallel to the yz plane we obtain an iterated integral that interchanges the order of integration; we have

$$\iint_R f(x, y) \, dA = \int_{a_1}^{b_1} \int_{a_2}^{b_2} f(x, y) \, dy \, dx \tag{5}$$

A sufficient condition for (4) and (5) to be valid is that the function be continuous on the rectangular region R.

▶ **EXAMPLE 3**   Evaluate the double integral

$$\iint_R (3y - 2x^2) \, dA$$

if R is the region consisting of all points (x, y) for which $-1 \le x \le 2$ and $1 \le y \le 3$.

Solution   With $a_1 = -1, b_1 = 2, a_2 = 1$, and $b_2 = 3$, we have from (4)

$$\iint_R (3y - 2x^2)\, dA = \int_1^3 \int_{-1}^2 (3y - 2x^2)\, dx\, dy$$

$$= \int_1^3 \left[\int_{-1}^2 (3y - 2x^2)\, dx \right] dy$$

$$= \int_1^3 \left[3xy - \tfrac{2}{3}x^3 \right]_{-1}^2 dy$$

$$= \int_1^3 (9y - 6)\, dy$$

$$= \tfrac{9}{2}y^2 - 6y \Big]_1^3$$

$$= 24$$

In Example 1 we found an approximate value of the double integral in the above example to be 25.

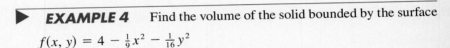

▶ **EXAMPLE 4**   Find the volume of the solid bounded by the surface

$$f(x, y) = 4 - \tfrac{1}{9}x^2 - \tfrac{1}{16}y^2$$

the planes $x = 3$ and $y = 2$, and the three coordinate planes.

Solution   Figure 7 shows the graph of the equation $z = f(x, y)$ in the first octant and the given solid. If V cubic units is the volume of the solid, then from Theorem 13.2.4.

$$V = \lim_{\|\Delta\| \to 0} \sum_{i=1}^n f(u_i, v_i)\, \Delta_i A$$

$$= \iint_R f(x, y)\, dA$$

$$= \int_0^3 \int_0^2 (4 - \tfrac{1}{9}x^2 - \tfrac{1}{16}y^2)\, dy\, dx$$

$$= \int_0^3 \left[4y - \tfrac{1}{9}x^2 y - \tfrac{1}{48}y^3 \right]_0^2 dx$$

$$= \int_0^3 \left(\tfrac{47}{6} - \tfrac{2}{9}x^2 \right) dx$$

$$= \tfrac{47}{6}x - \tfrac{2}{27}x^3 \Big]_0^3$$

$$= 21.5$$

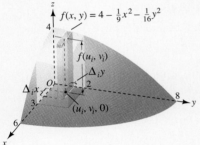

FIGURE 7

Conclusion: The volume is 21.5 cubic units.   ◀

In Example 2 we found an approximate value of the volume in the above example to be 21.59 cubic units.

Suppose now that R is the region in the xy plane bounded by the lines $x = a$ and $x = b$, where $a < b$, and by the curves $y = \phi_1(x)$ and

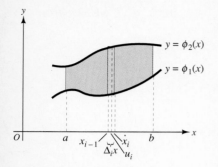

FIGURE 8

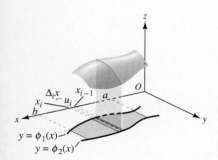

FIGURE 9

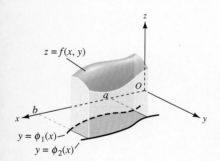

FIGURE 10

$y = \phi_2(x)$, where ϕ_1 and ϕ_2 are functions continuous on the closed interval $[a, b]$. Furthermore, $\phi_1(x) \leq \phi_2(x)$ whenever $a \leq x \leq b$ (see Figure 8). Let Δ be a partition of the interval $[a, b]$ defined by $\Delta: a = x_0 < x_1 < \ldots < x_n = b$. Consider the region R of Figure 8 to be divided into vertical strips with widths of $\Delta_i x$ units. A particular strip is shown in the figure. The intersection of the surface $z = f(x, y)$ and a plane $x = u_i$, where $x_{i-1} \leq u_i \leq x_i$, is a curve. A segment of this curve is over the ith vertical strip. The region under this curve segment and above the xy plane is shown in Figure 9 and the measure of the area of this region is given by

$$\int_{\phi_1(u_i)}^{\phi_2(u_i)} f(u_i, y) \, dy$$

The measure of the volume of the solid bounded above by the surface $z = f(x, y)$ and below by the ith vertical strip is approximately equal to

$$\left[\int_{\phi_1(u_i)}^{\phi_2(u_i)} f(u_i, y) \, dy \right] \Delta_i x$$

If we take the limit, as the norm of Δ approaches zero, of the sum of these measures of volume for n vertical strips of R from $x = a$ to $x = b$, we obtain the measure of the volume of the solid bounded above by the surface $z = f(x, y)$ and below by the region R in the xy plane. (See Figure 10.) This is the double integral of f on R; that is,

$$\lim_{\|\Delta\| \to 0} \sum_{i=1}^{n} \left[\int_{\phi_1(u_i)}^{\phi_2(u_i)} f(u_i, y) \, dy \right] \Delta_i x = \int_a^b \int_{\phi_1(x)}^{\phi_2(x)} f(x, y) \, dy \, dx$$

$$= \iint_R f(x, y) \, dy \, dx \qquad (6)$$

Sufficient conditions for (6) to be valid are that f be continuous on the closed region R and that ϕ_1 and ϕ_2 be smooth functions.

▶ **EXAMPLE 5** Express as both a double integral and an iterated integral the measure of the volume of the solid above the xy plane bounded by the elliptic paraboloid $z = x^2 + 4y^2$ and the cylinder $x^2 + 4y^2 = 4$. Evaluate the iterated integral to find the volume of the solid.

Solution Figure 11 shows the solid. We find the volume of the portion of the solid in the first octant, which from properties of symmetry is one-fourth of the required volume. The region R in the xy plane is that bounded by the x and y axes and the ellipse $x^2 + 4y^2 = 4$. This region appears in Figure 12, which also shows the ith subregion of a rectangular partition of R, where (u_i, v_i) is any point in this ith subregion. If V cubic units is the volume of the given solid, then by Theorem 13.2.4,

$$V = 4 \lim_{\|\Delta\| \to 0} \sum_{i=1}^{n} (u_i^2 + 4v_i^2) \, \Delta_i A$$

$$= 4 \iint_R (x^2 + 4y^2) \, dA$$

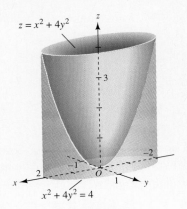

FIGURE 11

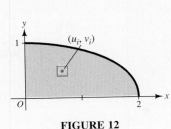

FIGURE 12

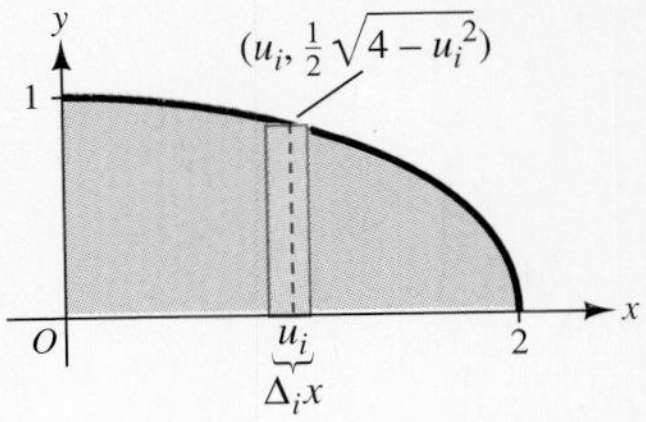

FIGURE 13

To express V as an iterated integral we divide the region R into n vertical strips. Figure 13 shows the region R and the ith vertical strip having width of $\Delta_i x$ units and length of $\frac{1}{2}\sqrt{4 - u_i^2}$ units, where $x_{i-1} \le u_i \le x_i$. From (6),

$$V = 4 \lim_{\|\Delta\| \to 0} \sum_{i=1}^{n} \left[\int_0^{\sqrt{4-u_i^2}/2} (u_i^2 + 4y^2)\, dy \right] \Delta_i x$$

$$= 4 \int_0^2 \int_0^{\sqrt{4-x^2}/2} (x^2 + 4y^2)\, dy\, dx$$

$$= 4 \int_0^2 \left[x^2 y + \tfrac{4}{3} y^3 \right]_0^{\sqrt{4-x^2}/2} dx$$

$$= 4 \int_0^2 \left[\tfrac{1}{2} x^2 \sqrt{4 - x^2} + \tfrac{1}{6}(4 - x^2)^{3/2} \right] dx$$

$$= \frac{4}{3} \int_0^2 (x^2 + 2)\sqrt{4 - x^2}\, dx$$

$$= -\tfrac{1}{3} x(4 - x^2)^{3/2} + 2x\sqrt{4 - x^2} + 8 \sin^{-1} \tfrac{1}{2} x \Big]_0^2$$

$$= 4\pi$$

Conclusion: The volume is 4π cubic units. ◀

Suppose the region R is bounded by the curves $x = \lambda_1(y)$ and $x = \lambda_2(y)$ and the lines $y = c$ and $y = d$, where $c < d$, and λ_1 and λ_2 are two functions continuous on the closed interval $[c, d]$ for which $\lambda_1(y) \le \lambda_2(y)$ whenever $c \le y \le d$. Consider a partition Δ of the interval $[c, d]$ and divide the region into horizontal strips, whose widths are $\Delta_i y$ units. See Figure 14, showing the ith horizontal strip. The intersection of the surface $z = f(x, y)$ and a plane $y = v_1$, where $y_{i-1} \le v_i \le y_i$ is a curve, and a segment of this curve is over the ith horizontal strip. Then, as in the derivation of (6), the measure of the volume of the solid bounded above by the surface $z = f(x, y)$ and below by the ith vertical strip is approximately equal to

$$\left[\int_{\lambda_1(v_i)}^{\lambda_2(v_i)} f(x, v_i)\, dx \right] \Delta_i y$$

Taking the limit, as $\|\Delta\|$ approaches zero, of the sum of these measures of volume for n horizontal strips of R from $y = c$ to $y = d$, we obtain the measure of the volume of the solid bounded above by the surface $z = f(x, y)$ and

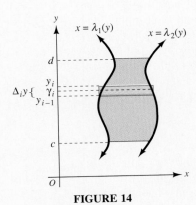

FIGURE 14

below by the region R in the xy plane. This measure of volume is the double integral of f on R. Hence

$$\lim_{\|\Delta\| \to 0} \sum_{i=1}^{n} \left[\int_{\lambda_1(v_i)}^{\lambda_2(v_i)} f(x, v_i)\, dx \right] \Delta_i y = \int_c^d \int_{\lambda_1(y)}^{\lambda_2(y)} f(x, y)\, dx\, dy$$

$$= \iint_R f(x, y)\, dx\, dy \qquad (7)$$

Sufficient conditions for (7) to be valid are that λ_1 and λ_2 be smooth functions and f be continuous on R. In applying both (6) and (7), sometimes it may be necessary to subdivide a region R into subregions on which these sufficient conditions hold.

▶   **EXAMPLE 6**   Express the volume of the solid of Example 5 by an iterated integral in which the order of integration is the reverse of that of Example 5. Compute the volume.

Solution   Again we find the volume of the solid in the first octant and multiply the result by 4. Figure 15 shows the region R in the xy plane and the ith horizontal strip whose width is $\Delta_i y$ units and whose length is $2\sqrt{1 - v_i^2}$ units. Then by (7),

$$V = 4 \lim_{\|\Delta\| \to 0} \sum_{i=1}^{n} \left[\int_0^{2\sqrt{1 - v_i^2}} (x^2 + 4v_i^2)\, dx \right] \Delta_i y$$

$$= 4 \int_0^1 \int_0^{2\sqrt{1 - y^2}} (x^2 + 4y^2)\, dx\, dy$$

$$= 4 \int_0^1 \left[\tfrac{1}{3}x^3 + 4y^2 x \right]_0^{2\sqrt{1 - y^2}} dy$$

$$= 4 \int_0^1 \left[\tfrac{8}{3}(1 - y^2)^{3/2} + 8y^2\sqrt{1 - y^2} \right] dy$$

$$= \frac{32}{3} \int_0^1 (2y^2 + 1)\sqrt{1 - y^2}\, dy$$

$$= -\tfrac{16}{3}y\,(1 - y^2)^{3/2} + 8y\sqrt{1 - y^2} + 8 \sin^{-1} y \Big]_0^1$$

$$= 4\pi$$

<u>Conclusion:</u>   The volume is 4π cubic units, which agrees with the answer of Example 5.   ◀

From the solutions of Examples 5 and 6 we see that the double integral $\iint_R (x^2 + 4y^2)\, dA$ can be evaluated by either of the iterated integrals.

$$\int_0^2 \int_0^{\sqrt{4 - x^2}/2} (x^2 + 4y^2)\, dy\, dx \quad \text{or} \quad \int_0^1 \int_0^{2\sqrt{1 - y^2}} (x^2 + 4y^2)\, dx\, dy$$

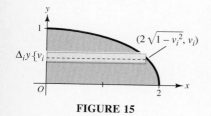

FIGURE 15

If in either (6) or (7), $f(x, y) = 1$ for all x and y, then the measure A of the area of a region R is expressed as a double integral. We have

$$A = \iint_R dy\, dx \quad \Leftrightarrow \quad A = \iint_R dx\, dy \tag{8}$$

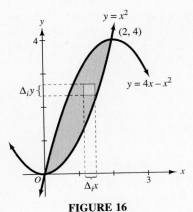

FIGURE 16

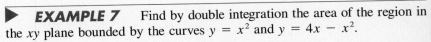

▶ **EXAMPLE 7** Find by double integration the area of the region in the xy plane bounded by the curves $y = x^2$ and $y = 4x - x^2$.

Solution The region appears in Figure 16. From (8),

$$A = \iint_R dy\, dx$$

$$= \int_0^2 \int_{x^2}^{4x - x^2} dy\, dx$$

$$= \int_0^2 (4x - x^2 - x^2)\, dx$$

$$= 2x^2 - \tfrac{2}{3}x^3 \Big]_0^2$$

$$= \tfrac{8}{3}$$

Conclusion: The area of the region is $\tfrac{8}{3}$ square units. ◀

EXERCISES 13.2

1. Find an approximate value of the double integral

$$\iint_R (3x - 2y + 1)\, dA$$

where R is the rectangular region having vertices $(0, -2)$ and $(3, 0)$. Take a partition of R formed by the lines $x = 1$, $x = 2$, and $y = -1$, and take (u_i, v_i) at the center of the ith subregion.

2. Find an approximate value of the double integral

$$\iint_R (y^2 - 4x)\, dA$$

where R is the rectangular region having vertices $(-1, 0)$ and $(1, 3)$. Take a partition of R formed by the lines $x = 0$, $y = 1$, and $y = 2$, and take (u_i, v_i) at the center of the ith subregion.

In Exercises 3 through 8, find an approximate value of the double integral, where R is the rectangular region having

the vertices P and Q, Δ is a partition of R, and (u_i, v_i) is at the center of each subregion.

3. $\displaystyle\iint_R (x^2 + y)\, dA$; $P(0, 0)$; $Q(4, 2)$; Δ: $x_1 = 0$, $x_2 = 1$, $x_3 = 2$, $x_4 = 3$, $y_1 = 0$, $y_2 = 1$

4. $\displaystyle\iint_R (2 - x - y)\, dA$; $P(0, 0)$; $Q(6, 4)$; Δ: $x_1 = 0$, $x_2 = 2$, $x_3 = 4$, $y_1 = 0$, $y_2 = 2$

5. $\displaystyle\iint_R (xy + 3y^2)\, dA$; $P(-2, 0)$; $Q(4, 6)$; Δ: $x_1 = -2$, $x_2 = 0$, $x_3 = 2$, $y_1 = 0$, $y_2 = 2$, $y_3 = 4$

6. $\displaystyle\iint_R (xy + 3y^2)\, dA$; $P(0, -2)$; $Q(6, 4)$; Δ: $x_1 = 0$, $x_2 = 2$, $x_3 = 4$, $y_1 = -2$, $y_2 = 0$, $y_3 = 2$

7. $\iint\limits_{R} (x^2y - 2xy^2) \, dA$; $P(-3, -2)$; $Q(1, 6)$;

   Δ: $x_1 = -3$, $x_2 = -1$, $y_1 = -2$, $y_2 = 0$, $y_3 = 2$, $y_4 = 4$

8. $\iint\limits_{R} (x^2y - 2xy^2) \, dA$; $P(-3, -2)$; $Q(1, 6)$;

   Δ: $x_1 = -3$, $x_2 = -2$, $x_3 = -1$, $x_4 = 0$, $y_1 = -2$, $y_2 = -1$, $y_3 = 0$, $y_4 = 1$, $y_5 = 2$, $y_6 = 3$, $y_7 = 4$, $y_8 = 5$

In Exercises 9 through 12, find an approximate value of the double integral where R is the rectangular region having the vertices P and Q, Δ is a partition of R, and (u_i, v_i) is an arbitrary point in each subregion.

9. The double integral, P, Q, and Δ are the same as in Exercise 3; $(u_1, v_1) = (0.25, 0.5)$; $(u_2, v_2) = (1.75, 0)$; $(u_3, v_3) = (2.5, 0.25)$; $(u_4, v_4) = (4, 1)$; $(u_5, v_5) = (0.75, 1.75)$; $(u_6, v_6) = (1.25, 1.5)$; $(u_7, v_7) = (2.5, 2)$; $(u_8, v_8) = (3, 1)$.

10. The double integral, P, Q, and Δ are the same as in Exercise 4; $(u_1, v_1) = (0.5, 1.5)$; $(u_2, v_2) = (3, 1)$; $(u_3, v_3) = (5.5, 0.5)$; $(u_4, v_4) = (2, 2)$; $(u_5, v_5) = (2, 2)$; $(u_6, v_6) = (5, 3)$.

11. The double integral, P, Q, and Δ are the same as in Exercise 5; $(u_1, v_1) = (-0.5, 0.5)$; $(u_2, v_2) = (1, 1.5)$; $(u_3, v_3) = (2.5, 2)$; $(u_4, v_4) = (-1.5, 3.5)$; $(u_5, v_5) = (0, 3)$; $(u_6, v_6) = (4, 4)$; $(u_7, v_7) = (-1, 4.5)$; $(u_8, v_8) = (1, 4.5)$; $(u_9, v_9) = (3, 4.5)$.

12. The double integral, P, Q, and Δ are the same as in Exercise 5; $(u_1, v_1) = (-2, 0)$; $(u_2, v_2) = (0, 0)$; $(u_3, v_3) = (2, 0)$; $(u_4, v_4) = (-2, 2)$; $(u_5, v_5) = (0, 2)$; $(u_6, v_6) = (2, 2)$; $(u_7, v_7) = (-2, 4)$; $(u_8, v_8) = (0, 4)$; $(u_9, v_9) = (2, 4)$.

13. Express the volume of the solid in the first octant bounded by the sphere $x^2 + y^2 + z^2 = 64$, the planes $x = 3$, $y = 3$, and the three coordinate planes as a double integral. To find an approximate value of the double integral take a partition of the region in the xy plane formed by the lines $x = 1$, $x = 2$, $y = 1$, and $y = 2$, and take (u_i, v_i) at the center of the ith subregion.

14. Express the volume of the solid bounded by the planes $z = 2x + y + 4$, $x = 2$, $y = 3$, and the three coordinate planes as a double integral. To find an approximate value of the double integral take a partition of the region in the xy plane formed by the lines $x = 1$, $y = 1$, and $y = 2$, and take (u_i, v_i) at the center of the ith subregion.

15. Express the volume of the solid bounded by the surface $z = 10 - \frac{1}{4}x^2 - \frac{1}{9}y^2$, the planes $x = 2$, $y = 2$, and the three coordinate planes as a double integral. To find an approximate value of the double integral take a partition of the region in the xy plane formed by the lines $x = 1$ and $y = 1$, and take (u_i, v_i) at the center of the ith subregion.

16. Express the volume of the solid bounded by the surface $100z = 300 - 25x^2 - 4y^2$, the planes $x = -1$, $x = 3$, $y = -3$, $y = 5$ and the xy plane as a double integral. To find an approximate value of the double integral take a partition of the region in the xy plane formed by the lines $x = 1$, $y = -1$, $y = 1$, and $y = 3$, and take (u_i, v_i) at the center of the ith subregion.

In Exercises 17 through 20, apply Theorem 13.2.8 to find a closed interval containing the value of the double integral.

17. $\iint\limits_{R} (2x + 5y) \, dA$, where R is the rectangular region having vertices $(0, 0)$, $(1, 0)$, $(1, 2)$, and $(0, 2)$.

18. $\iint\limits_{R} (x^2 + y^2) \, dA$, where R is the rectangular region having vertices $(0, 0)$, $(1, 0)$, $(1, 1)$, and $(0, 1)$.

19. $\iint\limits_{R} e^{xy} \, dA$, where R is the rectangular region having vertices $(0, 0)$, $(1, 0)$, $(1, 1)$, and $(0, 1)$.

20. $\iint\limits_{R} (\sin x + \sin y) \, dA$, where R is the rectangular region having vertices $(0, 0)$, $(\pi, 0)$, $(0, \pi)$, and (π, π). *Hint:* Use the result of Exercise 24 in Exercises 12.8.

In Exercises 21 through 30, evaluate the iterated integral.

21. $\displaystyle\int_{1}^{2} \int_{0}^{2x} xy^3 \, dy \, dx$

22. $\displaystyle\int_{0}^{4} \int_{0}^{y} dx \, dy$

23. $\displaystyle\int_{0}^{4} \int_{0}^{y} \sqrt{9 + y^2} \, dx \, dy$

24. $\displaystyle\int_{-1}^{1} \int_{1}^{e^x} \frac{x}{y} \, dy \, dx$

25. $\displaystyle\int_{1}^{4} \int_{y^2}^{y} \sqrt{\frac{y}{x}} \, dx \, dy$

26. $\displaystyle\int_{1}^{4} \int_{x^2}^{x} \sqrt{\frac{y}{x}} \, dy \, dx$

27. $\displaystyle\int_0^1 \int_0^1 |x - y| \, dy \, dx$

28. $\displaystyle\int_0^3 \int_0^x x^2 e^{xy} \, dy \, dx$

29. $\displaystyle\int_{\pi/2}^{\pi} \int_0^x \sin(4x - y) \, dy \, dx$

30. $\displaystyle\int_{\pi/2}^{\pi} \int_0^{y^2} \sin\frac{x}{y} \, dx \, dy$

In Exercises 31 through 38, find the exact value of the double integral.

31. The double integral is the same as in Exercise 1.

32. The double integral is the same as in Exercise 2.

33. The double integral is the same as in Exercise 3.

34. The double integral is the same as in Exercise 6.

35. $\displaystyle\iint_R \sin x \, dA$; R is the region bounded by the lines $y = 2x$, $y = \frac{1}{2}x$, and $x = \pi$.

36. $\displaystyle\iint_R \cos(x + y) \, dA$; R is the region bounded by the lines $y = x$ and $x = \pi$, and the x axis.

37. $\displaystyle\iint_R x^2 \sqrt{9 - y^2} \, dA$; R is the region bounded by the circle $x^2 + y^2 = 9$.

38. $\displaystyle\iint_R \frac{y^2}{x^2} \, dA$; R is the region bounded by the lines $y = x$ and $y = 2$, and the hyperbola $xy = 1$.

39. Find the volume of the solid under the plane $z = 4x$ and above the circle $x^2 + y^2 = 16$ in the xy plane.

40. Find the volume of the solid bounded by the planes $x = y + 2z + 1$, $x = 0$, $y = 0$, $z = 0$, and $3y + z - 3 = 0$.

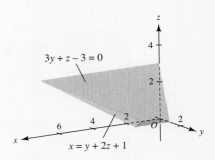

41. Find the volume of the solid in the first octant bounded by the two cylinders $x^2 + y^2 = 4$ and $x^2 + z^2 = 4$.

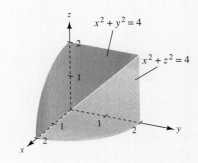

42. Find the volume of the solid in the first octant bounded by the paraboloid $z = 9 - x^2 - 3y^2$.

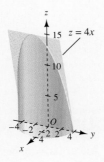

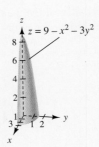

43. Find the volume of the solid in the first octant bounded by the surfaces $x + z^2 = 1$, $x = y$, and $x = y^2$.

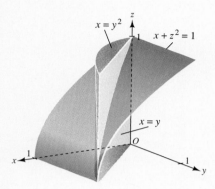

44. Find by double integration the volume of the portion of the solid in the first octant bounded by the sphere $x^2 + y^2 + z^2 = 16$.

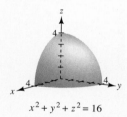

$x^2 + y^2 + z^2 = 16$

In Exercises 45 through 48, use double integrals to find the area of the region bounded by the curves in the xy plane. Sketch the region.

45. $y = x^3$ and $y = x^2$ **46.** $y^2 = 4x$ and $x^2 = 4y$

47. $y = x^2 - 9$ and $y = 9 - x^2$

48. $x^2 + y^2 = 16$ and $y^2 = 6x$

49. Express as an iterated integral the measure of the volume of the solid bounded by the ellipsoid

$$\frac{x^2}{a^2} + \frac{y^2}{b^2} + \frac{z^2}{c^2} = 1$$

50. Use double integration to find the area of the region in the first quadrant bounded by the parabola $y^2 = 4x$, the circle $x^2 + y^2 = 5$, and the x axis by two methods: **(a)** Integrate first with respect to x; **(b)** integrate first with respect to y. Compare the two methods of solution.

51. Find, by two methods, the volume of the solid below the plane $3x + 8y + 6z = 24$ and above the region in the first quadrant of the xy plane bounded by the parabola $y^2 = 2x$, the line $2x + 3y = 10$, and the x axis: **(a)** Integrate first with respect to x; **(b)** integrate first with respect to y. Compare the two methods of solution.

52. Given the iterated integral $\int_0^a \int_0^x \sqrt{a^2 - x^2} \, dy \, dx$. **(a)** Sketch the solid, the measure of whose volume is represented by the given iterated integral; **(b)** evaluate the iterated integral; **(c)** write the iterated integral that gives the measure of the volume of the same solid with the order of integration reversed.

53. Given the iterated integral

$$\frac{2}{3} \int_0^a \int_0^{\sqrt{a^2 - x^3}} (2x + y) \, dy \, dx$$

The instructions are the same as for Exercise 52.

54. Use double integration to find the volume of the solid common to two right-circular cylinders of radius r units, whose axes intersect at right angles. (See Exercise 60 in Exercises 4.9.)

In Exercises 55 and 56, the iterated integral cannot be evaluated exactly in terms of elementary functions by the given order of integration. Reverse the order of integration and perform the computation.

55. $\int_0^4 \int_{\sqrt{x}}^2 \sin \pi y^3 \, dy \, dx$

56. $\int_0^1 \int_y^1 e^{x^2} \, dx \, dy$

13.3 APPLICATIONS OF DOUBLE INTEGRALS

You learned in Section 13.2 how double integrals can be applied to find volumes of solids. In this section, you will learn other applications of double integrals such as finding centers of mass, moments of inertia, and surface area.

When applying single integrals to find the center of mass of a lamina, we can consider only homogeneous laminae, except in special cases. With double integrals, however, we can find the center of mass of either a homogeneous or a nonhomogeneous lamina.

Suppose we are given a lamina having the shape of a closed region R in the xy plane. Let $\rho(x, y)$ be the measure of the area density of the lamina at any point (x, y) of R where ρ is continuous on R. To find the total mass of the lamina we proceed as follows. Let Δ be a partition of R into n rectangles. If (u_i, v_i) is any point in the ith rectangle having an area of $\Delta_i A$ square units, then an approximation to the measure of the mass of the ith rectangle is given by $\rho(u_i, v_i) \, \Delta_i A$, and the measure of the total mass of the lamina is approximated by

$$\sum_{i=1}^{n} \rho(u_i, v_i) \, \Delta_i A,$$

Taking the limit of the above sum as the norm of Δ approaches zero, we express the measure M of the mass of the lamina by

$$M = \lim_{\|\Delta\| \to 0} \sum_{i=1}^{n} \rho(u_i, v_i) \, \Delta_i A$$

$$= \iint\limits_{R} \rho(x, y) \, dA \tag{1}$$

The measure of the moment of mass of the ith rectangle with respect to the x axis is approximated by $v_i \rho(u_i, v_i) \, \Delta_i A$. The sum of the measures of the moments of mass of the n rectangles with respect to the x axis is then approximated by the sum of n such terms. The measure M_x of the moment of mass with respect to the x axis of the entire lamina is given by

$$M_x = \lim_{\|\Delta\| \to 0} \sum_{i=1}^{n} v_i \rho(u_i, v_i) \, \Delta_i A$$

$$= \iint\limits_{R} y \rho(x, y) \, dA$$

Analogously, the measure M_y of its moment of mass with respect to the y axis is given by

$$M_y = \lim_{\|\Delta\| \to 0} \sum_{i=1}^{n} u_i \rho(u_i, v_i) \, \Delta_i A$$

$$= \iint\limits_{R} x \rho(x, y) \, dA \tag{2}$$

The center of mass of the lamina is denoted by the point $(\bar{x}, \bar{y})$ and

$$\bar{x} = \frac{M_y}{M} \qquad \bar{y} = \frac{M_x}{M}$$

▶ **EXAMPLE 1**   A lamina in the shape of an isosceles right triangle has an area density that varies as the square of the distance from the vertex of the right angle. If mass is measured in kilograms and distance is measured in meters, find the mass and the center of mass of the lamina.

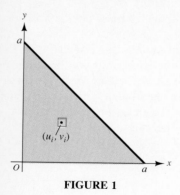

(u_i, v_i)

FIGURE 1

Solution   Choose the coordinate axes so that the vertex of the right triangle is at the origin and the sides of length a meters of the triangle are along the coordinate axes (see Figure 1). Let $\rho(x, y)$ kilograms per square meter be the area density of the lamina at the point (x, y). Then $\rho(x, y) = k(x^2 + y^2)$, where k is a constant. Therefore, if M kilograms is the mass of the lamina, we have, from (1),

$$
\begin{aligned}
M &= \lim_{\|\Delta\| \to 0} \sum_{i=1}^{n} k(u_i{}^2 + v_i{}^2)\, \Delta_i A \\
&= k \iint_R (x^2 + y^2)\, dA \\
&= \int_0^a \int_0^{a-x} (x^2 + y^2)\, dy\, dx \\
&= k \int_0^a \left[yx^2 + \tfrac{1}{3}y^3 \right]_0^{a-x} dx \\
&= k \int_0^a \left(\tfrac{1}{3}a^3 - a^2 x + 2ax^2 - \tfrac{4}{3}x^3 \right) dx \\
&= k \left(\tfrac{1}{3}a^4 - \tfrac{1}{2}a^4 + \tfrac{2}{3}a^4 - \tfrac{1}{3}a^4 \right) \\
&= \tfrac{1}{6}ka^4
\end{aligned}
$$

To find the center of mass, observe that because of symmetry it must lie on the line $y = x$. Therefore, if we find $\bar{x}$, we also have $\bar{y}$. From (2),

$$
\begin{aligned}
M_y &= \lim_{\|\Delta\| \to 0} \sum_{i=1}^{n} k u_i (u_i{}^2 + v_i{}^2)\, \Delta_i A \\
&= k \iint_R x(x^2 + y^2)\, dA \\
&= k \int_0^a \int_0^{a-x} (x^3 + xy^2)\, dy\, dx \\
&= k \int_0^a \left[x^3 y + \tfrac{1}{3}xy^3 \right]_0^{a-x} dx \\
&= k \int_0^a \left(\tfrac{1}{3}a^3 x - a^2 x^2 + 2ax^3 - \tfrac{4}{3}x^4 \right) dx \\
&= k \left(\tfrac{1}{6}a^5 - \tfrac{1}{3}a^5 + \tfrac{1}{2}a^5 - \tfrac{4}{15}a^5 \right) \\
&= \tfrac{1}{15}ka^5
\end{aligned}
$$

Because $M\bar{x} = M_y$, then $M\bar{x} = \tfrac{1}{15}ka^5$; and because $M = \tfrac{1}{6}ka^4$, we get $\bar{x} = \tfrac{2}{5}a$.

<u>**Conclusion:**</u>   The center of mass is at the point $(\tfrac{2}{5}a, \tfrac{2}{5}a)$.   ◀

The moment of mass of a lamina with respect to an axis is sometimes called the *first moment* of the lamina about the axis. Another moment of a lamina about an axis is the *moment of inertia,* called the *second moment* of the lamina. The moment of inertia is a measurement of the lamina's tendency to resist a change in rotational motion. To lead up to a definition of moment of inertia of a lamina, first consider a particle of mass m kilograms whose perpendicular distance from an axis is r meters. The moment of inertia of the particle about the axis is defined to be mr^2 kilogram-meters squared. The moment of inertia of a system of n particles about the axis is then the sum of the moments of inertia of all the particles. That is, if the ith particle has a mass of m_i kilograms and is at a distance of r_i meters from the axis, then I kilogram-meters squared is the moment of inertia of the system about the axis, where

$$I = \sum_{i=1}^{n} m_i r_i^2$$

By extending this concept to a continuous distribution of mass in a plane, such as a lamina, by processes similar to those previously applied, we have the following definition.

13.3.1 Definition of Moment of Inertia About an Axis

Suppose we are given a lamina occupying a region R in the xy plane such that the area density at the point (x, y) has measure $\rho(x, y)$, where ρ is continuous on R. Then the measure of the **moment of inertia** of the lamina about the x axis, denoted by I_x, is defined by

$$I_x = \lim_{\|\Delta\| \to 0} \sum_{i=1}^{n} v_i^2 \rho(u_i, v_i) \, \Delta_i A$$

$$= \iint\limits_{R} y^2 \rho(x, y) \, dA$$

Similarly, the measure of the **moment of inertia** of the lamina about the y axis, denoted by I_y, is defined by

$$I_y = \lim_{\|\Delta\| \to 0} \sum_{i=1}^{n} u_i^2 \, \rho(u_i, v_i) \, \Delta_i A$$

$$= \iint\limits_{R} x^2 \rho(x, y) \, dA$$

▶ **EXAMPLE 2**   A homogeneous straight wire has a constant linear density of k kilograms per meter. Find the moment of inertia of the wire about an axis perpendicular to the wire and passing through one end.

Solution   Let the wire be of length a meters, and suppose that it extends along the x axis from the origin. We find its moment of inertia about the y axis. Divide the wire into n segments; the length of the ith segment is $\Delta_i x$ meters. The mass of the ith segment is then $k \, \Delta_i x$ kilograms. Assume that the mass of the ith segment is concentrated at a single point u_i, where $x_{i-1} \le u_i \le x_i$. The measure of the moment of inertia of the ith segment about the y axis lies between $k x_{i-1}^2 \, \Delta_i x$ and $k x_i^2 \, \Delta_i x$ and is approximated by

$ku_i^2 \, \Delta_i x$. If the moment of inertia of the wire about the y axis is I_y kilogram-meters squared, then

$$I_y = \lim_{\|\Delta\| \to 0} \sum_{i=1}^{n} ku_i^2 \, \Delta_i x$$

$$= \int_0^a kx^2 \, dx$$

$$= \tfrac{1}{3} ka^3$$

Conclusion: The moment of inertia is $\tfrac{1}{3} ka^3$ kg-m^2.   ◄

The sum of the moments of inertia I_x and I_y of a lamina in the xy plane is called the *polar moment of inertia,* and it represents the moment of inertia of the lamina about the origin or the z axis.

13.3.2 Definition of Polar Moment of Inertia

Suppose we are given a lamina occupying a region R in the xy plane such that the area density at the point (x, y) has measure $\rho(x, y)$, where ρ is continuous on R. Then the measure of the **polar moment of inertia,** denoted by I_0, is defined by

$$I_0 = \lim_{\|\Delta\| \to 0} \sum_{i=1}^{n} (u_i^2 + v_i^2)\rho(u_i, v_i) \, \Delta_i A$$

$$= \iint\limits_R (x^2 + y^2)\rho(x, y) \, dA$$

▶   **EXAMPLE 3**   A homogeneous rectangular lamina has constant area density of k slugs per square foot. Find the moment of inertia of the lamina about one corner.

Solution   Suppose that the lamina is bounded by the lines $x = a$, $y = b$, the x axis, and the y axis. See Figure 2. If I_0 slug-feet squared is the moment of inertia about the origin, then

$$I_0 = \lim_{\|\Delta\| \to 0} \sum_{i=1}^{n} k(u_i^2 + v_i^2) \, \Delta_i A$$

$$= \iint\limits_R k(x^2 + y^2) \, dA$$

$$= k \int_0^b \int_0^a (x^2 + y^2) \, dx \, dy$$

$$= k \int_0^b \left[\tfrac{1}{3}x^3 + xy^2 \right]_0^a dy$$

$$= k \int_0^b (\tfrac{1}{3}a^3 + ay^2) \, dy$$

$$= \tfrac{1}{3} kab(a^2 + b^2)$$

Conclusion: The moment of inertia is $\tfrac{1}{3} kab(a^2 + b^2)$ slug-ft^2.   ◄

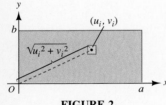

FIGURE 2

The *radius of gyration* of a lamina about an axis L is the distance from L at which the mass of the lamina can be concentrated without affecting the moment of inertia of the lamina about L. That is, if the mass M kilograms of a lamina is concentrated at a point r meters from L, the moment of inertia of the lamina about L is the same as that of a particle of mass M kilograms at a distance of r meters from L; this moment of inertia is Mr^2 kilogram-meters squared. Thus we have the following definition.

13.3.3 Definition of Radius of Gyration

If I is the measure of the moment of inertia about an axis L of a lamina and M is the measure of the total mass of the lamina, then the **radius of gyration** of the lamina about L has measure r, where

$$r^2 = \frac{I}{M}$$

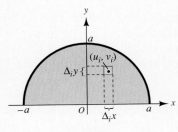

FIGURE 3

▶ **EXAMPLE 4**   Suppose that a lamina is in the shape of a semicircle and the measure of the area density of the lamina at any point is proportional to the measure of the distance of the point from the diameter. If mass is measured in kilograms and distance is measured in meters, find the radius of gyration of the lamina about the x axis.

Solution   Choose the x and y axes such that the semicircle is the top half of the circle $x^2 + y^2 = a^2$. See Figure 3. The area density of the lamina at the point (x, y) is then ky kilograms per square meter. So if M kilograms is the mass of the lamina, we have

$$M = \lim_{\|\Delta\| \to 0} \sum_{i=1}^{n} kv_i \, \Delta_i A$$

$$= \iint\limits_{R} ky \, dA$$

$$= \int_0^a \int_{-\sqrt{a^2-y^2}}^{\sqrt{a^2-y^2}} ky \, dx \, dy$$

$$= k \int_0^a \left[yx \right]_{-\sqrt{a^2-y^2}}^{\sqrt{a^2-y^2}} dy$$

$$= 2k \int_0^a y \sqrt{a^2 - y^2} \, dy$$

$$= -\tfrac{2}{3} k (a^2 - y^2)^{3/2} \Big]_0^a$$

$$= \tfrac{2}{3} k a^3$$

If I_x kilogram-meters squared is the moment of inertia of the lamina about the x axis, then

$$I_x = \lim_{\|\Delta\| \to 0} \sum_{i=1}^{n} v_i{}^2 (kv_i) \, \Delta_i A$$

$$= \iint\limits_{R} ky^3 \, dy \, dx$$

$$= \int_{-a}^{a} \int_{0}^{\sqrt{a^2-x^2}} ky^3 \, dy \, dx$$

$$= k \int_{-a}^{a} \left[\tfrac{1}{4} y^4 \right]_{0}^{\sqrt{a^2-x^2}} dx$$

$$= \tfrac{1}{4} k \int_{-a}^{a} (a^4 - 2a^2 x^2 + x^4) \, dx$$

$$= \tfrac{1}{4} k (2a^5 - \tfrac{4}{3} a^5 + \tfrac{2}{5} a^5)$$

$$= \tfrac{4}{15} ka^5$$

Therefore, if r meters is the radius of gyration,

$$r^2 = \frac{\tfrac{4}{15} ka^5}{\tfrac{2}{3} ka^3}$$

$$= \tfrac{2}{5} a^2$$

Thus $r = \tfrac{1}{5} \sqrt{10} \, a$.

<u>**Conclusion:**</u>   The radius of gyration is $\tfrac{1}{5} \sqrt{10} a$ meters.   ◀

The double integral can be used to determine the area of the portion of the surface $z = f(x, y)$ that lies over a closed region R in the xy plane. To show this we must first define what we mean by the measure of this area and then obtain a formula for computing it. Assume that f and its first partial derivatives are continuous on R, and suppose that $f(x, y) > 0$ on R. Let Δ be a partition of R into n rectangular subregions. The ith rectangle has dimensions $\Delta_i x$ units and $\Delta_i y$ units and an area of $\Delta_i A$ square units. Let (u_i, v_i) be any point in the ith rectangle, and at the point $Q(u_i, v_i, f(u_i, v_i))$ on the surface consider the tangent plane to the surface. Project vertically upward the ith rectangle onto the tangent plane and let $\Delta_i \sigma$ square units be the area of this projection. Figure 4 shows the region R, the portion of the surface above R, the ith rectangular subregion of R, and the projection of the ith rectangle onto the tangent plane to the surface at Q. The number $\Delta_i \sigma$ is an approximation to the measure of the area of the piece of the surface that lies above the ith rectangle. Because there are n such pieces, the summation

$$\sum_{i=1}^{n} \Delta_i \sigma$$

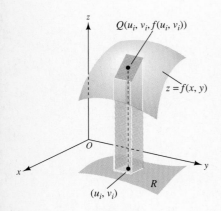

FIGURE 4

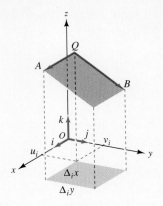

FIGURE 5

is an approximation to the measure σ of the area of the portion of the surface that lies above R. This leads to defining σ as follows:

$$\sigma = \lim_{\|\Delta\| \to 0} \sum_{i=1}^{n} \Delta_i \sigma \tag{3}$$

We now need to obtain a formula for computing this limit. To do this we find a formula for computing $\Delta_i \sigma$ as the measure of the area of a parallelogram. For simplicity in computation take the point (u_i, v_i) in the ith rectangle at the corner (x_{i-1}, y_{i-1}). Let $\mathbf{A}$ and $\mathbf{B}$ be vectors having as representations the directed line segments having initial points at Q and forming the two adjacent sides of the parallelogram whose area is $\Delta_i \sigma$ square units. See Figure 5. Then $\Delta_i \sigma = \| \mathbf{A} \times \mathbf{B} \|$. Because

$$\mathbf{A} = \Delta_i x \mathbf{i} + f_x(u_i, v_i)\, \Delta_i x \mathbf{k} \quad \text{and} \quad \mathbf{B} = \Delta_i y \mathbf{j} + f_y(u_i, v_i)\Delta_i y \mathbf{k}$$

then

$$\mathbf{A} \times \mathbf{B} = \begin{vmatrix} \mathbf{i} & \mathbf{j} & \mathbf{k} \\ \Delta_i x & 0 & f_x(u_i, v_i)\, \Delta_i x \\ 0 & \Delta_i y & f_y(u_i, v_i)\, \Delta_i y \end{vmatrix}$$

$$= -\Delta_i x\, \Delta_i y f_x(u_i, v_i)\mathbf{i} - \Delta_i x\, \Delta_i y f_y(u_i, v_i)\mathbf{j} + \Delta_i x\, \Delta_i y \mathbf{k}$$

Therefore

$$\Delta_i \sigma = \| \mathbf{A} \times \mathbf{B} \|$$
$$= \sqrt{f_x{}^2(u_i, v_i) + f_y{}^2(u_i, v_i) + 1}\; \Delta_i x\, \Delta_i y$$

Substituting this expression for $\Delta_i \sigma$ into (3) we get

$$\sigma = \lim_{\|\Delta\| \to 0} \sum_{i=1}^{n} \sqrt{f_x{}^2(u_i, v_i) + f_y{}^2(u_i, v_i) + 1}\; \Delta_i x\, \Delta_i y$$

This limit is a double integral that exists on R because of the continuity of f_x and f_y on R. We have, then, the following theorem.

13.3.4 Theorem

Suppose that f and its first partial derivatives are continuous on the closed region R in the xy plane. Then if σ square units is the area of the surface $z = f(x, y)$ that lies over R,

$$\sigma = \iint\limits_{R} \sqrt{f_x{}^2(x, y) + f_y{}^2(x, y) + 1}\; dx\, dy$$

▶ **EXAMPLE 5**   Find the area of the surface in the first octant cut from the cylinder $x^2 + z^2 = 16$ by the planes $x = 0$, $x = 2$, $y = 0$, and $y = 3$.

Solution   The given surface is shown in Figure 6. The region R is the rectangle in the first quadrant of the xy plane bounded by the lines $x = 2$ and $y = 3$. The surface has the equation $x^2 + z^2 = 16$. Solving for z we get

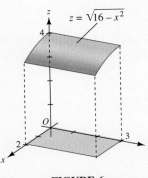

FIGURE 6

$z = \sqrt{16 - x^2}$. Hence $f(x, y) = \sqrt{16 - x^2}$. So if σ square units is the area of the surface, then from Theorem 13.3.4,

$$\sigma = \iint\limits_{R} \sqrt{f_x^{\,2}(x, y) + f_y^{\,2}(x, y) + 1}\; dx\, dy$$

$$= \int_0^3 \int_0^2 \sqrt{\left(\frac{-x}{\sqrt{16 - x^2}}\right)^2 + 0 + 1}\; dx\, dy$$

$$= \int_0^3 \int_0^2 \frac{4}{\sqrt{16 - x^2}}\; dx\, dy$$

$$= 4 \int_0^3 \left[\sin^{-1} \tfrac{1}{4}x\right]_0^2 dy$$

$$= 4 \int_0^3 \tfrac{1}{6}\pi\, dy$$

$$= 2\pi$$

__Conclusion:__ The surface area is 2π square units. ◄

Consider now the curve $y = F(x)$ with $a \le x \le b$, $F(x) > 0$ on $[a, b]$ and F' continuous on $[a, b]$. If this curve is rotated about the x axis, we obtain a surface of revolution. From Section 10.6 an equation of this surface is

$$y^2 + z^2 = [F(x)]^2 \qquad (4)$$

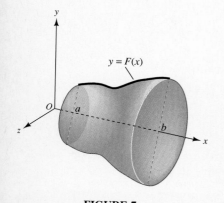

FIGURE 7

Figure 7 shows the surface of revolution. In the figure the xy plane is in the plane of the paper; however, we still have a right-handed system. We wish to obtain a formula for finding the area of this surface of revolution by using Theorem 13.3.4. From properties of symmetry, the area of the surface above the xz plane and in front of the xy plane is one-fourth of the area of the entire surface. Solving (4) for z and neglecting the negative square root because $z \ge 0$, we get $f(x, y) = \sqrt{[F(x)]^2 - y^2}$. The region R in the xy plane is that bounded by the x axis, the curve $y = F(x)$, and the lines $x = a$ and $x = b$. Computing the partial derivatives of f we obtain

$$f_x(x, y) = \frac{F(x)F'(x)}{\sqrt{[F(x)]^2 - y^2}} \qquad f_y(x, y) = \frac{-y}{\sqrt{[F(x)]^2 - y^2}}$$

We see that $f_x(x, y)$ and $f_y(x, y)$ do not exist on part of the boundary of R (when $y = -F(x)$ and when $y = F(x)$). The double integral obtained from Theorem 13.3.4 is

$$\iint\limits_{R} \sqrt{\frac{[F(x)]^2 [F'(x)]^2}{[F(x)]^2 - y^2} + \frac{y^2}{[F(x)]^2 - y^2} + 1}\; dy\, dx$$

$$= \iint\limits_{R} \frac{F(x)\sqrt{[F'(x)]^2 + 1}}{\sqrt{[F(x)]^2 - y^2}}\; dy\, dx$$

This double integral is improper because the integrand has an infinite discontinuity at each point of the boundary of R where $y = -F(x)$ and $y = F(x)$. Hence we evaluate the double integral by an iterated integral for which the inner integral is improper. If σ square units is the area of the surface of revolution

$$\sigma = 4 \int_a^b \left[F(x)\sqrt{[F'(x)]^2 + 1} \int_0^{F(x)} \frac{dy}{\sqrt{[F(x)]^2 - y^2}} \right] dx \qquad (5)$$

$$\int_0^{F(x)} \frac{dy}{\sqrt{[F(x)]^2 - y^2}} = \lim_{b \to F(x)^-} \int_0^b \frac{dy}{\sqrt{[F(x)]^2 - y^2}}$$

$$= \lim_{b \to F(x)^-} \left[\sin^{-1} \frac{y}{F(x)} \right]_0^b$$

$$= \lim_{b \to F(x)^-} \sin^{-1} \frac{b}{F(x)}$$

$$= \tfrac{1}{2}\pi$$

Therefore, from (5),

$$\sigma = 2\pi \int_a^b F(x)\sqrt{[F'(x)]^2 + 1}\ dx$$

We state this result as a theorem, where F is replaced by f.

13.3.5 Theorem

Suppose that the function f is positive on $[a, b]$ and f' is continuous on $[a, b]$. If σ square units is the area of the surface of revolution obtained by revolving the curve $y = f(x)$, with $a \le x \le b$, about the x axis, then

$$\sigma = 2\pi \int_a^b f(x)\sqrt{[f'(x)]^2 + 1}\ dx$$

▶ **EXAMPLE 6**   Find the area of the paraboloid of revolution generated by revolving the top half of the parabola $y^2 = 4px$, with $0 \le x \le h$, about the x axis.

Solution   The paraboloid of revolution appears in Figure 8. Solving the equation of the parabola for y, with $y \ge 0$, we obtain $y = 2p^{1/2}x^{1/2}$. So if σ square units is the area of the surface, from Theorem 13.3.5, with $f(x) = 2p^{1/2}x^{1/2}$,

$$\sigma = 2\pi \int_0^h 2p^{1/2}x^{1/2}\sqrt{\frac{p}{x} + 1}\ dx$$

$$= 4\pi p^{1/2} \int_0^h \sqrt{p + x}\ dx$$

$$= \tfrac{8}{3}\pi p^{1/2}(p + x)^{3/2} \Big]_0^h$$

$$= \tfrac{8}{3}\pi(\sqrt{p(p + h)^3} - p^2)$$

Conclusion: The area of the paraboloid of revolution is $\tfrac{8}{3}\pi(\sqrt{p(p + h)^3} - p^2)$ square units.   ◀

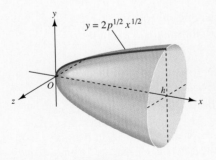

$y = 2p^{1/2}x^{1/2}$

FIGURE 8

EXERCISES 13.3

In Exercises 1 through 12, find the mass and center of mass of the lamina if the area density is as indicated. Mass is measured in kilograms and distance is measured in meters.

1. A lamina in the shape of the rectangular region bounded by the lines $x = 3$ and $y = 2$ and the coordinate axes. The area density at any point is xy^2 kilograms per square meter.

2. A lamina in the shape of the rectangular region bounded by the lines $x = 4$ and $y = 5$ and the coordinate axes. The area density at any point is $(x^2 + y)$ kilograms per square meter.

3. A lamina in the shape of the triangular region whose sides are segments of the coordinate axes and the line $x + 2y = 6$. The area density at any point is y^2 kilograms per square meter.

4. A lamina in the shape of the region in the first quadrant bounded by the parabola $y = x^2$, the line $y = 1$, and the y axis. The area density at any point is $(x + y)$ kilograms per square meter.

5. A lamina in the shape of the region in the first quadrant bounded by the parabola $x^2 = 8y$, the line $y = 2$, and the y axis. The area density varies as the distance from the line $y = -1$.

6. A lamina in the shape of the region bounded by the curve $y = e^x$, the line $x = 1$, and the coordinate axes. The area density varies as the distance from the x axis.

7. A lamina in the shape of the region in the first quadrant bounded by the circle $x^2 + y^2 = a^2$ and the coordinate axes. The area density varies as the sum of the distances from the two straight edges.

8. A lamina in the shape of the region bounded by the triangle whose sides are segments of the coordinate axes and the line $3x + 2y = 18$. The area density varies as the product of the distances from the coordinate axes.

9. A lamina in the shape of the region bounded by the curve $y = \sin x$ and the x axis from $x = 0$ to $x = \pi$. The area density varies as the distance from the x axis.

10. A lamina in the shape of the region bounded by the curve $y = \sqrt{x}$ and the line $y = x$. The area density varies as the distance from the y axis.

11. A lamina in the shape of the region in the first quadrant bounded by the circle $x^2 + y^2 = 4$ and the line $x + y = 2$. The area density at any point is xy kilograms per square meter.

12. A lamina in the shape of the region bounded by the circle $x^2 + y^2 = 1$ and the lines $x = 1$ and $y = 1$. The area density at any point is xy kilograms per square meter.

In Exercises 13 through 18, find the moment of inertia of the homogeneous lamina about the indicated axis if the area density is k kilograms per square meter and distance is measured in meters.

13. A lamina in the shape of the region bounded by $4y = 3x$, $x = 4$, and the x axis; about the x axis.

14. The lamina of Exercise 13; about the line $x = 4$.

15. A lamina in the shape of the region bounded by a circle of radius a meters; about its center.

16. A lamina in the shape of the region bounded by the parabola $x^2 = 4 - 4y$ and the x axis; about the x axis.

17. The lamina of Exercise 16; about the origin.

18. A lamina in the shape of the region bounded by a triangle of sides of lengths a meters, b meters, and c meters; about the side of length a meters.

In Exercises 19 through 22, find for the lamina each of the following: (a) the moment of inertia about the x axis; (b) the moment of inertia about the y axis, (c) the radius of gyration about the x axis, (d) the polar moment of inertia.

19. The lamina of Exercise 1

20. The lamina of Exercise 4

21. The lamina of Exercise 9

22. The lamina of Exercise 10

23. A lamina is in the shape of the region enclosed by the parabola $y = 2x - x^2$ and the x axis. Find the moment of inertia of the lamina about the line $y = 4$ if the area density varies as its distance from the line $y = 4$. Mass is measured in kilograms and distance is measured in meters.

24. A homogeneous lamina of area density k slugs per square foot is in the shape of the region bounded by the curve $x = \sqrt{y}$, the x axis, and the line $x = a$, where $a > 0$. Find the moment of inertia of the lamina about the line $x = a$.

25. Find the area of the surface cut from the plane $2x + y + z = 4$ by the planes $x = 0$, $x = 1$, $y = 0$, and $y = 1$.

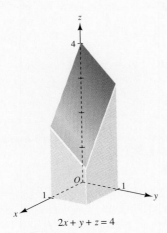

$$2x + y + z = 4$$

26. Find the area of the surface cut from the plane $z - 2x - y = 5$ by the planes $x = 0$, $x = 2$, $y = 0$, and $y = 4$.

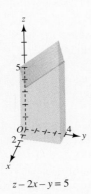

$$z - 2x - y = 5$$

27. Find the area of the portion of the surface of the plane $36x + 16y + 9z = 144$ cut by the coordinate planes.

28. Find the area of the surface cut from the plane $z = ax + by$ by the planes $x = 0$, $x = a$, $y = 0$, and $y = b$, where $a > 0$ and $b > 0$.

29. Find the area of the surface in the first octant cut from the cylinder $x^2 + y^2 = 9$ by the plane $x = z$.

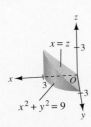

$$x^2 + y^2 = 9$$

30. Find the area of the surface cut from the cylinder $x^2 + y^2 = 25$ by the planes $x = 0$, $x = 1$, $z = 1$, and $z = 3$.

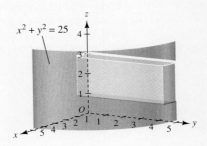

31. Let R be the triangular region in the xy plane with vertices at $(0, 0, 0)$, $(0, 4, 0)$, and $(2, 4, 0)$. Find the surface area of the part of the graph of $z - 5x - y^2 = 2$ that lies above R.

32. Find the area of the surface in the first octant cut from the cone $x^2 + y^2 = z^2$ by the plane $x + y = 4$.

33. Find the area of the surface of the portion of the cylinder $x^2 + z^2 = 4$ that is inside the cylinder $x^2 + y^2 = 4$.

34. Find the area of the surface of the portion of the cone $x^2 + y^2 = z^2$ inside the cylinder $x^2 + y^2 = 2x$.

35. Find the area of the surface of the portion of the cone $x^2 + y^2 = z^2$ between the cylinder $y^2 = x$ and the plane $x - y = 2$.

36. Find the area of the portion of the plane $x = z$ that lies between the planes $y = 0$ and $y = 6$ and within the hyperboloid $9x^2 - 4y^2 + 16z^2 = 144$.

37. The line segment from the origin to the point (a, b) is revolved about the x axis. Find the area of the surface of the cone generated.

38. Derive the formula for the area of the surface of a sphere by revolving a semicircle about its diameter.

39. Find the area of the surface of revolution obtained by revolving the arc of the catenary $y = a \cosh(x/a)$ from $x = 0$ to $x = a$ about the y axis.

40. Find the area of the surface of revolution obtained by revolving the catenary of Exercise 39 about the x axis.

41. The loop of the curve $18y^2 = x(6 - x)^2$ is revolved about the x axis. Find the area of the surface of revolution generated.

42. Find the area of the surface of revolution generated by revolving the arc of the curve $y = \ln x$ from $x = 1$ to $x = 2$ about the y axis.

43. A homogeneous lamina of area density k slugs per square foot is in the shape of the region bounded by an isosceles triangle having a base of length b feet and an altitude of length h feet. Find the radius of gyration of the lamina about its line of symmetry.

44. Suppose that f and its first partial derivatives are continuous on the closed region R in the xy plane. Show that if σ square units is the area of the portion of the surface $z = f(x, y)$ that lies over R, then

$$\sigma = \iint\limits_{R} \| \nabla g(x, y, z) \| \, dx \, dy$$

where $g(x, y, z) = z - f(x, y)$.

13.4 DOUBLE INTEGRALS IN POLAR COORDINATES

To define the double integral of a function on a closed region in the polar coordinate plane, we begin by considering the simplest kind of region. Let R be the region bounded by the rays $\theta = \alpha$ and $\theta = \beta$ and by the circles $r = a$ and $r = b$. Then let Δ be a *partition* of this region obtained by drawing rays through the pole and circles having centers at the pole. See Figure 1 showing a network of subregions called "curved" rectangles. The norm $\| \Delta \|$ of the partition is the length of the longest diagonal of the curved rectangles. Let the number of subregions be n, and let $\Delta_i A$ square units be the area of the ith curved rectangle. Because the area of the ith subregion is the difference of the areas of two circular sectors,

$$\Delta_i A = \tfrac{1}{2} r_i^2 (\theta_i - \theta_{i-1}) - \tfrac{1}{2} r_{i-1}^2 (\theta_i - \theta_{i-1})$$
$$= \tfrac{1}{2} (r_i - r_{i-1})(r_i + r_{i-1})(\theta_i - \theta_{i-1})$$

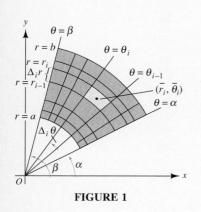

FIGURE 1

Let $\bar{r}_i = \tfrac{1}{2}(r_i + r_{i-1})$, $\Delta_i r = r_i - r_{i-1}$, and $\Delta_i \theta = \theta_i - \theta_{i-1}$. Then

$$\Delta_i A = \bar{r}_i \, \Delta_i r \, \Delta_i \theta$$

Take the point $(\bar{r}_i, \bar{\theta}_i)$ in the ith subregion, where $\theta_{i-1} \le \bar{\theta}_i \le \theta_i$, and form the sum

$$\sum_{i=1}^{n} f(\bar{r}_i, \bar{\theta}_i) \, \Delta_i A = \sum_{i=1}^{n} f(\bar{r}_i, \bar{\theta}_i) \bar{r}_i \, \Delta_i r \, \Delta_i \theta$$

It can be shown that if f is continuous on the region R, then the limit of this sum, as $\| \Delta \|$ approaches zero, exists and this limit will be the double integral of f on R. We write

$$\lim_{\|\Delta\| \to 0} \sum_{i=1}^{n} f(\bar{r}_i, \bar{\theta}_i) \, \Delta_i A = \iint\limits_{R} f(r, \theta) \, dA$$

$$\Leftrightarrow \quad \lim_{\|\Delta\| \to 0} \sum_{i=1}^{n} f(\bar{r}_i, \bar{\theta}_i) \bar{r}_i, \, \Delta_i r \, \Delta_i \theta = \iint\limits_{R} f(r, \theta) r \, dr \, d\theta$$

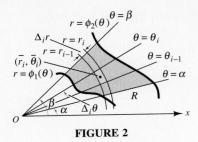

FIGURE 2

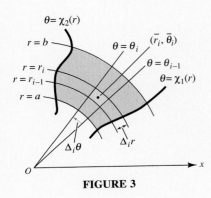

FIGURE 3

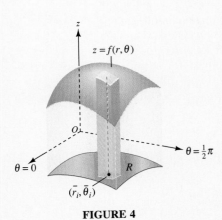

FIGURE 4

Observe that in polar coordinates, $dA = r\, dr\, d\theta$.

The double integral can be shown to be equal to an iterated integral having one of two possible forms:

$$\iint\limits_{R} f(r, \theta)\, dA = \int_{\alpha}^{\beta} \int_{a}^{b} f(r, \theta) r\, dr\, d\theta$$

$$= \int_{a}^{b} \int_{\alpha}^{\beta} f(r, \theta) r\, d\theta\, dr$$

We can define the double integral of a continuous function f of two variables on closed regions of the polar coordinate plane other than the one previously considered. For example, consider the region R bounded by the curves $r = \phi_1(\theta)$ and $r = \phi_2(\theta)$, where ϕ_1 and ϕ_2 are smooth functions, and by the lines $\theta = \alpha$ and $\theta = \beta$. See Figure 2. In the figure, $\phi_1(\theta) \leq \phi_2(\theta)$ for all θ in the closed interval $[\alpha, \beta]$. Then it can be shown that the double integral of f on R exists and equals an iterated integral, and we have

$$\iint\limits_{R} f(r, \theta)\, dA = \int_{\alpha}^{\beta} \int_{\phi_1(\theta)}^{\phi_2(\theta)} f(r, \theta) r\, dr\, d\theta$$

If the region R is bounded by the curves $\theta = \chi_1(r)$, and $\theta = \chi_2(r)$, where χ_1 and χ_2 are smooth functions, and by the circles $r = a$ and $r = b$, as shown in Figure 3, where $\chi_1(r) \leq \chi_2(r)$ for all r in the closed interval $[a, b]$, then

$$\iint\limits_{R} f(r, \theta)\, dA = \int_{a}^{b} \int_{\chi_1(r)}^{\chi_2(r)} f(r, \theta) r\, d\theta\, dr$$

We can interpret the double integral of a function on a closed region in the polar coordinate plane as the measure of the volume of a solid by using cylindrical coordinates. Figure 4 shows a solid having as its base a region R in the polar coordinate plane and bounded above by the surface $z = f(r, \theta)$, where f is continuous on R and $f(r, \theta) \geq 0$ on R. Take a partition of R giving a network of n curved rectangles. Construct the n solids for which the ith solid has as its base the ith curved rectangle and as its altitude $f(\bar{r}_i, \bar{\theta}_i)$ units, where $(\bar{r}_i, \bar{\theta}_i)$ is in the ith subregion. Figure 4 shows the ith solid. The measure of the volume of the ith solid is

$$f(\bar{r}_i, \bar{\theta}_i)\, \Delta_i A = f(\bar{r}_i, \bar{\theta}_i)\bar{r}_i\, \Delta_i r\, \Delta_i \theta$$

The sum of the measures of the volumes of the n solids is

$$\sum_{i=1}^{n} f(\bar{r}_i, \bar{\theta}_i)\bar{r}_i\, \Delta_i r\, \Delta_i \theta$$

If V cubic units is the volume of the given solid, then

$$V = \lim_{\|\Delta\| \to 0} \sum_{i=1}^{n} f(\bar{r}_i, \bar{\theta}_i)\bar{r}_i \, \Delta_i r \, \Delta_i \theta$$

$$= \iint_R f(r, \theta)r \, dr \, d\theta \qquad (1)$$

▶ **EXAMPLE 1** Find the volume of the solid in the first octant bounded by the cone $z = r$ and the cylinder $r = 3 \sin \theta$.

Solution The solid and the ith element are shown in Figure 5. Using (1) with $f(r, \theta) = r$, we have, where V cubic units is the volume of the given solid,

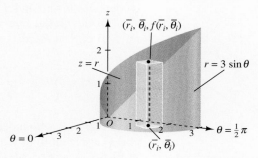

FIGURE 5

$$V = \lim_{\|\Delta\| \to 0} \sum_{i=1}^{n} \bar{r}_i \cdot \bar{r}_i \, \Delta_i r \, \Delta_i \theta$$

$$= \iint_R r^2 \, dr \, d\theta$$

$$= \int_0^{\pi/2} \int_0^{3 \sin \theta} r^2 \, dr \, d\theta$$

$$= \int_0^{\pi/2} \left[\tfrac{1}{3}r^3 \right]_0^{3 \sin \theta} d\theta$$

$$= 9 \int_0^{\pi/2} \sin^3 \theta \, d\theta$$

$$= -9 \cos \theta + 3 \cos^3 \theta \bigg]_0^{\pi/2}$$

$$= 6$$

Conclusion: The volume is 6 cubic units. ◀

▶ **EXAMPLE 2** Find the mass of the lamina in the shape of the region inside the semicircle $r = a \cos \theta, 0 \le \theta \le \tfrac{1}{2}\pi$, and whose measure of area density at any point is proportional to the measure of its distance from the pole. The mass is measured in kilograms and distance is measured in meters.

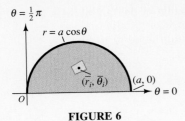

FIGURE 6

Solution Figure 6 shows a sketch of the lamina and the *i*th curved rectangle. The area density at the point (r, θ) is kr kilograms per square meter, where k is a constant. If M kilograms is the mass of the lamina, then

$$M = \lim_{\|\Delta\| \to 0} \sum_{i=1}^{n} (k\bar{r}_i)\bar{r}_i \, \Delta_i r \, \Delta_i \theta$$

$$= \iint_R kr^2 \, dr \, d\theta$$

$$= k \int_0^{\pi/2} \int_0^{a\cos\theta} r^2 \, dr \, d\theta$$

$$= \tfrac{1}{3} ka^3 \int_0^{\pi/2} \cos^3 \theta \, d\theta$$

$$= \tfrac{1}{3} ka^3 \left[\sin \theta - \tfrac{1}{3} \sin^3 \theta \right]_0^{\pi/2}$$

$$= \tfrac{2}{9} ka^3$$

Conclusion: The mass is $\tfrac{2}{9} ka^3$ kilograms. ◀

▶ **EXAMPLE 3**   Find the center of mass of the lamina in Example 2.

Solution   Let the cartesian coordinates of the center of mass of the lamina be $\bar{x}$ and $\bar{y}$, where, as is customary, the x axis is along the polar axis and the y axis is along the $\tfrac{1}{2}\pi$ axis. Let the cartesian coordinate representation of the point $(\bar{r}_i, \bar{\theta}_i)$ be $(\bar{x}_i, \bar{y}_i)$. Then if M_x kilogram-meters is the moment of mass of the lamina with respect to the x axis,

$$M_x = \lim_{\|\Delta\| \to 0} \sum_{i=1}^{n} \bar{y}_i (k\bar{r}_i)\bar{r}_i \, \Delta_i r \, \Delta_i \theta$$

Replacing $\bar{y}_i$ by $\bar{r}_i \sin \bar{\theta}_i$ we get

$$M_x = \lim_{\|\Delta\| \to 0} \sum_{i=1}^{n} k\bar{r}_i{}^3 \sin \bar{\theta}_i \, \Delta_i r \, \Delta_i \theta$$

$$= \iint_R kr^3 \sin \theta \, dr \, d\theta$$

$$= k \int_0^{\pi/2} \int_0^{a\cos\theta} r^3 \sin \theta \, dr \, d\theta$$

$$= \tfrac{1}{4} ka^4 \int_0^{\pi/2} \cos^4 \theta \sin \theta \, d\theta$$

$$= -\tfrac{1}{20} ka^4 \cos^5 \theta \Big]_0^{\pi/2}$$

$$= \tfrac{1}{20} ka^4$$

If M_y kilogram-meters is the moment of mass of the lamina with respect to the y axis, then

$$M_y = \lim_{\|\Delta\|\to 0} \sum_{i=1}^{n} \bar{x}_i (k\bar{r}_i)\bar{r}_i \, \Delta_i r \, \Delta_i \theta$$

Replacing $\bar{x}_i$ by $\bar{r}_i \cos \bar{\theta}_i$ we have

$$M_y = \lim_{\|\Delta\|\to 0} \sum_{i=1}^{n} k\bar{r}_i^3 \cos \bar{\theta}_i \, \Delta_i r \, \Delta_i \theta$$

$$= \iint_R kr^3 \cos \theta \, dr \, d\theta$$

$$= k \int_0^{\pi/2} \int_0^{a\cos\theta} r^3 \cos \theta \, dr \, d\theta$$

$$= \tfrac{1}{4}ka^4 \int_0^{\pi/2} \cos^5 \theta \, d\theta$$

$$= \tfrac{1}{4}ka^4 \left[\sin \theta - \tfrac{2}{3}\sin^3 \theta + \tfrac{1}{5}\sin^5 \theta \right]_0^{\pi/2}$$

$$= \tfrac{2}{15}ka^4$$

Therefore

$$\bar{x} = \frac{M_y}{M} \qquad \bar{y} = \frac{M_x}{M}$$

$$= \frac{\tfrac{2}{15}ka^4}{\tfrac{2}{9}ka^3} \qquad = \frac{\tfrac{1}{20}ka^4}{\tfrac{2}{9}ka^3}$$

$$= \tfrac{3}{5}a \qquad = \tfrac{9}{40}a$$

Conclusion: The center of mass is at the point $(\tfrac{3}{5}a, \tfrac{9}{40}a)$.   ◄

The next example shows how the area of a region in the polar plane can be found by double integration.

► **EXAMPLE 4** Find by double integration the area of the region enclosed by one leaf of the rose $r = \sin 3\theta$.

Solution The region and the ith curved rectangle appear in Figure 7. If A square units is the area of the region, then

$$A = \lim_{\|\Delta\|\to 0} \sum_{i=1}^{n} \Delta_i A$$

$$= \lim_{\|\Delta\|\to 0} \sum_{i=1}^{n} \bar{r}_i \, \Delta_i r \, \Delta_i \theta$$

$$= \iint_R r \, dr \, d\theta$$

$$= \int_0^{\pi/3} \int_0^{\sin 3\theta} r \, dr \, d\theta$$

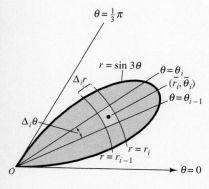

FIGURE 7

$$= \tfrac{1}{2} \int_0^{\pi/3} \sin^2 3\theta \, d\theta$$

$$= \tfrac{1}{4}\theta - \tfrac{1}{24} \sin 6\theta \Big]_0^{\pi/3}$$

$$= \tfrac{1}{12}\pi$$

<u>Conclusion:</u>   The area is $\tfrac{1}{12}\pi$ square units.   ◀

Sometimes it is easier to evaluate a double integral by using polar coordinates instead of cartesian coordinates as shown in the following examples.

▶ **EXAMPLE 5**   Evaluate the double integral

$$\iint\limits_R e^{-(x^2+y^2)} \, dA$$

where the region R is in the first quadrant and bounded by the circle $x^2 + y^2 = a^2$ and the coordinate axes.

Solution   Because $x^2 + y^2 = r^2$, and $dA = r \, dr \, d\theta$,

$$\iint\limits_R e^{-(x^2+y^2)} \, dA = \iint\limits_R e^{-r^2} r \, dr \, d\theta$$

$$= \int_0^{\pi/2} \int_0^a e^{-r^2} r \, dr \, d\theta$$

$$= -\tfrac{1}{2} \int_0^{\pi/2} \left[e^{-r^2} \right]_0^a d\theta$$

$$= -\tfrac{1}{2} \int_0^{\pi/2} (e^{-a^2} - 1) \, d\theta$$

$$= -\tfrac{1}{2}(e^{-a^2} - 1)\theta \Big]_0^{\pi/2}$$

$$= \tfrac{1}{4}\pi(1 - e^{-a^2})$$ ◀

▶ **EXAMPLE 6**   Find the surface area of the paraboloid $z = x^2 + y^2$ below the plane $z = 4$.

Solution   Figure 8 shows the given surface. From the equation of the paraboloid we see that $f(x, y) = x^2 + y^2$. The closed region in the xy plane bounded by the circle $x^2 + y^2 = 4$ is the region R. If σ square units is the required surface area, then from Theorem 13.3.4,

$$\sigma = \iint\limits_R \sqrt{f_x^2(x, y) + f_y^2(x, y) + 1} \, dx \, dy$$

$$= \iint\limits_R \sqrt{4(x^2 + y^2) + 1} \, dx \, dy$$

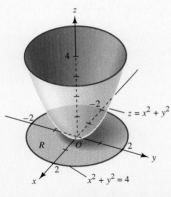

FIGURE 8

Because the integrand contains the terms $4(x^2 + y^2)$, the evaluation of the double integral is simplified by using polar coordinates. Then $x^2 + y^2 = r^2$. Because $dx\, dy = dA$, then $dx\, dy = r\, dr\, d\theta$. Furthermore, the limits for r are from 0 to 2 and the limits for θ are from 0 to 2π. Therefore

$$\sigma = \iint\limits_{R} \sqrt{4r^2 + 1}\; r\, dr\, d\theta$$

$$= \int_{0}^{2\pi} \int_{0}^{2} \sqrt{4r^2 + 1}\; r\, dr\, d\theta$$

$$= \int_{0}^{2\pi} \left[\tfrac{1}{12}(4r^2 + 1)^{3/2} \right]_{0}^{2} d\theta$$

$$= \tfrac{1}{6}\pi(17\sqrt{17} - 1)$$

Conclusion: The area of the paraboloid below the given plane is $\tfrac{1}{6}\pi(17\sqrt{17} - 1)$ square units.   ◀

▶ **EXAMPLE 7**   Find the area of the top half of the sphere

$$x^2 + y^2 + z^2 = a^2$$

Solution   The hemisphere appears in Figure 9. Solving the equation of the sphere for z and setting this equal to $f(x, y)$ we get

$$f(x, y) = \sqrt{a^2 - x^2 - y^2}$$

Because

$$f_x(x, y) = \frac{-x}{\sqrt{a^2 - x^2 - y^2}} \quad \text{and} \quad f_y(x, y) = \frac{-y}{\sqrt{a^2 - x^2 - y^2}}$$

f_x and f_y are not defined on the circle $x^2 + y^2 = a^2$, which is the boundary of the region R in the xy plane. Furthermore, the double integral obtained from Theorem 13.3.4 is

$$\iint\limits_{R} \frac{a}{\sqrt{a^2 - x^2 - y^2}}\, dx\, dy$$

which is improper because the integrand has an infinite discontinuity at each point of the boundary of R. We can take care of this situation by considering the region R' as that bounded by the circle $x^2 + y^2 = b^2$, where $b < a$, and then take the limit as $b \to a^-$. Furthermore, the computation is simplified if the double integral is evaluated by an iterated integral using polar coordinates. Then if σ square units is the area of the hemisphere,

$$\sigma = \lim_{b \to a^-} \int_{0}^{b} \int_{0}^{2\pi} \frac{a}{\sqrt{a^2 - r^2}}\; r\, d\theta\, dr$$

$$= 2\pi a \lim_{b \to a^-} \int_{0}^{b} \frac{r}{\sqrt{a^2 - r^2}}\, dr$$

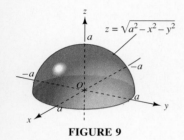

FIGURE 9

$z = \sqrt{a^2 - x^2 - y^2}$

$$= 2\pi a \lim_{b \to a^-} \left[-\sqrt{a^2 - r^2} \right]_0^b$$

$$= 2\pi a \lim_{b \to a^-} \left[-\sqrt{a^2 - b^2} + a \right]$$

$$= 2\pi a^2$$

<u>Conclusion:</u>   The area of the hemisphere is $2\pi a^2$ square units.   ◀

EXERCISES 13.4

In Exercises 1 through 6, use double integrals to find the area of the region.

1. The region inside the cardioid $r = 2(1 + \sin \theta)$.

2. One leaf of the rose $r = a \cos 2\theta$.

3. The region inside the cardioid $r = a(1 + \cos \theta)$ and outside the circle $r = a$.

4. The region inside the circle $r = 1$ and outside the lemniscate $r^2 = \cos 2\theta$.

5. The region inside the large loop of the limaçon

   $$r = 2 - 4 \sin \theta$$

   and outside the small loop.

6. The region inside the limaçon $r = 3 - \cos \theta$ and outside the circle $r = 5 \cos \theta$.

In Exercises 7 through 12, find the volume of the solid.

7. The solid bounded by the ellipsoid $z^2 + 9r^2 = 9$.

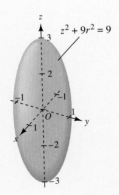

8. The solid cut out of the sphere $z^2 + r^2 = 4$ by the cylinder $r = 1$.

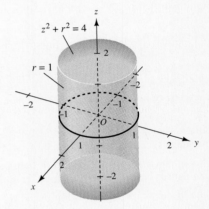

9. The solid cut out of the sphere $z^2 + r^2 = 16$ by the cylinder $r = 4 \cos \theta$.

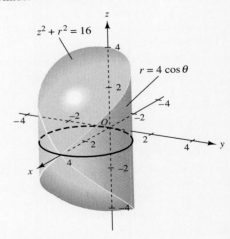

10. The solid above the polar plane bounded by the cone $z = 2r$ and the cylinder $r = 1 - \cos\theta$.

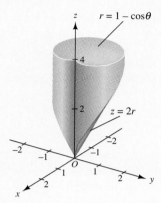

11. The solid bounded by the paraboloid $z = 4 - r^2$, the cylinder $r = 1$, and the polar plane.

12. The solid above the paraboloid $z = r^2$ and below the plane $z = 2r \sin\theta$.

In Exercises 13 through 19, find the mass and center of mass of the lamina if the area density is as indicated. Mass is measured in kilograms and distance is measured in meters.

13. A lamina in the shape of the region of Exercise 1. The area density varies as the distance from the pole.

14. A lamina in the shape of the region of Exercise 2. The area density varies as the distance from the pole.

15. A lamina in the shape of the region inside the limaçon $r = 2 - \cos\theta$. The area density varies as the distance from the pole.

16. A lamina in the shape of the region bounded by the limaçon $r = 2 + \cos\theta$, $0 \le \theta \le \pi$, and the polar axis. The area density at any point is $k \sin\theta$ kilograms per square meter.

17. The lamina of Exercise 16. The area density at any point is $kr \sin\theta$ kilograms per square meter.

18. A lamina in the shape of the region of Exercise 6. The area density varies as the distance from the pole.

19. A lamina in the shape of the region inside the small loop of the limaçon of Exercise 5. The area density varies as the distance from the pole.

In Exercises 20 through 24, find the moment of inertia of the lamina about the indicated axis or point if the area density is as indicated. Mass is measured in kilograms and distance is measured in meters.

20. A lamina in the shape of the region enclosed by the circle $r = \sin\theta$; about the $\frac{1}{2}\pi$ axis. The area density at any point is k kilograms per square meter.

21. The lamina of Exercise 20; about the polar axis. The area density at any point is k kilograms per square meter.

22. A lamina in the shape of the region bounded by the cardioid $r = a(1 - \cos\theta)$; about the pole. The area density at any point is k kilograms per square meter.

23. A lamina in the shape of the region bounded by the cardioid $r = a(1 + \cos\theta)$ and the circle $r = 2a \cos\theta$; about the pole. The area density at any point is k kilograms per square meter.

24. A lamina in the shape of the region enclosed by the lemniscate $r^2 = a^2 \cos 2\theta$; about the polar axis. The area density at any point is k kilograms per square meter.

25. A homogeneous lamina is in the shape of the region enclosed by one loop of the lemniscate $r^2 = \cos 2\theta$. Find the radius of gyration of the lamina about an axis perpendicular to the polar plane at the pole.

26. A lamina is in the shape of the region enclosed by the circle $r = 4$, and the area density varies as the distance from the pole. Find the radius of gyration of the lamina about an axis perpendicular to the polar plane at the pole.

27. Evaluate by polar coordinates the double integral

$$\iint\limits_{R} e^{x^2 + y^2}\, dA$$

where R is the region bounded by the circles $x^2 + y^2 = 1$ and $x^2 + y^2 = 9$.

28. Evaluate by polar coordinates the double integral

$$\iint\limits_{R} \frac{x}{\sqrt{x^2 + y^2}}\, dA$$

where R is the region in the first quadrant bounded by the circle $x^2 + y^2 = 1$ and the coordinate axes.

29. Find the area of the portion of the surface of the sphere $x^2 + y^2 + z^2 = 4x$ that is cut out by one nappe of the cone $y^2 + z^2 = x^2$.

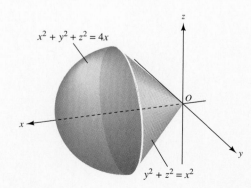

30. Find the area of the portion of the surface of the sphere $x^2 + y^2 + z^2 = 36$ that lies within the cylinder $x^2 + y^2 = 9$.

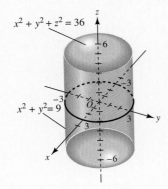

31. Find the area of the portion of the surface of the sphere $x^2 + y^2 + z^2 = 4z$ that lies within the paraboloid $x^2 + y^2 = 3z$.

32. For the sphere and paraboloid of Exercise 31, find the area of the portion of the surface of the paraboloid that lies within the sphere.

33. Find the area of the portion of the surface $xy = az$ in the first octant that lies inside the cylinder $x^2 + y^2 = a^2$.

34. Find the area of the surface cut from the hyperbolic paraboloid $y^2 - x^2 = 6z$ by the cylinder $x^2 + y^2 = 36$.

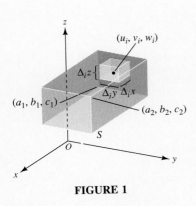

FIGURE 1

13.5 TRIPLE INTEGRALS

The extension of the double integral to the triple integral is analogous to the extension of the single integral to the double integral. The simplest type of region in R^3 is a rectangular parallelepiped bounded by six planes: $x = a_1$, $x = a_2$, $y = b_1$, $y = b_2$, $z = c_1$, and $z = c_2$, with $a_1 < a_2$, $b_1 < b_2$, and $c_1 < c_2$. Let f be a function of three variables and suppose that f is continuous on such a region S. A partition of this region is formed by dividing S into rectangular boxes by drawing planes parallel to the coordinate planes. Denote such a partition by Δ and suppose that n is the number of boxes. Let $\Delta_i V$ cubic units be the volume of the ith box. We choose an arbitrary point (u_i, v_i, w_i) in the ith box and form the sum

$$\sum_{i=1}^{n} f(u_i, v_i, w_i)\, \Delta_i V \tag{1}$$

Refer to Figure 1, which shows the rectangular parallelepiped together with the ith box. The *norm* $\|\Delta\|$ of the partition is the length of the longest diagonal of the boxes. If the sums of form (1) approach a limit as $\|\Delta\|$ approaches zero for any choices of the points (u_i, v_i, w_i), then we call this limit the **triple integral** of f on S and write

$$\lim_{\|\Delta\| \to 0} \sum_{i=1}^{n} f(u_i, v_i, w_i)\, \Delta_i V = \iiint_S f(x, y, z)\, dV$$

A sufficient condition for the triple integral of f on S to exist is that f be continuous on S.

Analogous to a double integral being equal to a twice-iterated integral, the triple integral is equal to a thrice-iterated integral. When S is the rectangular parallelepiped described above, and f is continuous on S, then

$$\iiint_S f(x, y, z)\, dV = \int_{a_1}^{a_2} \int_{b_1}^{b_2} \int_{c_1}^{c_2} f(x, y, z)\, dz\, dy\, dx$$

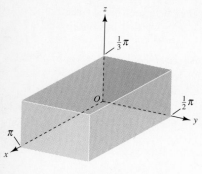

FIGURE 2

▶ **EXAMPLE 1**   Evaluate the triple integral

$$\iiint\limits_{S} xy \sin yz \, dV$$

if S is the rectangular parallelepiped bounded by the planes $x = \pi$, $y = \frac{1}{2}\pi$, $z = \frac{1}{3}\pi$, and the coordinate planes.

Solution   Figure 2 shows the rectangular parallelepiped S.

$$\iiint\limits_{S} xy \sin yz \, dV = \int_0^\pi \int_0^{\pi/2} \int_0^{\pi/3} xy \sin yz \, dz \, dy \, dx$$

$$= \int_0^\pi \int_0^{\pi/2} \left[-x \cos yz \right]_0^{\pi/3} dy \, dx$$

$$= \int_0^\pi \int_0^{\pi/2} x(1 - \cos \tfrac{1}{3}\pi y) \, dy \, dx$$

$$= \int_0^\pi x\left(y - \frac{3}{\pi} \sin \frac{1}{3}\pi y \right) \Bigg]_0^{\pi/2} dx$$

$$= \int_0^\pi x\left(\frac{\pi}{2} - \frac{3}{\pi} \sin \frac{\pi^2}{6} \right) dx$$

$$= \frac{x^2}{2} \left(\frac{\pi}{2} - \frac{3}{\pi} \sin \frac{\pi^2}{6} \right) \Bigg]_0^\pi$$

$$= \frac{\pi}{4} \left(\pi^2 - 6 \sin \frac{\pi^2}{6} \right) \qquad ◀$$

We now discuss how to define the triple integral of a continuous function of three variables on a region in R^3 other than a rectangular parallelepiped. Let S be the closed three-dimensional region bounded by the planes $x = a$ and $x = b$, the cylinders $y = \phi_1(x)$ and $y = \phi_2(x)$, and the surfaces $z = F_1(x, y)$ and $z = F_2(x, y)$, where the functions ϕ_1, ϕ_2, F_1, and F_2 are smooth. See Figure 3. Construct planes parallel to the coordinate planes,

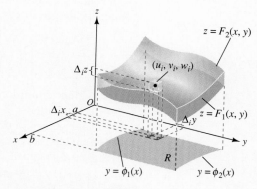

FIGURE 3

thereby forming a set of rectangular parallelepipeds that completely cover S. The parallelepipeds that are entirely inside S or on the boundary of S form a **partition** Δ of S. Choose some system of numbering so that they are numbered from 1 to n. The norm $\|\Delta\|$ of this partition of S is the length of the longest diagonal of any parallelepiped belonging to the partition. The volume of the ith parallelepiped is $\Delta_i V$ cubic units. Let f be a function of three variables that is continuous on S, and let (u_i, v_i, w_i) be an arbitrary point in the ith parallelepiped. Form the sum

$$\sum_{i=1}^{n} f(u_i, v_i, w_i)\, \Delta_i V$$

If this sum has a limit as $\|\Delta\|$ approaches zero, and if the limit is independent of the choice of the partitioning planes and the choices of the arbitrary points (u_i, v_i, w_i) in each parallelepiped, then the limit is called the **triple integral** of f on S, and we write

$$\lim_{\|\Delta\| \to 0} \sum_{i=1}^{n} f(u_i, v_i, w_i)\, \Delta_i V = \iiint\limits_{S} f(x, y, z)\, dV \qquad (2)$$

It can be proved in advanced calculus that a sufficient condition for the limit in (2) to exist is that f be continuous on S. Furthermore, under the condition imposed on the functions ϕ_1, ϕ_2, F_1, and F_2 that they be smooth, it can also be proved that the triple integral can be evaluated by the iterated integral

$$\int_{a}^{b} \int_{\phi_1(x)}^{\phi_2(x)} \int_{F_1(x, y)}^{F_2(x, y)} f(x, y, z)\, dz\, dy\, dx$$

Just as the double integral can be interpreted as the measure of the area of a plane region when $f(x, y) = 1$ on R, the triple integral can be interpreted as the measure of the volume of a three-dimensional region. If $f(x, y\, z) = 1$ on S, then (2) becomes

$$\lim_{\|\Delta\| \to 0} \sum_{i=1}^{n} \Delta_i V = \iiint\limits_{S} dV$$

and the triple integral is the measure of the volume of the region S.

▶ **EXAMPLE 2**   Find the volume of the solid of Example 5 in Section 13.2 by triple integration.

Solution   The solid lies above the xy plane bounded by the elliptic paraboloid $z = x^2 + 4y^2$ and the cylinder $x^2 + 4y^2 = 4$. See Figure 4. If V cubic units is the volume of the solid, then

$$V = \lim_{\|\Delta\| \to 0} \sum_{i=1}^{n} \Delta_i V$$

$$= \iiint\limits_{S} dV$$

where S is the region bounded by the solid. The z limits are from 0 (the value of z on the xy plane) to $x^2 + 4y^2$ (the value of z on the elliptic paraboloid).

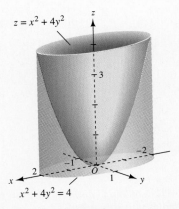

FIGURE 4

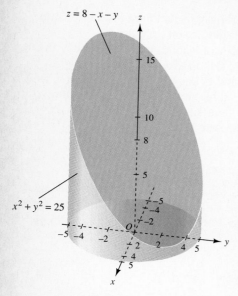

$z = 8 - x - y$

$x^2 + y^2 = 25$

FIGURE 5

The y limits for one-fourth of the volume are from 0 (the value of y on the xz plane) to $\frac{1}{2}\sqrt{4 - x^2}$ (the value of y on the cylinder). The x limits for the first octant are from 0 to 2. We evaluate the triple integral by an iterated integral and obtain

$$V = 4 \int_0^2 \int_0^{\sqrt{4-x^2}/2} \int_0^{x^2+4y^2} dz \, dy \, dx$$

$$= 4 \int_0^2 \int_0^{\sqrt{4-x^2}/2} (x^2 + 4y^2) \, dy \, dx$$

This is the same twice-iterated integral that we obtained in Example 5 in Section 13.2, and so the remainder of the solution is the same. ◀

▶ **EXAMPLE 3**   Find the volume of the solid bounded by the cylinder $x^2 + y^2 = 25$, the plane $x + y + z = 8$, and the xy plane.

Solution   The solid appears in Figure 5. The z limits for the iterated integral are from 0 to $8 - x - y$ (the value of z on the plane). The y limits are obtained from the boundary region in the xy plane, which is the circle $x^2 + y^2 = 25$. Hence the y limits are from $-\sqrt{25 - x^2}$ to $\sqrt{25 - x^2}$. The x limits are from -5 to 5. If V cubic units is the required volume,

$$V = \lim_{\|\Delta\|\to 0} \sum_{i=1}^{n} \Delta_i V$$

$$= \iiint_S dV$$

$$= \int_{-5}^{5} \int_{-\sqrt{25-x^2}}^{\sqrt{25-x^2}} \int_0^{8-x-y} dz \, dy \, dx$$

$$= \int_{-5}^{5} \int_{-\sqrt{25-x^2}}^{\sqrt{25-x^2}} (8 - x - y) \, dy \, dx$$

$$= \int_{-5}^{5} \left[(8 - x)y - \tfrac{1}{2}y^2 \right]_{-\sqrt{25-x^2}}^{\sqrt{25-x^2}} dx$$

$$= 2 \int_{-5}^{5} (8 - x)\sqrt{25 - x^2} \, dx$$

$$= 16 \int_{-5}^{5} \sqrt{25 - x^2} \, dx + \int_{-5}^{5} \sqrt{25 - x^2} \, (-2x) \, dx$$

$$= 16(\tfrac{1}{2}x\sqrt{25 - x^2} + \tfrac{25}{2}\sin^{-1}\tfrac{1}{5}x) + \tfrac{2}{3}(25 - x^2)^{3/2} \Big]_{-5}^{5}$$

$$= 200\pi$$

<u>Conclusion:</u>   The volume is 200π cubic units. ◀

▶ **EXAMPLE 4**   Find the mass of the solid above the xy plane bounded by the cone $9x^2 + z^2 = y^2$ and the plane $y = 9$ if the measure of the volume density at any point (x, y, z) in the solid is proportional to the

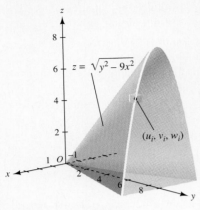

FIGURE 6

measure of the distance of the point from the xy plane. The volume density is measured in kilograms per cubic meter.

Solution Figure 6 shows the solid. Let M kilograms be the mass of the solid. The volume density at any point (x, y, z) in the solid is kz kilograms per cubic meter, where k is a constant. Then if (u_i, v_i, w_i) is any point in the ith rectangular parallelepiped of the partition,

$$M = \lim_{\|\Delta\| \to 0} \sum_{i=1}^{n} k\mu_i \, \Delta_i V$$

$$= \iiint\limits_{S} kz \, dV$$

$$= 2k \int_0^9 \int_0^{y/3} \int_0^{\sqrt{y^2 - 9x^2}} z \, dz \, dx \, dy$$

$$= 2k \int_0^9 \int_0^{y/3} \left[\tfrac{1}{2} z^2 \right]_0^{\sqrt{y^2 - 9x^2}} dx \, dy$$

$$= k \int_0^9 \int_0^{y/3} (y^2 - 9x^2) \, dx \, dy$$

$$= \tfrac{2}{9} k \int_0^9 y^3 \, dy$$

$$= \tfrac{729}{2} k$$

Conclusion: The mass is $\frac{729}{2} k$ kilograms. ◄

EXERCISES 13.5

In Exercises 1 through 8, evaluate the iterated integral.

1. $\int_0^1 \int_0^{1-x} \int_{2y}^{1+y^2} x \, dz \, dy \, dx$

2. $\int_1^2 \int_0^x \int_1^{x+xy} xy \, dz \, dy \, dx$

3. $\int_0^1 \int_0^x \int_0^{x+y} (x + y + z) \, dz \, dy \, dx$

4. $\int_0^2 \int_0^{\sqrt{4-y^2}} \int_0^{2-y} z \, dx \, dz \, dy$

5. $\int_{-1}^0 \int_e^{2e} \int_0^{\pi/3} y \ln z \tan x \, dx \, dz \, dy$

6. $\int_1^2 \int_y^{y^2} \int_0^{\ln x} ye^z \, dz \, dx \, dy$

7. $\int_0^{\pi/2} \int_z^{\pi/2} \int_0^{xz} \cos \frac{y}{z} \, dy \, dx \, dz$

8. $\int_0^2 \int_0^y \int_0^{\sqrt{3z}} \frac{z}{x^2 + z^2} \, dx \, dz \, dy$

In Exercises 9 through 18, evaluate the triple integral.

9. $\iiint\limits_{S} y \, dV$ if S is the region bounded by the tetrahedron formed by the plane $12x + 20y + 15z = 60$ and the coordinate planes.

10. $\iiint\limits_{S} (x^2 + z^2) \, dV$ if S is the same region as in Exercise 9.

11. $\iiint\limits_{S} z \, dV$ if S is the region bounded by the tetrahedron having vertices $(0, 0, 0)$, $(1, 1, 0)$, $(1, 0, 0)$, and $(1, 0, 1)$.

12. $\iiint\limits_{S} yz \, dV$ if S is the same region as in Exercise 11.

13. $\iiint\limits_{S} xy \, dV$ if S is the rectangular parallelepiped in the first octant bounded by the coordinate planes and the planes $x = 2$, $y = 3$, and $z = 4$.

14. $\iiint\limits_{S} x \, dV$ if S is the tetrahedron bounded by the planes $x + 2y + 3z = 6$, $x = 0$, $y = 0$, and $z = 0$.

15. $\iiint\limits_{S} dV$ if S is the region bounded by the surfaces $z = x^2 + y^2$ and $z = 27 - 2x^2 - 2y^2$.

16. $\iiint\limits_{S} y^2 \, dV$ if S is the region bounded by the cylinders $x^2 + y = 1$ and $z^2 + y = 1$ and the plane $y = 0$.

17. $\iiint\limits_{S} (xz + 3z) \, dV$ if S is the region bounded by the cylinder $x^2 + z^2 = 9$ and the planes $x + y = 3$, $z = 0$, and $y = 0$, above the xy plane.

18. $\iiint\limits_{S} xyz \, dV$ if S is the region bounded by the cylinders $x^2 + y^2 = 4$ and $x^2 + z^2 = 4$.

19. Find the volume of the solid in the first octant bounded below by the xy plane, above by the plane $z = y$, and laterally by the cylinder $y^2 = x$ and the plane $x = 1$.

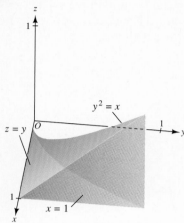

20. Find the volume of the solid in the first octant bounded by the cylinder $x^2 + z^2 = 16$, the plane $x + y = 2$, and the three coordinate planes.

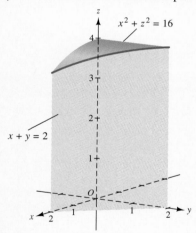

21. Find the volume of the solid in the first octant bounded by the cylinders $x^2 + y^2 = 4$ and $x^2 + 2z = 4$ and the three coordinate planes.

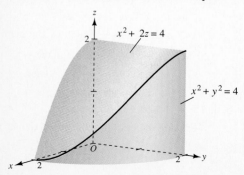

22. Find the volume of the solid bounded by the elliptic cone $4x^2 + 9y^2 - 36z^2 = 0$ and the plane $z = 1$.

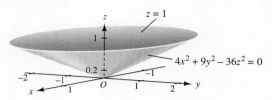

23. Find the volume of the solid above the elliptic paraboloid $3x^2 + y^2 = z$ and below the cylinder $x^2 + z = 4$.

24. Find the volume of the solid enclosed by the sphere $x^2 + y^2 + z^2 = a^2$.

25. Find the volume of the solid enclosed by the ellipsoid

$$\frac{x^2}{a^2} + \frac{y^2}{b^2} + \frac{z^2}{c^2} = 1$$

26. Find the volume of the solid bounded by the cylinders $z = 5x^2$ and $z = 3 - x^2$, the plane $y + z = 4$, and the xz plane.

27. Find the mass of the homogeneous solid bounded by the cylinder $z = 4 - x^2$, the plane $y = 5$, and the coordinate planes if the volume density at any point is k kilograms per cubic meter.

28. Find the mass of the solid enclosed by the tetrahedron formed by the plane $100x + 25y + 16z = 400$ and the coordinate planes if the volume density varies as the distance from the yz plane. The volume density is measured in kilograms per cubic meter.

29. Find the mass of the solid bounded by the cylinders $x = z^2$ and $y = x^2$, and the planes $x = 1$, $y = 0$, and $z = 0$. The volume density varies as the product of the distances from the three coordinate planes, and it is measured in kilograms per cubic meter.

30. Find the mass of the solid bounded by the surface $z = 4 - 4x^2 - y^2$ and the xy plane. The volume density at any point of the solid is $3z|x|$ kilograms per cubic meter.

31. Find the mass of the solid bounded by the surface $z = xy$ and the planes $x = 1$, $y = 1$, and $z = 0$. The volume density at any point of the solid is $3\sqrt{x^2 + y^2}$ kilograms per cubic meter.

32. A solid has the shape of a right-circular cylinder of base radius r meters and height h meters. Find the mass of the solid if the volume density varies as the distance from one of the bases. The volume density is measured in kilograms per cubic meter.

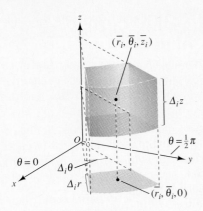

FIGURE 1

13.6 TRIPLE INTEGRALS IN CYLINDRICAL AND SPHERICAL COORDINATES

If a region S in R^3 has an axis of symmetry, triple integrals on S are easier to evaluate if cylindrical coordinates are used. If there is symmetry with respect to a point, it is convenient to choose that point as the origin and to use spherical coordinates. In this section we discuss the triple integral in these coordinates and apply them to physical problems.

To define the triple integral in cylindrical coordinates we construct a partition of the region S by drawing planes through the z axis, planes perpendicular to the z axis, and right-circular cylinders having the z axis as axis. Figure 1 shows a typical subregion. The elements of the constructed partition lie entirely in S. We call this partition a **cylindrical partition.** The measure of the length of the longest "diagonal" of any of the subregions is the **norm** of the partition. Let n be the number of subregions of the partition and $\Delta_i V$ cubic units be the volume of the ith subregion. The area of the base is $\bar{r}_i \, \Delta_i r \, \Delta_i \theta$ square units, where $\bar{r}_i = \frac{1}{2}(r_i + r_{i-1})$ as shown in Section 13.4. Hence if $\Delta_i z$ units is the altitude of the ith subregion,

$$\Delta_i V = \bar{r}_i \, \Delta_i r \, \Delta_i \theta \, \Delta_i z$$

Let f be a function of r, θ, and z, and suppose that f is continuous on S. Choose a point $(\bar{r}_i, \bar{\theta}_i, \bar{z}_i)$ in the ith subregion such that $\theta_{i-1} \le \bar{\theta}_i \le \theta_i$, and $z_{i-1} \le \bar{z}_i \le z_i$. Form the sum

$$\sum_{i=1}^{n} f(\bar{r}_i, \bar{\theta}_i, \bar{z}_i) \, \Delta_i V = \sum_{i=1}^{n} f(\bar{r}_i, \bar{\theta}_i, \bar{z}_i)\bar{r}_i \, \Delta_i r \, \Delta_i \theta \, \Delta_i z \qquad (1)$$

As the norm of Δ approaches zero, it can be shown, under suitable conditions on S, that the limit of this sum exists. The limit is called the **triple integral in cylindrical coordinates** of the function f on S, and we write

$$\lim_{\|\Delta\| \to 0} \sum_{i=1}^{n} f(\bar{r}_i, \bar{\theta}_i, \bar{z}_i) \, \Delta_i V = \iiint\limits_{S} f(r, \theta, z) \, dV$$

$$\Leftrightarrow \quad \lim_{\|\Delta\| \to 0} \sum_{i=1}^{n} f(\bar{r}_i, \bar{\theta}_i, \bar{z}_i)\bar{r}_i \, \Delta_i r \, \Delta_i \theta \, \Delta_i z = \iiint\limits_{R} f(r, \theta, z)r \, dr \, d\theta \, dz$$

Note that in cylindrical coordinates, $dV = r \, dr \, d\theta \, dz$. We can evaluate the triple integral by an iterated integral. For instance, suppose that the region S in R^3 is bounded by the planes $\theta = \alpha$ and $\theta = \beta$, with $\alpha < \beta$, by the cylinders $r = \lambda_1(\theta)$ and $r = \lambda_2(\theta)$, where λ_1 and λ_2 are smooth on $[\alpha, \beta]$ and $\lambda_1(\theta) \le \lambda_2(\theta)$ for $\alpha \le \theta \le \beta$, and by the surfaces $z = F_1(r, \theta)$ and $z = F_2(r, \theta)$, where F_1 and F_2 are functions of two variables that are smooth on some region R in the polar plane bounded by the curves $r = \lambda_1(\theta)$, $r = \lambda_2(\theta)$, $\theta = \alpha$, and $\theta = \beta$. Also, suppose that $F_1(r, \theta) \le F_2(r, \theta)$ for every point (r, θ) in R. Then the triple integral can be evaluated by an iterated integral by the formula

$$\iiint\limits_{S} f(r, \theta, z)r \, dr \, d\theta \, dz = \int_{\alpha}^{\beta} \int_{\lambda_1(\theta)}^{\lambda_2(\theta)} \int_{F_1(r,\theta)}^{F_2(r,\theta)} f(r, \theta, z)r \, dz \, dr \, d\theta$$

There are five other iterated integrals that can be used to evaluate the triple integral because there are six possible permutations of the three variables r, θ, and z.

Triple integrals and cylindrical coordinates are especially useful in finding the moment of inertia of a solid with respect to the z axis because the distance from the z axis to a point in the solid is determined by the coordinate r.

▶ **EXAMPLE 1**   A homogeneous solid in the shape of a right-circular cylinder has a radius of 2 m and an altitude of 4 m. Find the moment of inertia of the solid with respect to its axis.

Solution   Choose the coordinate planes so that the xy plane is the plane of the base of the solid and the z axis is the axis of the solid. Figure 2 shows the portion of the solid in the first octant together with the ith subregion of a cylindrical partition. Using cylindrical coordinates and taking the point $(\bar{r}_i, \bar{\theta}_i, \bar{z}_i)$ in the ith subregion with k kilograms per cubic meter as the volume density at any point, then if I_z kilogram-meters squared is the moment of inertia of the solid with respect to the z axis,

$$I_z = \lim_{\|\Delta\|\to 0} \sum_{i=1}^{n} \bar{r}_i^2 k\, \Delta_i V$$

$$= \iiint_S kr^2\, dV$$

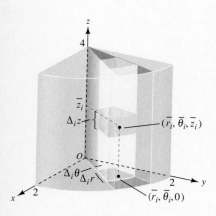

FIGURE 2

There are six different possible orders of integration. Figure 2 shows the order $dz\, dr\, d\theta$. Using this order, we have

$$I_z = \iiint_S kr^2\, dz\, r\, dr\, d\theta$$

$$= 4k \int_0^{\pi/2} \int_0^2 \int_0^4 r^3\, dz\, dr\, d\theta$$

In the first integration the blocks are summed from $z = 0$ to $z = 4$; the blocks become a column shown in green in the figure. In the second integration the columns are summed from $r = 0$ to $r = 2$; the columns become a wedge-shaped slice of the cylinder shown in blue in the figure. In the third integration the wedge-shaped slice is rotated from $\theta = 0$ to $\theta = \frac{1}{2}\pi$; this sweeps the wedge about the entire three-dimensional region in the first octant. We multiply by 4 to obtain the entire volume. Performing the integration we obtain.

$$I_z = 16k \int_0^{\pi/2} \int_0^2 r^3\, dr\, d\theta$$

$$= 64k \int_0^{\pi/2} d\theta$$

$$= 32k\pi$$

Conclusion: The moment of inertia is $32k\pi$ kg-m^2.   ◀

▶ **EXAMPLE 2**   Solve Example 1 by taking the order of integration as **(a)** $dr\, dz\, d\theta$; **(b)** $d\theta\, dr\, dz$.

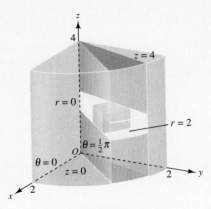

FIGURE 3

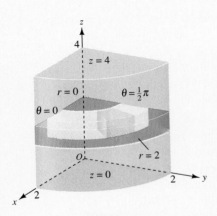

FIGURE 4

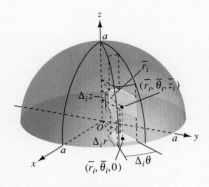

FIGURE 5

Solution

(a) Figure 3 represents the order $dr\,dz\,d\theta$. It shows the block summed from $r = 0$ to $r = 2$ to give a wedge-shaped sector shown in green. We then sum from $z = 0$ to $z = 4$ to give a wedge-shaped slice shown in blue. The slice is rotated from $\theta = 0$ to $\theta = \frac{1}{2}\pi$ to cover the first octant. Then

$$I_z = 4k \int_0^{\pi/2} \int_0^4 \int_0^2 r^3 \, dr \, dz \, d\theta$$

$$= 32k\pi$$

(b) Figure 4 represents the order $d\theta\,dr\,dz$. It shows the blocks summed from $\theta = 0$ to $\theta = \frac{1}{2}\pi$ to give a ring shown in green. These rings are summed from $r = 0$ to $r = 2$ to give a horizontal slice shown in blue. The horizontal slices are summed from $z = 0$ to $z = 4$. Therefore

$$I_z = 4k \int_0^4 \int_0^2 \int_0^{\pi/2} r^3 \, d\theta \, dr \, dz$$

$$= 32k\pi \qquad \blacktriangleleft$$

▶ **EXAMPLE 3** Find the mass of a solid hemisphere of radius a meters if the volume density at any point is proportional to the distance of the point from the axis of the solid and is measured in kilograms per cubic meter.

Solution If we choose the coordinate planes so that the origin is at the center of the sphere and the z axis is the axis of the solid, then an equation of the hemispherical surface above the xy plane is $z = \sqrt{a^2 - x^2 - y^2}$. Figure 5 shows this surface and the solid together with the ith subregion of a cylindrical partition. An equation of the hemisphere in cylindrical coordinates is $z = \sqrt{a^2 - r^2}$. If $(\bar{r}_i, \bar{\theta}_i, \bar{z}_i)$ is a point in the ith subregion, the volume density at this point is $k\bar{r}_i$ kilograms per cubic meter, where k is a constant; and if M kilograms is the mass of the solid, then

$$M = \lim_{\|\Delta\| \to 0} \sum_{i=1}^n k\bar{r}_i \, \Delta_i V$$

$$= \iiint_S kr \, dV$$

$$= k \int_0^{2\pi} \int_0^a \int_0^{\sqrt{a^2 - r^2}} r^2 \, dz \, dr \, d\theta$$

$$= k \int_0^{2\pi} \int_0^a r^2 \sqrt{a^2 - r^2} \, dr \, d\theta$$

$$= k \int_0^{2\pi} \left[-\tfrac{1}{4} r(a^2 - r^2)^{3/2} + \tfrac{1}{8} a^2 r \sqrt{a^2 - r^2} + \tfrac{1}{8} a^4 \sin^{-1} \frac{r}{a} \right]_0^a d\theta$$

$$= \tfrac{1}{16} ka^4 \pi \int_0^{2\pi} d\theta$$

$$= \tfrac{1}{8} ka^4 \pi^2$$

Conclusion: The mass of the solid hemisphere is $\tfrac{1}{8} ka^4 \pi^2$ kilograms. ◀

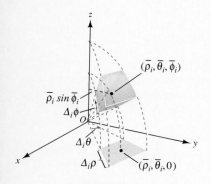

FIGURE 6

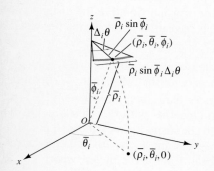

FIGURE 7

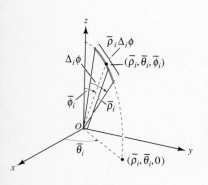

FIGURE 8

▶ **EXAMPLE 4**   Find the center of mass of the solid of Example 3.

Solution   Let the cartesian coordinate representation of the center of mass be $(\bar{x}, \bar{y}, \bar{z})$. Because of symmetry, $\bar{x} = 0$ and $\bar{y} = 0$. We need to calculate $\bar{z}$. If M_{xy} kg-m is the moment of mass of the solid with respect to the xy plane, then

$$
\begin{aligned}
M_{xy} &= \lim_{\|\Delta\| \to 0} \sum_{i=1}^{n} \bar{z}_i (k\bar{r}_i)\, \Delta_i V \\
&= \iiint_S kzr\, dV \\
&= k \int_0^{2\pi} \int_0^a \int_0^{\sqrt{a^2 - r^2}} zr^2\, dz\, dr\, d\theta \\
&= \tfrac{1}{2} k \int_0^{2\pi} \int_0^a (a^2 - r^2)r^2\, dr\, d\theta \\
&= \tfrac{1}{15} ka^5 \int_0^{2\pi} d\theta \\
&= \tfrac{2}{15} ka^5 \pi
\end{aligned}
$$

Because $M\bar{z} = M_{xy}$, we get $\bar{z} = M_{xy}/M$; thus

$$
\begin{aligned}
\bar{z} &= \frac{\tfrac{2}{15} ka^5 \pi}{\tfrac{1}{8} ka^4 \pi^2} \\
&= \frac{16}{15\pi} a
\end{aligned}
$$

<u>**Conclusion:**</u>   The center of mass is on the axis of the solid at a distance of $16a/15\pi$ meters from the plane of the base.   ◀

We now proceed to define the triple integral in spherical coordinates. A spherical partition of the three-dimensional region S is formed by planes containing the z axis, spheres with centers at the origin, and circular cones having vertices at the origin and the z axis as the axis. Figure 6 shows a typical subregion of the partition. If $\Delta_i V$ cubic units is the volume of the ith subregion, and $(\bar{\rho}_i, \bar{\theta}_i, \bar{\phi}_i)$ is a point in it, we can get an approximation to $\Delta_i V$ by considering the region as if it were a rectangular parallelepiped and taking the product of the measures of the three dimensions. These measures are $\bar{\rho}_i \sin \bar{\phi}_i \Delta_i \theta$, $\bar{\rho}_i \Delta_i \phi$, and $\Delta_i \rho$. Figures 7 and 8 show how the first two measures are obtained, and Figure 6 shows the dimension of measure $\Delta_i \rho$. Hence

$$
\Delta_i V = \bar{\rho}_i^{\,2} \sin \bar{\phi}_i \, \Delta_i \rho \, \Delta_i \theta \, \Delta_i \phi
$$

The **triple integral in spherical coordinates** of a function f on S is given by

$$\lim_{\|\Delta\| \to 0} \sum_{i=1}^{n} f(\bar{\rho}_i, \bar{\theta}_i, \bar{\phi}_i) \, \Delta_i V = \iiint\limits_{S} f(\rho, \theta, \phi) \, dV$$

$$\Leftrightarrow \quad \lim_{\|\Delta\| \to 0} \sum_{i=1}^{n} f(\bar{\rho}_i, \bar{\theta}_i, \bar{\phi}_i) \bar{\rho}_i^{\,2} \sin \bar{\phi}_i \, \Delta_i \rho \, \Delta_i \theta \, \Delta_i \phi$$

$$= \iiint\limits_{S} f(\rho, \theta, \phi) \rho^2 \sin \phi \, d\rho \, d\theta \, d\phi$$

The triple integral can be evaluated by an iterated integral. Observe that in spherical coordinates, $dV = \rho^2 \sin \phi \, d\rho \, d\theta \, d\phi$.

Spherical coordinates are especially useful in some problems involving spheres, as in the following example.

▶ **EXAMPLE 5**   Find the mass of the solid hemisphere of Example 3 if the volume density at any point is proportional to the distance of the point from the center of the base.

Solution   If $(\bar{\rho}_i, \bar{\theta}_i, \bar{\phi}_i)$ is a point in the ith subregion of a spherical partition, the volume density at this point is $k\bar{\rho}_i$ kilograms per cubic meter, where k is a constant. If M kilograms is the mass of the solid, then

$$M = \lim_{\|\Delta\| \to 0} \sum_{i=1}^{n} k\bar{\rho}_i \, \Delta_i V$$

$$= \iiint\limits_{S} k\rho \, dV$$

$$= 4k \int_{0}^{\pi/2} \int_{0}^{\pi/2} \int_{0}^{a} \rho^3 \sin \phi \, d\rho \, d\theta \, d\phi$$

$$= a^4 k \int_{0}^{\pi/2} \int_{0}^{\pi/2} \sin \phi \, d\theta \, d\phi$$

$$= \tfrac{1}{2} a^4 k\pi \int_{0}^{\pi/2} \sin \phi \, d\phi$$

$$= \tfrac{1}{2} a^4 k\pi \left[-\cos \phi \right]_{0}^{\pi/2}$$

$$= \tfrac{1}{2} a^4 k\pi$$

<u>Conclusion:</u>   The mass of the solid hemisphere is $\tfrac{1}{2} a^4 k\pi$ kilograms. ◀

It is interesting to compare the solution of Example 5, which uses spherical coordinates, with what is entailed when using cartesian coordinates. By the latter method, a partition of S is formed by dividing S into rectangular boxes by drawing planes parallel to the coordinate planes. If

(u_i, v_i, w_i) is any point in the ith subregion, and because $\rho = \sqrt{x^2 + y^2 + z^2}$, then

$$
\begin{aligned}
M &= \lim_{\|\Delta\| \to 0} \sum_{i=1}^{n} k\sqrt{u_i^2 + v_i^2 + w_i^2} \, \Delta_i V \\
&= \iiint\limits_{S} k\sqrt{x^2 + y^2 + z^2} \, dV \\
&= 4k \int_0^a \int_0^{\sqrt{a^2 - z^2}} \int_0^{\sqrt{a^2 - y^2 - z^2}} \sqrt{x^2 + y^2 + z^2} \, dx \, dy \, dz
\end{aligned}
$$

The computation involved in evaluating this integral is obviously much more complicated than that using spherical coordinates.

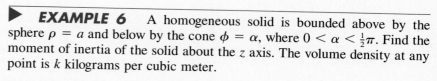

EXAMPLE 6   A homogeneous solid is bounded above by the sphere $\rho = a$ and below by the cone $\phi = \alpha$, where $0 < \alpha < \frac{1}{2}\pi$. Find the moment of inertia of the solid about the z axis. The volume density at any point is k kilograms per cubic meter.

Solution   The solid appears in Figure 9. Form a spherical partition of the solid and let $(\bar{\rho}_i, \bar{\theta}_i, \bar{\phi}_i)$ be a point in the ith subregion. The measure of the distance of the point $(\bar{\rho}_i, \bar{\theta}_i, \bar{\phi}_i)$ from the z axis is $\bar{\rho}_i \sin \bar{\phi}_i$. Hence if I_z kilogram-meters squared is the moment of inertia of the given solid about the z axis, then

$$
\begin{aligned}
I_z &= \lim_{\|\Delta\| \to 0} \sum_{i=1}^{n} (\bar{\rho}_i \sin \bar{\phi}_i)^2 k \, \Delta_i V \\
&= \iiint\limits_{S} k\rho^2 \sin^2 \phi \, dV \\
&= k \int_0^\alpha \int_0^{2\pi} \int_0^a (\rho^2 \sin^2 \phi)\rho^2 \sin \phi \, d\rho \, d\theta \, d\phi \\
&= \tfrac{1}{5} ka^5 \int_0^\alpha \int_0^{2\pi} \sin^3 \phi \, d\theta \, d\phi \\
&= \tfrac{2}{5} ka^5 \, \pi \int_0^\alpha \sin^3 \phi \, d\phi \\
&= \tfrac{2}{5} ka^5 \pi \left[-\cos \phi + \tfrac{1}{3} \cos^3 \phi \right]_0^\alpha \\
&= \tfrac{2}{15} ka^5 \pi (\cos^3 \alpha - 3 \cos \alpha + 2)
\end{aligned}
$$

Conclusion: The moment of inertia of the solid about the z axis is $\frac{2}{15} ka^5 \pi (\cos^3 \alpha - 3 \cos \alpha + 2)$ kg-m². ◀

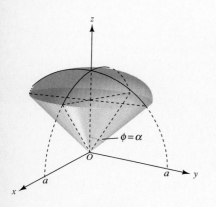

FIGURE 9

EXERCISES 13.6

In Exercises 1 through 6, evaluate the iterated integral.

1. $\int_0^{\pi/4} \int_0^a \int_0^{r\cos\theta} r \sec^3\theta \, dz \, dr \, d\theta$

2. $\int_0^{\pi/4} \int_{2\sin\theta}^{2\cos\theta} \int_0^{r\sin\theta} r^2 \cos\theta \, dz \, dr \, d\theta$

3. $\int_0^{\pi} \int_2^4 \int_0^1 re^z \, dz \, dr \, d\theta$

4. $\int_0^{2\pi} \int_0^{\pi} \int_0^2 \rho^3 \sin\phi \, d\rho \, d\phi \, d\theta$

5. $\int_0^{\pi/4} \int_0^{2a\cos\phi} \int_0^{2\pi} \rho^2 \sin\phi \, d\theta \, d\rho \, d\phi$

6. $\int_{\pi/4}^{\pi/2} \int_{\pi/4}^{\phi} \int_0^{a\csc\theta} \rho^3 \sin^2\theta \sin\phi \, d\rho \, d\theta \, d\phi$

7. Find the volume of the solid enclosed by the sphere $x^2 + y^2 + z^2 = a^2$ by using **(a)** cylindrical coordinates and **(b)** spherical coordinates.

8. If S is the solid in the first octant bounded by the sphere $x^2 + y^2 + z^2 = 16$ and the coordinate planes, evaluate the triple integral $\iiint\limits_S xyz \, dV$ by three methods: **(a)** using spherical coordinates; **(b)** using rectangular coordinates; **(c)** using cylindrical coordinates.

In Exercises 9 through 16, use cylindrical coordinates.

9. Find the volume of the solid in the first octant bounded by the cylinder $x^2 + y^2 = 1$ and the plane $z = x$.

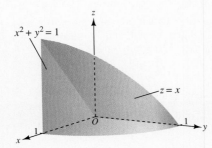

10. Find the volume of the solid bounded by the paraboloid $x^2 + y^2 + z = 1$ and the xy plane.

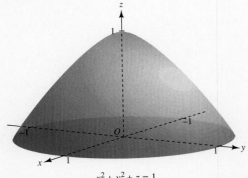

$x^2 + y^2 + z = 1$

11. Find the volume of the solid bounded by the paraboloid $x^2 + y^2 + z = 12$ and the plane $z = 8$.

12. Find the volume of the solid bounded by the cylinder $x^2 + y^2 = 2y$, the paraboloid $x^2 + y^2 = 2z$ and the xy plane.

13. Find the mass of the solid bounded by a sphere of radius a meters if the volume density varies as the square of the distance from the center. The volume density is measured in kilograms per cubic meter.

14. Find the mass of the solid in the first octant inside the cylinder $x^2 + y^2 = 4x$ and under the sphere $x^2 + y^2 + z^2 = 16$. The volume density varies as the distance from the xy plane, and it is measured in kilograms per cubic meter.

15. Find the moment of inertia with respect to the z axis of the homogeneous solid bounded by the cylinder $r = 5$, the cone $z = r$, and the xy plane. The volume density at any point is k slugs per cubic foot.

16. Find the moment of inertia of the solid bounded by a right circular cylinder of altitude h meters and radius a meters, with respect to the axis of the cylinder. The volume density varies as the distance from the axis of the cylinder, and it is measured in kilograms per cubic meter.

17. Find the mass of the solid in Exercise 13 by using spherical coordinates.

18. Use spherical coordinates to find the center of mass of the solid bounded by the hemisphere of Example 5. The volume density is the same as that in Example 5.

In Exercises 19 through 22, use spherical coordinates.

19. Find the volume of the solid inside the sphere $x^2 + y^2 + z^2 = 4z$ and above the cone $x^2 + y^2 = z^2$.

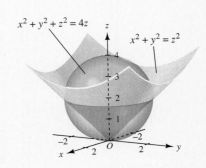

20. Find the volume of the solid inside the sphere
$x^2 + y^2 + z^2 = 2z$ and above the paraboloid
$x^2 + y^2 = z$.

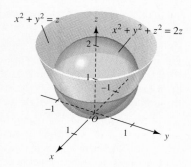

21. Find the moment of inertia with respect to the z axis
of the homogeneous solid inside the cylinder
$x^2 + y^2 - 2x = 0$, below the cone $x^2 + y^2 = z^2$,
and above the xy plane. The volume density at any
point is k kilograms per cubic meter.

22. Find the moment of inertia with respect to the z axis
of the homogeneous solid bounded by the sphere
$x^2 + y^2 + z^2 = 4$. The volume density at any point
is k slugs per cubic foot.

In Exercises 23 through 28, use the coordinate system that
you decide is best for the problem.

23. Find the mass of a solid hemisphere of radius 2 m if
the volume density varies as the distance from the
center of the base and is measured in kilograms per
cubic meter.

24. Find the mass of the homogeneous solid inside the
paraboloid $3x^2 + 3y^2 = z$ and outside the cone
$x^2 + y^2 = z^2$ if the constant volume density is k
kilograms per cubic meter.

25. Find the moment of inertia about a diameter of the
solid between two concentric spheres having radii a
feet and $2a$ feet. The volume density varies inversely
as the square of the distance from the center, and it
is measured in slugs per cubic foot.

26. Find the mass of the solid of Exercise 25. The volume density is the same as that in Exercise 25.

27. Find the center of mass of the solid inside the
paraboloid $x^2 + y^2 = z$ and outside the cone
$x^2 + y^2 = z^2$. The constant volume density is k kilograms per cubic meter.

28. Find the moment of inertia with respect to the z axis
of the homogeneous solid of Exercise 27.

In Exercises 29 through 32, evaluate the iterated integral
by using either cylindrical or spherical coordinates.

29. $\int_0^4 \int_0^3 \int_0^{\sqrt{9-x^2}} \sqrt{x^2 + y^2}\, dy\, dx\, dz$

30. $\int_0^1 \int_0^{\sqrt{1-x^2}} \int_0^{\sqrt{1-x^2-y^2}} \dfrac{z}{\sqrt{x^2 + y^2}}\, dz\, dy\, dx$

31. $\int_0^1 \int_0^{\sqrt{1-y^2}} \int_{\sqrt{x^2+y^2}}^{\sqrt{2-x^2-y^2}} z^2\, dz\, dx\, dy$

32. $\int_0^2 \int_0^{\sqrt{4-y^2}} \int_0^{\sqrt{4-x^2-y^2}} \dfrac{1}{x^2 + y^2 + z^2}\, dz\, dx\, dy$

CHAPTER 13 REVIEW

▶ SUGGESTIONS FOR REVIEW OF CHAPTER 13

1. Define the cylindrical coordinates of a point in three-
dimensional space.

2. Write the equations that express cartesian coordinates
in terms of cylindrical coordinates. Write the equations that express cylindrical coordinates in terms of
cartesian coordinates. Make a sketch showing how
these equations are obtained.

3. If the cylindrical-coordinate representation of a point
is (r, θ, z), describe each of the following surfaces
where c is a constant: (a) $r = c$; (b) $\theta = c$; (c) $z = c$.

4. Define the spherical coordinates of a point in three-dimensional space.

5. Write the equations that express cartesian coordinates
in terms of spherical coordinates. Write the equations
that express spherical coordinates in terms of cartesian
coordinates. Make a sketch showing how these equations are obtained.

6. If the spherical-coordinate representation of a point
is (ρ, θ, ϕ), describe each of the following surfaces
where c is a constant (a) $\rho = c$; (b) $\theta = c$; (c) $\phi = c$.

7. Define the limit of a Riemann sum of a function of two
variables.

8. Define the double integral of a function of two variables
on a closed rectangular region in the plane.

9. How can the definition in Suggestion 8 be extended to the double integral of a function over a more general region in the plane?

10. What is a geometrical interpretation of the double integral?

11. Make up an example showing how the volume of a solid is computed by a double integral.

12. How are iterated integrals used to evaluate double integrals? Make up an example.

13. Make up an example showing how the area of a plane region can be computed by a double integral.

14. Make up an example showing how the mass and center of mass of a lamina are computed by double integrals.

15. Make up an example showing how the moment of inertia about an axis is computed by a double integral.

16. Make up an example showing how the polar moment of inertia is computed by a double integral.

17. Make up an example showing how the radius of gyration of a lamina about an axis is computed by a double integral.

18. Make up an example showing how the area of a surface is computed by a double integral.

19. State the formula involving a single integral that gives the area of a surface of revolution. Make up an example showing the application of this formula.

20. Make up an example showing how a double integral in polar coordinates is used to compute the volume of a solid.

21. Make up an example showing how double integrals in polar coordinates are used to compute the mass and center of mass of a lamina.

22. Make up an example showing how the area of the region in the polar plane can be computed by double integration.

23. How can a double integral in rectangular coordinates be changed to a double integral in polar coordinates? Make up an example showing a case in which such a change in coordinates is desirable.

24. Define the triple integral of a function of three variables on a closed rectangular parallelepiped.

25. How are iterated integrals used to evaluate triple integrals? Make up an example.

26. Make up an example showing how the volume of a solid can be computed by triple integration.

27. Define a triple integral in cylindrical coordinates and a triple integral in spherical coordinates.

28. When is it advantageous to use a triple integral in cylindrical coordinates instead of one in rectangular coordinates? Make up an example.

29. When is it advantageous to use a triple integral in spherical coordinates instead of one in rectangular coordinates? Make up an example.

▶ MISCELLANEOUS EXERCISES FOR CHAPTER 13

1. Find a set of cylindrical coordinates for the point having spherical coordinates $(3, \pi, \frac{1}{3}\pi)$.

2. Find a set of spherical coordinates for the point having cartesian coordinates $(-3, \sqrt{3}, 2)$.

3. Find an equation in cylindrical coordinates of the graph of the equation: (a) $(x + y)^2 + 1 = z$; (b) $25x^2 + 4y^2 = 100$.

4. Find an equation in spherical coordinates of the graph of the equation: (a) $x^2 + y^2 + 4z^2 = 4$; (b) $4x^2 - 4y^2 + 9z^2 = 36$.

In Exercises 5 through 12, evaluate the iterated integral.

5. $\int_0^1 \int_x^{\sqrt{x}} x^2 y \, dy \, dx$

6. $\int_{-2}^2 \int_{-\sqrt{4-y^2}}^{\sqrt{4-y^2}} xy \, dx \, dy$

7. $\int_0^{\pi/2} \int_0^{2\sin\theta} r \cos^2\theta \, dr \, d\theta$

8. $\int_0^\pi \int_0^{3(1+\cos\theta)} r^2 \sin\theta \, dr \, d\theta$

9. $\int_0^1 \int_0^z \int_0^{y+z} e^x e^y e^z \, dx \, dy \, dz$

10. $\int_1^2 \int_3^x \int_0^{\sqrt{3}\,y} \dfrac{y}{y^2 + z^2} \, dz \, dy \, dx$

11. $\int_0^{\pi/2} \int_{\pi/6}^{\pi/2} \int_0^2 \rho^3 \sin\phi \cos\phi \, d\rho \, d\phi \, d\theta$

12. $\int_0^a \int_0^{\pi/2} \int_0^{\sqrt{a^2-z^2}} zre^{-r^2} \, dr \, d\theta \, dz$

In Exercises 13 through 16, evaluate the multiple integral.

13. $\iint_R xy \, dA$; R is the region in the first quadrant bounded by the circle $x^2 + y^2 = 1$ and the coordinate axes.

14. $\iint_R (x + y) \, dA$; R is the region bounded by the curve $y = \cos x$ and the x axis from $x = -\frac{1}{2}\pi$ to $x = \frac{1}{2}\pi$.

15. $\iiint_S z^2 \, dV$; S is the region bounded by the cylinders $x^2 + z = 1$ and $y^2 + z = 1$ and the xy plane.

16. $\iiint_S y \cos(x + z) \, dV$; S is the region bounded by the cylinder $x = y^2$ and the planes $x + z = \frac{1}{2}\pi$, $y = 0$, and $z = 0$.

17. Evaluate by polar coordinates the double integral

$$\iint\limits_{R} \frac{1}{x^2 + y^2} \, dA$$

where R is the region in the first quadrant bounded by the two circles $x^2 + y^2 = 1$ and $x^2 + y^2 = 4$.

18. Evaluate by polar coordinates the iterated integral

$$\int_0^1 \int_{\sqrt{3}y}^{\sqrt{4-y^2}} \ln(x^2 + y^2) \, dx \, dy$$

In Exercises 19 and 20, evaluate the iterated integral by reversing the order of integration.

19. $\int_0^1 \int_x^1 \sin y^2 \, dy \, dx$ 20. $\int_0^1 \int_0^{\cos^{-1}y} e^{\sin x} \, dx \, dy$

In Exercises 21 and 22, use double integrals to find the area of the region bounded by the curves in the xy plane. Sketch the region.

21. $y = x^2$ and $y = x^4$ 22. $y = \sqrt{x}$ and $y = x^3$

In Exercises 23 and 24, evaluate the iterated integral by changing to either cylindrical or spherical coordinates.

23. $\int_0^3 \int_0^{\sqrt{9-x^2}} \int_0^2 \sqrt{x^2 + y^2} \, dz \, dy \, dx$

24. $\int_0^2 \int_0^{\sqrt{4-x^2}} \int_0^{\sqrt{4-x^2-y^2}} z\sqrt{4 - x^2 - y^2} \, dz \, dy \, dx$

25. Use double integration to find the area of the region in the first quadrant bounded by the parabolas $x^2 = 4y$ and $x^2 = 8 - 4y$. Integrate first with respect to x.

26. Use double integration to find the area of the region in the xy plane bounded by the parabolas $y = 9 - x^2$ and $y = x^2 + 1$. Integrate first with respect to x.

27. Use double integration to find the area of the region in Exercise 25 by integrating first with respect to y.

28. Use double integration to find the area of the region in Exercise 26 by integrating first with respect to y.

29. Use double integration to find the volume of the solid bounded by the planes $x = y$, $y = 0$, $z = 0$, $x = 1$, and $z = 1$. Integrate first with respect to x.

30. Use double integration to find the volume of the solid above the xy plane bounded by the cylinder $x^2 + y^2 = 16$ and the plane $z = 2y$. Integrate first with respect to x.

31. Use double integration to find the volume of the solid in Exercise 29 by integrating first with respect to y.

32. Use double integration to find the volume of the solid in Exercise 30 by integrating first with respect to y.

33. Find the volume of the solid above the xy plane bounded by the surfaces $x^2 = 4y$, $y^2 = 4x$, and $x^2 = z - y$.

34. Find the mass of the lamina in the shape of the region bounded by the parabola $y = x^2$ and the line $x - y + 2 = 0$ if the area density at any point is x^2y^2 kilograms per square meter.

35. Find the area of the surface of the cylinder $x^2 + y^2 = 9$ lying in the first octant and between the planes $x = z$ and $3x = z$.

36. Find the area of the surface of the part of the cylinder $x^2 + y^2 = a^2$ that lies inside the cylinder $y^2 + z^2 = a^2$.

37. Use double integration to find the area of the region inside the circle $r = 1$ and to the right of the parabola $r(1 + \cos \theta) = 1$.

38. Find the mass of the lamina in the shape of the region exterior to the limaçon $r = 3 - \cos \theta$ and interior to the circle $r = 5 \cos \theta$ if the area density at any point is $2|\sin \theta|$ kilograms per square meter.

39. Find the center of mass of the rectangular lamina bounded by the lines $x = 3$ and $y = 2$ and the coordinate axes if the area density at any point is xy^2 kilograms per square meter.

40. Find the center of mass of the lamina in the shape of the region bounded by the parabolas $x^2 = 4 + 4y$ and $x^2 = 4 - 8y$ if the area density at any point is kx^2 kilograms per square meter.

41. Find the mass of the lamina in the shape of the region bounded by the polar axis and the curve $r = \cos 2\theta$, where $0 \leq \theta \leq \frac{1}{4}\pi$. The area density at any point is $r\theta$ kilograms per square meter.

42. Find the moment of inertia about the x axis of the lamina in the shape of the region bounded by the circle $x^2 + y^2 = a^2$ if the area density at any point is $k\sqrt{x^2 + y^2}$ kilograms per square meter.

43. Use cylindrical coordinates to find the volume of the solid bounded by the paraboloid $x^2 + y^2 = 4z$, the cylinder $x^2 + y^2 = 4ay$, and the plane $z = 0$.

44. Use spherical coordinates to find the mass of a spherical solid of radius a meters if the volume density at each point is proportional to the distance of the point from the center of the sphere. The volume density is measured in kilograms per cubic meter.

45. Use triple integration to find the volume of the solid bounded by the plane $z = 1$ and the smaller segment of the sphere $x^2 + y^2 + z^2 = 4$ cut off by this plane.

46. Use triple integration to find the volume of the solid in the first octant bounded by the plane $y + z = 8$, the cylinder $y = 2x^2$, the xy plane, and the yz plane.

47. Find the moment of inertia about the x axis of the lamina in the shape of the region bounded by the

curve $y = e^x$, the line $x = 2$, and the coordinate axes if the area density at any point is xy kilograms per square meter.

48. Find the moment of inertia of the lamina of Exercise 47 about the y axis.

49. Find the moment of inertia with respect to the $\frac{1}{2}\pi$ axis of the homogeneous lamina in the shape of the region bounded by the curve $r^2 = 4 \cos 2\theta$ if the area density at any point is k kilograms per square meter.

50. Find the mass of the lamina of Exercise 49.

51. Find the polar moment of inertia and the corresponding radius of gyration of the lamina of Exercise 49.

52. Find the moment of inertia about the y axis of the lamina in the shape of the region bounded by the parabola $y = x - x^2$ and the line $x + y = 0$ if the area density at any point is $(x + y)$ kilograms per square meter.

53. Find the mass of the solid bounded by the spheres $x^2 + y^2 + z^2 = 4$ and $x^2 + y^2 + z^2 = 9$ if the volume density at any point is $k\sqrt{x^2 + y^2 + z^2}$ kilograms per cubic meter.

54. Find the moment of inertia about the z axis of the solid of Exercise 53.

55. The homogeneous solid bounded by the cone $z^2 = 4x^2 + 4y^2$ between the planes $z = 0$ and $z = 4$ has a volume density at any point of k kilograms per cubic meter. Find the moment of inertia about the z axis for this solid.

56. Find the center of mass of the solid bounded by the sphere $x^2 + y^2 + z^2 - 6z = 0$ and the cone $x^2 + y^2 = z^2$, and above the cone, if the volume density at any point is kz kilograms per cubic meter.

INTRODUCTION TO THE CALCULUS OF VECTOR FIELDS

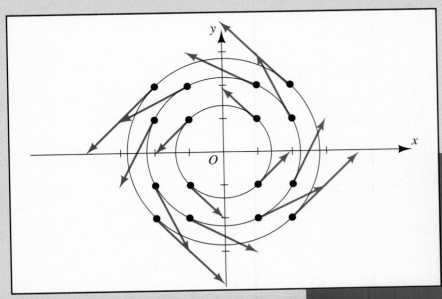

LOOKING AHEAD

This final chapter serves as a preview to topics developed fully in advanced calculus. As was the case with Chapter 13, the discussion in many places is informal and intuitive.

Vector fields, which are functions that associate vectors with points in space, and the *divergence* and *curl* of a vector are introduced in Section 14.1. Then in Section 14.2, *line integrals* are applied to find the work done by a force field in moving a particle along a curve. Line integrals independent of the path are discussed in Section 14.3, where an analogue of the second fundamental theorem of the calculus is presented for line integrals. Also in Section 14.3, the *law of conservation of energy*, a major concept in physics, is proved.

Green's theorem on line integrals over curves forms the subject matter of Section 14.4. This theorem is one of three important theorems in vector calculus named for mathematicians and scientists. The other two, *Gauss's divergence theorem* and *Stokes's theorem* are presented in the final section following Section 14.5 on *surface integrals*. Applications of these theorems in physics, chemistry, and engineering belong to courses in those disciplines. We include here applications of surface integrals to finding the mass of a surface and the flux of a velocity field across a surface.

14.1 VECTOR FIELDS

As preparation for our study of vector fields, we show how to determine if a given vector-valued function is the gradient of some real-valued function f, and if it is, how to find such a function f. First let us consider the problem of how to obtain f if its gradient is known. That is, we are given

$$\nabla f(x, y) = f_x(x, y)\mathbf{i} + f_y(x, y)\mathbf{j} \tag{1}$$

and we wish to find $f(x, y)$.

▷ **ILLUSTRATION 1**   Suppose

$$\nabla f(x, y) = (y^2 + 2x + 4)\mathbf{i} + (2xy + 4y - 5)\mathbf{j} \tag{2}$$

Then because Equation (1) must be satisfied, it follows that

$$f_x(x, y) = y^2 + 2x + 4 \tag{3}$$
$$f_y(x, y) = 2xy + 4y - 5 \tag{4}$$

By integrating both sides of (3) with respect to x,

$$f(x, y) = y^2x + x^2 + 4x + g(y) \tag{5}$$

Observe that the "constant" of integration is a function of y and independent of x because we are integrating with respect to x. If we now differentiate both sides of (5) partially with respect to y, we obtain

$$f_y(x, y) = 2xy + g'(y) \tag{6}$$

Equations (4) and (6) give two expressions for $f_y(x, y)$. Hence

$$2xy + 4y - 5 = 2xy + g'(y)$$

Therefore

$$g'(y) = 4y - 5$$
$$g(y) = 2y^2 - 5y + K$$

Substituting this value of $g(y)$ into (5) we have

$$f(x, y) = y^2x + x^2 + 4x + 2y^2 - 5y + K$$

where K is an arbitrary constant.   ◀

Every vector of the form $M(x, y)\mathbf{i} + N(x, y)\mathbf{j}$ is not necessarily a gradient, as shown in the next illustration.

▷ **ILLUSTRATION 2**   We show that there is no function f such that

$$\nabla f(x, y) = 3y\mathbf{i} - 2x\mathbf{j} \tag{7}$$

Assume that there is such a function. Then it follows that

$$f_x(x, y) = 3y \tag{8}$$
$$f_y(x, y) = -2x \tag{9}$$

We integrate both sides of (8) with respect to x and obtain

$$f(x, y) = 3xy + g(y)$$

We partially differentiate both sides of this equation with respect to y:

$$f_y(x, y) = 3x + g'(y)$$

Equating the right sides of this equation and (9) we obtain

$$3x + g'(y) = -2x$$
$$g'(y) = -5x$$

If both sides of this equation are differentiated with respect to x, it must follow that

$$0 = -5$$

which, of course, is not true. Thus the assumption that $3y\mathbf{i} - 2x\mathbf{j}$ is a gradient leads to a contradiction. ◀

We now investigate a condition that must be satisfied for a vector to be a gradient.

Suppose that M_y and N_x are continuous on an open disk B in R^2. If

$$M(x, y)\mathbf{i} + N(x, y)\mathbf{j} \tag{10}$$

is a gradient on B, then there is a function f such that

$$f_x(x, y) = M(x, y) \tag{11}$$
$$f_y(x, y) = N(x, y) \tag{12}$$

for all (x, y) in B. Because $M_y(x, y)$ exists on B, then, from (11),

$$M_y(x, y) = f_{xy}(x, y) \tag{13}$$

Furthermore, because $N_x(x, y)$ exists on B, then from (12)

$$N_x(x, y) = f_{yx}(x, y) \tag{14}$$

Because M_y and N_x are continuous on B, their equivalents f_{xy} and f_{yx} are also continuous on B. Thus, from Theorem 12.3.3, $f_{xy}(x, y) = f_{yx}(x, y)$ at all points in B. Therefore the left sides of (13) and (14) are equal at all points in B. We have proved that if M_y and N_x are continuous on an open disk B in R^2, a necessary condition for vector (10) to be a gradient on B is that

$$M_y(x, y) = N_x(x, y) \tag{15}$$

This equation is also a sufficient condition for vector (10) to be a gradient on B. If (15) holds, we can show how to find a function f such that vector (10) is a gradient. However, the proof that, whenever (15) holds, such a function exists belongs to a course in advanced calculus. The method for finding f is a generalization of that used in Illustration 1. We have the following theorem.

14.1.1 Theorem

Suppose that M and N are functions of two variables x and y defined on an open disk $B((x_0, y_0); r)$ in R^2, and M_y and N_x are continuous on B. Then the vector

$$M(x, y)\mathbf{i} + N(x, y)\mathbf{j}$$

is a gradient on B if and only if

$$M_y(x, y) = N_x(x, y)$$

at all points in B.

▷ **ILLUSTRATION 3**

(a) We apply Theorem 14.1.1 to the vector on the right side of Equation (2) in Illustration 1. Let

$$M(x, y) = y^2 + 2x + 4 \qquad N(x, y) = 2xy + 4y - 5$$
$$M_y(x, y) = 2y \qquad\qquad N_x(x, y) = 2y$$

Thus $M_y(x, y) = N_x(x, y)$, and therefore the vector is a gradient.

(b) If we apply Theorem 14.1.1 to the vector on the right side of Equation (7) in Illustration 2, with $M(x, y) = 3y$ and $N(x, y) = -2x$, we obtain

$$M_y(x, y) = 3 \qquad N_x(x, y) = -2$$

Hence $M_y(x, y) \neq N_x(x, y)$; thus the vector is not a gradient. ◀

▶ **EXAMPLE 1** Determine if the vector

$$(e^{-y} - 2x)\mathbf{i} - (xe^{-y} + \sin y)\mathbf{j}$$

is a gradient $\nabla f(x, y)$, and if it is, then find $f(x, y)$.

Solution We apply Theorem 14.1.1. Let

$$M(x, y) = e^{-y} - 2x \qquad N(x, y) = -xe^{-y} - \sin y$$
$$M_y(x, y) = -e^{-y} \qquad\quad N_x(x, y) = -e^{-y}$$

Therefore $M_y(x, y) = N_x(x, y)$; so the given vector is a gradient $\nabla f(x, y)$. Furthermore,

$$f_x(x, y) = e^{-y} - 2x \tag{16}$$
$$f_y(x, y) = -xe^{-y} - \sin y \tag{17}$$

Integrating both sides of (16) with respect to x we obtain

$$f(x, y) = xe^{-y} - x^2 + g(y) \tag{18}$$

where $g(y)$ is independent of x. We now partially differentiate both sides of (18) with respect to y and have

$$f_y(x, y) = -xe^{-y} + g'(y)$$

We equate the right members of this equation and (17) and get

$$-xe^{-y} + g'(y) = -xe^{-y} - \sin y$$
$$g'(y) = -\sin y$$
$$g(y) = \cos y + K$$

We substitute this expression for $g(y)$ into (18) and have

$$f(x, y) = xe^{-y} - x^2 + \cos y + K \qquad \blacktriangleleft$$

The following theorem is an extension of Theorem 14.1.1 to functions of three variables.

14.1.2 Theorem

Let M, N, and R be functions of three variables x, y, and z defined on an open ball $B((x_0, y_0, z_0); r)$ in R^3, and M_y, M_z, N_x, N_z, R_x, and R_y are continuous on B. Then the vector $M(x, y, z)\mathbf{i} + N(x, y, z)\mathbf{j} + R(x, y, z)\mathbf{k}$ is a gradient on B if and only if $M_y(x, y, z) = N_x(x, y, z)$, $M_z(x, y, z) = R_x(x, y, z)$, and $N_z(x, y, z) = R_y(x, y, z)$.

The proof of the "only if" part of this theorem is similar to the proof of the "only if" part of Theorem 14.1.1 and is left as an exercise (see Exercise 49). The proof of the "if" part is beyond the scope of this book.

▶ **EXAMPLE 2** Determine if the following vector is a gradient $\nabla f(x, y, z)$, and if it is, then find $f(x, y, z)$:

$$(e^x \sin z + 2yz)\mathbf{i} + (2xz + 2y)\mathbf{j} + (e^x \cos z + 2xy + 3z^2)\mathbf{k}$$

Solution We apply Theorem 14.1.2. Let

$$M(x, y, z) = e^x \sin z + 2yz \qquad N(x, y, z) = 2xz + 2y \qquad R(x, y, z) = e^x \cos z + 2xy + 3z^2$$
$$M_y(x, y, z) = 2z \qquad N_x(x, y, z) = 2z \qquad R_x(x, y, z) = e^x \cos z + 2y$$
$$M_z(x, y, z) = e^x \cos z + 2y \qquad N_z(x, y, z) = 2x \qquad R_y(x, y, z) = 2x$$

Therefore

$$M_y(x, y, z) = N_x(x, y, z) \qquad M_z(x, y, z) = R_x(x, y, z) \qquad N_z(x, y, z) = R_y(x, y, z)$$

Thus the given vector is a gradient $\nabla f(x, y, z)$. Furthermore,

$$f_x(x, y, z) = e^x \sin z + 2yz \qquad (19)$$
$$f_y(x, y, z) = 2xz + 2y \qquad (20)$$
$$f_z(x, y, z) = e^x \cos z + 2xy + 3z^2 \qquad (21)$$

Integrating both sides of (19) with respect to x we have

$$f(x, y, z) = e^x \sin z + 2xyz + g(y, z) \qquad (22)$$

where $g(y, z)$ is independent of x. We partially differentiate both sides of (22) with respect to y and obtain

$$f_y(x, y, z) = 2xz + g_y(y, z)$$

Equating the right sides of this equation and (20) we have

$$2xz + g_y(y, z) = 2xz + 2y$$
$$g_y(y, z) = 2y$$

We now integrate both sides of this equation with respect to y and get

$$g(y, z) = y^2 + h(z) \tag{23}$$

where h is independent of x and y. Substituting from (23) into (22) we obtain

$$f(x, y, z) = e^x \sin z + 2xyz + y^2 + h(z) \tag{24}$$

We now partially differentiate with respect to z both sides of (24):

$$f_z(x, y, z) = e^x \cos z + 2xy + h'(z)$$

Equating the right members of this equation and (21) we have

$$e^x \cos z + 2xy + h'(z) = e^x \cos z + 2xy + 3z^2$$
$$h'(z) = 3z^2$$
$$h(z) = z^3 + K$$

We substitute $z^3 + K$ for $h(z)$ in (24) and obtain

$$f(x, y, z) = e^x \sin z + 2xyz + y^2 + z^3 + K \qquad \blacktriangleleft$$

A *vector field* associates a vector with a point in space. For instance, if **F** is a vector-valued function defined on some open ball B in R^3 such that

$$\mathbf{F}(x, y, z) = M(x, y, z)\mathbf{i} + N(x, y, z)\mathbf{j} + R(x, y, z)\mathbf{k} \tag{25}$$

then **F** associates with each point (x, y, z) in B a vector, and **F** is called a **vector field.** This vector field has as its domain a subset of R^3 and as its range a subset of V_3. If the domain of a vector field is a set of points in a plane and its range is a set of vectors in V_2, then the vector field has an equation of the form

$$\mathbf{F}(x, y) = M(x, y)\mathbf{i} + N(x, y)\mathbf{j}$$

If, instead of a vector, a scalar is associated with a point in space, we have a scalar field; thus a scalar field is a real-valued function. An example of a scalar field is obtained by expressing the temperature at a point as a function of the coordinates of the point.

For an example of a vector field, consider the flow of a fluid, such as water through a pipe or blood through an artery. Assume that the fluid consists of infinitely many particles and that the velocity of a particle depends only on its position; thus the velocity is independent of time, and because of this fact the fluid flow is designated as a *steady-state* fluid flow. At a point (x, y, z) the velocity of the fluid is given by $\mathbf{F}(x, y, z)$ defined by an equation of the form (25). Thus **F** is a vector field called the **velocity field** of the fluid. Velocity fields can describe other motions, such as that of a wind or the rotation of a wheel. The vector fields that occur in this book will all be independent of time; they are termed **steady-state vector fields.**

We cannot show in a figure representations of all the vectors of a particular vector field. However, by drawing representations of some of the vectors we may get a visual description of the vector field, as indicated in the following example.

▶ **EXAMPLE 3** (a) Show on a figure the representations, having initial point at (x, y), of the vectors in the vector field

$$\mathbf{F}(x, y) = -y\mathbf{i} + x\mathbf{j}$$

where x is ± 1 or ± 2 and y is ± 1 or ± 2. (b) Prove that each representation is tangent to a circle having its center at the origin and has a length equal to the radius of the circle.

Solution

(a) Table 1 gives the vectors $\mathbf{F}(x, y)$ associated with the sixteen points (x, y). Representations of these vectors appear in Figure 1.

(b) Let

$$\mathbf{R}(x, y) = x\mathbf{i} + y\mathbf{j}$$

be the position vector whose terminal point is at (x, y). Then

$$\mathbf{R}(x, y) \cdot \mathbf{F}(x, y) = (x\mathbf{i} + y\mathbf{i}) \cdot (-y\mathbf{i} + x\mathbf{j})$$
$$= -xy + xy$$
$$= 0$$

Therefore $\mathbf{R}$ and $\mathbf{F}$ are orthogonal. Thus the representation of $\mathbf{F}$ whose initial point is at (x, y) is tangent to the circle having its center at the origin and radius $\|\mathbf{R}(x, y)\|$. Because

$$\|\mathbf{F}(x, y)\| = \sqrt{(-y)^2 + x^2}$$
$$= \|\mathbf{R}(x, y)\|$$

the length of each representation is equal to the radius of the circle. ◀

The vector field in Example 3 is similar to a velocity field determined by a wheel rotating at the origin.

An example of a vector field in V_3 arises from Newton's inverse square law of gravitational attraction. This law states that the measure of the magnitude of the gravitational force between two particles of mass M units and m units, respectively, is

$$\frac{GMm}{d^2}$$

where d units is the distance between the particles and G is the gravitational constant. Thus if a particle of mass M units is at the origin and a particle of mass 1 unit ($m = 1$) is at the point $P(x, y, z)$, then if $\mathbf{F}(x, y, z)$ is the gravitational force exerted by the particle at the origin on the particle at P,

$$\|\mathbf{F}(x, y, z)\| = \frac{GM(1)}{\|\mathbf{R}(x, y, z)\|^2}$$

Table 1

(x, y)	$\mathbf{F}(x, y)$
$(1, 1)$	$-\mathbf{i} + \mathbf{j}$
$(1, -1)$	$\mathbf{i} + \mathbf{j}$
$(-1, 1)$	$-\mathbf{i} - \mathbf{j}$
$(-1, -1)$	$\mathbf{i} - \mathbf{j}$
$(1, 2)$	$-2\mathbf{i} + \mathbf{j}$
$(1, -2)$	$2\mathbf{i} + \mathbf{j}$
$(-1, 2)$	$-2\mathbf{i} - \mathbf{j}$
$(-1, -2)$	$2\mathbf{i} - \mathbf{j}$
$(2, 1)$	$-\mathbf{i} + 2\mathbf{j}$
$(2, -1)$	$\mathbf{i} + 2\mathbf{j}$
$(-2, 1)$	$-\mathbf{i} - 2\mathbf{j}$
$(-2, -1)$	$\mathbf{i} - 2\mathbf{j}$
$(2, 2)$	$-2\mathbf{i} + 2\mathbf{j}$
$(2, -2)$	$2\mathbf{i} + 2\mathbf{j}$
$(-2, 2)$	$-2\mathbf{i} - 2\mathbf{j}$
$(-2, -2)$	$2\mathbf{i} - 2\mathbf{j}$

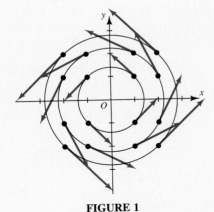

FIGURE 1

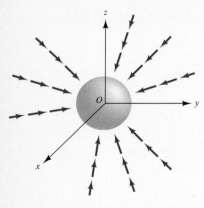

FIGURE 2

where $\mathbf{R}(x, y, z) = x\mathbf{i} + y\mathbf{j} + z\mathbf{k}$. To obtain the force vector $\mathbf{F}(x, y, z)$, we also need the direction of $\mathbf{F}$. Because this direction is toward the origin, it is the same as the direction of the unit vector $-\dfrac{1}{\|\mathbf{R}\|}\mathbf{R}$. With this direction and the magnitude given above, we have

$$\mathbf{F}(x, y, z) = \frac{GM}{\|\mathbf{R}(x, y, z)\|^2}\left(-\frac{\mathbf{R}(x, y, z)}{\|\mathbf{R}(x, y, z)\|}\right)$$

Because $\|\mathbf{R}(x, y, z)\| = \sqrt{x^2 + y^2 + z^2}$, we obtain

$$\mathbf{F}(x, y, z) = \frac{-GM}{(x^2 + y^2 + z^2)^{3/2}}(x\mathbf{i} + y\mathbf{j} + z\mathbf{k}) \qquad \textbf{(26)}$$

The vector field defined by (26) is called a **force field.** Figure 2 shows some of the representations of the vectors in this force field where the object at the origin is a sphere (for instance, the earth) and $\|\mathbf{R}\|$ is greater than the radius of the sphere. Each representation points toward the origin. Representations of vectors at points near the origin are longer than those at points farther away from the origin, and the lengths are the same at points having the same distance from the origin. With these properties, the force field defined by (26) is designated as a *central force field.*

The gradient of a scalar field is a vector field. If ϕ is a scalar field and $\mathbf{F}$ is the vector field defined by $\mathbf{F} = \nabla\phi$, then $\mathbf{F}$ is called a **gradient vector field,** and ϕ is termed a **potential function** for $\mathbf{F}$. A gradient vector field is also called a **conservative vector field.** The terminology *conservative* will be apparent after you read Section 14.3.

▷ **ILLUSTRATION 4**   Consider the vector field defined by

$$\mathbf{F}(x, y) = (y^2 + 2x + 4)\mathbf{i} + (2xy + 4y - 5)\mathbf{j}$$

From Illustration 1, if

$$\phi(x, y) = y^2x + x^2 + 4x + 2y^2 - 5y + K$$

then

$$\mathbf{F}(x, y) = \nabla\phi(x, y)$$

Thus $\mathbf{F}$ is a conservative vector field and ϕ is a potential function for $\mathbf{F}$.   ◀

The following illustration shows that the gravitational force field defined by (26) is conservative.

▷ **ILLUSTRATION 5**   In Example 6 of Section 12.6, we showed that if

$$V(x, y, z) = \frac{1}{\sqrt{x^2 + y^2 + z^2}}$$

then

$$\nabla V(x, y, z) = \frac{-1}{(x^2 + y^2 + z^2)^{3/2}}(x\mathbf{i} + y\mathbf{j} + z\mathbf{k})$$

Thus if

$$\phi(x, y, z) = \frac{GM}{\sqrt{x^2 + y^2 + z^2}}$$

$$\nabla\phi(x, y, z) = \frac{-GM}{(x^2 + y^2 + z^2)^{3/2}}(x\mathbf{i} + y\mathbf{j} + z\mathbf{k})$$

Comparing this equation and (26) we observe that

$$\mathbf{F}(x, y, z) = \nabla\phi(x, y, z)$$

Therefore $\mathbf{F}$ is conservative and ϕ is a potential function for $\mathbf{F}$. ◄

In the above two illustrations it was a simple matter to prove that the vector field was conservative because we knew a function ϕ for which $\mathbf{F}$ is its gradient. To decide if a given vector field is conservative, and if it is, to find a potential function, apply Theorems 14.1.1 and 14.1.2 as in Examples 1 and 2.

Two fields involving derivatives are associated with a vector field $\mathbf{F}$. One is called the *curl* of $\mathbf{F}$, which is a vector field, and the other is called the *divergence* of $\mathbf{F}$, which is a scalar field. Before giving their definitions, we show how the symbol ∇ is used as an operator.

If f is a scalar function of three variables x, y, and z, the gradient of f is

$$\nabla f(x, y, z) = f_x(x, y, z)\mathbf{i} + f_y(x, y, z)\mathbf{j} + f_z(x, y, z)\mathbf{k} \tag{27}$$

We shall now let the del operator ∇ in three dimensions be used to denote

$$\mathbf{i}\frac{\partial}{\partial x} + \mathbf{j}\frac{\partial}{\partial y} + \mathbf{k}\frac{\partial}{\partial z}$$

Therefore, ∇ operating on the scalar function f means

$$\nabla f = \frac{\partial f}{\partial x}\mathbf{i} + \frac{\partial f}{\partial y}\mathbf{j} + \frac{\partial f}{\partial z}\mathbf{k}$$

which agrees with (27).

14.1.3 Definition of the Curl of a Vector Field

Let F be a vector field on some open ball B in R^3 such that

$$\mathbf{F}(x, y, z) = M(x, y, z)\mathbf{i} + N(x, y, z)\mathbf{j} + R(x, y, z)\mathbf{k}$$

Then the **curl** of $\mathbf{F}$, denoted by curl $\mathbf{F}$, is defined by

$$\text{curl } \mathbf{F}(x, y, z) = \left(\frac{\partial R}{\partial y} - \frac{\partial N}{\partial z}\right)\mathbf{i} + \left(\frac{\partial M}{\partial z} - \frac{\partial R}{\partial x}\right)\mathbf{j} + \left(\frac{\partial N}{\partial x} - \frac{\partial M}{\partial y}\right)\mathbf{k}$$

if these partial derivatives exist.

A mnemonic device for computing curl $\mathbf{F}$ is to extend the notation for the cross product of two vectors to the "cross product" of the operator ∇ and the vector field $\mathbf{F}$ and write

$$\text{curl } \mathbf{F} = \nabla \times \mathbf{F}$$

$$= \begin{vmatrix} \mathbf{i} & \mathbf{j} & \mathbf{k} \\ \dfrac{\partial}{\partial x} & \dfrac{\partial}{\partial y} & \dfrac{\partial}{\partial z} \\ M & N & R \end{vmatrix}$$

As we indicated when determinant notation was first used for the cross product of two vectors, the elements of the determinant were not all real numbers as is customary. In the above "determinant" the first row contains vectors, the second row contains partial derivative operators, and the third row consists of scalar functions.

> ► **EXAMPLE 4**   Find curl $\mathbf{F}$ if $\mathbf{F}$ is the vector field defined by
>
> $$\mathbf{F}(x, y, z) = e^{2x}\mathbf{i} + 3x^2yz\mathbf{j} + (2y^2z + x)\mathbf{k}$$

Solution

$$\text{curl } \mathbf{F}(x, y, z) = \begin{vmatrix} \mathbf{i} & \mathbf{j} & \mathbf{k} \\ \dfrac{\partial}{\partial x} & \dfrac{\partial}{\partial y} & \dfrac{\partial}{\partial z} \\ e^{2x} & 3x^2yz & 2y^2z + x \end{vmatrix}$$

$$= (4yz - 3x^2y)\mathbf{i} + (0 - 1)\mathbf{j} + (6xyz - 0)\mathbf{k}$$

$$= (4yz - 3x^2y)\mathbf{i} - \mathbf{j} + 6xyz\mathbf{k} \qquad ◄$$

14.1.4 Definition of the Divergence of a Vector Field

Let F be a vector field on some open ball B in R^3 such that

$$\mathbf{F}(x, y, z) = M(x, y, z)\mathbf{i} + N(x, y, z)\mathbf{j} + R(x, y, z)\mathbf{k}$$

Then the **divergence** of $\mathbf{F}$, denoted by div $\mathbf{F}$, is defined by

$$\text{div } \mathbf{F}(x, y, z) = \frac{\partial M}{\partial x} + \frac{\partial N}{\partial y} + \frac{\partial R}{\partial z}$$

if these partial derivatives exist.

We extend the notation for the dot product of two vectors to the "dot product" of the operator ∇ and the vector field $\mathbf{F}$ to compute the divergence of $\mathbf{F}$, and we write

$$\text{div } \mathbf{F} = \nabla \cdot \mathbf{F}$$

$$= \left(\mathbf{i}\frac{\partial}{\partial x} + \mathbf{j}\frac{\partial}{\partial y} + \mathbf{k}\frac{\partial}{\partial z} \right) \cdot (M\mathbf{i} + N\mathbf{j} + R\mathbf{k})$$

$$= \frac{\partial M}{\partial x} + \frac{\partial N}{\partial y} + \frac{\partial R}{\partial z}$$

▶ **EXAMPLE 5** Find div **F** if **F** is the vector field of Example 4.

Solution

$$\text{div } \mathbf{F}(x, y, z) = \nabla \cdot \mathbf{F}(x, y, z)$$

$$= \frac{\partial}{\partial x}(e^{2x}) + \frac{\partial}{\partial y}(3x^2yz) + \frac{\partial}{\partial z}(2y^2z + x)$$

$$= 2e^{2x} + 3x^2z + 2y^2 \qquad \blacktriangleleft$$

A physical significance of curl **F** and div **F** in the study of fluid motion will be discussed in Sections 14.4–14.6. In this section we are concerned with learning how to compute them and to prove some of their properties. Two such properties are given in the following two theorems, whose proofs you are asked to provide in Exercises 47 and 48.

14.1.5 Theorem

Suppose **F** is a vector field on an open ball B in R^3 such that

$$\mathbf{F}(x, y, z) = M(x, y, z)\mathbf{i} + N(x, y, z)\mathbf{j} + R(x, y, z)\mathbf{k}$$

If the second partial derivatives of M, N, and R are continuous on B, then

$$\text{div(curl } \mathbf{F}) = 0$$

14.1.6 Theorem

If f is a scalar field on an open ball B in R^3 and the second partial derivatives of f are continuous on B, then

$$\text{curl}(\nabla f) = \mathbf{0}$$

The equation in Theorem 14.1.6 states that the curl of the gradient of f equals the zero vector. Consider now the divergence of the gradient of f, that is $\nabla \cdot (\nabla f)$, which can also be written as $\nabla \cdot \nabla f$ or $\nabla^2 f$. By definition,

$$\nabla^2 f(x, y, z) = \left(\mathbf{i}\frac{\partial}{\partial x} + \mathbf{j}\frac{\partial}{\partial y} + \mathbf{k}\frac{\partial}{\partial z}\right) \cdot \left(\frac{\partial f}{\partial x}\mathbf{i} + \frac{\partial f}{\partial y}\mathbf{j} + \frac{\partial f}{\partial z}\mathbf{k}\right)$$

$$\nabla^2 f(x, y, z) = \frac{\partial^2 f}{\partial x^2} + \frac{\partial^2 f}{\partial y^2} + \frac{\partial^2 f}{\partial z^2}$$

The expression on the right side of this equation is called the **Laplacian** of f. The following equation obtained by setting the Laplacian equal to zero is called **Laplace's equation:**

$$\frac{\partial^2 f}{\partial x^2} + \frac{\partial^2 f}{\partial y^2} + \frac{\partial^2 f}{\partial z^2} = 0$$

A scalar function satisfying Laplace's equation is said to be **harmonic.** These functions have important applications in physics in the study of heat transfer, electromagnetic radiation, acoustics, and so on.

If $\mathbf{F}$ is a vector field on some open disk B in R^2 such that $\mathbf{F}(x, y) = \mathbf{M}(x, y)\mathbf{i} + N(x, y)\mathbf{j}$, then the curl of $\mathbf{F}$ and divergence of $\mathbf{F}$ in two dimensions are defined by

$$\text{curl } \mathbf{F}(x, y) = \left(\frac{\partial N}{\partial x} - \frac{\partial M}{\partial y} \right)\mathbf{k} \qquad \text{div } \mathbf{F}(x, y) = \frac{\partial M}{\partial x} + \frac{\partial N}{\partial y}$$

if these partial derivatives exist. The Laplacian in two dimensions is defined by

$$\nabla^2 f(x, y) = \frac{\partial^2 f}{\partial x^2} + \frac{\partial^2 f}{\partial y^2}$$

▶ **EXAMPLE 6**   If $\mathbf{F}(x, y) = 3x^2 y\mathbf{i} - 2xy^3\mathbf{j}$, find **(a)** curl $\mathbf{F}(x, y)$ and **(b)** div $\mathbf{F}(x, y)$.

Solution   Let $M(x, y) = 3x^2 y$ and $N(x, y) = -2xy^3$.

(a) curl $\mathbf{F}(x, y) = \left(\dfrac{\partial N}{\partial x} - \dfrac{\partial M}{\partial y} \right)\mathbf{k}$ **(b)** div $\mathbf{F}(x, y) = \dfrac{\partial M}{\partial x} + \dfrac{\partial N}{\partial y}$

$\qquad\qquad\qquad = (-2y^3 - 3x^2)\mathbf{k}$ $\qquad\qquad\qquad = 6xy - 6xy^2$ ◀

EXERCISES 14.1

In Exercises 1 through 6, show on a figure the representations having initial point at (x, y) of the vectors in the vector field, where x is ± 1 or ± 2 and y is ± 1 or ± 2.

1. $\mathbf{F}(x, y) = x\mathbf{i} - y\mathbf{j}$ 　　 **2.** $\mathbf{F}(x, y) = -x\mathbf{i} + y\mathbf{j}$

3. $\mathbf{F}(x, y) = 4y\mathbf{i} + 3x\mathbf{j}$ 　　 **4.** $\mathbf{F}(x, y) = -3y\mathbf{i} + 4x\mathbf{j}$

5. $\mathbf{F}(x, y) = \dfrac{1}{\sqrt{x^2 + y^2}}(x\mathbf{i} + y\mathbf{j})$

6. $\mathbf{F}(x, y) = y\mathbf{i} + 2\mathbf{j}$

In Exercises 7 through 14, find a conservative vector field having the given potential function.

7. $f(x, y) = 3x^2 + 2y^3$

8. $f(x, y) = 2x^4 - 5x^2 y^2 + 4y^4$

9. $f(x, y) = \tan^{-1} x^2 y$ 　　 **10.** $f(x, y) = ye^x - xe^y$

11. $f(x, y, z) = 2x^3 - 3x^2 y + xy^2 - 4y^3$

12. $f(x, y, z) = \sqrt{x^2 + y^2 + z^2}$

13. $f(x, y, z) = x^2 y e^{-4z}$ 　　 **14.** $f(x, y, z) = z \sin(x^2 - y)$

In Exercises 15 through 20, determine if the vector field is conservative.

15. $\mathbf{F}(x, y) = (3x^2 - 2y^2)\mathbf{i} + (3 - 4xy)\mathbf{j}$

16. $\mathbf{F}(x, y) = (e^x e^y + 6e^{2x})\mathbf{i} + (e^x e^y - 2e^y)\mathbf{j}$

17. $\mathbf{F}(x, y) = y \cos(x + y)\mathbf{i} - x \sin(x + y)\mathbf{j}$

18. $\mathbf{F}(x, y, z) = (3x^2 + 2yz)\mathbf{i} + (2xz + 6yz)\mathbf{j}$
$\qquad\qquad\qquad + (2xy + 3y^2 - 2z)\mathbf{k}$

19. $\mathbf{F}(x, y, z) = (2ye^{2x} + e^z)\mathbf{i} + (3ze^{3y} + e^{2x})\mathbf{j}$
$\qquad\qquad\qquad + (xe^z + e^{3y})\mathbf{k}$

20. $\mathbf{F}(x, y, z) = y \sec^2 x\mathbf{i} + (\tan x - z \sec^2 y)\mathbf{j}$
$\qquad\qquad\qquad + x \sec z \tan z\mathbf{k}$

In Exercises 21 through 32, prove that the vector field is conservative, and find a potential function.

21. $\mathbf{F}(x, y) = y\mathbf{i} + x\mathbf{j}$ 　　　 **22.** $\mathbf{F}(x, y) = x\mathbf{i} + y\mathbf{j}$

23. $\mathbf{F}(x, y) = e^x \sin y\mathbf{i} + e^x \cos y\mathbf{j}$

24. $\mathbf{F}(x, y) = (\sin y \sinh x + \cos y \cosh x)\mathbf{i}$
$\qquad\qquad\qquad + (\cos y \cosh x - \sin y \sinh x)\mathbf{j}$

25. $\mathbf{F}(x, y) = (2xy^2 - y^3)\mathbf{i} + (2x^2 y - 3xy^2 + 2)\mathbf{j}$

26. $\mathbf{F}(x, y) = (3x^2 + 2y - y^2 e^x)\mathbf{i} + (2x - 2ye^x)\mathbf{j}$

27. $\mathbf{F}(x, y, z) = (x^2 - y)\mathbf{i} - (x - 3z)\mathbf{j} + (z + 3y)\mathbf{k}$

28. $\mathbf{F}(x, y, z) = yz\mathbf{i} + xz\mathbf{j} + xy\mathbf{k}$

29. $\mathbf{F}(x, y, z) = (ze^x + e^y)\mathbf{i} + (xe^y - e^z)\mathbf{j}$
$\qquad\qquad\qquad + (-ye^z + e^x)\mathbf{k}$

30. $\mathbf{F}(x, y, z) = (\tan y + 2xy \sec z)\mathbf{i}$
$\qquad\qquad + (x \sec^2 y + x^2 \sec z)\mathbf{j} + \sec z(x^2 y \tan z - \sec z)\mathbf{k}$

31. $\mathbf{F}(x, y, z) = (2x \cos y - 3)\mathbf{i}$
$\qquad - (x^2 \sin y + z^2)\mathbf{j} - (2yz - 2)\mathbf{k}$

32. $\mathbf{F}(x, y, z) = (2y^3 - 8xz^2)\mathbf{i} + (6xy^2 + 1)\mathbf{j}$
$\qquad\qquad\qquad - (8x^2z + 3z^2)\mathbf{k}$

In Exercises 33 through 42, find curl $\mathbf{F}$ *and div* $\mathbf{F}$ *for the vector field.*

33. $\mathbf{F}(x, y) = 2x\mathbf{i} + 3y\mathbf{j}$ **34.** $\mathbf{F}(x, y) = \cos x\mathbf{i} - \sin y\mathbf{j}$

35. $\mathbf{F}(x, y) = e^x \cos y\mathbf{i} + e^x \sin y\mathbf{j}$

36. $\mathbf{F}(x, y) = -\dfrac{y}{x}\mathbf{i} + \dfrac{1}{x}\mathbf{j}$

37. $\mathbf{F}(x, y, z) = x^2\mathbf{i} + y^2\mathbf{j} + z^2\mathbf{k}$

38. $\mathbf{F}(x, y, z) = xz^2\mathbf{i} + y^2\mathbf{j} + x^2z\mathbf{k}$

39. $\mathbf{F}(x, y, z) = \cos y\mathbf{i} + \cos z\mathbf{j} + \cos x\mathbf{k}$

40. $\mathbf{F}(x, y, z) = (y^2 + z^2)\mathbf{i} + xe^y \cos z\mathbf{j} - xe^y \cos z\mathbf{k}$

41. $\mathbf{F}(x, y, z) = \sqrt{x^2 + y^2 + 1}\,\mathbf{i}$
$\qquad\qquad\qquad + \sqrt{x^2 + y^2 + 1}\,\mathbf{j} + z^2\mathbf{k}$

42. $\mathbf{F}(x, y, z) = \dfrac{x}{(x^2 + y^2)^{3/2}}\mathbf{i} + \dfrac{y}{(x^2 + y^2)^{3/2}}\mathbf{j} + \mathbf{k}$

In Exercises 43 through 46, prove that the scalar function is harmonic by showing that its Laplacian is zero.

43. $f(x, y) = e^y \sin x + e^x \cos y$

44. $f(x, y) = \ln(\sqrt{x^2 + y^2})$

45. $f(x, y, z) = 2x^2 + 3y^2 - 5z^2$

46. $f(x, y, z) = (x^2 + y^2 + z^2)^{-1/2}$

47. Prove Theorem 14.1.5.   **48.** Prove Theorem 14.1.6.

49. Prove the "only if" part of Theorem 14.1.2.

50. Explain why the definition of the curl of a vector field applied in Theorem 14.1.2 indicates that the vector field $\mathbf{F}(x, y, z)$ is a gradient if and only if curl $\mathbf{F} = \mathbf{0}$.

14.2 LINE INTEGRALS

In Chapter 4, the geometric concept of area was used to motivate the definition of the definite integral. To motivate the definition of an integral of a vector field, we use the physical concept of work.

You learned in Section 10.3 that if a constant force of vector measure $\mathbf{F}$ moves a particle along a line from point A to point B, then if W is the measure of the work done,

$$\mathbf{W} = \mathbf{F} \cdot \mathbf{V}(\overrightarrow{AB}) \tag{1}$$

Suppose now that the force vector is not constant, and instead of the motion being along a line, it is along a curve. Let the force exerted on the particle at the point (x, y) in some open disk B in R^2 be given by the force field

$$\mathbf{F}(x, y) = M(x, y)\mathbf{i} + N(x, y)\mathbf{j}$$

where M and N are continuous on B. Let C be a curve lying in B and having the vector equation

$$\mathbf{R}(t) = f(t)\mathbf{i} + g(t)\mathbf{j} \qquad a \leq t \leq b$$

We require that the functions f and g be such that f' and g' be continuous on $[a, b]$ and not both zero anywhere on $[a, b]$; that is, according to Definition 9.1.1, curve C is smooth on $[a, b]$. We wish to define the work done by the variable force of vector measure $\mathbf{F}$ in moving the particle along C from the point $(f(a), g(a))$ to $(f(b), g(b))$. At a point $(f(t), g(t))$ on C the force vector is

$$\mathbf{F}(f(t), g(t)) = M(f(t), g(t))\mathbf{i} + N(f(t), g(t))\mathbf{j} \tag{2}$$

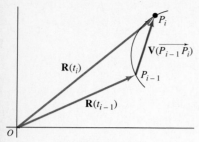

FIGURE 1

Let Δ be a partition of the interval $[a, b]$:

$$a = t_0 < t_1 < t_2 < \ldots < t_{n-1} < t_n = b$$

On C let P_i be the point $(x_i, y_i) = (f(t_i), g(t_i))$. Refer to Figure 1. The vector $\mathbf{V}(\overrightarrow{P_{i-1}P_i}) = \mathbf{R}(t_i) - \mathbf{R}(t_{i-1})$; therefore

$$\mathbf{V}(\overrightarrow{P_{i-1}P_i}) = f(t_i)\mathbf{i} + g(t_i)\mathbf{j} - [f(t_{i-1})\mathbf{i} + g(t_{i-1})\mathbf{j}]$$
$$\mathbf{V}(\overrightarrow{P_{i-1}P_i}) = [f(t_i) - f(t_{i-1})]\mathbf{i} + [g(t_i) - g(t_{i-1})]\mathbf{j} \qquad (3)$$

Because f' and g' are continuous on $[a, b]$, it follows from the mean-value theorem that there are numbers c_i and d_i in the open interval (t_{i-1}, t_i) such that

$$f(t_i) - f(t_{i-1}) = f'(c_i)(t_i - t_{i-1})$$
$$g(t_i) - g(t_{i-1}) = g'(d_i)(t_i - t_{i-1})$$

Letting $\Delta_i t = t_i - t_{i-1}$, and substituting from the above two equations into (3) we obtain

$$\mathbf{V}(\overrightarrow{P_{i-1}P_i}) = [f'(c_i)\mathbf{i} + g'(d_i)\mathbf{j}] \Delta_i t \qquad (4)$$

For each i consider the vector

$$\mathbf{F}_i = M(f(c_i), g(c_i))\mathbf{i} + N(f(d_i), g(d_i))\mathbf{j} \qquad (5)$$

Each of the vectors $\mathbf{F}_i (i = 1, 2, \ldots, n)$ is an approximation to the force vector $\mathbf{F}(f(t), g(t))$, given by (2), along the arc of C from P_{i-1} to P_i. Observe that even though c_i and d_i are in general different numbers in the open interval (t_{i-1}, t_i), the values of the vectors $\mathbf{F}(f(t), g(t))$ are close to the vector $\mathbf{F}_i$. Furthermore, we approximate the arc of C from P_{i-1} to P_i by the line segment $\overrightarrow{P_{i-1}P_i}$. Thus we apply formula (1) and obtain an approximation for the work done by the vector $\mathbf{F}(f(t), g(t))$ in moving a particle along the arc of C from P_{i-1} to P_i. Denoting this approximation by $\Delta_i W$, we have, from formula (1) and Equations (5) and (4)

$$\Delta_i W = [M(f(c_i), g(c_i))\mathbf{i} + N(f(d_i), g(d_i))\mathbf{j}] \cdot [f'(c_i)\mathbf{i} + g'(d_i)\mathbf{j}] \Delta_i t$$
$$\Leftrightarrow \quad \Delta_i W = [M(f(c_i), g(c_i))f'(c_i)] \Delta_i t + [N(f(d_i), g(d_i))g'(d_i)] \Delta_i t$$

An approximation of the measure of the work done by $F(f(t), g(t))$ along C is $\sum_{i=1}^{n} \Delta_i W$ or, equivalently,

$$\sum_{i=1}^{n} [M(f(c_i), g(c_i))f'(c_i)] \Delta_i t + \sum_{i=1}^{n} [N(f(d_i), g(d_i))g'(d_i)] \Delta_i t$$

Each of these sums is a Riemann sum. The first is a Riemann sum for the function having values $M(f(t), g(t))f'(t)$, and the second is a Riemann sum for the function having values $N(f(t), g(t))g'(t)$. If n increases without bound and each $\Delta_i t$ approaches zero, these two sums approach the definite integral:

$$\int_a^b [M(f(t), g(t))f'(t) + N(f(t), g(t))g'(t)] \, dt$$

We therefore have the following definition. In the definition we use the notation $\mathbf{F}(\mathbf{R}(t))$ in place of $\mathbf{F}(f(t), g(t))$.

14.2.1 Definition of Work Done by a Force Field on a Particle Moving along a Curve in R^2

Let C be a smooth curve lying in an open disk B in R^2 for which a vector equation of C is $\mathbf{R}(t) = f(t)\mathbf{i} + g(t)\mathbf{j}$. Furthermore, let a force field on B be defined by $\mathbf{F}(x, y) = M(x, y)\mathbf{i} + N(x, y)\mathbf{j}$, where M and N are continuous on B. Then if W is the measure of the **work** done by a force of vector measure $\mathbf{F}$ in moving a particle along C from $(f(a), g(a))$ to $(f(b), g(b))$,

$$W = \int_a^b [M(f(t), g(t))f'(t) + N(f(t), g(t))g'(t)]\, dt \qquad (6)$$

or, equivalently, by using vector notation,

$$W = \int_a^b \langle M(f(t), g(t)), N(f(t), g(t)) \rangle \cdot \langle f'(t), g'(t) \rangle\, dt$$

$$\Leftrightarrow W = \int_a^b \mathbf{F}(\mathbf{R}(t)) \cdot \mathbf{R}'(t)\, dt \qquad (7)$$

▶ **EXAMPLE 1**   Suppose a particle moves along the parabola $y = x^2$ from the point $A(-1, 1)$ to the point $B(2, 4)$. Find the total work done if the motion is caused by the force field

$$\mathbf{F}(x, y) = (x^2 + y^2)\mathbf{i} + 3x^2y\mathbf{j}$$

Assume the arc is measured in meters and the force is measured in newtons.

Solution   Figure 2 shows the arc of the parabola from A to B. Parametric equations of the parabola are

$$x = t \quad \text{and} \quad y = t^2 \quad -1 \le t \le 2$$

Thus a vector equation of the parabola is

$$\mathbf{R}(t) = t\mathbf{i} + t^2\mathbf{j} \quad \text{and} \quad \mathbf{R}'(t) = \mathbf{i} + 2t\mathbf{j}$$

Because $\mathbf{F}(x, y) = \langle x^2 + y^2, 3x^2y \rangle$, then

$$\mathbf{F}(\mathbf{R}(t)) = \mathbf{F}(t, t^2)$$
$$= \langle t^2 + t^4, 3t^4 \rangle$$

If W joules is the work done, then, from (7),

$$W = \int_{-1}^{2} \mathbf{F}(\mathbf{R}(t)) \cdot \mathbf{R}'(t)\, dt \qquad (8)$$

$$= \int_{-1}^{2} \langle t^2 + t^4, 3t^4 \rangle \cdot \langle 1, 2t \rangle\, dt$$

$$= \int_{-1}^{2} (t^2 + t^4 + 6t^5)\, dt$$

$$= \frac{t^3}{3} + \frac{t^5}{5} + t^6 \Big]_{-1}^{2}$$

$$= \tfrac{8}{3} + \tfrac{32}{5} + 64 - (-\tfrac{1}{3} - \tfrac{1}{5} + 1)$$

$$= \tfrac{363}{5}$$

<u>Conclusion:</u>   The work done is 72.6 joules.   ◀

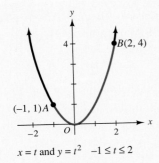

$x = t$ and $y = t^2$ $-1 \le t \le 2$

FIGURE 2

The integrals in Equations (6) and (7) are called *line integrals*. For the line integral of Equation (6), a common notation involving the differential form $M(x, y) \, dx + N(x, y) \, dy$ is

$$\int_C M(x, y) \, dx + N(x, y) \, dy$$

This notation is suggested by the fact that because parametric equations of C are $x = f(t)$ and $y = g(t)$, then $dx = f'(t) \, dt$ and $dy = g'(t) \, dt$. A vector notation for the line integral of Equation (7) is

$$\int_C \mathbf{F} \cdot d\mathbf{R}$$

This notation is suggested by considering the vector equation of C, which is $\mathbf{R}(t) = f(t)\mathbf{i} + g(t)\mathbf{j}$, and letting $d\mathbf{R} = \mathbf{R}'(t) \, dt$. Then

$$\mathbf{F}(\mathbf{R}(t)) \cdot d\mathbf{R} = \mathbf{F}(\mathbf{R}(t)) \cdot \mathbf{R}'(t) \, dt$$

We have, then, the following formal definition.

14.2.2 Definition of a Line Integral Over a Curve in R^2

Let C be a smooth curve lying in an open disk B in R^2 and having the vector equation

$$\mathbf{R}(t) = f(t)\mathbf{i} + g(t)\mathbf{j} \qquad a \le t \le b$$

Let $\mathbf{F}$ be a vector field on B defined by

$$\mathbf{F}(x, y) = M(x, y)\mathbf{i} + N(x, y)\mathbf{j}$$

where M and N are continuous on B. Then by using differential form notation the **line integral** of $M(x, y) \, dx + N(x, y) \, dy$ over C is given by

$$\int_C M(x, y) \, dx + N(x, y) \, dy$$

$$= \int_a^b [M(f(t), g(t))f'(t) + N(f(t), g(t))g'(t)] \, dt$$

or, equivalently, by using vector notation, the **line integral** of $\mathbf{F}$ over C is given by

$$\int_C \mathbf{F} \cdot d\mathbf{R} = \int_a^b \mathbf{F}(\mathbf{R}(t)) \cdot \mathbf{R}'(t) \, dt$$

We shall apply both the differential form and vector notations for line integrals.

▷   **ILLUSTRATION 1**   In Example 1, the integral in Equation (8) that defines W is a line integral. With vector notation, this line integral can be denoted by

$$\int_C \mathbf{F} \cdot d\mathbf{R}$$

where $\mathbf{F}(x, y) = (x^2 + y^2)\mathbf{i} + 3x^2y\mathbf{j}$ and $\mathbf{R}(t) = t\mathbf{i} + t^2\mathbf{j}$. With differential form notation, this line integral is written as

$$\int_C (x^2 + y^2)\, dx + 3x^2y\, dy \tag{9}$$

◄

If an equation of C is of the form $y = F(x)$, then x may be used as a parameter in place of t. In a similar manner, if an equation of C is of the form $x = G(y)$, then y may be used as a parameter in place of t.

▷ **ILLUSTRATION 2** In Example 1 and Illustration 1, the equation of C is $y = x^2$, which is of the form $y = F(x)$. Therefore we can use x as a parameter instead of t. Thus, in integral (9) of Illustration 1 we can replace y by x^2 and dy by $2x\, dx$, and we have

$$W = \int_{-1}^{2} (x^2 + x^4)\, dx + 3x^2x^2(2x\, dx)$$

$$= \int_{-1}^{2} (x^2 + x^4 + 6x^5)\, dx$$

This integral is the same as the third one appearing in the solution of Example 1, except that the variable is x instead of t. ◄

If the curve C in the definition of the line integral is the closed interval $[a, b]$ on the x axis, then $y = 0$ and $dy = 0$. Thus

$$\int_C M(x, y)\, dx + N(x, y)\, dy = \int_a^b M(x, 0)\, dx$$

Therefore, in such a case, the line integral reduces to a definite integral.

We can extend the concept of a line integral to include curves that are sectionally smooth. Recall from Section 9.1 that if an interval I can be partitioned into a finite number of subintervals on which curve C is smooth, then C is said to be *sectionally smooth* on I.

14.2.3 Definition of a Line Integral Over a Sectionally Smooth Curve in R^2

Let the curve C consist of the smooth arcs $C_1, C_2, \ldots, C_n$ lying in an open disk B in R^2 and define $\mathbf{R}(t)$ and $\mathbf{F}(x, y)$ as in Definition 14.2.2. Then the **line integral** of $M(x, y)\, dx + N(x, y)\, dy$ over C is defined by

$$\int_C M(x, y)\, dx + N(x, y)\, dy = \sum_{i=1}^{n} \left(\int_{C_i} M(x, y)\, dx + N(x, y)\, dy \right)$$

or, equivalently, by using vector notation, the line integral of $\mathbf{F}$ over C is defined by

$$\int_C \mathbf{F} \cdot d\mathbf{R} = \sum_{i=1}^{n} \left(\int_{a_i}^{b_i} \mathbf{F}(\mathbf{R}(t)) \cdot \mathbf{R}'(t)\, dt \right)$$

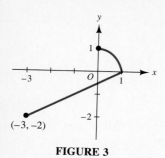

FIGURE 3

▶ **EXAMPLE 2**   Evaluate the line integral

$$\int_C 4xy \, dx + (2x^2 - 3xy) \, dy$$

if the curve C consists of the line segment from $(-3, -2)$ to $(1, 0)$ and the first quadrant arc of the circle $x^2 + y^2 = 1$ from $(1, 0)$ to $(0, 1)$, traversed in the counterclockwise direction.

Solution   Figure 3 shows the curve C composed of arcs C_1 and C_2. The arc C_1 is the line segment. An equation of the line through $(-3, -2)$ and $(1, 0)$ is $x - 2y = 1$. Therefore, C_1 can be represented parametrically by

$$x = 1 + 2t \qquad y = t \qquad -2 \le t \le 0$$

The arc C_2, which is the first quadrant arc of the circle $x^2 + y^2 = 1$, can be represented parametrically by

$$x = \cos t \qquad y = \sin t \qquad 0 \le t \le \tfrac{1}{2}\pi$$

Applying Definition 14.2.2 for each of the arcs C_1 and C_2 we have

$$\int_{C_1} 4xy \, dx + (2x^2 - 3xy) \, dy$$

$$= \int_{-2}^{0} 4(1 + 2t)t(2 \, dt) + [2(1 + 2t)^2 - 3(1 + 2t)t] \, dt$$

$$= \int_{-2}^{0} (8t + 16t^2 + 2 + 8t + 8t^2 - 3t - 6t^2) \, dt$$

$$= \int_{-2}^{0} (18t^2 + 13t + 2) \, dt$$

$$= 6t^3 + \tfrac{13}{2}t^2 + 2t \Big]_{-2}^{0}$$

$$= -(-48 + 26 - 4)$$

$$= 26$$

and

$$\int_{C_2} 4xy \, dx + (2x^2 - 3xy) \, dy$$

$$= \int_{0}^{\pi/2} 4 \cos t \sin t (-\sin t \, dt) + (2 \cos^2 t - 3 \cos t \sin t)(\cos t \, dt)$$

$$= \int_{0}^{\pi/2} (-4 \cos t \sin^2 t + 2 \cos^3 t - 3 \cos^2 t \sin t) \, dt$$

$$= \int_{0}^{\pi/2} [-4 \cos t \sin^2 t + 2 \cos t(1 - \sin^2 t) - 3 \cos^2 t \sin t] \, dt$$

$$= \int_{0}^{\pi/2} (2 \cos t - 6 \cos t \sin^2 t - 3 \cos^2 t \sin t) \, dt$$

$$= 2 \sin t - 2 \sin^3 t + \cos^3 t \Big]_{0}^{\pi/2}$$

$$= 2 - 2 - 1$$

$$= -1$$

Therefore, from Definition 14.2.3,

$$\int_C 4xy\,dx + (2x^2 - 3xy)\,dy = 26 + (-1)$$
$$= 25 \qquad \blacktriangleleft$$

The definition of a line integral in three dimensions requires the curve to be *smooth:* A curve in R^3 having the vector equation

$$\mathbf{R}(t) = f(t)\mathbf{i} + g(t)\mathbf{j} + h(t)\mathbf{k} \qquad a \le t \le b$$

is smooth if f', g', and h' are continuous on $[a, b]$ and not all zero anywhere on $[a, b]$.

14.2.4 Definition of a Line Integral Over a Curve in R^3

Let C be a smooth curve lying in an open ball B in R^3 and having the vector equation

$$\mathbf{R}(t) = f(t)\mathbf{i} + g(t)\mathbf{j} + h(t)\mathbf{k} \qquad a \le t \le b$$

Let $\mathbf{F}$ be a vector field on B defined by

$$\mathbf{F}(x, y, z) = M(x, y, z)\mathbf{i} + N(x, y, z)\mathbf{j} + R(x, y, z)\mathbf{k}$$

where M, N, and R are continuous on B. Then by using differential form notation the **line integral** of $M(x, y, z)\,dx + N(x, y, z)\,dy + R(x, y, z)\,dz$ over C is given by

$$\int_C M(x, y, z)\,dx + N(x, y, z)\,dy + R(x, y, z)\,dz$$
$$= \int_a^b [M(f(t), g(t), h(t))f'(t) + N(f(t), g(t), h(t))g'(t) + R(f(t), g(t), h(t))h'(t)]\,dt$$

or, equivalently, by using vector notation, the **line integral** of $\mathbf{F}$ over C is given by

$$\int_C \mathbf{F} \cdot d\mathbf{R} = \int_a^b \mathbf{F}(\mathbf{R}(t)) \cdot \mathbf{R}'(t)\,dt$$

▶ **EXAMPLE 3**   Evaluate the line integral

$$\int_C 3x\,dx + 2xy\,dy + z\,dz$$

if the curve C is the circular helix defined by the parametric equations

$$x = \cos t \qquad y = \sin t \qquad z = t \qquad 0 \le t \le 2\pi$$

Solution From the differential form notation for a line integral in Definition 14.2.4

$$\int_C 3x\,dx + 2xy\,dy + z\,dz$$

$$= \int_0^{2\pi} 3\cos t(-\sin t\,dt) + 2(\cos t)(\sin t)(\cos t\,dt) + t\,dt$$

$$= \int_0^{2\pi} (-3\sin t\cos t + 2\cos^2 t\sin t + t)\,dt$$

$$= -\tfrac{3}{2}\sin^2 t - \tfrac{2}{3}\cos^3 t + \tfrac{1}{2}t^2 \Big]_0^{2\pi}$$

$$= -\tfrac{3}{2}(0) - \tfrac{2}{3}(1) + \tfrac{1}{2}(4\pi^2) + \tfrac{3}{2}(0) + \tfrac{2}{3}(1) + \tfrac{1}{2}(0)$$

$$= 2\pi^2 \qquad \blacktriangleleft$$

We can define the work done by a force field in moving a particle along a curve in R^3 just as we did in Definition 14.2.1 for a curve in R^2. Such a definition is applied in the next example.

▶ **EXAMPLE 4**   A particle traverses the twisted cubic

$$\mathbf{R}(t) = t\mathbf{i} + t^2\mathbf{j} + t^3\mathbf{k} \qquad 0 \le t \le 1$$

Find the total work done if the motion is caused by the force field

$$\mathbf{F}(x, y, z) = e^x\mathbf{i} + xe^z\mathbf{j} + x\sin \pi y^2\mathbf{k}$$

Assume that the arc is measured in meters and the force is measured in newtons.

Solution   Figure 4 shows the twisted cubic from $t = 0$ to $t = 1$.

$$\mathbf{R}(t) = t\mathbf{i} + t^2\mathbf{j} + t^3\mathbf{k} \qquad \mathbf{R}'(t) = \mathbf{i} + 2t\mathbf{j} + 3t^2\mathbf{k}$$

Because $\mathbf{F}(x, y, z) = \langle e^x, xe^z, x\sin \pi y^2\rangle$, then

$$\mathbf{F}(\mathbf{R}(t)) = \mathbf{F}(t, t^2, t^3)$$

$$= \langle e^t, te^{t^3}, t\sin \pi t^4\rangle$$

If W joules is the work done, then from the vector notation for a line integral in Definition 14.2.4

$$W = \int_C \mathbf{F}\cdot d\mathbf{R}$$

$$= \int_0^1 \mathbf{F}(\mathbf{R}(t))\cdot \mathbf{R}'(t)\,dt$$

$$= \int_0^1 \langle e^t, te^{t^3}, t\sin \pi t^4\rangle \cdot \langle 1, 2t, 3t^2\rangle\,dt$$

$$= \int_0^1 (e^t + 2t^2e^{t^3} + 3t^3\sin \pi t^4)\,dt$$

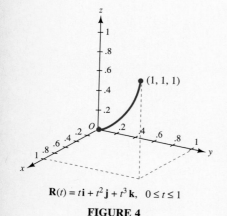

$\mathbf{R}(t) = t\mathbf{i} + t^2\mathbf{j} + t^3\mathbf{k}, \quad 0 \le t \le 1$

FIGURE 4

$$= e^t + \frac{2}{3}e^{t^3} - \frac{3}{4\pi}\cos\pi t^4 \Big]_0^1$$

$$= e + \frac{2}{3}e - \frac{3}{4\pi}\cos\pi - 1 - \frac{2}{3} + \frac{3}{4\pi}\cos 0$$

$$= \frac{5}{3}e + \frac{3}{2\pi} - \frac{5}{3}$$

$$\approx 3.34$$

Conclusion: The work done is 3.34 joules. ◄

EXERCISES 14.2

In Exercises 1 through 22, evaluate the line integral over the curve C.

1. $\int_C \mathbf{F} \cdot d\mathbf{R}$; $\mathbf{F}(x, y) = y\mathbf{i} + x\mathbf{j}$;
   C: $\mathbf{R}(t) = t\mathbf{i} + t^2\mathbf{j}$, $0 \le t \le 1$

2. $\int_C \mathbf{F} \cdot d\mathbf{R}$; $\mathbf{F}(x, y) = 2xy\mathbf{i} - 3x\mathbf{j}$;
   C: $\mathbf{R}(t) = 3t^2\mathbf{i} - t\mathbf{j}$, $0 \le t \le 1$

3. $\int_C \mathbf{F} \cdot d\mathbf{R}$; $\mathbf{F}(x, y) = 2xy\mathbf{i} + (x - 2y)\mathbf{j}$;
   C: $\mathbf{R}(t) = \sin t\mathbf{i} - 2\cos t\mathbf{j}$, $0 \le t \le \pi$

4. $\int_C \mathbf{F} \cdot d\mathbf{R}$; $\mathbf{F}(x, y) = xy\mathbf{i} - y^2\mathbf{j}$; C: $\mathbf{R}(t) = t^2\mathbf{i} + t^3\mathbf{j}$,
   from the point $(1, 1)$ to the point $(4, -8)$

5. $\int_C \mathbf{F} \cdot d\mathbf{R}$; $\mathbf{F}(x, y) = (x - y)\mathbf{i} + (y + x)\mathbf{j}$; C: the
   circle $x^2 + y^2 = 4$ from the point $(2, 0)$ in the
   counterclockwise direction

6. $\int_C \mathbf{F} \cdot d\mathbf{R}$; $\mathbf{F}(x, y) = (x - 2y)\mathbf{i} + xy\mathbf{j}$;
   C: $\mathbf{R}(t) = 3\cos t\mathbf{i} + 2\sin t\mathbf{j}$, $0 \le t \le \frac{1}{2}\pi$

7. $\int_C \mathbf{F} \cdot d\mathbf{R}$; $\mathbf{F}(x, y) = y\sin x\mathbf{i} - \cos x\mathbf{j}$; C: the line
   segment from $(\frac{1}{2}\pi, 0)$ to $(\pi, 1)$

8. $\int_C \mathbf{F} \cdot d\mathbf{R}$; $\mathbf{F}(x, y) = 9x^2y\mathbf{i} + (5x^2 - y)\mathbf{j}$; C: the
   curve $y = x^3 + 1$ from $(1, 2)$ to $(3, 28)$

9. $\int_C (x^2 + xy)\, dx + (y^2 - xy)\, dy$; C: the line $y = x$
   from the origin to the point $(2, 2)$

10. The line integral of Exercise 9; C: the parabola
    $x^2 = 2y$ from the origin to the point $(2, 2)$

11. The line integral of Exercise 9; C: the x axis from the
    origin to $(2, 0)$ and then the line $x = 2$ from $(2, 0)$ to
    $(2, 2)$

12. $\int_C yx^2\, dx + (x + y)\, dy$; C: the line $y = -x$ from
    the origin to the point $(1, -1)$

13. The line integral of Exercise 12; C: the curve
    $y = -x^3$ from the origin to the point $(1, -1)$

14. The line integral of Exercise 12; C: the y axis from
    the origin to $(0, -1)$ and then the line $y = -1$ from
    $(0, -1)$ to $(1, -1)$

15. $\int_C 3xy\, dx + (4x^2 - 3y)\, dy$; C: the line $y = 2x + 3$
    from $(0, 3)$ to $(3, 9)$ and then the parabola $y = x^2$
    from $(3, 9)$ to $(5, 25)$

16. $\int_C (xy - z)\, dx + e^x\, dy + y\, dz$; C: the line segment
    from $(1, 0, 0)$ to $(3, 4, 8)$

17. $\int_C (x + y)\, dx + (y + z)\, dy + (x + z)\, dz$; C: the
    line segment from the origin to the point $(1, 2, 4)$

18. The line integral of Exercise 16;
    C: $\mathbf{R}(t) = (t + 1)\mathbf{i} + t^2\mathbf{j} + t^3\mathbf{k}$, $0 \le t \le 2$

19. $\int_C \mathbf{F} \cdot d\mathbf{R}$; $\mathbf{F}(x, y, z) = z\mathbf{i} + x\mathbf{j} + y\mathbf{k}$; C: the circular
    helix $\mathbf{R}(t) = a\cos t\mathbf{i} + a\sin t\mathbf{j} + t\mathbf{k}$, $0 \le t \le 2\pi$

20. $\int_C \mathbf{F} \cdot d\mathbf{R}$; $\mathbf{F}(x, y, z) = 2xy\mathbf{i} + (6y^2 - xz)\mathbf{j} + 10z\mathbf{k}$;
    C: $\mathbf{R}(t) = t\mathbf{i} + t^2\mathbf{j} + t^3\mathbf{k}$, $0 \le t \le 1$

21. The line integral of Exercise 20; C: the line segment
    from the origin to the point $(0, 0, 1)$; then the line
    segment from $(0, 0, 1)$ to $(0, 1, 1)$; then the line
    segment from $(0, 1, 1)$ to $(1, 1, 1)$

22. The line integral of Exercise 20; C: the line segment
    from the origin to the point $(1, 1, 1)$

*In Exercises 23 through 36, find the total work done in
moving a particle along arc C if the motion is caused by
the force field F. Assume the arc is measured in meters
and the force is measured in newtons.*

23. $\mathbf{F}(x, y) = 2xy\mathbf{i} + (x^2 + y^2)\mathbf{j}$; C: the line segment
    from the origin to the point $(1, 1)$.

24. The force field of Exercise 23; C: the arc of the
    parabola $y^2 = x$ from the origin to the point $(1, 1)$

25. $\mathbf{F}(x, y) = (y - x)\mathbf{i} + x^2 y\mathbf{j}$; C: the line segment from the point $(1, 1)$ to $(2, 4)$

26. The force field of Exercise 25; C: the arc of the parabola $y = x^2$ from the point $(1, 1)$ to $(2, 4)$

27. The force field of Exercise 25; C: the line segment from $(1, 1)$ to $(2, 2)$ and then the line segment from $(2, 2)$ to $(2, 4)$

28. $\mathbf{F}(x, y) = -x^2 y\mathbf{i} + 2y\mathbf{j}$; C: the line segment from $(a, 0)$ to $(0, a)$

29. The force field of Exercise 28; C: $\mathbf{R}(t) = a \cos t\mathbf{i} + a \sin t\mathbf{j}$, $0 \le t \le \frac{1}{2}\pi$, $a > 0$

30. The force field of Exercise 28; C: the line segment from $(a, 0)$ to (a, a) and then the line segment from (a, a) to $(0, a)$

31. $\mathbf{F}(x, y, z) = (y + z)\mathbf{i} + (x + z)\mathbf{j} + (x + y)\mathbf{k}$; C: the line segment from the origin to the point $(1, 1, 1)$

32. $\mathbf{F}(x, y, z) = z^2\mathbf{i} + y^2\mathbf{j} + xz\mathbf{k}$; C: the line segment from the origin to the point $(4, 0, 3)$

33. $\mathbf{F}(x, y, z) = e^x\mathbf{i} + e^y\mathbf{j} + e^z\mathbf{k}$; C: $\mathbf{R}(t) = t\mathbf{i} + t^2\mathbf{j} + t^3\mathbf{k}$, $0 \le t \le 2$

34. $\mathbf{F}(x, y, z) = (xyz + x)\mathbf{i} + (x^2 z + y)\mathbf{j} + (x^2 y + z)\mathbf{k}$; C: the arc of Exercise 33

35. The force field of Exercise 34; C: the line segment from the origin to the point $(1, 0, 0)$; then the line segment from $(1, 0, 0)$ to $(1, 1, 0)$; then the line segment from $(1, 1, 0)$ to $(1, 1, 1)$

36. $\mathbf{F}(x, y, z) = x\mathbf{i} + y\mathbf{j} + (yz - x)\mathbf{k}$; C: $\mathbf{R}(t) = 2t\mathbf{i} + t^2\mathbf{j} + 4t^3\mathbf{k}$, $0 \le t \le 1$

14.3 LINE INTEGRALS INDEPENDENT OF THE PATH

You learned in Section 14.2 that the value of a line integral is determined by the integrand and a curve C between two points P_1 and P_2. Under certain conditions, however, the value of a line integral depends only on the integrand and the points P_1 and P_2 and not on the path P_1 to P_2. Such a line integral is said to be **independent of the path.**

▷ **ILLUSTRATION 1**   Suppose a force field

$$\mathbf{F}(x, y) = (y^2 + 2x + 4)\mathbf{i} + (2xy + 4y - 5)\mathbf{j}$$

moves a particle from the origin to the point $(1, 1)$. We show that the total work done is the same if the path is along **(a)** the line segment from the origin to $(1, 1)$; **(b)** the segment of the parabola $y = x^2$ from the origin to $(1, 1)$; and **(c)** the segment of the curve $x = y^3$ from the origin to $(1, 1)$.

If W is the measure of the work done, then

$$W = \int_C (y^2 + 2x + 4)\,dx + (2xy + 4y - 5)\,dy \tag{1}$$

(a) See Figure 1. An equation of C is $y = x$. We use x as the parameter and let $y = x$ and $dy = dx$ in (1). Then

$$W = \int_0^1 (x^2 + 2x + 4)\,dx + (2x^2 + 4x - 5)\,dx$$

$$= \int_0^1 (3x^2 + 6x - 1)\,dx$$

$$= x^3 + 3x^2 - x \Big]_0^1$$

$$= 3$$

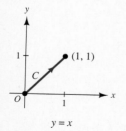

FIGURE 1

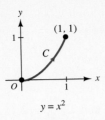

$$y = x^2$$

FIGURE 2

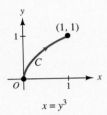

$$x = y^3$$

FIGURE 3

(b) See Figure 2. An equation of C is $y = x^2$. Again taking x as the parameter and in (1) letting $y = x^2$ and $dy = 2x\,dx$, we have

$$W = \int_0^1 (x^4 + 2x + 4)\,dx + (2x^3 + 4x^2 - 5)2x\,dx$$

$$= \int_0^1 (5x^4 + 8x^3 - 8x + 4)\,dx$$

$$= x^5 + 2x^4 - 4x^2 + 4x \Big]_0^1$$

$$= 3$$

(c) See Figure 3. An equation of C is $x = y^3$. We take y as the parameter and in (1) let $x = y^3$ and $dx = 3y^2\,dy$. Then

$$W = \int_0^1 (y^2 + 2y^3 + 4)3y^2\,dy + (2y^4 + 4y - 5)\,dy$$

$$= \int_0^1 (6y^5 + 5y^4 + 12y^2 + 4y - 5)\,dy$$

$$= y^6 + y^5 + 4y^3 + 2y^2 - 5y \Big]_0^1$$

$$= 3 \qquad \blacktriangleleft$$

In Illustration 1 you see that the value of the line integral is the same over three different paths from $(0, 0)$ to $(1, 1)$. Actually the value of the line integral is the same over any sectionally smooth curve from the origin to $(1, 1)$; this line integral is, therefore, independent of the path. This fact is proved in Illustration 2.

We now state and prove a theorem that not only gives conditions for which the value of a line integral is independent of the path but also gives a formula for finding the value.

14.3.1 Theorem

Let C be any sectionally smooth curve lying in an open disk B in R^2 from the point (x_1, y_1) to the point (x_2, y_2). If $\mathbf{F}$ is a conservative vector field continuous on B and ϕ is a potential function for $\mathbf{F}$, then the integral

$$\int_C \mathbf{F} \cdot d\mathbf{R}$$

is independent of the path C, and

$$\int_C \mathbf{F} \cdot d\mathbf{R} = \phi(x_2, y_2) - \phi(x_1, y_1)$$

Proof   We give the proof if C is smooth. If C is only sectionally smooth, then consider each piece separately; the following proof applies to each smooth piece.

Let parametric equations of C be

$$x = f(t) \qquad y = g(t) \qquad t_1 \le t \le t_2$$

Thus a vector equation of C is

$$\mathbf{R}(t) = f(t)\mathbf{i} + g(t)\mathbf{j} \qquad t_1 \le t \le t_2$$

Furthermore, the point (x_1, y_1) is $(f(t_1), g(t_1))$ and the point (x_2, y_2) is $(f(t_2), g(t_2))$. Because ϕ is a potential function for $\mathbf{F}$, $\nabla\phi(x, y) = \mathbf{F}(x, y)$ where $\mathbf{F}(x, y) = M(x, y)\mathbf{i} + N(x, y)\mathbf{j}$. Hence

$$\int_C \mathbf{F} \cdot d\mathbf{R} = \int_C \nabla\phi \cdot d\mathbf{R}$$

$$= \int_{t_1}^{t_2} \nabla\phi(\mathbf{R}(t)) \cdot \mathbf{R}'(t) \, dt$$

$$= \int_{t_1}^{t_2} \nabla\phi(f(t), g(t)) \cdot \mathbf{R}'(t) \, dt$$

$$= \int_{t_1}^{t_2} \langle M(f(t), g(t)), N(f(t), g(t)) \rangle \cdot \langle f'(t), g'(t) \rangle \, dt$$

$$= \int_{t_1}^{t_2} [M(f(t), g(t))f'(t) \, dt + N(f(t), g(t))g'(t) \, dt] \qquad \textbf{(2)}$$

Observe that because $M(x, y) \, dx + N(x, y) \, dy = d\phi(x, y)$, then

$$M(f(t), g(t))f'(t) \, dt + N(f(t), g(t))g'(t) \, dt = d\phi(f(t), g(t))$$

Substituting from this equation in (2) and then applying the second fundamental theorem of the calculus we get

$$\int_C \mathbf{F} \cdot d\mathbf{R} = \int_{t_1}^{t_2} d\phi(f(t), g(t))$$

$$= \phi(f(t), g(t)) \Big]_{t_1}^{t_2}$$

$$= \phi(f(t_2), g(t_2)) - \phi(f(t_1), g(t_1))$$

$$= \phi(x_2, y_2) - \phi(x_1, y_1)$$

which is what we wished to prove. ∎

Because of the resemblance of Theorem 14.3.1 to the second fundamental theorem of the calculus, it is sometimes called the **fundamental theorem for line integrals.** Because a conservative vector field has an unlimited number of potential functions all differing by an arbitrary constant K, we shall omit the arbitrary constant for the potential function ϕ when applying Theorem 14.3.1. Of course, what we are doing then is choosing as our potential function the one for which $K = 0$.

▷ **ILLUSTRATION 2** We use Theorem 14.3.1 to evaluate the line integral in Illustration 1:

$$\int_C (y^2 + 2x + 4)\, dx + (2xy + 4y - 5)\, dy$$

With vector notation this line integral is

$$\int_C \mathbf{F} \cdot d\mathbf{R}$$

where

$$\mathbf{F}(x, y) = (y^2 + 2x + 4)\mathbf{i} + (2xy + 4y - 5)\mathbf{j}$$

In Illustration 4 of Section 14.1 we showed that $\mathbf{F}$ is a conservative vector field having the potential function

$$\phi(x, y) = y^2 x + x^2 + 4x + 2y^2 - 5y$$

Therefore, from Theorem 14.3.1, the line integral is independent of the path, and C can be any sectionally smooth curve from $(0, 0)$ to $(1, 1)$. Furthermore, from Theorem 14.3.1,

$$\int_C (y^2 + 2x + 4)\, dx + (2xy + 4y - 5)\, dy = \phi(1, 1) - \phi(0, 0)$$

$$= 3 - 0$$

$$= 3$$

This result agrees with that of Illustration 1. ◀

▶ **EXAMPLE 1** Use the result of Example 1 in Section 14.1 to evaluate the line integral

$$\int_C \mathbf{F} \cdot d\mathbf{R}$$

if $\mathbf{F}(x, y) = (e^{-y} - 2x)\mathbf{i} - (xe^{-y} + \sin y)\mathbf{j}$ and C is the first quadrant arc of the circle

$$\mathbf{R}(t) = \pi \cos t\mathbf{i} + \pi \sin t\mathbf{j} \qquad 0 \le t \le \tfrac{1}{2}\pi$$

Solution From Example 1 in Section 14.1, we know that

$$\nabla(xe^{-y} - x^2 + \cos y) = (e^{-y} - 2x)\mathbf{i} - (xe^{-y} + \sin y)\mathbf{j}$$

Therefore $\mathbf{F}$ is a conservative vector field, and we apply Theorem 14.3.1 with $\phi(x, y) = xe^{-y} - x^2 + \cos y$. The point where $t = 0$ is $(\pi, 0)$ and the point where $t = \tfrac{1}{2}\pi$ is $(0, \pi)$.

$$\int_C \mathbf{F} \cdot d\mathbf{R} = \phi(0, \pi) - \phi(\pi, 0)$$

$$= \cos \pi - (\pi - \pi^2 + 1)$$

$$= \pi^2 - \pi - 2 \qquad ◀$$

If the value of a line integral is independent of the path, it is not necessary to find a potential function to compute the value. We show the procedure in the next example.

► **EXAMPLE 2**   Given the vector field

$$\mathbf{F}(x, y) = \frac{1}{y}\mathbf{i} - \frac{x}{y^2}\mathbf{j}$$

If C is any sectionally smooth curve from the point $A(5, -1)$ to the point $B(9, -3)$, show that the value of the line integral $\int_C \mathbf{F} \cdot d\mathbf{R}$ is independent of the path and evaluate it.

Solution   Let

$$M(x, y) = \frac{1}{y} \qquad N(x, y) = -\frac{x}{y^2}$$

$$M_y(x, y) = -\frac{1}{y^2} \qquad N_x(x, y) = -\frac{1}{y^2}$$

Because $M_y(x, y) = N_x(x, y)$, $\mathbf{F}$ is conservative. Therefore, the line integral is independent of the path.

We take for the path the line segment from A to B, shown in Figure 4. An equation of the line is $x + 2y = 3$. By letting $y = -t$ and $x = 3 + 2t$, a vector equation of the line is

$$\mathbf{R}(t) = (3 + 2t)\mathbf{i} - t\mathbf{j} \qquad 1 \le t \le 3$$

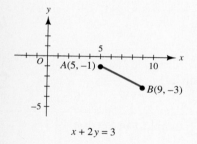

$x + 2y = 3$

FIGURE 4

We compute the value of the line integral by applying Definition 14.2.2.

$$\int_C \mathbf{F} \cdot d\mathbf{R} = \int_C \mathbf{F}(\mathbf{R}(t)) \cdot \mathbf{R}'(t) \, dt$$

$$= \int_1^3 \mathbf{F}(3 + 2t, -t) \cdot \langle 2, -1 \rangle \, dt$$

$$= \int_1^3 \left\langle -\frac{1}{t}, -\frac{3 + 2t}{t^2} \right\rangle \cdot \langle 2, -1 \rangle \, dt$$

$$= \int_1^3 \left(-\frac{2}{t} + \frac{3 + 2t}{t^2} \right) dt$$

$$= \int_1^3 \frac{3}{t^2} \, dt$$

$$= -\frac{3}{t} \Bigg]_1^3$$

$$= 2 \qquad \qquad ◄$$

Recall from Definition 9.1.2 that if for a curve C defined by the parametric equations $x = f(t)$ and $y = g(t)$, or the equivalent vector equation

$$\mathbf{R}(t) = f(t)\mathbf{i} + g(t)\mathbf{j} \qquad a \le t \le b$$

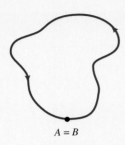

$A = B$

FIGURE 5

the initial point $A(f(a), g(a))$ and the point $B(f(b), g(b))$ coincide, then curve C is said to be *closed*. Figure 5 shows a smooth closed curve.

The following theorem regarding the line integral of a conservative vector field over a sectionally smooth closed curve follows immediately from Theorem 14.3.1.

14.3.2 Theorem

If C is any sectionally smooth closed curve lying in some open disk B in R^2 and $\mathbf{F}$ is a conservative vector field continuous on B, then

$$\int_C \mathbf{F} \cdot d\mathbf{R} = 0$$

Proof   We apply Theorem 14.3.1, and because C is closed, the point (x_1, y_1) coincides with the point (x_2, y_2). Therefore

$$\int_C \mathbf{F} \cdot d\mathbf{R} = \phi(x_2, y_2) - \phi(x_1, y_1)$$
$$= 0 \qquad \blacksquare$$

▶ **EXAMPLE 3**   A particle moves on the circle

$$\mathbf{R}(t) = 2 \cos t\mathbf{i} + 2 \sin t\mathbf{j} \qquad 0 \leq t \leq 2\pi$$

Find the total work done if the motion is caused by the force field

$$\mathbf{F}(x, y) = \left(\frac{xe^{2y}}{x^2 + 2}\right)\mathbf{i} + e^{2y} \ln (x^2 + 2)\mathbf{j}$$

Solution   Let

$$M(x, y) = \frac{xe^{2y}}{x^2 + 2} \qquad\qquad N(x, y) = e^{2y} \ln (x^2 + 2)$$

$$M_y(x, y) = \frac{2xe^{2y}}{x^2 + 2} \qquad\qquad N_x(x, y) = \frac{2xe^{2y}}{x^2 + 2}$$

Because $M_y(x, y) = N_x(x, y)$, $\mathbf{F}$ is conservative. Furthermore, the circle is a smooth closed curve. Therefore, if W is the measure of the work done, we have from Theorem 14.3.2

$$W = \int_C \mathbf{F} \cdot d\mathbf{R}$$
$$= 0 \qquad\qquad\qquad\qquad\qquad\qquad\qquad\qquad ◀$$

We now extend our discussion to functions of three variables. The statement of the following theorem and its proof are analogous to Theorem 14.3.1. You are asked to supply the proof in Exercise 32.

14.3.3 Theorem

Let C be any sectionally smooth curve lying in an open ball B in R^3 from the point (x_1, y_1, z_1) to (x_2, y_2, z_2). If $\mathbf{F}$ is a conservative vector field continuous on B and ϕ is a potential function for $\mathbf{F}$, then the line integral

$$\int_C \mathbf{F} \cdot d\mathbf{R}$$

is independent of the path C, and

$$\int_C \mathbf{F} \cdot d\mathbf{R} = \phi(x_2, y_2, z_2) - \phi(x_1, y_1, z_1)$$

▷ **ILLUSTRATION 3**   In Example 2 of Section 14.1 we showed that the vector field defined by

$$\mathbf{F}(x, y, z) = (e^x \sin z + 2yz)\mathbf{i} + (2xz + 2y)\mathbf{j} + (e^x \cos z + 2xy + 3z^2)\mathbf{k}$$

is a gradient $\nabla f(x, y, z)$, and

$$f(x, y, z) = e^x \sin z + 2xyz + y^2 + z^3$$

Thus $\mathbf{F}$ is a conservative vector field. Therefore, if C is any sectionally smooth curve from $(0, 0, 0)$ to $(1, -2, \pi)$, it follows from Theorem 14.3.3 that the line integral

$$\int_C \mathbf{F} \cdot d\mathbf{R}$$

is independent of the path and its value is

$$\begin{aligned} f(1, -2, \pi) - f(0, 0, 0) &= (e \sin \pi - 4\pi + 4 + \pi^3) - 0 \\ &= \pi^3 - 4\pi + 4 \end{aligned}$$ ◀

In the next example, we evaluate a line integral independent of the path when the integrand is written with differential form notation and parametric equations of the curve C are used instead of a vector equation.

▶ **EXAMPLE 4**   Show that the line integral

$$\int_C (4x + 2y - z)\, dx + (2x - 2y + z)\, dy + (-x + y + 2z)\, dz$$

is independent of the path, and evaluate the integral if C is any sectionally smooth curve from $(4, -2, 1)$ to $(-1, 2, 0)$.

Solution   Let

$$M(x, y, z) = 4x + 2y - z \qquad N(x, y, z) = 2x - 2y + z \qquad R(x, y, z) = -x + y + 2z$$
$$M_y(x, y, z) = 2 \qquad\qquad N_x(x, y, z) = 2 \qquad\qquad R_x(x, y, z) = -1$$
$$M_z(x, y, z) = -1 \qquad\qquad N_z(x, y, z) = 1 \qquad\qquad R_y(x, y, z) = 1$$

Because

$$M_y(x, y, z) = N_x(x, y, z) \qquad M_z(x, y, z) = R_x(x, y, z) \qquad N_z(x, y, z) = R_y(x, y, z)$$

the vector field $(4x + 2y - z)\mathbf{i} + (2x - 2y + z)\mathbf{j} + (-x + y + 2z)\mathbf{k}$ is conservative. Therefore from Theorem 14.3.3 the line integral is independent of the path. We take for the path the line segment from $(4, -2, 1)$ to $(-1, 2, 0)$. A set of direction numbers of this line is $[5, -4, 1]$. Therefore equations of the line are

$$\frac{x + 1}{5} = \frac{y - 2}{-4} = \frac{z}{1}$$

Parametric equations of the line segment are

$$x = -5t - 1 \qquad y = 4t + 2 \qquad z = -t \qquad -1 \le t \le 0$$

Therefore

$$\int_C (4x + 2y - z)\, dx + (2x - 2y + z)\, dy + (-x + y + 2z)\, dz$$

$$= \int_{-1}^{0} [4(-5t - 1) + 2(4t + 2) - (-t)](-5\, dt)$$

$$+ \int_{-1}^{0} [2(-5t - 1) - 2(4t + 2) + (-t)](4\, dt)$$

$$+ \int_{-1}^{0} [-(-5t - 1) + (4t + 2) + 2(-t)](-dt)$$

$$= \int_{-1}^{0} (-28t - 27)\, dt$$

$$= -14t^2 - 27t \Big]_{-1}^{0}$$

$$= -13 \qquad \blacktriangleleft$$

The line integral in Example 4 can be computed by finding a potential function for the conservative vector field $(4x + 2y - z)\mathbf{i} + (2x - 2y + z)\mathbf{j} + (-x + y + 2z)\mathbf{k}$. You are asked to do this in Exercise 31.

▶ **EXAMPLE 5**   Suppose $\mathbf{F}$ is the gravitational force field exerted by a particle of mass M units at the origin on a particle of mass 1 unit at the point $P(x, y, z)$. Then from Section 14.1,

$$\mathbf{F}(x, y, z) = \frac{-GM}{(x^2 + y^2 + z^2)^{3/2}} (x\mathbf{i} + y\mathbf{j} + z\mathbf{k})$$

Find the work done by the force $\mathbf{F}$ in moving a particle of mass 1 unit along a smooth curve C from $(0, 3, 4)$ to $(2, 2, 1)$.

Solution   In Illustration 5 of Section 14.1 we showed that **F** is conservative and that a potential function for **F** is given by

$$\phi(x, y, z) = \frac{GM}{\sqrt{x^2 + y^2 + z^2}}$$

If W is the measure of the work done in moving a particle of mass 1 unit along C,

$$W = \int_C \mathbf{F} \cdot d\mathbf{R}$$

From Theorem 14.3.3, the line integral is independent of the path, and

$$W = \phi(2, 2, 1) - \phi(0, 3, 4)$$

$$= \frac{GM}{\sqrt{2^2 + 2^2 + 1^2}} - \frac{GM}{\sqrt{0^2 + 3^2 + 4^2}}$$

$$= \frac{GM}{3} - \frac{GM}{5}$$

$$= \tfrac{2}{15} GM \qquad\qquad\qquad \blacktriangleleft$$

We now show how the results of this section lead to an important conclusion in physics. If the motion of a particle is caused by a conservative force field **F**, the **potential energy** of the particle at the point (x, y, z) is defined to be a scalar field E such that

$$\mathbf{F}(x, y, z) = -\nabla E(x, y, z)$$

That is, $-E$ is a potential function of **F**. We shall use the notation $E(P)$ to denote the potential energy of the particle at the point P. If W is the measure of the work done by **F** in moving a particle along a sectionally smooth curve C from point A to point B, then from Theorem 14.3.3,

$$W = \int_C \mathbf{F} \cdot d\mathbf{R}$$

$$W = -E(x, y, z)\Big]_A^B$$

$$W = -[E(B) - E(A)]$$

$$W = E(A) - E(B) \tag{3}$$

Thus W is the difference in the potential energies of the particle at A and B.

Now suppose that the particle is at point A at time t_1 and at point B at time t_2 and the curve C has the vector equation

$$\mathbf{R}(t) = f(t)\mathbf{i} + g(t)\mathbf{j} + h(t)\mathbf{k} \qquad t_1 \leq t \leq t_2$$

Then the velocity and acceleration vectors at t are $\mathbf{V}(t)$ and $\mathbf{A}(t)$ defined by

$$\mathbf{V}(t) = \mathbf{R}'(t) \quad \text{and} \quad \mathbf{A}(t) = \mathbf{V}'(t)$$

The speed of the particle at t is denoted by $v(t)$, where $v(t) = \| \mathbf{V}(t) \|$. Then another formula for computing W is given by

$$W = \int_C \mathbf{F} \cdot d\mathbf{R}$$

$$W = \int_{t_1}^{t_2} \mathbf{F}(\mathbf{R}(t)) \cdot \mathbf{R}'(t) \, dt$$

$$W = \int_{t_1}^{t_2} \mathbf{F}(\mathbf{R}(t)) \cdot \mathbf{V}(t) \, dt \tag{4}$$

Newton's second law of motion states that if a force $\mathbf{F}$ is acting on a particle of mass m units, then

$$\mathbf{F}(\mathbf{R}(t)) = m\mathbf{A}(t)$$
$$\Leftrightarrow \quad \mathbf{F}(\mathbf{R}(t)) = m\mathbf{V}'(t)$$

Substituting from this equation in (4) we have

$$W = \int_{t_1}^{t_2} m[\mathbf{V}'(t) \cdot \mathbf{V}(t)] \, dt$$

Because $D_t[\mathbf{V}(t) \cdot \mathbf{V}(t)] = 2\mathbf{V}'(t) \cdot \mathbf{V}(t)$ and $\mathbf{V}(t) \cdot \mathbf{V}(t) = [v(t)]^2$, we get

$$W = \tfrac{1}{2}m \int_{t_1}^{t_2} D_t[\mathbf{V}(t) \cdot \mathbf{V}(t)] \, dt$$

$$W = \tfrac{1}{2}m \int_{t_1}^{t_2} D_t[v(t)]^2 \, dt$$

$$W = \tfrac{1}{2}m[v(t)]^2 \Big]_{t_1}^{t_2}$$

$$W = \tfrac{1}{2}m[v(t_2)]^2 - \tfrac{1}{2}m[v(t_1)]^2 \tag{5}$$

In physics the **kinetic energy** of a particle is defined to be $\tfrac{1}{2}mv^2$. Therefore Equation (5) states that the work done in moving a particle along C from point A to point B is the change in kinetic energy of the particle. If we use the notation $K(P)$ to indicate the kinetic energy of a particle at point P, (5) can be written as

$$W = K(B) - K(A)$$

Equating the values of W from (3) and this equation, we have

$$E(A) - E(B) = K(B) - K(A)$$
$$E(A) + K(A) = E(B) + K(B)$$

The above equation states that the sums of the potential and kinetic energies are equal at the initial point A and the terminal point B. Because A and B can be any points on C, the sum of the two energies is constant along C; that is, the total energy of the particle remains unchanged during the motion. This fact is a major concept in physics called the **law of conservation of energy.** For this reason the terminology *conservative* is used for a force field that is a gradient.

EXERCISES 14.3

In Exercises 1 through 12, use the result of the indicated exercise in Exercises 14.1 to prove that the value of the line integral is independent of the path. Then evaluate the line integral by applying either Theorem 14.3.1 or 14.3.3 and using the potential function found in the indicated exercise. In each exercise, C is any sectionally smooth curve from point A to point B.

1. $\int_C y\, dx + x\, dy$; *A* is (1, 4) and *B* is (3, 2); Exercise 21

2. $\int_C x\, dx + y\, dy$; *A* is (−5, 2) and *B* is (1, 3); Exercise 22

3. $\int_C e^x \sin y\, dx + e^x \cos y\, dy$; *A* is (0, 0) and *B* is $(2, \frac{1}{2}\pi)$; Exercise 23

4. $\int_C (\sin y \sinh x + \cos y \cosh x)\, dx$
   $+ (\cos y \cosh x - \sin 2y \sinh x)\, dy$;
   A is (1, 0) and *B* is (2, π); Exercise 24

5. $\int_C (2xy^2 - y^3)\, dx + (2x^2y - 3xy^2 + 2)\, dy$; *A* is (−3, −1) and *B* is (1, 2); Exercise 25

6. $\int_C (3x^2 + 2y - y^2e^x)\, dx + (2x - 2ye^x)\, dy$; *A* is (0, 2) and *B* is (1, −3); Exercise 26

7. $\int_C (x^2 - y)\, dx - (x - 3z)\, dy + (z + 3y)\, dz$; *A* is (−3, 1, 2) and *B* is (3, 0, 4); Exercise 27

8. $\int_C yz\, dx + xz\, dy + xy\, dz$; *A* is (0, −2, 5) and *B* is (4, 1, −3); Exercise 28

9. $\int_C (ze^x + e^y)\, dx + (xe^y - e^z)\, dy + (-ye^z + e^x)\, dz$; *A* is (1, 0, 2) and *B* is (0, 2, 1); Exercise 29

10. $\int_C (\tan y + 2xy \sec z)\, dx + (x \sec^2 y + x^2 \sec z)\, dy$
    $+ \sec z(x^2y \tan z - \sec z)\, dz$;
    A is $(2, \frac{1}{6}\pi, 0)$ and *B* is $(3, \frac{1}{4}\pi, \frac{1}{3}\pi)$; Exercise 30

11. $\int_C (2x \cos y - 3)\, dx - (x^2 \sin y + z^2)\, dy$
    $- (2yz - 2)dz$;
    A is (−1, 0, 3) and *B* is (1, π, 0); Exercise 31

12. $\int_C (2y^3 - 8xz^2)\, dx + (6xy^2 + 1)\, dy$
    $- (8x^2z + 3z^2)\, dz$;
    A is (2, 0, 0) and *B* is (3, 2, 1); Exercise 32

*In Exercises 13 through 20, show that the value of the line integral $\int_C \mathbf{F} \cdot d\mathbf{R}$ for the given **F** and C is independent of the path, and evaluate the line integral.*

13. $\mathbf{F}(x, y) = 2(x - y)\mathbf{i} + 2(3y - x)\mathbf{j}$; *C* is the first quadrant arc of the circle $x^2 + y^2 = 9$ from the point on the *x* axis to the point on the *y* axis.

14. $\mathbf{F}(x, y) = (3x^2 + 6xy - 2y^2)\mathbf{i}$
    $+ (3x^2 - 4xy + 3y^2)\mathbf{j}$;
    C is the first quadrant arc of the ellipse $4x^2 + 9y^2 = 36$ from the point on the *x* axis to the point on the *y* axis.

15. $\mathbf{F}(x, y) = (4e^{2x} - 3e^x e^y)\mathbf{i} + (2e^{2y} - 3e^x e^y)\mathbf{j}$; *C* is the arc of the parabola $y^2 = 4x$ from the vertex to the endpoint of the latus rectum in the first quadrant.

16. $\mathbf{F}(x, y) = e^x \cos y\mathbf{i} - e^x \sin y\mathbf{j}$; *C* is the segment of the line $3x + 4y = 12$ from the point where it intersects the *y* axis to the point where it intersects the *x* axis.

17. $\mathbf{F}(x, y, z) = 2x\mathbf{i} + 3y^2\mathbf{j} + \mathbf{k}$; *C* is the trace of the ellipsoid $4x^2 + 4y^2 + z^2 = 9$ in the *xz* plane from the positive *x* axis to the positive *z* axis.

18. $\mathbf{F}(x, y, z) = (2xy + z^2)\mathbf{i} + (x^2 - 2yz)\mathbf{j}$
    $+ (2xz - y^2)\mathbf{k}$;
    C is the trace of the sphere $x^2 + y^2 + z^2 = 1$ in the *yz* plane from the positive *y* axis to the positive *z* axis.

19. $\mathbf{F}(x, y, z) = 2ye^{2x}\mathbf{i} + e^{2x}\mathbf{j} + 3z^2\mathbf{k}$; *C* is any sectionally smooth curve from the point (ln 2, 1, 1) to the point (ln 2, 2, 2).

20. $\mathbf{F}(x, y, z) = \left(\frac{1}{z} - \frac{y}{x^2}\right)\mathbf{i} + \left(\frac{1}{x} + \frac{z}{y^2}\right)\mathbf{j} - \left(\frac{1}{y} + \frac{x}{z^2}\right)\mathbf{k}$;
    C is any sectionally smooth curve from the point (1, 2, −1) to the point (2, 4, −2).

In Exercises 21 through 30, show that the value of the line integral is independent of the path, and compute the value in any convenient manner. In each exercise, C is any sectionally smooth curve from point A to point B.

21. $\int_C (2y - x)\, dx + (y^2 + 2x)\, dy$; *A* is (0, −1) and *B* is (1, 2).

22. $\int_C (\ln x + 2y)\, dx + (e^y + 2x)\, dy$; *A* is (3, 1) and *B* is (1, 3).

23. $\int_C \tan y\, dx + x \sec^2 y\, dy$; *A* is (−2, 0) and *B* is $(4, \frac{1}{4}\pi)$.

24. $\int_C \sin y\, dx + (\sin y + x \cos y)\, dy$; *A* is (−2, 0) and *B* is $(2, \frac{1}{6}\pi)$.

25. $\int_C \frac{2y}{(xy + 1)^2}\, dx + \frac{2x}{(xy + 1)^2}\, dy$; *A* is (0, 2) and *B* is (1, 0).

26. $\int_C \dfrac{x}{x^2 + y^2 + z^2}\, dx + \dfrac{y}{x^2 + y^2 + z^2}\, dy$

$$+ \dfrac{z}{x^2 + y^2 + z^2}\, dz;$$

A is $(1, 0, 0)$ and B is $(1, 2, 3)$.

27. $\int_C (y + z)\, dx + (x + z)\, dy + (x + y)\, dz;$ A is $(0, 0, 0)$ and B is $(1, 1, 1)$.

28. $\int_C (yz + x)\, dx + (xz + y)\, dy + (xy + z)\, dz;$ A is $(0, 0, 0)$ and B is $(1, 1, 1)$.

29. $\int_C (e^x \sin y + yz)\, dx + (e^x \cos y + z \sin y + xz)\, dy$
$$+ (xy - \cos y)\, dz;$$

A is $(2, 0, 1)$ and B is $(0, \pi, 3)$.

30. $\int_C (2x \ln yz - 5ye^x)\, dx - (5e^x - x^2y^{-1})\, dy$
$$+ (x^2z^{-1} + 2z)\, dz;$$

A is $(2, 1, 1)$ and B is $(3, 1, e)$.

31. Evaluate the line integral in Example 4 by finding a potential function for the conservative vector field

$$(4x + 2y - z)\mathbf{i} + (2x - 2y + z)\mathbf{j} + (-x + y + 2z)\mathbf{k}$$

and applying Theorem 14.3.3.

32. Prove Theorem 14.3.3.

In Exercises 33 through 36, find the total work done in moving a particle along arc C if the motion is caused by the force field $\mathbf{F}$. Assume the arc is measured in meters and the force is measured in newtons. Hint: First show that $\mathbf{F}$ is conservative.

33. $\mathbf{F}(x, y) = 3(x + y)^2\mathbf{i} + 3(x + y)^2\mathbf{j};$ C: the arc of the parabola $y = x^2$ from the vertex to the point $(2, 4)$

34. $\mathbf{F}(x, y) = (2xy - 5y + 2y^2)\mathbf{i} + (x^2 - 5x + 4xy)\mathbf{j};$ C: the quarter circle $\mathbf{R}(t) = 2 \cos t\mathbf{i} + 2 \sin t\mathbf{j},$ $0 \le t \le \tfrac{1}{2}\pi$

35. $\mathbf{F}(x, y, z) = 2y^2z^3\mathbf{i} + 4xyz^3\mathbf{j} + 6xy^2z^2\mathbf{k};$ C: the arc of $\mathbf{R}(t) = t\mathbf{i} + t^2\mathbf{j} + t^3\mathbf{k}$ from $t = 1$ to $t = 2$

36. $\mathbf{F}(x, y, z) = 4y^2z\mathbf{i} + 8xyz\mathbf{j} + 4(3z^3 + xy^2)\mathbf{k};$ C: the arc of $\mathbf{R}(t) = 3 \cos t\mathbf{i} + 3 \sin t\mathbf{j} + t\mathbf{k}$ from $t = 0$ to $t = \tfrac{1}{3}\pi$

37. If $\mathbf{F}$ is the inverse-square force field defined by

$$\mathbf{F}(x, y, z) = \dfrac{k(x\mathbf{i} + y\mathbf{j} + z\mathbf{k})}{(x^2 + y^2 + z^2)^{3/2}}$$

where k is a positive constant, find the work done by $\mathbf{F}$ in moving a particle along the segment of a line from the point $(3, 0, 0)$ to $(3, 0, 4)$. Evaluate the line integral by two methods: **(a)** Use a potential function for $\mathbf{F}$; **(b)** do not use a potential function for $\mathbf{F}$.

14.4 GREEN'S THEOREM

Green's theorem, named for the English mathematician and physicist George Green (1793–1841) who presented it in a paper on applications of mathematics to electricity and magnetism, expresses a double integral over a plane region R in terms of a line integral around a boundary curve of R.

At this time you should review Definitions 9.1.1–9.1.3 pertaining to curves that are *smooth, closed,* and *simple,* respectively. The statement of Green's theorem refers to a line integral around a sectionally smooth simple closed curve C that forms the boundary of a plane region, and the direction along C is counterclockwise. Figure 1 shows such a region R with the required boundary curve C. The line integral around C in the counterclockwise direction is denoted by $\oint_C$.

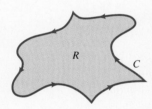

FIGURE 1

14.4.1 Green's Theorem

Let M and N be functions of two variables x and y such that they have continuous first partial derivatives on an open disk B in R^2. If C is a sectionally smooth simple closed curve lying entirely in B, and if R is the region bounded by C, then

$$\oint_C M(x, y)\, dx + N(x, y)\, dy = \iint_R \left(\dfrac{\partial N}{\partial x} - \dfrac{\partial M}{\partial y}\right) dA$$

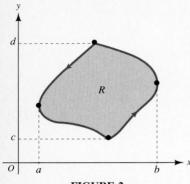

FIGURE 2

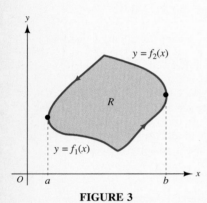

FIGURE 3

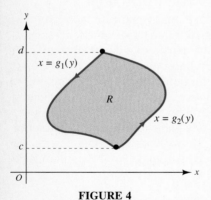

FIGURE 4

The proof of Green's theorem for all regions bounded by curves that are sectionally smooth, simple, and closed belongs to a course in advanced calculus. However, we shall prove the theorem for a particular kind of region, one for which each horizontal line and each vertical line intersect it in at most two points. The proof follows.

Proof   Let R be a region in the xy plane that can be defined by either

$$R = \{(x, y) \mid a \le x \le b, f_1(x) \le y \le f_2(x)\} \tag{1}$$

or

$$R = \{(x, y) \mid c \le y \le d, g_1(y) \le x \le g_2(y)\} \tag{2}$$

where the functions f_1, f_2, g_1, and g_2 are smooth. Figure 2 shows such a region R, regarded as being defined by (1) in Figure 3 and by (2) in Figure 4. The proof consists of showing that

$$\oint_C M(x, y)\, dx = -\iint_R \frac{\partial M}{\partial y}\, dA \tag{3}$$

and

$$\oint_C N(x, y)\, dy = \iint_R \frac{\partial N}{\partial x}\, dA \tag{4}$$

To prove (3) we treat R as a region defined by (1). Refer to Figure 3. Let C_1 be the graph of $y = f_1(x)$ from $x = a$ to $x = b$; that is, C_1 is the lower part of the boundary curve C going from left to right. Let C_2 be the graph of $y = f_2(x)$ from $x = b$ to $x = a$; that is, C_2 is the upper part of the boundary curve C going from right to left. Consider the line integral $\oint_C M(x, y)\, dx$.

$$\oint_C M(x,y)\, dx = \int_{C_1} M(x, y)\, dx + \int_{C_2} M(x, y)\, dx$$

$$= \int_a^b M(x, f_1(x))\, dx + \int_b^a M(x, f_2(x))\, dx$$

$$= \int_a^b M(x, f_1(x))\, dx - \int_a^b M(x, f_2(x))\, dx$$

$$= \int_a^b [M(x, f_1(x)) - M(x, f_2(x))]\, dx \tag{5}$$

We now deal with the double integral $\displaystyle\iint_R \frac{\partial M}{\partial y}\, dA$, where R is still considered to be defined by (1). Then

$$\iint_R \frac{\partial M}{\partial y}\, dA = \int_a^b \int_{f_1(x)}^{f_2(x)} \frac{\partial M}{\partial y}\, dy\, dx$$

$$= \int_a^b \left(\int_{f_1(x)}^{f_2(x)} \frac{\partial M}{\partial y}\, dy \right) dx$$

$$= \int_a^b M(x, y) \Bigg]_{f_1(x)}^{f_2(x)} dx$$

$$= \int_a^b [M(x, f_2(x)) - M(x, f_1(x))] \, dx \tag{6}$$

By comparing (5) and (6) it follows that (3) holds.

To prove (4), R is regarded as a region defined by (2), as in Figure 4. The details of the proof are left as an exercise (see Exercise 43).

By adding corresponding members of Equations (3) and (4) we obtain Green's theorem for this region R.   ∎

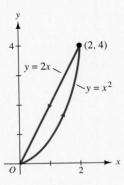

FIGURE 5

▷ **ILLUSTRATION 1**   We apply Green's theorem to evaluate the line integral $\oint_C y^2 \, dx + 4xy \, dy$, where C is the closed curve consisting of the arc of the parabola $y = x^2$ from the origin to the point $(2, 4)$ and the line segment from $(2, 4)$ to the origin. The region R with the boundary C is shown in Figure 5. From Green's theorem,

$$\oint_C y^2 \, dx + 4xy \, dy = \iint_R \left[\frac{\partial}{\partial x}(4xy) - \frac{\partial}{\partial y}(y^2) \right] dA$$

$$= \int_0^2 \int_{x^2}^{2x} (4y - 2y) \, dy \, dx$$

$$= \int_0^2 y^2 \Bigg]_{x^2}^{2x} dx$$

$$= \int_0^2 (4x^2 - x^4) \, dx$$

$$= \tfrac{4}{3}x^3 - \tfrac{1}{5}x^5 \Bigg]_0^2$$

$$= \tfrac{64}{15}$$

To show the advantage of using Green's theorem we evaluate the same line integral by the method of Section 14.2. If C_1 is the arc of the parabola $y = x^2$ from $(0, 0)$ to $(2, 4)$ and C_2 is the line segment from $(2, 4)$ to $(0, 0)$ then

$$\oint_C y^2 \, dx + 4xy \, dy = \int_{C_1} y^2 \, dx + 4xy \, dy + \int_{C_2} y^2 \, dx + 4xy \, dy$$

Parametric equations for C_1 are

$$x = t \qquad y = t^2 \qquad 0 \le t \le 2$$

Therefore

$$\int_{C_1} y^2 \, dx + 4xy \, dy = \int_0^2 (t^2)^2 \, dt + 4(t)(t^2)(2t \, dt)$$

$$= \int_0^2 9t^4 \, dt$$

$$= \frac{9}{5} t^5 \Big]_0^2$$

$$= \frac{288}{5}$$

Arc C_2 can be represented parametrically by

$$x = t \qquad y = 2t \qquad \text{from } t = 2 \text{ to } t = 0$$

Thus

$$\int_{C_2} y^2 \, dx + 4xy \, dy = \int_2^0 (2t)^2 \, dt + 4(t)(2t)(2 \, dt)$$

$$= \int_2^0 20t^2 \, dt$$

$$= \frac{20}{3} t^3 \Big]_2^0$$

$$= -\frac{160}{3}$$

Hence

$$\oint_C y^2 \, dx + 4xy \, dy = \frac{288}{5} - \frac{160}{3}$$

$$= \frac{64}{15}$$

which agrees with the result obtained by using Green's theorem.   ◀

▶ **EXAMPLE 1**   Use Green's theorem to find the total work done in moving an object in the counterclockwise direction once around the circle $x^2 + y^2 = a^2$ if the motion is caused by the force field $\mathbf{F}(x, y) = (\sin x - y)\mathbf{i} + (e^y - x^2)\mathbf{j}$. Assume the arc is measured in meters and the force is measured in newtons.

Solution   If W joules is the work done, then

$$W = \oint_C (\sin x - y) \, dx + (e^y - x^2) \, dy$$

where C is the circle $x^2 + y^2 = a^2$. From Green's theorem,

$$W = \iint_R \left[\frac{\partial}{\partial x}(e^y - x^2) - \frac{\partial}{\partial y}(\sin x - y) \right] dA$$

$$= \iint_R (-2x + 1) \, dA$$

We use polar coordinates to evaluate the double integral, with $x = r \cos \theta$ and $dA = r \, dr \, d\theta$. Then

$$W = \int_0^{2\pi} \int_0^a (-2r \cos \theta + 1) r \, dr \, d\theta$$

$$= \int_0^{2\pi} \int_0^a (-2r^2 \cos \theta + r) \, dr \, d\theta$$

$$= \int_0^{2\pi} \left. -\frac{2}{3} r^3 \cos \theta + \frac{r^2}{2} \right]_0^a d\theta$$

$$= \int_0^{2\pi} \left(-\frac{2}{3} a^3 \cos \theta + \frac{a^2}{2} \right) d\theta$$

$$= \left. -\frac{2}{3} a^3 \sin \theta + \frac{a^2}{2} \theta \right]_0^{2\pi}$$

$$= \pi a^2$$

Conclusion: The work done is πa^2 joules.   ◀

The following theorem, which is a consequence of Green's theorem, gives a useful method for computing the area of a region bounded by a sectionally smooth simple closed curve.

14.4.2 Theorem

If R is a region having as its boundary a sectionally smooth simple closed curve C, and A square units is the area of R, then

$$A = \frac{1}{2} \oint_C x \, dy - y \, dx$$

Proof   In the statement of Green's theorem, let $M(x, y) = -\frac{1}{2}y$ and $N(x, y) = \frac{1}{2}x$. Then

$$\oint_C -\frac{1}{2} y \, dx + \frac{1}{2} x \, dy = \iint_R \left[\frac{\partial}{\partial x}\left(\frac{1}{2}x \right) - \frac{\partial}{\partial y}\left(-\frac{1}{2}y \right) \right] dA$$

$$= \iint_R \left(\frac{1}{2} + \frac{1}{2} \right) dA$$

$$= \iint_R dA$$

Because $\iint_R dA$ is the measure of the area of R,

$$\frac{1}{2} \oint_C x \, dy - y \, dx = A$$

▶ **EXAMPLE 2**   Use Theorem 14.4.2 to find the area of the region enclosed by the ellipse

$$\frac{x^2}{a^2} + \frac{y^2}{b^2} = 1$$

Solution   Parametric equations for the ellipse are

$$x = a \cos t \qquad y = b \sin t \qquad 0 \le t \le 2\pi$$

Then $dx = -a \sin t \, dt$ and $dy = b \cos t \, dt$. If C is the ellipse and A square units is the area of the region enclosed by C, then from Theorem 14.4.2,

$$A = \frac{1}{2} \oint_C x \, dy - y \, dx$$

$$= \frac{1}{2} \int_0^{2\pi} [(a \cos t)(b \cos t \, dt) - (b \sin t)(-a \sin t \, dt)]$$

$$= \frac{1}{2} \int_0^{2\pi} ab(\cos^2 t + \sin^2 t) \, dt$$

$$= \frac{1}{2} ab \int_0^{2\pi} dt$$

$$= \pi ab$$

<u>Conclusion:</u>   The area is πab square units.   ◀

▶ **EXAMPLE 3**   Use Green's theorem to evaluate the line integral

$$\oint_C (x^4 - 3y) \, dx + (2y^3 + 4x) \, dy$$

if C is the ellipse $\dfrac{x^2}{9} + \dfrac{y^2}{4} = 1$.

Solution   From Green's theorem,

$$\oint_C (x^4 - 3y) \, dx + (2y^3 + 4x) \, dy = \iint_R \left[\frac{\partial}{\partial x}(2y^3 + 4x) - \frac{\partial}{\partial y}(x^4 - 3y) \right] dA$$

$$= \iint_R (4 + 3) \, dA$$

$$= 7 \iint_R dA$$

The double integral $\iint_R dA$ is the measure of the area of the region enclosed by the ellipse. From Example 2 with $a = 3$ and $b = 2$, the area of the region enclosed by the ellipse is 6π square units. Therefore

$$\oint_C (x^4 - 3y) \, dx + (2y^3 + 4x) \, dy = 42\pi$$ ◀

There are two vector forms of Green's theorem that we shall proceed to obtain. Let C be a sectionally smooth simple closed curve in the xy plane. Suppose a vector equation of C is

$$\mathbf{R}(s) = x\mathbf{i} + y\mathbf{j}$$

and $x = f(s)$ and $y = g(s)$, where s units is the length of arc measured in the counterclockwise direction from a particular point P_0 on C to the point P on C. Then if $\mathbf{T}(s)$ is the unit tangent vector of C at P, $\mathbf{T}(s) = D_s \mathbf{R}(s)$. Thus

$$\mathbf{T}(s) = \frac{dx}{ds}\mathbf{i} + \frac{dy}{ds}\mathbf{j} \qquad (7)$$

The vector $\mathbf{N}(s)$ defined by

$$\mathbf{N}(s) = \frac{dy}{ds}\mathbf{i} - \frac{dx}{ds}\mathbf{j} \qquad (8)$$

is a unit normal vector of C at P. This unit normal vector is selected rather than its negative so that when the direction along C is counterclockwise, $\mathbf{N}(s)$ will point outward from the region R bounded by C. It is called the **unit outward normal.** See Figure 6. Let

$$\mathbf{F}(x, y) = M(x, y)\mathbf{i} + N(x, y)\mathbf{j}$$

where M and N satisfy the hypothesis of Green's theorem. Because

$$\mathbf{F}(x, y) \cdot \mathbf{N}(s) \, ds = [M(x, y)\mathbf{i} + N(x, y)\mathbf{j}] \cdot \left(\frac{dy}{ds}\mathbf{i} - \frac{dx}{ds}\mathbf{j}\right) ds$$

$$= M(x, y) \, dy - N(x, y) \, dx$$

then

$$\oint_C \mathbf{F}(x, y) \cdot \mathbf{N}(s) \, ds = \oint_C -N(x, y) \, dx + \mathbf{M}(x, y) \, dy$$

We apply Green's theorem to the line integral on the right side of this equation and we have

$$\oint_C \mathbf{F}(x, y) \cdot \mathbf{N}(s) \, ds = \iint_R \left[\frac{\partial M}{\partial x} - \frac{\partial}{\partial y}(-N)\right] dA$$

$$= \iint_R \left(\frac{\partial M}{\partial x} + \frac{\partial N}{\partial y}\right) dA$$

$$= \iint_R \text{div } \mathbf{F} \, dA$$

This vector form of Green's theorem is stated formally as the following theorem, named after the German mathematician and scientist Karl Gauss (1777–1855).

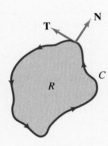

FIGURE 6

14.4.3 Gauss's Divergence Theorem in the Plane

Let the functions M and N, the curve C, and the region R be as defined in Green's theorem. If $\mathbf{F}(x, y) = M(x, y)\mathbf{i} + N(x, y)\mathbf{j}$ and $\mathbf{N}(s)$ is the unit outward normal vector of C at P, where s units is the length of arc measured in the counterclockwise direction from a particular point P_0 on C to P, then

$$\oint_C \mathbf{F} \cdot \mathbf{N}\, ds = \iint_R \operatorname{div} \mathbf{F}\, dA$$

▶ **EXAMPLE 4**   Verify Gauss's divergence theorem in the plane if

$$\mathbf{F}(x, y) = 2y\mathbf{i} + 5x\mathbf{j}$$

and R is the region bounded by the circle $x^2 + y^2 = 1$.

Solution   The boundary of R is the unit circle that can be represented parametrically by

$$x = \cos s \qquad y = \sin s \qquad 0 \le s \le 2\pi$$

where s units is the length of arc from the point where $s = 0$ to the point P on C. Then a vector equation of C is

$$\mathbf{R}(s) = \cos s\,\mathbf{i} + \sin s\,\mathbf{j} \qquad 0 \le s \le 2\pi$$

From (8) the unit outward normal is

$$\mathbf{N}(s) = \cos s\,\mathbf{i} + \sin s\,\mathbf{j}$$

At a point $P(\cos s, \sin s)$ on C, $\mathbf{F}$ is $2\sin s\,\mathbf{i} + 5\cos s\,\mathbf{j}$. Therefore

$$\oint_C \mathbf{F} \cdot \mathbf{N}\, ds = \int_0^{2\pi} (2\sin s\,\mathbf{i} + 5\cos s\,\mathbf{j}) \cdot (\cos s\,\mathbf{i} + \sin s\,\mathbf{j})\, ds$$

$$= \int_0^{2\pi} (2\sin s \cos s + 5\sin s \cos s)\, ds$$

$$= 7\int_0^{2\pi} \sin s \cos s\, ds$$

$$= \frac{7}{2}\sin^2 s \Big]_0^{2\pi}$$

$$= 0$$

Because $M = 2y$, $\dfrac{\partial M}{\partial x} = 0$, and because $N = 5x$, $\dfrac{\partial N}{\partial y} = 0$. Thus

$$\iint_R \operatorname{div} \mathbf{F}\, dA = \iint_R \left(\frac{\partial M}{\partial x} + \frac{\partial N}{\partial y}\right) dA$$

$$= 0$$

We have therefore verified Gauss's divergence theorem in the plane for this $\mathbf{F}$ and R.   ◀

Note in Example 4 that $\iint_R \text{div } \mathbf{F} \; dA$ is easier to compute than $\oint_C \mathbf{F} \cdot \mathbf{N} \; ds$.

If $\mathbf{F}$ is a vector field and div $\mathbf{F} = 0$, then $\mathbf{F}$ is said to be **divergence free.** The vector field in Example 4 is divergence free. In the study of hydrodynamics (fluid motion), if the velocity field of a fluid is divergence free, the fluid is called **incompressible.** In the theory of electricity and magnetism, a vector field that is divergence free is said to be **solenoidal.**

We now use Gauss's divergence theorem in the plane to give a physical interpretation of the divergence of a vector field. Let the functions M and N, the region R, and the curve C be as defined in Green's theorem. Suppose $\mathbf{F}$ is the velocity field of a two-dimensional fluid (constant depth) and $\mathbf{F}$ is defined by $\mathbf{F}(x, y) = M(x, y)\mathbf{i} + N(x, y)\mathbf{j}$. Suppose that the fluid flows through region R having curve C as its boundary, for which the direction along C is counterclockwise. We assume that the fluid has a constant density in R, and for convenience let the density have unit measure. The flow of the velocity field $\mathbf{F}$ across C is the rate at which the fluid crosses C in a direction perpendicular to C. We shall show how this flow can be expressed as a line integral.

Let s denote the length of arc of curve C measured from a particular point P_0 to a point P. Divide the curve C into n arcs and let $\Delta_i s$ be the length of the ith arc containing the point $P_i(x_i, y_i)$ where s_i is the length of arc of C from P_0 to P_i. Because $\mathbf{F}$ is continuous, an approximation of the velocity of the fluid at each point of the ith arc is $\mathbf{F}(x_i, y_i)$. The amount of fluid that crosses the arc per unit of time is given approximately by the area of a parallelogram having one pair of opposite sides of length $\Delta_i s$ units and an altitude of length $\mathbf{F}(x_i, y_i) \cdot \mathbf{N}(s_i)$ units, where $\mathbf{N}(s_i)$ is the unit outward normal vector of C at $P_i(x_i, y_i)$. See Figure 7. The area of the parallelogram is $\mathbf{F}(x_i, y_i) \cdot \mathbf{N}(s_i) \, \Delta_i s$ square units. The total amount of fluid that crosses C per unit of time is given approximately by

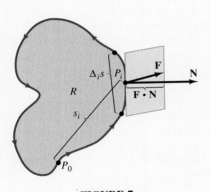

FIGURE 7

$$\sum_{i=1}^{n} \mathbf{F}(x_i, y_i) \cdot \mathbf{N}(s_i) \, \Delta_i s$$

Taking the limit of this summation as n increases without bound and as each $\Delta_i s$ approaches zero we obtain the line integral

$$\oint_C \mathbf{F}(x, y) \cdot \mathbf{N}(s) \; ds$$

which is called the **flux** of $\mathbf{F}$ across C.

Now let $\bar{P}(\bar{x}, \bar{y})$ be a particular point in region R. Consider a circle having its center at $\bar{P}$ and having a small radius δ, and denote this circle by C_δ. Let R_δ be the region enclosed by C_δ. Then

$$\text{flux of } \mathbf{F} \text{ across } C_\delta = \oint_{C_\delta} \mathbf{F}(x, y) \cdot \mathbf{N} \; ds$$

Applying Theorem 14.4.3 we have

$$\text{flux of } \mathbf{F} \text{ across } C_\delta = \iint_{R_\delta} \text{div } \mathbf{F} \; dA$$

If M_x and N_y are continuous on R_δ, then div $\mathbf{F}$ is continuous there, and for small δ, div $\mathbf{F}$ on R_δ is approximately div $\mathbf{F}(\bar{x}, \bar{y})$. Thus

$$\text{flux of } \mathbf{F} \text{ across } C_\delta \approx \iint_R \text{div } \mathbf{F}(\bar{x}, \bar{y}) \, dA$$

Because div $\mathbf{F}(\bar{x}, \bar{y})$ is constant and $\iint_{R_\delta} dA$ is the measure of the area of a circle of radius δ, we have

$$\text{flux of } \mathbf{F} \text{ across } C_\delta \approx \text{div } \mathbf{F}(\bar{x}, \bar{y})(\pi\delta^2) \tag{9}$$

Remember that the flux of $\mathbf{F}$ across C_δ is the total amount of fluid that crosses C_δ per unit of time. Therefore, from (9), div $\mathbf{F}(x, y)$ can be interpreted as the approximate measure of the rate of flow of the fluid per unit area away from the point $(\bar{x}, \bar{y})$. If div $\mathbf{F}(\bar{x}, \bar{y}) > 0$, the fluid is said to have a **source** at $(\bar{x}, \bar{y})$. If div $\mathbf{F}(\bar{x}, \bar{y}) < 0$, the fluid has a **sink** at $(\bar{x}, \bar{y})$. If $\mathbf{F}$ is divergence free at all points in a region, then there are no sources or sinks in the region. As mentioned above, in such a case the fluid is incompressible.

The word *flux* normally means flow; however, the terminology *flux* is applied to vector fields in general, not just to those associated with the velocity of a fluid. Thus if $\mathbf{F}$ is a vector field

$$\text{flux of } \mathbf{F} \text{ across } C = \oint_C \mathbf{F} \cdot \mathbf{N} \, ds \tag{10}$$

▶ **EXAMPLE 5** The velocity field of a fluid is defined by

$$\mathbf{F}(x, y) = (5x - y)\mathbf{i} + (x^2 - 3y)\mathbf{j}$$

Find the rate of flow of the fluid out of a region R bounded by a smooth closed curve C and whose area is 150 cm².

Solution The rate of flow of the fluid is given by the flux of $\mathbf{F}$ across C. From (10) and Gauss's divergence theorem in the plane,

$$\text{flux} = \oint_C \mathbf{F} \cdot \mathbf{N} \, ds$$

$$= \iint_R \text{div } \mathbf{F} \, dA$$

$$= \iint_R \left[\frac{\partial}{\partial x}(5x - y) + \frac{\partial}{\partial y}(x^2 - 3y) \right] dA$$

$$= \iint_R (5 - 3) \, dA$$

$$= 2 \iint_R dA$$

Because the area of R is 150 cm², $\iint_R dA = 150$. Thus

$$\text{flux} = 300$$

Conclusion: The rate of flow of the fluid out of the region is 300 cm² per unit of time. ◀

To obtain the second vector form of Green's theorem we consider the dot product of $\mathbf{F}(x, y)$ and the unit tangent vector $\mathbf{T}(s)$ defined by Equation (7). We have

$$\mathbf{F}(x, y) \cdot \mathbf{T}(s) \, ds = [M(x, y)\mathbf{i} + N(x, y)\mathbf{j}] \cdot \left(\frac{dx}{ds}\mathbf{i} + \frac{dy}{ds}\mathbf{j}\right) ds$$

$$= M(x, y) \, dx + N(x, y) \, dy$$

Thus

$$\oint_C \mathbf{F}(x, y) \cdot \mathbf{T}(s)ds = \oint_C M(x, y) \, dx + N(x, y) \, dy \qquad \text{(11)}$$

The curl of $\mathbf{F}$ in two dimensions was defined in Section 14.1 as

$$\text{curl } \mathbf{F}(x, y) = \left(\frac{\partial N}{\partial x} - \frac{\partial M}{\partial y}\right) \mathbf{k}$$

Therefore

$$\text{curl } \mathbf{F}(x, y) \cdot \mathbf{k} = \left(\frac{\partial N}{\partial x} - \frac{\partial M}{\partial y}\right) \mathbf{k} \cdot \mathbf{k}$$

$$\text{curl } \mathbf{F}(x, y) \cdot \mathbf{k} = \frac{\partial N}{\partial x} - \frac{\partial M}{\partial y}$$

Hence from this equation and (11), the equation of Green's theorem can be written

$$\oint_C \mathbf{F}(x, y) \cdot \mathbf{T}(s) \, ds = \iint_R \text{curl } \mathbf{F}(x, y) \cdot \mathbf{k} \, dA$$

This vector form of Green's theorem is stated formally as the following theorem named after the Irish mathematician and physicist George Stokes (1819–1903).

14.4.4 Stokes's Theorem in the Plane

Let the functions M and N, the curve C, and the region R be as defined in Green's theorem. If $\mathbf{F}(x, y) = M(x, y)\mathbf{i} + N(x, y)\mathbf{j}$ and $\mathbf{T}(s)$ is the unit tangent vector of C at P, where s units is the length of arc measured from a particular point P_0 on C to P, then

$$\oint_C \mathbf{F} \cdot \mathbf{T} \, ds = \iint_R \text{curl } \mathbf{F} \cdot \mathbf{k} \, dA$$

▶ **EXAMPLE 6**   Verify Stokes's theorem in the plane for $\mathbf{F}$ and region R of Example 4.

Solution   As in Example 4, the vector field $\mathbf{F}$ is defined by

$$\mathbf{F}(x, y) = 2y\mathbf{i} + 5x\mathbf{j}$$

and a vector equation of C is

$$\mathbf{R}(s) = \cos s\mathbf{i} + \sin s\mathbf{j} \qquad 0 \leq s \leq 2\pi$$

Because $\mathbf{T}(s) = D_s \mathbf{R}(s)$,

$$\mathbf{T}(s) = -\sin s\mathbf{i} + \cos s\mathbf{j}$$

At a point $P(\cos s, \sin s)$ on C, $\mathbf{F}$ is $2 \sin s\mathbf{i} + 5 \cos s\mathbf{j}$. Therefore

$$\oint_C \mathbf{F} \cdot \mathbf{T} \, ds = \int_0^{2\pi} (2 \sin s\mathbf{i} + 5 \cos s\mathbf{j}) \cdot (-\sin s\mathbf{i} + \cos s\mathbf{j}) \, ds$$

$$= \int_0^{2\pi} (-2 \sin^2 s + 5 \cos^2 s) \, ds$$

$$= -2 \int_0^{2\pi} \frac{1 - \cos 2s}{2} \, ds + 5 \int_0^{2\pi} \frac{1 + \cos 2s}{2} \, ds$$

$$= -s + \tfrac{1}{2} \sin 2s + \tfrac{5}{2}s + \tfrac{5}{4} \sin 2s \Big]_0^{2\pi}$$

$$= \tfrac{3}{2}s + \tfrac{7}{4} \sin 2s \Big]_0^{2\pi}$$

$$= 3\pi$$

Because $N = 5x$, $\dfrac{\partial N}{\partial x} = 5$, and because $M = 2y$, $\dfrac{\partial M}{\partial y} = 2$. Thus

$$\iint_R \text{curl } \mathbf{F} \cdot \mathbf{k} \, dA = \iint_R \left(\frac{\partial N}{\partial x} - \frac{\partial M}{\partial y} \right) dA$$

$$= \iint_R (5 - 2) \, dA$$

$$= 3 \iint_R dA$$

$$= 3\pi$$

Therefore Stokes's theorem in the plane is verified for this $\mathbf{F}$ and R.   ◀

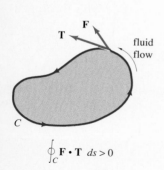

$$\oint_C \mathbf{F} \cdot \mathbf{T} \, ds > 0$$

FIGURE 8

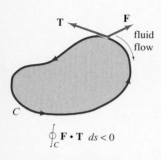

$$\oint_C \mathbf{F} \cdot \mathbf{T} \, ds < 0$$

FIGURE 9

If $\mathbf{F}$ is the velocity field of a fluid, the dot product $\mathbf{F} \cdot \mathbf{T}$ is the tangential component of $\mathbf{F}$ and the line integral $\oint_C \mathbf{F} \cdot \mathbf{T} \, ds$ is called the **circulation** of $\mathbf{F}$ around the closed curve C. In an intuitive sense, we can think of the circulation as being the sum of the tangential components of $\mathbf{F}$ around C. If motion around C is in the counterclockwise direction and $\oint_C \mathbf{F} \cdot \mathbf{T} \, ds > 0$, the fluid is circulating counterclockwise; see Figure 8. If $\oint_C \mathbf{F} \cdot \mathbf{T} \, ds < 0$, the circulation of the fluid is clockwise; see Figure 9.

Let $\overline{P}(\overline{x}, \overline{y})$ be a particular point in region R and let C_δ be the circle having its center at $\overline{P}$ and having a small radius δ. If R_δ is the region enclosed by C_δ,

$$\oint_{C_\delta} \mathbf{F} \cdot \mathbf{T} \, ds = \iint_{R_\delta} \text{curl } \mathbf{F} \cdot \mathbf{k} \, dA$$

If M_y and N_x are continuous on R_δ, then curl $\mathbf{F} \cdot \mathbf{k}$ is continuous there and for small δ, curl $\mathbf{F} \cdot \mathbf{k}$ on R_δ is approximately curl $\mathbf{F}(\bar{x}, \bar{y}) \cdot \mathbf{k}$. Therefore

$$\oint_{C_\delta} \mathbf{F} \cdot \mathbf{T} \, ds \approx \text{curl } \mathbf{F}(\bar{x}, \bar{y}) \cdot \mathbf{k} \iint_{R_\delta} dA$$

$$\oint_{C_\delta} \mathbf{F} \cdot \mathbf{T} \, ds \approx \text{curl } \mathbf{F}(\bar{x}, \bar{y}) \cdot \mathbf{k}(\pi\delta^2)$$

Thus we interpret curl $\mathbf{F}(\bar{x}, \bar{y}) \cdot \mathbf{k}$ as the approximate measure of the rate of circulation per unit area in the counterclockwise direction at the point $\bar{P}$. When $\mathbf{F}$ and $\mathbf{T}$ are orthogonal vectors, $\mathbf{F} \cdot \mathbf{T} = 0$ and then curl $\mathbf{F} = \mathbf{0}$. In such a case $\mathbf{F}$ is said to be **irrotational.** This terminology is used even if $\mathbf{F}$ is not the velocity field of a fluid.

EXERCISES 14.4

In Exercises 1 through 8, evaluate the line integral by Green's theorem. Then verify the result by the method of Section 14.2.

1. $\oint_C 4y \, dx + 3x \, dy$, where C is the square with vertices at $(0, 0)$, $(1, 0)$, $(1, 1)$, and $(0, 1)$.

2. $\oint_C y^2 \, dx + x^2 \, dy$, where C is the square of Exercise 1.

3. $\oint_C 2xy \, dx - x^2y \, dy$, where C is the triangle with vertices at $(0, 0)$, $(1, 0)$, and $(0, 1)$.

4. The line integral of Exercise 3, where C is the triangle with vertices at $(0, 0)$, $(1, 0)$, and $(1, 1)$.

5. $\oint_C x^2y \, dx - y^2x \, dy$, where C is the circle $x^2 + y^2 = 1$.

6. $\oint_C (x^2 - y^2) \, dx + 2xy \, dy$, where C is the circle $x^2 + y^2 = 1$.

7. The line integral of Exercise 5, where C is the closed curve consisting of the arc of $4y = x^3$ from $(0, 0)$ to $(2, 2)$ and the line segment from $(2, 2)$ to $(0, 0)$.

8. The line integral of Exercise 6, where C is the closed curve of Exercise 7.

In Exercises 9 through 20, use Green's theorem to evaluate the line integral.

9. $\oint_C (x + y) \, dx + xy \, dy$, where C is the closed curve determined by the x axis, the line $x = 2$, and the curve $4y = x^3$.

10. $\oint_C y^2 \, dx + x^2 \, dy$, where C is the closed curve determined by the x axis, the line $x = 1$, and the curve $y = x^2$.

11. $\oint_C (-x^2 + x) \, dy$, where C is the closed curve determined by the line $x - 2y = 0$ and the parabola $x = 2y^2$.

12. $\oint_C (x^2 + y) \, dx$, where C is the closed curve determined by the x axis and the parabola $y = 4 - x^2$.

13. $\oint_C \cos y \, dx + \cos x \, dy$, where C is the rectangle with vertices at $(0, 0)$, $(\frac{1}{3}\pi, 0)$, $(\frac{1}{3}\pi, \frac{1}{4}\pi)$, and $(0, \frac{1}{4}\pi)$.

14. $\oint_C e^{x+y} \, dx + e^{x+y} \, dy$, where C is the circle $x^2 + y^2 = 4$.

15. $\oint_C (\sin^4 x + e^{2x}) \, dx + (\cos^3 y - e^y) \, dy$, where C is the curve $x^4 + y^4 = 16$.

16. $\oint_C x \sin y \, dx - y \cos x \, dy$, where C is the rectangle with vertices at $(0, 0)$, $(\frac{1}{2}\pi, 0)$, $(\frac{1}{4}\pi, \frac{1}{2}\pi)$, and $(0, \frac{1}{4}\pi)$.

17. $\oint_C \dfrac{x^2y}{x^2 + 1} \, dx - \tan^{-1} x \, dy$, where C is the ellipse $4x^2 + 25y^2 = 100$.

18. $\oint_C e^y \cos x \, dx + e^y \sin x \, dy$, where C is the curve $x^6 + y^4 = 10$.

19. $\oint_C (e^x - x^2y) \, dx + 3x^2y \, dy$, where C is the closed curve determined by $y = x^2$ and $x = y^2$.

20. $\oint_C \tan y \, dx - x \tan^2 y \, dy$, where C is the ellipse $x^2 + 4y^2 = 1$.

In Exercises 21 through 26, use Theorem 14.4.2 to find the area of the region.

21. The region having as its boundary the quadrilateral with vertices at $(0, 0)$, $(4, 0)$, $(3, 2)$, and $(1, 1)$.

22. The region having as its boundary the circle $x^2 + y^2 = a^2$.

23. The region bounded by the graphs of $y = x^2$ and $y = \sqrt{x}$.

24. The region bounded by the parabola $y = 2x^2$ and the line $y = 8x$.

25. The region bounded by the hypocycloid having parametric equations

$$x = a \cos^3 t \qquad y = a \sin^3 t$$

where $a > 0$ and $0 \leq t \leq 2\pi$.

26. The region bounded below by the x axis and above by one arch of the cycloid having parametric equations

$$x = t - \sin t \qquad y = 1 - \cos t \qquad 0 \leq t \leq 2\pi$$

*In Exercises 27 through 30, verify Gauss's divergence theorem in the plane and Stokes's theorem in the plane for **F** and R.*

27. $\mathbf{F}(x, y) = 3x\mathbf{i} + 2y\mathbf{j}$ and R is the region bounded by the circle $x^2 + y^2 = 1$.

28. $\mathbf{F}(x, y) = 3y\mathbf{i} - 2x\mathbf{j}$ and R is the region bounded by $x^{2/3} + y^{2/3} = 1$.

29. $\mathbf{F}(x, y) = x^2\mathbf{i} + y^2\mathbf{j}$ and R is the region bounded by the ellipse $4x^2 + 25y^2 = 100$.

30. $\mathbf{F}(x, y) = y^2\mathbf{i} + x^2\mathbf{j}$ and R is the region bounded by the circle $x^2 + y^2 = 4$.

*In Exercises 31 through 34, use Green's theorem to find the total work done in moving an object in the counterclockwise direction once around curve C if the motion is caused by the force field **F**(x, y). Assume the arc is measured in meters and the force is measured in newtons.*

31. C is the ellipse $x^2 + 4y^2 = 16$;
$\mathbf{F}(x, y) = (3x + y)\mathbf{i} + (4x - 5y)\mathbf{j}$.

32. C is the circle $x^2 + y^2 = 25$;
$\mathbf{F}(x, y) = (e^x + y^2)\mathbf{i} + (x^2y + \cos y)\mathbf{j}$.

33. C is the triangle with vertices at $(0, 0)$, $(2, 0)$, and $(0, 2)$; $\mathbf{F}(x, y) = (e^{x^2} + y^2)\mathbf{i} + (e^{y^2} + x^2)\mathbf{j}$.

34. C consists of the top half of the ellipse $9x^2 + 4y^2 = 36$ and the interval $[-2, 2]$ on the x axis; $\mathbf{F}(x, y) = (xy + y^2)\mathbf{i} + xy\mathbf{j}$.

*In Exercises 35 through 38, find the rate of flow of the fluid out of a region R bounded by curve C if **F** is the velocity field of the fluid. Assume the velocity is measured in centimeters per second and the area of R is measured in square centimeters.*

35. $\mathbf{F}(x, y) = (y^2 + 6x)\mathbf{i} + (2y - x^2)\mathbf{j}$; C is the ellipse $x^2 + 4y^2 = 4$.

36. $\mathbf{F}(x, y) = (5x - y^2)\mathbf{i} + (3x - 2y)\mathbf{j}$; C is the right triangle having vertices at $(1, 2)$, $(4, 2)$, and $(4, 6)$.

37. $\mathbf{F}(x, y) = x^3\mathbf{i} + y^3\mathbf{j}$; C is the circle $x^2 + y^2 = 1$.

38. $\mathbf{F}(x, y) = xy^2\mathbf{i} + yx^2\mathbf{j}$; C is the circle $x^2 + y^2 = 9$.

*In Exercises 39 through 42, **F** is the velocity field of a fluid around the closed curve C, where motion around C is in the counterclockwise direction. Use Stokes's theorem in the plane to compute $\oint_C \mathbf{F} \cdot \mathbf{T}\, ds$, and from the result determine which of the following applies; (i) the circulation of the fluid is counterclockwise; (ii) the circulation of the fluid is clockwise; (iii) **F** is irrotational.*

39. $\mathbf{F}(x, y) = 4y\mathbf{i} + 6x\mathbf{j}$; C is the triangle having vertices at $(0, 0)$, $(3, 0)$, and $(3, 5)$.

40. $\mathbf{F}(x, y) = 8y\mathbf{i} + 3x\mathbf{j}$; C is the ellipse $4x^2 + 9y^2 = 1$.

41. $\mathbf{F}(x, y) = \sin^2 x\mathbf{i} + \cos^2 y\mathbf{j}$; C is the ellipse $9x^2 + y^2 = 9$.

42. $\mathbf{F}(x, y) = y^3\mathbf{i} + x^3\mathbf{j}$; C is the circle $x^2 + y^2 = 25$.

43. Prove $\oint_C N(x, y)\, dy = \iint\limits_R \dfrac{\partial N}{\partial x}\, dA$ if R is the region defined by

$$R = \{(x, y) \mid c \leq y \leq d, g_1(y) \leq x \leq g_2(y)\}$$

where g_1 and g_2 are smooth.

14.5 SURFACE INTEGRALS

The idea of a *surface integral* is an extension of the concept of a line integral to three dimensions. We begin by considering a closed region in the xy plane. Let us denote this region by D, instead of R, to avoid confusion with the function defined by $R(x, y, z)$ used later in the discussion. Suppose S is a surface lying over D and having the equation $z = f(x, y)$, where f and its first partial derivatives are continuous on D. Then if σ is the measure of the area of the surface S, we have, from Theorem 13.3.4,

$$\sigma = \iint\limits_D \sqrt{f_x{}^2(x, y) + f_y{}^2(x, y) + 1}\; dx\, dy \tag{1}$$

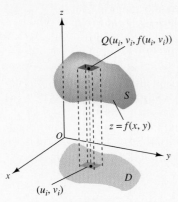

FIGURE 1

We can generalize the integral in (1) by considering a function G of the three variables x, y, and z, where G is continuous on S. We proceed in a manner similar to the discussion in Section 13.3 leading up to the statement of Theorem 13.3.4. Let Δ be a partition of region D into n rectangular subregions, where the ith rectangle has dimensions of measures $\Delta_i x$ and $\Delta_i y$ and an area of measure $\Delta_i A$. Let (u_i, v_i) be any point in the ith rectangle, and at the point $Q(u_i, v_i, f(u_i, v_i))$ on the surface S consider the tangent plane to the surface. Project vertically upward the ith rectangle onto the tangent plane, and let $\Delta_i \sigma$ be the measure of the area of this projection. See Figure 1. The number $\Delta_i \sigma$ is an approximation to the measure of the area of the piece of the surface that lies above the ith rectangle. We showed in Section 13.3 that

$$\Delta_i \sigma = \sqrt{f_x^2(u_i, v_i) + f_y^2(u_i, v_i) + 1} \; \Delta_i A \qquad (2)$$

If we form the sum

$$\sum_{i=1}^{n} G(u_i, v_i, f(u_i, v_i)) \; \Delta_i \sigma$$

and take the limit of this sum as the norm of the partition approaches zero, we have

$$\lim_{\|\Delta\| \to 0} \sum_{i=1}^{n} G(u_i, v_i, f(u_i, v_i)) \; \Delta_i \sigma \qquad (3)$$

This limit is called the **surface integral** of G over S and is denoted by

$$\iint\limits_{S} G(x, y, z) \, d\sigma$$

To obtain a formula for evaluating this surface integral, we substitute from (2) into (3) and we have

$$\lim_{\|\Delta\| \to 0} \sum_{i=1}^{n} G(u_i, v_i, f(u_i, v_i)) \sqrt{f_x^2(u_i, v_i) + f_y^2(u_i, v_i) + 1} \; \Delta_i A$$

This limit is a double integral over the region D in the xy plane. Thus

$$\iint\limits_{S} G(x, y, z) \, d\sigma$$

$$= \iint\limits_{D} G(x, y, f(x, y)) \sqrt{f_x^2(x, y) + f_y^2(x, y) + 1} \; dA \qquad (4)$$

If $G(x, y, z) = 1$, then (4) becomes

$$\iint\limits_{S} d\sigma = \iint\limits_{D} \sqrt{f_x^2(x, y) + f_y^2(x, y) + 1} \; dA$$

Comparing this equation with (1), we observe that for this G the surface integral of G over S gives the measure of the area of surface S.

For the surface integral in (4), $z = f(x, y)$ is an equation of the surface S that is projected onto the region D in the xy plane. If an equation of surface

S is of the form $y = g(x, z)$ and S is projected onto a region D in the xz plane, and g and its first partial derivatives are continuous on D, then

$$\iint\limits_{S} G(x, y, z) \, d\sigma$$

$$= \iint\limits_{D} G(x, g(x, z), z)\sqrt{g_x^{\,2}(x, z) + g_z^{\,2}(x, z) + 1} \, dA \qquad \textbf{(5)}$$

Furthermore, if an equation of surface S is of the form $x = h(y, z)$ and S is projected onto a region D in the yz plane, and h and its first partial derviatives are continuous on D, then

$$\iint\limits_{S} G(x, y, z) \, d\sigma$$

$$= \iint\limits_{D} G(h(y, z), y, z)\sqrt{h_y^{\,2}(y, z) + h_z^{\,2}(y, z) + 1} \, dA \qquad \textbf{(6)}$$

▶ **EXAMPLE 1**   Evaluate the surface integral

$$\iint\limits_{S} x^2 z^2 \, d\sigma$$

where S is the portion of the cone $x^2 + y^2 = z^2$ between the planes $z = 1$ and $z = 2$.

Solution   Figure 2 shows the surface S and the projection of S onto the region D in the xy plane. Region D is bounded by the two circles of radii 1 and 2 whose centers are at the origin. We solve the equation of S for z, where $z \geq 0$, and we obtain $z = \sqrt{x^2 + y^2}$. Therefore

$$f(x, y) = \sqrt{x^2 + y^2} \qquad f_x(x, y) = \frac{x}{\sqrt{x^2 + y^2}} \qquad f_y(x, y) = \frac{y}{\sqrt{x^2 + y^2}}$$

From (4), with $G(x, y, z) = x^2 z^2$, we obtain

$$\iint\limits_{S} x^2 z^2 \, d\sigma = \iint\limits_{D} x^2(x^2 + y^2)\sqrt{\frac{x^2}{x^2 + y^2} + \frac{y^2}{x^2 + y^2} + 1} \, dA$$

$$= \iint\limits_{D} x^2(x^2 + y^2)\sqrt{2} \, dA$$

We evaluate the double integral by using polar coordinates, where $x = r \cos \theta$, $x^2 + y^2 = r^2$, and $dA = r \, dr \, d\theta$. Therefore

$$\iint\limits_{S} x^2 z^2 \, d\sigma = \sqrt{2} \int_0^{2\pi} \int_1^2 (r^2 \cos^2 \theta) r^2 (r \, dr \, d\theta)$$

$$= \sqrt{2} \int_0^{2\pi} \int_1^2 \cos^2 \theta \, r^5 \, dr \, d\theta$$

$$= \sqrt{2} \int_0^{2\pi} \left[\cos^2 \theta \, \frac{r^6}{6} \right]_1^2 d\theta$$

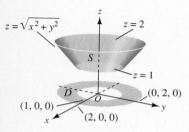

$z = \sqrt{x^2 + y^2}$ $z = 2$

$z = 1$

$(1, 0, 0)$ $(0, 2, 0)$

$(2, 0, 0)$

FIGURE 2

$$= \frac{21\sqrt{2}}{2} \int_0^{2\pi} \frac{1 + \cos 2\theta}{2} \, d\theta$$

$$= \frac{21\sqrt{2}}{4} \left[\theta + \frac{\sin 2\theta}{2} \right]_0^{2\pi}$$

$$= \frac{21\pi}{\sqrt{2}}$$

◀

If the measure of the area density at the point (x, y, z) on a surface S is $\rho(x, y, z)$, and if M is the measure of the mass of S, then

$$M = \iint_S \rho(x, y, z) \, d\sigma \tag{7}$$

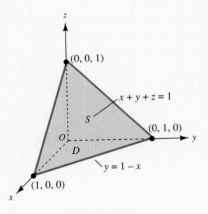

FIGURE 3

▶ **EXAMPLE 2**   Find the mass of the portion of the plane $x + y + z = 1$ in the first octant if the area density at any point (x, y, z) on the surface is kx^2 kilograms per square meter, where k is a constant.

Solution   Figure 3 shows S, which is the surface of the given plane in the first octant, and the region D, which is the projection of S onto the xy plane. We solve the equation of the plane for z and obtain $z = 1 - x - y$. Thus

$$f(x, y) = 1 - x - y \qquad f_x(x, y) = -1 \qquad f_y(x, y) = -1$$

From (7), with $\rho(x, y, z) = kx^2$, if M kilograms is the mass of the surface,

$$M = \iint_S kx^2 \, d\sigma$$

$$= \iint_D kx^2 \sqrt{f_x{}^2(x, y) + f_y{}^2(x, y) + 1} \, dA$$

$$= \iint_D kx^2 \sqrt{(-1)^2 + (-1)^2 + 1} \, dA$$

$$= \sqrt{3} \, k \int_0^1 \int_0^{1-x} x^2 \, dy \, dx$$

$$= \sqrt{3} \, k \int_0^1 \left[x^2 y \right]_0^{1-x} dx$$

$$= \sqrt{3} \, k \int_0^1 (x^2 - x^3) \, dx$$

$$= \sqrt{3} \, k \left[\frac{x^3}{3} - \frac{x^4}{4} \right]_0^1$$

$$= \tfrac{1}{12} \sqrt{3} \, k$$

<u>**Conclusion:**</u>   The mass is $\tfrac{1}{12}\sqrt{3} \, k$ kilograms.

◀

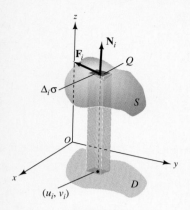

(u_i, v_i)

FIGURE 4

We now give an application of surface integrals to fluid flow. Let **F** be the velocity field of a fluid defined by

$$\mathbf{F}(x, y, z) = M(x, y, z)\mathbf{i} + N(x, y, z)\mathbf{j} + R(x, y, z)\mathbf{k}$$

Furthermore, suppose that the fluid flows through a surface S having the equation $z = f(x, y)$, which lies over a closed region D in the xy plane. Assume that f and its first partial derivatives are continuous on D. At each point of S there are two unit normal vectors to S. The unit normal having a positive **k** component is called the **unit upper normal** and the one having a negative **k** component is called the **unit lower normal.**

As in our discussion preceding Equation (2), take a partition of D into n rectangular subregions. Choose a point (u_i, v_i) in the ith rectangle. Project vertically upward the ith rectangle onto the tangent plane at the point $Q(u_i, v_i, f(u_i, v_i))$ on S and let $\Delta_i\sigma$, given by (2), be an approximation to the measure of the area of this projection. Again refer to Figure 1. Now let $\mathbf{N}_i$ be the unit upper normal to S at point Q and let $\mathbf{F}_i$ be the velocity vector of the fluid at Q. The amount of fluid that crosses the projection per unit of time is given approximately by the volume of the parallelepiped having a base of area $\Delta_i\sigma$ square units and an altitude of length $\mathbf{F}_i \cdot \mathbf{N}_i$ units. See Figure 4. The measure of the volume of the parallelepiped is $\mathbf{F}_i \cdot \mathbf{N}_i \, \Delta_i\sigma$. The total amount of fluid that crosses S per unit of time is given approximately by

$$\sum_{i=1}^{n} \mathbf{F}_i \cdot \mathbf{N}_i \, \Delta_i\sigma$$

Taking the limit of this summation as n increases without bound and each $\Delta_i\sigma$ approaches zero, we obtain the surface integral

$$\iint\limits_{S} \mathbf{F} \cdot \mathbf{N} \, d\sigma \tag{8}$$

which is called the **flux** of **F** across S.

To evaluate surface integral (8), write the equation of S in the form $g(x, y, z) = 0$, where

$$g(x, y, z) = z - f(x, y)$$

From Theorem 12.7.2, a unit normal vector of the surface defined by $g(x, y, z) = 0$ is

$$\mathbf{N} = \frac{\nabla g}{\|\nabla g\|}$$

$$= \frac{-f_x(x, y)\mathbf{i} - f_y(x, y)\mathbf{j} + \mathbf{k}}{\sqrt{f_x{}^2(x, y) + f_y{}^2(x, y) + 1}}$$

Thus

$$\iint\limits_{S} \mathbf{F} \cdot \mathbf{N} \, d\sigma = \iint\limits_{S} (M\mathbf{i} + N\mathbf{j} + R\mathbf{k}) \cdot \left(\frac{-f_x\mathbf{i} - f_y\mathbf{j} + \mathbf{k}}{\sqrt{f_x{}^2 + f_y{}^2 + 1}} \right) d\sigma$$

$$= \iint\limits_{D} \frac{-Mf_x - Nf_y + R}{\sqrt{f_x{}^2 + f_y{}^2 + 1}} \left(\sqrt{f_x{}^2 + f_y{}^2 + 1} \right) dA$$

Therefore, we conclude that

$$\iint\limits_{S} \mathbf{F} \cdot \mathbf{N}\, d\sigma = \iint\limits_{D} (-Mf_x - Nf_y + R)\, dA \qquad (9)$$

where $\mathbf{N}$ is a unit upper normal. If $\mathbf{N}$ is a unit lower normal (where the component of $\mathbf{k}$ is negative)

$$\iint\limits_{S} \mathbf{F} \cdot \mathbf{N}\, d\sigma = \iint\limits_{D} (Mf_x + Nf_y - R)\, dA \qquad (10)$$

This formula is proved in a manner similar to that used to prove (9).

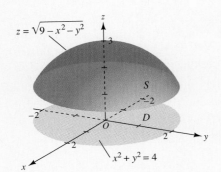

FIGURE 5

▶ **EXAMPLE 3**   The velocity field of a fluid is given by

$$\mathbf{F}(x, y, z) = y\mathbf{i} - x\mathbf{j} + 8\mathbf{k}$$

and surface S is that part of the sphere $x^2 + y^2 + z^2 = 9$ that is above the region D in the xy plane enclosed by the circle $x^2 + y^2 = 4$. Find the flux of $\mathbf{F}$ across S.

Solution   Figure 5 shows the surface S and the region D in the xy plane. We solve the equation of the sphere for z, with $z > 0$, and obtain $z = \sqrt{9 - x^2 - y^2}$. Therefore

$$f(x, y) = \sqrt{9 - x^2 - y^2} \qquad f_x = \frac{-x}{\sqrt{9 - x^2 - y^2}} \qquad f_y = \frac{-y}{\sqrt{9 - x^2 - y^2}}$$

$$f_x = -\frac{x}{z} \qquad\qquad f_y = -\frac{y}{z}$$

From the definition of flux we have

$$\text{flux of } \mathbf{F} \text{ across } S = \iint\limits_{S} \mathbf{F} \cdot \mathbf{N}\, d\sigma$$

From the given velocity field, $M = y$, $N = -x$, and $R = 8$. Therefore, from (9),

$$\text{flux of } \mathbf{F} \text{ across } S = \iint\limits_{D} (-Mf_x - Nf_y + R)\, dA$$

$$= \iint\limits_{D} \left[-y\left(-\frac{x}{z}\right) - (-x)\left(-\frac{y}{z}\right) + 8 \right] dA$$

$$= 8 \iint\limits_{D} dA$$

Because D is the region enclosed by the circle $x^2 + y^2 = 4$, $A = 4\pi$. Thus

$$\text{flux of } \mathbf{F} \text{ across } S = 8(4\pi)$$
$$= 32\pi$$

Conclusion: The rate of flow of the fluid across S is 32π cubic units of volume per unit of time.   ◀

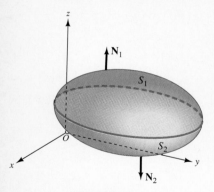

FIGURE 6

Suppose S is a closed surface, examples of which are rectangular parallelepipeds, spheres, and ellipsoids. When using (8) to compute the flux of F across a closed surface, we select N as a **unit outward normal,** which is a normal whose direction is away from the solid bounded by the surface. In particular, if S is an ellipsoid, as shown in Figure 6, we consider S as consisting of an upper surface S_1 and a lower surface S_2, as indicated in the figure. In such a case the flux of $\mathbf{F}$ across $\mathbf{S}$ is

$$\iint_S \mathbf{F} \cdot \mathbf{N}\, d\sigma = \iint_{S_1} \mathbf{F} \cdot \mathbf{N}_1\, d\sigma + \iint_{S_2} \mathbf{F} \cdot \mathbf{N}_2\, d\sigma$$

For the surface integral across S_1, $\mathbf{N}_1$ is a unit upper normal, and for the surface integral across S_2, $\mathbf{N}_2$ is a unit lower normal.

▶ **EXAMPLE 4**   The velocity field of a fluid is given by $\mathbf{F}(x, y, z) = 5z\,\mathbf{k}$, and S is the sphere $x^2 + y^2 + z^2 = 16$. Find the flux of $\mathbf{F}$ across S if length is measured in centimeters and time is measured in hours.

Solution   Figure 7 shows the sphere and the region D in the xy plane, which is the circle $x^2 + y^2 = 16$. Because $\mathbf{F}(x, y, z) = 5z\,\mathbf{k}$, $M = 0$, $N = 0$, and $R = 5z$. The flux of $\mathbf{F}$ across S is

$$\iint_S \mathbf{F} \cdot \mathbf{N}\, d\sigma = \iint_{S_1} \mathbf{F} \cdot \mathbf{N}_1\, d\sigma + \iint_{S_2} \mathbf{F} \cdot \mathbf{N}_2\, d\sigma \qquad (11)$$

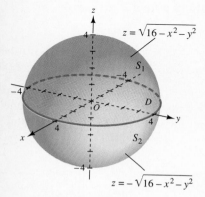

FIGURE 7

where S_1 is the top half of the sphere and S_2 is the bottom half. For S_1, $\mathbf{N}_1$ is a unit upper normal and an equation of S_1 is $z = \sqrt{16 - x^2 - y^2}$. Thus $f(x, y) = \sqrt{16 - x^2 - y^2}$. From (9),

$$\iint_{S_1} \mathbf{F} \cdot \mathbf{N}_1\, d\sigma = \iint_D [-Mf_x - Nf_y + R]\, dA$$

$$= \iint_D 5z\, dA$$

$$= 5 \iint_D \sqrt{16 - x^2 - y^2}\, dA$$

$$= 5 \int_0^{2\pi} \int_0^4 \sqrt{16 - r^2}\, r\, dr\, d\theta$$

$$= 5 \int_0^{2\pi} -\frac{1}{3}(16 - r^2)^{3/2} \Big]_0^4 d\theta$$

$$= \frac{320}{3} \int_0^{2\pi} d\theta$$

$$= \frac{640}{3}\pi$$

For S_2, $\mathbf{N}_2$ is a unit lower normal and as an equation of S_2 we have $z = -\sqrt{16 - x^2 - y^2}$. Therefore $f(x, y) = -\sqrt{16 - x^2 - y^2}$. From (10),

$$\iint\limits_{S_2} \mathbf{F} \cdot \mathbf{N}_2 \, d\sigma = \iint\limits_{D} [Mf_x + Nf_y - R] \, dA$$

$$= \iint\limits_{D} -5z \, dA$$

$$= 5 \iint\limits_{D} \sqrt{16 - x^2 - y^2} \, dA$$

As in the computation for the flux of $\mathbf{F}$ across S_1 we get

$$\iint\limits_{S_2} \mathbf{F} \cdot \mathbf{N} \, d\sigma = \tfrac{640}{3} \pi$$

Hence from (11),

$$\iint\limits_{S} \mathbf{F} \cdot \mathbf{N} \, d\sigma = \tfrac{640}{3} \pi + \tfrac{640}{3} \pi$$

$$= \tfrac{1280}{3} \pi$$

Conclusion: The rate of flow of the fluid across the sphere is $\tfrac{1280}{3} \pi$ cm³/hr. ◀

The concept of flux is not limited to velocity fields of fluids. For instance, if $\mathbf{F}$ is an electric field, then surface integral (8) is an electric flux, and if $\mathbf{F}$ is a magnetic field, the surface integral is a magnetic flux. Surface integral (8) could also represent a flux of heat.

EXERCISES 14.5

In Exercises 1 through 14, evaluate the surface integral $\iint\limits_{S} G(x, y, z) \, d\sigma$ *for G and S.*

1. $G(x, y, z) = z$; S is the hemisphere $x^2 + y^2 + z^2 = 4$ above the xy plane.

2. $G(x, y, z) = x$; S is the portion of the plane $x + y + z = 1$ in the first octant.

3. $G(x, y, z) = x + 2y - z$; S is the portion of the plane $x + y + z = 2$ in the first octant.

4. $G(x, y, z) = z$; S is the portion of the plane $2x + 3y + z = 6$ in the first octant.

5. $G(x, y, z) = xyz$; S is the same as in Exercise 4.

6. $G(x, y, z) = x^2$; S is the portion of the cylinder $x^2 + y^2 = 1$ between the xy plane and the plane $z = 1$ in the first octant.

7. $G(x, y, z) = x$; S is the portion of the cylinder $z = x^2$ in the first octant bounded by the coordinate planes and the planes $x = 1$ and $y = 2$.

8. $G(x, y, z) = y$; S is the portion of the cylinder $z = 4 - y^2$ in the first octant bounded by the coordinate planes and the plane $x = 3$.

9. $G(x, y, z) = z^2$; S is the portion of the cone $x^2 + y^2 = z^2$ between the planes $z = 1$ and $z = 2$.

10. $G(x, y, z) = xyz$; S is the portion of the cone $x^2 + y^2 = z^2$ between the planes $z = 1$ and $z = 2$.

11. $G(x, y, z) = x + y$; S is the portion of the plane $4x + 3y + 6z = 12$ in the first octant.

12. $G(x, y, z) = \sqrt{x^2 + y^2 + z^2}$; S is the portion of the cone $x^2 + y^2 = z^2$ between the xy plane and the plane $z = 2$.

13. $G(x, y, z) = xyz$; S is the portion of the cylinder $x^2 + z^2 = 4$ between the planes $y = 1$ and $y = 3$.

14. $G(x, y, z) = x^2$; S is the hemisphere $x^2 + y^2 + z^2 = 9$ above the xy plane. *Hint:* The surface integral is improper. See Example 7 in Section 13.4.

In Exercises 15 through 20, find the mass of the surface S if the area density at any point (x, y, z) on the surface is $\rho(x, y, z)$ kilograms per square meter.

15. S is that part of the sphere $x^2 + y^2 + z^2 = 4$ above the region in the xy plane enclosed by the circle $x^2 + y^2 = 1$; $\rho(x, y, z) = k\sqrt{x^2 + y^2 + z^2}$, where k is a constant.

16. S is the portion of the plane $3x + 2y + z = 6$ in the first octant; $\rho(x, y, z) = y + 2z$.

17. S is the portion of the paraboloid $z = 9 - x^2 - y^2$ above the xy plane; $\rho(x, y, z) = 1/\sqrt{4x^2 + 4y^2 + 1}$.

18. S is the hemisphere $x^2 + y^2 + z^2 = 1$ below the xy plane; $\rho(x, y, z) = x^2 + y^2$. See the hint for Exercise 14.

19. S is the portion of the cone $x^2 + y^2 = z^2$ between the planes $z = 2$ and $z = 3$; $\rho(x, y, z) = y^2z^2$.

20. S is the portion of the sphere $x^2 + y^2 + z^2 = 16$ in the first octant; $\rho(x, y, z) = kz^2$, where k is a constant.

*In Exercises 21 through 24, find the flux of **F** across the surface S where $\mathbf{F}(x, y, z)$ gives the velocity field of a fluid.*

21. $\mathbf{F}(x, y, z) = x\mathbf{i} + y\mathbf{j} + z\mathbf{k}$; S is the portion of the plane $3x + 2y + z = 6$ in the first octant.

22. $\mathbf{F}(x, y, z)$ is the same as in Exercise 21; S is that part of the sphere $x^2 + y^2 + z^2 = 1$ above the region in the xy plane enclosed by the circle $4x^2 + 4y^2 = 1$.

23. $\mathbf{F}(x, y, z) = -2y\mathbf{i} + 2x\mathbf{j} + 5\mathbf{k}$; S is that part of the sphere $x^2 + y^2 + z^2 = 16$ above the region in the xy plane enclosed by the circle $x^2 + y^2 = 9$.

24. $\mathbf{F}(x, y, z) = 3x\mathbf{i} + 3y\mathbf{i} + 6z\mathbf{k}$; S is the portion of the paraboloid $z = 4 - x^2 - y^2$ above the xy plane.

25. Suppose $\mathbf{F}(x, y, z) = x^2\mathbf{i} + xy\mathbf{j} + 2z\mathbf{k}$, and S is the cube in the first octant bounded by the coordinate planes and the planes $x = 1$, $y = 1$, and $z = 1$. Find the flux of **F** across S by evaluating six surface integrals, one for each face of the cube.

26. If $\mathbf{F}(x, y, z) = 3x\mathbf{i} + y^2\mathbf{j} + yz\mathbf{k}$ and S is the cube of Exercise 25, find the flux of **F** across S by evaluating six surface integrals, one for each face of the cube.

14.6 GAUSS'S DIVERGENCE THEOREM AND STOKES'S THEOREM

The two vector forms of Green's theorem, Gauss's divergence theorem in the plane and Stokes's theorem in the plane, can be generalized in three dimensions. A rigorous presentation of these theorems belongs to a course in advanced calculus. In this section, however, we present a brief introduction to them.

14.6.1 Gauss's Divergence Theorem

Let M, N, and R be functions of three variables x, y, and z that have continuous first partial derivatives on an open ball B in R^3. Let S be a sectionally smooth closed surface lying in B, and let E be the region bounded by S. If

$$\mathbf{F}(x, y, z) = M(x, y, z)\mathbf{i} + N(x, y, z)\mathbf{j} + R(x, y, z)\mathbf{k}$$

and **N** is a unit outward normal vector of S, then

$$\iint\limits_{S} \mathbf{F} \cdot \mathbf{N} \, d\sigma = \iiint\limits_{E} \text{div } \mathbf{F} \, dV$$

This theorem states that the flux of **F** across the boundary S of a region E in R^3 is the triple integral of the divergence of **F** over E. Its proof is beyond the scope of this book. The following example verifies it for a particular **F** and S.

▶ **EXAMPLE 1**   Use Gauss's divergence theorem to solve Example 4 of Section 14.5.

Solution $\mathbf{F}(x, y, z) = 5z\mathbf{k}$ and S is the sphere $x^2 + y^2 + z^2 = 16$. From Gauss's divergence theorem, the flux of **F** across S is

$$\iint\limits_{S} \mathbf{F} \cdot \mathbf{N}\, d\sigma = \iiint\limits_{E} \operatorname{div} \mathbf{F}\, dV$$

Since $\mathbf{F}(x, y, z) = 5z\mathbf{k}$, $\operatorname{div} \mathbf{F} = \dfrac{\partial}{\partial z}(5z)$; that is, $\operatorname{div} \mathbf{F} = 5$. Thus

$$\iint\limits_{S} \mathbf{F} \cdot \mathbf{N}\, d\sigma = 5 \iiint\limits_{E} dV$$

Because the volume of E is the volume of a sphere of radius 4, we have

$$\iint\limits_{S} \mathbf{F} \cdot \mathbf{N}\, d\sigma = 5[\tfrac{4}{3}\pi(4)^3]$$
$$= \tfrac{1280}{3}\pi \qquad\qquad ◀$$

By comparing the solution of the above example with that of Example 4 in Section 14.5, observe how Gauss's divergence theorem can simplify the computation of a surface integral.

▶ **EXAMPLE 2**   If $\mathbf{F}(x, y, z) = x^2 y\mathbf{i} + y^2\mathbf{i} + yz\mathbf{k}$, and S is the cube in the first octant bounded by the planes $x = 1$, $y = 1$, $z = 1$, and the coordinate planes, find the flux of **F** across S.

Solution   The cube appears in Figure 1. The flux of **F** across S is

$$\iint\limits_{S} \mathbf{F} \cdot \mathbf{N}\, d\sigma$$

To compute this surface integral directly we would have to evaluate six surface integrals, one for each face of the cube. By applying Gauss's divergence theorem with

$$\operatorname{div} \mathbf{F} = \frac{\partial}{\partial x}(x^2 y) + \frac{\partial}{\partial y}(y^2) + \frac{\partial}{\partial z}(xz)$$
$$= 2xy + 2y + x$$

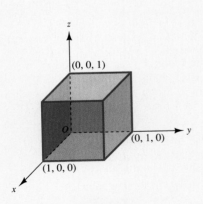

FIGURE 1

we have

$$\iint_S \mathbf{F} \cdot \mathbf{N} \, d\sigma = \iiint_E \text{div } \mathbf{F} \, dV$$

$$= \int_0^1 \int_0^1 \int_0^1 (2xy + 2y + x) \, dz \, dy \, dx$$

$$= \int_0^1 \int_0^1 (2xy + 2y + x) \, dy \, dx$$

$$= \int_0^1 \left[xy^2 + y^2 + xy \right]_0^1 dx$$

$$= \int_0^1 (2x + 1) \, dx$$

$$= x^2 + x \Big]_0^1$$

$$= 2$$

<u>Conclusion:</u> The rate of flow of the fluid across S is 2 cubic units of volume per unit of time. ◄

The second vector form of Green's theorem, known as Stokes's theorem in the plane states that

$$\oint_C \mathbf{F} \cdot \mathbf{T} \, ds = \iint_D \text{curl } \mathbf{F} \cdot \mathbf{k} \, dA$$

where C is a sectionally smooth simple closed curve in R^2 and D is the region bounded by C. We now extend this theorem to three-dimensional space.

14.6.2 Stokes's Theorem

Let M, N, and R be functions of three variables x, y, and z that have continuous first partial derivatives on an open ball B in R^3. Let S be a sectionally smooth surface lying in B and let C be a sectionally smooth simple closed curve that is the boundary of S. If

$$\mathbf{F}(x, y, z) = M(x, y, z)\mathbf{i} + N(x, y, z)\mathbf{j} + R(x, y, z)\mathbf{k}$$

$\mathbf{N}$ is a unit upward normal vector of S and $\mathbf{T}$ is a unit tangent vector to C where s units is the length of arc measured from a particular point P_0 on C to P, then

$$\oint_C \mathbf{F} \cdot \mathbf{T} \, ds = \iint_S \text{curl } \mathbf{F} \cdot \mathbf{N} \, d\sigma$$

Stokes's theorem states that the line integral of the tangential component of a vector field $\mathbf{F}$ around the boundary C of a surface S can be computed by evaluating the surface integral of the normal component of the curl of $\mathbf{F}$ over S. Our Theorem 14.6.2 is restricted to surfaces for which $\mathbf{N}$ is an upward normal of S. A complete statement of Stokes's theorem,

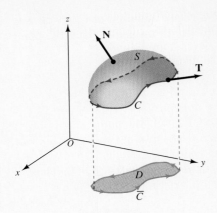

FIGURE 2

involving surfaces having an orientation and for which a unit normal **N** can be adequately defined, can be found in an advanced calculus text. The proof of the theorem can also be found there.

Figure 2 shows a surface S with boundary curve C for which Theorem 14.6.2 applies. An equation of S is of the form $z = f(x, y)$, where f has continuous first partial derivatives on region D that is the projection of S onto the xy plane. Curve $\overline{C}$ is the projection of C onto the xy plane, and D and $\overline{C}$ are defined as in Green's theorem. The positive direction along C is the same as the positive direction along $\overline{C}$, which is counterclockwise. Figure 2 also shows representations of vectors **N** and **T**.

Another form of the equation of Stokes's theorem is obtained by writing $d\mathbf{R}$ in place of $\mathbf{T}\, ds$ in the line integral on the left. We then have

$$\oint_C \mathbf{F} \cdot d\mathbf{R} = \iint_S \text{curl } \mathbf{F} \cdot \mathbf{N}\, d\sigma \tag{1}$$

▶ **EXAMPLE 3**   Let the force field **F** be defined by

$$\mathbf{F}(x, y, z) = -4y\mathbf{i} + 2z\mathbf{j} + 3x\mathbf{k}$$

and let a vector equation of C be $\mathbf{R}(t) = 3 \cos t\mathbf{i} + 3 \sin t\mathbf{j} + \mathbf{k}$. Suppose S is the portion of the paraboloid $z = 10 - x^2 - y^2$ above the plane $z = 1$. Verify Stokes's theorem for this **F**, C, and S by computing each of the following: **(a)** $\oint_C \mathbf{F} \cdot d\mathbf{R}$; **(b)** $\oint_C \mathbf{F} \cdot \mathbf{T}\, ds$; **(c)** $\iint_S \text{curl } \mathbf{F} \cdot \mathbf{N}\, d\sigma$.

Solution   Figure 3 shows the surface S and the region D, which is the projection of S onto the xy plane. Region D is bounded by the circle $x^2 + y^2 = 9$. The curve C, which is the boundary of S, is the circle having its center at $(0, 0, 1)$ and radius 3, in the plane $z = 1$.

(a) We are given the following vector equation of C:

$$\mathbf{R}(t) = 3 \cos t\mathbf{i} + 3 \sin t\mathbf{j} + \mathbf{k} \qquad 0 \le t \le 2\pi \tag{2}$$

Thus

$$\mathbf{R}'(t) = -3 \sin t\mathbf{i} + 3 \cos t\mathbf{j} \tag{3}$$

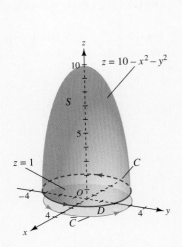

FIGURE 3

$$\oint_C \mathbf{F} \cdot d\mathbf{R} = \int_C \mathbf{F}(\mathbf{R}(t)) \cdot \mathbf{R}'(t)\, dt$$

$$= \int_0^{2\pi} (-12 \sin t\mathbf{i} + 2\mathbf{j} + 9 \cos t\mathbf{k}) \cdot (-3 \sin t\mathbf{i} + 3 \cos t\mathbf{j})\, dt$$

$$= \int_0^{2\pi} (36 \sin^2 t + 6 \cos t)\, dt$$

$$= 36 \int_0^{2\pi} \frac{1 - \cos 2t}{2}\, dt + 6 \int_0^{2\pi} \cos t\, dt$$

$$= 18t - 9 \sin 2t + 6 \sin t \Big]_0^{2\pi}$$

$$= 36\pi$$

(b) To compute $\oint_C \mathbf{F} \cdot \mathbf{T}\, ds$, we obtain a vector equation of C having s as a parameter, where s units is the arc length measured from the point where $t = 0$. Because $\dfrac{ds}{dt} = \|\mathbf{R}'(t)\|$ we have from (3)

$$\frac{ds}{dt} = \sqrt{9\sin^2 t + 9\cos^2 t}$$

$$= 3\sqrt{\sin^2 t + \cos^2 t}$$

$$= 3$$

Therefore, $s = 3t + C$, and since $s = 0$ when $t = 0$, $C = 0$. Thus

$$s = 3t$$

From (2) with $t = \tfrac{1}{3}s$, we obtain

$$\mathbf{R}(s) = 3\cos \tfrac{1}{3}s\,\mathbf{i} + 3\sin \tfrac{1}{3}s\,\mathbf{j} + \mathbf{k} \qquad 0 \le s \le 6\pi$$

Because $\mathbf{T}(s) = D_s\mathbf{R}(s)$, we have

$$\mathbf{T}(s) = -\sin \tfrac{1}{3}s\,\mathbf{i} + \cos \tfrac{1}{3}s\,\mathbf{j} \qquad 0 \le s \le 6\pi$$

We have then

$$\oint_C \mathbf{F} \cdot \mathbf{T}\, ds = \int_C \mathbf{F}(\mathbf{R}(s)) \cdot \mathbf{T}(s)\, ds$$

$$= \int_0^{6\pi} (-12\sin \tfrac{1}{3}s\,\mathbf{i} + 2\mathbf{j} + 9\cos \tfrac{1}{3}s\,\mathbf{k}) \cdot (-\sin \tfrac{1}{3}s\,\mathbf{i} + \cos \tfrac{1}{3}s\,\mathbf{j})\, ds$$

$$= \int_0^{6\pi} (12\sin^2 \tfrac{1}{3}s + 2\cos \tfrac{1}{3}s)\, ds$$

$$= 12\int_0^{6\pi} \frac{1 - \cos \tfrac{2}{3}s}{2}\, ds + 2\int_0^{6\pi} \cos \tfrac{1}{3}s\, ds$$

$$= 6s - 9\sin \tfrac{2}{3}s + 6\sin \tfrac{1}{3}s \Big]_0^{6\pi}$$

$$= 36\pi$$

(c) We first compute curl $\mathbf{F}$.

$$\text{curl } \mathbf{F} = \begin{vmatrix} \mathbf{i} & \mathbf{j} & \mathbf{k} \\ \dfrac{\partial}{\partial x} & \dfrac{\partial}{\partial y} & \dfrac{\partial}{\partial z} \\ -4y & 2z & 3x \end{vmatrix}$$

$$= -2\mathbf{i} - 3\mathbf{j} + 4\mathbf{k}$$

Thus

$$\iint_S \text{curl } \mathbf{F} \cdot \mathbf{N}\, d\sigma = \iint_S (-2\mathbf{i} - 3\mathbf{j} + 4\mathbf{k}) \cdot \mathbf{N}\, d\sigma$$

To evaluate this surface integral we apply (9) of Section 14.5 because $\mathbf{N}$ is a unit upper normal. The vector field is $-2\mathbf{i} - 3\mathbf{j} + 4\mathbf{k}$; thus

$M = -2$, $N = -3$, and $R = 4$. Because an equation of the surface is $z = 10 - x^2 - y^2$,

$$f(x, y) = 10 - x^2 - y^2 \qquad f_x(x, y) = -2x \qquad f_y(x, y) = -2y$$

Therefore,

$$\iint_S \text{curl } \mathbf{F} \cdot \mathbf{N} \, d\sigma = \iint_D [-(-2)(-2x) - (-3)(-2y) + 4] \, dA$$

$$= \iint_D (-4x - 6y + 4) \, dA$$

$$= \int_0^{2\pi} \int_0^3 (-4r \cos \theta - 6r \sin \theta + 4)r \, dr \, d\theta$$

$$= \int_0^{2\pi} \left[-\frac{4}{3}r^3 \cos \theta - 2r^3 \sin \theta + 2r^2 \right]_0^3 d\theta$$

$$= \int_0^{2\pi} (-36 \cos \theta - 54 \sin \theta + 18) \, d\theta$$

$$= -36 \sin \theta + 54 \cos \theta + 18\theta \Big]_0^{2\pi}$$

$$= 36\pi$$

The results of parts (a), (b), and (c) are all 36π. We have therefore verified Stokes's theorem for this $\mathbf{F}$, C, and S. ◀

▶ **EXAMPLE 4** Use Stokes's theorem to evaluate the line integral

$$\oint_C \mathbf{F} \cdot \mathbf{T} \, ds$$

if $\mathbf{F}(x, y, z) = xz\mathbf{i} + xy\mathbf{j} + y^2\mathbf{k}$ and C is the boundary of the surface consisting of the portion of the cylinder $z = 4 - x^2$ in the first octant that is cut off by the coordinate planes and the plane $y = 3$.

Solution Figure 4 shows the surface S and the boundary curve C that is composed of the four arcs C_1, C_2, C_3, and C_4. From Stokes's theorem,

$$\oint_C \mathbf{F} \cdot \mathbf{T} \, ds = \iint_S \text{curl } \mathbf{F} \cdot \mathbf{N} \, d\sigma$$

$$\text{curl } \mathbf{F} = \begin{vmatrix} \mathbf{i} & \mathbf{j} & \mathbf{k} \\ \dfrac{\partial}{\partial x} & \dfrac{\partial}{\partial y} & \dfrac{\partial}{\partial z} \\ xz & xy & y^2 \end{vmatrix}$$

$$= 2y\mathbf{i} + x\mathbf{j} + y\mathbf{k}$$

Thus

$$\oint_C \mathbf{F} \cdot \mathbf{T} \, ds = \iint_S (2y\mathbf{i} + x\mathbf{j} + y\mathbf{k}) \cdot \mathbf{N} \, d\sigma$$

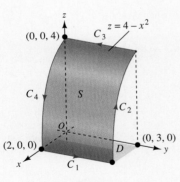

FIGURE 4

Because $\mathbf{N}$ is a unit upper normal vector, we compute the value of the surface integral by applying (9) of Section 14.5. Because the vector field is $2y\mathbf{i} + x\mathbf{j} + y\mathbf{k}$, then $M = 2y$, $N = x$, and $R = y$. An equation of S is $z = 4 - x^2$. Therefore

$$f(x, y) = 4 - x^2 \qquad f_x(x, y) = -2x \qquad f_y(x, y) = 0$$

Hence, we have

$$\oint_C \mathbf{F} \cdot \mathbf{T} \, ds = \iint_D [-(2y)(-2x) - x(0) + y] \, dA$$

$$= \iint_D (4xy + y) \, dA$$

Region D is enclosed by the rectangle in the xy plane bounded by the x and y axes and the lines $x = 2$ and $y = 3$. Therefore

$$\oint_C \mathbf{F} \cdot \mathbf{T} \, ds = \int_0^2 \int_0^3 (4xy + y) \, dy \, dx$$

$$= \int_0^2 \left[2xy^2 + \frac{1}{2}y^2 \right]_0^3 dx$$

$$= \int_0^2 (18x + \tfrac{9}{2}) \, dx$$

$$= 9x^2 + \tfrac{9}{2}x \Big]_0^2$$

$$= 45$$

◀

EXERCISES 14.6

In Exercises 1 through 4, verify Gauss's divergence theorem for $\mathbf{F}$ *and* S.

1. $\mathbf{F}(x, y, z) = 2z\mathbf{k}$; S is the sphere $x^2 + y^2 + z^2 = 1$.

2. $\mathbf{F}(x, y, z) = x\mathbf{i} + y\mathbf{j} + z\mathbf{k}$; S is the sphere $x^2 + y^2 + z^2 = 9$.

3. $\mathbf{F}(x, y, z) = xy\mathbf{i} + xy\mathbf{j}$; S is the cube bounded by the coordinate planes and the planes $x = 1$, $y = 1$, and $z = 1$.

4. $\mathbf{F}(x, y, z) = 4x\mathbf{i} - 2y\mathbf{j} + z\mathbf{k}$; S is the boundary of the region enclosed by the paraboloid $z = x^2 + y^2$ and the plane $z = 4$.

In Exercises 5 through 8, for the $\mathbf{F}$ *and* S *of the indicated exercise in Exercises 14.5, find the flux of* $\mathbf{F}$ *across* S *by Gauss's divergence theorem.*

5. Exercise 21

6. Exercise 22

7. Exercise 25

8. Exercise 26

In Exercises 9 through 16, use Gauss's divergence theorem to evaluate the surface integral $\iint_S \mathbf{F} \cdot \mathbf{N} \, d\sigma$ *for* $\mathbf{F}$ *and* S.

9. $\mathbf{F}(x, y, z) = x^2yz\mathbf{i} + xy^2z\mathbf{j} + xyz^2\mathbf{k}$; S is the cube in the first octant bounded by the coordinate planes and the planes $x = 1$, $y = 2$, and $z = 3$.

10. $\mathbf{F}(x, y, z) = 6x\mathbf{i} + 3y\mathbf{j} + 2z\mathbf{k}$; S is the tetrahedron having vertices at the origin and the points $(3, 0, 0)$, $(0, 1, 0)$, and $(0, 0, 2)$.

11. $\mathbf{F}(x, y, z) = x\mathbf{i} + y\mathbf{j} + z\mathbf{k}$; S is the sphere $x^2 + y^2 + z^2 = 4$.

12. $\mathbf{F}(x, y, z) = x\mathbf{i} + y\mathbf{j} + z\mathbf{k}$; S is the boundary of the region enclosed on the side by the cylinder $x^2 + y^2 = 9$, below by the xy plane, and above by the plane $z = 4$.

13. $\mathbf{F}(x, y, z) = x^2\mathbf{i} + y^2\mathbf{j} + z^2\mathbf{k}$; S is the surface of Exercise 12.

14. $\mathbf{F}(x, y, z) = x^2\mathbf{i} + y^2\mathbf{j} + z^2\mathbf{k}$; S is the surface of Exercise 11.

15. $\mathbf{F}(x, y, z) = 2x\mathbf{i} + 2yz\mathbf{j} + 3z\mathbf{k}$; S is the boundary of the region enclosed by the coordinate planes and the plane $x + y + z = 1$.

16. $\mathbf{F}(x, y, z) = \dfrac{x\mathbf{i} + y\mathbf{j} + z\mathbf{k}}{x^2 + y^2 + z^2}$; S is the boundary of the region outside the sphere $x^2 + y^2 + z^2 = 1$ and inside the sphere $x^2 + y^2 + z^2 = 4$.

In Exercises 17 through 22, verify Stokes's theorem for $\mathbf{F}$ *and S.*

17. $\mathbf{F}(x, y, z) = y^2\mathbf{i} + x^2\mathbf{j} + z^2\mathbf{k}$; S is the hemisphere $x^2 + y^2 + z^2 = 1$ above the xy plane.

18. $\mathbf{F}(x, y, z) = x^2\mathbf{i} + y^2\mathbf{j} + z^2\mathbf{k}$; S is the hemisphere $x^2 + y^2 + z^2 = 1$ below the xy plane.

19. $\mathbf{F}(x, y, z) = y^2\mathbf{i} + x\mathbf{j} + z^2\mathbf{k}$; S is the portion of the paraboloid $z = x^2 + y^2$ below the plane $z = 1$.

20. $\mathbf{F}(x, y, z) = xy\mathbf{i} + y^2\mathbf{j} + 2\mathbf{k}$; S is the surface of Exercise 19.

21. $\mathbf{F}(x, y, z) = -3y\mathbf{i} + 3x\mathbf{j} + 2\mathbf{k}$; S is the portion of the plane $z = 1$ inside the cylinder $x^2 + y^2 = 9$.

22. $\mathbf{F}(x, y, z) = 2z\mathbf{i} + 3x\mathbf{j} + 4z\mathbf{k}$; S is the portion of the paraboloid $z = 4 - x^2 - y^2$ above the xy plane.

In Exercises 23 through 28, use Stokes's theorem to evaluate the line integral $\oint_C \mathbf{F} \cdot \mathbf{T}\, ds$ for $\mathbf{F}$ and C.

23. $\mathbf{F}(x, y, z) = 4y\mathbf{i} - 3z\mathbf{j} + x\mathbf{k}$; C is the triangle having vertices at $(1, 0, 0)$, $(0, 1, 0)$, and $(0, 0, 1)$.

24. $\mathbf{F}(x, y, z) = (y - x)\mathbf{i} + (x - z)\mathbf{j} + (x - y)\mathbf{k}$; C is the triangle having vertices at $(2, 0, 0)$, $(0, 2, 0)$, and $(0, 0, 1)$.

25. $\mathbf{F}(x, y, z) = -y\mathbf{i} + x\mathbf{j} + z\mathbf{k}$; C is the circle $x^2 + y^2 = 4$ in the xy plane.

26. $\mathbf{F}(x, y, z) = yz\mathbf{i} + xy\mathbf{j} + xz\mathbf{k}$; C is the square having vertices at $(0, 0, 0)$, $(2, 0, 0)$, $(0, 2, 0)$, and $(2, 2, 0)$.

27. $\mathbf{F}(x, y, z) = (2y + \sin^{-1} x)\mathbf{i} + e^{y^2}\mathbf{j} + (x + \ln(z^2 + 4))\mathbf{k}$; C is the triangle having vertices at $(1, 0, 0)$, $(0, 1, 0)$, and $(0, 0, 2)$.

28. $\mathbf{F}(x, y, z) = (2z - e^x)\mathbf{i} + (x^3 + \sin y)\mathbf{j} + (y^2 - \tan z)\mathbf{k}$; C has the equation $\mathbf{R}(t) = \cos t\,\mathbf{i} + \sin t\,\mathbf{j} + \mathbf{k}$, $0 \le t \le 2\pi$.

29. Explain why Gauss's divergence theorem and Stokes's theorem are three-dimensional versions of Green's theorem.

CHAPTER 14 REVIEW

▶ SUGGESTIONS FOR REVIEW OF CHAPTER 14

1. State a condition you can use to determine if a vector in the plane is a gradient. Make up an example.

2. Do Suggestion 1 for a vector in three dimensions. Make up an example.

3. What is a vector field? Make up an example of a vector field in the plane and one in three dimensions.

4. What is a conservative vector field, and what is a potential function for a conservative vector field? Make up an example of each.

5. Define the curl of a vector field in three dimensions. Make up an example.

6. Define the divergence of a vector field in three dimensions. Make up an example.

7. State a mnemonic device, involving determinant notation, for computing curl $\mathbf{F}$. Make up an example.

8. How do you compute the work done by a force field on a particle moving along a curve? Make up an example.

9. What is a line integral? Make up an example of a line integral expressed in both differential form notation and vector notation.

10. What is meant by a line integral independent of the path? Make up an example.

11. State a theorem giving conditions for which a line integral of a vector field in the plane is independent of the path. Make up an example.

12. Do Suggestion 11 for a line integral of a vector field in three dimensions.

13. State the formula of the fundamental theorem of line integrals that gives the value of a line integral independent of the path. Make up an example both in the plane and in three dimensions.

14. State Green's theorem.

15. Make up an example showing how Green's theorem is applied to evaluate a line integral.

16. State the theorem which gives a method for computing the area of a plane region bounded by a sectionally smooth simple closed curve. Make up an example.

17. State Gauss's divergence theorem in the plane. Make up an example showing how this theorem relates flux to the divergence of a vector field in the plane.

18. State Stokes's theorem in the plane. Make up an example showing how this theorem relates circulation to the curl of a vector field in the plane.

19. What is a surface integral? Make up an example.

20. How can you compute the mass of a surface by a surface integral? Make up an example.

21. How are surface integrals applied to compute the flux of a vector field across a surface?

22. State Gauss's divergence theorem in three dimensions. Make up an example showing how this theorem relates flux to the divergence of a vector field in three dimensions.

23. State Stokes's theorem in three dimensions. Make up an example showing how this theorem relates circulation to the curl of a vector field in three dimensions.

▶ MISCELLANEOUS EXERCISES FOR CHAPTER 14

In Exercises 1 through 4, determine if the vector is a gradient, and if it is, find a function having the gradient.

1. $2xe^{x^2} \ln y\, \mathbf{i} + \dfrac{e^{x^2}}{y}\mathbf{j}$

2. $(e^x \tan y - \sec y)\mathbf{i} - \sec y(x \tan y - e^x \sec y)\mathbf{j}$

3. $\left(\dfrac{-y}{(x+z)^2} + \dfrac{1}{x^2}\right)\mathbf{i} + \dfrac{1}{x+z}\mathbf{j} + \left(\dfrac{-y}{(x+z)^2} + \dfrac{2}{z^2}\right)\mathbf{k}$

4. $y(\cos x - z \sin x)\mathbf{i} + z(\cos x + \sin y)\mathbf{j} - (\cos y - y \cos x)\mathbf{k}$

In Exercises 5 and 6, find a conservative vector field having the potential function f.

5. (a) $f(x, y) = 2x^2y + 3xy^3$;
   (b) $f(x, y, z) = xe^y - yze^y$

6. (a) $f(x, y) = e^x \cos y + x \sin y$;
   (b) $f(x, y, z) = \dfrac{1}{x^2 + y^2 + z^2}$

In Exercises 7 through 10, prove that the vector field $\mathbf{F}$ is conservative, and find a potential function.

7. $\mathbf{F}(x, y) = \dfrac{2y^2}{1+4x^2y^4}\mathbf{i} + \dfrac{4xy}{1+4x^2y^4}\mathbf{j}$

8. $\mathbf{F}(x, y, z) = (6x - 4y)\mathbf{i} + (z - 4x)\mathbf{j} + (y - 8z)\mathbf{k}$

9. $\mathbf{F}(x, y, z) = z^2 \sec^2 x\,\mathbf{i} + 2ye^{3z}\mathbf{j} + (3y^2e^{3z} + 2z \tan x)\mathbf{k}$

10. $\mathbf{F}(x, y) = (y \sin x - \sin y)\mathbf{i} - (x \cos y + \cos x)\mathbf{j}$

In Exercises 11 through 14, find curl $\mathbf{F}$ and div $\mathbf{F}$.

11. $\mathbf{F}(x, y, z) = e^{yz}\mathbf{i} + e^{xz}\mathbf{j} + e^{xy}\mathbf{k}$

12. $\mathbf{F}(x, y) = \sin y\,\mathbf{i} + \sin x\,\mathbf{k}$

13. $\mathbf{F}(x, y) = \dfrac{1}{y}\mathbf{i} - \dfrac{2x}{y}\mathbf{j}$

14. $\mathbf{F}(x, y, z) = \dfrac{x}{y}\mathbf{i} + \dfrac{y}{z}\mathbf{j} + \dfrac{z}{x}\mathbf{k}$

In Exercises 15 through 22, evaluate the line integral over curve C.

15. $\int_C \mathbf{F} \cdot d\mathbf{R}$; $\mathbf{F}(x, y) = 3y\mathbf{i} - 4x\mathbf{j}$; C: $\mathbf{R}(t) = 2t^2\mathbf{i} - t\mathbf{j}, 0 \le t \le 1$.

16. $\int_C \mathbf{F} \cdot d\mathbf{R}$; $\mathbf{F}(x, y) = (x + y)\mathbf{i} + (y - x)\mathbf{j}$; C: $\mathbf{R}(t) = t^3\mathbf{i} + t^2\mathbf{j}$ from the point (8, 4) to the point (1, 1).

17. $\int_C (2x + 3y)\, dx + xy\, dy$; C: $\mathbf{R}(t) = 4 \sin t\mathbf{i} - \cos t\mathbf{j}, 0 \le t \le \frac{1}{2}\pi$.

18. $\int_C (2x + y)\, dx + (x - 2y)\, dy$; C: $x^2 + y^2 = 9$.

19. $\int_C y^2\, dx + z^2\, dy + x^2\, dz$; C: $\mathbf{R}(t) = (t - 1)\mathbf{i} + (t + 1)\mathbf{j} + t^2\mathbf{k}, 0 \le t \le 1$.

20. $\int_C xe^y\, dx - xe^z\, dy + e^z\, dz$; C: $\mathbf{R}(t) = t\mathbf{i} + t^2\mathbf{j} + t^3\mathbf{k}, 0 \le t \le 1$.

21. $\int_C \mathbf{F} \cdot d\mathbf{R}$; $\mathbf{F}(x, y, z) = 3xy\mathbf{i} + (4y^2 - xz)\mathbf{j} + 6z\mathbf{k}$; C: the twisted cubic $\mathbf{R}(t) = t\mathbf{i} + t^2\mathbf{j} + t^3\mathbf{k}, 0 \le t \le 1$.

22. $\int_C \mathbf{F} \cdot d\mathbf{R}$; $\mathbf{F}(x, y, z) = 2x\mathbf{i} + 3y\mathbf{i} + z\mathbf{k}$; C: the circular helix $\mathbf{R}(t) = 2 \cos t\mathbf{i} + 2 \sin t\mathbf{j} + t\mathbf{k}, 0 \le t \le 2\pi$.

In Exercises 23 through 30, prove that the value of the line integral is independent of the path, and compute the value in any convenient manner. In each exercise C is any sectionally smooth curve from point A to point B.

23. $\int_C 2xe^y\, dx + x^2e^y\, dy$; A is (1, 0) and B is (3, 2).

24. $\int_C \left(\dfrac{1}{y} - y\right) dx + \left(-\dfrac{x}{y^2} - x\right) dy$; A is (0, 1) and B is (6, 3).

25. $\int_C \mathbf{F} \cdot d\mathbf{R}$;
    $\mathbf{F}(x, y) = (\cos y - y \cos x)\mathbf{i} - (\sin x + x \sin y)\mathbf{j}$
    A is $(0, \frac{1}{2}\pi)$ and B is $(\pi, 0)$.

26. $\int_C \mathbf{F} \cdot d\mathbf{R}$;

$$\mathbf{F}(x, y) = (2xy - 2y)\mathbf{i} + (x^2 - 2x + 3y^2)\mathbf{j}$$

A is $(2, -1)$ and B is $(3, 2)$.

27. $\int_C 3y \, dx + (3x + 4y) \, dy - 2z \, dz$; A is $(0, 1, -1)$ and B is $(1, 2, 0)$.

28. $\int_C z \sin y \, dx + xz \cos y \, dy + x \sin y \, dz$; A is $(0, 0, 0)$ and B is $(2, 3, \frac{1}{2}\pi)$.

29. $\int_C \mathbf{F} \cdot d\mathbf{R}$;

$$\mathbf{F}(x, y, z) = \left(\frac{1}{y} - \frac{2z}{x^2}\right)\mathbf{i} - \left(\frac{1}{z} + \frac{x}{y^2}\right)\mathbf{j} + \left(\frac{2}{x} + \frac{y}{z^2}\right)\mathbf{k}$$

A is $(2, -1, 1)$ and B is $(4, 2, -2)$.

30. $\int_C \mathbf{F} \cdot d\mathbf{R}$;

$$\mathbf{F}(x, y, z) = (2xy + 3yz)\mathbf{i} + (x^2 - 4yz + 3xz)\mathbf{j} + (3xy - 2y^2)\mathbf{k}$$

A is $(0, 2, 1)$ and B is $(1, -1, 4)$.

In Exercises 31 through 34, use Green's theorem to evaluate the line integral.

31. $\oint_C (3x + 2y) \, dx + (3x + y^2) \, dy$, where C is the ellipse $16x^2 + 9y^2 = 144$.

32. $\oint_C \ln(y + 1) \, dx - \dfrac{xy}{y + 1} \, dy$, where C is the closed curve determined by the curve $\sqrt{x} + \sqrt{y} = 2$ and the intervals $[0, 4]$ on the x and y axes.

33. $\oint_C e^x \sin y \, dx + e^x \cos y \, dy$; where C is any smooth closed curve.

34. $\oint_C (x^2 - y^3) \, dx + (y^2 + x^3) \, dy$; where C is the circle $x^2 + y^2 = 1$.

In Exercises 35 and 36, use Theorem 14.4.2 to find the area of the region.

35. The region enclosed by the parabola $y = x^2$ and the line $y = x + 2$.

36. The region enclosed by the two parabolas $y = x^2$ and $x^2 = 18 - y$.

In Exercises 37 through 40, find the total work done in moving an object along C if the motion is caused by the force field. Assume the arc is measured in meters and the force is measured in newtons.

37. $\mathbf{F}(x, y) = 2x^2 y\mathbf{i} + (x^2 + 3y)\mathbf{j}$; C: the arc of the parabola $y = 3x^2 + 2x + 4$ from $(0, 4)$ to $(1, 9)$.

38. $\mathbf{F}(x, y) = xy^2\mathbf{i} - x^2 y\mathbf{j}$; C: the arc of the circle $x^2 + y^2 = 4$ from $(2, 0)$ to $(0, 2)$.

39. $\mathbf{F}(x, y, z) = (xy - z)\mathbf{i} + y\mathbf{j} + z\mathbf{k}$; C: the line segment from the origin to the point $(4, 1, 2)$.

40. $\mathbf{F}(x, y, z) = xyz\mathbf{i} + e^y\mathbf{j} + (x + z)\mathbf{k}$; C: $\mathbf{R}(t) = 3t\mathbf{i} + t^2\mathbf{j} + 2t\mathbf{k}$; $0 \leq t \leq 3$.

In Exercises 41 and 42, verify Gauss's divergence theorem in the plane and Stokes's theorem in the plane for $\mathbf{F}$ and R.

41. $\mathbf{F}(x, y) = 4y\mathbf{i} + 3x\mathbf{j}$, and R is the region bounded by $x^{2/3} + y^{2/3} = 1$.

42. $\mathbf{F}(x, y) = 3x^2\mathbf{i} + 4y^2\mathbf{j}$ and R is the region bounded by the ellipse $9x^2 + 16y^2 = 144$.

In Exercises 43 and 44, use Green's theorem to find the total work done in moving an object in the counterclockwise direction once around C if the motion is caused by the force field $\mathbf{F}(x, y)$. Assume the arc is measured in meters and the force is measured in newtons.

43. C is the circle $x^2 + y^2 = 4$; $\mathbf{F}(x, y) = (xy^2 + \cos x)\mathbf{i} + (x^2 + e^y)\mathbf{j}$.

44. C is the ellipse $9x^2 + y^2 = 9$; $\mathbf{F}(x, y) = (2x - 3y)\mathbf{i} + (x + 2y)\mathbf{j}$.

In Exercises 45 and 46, find the rate of flow of the fluid out of the region R bounded by C if $\mathbf{F}(x, y)$ is the velocity field of the fluid. Assume the velocity is measured in centimeters per second and the area of R is measured in square centimeters.

45. $\mathbf{F}(x, y) = (4x - 3y)\mathbf{i} + (5y - 4x^2)\mathbf{j}$; C is the right triangle with vertices at $(0, 1)$, $(0, 4)$, and $(4, 4)$.

46. $\mathbf{F}(x, y) = (y^2 + 12x)\mathbf{i} + (4y - x^2)\mathbf{j}$; C is the ellipse $x^2 + 4y^2 = 16$.

47. Find the value of the line integral

$$\int_C \frac{-y}{x^2 + y^2} \, dx + \frac{x}{x^2 + y^2} \, dy$$

if C is the arc of the circle $x^2 + y^2 = 4$ from $(\sqrt{2}, \sqrt{2})$ to $(-\sqrt{2}, \sqrt{2})$.

48. Apply Green's theorem to compute the area of the quadrilateral having vertices at the points $(0, 0)$, $(3, 2)$, $(1, 5)$, and $(-2, 1)$.

49. Evaluate the surface integral $\int\int_S xy \, d\sigma$, where S is the portion of the plane $3x + 2y - z = 0$ in the first octant below the plane $z = 6$.

50. Evaluate the surface integral $\int\int_S x^2 \, d\sigma$, where S is the portion of the cylinder $x^2 + y^2 = 1$ in the first octant bounded by the xy plane and the plane $z = 1$.

51. Evaluate the surface integral $\int\int_S x \, d\sigma$, where S is the portion of the cylinder $z = 9 - x^2$ in the first octant bounded by the coordinate planes and the plane $y = 2$.

52. Evaluate the surface integral $\iint_S xyz \, d\sigma$, where S is the portion of the cylinder $y^2 + z^2 = 9$ between the planes $x = 1$ and $x = 4$.

53. Find the mass of the portion of the sphere $x^2 + y^2 + z^2 = 4$ in the first octant if the area density at any point (x, y, z) on the surface is kz^2 kilograms per square meter, where k is a constant.

54. Find the mass of the hemisphere $x^2 + y^2 + z^2 = 4$ above the xy plane if the area density at any point (x, y, z) on the surface is $(4 - z)$ kilograms per square meter. *Hint:* The surface integral is improper. See Example 7 in Section 13.4.

55. A funnel is in the shape of the portion of the cone $x^2 + y^2 = z^2$ between the planes $z = 1$ and $z = 4$. If the area density at any point (x, y, z) on the surface is $(10 - z)$ kilograms per square meter, find the mass of the funnel.

56. Suppose surface S is that part of the sphere $x^2 + y^2 + z^2 = 9$ that is above the region D in the xy plane enclosed by the circle $x^2 + y^2 = 1$. If the velocity field of a fluid is given by

$$\mathbf{F}(x, y, z) = -y\mathbf{i} + x\mathbf{j} + 3\mathbf{k}$$

find the flux of $\mathbf{F}$ across S.

57. The velocity field of a fluid is given by

$$\mathbf{F}(x, y, z) = 2x\mathbf{i} + 2y\mathbf{j} + 3z\mathbf{k}$$

and surface S is that portion of the paraboloid $z = 4 - x^2 - y^2$ above the xy plane. Find the flux of $\mathbf{F}$ across S.

58. Verify Gauss's divergence theorem if $\mathbf{F}(x, y, z) = \frac{1}{2}z\mathbf{i}$ and S is the sphere $x^2 + y^2 + z^2 = 4$.

In Exercises 59 and 60, use Gauss's divergence theorem to evaluate the surface integral $\iint_S \mathbf{F} \cdot \mathbf{N} \, d\sigma$ for $\mathbf{F}$ and S.

59. $\mathbf{F}(x, y, z) = 2x\mathbf{i} + y\mathbf{j} + 2z\mathbf{k}$; S is the boundary of the region enclosed on the side by the cylinder $x^2 + y^2 = 16$, below by the xy plane and above by the plane $z = 2$.

60. $\mathbf{F}(x, y, z) = x^2\mathbf{i} + y^2\mathbf{j} + z^2\mathbf{k}$; S is the boundary of the region enclosed by the cone $z = \sqrt{x^2 + y^2}$ and the plane $z = 1$.

In Exercises 61 and 62, verify Stokes's theorem for $\mathbf{F}$ and S.

61. $\mathbf{F}(x, y, z) = z\mathbf{i} + 4x\mathbf{j} + 2z\mathbf{k}$; S is the portion of the paraboloid $z = 9 - x^2 - y^2$ above the xy plane.

62. $\mathbf{F}(x, y, z) = xy\mathbf{i} + yz\mathbf{j} + xz\mathbf{k}$; S is the hemisphere $x^2 + y^2 + z^2 = 16$ above the xy plane.

In Exercises 63 and 64, use Stokes's theorem to evaluate the line integral $\oint_C \mathbf{F} \cdot \mathbf{T} \, ds$ for $\mathbf{F}$ and C.

63. $\mathbf{F}(x, y, z) = (z + \ln(x^2 + 1))\mathbf{i} + \cos(y - x^2)\mathbf{j} + (3y^2 - e^z)\mathbf{k}$; C: $\mathbf{R}(t) = \cos t\mathbf{i} + \sin t\mathbf{j} + \mathbf{k}$, $0 \le t \le 2\pi$.

64. $\mathbf{F}(x, y, z) = -2y\mathbf{i} + 3x\mathbf{j} + z\mathbf{k}$; C is the circle $x^2 + y^2 = 1$ in the xy plane.

In Exercises 65 and 66, prove the identity if f is a real-valued function and $\mathbf{V}$ is a vector-valued function.

65. $\text{div}(f\mathbf{V}) = \nabla f \cdot \mathbf{V} + f \, \text{div } \mathbf{V}$

66. $\text{curl}(f\mathbf{V}) = \nabla f \times \mathbf{V} + f \, \text{curl } \mathbf{V}$

APPENDIX

PRECALCULUS TOPICS

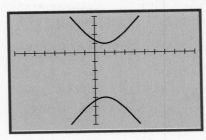

[−8, 10] by [−8, 4]

$x = 2 \tan t + 1$ and $y = 3 \sec t - 2$

A.1 REAL NUMBERS AND INEQUALITIES

The **real number system** consists of a set R of elements called **real numbers** and two operations called **addition** and **multiplication,** denoted by the symbols $+$ and $\cdot$, respectively. If a and b are elements of the set R, $a + b$ indicates the **sum** of a and b, and $a \cdot b$ (or ab) indicates their **product.** The operation of subtraction is defined by the equation

$$a - b = a + (-b)$$

where $-b$ denotes the **negative** of b such that $b + (-b) = 0$. The operation of **division** is defined by the equation

$$a \div b = a \cdot b^{-1} \qquad b \neq 0$$

where b^{-1} denotes the **reciprocal** of b such that $b \cdot b^{-1} = 1$.

    The real number system can be completely described by a set of axioms (the word **axiom** is used to indicate a formal statement assumed to be true without proof). With these axioms we can derive the properties of the real number from which follow the familiar algebraic operations of addition, subtraction, multiplication, and division, as well as the algebraic concepts of solving equations, factoring, and so forth.

    Properties that can be shown to be logical consequences of axioms are **theorems.** In the statement of most theorems there are two parts: the "if" part, called the **hypothesis,** and the "then" part, called the **conclusion.** The argument verifying a theorem is a **proof.** A proof consists in showing that the conclusion follows from the assumed truth of the hypothesis.

A real number is either positive, negative, or zero, and any real number can be classified as either *rational* or *irrational*. A **rational number** is one that can be expressed as the ratio of two integers. That is, a rational number is of the form p/q, where p and q are integers and $q \neq 0$. The rational numbers consist of the following:

The **integers** (positive, negative, and zero)

$$\ldots, -5, -4, -3, -2, -1, 0, 1, 2, 3, 4, 5, \ldots$$

The positive and negative **fractions,** such as

$$\frac{2}{7} \qquad -\frac{4}{5} \qquad \frac{83}{5}$$

The positive and negative **terminating decimals,** such as

$$2.36 = \frac{236}{100} \qquad -0.003251 = -\frac{3,251}{1,000,000}$$

The positive and negative **nonterminating repeating decimals,** such as

$$0.333\ldots = \tfrac{1}{3} \qquad -0.549549549\ldots = -\tfrac{61}{111}$$

The real numbers that are not rational are called **irrational numbers.** These are positive and negative **nonterminating nonrepeating** decimals, for example,

$$\sqrt{3} = 1.732\ldots \qquad \pi = 3.14159\ldots$$

From time to time we will use some set notation and terminology. The idea of *set* is used extensively in mathematics and is such a basic concept that it is not given a formal definition here. We can say that a **set** is a collection of objects, and the objects in a set are called **elements.** If every element of a set S is also an element of a set T, then S is a **subset** of T. In calculus we are concerned with the set R of real numbers. Two subsets of R are the set N of natural numbers (the positive integers) and the set Z of integers.

We use the symbol $\in$ to indicate that a specific element belongs to a set. Hence we may write $8 \in N$, which is read "8 is an element of N." The notation $a, b \in S$ indicates that both a and b are elements of S. The symbol $\notin$ is read "is not an element of." Thus we read $\tfrac{1}{2} \notin N$ as "$\tfrac{1}{2}$ is not an element of N."

A pair of braces { } used with words or symbols can describe a set. If S is the set of natural numbers less than 6, we can write the set S as

$$\{1, 2, 3, 4, 5\}$$

We can also write the set S as

$$\{x, \text{ such that } x \text{ is a natural number less than } 6\}$$

where the symbol x is called a *variable*. A **variable** is a symbol used to represent any element of a given set.

The set S can be written as follows with **set-builder notation,** where a vertical bar replaces the words *such that:*

$$\{x \mid x \text{ is a natural number less than } 6\}$$

which is read "the set of all x such that x is a natural number less than 6."

Two sets A and B are said to be **equal,** written $A = B$, if A and B have identical elements. The **union** of two sets A and B, denoted by $A \cup B$ and read "A union B," is the set of all elements that are in A or in B or in both A and B. The **intersection** of A and B, denoted by $A \cap B$ and read "A intersection B," is the set of only those elements that are in both A and B. The set that contains no elements is called the **empty set** and is denoted by $\emptyset$.

▷ **ILLUSTRATION 1**   Suppose $A = \{2, 4, 6, 8, 10, 12\}$, $B = \{1, 4, 9, 16\}$, and $C = \{2, 10\}$. Then

$$A \cup B = \{1, 2, 4, 6, 8, 9, 10, 12, 16\} \qquad A \cap B = \{4\}$$
$$B \cup C = \{1, 2, 4, 9, 10, 16\} \qquad B \cap C = \emptyset$$
◀

There is an ordering for the set R by means of a relation denoted by the symbols $<$ (read "is less than") and $>$ (read "is greater than").

A.1.1 Definition of $<$ and $>$

Given $a, b \in R$,

(i) $a < b$ if and only if $b - a$ is positive;
(ii) $a > b$ if and only if $a - b$ is positive.

▷ **ILLUSTRATION 2**

$3 < 5$ because $5 - 3 = 2$, and 2 is positive
$-10 < -6$ because $-6 - (-10) = 4$, and 4 is positive
$7 > 2$ because $7 - 2 = 5$, and 5 is positive
$-2 > -7$ because $-2 - (-7) = 5$, and 5 is positive
$\frac{3}{4} > \frac{2}{3}$ because $\frac{3}{4} - \frac{2}{3} = \frac{1}{12}$, and $\frac{1}{12}$ is positive
◀

We now define the symbols $\leq$ (read "is less than or equal to") and $\geq$ (read "is greater than or equal to").

A.1.2 Definition of $\leq$ and $\geq$

Given $a, b \in R$,

(i) $a \leq b$ if and only if   either $a < b$ or $a = b$;
(ii) $a \geq b$ if and only if   either $a > b$ or $a = b$.

The statements $a < b$, $a > b$, $a \leq b$, and $a \geq b$ are called **inequalities.** In particular, $a < b$ and $a > b$ are called **strict** inequalities, whereas $a \leq b$ and $a \geq b$ are called **nonstrict** inequalities.

From the definition of $<$ and $>$,

$a > 0$ if and only if a is positive
$a < 0$ if and only if a is negative

The following theorem gives properties of inequalities. These properties can be proved by using axioms for the set R and the above definitions.

A.1.3 Theorem   Properties of < and >

Given $a, b, c, d, \in R$,

(i) if $a > 0$ and $b > 0$, then $a + b > 0$;
(ii) if $a > 0$ and $b > 0$, then $ab > 0$;
(iii) if $a < b$ and $b < c$, then $a < c$; (transitive property)
(iv) if $a < b$, then $a + c < b + c$;
(v) if $a < b$ and $c < d$, then $a + c < b + d$;
(vi) if $a < b$ and $c > 0$, then $ac < bc$;
(vii) if $a < b$ and $c < 0$, then $ac > bc$.

Property (i) above states that the sum of two positive numbers is positive and property (ii) states that the product of two positive numbers is positive.

▷ **ILLUSTRATION 3**

(a) If $x < 5$ and $5 < y$, then by the transitive property (iii), $x < y$.
(b) If $x < y$, then from property (iv), x + 4 < y + 4. For instance, $3 < 9$; thus $3 + 4 < 9 + 4$ or, equivalently, $7 < 13$. Furthermore, if $x < y$, then $x - 11 < y - 11$. For instance, $3 < 9$; thus $3 - 11 < 9 - 11$ or, equivalently, $-8 < -2$.
(c) If $x < 8$ and $y < -3$, then from property (v), $x + y < 8 + (-3)$; that is, $x + y < 5$.
(d) If $x < y$, then from property (v) $7x < 7y$. For instance, because $5 < 8$, then $7 \cdot 5 < 7 \cdot 8$ or, equivalently, $35 < 56$.
(e) Because $4 < 6$, and if $z < 0$, then from property (vii), $4z > 6z$. For instance, because $4 < 6$, then $4(-3) > 6(-3)$ or, equivalently, $-12 > -18$.   ◀

Property (vi) states that if both sides of an inequality are multiplied by a positive number, the direction of the inequality remains unchanged, whereas property (vii) states that if both sides are multiplied by a negative number, the direction of the inequality is reversed. Properties (vi) and (vii) also hold for division because dividing both sides of an inequality by a number $d(d \neq 0)$ is equivalent to multiplying them by $1/d$.

A number x is **between** a and b if $a < x$ and $x < b$. We can write this as a **continued inequality** as follows:

$$a < x < b$$

Another continued inequality is

$$a \leq x \leq b$$

which means that both $a \leq x$ and $x \leq b$. Other continued inequalities are $a \leq x < b$ and $a < x \leq b$.

▶ **EXAMPLE 1**   With set notation and one or more of the symbols $<$, $>$, $\leq$, and $\geq$, denote the set: **(a)** the set of all x such that x is between -2 and 2; **(b)** the set of all t such that $4t - 1$ is nonnegative; **(c)** the set of all y such that $y + 3$ is positive and less than or equal to 15; **(d)** the set of all z such that $2z$ is greater than or equal to -5 and less than -1.

Solution

(a) $\{x \mid -2 < x < 2\}$ **(b)** $\{t \mid 4t - 1 \geq 0\}$

(c) $\{y \mid 0 < y + 3 \leq 15\}$ **(d)** $\{z \mid -5 \leq 2z < -1\}$ ◀

We now give a geometric interpretation to the set R of real numbers by associating them with points on a horizontal line called an **axis.** A point, called the **origin,** is chosen to represent the number 0. A unit of distance is selected arbitrarily. Then each positive integer n is represented by the point at a distance of n units to the right of the origin, and each negative integer $-n$ is represented by the point at a distance of n units to the left of the origin. We call these points **unit points.** They are labeled with the numbers with which they are associated. For example, 4 is represented by the point 4 units to the right of the origin and -4 is represented by the point 4 units to the left of the origin. Figure 1 shows the unit points representing 0 and the first 12 positive integers and their corresponding negative integers.

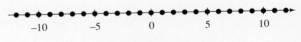

FIGURE 1

The rational numbers are associated with points on the axis of Figure 1 by dividing the segments between points representing successive integers. For instance, if the segment from 0 to 1 is divided into seven equal parts, the endpoint of the first such subdivision is associated with $\frac{1}{7}$, the endpoint of the second is associated with $\frac{2}{7}$, and so on. The point associated with the number $\frac{24}{7}$ is three-sevenths of the distance from the unit point 3 to the unit point 4. A negative rational number, in a similar manner, is associated with a point to the left of the origin. Figure 2 shows some of the points associated with rational numbers.

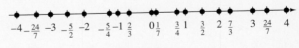

FIGURE 2

Geometric constructions can be used to find points corresponding to certain irrational numbers, such as $\sqrt{2}$, $\sqrt{3}$, $\sqrt{5}$, and so on. (See Exercises 35 and 36.) Points corresponding to other irrational numbers can be found by using decimal approximations. For example, a point corresponding to the number π can be approximated using some of the digits in the decimal representation 3.14159 . . . .

Every irrational number can be associated with a unique point on the axis, and every point that does not correspond to a rational number can be associated with an irrational number. This fact is guaranteed by the Axiom of Completeness (Axiom 8.2.9), whose statement appears in Section 8.2 because it requires some terminology best introduced and discussed there. Thus a one-to-one correspondence exists between the set R and the set of points on an axis. For this reason the horizontal axis is referred to as the **real-number line.** Because the points on this line are identified with the numbers they represent, the same symbol is used for that number and the point.

▷   **ILLUSTRATION 4**   Consider the set $\{x \mid -6 < x \leq 4\}$. This set is represented on the real-number line in Figure 3. The bracket at 4 indicates that 4 is in the set, and the parenthesis at -6 indicates that -6 is not in the set.   ◀

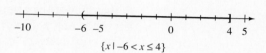

$\{x \mid -6 < x \leq 4\}$

FIGURE 3

The set of all numbers x satisfying the continued inequality $a < x < b$ is called an **open interval** and is denoted by (a, b). Therefore,

$$(a, b) = \{x \mid a < x < b\}$$

The **closed interval** from a to b is the open interval (a, b) together with the two endpoints a and b and is denoted by $[a, b]$. Thus,

$$[a, b] = \{x \mid a \leq x \leq b\}$$

Figure 4 illustrates the open interval (a, b), and Figure 5 shows the closed interval $[a, b]$.

The **interval half-open on the left** is the open interval (a, b) together with the right endpoint b. It is denoted by $(a, b]$; so

$$(a, b] = \{x \mid a < x \leq b\}$$

We define an **interval half-open on the right** in a similar way and denote it by $[a, b)$. Thus

$$[a, b) = \{x \mid a \leq x < b\}$$

The interval $(a, b]$ appears in Figure 6, and the interval $[a, b)$ is shown in Figure 7.

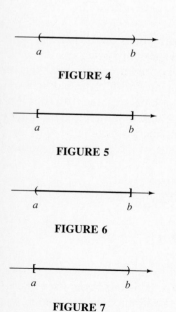

FIGURE 4

FIGURE 5

FIGURE 6

FIGURE 7

We shall use the symbol $+\infty$ (positive infinity) and the symbol $-\infty$ (negative infinity); however, take care not to confuse these symbols with real numbers, for they do not obey the properties of the real numbers. We have the following intervals:

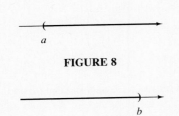

a

FIGURE 8

$$(a, +\infty) = \{x \mid x > a\}$$
$$(-\infty, b) = \{x \mid x < b\}$$
$$[a, +\infty) = \{x \mid x \geq a\}$$
$$(-\infty, b] = \{x \mid x \leq b\}$$
$$(-\infty, +\infty) = R$$

b

FIGURE 9

Figure 8 shows the interval $(a, +\infty)$, and Figure 9 illustrates the interval $(-\infty, b)$. Note that $(-\infty, +\infty)$ denotes the set of all real numbers.

For each of the intervals (a, b), $[a, b]$, $[a, b)$, and $(a, b]$ the numbers a and b are called the **endpoints** of the interval. The closed interval $[a, b]$ contains both its endpoints, whereas the open interval (a, b) contains neither endpoint. The interval $[a, b)$ contains its left endpoint but not its right one, and the interval $(a, b]$ contains its right endpoint but not its left one. An open interval can be thought of as one that contains none of its endpoints, and a closed interval can be regarded as one that contains all of its endpoints. Consequently, the interval $[a, +\infty)$ is considered to be a closed interval because it contains its only endpoint a. Similarly, $(-\infty, b]$ is a closed interval, whereas $(a, +\infty)$ and $(-\infty, b)$ are open. The intervals $[a, b)$ and $(a, b]$ are neither open nor closed. The interval $(-\infty, +\infty)$ has no endpoints, and it is considered both open and closed.

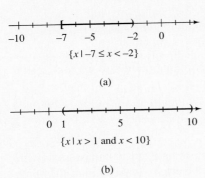

$\{x \mid -7 \leq x < -2\}$

(a)

$\{x \mid x > 1 \text{ and } x < 10\}$

(b)

$\{x \mid x \leq -5 \text{ or } x \geq 5\}$

(c)

$\{x \mid x \geq 2\} \cap \{x \mid x < 9\}$

(d)

$\{x \mid x < 0\} \cup \{x \mid x \geq 3\}$

(e)

FIGURE 10

▶ **EXAMPLE 2**   Show the set on the real-number line and represent the set by interval notation.

(a) $\{x \mid -7 \leq x < -2\}$ (b) $\{x \mid x > 1 \text{ and } x < 10\}$
(c) $\{x \mid x \leq -5 \text{ or } x \geq 5\}$ (d) $\{x \mid x \geq 2\} \cap \{x \mid x < 9\}$
(e) $\{x \mid x < 0\} \cup \{x \mid x \geq 3\}$

Solution   The sets are shown on the real-number line in Figure 10 (a), (b), (c), (d), and (e), respectively. With interval notation, we have

(a) $\{x \mid -7 \leq x < -2\} = [-7, -2)$
(b) $\{x \mid x > 1 \text{ and } x < 10\} = (1, 10)$
(c) $\{x \mid x \leq -5 \text{ or } x \geq 5\} = (-\infty, -5] \cup [5, +\infty)$
(d) $\{x \mid x \geq 2\} \cap \{x \mid x < 9\} = [2, 9)$
(e) $\{x \mid x < 0\} \cup \{x \mid x \geq 3\} = (-\infty, 0) \cup [3, +\infty)$ ◀

▶ **EXAMPLE 3**   Show the interval on the real-number line and use set notation and inequality symbols to denote the interval: (a) $(-2, 4)$; (b) $[3, 7]$; (c) $[1, 6)$; (d) $(-4, 0]$; (e) $[0, +\infty)$; (f) $(-\infty, 5)$.

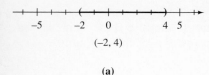

(−2, 4)

(a)

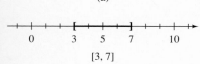

[3, 7]

(b)

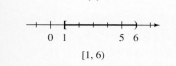

[1, 6)

(c)

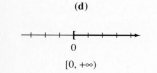

(−4, 0]

(d)

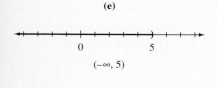

[0, +∞)

(e)

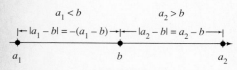

(−∞, 5)

(f)

FIGURE 11

FIGURE 12

Solution The intervals are shown on the real-number line in Figure 11(a), (b), (c), (d), (e), and (f), respectively. With set notation we have

(a) $(-2, 4) = \{x \mid -2 < x < 4\}$ **(b)** $[3, 7] = \{x \mid 3 \le x \le 7\}$
(b) $[1, 6) = \{x \mid 1 \le x < 6\}$ **(d)** $(-4, 0] = \{x \mid -4 < x \le 0\}$
(e) $[0, +\infty) = \{x \mid x \ge 0\}$ **(f)** $(-\infty, 5) = \{x \mid x < 5\}$ ◄

The concept of the *absolute value* of a number is used in some important definitions in calculus.

A.1.4 Definition of Absolute Value

If a is a real number, the **absolute value** of a, denoted by $|a|$, is a if a is nonnegative and is $-a$ if a is negative. With symbols we write

$$|a| = \begin{cases} a & \text{if } a \ge 0 \\ -a & \text{if } a < 0 \end{cases}$$

▷ **ILLUSTRATION 5**   If in the preceding definition we take a as 6, 0, and -6, we have, respectively,

$$|6| = 6 \qquad |0| = 0 \qquad |-6| = -(-6)$$
$$= 6 \qquad ◄$$

The absolute value of a number can be considered as its distance (without regard to direction, left or right) from the origin. In particular, the points 6 and -6 are each six units from the origin.

From the definition of absolute value

$$|a - b| = \begin{cases} a - b & \text{if } a - b \ge 0 \\ -(a - b) & \text{if } a - b < 0 \end{cases}$$

or, equivalently

$$|a - b| = \begin{cases} a - b & \text{if } a \ge b \\ b - a & \text{if } a < b \end{cases}$$

On the real-number line, $|a - b|$ units can be interpreted as the distance between a and b without regard to direction. See Figure 12.

▶ **EXAMPLE 4**   Show the points corresponding to the numbers $-10, -7, -5, -3, 0, 3, 5, 7,$ and 10 on the real-number line. Find the distance between u and v in the following cases: **(a)** $u = 10, v = 3$; **(b)** $u = 3, v = 7$; **(c)** $u = 5, v = -3$; **(d)** $u = -7, v = 0$; **(e)** $u = -3, v = -5$; **(f)** $u = -10, v = -7$.

Solution Figure 13 shows the points corresponding to the given numbers on the real-number line. In each part the distance between u and v is $|u - v|$ units:

FIGURE 13

(a) $|u - v| = |10 - 3|$
$= |7|$
$= 7$

(b) $|u - v| = |3 - 7|$
$= |-4|$
$= 4$

(c) $|u - v| = |5 - (-3)|$
$= |8|$
$= 8$

(d) $|u - v| = |-7 - 0|$
$= |-7|$
$= 7$

(e) $|u - v| = |-3 - (-5)|$
$= |2|$
$= 2$

(f) $|u - v| = |-10 - (-7)|$
$= |-3|$
$= 3$ ◄

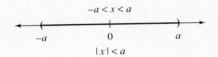

FIGURE 14

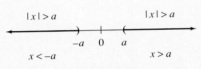

FIGURE 15

We will be working with inequalities involving absolute value. The inequality $|x| < a$, where $a > 0$, states that on the real-number line the distance from the origin to the point x is less than a units; that is $-a < x < a$. See Figure 14. The inequality $|x| > a$, where $a > 0$, states that on the real-number line the distance from the origin to the point x is greater than a units; that is, either $x > a$ or $x < -a$. See Figure 15. We state these two results formally. The double arrow ⇔ is used here and throughout the text to indicate that the statement preceding it and the statement following it are equivalent.

$$|x| < a \quad\Leftrightarrow\quad -a < x < a \qquad \text{where } a > 0 \qquad (1)$$
$$|x| > a \quad\Leftrightarrow\quad x > a \ \text{ or } \ x < -a \qquad \text{where } a > 0 \qquad (2)$$

You may recall from algebra that the symbol $\sqrt{a}$, where $a \geq 0$, is defined as the unique *nonnegative* number x such that $x^2 = a$. We read $\sqrt{a}$ as "the principal square root of a." For example,

$$\sqrt{4} = 2 \qquad \sqrt{0} = 0 \qquad \sqrt{\tfrac{9}{25}} = \tfrac{3}{5}$$

Note: $\sqrt{4} \neq -2$ even though $(-2)^2 = 4$, because $\sqrt{4}$ denotes only the *positive* square root of 4. The *negative* square root of 4 is designated by $-\sqrt{4}$.

Because we are concerned only with real numbers in calculus, $\sqrt{a}$ is not defined if $a < 0$.

From the definition of $\sqrt{a}$ it follows that

$$\sqrt{x^2} = |x|$$

▷ **ILLUSTRATION 6**

$$\sqrt{5^2} = |5| \qquad \sqrt{(-3)^2} = |-3|$$
$$= 5 \qquad\qquad = 3 \qquad ◄$$

The properties of absolute value given in the following theorem are useful in calculus.

A.1.5 Theorem

Given $a, b \in R$,

(i) $|ab| = |a||b|$

(ii) $\left|\dfrac{a}{b}\right| = \dfrac{|a|}{|b|}$ if $b \neq 0$

Proof of (i)

$$
\begin{aligned}
|ab| &= \sqrt{(ab)^2} \\
&= \sqrt{a^2 b^2} \\
&= \sqrt{a^2} \cdot \sqrt{b^2} \\
&= |a| \cdot |b|
\end{aligned}
$$

∎

The proof of (ii) is similar.

In calculus we often want to replace one inequality with an equivalent but simpler one, as in the following example.

▶ **EXAMPLE 5**   Show that the inequality

$$|(3x + 2) - 8| < 1 \quad \text{is equivalent to} \quad |x - 2| < \tfrac{1}{3}$$

Solution   The following inequalities are equivalent:

$$
\begin{aligned}
|(3x + 2) - 8| &< 1 \\
|3x - 6| &< 1 \\
|3(x - 2)| &< 1 \\
|3||x - 2| &< 1 \\
3|x - 2| &< 1 \\
|x - 2| &< \tfrac{1}{3}
\end{aligned}
$$

◀

The next theorem, called the *triangle inequality*, and its two corollaries given in Theorem A.1.7 are used frequently in proving calculus theorems.

A.1.6 Theorem   The Triangle Inequality

Given $a, b \in R$,

$$|a + b| \leq |a| + |b|$$

Proof   By the definition of absolute value, either $a = |a|$ or $a = -|a|$; thus

$$-|a| \leq a \leq |a|$$

Furthermore,

$$-|b| \leq b \leq |b|$$

From these two continued inequalities and property (v) of Theorem A.1.3

$$-(|a| + |b|) \leq a + b \leq |a| + |b|$$

Hence from statement (1) with $\leq$ instead of $<$, we have

$$|a + b| \leq |a| + |b|$$ ∎

We demonstrate the content of the triangle inequality in the following illustration with four particular cases.

▷ **ILLUSTRATION 7**   If $a = 3$ and $b = 4$, then

$$
\begin{aligned}
|a + b| &= |3 + 4| & |a| + |b| &= |3| + |4| \\
&= |7| & &= 3 + 4 \\
&= 7 & &= 7
\end{aligned}
$$

If $a = -3$ and $b = 4$, then

$$
\begin{aligned}
|a + b| &= |-3 + 4| & |a| + |b| &= |-3| + |4| \\
&= |1| & &= 3 + 4 \\
&= 1 & &= 7
\end{aligned}
$$

If $a = 3$ and $b = -4$, then

$$
\begin{aligned}
|a + b| &= |3 + (-4)| & |a| + |b| &= |3| + |-4| \\
&= |-1| & &= 3 + 4 \\
&= 1 & &= 7
\end{aligned}
$$

If $a = -3$ and $b = -4$, then

$$
\begin{aligned}
|a + b| &= |-3 + (-4)| & |a| + |b| &= |-3| + |-4| \\
&= |-7| & &= 3 + 4 \\
&= 7 & &= 7
\end{aligned}
$$

In each case $|a + b| \leq |a| + |b|$.   ◀

A.1.7 Theorem

Given $a, b \in R$,

(i) $|a - b| \leq |a| + |b|$
(ii) $|a| - |b| \leq |a - b|$

Proof of (i)

$$|a - b| = |a + (-b)| \leq |a| + |(-b)| = |a| + |b|$$

Proof of (ii)

$$|a| = |(a - b) + b| \leq |a - b| + |b|$$

Thus, subtracting $|b|$ from both sides of the inequality, we have

$$|a| - |b| \leq |a - b|$$ ∎

EXERCISES A.1

In Exercises 1 and 2, arrange the elements of the given subset of R in the same order as their corresponding points from left to right on the real-number line.

1. $\{-2, 3, 21, 5, -7, \frac{2}{3}, \sqrt{2}, -\frac{7}{4}, -\sqrt{5}, -10,$
$0, \frac{3}{4}, -\frac{5}{3}, -1\}$

2. $\{\frac{11}{3}, \pi, -8, -\sqrt{2}, 3, -\sqrt{3}, 4, \frac{21}{4}, -\frac{3}{2}, 1.26, \frac{1}{2}\pi\}$

In Exercises 3 through 6, use set notation and one or more of the symbols $<$, $>$, $\leq$, and $\geq$ to denote the set.

3. **(a)** The set of all x such that x is greater than -9 and less than 8; **(b)** the set of all y between -12 and -3; **(c)** the set of all z such that $4z - 5$ is negative.

4. **(a)** The set of all x between -5 and 3; **(b)** the set of all y such that y is greater than or equal to -26 and less than -16; **(c)** the set of all t such that $8t - 4$ is positive.

5. **(a)** The set of all x such that $2x + 4$ is nonnegative; **(b)** the set of all r such that r is greater than or equal to 2 and less than 8; **(c)** the set of all a such that $a - 2$ is greater than -5 and less than or equal to 7.

6. **(a)** The set of all s such that $2s + 3$ is nonpositive; **(b)** the set of all x such that $3x$ is greater than 10 and less than or equal to 20; **(c)** the set of all z such that $2z + 5$ is between and including -1 and 15.

In Exercises 7 through 14 do the following: (i) show the set on the real-number line; (ii) represent the set by interval notation; (iii) describe the set in words similar to the descriptions in Exercises 3 through 6.

7. **(a)** $\{x \mid x > 2\}$ **(b)** $\{x \mid -4 < x \leq 4\}$
8. **(a)** $\{x \mid x \leq 8\}$ **(b)** $\{x \mid 3 < x < 9\}$
9. **(a)** $\{x \mid x > 2 \text{ and } x < 12\}$
    (b) $\{x \mid x \leq -4 \text{ or } x > 4\}$
10. **(a)** $\{x \mid x \geq -5 \text{ and } x \leq 5\}$
    (b) $\{x \mid x < 3 \text{ or } x > 6\}$
11. **(a)** $\{x \mid x > 2\} \cap \{x \mid x < 12\}$
    (b) $\{x \mid x \leq -4\} \cup \{x \mid x > 4\}$
12. **(a)** $\{x \mid x \geq -5\} \cap \{x \mid x \leq 5\}$
    (b) $\{x \mid x < 3\} \cup \{x \mid x > 6\}$
13. **(a)** $\{x \mid x > -4\} \cap \{x \mid x \leq 0\}$
    (b) $\{x \mid x \leq 0\} \cup \{x \mid x \leq 7\}$
14. **(a)** $\{x \mid x > -8\} \cap \{x \mid x \leq 0\}$
    (b) $\{x \mid x > 2\} \cup \{x \mid x > 10\}$

In Exercises 15 through 18, show the interval on the real-number line and use set notation and inequality symbols to denote the interval.

15. **(a)** $(2, 7)$ **(b)** $[-3, 6]$
    (c) $(-5, 4]$ **(d)** $[-10, -2)$
16. **(a)** $(-5, 5)$ **(b)** $[1, 9]$
    (c) $[-8, 3)$ **(d)** $(-7, 0]$
17. **(a)** $[3, +\infty)$ **(b)** $(-\infty, 0]$
    (c) $(-4, +\infty)$ **(d)** $(-\infty, +\infty)$
18. **(a)** $(-\infty, -2]$ **(b)** $(-1, +\infty)$
    (c) $(-\infty, 10)$ **(d)** $[0, +\infty]$

In Exercises 19 and 20, write the number without absolute-value bars.

19. **(a)** $|7|$ **(b)** $\left|-\frac{3}{4}\right|$
    (c) $|3 - \sqrt{3}|$ **(d)** $|\sqrt{3} - 3|$
20. **(a)** $\left|\frac{1}{3}\right|$ **(b)** $|-8|$
    (c) $|\pi - 2|$ **(d)** $|3 - \pi|$

In Exercises 21 through 24, show the points corresponding to u and v on the real-number line and then find the distance between u and v.

21. **(a)** $u = 8, v = 2$ **(b)** $u = -8, v = 2$
    (c) $u = 8, v = -2$ **(d)** $u = -8, v = -2$
22. **(a)** $u = 6, v = 4$ **(b)** $u = -6, v = 4$
    (c) $u = 6, v = -4$ **(d)** $u = -6, v = -4$
23. **(a)** $u = t, v = 2t, \text{ and } t > 0$
    (b) $u = t, v = 2t, \text{ and } t < 0$
24. **(a)** $u = t, v = \frac{1}{2}t, \text{ and } t > 0$
    (b) $u = t, v = \frac{1}{2}t, \text{ and } t < 0$

In Exercises 25 through 30, show that the two inequalities are equivalent.

25. $|(2x - 3) - 9| < 1; |x - 6| < \frac{1}{2}$
26. $|(2x + 3) - 1| < 1; |x + 6| < \frac{1}{2}$
27. $|(3x - 5) - 1| < \frac{1}{2}; |x - 2| < \frac{1}{6}$
28. $|(5x - 2) - 3| < \frac{1}{2}; |x - 1| < \frac{1}{10}$
29. $|(\frac{1}{2}x - 5) + 7| < \frac{1}{8}; |x + 4| < \frac{1}{4}$
30. $|(\frac{1}{4}x - 1) + 2| < \frac{1}{6}; |x + 4| < \frac{2}{3}$

In Exercises 31 and 32, verify the triangle inequality for the values of a and b.

31. **(a)** $a = 5 \text{ and } b = 7$ **(b)** $a = 5 \text{ and } b = -7$
    (c) $a = -5 \text{ and } b = 7$ **(d)** $a = -5 \text{ and } b = -7$
32. **(a)** $a = \frac{1}{2} \text{ and } b = \frac{1}{3}$ **(b)** $a = -\frac{1}{2} \text{ and } b = \frac{1}{3}$
    (c) $a = \frac{1}{2} \text{ and } b = -\frac{1}{3}$ **(d)** $a = -\frac{1}{2} \text{ and } b = -\frac{1}{3}$

In Exercises 33 and 34, use the triangle inequality to prove the statement.

33. If $|x - 1| < \frac{1}{3}$ and $|y + 1| < \frac{1}{4}$, then $|x + y| < \frac{7}{12}$.

34. If $|x - 1| < \frac{1}{3}$ and $|y - 1| < \frac{1}{4}$, then $|x - y| < \frac{7}{12}$.

35. To determine the point on the real-number line corresponding to the irrational number $\sqrt{2}$, use the construction indicated in the figure below: From the point 1, a line segment of length one unit is drawn perpendicular to the axis. Then a right triangle is formed by connecting the endpoint of this segment with the origin. The length of the hypotenuse of this right triangle is $\sqrt{2}$ units. (This fact follows from the Pythagorean theorem, which states that c^2 has the same value as $a^2 + b^2$, where c units is the length of the hypotenuse, and a units and b units are the lengths of the other two sides.) An arc of a circle having its center at the origin and a radius of $\sqrt{2}$ is then drawn; the point where this arc intersects the axis is $\sqrt{2}$. Use this method to determine the point corresponding to $\sqrt{5}$.

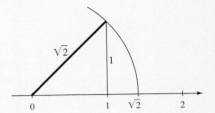

36. Determine the point on the real-number line corresponding to the irrational number $\sqrt{10}$. *Hint:* See Exercise 35.

A.2 COORDINATES AND GRAPHS OF EQUATIONS

The origination of analytic geometry is credited to René Descartes (1596–1650), a French mathematician and philosopher. In his book *Geometry,* published in 1635, Descartes established the union of algebra and geometry by a *rectangular cartesian* (named for Descartes) *coordinate system.* This coordinate system utilizes *ordered pairs* of real numbers.

Any two real numbers form a pair, and when the order of appearance of the numbers is significant, we call it an **ordered pair.** If x is the first real number and y is the second, this ordered pair is denoted by (x, y). Observe that the ordered pair $(5, 2)$ is different from the ordered pair $(2, 5)$.

The set of all ordered pairs of real numbers is called the **number plane,** denoted by R^2, and each ordered pair (x, y) is a **point** in the number plane. Just as R, the set of real numbers, can be identified with points on an axis (a one-dimensional space), we can identify R^2 with points in a geometric plane (a two-dimensional space). A horizontal line, called the **x axis,** is chosen in the geometric plane. A vertical line, called the **y axis,** is selected, and the point of intersection of the x axis and the y axis is called the **origin,** denoted by the letter O. The units of measurement along the two axes are usually the same. We establish the positive direction on the x axis to the right of the origin, and the positive direction on the y axis above the origin. See Figure 1.

We now associate an ordered pair of real numbers (x, y) with a point in the geometric plane. At the point x on the horizontal axis and the point y on the vertical axis, line segments are drawn perpendicular to the respective axes. The intersection of these two perpendicular line segments is the point P associated with the ordered pair (x, y). Refer to Figure 2. The first number x of the pair is called the **abscissa** (or **x coordinate**) of P, and the second number y is called the **ordinate** (or **y coordinate**) of P. If the abscissa is

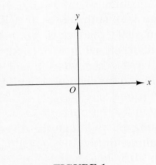

FIGURE 1

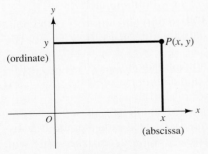

FIGURE 2

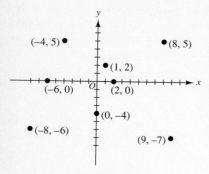

FIGURE 3

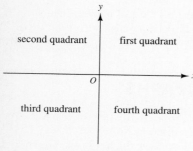

FIGURE 4

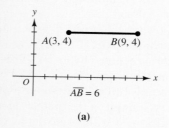

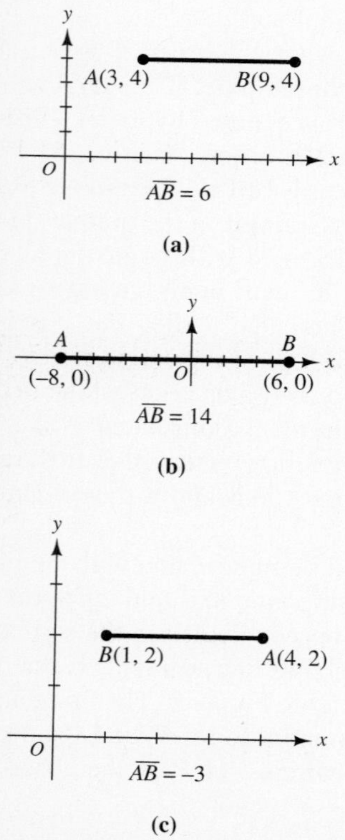

(a)

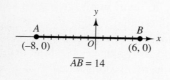

(b)

positive, P is to the right of the y axis; and if it is negative, P is to the left of the y axis. If the ordinate is positive, P is above the x axis; and if it is negative, P is below the x axis. The abscissa and ordinate of a point are called the **rectangular cartesian coordinates** of the point. There is a one-to-one correspondence between the points in a geometric plane and R^2; that is, with each point there corresponds a unique ordered pair (x, y), and with each ordered pair (x, y) there is associated only one point. This one-to-one correspondence is called a **rectangular cartesian coordinate system.** Figure 3 illustrates a rectangular cartesian coordinate system with some points located.

The x and y axes are called **coordinate axes.** They divide the plane into four parts, called **quadrants.** The first quadrant is the one in which the abscissa and the ordinate are both positive, that is, the upper right quadrant. The other quadrants are numbered in the counterclockwise direction, with the fourth being the lower right quadrant. See Figure 4.

Because of the one-to-one correspondence, we identify R^2 with the geometric plane. For this reason we call an ordered pair (x, y) a point.

We now discuss the problem of finding the distance between two points in R^2. If A is the point (x_1, y_1) and B is the point (x_2, y_1) (that is, A and B have the same ordinate but different abscissas), then the **directed distance** from A to B is denoted by $\overline{AB}$, and we define

$$\overline{AB} = x_2 - x_1$$

▷ **ILLUSTRATION 1**   Refer to Figure 5(a), (b), and (c). If A is the point $(3, 4)$ and B is the point $(9, 4)$, then $\overline{AB} = 9 - 3$; that is, $\overline{AB} = 6$. If A is the point $(-8, 0)$ and B is the point $(6, 0)$, then $\overline{AB} = 6 - (-8)$; that is, $\overline{AB} = 14$. If A is the point $(4, 2)$ and B is $(1, 2)$, then $\overline{AB} = 1 - 4$; that is, $\overline{AB} = -3$. We see that $\overline{AB}$ is positive if B is to the right of A, and $\overline{AB}$ is negative if B is to the left of A.   ◀

If C is the point (x_1, y_1) and D is the point (x_1, y_2), then the **directed distance** from C to D, denoted by $\overline{CD}$, is defined by

$$\overline{CD} = y_2 - y_1$$

▷ **ILLUSTRATION 2**   Refer to Figure 6(a) and (b). If C is the point $(1, -2)$ and D is $(1, -8)$, then $\overline{CD} = -8 - (-2)$; that is, $\overline{CD} = -6$. If C is the point $(-2, -3)$ and D is $(-2, 4)$, then $\overline{CD} = 4 - (-3)$; that is, $\overline{CD} = 7$. The number $\overline{CD}$ is positive if D is above C, and $\overline{CD}$ is negative if D is below C.   ◀

Observe that the terminology *directed distance* indicates both a distance and a direction (positive or negative). If we are concerned only with

(c)

FIGURE 5

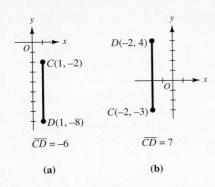

$\overline{CD} = -6$ (a)

$\overline{CD} = 7$ (b)

FIGURE 6

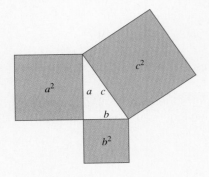

FIGURE 7

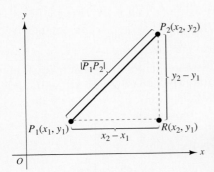

FIGURE 8

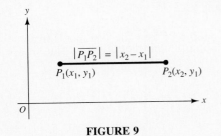

FIGURE 9

the length of the line segment between two points P_1 and P_2 (that is, the distance between the points P_1 and P_2 without regard to direction), then we use the terminology *undirected distance*. We denote the **undirected distance** from P_1 to P_2 by $|\overline{P_1 P_2}|$, which is a nonnegative number. If we use the word *distance* without an adjective *directed* or *undirected,* it is understood that we mean an undirected distance.

We now wish to obtain a formula for computing the distance $|\overline{P_1 P_2}|$ if $P_1(x_1, y_1)$ and $P_2(x_2, y_2)$ are any two points in the plane. We use the Pythagorean theorem from plane geometry, which we now state. Refer to Figure 7.

A.2.1 Theorem   The Pythagorean Theorem

In a right triangle, if a and b are the lengths of the perpendicular sides and c is the length of the hypotenuse, then

$$a^2 + b^2 = c^2$$

Figure 8 shows P_1 and P_2 in the first quadrant and the point $R(x_2, y_1)$. Note that $|\overline{P_1 P_2}|$ is the length of the hypotenuse of the right triangle $P_1 R P_2$. From the Pythagorean theorem, we have

$$|\overline{P_1 P_2}|^2 = |\overline{P_1 R}|^2 + |\overline{RP_2}|^2$$
$$|\overline{P_1 P_2}| = \sqrt{|\overline{P_1 R}|^2 + |\overline{RP_2}|^2}$$
$$|\overline{P_1 P_2}| = \sqrt{(x_2 - x_1)^2 + (y_2 - y_1)^2}$$

In this formula we do not have a $\pm$ symbol in front of the radical because $|\overline{P_1 P_2}|$ is a nonnegative number. The formula holds for all possible positions of P_1 and P_2 in all four quadrants. The length of the hypotenuse is always $|\overline{P_1 P_2}|$, and the lengths of the legs are always $|\overline{P_1 R}|$ and $|\overline{RP_2}|$. We have then the following theorem.

A.2.2 Theorem   The Distance Formula

The distance between two points $P_1(x_1, y_1)$ and $P_2(x_2, y_2)$ is given by

$$|\overline{P_1 P_2}| = \sqrt{(x_2 - x_1)^2 + (y_2 - y_1)^2}$$

If P_1 and P_2 are on the same horizontal line, as in Figure 9, then $y_2 = y_1$ and

$$|\overline{P_1 P_2}| = \sqrt{(x_2 - x_1)^2 + 0^2}$$
$$\Leftrightarrow |\overline{P_1 P_2}| = |x_2 - x_1| \qquad \text{(because } \sqrt{a^2} = |a|\text{)}$$

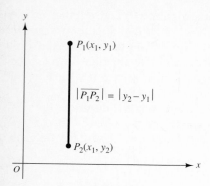

FIGURE 10

Furthermore, if P_1 and P_2 are on the same vertical line, as in Figure 10, then $x_2 = x_1$, and

$$|\overline{P_1P_2}| = \sqrt{0^2 + (y_2 - y_1)^2}$$
$$\Leftrightarrow |\overline{P_1P_2}| = |y_2 - y_1|$$

We now obtain the formulas for finding the midpoint of a line segment. Let $M(x, y)$ be the midpoint of the line segment from $P_1(x_1, y_1)$ to $P_2(x_2, y_2)$. Refer to Figure 11. Because triangles P_1RM and MTP_2 are congruent,

$$|\overline{P_1R}| = |\overline{MT}| \quad \text{and} \quad |\overline{RM}| = |\overline{TP_2}|$$

Thus

$$x - x_1 = x_2 - x \qquad y - y_1 = y_2 - y$$
$$2x = x_1 + x_2 \qquad 2y = y_1 + y_2$$
$$x = \frac{x_1 + x_2}{2} \qquad y = \frac{y_1 + y_2}{2}$$

We have proved the following theorem.

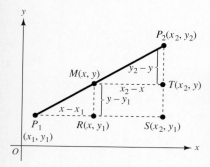

FIGURE 11

A.2.3 Theorem   The Midpoint Formulas

If $M(x, y)$ is the midpoint of the line segment from $P_1(x_1, y_1)$ to $P_2(x_2, y_2)$, then

$$x = \frac{x_1 + x_2}{2} \qquad y = \frac{y_1 + y_2}{2}$$

In the derivation of the formulas, we assumed that $x_2 > x_1$ and $y_2 > y_1$. The same formulas are obtained by using any orderings of these numbers.

▶ **EXAMPLE 1** **(a)** Determine the coordinates of the midpoint M of the line segment from $A(5, -3)$ to $B(-1, 6)$. **(b)** Locate the points A, M, and B, and show that $|\overline{AM}| = |\overline{MB}|$.

Solution

(a) From the midpoint formulas, if M is the point (x, y)

$$x = \frac{5 - 1}{2} \qquad y = \frac{-3 + 6}{2}$$
$$= 2 \qquad\qquad = \tfrac{3}{2}$$

Thus M is the point $(2, \tfrac{3}{2})$.

(b) Figure 12 shows the points A, M, and B. From the distance formula

$$|\overline{AM}| = \sqrt{(2 - 5)^2 + (\tfrac{3}{2} + 3)^2} \qquad\qquad |\overline{MB}| = \sqrt{(-1 - 2)^2 + (6 - \tfrac{3}{2})^2}$$
$$= \sqrt{9 + \tfrac{81}{4}} \qquad\qquad\qquad = \sqrt{9 + \tfrac{81}{4}}$$
$$= \tfrac{3}{2}\sqrt{13} \qquad\qquad\qquad = \tfrac{3}{2}\sqrt{13}$$

Therefore $|\overline{AM}| = |\overline{MB}|$.   ◀

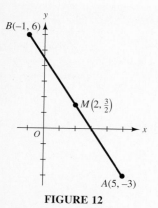

FIGURE 12

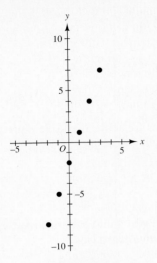

FIGURE 13

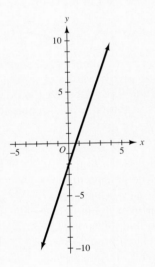

$y = 3x - 2$

FIGURE 14

We have demonstrated how a rectangular cartesian coordinate system can be used to obtain geometric facts by algebra. We now show how such a coordinate system enables us to associate a *graph* (a geometric concept) with an *equation* (an algebraic concept).

An **algebraic equation** in two variables x and y is a statement that two algebraic expressions in x and y are equal. When x and y are replaced by specific numbers, say a and b, the resulting statement may be either true or false. If it is true, the ordered pair (a, b) is called a solution of the equation.

▷ **ILLUSTRATION 3**   Consider the equation

$$y = 3x - 2 \qquad (1)$$

where (x, y) is a point in R^2. If x is replaced by 2 in the equation, we see that $y = 4$; thus the ordered pair $(2, 4)$ is a solution. If any number is substituted for x in the right side of (1), a corresponding value for y is obtained. Therefore, (1) has an unlimited number of solutions. The solutions obtained from Table 1 are $(-2, -8)$, $(-1, -5)$, $(0, -2)$, $(1, 1)$, $(2, 4)$, and $(3, 7)$. ◀

Table 1

x	-2	-1	0	1	2	3
$y = 3x - 2$	-8	-5	-2	1	4	7

A.2.4 Definition of the Graph of an Equation

The **graph of an equation** in R^2 is the set of all points in R^2 whose coordinates are solutions of the equation.

Because Equation (1) has an unlimited number of solutions, its graph consists of an unlimited number of points. The six points, given by Table 1 and shown in Figure 13, appear to lie on a line. In fact, you will learn in Appendix Section A.3 that every solution of Equation (1) corresponds to a point on the line, and conversely, the coordinates of each point on the line satisfy (1). The line is, therefore, the graph of the equation. This graph is sketched in Figure 14, where the arrowheads indicate that the line continues in both directions. The coordinates of any point (x, y) on the line satisfy (1), and the coordinates of any point not on the line do not satisfy the equation.

Recall from the section at the beginning of the book titled *Preparation for Your Study of Calculus*, we indicated that graphs will be obtained in two ways: (i) by hand, where we use the terminology *sketch the graph;* (ii) on a graphics calculator, where we state *plot the graph.*

▷ **ILLUSTRATION 4**   The graph of the equation

$$y = 3x - 2$$

plotted in the $[-12, 12]$ by $[-8, 8]$ window appears in Figure 15. Compare Figures 14 and 15, showing the same line. ◀

$[-12, 12]$ by $[-8, 8]$

$y = 3x - 2$

FIGURE 15

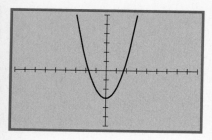

$[-9, 9]$ by $[-6, 6]$

$y = x^2 - 3$

FIGURE 16

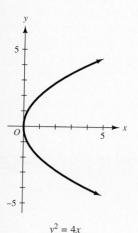

$y^2 = 4x$

FIGURE 17

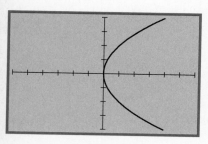

$[-6, 6]$ by $[-4, 4]$

$y_1 = 2\sqrt{x}$ and $y_2 = -2\sqrt{x}$

FIGURE 18

▷ **ILLUSTRATION 5**   The graph of the equation

$$y = x^2 - 3$$

plotted in the $[-9, 9]$ by $[-6, 6]$ window appears in Figure 16.   ◀

The graph of the equation in Illustration 5 is a *parabola*. We discuss *parabolas* in detail in Appendix Section A.4.

Most graphics calculators can plot graphs for more than one equation in the same window. We do this in the following example.

▶ **EXAMPLE 2**   **(a)** Sketch the graph of the equation

$$y^2 = 4x$$

by locating the points for which x is 0, 1, 2, 3, and 4 and connnecting these points by a curve. **(b)** Plot the graphs of the two equations

$$y = 2\sqrt{x} \quad \text{and} \quad y = -2\sqrt{x}$$

in the same window. **(c)** Why are the curves obtained in parts (a) and (b) identical?

Solution

(a) Because y^2 is nonnegative, values of x are restricted to nonnegative numbers. For each positive value of x there are two values of y. Table 2 gives the values of y when x is 0, 1, 2, 3, and 4. By locating the points whose coordinates are the x and y values in the table and connecting these points we obtain the graph sketched in Figure 17.

Table 2

x	0	1	1	2	2	3	3	4	4
$y^2 = 4x$	0	2	-2	$2\sqrt{2}$	$-2\sqrt{2}$	$2\sqrt{3}$	$-2\sqrt{3}$	4	-4

(b) On a graphics calculator we let

$$y_1 = 2\sqrt{x} \quad \text{and} \quad y_2 = -2\sqrt{x}$$

and plot the graphs of these two equations in the same $[-6, 6]$ by $[-4, 4]$ window as shown in Figure 18.

(c) The equation $y^2 = 4x$ is equivalent to the two equations $y = 2\sqrt{x}$ and $y = -2\sqrt{x}$. Therefore the union of the graphs of y_1 and y_2 plotted in part (b) is the same as the graph sketched in part (a).   ◀

The curve in Example 2 is also a *parabola*.

▶ **EXAMPLE 3**   **(a)** Plot the graph of the equation $y = |x|$. **(b)** Sketch the graph of the equation in part (a).

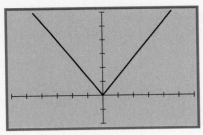

[–6, 6] by [–2, 6]

$y = \text{ABS}(x)$

FIGURE 19

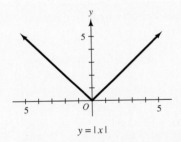

$y = |x|$

FIGURE 20

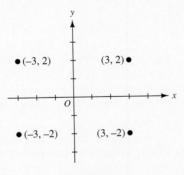

FIGURE 21

Solution

(a) Computing the absolute value of a number is *built-in* on a graphics calculator and on most calculators is denoted by ABS. We let

$$y = \text{ABS}(x)$$

and plot the graph in the $[-6, 6]$ by $[-2, 6]$ window shown in Figure 19.

(b) From the definition of the absolute value of a number,

$$y = \begin{cases} x & \text{if } x \geq 0 \\ -x & \text{if } x < 0 \end{cases}$$

Table 3 gives some values of x and y satisfying the equation, and the graph is sketched in Figure 20, which agrees with Figure 19.

Table 3

x	0	1	2	3	4	-1	-2	-3	-4
$y = \lvert x \rvert$	0	1	2	3	4	1	2	3	4

◀

Symmetry is an important property of graphs, especially helpful when sketching graphs.

A.2.5 Definition of Symmetry of Two Points

Two points P and Q are said to be **symmetric with respect to a line** if and only if the line is the perpendicular bisector of the line segment PQ. Two points P and Q are said to be **symmetric with respect to a third point** if and only if the third point is the midpoint of the line segment PQ.

▷ **ILLUSTRATION 6**   The points $(3, 2)$ and $(3, -2)$ are symmetric with respect to the x axis, the points $(3, 2)$ and $(-3, 2)$ are symmetric with respect to the x axis, and the points $(3, 2)$ and $(-3, -2)$ are symmetric with respect to the origin. See Figure 21. ◀

In general, the points (x, y) and $(x, -y)$ are symmetric with respect to the x axis; (x, y) and $(-x, y)$ are symmetric with respect to the y axis; and (x, y) and $(-x, -y)$ are symmetric with respect to the origin.

A.2.6 Definition of Symmetry of a Graph

The graph of an equation is **symmetric with respect to a line l** if and only if for every point P on the graph there is a point Q also on the graph such that P and Q are symmetric with respect to l. The graph of an equation is **symmetric with respect to a point R** if and only if for every point P on the graph there is a point S also on the graph such that P and S are symmetric with respect to R.

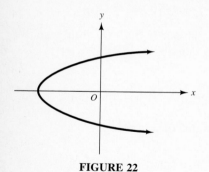

FIGURE 22

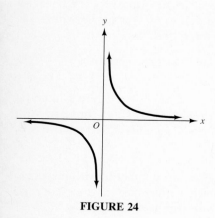

FIGURE 23

Figure 22 shows a graph symmetric with respect to the x axis, Figure 23 shows one symmetric with respect to the y axis, and Figure 24 shows one symmetric with respect to the origin.

From the definition of symmetry of a graph, it follows that if a point (x, y) is on a graph symmetric with respect to the x axis, then the point $(x, -y)$ also must be on the graph. And if both the points (x, y) and $(x, -y)$ are on the graph, then the graph is symmetric with respect to the x axis. Therefore the coordinates of the point $(x, -y)$ as well as (x, y) must satisfy an equation of the graph. Hence the graph of an equation in x and y is symmetric with respect to the x axis if and only if an equivalent equation is obtained when y is replaced by $-y$ in the equation. We have thus proved part (i) in the following symmetry tests. The proofs of parts (ii) and (iii) are similar.

A.2.7 Theorem   Symmetry Tests

The graph of an equation in x and y is

(i) symmetric with respect to the x axis if and only if an equivalent equation is obtained when y is replaced by $-y$ in the equation;

(ii) symmetric with respect to the y axis if and only if an equivalent equation is obtained when x is replaced by $-x$ in the equation.

(iii) symmetric with respect to the origin if and only if an equivalent equation is obtained when x is replaced by $-x$ and y is replaced by $-y$ in the equation.

▷ **ILLUSTRATION 7**   Refer to the graph in Figure 16, symmetric with respect to the y axis and having the equation

$$y = x^2 - 3$$

If x is replaced by $-x$, we obtain the equation

$$y = (-x)^2 - 3$$
$$\Leftrightarrow y = x^2 - 3$$

◀

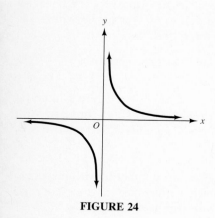

FIGURE 24

▷ **ILLUSTRATION 8**   The graph sketched in Figure 17 is symmetric with respect to the x axis, and its equation is

$$y^2 = 4x$$

Replacing y by $-y$ in this equation, we obtain

$$(-y)^2 = 4x$$
$$\Leftrightarrow \quad y^2 = 4x$$

◀

▶ **EXAMPLE 4**   Test for symmetry the graph of the equation

$$y = \tfrac{1}{2}x^3$$

Then plot the graph.

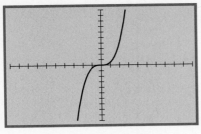

[−10, 10] by [−10, 10]

$$y = \tfrac{1}{2}x^3$$

FIGURE 25

Solution We test for symmetry. If x is replaced by $-x$ and y is replaced by $-y$ in the given equation, we have

$$-y = \tfrac{1}{2}(-x)^3$$
$$\Leftrightarrow \quad y = \tfrac{1}{2}x^3$$

Therefore, by symmetry test (iii), the graph is symmetric with respect to the origin. The graph is neither symmetric with respect to the x axis, nor symmetric with respect to the y axis, as symmetry tests (i) and (ii) will verify.

The graph of the given equation, plotted in the $[-10, 10]$ by $[-10, 10]$ window, appears in Figure 25. Observe the symmetry with respect to the origin. ◀

EXERCISES A.2

In Exercises 1 and 2, locate the point P on a rectangular cartesian coordinate system and state the quadrant in which it lies.

1. (a) $P(3,7)$ **(b)** $P(-4, -6)$
   (c) $P(2, -5)$ **(d)** $P(-1, 4)$

2. (a) $P(5, 6)$ **(b)** $P(8, -1)$
   (c) $P(-7, -2)$ **(d)** $P(-9, 3)$

In Exercises 3 through 8, locate the point P and each of the following points as may apply: (a) The point Q such that the line through Q and P is perpendicular to the x axis and bisected by it. Give the coordinates of Q. (b) The point R such that the line through P and R is perpendicular to and bisected by the y axis. Give the coordinates of R. (c) The point S such that the line through P and S is bisected by the origin. Give the coordinates of S. (d) The point T such that the line through P and T is perpendicular to and bisected by the 45° line through the origin bisecting the first and third quadrants. Give the coordinates of T.

3. $P(1, -2)$ **4.** $P(-2, 2)$ **5.** $P(2, 2)$
6. $P(-2, -2)$ **7.** $P(-1, -3)$ **8.** $P(0, -3)$

In Exercises 9 and 10, do the following: (a) determine the coordinates of the midpoint M of the line segment from A to B; (b) locate the points A , M, and B and show that $|\overline{AM}| = |\overline{MB}|$.

9. $A(-4, 7)$ and $B(1, -3)$ **10.** $A(3, 4)$ and $B(4, -3)$

In Exercises 11 and 12, draw the triangle having vertices at A , B, and C and find the lengths of the sides.

11. $A(4, -5)$, $B(-2, 3)$, $C(-1, 7)$

12. $A(2, 3)$, $B(3, -3)$, $C(-1, -1)$

13. A median of a triangle is a line segment from a vertex to the midpoint of the opposite side. Find the length of the medians of the triangle having vertices $A(2, 3)$, $B(3, -3)$, and $C(-1, -1)$.

14. Find the length of the medians of the triangle having vertices $A(-3, 5)$, $B(2, 4)$, and $C(-1, -4)$.

15. Prove that the triangle with vertices $A(3, -6)$, $B(8, -2)$, and $C(-1, -1)$ is a right triangle. *Hint:* Use the converse of the Pythagorean theorem.

16. Find the midpoints of the diagonals of the quadrilateral whose vertices are $(0, 0)$, $(0, 4)$, $(3, 5)$, and $(3, 1)$.

17. Prove that the points $A(-7, 2)$, $B(3, -4)$, and $C(1, 4)$ are the vertices of an isosceles triangle.

18. Prove that the points $A(-4, -1)$, $B(-2, -3)$, $C(4, 3)$, and $D(2, 5)$ are the vertices of a rectangle.

19. By using the distance formula, prove that the points $(-3, 2)$, $(1, -2)$, and $(9, -10)$ lie on a line.

20. Determine whether the points $(14, 7)$, $(2, 2)$, and $(-4, -1)$ lie on a line by using the distance formula.

21. Prove that the points $A(6, -13)$, $B(-2, 2)$, $C(13, 10)$, and $D(21, -5)$ are the vertices of a square. Find the length of a diagonal.

22. If one end of a line segment is the point $(-4, 2)$ and the midpoint is $(3, -1)$, find the coordinates of the other end of the line segment.

23. The abscissa of a point is -6, and its distance from the point $(1, 3)$ is $\sqrt{74}$. Find the ordinate of the point.

24. Given the two points $A(-3, 4)$ and $B(2, 5)$, find the coordinates of a point P on the line through A and B and not between A and B such that P is **(a)** twice as far from A as from B and **(b)** twice as far from B as from A.

In Exercises 25 through 32, do the following: (a) test the graph of equation (i) for symmetry; (b) sketch the graph of equation (i); (c) plot the graphs of equations (ii) and (iii) in the same window; (d) compare the curves obtained in parts (b) and (c).

25. (i) $y^2 = 9x$ **(ii)** $y = 3\sqrt{x}$ **(iii)** $y = -3\sqrt{x}$
26. (i) $y^2 = \frac{1}{4}x$ **(ii)** $y = \frac{1}{2}\sqrt{x}$ **(iii)** $y = -\frac{1}{2}\sqrt{x}$
27. (i) $y^2 = -\frac{1}{4}x$ **(ii)** $y = \frac{1}{2}\sqrt{-x}$
    (iii) $y = -\frac{1}{2}\sqrt{-x}$
28. (i) $y^2 = -4x$ **(ii)** $y = 2\sqrt{-x}$
    (iii) $y = -2\sqrt{-x}$
29. (i) $y^2 = 1 - x^2$ **(ii)** $y = \sqrt{1 - x^2}$
    (iii) $y = -\sqrt{1 - x^2}$
30. (i) $y^2 = 9 - x^2$ **(ii)** $y = \sqrt{9 - x^2}$
    (iii) $y = -\sqrt{9 - x^2}$
31. (i) $y^2 = x^2 - 4$ **(ii)** $y = \sqrt{x^2 - 4}$
    (iii) $y = -\sqrt{x^2 - 4}$
32. (i) $y^2 = x^2 - 16$ **(ii)** $y = \sqrt{x^2 - 16}$
    (iii) $y = -\sqrt{x^2 - 16}$

In Exercises 33 and 34, sketch the graph of the equation.

33. (a) $y = |x - 2|$ **(b)** $y = |x + 2|$
    (c) $y = |x| - 2$ **(d)** $y = |x| + 2$
34. (a) $y = 2|x - 3|$ **(b)** $y = 2|x + 3|$
    (c) $y = 2|x| - 6$ **(d)** $y = 2|x| + 6$

In Exercises 35 through 38, test the graph of the equation for symmetry and then plot the graph.

35. (a) $y = x^3$ **(b)** $y = -x^3$
    (c) $y = \frac{1}{8}x^3$ **(d)** $y = -\frac{1}{8}x^3$

36. (a) $y = 2x^3$ **(b)** $y = -2x^3$
    (c) $y = \frac{1}{6}x^3$ **(d)** $y = -\frac{1}{6}x^3$
37. (a) $y = 2x^4$ **(b)** $y = -2x^4$
    (c) $y = \frac{1}{4}x^4$ **(d)** $y = -\frac{1}{4}x^4$
38. (a) $y = 4x^4$ **(b)** $y = -4x^4$
    (c) $y = \frac{1}{2}x^4$ **(d)** $y = -\frac{1}{2}x^4$

In Exercises 39 through 44, plot the graph of each equation in the same window.

39. $y = x^2, y = (x + 2)^2, y = (x - 2)^2, y = (x - 4)^2$
40. $y = x^2, y = x^2 + 2, y = x^2 - 2, y = x^2 - 4$
41. $y = x^2, y = 2x^2, y = -2x^2, y = 4x^2$
42. $y = x^2, y = \frac{1}{2}x^2, y = -\frac{1}{2}x^2, y = \frac{1}{4}x^2$
43. $y = |x|, y = |x| + 3, y = |x| - 3,$
    $y = |x| - 4$
44. $y = |x|, y = |x + 3|, y = |x - 3|,$
    $y = |x - 4|$
45. Describe how the graphs in Exercise 39 are similar and how they differ. Do the same for the graphs in Exercise 41.
46. Follow the instructions of Exercise 45 for the graphs in Exercises 40 and 42.
47. Follow the instructions of Exercise 45 for the graphs in Exercises 43 and 44.
48. Use the definitions of symmetry to explain why a graph symmetric with respect to both coordinate axes is also symmetric with respect to the origin.

A.3 LINES

Suppose the cost of hiring a one-passenger plane from a private airline is $310 for the plane and pilot plus 75 cents per mile flown. Then if y dollars is the cost of a trip of x miles,

$$y = 0.75x + 310$$

Figure 1 shows the graph of this equation plotted in the $[0, 1200]$ by $[0, 800]$ window, with scales of 100 on the axes. The graph appears to be a line. That the graph is indeed a line is established in Theorem A.3.4. Observe that for each 100-unit increase in x, y increases by 75 units, or, equivalently, for each 1-unit increase in x, y increases by 0.75 unit. Thus the ratio of the change in y to the change in x is a constant 0.75. This constant ratio is called the *slope* of the line. We proceed now to arrive at a formal definition of slope.

Let l be a nonvertical line and $P_1(x_1, y_1)$ and $P_2(x_2, y_2)$ be any two distinct points on l. Figure 2 shows such a line. In the figure R is the point (x_2, y_1), and the points P_1, P_2, and R are vertices of a right triangle; further-

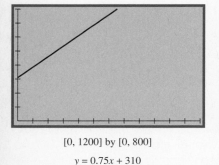

$[0, 1200]$ by $[0, 800]$

$y = 0.75x + 310$

FIGURE 1

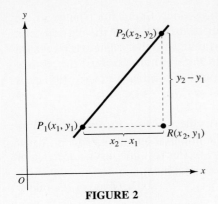

FIGURE 2

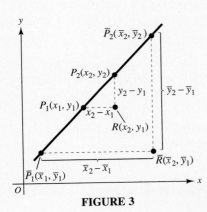

FIGURE 3

more, $\overline{P_1R} = x_2 - x_1$ and $\overline{RP_2} = y_2 - y_1$. The number $y_2 - y_1$ gives the measure of the change in the ordinate from P_1 to P_2, and it may be positive, negative, or zero. The number $x_2 - x_1$ gives the measure of the change in the abscissa from P_1 to P_2, and it may be positive or negative. Because the line l is not vertical, $x_2 \neq x_1$, and therefore $x_2 - x_1$ may not be zero. Let

$$m = \frac{y_2 - y_1}{x_2 - x_1} \tag{1}$$

The value of m computed from this equation is independent of the choice of the two points P_1 and P_2 on l. To show this, suppose we choose two different points $\overline{P}_1(\overline{x}_1, \overline{y}_1)$ and $\overline{P}_2(\overline{x}_2, \overline{y}_2)$ on line l, and compute a number $\overline{m}$ from (1).

$$\overline{m} = \frac{\overline{y}_2 - \overline{y}_1}{\overline{x}_2 - \overline{x}_1}$$

We shall show that $\overline{m} = m$. Refer to Figure 3. Triangles $\overline{P}_1\,\overline{R}P_2$ and P_1RP_2 are similar; so the lengths of corresponding sides are proportional. Therefore

$$\frac{\overline{y}_2 - \overline{y}_1}{\overline{x}_2 - \overline{x}_1} = \frac{y_2 - y_1}{x_2 - x_1}$$

or

$$\overline{m} = m$$

Thus the value of m computed from (1) is the same number no matter what two points on l are selected. This number m is called the *slope* of the line.

A.3.1 Definition of the Slope of a Line

If $P_1(x_1, y_1)$ and $P_2(x_2, y_2)$ are any two distinct points on line l, which is not parallel to the y axis, then the **slope** of l, denoted by m, is given by

$$m = \frac{y_2 - y_1}{x_2 - x_1}$$

Multiplying on both sides of the preceding equation by $x_2 - x_1$, we obtain

$$y_2 - y_1 = m(x_2 - x_1)$$

It follows from this equation that if we consider a particle moving along a line, the change in the ordinate of the particle is equal to the product of the slope and the change in the abscissa.

▷ **ILLUSTRATION 1**   If l is the line through the points $P_1(2, 1)$ and $P_2(4, 7)$ and m is the slope of l, then

$$m = \frac{7 - 1}{4 - 2}$$
$$= 3$$

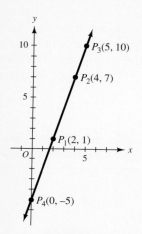

FIGURE 4

Refer to Figure 4. If a particle is moving along line l, the change in the ordinate is 3 times the change in the abscissa. That is, if the particle is at $P_2(4, 7)$ and the abscissa is increased by 1 unit, then the ordinate is increased by 3 units, and the particle is at the point $P_3(5, 10)$. Similarly, if the particle is at $P_1(2, 1)$ and the abscissa is decreased by 2 units, then the ordinate is decreased by 6 units, and the particle is at $P_4(0, -5)$. ◀

If the slope of a line is positive, then as the abscissa of a point on the line increases, the ordinate increases. Such a line is shown in Figure 5. A line whose slope is negative appears in Figure 6. For this line, as the abscissa of a point on the line increases, the ordinate decreases.

If a line is parallel to the x axis, then $y_2 = y_1$; so the slope of the line is zero. If a line is parallel to the y axis, $x_2 = x_1$; thus the fraction $\dfrac{y_2 - y_1}{x_2 - x_1}$ is meaningless because we cannot divide by zero. For this reason lines parallel to the y axis are excluded in the definition of slope. The slope of a vertical line is, therefore, not defined.

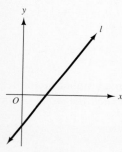

FIGURE 5

▶ **EXAMPLE 1** For each pair of points, sketch the line through them and find its slope: **(a)** $A(3, 7)$ and $B(-2, -4)$; **(b)** $A(-2, 5)$ and $B(2, -3)$; **(c)** $A(-3, 4)$ and $B(5, 4)$; **(d)** $A(5, 3)$ and $B(5, -1)$.

Solution The lines appear in Figure 7(a)–(d). We compute the slope from the definition.

(a) $m = \dfrac{-4 - 7}{-2 - 3}$ **(b)** $m = \dfrac{-3 - 5}{2 - (-2)}$ **(c)** $m = \dfrac{4 - 4}{5 - (-3)}$

$ = \dfrac{-11}{-5}$ $= -\dfrac{8}{4}$ $= \dfrac{0}{8}$

$ = \tfrac{11}{5}$ $= -2$ $= 0$

(d) Because the line is vertical, the slope is not defined. If you attempt to use the definition to compute the slope, you obtain zero in the denominator. ◀

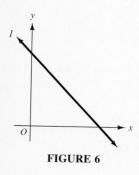

FIGURE 6

▷ **ILLUSTRATION 2**

(a) Suppose a line contains the point $P(5, 2)$ and its slope is $\tfrac{3}{4}$. To determine another point on the line, we start at P, and because the slope is $\tfrac{3}{4}$, we go 4 units to the right and then 3 units upward. We have then the point $Q(9, 5)$ also on the line. The line is sketched through points P and Q as in Figure 8.

(b) If a line through $P(5, 2)$ has the negative slope $-\tfrac{3}{4}$, we obtain another point on the line by starting at P and then going 4 units to the right and 3 units downward. This gives the point $Q(9, -1)$. Figure 9 shows the line through these points P and Q. ◀

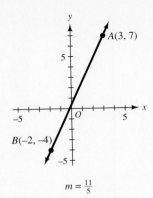

$$m = \frac{11}{5}$$

(a)

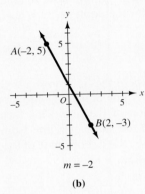

$$m = -2$$

(b)

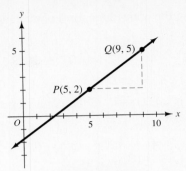

FIGURE 8   **FIGURE 9**

In Appendix Section A.2 we defined the graph of an equation. We now define what we mean by an *equation of a graph*.

A.3.2 Definition of an Equation of a Graph

An **equation of a graph** is an equation that is satisfied by the coordinates of those, and only those, points on the graph.

From this definition, it follows that an equation of a graph has the following properties:

1. If a point $P(x, y)$ is on the graph, then its coordinates satisfy the equation.
2. If a point $P(x, y)$ is not on the graph, then its coordinates do not satisfy the equation.

To obtain an equation of a line, we use the fact that a point $P_1(x_1, y_1)$ and a slope m determine a unique line. Let $P(x, y)$ be any point on the line except P_1. Then because the slope of the line through P_1 and P is m, we have from the definition of slope

$$\frac{y - y_1}{x - x_1} = m$$

$$y - y_1 = m(x - x_1)$$

This equation is called the **point-slope form** of an equation of the line. It gives an equation of the line if a point $P_1(x_1, y_1)$ on the line and the slope of the line are known.

▷ **ILLUSTRATION 3**   To find an equation of the line through the points $A(6, -3)$ and $B(-2, 3)$, we first compute m.

$$m = \frac{3 - (-3)}{-2 - 6}$$

$$= \frac{6}{-8}$$

$$= -\frac{3}{4}$$

(c)

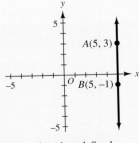

slope is undefined

(d)

FIGURE 7

$m = 0$ (c)

Using the point-slope form of an equation of the line with A as P_1, we have

$$y - (-3) = -\tfrac{3}{4}(x - 6)$$
$$4y + 12 = -3x + 18$$
$$3x + 4y - 6 = 0$$

If B is taken as P_1 in the point-slope form, we have

$$y - 3 = -\tfrac{3}{4}[x - (-2)]$$
$$4y - 12 = -3x - 6$$
$$3x + 4y - 6 = 0$$

which of course is the same equation.   ◀

If in the point-slope form we choose the particular point $(0, b)$ (that is, the point where the line intersects the y axis) for the point (x_1, y_1), we have

$$y - b = m(x - 0)$$

$\Leftrightarrow$ $\boxed{y = mx + b}$

The number b, the ordinate of the point where the line intersects the y axis, is the y **intercept** of the line. Consequently, the preceding equation is called the **slope-intercept form** of an equation of the line. This form is especially useful because it enables us to find the slope of a line from its equation. It is also important because it expresses the y coordinate of a point on the line explicitly in terms of its x coordinate.

▶ **EXAMPLE 2**   Find the slope of the line having the equation

$$6x + 5y - 7 = 0$$

Solution   We solve the equation for y.

$$5y = -6x + 7$$
$$y = -\tfrac{6}{5}x + \tfrac{7}{5}$$

This equation is in the slope-intercept form where $m = -\tfrac{6}{5}$ and $b = \tfrac{7}{5}$. Therefore the slope is $-\tfrac{6}{5}$.   ◀

Because the slope of a vertical line is undefined, we cannot apply the point-slope form to obtain its equation. We use instead the following theorem, which also gives an equation of a horizontal line.

A.3.3 Theorem

(i) An equation of the vertical line having x intercept a is

$$x = a$$

(ii) An equation of the horizontal line having y intercept b is

$$y = b$$

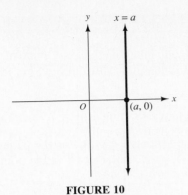

FIGURE 10

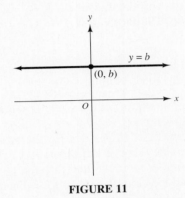

FIGURE 11

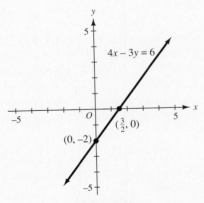

FIGURE 12

Proof

(i) Figure 10 shows the vertical line that intersects the x axis at the point $(a, 0)$. This line contains those and only those points on the line having the same abscissa. So $P(x, y)$ is any point on the line if and only if

$$x = a$$

(ii) The horizontal line that intersects the y axis at the point $(0, b)$ appears in Figure 11. For this line, $m = 0$. Therefore, from the slope-intercept form an equation of this line is

$$y = b$$ ∎

We have shown that an equation of a nonvertical line is of the form $y = mx + b$, and an equation of a vertical line is of the form $x = a$. Because each of these equations is a special case of an equation of the form

$$Ax + By + C = 0 \tag{2}$$

where A, B, and C are constants and A and B are not both zero, it follows that every line has an equation of the form (2). The converse of this fact is given by the next theorem.

A.3.4 Theorem

The graph of the equation

$$Ax + By + C = 0$$

where A, B, and C are constants and where not both A and B are zero, is a line.

The proof of this theorem is left as an exercise. See Exercise 51.

Because the graph of (2) is a line, it is called a **linear equation;** it is the general equation of the first degree in x and y.

To plot a line on a graphics calculator, we first write its equation in slope-intercept form as we did with Figure 1. To sketch a line by hand, we need only determine the coordinates of two points on the line, locate the points, and then draw the line. Any two points will suffice, but for convenience we usually choose the two points where the line intersects the axes.

▷ **ILLUSTRATION 4**   To sketch the line having the equation

$$4x - 3y = 6$$

we first find the x intercept a and the y intercept b. In the equation, we substitute 0 for y and get $a = \frac{3}{2}$. Substituting 0 for x, we obtain $b = -2$. Thus we have the line appearing in Figure 12.   ◀

An application of slopes is given by the following theorem.

A-28 **APPENDIX**

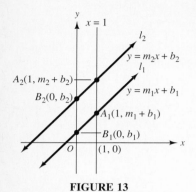

FIGURE 13

If l_1 and l_2 are two distinct nonvertical lines having slopes m_1 and m_2, respectively, then l_1 and l_2 are parallel if and only if $m_1 = m_2$.

Proof   Let equations of l_1 and l_2 be, respectively,

$$y = m_1 x + b_1 \quad \text{and} \quad y = m_2 x + b_2$$

See Figure 13, showing the two lines intersecting the y axis at the points $B_1(0, b_1)$ and $B_2(0, b_2)$. Let the vertical line $x = 1$ intersect l_1 at the point $A_1(1, m_1 + b_1)$ and l_2 at the point $A_2(1, m_2 + b_2)$. Then

$$|\overline{B_1 B_2}| = b_2 - b_1 \quad \text{and} \quad |\overline{A_1 A_2}| = (m_2 + b_2) - (m_1 + b_1)$$

The two lines are parallel if and only if the vertical distances $|\overline{B_1 B_2}|$ and $|\overline{A_1 A_2}|$ are equal; that is, l_1 and l_2 are parallel if and only if

$$b_2 - b_1 = (m_2 + b_2) - (m_1 + b_1)$$
$$b_2 - b_1 = m_2 + b_2 - m_1 - b_1$$
$$m_1 = m_2$$

Thus l_1 and l_2 are parallel if and only if $m_1 = m_2$. ∎

▷   **ILLUSTRATION 5**   Let l_1 be the line through the points $A(1, 2)$ and $B(3, -6)$ and m_1 be the slope of l_1; and let l_2 be the line through the points $C(2, -5)$ and $D(-1, 7)$ and m_2 be the slope of l_2. See Figure 14. Then

$$m_1 = \frac{-6 - 2}{3 - 1} \qquad m_2 = \frac{7 - (-5)}{-1 - 2}$$
$$= \frac{-8}{2} \qquad\qquad = \frac{12}{-3}$$
$$= -4 \qquad\qquad = -4$$

Because $m_1 = m_2$, then from Theorem A.3.5 l_1 and l_2 are parallel. ◀

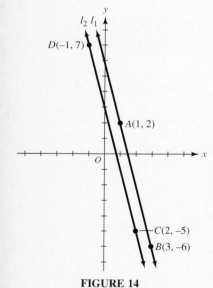

FIGURE 14

Any two distinct points determine a line. Three distinct points may or may not lie on the same line. If three or more points lie on the same line, they are said to be **collinear.** Hence three points A, B, and C are collinear if and only if the line through the points A and B is the same as the line through the points B and C. Because the line through A and B and the line through B and C both contain the point B, they are the same line if and only if their slopes are equal.

▶   **EXAMPLE 3**   Determine by means of slopes if the points $A(-3, -4)$, $B(2, -1)$, and $C(7, 2)$ are collinear.

Solution   If m_1 is the slope of the line through A and B, and m_2 is the slope of the line B and C, then

$$m_1 = \frac{-1 - (-4)}{2 - (-3)} \qquad m_2 = \frac{2 - (-1)}{7 - 2}$$
$$= \frac{3}{5} \qquad\qquad = \frac{3}{5}$$

Hence $m_1 = m_2$. Therefore the line through A and B and the line through B and C have the same slope and contain the common point B. Thus they are the same line, and therefore A, B, and C are collinear. ◄

We now state and prove a theorem regarding the slopes of two perpendicular lines.

A.3.6 Theorem

Two nonvertical lines l_1 and l_2 having slopes m_1 and m_2, respectively, are perpendicular if and only if $m_1 m_2 = -1$.

Proof   Let us choose the coordinate axes so that the origin is at the point of intersection of l_1 and l_2. See Figure 15. Because neither l_1 nor l_2 is vertical, these two lines intersect the line $x = 1$ at points P_1 and P_2, respectively. The abscissa of both P_1 and P_2 is 1. Let $\bar{y}$ be the ordinate of P_1. Because l_1 contains the points $(0, 0)$ and $(1, \bar{y})$ and its slope is m_1, then

$$m_1 = \frac{\bar{y} - 0}{1 - 0}$$

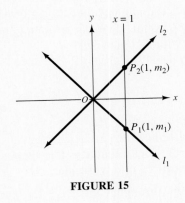

FIGURE 15

Thus $\bar{y} = m_1$. Similarly, the ordinate of P_2 is shown to be m_2. From the Pythagorean theorem and its converse, triangle $P_1 O P_2$ is a right triangle if and only if

$$|\overline{OP_1}|^2 + |\overline{OP_2}|^2 = |\overline{P_1 P_2}|^2 \tag{3}$$

Applying the distance formula, we obtain

$$|\overline{OP_1}|^2 = (1 - 0)^2 + (m_1 - 0)^2 \qquad |\overline{OP_2}|^2 = (1 - 0)^2 + (m_2 - 0)^2$$
$$= 1 + m_1^2 \qquad\qquad\qquad = 1 + m_2^2$$
$$|\overline{P_1 P_2}|^2 = (1 - 1)^2 + (m_2 - m_1)^2$$
$$= m_2^2 - 2m_1 m_2 + m_1^2$$

Substituting into (3), we can conclude that $P_1 O P_2$ is a right triangle if and only if

$$1 + m_1^2 + 1 + m_2^2 = m_2^2 - 2m_1 m_2 + m_1^2$$
$$2 = -2m_1 m_2$$
$$m_1 m_2 = -1 \qquad\qquad\blacksquare$$

Because $m_1 m_2 = -1$ is equivalent to

$$m_1 = -\frac{1}{m_2} \quad \text{and} \quad m_2 = -\frac{1}{m_1}$$

Theorem A.3.6 states that two nonvertical lines are perpendicular if and only if the slope of one of them is the negative reciprocal of the slope of the other.

► **EXAMPLE 4**   Given the line l having the equation

$$5x + 4y - 20 = 0$$

find an equation of the line through the point $(2, -3)$ and **(a)** parallel to l and **(b)** perpendicular to l.

Solution   We first determine the slope of l by writing its equation in the slope-intercept form. Solving the equation for y, we have

$$4y = -5x + 20$$
$$y = -\tfrac{5}{4}x + 5$$

The slope of l is the coefficient of x, which is $-\tfrac{5}{4}$.

(a) The slope of a line parallel to l is also $-\tfrac{5}{4}$. Because the required line contains the point $(2, -3)$, we use the point-slope form, which gives

$$y - (-3) = -\tfrac{5}{4}(x - 2)$$
$$4y + 12 = -5x + 10$$
$$5x + 4y + 2 = 0$$

(b) The slope of a line perpendicular to l is the negative reciprocal of $-\tfrac{5}{4}$, which is $\tfrac{4}{5}$. From the point-slope form, an equation of the line through $(2, -3)$ and having slope $\tfrac{4}{5}$ is

$$y - (-3) = \tfrac{4}{5}(x - 2)$$
$$5y + 15 = 4x - 8$$
$$4x - 5y - 23 = 0$$

▶ **EXAMPLE 5**   Prove by means of slopes that the four points $A(6, 2)$, $B(8, 6)$, $C(4, 8)$, and $D(2, 4)$ are vertices of a rectangle.

Solution   See Figure 16, where l_1 is the line through A and B, l_2 is the line through B and C, and l_3 is the line through D and C, and l_4 is the line through A and D; m_1, m_2, m_3, and m_4 are their respective slopes.

$$m_1 = \frac{6 - 2}{8 - 6} \qquad m_2 = \frac{8 - 6}{4 - 8} \qquad m_3 = \frac{8 - 4}{4 - 2} \qquad m_4 = \frac{4 - 2}{2 - 6}$$

$$= 2 \qquad\qquad = -\frac{1}{2} \qquad\qquad = 2 \qquad\qquad = -\frac{1}{2}$$

Because $m_1 = m_3$, l_1 is parallel to l_3; and because $m_2 = m_4$, l_2 is parallel to l_4. Because $m_1 m_2 = -1$, l_1 and l_2 are perpendicular. Therefore, the quadrilateral has its opposite sides parallel, and a pair of adjacent sides are perpendicular. Thus the quadrilateral is a rectangle.   ◀

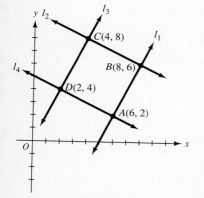

FIGURE 16

EXERCISES A.3

In Exercises 1 through 6, sketch the line through points A and B and determine the slope of the line.

1. (a) $A(1, 4)$, $B(6, 5)$ **(b)** $A(2, -3)$, $B(-4, 3)$

2. (a) $A(5, 2)$, $B(-2, -3)$ **(b)** $A(-4, 2)$, $B(8, 5)$

3. (a) $A(-4, 3)$, $B(0, 0)$ **(b)** $A(\tfrac{1}{3}, \tfrac{1}{2})$, $B(-\tfrac{5}{6}, \tfrac{2}{3})$

4. (a) $A(7, 0)$, $B(0, -6)$ **(b)** $A(-\tfrac{3}{4}, \tfrac{1}{8})$, $B(\tfrac{5}{4}, -\tfrac{1}{2})$

5. (a) $A(1, 5)$, $B(-2, 5)$
   (b) $A(-2.1, 0.3)$, $B(2.3, 1.4)$

6. (a) $A(3, -5)$, $B(3, 4)$
   (b) $A(5.2, -3.5)$, $B(-6.3, -1.4)$

In Exercises 7 and 8, sketch the line through point P and having slope m.

7. (a) $P(3, 4)$, $m = \tfrac{2}{5}$ **(b)** $P(-1, 6)$, $m = -3$

8. (a) $P(4, 3)$, $m = 2$ **(b)** $P(2, -5)$, $m = -\tfrac{4}{3}$

In Exercises 9 through 20, find an equation of the line satisfying the conditions.

9. **(a)** The slope is 4 and through the point $(2, -3)$;
   (b) through the two points $(-1, -5)$ and $(3, 6)$.

10. **(a)** The slope is -2 and through the point $(-4, 3)$;
    (b) through the two points $(3, 1)$ and $(-5, 4)$.

11. **(a)** The slope is $-\frac{2}{3}$ and the y intercept is 1;
    (b) the slope is 2 and the x intercept is $-\frac{4}{3}$.

12. **(a)** The slope is $\frac{3}{5}$ and the y intercept is -4;
    (b) the slope is -2 and the x intercept is 4.

13. **(a)** Through the point $(1, -7)$ and parallel to the x axis; **(b)** through the point $(2, 6)$ and parallel to the y axis.

14. **(a)** Through the point $(-5, 2)$ and parallel to the x axis; **(b)** through the point $(-3, -4)$ and parallel to the y axis.

15. **(a)** The x intercept is -3 and the y intercept is 4;
    (b) through the origin and bisecting the angle between the axes in the first and third quadrants.

16. **(a)** The x intercept is 5 and the y intercept is -6;
    (b) through the origin and bisecting the angle between the axes in the second and fourth quadrants.

17. Through the point $(-2, 3)$ and parallel to the line whose equation is $2x - y - 2 = 0$.

18. Through the point $(1, 4)$ and parallel to the line whose equation is $2x - 5y + 7 = 0$.

19. Through the point $(2, 4)$ and perpendicular to the line whose equation is $x - 5y + 10 = 0$.

20. Through the origin and perpendicular to the line whose equation is $2x - 5y + 6 = 0$.

In Exercises 21 through 24, find the slope and y intercept of the line having the given equation, and sketch the line.

21. **(a)** $x + 3y - 6 = 0$ **(b)** $4y - 9 = 0$

22. **(a)** $8x - 4y = 5$ **(b)** $3y - 5 = 0$

23. **(a)** $7x - 8y = 0$ **(b)** $x = 6 - 2y$

24. **(a)** $x = 4y - 2$ **(b)** $4x = 3y$

In Exercises 25 and 26, find an equation of the line through the two points, and write the equation in slope-intercept form; sketch the line.

25. $(1, 3)$ and $(2, -2)$ 26. $(3, -5)$ and $(1, -2)$

27. Show that the lines having the equations $3x + 5y + 7 = 0$ and $6x + 10y - 5 = 0$ are parallel, and sketch their graphs.

28. Show that the lines having the equations $4x - 3y + 12 = 0$ and $8x - 6y + 15 = 0$ are parallel, and sketch their graphs.

29. Show that the lines having the equations $2x - 3y + 6 = 0$ and $3x + 2y - 12 = 0$ are perpendicular, and sketch their graphs.

30. Show that the lines having the equations $2y = 10 - 5x$ and $5y = 2x + 20$ are perpendicular, and sketch their graphs.

31. Find the value of k such that the lines whose equations are $3x + 6ky = 7$ and $9kx + 8y = 15$ are parallel.

32. Find the value of k such that the lines whose equations are $3kx + 8y = 5$ and $6y - 4kx = -1$ are perpendicular.

In Exercises 33 through 36, determine by means of slopes if the points are collinear.

33. **(a)** $(2, 3)$, $(-4, -7)$, $(5, 8)$
    (b) $(2, -1)$, $(1, 1)$, $(3, 4)$

34. **(a)** $(4, 6)$, $(1, 2)$, $(-5, -4)$
    (b) $(-3, 6)$, $(3, 2)$, $(9, -2)$

35. **(a)** $(2, 5)$, $(-1, 4)$, $(3, -2)$
    (b) $(0, 2)$, $(-3, -1)$, $(4, 6)$

36. **(a)** $(-1, 2)$, $(7, 4)$, $(2, -1)$
    (b) $(4, -9)$, $(4, 1)$, $(4, 8)$

37. Show by means of slopes that the four points $(0, 0)$, $(-2, 1)$, $(3, 4)$, and $(5, 3)$ are vertices of a parallelogram (a quadrilateral with opposite sides parallel).

38. Show by means of slopes that the four points $(-4, -1)$, $(3, \frac{8}{3})$, $(8, -4)$, and $(2, -9)$ are vertices of a trapezoid (a quadrilateral with one pair of opposite sides parallel).

39. Show by means of slopes that the three points $(3, 1)$, $(6, 0)$, and $(4, 4)$ are the vertices of a right triangle, and find the area of the triangle.

40. Show by means of slopes that the points $(-6, 1)$, $(-4, 6)$, $(4, -3)$, and $(6, 2)$ are the vertices of a rectangle.

41. The producer of a particular commodity has a total cost consisting of a weekly overhead of $3000 and a manufacturing cost of $25 per unit. **(a)** If x units are produced per week and y dollars is the total weekly cost, write an equation involving x and y. **(b)** Sketch the graph of the equation in part (a).

42. A producer's total cost consists of a manufacturing cost of $20 per unit and a fixed daily overhead. **(a)** If the total cost of producing 200 units in 1 day is $4500, determine the fixed daily overhead. **(b)** If x units are produced per day and y dollars is the total daily cost, write an equation involving x and y. **(c)** Sketch the graph of the equation in part (b).

43. Do Exercise 42 if the producer's cost is $30 per unit, and the total cost of producing 200 units in 1 day is $6600.

44. The graph of an equation relating the temperature reading in Celsius degrees and the temperature reading in Fahrenheit degrees is a line. Water freezes at 0° Celsius and 32° Fahrenheit, and water boils at 100° Celsius and 212° Fahrenheit.   **(a)** If y degrees Fahrenheit corresponds to x degrees Celsius, write an equation involving x and y.   **(b)** Sketch the graph of the equation in part (a).   **(c)** What is the Fahrenheit temperature corresponding to 20° Celsius?   **(d)** What is the Celsius temperature corresponding to 86° Fahrenheit?

45. Find the ordinate of the point whose abscissa is -3 and that is collinear with the points $(3, 2)$ and $(0, 5)$.

46. The equation

$$\frac{x}{a} + \frac{y}{b} = 1$$

where a and b are the x and y intercepts, respectively, is the *intercept form* of an equation of a line. Explain how you can obtain this form from the slope-intercept form and the relationship between the slope and the intercepts.

47. If you know the coordinates of the three vertices A, B, and C of a triangle, explain how you would find an equation of the median from A to the side through B and C.

48. For the triangle of Exercise 47, explain how you would find an equation of the altitude from A to the side through B and C.

49. Apply your explanation in Exercise 47 to find equations of the three medians of the triangle having vertices at $(3, -2)$, $(2, 4)$, and $(-1, 1)$.

50. Apply your explanation in Exercise 48 to find equations of the three altitudes of the triangle of Exercise 49.

51. Prove Theorem A.3.4: The graph of the equation $Ax + By + C = 0$, where A, B, and C are constants and where not both A and B are zero, is a line. *Hint:* Consider two cases $B \neq 0$ and $B = 0$. If $B \neq 0$, show that the equation is that of a line having slope $-A/B$ and y intercept $-C/B$. If $B = 0$, show that the equation is that of a vertical line.

A.4 PARABOLAS

We introduced parabolas in Appendix Section A.2. The graphs in Figures 16 and 17 of that section are parabolas. These curves have many important applications. They are used in the design of parabolic mirrors, searchlights, and automobile headlights. The path of a projectile is a parabola if motion is considered to be in a plane and air resistance is neglected. Arches are sometimes parabolic in appearance; and the cable of a suspension bridge could hang in the form of a parabola. Dish antennas for receiving satellite television signals are also parabolic in shape.

In the definition of a parabola we refer to the distance from a point to a line. By such a distance, we mean the length of the perpendicular line segment from the point to the line. See Figure 1, where $|\overline{PQ}|$ is the distance from point P to line l.

A.4.1 Definition of a Parabola

A **parabola** is the set of all points in a plane equidistant from a fixed point and a fixed line. The fixed point is called the **focus,** and the fixed line is called the **directrix.**

We now derive an equation of a parabola from the definition. For this equation to be as simple as possible, we choose the y axis as perpendicular to the directrix and containing the focus. The origin is taken as the point on the y axis midway between the focus and the directrix. Observe that we are choosing the axes (*not* the parabola) in a special way. See Figure 2.

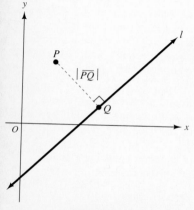

FIGURE 1

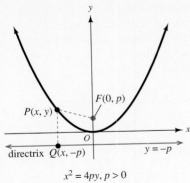

$x^2 = 4py, p > 0$

FIGURE 2

Let p be the directed distance $\overline{OF}$. The focus is the point $F(0, p)$, and the directrix is the line having the equation $y = -p$. A point $P(x, y)$ is on the parabola if and only if P is equidistant from F and the directrix. That is, if $Q(x, -p)$ is the foot of the perpendicular line from P to the directrix, then P is on the parabola if and only if

$$|\overline{FP}| = |\overline{QP}|$$

Because

$$|\overline{FP}| = \sqrt{x^2 + (y - p)^2}$$

and

$$|\overline{QP}| = \sqrt{(x - x)^2 + (y + p)^2}$$

the point P is on the parabola if and only if

$$\sqrt{x^2 + (y - p)^2} = \sqrt{(y + p)^2}$$

By squaring on both sides of the equation, we obtain

$$x^2 + y^2 - 2py + p^2 = y^2 + 2py + p^2$$
$$x^2 = 4py$$

We state this result formally as the following theorem.

A.4.2 Theorem   Equation of a Parabola

An equation of the parabola having its focus at $(0, p)$ and having as its directrix the line $y = -p$ is

$$x^2 = 4py$$

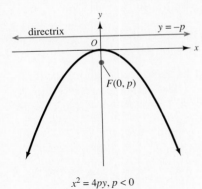

$x^2 = 4py, p < 0$

FIGURE 3

In Figure 2, p is positive; p may be negative, however, because it is the directed distance $\overline{OF}$. Figure 3 shows a parabola for $p < 0$.

From Figures 2 and 3 we see that for the equation $x^2 = 4py$ the parabola opens upward if $p > 0$ and downward if $p < 0$. The line through the focus perpendicular to the directrix is called the **axis** of the parabola. The axis of the parabolas of Figures 2 and 3 is the y axis. The intersection of the parabola with its axis is called the **vertex**, which of course is midway between the focus and directrix. The vertex of the parabolas in Figures 2 and 3 is the origin.

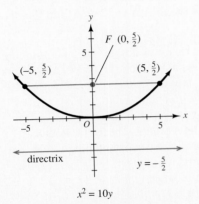

$x^2 = 10y$

FIGURE 4

▷ **ILLUSTRATION 1**   The graph of the equation

$$x^2 = 10y$$

is a parabola whose vertex is at the origin and whose axis is the y axis. Because $4p = 10$, $p = \frac{5}{2} > 0$, and therefore the parabola opens upward. The focus is at the point $F(0, \frac{5}{2})$, and an equation of the directrix is $y = -\frac{5}{2}$. Two points on the parabola are $(5, \frac{5}{2})$ and $(-5, \frac{5}{2})$. These points are the endpoints of a chord through the focus and perpendicular to the axis of the parabola. This chord is called the **latus rectum** of the parabola. In Exercise 41 you are asked to prove that the length of the latus rectum of a parabola is $|4p|$. When sketching a parabola, it is helpful to plot the endpoints of the latus rectum. Figure 4 shows the parabola, focus, directrix, and latus rectum. ◀

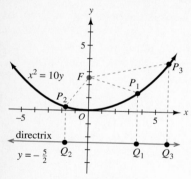

FIGURE 5

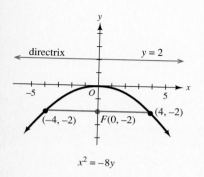

$x^2 = -8y$

FIGURE 6

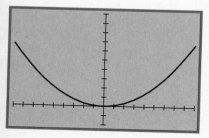

$[-9, 9]$ by $[-2, 10]$

$y = \frac{1}{12}x^2$

FIGURE 7

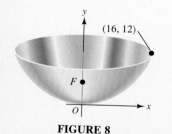

FIGURE 8

The parabola of Figure 4 with three points P_1, P_2, and P_3 on it appears in Figure 5. Because the definition of a parabola states that any point on the parabola is equidistant from the focus and directrix,

$$|\overline{FP_1}| = |\overline{Q_1 P_1}| \qquad |\overline{FP_2}| = |\overline{Q_2 P_2}| \qquad |\overline{FP_3}| = |\overline{Q_3 P_3}|$$

▶ **EXAMPLE 1**   Sketch the parabola having the equation

$$x^2 = -8y$$

and find the focus, an equation of the directrix, and the endpoints of the latus rectum.

Solution   The graph is a parabola whose vertex is at the origin and whose axis is the y axis. Because $4p = -8$, $p = -2$, and because $p < 0$, the parabola opens downward. The focus is at the point $F(0, -2)$, and an equation of the directrix is $y = 2$. The endpoints of the latus rectum are $(4, -2)$ and $(-4, -2)$. These points are obtained by substituting -2 for y in the equation of the parabola and solving for x. The parabola is sketched in Figure 6, which also shows the focus and directrix.   ◀

Of course, you can check the parabola in Example 1 by plotting the graph of the equation $y = -\frac{1}{8}x^2$ on your graphics calculator.

▶ **EXAMPLE 2**   Find an equation of the parabola having its focus at $(0, 3)$ and as its directrix the line $y = -3$. Plot the parabola.

Solution   Because the focus is on the y axis and is also above the directrix, the parabola opens upward and $p = 3$. The vertex is at the origin. An equation of the parabola is of the form $x^2 = 4py$ with $4p = 12$. Thus the required equation is

$$x^2 = 12y$$

To plot the parabola, we write the equation as $y = \frac{1}{12}x^2$. See Figure 7.   ◀

▶ **EXAMPLE 3**   A parabolic mirror has a depth of 12 cm at the center, and the distance across the top of the mirror is 32 cm. Find the distance from the vertex to the focus.

Solution   See Figure 8. We choose the coordinate axes so that the parabola has its vertex at the origin, has its axis along the y axis, and opens upward. An equation of the parabola is, therefore, of the form

$$x^2 = 4py$$

where p centimeters is the distance from the vertex to the focus. Because the point $(16, 12)$ is on the parabola, its coordinates satisfy the equation, and we have

$$16^2 = 4p(12)$$
$$p = \tfrac{16}{3}$$

Conclusion: The distance from the vertex to the focus is $\frac{16}{3}$ cm.   ◀

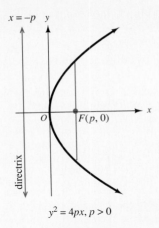

$$x = -p$$

$$y^2 = 4px, p > 0$$

FIGURE 9

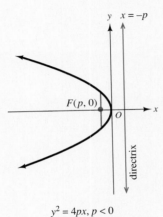

$$y^2 = 4px, p < 0$$

FIGURE 10

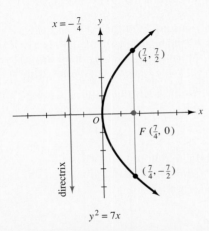

$$x = -\frac{7}{4}$$

$$\left(\frac{7}{4}, \frac{7}{2}\right)$$

$$F\left(\frac{7}{4}, 0\right)$$

$$\left(\frac{7}{4}, -\frac{7}{2}\right)$$

$$y^2 = 7x$$

FIGURE 11

Some parabolas have horizontal axes. The parabola having the equation

$$y^2 = 7x$$

is an example. This equation is of the form

$$y^2 = 4px$$

which can be obtained from the equation $x^2 = 4py$ by interchanging x and y. A parabola having the equation $y^2 = 4px$ has its vertex at the origin, the x axis as its axis, and its focus at the point $F(p, 0)$; an equation of its directrix is $x = -p$. If $p > 0$, the parabola opens to the right, as in Figure 9, and if $p < 0$, the parabola opens to the left, as in Figure 10.

These results are summarized in the following theorem.

A.4.3 Theorem   Equation of a Parabola

An equation of the parabola having its focus at $(p, 0)$ and its directrix the line $x = -p$ is

$$y^2 = 4px$$

Plotting a Parabola

To plot the graph of an equation of the form $y^2 = 4px$:

1. Solve for y by taking the square root of both sides of the equation and obtain the two equations

$$y = \sqrt{4px} \quad \text{and} \quad y = -\sqrt{4px}$$

2. The union of the graphs of these two equations gives the graph of

$$y^2 = 4px$$

▶ **EXAMPLE 4**   Sketch the parabola having the equation

$$y^2 = 7x$$

and find the focus, an equation of the directrix, and the endpoints of the latus rectum. Check the graph by plotting it.

Solution   The given equation is of the form $y^2 = 4px$; the vertex is, therefore, at the origin, and the x axis is the axis. Because $4p = 7$, $p = \frac{7}{4} > 0$; thus the parabola opens to the right. The focus is at the point $F(\frac{7}{4}, 0)$, and an equation of the directrix is $x = -\frac{7}{4}$. To obtain the endpoints of the latus rectum, let $x = \frac{7}{4}$ in the given equation, and we have

$$y^2 = \frac{49}{4}$$
$$y = \pm\frac{7}{2}$$

The endpoints of the latus rectum are, therefore, $(\frac{7}{4}, \frac{7}{2})$ and $(\frac{7}{4}, -\frac{7}{2})$. The parabola is sketched in Figure 11, which also shows the focus and directrix.

To plot the parabola, we plot the graphs of

$$y = \sqrt{7x} \quad \text{and} \quad y = -\sqrt{7x}$$

in the same window.   ◀

EXERCISES A.4

In Exercises 1 through 16, for the parabola having the given equation, find (a) the vertex, (b) the axis, (c) the focus, (d) an equation of the directrix, and (e) the endpoints of the latus rectum. Sketch the parabola.

1. $x^2 = 4y$
2. $x^2 = 8y$
3. $x^2 = -16y$
4. $x^2 = -12y$
5. $x^2 - y = 0$
6. $x^2 - 2y = 0$
7. $y^2 = 12x$
8. $y^2 = -6x$
9. $y^2 = -8x$
10. $y^2 = x$
11. $y^2 - 5x = 0$
12. $y^2 + 3x = 0$
13. $3x^2 + 8y = 0$
14. $2x^2 + 5y = 0$
15. $2y^2 - 9x = 0$
16. $3y^2 - 4x = 0$

In Exercises 17 through 22, plot the parabola having the given equation.

17. (a) $y = 4x^2$ (b) $y = -4x^2$
    (c) $x = 4y^2$ (d) $x = -4y^2$
18. (a) $y = 2x^2$ (b) $y = -2x^2$
    (c) $x = 2y^2$ (d) $x = -2y^2$
19. (a) $y = \frac{1}{4}x^2$ (b) $y = -\frac{1}{4}x^2$
    (c) $x = \frac{1}{4}y^2$ (d) $x = -\frac{1}{4}y^2$
20. (a) $y = \frac{1}{2}x^2$ (b) $y = -\frac{1}{2}x^2$
    (c) $x = \frac{1}{2}y^2$ (d) $x = -\frac{1}{2}y^2$
21. (a) $x^2 - 16y = 0$ (b) $x^2 + 16y = 0$
    (c) $y^2 - 16x = 0$ (d) $y^2 + 16x = 0$
22. (a) $4x^2 - 3y = 0$ (b) $4x^2 + 3y = 0$
    (c) $4y^2 - 3x = 0$ (d) $4y^2 + 3x = 0$

In Exercises 23 through 36, find an equation of the parabola having the given properties. Sketch the parabola and then check your graph by plotting it on your graphics calculator.

23. Focus, $(0, 4)$; directrix, $y = -4$
24. Focus, $(0, -2)$; directrix, $y = 2$
25. Focus, $(0, -5)$; directrix, $y - 5 = 0$
26. Focus, $(0, -\frac{1}{2})$; directrix, $2y - 1 = 0$
27. Focus, $(2, 0)$; directrix, $x = -2$
28. Focus, $(1, 0)$; directrix, $x = -1$
29. Focus, $(-\frac{5}{3}, 0)$; directrix, $5 - 3x = 0$
30. Focus, $(-\frac{3}{2}, 0)$; directrix, $2x - 3 = 0$
31. Vertex, the origin; opens upward; through the point $(6, 3)$
32. Vertex, the origin; opens downward; through the point $(-4, -2)$
33. Vertex, the origin; directrix, $2x = 3$

34. Vertex, the origin; directrix, $2y + 5 = 0$
35. Vertex, the origin; y axis is its axis; through the point $(-2, 4)$
36. Vertex, the origin; x axis is its axis; through the point $(-3, 3)$

In Exercises 37 through 40, solve the word problem by finding an equation of a parabola as a mathematical model of the situation. Complete the exercise by writing a conclusion.

37. A reflecting telescope has a parabolic mirror for which the distance from the vertex to the focus is 30 ft. If the distance across the top of the mirror is 64 in., how deep is the mirror at the center?

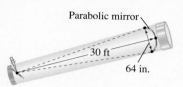

38. A parabolic arch has a height of 20 m and a width of 36 m at the base. If the vertex of the parabola is at the top of the arch, at which height above the base is it 18 m wide?

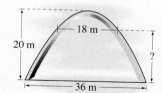

39. The cable of a suspension bridge hangs in the form of a parabola when the load is uniformly distributed horizontally. The distance between two towers is 150 m, the points of support of the cable on the towers are 22 m above the roadway, and the lowest point on the cable is 7 m above the roadway. Find the vertical distance to the cable from a point in the roadway 15 m from the foot of a tower.

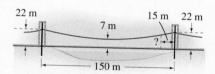

40. Assume that water issuing from the end of a horizontal pipe 25 ft above the ground describes a parabolic curve, the vertex of the parabola being at the end of the pipe. If at a point 8 ft below the line of the pipe the flow of water has curved outward 10 ft beyond a vertical line through the end of the pipe, how far beyond this vertical line will the water strike the ground?

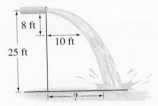

41. Prove that the length of the latus rectum of a parabola is $|4p|$.

42. Find an equation of the parabola whose vertex is at the origin and for which the endpoints of the latus rectum are at $(-8, 4)$ and $(8, 4)$.

43. The endpoints of the latus rectum of a parabola are $(5, k)$ and $(-5, k)$. If the vertex of the parabola is at the origin and the parabola opens downward, find: **(a)** the value of k; **(b)** an equation of the parabola.

44. Find all points on the parabola $y^2 = 8x$ such that the focus, the point itself, and the foot of the perpendicular drawn from the point to the directrix are vertices of an equilateral triangle.

45. Plot the graphs of $y = x^2$ and $y = x^4$. Explain why the graph of the first equation is a parabola and why the graph of the second is not. Use the definition of a parabola in your explanation.

A.5 CIRCLES

You learned in the previous section that parabolas have second-degree equations involving just one second-degree term. Another curve having second-degree equations is the *circle*, but these equations have two second-degree terms, one involving x and one involving y.

A.5.1 Definition of a Circle

A **circle** is the set of all points in a plane equidistant from a fixed point. The fixed point is called the **center** of the circle, and the constant equal distance is called the **radius** of the circle.

To obtain an equation of the circle having center at $C(h, k)$ and radius r, we use the distance formula. Refer to Figure 1. The point $P(x, y)$ is on the circle if and only if $|\overline{PC}| = r$; that is, if and only if

$$\sqrt{(x - h)^2 + (y - k)^2} = r$$

This equation is true if and only if

$$(x - h)^2 + (y - k)^2 = r^2 \qquad (r > 0)$$

This equation is satisfied by the coordinates of those and only those points that lie on the circle, and therefore it is an equation of the circle. We state this result formally in the following theorem.

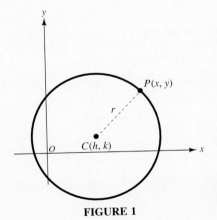

FIGURE 1

A.5.2 Theorem   Equation of a Circle

The circle with center at the point (h, k) and radius r has as an equation

$$(x - h)^2 + (y - k)^2 = r^2$$

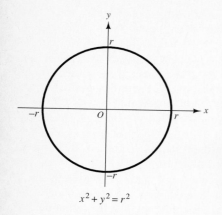

$$x^2 + y^2 = r^2$$

FIGURE 2

If the center of a circle is at the origin, then $h = 0$ and $k = 0$; therefore, its equation is

$$x^2 + y^2 = r^2$$

Such a circle appears in Figure 2. If the radius of a circle is 1, it is called a **unit circle.**

If the center and radius of a circle are known, the circle can be drawn by using a compass.

Plotting a Circle

To plot the circle having the equation

$$x^2 + y^2 = r^2$$

1. Solve this equation for y and obtain

$$y = \sqrt{r^2 - x^2} \quad \text{and} \quad y = -\sqrt{r^2 - x^2}$$

The graph of each of these equations is a semicircle.
2. Plotting these two semicircles in the same window gives the desired circle.

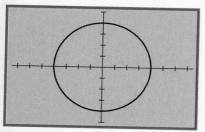

$[-7.5, 7.5]$ by $[-5, 5]$

$y = \sqrt{16 - x^2}$ and $y = -\sqrt{16 - x^2}$

FIGURE 3

▷   **ILLUSTRATION 1**   The graph of the equation

$$x^2 + y^2 = 16$$

is the circle with center at the origin and radius 4. Solving this equation for y, we obtain

$$y = \sqrt{16 - x^2} \quad \text{and} \quad y = -\sqrt{16 - x^2}$$

We plot these two semicircles in the same window and obtain the circle shown in Figure 3.   ◀

▶   **EXAMPLE 1**   Find an equation of the circle having a diameter with endpoints at $A(-2, 3)$ and $B(4, 5)$. Plot the circle.

Solution   The midpoint of the line segment from A to B is the center of the circle. See Figure 4. If $C(h, k)$ is the center of the circle, then

$$h = \frac{-2 + 4}{2} \qquad k = \frac{3 + 5}{2}$$

$$= 1 \qquad\qquad = 4$$

The center is at $C(1, 4)$. The radius of the circle can be computed as either $|\overline{CA}|$ or $|\overline{CB}|$. If $r = |\overline{CA}|$, then

$$r = \sqrt{(1 + 2)^2 + (4 - 3)^2}$$

$$= \sqrt{10}$$

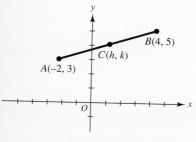

FIGURE 4

An equation of the circle is therefore

$$(x - 1)^2 + (y - 4)^2 = 10$$
$$x^2 + y^2 - 2x - 8y + 7 = 0$$

To plot the circle, we first solve the equation for y by treating it as a quadratic equation in y:

$$y^2 - 8y + (x^2 - 2x + 7) = 0$$

From the quadratic formula where a is 1, b is -8, and c is $x^2 - 2x + 7$, we have

$$
\begin{aligned}
y &= \frac{-b \pm \sqrt{b^2 - 4ac}}{2a} \\
&= \frac{-(-8) \pm \sqrt{(-8)^2 - 4(1)(x^2 - 2x + 7)}}{2(1)} \\
&= \frac{8 \pm \sqrt{64 - 4x^2 + 8x - 28}}{2} \\
&= \frac{8 \pm \sqrt{36 + 8x - 4x^2}}{2} \\
&= \frac{8 \pm 2\sqrt{9 + 2x - x^2}}{2} \\
&= 4 \pm \sqrt{9 + 2x - x^2}
\end{aligned}
$$

In the same window, we plot the graphs of

$$y = 4 + \sqrt{9 + 2x - x^2} \quad \text{and} \quad y = 4 - \sqrt{9 + 2x - x^2}$$

to obtain the circle appearing in Figure 5.

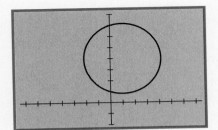

[-7.5, 7.5] by [-2, 8]

$y = 4 + \sqrt{9 + 2x - x^2}$

and $y = 4 - \sqrt{9 + 2x - x^2}$

FIGURE 5

The equation $(x - h)^2 + (y - k)^2 = r^2$ is called the **center-radius form** of an equation of a circle. If we remove parentheses and combine like terms, we obtain

$$x^2 + y^2 - 2hx - 2ky + (h^2 + k^2 - r^2) = 0$$

By letting $D = -2h$, $E = -2k$, and $F = h^2 + k^2 - r^2$, this equation becomes

$$x^2 + y^2 + Dx + Ey + F = 0$$

which is called the **general form** of an equation of a circle. Because every circle has a center and radius, its equation can be put in the center-radius form, and hence into the general form, as we did in Example 1. If we start with an equation of a circle in the general form, we can write it in the center-radius form by completing the square. The next example shows the procedure.

▶ **EXAMPLE 2**   Find the center and radius of the circle having the equation

$$x^2 + y^2 + 6x - 4y - 23 = 0$$

Solution   The given equation may be written as

$$(x^2 + 6x) + (y^2 - 4y) = 23$$

Completing the squares of the terms in parentheses by adding 9 and 4 on both sides of the equation, we have

$$(x^2 + 6x + 9) + (y^2 - 4y + 4) = 23 + 9 + 4$$
$$(x + 3)^2 + (y - 2)^2 = 36$$

This equation is in the center-radius form; thus it is an equation of a circle with its center at $(-3, 2)$ and radius 6.   ◀

Some equations of the form

$$x^2 + y^2 + Dx + Ey + F = 0$$

have graphs that are not circles. Suppose when we complete the squares we obtain

$$(x - h)^2 + (y - k)^2 = d \qquad \text{where } d < 0$$

No real values of x and y satisfy this equation; thus the equation has no graph. In such a case we state that the graph is the empty set. See Exercise 32.

If when completing the squares, we obtain

$$(x - h)^2 + (y - k)^2 = 0$$

the only real values of x and y satisfying this equation are $x = h$ and $y = k$. Thus the graph is the single point (h, k). See Exercise 31.

The definition of the tangent line to a general curve at a point on the curve requires the concept of *limit*. For a circle, however, the plane-geometry definition states that a tangent line at a point P on a circle is the line intersecting the circle at only one point.

▶ **EXAMPLE 3**   Find an equation of the tangent line to the circle

$$x^2 + y^2 - 6x - 2y - 15 = 0$$

at the point $(6, 5)$. Plot the circle and tangent line in the same window.

Solution   We write the equation of the circle in the center-radius form by completing the squares:

$$(x^2 - 6x) + (y^2 - 2y) = 15$$
$$(x^2 - 6x + 9) + (y^2 - 2y + 1) = 15 + 9 + 1$$
$$(x - 3)^2 + (y - 1)^2 = 25$$

From this equation, the center of the circle is at $C(3, 1)$ and the radius is 5. Figure 6 shows the circle and a piece of the tangent line at $P(6, 5)$. If m_1 is the slope of the line through C and P,

$$m_1 = \frac{5 - 1}{6 - 3}$$
$$= \tfrac{4}{3}$$

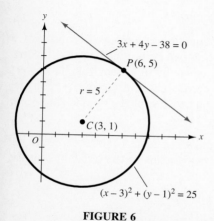

FIGURE 6

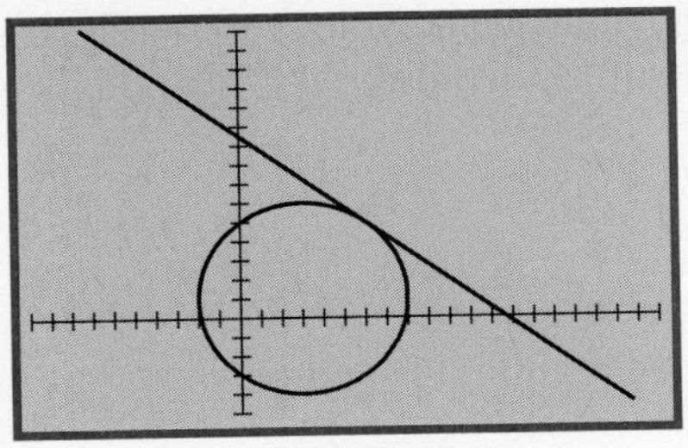

[−10, 20] by [−5, 15]

$y = 1 + \sqrt{25 - (x - 3)^2}$ and

$y = 1 - \sqrt{25 - (x - 3)^2}$ and

$y = -\frac{3}{4}x + \frac{38}{4}$

FIGURE 7

From plane geometry, we know that the tangent line is perpendicular to the line through C and P. Therefore, if m_2 is the slope of the tangent line,

$$m_2 m_1 = -1$$
$$m_2(\tfrac{4}{3}) = -1$$
$$m_2 = -\tfrac{3}{4}$$

Hence from the point-slope form of an equation of the line through $(6, 5)$ with slope $-\frac{3}{4}$, we have as the required equation

$$y - 5 = -\frac{3}{4}(x - 6)$$
$$4y - 20 = -3x + 18$$
$$3x + 4y - 38 = 0$$

Figure 7 shows the circle and tangent line plotted in the same window. ◀

EXERCISES A.5

In Exercises 1 through 8, sketch the graph of the equation.

1. (a) $y = \sqrt{4 - x^2}$ (b) $y = -\sqrt{4 - x^2}$
(c) $x^2 + y^2 = 4$

2. (a) $y = \sqrt{25 - x^2}$ (b) $y = -\sqrt{25 - x^2}$
(c) $x^2 + y^2 = 25$

3. $9x^2 + 9y^2 = 1$ **4.** $4x^2 + 4y^2 = 1$

5. $(x - 3)^2 + (y + 4)^2 = 16$

6. $(x + 1)^2 + (y - 5)^2 = 36$

7. $(x + 4)^2 + y^2 = 1$ **8.** $x^2 + (y - 2)^2 = 9$

In Exercises 9 through 14, plot the graph of the equation.

9. $x^2 + y^2 = 36$ **10.** $x^2 + y^2 = 16$

11. $4x^2 + 4y^2 = 81$ **12.** $9x^2 + 9y^2 = 49$

13. $(x + 2)^2 + (y - 3)^2 = 100$

14. $(x - 4)^2 + (y + 7)^2 = 64$

In Exercises 15 through 20, find an equation of the circle with center at C and radius r. Write the equation in both the center-radius form and the general form. Plot the circle.

15. $C(4, -3)$, $r = 5$ **16.** $C(0, 0)$, $r = 8$

17. $C(-5, -12)$, $r = 3$ **18.** $C(-1, 1)$, $r = 2$

19. $C(0, 7)$, $r = 1$ **20.** $C(-3, 0)$, $r = 4$

In Exercises 21 through 24, find an equation of the circle satisfying the given conditions. Plot the circle.

21. Center is at $(1, 2)$ and through the point $(3, -1)$.

22. Center is at $(-3, 4)$ and through the point $(2, 0)$.

23. Diameter has endpoints at $(3, -4)$ and $(7, 2)$.

24. Diameter has endpoints at $(-1, -5)$ and $(4, -6)$.

In Exercises 25 through 30, find the center and radius of the circle. Sketch the circle.

25. $x^2 + y^2 - 6x - 8y + 9 = 0$

26. $x^2 + y^2 - 10x - 10y + 25 = 0$

27. $x^2 + y^2 + 2x + 10y + 18 = 0$

28. $x^2 + y^2 + 6x - 1 = 0$

29. $3x^2 + 3y^2 + 4y - 7 = 0$

30. $2x^2 + 2y^2 - 2x + 2y + 7 = 0$

31. Prove that the graph of

$$x^2 + y^2 - 4x + 10y + 29 = 0$$

is a point.

32. Prove that the graph of

$$x^2 + y^2 + 8x - 6y + 30 = 0$$

is the empty set.

In Exercises 33 through 38, determine whether the graph is a circle, a point, or the empty set.

33. $x^2 + y^2 - 2x + 10y + 19 = 0$

34. $x^2 + y^2 + 2x - 4y + 5 = 0$

35. $x^2 + y^2 - 10x + 6y + 36 = 0$

36. $4x^2 + 4y^2 + 24x - 4y + 1 = 0$

37. $2x^2 + 2y^2 - 2x + 6y + 5 = 0$

38. $9x^2 + 9y^2 + 6x - 6y + 5 = 0$

In Exercises 39 through 42, find an equation of the line tangent to the circle at point P. Plot the circle and tangent line in the same window.

39. $x^2 + y^2 = 25$; $P(-4, 3)$

40. $16x^2 + 16y^2 = 25$; $P(\frac{3}{4}, -1)$

41. $x^2 + y^2 - 4x + 6y - 12 = 0$; $P(5, 1)$

42. $x^2 + y^2 + 14x - 8y - 35 = 0$; $P(-1, -4)$

43. Use analytic geometry to prove that an angle inscribed in a semicircle is a right angle.

44. Use analytic geometry to prove that a line from the center of any circle bisecting any chord is perpendicular to the chord.

45. What inequality involving D, E, and F is necessary for the graph of the equation

$$x^2 + y^2 + Dx + Ey + F = 0$$

to be a circle?

46. From the origin, chords of the circle

$$x^2 + y^2 + 4x = 0$$

are drawn. Prove that the set of midpoints of these chords is a circle.

47. The circumscribed circle of a triangle is the circle containing the three vertices of the triangle. Given the three vertices, explain how you can determine the center and radius of the circumscribed circle.

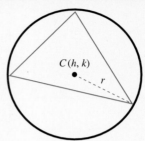

48. Use your explanation in Exercise 47 to find the center and radius of the circumscribed circle of the triangle having vertices at $(-3, 2)$, $(4, -1)$, and $(5, 2)$.

49. Describe the set of points (x, y) in R^2 for which
(a) $x^2 + y^2 \leq 1$ **(b)** $1 < x^2 + y^2 \leq 4$
(c) $x^2 + y^2 > 4$

50. Use the fact that $ab = 0$ if and only if $a = 0$ or $b = 0$ to write an equation of each of the following graphs: **(a)** the graph consisting of all points on either of two circles, each having its center at the origin and one having radius 2 and the other having radius 3; **(b)** the graph consisting of the origin and all points on the unit circle whose center is the origin.

A.6 TRANSLATION OF AXES

The shape of a graph is not affected by the position of the coordinate axes, but its equation is affected. For example, a circle with a radius of 3 and having its center at the point $(4, -1)$ has the equation

$$(x - 4)^2 + (y + 1)^2 = 9$$

However, if the coordinate axes are chosen so that the origin is at the center, the same circle has the simpler equation

$$x^2 + y^2 = 9$$

If we may select the coordinate axes as we please, we generally do so in such a way that the equations will be as simple as possible. If the axes are given, however, we may wish to find a simpler equation of a particular graph relative to a different set of axes. If these different axes are chosen parallel to the given ones, we say that there has been a **translation of axes.**

In particular, let the given x and y axes be translated to new axes x' and y' having origin (h, k) with respect to the given axes. Also assume that the positive numbers lie on the same side of the origin on the x' and y' axes as on the x and y axes. See Figure 1. A point P in the plane having coordinates (x, y) with respect to the given coordinate axes will have coordinates (x', y') with respect to the new axes. We now obtain relationships between these two sets of coordinates. We draw two lines through P, one parallel to the y and y' axes and one parallel to the x and x' axes. Let the first line intersect the

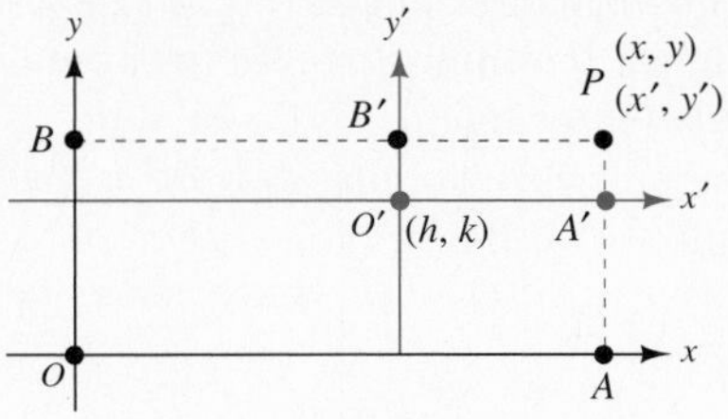

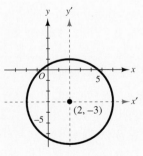

FIGURE 1

x axis at the point A and the x' axis at the point A', and let the second line intersect the y axis at the point B and the y' axis at the point B'. These lines are shown in Figure 1.

With respect to the x and y axes, the coordinates of P are (x, y), the coordinates of A are $(x, 0)$, and the coordinates of A' are (x, k). Because $\overline{A'P} = \overline{AP} - \overline{AA'}$,

$$y' = y - k$$

With respect to the x and y axes, the coordinates of B are $(0, y)$, and the coordinates of B' are (h, y). Because $\overline{B'P} = \overline{BP} - \overline{BB'}$,

$$x' = x - h$$

We state these results formally in the following theorem.

A.6.1 Theorem   Equations for Translating the Axes

If (x, y) represents a point P with respect to a given set of axes, and (x', y') is a representation of P after the axes are translated to a new origin having coordinates (h, k) with respect to the given axes, then

$$x' = x - h \qquad \text{and} \qquad y' = y - k$$

▶   **EXAMPLE 1**   Given the equation

$$x^2 + y^2 - 4x + 6y - 3 = 0$$

translate the axes so that the equation of the graph with respect to the x' and y' axes contains no first-degree terms.

Solution   We rewrite the given equation as

$$(x^2 - 4x) + (y^2 + 6y) = 3$$

Completing the squares of the terms in parentheses by adding 4 and 9 on both sides of the equation, we have

$$(x^2 - 4x + 4) + (y^2 + 6y + 9) = 3 + 4 + 9$$
$$(x - 2)^2 + (y + 3)^2 = 16$$

If we let $x' = x - 2$ and $y' = y + 3$, we obtain

$$x'^2 + y'^2 = 16$$

The graph of this equation with respect to the x' and y' axes is a circle with its center at the origin and radius 4. Because the substitutions of $x' = x - 2$ and $y' = y + 3$ result in a translation of axes to a new origin of $(2, -3)$, the graph of the given equation with respect to the x and y axes is a circle with center at $(2, -3)$ and radius 4. This result agrees with our discussion of circles in Appendix Section A.5. Figure 2 shows the circle with both sets of axes.   ◀

$(x - 2)^2 + (y + 3)^2 = 16$

FIGURE 2

We now apply translation of axes to find the general equation of a parabola having its vertex at the point (h, k) and either a vertical or a

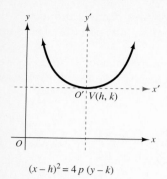

$(x-h)^2 = 4p(y-k)$

FIGURE 3

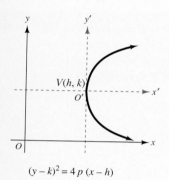

$(y-k)^2 = 4p(x-h)$

FIGURE 4

horizontal axis. In particular, let the axis be vertical. Let the x' and y' axes be such that the origin is at $V(h, k)$. See Figure 3. With respect to the x' and y' axes, an equation of the parabola in this figure is

$$x'^2 = 4py'$$

To obtain an equation of this parabola with respect to the x and y axes, we let $x' = x - h$ and $y' = y - k$, which gives

$$(x - h)^2 = 4p(y - k)$$

In Figure 4 the axis of the parabola is horizontal, and the vertex is at $V(h, k)$. By a similar argument, its equation with respect to the x and y axes is

$$(y - k)^2 = 4p(x - h)$$

We have obtained the standard forms of an equation of a parabola, which we state in the next theorem.

> **A.6.2 Theorem   Standard Forms of an Equation of a Parabola**
>
> If p is the directed distance from the vertex to the focus, an equation of the parabola with its vertex at (h, k) and with its axis vertical is
>
> $$(x - h)^2 = 4p(y - k)$$
>
> A parabola with the same vertex and with its axis horizontal has the equation
>
> $$(y - k)^2 = 4p(x - h)$$

The graph of any quadratic equation of the form

$$y = ax^2 + bx + c \qquad \textbf{(1)}$$

where a, b, and c are constants and $a \neq 0$ is a parabola whose axis is vertical. This statement can be proved by showing that (1) is equivalent to an equation of the form

$$(x - h)^2 = 4p(y - k)$$

You are asked to do this in Exercise 49. The equation in the following example is the special case of (1) where a is $-\frac{1}{4}$, b is 1, and c is 6.

▶ **EXAMPLE 2**   Given the parabola having the equation

$$y = -\tfrac{1}{4}x^2 + x + 6$$

find the vertex, an equation of the axis, the focus, and the endpoints of the latus rectum. Sketch the parabola from these properties, and check the graph on a graphics calculator.

Solution   The given equation is equivalent to

$$4y = -x^2 + 4x + 24$$
$$x^2 - 4x = -4y + 24$$

Completing the square on the left by adding 4 to each side, we get

$$x^2 - 4x + 4 = -4y + 24 + 4$$
$$(x - 2)^2 = -4y + 28$$
$$(x - 2)^2 = -4(y - 7)$$

This equation is of the form

$$(x - h)^2 = 4p(y - k)$$

with $h = 2$, $k = 7$, and $p = -1$. Therefore its graph is a parabola with vertex at $(2, 7)$, and the axis is vertical. Thus the axis has the equation $x = 2$. Because $p < 0$, it opens downward. Furthermore, the focus is the point on the axis 1 unit below the vertex; thus the focus is at $(2, 6)$. Because the length of the latus rectum is $4p = 4$, its endpoints are 2 units to the right and left of the focus at $(4, 6)$ and $(0, 6)$.

Figure 5 shows the parabola sketched from these properties. A graphics calculator verifies this graph. ◄

If x and y are interchanged in (1), we have the equation

$$x = ay^2 + by + c \qquad \textbf{(2)}$$

The graph of any equation of this form is a parabola whose axis is horizontal. This fact can be verified by showing that (2) is equivalent to an equation of the form

$$(y - k)^2 = 4p(x - h)$$

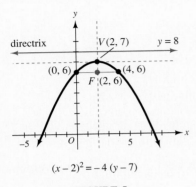

$(x - 2)^2 = -4(y - 7)$

FIGURE 5

▶ **EXAMPLE 3**   Follow the instructions of Example 2 for the parabola having the equation

$$x = 2y^2 + 8y + 11$$

Solution   The given equation is equivalent to

$$2y^2 + 8y = x - 11$$
$$2(y^2 + 4y) = x - 11$$

To complete the square of the expression within the parentheses on the left, we add 4 to $y^2 + 4y$. We are actually adding 8 to the left side; so we also add 8 to the right side, and we have

$$2(y^2 + 4y + 4) = x - 11 + 8$$
$$2(y + 2)^2 = x - 3$$
$$(y + 2)^2 = \tfrac{1}{2}(x - 3)$$

This equation is of the form

$$(y - k)^2 = 4p(x - h)$$

with $h = 3$, $k = -2$, and $p = \frac{1}{8}$. Therefore the parabola has its vertex at $(3, -2)$, its axis is the horizontal line $y = -2$, and because $p > 0$, it opens to the right. Because the focus is $\frac{1}{8}$ unit to the right of the vertex, it is at the point $(\frac{25}{8}, -2)$. The length of the latus rectum is $|4p| = \frac{1}{2}$; thus the

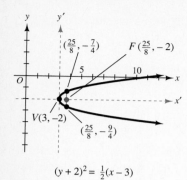

$(y + 2)^2 = \frac{1}{2}(x - 3)$

FIGURE 6

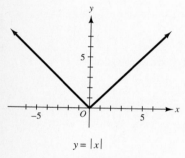

$y = |x|$

FIGURE 7

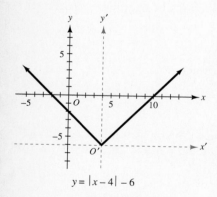

$y = |x - 4| - 6$

FIGURE 8

endpoints of the latus rectum are $\frac{1}{4}$ unit above and below the focus at $(\frac{25}{8}, -\frac{7}{4})$ and $(\frac{25}{8}, -\frac{9}{4})$.

The parabola sketched from these properties appears in Figure 6. To plot the parabola on a graphics calculator, we first write the given equation as

$$2y^2 + 8y + (11 - x) = 0$$

and then solve for y in terms of x by the quadratic formula where a is 2, b is 8, and c is $(11 - x)$. We get two values for y:

$$y = -2 + \frac{1}{2}\sqrt{2x - 6} \quad \text{and} \quad y = -2 - \frac{1}{2}\sqrt{2x - 6}$$

When we plot the graphs of these two equations in the same window, we obtain the parabola in Figure 6. ◄

In the next two examples, we apply translation of axes to other graphs.

► **EXAMPLE 4** From the graph of $y = |x|$ and a suitable translation of axes, obtain the graph of $y = |x - 4| - 6$.

Solution The graph of $y = |x|$ appears in Figure 20 of Appendix Section A.2. We reproduce it here in Figure 7. The equation

$$y = |x - 4| - 6$$

is equivalent to

$$y + 6 = |x - 4|$$

To obtain the graph of this equation, we let

$$x' = x - 4 \quad \text{and} \quad y' = y + 6$$

We have translated the axes to the new origin $(4, -6)$, and the equation becomes $y' = |x'|$. The graph of this equation with respect to the x' and y' axes is the same as the graph in Figure 7 with respect to the x and y axes. Thus we obtain the graph shown in Figure 8. ◄

► **EXAMPLE 5** Use the graph of $y = \frac{1}{2}x^3$ from Example 4 of Appendix Section A.2 along with a suitable translation of axes to obtain the graph of the equation

$$y = \frac{1}{2}(x + 5)^3 + 3$$

Solution Figure 9 shows the graph of $y = \frac{1}{2}x^3$. The equation

$$y = \frac{1}{2}(x + 5)^3 + 3$$

is equivalent to

$$y - 3 = \frac{1}{2}(x + 5)^3$$

To obtain the graph of this equation, we let

$$x' = x + 5 \quad \text{and} \quad y' = y - 3$$

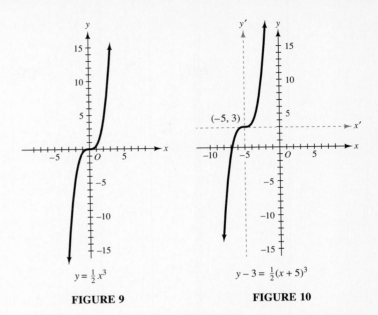

$$y = \tfrac{1}{2} x^3$$

FIGURE 9

$$y - 3 = \tfrac{1}{2}(x + 5)^3$$

FIGURE 10

We have translated the axes to the new origin $(-5, 3)$, and the equation becomes $y' = \tfrac{1}{2} x'^3$. Figure 10 shows the graph of this equation with respect to the x' and y' axes. It is the same as the graph in Figure 9 with respect to the x and y axes. ◄

EXERCISES A.6

In Exercises 1 through 4, translate the axes so that an equation of the graph with respect to the new axes contains no first-degree terms. Draw the original and new axes and sketch the graph.

1. $x^2 + y^2 + 6x + 4y = 0$

2. $x^2 + y^2 - 2x - 8y + 1 = 0$

3. $x^2 + y^2 + x - 2y + 1 = 0$

4. $x^2 + y^2 - 10x + 4y + 13 = 0$

In Exercises 5 and 6, translate the axes so that an equation of the graph with respect to the new x' and y' axes contains no first-degree term in x' and no constant term. Draw the original and new axes and sketch the graph.

5. $x^2 - 4x - 8y - 28 = 0$

6. $x^2 + 4x + 2y = 0$

In Exercises 7 and 8, translate the axes so that an equation of the graph with respect to the new x' and y' axes contains no first-degree term in y' and no constant term. Draw the original and new axes and sketch the graph.

7. $y^2 + 6x + 7y + 39 = 0$

8. $2y^2 - 2x - 4y + 3 = 0$

In Exercises 9 through 24, for the given parabola, find (a) the vertex, (b) an equation of the axis, (c) the focus, (d) an equation of the directrix, and (e) the endpoints of the latus rectum. (f) Sketch the parabola from these properties and check your graph on your graphics calculator.

9. $y = x^2 - 4$

10. $y = x^2 + 4x$

11. $y = -x^2 + 4x - 5$

12. $y = x^2 + 6x - 2$

13. $x = y^2 - 6y$

14. $x = -y^2 + 1$

15. $x^2 - 6x - 4y + 13 = 0$

16. $x^2 - 4x + 8y + 28 = 0$

17. $y^2 + 4x + 12y = 0$

18. $y^2 - 12x - 14y + 25 = 0$

19. $y = -\tfrac{1}{2} x^2 + 4x - 5$

20. $y = \tfrac{1}{16} x^2 + \tfrac{1}{2} x$

21. $y = \tfrac{1}{8} x^2 - \tfrac{1}{2} x - \tfrac{3}{2}$

22. $x = 2y^2 + 10y + 3$

23. $x = -2y^2 - 8y - 5$

24. $x = -\tfrac{1}{4} y^2 - \tfrac{3}{2} y - 2$

In Exercises 25 through 28, plot the parabola having the given equation.

25. $y^2 - 4x - 2y + 9 = 0$

26. $4y^2 - x + 16y + 12 = 0$

27. $5y^2 - 4x + 10y + 17 = 0$
28. $3y^2 + 8x - 12y + 20 = 0$

In Exercises 29 through 46, do the following: (a) sketch the graph of the first equation; (b) from the graph obtained in part (a) and a suitable translation of axes, sketch the graph of the second equation. (c) Check your graphs in parts (a) and (b) by plotting them in the same window.

29. $y = |x|; y = |x - 2|$
30. $y = |x|; y = |x + 3|$
31. $y = |x|; y = |x| + 3$
32. $y = |x|; y = |x| - 2$
33. $y = |x|; y = |x + 4| - 5$
34. $y = |x|; y = |x - 1| + 6$
35. $y = x^3; y = (x - 4)^3$
36. $2y = -x^3; 2y + 2 = -x^3$
37. $y = x^3; y = (x + 1)^3 + 1$
38. $2y = -x^3; 2y = -(x - 4)^3 + 4$
39. $y = \sqrt{x}; y = \sqrt{x - 2} + 4$
40. $y = \sqrt{x}; y = \sqrt{x + 3} - 2$
41. $y = x^2; y = (x - 4)^2$

42. $y = x^2; y = (x + 3)^2$
43. $y = x^2; y = x^2 + 3$
44. $y = x^2; y = x^2 - 4$
45. $y = x^2; y = (x + 1)^2 - 5$
46. $y = x^2; y = (x - 2)^2 + 1$
47. Given the parabola having the equation

$$y = ax^2 + bx + c$$

with $a \neq 0$, find the coordinates of the vertex.
48. Find the coordinates of the focus of the parabola in Exercise 47.
49. Show that the equation $y = ax^2 + bx + c$ is equivalent to an equation of the form $(x - h)^2 = 4p(y - k)$ by solving the second equation for y.
50. If a parabola has its focus at the origin and the x axis as its axis, prove that it must have an equation of the form $y^2 = 4kx + 4k^2, k \neq 0$.
51. **(a)** Show that the equation $y = x^2 + bx + c$ can be written in the form $y = (x - h)^2 + k$. **(b)** Explain how to sketch the graph of $y = (x - h)^2 + k$ from the graph of $y = x^2$. In your explanation make up a particular example.

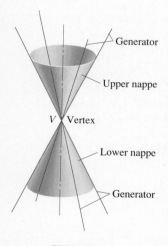

FIGURE 1

A.7 ELLIPSES

To consider the geometry of conic sections, we regard a cone as having two nappes, each extending indefinitely far. A portion of a right-circular cone of two nappes appears in Figure 1. A line lying in the cone is called a **generator** (or **element**) of the cone. All generators of a cone contain the point V called the **vertex.**

   An *ellipse* is obtained as a conic section if the cutting plane is parallel to no generator, in which case the cutting plane intersects each generator as in Figure 2. A special case of the ellipse is a circle, which is formed if the cutting plane intersecting each generator is also perpendicular to the axis of the cone. See Figure 3. We now define an ellipse as a set of points in a plane. At the end of this section we prove that this definition is a consequence of the definition of an ellipse as a section of a cone.

A.7.1 Definition of an Ellipse

An **ellipse** is the set of points in a plane the sum of whose distances from two fixed points is a constant. Each fixed point is called a **focus.**

   Let the undirected distance between the foci (the plural of focus) be $2c$ where $c > 0$. To obtain an equation of an ellipse, we select the x axis as the line through F and F', and we choose the origin as the midpoint of the segment between F and F'. See Figure 4. The foci F and F' have coordinates $(c, 0)$ and $(-c, 0)$, respectively. Let the constant sum referred to in the

Ellipse

FIGURE 2

Circle

FIGURE 3

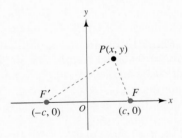

FIGURE 4

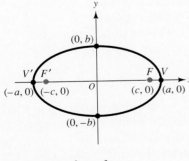

$$\frac{x^2}{a^2} + \frac{y^2}{b^2} = 1$$

FIGURE 5

definition be $2a$. Then $a > c$, and the point $P(x, y)$ in Figure 4 is any point on the ellipse if and only if

$$|\overline{FP}| + |\overline{F'P}| = 2a$$

Because

$$|\overline{FP}| = \sqrt{(x - c)^2 + y^2} \quad \text{and} \quad |\overline{F'P}| = \sqrt{(x + c)^2 + y^2}$$

P is on the ellipse if and only if

$$\sqrt{(x - c)^2 + y^2} + \sqrt{(x + c)^2 + y^2} = 2a$$

To simplify this equation requires eliminating the radicals and performing some algebraic manipulations, which you are asked to do in Exercise 35. When this is done, we obtain

$$\frac{x^2}{a^2} + \frac{y^2}{b^2} = 1$$

where $b^2 = a^2 - c^2$. The following theorem states this result formally.

> **A.7.2 Theorem   Equation of an Ellipse**
>
> If $2a$ is the constant referred to in the definition of an ellipse, if the foci are at $(c, 0)$ and $(-c, 0)$, and if $b^2 = a^2 - c^2$, then an equation of the ellipse is
>
> $$\frac{x^2}{a^2} + \frac{y^2}{b^2} = 1$$

To sketch this ellipse, first observe from the equation that the graph is symmetric with respect to both the x and y axes. If we replace y by 0 in the equation, we get $x = \pm a$, and if we replace x by 0, we obtain $y = \pm b$. Therefore the graph intersects the x axis at $(a, 0)$ and $(-a, 0)$, and it intersects the y axis at $(0, b)$ and $(0, -b)$. Because $b^2 = a^2 - c^2$, it follows that $a > b$. See Figure 5 and refer to it as you read the next paragraph.

The line through the foci is called the **principal axis.** For this ellipse the x axis is the principal axis. The points of intersection of the ellipse and its principal axis are called the **vertices.** Thus for this ellipse the vertices are at $V(a, 0)$ and $V'(-a, 0)$. The point on the principal axis that lies halfway between the two vertices is called the **center.** The origin is the center of this ellipse. The segment of the principal axis between the two vertices is called the **major axis,** and its length is $2a$ units. For this ellipse the segment of the y axis between the points $(0, b)$ and $(0, -b)$ is called the **minor axis.** Its length is $2b$ units.

An ellipse is called a **central conic** in contrast to a parabola, which has no center because it has only one vertex.

▶ **EXAMPLE 1**   For the ellipse having the equation

$$\frac{x^2}{25} + \frac{y^2}{16} = 1$$

find the vertices, endpoints of the minor axis, and foci. Sketch the ellipse and show the foci.

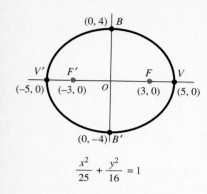

$$\frac{x^2}{25} + \frac{y^2}{16} = 1$$

FIGURE 6

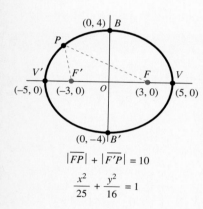

$$|\overline{FP}| + |\overline{F'P}| = 10$$

$$\frac{x^2}{25} + \frac{y^2}{16} = 1$$

FIGURE 7

Solution   Because the form of the equation is

$$\frac{x^2}{a^2} + \frac{y^2}{b^2} = 1$$

the center of the ellipse is at the origin and the principal axis is the x axis. Because $a^2 = 25$ and $b^2 = 16$, $a = 5$ and $b = 4$. Therefore the vertices are at $V(5, 0)$ and $V'(-5, 0)$, and the endpoints of the minor axis are at $B(0, 4)$ and $B'(0, -4)$.

   To find the foci, we solve for c from the equation $b^2 = a^2 - c^2$ with $a^2 = 25$ and $b^2 = 16$. Thus, because $c > 0$,

$$16 = 25 - c^2$$
$$c^2 = 9$$
$$c = 3$$

Therefore the foci are at $F(3, 0)$ and $F'(-3, 0)$.

   As an aid in sketching the ellipse, we find a point on it in the first quadrant by substituting 3 for x in the equation and solving for y. (Of course, any other value of x between 0 and 5 can be used.) By symmetry we have corresponding points in the other three quadrants. Figure 6 shows the ellipse and the foci.   ◀

   Observe from the definition of an ellipse that if P is any point on the ellipse of Example 1, then $|\overline{FP}| + |\overline{F'P}| = 10$. In Figure 7 we have taken P in the second quadrant.

   To plot an ellipse on a graphics calculator, we can do what we did in Appendix Section A.5 for graphs of circles. That is, we treat the equation of the ellipse as quadratic in y and solve it to obtain two equations defining y as two functions of x.

▷   **ILLUSTRATION 1**   Solving the equation of the ellipse in Example 1 for y, by first multiplying both sides of the equation by 400, we have

$$16x^2 + 25y^2 = 400$$
$$25y^2 = 400 - 16x^2$$
$$25y^2 = 16(25 - x^2)$$
$$y^2 = \tfrac{16}{25}(25 - x^2)$$
$$y = \pm \tfrac{4}{5}\sqrt{25 - x^2}$$

In the same window on a graphics calculator, we plot the graphs of

$$y_1 = \tfrac{4}{5}\sqrt{25 - x^2} \qquad \text{and} \qquad y_2 = -\tfrac{4}{5}\sqrt{25 - x^2}$$

to obtain the ellipse that appears in Figure 6.   ◀

   Another method of plotting an ellipse on a graphics calculator is explained in Appendix Section A.9. This method utilizes parametric equations of the ellipse that involve trigonometric functions.

   The paths of many comets and the orbits of planets and satellites are ellipses. Arches of bridges are sometimes elliptical in shape, and ellipses are used in making machine gears. An application of the ellipse in architecture for so-called whispering galleries uses its reflective property. In whispering galleries the ceilings have cross sections that are arcs of ellipses with common foci. A person located at one focus F can hear another person whispering at the other focus F' because the sound waves originating from the whisperer at F' hit the ceiling and are reflected by the ceiling to the listener at F. A famous example of a whispering gallery is under the dome of the Capitol in Washington, D.C. Another is at the Mormon Tabernacle in Salt Lake City.

▶ **EXAMPLE 2**   An arch in the form of a semiellipse is 48 ft wide at the base and has a height of 20 ft. How wide is the arch at a height of 10 ft above the base?

Solution   Figure 8 shows a sketch of the arch and the coordinate axes chosen so that the x axis is along the base and the origin is at the midpoint of the base. Then the ellipse has its principal axis on the x axis, its center at the origin, $a = 24$, and $b = 20$. Thus an equation of the ellipse is

$$\frac{x^2}{576} + \frac{y^2}{400} = 1$$

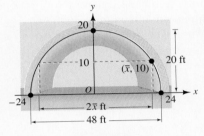

FIGURE 8

Let $2\bar{x}$ be the number of feet in the width of the arch at a height of 10 ft above the base. Therefore the point $(\bar{x}, 10)$ is on the ellipse. Thus

$$\frac{\bar{x}^2}{576} + \frac{100}{400} = 1$$

$$\bar{x}^2 = 432$$

$$\bar{x} = 12\sqrt{3}$$

Conclusion: At a height of 10 ft above the base the width of the arch is $24\sqrt{3}$ ft.   ◀

If an ellipse has its center at the origin and principal axis on the y axis, then an equation of the ellipse is of the form

$$\frac{y^2}{a^2} + \frac{x^2}{b^2} = 1$$

This equation is obtained by interchanging x and y in the equation

$$\frac{y^2}{a^2} + \frac{x^2}{b^2} = 1$$

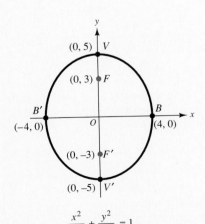

$$\frac{x^2}{16} + \frac{y^2}{25} = 1$$

FIGURE 9

▷ **ILLUSTRATION 2**   Because for an ellipse $a > b$, it follows that the ellipse having the equation

$$\frac{x^2}{16} + \frac{y^2}{25} = 1$$

has its principal axis on the y axis. This ellipse has the same shape as the ellipse of Example 1. The vertices are at $(0, 5)$ and $(0, -5)$, the endpoints of the minor axis are at $(4, 0)$ and $(-4, 0)$, and the foci are at $(0, 3)$ and $(0, -3)$. Figure 9 shows this ellipse.   ◀

Suppose the center of an ellipse is at the point (h, k) rather than at the origin, and the principal axis is parallel to one of the coordinate axes. Then by a translation of axes so that the point (h, k) is the new origin, an equation of the ellipse is

$$\frac{x'^2}{a^2} + \frac{y'^2}{b^2} = 1$$

if the principal axis is horizontal, and

$$\frac{y'^2}{a^2} + \frac{x'^2}{b^2} = 1$$

if the principal axis is vertical. Because $x' = x - h$ and $y' = y - k$, we obtain the following standard forms of an equation of an ellipse.

A.7.3 Theorem   Standard Forms of an Equation of an Ellipse

If the center of an ellipse is at (h, k) and the distance between the vertices is $2a$, then an equation of the ellipse is of the form

$$\frac{(x - h)^2}{a^2} + \frac{(y - k)^2}{b^2} = 1 \qquad (a > b) \tag{1}$$

if the principal axis is horizontal, and

$$\frac{(y - k)^2}{a^2} + \frac{(x - k)^2}{b^2} = 1 \qquad (a > b) \tag{2}$$

if the principal axis is vertical.

By expanding $(x - h)^2$ and $(y - k)^2$ and simplifying, we can write each of Equations (1) and (2) in the form

$$Ax^2 + Cy^2 + Dx + Ey + F = 0 \tag{3}$$

where A and C have the same sign. In the following example, we start with an equation in this form and complete squares to write it in a standard form of an equation of an ellipse.

▶ **EXAMPLE 3**   Show that the graph of the equation

$$25x^2 + 16y^2 + 150x - 128y - 1119 = 0$$

is an ellipse. Find the center, an equation of the principal axis, the vertices, the endpoints of the minor axis, and the foci. Sketch the ellipse and check the graph on a graphics calculator.

Solution   To write this equation in one of the standard forms, we begin by completing the squares in x and y. We have then

$$25(x^2 + 6x) + 16(y^2 - 8y) = 1119$$
$$25(x^2 + 6x + 9) + 16(y^2 - 8y + 16) = 1119 + 225 + 256$$
$$25(x + 3)^2 + 16(y - 4)^2 = 1600$$

$$\frac{25(x+3)^2}{1600} + \frac{16(y-4)^2}{1600} = 1$$

$$\frac{(x+3)^2}{64} + \frac{(y-4)^2}{100} = 1$$

This equation is of the form

$$\frac{(y-k)^2}{a^2} + \frac{(x-h)^2}{b^2} = 1 \qquad (a > b)$$

where (h, k) is $(-3, 4)$, $a^2 = 100$, and $b^2 = 64$. Therefore the graph is an ellipse whose center is at $(-3, 4)$ and whose principal axis is the vertical line having the equation $x = -3$. Because $a = 10$ and $b = 8$, the vertices are at $V(-3, 14)$ and $V'(-3, -6)$ and the endpoints of the minor axis are at $B(5, 4)$ and $B'(-11, 4)$. To find the foci, we use the equation $b^2 = a^2 - c^2$ with $c > 0$ and obtain

$$64 = 100 - c^2$$
$$c^2 = 36$$
$$c = 6$$

Thus the foci are at $F(-3, 10)$ and $F'(-3, -2)$. By locating a few more points (in particular where the ellipse intersects the x and y axes), we get the ellipse appearing in Figure 10.

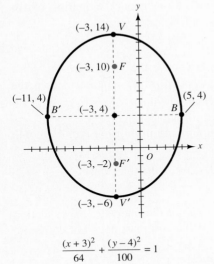

$$\frac{(x+3)^2}{64} + \frac{(y-4)^2}{100} = 1$$

FIGURE 10

In the next two illustrations, we again have equations in form (3).

▷ **ILLUSTRATION 3**   Suppose that (3) is

$$6x^2 + 9y^2 - 24x - 54y + 115 = 0$$

which can be written as

$$6(x^2 - 4x) + 9(y^2 - 6y) = -115$$

Completing the squares in x and y, we get

$$6(x^2 - 4x + 4) + 9(y^2 - 6y + 9) = -115 + 24 + 81$$
$$6(x - 2)^2 + 9(y - 3)^2 = -10$$

Because the right side of this equation is negative and the left side is nonnegative for all points (x, y), the graph is the empty set.

▷ **ILLUSTRATION 4**   Because the equation

$$6x^2 + 9y^2 - 24x - 54y + 105 = 0$$

can be written as

$$6(x - 2)^2 + 9(y - 3)^2 = 0$$

its graph is the point $(2, 3)$.

We can prove in general that the graph of any equation of the form (3) is either an ellipse, as in Example 3, a point, or the empty set. When the graph is a point or the empty set, as in Illustrations 3 and 4, it is said to be **degenerate.**

Observe that (3) is the special case of the general equation of the second degree in two variables,

$$Ax^2 + Bxy + Cy^2 + Dx + Ey + F = 0 \qquad (4)$$

where $B = 0$ and $AC > 0$ (that is, A and C have the same sign).

The conclusions in the preceding discussion are summarized in the following theorem.

A.7.4 Theorem

If in the general second-degree equation (4), $B = 0$ and $AC > 0$, then the graph is either an ellipse, a point, or the empty set.

The degenerate case of an ellipse, a point, is obtained as a conic section if the cutting plane contains the vertex of the cone but does not contain a generator. See Figure 11.

If $A = C$ in (3), the equation becomes

$$Ax^2 + Ay^2 + Dx + Ey + F = 0$$

which when dividing by A gives

$$x^2 + y^2 + \frac{D}{A}x + \frac{E}{A}y + \frac{F}{A} = 0$$

In Appendix Section A.5 we learned that the graph of this equation is either a circle, a point, or the empty set. This statement agrees with Theorem A.7.4 because a circle is a limiting form of an ellipse. This fact can be shown by considering the equation relating a, b, and c for an ellipse:

$$b^2 = a^2 - c^2$$

From this equation we see that if $c = 0$, $b^2 = a^2$, and then the standard forms of an equation of an ellipse become

$$\frac{(x - h)^2}{a^2} + \frac{(y - k)^2}{a^2} = 1$$

$$\Leftrightarrow \quad (x - h)^2 + (y - k)^2 = a^2$$

which is an equation of a circle having its center at (h, k) and radius a. Furthermore, when $c = 0$, the foci are coincident at the center of the circle.

Point

FIGURE 11

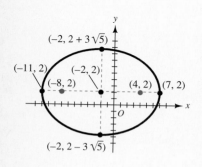

$$\frac{(x + 2)^2}{81} + \frac{(y - 2)^2}{45} = 1$$

FIGURE 12

► **EXAMPLE 4**   Find an equation of the ellipse having foci at $(-8, 2)$ and $(4, 2)$ and for which the constant referred to in the definition is 18. Sketch the ellipse.

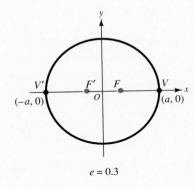

$e = 0.3$

(a)

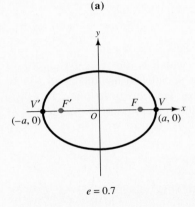

$e = 0.7$

(b)

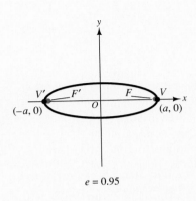

$e = 0.95$

(c)

FIGURE 13

Solution   The center of the ellipse is halfway between the foci and is the point $(-2, 2)$. The distance between the foci of an ellipse is $2c$, and the distance between $(-8, 2)$ and $(4, 2)$ is 12. Therefore $c = 6$. The constant referred to in the definition is $2a$; thus $2a = 18$ and $a = 9$. Because $b^2 = a^2 - c^2$,

$$b^2 = 81 - 36$$
$$b^2 = 45$$
$$b = 3\sqrt{5}$$

The principal axis is parallel to the x axis; hence an equation of the ellipse is of the form

$$\frac{(x - h)^2}{a^2} + \frac{(y - k)^2}{b^2} = 1$$

Because (h, k) is the point $(-2, 2)$, $a = 9$, and $b = 3\sqrt{5}$, the required equation is

$$\frac{(x + 2)^2}{81} + \frac{(y - 2)^2}{45} = 1$$

This ellipse appears in Figure 12.   ◀

Some ellipses are almost circular, which happens when the foci are close together. Some ellipses are "flat," which occurs when the foci and vertices are near each other. The shape of an ellipse (its "roundness" or "flatness") is given by the *eccentricity,* which we now formally define.

A.7.5 Definition of Eccentricity of an Ellipse

The **eccentricity** e of an ellipse is the ratio of the undirected distance between the foci to the undirected distance between the vertices; that is,

$$e = \frac{c}{a}$$

Because $c^2 = a^2 - b^2$, then $c < a$; therefore, $0 < e < 1$. When the foci are close together, e is close to zero, and the shape of the ellipse is close to that of a circle. See Figure 13(a) showing an ellipse for which $e = 0.3$. If a remains fixed, then as e increases the flatness of the ellipse increases. Figures 13(b) and 13(c) show ellipses with eccentricities of 0.7 and 0.95, respectively, each with the same value of a as in Figure 13(a). The limiting forms of the ellipse are a circle of diameter $2a$ and a line segment of length $2a$.

As promised, we now prove that the definition of an ellipse as a set of points in a plane follows from the definition of an ellipse as a conic section. This proof, sometimes referred to as the "ice cream cone proof," was

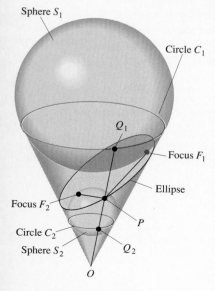

Sphere S_1

Circle C_1

Q_1

Focus F_1

Ellipse

Focus F_2

P

Circle C_2

Sphere S_2

Q_2

O

FIGURE 14

presented in 1822 by the Belgian mathematician G. P. Dandelin (1794–1847). Refer to Figure 14, which shows one nappe of a cone having vertex at O and a cutting plane intersecting the cone in an ellipse. Two spheres S_1 and S_2 are inscribed in the cone. Sphere S_1 is tangent to the cone along the circle C_1 and tangent to the cutting plane at point F_1. Sphere S_2 is tangent to the cone along the circle C_2 and tangent to the cutting plane at point F_2. The planes of the circles C_1 and C_2 are parallel. We shall prove that F_1 and F_2 are the foci of the ellipse by showing that if P is any point on the ellipse, $|\overline{PF_1}| + |\overline{PF_2}|$ is a constant. To demonstrate this, we draw the line through points O and P on the surface of the cone. Points Q_1 and Q_2 are the intersections of this line with the circles C_1 and C_2, respectively. Because PF_1 and PQ_1 are two tangent lines to sphere S_1 from the point P, it follows that

$$|\overline{PF_1}| = |\overline{PQ_1}|$$

Also PF_2 and PQ_2 are two tangent lines to sphere S_2 from the point P. Thus

$$|\overline{PF_2}| = |\overline{PQ_2}|$$

Therefore

$$|\overline{PF_1}| + |\overline{PF_2}| = |\overline{PQ_1}| + |\overline{PQ_2}|$$

Observe that $|\overline{PQ_1}| + |\overline{PQ_2}| = |\overline{Q_1Q_2}|$, which is the distance measured along the surface of the cone between the parallel planes of the circles C_1 and C_2. This distance will be the same for any choice of point P on the ellipse. Therefore $|\overline{PF_1}| + |\overline{PF_2}|$ is a constant, and F_1 and F_2 are the foci of the ellipse.

EXERCISES A.7

In Exercises 1 through 16, for the ellipse having the given equation, find (a) the center, (b) the principal axis, (c) the vertices, (d) the endpoints of the minor axis, and (e) the foci. (f) Sketch the ellipse and show the foci. Check your graph on your graphics calculator.

1. $\dfrac{x^2}{25} + \dfrac{y^2}{9} = 1$ **2.** $\dfrac{x^2}{100} + \dfrac{y^2}{64} = 1$

3. $\dfrac{x^2}{4} + \dfrac{y^2}{16} = 1$ **4.** $\dfrac{x^2}{25} + \dfrac{y^2}{169} = 1$

5. $9x^2 + 25y^2 = 900$ **6.** $4x^2 + 9y^2 = 36$

7. $9x^2 + y^2 = 9$ **8.** $25x^2 + 4y^2 = 100$

9. $4x^2 + 9y^2 - 16x - 18y - 11 = 0$

10. $x^2 + 4y^2 - 6x + 8y - 3 = 0$

11. $4x^2 + y^2 + 8x - 4y - 92 = 0$

12. $2x^2 + 2y^2 - 2x + 18y + 33 = 0$

13. $4x^2 + 4y^2 + 20x - 32y + 89 = 0$

14. $25x^2 + y^2 - 4y - 21 = 0$

15. $x^2 + 3y^2 - 4x - 23 = 0$

16. $2x^2 + 3y^2 - 4x + 12y + 2 = 0$

In Exercises 17 and 18, determine whether the graph of the equation is an ellipse, a point, or the empty set.

17. $4x^2 + y^2 - 8x + 2y + 5 = 0$

18. $2x^2 + 3y^2 + 8x - 6y + 20 = 0$

In Exercises 19 through 28, find an equation of the ellipse having the given properties and sketch the ellipse. Check your graph on your graphics calculator.

19. Vertices at $(-\frac{5}{2}, 0)$ and $(\frac{5}{2}, 0)$ and one focus at $(\frac{3}{2}, 0)$.

20. Foci at $(-5, 0)$ and $(5, 0)$ and for which the constant referred to in the definition is 20.

21. Foci at $(0, 3)$ and $(0, -3)$ and for which the constant referred to in the definition is $6\sqrt{3}$.

22. Center at the origin, its foci on the x axis, the length of the major axis equal to 3 times the length of the minor axis, and passing through the point $(3, 3)$.

23. Vertices at $(2, 0)$ and $(-2, 0)$ and through the point $(-1, \frac{1}{2}\sqrt{3})$.

24. Vertices at $(0, 5)$ and $(0, -5)$ and through the point $(2, -\frac{5}{3}\sqrt{5})$.

25. Center at $(4, -2)$, a vertex at $(9, -2)$, and one focus at $(0, -2)$.

26. A focus at $(2, -3)$, a vertex at $(2, 4)$, and center on the x axis.

27. Foci at $(-1, -1)$ and $(-1, 7)$ and the semimajor axis of length 8 units.

28. Foci at $(2, 3)$ and $(2, -7)$ and the length of the semiminor axis is two-thirds of the length of the semimajor axis.

In Exercises 29 through 32, solve the word problem and be sure to write a conclusion.

29. The ceiling in a hallway 10 m wide is in the shape of a semiellipse and is 9 m high in the center and 6 m high at the side walls. Find the height of the ceiling 2 m from either wall.

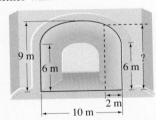

30. The orbit of the earth around the sun is elliptical in shape with the sun at one focus and a semimajor axis of length 92.96 million miles. If the eccentricity of the ellipse is 0.0167, find **(a)** how close the earth gets to the sun and **(b)** the greatest possible distance between the earth and the sun.

31. Suppose that the orbit of a planet is in the shape of an ellipse with a major axis whose length is 500 million km. If the distance between the foci is 400 million km, find an equation of the orbit.

32. The arch of a bridge is in the shape of a semiellipse having a horizontal span of 40 m and a height of 16 m at its center. How high is the arch 9 m to the right or left of the center?

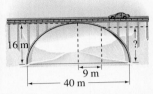

33. To trace the ellipse defined by the equation $4x^2 + 9y^2 = 36$, use the following procedure and explain why it works: First determine the points of intersection of the ellipse with the coordinate axes. Obtain the foci on the x axis by using a compass with its center at one of the points of intersection with the y axis and with radius of 3. Then fasten thumbtacks at each focus. Take a piece of string of length 6 and attach one end at one thumbtack and the other end at the other thumbtack. Place a pencil against the string and make it tight. Move the pencil against the string and trace the ellipse.

34. Use a procedure similar to that of Exercise 33 to trace the ellipse having the equation $16x^2 + 9y^2 = 144$. Explain why your procedure works.

35. Show that the equation

$$\sqrt{(x - c)^2 + y^2} + \sqrt{(x + c)^2 + y^2} = 2a$$

can be simplified to

$$\frac{x^2}{a^2} + \frac{y^2}{b^2} = 1$$

where $b^2 = a^2 - c^2$.

36. For the ellipse whose equation is

$$\frac{(x - h)^2}{a^2} + \frac{(y - k)^2}{b^2} = 1$$

where $a > b > 0$, find the coordinates of the foci in terms of h, k, a, and b.

Hyperbola

FIGURE 1

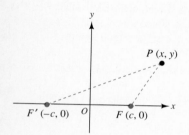

FIGURE 2

A.8 HYPERBOLAS

When a cutting plane intersects both nappes of a cone and is parallel to two generators, the conic section obtained is a *hyperbola,* shown in Figure 1. The following definition of a hyperbola as a set of points in a plane can be proved from its definition as a conic section. The proof, similar to that used for an ellipse in Appendix Section A.7, involves a sphere in each nappe of the cone.

A.8.1   Definition of a Hyperbola

A **hyperbola** is the set of points in a plane, the absolute value of the difference of whose distances from two fixed points is a constant. The two fixed points are called the **foci.**

To obtain an equation of a hyperbola, we begin as we did with the ellipse by letting the undirected distance between the foci be $2c$, where $c > 0$. Then we choose the x axis as the line through the foci F and F', and we take the origin as the midpoint of the segment between F and F'. See Figure 2. The points $(c, 0)$ and $(-c, 0)$ are the foci F and F', respectively. Let $2a$ be the constant referred to in the definition. It can be shown that $c > a$. The point $P(x, y)$ in Figure 2 is any point on the hyperbola if and only if

$$||\overline{FP}| - |\overline{F'P}|| = 2a$$

Because

$$|\overline{FP}| = \sqrt{(x - c)^2 + y^2} \quad \text{and} \quad |\overline{F'P}| = \sqrt{(x + c)^2 + y^2}$$

P is on the hyperbola if and only if

$$|\sqrt{(x - c)^2 + y^2} - \sqrt{(x + c)^2 + y^2}| = 2a$$

or, equivalently, without absolute-value bars,

$$\sqrt{(x - c)^2 + y^2} - \sqrt{(x + c)^2 + y^2} = \pm 2a$$

This equation can be simplified by eliminating the radicals and performing some algebraic manipulations. You are asked to do this in Exercise 43. The resulting equation is

$$\frac{x^2}{a^2} - \frac{y^2}{b^2} = 1$$

where $b^2 = c^2 - a^2$. We have then the following theorem.

A.8.2 Theorem   Equation of a Hyperbola

If $2a$ is the constant referred to in the definition of a hyperbola, if the foci are at $(c, 0)$ and $(-c, 0)$, and if $b^2 = c^2 - a^2$, then an equation of the hyperbola is

$$\frac{x^2}{a^2} - \frac{y^2}{b^2} = 1$$

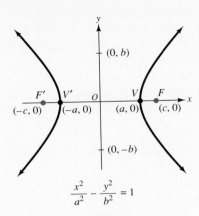

$$\frac{x^2}{a^2} - \frac{y^2}{b^2} = 1$$

FIGURE 3

We now show how to sketch this hyperbola, which appears in Figure 3. Observe from the equation that the graph is symmetric with respect to both the x and y axes. As with the ellipse, the line through the foci is called the **principal axis.** Thus for this hyperbola the x axis is the principal axis. The points where the hyperbola intersects the principal axis are called the **vertices,** and the point that is halfway between the vertices is called the **center.** For this hyperbola the vertices are at $V(a, 0)$ and $V'(-a, 0)$ and the center is at the origin. The segment $V'V$ of the principal axis is called the **transverse axis,** and its length is $2a$ units.

Substituting 0 for x in the equation of the hyperbola, we get $y^2 = -b^2$, which has no real solutions. Consequently, the hyperbola does not intersect the y axis. However, the line segment having extremities at the points $(0, -b)$ and $(0, b)$ is called the **conjugate axis,** and its length is $2b$ units. If we solve the equation of the hyperbola for y in terms of x, we have

$$y = \pm \frac{b}{a}\sqrt{x^2 - a^2}$$

We conclude from this equation that if $|x| < a$, there is no real value of y. Thus there are no points (x, y) on the hyperbola for which $-a < x < a$. We also observe that if $|x| > a$, then y has two real values. Thus the hyperbola has two *branches.* One branch contains the vertex $V(a, 0)$ and extends indefinitely to the right of V. The other branch contains the vertex $V'(-a, 0)$ and extends indefinitely to the left of V'.

As was the case with an ellipse, because the hyperbola has a center it is called a **central conic.**

▶ **EXAMPLE 1**   Find the vertices and foci of the hyperbola having the equation

$$\frac{x^2}{9} - \frac{y^2}{16} = 1$$

Sketch the hyperbola and show the foci.

Solution   Because the equation is of the form

$$\frac{x^2}{a^2} - \frac{y^2}{b^2} = 1$$

the center of the hyperbola is at the origin and the principal axis is the x axis. Because $a^2 = 9$ and $b^2 = 16$, $a = 3$ and $b = 4$. The vertices are therefore at $V(3, 0)$ and $V'(-3, 0)$. The number of units in the length of the transverse axis is $2a = 6$, and the number of units in the length of the conjugate axis is $2b = 8$. Because $b^2 = c^2 - a^2$, with $c > 0$, we have

$$16 = c^2 - 9$$
$$c^2 = 16 + 9$$
$$c^2 = 25$$
$$c = 5$$

Hence the foci are at $F(5, 0)$ and $F'(-5, 0)$. A sketch of the hyperbola with its foci appears in Figure 4. ◀

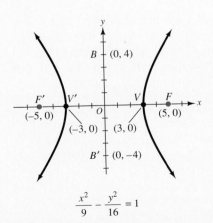

$$\frac{x^2}{9} - \frac{y^2}{16} = 1$$

FIGURE 4

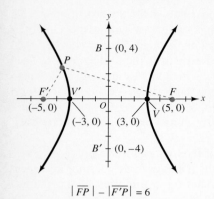

$$|\overline{FP}| - |\overline{F'P}| = 6$$

(a)

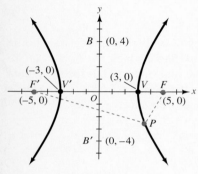

$$|\overline{F'P}| - |\overline{FP}| = 6$$

(b)

$$\frac{x^2}{9} - \frac{y^2}{16} = 1$$

FIGURE 5

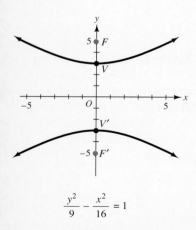

$$\frac{y^2}{9} - \frac{x^2}{16} = 1$$

FIGURE 6

From the definition of a hyperbola, if P is any point on the hyperbola of Example 1, $||\overline{FP}| - |\overline{F'P}|| = 6$. See Figure 5(a) and (b); in (a) P is in the second quadrant and $|\overline{FP}| - |\overline{F'P}| = 6$; in (b) P is in the fourth quadrant and $|\overline{F'P}| - |\overline{FP}| = 6$.

▶ **EXAMPLE 2**   Find an equation of the hyperbola having a focus at $(5, 0)$ and the ends of its conjugate axis at $(0, 2)$ and $(0, -2)$.

Solution   Because the ends of the conjugate axis are at $(0, 2)$ and $(0, -2)$, $b = 2$, the principal axis is on the x axis, and the center is at the origin. Hence an equation is of the form

$$\frac{x^2}{a^2} - \frac{y^2}{b^2} = 1$$

Because a focus is at $(5, 0)$, $c = 5$, and because $b^2 = c^2 - a^2$, $a^2 = 25 - 4$. Thus $a = \sqrt{21}$, and an equation of the hyperbola is

$$\frac{x^2}{21} - \frac{y^2}{4} = 1 \qquad ◀$$

If in the equation

$$\frac{x^2}{a^2} - \frac{y^2}{b^2} = 1$$

x and y are interchanged, we obtain

$$\frac{y^2}{a^2} - \frac{x^2}{b^2} = 1$$

which is an equation of a hyperbola having its center at the origin and its principal axis on the y axis.

▷ **ILLUSTRATION 1**   The equation

$$\frac{y^2}{9} - \frac{x^2}{16} = 1$$

can be obtained from the one in Example 1 by interchanging x and y. The graph of this equation is a hyperbola having its center at the origin, the y axis as its principal axis, its vertices at $V(0, 3)$ and $V'(0, -3)$, and its foci at $F(0, 5)$ and $F'(0, -5)$. Figure 6 shows the hyperbola and its foci.   ◀

As we did with circles in Appendix Section A.5 and with an ellipse in Illustration 1 of Appendix Section A.7, we can plot a hyperbola on a graphics calculator by first defining y as two functions of x obtained by solving the equation of the hyperbola for y. As with an ellipse, however, it is easier to plot the graph from parametric equations of the hyperbola, and the method is explained in Appendix Section A.9.

In the standard equation of an ellipse, we know that $a > b$. For a hyperbola, however, there is no general inequality involving a and b. For instance, in Example 1 where $a = 3$ and $b = 4$, $a < b$; but in Example 2 where $a = \sqrt{21}$ and $b = 2$, $a > b$. Furthermore a may equal b, in which

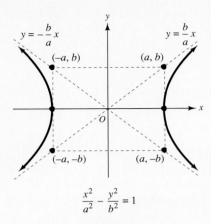

$$\frac{x^2}{a^2} - \frac{y^2}{b^2} = 1$$

FIGURE 7

case the hyperbola is **equilateral.** The equilateral hyperbola having the equation

$$x^2 - y^2 = 1$$

is called the **unit hyperbola.**

Refer now to Figure 7, showing the hyperbola having the equation

$$\frac{x^2}{a^2} - \frac{y^2}{b^2} = 1$$

The diagonal dashed lines in the figure are *asymptotes* of the hyperbola. In Sections 1.7 and 3.7, we discuss vertical, horizontal, and oblique asymptotes of a graph and give formal definitions involving the *limit* concept. Intuitively, however, we can state that if the undirected distance between a graph and a line gets smaller and smaller (but not zero) as either $|x|$ or $|y|$ gets larger and larger, then the line is an asymptote of the graph.

Observe in Figure 7 that the diagonals of the rectangle having vertices at (a, b), $(a, -b)$, $(-a, b)$, and $(-a, -b)$ are on the asymptotes of the hyperbola. This rectangle is called the **auxiliary rectangle;** its sides have lengths $2a$ and $2b$. The vertices of the hyperbola are the points of intersection of the principal axis and the auxiliary rectangle. A fairly good graph of a hyperbola can be sketched by first drawing the auxiliary rectangle. By extending the diagonals of the rectangle, we have the asymptotes. Through each vertex we draw a branch of the hyperbola by using the asymptotes as guides. Observe that because $a^2 + b^2 = c^2$, the circle having its center at the origin and passing through the vertices of the auxiliary rectangle also passes through the foci of the hyperbola.

▶ **EXAMPLE 3**   Find the vertices of the hyperbola having the equation

$$x^2 - 4y^2 = 16$$

Sketch the hyperbola and show the auxiliary rectangle and asymptotes.

Solution   The given equation is equivalent to

$$\frac{x^2}{16} - \frac{y^2}{4} = 1$$

Therefore the hyperbola has its center at the origin, and its principal axis is the x axis. Because $a^2 = 16$ and $b^2 = 4$, $a = 4$ and $b = 2$. The vertices are at $V(4, 0)$ and $V'(-4, 0)$, and the sides of the auxiliary rectangle have lengths $2a = 8$ and $2b = 4$. Figure 8 shows the auxiliary rectangle and the asymptotes. These asymptotes are used as guides to sketch the hyperbola appearing in the figure.   ◀

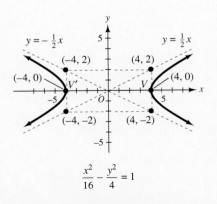

$$\frac{x^2}{16} - \frac{y^2}{4} = 1$$

FIGURE 8

A convenient device can be used to obtain equations of the asymptotes of a hyperbola. For instance, for the hyperbola having the equation $\frac{x^2}{a^2} - \frac{y^2}{b^2} = 1$, we replace the right side by zero and obtain

$$\frac{x^2}{a^2} - \frac{y^2}{b^2} = 0$$

Upon factoring, this equation becomes

$$\left(\frac{x}{a} - \frac{y}{b}\right)\left(\frac{x}{a} + \frac{y}{b}\right) = 0$$

which is equivalent to the two equations

$$\frac{x}{a} - \frac{y}{b} = 0 \quad \text{and} \quad \frac{x}{a} + \frac{y}{b} = 0$$

$$\Leftrightarrow \qquad y = \frac{b}{a}x \quad \text{and} \quad y = -\frac{b}{a}x$$

which are equations of the asymptotes of the given hyperbola.

▷ **ILLUSTRATION 2**   An equation of the hyperbola of Example 3 is

$$\frac{x^2}{16} - \frac{y^2}{4} = 1$$

To obtain equations of the asymptotes we replace the right side by zero, and we have

$$\frac{x^2}{16} - \frac{y^2}{4} = 0$$

$$\left(\frac{x}{4} - \frac{y}{2}\right)\left(\frac{x}{4} + \frac{y}{2}\right) = 0$$

$$\frac{x}{4} - \frac{y}{2} = 0 \qquad\qquad \frac{x}{4} + \frac{y}{2} = 0$$

$$y = \tfrac{1}{2}x \qquad \text{and} \qquad y = -\tfrac{1}{2}x$$

◀

Suppose the center of a hyperbola is at (h, k) and its principal axis is parallel to one of the coordinate axes. Then by a translation of axes so that the point (h, k) is the new origin, an equation of the hyperbola is

$$\frac{x'^2}{a^2} - \frac{y'^2}{b^2} = 1$$

if the principal axis is horizontal, and

$$\frac{y'^2}{a^2} - \frac{x'^2}{b^2} = 1$$

if the principal axis is vertical. If we replace x' by $x - h$ and y' by $y - k$, we obtain the following standard forms of an equation of a hyperbola.

A.8.3 Theorem   Standard Forms of an Equation of a Hyperbola

If the center of a hyperbola is at (h, k) and the distance between the vertices is $2a$, then an equation of the hyperbola is of the form

$$\frac{(x - h)^2}{a^2} - \frac{(y - k)^2}{b^2} = 1$$

if the principal axis is horizontal, and

$$\frac{(y - k)^2}{a^2} - \frac{(x - h)^2}{b^2} = 1$$

if the principal axis is vertical.

By expanding $(x - h)^2$ and $(y - k)^2$ and simplifying, we can write each of these equations in the form

$$Ax^2 + Cy^2 + Dx + Ey + F = 0 \qquad \textbf{(1)}$$

where A and C have opposite signs. The next example involves an equation of this form.

▶ **EXAMPLE 4**   Show that the graph of the equation

$$9x^2 - 4y^2 - 18x - 16y + 29 = 0$$

is a hyperbola. Find the center, an equation of the principal axis, and the vertices. Sketch the hyperbola and show the auxiliary rectangle and asymptotes.

Solution   We begin by completing the squares in x and y. We have

$$9(x^2 - 2x) - 4(y^2 + 4y) = -29$$
$$9(x^2 - 2x + 1) - 4(y^2 + 4y + 4) = -29 + 9 - 16$$
$$9(x - 1)^2 - 4(y + 2)^2 = -36$$
$$\frac{(y + 2)^2}{9} - \frac{(x - 1)^2}{4} = 1$$

This equation is that of a hyperbola whose center is at $(1, -2)$ and whose principal axis is the vertical line having the equation $x = 1$. Because $a^2 = 9$ and $b^2 = 4$, $a = 3$ and $b = 2$. The vertices are on the principal axis and 3 units above and below the center; thus they are at $V(1, 1)$ and $V'(1, -5)$. The auxiliary rectangle has sides of lengths $2a = 6$ and $2b = 4$; it appears in Figure 9 along with the asymptotes and the hyperbola.   ◀

In the following illustration we have another equation in the form of (1).

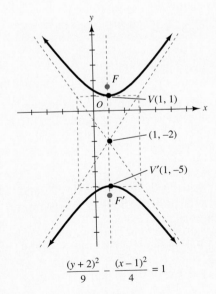

$$\frac{(y + 2)^2}{9} - \frac{(x - 1)^2}{4} = 1$$

FIGURE 9

▷ **ILLUSTRATION 3**   The equation

$$4x^2 - 12y^2 + 24x + 96y - 156 = 0$$

can be written as

$$4(x^2 + 6x) - 12(y^2 - 8y) = 156$$

and upon completing the squares in x and y we have

$$4(x^2 + 6x + 9) - 12(y^2 - 8y + 16) = 156 + 36 - 192$$
$$4(x + 3)^2 - 12(y - 4)^2 = 0$$
$$(x + 3)^2 - 3(y - 4)^2 = 0$$
$$[(x + 3) - \sqrt{3}(y - 4)][(x + 3) + \sqrt{3}(y - 4)] = 0$$
$$x + 3 - \sqrt{3}(y - 4) = 0 \quad \text{and} \quad x + 3 + \sqrt{3}(y - 4) = 0$$

which are equations of two lines through the point $(-3, 4)$.   ◀

We can prove in general that the graph of any equation of the form (1) is either a hyperbola or two intersecting lines. The results of Example 4 and Illustration 3 are particular cases of this fact.

Equation (1) is the special case of the general equation of the second degree in two variables,

$$Ax^2 + Bxy + Cy^2 + Dx + Ey + F = 0 \tag{2}$$

where $B = 0$ and $AC < 0$ (that is, A and C have opposite signs).

The following theorem summarizes the conclusions in the preceding discussion.

A.8.4 Theorem

If in the general second-degree equation (2), $B = 0$ and $AC < 0$, then the graph is either a hyperbola or two intersecting lines.

The degenerate case of a hyperbola, two intersecting lines, is obtained as a conic section if the cutting plane contains the vertex of the cone and two generators, as shown in Figure 10.

Two intersecting lines

FIGURE 10

▶ **EXAMPLE 5**   The vertices of a hyperbola are at $(-5, -3)$ and $(-5, -1)$, and the endpoints of the conjugate axis are at $(-7, -2)$ and $(-3, -2)$. Find an equation of the hyperbola and equations of the asymptotes. Sketch the hyperbola and the asymptotes.

Solution   The distance between the vertices is $2a$; hence $2a = 2$ and $a = 1$. The length of the conjugate axis is $2b$; thus $2b = 4$ and $b = 2$. Because the principal axis is vertical, an equation of the hyperbola is of the form

$$\frac{(y - k)^2}{a^2} - \frac{(x - h)^2}{b^2} = 1$$

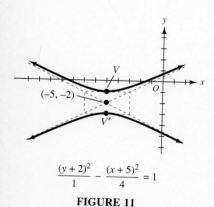

$$\frac{(y + 2)^2}{1} - \frac{(x + 5)^2}{4} = 1$$

FIGURE 11

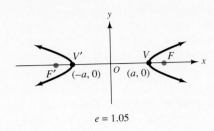

$e = 1.05$

(a)

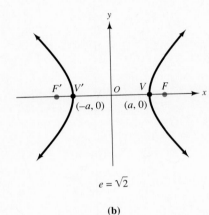

$e = \sqrt{2}$

(b)

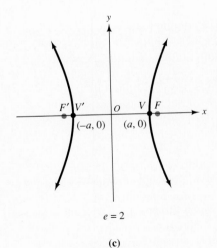

$e = 2$

(c)

FIGURE 12

The center (h, k) is halfway between the vertices and is therefore at the point $(-5, -2)$. Hence an equation of the hyperbola is

$$\frac{(y + 2)^2}{1} - \frac{(x + 5)^2}{4} = 1$$

Replacing the right side by zero to obtain equations of the asymptotes, we have

$$\left(\frac{y + 2}{1} - \frac{x + 5}{2}\right)\left(\frac{y + 2}{1} + \frac{x + 5}{2}\right) = 0$$

$$y + 2 = \tfrac{1}{2}(x + 5) \quad \text{and} \quad y + 2 = -\tfrac{1}{2}(x + 5)$$

The hyperbola and the asymptotes appear in Figure 11.   ◀

As with an ellipse, an indication of the shape of a hyperbola is given by its *eccentricity*, defined exactly the same as for an ellipse; that is, if e is the **eccentricity** of a hyperbola,

$$e = \frac{c}{a}$$

For a hyperbola, however, $e > 1$. This follows from the fact that $c > a$ because for a hyperbola

$$c^2 = a^2 + b^2 \qquad\qquad\qquad \textbf{(3)}$$

From this equation, when $a = b$, we obtain $c = \sqrt{2}a$. Thus the eccentricity of an equilateral hyperbola is $\sqrt{2}$. See Figure 12(b). If e approaches 1 and a remains fixed, then c approaches a and from Equation (3) b approaches 0, so that the shape of the hyperbola becomes "thin" around its principal axis. Figure 12(a) shows a hyperbola with $e = 1.05$ and the same value of a as in Figure 12(b). If e increases as a remains fixed, then c increases and b increases, and the hyperbola becomes "fat" around its principal axis. See Figure 12(c) for a hyperbola with $e = 2$ and the same value of a as in Figures 12(a) and 12(b).

The property of the hyperbola given in its definition forms the basis of several important navigational systems. These systems involve a network of pairs of radio transmitters at fixed positions at a known distance from one another. The transmitters send out radio signals received by a navigator. The difference in arrival time of the two signals determines the difference $2a$ of the distances from the navigator. Thus the navigator's position is known to be somewhere along one arc of a hyperbola having foci at the locations of the two transmitters. One arc, rather than both, is determined because of the signal delay between the two transmitters that is built into the system. The procedure is then repeated for a different pair of radio transmitters, and another arc of a hyperbola that contains the navigator's position is determined. The point of intersection of the two hyperbolic arcs is the

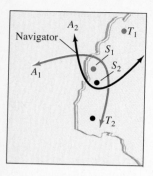

FIGURE 13

actual position. For example, in Figure 13 suppose a pair of transmitters is located at points T_1 and S_1 and the signals from this pair determine the hyperbolic arc A_1. Another pair of transmitters is located at points T_2 and S_2 and hyperbolic arc A_2 is determined from their signals. Then the intersection of A_1 and A_2 is the position of the navigator.

The hyperbola has a reflective property used in the design of certain telescopes. Hyperbolas are also used in combat to locate the position of enemy guns by the sound of their firing, a practice called *sound ranging*. Some comets move in hyperbolic orbits. If a quantity varies inversely as another quantity, such as pressure and volume in Boyle's law for a perfect gas ($PV = k$), the graph is a hyperbola as you will learn in Appendix Section A.10.

EXERCISES A.8

In Exercises 1 through 6, for the hyperbola having the equation, find (a) the center, (b) the principal axis, (c) the vertices, and (d) the foci. (e) Sketch the hyperbola and show the foci.

1. $\dfrac{x^2}{64} - \dfrac{y^2}{36} = 1$

2. $\dfrac{x^2}{4} - \dfrac{y^2}{4} = 1$

3. $\dfrac{y^2}{25} - \dfrac{x^2}{144} = 1$

4. $\dfrac{y^2}{16} - \dfrac{x^2}{9} = 1$

5. $9x^2 - 4y^2 = 36$

6. $25y^2 - 4x^2 = 100$

In Exercises 7 through 20, for the hyperbola having the equation, find (a) the center, (b) the principal axis, and (c) the vertices. (d) Sketch the hyperbola and show the auxiliary rectangle and asymptotes.

7. $\dfrac{x^2}{25} - \dfrac{y^2}{16} = 1$

8. $\dfrac{x^2}{9} - \dfrac{y^2}{25} = 1$

9. $\dfrac{y^2}{4} - \dfrac{x^2}{16} = 1$

10. $\dfrac{y^2}{100} - \dfrac{x^2}{49} = 1$

11. $25y^2 - 36x^2 = 900$

12. $4x^2 - 9y^2 = 144$

13. $x^2 - y^2 + 6x - 4y - 4 = 0$

14. $9y^2 - 4x^2 + 32x - 36y - 64 = 0$

15. $9x^2 - 16y^2 + 54x - 32y - 79 = 0$

16. $9y^2 - 25x^2 - 50x - 72y - 106 = 0$

17. $3y^2 - 4x^2 - 8x - 24y - 40 = 0$

18. $2x^2 - y^2 + 12x + 8y - 6 = 0$

19. $4y^2 - 9x^2 + 16y + 18x = 29$

20. $4x^2 - y^2 + 56x + 2y + 195 = 0$

In Exercises 21 through 26, find equations of the asymptotes of the hyperbola of the given exercise.

21. Exercise 7

22. Exercise 10

23. Exercise 13

24. Exercise 16

25. Exercise 19

26. Exercise 18

In Exercises 27 through 36, find an equation of the hyperbola satisfying the conditions and sketch the hyperbola.

27. Vertices at $(-2, 0)$ and $(2, 0)$ and a conjugate axis of length 6.

28. Foci at $(0, 5)$ and $(0, -5)$ and a vertex at $(0, 4)$.

29. Center at the origin, its foci on the y axis, and passing through the points $(-2, 4)$ and $(-6, 7)$.

30. Endpoints of its conjugate axis at $(0, -3)$ and $(0, 3)$ and one focus at $(5, 0)$.

31. One focus at $(26, 0)$ and asymptotes the lines $12y = \pm 5x$.

32. Center at $(3, -5)$, a vertex at $(7, -5)$, and a focus at $(8, -5)$.

33. Center at $(-2, -1)$, a vertex at $(-2, 11)$, and a focus at $(-2, 14)$.

34. Foci at $(3, 6)$ and $(3, 0)$ and passing through the point $(5, 3 + \frac{6}{5}\sqrt{5})$.

35. Foci at $(-1, 4)$ and $(7, 4)$ and length of the transverse axis is $\frac{8}{3}$.

36. One focus at $(-3 - 3\sqrt{13}, 1)$, asymptotes intersecting at $(-3, 1)$, and one asymptote passing through the point $(1, 7)$.

37. The vertices of a hyperbola are at $(-3, -1)$ and $(-1, -1)$ and the distance between the foci is $2\sqrt{5}$. Find **(a)** an equation of the hyperbola and **(b)** equations of the asymptotes.

38. The foci of a hyperbola are at $(2, 7)$ and $(2, -7)$ and the distance between the vertices is $8\sqrt{3}$. Find **(a)** an equation of the hyperbola and **(b)** equations of the asymptotes.

39. Find an equation of the hyperbola whose foci are the vertices of the ellipse $7x^2 + 11y^2 = 77$ and whose vertices are the foci of this ellipse.

40. Find an equation of the ellipse whose foci are the vertices of the hyperbola $11x^2 - 7y^2 = 77$ and whose vertices are the foci of this hyperbola.

41. The cost of the production of a commodity is \$12 less per unit at a point A than it is at a point B, and the distance between A and B is 100 km. Assuming that the route of delivery of the commodity is along a straight line and that the delivery cost is 20 cents per unit per kilometer, find the curve at any point of which the commodity can be supplied from either A or B at the same total cost. *Hint:* Take points A and B at $(-50, 0)$ and $(50, 0)$, respectively.

42. Two LORAN (long-range navigation) stations A and B lie on a line running east and west, and A is 80 miles due east of B. An airplane is traveling east on a straight-line course that is 60 miles north of the line through A and B. Signals are sent at the same time from A and B, and the signal from A reaches the plane 350 μsec (microseconds) before the one from B. If the signals travel at the rate of 0.2 mi/μsec, locate the position of the plane by the definition of a hyperbola.

43. Show that the equation
$$\sqrt{(x - c)^2 + y^2} - \sqrt{(x + c)^2 + y^2} = \pm 2a$$
can be simplified to
$$\frac{x^2}{a^2} - \frac{y^2}{b^2} = 1$$
where $b^2 = c^2 - a^2$.

44. For a hyperbola the eccentricity e is greater than 1, and for an ellipse $0 < e < 1$. Explain why the eccentricity of a parabola is equal to 1.

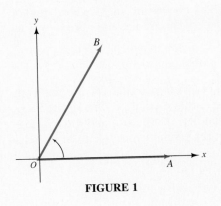

FIGURE 1

A.9 THE TRIGONOMETRIC FUNCTIONS

Even though you have studied trigonometry in a previous course, a brief review of the trigonometric functions is presented here because of their importance in calculus.

In geometry an **angle** is defined as the union of two rays called the **sides,** having a common endpoint called the **vertex.** Any angle is congruent to some angle having its vertex at the origin and one side, called the **initial side,** lying on the positive side of the x axis. Such an angle is said to be in **standard position.** Figure 1 shows an angle AOB in standard position with OA as the initial side. The other side, OB, is called the **terminal side.** The angle AOB can be formed by rotating the side OA to the side OB, and under such a rotation the point A moves along the circumference of a circle having its center at O and radius $|\overline{OA}|$ to the point B.

In dealing with problems involving angles of triangles, the measurement of an angle is usually given in degrees. However, in calculus we are concerned with trigonometric functions of real numbers, and these functions are defined in terms of *radian measure.*

The length of an arc of a circle is used to define the radian measure of an angle.

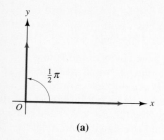

(a)

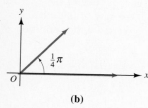

(b)

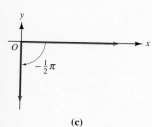

(c)

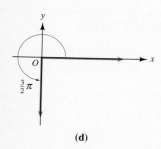

(d)

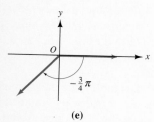

(e)

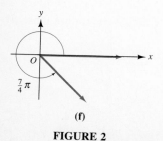

(f)

FIGURE 2

A.9.1 Definition of Radian Measure

Let AOB be an angle in standard position and $|\overline{OA}| = 1$. If s units is the length of the arc of the circle traveled by point A as the initial side OA is rotated to the terminal side OB, the **radian measure,** t, of angle AOB is given by

$$t = s \quad \text{if the rotation is counterclockwise}$$

and

$$t = -s \quad \text{if the rotation is clockwise}$$

▷ **ILLUSTRATION 1**   From the fact that the measure of the length of the unit circle's circumference is 2π, the radian measures of the angles in Figure 2(a)–(f) are determined. They are $\frac{1}{2}\pi, \frac{1}{4}\pi, -\frac{1}{2}\pi, \frac{3}{2}\pi, -\frac{3}{4}\pi$, and $\frac{7}{4}\pi$, respectively.   ◀

In Definition A.9.1, there may be more than one complete revolution in the rotation of OA.

▷ **ILLUSTRATION 2**   Figure 3(a) shows an angle whose radian measure is $\frac{5}{2}\pi$, and Figure 3(b) shows one whose radian measure is $-\frac{13}{4}\pi$.   ◀

An angle formed by one complete revolution so that OA is coincident with OB has degree measure of 360 and radian measure of 2π. Hence there is the following correspondence between degree measure and radian measure (where the symbol $\sim$ indicates that the given measurements are for the same or congruent angles):

$$360° \sim 2\pi \text{ rad} \qquad 180° \sim \pi \text{ rad}$$

From this it follows that

$$1° \sim \frac{1}{180}\pi \text{ rad} \qquad 1 \text{ rad} \sim \frac{180°}{\pi}$$

$$\approx 57°18'$$

Note that the symbol $\approx$ before $57°18'$ indicates that 1 rad and approximately $57°18'$ are measurements for the same or congruent angles.

From this correspondence the measurement of an angle can be converted from one system of units to the other.

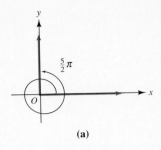

(a)

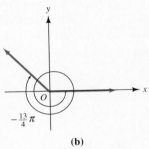

(b)

FIGURE 3

Table 1

Degree Measure	Radian Measure
30	$\frac{1}{6}\pi$
45	$\frac{1}{4}\pi$
60	$\frac{1}{3}\pi$
90	$\frac{1}{2}\pi$
120	$\frac{2}{3}\pi$
135	$\frac{3}{4}\pi$
150	$\frac{5}{6}\pi$
180	π
270	$\frac{3}{2}\pi$
360	2π

▶ **EXAMPLE 1**   Find: **(a)** the equivalent radian measurement for $162°$; **(b)** the equivalent degree measurement for $\frac{5}{12}\pi$.

Solution

(a) $162° \sim 162 \cdot \dfrac{1}{180}\pi$ rad   **(b)** $\frac{5}{12}\pi$ rad $\sim \dfrac{5}{12}\pi \cdot \dfrac{180°}{\pi}$

$162° \sim \frac{9}{10}\pi$ rad $\frac{5}{12}\pi$ rad $\sim 75°$ ◀

Table 1 gives the corresponding degree and radian measures of certain angles.

We now define the *sine* and *cosine* functions of any real number.

A.9.2 Definition of Sine and Cosine of a Real Number

Suppose that t is a real number. Place an angle, having radian measure t, in standard position and let point P be at the intersection of the terminal side of the angle with the unit circle having its center at the origin. If P is the point (x, y), then the **sine** function is defined by

$$\sin t = y$$

and the **cosine** function is defined by

$$\cos t = x$$

From this definition, $\sin t$ and $\cos t$ are defined for any value of t. Therefore the domain of the sine and cosine is the set of all real numbers. Figure 4 shows the point $(\cos t, \sin t)$ when $0 < t < \frac{1}{2}\pi$, and Figure 5 shows the point $(\cos t, \sin t)$ when $-\frac{3}{2}\pi < t < -\pi$.

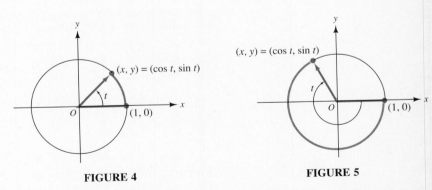

FIGURE 4   **FIGURE 5**

The largest value either function may have is 1 and the smallest value is -1. We will show later that the sine and cosine functions assume all values between -1 and 1, and from this fact it follows that the range of the two functions is $[-1, 1]$.

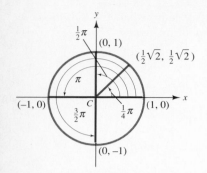

FIGURE 6

Table 2

t	$\sin t$	$\cos t$
0	0	1
$\frac{1}{6}\pi$	$\frac{1}{2}$	$\frac{1}{2}\sqrt{3}$
$\frac{1}{4}\pi$	$\frac{1}{2}\sqrt{2}$	$\frac{1}{2}\sqrt{2}$
$\frac{1}{3}\pi$	$\frac{1}{2}\sqrt{3}$	$\frac{1}{2}$
$\frac{1}{2}\pi$	1	0
$\frac{2}{3}\pi$	$\frac{1}{2}\sqrt{3}$	$-\frac{1}{2}$
$\frac{3}{4}\pi$	$\frac{1}{2}\sqrt{2}$	$-\frac{1}{2}\sqrt{2}$
$\frac{5}{6}\pi$	$\frac{1}{2}$	$-\frac{1}{2}\sqrt{3}$
π	0	-1
$\frac{3}{2}\pi$	-1	0
2π	0	1

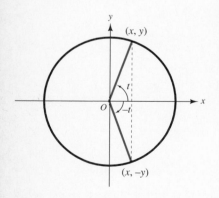

FIGURE 7

For certain values of t, the sine and cosine are easily obtained from a figure. In Figure 6 we observe that $\sin 0 = 0$ and $\cos 0 = 1$, $\sin \frac{1}{4}\pi = \frac{1}{2}\sqrt{2}$ and $\cos \frac{1}{4}\pi = \frac{1}{2}\sqrt{2}$, $\sin \frac{1}{2}\pi = 1$ and $\cos \frac{1}{2}\pi = 0$, $\sin \pi = 0$ and $\cos \pi = -1$, $\sin \frac{3}{2}\pi = -1$ and $\cos \frac{3}{2}\pi = 0$. Table 2 gives these values and some others that are frequently used.

An equation of the unit circle having its center at the origin is $x^2 + y^2 = 1$. Because $x = \cos t$ and $y = \sin t$, it follows that

$$\sin^2 t + \cos^2 t = 1 \tag{1}$$

Note that $\sin^2 t + \cos^2 t$ stands for $(\sin t)^2$ and $(\cos t)^2$. Equation (1) is an identity because it is valid for any real number t. It is called the **fundamental Pythagorean identity** showing the relationship between the sine and cosine values and can be used to compute one of them when the other is known.

Figures 7 and 8 show angles having a negative radian measure of $-t$ and corresponding angles having a positive radian measure of t. From these figures observe that

$$\sin(-t) = -\sin t \quad \text{and} \quad \cos(-t) = \cos t$$

These equations hold for any real number t because the points where the terminal sides of the angles (having radian measures t and $-t$) intersect the unit circle have equal abscissas and ordinates that differ only in sign. Hence they are identities. From these identities it follows that the sine is an odd function and the cosine is an even function.

From Definition A.9.2 we can obtain the following identities:

$$\sin(t + 2\pi) = \sin t \quad \text{and} \quad \cos(t + 2\pi) = \cos t \tag{2}$$

The property of sine and cosine stated by these two equations is called **periodicity.**

A.9.3 Definition of a Periodic Function

A function f is said to be **periodic** if there exists a positive real number p such that whenever x is in the domain of f, then $x + p$ is also in the domain of f, and

$$f(x + p) = f(x)$$

The smallest such positive real number p is called the **period** of f.

Compare this definition with Equations (2). Because 2π can be shown to be the smallest positive number p having the property that $\sin(t + p) = \sin t$ and $\cos(t + p) = \cos t$, the sine and cosine are periodic with period 2π; that is, whenever the value of the independent variable t is increased by 2π, the value of each of the functions is repeated. It is because of the periodicity of the sine and cosine that these functions have important applications in connection with periodically repetitive phenomena, such as wave motion, alternating electrical current, vibrating strings, oscillating pendulums, business cycles, and biological rhythms.

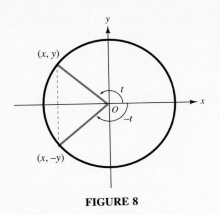

FIGURE 8

▶ **EXAMPLE 2**   Use the periodicity of the sine and cosine functions as well as the values of $\sin t$ and $\cos t$ when $0 \leq t < 2\pi$ to find an exact value of each of the following: **(a)** $\sin \frac{17}{4}\pi$; **(b)** $\cos \frac{7}{3}\pi$; **(c)** $\sin \frac{15}{2}\pi$; **(d)** $\cos(-\frac{7}{6}\pi)$

Solution

(a) $\sin \frac{17}{4}\pi = \sin(\frac{1}{4}\pi + 2 \cdot 2\pi)$
$= \sin \frac{1}{4}\pi$
$= \frac{1}{2}\sqrt{2}$

(b) $\cos \frac{7}{3}\pi = \cos(\frac{1}{3}\pi + 2\pi)$
$= \cos \frac{1}{3}\pi$
$= \frac{1}{2}$

(c) $\sin \frac{15}{2}\pi = \sin(\frac{3}{2}\pi + 3 \cdot 2\pi)$
$= \sin \frac{3}{2}\pi$
$= -1$

(d) $\cos(-\frac{7}{6}\pi) = \cos[\frac{5}{6}\pi + (-1)2\pi]$
$= \cos \frac{5}{6}\pi$
$= -\frac{1}{2}\sqrt{3}$ ◀

We now define the other four trigonometric functions in terms of the sine and cosine.

A.9.4 Definition of the Tangent, Secant, Cotangent, and Cosecant Functions of a Real Number

The **tangent** and **secant** functions are defined by

$$\tan t = \frac{\sin t}{\cos t} \qquad \sec t = \frac{1}{\cos t}$$

for all real numbers t for which $\cos t \neq 0$.

The **cotangent** and **cosecant** functions are defined by

$$\cot t = \frac{\cos t}{\sin t} \qquad \csc t = \frac{1}{\sin t}$$

for all real numbers t for which $\sin t \neq 0$.

The tangent and secant functions are not defined when $\cos t = 0$. Therefore the domain of the tangent and secant functions is the set of all real numbers except numbers of the form $\frac{1}{2}\pi + k\pi$, where k is any integer. Similarly, because $\cot t$ and $\csc t$ are not defined when $\sin t = 0$, the domain of the cotangent and cosecant functions is the set of all real numbers except numbers of the form $k\pi$, where k is any integer.

It can be shown that the tangent and cotangent are periodic with period π; that is,

$$\tan(t + \pi) = \tan t \quad \text{and} \quad \cot(t + \pi) = \cot t$$

Furthermore, the secant and cosecant are periodic with period 2π; therefore

$$\sec(t + 2\pi) = \sec t \quad \text{and} \quad \csc(t + 2\pi) = \csc t$$

By using the fundamental Pythagorean identity (1) and Definition A.9.4, we obtain two other important identities. One of these identities is obtained by dividing both sides of (1) by $\cos^2 t$, and the other is obtained by dividing both sides of (1) by $\sin^2 t$. We have

$$\frac{\sin^2 t}{\cos^2 t} + \frac{\cos^2 t}{\cos^2 t} = \frac{1}{\cos^2 t} \quad \text{and} \quad \frac{\sin^2 t}{\sin^2 t} + \frac{\cos^2 t}{\sin^2 t} = \frac{1}{\sin^2 t}$$

$$\tan^2 t + 1 = \sec^2 t \quad \text{and} \quad 1 + \cot^2 t = \csc^2 t$$

These two identities are also called Pythagorean identities.

Three other important identities that follow from Definition A.9.4 are

$$\sin t \csc t = 1 \qquad \cos t \sec t = 1 \qquad \tan t \cot t = 1$$

These three identities, the three Pythagorean identities, and the two identities in Definition A.9.4 that define the tangent and cotangent are the *eight fundamental trigonometric identities*. These as well as other formulas from trigonometry appear later in the book.

We have defined the trigonometric functions with real-number domains. There are important uses of trigonometric functions for which the domains are sets of angles. For these purposes, we define a trigonometric function of an angle θ as the corresponding function of the real number t, where t is the radian measure of θ.

A.9.5 Definition of the Trigonometric Functions of an Angle

If θ is an angle having radian measure t, then

$$\sin \theta = \sin t \qquad \cos \theta = \cos t \qquad \tan \theta = \tan t$$
$$\cot \theta = \cot t \qquad \sec \theta = \sec t \qquad \csc \theta = \csc t$$

When considering a trigonometric function of an angle θ, often the measurement of the angle is used in place of θ. For instance, if the degree measure of an angle θ is 60 (or, equivalently, the radian measure of θ is $\frac{1}{3}\pi$), then in place of $\sin \theta$ we could write $\sin 60°$ or $\sin \frac{1}{3}\pi$. Notice that when the measurement of an angle is in degrees, the degree symbol is written. However, when there is no symbol attached, the measurement of the angle is in radians. For example, $\cos 2°$ means the cosine of an angle having degree measure 2, while $\cos 2$ means the cosine of an angle having radian measure 2. This is consistent with the fact that the cosine of an angle having radian measure 2 is equal to the cosine of the real number 2.

We now explain how parametric equations involving trigonometric functions can be used to plot ellipses and hyperbolas on a graphics calculator.

To plot the ellipse

$$\frac{x^2}{a^2} + \frac{y^2}{b^2} = 1 \tag{3}$$

we use the parametric equations

$$x = a \cos t \quad \text{and} \quad y = b \sin t$$

To show that these equations represent the ellipse, we eliminate t from the equations. We first write the equations as

$$\frac{x}{a} = \cos t \quad \text{and} \quad \frac{y}{b} = \sin t$$

Squaring on both sides of each equation and adding gives

$$\frac{x^2}{a^2} + \frac{y^2}{b^2} = \cos^2 t + \sin^2 t$$

$$\frac{x^2}{a^2} + \frac{y^2}{b^2} = 1$$

which is Equation (3).

▶ **EXAMPLE 3**   Plot the ellipse of Example 1 in Appendix Section A.7 by using parametric equations.

Solution   A cartesian equation of the ellipse is

$$\frac{x^2}{25} + \frac{y^2}{16} = 1$$

Parametric equations of this ellipse are

$$x = 5 \cos t \quad \text{and} \quad y = 4 \sin t$$

On our graphics calculator in parametric mode, we let t take on all numbers in the closed interval $[0, 2\pi]$. Figure 9 shows the graph plotted in the $[-6, 6]$ by $[-4, 4]$ window with $t_{\text{step}} = 0.05$. Compare this graph with Figure 6 in Appendix Section A.7 obtained by sketching the graph by hand.   ◀

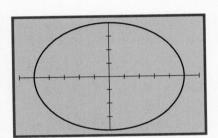

[−6, 6] by [−4, 4]

$x = 5 \cos t$ and $y = 4 \sin t$

FIGURE 9

To plot an ellipse whose principal axis is horizontal, use the parametric equations

$$x = a \cos t + h \quad \text{and} \quad y = b \sin t + k$$

In Exercise 34, you are asked to show that these are parametric equations of the ellipse having the cartesian equation

$$\frac{(x - h)^2}{a^2} + \frac{(y - k)^2}{b^2} = 1$$

If the principal axis is vertical, use the parametric equations

$$x = b \cos t + h \quad \text{and} \quad y = a \sin t + k$$

To plot the hyperbola having the cartesian equation

$$\frac{(x - h)^2}{a^2} - \frac{(y - k)^2}{b^2} = 1$$

use the parametric equations

$$x = a \sec t + h \quad \text{and} \quad y = b \tan t + k$$

where t is in the interval $[0, 2\pi]$. This method is based on the identity $\sec^2 t - \tan^2 t = 1$. See Exercise 43. If the hyperbola has the cartesian equation

$$\frac{(y - k)^2}{a^2} - \frac{(x - h)^2}{b^2} = 1$$

use the parametric equations

$$x = b \tan t + h \quad \text{and} \quad y = a \sec t + k$$

See Exercise 44.

▶ **EXAMPLE 4**   Plot the hyperbola of Example 4 in Appendix Section A.8 by using parametric equations.

Solution   A cartesian equation in standard cartesian form for this hyperbola is

$$\frac{(y + 2)^2}{9} - \frac{(x - 1)^2}{4} = 1$$

Parametric equations of this hyperbola are

$$x = 2 \tan t + 1 \quad \text{and} \quad y = 3 \sec t - 2$$

Figure 10 shows the graph of these parametric equations plotted in the $[-8, 10]$ by $[-8, 4]$ window for t in the closed interval $[0, 2\pi]$ with $t_{\text{step}} = 0.05$. Compare this graph with Figure 9 in Appendix Section A.8 obtained by sketching the graph by hand.   ◀

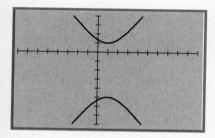

[−8, 10] by [−8, 4]

$x = 2 \tan t + 1$ and $y = 3 \sec t - 2$

FIGURE 10

EXERCISES A.9

In Exercises 1 and 2, find the equivalent radian measurement.

1. (a) $60°$ **(b)** $135°$ **(c)** $210°$ **(d)** $-150°$
   (e) $20°$ **(f)** $450°$ **(g)** $-75°$ **(h)** $100°$

2. (a) $45°$ **(b)** $120°$ **(c)** $240°$ **(d)** $-225°$
   (e) $15°$ **(f)** $540°$ **(g)** $-48°$ **(h)** $2°$

In Exercises 3 and 4, find the equivalent degree measurement.

3. (a) $\frac{1}{4}\pi$ rad **(b)** $\frac{2}{3}\pi$ rad **(c)** $\frac{11}{6}\pi$ rad
   (d) $-\frac{1}{2}\pi$ rad **(e)** $\frac{1}{2}$ rad **(f)** 3π rad
   (g) -2 rad **(h)** $\frac{1}{12}\pi$ rad

4. (a) $\frac{1}{6}\pi$ rad **(b)** $\frac{4}{3}\pi$ rad **(c)** $\frac{3}{4}\pi$ rad
   (d) -5π rad **(e)** $\frac{1}{3}$ rad **(f)** -5 rad
   (g) $\frac{11}{12}\pi$ rad **(h)** 0.2 rad

In Exercises 5 through 12, determine the exact function value.

5. (a) $\sin \frac{1}{6}\pi$ **(b)** $\cos \frac{1}{4}\pi$ **(c)** $\sin(-\frac{3}{2}\pi)$
   (d) $\cos \frac{1}{3}\pi$

6. (a) $\cos \frac{1}{3}\pi$ **(b)** $\sin \frac{1}{4}\pi$
   (c) $\cos(-\frac{1}{2}\pi)$ **(d)** $\sin(-2\pi)$

7. (a) $\cos \frac{5}{6}\pi$ **(b)** $\sin \frac{3}{4}\pi$
   (c) $\cos 3\pi$ **(d)** $\sin(-5\pi)$

8. (a) $\sin \frac{4}{3}\pi$ **(b)** $\cos(-\frac{1}{6}\pi)$
   (c) $\sin 7\pi$ **(d)** $\cos(-\frac{5}{2}\pi)$

9. (a) $\tan \frac{1}{3}\pi$ **(b)** $\cot \frac{1}{4}\pi$ **(c)** $\sec(-\pi)$ **(d)** $\csc \frac{1}{2}\pi$

10. (a) $\cot \frac{1}{6}\pi$ **(b)** $\tan \frac{1}{4}\pi$ **(c)** $\csc(-\frac{3}{2}\pi)$ **(d)** $\sec \pi$

11. (a) $\sec(-\frac{1}{6}\pi)$ **(b)** $\csc \frac{3}{4}\pi$
   (c) $\tan \frac{5}{6}\pi$ **(d)** $\cot(-\frac{3}{4}\pi)$

12. (a) $\csc(-\frac{1}{3}\pi)$ **(b)** $\sec \frac{5}{6}\pi$
   (c) $\tan \frac{3}{4}\pi$ **(d)** $\cot \frac{3}{2}\pi$

In Exercises 13 through 20, use the periodicity of the sine, cosine, secant, and cosecant functions as well as the values of $\sin t$, $\cos t$, $\sec t$, and $\csc t$ when $0 \leq t < 2\pi$ to find the exact function value.

13. (a) $\sin \frac{9}{4}\pi$ **(b)** $\cos \frac{9}{4}\pi$ **(c)** $\sec \frac{9}{4}\pi$ **(d)** $\csc \frac{9}{4}\pi$

14. (a) $\sin \frac{17}{6}\pi$ **(b)** $\cos \frac{17}{6}\pi$
   (c) $\sec \frac{17}{6}\pi$ **(d)** $\csc \frac{17}{6}\pi$

15. (a) $\sin(-\frac{2}{3}\pi)$ **(b)** $\cos(-\frac{2}{3}\pi)$
  (c) $\sec(-\frac{2}{3}\pi)$ **(d)** $\csc(-\frac{2}{3}\pi)$

16. (a) $\sin(-\frac{5}{4}\pi)$ **(b)** $\cos(-\frac{5}{4}\pi)$
  (c) $\sec(-\frac{5}{4}\pi)$ **(d)** $\csc(-\frac{5}{4}\pi)$

17. (a) $\sin 8\pi$ **(b)** $\cos 10\pi$ **(c)** $\sec 7\pi$ **(d)** $\csc 9\pi$

18. (a) $\sin \frac{7}{2}\pi$ **(b)** $\cos \frac{5}{2}\pi$ **(c)** $\sec \frac{11}{2}\pi$ **(d)** $\csc \frac{9}{2}\pi$

19. (a) $\sin(-\frac{7}{2}\pi)$ **(b)** $\cos(-\frac{5}{2}\pi)$
  (c) $\sec(-\frac{11}{2}\pi)$ **(d)** $\csc(-\frac{9}{2}\pi)$

20. (a) $\sin(-8\pi)$ **(b)** $\cos(-10\pi)$
  (c) $\sec(-7\pi)$ **(d)** $\csc(-9\pi)$

In Exercises 21 through 24, use the periodicity of the tangent and cotangent functions as well as the values of $\tan t$ and $\cot t$ when $0 \le t < \pi$ to find the exact function value.

21. (a) $\tan \frac{7}{4}\pi$ **(b)** $\cot \frac{7}{4}\pi$
  (c) $\tan(-\frac{5}{6}\pi)$ **(d)** $\cot(-\frac{5}{6}\pi)$

22. (a) $\tan \frac{4}{3}\pi$ **(b)** $\cot \frac{4}{3}\pi$
  (c) $\tan(-\frac{1}{6}\pi)$ **(d)** $\cot(-\frac{1}{6}\pi)$

23. (a) $\tan \frac{11}{3}\pi$ **(b)** $\cot \frac{11}{3}\pi$
  (c) $\tan(-5\pi)$ **(d)** $\cot(-\frac{9}{2}\pi)$

24. (a) $\tan(-\frac{11}{4}\pi)$ **(b)** $\cot(-\frac{11}{4}\pi)$
  (c) $\tan 11\pi$ **(d)** $\cot \frac{15}{2}\pi$

In Exercises 25 through 30, find all values of t in the interval $[0, 2\pi]$ for which the equation is satisfied.

25. (a) $\sin t = 1$ **(b)** $\cos t = -1$
  (c) $\tan t = 1$ **(d)** $\sec t = 1$

26. (a) $\sin t = -1$ **(b)** $\cos t = 1$
  (c) $\tan t = -1$ **(d)** $\csc t = 1$

27. (a) $\sin t = 0$ **(b)** $\cos t = 0$
  (c) $\tan t = 0$ **(d)** $\cot t = 0$

28. (a) $\sin t = \frac{1}{2}$ **(b)** $\cos t = -\frac{1}{2}$
  (c) $\cot t = 1$ **(d)** $\sec t = 2$

29. (a) $\sin t = -\frac{1}{2}$ **(b)** $\cos t = \frac{1}{2}$
  (c) $\cot t = -1$ **(d)** $\csc t = 2$

30. (a) $\sin t = -\frac{1}{2}\sqrt{2}$ **(b)** $\cos t = \frac{1}{2}\sqrt{2}$
  (c) $\tan t = -\frac{1}{3}\sqrt{3}$ **(d)** $\cot t = \frac{1}{3}\sqrt{3}$

31. For what values of t in $[0, 2\pi)$ is (a) $\tan t$ undefined and (b) $\csc t$ undefined?

32. For what values of t in $[0, \pi)$ is (a) $\cot t$ undefined and (b) $\sec t$ undefined?

33. For what values of t in $[\pi, 2\pi)$ is (a) $\cot t$ undefined and (b) $\sec t$ undefined?

34. Show that the ellipse having the equation

$$\frac{(x - h)^2}{a^2} + \frac{(y - k)^2}{b^2} = 1$$

has the parametric equations $x = a \cos t + h$ and $y = b \sin t + k$.

In Exercises 35 through 42, write parametric equations defining the ellipse of the given exercise in Exercises A. 7, and use them to plot the ellipse.

35. Exercise 1   **36.** Exercise 2
37. Exercise 3   **38.** Exercise 4
39. Exercise 9   **40.** Exercise 10
41. Exercise 11   **42.** Exercise 14

43. Show that the hyperbola having the equation

$$\frac{(x - h)^2}{a^2} - \frac{(y - k)^2}{b^2} = 1$$

has the parametric equations $x = a \sec t + h$ and $y = b \tan t + k$.

44. Show that the hyperbola having the equation

$$\frac{(y - k)^2}{a^2} - \frac{(x - h)^2}{b^2} = 1$$

has the parametric equations $x = b \tan t + h$ and $y = a \sec t + k$.

In Exercises 45 through 52, write parametric equations defining the hyperbola of the given exercise in Exercises A.8, and use them to plot the hyperbola.

45. Exercise 1   **46.** Exercise 2
47. Exercise 3   **48.** Exercise 4
49. Exercise 13   **50.** Exercise 14
51. Exercise 17   **52.** Exercise 18

A.10 THE GENERAL EQUATION OF THE SECOND DEGREE IN TWO VARIABLES AND ROTATION OF AXES

You learned in Appendix Section A.7 and A.8 that the graph of the general second-degree equation in two variables,

$$Ax^2 + Bxy + Cy^2 + Dx + Ey + F = 0 \tag{1}$$

is an ellipse or a degenerate case if $B = 0$ and $AC > 0$, and a hyperbola or the degenerate case if $B = 0$ and $AC < 0$.

Parabola

FIGURE 1

We now consider (1) where $B = 0$ and $AC = 0$. In such a case either $A = 0$ or $C = 0$, but not both, for if the three numbers A, B, and C are all zero, (1) is not a second-degree equation. Suppose in (1) that $B = 0$, $A = 0$, and $C \neq 0$. Then (1) becomes

$$Cy^2 + Dx + Ey + F = 0 \tag{2}$$

If $D \neq 0$, you learned in Appendix Section A.6 that the graph of this equation is a parabola, the third conic section. The parabola is obtained as a conic section if the cutting plane is parallel to one and only one generator of a conic. See Figure 1.

In Appendix Section A.4, we defined a parabola as a set of points in a plane. The proof that this definition follows from its definition as a conic section is similar to that for an ellipse. For a parabola, however, you need only one sphere tangent to the cutting plane at the focus and tangent to the cone along a circle. The intersection of the plane of the circle with the cutting plane is the directrix of the parabola.

The degenerate cases of a parabola, occurring if $D = 0$ in (2), are two parallel lines, one line, or the empty set.

 ILLUSTRATION 1   The graph of the equation

$$4y^2 - 9 = 0$$

is two parallel lines: $2y - 3 = 0$ and $2y + 3 = 0$. The graph of the equation

$$9y^2 + 6y + 1 = 0$$

is one line because the equation is equivalent to $(3y + 1)^2 = 0$. Because the equation

$$2y^2 + y + 1 = 0$$

has no real solutions, its graph is the empty set.   ◄

A discussion similar to the above can be given if, in (1), $B = 0$, $C = 0$, and $A \neq 0$. We summarize the results in the following theorem.

A.10.1 Theorem

In the general second-degree equation (1), if $B = 0$ and either $A = 0$ and $C \neq 0$ or $C = 0$ and $A \neq 0$, then the graph is one of the following: a parabola, two parallel lines, one line, or the empty set.

Line

FIGURE 2

The degenerate case of a parabola, one line, is obtained as a conic section if the cutting plane contains the vertex of the cone and only one generator, as in Figure 2. The degenerate parabola consisting of two parallel lines cannot be obtained as a plane section of a cone unless we consider a circular cylinder as a degenerate cone with its vertex at infinity. Then a plane parallel to the elements of the cylinder and cutting two distinct elements produces the two parallel lines.

From the theorems of Appendix Sections A.7 and A.8 and the preceding theorem in this section, we may conclude that the graph of the general second-degree equation in two variables when $B = 0$ is either a conic or a degenerate conic. The type of conic can be determined from the product of A and C. We have the following theorem.

A.10.2 Theorem

The graph of the equation

$$Ax^2 + Cy^2 + Dx + Ey + F = 0$$

where A and C are not both zero, is either a conic or a degenerate conic. If it is a conic, then the graph is

(i) a *parabola* if either $A = 0$ or $C = 0$, that is, if $AC = 0$;
(ii) an *ellipse* if A and C have the same sign, that is, if $AC > 0$;
(iii) a *hyperbola* if A and C have opposite signs, that is, if $AC < 0$.

▶ **EXAMPLE 1**   Identify the graph of each of the following equations as the type of conic or degenerate conic.

(a) $9x^2 + y^2 - 18x + 4y + 4 = 0$ (b) $x^2 + 4y^2 = 0$

(c) $2x^2 + 12x - 5y + 28 = 0$ (d) $x^2 - 4 = 0$

(e) $3x^2 - 2y^2 + 12x - 4y - 2 = 0$ (f) $x^2 - 4y^2 = 0$

Solution   In each part, we have a second-degree equation in two variables. The graph is, therefore, a conic or else it degenerates. From Theorem A.10.2, the product AC determines the type of conic.

(a) Because $A = 9$ and $C = 1$, $AC = 9 > 0$. Therefore, the graph is an ellipse or else degenerates. By completing squares, the equation can be written as

$$(x - 1)^2 + \frac{(y + 2)^2}{9} = 1$$

Thus the graph is an ellipse.

(b) Because the only ordered pair satisfying this equation is $(0, 0)$, the graph is the origin, a degenerate ellipse.

(c) Because $C = 0$, $AC = 0$. So the graph is a parabola or degenerates. By completing squares, we can write the equation as

$$(x + 3)^2 = \tfrac{5}{2}(y - 2)$$

which is an equation of a parabola.

(d) Because the equation $x^2 - 4 = 0$ is equivalent to the equation $(x - 2)(x + 2) = 0$, its graph consists of the two parallel lines $x = 2$ and $x = -2$, a degenerate parabola.

(e) Because $A = 3$ and $C = -2$, $AC = -6 < 0$. The graph is, therefore, a hyperbola, or else it degenerates. The equation is equivalent to

$$\frac{(x + 2)^2}{4} - \frac{(y + 1)^2}{6} = 1$$

whose graph is a hyperbola.

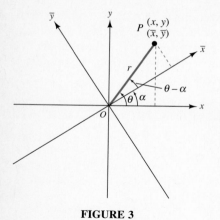

FIGURE 3

(f) The equation is equivalent to $(x - 2y)(x + 2y) = 0$; thus its graph consists of the two intersecting lines $x = 2y$ and $x = -2y$, a degenerate hyperbola. ◀

We now discuss the graph of the general second-degree equation in two variables where $B \neq 0$, that is, an equation having an xy term. We transform such an equation into one having no xy term by rotating the coordinate axes. While a translation of axes gives a new coordinate system whose axes are parallel to the original x and y axes, a rotation of axes gives a coordinate system that will in general have axes that are *not* parallel to the original ones.

Suppose we have two rectangular cartesian coordinate systems with the same origin. Let one system be the xy system and the other the $\bar{x}\bar{y}$ system. Suppose further that the $\bar{x}$ axis makes an angle α with the x axis. See Figure 3. Of course, the $\bar{y}$ axis then makes an angle α with the y axis. In such a case we state that the xy system of coordinates is *rotated* through an angle α to form the $\bar{x}\bar{y}$ system of coordinates. A point P having coordinates (x, y) with respect to the original coordinate system will have coordinates $(\bar{x}, \bar{y})$ with respect to the new one. We now obtain relationships between these two sets of coordinates.

In Figure 3, let r denote the undirected distance $|\overline{OP}|$ and let θ be the angle measured from the x axis to the line segment OP. From the figure we observe that

$$x = r \cos \theta \quad \text{and} \quad y = r \sin \theta \tag{3}$$

Also from Figure 3

$$\bar{x} = r \cos(\theta - \alpha) \quad \text{and} \quad \bar{y} = r \sin(\theta - \alpha)$$

With the cosine and sine difference identities these two equations become

$$\bar{x} = r \cos \theta \cos \alpha + r \sin \theta \sin \alpha$$

and

$$\bar{y} = r \sin \theta \cos \alpha - r \cos \theta \sin \alpha$$

Substituting from Equations (3) into the preceding equations, we get

$$\bar{x} = x \cos \alpha + y \sin \alpha \quad \text{and} \quad \bar{y} = -x \sin \alpha + y \cos \alpha \tag{4}$$

Solving Equations (4) simultaneously for x and y in terms of $\bar{x}$ and $\bar{y}$ (see Exercise 38), we obtain

$$x = \bar{x} \cos \alpha - \bar{y} \sin \alpha \quad \text{and} \quad y = \bar{x} \sin \alpha + \bar{y} \cos \alpha \tag{5}$$

We state these results formally.

A.10.3 Theorem   Formulas for Rotation of Axes

If (x, y) represents a point P with respect to a given set of axes and $(\bar{x}, \bar{y})$ is a representation of P after the axes have been rotated through an angle α, then

(i) $x = \bar{x} \cos \alpha - \bar{y} \sin \alpha$ and $y = \bar{x} \sin \alpha + \bar{y} \cos \alpha$
(ii) $\bar{x} = x \cos \alpha + y \sin \alpha$ and $\bar{y} = -x \sin \alpha + y \cos \alpha$

▶ **EXAMPLE 2**   Given the equation

$$xy = 1$$

(a) Find an equation of the graph with respect to the x and y axes after a rotation of axes through an angle of radian measure $\frac{1}{4}\pi$. **(b)** Sketch the graph and show both sets of axes.

Solution

(a) With $\alpha = \frac{1}{4}\pi$ in (i) of Theorem A.10.3, we obtain

$$x = \frac{1}{\sqrt{2}}\bar{x} - \frac{1}{\sqrt{2}}\bar{y} \quad \text{and} \quad y = \frac{1}{\sqrt{2}}\bar{x} + \frac{1}{\sqrt{2}}\bar{y}$$

Substituting these expressions for x and y in the equation $xy = 1$, we get

$$\left(\frac{1}{\sqrt{2}}\bar{x} - \frac{1}{\sqrt{2}}\bar{y}\right)\left(\frac{1}{\sqrt{2}}\bar{x} + \frac{1}{\sqrt{2}}\bar{y}\right) = 1$$

$$\frac{\bar{x}^2}{2} - \frac{\bar{y}^2}{2} = 1$$

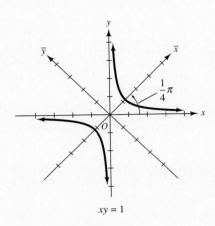

$xy = 1$

FIGURE 4

(b) This is an equation of an equilateral hyperbola whose asymptotes are the bisectors of the quadrants in the $\bar{x}\bar{y}$ system. Thus the graph of the equation $xy = 1$ is an equilateral hyperbola lying in the first and third quadrants and the asymptotes are the x and y axes. See Figure 4 for the required graph.   ◀

From Theorem A.10.1 we know that when $B = 0$ and A and C are not both zero, the graph of (1), the general second-degree equation in two variables, is either a conic or a degenerate conic. We now show that if $B = 0$, then any equation of the form (1) can be transformed by a suitable rotation of axes into an equation of the form

$$\bar{A}\bar{x}^2 + \bar{C}\bar{y}^2 + \bar{D}\bar{x} + \bar{E}\bar{y} + \bar{F} = 0 \tag{6}$$

where $\bar{A}$ and $\bar{C}$ are not both zero.

If the xy system is rotated through an angle α, then to obtain an equation of the graph of (1) with respect to the $\bar{x}\bar{y}$ system, we replace x by $\bar{x}\cos\alpha - \bar{y}\sin\alpha$ and y by $\bar{x}\sin\alpha + \bar{y}\cos\alpha$. We get

$$\bar{A}\bar{x}^2 + \bar{B}\bar{x}\bar{y} + \bar{C}\bar{y}^2 + \bar{D}\bar{x} + \bar{E}\bar{y} + \bar{F} = 0 \tag{7}$$

where

$$\bar{A} = A\cos^2\alpha + B\sin\alpha\cos\alpha + C\sin^2\alpha$$
$$\bar{B} = -2A\sin\alpha\cos\alpha + B(\cos^2\alpha - \sin^2\alpha) + 2C\sin\alpha\cos\alpha$$
$$\bar{C} = A\sin^2\alpha - B\sin\alpha\cos\alpha + C\cos^2\alpha$$

We wish to find an α so that the rotation transforms (1) into an equation of the form (6). Setting the expression for $\bar{B}$ equal to zero, we have

$$B(\cos^2\alpha - \sin^2\alpha) + (C - A)(2\sin\alpha\cos\alpha) = 0$$

or, equivalently, with trigonometric identities,

$$B\cos 2\alpha + (C - A)\sin 2\alpha = 0$$

Because $B \neq 0$, this gives

$$\cot 2\alpha = \frac{A - C}{B}$$

We have shown that a rotation of axes through an angle α satisfying this equation will transform (1), the general second-degree equation in two variables, where $B \neq 0$, to an equation of the form (6). We now wish to show that $\bar{A}$ and $\bar{C}$ in (6) are not both zero. To prove this, notice that (7) is obtained from (1) by rotating the axes through the angle α. Also (1) can be obtained from (7) by rotating the axes back through the angle $-\alpha$. If $\bar{A}$ and $\bar{C}$ in (7) were both zero then the substitutions

$$\bar{x} = x \cos \alpha + y \sin \alpha \quad \text{and} \quad \bar{y} = -x \sin \alpha + y \cos \alpha$$

in that equation would result in the equation

$$\bar{D}(x \cos \alpha + y \sin \alpha) + \bar{E}(-x \sin \alpha + y \cos \alpha) + \bar{F} = 0$$

This equation is of the first degree and hence different from (1) because we have assumed that at least $B \neq 0$. We have therefore proved the following theorem.

A.10.4 Theorem

If $B \neq 0$, the equation

$$Ax^2 + Bxy + Cy^2 + Dx + Ey + F = 0$$

can be transformed into the equation

$$\bar{A}\bar{x}^2 + \bar{C}\bar{y}^2 + \bar{D}\bar{x} + \bar{E}\bar{y} + \bar{F} = 0$$

where $\bar{A}$ and $\bar{C}$ are not both zero, by a rotation of axes through an angle α for which

$$\cot 2\alpha = \frac{A - C}{B}$$

By Theorems A.10.2 and A10.4, the graph of the general second-degree equation in two variables is either a conic or a degenerate conic. To determine which type of conic is the graph of a particular equation, we examine the expression $B^2 - 4AC$.

We use the fact that A, B, and C of (1) and $\bar{A}$, $\bar{B}$, and $\bar{C}$ of (7) satisfy the equation

$$B^2 - 4AC = \bar{B}^2 - 4\bar{A}\bar{C} \tag{8}$$

which can be proved by substituting the expressions for $\bar{A}$, $\bar{B}$, and $\bar{C}$ given after Equation (7) in the right side. You are asked to do this in Exercise 37.

The expression $B^2 - 4AC$ is called the **discriminant** and Equation (8) states that the discriminant of the general quadratic equation in two variables is **invariant** under a rotation of axes.

If the angle of rotation is chosen so that $\bar{B} = 0$, then (8) becomes

$$B^2 - 4AC = -4\bar{A}\bar{C} \tag{9}$$

Except for degenerate cases, by applying Theorem A.10.2, the graph of the equation

$$\overline{A}\overline{x}^2 + \overline{C}\overline{y}^2 + \overline{D}\overline{x} + \overline{E}\overline{y} + \overline{F} = 0$$

is a parabola if $\overline{A}\,\overline{C} = 0$, an ellipse if $\overline{A}\,\overline{C} > 0$, and a hyperbola if $\overline{A}\,\overline{C} < 0$; or, equivalently, a parabola if $-4\overline{A}\,\overline{C} = 0$, an ellipse if $-4\overline{A}\,\overline{C} < 0$, and a hyperbola if $-4\overline{A}\,\overline{C} > 0$. From these facts and Equation (9) it follows that, except for degenerate cases, the graph of (1), the general second-degree equation, is a parabola, an ellipse, or a hyperbola depending on whether the discriminant $B^2 - 4AC$ is zero, negative, or positive. We have proved the following theorem.

A.10.5 Theorem

The graph of the equation

$$Ax^2 + Bxy + Cy^2 + Dx + Ey + F = 0$$

is either a conic or a degenerate conic. If the graph is a conic, then it is

(i) a *parabola* if $B^2 - 4AC = 0$;
(ii) an *ellipse* if $B^2 - 4AC < 0$;
(iii) a *hyperbola* if $B^2 - 4AC > 0$.

▶ **EXAMPLE 3**   (a) Identify the graph of the equation

$$17x^2 - 12xy + 8y^2 - 80 = 0$$

(b) Simplify the equation by a rotation of axes. (c) Sketch the graph of the equation and show both sets of axes.

Solution

(a) From the equation, $A = 17$, $B = -12$, and $C = 8$.

$$B^2 - 4AC = (-12)^2 - 4(17)(8)$$

Because $B^2 - 4AC < 0$, from Theorem A.10.5 the graph is an ellipse or else it degenerates.

(b) To eliminate the xy term by a rotation of axes, we must choose an α such that

$$\cot 2\alpha = \frac{A - C}{B}$$

$$= \frac{17 - 8}{-12}$$

$$= -\tfrac{3}{4}$$

There is a 2α in the interval $(0, \pi)$ for which $\cot 2\alpha = -\tfrac{3}{4}$. Therefore α is in the interval $(0, \tfrac{1}{2}\pi)$. To apply the formulas for rotation of axes, it is not necessary to find α so long as we find $\cos \alpha$ and $\sin \alpha$. These functions can be found from the value of $\cot 2\alpha$ by the trigonometric identities

$$\cos \alpha = \sqrt{\frac{1 + \cos 2\alpha}{2}} \quad \text{and} \quad \sin \alpha = \sqrt{\frac{1 - \cos 2\alpha}{2}}$$

Because $\cot 2\alpha = -\frac{3}{4}$ and $0 < \alpha < \frac{1}{2}\pi$, it follows that $\cos 2\alpha = -\frac{3}{5}$. So

$$\cos \alpha = \sqrt{\frac{1 - \frac{3}{5}}{2}} \quad \text{and} \quad \sin \alpha = \sqrt{\frac{1 + \frac{3}{5}}{2}}$$

$$= \frac{1}{\sqrt{5}} \qquad\qquad = \frac{2}{\sqrt{5}}$$

Substituting $x = \bar{x}/\sqrt{5} - 2\bar{y}/\sqrt{5}$ and $y = 2\bar{x}/\sqrt{5} + \bar{y}/\sqrt{5}$ in the given equation, we obtain

$$17\left(\frac{\bar{x}^2 - 4\bar{x}\,\bar{y} + 4\bar{y}^2}{5}\right) - 12\left(\frac{2\bar{x}^2 - 3\bar{x}\,\bar{y} + 2\bar{y}^2}{5}\right) + 8\left(\frac{4\bar{x}^2 + 4\bar{x}\,\bar{y} + \bar{y}^2}{5}\right) - 80 = 0$$

Upon simplification this equation becomes

$$\bar{x}^2 + 4\bar{y}^2 = 16$$
$$\frac{\bar{x}^2}{16} + \frac{\bar{y}^2}{4} = 1$$

The graph is, therefore, an ellipse whose major axis is 8 units long and whose minor axis is 4 units long.

(c) We apply the information obtained in part (b) to sketch the ellipse. Figure 5 shows this ellipse and both sets of axes. ◀

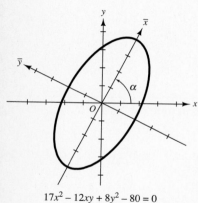

$17x^2 - 12xy + 8y^2 - 80 = 0$

FIGURE 5

As you can see from the above example, sketching the graph of a second-degree equation, having an xy term, by a rotation of axes often requires tedious computations. As shown in the next example, plotting such a graph on a graphics calculator can also entail complicated calculations when you first express y as two functions of x.

▶ **EXAMPLE 4**   Plot the graph of the equation of Example 3.

Solution   The equation defines y as two functions of x. To determine these functions we treat the equation as quadratic in y and write it as

$$8y^2 - 12xy + (17x^2 - 80) = 0$$

From the quadratic formula with $a = 8$, $b = -12x$, and $c = 17x^2 - 80$, we have

$$y = \frac{-b \pm \sqrt{b^2 - 4ac}}{2a}$$

$$= \frac{-(-12x) \pm \sqrt{(-12x)^2 - 4(8)(17x^2 - 80)}}{2(8)}$$

$$= \frac{12x \pm 4\sqrt{160 - 25x^2}}{16}$$

$$= \frac{3x \pm \sqrt{160 - 25x^2}}{4}$$

In the window $[-7.5, 7.5]$ by $[-5, 5]$ we plot the graphs of

$$y_1 = \frac{3x + \sqrt{160 - 25x^2}}{4} \quad \text{and} \quad y_2 = \frac{3x - \sqrt{160 - 25x^2}}{4}$$

to obtain the ellipse in Figure 5. ◀

EXERCISES A.10

In Exercises 1 through 4, identify the graph of the equation as the type of conic or degenerate conic.

1. (a) $x^2 - 4y^2 - 6x - 24y - 31 = 0$
   (b) $4x^2 + y^2 + 8x - 14y - 47 = 0$
   (c) $y^2 + 4x - 8y + 4 = 0$
   (d) $x^2 - 16y^2 = 0$

2. (a) $2x^2 + y^2 + 8x - 2y - 9 = 0$
   (b) $2x^2 - 3y^2 + 16x + 12y + 38 = 0$
   (c) $16y^2 + 24y + 9 = 0$
   (d) $4x^2 + 16x - 3y + 19 = 0$

3. (a) $3x^2 + 5y^2 + 6x - 20y + 23 = 0$
   (b) $4x^2 - 5y^2 + 16x + 10y + 111 = 0$
   (c) $2x^2 - 16x - 5y + 22 = 0$
   (d) $9x^2 + 30x + 29 = 0$

4. (a) $5y^2 + 4x + 10y - 3 = 0$
   (b) $3x^2 + 7y^2 - 6x + 28y + 37 = 0$
   (c) $2x^2 - 3y^2 - 12x - 6y + 15 = 0$
   (d) $4x^2 - 9y^2 - 40x - 54y + 55 = 0$

In Exercises 5 through 8, (a) identify the graph of the equation, (b) find an equation of the graph with respect to the x and y axes after a rotation of axes through an angle of radian measure $\frac{1}{4}\pi$, and (c) sketch the graph and show both sets of axes.

5. $xy = 8$

6. $xy = -4$

7. $x^2 - y^2 = 8$

8. $y^2 - x^2 = 16$

In Exercises 9 through 16, (a) identify the graph of the equation, (b) remove the xy term by a rotation of axes, and (c) sketch the graph and show both sets of axes.

9. $24xy - 7y^2 + 36 = 0$

10. $4xy + 3x^2 = 4$

11. $x^2 + 2xy + y^2 - 8x + 8y = 0$

12. $x^2 + xy + y^2 = 3$

13. $xy + 16 = 0$

14. $5x^2 + 6xy + 5y^2 = 9$

15. $31x^2 + 10\sqrt{3}xy + 21y^2 = 144$

16. $6x^2 + 20\sqrt{3}\,xy + 26y^2 = 324$

In Exercises 17 through 26, (a) identify the graph of the equation, (b) simplify the equation by a rotation and translation of axes, and (c) sketch the graph and show the three sets of axes.

17. $x^2 + xy + y^2 - 3y - 6 = 0$

18. $19x^2 + 6xy + 11y^2 - 26x + 38y + 31 = 0$

19. $17x^2 - 12xy + 8y^2 - 68x + 24y - 12 = 0$

20. $x^2 - 10xy + y^2 + x + y + 1 = 0$

21. $x^2 + 2xy + y^2 + x - y - 4 = 0$

22. $16x^2 - 24xy + 9y^2 - 60x - 80y + 400 = 0$

23. $11x^2 - 24xy + 4y^2 + 30x + 40y - 45 = 0$

24. $3x^2 - 4xy + 8x - 1 = 0$

25. $4x^2 + 4xy + y^2 - 6x + 12 = 0$

26. $x^2 + 2xy + y^2 - x - 3y = 0$

In Exercises 27 through 34, plot the graph of the equation of the indicated exercises.

27. Exercise 9

28. Exercise 10

29. Exercise 11

30. Exercise 12

31. Exercise 17

32. Exercise 18

33. Exercise 21

34. Exercise 22

35. Show that the graph of $\sqrt{x} + \sqrt{y} = 1$ is part of a parabola by rotating the axes through an angle of radian measure $\frac{1}{4}\pi$. *Hint:* Eliminate the radicals in the equation before applying the formulas for rotation of axes.

36. Given the equation $(a^2 + b^2)xy = 1$, where $a > 0$ and $b > 0$, find an equation of the graph with respect to the $\bar{x}$ and $\bar{y}$ axes after a rotation of the axes through an angle of radian measure $\tan^{-1}(b/a)$.

37. Show that for the general second-degree equation in two variables, the discriminant $B^2 - 4AC$ is invariant under a rotation of axes.

38. Derive Equations (5) by solving Equations (4) for x and y in terms of $\bar{x}$ and $\bar{y}$. *Hint:* To solve for x, multiply both sides of the first equation by $\cos \alpha$ and both sides of the second equation by $\sin \alpha$ and then sub-

tract corresponding members of the resulting equations. Use a similar procedure to solve for y.

39. Rotation of axes makes neither a change in the graph nor a change in the position of the graph in the plane. Explain when rotation of axes is an advantage to sketching the graph of a second-degree equation in two variables and when it is a disadvantage.

A.11 PARTIAL FRACTIONS

You already know how to combine two or more rational expressions into one rational expression by addition or subtraction. For example,

$$\frac{3}{x + 2} + \frac{4}{x - 3} = \frac{7x - 1}{(x + 2)(x - 3)}$$

It is sometimes necessary to do the reverse, that is, to express a single rational expression as a sum of two or more simpler quotients, called **partial fractions.** We need to do this in calculus to perform the operation of integration on some rational functions. Often systems of equations are used to decompose a rational expression into partial fractions.

Consider a rational function H defined by

$$H(x) = \frac{P(x)}{Q(x)}$$

where $P(x)$ and $Q(x)$ are polynomials. We shall assume that we have a **proper fraction,** that is, one for which the degree of $P(x)$ is less than the degree of $Q(x)$. If we have a rational function for which the degree of the numerator is not less than the degree of the denominator, then we have an **improper fraction,** and in that case we divide the numerator by the denominator until a proper fraction is obtained. For instance,

$$\frac{x^4 - 10x^2 + 3x + 1}{x^2 - 4} = x^2 - 6 + \frac{3x - 23}{x^2 - 4}$$

In general, then, we are concerned with a method of decomposing a proper fraction of the form $P(x)/Q(x)$ into two or more partial fractions. The denominators of the partial fractions are obtained by factoring $Q(x)$ into a product of linear and quadratic factors. Sometimes it may be difficult to find these factors. However, a theorem from algebra states that a polynomial with real coefficients can be expressed as a product of linear or quadratic polynomials with real coefficients.

After $Q(x)$ has been factored into products of linear or quadratic factors, the method of determining the partial fractions depends on the nature of these factors. We consider various cases separately.

Case 1: The factors of $Q(x)$ are all linear, and none is repeated. That is,

$$Q(x) = (a_1x + b_1)(a_2x + b_1) \cdot \ldots \cdot (a_nx + b_n)$$

where no two of the factors are identical. In this case we write

$$\frac{P(x)}{Q(x)} = \frac{A_1}{a_1x + b_1} + \frac{A_2}{a_2x + b_2} + \ldots + \frac{A_n}{a_nx + b_n}$$

where $A_1, A_2, \ldots, A_n$ are constants to be determined. Observe that this equation is an identity because it is true for each value of x for which a denominator is not zero. The following illustration shows a method for determining the values of A_i.

▷ **ILLUSTRATION 1**   To decompose the fraction

$$\frac{7x - 1}{x^2 - x - 6}$$

into partial fractions, we factor the denominator and obtain

$$\frac{7x - 1}{x^2 - x - 6} = \frac{7x - 1}{(x + 2)(x - 3)}$$

Therefore we have

$$\frac{7x - 1}{(x + 2)(x - 3)} = \frac{A}{x + 2} + \frac{B}{x - 3} \qquad \textbf{(1)}$$

Equation (1) is an identity for all x except -2 and 3. By multiplying on both sides of the equation by the LCD, we obtain

$$7x - 1 = A(x - 3) + B(x + 2)$$

This equation is an identity. It is true for all values of x including -2 and 3. We now find the constants A and B. Substituting 3 for x in the preceding equation, we get

$$20 = 5B \quad \Leftrightarrow \quad B = 4$$

Substituting -2 for x in the same equation, we obtain

$$-15 = -15A \quad \Leftrightarrow \quad A = 3$$

With these values for A and B, we have from (1)

$$\frac{7x - 1}{(x + 2)(x - 3)} = \frac{3}{x + 2} + \frac{4}{x - 3}$$

Observe that this equation is equivalent to the one at the beginning of this section. ◀

▶ **EXAMPLE 1**   Decompose the fraction

$$\frac{x - 1}{x^3 - x^2 - 2x}$$

into partial fractions.

Solution   We factor the denominator and have

$$\frac{x - 1}{x^3 - x^2 - 2x} = \frac{x - 1}{x(x - 2)(x + 1)}$$

Thus we have

$$\frac{x - 1}{x(x - 2)(x + 1)} = \frac{A}{x} + \frac{B}{x - 2} + \frac{C}{x + 1} \qquad \textbf{(2)}$$

Equation (2) is an identity for all x except 0, 2 and -1. We multiply on both sides of the equation by the LCD and get

$$x - 1 = A(x - 2)(x + 1) + Bx(x + 1) + Cx(x - 2)$$

This equation is an identity that is true for all values of x including 0, 2, and -1. To find the constants, we first substitute 0 for x and obtain

$$-1 = -2A \quad \Leftrightarrow \quad A = \tfrac{1}{2}$$

Substituting 2 for x, we get

$$1 = 6B \quad \Leftrightarrow \quad B = \tfrac{1}{6}$$

Substituting -1 for x, we obtain

$$-2 = 3C \quad \Leftrightarrow \quad C = -\tfrac{2}{3}$$

With these values for A, B, and C we have from (2)

$$\frac{x - 1}{x(x - 2)(x + 1)} = \frac{\tfrac{1}{2}}{x} + \frac{\tfrac{1}{6}}{x - 2} + \frac{-\tfrac{2}{3}}{x + 1}$$

$$\Leftrightarrow \quad \frac{x - 1}{x(x - 2)(x + 1)} = \frac{1}{2x} + \frac{1}{6(x - 2)} - \frac{2}{3(x + 1)} \qquad \blacktriangleleft$$

Case 2: The factors of $Q(x)$ are all linear, and some are repeated.

Suppose that $(ax + b)^p$ occurs as a factor of $Q(x)$. Then $ax + b$ is said to be a p-fold factor of $Q(x)$, and corresponding to this factor there will be the sum of p partial fractions.

$$\frac{A_1}{ax + b} + \frac{A_2}{(ax + b)^2} + \cdots + \frac{A_{p-1}}{(ax + b)^{p-1}} + \frac{A_p}{(ax + b)^p}$$

where $A_1, A_2, \ldots, A_p$ are constants to be determined. Example 2 illustrates this case and the method of determining each A_i.

▶ **EXAMPLE 2**   Decompose the fraction

$$\frac{x^4 + x^2 + 16x - 12}{x^3(x - 2)^2}$$

into partial fractions.

Solution   We write the given fraction as a sum of partial fractions as follows:

$$\frac{x^4 + x^2 + 16x - 12}{x^3(x - 2)^2} = \frac{A}{x} + \frac{B}{x^2} + \frac{C}{x^3} + \frac{D}{x - 2} + \frac{E}{(x - 2)^2} \qquad \textbf{(3)}$$

Multiplying on both sides of (3) by the LCD, we get

$$x^4 + x^2 + 16x - 12 = Ax^2(x - 2)^2 + Bx(x - 2)^2 + C(x - 2)^2 + Dx^3(x - 2) + Ex^3 \qquad \textbf{(4)}$$

We substitute 0 for x in this equation and obtain

$$-12 = 4C \quad \Leftrightarrow \quad C = -3$$

Substituting 2 for x in (4), we get

$$40 = 8E \quad \Leftrightarrow \quad E = 5$$

With these values for C and E in (4) and expanding the powers of the binomials, we have

$$x^4 + x^2 + 16x - 12 = Ax^2(x^2 - 4x + 4) + Bx(x^2 - 4x + 4) - 3(x^2 - 4x + 4) + Dx^3(x - 2) + 5x^3$$
$$x^4 + x^2 + 16x - 12 = (A + D)x^4 + (-4A + B - 2D + 5)x^3 + (4A - 4B - 3)x^2 + (4B + 12)x - 12$$

Because this equation is an identity, the coefficients on the left must equal the corresponding coefficients on the right. Therefore we have the following system of equations:

$$\begin{cases} A + D = 1 \\ -4A + B - 2D + 5 = 0 \\ 4A - 4B - 3 = 1 \\ 4B + 12 = 16 \end{cases}$$

From the fourth equation, $B = 1$. Replacing B by 1 in the equation and solving for A, we get $A = 2$. With $A = 2$ in the first equation, we obtain $D = -1$. We use the second equation as a check:

$$-4A + B - 2D + 5 = -4(2) + 1 - 2(-1) + 5$$
$$= 0$$

Thus the values of the constants are as follows:

$$A = 2 \qquad B = 1 \qquad C = -3 \qquad D = -1 \qquad E = 5$$

With these values we have from (3)

$$\frac{x^4 + x^2 + 16x - 12}{x^3(x - 2)^2} = \frac{2}{x} + \frac{1}{x^2} - \frac{3}{x^3} - \frac{1}{x - 2} + \frac{5}{(x - 2)^2} \qquad \blacktriangleleft$$

Case 3: The factors of $Q(x)$ are linear and quadratic, and none of the quadratic factors is repeated.

Corresponding to the quadratic factor $ax^2 + bx + c$ in the denominator is the partial fraction of the form

$$\frac{Ax + B}{ax^2 + bx + c}$$

▶ **EXAMPLE 3** Decompose the fraction

$$\frac{x^2 - x - 5}{x^3 + x^2 - 2}$$

into partial fractions.

Solution   We attempt to factor the denominator by using synthetic division to divide $x^3 + x^2 - 2$ by linear expressions of the form $x - r$, where r is an integer factor of -2. The division by $x - 1$ is as follows:

$$\underline{1|}\quad \begin{array}{cccc} 1 & 1 & 0 & -2 \\ & 1 & 2 & 2 \\ \hline 1 & 2 & 2 & 0 \end{array}$$

Therefore $x^3 + x^2 - 2 = (x - 1)(x^2 + 2x + 2)$. The given fraction is written as a sum of partial fractions in the following way:

$$\frac{x^2 - x - 5}{(x - 1)(x^2 + 2x + 2)} = \frac{Ax + B}{x^2 + 2x + 2} + \frac{C}{x - 1} \tag{5}$$

Multiplying on both sides by the LCD, we have

$$x^2 - x - 5 = (Ax + B)(x - 1) + C(x^2 + 2x + 2) \tag{6}$$

We compute C by substituting 1 for x in (6), and we get

$$-5 = 5C \quad \Leftrightarrow \quad C = -1$$

We replace C by -1 in (6) and multiply on the right side to obtain

$$x^2 - x - 5 = (A - 1)x^2 + (B - A - 2)x + (-B - 2)$$

Equating coefficients of like powers of x gives the system

$$\begin{cases} A - 1 = 1 \\ B - A - 2 = -1 \\ -B - 2 = -5 \end{cases}$$

Therefore

$$A = 2 \qquad B = 3$$

Substituting the values of A, B, and C in (5), we obtain

$$\frac{x^2 - x - 5}{(x - 1)(x^2 + 2x + 2)} = \frac{2x + 3}{x^2 + 2x + 2} - \frac{1}{x - 1} \qquad \blacktriangleleft$$

Case 4: The factors of $Q(x)$ are linear and quadratic, and some of the quadratic factors are repeated.

If $ax^2 + bx + c$ is a p-fold quadratic factor of $Q(x)$, then corresponding to this factor $(ax^2 + bx + c)^p$, we have the sum of the following p partial fractions:

$$\frac{A_1 x + B_1}{ax^2 + bx + c} + \frac{A_2 x + B_2}{(ax^2 + bx + c)^2} + \cdots + \frac{A_p x + B_p}{(ax^2 + bx + c)^p}$$

▷ **ILLUSTRATION 2**   If the denominator contains the factor $(x^2 - 5x + 2)^3$, we have, corresponding to this factor, the sum of partial fractions

$$\frac{Ax + B}{x^2 - 5x + 2} + \frac{Cx + D}{(x^2 - 5x + 2)^2} + \frac{Ex + F}{(x^2 - 5x + 2)^3} \qquad \blacktriangleleft$$

▶ **EXAMPLE 4** Decompose the fraction

$$\frac{3x^4 - 12x^3 + 4x^2 + 11x + 4}{x(x^2 - 3x - 2)^2}$$

into partial fractions.

Solution The given fraction is written as a sum of partial fractions as follows:

$$\frac{3x^4 - 12x^3 + 4x^2 + 11x + 4}{x(x^2 - 3x - 2)^2} = \frac{Ax + B}{x^2 - 3x - 2} + \frac{Cx + D}{(x^2 - 3x - 2)^2} + \frac{E}{x} \qquad (7)$$

We multiply on both sides by the LCD and get

$$3x^4 - 12x^3 + 4x^2 + 11x + 4 = x(Ax + B)(x^2 - 3x - 2) + x(Cx + D) + E(x^2 - 3x - 2)^2 \qquad (8)$$

Substituting 0 for x in this equation, we obtain

$$4 = 4E \quad \Leftrightarrow \quad E = 1$$

With $E = 1$ in (8) and multiplying the polynomials, we get

$$3x^4 - 12x^3 + 4x^2 + 11x + 4$$
$$= Ax^4 - 3Ax^3 - 2Ax^2 + Bx^3 - 3Bx^2 - 2Bx + Cx^2 + Dx + x^4 + 9x^2 + 4 - 6x^3 - 4x^2 + 12x$$
$$= (A + 1)x^4 + (-3A + B - 6)x^3 + (-2A - 3B + C + 5)x^2 + (-2B + D + 12)x + 4$$

We equate the coefficients of corresponding powers of x and obtain the system

$$\begin{cases} A + 1 = 3 \\ -3A + B - 6 = -12 \\ -2A - 3B + C + 5 = 4 \\ -2B + D + 12 = 11 \end{cases}$$

We solve this system to obtain

$$A = 2 \quad B = 0 \quad C = 3 \quad D = -1 \quad E = 1$$

Substituting these values in (7), we have

$$\frac{3x^4 - 12x^3 + 4x^2 + 11x + 4}{x(x^2 - 3x - 2)^2} = \frac{2x}{x^2 - 3x - 2} + \frac{3x - 1}{(x^2 - 3x - 2)^2} + \frac{1}{x} \qquad ◀$$

Observe that in each of the examples, the number of constants to be determined is equal to the degree of the denominator of the original fraction being decomposed into partial fractions. This situation is always the case.

EXERCISES A.11

In Exercises 1 through 10, decompose the fraction into partial fractions.

1. $\dfrac{12}{x^2 - 4}$

2. $\dfrac{1}{2x^2 - x}$

3. $\dfrac{x - 1}{x^2 + x}$

4. $\dfrac{x + 15}{x^2 - 9}$

5. $\dfrac{x + 5}{x^2 - 4x + 3}$

6. $\dfrac{3x}{x^2 + x - 2}$

7. $\dfrac{x + 12}{3x^2 - 5x - 2}$

8. $\dfrac{3x - 7}{4x^2 + 3x - 1}$

9. $\dfrac{3x^2 + 3x - 12}{6x^3 + 5x^2 - 6x}$

10. $\dfrac{2x^2 - 11x - 9}{x^3 - 2x^2 - 3x}$

In Exercises 11 through 14, express the improper fraction as the sum of a polynomial and partial fractions.

11. $\dfrac{2x^3 + 4}{x^2 - 4}$

12. $\dfrac{x^3 + 5}{x^2 - 1}$

13. $\dfrac{4x^3 - 8x^2 - 10x + 30}{2x^2 + x - 6}$

14. $\dfrac{6x^3 + x^2 - 5x - 7}{3x^2 - x - 2}$

In Exercises 15 through 38, decompose the fraction into partial fractions.

15. $\dfrac{3x^2 + 13x - 10}{x^3 - 2x^2}$

16. $\dfrac{x^2 + x + 1}{x^4 - x^3}$

17. $\dfrac{x^2 - 11x + 6}{(x + 2)(x^2 - 4x + 4)}$

18. $\dfrac{x^2 + 11}{(x - 5)(x^2 + 2x + 1)}$

19. $\dfrac{3x + 15}{(2x^2 - x - 1)^2}$

20. $\dfrac{9x^3 - 8x^2 - 4x + 48}{(x^2 - 4)^2}$

21. $\dfrac{x^3 + 6x - 4}{(x - 2)^3}$

22. $\dfrac{x^2 + 2}{(x - 3)^3}$

23. $\dfrac{3x^2 - x + 4}{x^3 + x^2 + x}$

24. $\dfrac{3x + 8}{x^3 + 4x}$

25. $\dfrac{3x^2 + 2x - 4}{x^3 - 8}$

26. $\dfrac{x^2 - 6x + 2}{x^3 + 1}$

27. $\dfrac{2x^2 - 7x + 1}{x^3 - x^2 + x - 1}$

28. $\dfrac{3x^2 - 9x + 8}{x^3 + x^2 + 3x + 3}$

29. $\dfrac{11x^2 + 11x + 8}{2x^3 + 8x^2 + 3x + 12}$

30. $\dfrac{3x^2 + 2x + 3}{x^4 + x^3 + x^2 + x}$

31. $\dfrac{3x^2 - 4x}{(x^2 + 1)(x^2 - x - 1)}$

32. $\dfrac{4x - 3}{x^4 + 2x^3 + 3x^2}$

33. $\dfrac{x + 6}{x^4 + 2x^3 + 3x^2}$

34. $\dfrac{3x^4 + 4}{x^4 + 4x^2 + 4}$

35. $\dfrac{x^3 - x^2}{x^4 + 2x^2 + 1}$

36. $\dfrac{x^4 + 2x^2 - 2x - 4}{(x^2 + 3)^3}$

37. $\dfrac{x^4 + x^3 - 5x^2 - 14x - 1}{x^5 - x^4 + 4x^3 - 4x^2 + 4x - 4}$

38. $\dfrac{11x - 28}{x^5 + 2x^4 + 2x^3 + 4x^2 + x + 2}$

SUPPLEMENTARY SECTIONS

1.5 SUPPLEMENT

▶ **EXAMPLE 6**   Use the definition of a limit to prove that

$$\lim_{x \to 2} x^2 = 4$$

SOLUTION   Because x^2 is defined for all real numbers, any open interval containing 2 will satisfy the first requirement of Definition 1.5.1. We must show that for any $\epsilon > 0$ there exists a $\delta > 0$ such that

$$\text{if} \quad 0 < |x - 2| < \delta \quad \text{then} \quad |x^2 - 4| < \epsilon$$
$$\Leftrightarrow \text{if} \quad 0 < |x - 2| < \delta \quad \text{then} \quad |x - 2||x + 2| < \epsilon \tag{4}$$

Observe that on the right end of (4), in addition to the factor $|x - 2|$ we have the factor $|x + 2|$. Thus to prove (4) we wish to place a restriction on δ that will give us an inequality involving $|x + 2|$. Such a restriction is to choose the open interval required by Definition 1.5.1 to be the interval (1, 3), and this implies that $\delta \le 1$. Then

$$0 < |x - 2| < \delta \quad \text{and} \quad \delta \le 1$$
$$\Rightarrow \quad 0 < |x - 2| < 1$$
$$\Rightarrow \quad -1 < x - 2 < 1$$
$$\Rightarrow \quad 3 < x + 2 < 5$$
$$\Rightarrow \quad |x + 2| < 5$$

Thus

$$0 < |x - 2| < \delta \quad \text{and} \quad \delta \le 1$$
$$\Rightarrow \quad 0 < |x - 2| < \delta \quad \text{and} \quad |x + 2| < 5$$
$$\Rightarrow \quad |x - 2||x + 2| < \delta \cdot 5$$

Remember statement (4) is our goal. Thus we should require that

$$\delta \cdot 5 \le \epsilon \quad \Leftrightarrow \quad \delta \le \epsilon/5$$

We have now put two restrictions on δ: $\delta \le 1$ and $\delta \le \epsilon/5$. So that both restrictions hold we take δ as the smaller of the two numbers 1 and $\epsilon/5$; with symbols we write this as $\delta = \min(1, \epsilon/5)$. Using this δ, we have the following argument:

$$0 < |x - 2| < \delta$$
$$\Rightarrow \quad |x - 2| < \frac{\epsilon}{5} \quad \text{and} \quad |x + 2| < 5$$
$$\Rightarrow \quad |x - 2||x + 2| < \frac{\epsilon}{5} \cdot 5$$
$$\Rightarrow \quad |x^2 - 4| < \epsilon$$

We have, therefore, demonstrated that for any $\epsilon > 0$ the choice of $\delta = \min(1, \epsilon/5)$ makes the following statement true:

$$\text{if} \quad 0 < |x - 2| < \delta \quad \text{then} \quad |x^2 - 4| < \epsilon$$

This proves that $\lim_{x \to 2} x^2 = 4$.   ◀

1.5.5 Limit Theorem 4   Limit of the Sum and Difference of Two Functions

If $\lim_{x \to a} f(x) = L$ and $\lim_{x \to a} g(x) = M$, then

$$\lim_{x \to a} [f(x) \pm g(x)] = L \pm M$$

Proof   We shall prove the theorem with the plus sign. Given

$$\lim_{x \to a} f(x) = L \tag{5}$$

and

$$\lim_{x \to a} g(x) = M \tag{6}$$

we wish to prove that

$$\lim_{x \to a} [f(x) + g(x)] = L + M$$

We use Definition 1.5.1; that is, for any $\epsilon > 0$ we must show that there exists a $\delta > 0$ such that

$$\text{if} \quad 0 < |x - a| < \delta \quad \text{then} \quad |[f(x) + g(x)] - (L + M)| < \epsilon \tag{7}$$

Because (5) is given, it follows from the definition of a limit that for $\frac{1}{2}\epsilon > 0$ there exists a $\delta_1 > 0$ such that

$$\text{if} \quad 0 < |x - a| < \delta_1 \quad \text{then} \quad |f(x) - L| < \tfrac{1}{2}\epsilon$$

Similarly, from (6), for $\frac{1}{2}\epsilon > 0$ there exists a $\delta_2 > 0$ such that

$$\text{if} \quad 0 < |x - a| < \delta_2 \quad \text{then} \quad |g(x) - M| < \tfrac{1}{2}\epsilon$$

Now let δ be the smaller of the two numbers δ_1 and δ_2. Therefore $\delta \le \delta_1$ and $\delta \le \delta_2$. So

$$\text{if} \quad 0 < |x - a| < \delta \quad \text{then} \quad |f(x) - L| < \tfrac{1}{2}\epsilon$$

and

$$\text{if} \quad 0 < |x - a| < \delta \quad \text{then} \quad |g(x) - M| < \tfrac{1}{2}\epsilon$$

Hence if $0 < |x - a| < \delta$, then

$$
\begin{aligned}
|[f(x) + g(x)] - (L + M)| &= |(f(x) - L) + (g(x) - M)| \\
&\le |f(x) - L| + |g(x) - M| \\
&< \tfrac{1}{2}\epsilon + \tfrac{1}{2}\epsilon \\
&= \epsilon
\end{aligned}
$$

In this way we have obtained statement (7), thereby proving that

$$\lim_{x \to a} [f(x) + g(x)] = L + M$$

■

The proof of Limit Theorem 4 using the minus sign is left as an exercise (see Supplementary Exercise 9).

The proof of Limit Theorem 6 (1.5.7) is more sophisticated than those of Limit Theorems 1–5. The steps of the proof are indicated in Supplementary Exercises 11 and 12.

1.5.12 Theorem

If a is any real number except zero

$$\lim_{x \to a} \frac{1}{x} = \frac{1}{a}$$

Proof   We prove the theorem if $a > 0$. The proof for $a < 0$ is left as an exercise (see Supplementary Exercise 14).

Because $1/x$ is defined for every x except zero, the open interval required by Definition 1.5.1 can be any open interval containing a but not containing 0. We must show that for any $\epsilon > 0$ there exists a $\delta > 0$ such that

$$\text{if} \quad 0 < |x - a| < \delta \quad \text{then} \quad \left| \frac{1}{x} - \frac{1}{a} \right| < \epsilon \tag{8}$$

Because

$$\left| \frac{1}{x} - \frac{1}{a} \right| = \left| \frac{a - x}{ax} \right|$$

$$= \frac{|x - a|}{|a|\,|x|}$$

$$= |x - a| \cdot \frac{1}{a|x|} \qquad \text{(because } a > 0\text{)}$$

statement (8) is equivalent to

$$\text{if} \quad 0 < |x - a| < \delta \quad \text{then} \quad |x - a| \cdot \frac{1}{a|x|} < \epsilon \tag{9}$$

On the right end of (9), in addition to the factor $|x - a|$ we have the quotient $\dfrac{1}{a|x|}$. Therefore, to prove (9) we need to restrict δ so that we will have an inequality involving $\dfrac{1}{a|x|}$. By choosing the open interval required by Definition 1.5.1 to be the interval $(\tfrac{1}{2}a, \tfrac{3}{2}a)$, which contains a but not 0, we are implying that $\delta \le \tfrac{1}{2}a$. Then

$$0 < |x - a| < \delta \quad \text{and} \quad \delta \le \tfrac{1}{2}a$$

$$\Rightarrow \qquad |x - a| < \tfrac{1}{2}a$$

$$\Rightarrow \quad -\tfrac{1}{2}a < x - a < \tfrac{1}{2}a$$

$$\Rightarrow \qquad \tfrac{1}{2}a < x < \tfrac{3}{2}a$$

$$\Rightarrow \qquad \tfrac{1}{2}a < |x| < \tfrac{3}{2}a \qquad \text{(because } a > 0\text{)}$$

$$\Rightarrow \qquad \frac{2}{3a} < \frac{1}{|x|} < \frac{2}{a}$$

$$\Rightarrow \qquad \frac{2}{3a^2} < \frac{1}{a|x|} < \frac{2}{a^2} \tag{10}$$

Now

$$0 < |x - a| < \delta \quad \text{and} \quad \frac{1}{a|x|} < \frac{2}{a^2}$$

$$\Rightarrow \quad |x - a| \cdot \frac{1}{a|x|} < \delta \cdot \frac{2}{a^2} \qquad \qquad \textbf{(11)}$$

Because our goal is to have $|x - a| \cdot \dfrac{1}{a|x|} < \epsilon$, statement (11) indicates that we should require $\delta \cdot \dfrac{2}{a^2} \leq \epsilon$, that is, $\delta \leq \frac{1}{2}a^2\epsilon$. Thus with the two restrictions on δ we choose $\delta = \min(\frac{1}{2}a, \frac{1}{2}a^2\epsilon)$. With this δ we have the following argument:

$$0 < |x - a| < \delta$$

$$\Rightarrow \quad |x - a| \cdot \frac{1}{a|x|} < \delta \cdot \frac{1}{a|x|}$$

$$\Rightarrow \quad \frac{|x - a|}{|a||x|} < \delta \cdot \frac{1}{a|x|} \qquad \text{(because } a > 0\text{)}$$

$$\Rightarrow \quad \left| \frac{a - x}{ax} \right| < \delta \cdot \frac{1}{a|x|}$$

$$\Rightarrow \quad \left| \frac{1}{x} - \frac{1}{a} \right| < \delta \cdot \frac{1}{a|x|}$$

$$\Rightarrow \quad \left| \frac{1}{x} - \frac{1}{a} \right| < \delta \cdot \frac{2}{a^2} \qquad \text{(from (10))}$$

$$\Rightarrow \quad \left| \frac{1}{x} - \frac{1}{a} \right| < \frac{1}{2}a^2\epsilon \cdot \frac{2}{a^2} \qquad \text{(because } \delta \leq \frac{1}{2}a^2\epsilon\text{)}$$

$$\Rightarrow \quad \left| \frac{1}{x} - \frac{1}{a} \right| < \epsilon$$

Thus we have shown that for any $\epsilon > 0$, if $\delta = \min(\frac{1}{2}a, \frac{1}{2}a^2\epsilon)$, then the following statement is true:

$$\text{if} \quad 0 < |x - a| < \delta \quad \text{then} \quad \left| \frac{1}{x} - \frac{1}{a} \right| < \epsilon$$

which is statement (8). ∎

The proof of Theorem 1.5.13 makes use of the following formula, where n is any positive integer:

$$a^n - b^n = (a - b)(a^{n-1} + a^{n-2}b + a^{n-3}b^2 + \ldots + ab^{n-2} + b^{n-1}) \qquad \textbf{(12)}$$

This formula follows from

$$a(a^{n-1} + a^{n-2}b + \ldots + ab^{n-2} + b^{n-1}) = a^n + a^{n-1}b + \ldots + ab^{n-1}$$

and

$$b(a^{n-1} + a^{n-2}b + \ldots + ab^{n-2} + b^{n-1}) = a^{n-1}b + \ldots + ab^{n-1} + b^n$$

by subtracting the terms of the second equation from those of the first.

1.5.13 Theorem

If $a > 0$ and n is a positive integer, or if $a \leq 0$ and n is an odd positive integer, then

$$\lim_{x \to a} \sqrt[n]{x} = \sqrt[n]{a}$$

Proof We prove the theorem if $a > 0$ and n is a positive integer. The case when $a \leq 0$ and n is an odd positive integer is left as an exercise (see Supplementary Exercise 15).

Because $\sqrt[n]{x}$ is defined for every nonnegative number, the open interval required by Definition 1.5.1 can be any open interval containing a and having a nonnegative number as its left endpoint. We must show that for any $\epsilon > 0$ there exists a $\delta > 0$ such that

$$\text{if} \quad 0 < |x - a| < \delta \quad \text{then} \quad |\sqrt[n]{x} - \sqrt[n]{a}| < \epsilon \tag{13}$$

To express $|\sqrt[n]{x} - \sqrt[n]{a}|$ in terms of $|x - a|$ we use (12)

$$|\sqrt[n]{x} - \sqrt[n]{a}| = \left| \frac{(x^{1/n} - a^{1/n})[(x^{1/n})^{n-1} + (x^{1/n})^{n-2}a^{1/n} + \ldots + x^{1/n}(a^{1/n})^{n-2} + (a^{1/n})^{n-1}]}{(x^{1/n})^{n-1} + (x^{1/n})^{n-2}a^{1/n} + \ldots + x^{1/n}(a^{1/n})^{n-2} + (a^{1/n})^{n-1}} \right|$$

If (12) is applied to the numerator,

$$|\sqrt[n]{x} - \sqrt[n]{a}| = |x - a| \cdot \left| \frac{1}{x^{(n-1)/n} + x^{(n-2)/n}a^{1/n} + \ldots + x^{1/n}a^{(n-2)/n} + a^{(n-1)/n}} \right|$$

In the above equation we let

$$|\phi(x)| = |x^{(n-1)/n} + x^{(n-2)/n}a^{1/n} + \ldots + x^{1/n}a^{(n-2)/n} + a^{(n-1)/n}|$$

and obtain

$$|\sqrt[n]{x} - \sqrt[n]{a}| = |x - a| \cdot \frac{1}{|\phi(x)|} \tag{14}$$

Thus statement (13) is equivalent to

$$\text{if} \quad 0 < |x - a| < \delta \quad \text{then} \quad |x - a| \cdot \frac{1}{|\phi(x)|} < \epsilon \tag{15}$$

On the right end of (15), in addition to the factor $|x - a|$ we have the fraction $\dfrac{1}{|\phi(x)|}$. Hence to prove (15) we need to restrict δ so that we will have an inequality involving this fraction. If we choose the open interval stipulated in Definition 1.5.1 as the interval $(0, 2a)$, we are requiring that $\delta \leq a$. Then

$$0 < |x - a| < \delta \quad \text{and} \quad \delta \leq a$$

$$\Rightarrow \quad |x - a| < a$$

$$\Rightarrow \quad -a < x - a < a$$

$$\Rightarrow \quad 0 < x < 2a$$

$$\Rightarrow \quad a^{(n-1)/n} < |\phi(x)| \qquad \text{(because } x > 0\text{)}$$

$$\Rightarrow \quad \frac{1}{|\phi(x)|} < \frac{1}{a^{(n-1)/n}} \tag{16}$$

Now

$$0 < |x - a| < \delta \quad \text{and} \quad \frac{1}{|\phi(x)|} < \frac{1}{a^{(n-1)/n}}$$

$$\Rightarrow \quad |x - a| \cdot \frac{1}{|\phi(x)|} < \delta \cdot \frac{1}{a^{(n-1)/n}} \qquad (17)$$

Our goal is to have $|x - a| \cdot \dfrac{1}{|\phi(x)|} < \epsilon$. Thus statement (17) tells us that we should require $\delta \cdot \dfrac{1}{a^{(n-1)/n}} \leq \epsilon$, that is, $\delta \leq a^{(n-1)/n}\epsilon$. Thus we choose $\delta = \min(a, a^{(n-1)/n}\epsilon)$. With this δ we have the following argument:

$$0 < |x - a| < \delta$$

$$\Rightarrow \quad |x - a| \cdot \frac{1}{|\phi(x)|} < \delta \cdot \frac{1}{|\phi(x)|}$$

$$\Rightarrow \quad |\sqrt[n]{x} - \sqrt[n]{a}| < \delta \cdot \frac{1}{|\phi(x)|} \qquad \text{(from (14))}$$

$$\Rightarrow \quad |\sqrt[n]{x} - \sqrt[n]{a}| < \delta \cdot \frac{1}{a^{(n-1)/n}} \qquad \text{(from (16))}$$

$$\Rightarrow \quad |\sqrt[n]{x} - \sqrt[n]{a}| < a^{(n-1)/n}\epsilon \cdot \frac{1}{a^{(n-1)/n}} \qquad \text{(because } \delta \leq a^{(n-1)/n}\epsilon\text{)}$$

$$\Rightarrow \quad |\sqrt[n]{x} - \sqrt[n]{a}| < \epsilon$$

We have demonstrated that for any $\epsilon > 0$, if $\delta = \min(a, a^{(n-1)/n}\epsilon)$, then

$$\text{if} \quad 0 < |x - a| < \delta \quad \text{then} \quad |\sqrt[n]{x} - \sqrt[n]{a}| < \epsilon$$

which is statement (13).

■

1.5.16 Theorem

If $\lim\limits_{x \to a} f(x) = L_1$ and $\lim\limits_{x \to a} f(x) = L_2$, then $L_1 = L_2$

Proof We shall assume that $L_1 \neq L_2$, and show that this assumption leads to a contradiction. Because $\lim\limits_{x \to a} f(x) = L_1$, it follows from Definition 1.5.1 that for any $\epsilon > 0$ there exists a $\delta_1 > 0$ such that

$$\text{if} \quad 0 < |x - a| < \delta_1 \quad \text{then} \quad |f(x) - L_1| < \epsilon \qquad (18)$$

Also, because $\lim\limits_{x \to a} f(x) = L_2$, there exists a $\delta_2 > 0$ such that

$$\text{if} \quad 0 < |x - a| < \delta_2 \quad \text{then} \quad |f(x) - L_2| < \epsilon \qquad (19)$$

Now, writing $L_1 - L_2$ as $L_1 - f(x) + f(x) - L_2$ and applying the triangle inequality we have

$$|L_1 - L_2| = |[L_1 - f(x)] + [f(x) - L_2]|$$
$$\leq |L_1 - f(x)| + |f(x) - L_2| \qquad (20)$$

So from (18), (19), and (20) we may conclude that for any $\epsilon > 0$ there exists a $\delta_1 > 0$ and a $\delta_2 > 0$ such that

$$\text{if } 0 < |x - a| < \delta_1 \text{ and } 0 < |x - a| < \delta_2 \text{ then } |L_1 - L_2| < \epsilon + \epsilon \quad \textbf{(21)}$$

If δ is the smaller of δ_1 and δ_2, then $\delta \leq \delta_1$ and $\delta \leq \delta_2$, and (21) states that for any $\epsilon > 0$ there exists a $\delta > 0$ such that

$$\text{if } 0 < |x - a| < \delta \quad \text{then} \quad |L_1 - L_2| < 2\epsilon \quad \textbf{(22)}$$

However, if $\epsilon = \frac{1}{2}|L_1 - L_2|$, then (22) states that there exists a $\delta > 0$ such that

$$\text{if } 0 < |x - a| < \delta \quad \text{then} \quad |L_1 - L_2| < |L_1 - L_2|$$

Obviously $|L_1 - L_2|$ is not less than itself. So we have a contradiction and our assumption is false. Thus $L_1 = L_2$, and the theorem is proved. ∎

SUPPLEMENTARY EXERCISES 1.5

In Exercises 1 through 8, prove the limit is the indicated number by applying Definition 1.5.1.

1. $\lim_{x \to 1} x^2 = 1$
2. $\lim_{x \to -3} x^2 = 9$
3. $\lim_{x \to 5} (x^2 - 3x) = 10$
4. $\lim_{x \to 2} (x^2 + 2x - 1) = 7$
5. $\lim_{x \to -3} (5 - x - x^2) = -1$
6. $\lim_{x \to -1} (3 + 2x - x^2) = 0$
7. $\lim_{x \to 2} (6x^2 - 13x + 5) = 3$
8. $\lim_{x \to 1} (4x^2 - 13x + 12) = 3$

9. Use Definition 1.5.1 to prove that if

$$\lim_{x \to a} f(x) = L \quad \text{and} \quad \lim_{x \to a} g(x) = M$$

then

$$\lim_{x \to a} [f(x) - g(x)] = L - M$$

10. Prove Limit Theorem 5 by applying Limit Theorem 4 and mathematical induction.

11. Use Definition 1.5.1 to prove that if

$$\lim_{x \to a} f(x) = L \quad \text{and} \quad \lim_{x \to a} g(x) = 0$$

then

$$\lim_{x \to a} [f(x) \cdot g(x)] = 0$$

Hint: To prove that $\lim_{x \to a} [f(x) \cdot g(x)] = 0$ we must show that for any $\epsilon > 0$ there exists a $\delta > 0$ such that if $0 < |x - a| < \delta$, then $|f(x) \cdot g(x)| < \epsilon$. First show that there is a $\delta_1 > 0$ such that if $0 < |x - a| < \delta_1$, then $|f(x)| < 1 + |L|$, by applying Definition 1.5.1 to $\lim_{x \to a} f(x) = L$ with $\epsilon = 1$ and $\delta = \delta_1$, and then use the triangle inequality. Then show that there is a $\delta_2 > 0$ such that if $0 < |x - a| < \delta_2$, then $|g(x)| < \epsilon/(1 + |L|)$ by applying Definition 1.5.1 to $\lim_{x \to a} g(x) = 0$. By taking δ as the smaller of the two numbers δ_1 and δ_2, the theorem is proved.

12. Prove Limit Theorem 6: If $\lim_{x \to a} f(x) = L$ and $\lim_{x \to a} g(x) = M$, then

$$\lim_{x \to a} [f(x) \cdot g(x)] = L \cdot M$$

Hint: Let

$$f(x) \cdot g(x) = [f(x) - L]g(x) + L[g(x) - M] + L \cdot M.$$

Apply Limit Theorem 5 and the result of Supplementary Exercise 11.

13. Prove Limit Theorem 7 by applying Limit Theorem 6 and mathematical induction.

14. Prove Theorem 1.5.12 if $a < 0$.

15. Prove Theorem 1.5.13 if $a \leq 0$ and n is an odd positive integer.

1.7 SUPPLEMENT

1.7.4 Limit Theorem 12

If a is any real number, and if $\lim\limits_{x \to a} f(x) = 0$ and $\lim\limits_{x \to a} g(x) = c$, where c is a constant not equal to 0, then

(i) if $c > 0$ and if $f(x) \to 0$ through positive values of $f(x)$,

$$\lim_{x \to a} \frac{g(x)}{f(x)} = +\infty$$

(ii) if $c > 0$ and if $f(x) \to 0$ through negative values of $f(x)$,

$$\lim_{x \to a} \frac{g(x)}{f(x)} = -\infty$$

(iii) if $c < 0$ and if $f(x) \to 0$ through positive values of $f(x)$,

$$\lim_{x \to a} \frac{g(x)}{f(x)} = -\infty$$

(iv) if $c < 0$ and if $f(x) \to 0$ through negative values of $f(x)$,

$$\lim_{x \to a} \frac{g(x)}{f(x)} = +\infty$$

The theorem is also valid if "$x \to a$" is replaced by "$x \to a^+$" or "$x \to a^-$."

Proof of Part (i)   To prove that

$$\lim_{x \to a} \frac{g(x)}{f(x)} = +\infty$$

we must show that for any $N > 0$ there exists a $\delta > 0$ such that

$$\text{if} \quad 0 < |x - a| < \delta \quad \text{then} \quad \frac{g(x)}{f(x)} > N \tag{7}$$

Since $\lim\limits_{x \to a} g(x) = c > 0$, by taking $\epsilon = \frac{1}{2}c$ in Definition 1.5.1 it follows that there exists a $\delta_1 > 0$ such that

$$\text{if} \quad 0 < |x - a| < \delta_1 \quad \text{then} \quad |g(x) - c| < \tfrac{1}{2}c$$
$$\Leftrightarrow \quad \text{if} \quad 0 < |x - a| < \delta_1 \quad \text{then} \quad -\tfrac{1}{2}c < g(x) - c < \tfrac{1}{2}c$$
$$\Leftrightarrow \quad \text{if} \quad 0 < |x - a| < \delta_1 \quad \text{then} \quad \tfrac{1}{2}c < g(x) < \tfrac{3}{2}c$$

So there exists a $\delta_1 > 0$ such that

$$\text{if} \quad 0 < |x - a| < \delta_1 \quad \text{then} \quad g(x) > \tfrac{1}{2}c \tag{8}$$

Now $\lim\limits_{x \to a} f(x) = 0$. Thus for any $\epsilon > 0$ there exists a $\delta_2 > 0$ such that

$$\text{if} \quad 0 < |x - a| < \delta_2 \quad \text{then} \quad |f(x)| < \epsilon$$

Since $f(x)$ is approaching zero through positive values of $f(x)$, the absolute value bars around $f(x)$ can be removed; hence for any $\epsilon > 0$ there exists a $\delta_2 > 0$ such that

$$\text{if} \quad 0 < |x - a| < \delta_2 \quad \text{then} \quad 0 < f(x) < \epsilon \tag{9}$$

From statements (8) and (9) we can conclude that for any $\epsilon > 0$ there exist a $\delta_1 > 0$ and a $\delta_2 > 0$ such that

$$\text{if} \quad 0 < |x - a| < \delta_1 \quad \text{and} \quad 0 < |x - a| < \delta_2 \quad \text{then} \quad \frac{g(x)}{f(x)} > \frac{\frac{1}{2}c}{\epsilon}$$

Hence, if $\epsilon = c/(2N)$ and $\delta = \min(\delta_1, \delta_2)$, then

$$\text{if} \quad 0 < |x - a| < \delta \quad \text{then} \quad \frac{g(x)}{f(x)} > \frac{\frac{1}{2}c}{c/(2N)} = N$$

which is statement (7). Hence part (i) is proved.   ∎

SUPPLEMENTARY EXERCISES 1.7

1. Prove that $\lim\limits_{x \to 2} \dfrac{3}{(x - 2)^2} = +\infty$ by using Definition 1.7.1.

2. Prove that $\lim\limits_{x \to 4} \dfrac{-2}{(x - 4)^2} = -\infty$ by using Definition 1.7.2.

3. Prove part (ii) of Limit Theorem 11 (1.7.3).

4. Prove part (ii) of Limit Theorem 12 (1.7.4).

5. Prove part (iii) of Limit Theorem 12 (1.7.4).

6. Prove part (iv) of Limit Theorem 12 (1.7.4).

7. Prove Theorem 1.7.5.

8. Prove Theorem 1.7.6.

9. Prove Theorem 1.7.7.

10. Use Definition 1.7.1 to prove that

$$\lim_{x \to -3} \left| \frac{5 - x}{3 + x} \right| = +\infty.$$

1.10 SUPPLEMENT

1.10.1 The Squeeze Theorem

Suppose that the functions f, g, and h are defined on some open interval I containing a except possibly at a itself, and that $f(x) \leq g(x) \leq h(x)$ for all x in I for which $x \neq a$. Also suppose that $\lim\limits_{x \to a} f(x)$ and $\lim\limits_{x \to a} h(x)$ both exist and are equal to L. Then $\lim\limits_{x \to a} g(x)$ exists and is equal to L.

Proof   To prove that $\lim\limits_{x \to a} g(x) = L$ we must show that for any $\epsilon > 0$ there is a $\delta > 0$ such that

$$\text{if} \quad 0 < |x - a| < \delta \quad \text{then} \quad |g(x) - L| < \epsilon \tag{19}$$

We are given that

$$\lim_{x \to a} f(x) = L \quad \text{and} \quad \lim_{x \to a} h(x) = L$$

and so for any $\epsilon > 0$ there is a $\delta_1 > 0$ such that

$$\text{if} \quad 0 < |x - a| < \delta_1 \quad \text{then} \quad |f(x) - L| < \epsilon$$
$$\Leftrightarrow \quad \text{if} \quad 0 < |x - a| < \delta_1 \quad \text{then} \quad L - \epsilon < f(x) < L + \epsilon \quad \text{(20)}$$

and a $\delta_2 > 0$ such that

$$\text{if} \quad 0 < |x - a| < \delta_2 \quad \text{then} \quad |h(x) - L| < \epsilon$$
$$\Leftrightarrow \quad \text{if} \quad 0 < |x - a| < \delta_2 \quad \text{then} \quad L - \epsilon < h(x) < L + \epsilon \quad \text{(21)}$$

Let $\delta = \min(\delta_1, \delta_2)$, and so $\delta \leq \delta_1$ and $\delta \leq \delta_2$. Therefore it follows from statement (20) that

$$\text{if} \quad 0 < |x - a| < \delta \quad \text{then} \quad L - \epsilon < f(x) \quad \text{(22)}$$

and from statement (21) that

$$\text{if} \quad 0 < |x - a| < \delta \quad \text{then} \quad h(x) < L + \epsilon \quad \text{(23)}$$

We are given that

$$f(x) \leq g(x) \leq h(x) \quad \text{(24)}$$

From statements (22), (23), and (24),

$$\text{if} \quad 0 < |x - a| < \delta \quad \text{then} \quad L - \epsilon < f(x) \leq g(x) \leq h(x) < L + \epsilon$$

Therefore

$$\text{if} \quad 0 < |x - a| < \delta \quad \text{then} \quad L - \epsilon < g(x) < L + \epsilon$$
$$\Leftrightarrow \quad \text{if} \quad 0 < |x - a| < \delta \quad \text{then} \quad |g(x) - L| < \epsilon$$

which is statement (19). Hence

$$\lim_{x \to a} g(x) = L$$

∎

2.8 SUPPLEMENT

An important part of the proof of the chain rule consists of introducing a new function F that has useful properties. This device of "making up" a function is a common one for mathematicians.

2.8.1 Theorem   The Chain Rule

If the function g is differentiable at x and the function f is differentiable at $g(x)$, then the composite function $f \circ g$ is differentiable at x and

$$(f \circ g)'(x) = f'(g(x))g'(x) \quad \text{(15)}$$

Proof   Let x_1 be any number in the domain of g such that g is differentiable at x_1 and f is differentiable at $g(x_1)$. Form the function F defined by

$$F(t) = \begin{cases} \dfrac{f(t) - f(g(x_1))}{t - g(x_1)} & \text{if } t \neq g(x_1) \\ f'(g(x_1)) & \text{if } t = g(x_1) \end{cases} \quad \text{(16)}$$

Then

$$\lim_{t \to g(x_1)} F(t) = \lim_{t \to g(x_1)} \frac{f(t) - f(g(x_1))}{t - g(x_1)}$$

From (7) in Section 2.1, the function on the right-hand side of this equation is $f'(g(x_1))$. Therefore

$$\lim_{t \to g(x_1)} F(t) = f'(g(x_1)) \tag{17}$$

But from (16)

$$f'(g(x_1)) = F(g(x_1))$$

Substituting from this equation into (17) we get

$$\lim_{t \to g(x_1)} F(t) = F(g(x_1))$$

Therefore F is continuous at $g(x_1)$. Furthermore, from (16),

$$F(t) = \frac{f(t) - f(g(x_1))}{t - g(x_1)} \qquad \text{if } t \neq g(x_1)$$

Multiplying both sides of this equation by $t - g(x_1)$ gives

$$f(t) - f(g(x_1)) = F(t)[t - g(x_1)] \qquad \text{if } t \neq g(x_1) \tag{18}$$

Observe that (18) holds even if $t = g(x_1)$ because the left-hand side is

$$f(g(x_1)) - f(g(x_1)) = 0$$

and the right-hand side is

$$F(g(x_1))[g(x_1) - g(x_1)] = 0$$

Therefore the stipulation in (18) that $t \neq g(x_1)$ is not necessary, and we write

$$f(t) - f(g(x_1)) = F(t)[t - g(x_1)] \tag{19}$$

Now let h be the composite function $f \circ g$, so that

$$h(x) = f(g(x)) \tag{20}$$

Then from (7) in Section 2.1, if the limit exists,

$$h'(x_1) = \lim_{x \to x_1} \frac{h(x) - h(x_1)}{x - x_1}$$

Substituting from (20) in the right-hand side of this equation we get

$$h'(x_1) = \lim_{x \to x_1} \frac{f(g(x)) - f(g(x_1))}{x - x_1} \tag{21}$$

if the limit exists. Now by letting $t = g(x)$ in (19) it follows that for every x in the domain of g such that $g(x)$ is in the domain of f,

$$f(g(x)) - f(g(x_1)) = F(g(x))[g(x) - g(x_1)]$$

Substituting from this equation into (21) we have

$$h'(x_1) = \lim_{x \to x_1} \frac{F(g(x))[g(x) - g(x_1)]}{x - x_1}$$

Thus if the limits exist,

$$h'(x_1) = \lim_{x \to x_1} F(g(x)) \cdot \lim_{x \to x_1} \frac{g(x) - g(x_1)}{x - x_1} \tag{22}$$

Because F is continuous at $g(x_1)$,

$$\lim_{x \to x_1} F(g(x)) = F(g(x_1)) \tag{23}$$

But from (16),

$$F(g(x_1)) = f'(g(x_1))$$

Substituting from this equation into (23) we get

$$\lim_{x \to x_1} F(g(x)) = f'(g(x_1)) \tag{24}$$

Furthermore, because g is differentiable at x_1,

$$\lim_{x \to x_1} \frac{g(x) - g(x_1)}{x - x_1} = g'(x_1)$$

Substituting from (24) and this equation into (22) and replacing $h'(x_1)$ by $(f \circ g)'(x_1)$ we have

$$(f \circ g)'(x_1) = f'(g(x_1)) \cdot g'(x_1)$$

which is (15) with x replaced by x_1. Thus we have proved the chain rule. ∎

4.5 SUPPLEMENT

4.5.11 Theorem

If the functions f and g are integrable on $[a, b]$, then $f + g$ is integrable on $[a, b]$ and

$$\int_a^b [f(x) + g(x)] \, dx = \int_a^b f(x) \, dx + \int_a^b g(x) \, dx$$

Proof   The functions f and g are integrable on $[a, b]$; thus let

$$\int_a^b f(x) \, dx = M \quad \text{and} \quad \int_a^b g(x) \, dx = N$$

To prove that $\int_a^b [f(x) + g(x)] \, dx = M + N$, we must show that for any $\epsilon > 0$ there exists a $\delta > 0$ such that for all partitions Δ and for any w_i in $[x_{i-1}, x_i]$, if $\|\Delta\| < \delta$, then

$$\left| \sum_{i=1}^n [f(w_i) + g(w_i)] \, \Delta_i x - (M + N) \right| < \epsilon$$

Because

$$M = \lim_{\|\Delta\| \to 0} \sum_{i=1}^n f(w_i) \, \Delta_i x \quad \text{and} \quad N = \lim_{\|\Delta\| \to 0} \sum_{i=1}^n g(w_i) \, \Delta_i x$$

it follows that for any $\epsilon > 0$ there exist a $\delta_1 > 0$ and a $\delta_2 > 0$ such that for all partitions Δ and for any w_i in $[x_{i-1}, x_i]$, if $\|\Delta\| < \delta_1$ and $\|\Delta\| < \delta_2$, then

$$\left| \sum_{i=1}^{n} f(w_i)\, \Delta_i x - M \right| < \frac{\epsilon}{2} \quad \text{and} \quad \left| \sum_{i=1}^{n} g(w_i)\, \Delta_i x - N \right| < \frac{\epsilon}{2}$$

Therefore, if $\delta = \min(\delta_1, \delta_2)$, then for any $\epsilon > 0$, for all partitions Δ and for any w_i in $[x_{i-1}, x_i]$, if $\|\Delta\| < \delta$,

$$\left| \sum_{i=1}^{n} f(w_i)\, \Delta_i x - M \right| + \left| \sum_{i=1}^{n} g(w_i)\, \Delta_i x - N \right| < \frac{\epsilon}{2} + \frac{\epsilon}{2} = \epsilon \qquad (13)$$

By the triangle inequality we have

$$\left| \left(\sum_{i=1}^{n} f(w_i)\, \Delta_i x - M \right) + \left(\sum_{i=1}^{n} g(w_i)\, \Delta_i x - N \right) \right|$$

$$\leq \left| \sum_{i=1}^{n} f(w_i)\, \Delta_i x - M \right| + \left| \sum_{i=1}^{n} g(w_i)\, \Delta_i x - N \right| \qquad (14)$$

From inequalities (13) and (14) we have

$$\left| \left(\sum_{i=1}^{n} f(w_i)\, \Delta_i x + \sum_{i=1}^{n} g(w_i)\, \Delta_i x \right) - (M + N) \right| < \epsilon \qquad (15)$$

From Theorem 4.4.4,

$$\sum_{i=1}^{n} f(w_i)\, \Delta_i x + \sum_{i=1}^{n} g(w_i)\, \Delta_i x = \sum_{i=1}^{n} [f(w_i) + g(w_i)]\, \Delta_i x$$

So by substituting from this equation into (15) we are able to conclude that for any $\epsilon > 0$, for all partitions Δ and for any w_i in $[x_{i-1}, x_i]$, if $\|\Delta\| < \delta$ where $\delta = \min(\delta_1, \delta_2)$, then

$$\left| \sum_{i=1}^{n} [f(w_i) + g(w_i)]\, \Delta_i x - (M + N) \right| < \epsilon$$

This proves that $f + g$ is integrable on $[a, b]$ and that

$$\int_a^b [f(x) + g(x)]\, dx = \int_a^b f(x)\, dx + \int_a^b g(x)\, dx$$

∎

4.5.12 Theorem

If the function f is integrable on the closed intervals $[a, b]$, $[a, c]$, and $[c, b]$, then

$$\int_a^b f(x)\, dx = \int_a^c f(x)\, dx + \int_c^b f(x)\, dx$$

where $a < c < b$.

Proof   Let Δ be a partition of $[a, b]$. Form the partition Δ' of $[a, b]$ in the following way. If c is one of the partitioning points of Δ (i.e., $c = x_i$ for some i), then Δ' is exactly the same as Δ. If c is not one of the partitioning points of Δ but is contained in the subinterval $[x_{i-1}, x_i]$, then the partition Δ' has as its partitioning points all the partitioning points of Δ and, in addition, the point c. Therefore the subintervals of the partition Δ' are the same as the subintervals of Δ, with the exception that the subinterval $[x_{i-1}, x_i]$ of Δ is divided into the two subintervals $[x_{i-1}, c]$ and $[c, x_i]$.

If $\| \Delta' \|$ is the norm of Δ' and if $\| \Delta \|$ is the norm of Δ, then

$$\| \Delta' \| \leq \| \Delta \|$$

If in the partition Δ' the interval $[a, c]$ is divided into r subintervals and the interval $[c, b]$ is divided into $(n - r)$ subintervals, then the part of the partition Δ' from a to c gives a Riemann sum of the form

$$\sum_{i=1}^{r} f(w_i)\, \Delta_i x$$

and the other part of the partition Δ', from c to b, gives a Riemann sum of the form

$$\sum_{i=r+1}^{n} f(w_i)\, \Delta_i x$$

Using the definition of the definite integral and properties of sigma notation we have

$$\int_a^b f(x)\, dx = \lim_{\|\Delta\| \to 0} \sum_{i=1}^{n} f(w_i)\, \Delta_i x$$

$$= \lim_{\|\Delta\| \to 0} \left[\sum_{i=1}^{r} f(w_i)\, \Delta_i x + \sum_{i=r+1}^{n} f(w_i)\, \Delta_i x \right]$$

$$= \lim_{\|\Delta\| \to 0} \sum_{i=1}^{r} f(w_i)\, \Delta_i x + \lim_{\|\Delta\| \to 0} \sum_{i=r+1}^{n} f(w_i)\, \Delta_i x$$

Because $0 < \| \Delta' \| \leq \| \Delta \|$, we can replace $\| \Delta \| \to 0$ by $\| \Delta' \| \to 0$, giving

$$\int_a^b f(x)\, dx = \lim_{\|\Delta'\| \to 0} \sum_{i=1}^{r} f(w_i)\, \Delta_i x + \lim_{\|\Delta'\| \to 0} \sum_{i=r+1}^{n} f(w_i)\, \Delta_i x$$

Applying the definition of the definite integral to the right side of the above equation we have

$$\int_a^b f(x)\, dx = \int_a^c f(x)\, dx + \int_c^b f(x)\, dx$$

∎

5.1 SUPPLEMENT

We deferred the proofs of two theorems to this supplement, and the proof of one theorem to the supplementary exercises. The first of these theorems is the inverse function theorem for increasing functions.

5.1.5 Theorem (Inverse Function Theorem)

Suppose that the function f is continuous and increasing on the closed interval $[a, b]$. Then

(i) f has an inverse f^{-1} defined on $[f(a), f(b)]$;
(ii) f^{-1} is increasing on $[f(a), f(b)]$;
(iii) f^{-1} is continuous on $[f(a), f(b)]$.

Proof of (i)   If f is continuous on $[a, b]$ and if k is any number such that $f(a) < k < f(b)$, then by the intermediate-value theorem 1.9.8 there exists a number c in (a, b) such that $f(c) = k$. Therefore the range of f is the closed interval $[f(a), f(b)]$. Because f is increasing on $[a, b]$, f is one-to-one and so f has an inverse f^{-1}. Because the domain of f^{-1} is the range of f, f^{-1} is defined on $[f(a), f(b)]$.

Proof of (ii)   To prove that f^{-1} is increasing on $[f(a), f(b)]$ we must show that

$$\text{if}\quad y_1 < y_2\quad\text{then}\quad f^{-1}(y_1) < f^{-1}(y_2)$$

where y_1 and y_2 are two numbers in $[f(a), f(b)]$. Because f^{-1} is defined on $[f(a), f(b)]$, there exist numbers x_1 and x_2 in $[a, b]$ such that $y_1 = f(x_1)$ and $y_2 = f(x_2)$. Therefore

$$f^{-1}(y_1) = f^{-1}(f(x_1))\quad\text{and}\quad f^{-1}(y_2) = f^{-1}(f(x_2))$$
$$\Leftrightarrow\quad f^{-1}(y_1) = x_1\qquad\qquad\text{and}\quad f^{-1}(y_2) = x_2 \qquad\qquad\textbf{(8)}$$

If $x_2 < x_1$, then because f is increasing on $[a, b]$, $f(x_2) < f(x_1)$ or, equivalently, $y_2 < y_1$. But $y_1 < y_2$; therefore x_2 cannot be less than x_1.

If $x_2 = x_1$, then because f is a function, $f(x_1) = f(x_2)$ or, equivalently, $y_1 = y_2$, but this also contradicts the fact that $y_1 < y_2$. Therefore $x_2 \neq x_1$.

So if x_2 is not less than x_1 and $x_2 \neq x_1$, it follows that $x_1 < x_2$; hence, from the two equations in (8), $f^{-1}(y_1) < f^{-1}(y_2)$. Thus we have proved that f^{-1} is increasing on $[f(a), f(b)]$.

Proof of (iii)   To prove that f^{-1} is continuous on the closed interval $[f(a), f(b)]$ we must show that if r is any number in the open interval $(f(a), f(b))$, then f^{-1} is continuous at r, and f^{-1} is continuous from the right at $f(a)$, and f^{-1} is continuous from the left at $f(b)$.

We prove that f^{-1} is continuous at any r in the open interval $(f(a), f(b))$ by showing that Theorem 1.8.6 holds at r. We wish to show that, for any $\epsilon > 0$ small enough so that $f^{-1}(r) - \epsilon$ and $f^{-1}(r) + \epsilon$ are both in $[a, b]$, there exists a $\delta > 0$ such that

$$\text{if}\quad |y - r| < \delta\quad\text{then}\quad |f^{-1}(y) - f^{-1}(r)| < \epsilon$$

Let $f^{-1}(r) = s$. Then $f(s) = r$. Because, from (i), f^{-1} is increasing on $[f(a), f(b)]$, we conclude that $a < s < b$. Therefore

$$a \leq s - \epsilon < s < s + \epsilon \leq b$$

Because f is increasing on $[a, b]$,

$$f(a) \leq f(s - \epsilon) < r < f(s + \epsilon) \leq f(b) \qquad\qquad\textbf{(9)}$$

Let δ be the smaller of the two numbers $r - f(s - \epsilon)$ and $f(s + \epsilon) - r$; so $\delta \leq r - f(s - \epsilon)$ and $\delta \leq f(s + \epsilon) - r$ or, equivalently,

$$f(s - \epsilon) \leq r - \delta\quad\text{and}\quad r + \delta \leq f(s + \epsilon) \qquad\qquad\textbf{(10)}$$

If $|y - r| < \delta$, then $-\delta < y - r < \delta$ or, equivalently,

$$r - \delta < y < r + \delta$$

From this inequality and (9) and (10), we have

$$\text{if}\quad |y - r| < \delta\quad\text{then}\quad f(a) \leq f(s - \epsilon) < y < f(s + \epsilon) \leq f(b)$$

Because f^{-1} is increasing on $[f(a), f(b)]$, it follows from the above that

$$\text{if} \quad |y - r| < \delta \quad \text{then} \quad f^{-1}(f(s - \epsilon)) < f^{-1}(y) < f^{-1}(f(s + \epsilon))$$
$$\Leftrightarrow \quad \text{if} \quad |y - r| < \delta \quad \text{then} \quad s - \epsilon < f^{-1}(y) < s + \epsilon$$
$$\Leftrightarrow \quad \text{if} \quad |y - r| < \delta \quad \text{then} \quad -\epsilon < f^{-1}(y) - s < \epsilon$$
$$\Leftrightarrow \quad \text{if} \quad |y - r| < \delta \quad \text{then} \quad |f^{-1}(y) - f^{-1}(r)| < \epsilon$$

So f^{-1} is continuous on the open interval $(f(a), f(b))$.

The proofs that f^{-1} is continuous from the right at $f(a)$ and continuous from the left at $f(b)$ appear as an exercise. See Supplementary Exercise 1. ∎

You are asked to prove parts (i)–(iii) of the inverse function theorem for decreasing functions in Supplementary Exercises 2–4, respectively.

We now restate the other theorem whose proof we deferred.

5.1.7 Theorem

Suppose that the function f is continuous and monotonic on the closed interval $[a, b]$, and let $y = f(x)$. If $f'(x)$ exists and is not zero for all x in $[a, b]$, then the derivative of the inverse function f^{-1}, defined by $x = f^{-1}(y)$, is given by

$$\frac{dx}{dy} = \frac{1}{\dfrac{dy}{dx}}$$

Proof   Because f is continuous and monotonic on $[a, b]$, then by Theorems 5.1.5 and 5.1.6, f has an inverse that is continuous and monotonic on $[f(a), f(b)]$ (or $[f(b), f(a)]$ if $f(b) < f(a)$).

If x is a number in $[a, b]$, let Δx be an increment of x, $\Delta x \neq 0$, such that $x + \Delta x$ is also in $[a, b]$. Then the corresponding increment of y is given by

$$\Delta y = f(x + \Delta x) - f(x) \tag{11}$$

$\Delta y \neq 0$ since $\Delta x \neq 0$ and f is monotonic on $[a, b]$; that is, either

$$f(x + \Delta x) < f(x) \quad \text{or} \quad f(x + \Delta x) > f(x) \quad \text{on } [a, b]$$

If x is in $[a, b]$ and $y = f(x)$, then y is in $[f(a), f(b)]$ (or $[f(b), f(a)]$). Also, if $x + \Delta x$ is in $[a, b]$, then $y + \Delta y$ is in $[f(a), f(b)]$ (or $[f(b), f(a)]$) because $y + \Delta y = f(x + \Delta x)$ by (11). So

$$x = f^{-1}(y) \quad \text{and} \quad x + \Delta x = f^{-1}(y + \Delta y)$$

From these two equations, we have

$$\Delta x = f^{-1}(y + \Delta y) - f^{-1}(y) \tag{12}$$

From the definition of a derivative,

$$\frac{dx}{dy} = \lim_{\Delta y \to 0} \frac{f^{-1}(y + \Delta y) - f^{-1}(y)}{\Delta y}$$

Substituting from (11) and (12) into the above equation we get

$$\frac{dx}{dy} = \lim_{\Delta y \to 0} \frac{\Delta x}{f(x + \Delta x) - f(x)}$$

and because $\Delta x \neq 0$,

$$\frac{dx}{dy} = \lim_{\Delta y \to 0} \frac{1}{\dfrac{f(x + \Delta x) - f(x)}{\Delta x}} \tag{13}$$

Before we find the limit in (13) we show that under the hypothesis of this theorem $\Delta x \to 0$ is equivalent to $\Delta y \to 0$. First we show that $\lim\limits_{\Delta y \to 0} \Delta x = 0$. From (12),

$$\lim_{\Delta y \to 0} \Delta x = \lim_{\Delta y \to 0} \left[f^{-1}(y + \Delta y) - f^{-1}(y) \right]$$

Because f^{-1} is continuous on $[f(a), f(b)]$ (or $[f(b), f(a)]$), the limit on the right side of the above equation is zero. So

$$\lim_{\Delta y \to 0} \Delta x = 0 \tag{14}$$

Now we demonstrate that $\lim\limits_{\Delta x \to 0} \Delta y = 0$. From (11),

$$\lim_{\Delta x \to 0} \Delta y = \lim_{\Delta x \to 0} \left[f(x + \Delta x) - f(x) \right]$$

Because f is continuous on $[a, b]$, the limit on the right side of the above equation is zero, and therefore

$$\lim_{\Delta x \to 0} \Delta y = 0$$

From this equation and (14) it follows that

$$\Delta x \to 0 \quad \text{if and only if} \quad \Delta y \to 0$$

From this statement and by applying the theorem regarding the limit of a quotient to (13) we have

$$\frac{dx}{dy} = \frac{1}{\lim\limits_{\Delta x \to 0} \dfrac{f(x + \Delta x) - f(x)}{\Delta x}} \tag{13}$$

Because f is differentiable on $[a, b]$, the limit in the denominator of the above is $f'(x)$ or, equivalently, $\dfrac{dy}{dx}$. Thus

$$\frac{dx}{dy} = \frac{1}{\dfrac{dy}{dx}}$$

∎

SUPPLEMENTARY EXERCISES 5.1

1. Given that the function f is continuous and increasing on the closed interval $[a, b]$, by assuming Theorem 5.1.5 (i) and (ii) prove that f^{-1} is continuous from the right at $f(a)$ and continuous from the left at $f(b)$.

2. Prove Theorem 5.1.6(i).

3. Prove Theorem 5.1.6(ii).

4. Prove Theorem 5.1.6(iii).

8.2 SUPPLEMENT

8.2.10 Theorem

A bounded monotonic sequence is convergent.

Proof   We prove the theorem for the case when the monotonic sequence is increasing. Let the sequence be $\{a_n\}$.

Because $\{a_n\}$ is bounded, there is an upper bound for the sequence. By the axiom of completeness, $\{a_n\}$ has a least upper bound that we call B. Then if ϵ is a positive number, $B - \epsilon$ cannot be an upper bound of the sequence because $B - \epsilon < B$ and B is the least upper bound of the sequence. So for some positive integer N,

$$B - \epsilon < a_N \tag{9}$$

Because B is the least upper bound of $\{a_n\}$, by Definition 8.2.6 it follows that

$$a_n \leq B \qquad \text{for every positive integer } n \tag{10}$$

Because $\{a_n\}$ is an increasing sequence, we have from Definition 8.2.5(i)

$$a_n \leq a_{n+1} \qquad \text{for every positive integer } n$$

and so

$$\text{if} \quad n \geq N \quad \text{then} \quad a_N \leq a_n$$

From this statement and (9) and (10) it follows that

$$\text{if} \quad n \geq N \quad \text{then} \quad B - \epsilon < a_N \leq a_n \leq B < B + \epsilon$$

from which we get

$$\text{if} \quad n \geq N \quad \text{then} \quad B - \epsilon < a_n < B + \epsilon$$
$$\Leftrightarrow \quad \text{if} \quad n \geq N \quad \text{then} \quad -\epsilon < a_n - B < \epsilon$$
$$\Leftrightarrow \quad \text{if} \quad n \geq N \quad \text{then} \quad |a_n - B| < \epsilon$$

But by Definition 8.2.2, this statement is the condition that $\lim\limits_{n \to +\infty} a_n = B$. Therefore the sequence $\{a_n\}$ is convergent.

To prove the theorem when $\{a_n\}$ is a decreasing sequence, consider the sequence $\{-a_n\}$, which will be increasing, and apply the above results. We leave it as an exercise to fill in the steps (see Supplementary Exercise 1). ∎

8.2.13 Theorem

A convergent monotonic sequence is bounded.

Proof   We prove the theorem for the case when the monotonic sequence is increasing. Let the sequence be $\{a_n\}$.

To prove that $\{a_n\}$ is bounded, it must be shown that it has a lower bound and an upper bound. Because $\{a_n\}$ is an increasing sequence, its first element serves as a lower bound. We must now find an upper bound.

Because $\{a_n\}$ is convergent, the sequence has a limit; call this limit L. Therefore $\lim_{n\to\infty} a_n = L$, and so by Definition 8.1.2, for any $\epsilon > 0$ there exists a number $N > 0$ such that if n is an integer and

$$\text{if} \quad n > N \quad \text{then} \quad |a_n - L| < \epsilon$$
$$\Leftrightarrow \quad \text{if} \quad n > N \quad \text{then} \quad -\epsilon < a_n - L < \epsilon$$
$$\Leftrightarrow \quad \text{if} \quad n > N \quad \text{then} \quad L - \epsilon < a_n < L + \epsilon$$

Because $\{a_n\}$ is increasing, it follows from this statement that

$$a_n < L + \epsilon \quad \text{for all positive integers } n$$

Therefore $L + \epsilon$ will serve as an upper bound of the sequence $\{a_n\}$.

To prove the theorem when $\{a_n\}$ is a decreasing sequence, do as suggested in the proof of Theorem 8.2.10. Consider the sequence $\{-a_n\}$, which will be increasing, and apply the above results. You are asked to provide this proof in Supplementary Exercise 2. ∎

SUPPLEMENTARY EXERCISES 8.2

1. Use the fact that Theorem 8.2.10 holds for an increasing sequence to prove that the theorem holds when $\{a_n\}$ is a decreasing sequence. *Hint:* Consider the sequence $\{-a_n\}$.

2. Prove Theorem 8.2.13 when $\{a_n\}$ is a decreasing sequence by a method similar to that used in Exercise 1.

8.5 SUPPLEMENT

8.5.4 Theorem

Consider the alternating series $\sum_{n=1}^{+\infty} (-1)^{n+1} a_n \left[\text{or } \sum_{n=1}^{+\infty} (-1)^n a_n \right]$, where $a_n > 0$ and $a_{n+1} < a_n$ for all positive integers n, and $\lim_{n\to+\infty} a_n = 0$. If R_k is the remainder obtained by approximating the sum of the series by the sum of the first k terms, $|R_k| < a_{k+1}$.

Proof   The given series converges by the alternating-series test. Assume that the odd-numbered terms of the given series are positive and the even-numbered terms are negative. Then from (3) in the proof of Theorem 8.5.2, the sequence $\{s_{2n}\}$ is increasing. So if S is the sum of the given series,

$$s_{2k} < s_{2k+2} < S \quad \text{for all } k \geq 1 \tag{11}$$

To show that the sequence $\{s_{2n-1}\}$ is decreasing we write

$$s_{2n-1} = a_1 - (a_2 - a_3) - (a_4 - a_5) - \ldots - (a_{2n-2} - a_{2n-1})$$

Because $a_{n+1} < a_n$, each quantity in parentheses is positive. Therefore, because $a_1 > 0$

$$s_1 > s_3 > s_5 > \ldots > s_{2n-1} > \ldots$$

Hence the sequence $\{s_{2n-1}\}$ is decreasing. Thus

$$S < s_{2k+1} < s_{2k-1} \qquad \text{for all } k \geq 1 \tag{12}$$

Because $S < s_{2k+1}$

$$S - s_{2k} < s_{2k+1} - s_{2k} = a_{2k+1} \qquad \text{for all } k \geq 1 \tag{13}$$

From (11), $s_{2k} < S$. Hence

$$0 < S - s_{2k} \qquad \text{for all } k \geq 1$$

Therefore, from this inequality and (13),

$$0 < S - s_{2k} < a_{2k+1} \qquad \text{for all } k \geq 1 \tag{14}$$

From (11), $-S < -s_{2k}$. Hence

$$s_{2k-1} - S < s_{2k-1} - s_{2k} = a_{2k} \qquad \text{for all } k \geq 1 \tag{15}$$

From (12),

$$0 < s_{2k-1} - S \qquad \text{for all } k \geq 1$$

Then from this inequality and (15),

$$0 < s_{2k-1} - S < a_{2k} \qquad \text{for all } k \geq 1 \tag{16}$$

Because from Definition 8.5.3, $R_k = S - s_k$, then (14) can be written as

$$0 < R_{2k} < a_{2k+1} \qquad \text{for all } k \geq 1 \tag{17}$$

and (16) can be written as

$$0 < -R_{2k-1} < a_{2k} \qquad \text{for all } k \geq 1$$

Combining this inequality and (17) we have

$$|R_k| < a_{k+1} \qquad \text{for all } k \geq 1$$

and the theorem is proved.   ∎

8.8 SUPPLEMENT

8.8.1 Theorem

If $\displaystyle\sum_{n=0}^{+\infty} c_n x^n$ is a power series having a radius of convergence of $R > 0$, then $\displaystyle\sum_{n=1}^{+\infty} n c_n x^{n-1}$ also has R as its radius of convergence.

Proof   Let x be any number in the open interval $(-R, R)$. Then $|x| < R$. Choose a number x_1 such that $|x| < |x_1| < R$. Because $|x_1| < R$, $\displaystyle\sum_{n=0}^{+\infty} c_n x_1^n$ is convergent. Hence $\displaystyle\lim_{n \to +\infty} c_n x_1^n = 0$. So if we take $\epsilon = 1$ in Definition 3.7.1, there exists a number $N > 0$ such that

$$\text{if} \quad n > N \quad \text{then} \quad |c_n x_1^n| < 1$$

Let M be the largest of the numbers $|c_1x_1|, |c_2x_1{}^2|, |c_3x_1{}^3|, \ldots, |c_Nx_1{}^N|$, 1. Then

$$|c_nx_1{}^n| \leq M \qquad \text{for all positive integers } n \tag{7}$$

Now

$$|nc_nx^{n-1}| = \left| nc_n \cdot \frac{x^{n-1}}{x_1{}^n} \cdot x_1{}^n \right|$$

$$= n \frac{|c_nx_1{}^n|}{|x_1|} \left| \frac{x}{x_1} \right|^{n-1}$$

From (7) and the above equation,

$$|nc_nx^{n-1}| \leq n \frac{M}{|x_1|} \left| \frac{x}{x_1} \right|^{n-1} \tag{8}$$

If the ratio test is applied to the series

$$\frac{M}{|x_1|} \sum_{n=1}^{+\infty} n \left| \frac{x}{x_1} \right|^{n-1} \tag{9}$$

then

$$\lim_{n \to +\infty} \left| \frac{u_{n+1}}{u_n} \right| = \lim_{n \to +\infty} \left| \frac{(n+1)|x|^n}{|x_1|^n} \cdot \frac{|x_1|^{n-1}}{n|x|^{n-1}} \right|$$

$$= \left| \frac{x}{x_1} \right| \lim_{n \to +\infty} \frac{n+1}{n}$$

$$= \left| \frac{x}{x_1} \right| < 1$$

Therefore series (9) is absolutely convergent; so from (8) and the comparison test, the series $\sum_{n=1}^{+\infty} nc_nx^{n-1}$ is also absolutely convergent. Because x is any number in $(-R, R)$, it follows that if the radius of convergence of $\sum_{n=1}^{+\infty} nc_nx^{n-1}$ is R', then $R' \geq R$.

To complete the proof we must show that R' cannot be greater than R. Assume that $R' > R$, and let x_2 be a number such that $R < |x_2| < R'$. Because $|x_2| > R$, it follows that

$$\sum_{n=0}^{+\infty} c_nx_2{}^n \text{ is divergent} \tag{10}$$

Because $|x_2| < R'$, it follows that $\sum_{n=1}^{+\infty} nc_nx_2{}^{n-1}$ is absolutely convergent. Furthermore,

$$|x_2| \sum_{n=1}^{+\infty} |nc_nx_2{}^{n-1}| = \sum_{n=1}^{+\infty} |nc_nx_2{}^n|$$

and so from Theorem 8.3.6,

$$\sum_{n=1}^{+\infty} |nc_nx_2{}^n| \text{ is convergent} \tag{11}$$

If n is any positive integer,

$$\left|c_n x_2{}^n\right| \le n\left|c_n x_2{}^n\right| = \left|nc_n x_2{}^n\right|$$

From this inequality, statement (11), and the comparison test it follows that $\sum_{n=1}^{+\infty}\left|c_n x_2{}^n\right|$ is convergent. Therefore the series $\sum_{n=0}^{+\infty} c_n x_2{}^n$ is convergent, which contradicts statement (10). Hence the assumption that $R' > R$ is false. Therefore R' cannot be greater than R; and because it was shown that $R' \ge R$, it follows that $R' = R$, which proves the theorem. ∎

8.8.3 Theorem

Let $\sum_{n=0}^{+\infty} c_n x^n$ be a power series whose radius of convergence is $R > 0$. If f is the function defined by

$$f(x) = \sum_{n=0}^{+\infty} c_n x^n \tag{12}$$

then $f'(x)$ exists for every x in the open interval $(-R, R)$ and

$$f'(x) = \sum_{n=1}^{+\infty} nc_n x^{n-1}$$

Proof Let x and a be two distinct numbers in the open interval $(-R, R)$. Taylor's formula (formula (2) in Section 8.1), with $n = 1$, is

$$f(x) = f(a) + \frac{f'(a)}{1!}(x - a) + \frac{f''(z)}{2!}(x - a)^2$$

From this formula with $f(x) = x^n$ it follows that for every positive integer n,

$$x^n = a^n + na^{n-1}(x - a) + \tfrac{1}{2}n(n - 1)(z_n)^{n-2}(x - a)^2 \tag{13}$$

where z_n is between a and x for every positive integer n. From (12),

$$f(x) - f(a) = \sum_{n=0}^{+\infty} c_n x^n - \sum_{n=0}^{+\infty} c_n a^n$$

$$= c_0 + \sum_{n=1}^{+\infty} c_n x^n - c_0 - \sum_{n=1}^{+\infty} c_n a^n$$

$$= \sum_{n=1}^{+\infty} c_n(x^n - a^n)$$

Dividing by $x - a$ (because $x \ne a$) and using (13) we have from the above equation

$$\frac{f(x) - f(a)}{x - a} = \frac{1}{x - a}\sum_{n=1}^{+\infty} c_n[na^{n-1}(x - a) + \tfrac{1}{2}n(n - 1)(z_n)^{n-2}(x - a)^2]$$

So

$$\frac{f(x) - f(a)}{x - a} = \sum_{n=1}^{+\infty} nc_n a^{n-1} + \tfrac{1}{2}(x - a)\sum_{n=2}^{+\infty} n(n - 1)c_n(z_n)^{n-2} \tag{14}$$

Because a is in $(-R, R)$, we conclude from Theorem 8.8.1 that

$$\sum_{n=1}^{+\infty} nc_n a^{n-1}$$ is absolutely convergent.

Because both a and x are in $(-R, R)$, there is some number $K > 0$ such that $|a| < K < R$ and $|x| < K < R$. Thus from Theorem 8.8.2

$$\sum_{n=2}^{+\infty} n(n-1)c_n K^{n-2}$$

is absolutely convergent. Then because

$$\left| n(n-1)c_n(z_n)^{n-2} \right| < \left| n(n-1)c_n K^{n-2} \right| \tag{15}$$

for each z_n, we can conclude from the comparison test that

$$\sum_{n=2}^{+\infty} n(n-1)c_n(z_n)^{n-2}$$

is absolutely convergent.

From (14)

$$\left| \frac{f(x) - f(a)}{x - a} - \sum_{n=1}^{+\infty} nc_n a^{n-1} \right| = \left| \tfrac{1}{2}(x-a) \sum_{n=2}^{+\infty} n(n-1)c_n(z_n)^{n-2} \right| \tag{16}$$

However, if $\sum\limits_{n=1}^{+\infty} u_n$ is absolutely convergent, then

$$\left| \sum_{n=1}^{+\infty} u_n \right| \le \sum_{n=1}^{+\infty} |u_n|$$

Applying this to the right side of (16) we obtain

$$\left| \frac{f(x) - f(a)}{x - a} - \sum_{n=1}^{+\infty} nc_n a^{n-1} \right| \le \tfrac{1}{2}|x-a| \sum_{n=2}^{+\infty} n(n-1)|c_n| \, |z_n|^{n-2}$$

From this inequality and (15)

$$\left| \frac{f(x) - f(a)}{x - a} - \sum_{n=1}^{+\infty} nc_n a^{n-1} \right| \le \tfrac{1}{2}|x-a| \sum_{n=2}^{+\infty} n(n-1)|c_n| K^{n-2} \tag{17}$$

where $0 < K < R$. Because the series on the right side of (17) is absolutely convergent, the limit of the right side, as x approaches a, is zero. Therefore, from (17) and the squeeze theorem,

$$\lim_{x \to a} \frac{f(x) - f(a)}{x - a} = \sum_{n=1}^{+\infty} nc_n a^{n-1}$$

$$\Leftrightarrow \qquad f'(a) = \sum_{n=1}^{+\infty} nc_n a^{n-1}$$

and because a may be any number in the open interval $(-R, R)$, the theorem is proved.   ∎

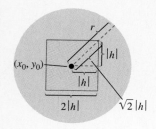

FIGURE 1

12.3 SUPPLEMENT

12.3.3 Theorem

Suppose that f is a function of two variables x and y defined on an open disk $B((x_0, y_0); r)$ and f_x, f_y, f_{xy}, and f_{yx} also are defined on B. Furthermore, suppose that f_{xy} and f_{yx} are continuous on B. Then

$$f_{xy}(x_0, y_0) = f_{yx}(x_0, y_0)$$

Proof   Consider a square having its center at (x_0, y_0) and the length of its side $2|h|$ such that $0 < \sqrt{2}|h| < r$. Then all the points in the interior of the square and on the sides of the square are in the open disk B (see Figure 1). So the points $(x_0 + h, y_0 + h)$, $(x_0 + h, y_0)$, and $(x_0, y_0 + h)$ are in B. Let Δ be defined by

$$\Delta = f(x_0 + h, y_0 + h) - f(x_0 + h, y_0) - f(x_0, y_0 + h) + f(x_0, y_0) \tag{13}$$

Consider the function G defined by

$$G(x) = f(x, y_0 + h) - f(x, y_0) \tag{14}$$

Then

$$G(x + h) = f(x + h, y_0 + h) - f(x + h, y_0)$$

So (13) can be written as

$$\Delta = G(x_0 + h) - G(x_0) \tag{15}$$

From (14),

$$G'(x) = f_x(x, y_0 + h) - f_x(x, y_0) \tag{16}$$

Now, because $f_x(x, y_0 + h)$ and $f_x(x, y_0)$ are defined on B, $G'(x)$ exists if x is in the closed interval having endpoints at x_0 and $x_0 + h$. Hence G is continuous if x is in this closed interval. By the mean-value theorem there is a number c_1 between x_0 and $x_0 + h$ such that

$$\frac{G(x_0 + h) - G(x_0)}{(x_0 + h) - x_0} = G'(c_1)$$

$$G(x_0 + h) - G(x_0) = hG'(c_1)$$

Substituting from this equation into (15) we get

$$\Delta = hG'(c_1)$$

From this equation and replacing x by c_1 in (16), we have

$$\Delta = h[f_x(c_1, y_0 + h) - f_x(c_1, y_0)] \tag{17}$$

Now if g is the function defined by

$$g(y) = f_x(c_1, y) \tag{18}$$

we can write (17) as

$$\Delta = h[g(y_0 + h) - g(y_0)] \tag{19}$$

From (18),

$$g'(y) = f_{xy}(c_1, y) \tag{20}$$

Because $f_{xy}(c_1, y)$ is defined on B, $g'(y)$ exists if y is in the closed interval having endpoints at y_0 and $y_0 + h$; hence g is continuous if y is in this closed interval. Therefore, by the mean-value theorem there is a number d_1 between y_0 and $y_0 + h$ such that

$$g(y_0 + h) - g(y_0) = hg'(d_1)$$

Substituting from this equation into (19) we get $\Delta = h^2 g'(d_1)$; so from (20)

$$\Delta = h^2 f_{xy}(c_1, d_1) \tag{21}$$

for some point (c_1, d_1) in the open disk B. We define a function ϕ by

$$\phi(y) = f(x_0 + h, y) - f(x_0, y) \tag{22}$$

and so $\phi(y + h) = f(x_0 + h, y + h) - f(x_0, y + h)$. Therefore (13) can be written as

$$\Delta = \phi(y_0 + h) - \phi(y_0) \tag{23}$$

From (22),

$$\phi'(y) = f_y(x_0 + h, y) - f_y(x_0, y) \tag{24}$$

Because, by hypothesis, each term on the right side of (24) exists on B, ϕ' exists if y is in the closed interval having y_0 and $y_0 + h$ as endpoints. Therefore ϕ is continuous on this closed interval. So by the mean-value theorem there is a number d_2 between y_0 and $y_0 + h$ such that

$$\phi(y_0 + h) - \phi(y_0) = h\phi'(d_2)$$

From this equation, (23), and (24),

$$\Delta = h[f_y(x_0 + h, d_2) - f_y(x_0, d_2)] \tag{25}$$

We define the function χ by

$$\chi(x) = f_y(x, d_2) \tag{26}$$

and write (25) as

$$\Delta = h[\chi(x_0 + h) - \chi(x_0)] \tag{27}$$

From (26),

$$\chi'(x) = f_{yx}(x, d_2) \tag{28}$$

and by the mean-value theorem there is a number c_2 between x_0 and $x_0 + h$ such that

$$\chi(x_0 + h) - \chi(x_0) = h\chi'(c_2)$$

From this equation, (27), and (28),

$$\Delta = h^2 f_{yx}(c_2, d_2)$$

With this expression for Δ, and (21) we get

$$h^2 f_{xy}(c_1, d_1) = h^2 f_{yx}(c_2, d_2)$$

and because $h \neq 0$, we can divide by h^2, which gives

$$f_{xy}(c_1, d_1) = f_{yx}(c_2, d_2) \tag{29}$$

where (c_1, d_1) and (c_2, d_2) are in B.

Because c_1 and c_2 are each between x_0 and $x_0 + h$, we have $c_1 = x_0 + \epsilon_1 h$, where $0 < \epsilon_1 < 1$, and $c_2 = x_0 + \epsilon_2 h$, where $0 < \epsilon_2 < 1$. Similarly, because both d_1 and d_2 are between y_0 and $y_0 + h$, we have $d_1 = y_0 + \epsilon_3 h$, where $0 < \epsilon_3 < 1$, and $d_2 = y_0 + \epsilon_4 h$, where $0 < \epsilon_4 < 1$. Making these substitutions in (29) gives

$$f_{xy}(x_0 + \epsilon_1 h, y_0 + \epsilon_3 h) = f_{yx}(x_0 + \epsilon_2 h, y_0 + \epsilon_4 h)$$

Because f_{xy} and f_{yx} are continuous on B, upon taking the limit of both sides of this equation as h approaches zero we obtain

$$f_{xy}(x_0, y_0) = f_{yx}(x_0, y_0)$$

■

12.4 SUPPLEMENT

12.4.4 Theorem

Let f be a function of x and y such that $D_1 f$ and $D_2 f$ exist on an open disk $B(P_0; r)$, where P_0 is the point (x_0, y_0). Then if $D_1 f$ and $D_2 f$ are continuous at P_0, f is differentiable at P_0.

Proof   See Figure 1, where the point $(x_0 + \Delta x, y_0 + \Delta y)$ is in $B(P_0; r)$. Then

$$\Delta f(x_0, y_0) = f(x_0 + \Delta x, y_0 + \Delta y) - f(x_0, y_0)$$

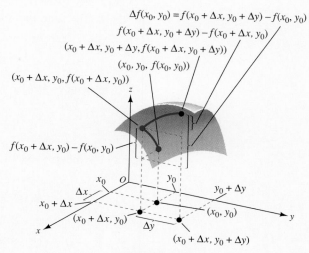

FIGURE 1

Adding and subtracting $f(x_0 + \Delta x, y_0)$ on the right side of this equation, we get

$$\Delta f(x_0, y_0) = [f(x_0 + \Delta x, y_0) - f(x_0, y_0)] + [f(x_0 + \Delta x, y_0 + \Delta y) - f(x_0 + \Delta x, y_0)] \qquad (9)$$

In the plane $y = y_0$, y is constant and x changes. Because $D_1 f$ exists in the plane $y = y_0$, we know from the mean-value theorem that there is some number c between x_0 and $x_0 + \Delta x$, such that

$$\frac{f(x_0 + \Delta x, y_0) - f(x_0, y_0)}{(x_0 + \Delta x) - x_0} = D_1 f(c, y_0)$$

$$f(x_0 + \Delta x, y_0) - f(x_0, y_0) = (\Delta x) D_1 f(c, y_0) \qquad (10)$$

In the plane $x = x_0 + \Delta x$, x is constant and y changes. Because $D_2 f$ exists in the plane $x = x_0 + \Delta x$, the mean-value theorem states that there is some number d between y_0 and $y_0 + \Delta y$, such that

$$f(x_0 + \Delta x, y_0 + \Delta y) - f(x_0 + \Delta x, y_0) = (\Delta y) D_2 f(x_0 + \Delta x, d)$$

Substituting from this equation and (10) in (9) we obtain

$$\Delta f(x_0, y_0) = (\Delta x) D_1 f(c, y_0) + (\Delta y) D_2 f(x_0 + \Delta x, d) \qquad (11)$$

Because $(x_0 + \Delta x, y_0 + \Delta y)$ is in $B(P_0; r)$, c is between x_0 and $x_0 + \Delta x$, and $D_1 f$ is continuous at P_0,

$$\lim_{(\Delta x, \Delta y) \to (0,0)} D_1 f(c, y_0) = D_1 f(x_0, y_0) \qquad (12)$$

and because d is between y_0 and $y_0 + \Delta y$ and $D_2 f$ is continuous at P_0,

$$\lim_{(\Delta x, \Delta y) \to (0,0)} D_2 f(x_0 + \Delta x, d) = D_2 f(x_0, y_0) \qquad (13)$$

If

$$\epsilon_1 = D_1 f(c, y_0) - D_1 f(x_0, y_0) \qquad (14)$$

and

$$\epsilon_2 = D_2 f(x_0 + \Delta x, d) - D_2 f(x_0, y_0) \qquad (15)$$

Then from (12) and (13), respectively,

$$\lim_{(\Delta x, \Delta y) \to (0,0)} \epsilon_1 = 0 \quad \text{and} \quad \lim_{(\Delta x, \Delta y) \to (0,0)} \epsilon_2 = 0 \qquad (16)$$

Substituting from (14) and (15) into (11) we get

$$\Delta f(x_0, y_0) = \Delta x [D_1 f(x_0, y_0) + \epsilon_1] + \Delta y [D_2 f(x_0, y_0) + \epsilon_2]$$

$$\Delta f(x_0, y_0) = D_1 f(x_0, y_0)\, \Delta x + D_2 f(x_0, y_0)\, \Delta y + \epsilon_1\, \Delta x + \epsilon_2\, \Delta y$$

From this equation and (16), Definition 12.4.2 holds; so f is differentiable at (x_0, y_0). ∎

12.8 SUPPLEMENT

12.8.5 Theorem   Second-Derivative Test

Let f be a function of two variables such that f and its first- and second-order partial derivatives are continuous on some open disk $B((a, b); r)$. Suppose further that $f_x(a, b) = 0$ and $f_y(a, b) = 0$. Let

$$D(a, b) = f_{xx}(a, b)f_{yy}(a, b) - [f_{xy}(a, b)]^2$$

(i) f has a relative minimum value at (a, b) if

$$D(a, b) > 0 \quad \text{and} \quad f_{xx}(a, b) > 0 \quad (\text{or } f_{yy}(a, b) > 0)$$

(ii) f has a relative maximum value at (a, b) if

$$D(a, b) > 0 \quad \text{and} \quad f_{xx}(a, b) < 0 \quad (\text{or } f_{yy}(a, b) < 0)$$

(iii) $f(a, b)$ is not a relative extremum, but f has a saddle point at $(a, b, f(a, b))$ if

$$D(a, b) < 0$$

(iv) No conclusion regarding relative extrema can be made if

$$D(a, b) = 0$$

Proof of part (i)   For simplicity of notation let us define

$$D(x, y) = f_{xx}(x, y)f_{yy}(x, y) - [f_{xy}(x, y)]^2$$

We are given $D(a, b) > 0$ and $f_{xx}(a, b) > 0$, we wish to prove that $f(a, b)$ is a relative minimum function value. Because f_{xx}, f_{xy}, and f_{yy} are continuous on $B((a, b); r)$, then D is also continuous on B. Hence there exists an open disk $B'((a, b); r')$, where $r' \leq r$, such that $D(x, y) > 0$ and $f_{xx}(x, y) > 0$ for every point (x, y) in B'. Let h and k be constants, not both zero, such that the point $(a + h, b + k)$ is in B'. Then the two equations

$$x = a + ht \quad \text{and} \quad y = b + kt \qquad 0 \leq t \leq 1$$

define all the points on the line segment from (a, b) to $(a + h, b + k)$, and all these points are in B'. Let F be the function of one variable defined by

$$F(t) = f(a + ht, b + kt) \tag{5}$$

By Taylor's formula (formula (2), Section 8.1),

$$F(t) = F(0) + F'(0)t + \frac{F''(z)}{2!}t^2$$

where z is between 0 and t. If $t = 1$ in this equation, we get

$$F(1) = F(0) + F'(0) + \tfrac{1}{2}F''(z) \tag{6}$$

where $0 < z < 1$. Because $F(0) = f(a, b)$ and $F(1) = f(a + h, b + k)$, then from (6)

$$f(a + h, b + k) = f(a, b) + F'(0) + \tfrac{1}{2}F''(z) \tag{7}$$

where $0 < z < 1$.

To find $F'(t)$ and $F''(t)$ from (5) we use the chain rule and obtain

$$F'(t) = hf_x(a + ht, b + kt) + kf_y(a + ht, b + kt) \tag{8}$$

and

$$F''(t) = h^2 f_{xx} + hk f_{yx} + hk f_{xy} + k^2 f_{yy}$$

where each second partial derivative is evaluated at $(a + ht, b + kt)$. From Theorem 12.3.3, $f_{xy}(x, y) = f_{yx}(x, y)$ for all (x, y) in B'. So

$$F''(t) = h^2 f_{xx} + 2hk f_{xy} + k^2 f_{yy} \tag{9}$$

where each second partial derivative is evaluated at $(a + ht, b + kt)$. Substituting 0 for t in (8) and z for t in (9) we get

$$F'(0) = hf_x(a, b) + kf_y(a, b)$$
$$= 0$$

and

$$F''(z) = h^2 f_{xx} + 2hk f_{xy} + k^2 f_{yy}$$

where each second partial derivative is evaluated at $(a + hz, b + kz)$, where $0 < z < 1$. Substituting these values of $F'(0)$ and $F''(z)$ into (7) we obtain

$$f(a + h, b + k) - f(a, b) = \tfrac{1}{2}(h^2 f_{xx} + 2hk f_{xy} + k^2 f_{yy}) \tag{10}$$

The terms in parentheses on the right side of (10) can be written as

$$h^2 f_{xx} + 2hk f_{xy} + k^2 f_{yy} = f_{xx}\left[h^2 + 2hk\frac{f_{xy}}{f_{xx}} + \left(k\frac{f_{xy}}{f_{xx}}\right)^2 - \left(k\frac{f_{xy}}{f_{xx}}\right)^2 + k^2\frac{f_{yy}}{f_{xx}}\right]$$

So from (10)

$$f(a + h, b + k) - f(a, b) = \frac{f_{xx}}{2}\left[\left(h + \frac{f_{xy}}{f_{xx}}k\right)^2 + \frac{f_{xx}f_{yy} - f_{xy}^2}{f_{xx}^2}k^2\right] \tag{11}$$

Because $f_{xx}f_{yy} - f_{xy}^2$ evaluated at $(a + hz, b + kz)$ equals

$$D(a + hz, b + kz) > 0$$

then the expression in brackets on the right side of (11) is positive. Furthermore, because $f_{xx}(a + hz, b + kz) > 0$, then from (11)

$$f(a + h, b + k) - f(a, b) > 0$$

Hence we have proved that

$$f(a + h, b + k) > f(a, b)$$

for every point $(a + h, b + k) \neq (a, b)$ in B'. Therefore, by Definition 12.7.1(ii) $f(a, b)$ is a relative minimum value of f. ∎

SUPPLEMENTARY EXERCISES 12.8

1. Prove part (ii) of Theorem 12.8.5.

2. Prove part (iii) of Theorem 12.8.5.

FORMULAS FROM TRIGONOMETRY

THE EIGHT FUNDAMENTAL TRIGONOMETRIC IDENTITIES

$$\sin x \csc x = 1 \qquad \cos x \sec x = 1 \qquad \tan x \cot x = 1$$

$$\tan x = \frac{\sin x}{\cos x} \qquad \cot x = \frac{\cos x}{\sin x}$$

$$\sin^2 x + \cos^2 x = 1 \qquad 1 + \tan^2 x = \sec^2 x \qquad 1 + \cot^2 x = \csc^2 x$$

SUM AND DIFFERENCE IDENTITIES

$$\sin(u + v) = \sin u \cos v + \cos u \sin v$$

$$\sin(u - v) = \sin u \cos v - \cos u \sin v$$

$$\cos(u + v) = \cos u \cos v - \sin u \sin v$$

$$\cos(u - v) = \cos u \cos v + \sin u \sin v$$

$$\tan(u + v) = \frac{\tan u + \tan v}{1 - \tan u \tan v} \qquad \tan(u - v) = \frac{\tan u - \tan v}{1 + \tan u \tan v}$$

MULTIPLE-MEASURE IDENTITIES

$$\sin 2u = 2 \sin u \cos u$$

$$\cos 2u = \cos^2 u - \sin^2 u$$

$$\cos 2u = 1 - 2 \sin^2 u \qquad \cos 2u = 2 \cos^2 u - 1$$

$$\tan 2u = \frac{2 \tan u}{1 - \tan^2 u}$$

$$\sin^2 u = \frac{1 - \cos 2u}{2} \qquad \cos^2 u = \frac{1 + \cos 2u}{2}$$

$$\tan^2 u = \frac{1 - \cos 2u}{1 + \cos 2u}$$

$$\sin^2 \tfrac{1}{2}t = \frac{1 - \cos t}{2} \qquad \cos^2 \tfrac{1}{2}t = \frac{1 + \cos t}{2}$$

$$\tan \tfrac{1}{2}t = \frac{1 - \cos t}{\sin t} \qquad \tan \tfrac{1}{2}t = \frac{\sin t}{1 + \cos t}$$

IDENTITIES FOR THE PRODUCT, SUM, AND DIFFERENCE OF SINE AND COSINE

$$\sin u \cos v = \tfrac{1}{2}[\sin(u + v) + \sin(u - v)]$$

$$\cos u \sin v = \tfrac{1}{2}[\sin(u + v) - \sin(u - v)]$$

$$\cos u \cos v = \tfrac{1}{2}[\cos(u + v) + \cos(u - v)]$$

$$\sin u \sin v = \tfrac{1}{2}[\cos(u - v) - \cos(u + v)]$$

$$\sin s + \sin t = 2 \sin\left(\frac{s + t}{2}\right) \cos\left(\frac{s - t}{2}\right)$$

$$\sin s - \sin t = 2 \cos\left(\frac{s + t}{2}\right) \sin\left(\frac{s - t}{2}\right)$$

$$\cos s + \cos t = 2 \cos\left(\frac{s + t}{2}\right) \cos\left(\frac{s - t}{2}\right)$$

$$\cos s - \cos t = -2 \sin\left(\frac{s + t}{2}\right) \sin\left(\frac{s - t}{2}\right)$$

SOME REDUCTION FORMULAS

$$\sin(-x) = -\sin x \qquad \cos(-x) = \cos x \qquad \tan(-x) = -\tan x$$
$$\sin(\tfrac{1}{2}\pi - x) = \cos x \qquad \cos(\tfrac{1}{2}\pi - x) = \sin x$$
$$\tan(\tfrac{1}{2}\pi - x) = \cot x$$
$$\sin(\tfrac{1}{2}\pi + x) = \cos x \qquad \cos(\tfrac{1}{2}\pi + x) = -\sin x$$
$$\tan(\tfrac{1}{2}\pi + x) = -\cot x$$
$$\sin(\pi - x) = \sin x \qquad \cos(\pi - x) = -\cos x$$
$$\tan(\pi - x) = -\tan x$$

LAW OF SINES AND LAW OF COSINES

a, b, and c represent the measures of the sides of a triangle: α, β, and γ represent the measures of the angles opposite the sides of measures a, b, and c, respectively.

$$\frac{a}{\sin \alpha} = \frac{b}{\sin \beta} = \frac{c}{\sin \gamma} \qquad c^2 = a^2 + b^2 - 2ab \cos \gamma$$

FORMULAS FROM GEOMETRY

The following symbols are used for the measure:
r: radius h: altitude b: base a: base C: circumference
A: area S: surface area B: area of base V: volume

Circle: $A = \pi r^2$; $C = 2\pi r$

Triangle: $A = \frac{1}{2}bh$

Rectangle and parallelogram: $A = bh$

Trapezoid: $A = \frac{1}{2}(a + b)h$

Right circular cylinder: $V = \pi r^2 h$; $S = 2\pi rh$

Right circular cone: $V = \frac{1}{3}\pi r^2 h$; $S = \pi r\sqrt{r^2 + h^2}$

Sphere: $V = \frac{4}{3}\pi r^3$; $S = 4\pi r^2$

Prism (with parallel bases): $V = Bh$

Pyramid: $V = \frac{1}{3}Bh$

The Greek alphabet

α	alpha	ι	iota	ρ	rho
β	beta	κ	kappa	σ	sigma
γ	gamma	λ	lambda	τ	tau
δ	delta	μ	mu	υ	upsilon
ϵ	epsilon	ν	nu	φ	phi
ζ	zeta	ξ	xi	χ	chi
η	eta	o	omicron	ψ	psi
θ	theta	π	pi	ω	omega

ANSWERS TO ODD-NUMBERED EXERCISES

EXERCISES 1.1   (page 10)

1. (a) domain: $[4, +\infty)$;   (b) domain: $(-\infty, -2] \cup [2, +\infty)$;   (c) domain: $[-2, 2]$;   (d) not a function

3. (a) domain: $(-\infty, +\infty)$;   (b) not a function;   (c) domain: $(-\infty, +\infty)$;   (d) domain: $(-\infty, +\infty)$

5. (a) 5;   (b) -5;   (c) -1;   (d) $2a + 1$;   (e) $2x + 1$;   (f) $4x - 1$;
   (g) $4x - 2$;   (h) $2x + 2h - 1$;   (i) $2x + 2h - 2$;   (j) 2

7. (a) -5;   (b) -6;   (c) -3;   (d) 30;   (e) $2h^2 + 9h + 4$;   (f) $8x^4 + 10x^2 - 3$;   (g) $2x^4 - 7x^2$;
   (h) $2x^2 + (4h + 5)x + (2h^2 + 5h - 3)$;   (i) $2x^2 + 5x + (2h^2 + 5h - 6)$;   (j) $4x + 2h + 5$

9. (a) $\sqrt{x + 18}$;   (b) $|x|$;   (c) x^2;   (d) $|x + 3|$;   (e) $|x^2 - 3|$;   (f) $\dfrac{1}{\sqrt{x + h + 9} + \sqrt{x + 9}}$

11. domain: $(-\infty, +\infty)$;
    range: $(-\infty, +\infty)$

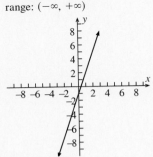

13. domain: $(-\infty, +\infty)$;
    range: $[0, +\infty)$

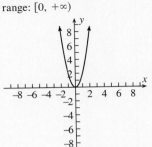

15. domain: $(-\infty, +\infty)$;
    range: $(-\infty, 5]$

17. domain: $[1, +\infty)$;
    range: $[0, +\infty)$

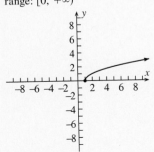

19. domain $(-\infty, -2] \cup [2, +\infty)$;
    range: $[0, +\infty)$

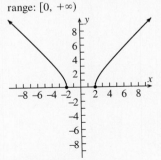

21. domain: $[-3, 3]$;
    range: $[0, 3]$

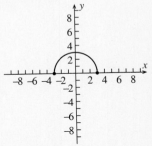

23. domain: $(-\infty, +\infty)$;
    range: $[0, +\infty)$

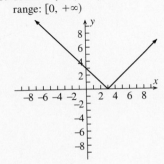

25. domain: $(-\infty, +\infty)$;
    range: $[0, +\infty)$

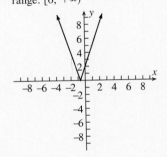

27. domain: $\{x \mid x \neq -5\}$;
    range: $\{y \mid y \neq -10\}$

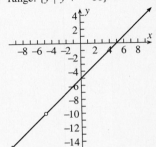

29. domain: $\{x \mid x \neq 1\}$;
range: $\{y \mid y \neq -2\}$

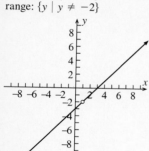

31. domain: $(-\infty, +\infty)$;
range: $\{-2, 2\}$

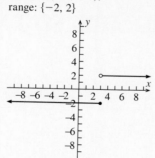

33. domain: $(-\infty, +\infty)$;
range: $\{y \mid y \neq 3\}$

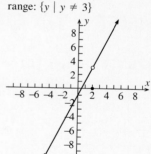

35. domain: $(-\infty, +\infty)$;
range: $[-4, +\infty)$

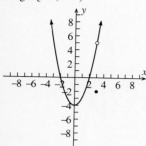

37. domain: $(-\infty, +\infty)$;
range: $(-\infty, +\infty)$

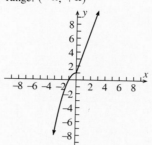

39. domain: $(-\infty, +\infty)$;
range: $(-\infty, 6)$

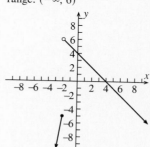

41. domain: $(-\infty, +\infty)$;
range: $(-\infty, -2) \cup [0, 5]$

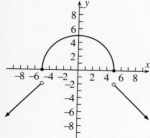

43. domain: $\{x \mid x \neq 2\}$;
range: $[0, +\infty)$

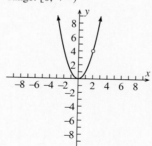

45. domain: $(-\infty, +\infty)$;
range: $\{\text{integers}\}$

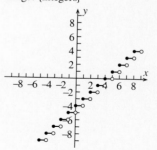

47. (a)

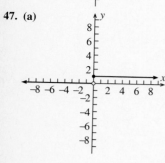

(b) $U(x - 1)$
$= \begin{cases} 0 & \text{if } x < 1 \\ 1 & \text{if } 1 \leq x \end{cases}$

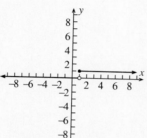

(c) $U(x) - 1$
$= \begin{cases} -1 & \text{if } x < 0 \\ 0 & \text{if } 0 \leq x \end{cases}$

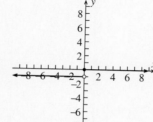

(d) $U(x) - U(x - 1)$
$= \begin{cases} 0 & \text{if } x < 0 \\ 1 & \text{if } 0 \leq x < 1 \\ 0 & \text{if } 1 \leq x \end{cases}$

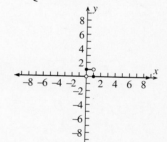

49. (a)

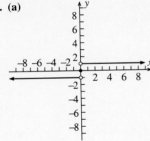

(b) $x \operatorname{sgn} x$

$$= \begin{cases} -x & \text{if } x < 0 \\ 0 & \text{if } x = 0 \\ x & \text{if } 0 < x \end{cases} = |x|$$

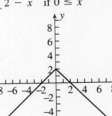

(c) $2 - x \operatorname{sgn} x$

$$= \begin{cases} 2 + x & \text{if } x < 0 \\ 2 - x & \text{if } 0 \le x \end{cases}$$

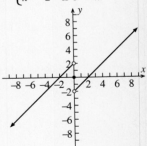

(d) $x - 2 \operatorname{sgn} x$

$$= \begin{cases} x + 2 & \text{if } x < 0 \\ 0 & \text{if } x = 0 \\ x - 2 & \text{if } 0 < x \end{cases}$$

51. $f(x) = \begin{cases} -2x - 2 & \text{if } -2 \le x < -1 \\ x + 1 & \text{if } -1 \le x < 0 \\ -x + 1 & \text{if } 0 \le x < 1 \\ 2x - 2 & \text{if } 1 \le x \le 2 \end{cases}$

53. $f_1(x) = x, f_2(x) = -x$; or, $f_1(x) = |x|, f_2(x) = -|x|$

55. (a) $f(x) = \begin{cases} x^2 - 1 & \text{if } x \le -1 \\ 1 - x^2 & \text{if } -1 < x < 1 \\ x^2 - 1 & \text{if } 1 \le x \end{cases}$

(b)

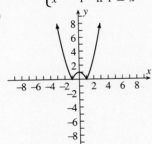

57. (a) $f(x) = \begin{cases} x^2 - 5x & \text{if } x < 0 \\ 5x - x^2 & \text{if } 0 \le x \le 5 \\ x^2 - 5x & \text{if } 5 < x \end{cases}$

(b)

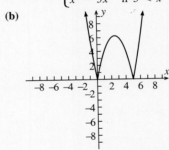

59. domain: $(-\infty, +\infty)$;
range: $[0, 1)$

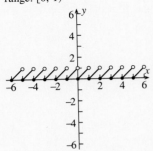

61. $N\text{:} f(x) = \begin{cases} x & \text{if } 0 \le x < 1 \\ 2 - x & \text{if } 1 \le x < 2 \\ x - 2 & \text{if } 2 \le x \le 3 \end{cases}$;

$V\text{:} f(x) = |x| \quad \text{if } -1 \le x \le 1$

EXERCISES 1.2 (page 20)

1. (a) $x^2 + x - 6$, domain: $(-\infty, +\infty)$; **(b)** $-x^2 + x - 4$, domain: $(-\infty, +\infty)$; **(c)** $x^3 - 5x^2 - x + 5$, domain: $(-\infty, +\infty)$;

(d) $\dfrac{x - 5}{x^2 - 1}$, domain: $\{x \mid x \ne -1, x \ne 1\}$; **(e)** $\dfrac{x^2 - 1}{x - 5}$, domain: $\{x \mid x \ne 5\}$

3. **(a)** $\dfrac{x^2 + 2x - 1}{x^2 - x}$, domain: $\{x \mid x \neq 0, x \neq 1\}$;   **(b)** $\dfrac{x^2 + 1}{x^2 - x}$, domain: $\{x \mid x \neq 0, x \neq 1\}$ **(c)** $\dfrac{x + 1}{x^2 - x}$, domain: $\{x \mid x \neq 0, x \neq 1\}$;

(d) $\dfrac{x^2 + x}{x - 1}$, domain: $\{x \mid x \neq 0, x \neq 1\}$;   **(e)** $\dfrac{x - 1}{x^2 + x}$, domain: $\{x \mid x \neq -1, x \neq 0, x \neq 1\}$

5. **(a)** $\sqrt{x} + x^2 - 1$, domain: $[0, +\infty)$;   **(b)** $\sqrt{x} - x^2 + 1$, domain: $[0, +\infty)$ **(c)** $\sqrt{x}\,(x^2 - 1)$, domain: $[0, +\infty)$;

(d) $\dfrac{\sqrt{x}}{x^2 - 1}$, domain: $[0, 1) \cup (1, +\infty)$;   **(e)** $\dfrac{x^2 - 1}{\sqrt{x}}$, domain: $(0, +\infty)$

7. **(a)** $x^2 + 3x - 1$, domain: $(-\infty, +\infty)$;   **(b)** $x^2 - 3x + 3$, domain: $(-\infty, +\infty)$ **(c)** $3x^3 - 2x^2 + 3x - 2$, domain: $(-\infty, +\infty)$;

(d) $\dfrac{x^2 + 1}{3x - 2}$, domain: $\{x \mid x \neq \frac{2}{3}\}$;   **(e)** $\dfrac{3x - 2}{x^2 + 1}$, domain: $(-\infty, +\infty)$

9. **(a)** $\dfrac{x^2 + 2x - 2}{x^2 - x - 2}$, domain: $\{x \mid x \neq -1, x \neq 2\}$;   **(b)** $\dfrac{-x^2 - 2}{x^2 - x - 2}$, domain: $\{x \mid x \neq -1, x \neq 2\}$;

(c) $\dfrac{x}{x^2 - x - 2}$, domain: $\{x \mid x \neq -1, x \neq 2\}$;   **(d)** $\dfrac{x - 2}{x^2 + x}$, domain: $\{x \mid x \neq -1, x \neq 0, x \neq 2\}$;

(e) $\dfrac{x^2 + x}{x - 2}$, domain: $\{x \mid x \neq -1, x \neq 2\}$ **11.** 15   **13.** $\frac{5}{3}$

15. **(a)** $x + 5$, domain: $(-\infty, +\infty)$;   **(b)** $x + 5$, domain: $(-\infty, +\infty)$;   **(c)** $x - 4$, domain: $(-\infty, +\infty)$;

(d) $x + 14$, domain: $(-\infty, +\infty)$ **17.** **(a)** $x^2 - 6$, domain: $(-\infty, +\infty)$;   **(b)** $x^2 - 10x + 24$, domain: $(-\infty, +\infty)$;

(c) $x - 10$, domain: $(-\infty, +\infty)$;   **(d)** $x^4 - 2x^2$, domain: $(-\infty, +\infty)$ **19.** **(a)** $\sqrt{x^2 - 4}$, domain: $(-\infty, -2] \cup [2, +\infty)$;

(b) $x - 4$, domain: $[2, +\infty)$;   **(c)** $\sqrt{\sqrt{x - 2} - 2}$, domain: $[6, +\infty)$;   **(d)** $x^4 - 4x^2 + 2$, domain: $(-\infty, +\infty)$

21. **(a)** $\dfrac{1}{\sqrt{x}}$, domain: $(0, +\infty)$;   **(b)** $\dfrac{1}{\sqrt{x}}$, domain: $(0, +\infty)$;   **(c)** x, domain: $\{x \mid x \neq 0\}$;   **(d)** $\sqrt[4]{x}$, domain: $[0, +\infty)$

23. **(a)** $|x + 2|$, domain: $(-\infty, +\infty)$;   **(b)** $|x| + 2$, domain: $(-\infty, +\infty)$;   **(c)** $|x|$, domain: $(-\infty, +\infty)$;

(d) $|x + 2| + 2$, domain: $(-\infty, +\infty)$ **25.** **(a)** $|x|$, domain: $(-\infty, +\infty)$;   **(b)** x, domain: $(-\infty, +\infty)$;

(c) $\sqrt[4]{x}$, domain: $[0, +\infty)$;   **(d)** $\sqrt[4]{-x}$, domain: $(-\infty, 0]$ **27.** $f(x) = \sqrt{x} - 4$, $g(x) = x^2$; or, $f(x) = \sqrt{x}$, $g(x) = x^2 - 4$

29. $f(x) = x^3$, $g(x) = \dfrac{1}{x - 2}$; or, $f(x) = \left(\dfrac{1}{x}\right)^3$, $g(x) = x - 2$

31. $f(x) = x^4$, $g(x) = x^2 + 4x - 5$; or, $f(x) = (x - 5)^4$, $g(x) = x^2 + 4x$ **33.** **(a)** even;   **(b)** neither

35. **(a)** odd;   **(b)** even   **37.** **(a)** odd;   **(b)** even   **39.** **(a)** odd;   **(b)** even;   **(c)** even

41. **(a)** $\begin{cases} -1 & \text{if } x < 0 \\ 1 & \text{if } 0 < x \end{cases}$ **(c)** odd   **43.** **(a)** $\begin{cases} 4 & \text{if } x < -2 \\ -2x & \text{if } -2 \leq x < 2 \\ -4 & \text{if } 2 \leq x \end{cases}$ **(c)** odd   **45.** No

51. $\text{sgn}(U(x)) = U(\text{sgn}(x)) = U(x)$; see figure for answer to Exercises 1.1 Ex. 47(a)

53. **(a)** odd;   **(b)** even;   **(c)** even

55. $(g \circ f)(x) = \begin{cases} 0 & \text{if } x \leq 0 \text{ or if } 1 < x \\ x & \text{if } 0 < x \leq \frac{1}{2} \\ 1 & \text{if } \frac{1}{2} < x \leq 1 \end{cases}$

57. $2x - 3$, $-2x + 3$

59. The function defined by $f(x) = 0$

EXERCISES 1.3 *(page 27)*

1. **(a)** w workers, P dollars: $P(w) = 67.5w$;   **(b)** \$1012.50

3. **(a)** x ft, P sec: $P(x) = \sqrt{\dfrac{x}{2}}$;   **(b)** 1 sec

5. (a) x lbs, C dollars:

$$C(x) = \begin{cases} 2.2x & \text{if } 0 < x \le 50 \\ 2.1x & \text{if } 50 < x \le 200 \\ 2.05x & \text{if } 200 < x \end{cases}$$

(b)

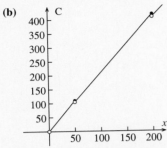

(c) $110, 107.10, 109.20, 111.30, 420, 414.10, 418.20, 422.30

7. (a) x minutes, y cents: $y(x) = 10 - 30[\![-x]\!]$

(b)

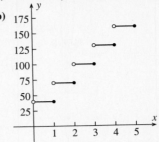

(c) 40¢, 70¢, $1, $1, $1.30, $1.60

9. (a) $f(t) = \dfrac{2\,000\,000}{(t^2 + 7t + 100)^2}$;   **(b)** 78

11. (a) The surface area of the balloon after t seconds is $36\pi t^2$ cm^2;   **(b)** 576π cm$^2 \approx 1810$ cm^2

13. (a) x meters, A sq meters: $A(x) = 120x - x^2$;   **(b)** $[0, 120]$;   **(c)** 60 m $\times$ 60 m

15. (a) x meters, A sq meters: $A(x) = 120x - \frac{1}{2}x^2$;   **(b)** $[0, 240]$;   **(c)** 120 m $\times$ 60 m

17. (a) x in., V cu in.: $V(x) = 4x^3 - 46x^2 + 120x$;   **(b)** $[0, 4]$;   **(c)** 1.7 in., 91 in.^{3}

19. (a) x in., V cu in.: $V(x) = 4x^3 - 54x^2 + 180x$;   **(b)** $[0, 6]$;   **(c)** 2.21 in., 177 in.^{3}

21. (a) r in., C dollars: $C(r) = k\left(\dfrac{120}{r} + 4\pi r^2\right)$, where $k/$in.^{2} is the cost of material for the top and bottom;

(b) $\{r \mid r > 0\}$;   **(c)** 1.68 in.   **23. (a)** x in., A sq in.: $A(x) = 3x + \dfrac{48}{x} + 30$;   **(b)** $(0, +\infty)$;   **(c)** 6 in. $\times$ 9 in.

25. (a) x in., V cu in.: $V(x) = \frac{1}{16}x(100 - x)^2$;   **(b)** $[20, 100]$;   **(c)** 33 in. $\times$ 17 in. $\times$ 17 in.

27. (a) $f(x) = \frac{9}{490,000}x(5000 - x)$;   **(b)** 17.6 people per day;   **(c)** 2500

EXERCISES 1.4 *(page 39)*

(Note. Any value for δ smaller than those given is also correct.) **1.** 0.1   **3.** 0.23   **5.** 0.005   **7.** 0.01   **9.** 0.005
11. 0.01   **13.** 0.015   **15.** 0.268   **17.** 0.082   **19.** 0.095   **21.** 0.183   **23.** 0.084   **25.** 0.23   **27.** 0.01
29. 0.015   **31.** $\frac{1}{14}$ **33.** $\frac{2}{15}$ **35.** $\frac{1}{15}$ **37.** within 1 min   **39.** within 0.01 ft   **41.** within $\frac{2}{7}$ in.   **43.** within $\frac{1}{8}$ sec

EXERCISES 1.5 *(page 51)*

11. 8   **13.** 7   **15.** 5.0   **17.** $\frac{1}{2}$ **19.** $-\frac{1}{22}$ **21.** $\frac{3}{2}$ **23.** $\frac{2}{3}$
25. (a) 0.3333, 0.2857, 0.2564, 0.2506, 0.2501; 0.2000, 0.2222, 0.2439, 0.2494, 0.2499;   **(b)** $\frac{1}{4}$
27. (a) 0.2500, 0.2000, 0.1549, 0.1441, 0.1430, 0.1429; 0, 0.0769, 0.1304, 0.1416, 0.1427, 0.1428;   **(b)** $\frac{1}{7}$
29. (a) 0.1716, 0.1690, 0.1671, 0.1667, 0.1667; 0.1623, 0.1644, 0.1662, 0.1666, 0.1667;   **(b)** $\frac{1}{6}$
31. 14   **33.** -6 **35.** $\frac{16}{7}$ **37.** 12   **39.** $\sqrt{\frac{6}{5}} = \frac{1}{5}\sqrt{30}$ **41.** $\frac{1}{2}$ **43.** $\frac{1}{4}\sqrt{2}$ **45.** -1
49. 0/0 is not defined; 2   **51.** 0/0 is not defined; $\frac{1}{6}$
53. $\lim\limits_{x \to 2} f(x) = 3; f(2) = 1$

55. (a) $f(x) = \begin{cases} x + 3 & \text{if } x \ne 3 \\ 2 & \text{if } x = 3 \end{cases}$;   **(b)** 0, 3, 2;   **(c)** 0, 3, 6

57. (a) $f(x) = \begin{cases} 5 & \text{if } x = -4 \\ 6 & \text{if } x = 3 \\ \sqrt{25 - x^2} & \text{if } x \in [-5, -4) \cup (-4, 3) \cup (3, 5] \end{cases}$;

(b) 5, 4, 6, 3;   **(c)** 3, 4, 4, 3

59.

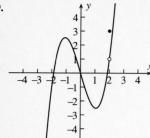

61.

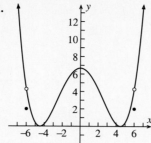

EXERCISES 1.6 (page 57)

1. (a) -3; **(b)** 2; **(c)** does not exist because $\lim\limits_{x \to 1^+} f(x) \neq \lim\limits_{x \to 1^-} f(x)$

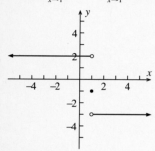

3. (a) 8; **(b)** 0; **(c)** does not exist because $\lim\limits_{t \to -4^+} f(t) \neq \lim\limits_{t \to -4^-} f(t)$

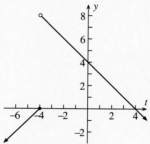

5. (a) 4; **(b)** 4; **(c)** 4

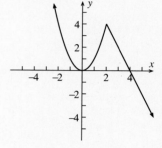

7. (a) 5; **(b)** 5; **(c)** 5

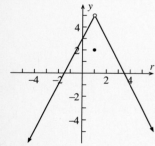

9. (a) 0; **(b)** 0; **(c)** 0

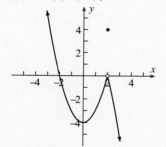

11. (a) 0; **(b)** 0; **(c)** 0

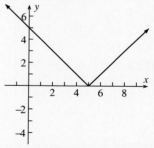

13. (a) -4; **(b)** -4; **(c)** -4

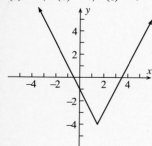

15. (a) 1; **(b)** -1; **(c)** does not exist because $\lim\limits_{x \to 0^+} f(x) \neq \lim\limits_{x \to 0^-} f(x)$

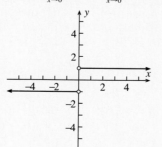

17. (a) 2; **(b)** 0; **(c)** does not exist because $\lim\limits_{x \to -2^-} f(x) \neq \lim\limits_{x \to -2^+} f(x)$;
(d) 0; **(e)** -2; **(f)** does not exist because $\lim\limits_{x \to 2^-} f(x) \neq \lim\limits_{x \to 2^+} f(x)$

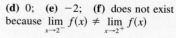

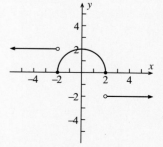

19. (a) 0; **(b)** 0; **(c)** 0

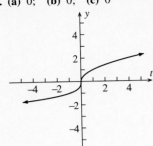

21. (a) 0; **(b)** 0; **(c)** 0; **(d)** 0; **(e)** 0; **(f)** 0

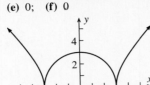

23. (a) −2; **(b)** 2; **(c)** does not exist
25. (a) 2; **(b)** 1; **(c)** does not exist
27. (a) −1; **(b)** 1; **(c)** does not exist

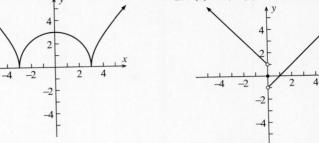

29. −6   **31.** $a = -\frac{3}{2}, b = 1$

37.

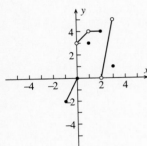

35. (a) 0; **(b)** 3; **(c)** 0; **(d)** does not exist; **(e)** 5; **(f)** 5; **(g)** 5; **(h)** 2; **(i)** 2
(j) 2; **(k)** 0
39. (a) 110; **(b)** 105; **(c)** 420; **(d)** 410   **41. (a)** 40; **(b)** 70; **(c)** 70; **(d)** 160
43. (a) $\lim_{x\to1^-} f(x) = 4$, $\lim_{x\to1^+} f(x) = 2$; **(b)** $\lim_{x\to1^-} g(x) = 1$, $\lim_{x\to1^+} g(x) = 2$;

(c) $f(x)g(x) = \begin{cases} x^4 + 3x^2 & \text{if } x \le 1 \\ 2x + 2 & \text{if } x > 1 \end{cases}$; **(d)** 4

EXERCISES 1.7 (page 69)

1. (a) 1, 2, 10, 100, 1000, 10,000; **(c)** $+\infty$ **3. (a)** 1, 4, 100, 10,000, 1,000,000, 100,000,000; 1, 4, 100, 10,000, 1,000,000,
100,000,000; **(c)** $+\infty$ **5. (a)** −4, −7, −31, −301, −3001, −30,001; **(c)** $-\infty$ **7. (a)** −2, −5, −29, −299, −2999,
−29,999; **(c)** $-\infty$ **9. (a)** 5, 9, 41, 401, 4001, 40,001; **(c)** $+\infty$ **11. (a)** 2.3, 4.3, 20.3, 200.3, 2000.5, 20,037; **(c)** $+\infty$
13. $+\infty$ **15.** $-\infty$ **17.** $-\infty$ **19.** $+\infty$ **21.** $-\infty$ **23.** $+\infty$ **25.** $+\infty$ **27.** $-\infty$ **29.** $-\infty$ **31.** $-\infty$
33. (b) $-\frac{5}{2}$; **(c)** $-\frac{5}{2}$; **(d)** $-\infty$; **(e)** $+\infty$
35. (a) $x = 0$;   **(b)** $x = 0$;   **(c)** $x = 0$;   **(d)** $x = 0$

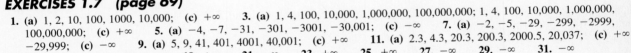

37. $x = 4$ **39.** $x = -3$ **41.** $x = -3$ **43.** $x = -5, x = -3$

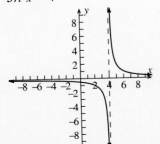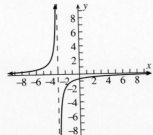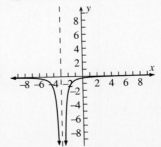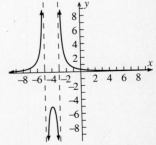

45. (a) 0; **(b)** $-\infty$ **(c)** $+\infty$; **(d)** 0; **(e)** $+\infty$; **(f)** $+\infty$; **(g)** $+\infty$; **(h)** 1; **(i)** $-\infty$; **(j)** 0

47.

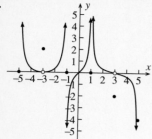

49. $+\infty$

EXERCISES 1.8 (page 80)

1. $-3; f(-3)$ does not exist   **3.** $-3; \lim_{x\to -3} g(x) \neq g(-3)$ **5.** $4; h(4)$ does not exist   **7.** $4; \lim_{x\to 4} f(x)$ does not exist

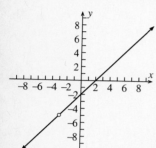

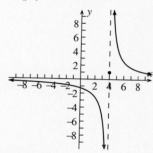

9. $0; \lim_{x\to 0} f(x)$ does not exist   **11.** $2; \lim_{t\to 2} g(t) \neq g(2)$ **13.** $0; f(0)$ does not exist

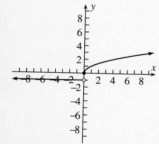

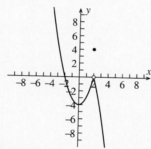

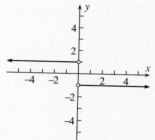

15. (a) removable; **(b)** 4   **17. (a)** removable; **(b)** 6   **19. (a)** removable; **(b)** $\frac{1}{6}$ **21. (a)** removable; **(b)** $-\frac{1}{4}\sqrt{2}$
23. (a) removable; **(b)** $\frac{1}{12}$ **25. (a)** removable; **(b)** 1   **27. (a)** essential   **29.** all real numbers
31. all real numbers except 3   **33.** all real numbers except -2 and 2   **35.** all real numbers except 2
37. all real numbers except -1 and 3   **39.** all real numbers
41. $k = 5$ **43.** $c = -3, k = 4$

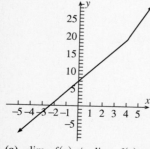

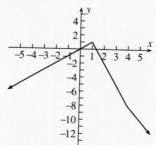

45. (a) $\lim_{x\to -3^-} f(x) \neq \lim_{x\to -3^+} f(x)$, essential; **(b)** $\lim_{x\to 1} f(x) \neq f(1)$, removable: define $f(1) = 5$; **(c)** $\lim_{x\to 3^-} f(x)$ does not exist, essential

47.

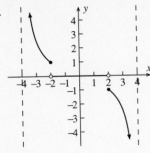

49. 50: $\lim\limits_{x \to 50^-} f(x) \neq \lim\limits_{x \to 50^+} f(x)$; 200: $\lim\limits_{x \to 200^-} f(x) \neq \lim\limits_{x \to 200^+} f(x)$

51. $\lim\limits_{x \to n^-} g(x) \neq \lim\limits_{x \to n^+} g(x)$ for any positive integer n

59. $f(x) = \begin{cases} 0 & \text{if } x < a \\ 1 & \text{if } a \leq x \end{cases}$; $g(x) = \begin{cases} 1 & \text{if } x < a \\ 0 & \text{if } a \leq x \end{cases}$

EXERCISES 1.9 (page 90)

1. (a) $(f \circ g)(x) = \sqrt{9 - x^2}$, continuous at all numbers in $(-3, 3)$;
   (b) $(f \circ g)(x) = \sqrt{x^2 - 16}$, continuous at all numbers in $(-\infty, -4) \cup (4, +\infty)$

3. (a) $(f \circ g)(x) = \dfrac{1}{\sqrt{x - 2}}$, continuous at all numbers in $(2, +\infty)$;

   (b) $(f \circ g)(x) = \dfrac{1}{\sqrt{x} - 2}$, continuous at all positive numbers except 4

5. $(f \circ g)(x) = \dfrac{\sqrt{4 - x^2}}{\sqrt{|x| - 1}}$, continuous at all numbers in $(-2, -1) \cup (1, 2)$

7. all real numbers except -5; continuous on $(3, 7)$, $(-5, +\infty)$, $[-10, -5)$; discontinuous on $[-6, 4]$, $(-\infty, 0)$, $[-5, +\infty)$

9. all real numbers except 1 and -1; continuous on $(0, 1)$, $(-1, 1)$, $(-1, 0]$, $(1, +\infty)$; discontinuous on $[0, 1]$, $(-\infty, -1]$

11. $(-\infty, -3] \cup [3, +\infty)$; continuous on $(-\infty, -3)$, $(3, +\infty)$, $(-\infty, -3]$, $[3, +\infty)$; discontinuous on $(-3, 3)$

13. all real numbers except 1; continuous on $(-\infty, 1)$, $(1, +\infty)$; discontinuous on $(-\infty, 1]$, $[-1, 1]$, $(-1, \infty)$

15. $[-2, 2]$; continuous on $(-2, 2)$, $[-2, 2]$, $(-2, 2]$, $[-2, 2)$; discontinuous on $(-\infty, -2]$ and $(2, +\infty)$

17. (a) $[-3, 3]$; **(b)** $(-\infty, -4] \cup [4, +\infty)$ **19. (a)** $(2, +\infty)$; **(b)** $[0, 4) \cup (4, +\infty)$ **21.** $[-2, -1) \cup (1, 2]$

23. $(-\infty, -2) \cup [-2, 2] \cup (2, +\infty)$

25.

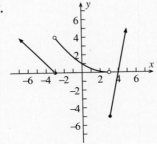

27.

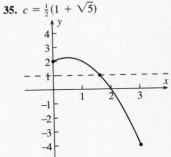

35. $c = \frac{1}{2}(1 + \sqrt{5})$

37. $c = -4$

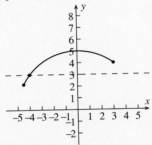

39. f is discontinuous at -2

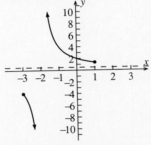

41. f is discontinuous at 1

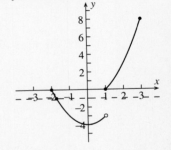

43. $-2.67, 0.52, 2.15$ **45.** $-1, 1.17$ **49.** $[0, c)$ **55.** no

EXERCISES 1.10 *(page 101)*

1. 4   **3.** $\frac{9}{7}$ **5.** $\frac{3}{5}$ **7.** $\frac{1}{9}$ **9.** 0   **11.** 0   **13.** 12   **15.** $\frac{1}{2}$ **17.** 0   **19.** 3   **21.** $+\infty$ **23.** 0
25. -1 **29.** 0   **31.** -4 **33.** 1   **35.** 0   **45.** does not exist

MISCELLANEOUS EXERCISES FOR CHAPTER 1   *(page 103)*

1. (a) 3;   (b) 0;   (c) -5;   (d) $-x^2 + 2x + 3$;   (e) $4 - x^4$;   (f) $-2x - h$

3. (a) $\sqrt{x + 2} + x^2 - 4$, domain: $[-2, +\infty)$;   (b) $\sqrt{x + 2} - x^2 + 4$, domain: $[-2, +\infty)$;

 (c) $\sqrt{x + 2}\,(x^2 - 4)$, domain: $[-2, +\infty)$;   (d) $\dfrac{\sqrt{x + 2}}{x^2 - 4}$, domain: $(-2, 2) \cup (2, +\infty)$;

 (e) $\dfrac{x^2 - 4}{\sqrt{x + 2}}$, domain: $(-2, +\infty)$;   (f) $\sqrt{x^2 - 2}$, domain: $(-\infty, -\sqrt{2}] \cup [\sqrt{2}, +\infty)$;   (g) $x - 2$, domain: $(-2, +\infty)$

5. (a) $\dfrac{1}{x^2} + \sqrt{x}$, domain: $(0, +\infty)$;   (b) $\dfrac{1}{x^2} - \sqrt{x}$, domain: $(0, +\infty)$;   (c) $\dfrac{1}{\sqrt{x^3}}$, domain: $(0, +\infty)$;   (d) $\dfrac{1}{\sqrt{x^5}}$, domain: $(0, +\infty)$;

 (e) $\sqrt{x^5}$, domain: $(0, +\infty)$;   (f) $\dfrac{1}{x}$, domain: $(0, +\infty)$;   (g) $\dfrac{1}{|x|}$, domain: $x \neq 0$ **7.** (a) odd;   (b) even;   (c) neither;   (d) odd

9. (a) domain: $(-\infty, +\infty)$, range: $(-\infty, +\infty)$;   (b) domain: $(-\infty, +\infty)$, range: $[-4, +\infty)$;   (c) domain: $(-\infty, -4] \cup [4, +\infty)$, range:
 $[0, +\infty)$;   (d) domain: $[-4, 4]$, range: $[0, 4]$;   (e) domain: $(-\infty, +\infty)$, range: $[0, +\infty)$;   (f) domain: $(-\infty, +\infty)$, range: $(-\infty, 5]$

11. (a) domain: $\{x \mid x \neq -4\}$;   (b) domain: $(-\infty, +\infty)$;   **13.** (a) domain: $(-\infty, +\infty)$;   (b) domain: $(-\infty, +\infty)$;
 range: $\{y \mid y \neq -8\}$ range: $\{y \mid y \neq -8\}$ range: $[3, +\infty)$ range: $[-1, +\infty)$

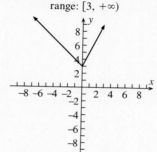
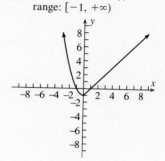

(Note on Exercises 15–25: Any value for δ smaller than those given is also correct.)

15. (a) 0.025;   (c) 0.025   **17.** (a) 0.1;   (c) 0.1   **19.** (a) 0.074;   (b) 0.06   **21.** $\frac{1}{2}\epsilon$ **23.** $\frac{1}{3}\epsilon$ **25.** $\frac{1}{4}\epsilon$
27. 9   **29.** -6 **31.** $\sqrt[3]{2}$ **33.** $-\frac{1}{6}$ **35.** $-\frac{5}{2}$ **37.** $\frac{1}{3}$ **39.** $\frac{3}{10}$ **41.** $-\infty$
43. (a) 8;   (b) 8;   (c) 8;   **45.** (a) -1;   (b) 1;   (c) does not exist   **47.** (a) -8;   (b) 0;   (c) does not exist

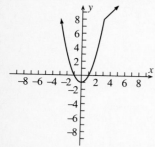
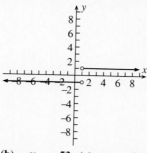
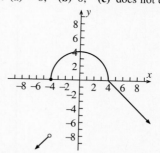

49. (a) $+\infty$;   (b) $-\infty$ **51.** (a) $+\infty$;   (b) $-\infty$ **53.** (a) $+\infty$;   (b) $-\infty$ **55.** $\frac{1}{3}$ **57.** $\frac{5}{2}$ **59.** 0   **61.** $\frac{1}{3}$

63. $x = 4$

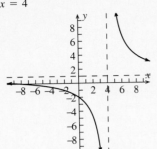

65. $x = 0$

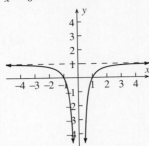

67. $x = 2, x = -2$

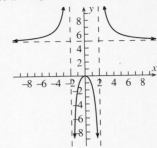

69. $-2, 1; f(-2)$ and $f(1)$ do not exist

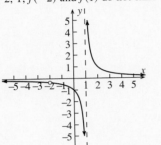

71. -2; $\lim\limits_{x \to -2} g(x)$ does not exist

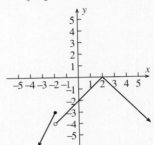

73. $0, 1; h(0)$ does not exist, $\lim\limits_{x \to 1} h(x)$ does not exist

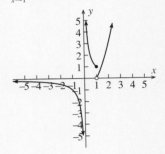

75. removable; $\frac{6}{5}$ **77.** essential   **79.** removable; -1 **81.** removable; 6

83. **(a)** $(f \circ g)(x) = \sqrt{25 - x^2}$, continuous at all numbers in $(-5, 5)$;

(b) $(f \circ g)(x) = \dfrac{\sqrt{x^2 - 4}}{\sqrt{3 - |x|}}$, continuous at all numbers in $(-3, -2) \cup (2, 3)$;

(c) $(f \circ g)(x) = \begin{cases} 1 & \text{if } x < -1 \\ 0 & \text{if } x = -1 \\ -1 & \text{if } -1 < x < 1 \\ 0 & \text{if } x = 1 \\ 1 & \text{if } x > 1 \end{cases}$, continuous at all real numbers except -1 and 1

85. $a = 10, b = -23$

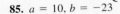

87. **(b)** all values of a;   **(c)** all nonintegers

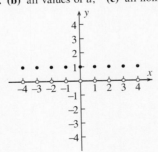

89. **(a)** $[-5, 5]$;   **(b)** $(-\infty, -5] \cup [5, +\infty)$
91. **(a)** $(-\infty, 2) \cup (2, +\infty)$;
(b) $(-\infty, -2) \cup (-2, 2) \cup (2, +\infty)$

93. $2 - \sqrt{13} \approx -1.6056$

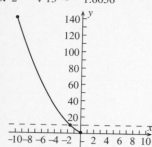

95. $-1 + \sqrt{7} \approx 1.6458$

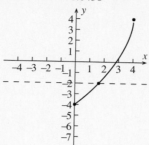

97. (a) 0;
(b) $-\infty$;
(c) 3;
(d) $-\infty$;
(e) $+\infty$;
(f) 1;
(g) 4;
(h) -3, removable, $f(-3) = 0$;
-2, essential; 0, removable,
$f(0) = 3$; 2, essential; 3, essential

99.

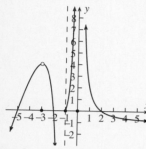

101.

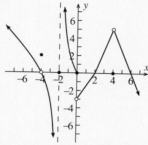

103. (a) cut x in. squares, $V = (14 - 2x)(18 - 2x)x$;   **(b)** $[0, 7]$;   **(c)** 2.60 in.; 293 in.^{3}

105. (a) x in. is width, $A = 82 + 8x + \dfrac{200}{x}$;   **(b)** $(0, +\infty)$;   **(d)** 9 m wide by 18 m long

107. $F(x) = \begin{cases} -1 \cdot 0 = 0 & \text{if } x < -1 \\ -1 \cdot 1 = -1 & \text{if } -1 \le x < 0 \\ 0 \cdot 1 = 0 & \text{if } x = 0 \\ 1 \cdot 1 = 1 & \text{if } x > 0 \end{cases}$

F is discontinuous at -1 and 0 because the
left- and right-hand limits disagree there

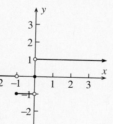

109. 0   **111. (a)** yes;   **(b)** yes

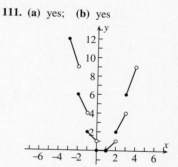

EXERCISES 2.1 *(page 116)*

1. $y = -4x + 13$

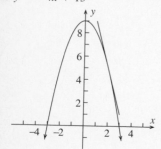

3. $y = -4x - 8$

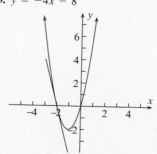

5. $y = 3x + 1$

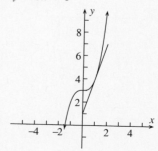

7. (a) $6x_1 - 12$;   **(b)** $(2, 4)$ **9. (a)** $3x_1{}^2 - 12x_1 + 9$;   **(b)** $(1, 2), (3, -2)$

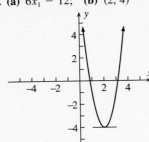

11. tangent: $y = \frac{1}{4}x + \frac{5}{4}$; normal: $y = -4x + 14$ **13.** tangent: $y = -10x - 16$; normal: $y = \frac{1}{10}x + \frac{21}{5}$

15. tangent: $y = -x + 3$; normal: $y = x - 1$

17. (a and c) 5.30, 5.27, 5.24, 5.21, 5.18, 5.15, 5.12, 5.09, 5.06, 5.03; 4.70, 4.73, 4.76, 4.79, 4.82, 4.85, 4.88, 4.91, 4.94, 4.97
    (b and d) 5

19. (a and c) $-0.2516, -0.2514, -0.2513, -0.2511, -0.2509, -0.2508, -0.2506, -0.2505, -0.2503, -0.2502; -0.2485, -0.2486,$
    $-0.2488, -0.2489, -0.2491, -0.2492, -0.2494, -0.2495, -0.2497, -0.2498;$ **(b and d)** $-\frac{1}{4}$

21. $-\frac{1}{2}$ **23.** 1   **25.** 0   **27.** 0   **29.** -1 **31.** 0   **33.** 7   **35.** $5 - 4x$ **37.** $-3x^2$

39. $\dfrac{-13}{(3r - 2)^2}$ **41.** $3 - \dfrac{12}{x^3}$ **43.** $-\frac{1}{2}(x - 1)^{-3/2}$ **45.** $y = 8x - 5$ **47.** $4x + 4y - 11 = 0$ **51.** $g(a)$ **53.** $2a$

EXERCISES 2.2   (page 125)

1. (a)

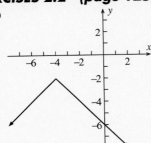

(b) yes;
(c) 1, −1;
(d) no

3. (a)

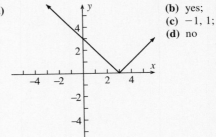

(b) yes;
(c) −1, 1;
(d) no

5. (a)

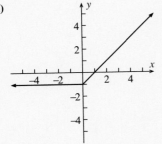

(b) yes;
(c) 0, 1;
(d) no

7. (a)

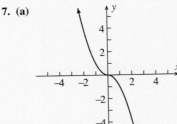

(b) yes;
(c) 0, 0;
(d) yes

9. (a)

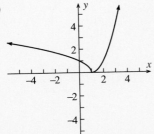

(b) yes;
(c) does not exist, 0;
(d) no

11. (a)

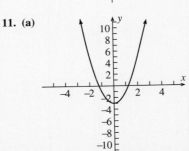

(b) yes;
(c) 8, 8;
(d) yes

13. (a)

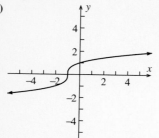

(b) yes;
(c) neither exists;
(d) no

15. (a)

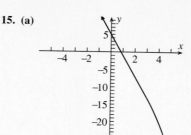

(b) yes;
(c) $-6, -6$;
(d) yes

17. (a)

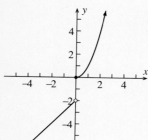

(b) no;
(c) 1, 0;
(d) no

19. (a)

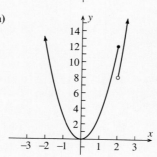

(b) no;
(c) 12, 12;
(d) no

21. (a) $f(x) = \begin{cases} 1 - x^2 & \text{if } x \le -1 \\ x + 1 & \text{if } -1 < x \le 0; \\ -x + 1 & \text{if } 0 < x \le 1 \\ x - 1 & \text{if } x \ge 1 \end{cases}$

(b) 2; **(c)** 1; **(d)** 1;
(e) -1; **(f)** -1;
(g) 1; **(h)** $-1, 0, 1$

23. (a) $\begin{cases} \frac{1}{2}x + \frac{3}{2} & \text{if } x \le -1 \\ -x^{1/3} & \text{if } -1 < x \le 0 \\ x^{1/3} & \text{if } 0 < x \le 1; \\ x & \text{if } x > 1 \end{cases}$

(b) $\frac{1}{2}$; **(c)** $-\frac{1}{3}$;
(d) $-\infty$; **(e)** $+\infty$;
(f) $\frac{1}{3}$; **(g)** 1; **(h)** $-1, 0, 1$

25. (a) $f(x) = \begin{cases} -2x - 1 & \text{if } x \le -1 \\ x^2 & \text{if } -1 < x \le 0 \\ -x^2 & \text{if } 0 < x \le 1; \\ x - 2 & \text{if } x > 1 \end{cases}$

(b) -2; **(c)** -2;
(d) 0; **(e)** 0;
(f) -2; **(g)** 1; **(h)** 1

27.

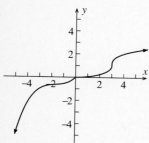

29.

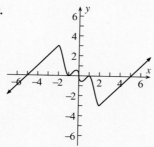

31. yes

33. (a) 3; **(b)**
(c) no

35. $a = 2, b = -1$

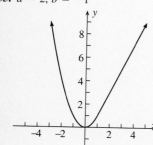

37. (a) $f(x) = \begin{cases} 15x & \text{if } 0 \le x \le 150 \\ 22.5x - 0.05x^2 & \text{if } 150 < x \le 250 \end{cases}$; **(c)** no

39. (a) $f(x) = \begin{cases} 600x & \text{if } 0 \le x \le 20 \\ 900x - 15x^2 & \text{if } 20 < x \le 60 \end{cases}$; **(c)** no

43. (a) 0; **(b)** 1; **(c)** does not exist

47. (a) 0 for all real numbers; **(b)** 0 if $x \ne 0$

EXERCISES 2.3 (page 131)

1. all are 5   **3. (a)** $-0.250019, -0.250016, -0.250012, -0.250009, -0.250006, -0.250005, -0.250004, -0.250002,$ $-0.250001, -0.250000$; the same 10 numbers; $-\frac{1}{4}$ **9. (a)** 2;   **(b)** $y = 2x - 3$ **11. (a)** 4;   **(b)** $y = 4x - 13$
13. (a) $-\frac{5}{3} \approx -1.6667$;   **(b)** $y = -\frac{5}{3}x - \frac{16}{3} \approx -1.6667x - 5.3333$ **15. (a)** 0.4;   **(b)** $y = 0.4x - 0.4$
17. (a) 1.3818;   **(b)** $y = 1.3818x - 0.5403$ **19. (a)** -0.8317;   **(b)** $y = -0.8317x + 1.2591$
23. (b) and **(d)** $x > 0$;   **(c)** and **(e)** $x < 0$ **25. (b)** and **(d)** $x < 0$;   **(c)** and **(e)** $x > 0$ **27. (a)** 100   **29. (b)** 0

EXERCISES 2.4 (page 141)

1. 7   **3.** $-2 - 2x$ **5.** $3x^2 - 6x + 5$ **7.** $x^7 - 4x^3$ **9.** $t^3 - t$ **11.** $4\pi r^2$
13. $2x + 3 - \dfrac{2}{x^3}$ **15.** $16x^3 + \dfrac{1}{x^5}$ **17.** $-\dfrac{6}{x^3} - \dfrac{20}{x^5}$ **19.** $3\sqrt{3}s^2 - 2\sqrt{3}s$ **21.** $70x^6 + 60x^4 - 15x^2 - 6$
23. $-18y^2(7 - 3y^3)$ **25.** $10x^4 - 24x^3 + 12x^2 + 2x - 3$ **27.** $-\dfrac{1}{(x-1)^2}$ **29.** $-\dfrac{4(x+1)}{(x-1)^3}$ **31.** $\dfrac{5(1 - 2t^2)}{(1 + 2t^2)^2}$
33. $\dfrac{48y^2}{(y^3 + 8)^2}$ **35.** $\dfrac{6(x^2 + 10x + 1)}{(x + 5)^2}$
37. $f'(x) = 30x^4 + 12x^3 - 6x^2 + 10x - 8$; $f''(x) = 120x^3 + 36x^2 - 12x + 10$; $f'''(x) = 360x^2 + 72x - 12$; $f^{(4)}(x) = 720x + 72$; $f^{(5)}(x) = 720$; $f^{(n)}(x) = 0$ if $n \geq 6$ **39.** $-10t^{-6}$ **41.** $2 + 6x^{-4}$ **43.** $y = 12x - 20$
45. $y = -\frac{1}{20}x - \frac{24}{5}$ **47.** $y = 2x - 3$ **49.** $x + 8y + 2 = 0$; $x + 8y - 2 = 0$ **51.** $28x - y = 99$; $4x - y = 3$
55. $2(3x + 2)(6x^2 + 2x - 3)$ **57.** $3(2x^2 + x + 1)^2(4x + 1)$

EXERCISES 2.5 (page 152)

1. $v(t) = 6t$; 18   **3.** $v(t) = -\dfrac{1}{4t^2}$; -1 **5.** $v(t) = 6t^2 - 2t$; 8   **7.** $v(t) = \dfrac{8}{(4 + t)^2}$; $\dfrac{1}{2}$
9. $t < -3$, moving to right; $-3 < t < 1$, moving to left; $t > 1$, moving to right; changes direction when $t = -3$ and $t = 1$
11. $t < -2$, moving to right; $-2 < t < \frac{1}{2}$, moving to left; $t > \frac{1}{2}$, moving to right; changes direction when $t = -2$ and $t = \frac{1}{2}$
13. $t < -3$, moving to left; $-3 < t < 3$, moving to right; $t > 3$, moving to left; changes direction when $t = -3$ and $t = 3$
17. (a) $s = -16t^2 + 256$;   **(b)** -32 ft/sec, -64 ft/sec;   **(c)** 4 sec;   **(d)** -128 ft/sec
19. (a) $s = -16t^2 - 48t + 160$;   **(b)** -80 ft/sec, -96 ft/sec;   **(c)** 2 sec;   **(d)** -112 ft/sec
21. (a) $s = -16t^2 + 560t$;   **(b and c)** 17.5 sec, 4900 ft;   **(d)** 240 ft/sec, -240 ft/sec;   **(e)** 240 ft/sec, 240 ft/sec;   **(f)** 560 ft/sec
23.

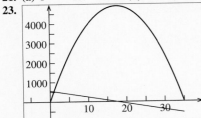

25. $\frac{3}{2}$ sec; $\frac{7}{4}$ ft; $-\frac{1}{4}$ ft/sec

27. $v = 3t^2 - 18t + 15$; $a = 6t - 18$; when $0 < t < 1$, the particle is at the right of the origin, it is moving to the right, the velocity is decreasing, and the speed is decreasing; when $1 < t < \frac{1}{2}(9 - \sqrt{21})$, the particle is at the right of the origin, it is moving to the left, the velocity is decreasing, and the speed is increasing; when $\frac{1}{2}(9 - \sqrt{21}) < t < 3$, the particle is at the left of the origin, it is moving to the left, the velocity is decreasing, and the speed is increasing; when $3 < t < 5$, the particle is at the left of the origin, it is moving to the left, the velocity is increasing, and the speed is decreasing; when $5 < t < \frac{1}{2}(9 + \sqrt{21})$, the particle is at the left of the origin, it is moving to the right, the velocity is increasing, and the speed is increasing; when $\frac{1}{2}(9 + \sqrt{21}) < t$, the particle is at the right of the origin, it is moving to the right, the velocity is increasing, and the speed is increasing
31. (a) 44 ft;   **(b)** -22 ft/sec;   **(c)** 22 ft/sec   **33. (a)** 8.25 m/sec;   **(b)** 12.96 m/sec   **35.** 160 cm/sec

EXERCISES 2.6 (page 160)

1. (a) 8.6;   **(b)** 8.3;   **(c)** 8.1;   **(d)** 8.05;   **(e)** 8   **3. (a)** $65,000,000k$;   **(b)** $32,000,000k$ **5. (a)** $2\pi r$;   **(b)** 2π
7. $\frac{5}{32}\pi x^2$ **9. (a)** $1.2 - 0.24t$;   **(b)** $101.12°$, $0.48°$/day;   **(c)** $100.52°$, $-0.72°$/day;   **(d)** $101.6°$ at 5 days
11. (a) 9π $\mu m^3/\mu m$;   **(b)** 16π $\mu m^3/\mu m$ **13. (a)** 12π $\mu m^2/\mu m$;   **(b)** 16π $\mu m^2/\mu m$ **15. (a)** $2.9°$/hr;   **(b)** $-3°$/hr
17. (a) 18,750 liters/min;   **(b)** 17,500 liters/min   **19. (a)** $C'(x) = 3 + 2x$;   **(b)** \$83;   **(c)** \$84
21. (a) $R'(x) = 600 - \frac{3}{20}x^2$;   **(b)** \$540;   **(c)** \$536.95
23. (a) \$3.6 million per year;   **(b)** 23.1 percent;   **(c)** \$6.8 million per year;   **(d)** 18.7 percent

25. (a) 920 people per year; (b) 6.1 percent; (c) 1400 people per year; (d) 6.4 percent
27. (a) profitable; (b) not profitable; (c) 90   **29.** $y'(-1) = 5$, $y'(\frac{1}{2}) = -\frac{7}{4}$
31. (a) 3.2 m/min; (b) 16 m/min; (c) 16 m/min

EXERCISES 2.7 (page 170)

3. $3 \cos x$ **5.** $\sec^2 x - \csc^2 x$ **7.** $2(\cos t - t \sin t)$ **9.** $x \cos x$ **11.** $4 \cos 2x$ **13.** $-x^2 \sin x$
15. $3 \sec x(2 \tan^2 x + 1)$ **17.** $-\sin y \cot y - \cos y \csc^2 y$
19. $-\dfrac{2(z+1)\sin z + 2 \cos z}{(z+1)^2}$ **21.** $\dfrac{1}{\cos x - 1}$ **23.** $\dfrac{1 - 4 \sec t + \sin^2 t}{\cos t(\cos t - 4)^2}$ **25.** $\dfrac{2 \cos y}{(1 - \sin y)^2}$
27. $(1 - \cos x)(x + \cos x) + (1 - \sin x)(x - \sin x)$ **29.** $-\dfrac{5 \csc t \cot t}{(\csc t + 2)^2}$ **31.** 1   **33.** $-\dfrac{2}{\pi}$
35. π^2 **37.** 2   **39.** $\sqrt{2}$ **41.** $-\frac{10}{3}$
43. (a) 0.0226, 0.2674, 0.4559, 0.4956, 0.4995; 0.8188, 0.6915, 0.5424, 0.5043, 0.5006; (b) $\frac{1}{2}$
45. (a) 2.2305, 2.0203, 2.0020, 2.0002, 2.0000; 1.8237, 1.9803, 1.9980, 1.9998, 2.0000; (b) 2
47. (a) $-0.4771, -0.4886, -0.4977, -0.4989, -0.4998; -0.5224, -0.5113, -0.5023, -0.5011, -0.5002$; (b) $-\frac{1}{2}$
49. (a) 0.4929, 0.5736, 0.6468, 0.6567, 0.6647; 0.9116, 0.7770, 0.6872, 0.6768, 0.6687; (b) $\frac{2}{3}$
51. (a) $x - y = 0$; (b) $x - 2y + \sqrt{3} - \frac{1}{3}\pi = 0$; (c) $x + y - \pi = 0$
53. (a) $x - y = 0$; (b) $4x - 2y + 2 - \pi = 0$; (c) $4x - 2y - 2 + \pi = 0$
55. (a) $4 \cos t$; (b) $v(0) = 4$, $v(\frac{1}{3}\pi) = 2$, $v(\frac{1}{2}\pi) = 0$, $v(\frac{2}{3}\pi) = -2$, $v(\pi) = -4$
57. (a) $3 \sin t$; (b) $v(0) = 0$, $v(\frac{1}{6}\pi) = \frac{3}{2}$, $v(\frac{1}{3}\pi) = \frac{3}{2}\sqrt{3}$, $v(\frac{1}{2}\pi) = 3$, $v(\frac{2}{3}\pi) = \frac{3}{2}\sqrt{3}$, $v(\frac{5}{6}\pi) = \frac{3}{2}$, $v(\pi) = 0$
59. (a) $\frac{1}{9}\sqrt{2}W$; (b) $2W$

EXERCISES 2.8 (page 181)

1. $6(2x + 1)^2$ **3.** $8(x + 2)(x^2 + 4x - 5)^3$ **5.** $2(2t^4 - 7t^3 + 2t - 1)(8t^3 - 21t^2 + 2)$
7. $\dfrac{-4x}{(x^2 + 4)^3}$ **9.** $-12(\sin 3x + \cos 4x)$ **11.** $2 \sec 2x \tan^3 2x$ **13.** $2 \sec^2 x \tan x(2 \tan^2 x + 1)$
15. $4 \cot t \csc^2 t$ **17.** $\dfrac{18(x - 7)}{(x + 2)^2}$ **19.** $6t \sin(6t^2 - 2)$ **21.** $6(\tan^2 x - x^2)^2(\tan x \sec^2 x - x)$
23. $-12 \cos 3x \sin(\sin 3x)$ **25.** $y = 24x - 39$ **27.** (a) $v = \frac{3}{2}\pi \cos \frac{1}{4}\pi t$, $a = -\frac{3}{8}\pi^2 \sin \frac{1}{4}\pi t$; (c) $A = 6$, $p = 8$, $f = \frac{1}{8}$
29. (a) $v = -8\pi \sin \pi(2t - \frac{1}{3})$, $a = -16\pi^2 \cos \pi(2t - \frac{1}{3})$; (c) $A = 4$, $p = 1$, $f = 1$
31. (a) $-bk \sin(kt + c)$; (b) $-bk^2 \cos(kt + c)$ **33.** (a) $v = 5\pi \cos \pi t - 3\pi \sin \pi t$, $a = -5\pi^2 \sin \pi t - 3\pi^2 \cos \pi t$
35. (a) $v = -20 \sin 4t$, $a = -80 \cos 4t$ **39.** (a) $\frac{1}{28}$; (b) $\frac{4}{7}$ **41.** -0.6 rad/sec
43. (a) $6000 \cos \frac{12}{5}\pi \approx 5824$ volts/sec; (b) $6000\pi \approx 18,850$ volts/sec   **45.** decreasing by 16.6 toys per month
47. (a) $3x^4$; (b) $6x^5$ **53.** (b) $f'(x) = \begin{cases} 2x \sin(1/x) - \cos(1/x) & \text{if } x \neq 0 \\ 0 & \text{if } x = 0 \end{cases}$

EXERCISES 2.9 (page 190)

1. $x^{-1/2}(2 - \frac{5}{2}x^{-1})$ **3.** $\dfrac{4x}{\sqrt{1 + 4x^2}}$ **5.** $\dfrac{-2}{(5 - 3x)^{1/3}}$ **7.** $\dfrac{y}{(25 - y^2)^{3/2}}$ **9.** $-\dfrac{\sin \sqrt{t}}{\sqrt{t}}$ **11.** $-\dfrac{\sqrt{3}}{2\sqrt{r}} \csc^2 \sqrt{3r}$
13. $\dfrac{\cos t}{\sqrt{\sin t}(1 - \sin t)^{3/2}}$ **15.** $\dfrac{-1}{4\sqrt{9 + \sqrt{9 - x}}\sqrt{9 - x}}$ **17.** $-\dfrac{x}{y}$ **19.** $\dfrac{8y - 3x^2}{3y^2 - 8x}$ **21.** $-\dfrac{y^2}{x^2}$
23. $-\dfrac{\sqrt{y}}{\sqrt{x}}$ **25.** $\dfrac{x - xy^2}{x^2y - y}$ **27.** $\dfrac{\sin(x - y)}{\sin(x - y) - 1}$ **29.** $\dfrac{\tan x \sec^2 x}{\cot y \csc^2 y}$ **31.** $\dfrac{y \sin x - \sin y}{x \cos y + \cos x}$
33. $y = \frac{4}{5}x + \frac{9}{5}$ **35.** $y = -\frac{4}{9}x + \frac{22}{9}$ **37.** $(1, 0)$, $(\frac{1}{3}, \frac{4}{3})$
39. (a) $f_1(x) = 2\sqrt{x - 2}$, domain: $x \geq 2$; $f_2(x) = -2\sqrt{x - 2}$, domain: $x \geq 2$;
(b)   (c)

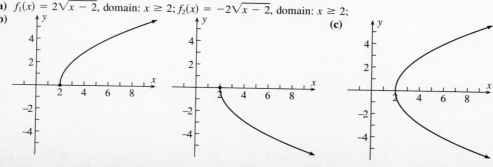

(d) $f_1'(x) = (x - 2)^{-1/2}$, domain: $x > 2$; $f_2'(x) = -(x - 2)^{-1/2}$, domain: $x > 2$;   **(e)** $\dfrac{2}{y}$;   **(f)** $x - y - 1 = 0$, $x + y - 1 = 0$

41. (a) $f_1(x) = \sqrt{x^2 - 9}$, domain: $|x| \geq 3$; $f_2(x) = -\sqrt{x^2 - 9}$, domain: $|x| \geq 3$;

(b)

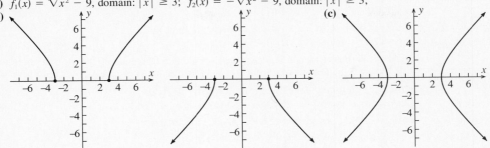

(d) $f_1'(x) = x(x^2 - 9)^{-1/2}$, domain: $|x| > 3$; $f_2'(x) = -x(x^2 - 9)^{-1/2}$, domain: $|x| > 3$;   **(e)** $\dfrac{x}{y}$;

(f) $5x + 4y + 9 = 0$; $5x - 4y + 9 = 0$

47. (a) 0;   **(b)** $\frac{1}{2}$;   **(c)** no value of t **49. (a)** 50 cents per liter;   **(b)** 25   **51.** 100   **53.** 2.7 km/min

57. $\dfrac{2x(x^2 - 4)}{|x^2 - 4|}$ **59.** $f'(x) = 3x|x|$; $f''(x) = 6|x|$

61. (a) $-0.1957h$ ft/sec;   **(b)** $0.14454h$ ft/sec;   **(c)** $0.1035h$ ft/sec;   **(d)** $0.0430h$ ft/sec

63. $\sqrt{3}x - y + \frac{1}{2}\sqrt{3} = 0$; $\sqrt{3}x + y + \frac{1}{2}\sqrt{3} = 0$

EXERCISES 2.10 (page 197)

1. -3 **3.** -2 **5.** $-\frac{1}{2}\sqrt{3}$ **7.** $-\frac{3}{4}$ **9.** $\frac{9}{5}$ ft/sec   **11.** $\dfrac{1}{2\pi}$ ft/min   **13.** $\dfrac{5}{8\pi}$ m/min   **15.** $\frac{25}{3}$ ft/sec

17. 0.001π cm³/day   **19.** 0.004π cm²/day   **21.** $\dfrac{6}{25\pi}$ m/min   **23.** 1800 lb/ft² per min   **25.** 128π cm²/sec   **27.** 14 ft/sec

29. \$1020 per week   **31.** 875 units per month   **33.** decreasing at the rate of 55 shirts per week

37. 22 m³/min   **39.** $\frac{1}{194}(3\sqrt{97} + 97)$ft/sec ≈ 0.65 ft/sec   **41.** $\frac{2000}{9}$ ft/sec   **43.** $\frac{2}{25}$ rad/sec

MISCELLANEOUS EXERCISES FOR CHAPTER 2 (page 203)

1. $15x^2 - 14x + 2$ **3.** $\dfrac{x}{2} - \dfrac{8}{x^3}$ **5.** $x^{-1/2} + \frac{1}{4}x^{-3/2}$ **7.** $60t^4 - 39t^2 - 6t - 4$ **9.** $\dfrac{-6x^2}{(x^3 - 1)^2}$

11. $4(2s^3 - 3s + 7)^3(6s^2 - 3)$ **13.** $x(4x^2 - 13)(x^2 - 1)^{1/2}(x^2 - 4)^{-1/2}$

15. $(x + 1)\sin x + x \cos x$ **17.** $\dfrac{2 \sec^2 4t}{\sqrt{\tan 4t}}$ **19.** $-3 \sin 3w \cos(\cos 3w) - \cos w \cos 3w + 3 \sin w \sin 3w$

21. $\dfrac{8x(1 - x^2)}{(x^2 + 1)^3}$ **23.** $\dfrac{(1 + x)\sec^2 x - \tan x}{(1 + x)^2}$ **25.** $\dfrac{8x}{3y^2 - 8y}$ **27.** $\dfrac{y - \sec^2 x}{\sec^2 y - x}$

29. (a) $f(x) = \begin{cases} x^2 - 4 & \text{if } x \leq -2 \\ 4 - x^2 & \text{if } -2 < x \leq 0 \\ 4 - 2x & \text{if } 0 < x \leq 2 \\ 2 - \frac{1}{2}x^2 & \text{if } x > 2 \end{cases}$;   **31.**

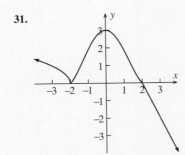

(b) -4;   **(c)** 4;   **(d)** 0;

(e) -2;   **(f)** -2;

(g) -2;   **(h)** $-2, 0$

33. $y = 9x - 17$ **35.** $x - 2y + 9 = 0; 27x - 54y - 7 = 0$ **37.** $5x - 4y - 6 = 0; 4x + 5y - 13 = 0$
39. $(-1, 0)$ **41.** $-3(3 - 2x)^{-5/2}$ **43.** $x < -3$ or $x > -1$
45. moving to the right: $t < -2$ and $t > 1$; moving to the left: $-2 < t < 1$; reverses direction: $t = -2, 1$
47.

	s	v	a	Conclusion
$0 \le t < 1$	$+$	$-$	$+$	Particle is right of the origin, and it is moving to the left. The velocity is increasing. The speed is decreasing.
$t = 1$	0	0	$+$	Particle is at the origin, and it is changing its direction of motion from left to right. The velocity is increasing. The speed is increasing.
$1 < t < 2$	$+$	$+$	$+$	Particle is right of the origin, and it is moving to the right. The velocity is increasing. The speed is increasing.
$t = 2$	$+$	$+$	0	Particle is right of the origin, and it is moving to the right. The velocity is not changing; so the speed is not changing.
$2 < t < 3$	$+$	$+$	$-$	Particle is right of the origin, and it is moving to the right. The velocity is decreasing. The speed is decreasing.
$t = 3$	$+$	0	$-$	Particle is right of the origin, and it is changing its direction of motion from right to left. The velocity is decreasing. The speed is increasing.
$3 < t < 4$	$+$	$-$	$-$	Particle is right of the origin, and it is moving to the left. The velocity is decreasing. The speed is increasing.
$t = 4$	0	$-$	$-$	Particle is at the origin, and it is moving to the left. The velocity is decreasing. The speed is increasing.
$4 < t$	$-$	$-$	$-$	Particle is left of the origin, and it is moving to the left. The velocity is decreasing. The speed is increasing.

49. $t = 2^{-1}3^{-4/3}; s = \frac{3}{4}\sqrt[3]{3} + 1; v = 3^{5/3}$ **51. (a)** $s = 200 - 16t^2$; **(b)** -32 ft/sec, -96 ft/sec; **(c)** 3.54 sec; **(d)** 113 ft/sec
53. (a) $s = -16t^2 + 96t + 112$; (b and c) 3 sec, 256 ft; (d and e) 7 sec; **(f)** 32 ft/sec, -32 ft/sec; **(g)** both 32 ft/sec;
(h) -128 ft/sec
55. (a) $v = -2\sin 2t + 4\cos 2t, a = -4\cos 2t - 8\sin 2t$
57. (a) $f(x) = \begin{cases} 200x & \text{if } 0 \le x \le 800 \\ 360x - 0.2x^2 & \text{if } 800 < x \le 1800 \end{cases}$; **(c)** no   **59. (a)** 8.005; **(b)** 8   **61. (a)** 3312.2; **(b)** 3212.5
63. $-\frac{1}{3}$ **65.** $\dfrac{2}{\sqrt{4x - 3}}$ **67.** $\frac{1}{2}$ **69.** $2(|x + 1| - |x|)\left(\dfrac{x + 1}{|x + 1|} - \dfrac{x}{|x|}\right)$
71. (a) $v = \frac{5}{6}\pi\cos\frac{1}{6}\pi t, a = -\frac{5}{36}\pi^2\sin\frac{1}{6}\pi t$; **(c)** $A = 5, p = 12, f = \frac{1}{12}$
73. (a) $v = -6\sin(3t + \frac{1}{3}\pi) + 12\cos(3t - \frac{1}{6}\pi), a = -18\cos(3t + \frac{1}{3}\pi) - 36\sin(3t - \frac{1}{6}\pi)$
77. (a) $C'(x) = 2x + 40$; **(b)** 80; **(c)** 81 **79.** 648 fish/week   **81.** 12.4 knots
83. $\dfrac{512}{625\pi}$ in./sec ≈ 0.26 in./sec   **85.** 9.6 ft/sec
87. (a)

(b) continuous at 3; **(c)** not differentiable at 3   **89. (a)**

(b) 0; **(c)** 0

91. $a = -\frac{1}{2}, b = \frac{3}{2}$ **97.** $f(x) = |x|, g(x) = x^2$ **101.** no; if $f(x) = \dfrac{1}{x - 1}$ and $g(x) = x + 1$, then f and g are differentiable
at 0; however $(f \circ g)(x) = \dfrac{1}{x}$ and $f \circ g$ is not differentiable at 0

EXERCISES 3.1 (page 218)

1. $\frac{1}{3}, -5$ **3.** $0, 2$ **5.** $-1 + \sqrt{10}, -1 - \sqrt{10}$ **7.** $2, -1, \frac{1}{5}$ **9. (a)** $-5, -\frac{1}{4}, -3$ **11. (a)** $-2, 2, 0$
13. (a) $2 + 2\sqrt{2}, 2 - 2\sqrt{2}$ **15.** $\frac{1}{8}(2k + 1)\pi$, where k is any integer   **17.** $\frac{1}{3}k\pi$, where k is any integer

19. abs. min.: $f(2) = -2$

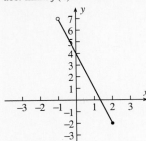

21. no absolute extrema

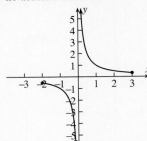

23. abs. min.: $f(-\frac{2}{3}\pi) = -1$; abs. max.: $f(0) = 2$

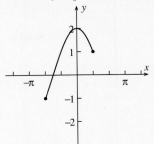

25. abs. min.: $f(-3) = 0$

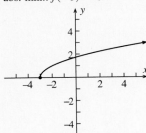

27. abs. min.: $h(5) = 1$

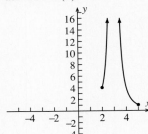

29. abs. min.: $f(4) = 1$

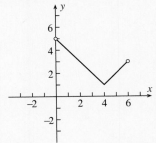

31. abs. min.: $g(0) = 2$

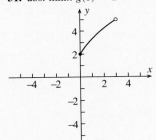

33. abs. max.: $f(5) = 2$

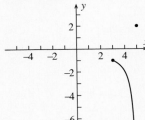

35. abs. min.: $f(2) = 0$

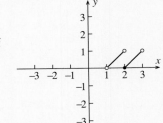

37. abs. min.: $g(0) = 1$

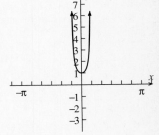

39. (a) abs. min.: $f(-2) = 0$; abs. max.: $f(-4) = 144$ **(b)** abs. min.: $f(-2) = f(2) = 0$; abs. max.: $f(-3) = 25$
41. abs. min.: $f(-\frac{1}{2}\pi) = -2$; abs. max.: $f(\frac{1}{2}\pi) = 2$ **43.** abs. min.: $g(-1) = -1$; abs. max.: $g(2) = \frac{1}{2}$
45. abs. min.: $f(-1) = 0$; abs. max.: $f(1) = \sqrt[3]{4}$ **47.** abs. min.: $f(-3) = -46$; abs. max.: $f(-1) = -10$
49. abs. min.: $g(0) = 2$; abs. max.: $g(\frac{1}{2}\pi) = 2\sqrt{2}$ **51.** abs. min.: $f(0) = 3$; abs. max.: $f(2) = 5$
53. abs. min.: $f(0) = 0$; abs. max.: $f(-3) = 3$ **55.** abs. min.: $F(-3) = -13$; abs. max.: $F(3) = 7$ **59.** no

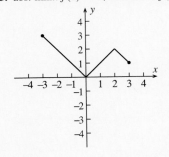

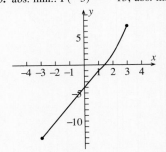

EXERCISES 3.2 (page 226)
1. (a) 1;   **(b)** $\frac{1}{3}$ **15.** 225   **17.** 30   **19.** 6, 6   **21.** P is $20/\sqrt{39} \approx 3.2$ km from B **23.** radius: $3\sqrt{2}$ in., height: $6\sqrt{2}$ in.
25. (a) $\sqrt{50 - 6\sqrt{41}}$ units $= (\sqrt{41} - 3)$ units ≈ 3.4 units;   **(b)** $\sqrt{50 + 6\sqrt{41}}$ units $= (\sqrt{41} + 3)$ units ≈ 9.4 units

27. $\frac{2}{3}k$ **29.** breadth is $48\sqrt{3}$ cm; depth is $48\sqrt{6}$ cm

31. (a) radius of circle is $\dfrac{5}{\pi + 4}$ ft and length of side of square is $\dfrac{10}{\pi + 4}$ ft;   **(b)** radius of circle is $\dfrac{5}{\pi}$ ft and there is no square

33. $\frac{1}{4}\pi$ **35.** 7 produce A; 8 produce B

EXERCISES 3.3   (page 234)

1. 2   **3.** $\frac{1}{4}\pi$ **5. (b)** (i), (ii), (iii) satisfied;   **(c)** $(\frac{3}{4}, -\frac{9}{8}\sqrt[3]{6})$
7. (b) (i) not satisfied   **9. (b)** (ii) not satisfied   **11.** $\frac{1}{2}$
13. $\frac{8}{27}$ **15.** 0   **17.** 4   **19.** $\cos c = \frac{2}{\pi}$; $c \approx 0.8807$ **21.** (i) not satisfied   **23.** (ii) not satisfied

EXERCISES 3.4   (page 242)

1. extrema: $f(2) = -5$, rel. min.; increasing: $[2, +\infty)$; decreasing: $(-\infty, 2]$

3. extrema: $f(-\frac{1}{3}) = \frac{5}{27}$, rel. max.; $f(1) = -1$, rel. min.; increasing: $(-\infty, -\frac{1}{3}], [1, +\infty)$; decreasing: $[-\frac{1}{3}, 1]$

5. extrema: $f(0) = 0$, rel. min.; $f(1) = \frac{1}{4}$, rel. max.; $f(2) = 0$, rel. min.; increasing: $[0, 1], [2, +\infty)$; decreasing: $(-\infty, 0], [1, 2]$

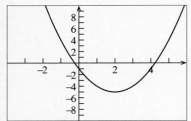

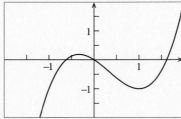

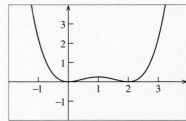

7. extrema: $f(-\pi) = -4$, rel. min.; $f(\pi) = 4$, rel. max.; increasing: $[-\pi, \pi]$; decreasing; $[-2\pi, -\pi], [\pi, 2\pi]$

9. extrema: no relative extrema; increasing: $(0, +\infty)$; decreasing: nowhere

11. extrema: $f(\frac{1}{5}) = \frac{3456}{3125}$, rel. max.; $f(1) = 0$, rel. min.; increasing: $(-\infty, \frac{1}{5}]$, $[1, +\infty)$; decreasing: $[\frac{1}{5}, 1]$

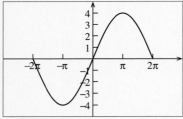

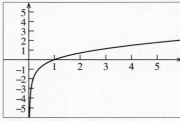

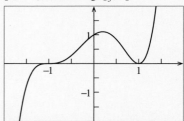

13. extrema: $f(-1) = 2$, rel. max.; $f(1) = -2$, rel. min.; increasing: $(-\infty, -1], [1, +\infty)$; decreasing: $[-1, 1]$

15. extrema: $f(\frac{1}{8}) = -\frac{1}{4}$, rel. min.; increasing: $[\frac{1}{8}, +\infty)$; decreasing: $(-\infty, \frac{1}{8}]$

17. extrema: no relative extrema; increasing: $[0, +\infty)$; decreasing nowhere

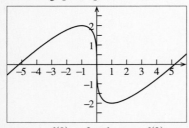

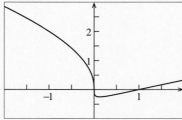

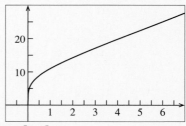

19. extrema: $f(0) = 2$, rel. max.; $f(3) = -25$, rel. min.; increasing: $(-\infty, 0], [3, +\infty)$; decreasing: $[0, 3]$
21. extrema: $f(-2) = -\frac{1}{15}$, rel. max.; $f(-1) = -\frac{23}{15}$, rel. min.; $f(1) = \frac{53}{15}$, rel. max.; $f(2) = \frac{31}{15}$, rel. min.; increasing: $(-\infty, -2], [-1, 1], [2, +\infty)$; decreasing: $[-2, -1], [1, 2]$
23. extrema: $f(\sqrt[3]{2}) = \frac{3}{2}\sqrt[3]{2}$, rel. min.; increasing: $(-\infty, 0), [\sqrt[3]{2}, +\infty)$; decreasing: $(0, \sqrt[3]{2})$
25. extrema: $f(2) = 4$, rel. max.; increasing: $(-\infty, 2]$; decreasing: $[2, 3]$
27. extrema: $f(4) = 2$, rel. max.; increasing: $(-\infty, 4]$; decreasing: $[4, +\infty)$

29. extrema: $f(-\frac{1}{4}\pi) = f(\frac{1}{4}\pi) = -\frac{1}{2}$, rel. max.; $f(0) = \frac{1}{2}$, rel. min.; (end points cannot be relative extrema);
increasing: $[-\frac{1}{2}\pi, -\frac{3}{8}\pi)$, $(-\frac{3}{8}\pi, -\frac{1}{4}\pi]$, $[0, \frac{1}{8}\pi)$, $(\frac{1}{8}\pi, \frac{1}{4}\pi]$; decreasing: $[-\frac{1}{4}\pi, -\frac{1}{8}\pi)$, $(-\frac{1}{8}\pi, 0]$, $[\frac{1}{4}\pi, \frac{3}{8}\pi)$, $(\frac{3}{8}\pi, \frac{1}{2}\pi]$

31. extrema: $f(4) = \frac{1}{4}\sqrt[3]{4}$, rel. max.; increasing: $(-4, 4]$; decreasing: $(-\infty, -4)$, $[4, +\infty)$

33. extrema: $f(-2) = 5$, rel. max.;
$f(0) = 1$, rel. min.;
increasing: $(-\infty, -2]$, $[0, +\infty)$;
decreasing: $[-2, 0]$

35. extrema: $f(-1) = 2$, rel. max.;
$f(0) = 1$, rel. min.; $f(2) = 5$,
rel. max.; increasing: $(-\infty, -1]$, $[0, 2]$;
decreasing: $[-1, 0]$, $[2, +\infty)$

37. extrema: $f(-9) = -8$, rel. min.;
$f(-7) = -4$, rel. max.; $f(-4) = -5$,
rel. min.; $f(0) = -3$, rel. max.;
$f(2) = -7$, rel. min.;
increasing: $[-9, -7]$, $[-4, 0]$, $[2, +\infty)$;
decreasing: $(-\infty, -9]$, $[-7, -4]$, $[0, 2]$

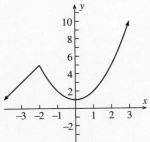
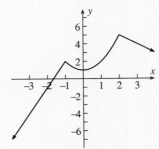
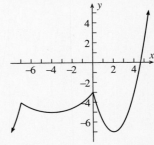

39. critical numbers: $-3, 1, 3$; increasing: $(-\infty, -3]$, $[1, 3]$; decreasing: $[-3, 1]$, $[3, +\infty)$; extrema: rel. max.: $-3, 3$; rel. min.: 1
41. critical numbers: $0, 2$; increasing: $(-\infty, 0]$, $[2, +\infty)$; decreasing: $[0, 2]$; extrema: rel. max.: 0, rel. min.: 2
43. critical numbers: $1, -2, 0, 2$; increasing: $[-2, 0]$, $[1, +\infty)$; decreasing: $(-\infty, -2]$, $[0, 1]$; extrema: rel. max.: 0; rel. min.: $-2, 1$

45. (a) 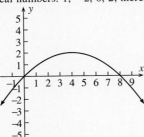 **(b)** 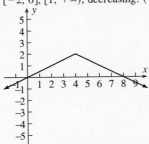 **(c)**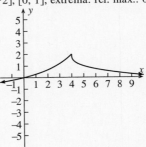

47. $a = -3, b = 7$ **49.** $a = -2, b = 9, c = -12, d = 7$ **57.** no

EXERCISES 3.5 *(page 254)*

1. pt. of infl.: $(-\frac{1}{2}, \frac{15}{2})$; concave downward for $x < -\frac{1}{2}$; concave upward for $x > -\frac{1}{2}$
3. pts. of infl.: $(0, 0)$, $(4, -256)$; concave upward for $x < 0$ and $x > 4$; concave downward for $0 < x < 4$
5. pts. of infl.: $(-1, \frac{1}{2})$, $(1, \frac{1}{2})$; concave upward for $x < -1$ and $x > 1$; concave downward for $-1 < x < 1$
7. pts. of infl.: $(-\frac{1}{3}\pi, 0)$, $(0, 0)$, $(\frac{1}{3}\pi, 0)$; concave upward for $-\frac{1}{3}\pi < x < 0$, and $\frac{1}{3}\pi < x < \frac{1}{2}\pi$; concave downward for
$-\frac{1}{2}\pi < x < -\frac{1}{3}\pi$ and $0 < x < \frac{1}{3}\pi$
9. pt. of infl.: $(0, 0)$; concave downward for $x < 0$; concave upward for $x > 0$
11. pt. of infl.: $(1, 0)$; concave downward for $x < 1$; concave upward for $x > 1$
13. pt. of infl.: $(-2, 0)$; concave upward for $x < -2$; concave downward for $x > -2$
15. pt. of infl.: $(0, 0)$; concave downward for $-\pi < x < 0$; concave upward for $0 < x < \pi$
17. no pt. of infl.;
concave upward for $x < 2$;
concave downward for $x > 2$

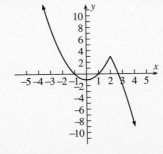

19. $(0, 0)$;
concave upward for $x < 0$;
concave downward for $x > 0$

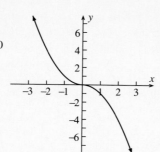

21. $(0, 0)$;
concave downward for $x < 0$;
concave upward for $x > 0$

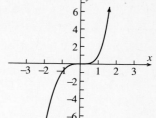

23. (a)   **(b)**

25. (a)   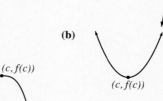   **(b)**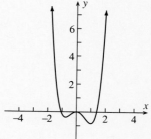

27. (a)      **(b)**

29.

31. $f(\frac{3}{2}) = \frac{81}{4}$, rel. max.;
$f(-1) = -11$, rel. min.;

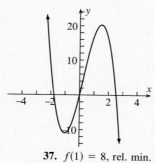

33. $g(-\frac{3}{4}) = -\frac{99}{256}$, rel. min.;
$g(0) = 0$, rel. max.;
$g(1) = -\frac{5}{6}$, rel. min.

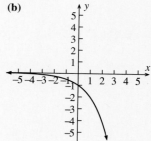

35. $f(\frac{1}{3}\pi) = -1$, rel. min.;
$f(0) = 1$, rel. max.

37. $f(1) = 8$, rel. min.

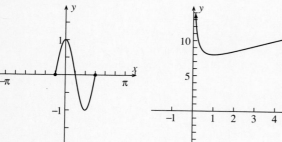

39. (a)   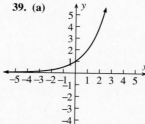   **(b)**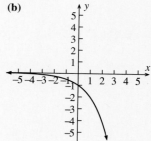

41. (a) $(k\pi, 0)$ where k is any integer;   **(b)** 1

43. $\csc(\frac{1}{2}\pi + 2k\pi) = 1$, where k is any integer, rel. min.; $\csc(\frac{1}{2}\pi + 2k\pi) = -1$, where k is any integer, rel. max.

45. (a)   **(b)**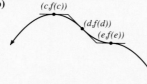

47. (a) 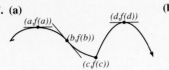 **(b)**   **49. (a)** 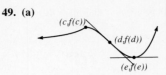 **(b)**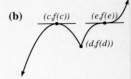

51. $a = -1, b = 3$ **53.** $a = 2, b = -6, c = 0, d = 3$ **55.** f has a rel. min. at $x = \frac{1}{2}\sqrt{2}$ and a rel. max. at $x = -\frac{1}{2}\sqrt{3}$

57. f is continuous; f' and f'' need not be continuous   **59.** at 10:40 A.M.

EXERCISES 3.6 (page 259)

1. pts. of infl.: $-1, 2$;
concave upward: $(-1, 2)$;
concave downward: $x < -1, x > 2$

3. no pt. of infl.;
concave upward: $x < 0, x > 0$

5. pts. of infl.: $-1, 2$;
concave upward: $x < -1, x > 2$;
concave downward: $(-1, 1), (1, 2)$

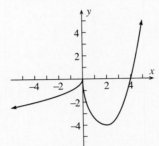

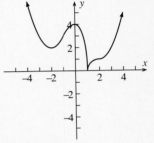

7. increasing: $(-\infty, +\infty)$; no extrema;
concave upward: $x > 0$;
concave downward: $x < 0$

9. increasing: $(-1, 1)$;
decreasing: $x < -1, x > 1$;
extrema: $x = -1$, rel. min.;
$x = 1$, rel. max.;
concave upward: $x < 0$;
concave downward: $x > 0$;
no pt. of infl.

11. increasing: $x < 2$;
decreasing: $x > 2$;
extrema: $x = 2$, rel. max.;
concave upward: $x < 0$;
concave downward: $x > 0$;
pt. of infl.: $x = 0$

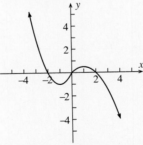

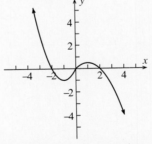

13. increasing: $x < -2, x > 0$;
decreasing: $(-2, 0)$; extrema: $x = -2$,
rel. max.; $x = 0$, rel. min.;
concave upward: $x < -2, (-2, 2)$;
concave downward: $x > 2$;
pt. of infl.: $x = 2$

15. increasing: $x < 0$; decreasing: $x > 0$;
extrema: $x = 0$, rel. max.;
concave upward: $(-2, 0), (0, 2)$;
concave downward: $x < -2, x > 2$;
pts. of infl.: $x = -2, x = 2$

17. increasing: $(-1, 0), x > 1$;
decreasing: $x < -1, (0, 1)$;
extrema: $x = -1$, rel. min.;
$x = 0$, rel. max.; $x = 1$, rel. min.;
concave upward: $x < -1, x > 1$;
concave downward: $(-1, 1)$;
no pt. of infl.

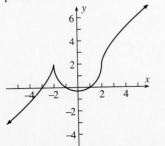

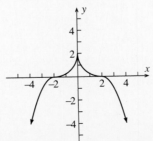

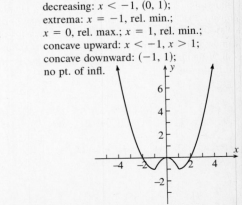

19. increasing: $x < -1$, $x > 2$; decreasing: $(-1, 2)$;
extrema: $x = -1$, rel. max.; $x = 2$, rel. min.;
concave upward: $x > 0$; concave downward: $x < 0$;
pt. of infl.: $x = 0$

21. increasing: $(-2, 3)$; decreasing: $x < -3$, $x > 3$;
extrema: $x = -2$, rel. min.; $x = 3$, rel. max.;
concave upward: $x < -1$, $(0, 1)$;
concave downward: $(-1, 0)$, $x > 1$;
pts. of infl.: $x = -1$, $x = 1$

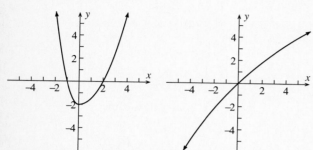
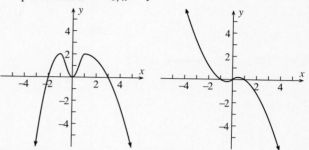

23. increasing: $(1, 3)$; decreasing: $x < 1$, $x > 3$;
extrema: $x = 1$, rel. min.; $x = 3$, rel. max.;
concave upward: $(0, 2)$, $x > 3$;
concave downward: $x < 0$, $(2, 3)$;
pts. of infl.: $x = 0$, $x = 2$

25. increasing: $x < -3$, $x > 2$; decreasing: $(-3, 2)$;
extrema: $x = -3$, rel. max.; $x = 2$, rel. min.;
concave upward: $x < -3$, $(-3, -1)$, $x > 1$;
concave downward: $(-1, 1)$; pt. of infl.: $x = 1$

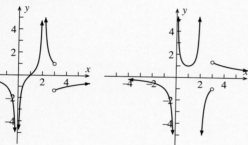
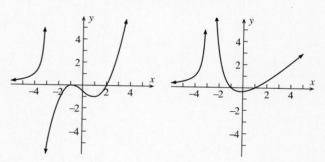

31.

EXERCISES 3.7 (page 274)

1. 4, 1, 0.25, 0.1111, 0.0625, 0.0400, 0.0004, 0.000004; 4, 1, 0.25, 0.1111, 0.0625, 0.0400, 0.0004, 0.000004; (a–e) 0
3. 1, 0.1250, 0.0156, 0.0046, 0.0020, 0.0010, 10^{-6}, 10^{-9}; -1, -0.1250, -0.0156, -0.0046, -0.0020, -0.0010, -10^{-6}, -10^{-9};
(a–e) 0
5. 0, -1.5, -2.4, -2.823, -2.919, -2.953, -2.970, -2.9997, -2.999997; 0, -1.5, -2.4, -2.823, -2.919, -2.953, -2.970,
-2.9997, -2.999997; (a–e) -3
7. 3, 2.273, 2.158, 2.015, 2.0015, 2.00015, 2.000015; 1.4, 1.769, 1.857, 1.985, 1.9985, 1.99985, 1.999985; (a–e) 2
9. 0.75, 0.1944, 0.1100, 0.0101, 0.001001, 0.0001, 0.00001; -0.25, -0.1389, -0.0900, -0.0099, -0.0010, -0.0001, -0.00001;
(a–e) 0
11. $\frac{2}{5}$ **13.** $-\frac{2}{5}$ **15.** $\frac{7}{3}$ **17.** 0   **19.** $+\infty$ **21.** $\frac{1}{2}$ **23.** $+\infty$ **25.** $-\infty$ **27.** 1   **29.** -1 **31.** 0   **33.** $-\infty$

35. $y = 2, x = 3$

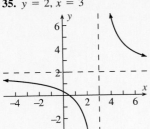

37. $y = 1, x = 0$

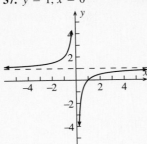

39. $y = 0, x = -2, x = 2$

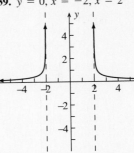

41. $y = 4, x = -3, x = 3$

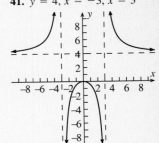

43. $y = 0, x = \frac{2}{3}, x = -\frac{5}{2}$

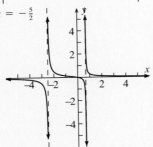

45. $x = -\sqrt{2}, x = \sqrt{2}$
$y = -4x, y = 4x$

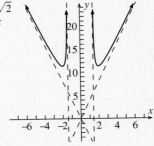

47. $x = 1, y = x + 1$ **49.** $x = 3, y = x + 3$ **51.** $x = -2, y = x - 6$ **53.** $x = 0, y = x + 2$

55. **(a)** 1; **(b)** 0; **(c)** 1;   **57.**

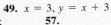
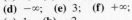

(d) $-\infty$; **(e)** 3; **(f)** $+\infty$;

69. 0

(g) 1; **(h)** -2

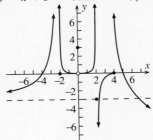

EXERCISES 3.8 (page 282)

1. $f(0) = 1$, rel. min.; $(\frac{1}{2}, \frac{23}{16})$, $(1, 2)$,
pts. of infl.; decreasing: $(-\infty, 0]$;
increasing: $[0, +\infty)$;
concave upward: $x < \frac{1}{2}, x > 1$;
concave downward: $(\frac{1}{2}, 1)$

3. $f(-1) = \frac{7}{12}$, rel. min.; $f(0) = 1$,
rel. max.; $f(2) = -\frac{5}{3}$, rel. min.;
pts. of infl.: $x = \frac{1}{3}(1 \pm \sqrt{7})$;
decreasing: $(-\infty, -1], [0, 2]$;
increasing: $[-1, 0], [2, +\infty)$;
concave upward: $x < \frac{1}{3}(1 - \sqrt{7})$,
$x > \frac{1}{3}(1 + \sqrt{7})$; concave downward:
$\frac{1}{3}(1 - \sqrt{7}) < x < \frac{1}{3}(1 + \sqrt{7})$

5. $f(0) = 2$, rel. min.;
no pts. of infl.; decreasing: $(-\infty, 0]$;
increasing: $[0, +\infty)$; concave upward
everywhere

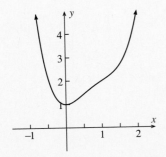

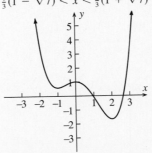

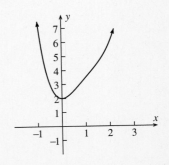

7. $f(0) = 0$, rel. min.;
no pts. of infl.; decreasing: $(-\infty, 0]$;
increasing: $[0, +\infty)$; concave upward
everywhere

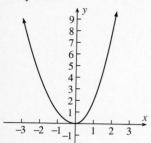

9. no relative extrema; $(0, 0)$ pt.
of infl.; increasing: $(-\infty, +\infty)$;
concave downward: $(-\infty, 0)$;
concave upward on $(0, +\infty)$

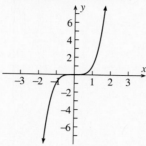

11. no relative extrema; $(2, 0)$ pt.
of infl.; decreasing: $(-\infty, +\infty)$;
concave upward: $x < 2$;
concave downward: $x > 2$

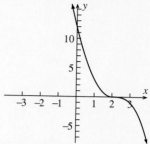

13. $f(\frac{4}{5}) = \frac{26,244}{3,125}$, rel. max.;
$f(2) = 0$, rel. min.;
pts. of infl.: $(-1, 0)$,
$x = \frac{1}{10}(8 \pm 3\sqrt{6})$; increasing: $(-\infty, \frac{4}{5}]$,
$[2, +\infty)$; decreasing: $[\frac{4}{5}, 2]$;
concave downward: $x < -1$,
$(\frac{1}{10}(8 - 3\sqrt{6}), \frac{1}{10}(8 + 3\sqrt{6}))$;
concave upward: $(-1, \frac{1}{10}(8 - 3\sqrt{6}))$,
$x > \frac{1}{10}(8 + 3\sqrt{6})$

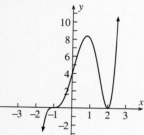

15. $(\frac{1}{2}\pi, 0)$, rel. min.; no pts.
of infl.; increasing: $[0, \frac{1}{2}\pi)$, $[\frac{1}{2}\pi, \pi]$;
concave downward: $0 < x < \frac{1}{2}\pi$,
$\frac{1}{2}\pi < x < \pi$

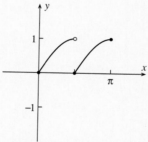

17. $f(0) = 0$, rel. max.; $f(2) = 4$,
rel. min.; no pts. of infl.;
increasing: $(-\infty, 0]$, $[2, +\infty)$;
decreasing: $[0, 1)$ and $(1, 2]$;
concave downward: $x < 1$;
concave upward: $x > 1$; $x = 1$ and
$y = x + 1$ are asymptotes

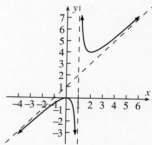

19. $f(0) = -1$, rel. max.; no pts.
of infl.; increasing: $(-\infty, -1)$ and
$(-1, 0]$; decreasing: $[0, 1)$ and $(1, +\infty)$;
concave upward: $x < -1$, $x > 1$;
concave downward: $-1 < x < 1$;
$y = 1$, $x = -1$, and $x = 1$ are
asymptotes

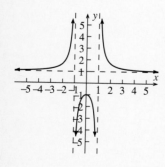

21. $f(-1) = -1$, rel. min.; $f(1) = 1$,
rel. max.; $(-\sqrt{3}, -\frac{1}{2}\sqrt{3})$, $(0, 0)$,
$(\sqrt{3}, \frac{1}{2}\sqrt{3})$, pts. of infl.;
decreasing: $(-\infty, -1]$, $[1, +\infty)$;
increasing: $[-1, 1]$; concave
downward: $x < -\sqrt{3}$, $0 < x < \sqrt{3}$;
concave upward: $-\sqrt{3} < x < 0$,
$x > \sqrt{3}$; $y = 0$ is an asymptote

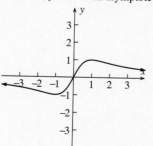

23. $f(-1) = 0$, rel. max.;
$f(1) = -\sqrt[3]{4}$, rel. min.; pt.
of infl.: $(2, 0)$; decreasing: $[-1, 1]$;
increasing: $(-\infty, -1]$, $[1, +\infty)$;
concave downward: $x > 2$;
concave upward: $x < -1$, $(-1, 2)$;
$y = x$ is an asymptote

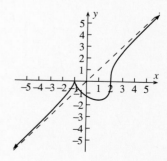

25. $x_1 = -\frac{1}{2}\sqrt{29} - \frac{1}{2}$, $x_2 = \frac{1}{2}\sqrt{29} - \frac{1}{2}$,
$x_3 = -\frac{1}{6}(\sqrt{87} + 3)$, $x_4 = \frac{1}{6}(\sqrt{87} - 3)$;
$f(x_1) = f(x_2) = -25$, rel. min.;
$f(-\frac{1}{2}) = \frac{441}{16}$, rel. max.;
pts. of infl.: $(x_3, -\frac{59}{36})$, $(x_4, -\frac{59}{36})$;
increasing: $[x_1, -\frac{1}{2}], [x_2, +\infty)$;
decreasing: $(-\infty, x_1], (-\frac{1}{2}, x_2]$;
concave upward: $x < x_3, x > x_4$;
concave downward: (x_3, x_4)

27. $f(-5) = f(5) = 0$, rel. min.;
$f(0) = 25$, rel. max.; no pt. of
infl.: increasing: $[-5, 0], [5, +\infty)$;
decreasing: $(-\infty, -5], [0, 5]$;
concave upward: $x < -5, x > 5$;
concave downward: $-5 < x < 5$

29. $f(-1) = -3$, rel. min.;
pts. of infl.: $(0, 0), (2, 6\sqrt[3]{2})$
increasing: $[-1, +\infty)$;
decreasing: $(-\infty, -1]$;
concave upward: $x < 0, x > 2$;
concave downward: $-1 < x < 2$

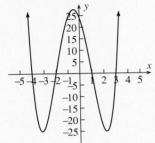
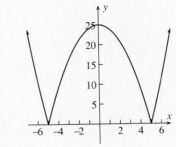
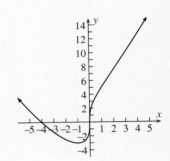

31. $f(-\frac{3}{4}\pi) = -\sqrt{2}$, rel. min.;
$f(\frac{1}{4}\pi) = \sqrt{2}$, rel. max.;
$(-\frac{1}{4}\pi, 0), (\frac{3}{4}\pi, 0)$, pts. of infl.;
increasing: $[-\frac{3}{4}\pi, \frac{1}{4}\pi]$;
decreasing: $[-\pi, -\frac{3}{4}\pi], [\frac{1}{4}\pi, \pi]$;
concave downward: $(-\frac{1}{4}\pi, \frac{3}{4}\pi)$;
concave upward: $(-\pi, -\frac{1}{4}\pi)$,
$(\frac{3}{4}\pi, \pi)$

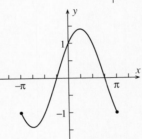

EXERCISES 3.9   (page 289)

1. height, $60/\sqrt[3]{225\pi} \approx 6.73$ in.; radius, $\sqrt[3]{15/\pi} \approx 1.68$ in.   **5.** 45 m by 60 m   **7.** 12 in. by 4 in. by 6 in.   **9.** 90 km/hr
11. 1.44 sec   **13.** $2x - y + 1 = 0$ **15.** 1 month; 7.5 percent   **17.** 40 units   **19.** \$1500   **21.** $\frac{3}{5}\sqrt{10}$ units; $(\frac{9}{5}, \frac{3}{5})$
23. radius of semicircle, $\dfrac{32}{4 + \pi}$ ft; height of rectangle, $\dfrac{32}{4 + \pi}$ ft   **25.** $5\sqrt{5}$ ft   **27.** $\sqrt{2}$ **29.** $2\sqrt{2}$ **31.** $\frac{1}{2}\pi$

EXERCISES 3.10   (page 302)

1. 4.1179   **3.** -1.1673 **5.** 2.649   **7.** 0.507   **9.** -1.128 **11.** 1.73205   **13.** 1.81712   **15.** 0.7391   **17.** 0.8767
19. (a) $1 + 2(x - 1)$;   (c) f: 0.81, 0.9801, 1, 1.0201, 1.21; approximation: 0.8, 0.98, 1.02, 1.2
21. (a) $2 + (x - 1)$;   (c) f: 1.897, 1.98997, 2, 2.00998, 2.0976; approximation: 1.9, 1.99, 2, 2.01, 2.1
23. (a) $0.54030 - 0.84147(x - 1)$;   (c) f: 0.6216, 0.54869, 0.54030, 0.53186, 0.4536; approximation: 0.6244, 0.54871, 0.54030,
0.53189, 0.4562
25. $dy = 2, \Delta = 2.25$ **27.** $dy = \frac{1}{12} \approx .083, \Delta y \approx .080$ **29.** (a) 0.0309;   (b) 0.03;   (c) 0.0009
31. (a) $\frac{1}{42} \approx 0.0238$;   (b) $\frac{1}{40} = 0.025$;   (c) $-\frac{1}{840} \approx -0.0012$ **33.** (a) -0.875;   (b) -1.5;   (c) 0.625
35. $3(3x^2 - 2x + 1)^2(6x - 2)\, dx$ **37.** $x(5x + 6)(2x + 3)^{-1/2}\, dx$ **39.** $\dfrac{(1 - 2\sin x + 2\cos x)\, dx}{(2 - \sin x)^2}$
41. $2\tan x \sec^2 x(2\tan^2 x + 1)\, dx$ **43.** (a) 6.75 cm^3;   (b) 0.3 cm^2 **45.** $\frac{12}{5}\pi$ m^3 **47.** 0.4π cm^2 **49.** 0.9π cm^3
51. 4 percent   **53.** 10 ft^3 **57.** 2.0288, 4.9132   **59.** 3.14159

MISCELLANEOUS EXERCISES FOR CHAPTER 3 (page 306)

1. abs. min.: $f(-5) = 0$

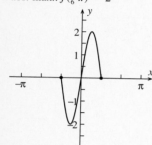

3. abs. min.: $f(3) = 0$;
abs. max.: $f(0) = 9$

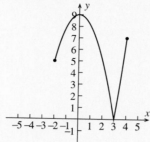

5. no absolute extrema

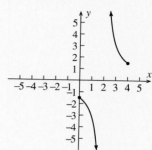

7. abs. min.: $f(-\frac{1}{6}\pi) = -2$;
abs. max.: $f(\frac{1}{6}\pi) = 2$

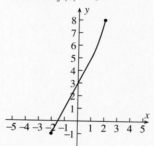

9. abs. min.: $f(-2) = -1$;
abs. max.: $f(2) = 8$

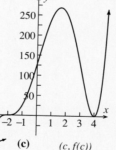

11. **(a)** abs. min.: $f(\sqrt{6}) = 0$;
abs. max.: $f(3) = 9$;
(b) abs. min.: $f(\sqrt{6}) = 0$;
abs max: $f(-4) = 100$

13. abs. min.: $f(-1) \approx -0.301$;
abs. max.: $f(\frac{1}{4}\pi) = \sqrt{2}$

15. $\frac{1}{3}(1 - \sqrt{13})$

17. $-\frac{13}{4}$ **19.** 1.269, 1.872

23. $f'(1)$ does not exist

25 and 37. $f(-2) = 0$, rel. max.; $f(0) = -4$, rel. min.; $(-1, -2)$, pt. of infl.; increasing: $(-\infty, -2]$ and $[0, +\infty)$; decreasing: $[-2, 0]$; concave downward for $x < -1$; concave upward for $x > -1$

27 and 39. no relative extrema; pt. of infl.: $(3, 1)$; increasing: $(-\infty, +\infty)$; concave downward: $x < 3$; concave upward: $x > 3$

29 and 41. no relative extrema; pt. of infl.: $(0, 0)$; decreasing: $(-\frac{1}{2}\pi, \frac{1}{2}\pi)$; concave downward: $(0, \frac{1}{2}\pi)$; concave upward: $(-\frac{1}{2}\pi, 0)$

31 and 43. $f(-1) = 0$, rel. min.; $f(0) = 9$, rel. max.; $f(3) = 0$, rel. min.; pts. of infl. at $x = \pm\frac{3}{5}\sqrt{5}$; decreasing: $(-\infty, -1]$ and $[0, 3]$; increasing: $[-1, 0]$ and $[3, +\infty)$; concave upward: $x < -\frac{3}{5}\sqrt{5}$ and $x > \frac{3}{5}\sqrt{5}$; concave downward: $-\frac{3}{5}\sqrt{5} < x < \frac{3}{5}\sqrt{5}$

33. $f(\frac{8}{5}) = \frac{839,808}{3125}$, rel. max.; $f(4) = 0$,
rel. min.; pts. of infl.: $x = -2$,
$x = \frac{1}{5}(8 \pm 3\sqrt{6})$; increasing: $(-\infty, \frac{8}{5}]$,
$[4, +\infty)$; decreasing: $[\frac{8}{5}, 4]$;
concave upward: $-2 < x < \frac{1}{5}(8 - 3\sqrt{6})$,
$x > \frac{1}{5}(8 + 3\sqrt{6})$; concave downward:
$x < -2, \frac{1}{5}(8 - 3\sqrt{6}) < x < \frac{1}{5}(8 + 3\sqrt{6})$

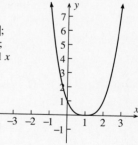

35. $f(1) = 0$, rel. min.;
no pts. of infl.;
decreasing: $(-\infty, 1]$;
increasing: $[1, +\infty)$;
concave upward: all x

45. (a)

$(c, f(c))$

(b)

$(c, f(c))$

(c)

$(c, f(c))$

(d)

$(c, f(c))$

47. (a)

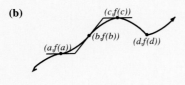

(b)

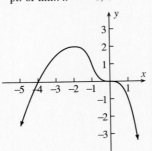

49. increasing: $(-\infty, -2]$;
decreasing: $(-2, +\infty)$;
rel. max.: $x = -2$;
concave upward: $(-1, 0)$;
concave downward: $x < -1, x > 0$;
pt. of infl.: $x = -1, 0$

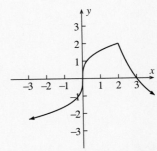

51. increasing: $(-\infty, 2]$; decreasing: $[2, +\infty)$;
rel. max.: $x = 2$, concave upward:
$x < 0, x > 2$; concave downward: $(0, 2)$;
pt. of infl.: $x = 0$

53. increasing: $(-\infty, -3], [1, 3.5]$; decreasing: $[-3, 1], [3.5, +\infty)$;
rel. max.: $x = -3, x = 3.5$; rel. min.: $x = 1$;
concave upward: $(-1, 2.5)$; concave downward: $x < -1$,
$x > 2.5$; pt. of infl.: $x = -1, x = 2.5$

55. increasing: $[-1, 1], [2.5, +\infty)$; decreasing: $(-\infty, -1], [1, 2.5)$;
rel. max.: $x = 1$; rel. min.: $x = -1, x = 2.5$;
concave upward: $x < 1, x > 1$; no pt. of infl.

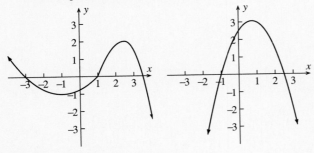

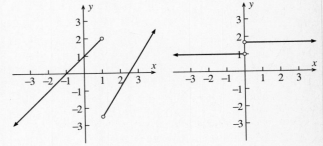

57. 3   **59.** $-\infty$ **61.** 0
67. $x_1 = \frac{1}{16}(9 - \sqrt{561})$, $x_2 = \frac{1}{16}(9 + \sqrt{561})$,
$x_3 = -\frac{1}{8}(\sqrt{137} + 5)$, $x_4 = \frac{1}{8}(\sqrt{137} - 5)$;
increasing: $[-3, x_1], [x_2, +\infty)$; relative min.: $f(-3) = 0$,
$f(x_2) \approx -75.1$; rel. max.: $f(x_1) \approx 48.1$;
concave upward: $x < x_3, x > x_4$;
concave downward: (x_3, x_4); pt. of infl.: $x = x_3, x = x_4$

63. $x = 2, x = -2, y = 5$ **65.** $x = 3, y = x + 3$
69. increasing: $[-2\sqrt{2}, 2\sqrt{2}]$; decreasing: $(-\infty, -2\sqrt{2}]$,
$[2\sqrt{2}, +\infty)$;
rel. min.: $f(-2\sqrt{2}) = -4\sqrt{2}$;
rel. max.: $f(2\sqrt{2}) = 4\sqrt{2}$
concave upward: $x < 0$; concave downward: $x > 0$
pt. of infl.: $(0, 0)$

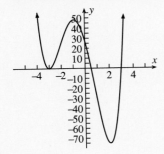

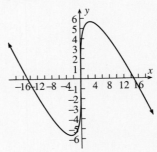

71. $\sqrt{A^2 + B^2}$ **73.** $a = 2, b = -6, c = 3$ **79.** 900   **81.** 12 km from point on bank nearest A **83.** $2000   **85.** $1800
87. 1500   **89.** 25 radios; $525   **91.** $\frac{125}{8}$ m   **93.** $\frac{512}{27}\pi$ in.^{3} **95.** radius is $\frac{3}{2}r$ cm and altitude is $3h$ cm
99. the wire should be cut in half   **101.** 1000; $11   **103.** -0.482 **105.** 4.4934
107. 1; f: 0.9998, 0.999998, 1, 0.999998, 0.9998; approximation: 1, 1, 1, 1, 1   **109. (a)** -0.16;   **(b)** -0.64
111. 2π in.^{3} **113.** 1 percent   **117. (a)**

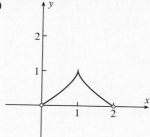

(c)

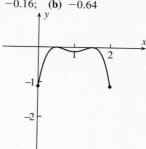

EXERCISES 4.1   (page 324)

1. $\frac{3}{5}x^5 + C$ **3.** $-\dfrac{1}{2x^2} + C$ **5.** $2u^{5/2} + C$ **7.** $3x^{2/3} + C$ **9.** $\frac{9}{5}t^{10/3} + C$ **11.** $\frac{1}{3}y^6 - \frac{3}{4}y^4 + C$
13. $\frac{8}{5}x^5 + x^4 - 2x^3 - 2x^2 + 5x + C$ **15.** $\frac{2}{5}x^{5/2} + \frac{2}{3}x^{3/2} + C$ **17.** $-\frac{1}{x^2} - \frac{3}{x} + 5x + C$ **19.** $\frac{2}{5}x^{5/2} + \frac{8}{3}x^{3/2} - 8x^{1/2} + C$
21. $\frac{3}{4}x^{4/3} + \frac{3}{2}x^{2/3} + C$ **23.** $-3\cos t - 2\sin t + C$ **25.** $\sec x + C$ **27.** $-4\csc x + 2\tan x + C$
29. $-2\cot\theta - 3\tan\theta + \theta + C$
31. (a)

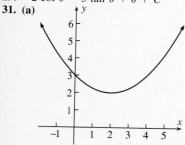

33. (a)

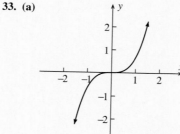

35.

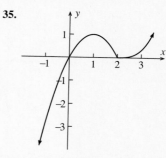

(b)

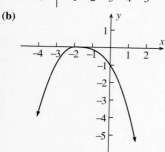

(b)

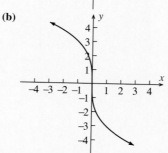

37. $y = x^2 - 3x + 2$ **39.** $3y = -2x^3 + 3x^2 + 2x + 6$ **41.** $12y = -x^4 + 6x^2 - 20x + 27$
43. $C(x) = x^3 + 4x^2 + 4x + 6$ **45. (a)** $C(x) = 3x^2 + 8$;   **(b)** $800   **47. (a)** $R(x) = 15x - 2x^2$;   **(b)** $p = 15 - 2x$
49. 117π m^3 **53.** $g'(x)$ does not exist at $x = 0$

EXERCISES 4.2   (page 334)

1. $-\frac{1}{6}(1 - 4y)^{3/2} + C$ **3.** $\frac{3}{8}(x^2 - 9)^{4/3} + C$ **5.** $\frac{1}{33}(x^3 - 1)^{11} + C$ **7.** $\dfrac{1}{32(1 - 2y^4)^4} + C$ **9.** $\frac{3}{11}(x - 2)^{11/3} + C$
11. $\frac{2}{5}(x + 2)^{5/2} - \frac{4}{3}(x + 2)^{3/2} + C$ **13.** $-\frac{2}{5}(1 - r)^{-5} + \frac{1}{3}(1 - r)^{-6} + C$
15. $-\frac{3}{4}(3 - 2x)^{3/2} + \frac{3}{10}(3 - 2x)^{5/2} - \frac{1}{28}(3 - 2x)^{7/2} + C$

17. $\frac{1}{4}\sin 4\theta + C$ **19.** $-2\cos x^3 + C$ **21.** $\frac{1}{5}\tan 5x + C$ **23.** $-\frac{1}{6}\csc 3y^2 + C$ **25.** $\frac{1}{6}(2+\sin x)^6 + C$

27. $-2\left(1+\frac{1}{3x}\right)^{3/2} + C$ **29.** $-\frac{3}{2}(1+\cos x)^{4/3} + C$ **31.** $-\frac{1}{3}\cos^3 t + C$ **33.** $\frac{1}{2}\tan 2x - \frac{1}{2}\cot 2x + C$

35. $\frac{2}{3}\sqrt{x^3+3x^2+1} + C$ **37.** $\frac{3}{4}(3-y)^{4/3} - 18(3-y)^{1/3} + C$ **39.** $\frac{3}{5}(r^{1/3}+2)^5 + C$ **41.** $\sqrt{x^2+4} + \frac{4}{\sqrt{x^2+4}} + C$

43. $\cos(\cos x) + C$ **45.** $C(x) = \frac{6}{5}\sqrt{5x+4} + \frac{38}{5}$ **47.** $p = \frac{4x+22}{x+5}$ **49.** $\frac{1}{6}$ coulombs **51.** \$325 **53.** 3.1 μm^3

55. (a) $2x^4 + 4x^3 + 3x^2 + x + C$; (b) $\frac{1}{8}(2x+1)^4 + \overline{C}$; (c) $C = \frac{1}{8} + \overline{C}$

57. (a) $\frac{2}{3}x^{3/2} - 2x + 2x^{1/2} + C$; (b) $\frac{2}{3}(\sqrt{x}-1)^3 + \overline{C}$; (c) $C = -\frac{2}{3} + \overline{C}$

59. (a) $\sin^2 x + C_1$; (b) $-\cos^2 x + C_2$; (c) $-\frac{1}{2}\cos 2x + C_3$; (d) $C_2 = C_1 + 1$; $C_3 = C_1 + \frac{1}{2}$

EXERCISES 4.3 (page 343)

1. $y = 2x^2 - 5x + C$ **3.** $y = x^3 + x^2 - 7x + C$ **5.** $y = \frac{-2}{3x^2+C}$ **7.** $2\sqrt{1+u^2} = 3v^2 + C$

9. $\tan x - \tan y + y = C$ **11.** $y = \frac{5}{12}x^4 + \frac{1}{2}x^2 + C_1 x + C_2$ **13.** $s = -\frac{1}{9}(\sin 3t + \cos 3t) + C_1 t + C_2$

15. $y = \frac{1}{3}x^3 - x^2 - 4x + 6$ **17.** $4\sin 3x + 6\cos 2y + 7 = 0$ **19.** $u = 3v^4 + 4v^3 + 2v^2 + 2v$

21. $s = \frac{1}{3}(2t+4)^{3/2} - \frac{8}{3}$ **23.** $v = 2 + 5t - t^2$; $s = 2t + \frac{5}{2}t^2 - \frac{1}{3}t^3$ **25.** $v = \frac{1}{3}t^3 + t^2 - 4$; $s = \frac{1}{12}t^4 + \frac{1}{3}t^3 - 4t + 1$

27. $v = -2\sqrt{2}\sin(2t - \frac{1}{4}\pi)$; $s = \sqrt{2}\cos(2t - \frac{1}{4}\pi)$ **29.** $1600s = v^2 + 1200$ **31.** $5s^2 + 4s = v^2 + 12$

33. At t sec, its position is s cm to the right of the origin, where $s = (-3\cos 3\pi t + 3)/\pi$.
   (a) $s = (\frac{9}{4} - \frac{3}{4}\sqrt{5})/\pi \approx 0.1824$; (b) $s = 3/\pi \approx 0.9549$; (c–d) $s = (\frac{15}{4} - \frac{3}{4}\sqrt{5})/\pi \approx 0.6598$

35. (a) 0.625 sec; (b) 6.25 ft; (c) 1.25 sec; (e) 20.0 ft/sec **37.** (a) 5.89 sec; (b) 188 ft/sec

39. (a) 3.39 sec; (b) 98.5 ft/sec **41.** (a) 3.54 sec; (b) 113 ft/sec

43. (a) $s = -4.9t^2 + 150t + 2$; (b) 523.6 m; (c) 3.79 sec; 26.8 sec **45.** $\frac{15}{241}$ rad/sec ≈ 0.06 rad/sec **47.** 1.62 m/sec²

49. (a) 3.47 sec; (b) 48.2 m **51.** 20 m/sec = 72 km/hr **53.** $x^2 + 2y^2 = C$

EXERCISES 4.4 (page 355)

1. 51 **3.** 147 **5.** 2025 **7.** $\frac{73}{12}$ **9.** $\frac{63}{4}$ **11.** $\frac{7}{12}$ **13.** 10,400 **15.** $2^n - 1$ **17.** $\frac{100}{101}$ **19.** $n^4 - \frac{2}{3}n^3 - 3n^2 - \frac{4}{3}n$

21. $\frac{8}{3}$ sq units **23.** $\frac{5}{3}$ sq units **25.** 9 sq units **27.** $\frac{17}{4}$ sq units **29.** $\frac{27}{4}$ sq units **31.** $\frac{1}{2}h(b_1 + b_2)$ sq units

33. 9 sq units **35.** 15 sq units **37.** 1.0349 sq units **39.** 1.8530 sq units **41.** 1.5912 sq units

EXERCISES 4.5 (page 367)

1. $\frac{247}{32}$ **3.** 1.14 **5.** $\frac{\pi}{24}(10 + \sqrt{2} + 3\sqrt{3})$ **7.** (a) 0.2672; (b) 0.3 **9.** (a) 2.6725; (b) 2.6339 **11.** 2

13. π **15.** 6 **17.** 12 **19.** 10 **21.** $\frac{5}{2}$ **23.** 28 **25.** $\frac{\pi}{2}$ **27.** 0 **29.** (a) 12; (b) 49; (c) -5

31. 15 **33.** 0 **35.** -21 **37.** $-\frac{3}{2}$ **39.** $4 + \pi$ **41.** $\frac{33}{2}\pi$ **49.** $\int_0^2 x^2\, dx$ **51.** $\int_1^2 \frac{1}{x^2}\, dx$

EXERCISES 4.6 (page 376)

1. $\geq$ **3.** $\leq$ **5.** $[0, 0.125]$ **7.** $[2, 2\sqrt{3}]$ **9.** $[\frac{\pi}{12}, \frac{\pi}{12}\sqrt{3}]$ **11.** $[0, 1.5]$ **13.** $[0, \frac{25}{32}]$ **15.** $[2, 2.5]$ **17.** $[-2, \frac{2}{3}]$

19. $[-\frac{2}{3}\pi, 0]$ **21.** 1.15 **23.** 1.55 **25.** 2.58 **27.** 0 **29.** 2.66 **31.** 0.66 **41.** $\frac{1}{2}$, occurring at $x = \frac{1}{2}$

43. $\frac{2}{\pi} \approx \sin 0.69$ **45.** $v = 32t$; 32 **47.** π

EXERCISES 4.7 (page 387)

1. 12 **3.** 36 **5.** $\frac{3}{2}$ **7.** $\frac{3}{16}$ **9.** $\frac{134}{3}$ **11.** -8 **13.** 1 **15.** $\frac{2}{9}(27 - 2\sqrt{2})$ **17.** $2 - \sqrt[3]{2}$

19. $\frac{104}{5}$ **21.** $\frac{29}{2}$ **23.** $\frac{2}{3}\sqrt{2}$ **25.** $\frac{256}{15}$ **27.** $\frac{5}{6}$ **29.** $\frac{6215}{12}$ **31.** 0 **33.** $\frac{3}{2}$ **35.** $\sqrt{4+x^6}$ **37.** $-\sqrt{\sin x}$

39. $\frac{2}{3+x^2}$ **41.** $3x^2\sqrt[3]{x^6+1}$ **43.** 1 **45.** 6, occurring at $x = \sqrt{3}$ **47.** 27 **49.** $\sqrt{2 - \frac{3}{4}(\sin\frac{8}{3})} \approx 1.2873$ **59.** $\frac{188}{3}$

EXERCISES 4.8 *(page 396)*

1. $\frac{32}{3}$ sq units   **3.** $\frac{22}{3}$ sq units   **5.** $\frac{52}{3}$ sq units   **7.** $\frac{343}{6}$ sq units   **9.** 1 sq unit   **11.** 1 sq unit   **13.** $\frac{32}{3}$ sq units
15. $\frac{32}{3}$ sq units   **17.** $\frac{1}{6}$ sq units   **19.** $\frac{12}{5}$ sq units   **21.** $\frac{9}{2}$ sq units   **23.** $\frac{8}{3}\sqrt{2}$ sq units   **25.** $\frac{5}{12}$ sq units   **27.** $\frac{27}{10}$ sq units
29. $\frac{64}{3}$ sq units   **31.** $\frac{253}{12}$ sq units   **33.** $\frac{37}{12}$ sq units   **35.** $(\sqrt{2}-1)$ sq units   **37.** $\frac{7}{3}$ sq units
39. **(a)** $\pm\sqrt{2} \approx 1.4142$;   **(c)** $\frac{56}{15}\sqrt{2}$ sq units ≈ 5.2797 sq units   **41.** **(a)** ± 1.4045;   **(c)** 2.2032 sq units
43. **(a)** 1.3146;   **(c)** 3.7545 sq units   **45.** **(a)** 1.1274;   **(c)** 2.8079 sq units   **47.** 12 sq units   **49.** $\frac{128}{5}$ sq units
51. 64 sq units   **53.** $(\frac{1}{2}\pi - 1)$ sq units   **55.** $(1 - \frac{1}{4}\pi)$ sq units   **57.** $\frac{16}{3}p^2$ sq units   **59.** 32   **61.** $m = \frac{3}{2}K$
63. The domain of $A(h)$ is $[0, r]$

EXERCISES 4.9 *(page 407)*

1. $\frac{4}{3}\pi r^3$ cu units   **3.** $\frac{127}{7}\pi$ cu units   **5.** 64π cu units   **7.** $\frac{704}{5}\pi$ cu units   **9.** $\frac{384}{7}\pi$ cu units   **11.** $\frac{3456}{35}\pi$ cu units
13. $\frac{256}{15}\pi$ cu units   **15.** $\frac{128}{15}\pi$ cu units   **17.** $\frac{4}{3}\pi r^3$ cu units   **19.** $\frac{1}{3}\pi h(a^2 + ab + b^2)$ cu units   **21.** π cu units
23. $\frac{1}{2}\pi^2$ cu units   **25.** $(4\pi - \frac{1}{2}\pi^2)$ cu units   **27.** $(\sqrt{3}\pi - \frac{1}{3}\pi^2)$ cu units   **29.** $\frac{1250}{3}\pi$ cu units   **31.** $\frac{64}{5}\pi$ cu units
33. $\frac{261}{32}\pi$ cu units   **35.** $\frac{16}{3}\pi$ cu units   **37.** $(\frac{8}{3}\pi^2 - 2\sqrt{3}\pi)$ cu units   **39.** 2   **41.** 15.15 cu units
43. 39.69 cu units   **45.** 2.822 cu units   **47.** 6.923 cu units   **49.** 20.28 cu units   **51.** $32\sqrt{2}$ cu units   **53.** $\frac{1372}{3}\sqrt{3}$ cm^3
55. $\frac{686}{3}$ cm^3 **57.** $\frac{8}{3}r^3$ cu units   **59.** 396.9 cu units   **61.** $\frac{2}{3}r^3$ cm^3 **63.** 180π cm^3

EXERCISES 4.10 *(page 414)*

1–11. See answers to Exercises 4.9. Ex. 5–15
13. $\frac{1}{2}\pi$ cu units   **15.** $\frac{3}{10}\pi$ cu units   **17.** $\frac{5}{6}\pi$ cu units   **19.** $\frac{49}{30}\pi$ cu units   **21.** 16π cu units   **23.** $\frac{512}{15}\pi$ cu units
25. $\frac{32}{15}\pi p^3$ cu units   **27.** $\frac{8}{5}\pi$ cu units   **29.** $\frac{11}{10}\pi$ cu units   **31.** $\frac{152}{15}\pi$ cu units   **33.** $\frac{16}{3}\pi$ cu units
35. $\frac{32}{15}\pi$ cu units   **37.** $\frac{1}{2}(2 + \sqrt{2})\pi$ cu units   **39.** π cu units   **41.** 20.37 cu units   **43.** 62.67 cu units
45. 2.038 cu units   **47.** 7.707 cu units   **49.** 6.763 cu units   **51.** $\frac{224}{3}\pi$ cu units   **53.** $\sqrt[7]{2744}$

MISCELLANEOUS EXERCISES FOR CHAPTER 4 *(page 417)*

1. $\frac{1}{2}x^4 - \frac{1}{3}x^3 + 3x + C$ **3.** $\frac{2}{15}(x^5 - 1)^{3/2} + C$ **5.** $\frac{1}{3}\sqrt{2s + 3}(s - 3) + C$ **7.** $\frac{1}{3}\tan 3\theta - \theta + C$
9. $5\sin x - 3\sec x + C$ **11.** $\frac{56}{3}$ **13.** $\frac{11}{4}$ **15.** $\frac{5}{4}$ **17.** $\frac{1}{2}$ **19.** $\frac{652}{15}$ **21.** $4 - \frac{1}{2}\pi$ **23.** $y^2 = \dfrac{1}{2x^{-1} + C} + 1$
25. $y = \frac{1}{15}(2x - 1)^{5/2} + C_1 x + C_2$ **27.** $y = 10x - 2x^2 - 9$ **29.** **(a)** $R(x) = \frac{1}{4}x^3 - 5x^2 + 12x$;   **(b)** $p = \frac{1}{4}x^2 - 5x + 12$
31. **(a)** $V = \frac{2}{3}(t + 1)^{3/2} + \frac{1}{3}t^2 + \frac{74}{3}$;   **(b)** 64 cm^3 **33.** 1.46 cm^3 **35.** \$5
37. $v = 3\sin 2t + 3$; $s = -\frac{3}{2}\cos 2t + 3t + \frac{1}{2}(5 - 3\pi)$
39. At t sec, its position is s cm to the right of the origin, where $s = \dfrac{3\sin 2\pi t}{2\pi}$.

    (a) $s \approx 0.4541$;   **(b–c)** $s \approx -0.4541$;   **(d)** $s = \dfrac{3}{2\pi} \approx 0.4775$
41. **(a)** $25\sqrt{3}$ sec ≈ 43 sec;   **(b)** $800\sqrt{3}$ ft/sec ≈ 1400 ft/sec   **43.** **(a)** $\frac{3}{2}$ sec;   **(b)** 100 ft;   **(c)** 4 sec;   **(d)** -80 ft/sec
45. **(a)** 1500 m/sec;   **(b)** 45000 m
47. $(11 + \sqrt{187})$ sec ≈ 25 sec; $88(14 + \sqrt{187})$ ft ≈ 2400 ft; $(88 + 8\sqrt{187})$ ft/sec ≈ 200 ft/sec   **49.** $\sqrt[3]{2} - 5$
53. $[0, \pi]$ **55.** $\frac{313}{2}$ **57.** $-(3x^2 - 4)^{3/2}$ **59.** $\dfrac{1}{x}$ **61.** 0   **63.** $\frac{42,304}{175}$ **67.** $\frac{46}{3}$ sq units   **69.** $\frac{224}{3}$ sq units
71. 36 sq units   **73.** 21.88 sq units   **75.** 0.9678 sq units   **77.** $\frac{1}{12}$ sq units   **79.** $2\sqrt{2}$ sq units   **81.** $(\frac{1}{2}\pi - 1)$ sq units
83. $\frac{1}{9}\pi$ cu units   **85.** π cu units   **87.** π cu units   **89.** 250π cu units   **91.** 1024 cu units   **93.** 3π cu units
95. $\frac{25}{6}\pi$ cu units   **97.** 558π cm^3 **99–101.** 44.96 cu units   **103.** 1.535 cu units   **105.** 25.17 cu units   **107.** 90 ft^3
109. $\frac{832}{3}\pi$ cu units   **111.** $\frac{1}{4}\pi^2$ cu units   **113.** 12; $c = \sqrt{3}$ **119.** $\frac{1}{6}\pi + \sqrt{3}$

EXERCISES 5.1 *(page 437)*

1. **(a)** one-to-one;   **(b)** not one-to-one;   **(c)** one-to-one   **3.** **(a)** one-to-one;   **(b)** one-to-one;   **(c)** not one-to-one
5. **(a)** one-to-one;   **(b)** one-to-one;   **(c)** one-to-one
7. **(a)** $f^{-1}(x) = \frac{1}{5}(x + 7)$, domain: $(-\infty, +\infty)$, range: $(-\infty, +\infty)$;   **(b)** no inverse
9. **(a)** $f^{-1}(x) = 4 - \sqrt[3]{x}$, domain: $(-\infty, +\infty)$, range: $(-\infty, +\infty)$;   **(b)** $h^{-1}(x) = \frac{1}{2}x^2 + 3$, domain: $[0, +\infty)$, range: $[3, +\infty)$
11. **(a)** $F^{-1}(x) = x^3 - 1$, domain: $(-\infty, +\infty)$, range: $(-\infty, +\infty)$;   **(b)** no inverse

13. (a) $f^{-1}(x) = \frac{1}{32}x^5$, domain: $(-\infty, +\infty)$, range: $(-\infty, +\infty)$; **(b)** $f^{-1}(x) = \frac{x+3}{1-x}$, domain: $\{x \mid x \neq 1\}$, range: $\{y \mid y \neq -1\}$

15. (a) $g^{-1}(x) = \sqrt{x-5}$, domain: $[5, +\infty)$, range: $[0, +\infty)$; **(b)** $f^{-1}(x) = \frac{1}{2}(\sqrt[3]{x} - 1)$, domain: $[0, 8]$, range: $[-\frac{1}{2}, \frac{1}{2}]$

17. $F^{-1}(x) = \sqrt{9 - x^2}$, domain: $[0, 3]$, range: $[0, 3]$ **25. (a)** $\frac{2}{3}$; **(b)** $\frac{1}{10}$ **27. (a)** $\frac{1}{12}$; **(b)** $\frac{1}{21}$ **29. (a)** -2; **(b)** $-\frac{1}{4}$

31. (a) $-\frac{1}{\sqrt{3}}$; **(b)** $-\frac{1}{4}$ **33.** 0.09426 **35.** $\sqrt{\frac{1}{840}(1 + \sqrt{21})} \approx 0.08152$ **37.** 1.334 **39.** $\frac{1}{3}$ **41.** $f^{-1}(x) = \frac{1}{4}(x + 3)$

43. $f^{-1}(x) = \sqrt[3]{x} - 2$ **45.** $f^{-1}(x) = \frac{4x-1}{3-2x}$ **47.** $f^{-1}(x) = \frac{5}{9}(x - 32)$ **49.** $v(m) = c\sqrt{1 - \left(\frac{m_0}{m}\right)^2}$ **51. (b)** 6; **(c)** $\frac{1}{6}$

55. -1 **59. (b)** $f_1(x) = x^2 + 4, x \geq 0; f_2(x) = x^2 + 4, x \leq 0$; **(c)** $f_1^{-1}(x) = \sqrt{x - 4}, x \geq 4; f_2^{-1}(x) = -\sqrt{x - 4}, x \geq 4$

61. $f^{-1}(x) = \begin{cases} x & \text{if } x < 1 \\ \sqrt{x} & \text{if } 1 \leq x \leq 81 \\ \left(\frac{x}{27}\right)^2 & \text{if } 81 < x \end{cases}$ **63.** $(f^{-1})'(0) = \frac{1}{5}$ **65.** $(f^{-1})'(0) = \frac{1}{3\pi^2}$

EXERCISES 5.2   (page 449)

5. $\frac{5}{4 + 5x}$ **7.** $\frac{5}{8 + 10x}$ **9.** $\frac{6}{3t + 1}$ **11.** $\frac{6 \ln(3t + 1)}{3t + 1}$ **13.** $-\frac{2x}{12 - 3x^2}$ **15.** $\frac{5 \cos 5y}{\sin 5y}$ **17.** $-\frac{\sin(\ln x)}{x}$

19. $2 \sec 2x$ **21.** $\frac{\sec^2 x}{2 \tan x}$ **23.** $-\frac{17}{2(2w - 5)(3w + 1)}$ **25.** $\frac{\ln x - 1}{(\ln x)^2}$ **27.** $\frac{1 - 2x - x^2}{3(x + 1)(x^2 + 1)}$ **29.** $\frac{1}{2(1 + \sqrt{x + 1})}$

31. $-\frac{xy + y}{xy + x}$ **33.** $x + y$ **35.** $\frac{4x^2y - xy - 2y}{6xy^2 + x}$

39.

41.

43.

45.

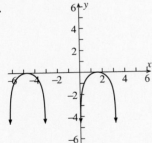

49. $x - 2y = 2 - 2 \ln x$ **51.** $x + y = 1$ **53.** $-\frac{1}{2}$
55. (a) \$5 per \$1 change in advertising expense; **(b)** \$688

EXERCISES 5.3   (page 457)

1. $\frac{3x^2}{x^3 + 1}$ **3.** $-\frac{3 \sin 3x}{\cos 3x}$ **5.** $4 \sec 4x$ **7.** $\frac{4 - x^2}{x(x^2 + 4)}$ **9.** $2x(x + 1)^6(x - 1)^2(6x^2 - 2x - 1)$

11. $\frac{x(x - 1)(x + 2)^2}{(x - 4)^6}(2x^3 - 30x^2 - 6x + 16)$ **13.** $\frac{8x^9 - 4x^7 + 15x^2 + 10}{5(x^7 + 1)^{6/5}}$ **15.** $-\frac{1}{2} \ln|3 - 2x| + C$

17. $\frac{1}{5} \ln|5x^3 - 1| + C$ **19.** $\ln|\ln y| + C$ **21.** $\frac{1}{5} \ln(1 - \cos 5x) + C$ **23.** $\ln(1 + \sin 2x) + \frac{1}{2} \ln|\cos 2x| + C$

25. $x^2 + 4 \ln|x^2 - 4| + C$ **27.** $\frac{1}{3} \ln^3(3x) + C$ **29.** $\ln|\ln^2(x) + \ln x| + C$ **31.** $\ln|\sec(\ln x)| + C$ **33.** $\frac{3}{2} \ln 2$

35. $\frac{1}{2} \ln \frac{4}{7}$ **37.** $4 + \ln 2$ **39.** $\frac{1}{2} \ln 3$ **41.** $\frac{1}{2} \ln(4 + 2\sqrt{3})$ **43.** $\frac{1}{\ln 4}$ **47.** $\frac{1}{4} \ln 5 \approx 0.40236$

49. $2000 \ln 2 \text{ lb/ft}^2 \approx 1386 \text{ lb/ft}^2$ **51.** $\ln 4$ sq units ≈ 1.38629 sq units   **53.** $\pi(11 + 8 \ln 2)$ cu units ≈ 51.97821 cu units

EXERCISES 5.4   (page 467)

1. (a) 2.665; **(b)** 2.565   **3. (a)** 15.15; **(b)** 5.616   **5.** $5e^{5x}$ **7.** $-6xe^{-3x^2}$ **9.** $-e^{\cos x}\sin x$ **11.** $e^{2x}\cos e^x + e^x\sin e^x$

13. $\dfrac{e^{\sqrt{x}}\sec^2 e^{\sqrt{x}}}{2\sqrt{x}}$ **15.** $\dfrac{4}{(e^x + e^{-x})^2}$ **17.** $2x$ **19.** $2e^{2x}\sec e^{2x}\tan e^{2x} + 2e^{2\sec x}\sec x\tan x$ **21.** $-e^{y-x}$

23. $-\dfrac{y^2 + 2ye^{2x}}{2e^{2x} + 3xy}$ **25.** $-\frac{1}{5}e^{2-5x} + C$ **27.** $e^x - e^{-x} + C$ **29.** $\dfrac{1}{6(1 - 2e^{3x})} + C$ **31.** $e^x - 3\ln(e^x + 3) + C$

33. e^2 **35.** 2   **37.** $\frac{1}{2}$ **39.** $\frac{1}{2}(e^4 - 1)$ **41. (a)** 1; **(b)** 0; **(c)** e; **(d)** no, but $\lim\limits_{x\to-\infty} e^x = 0$ **43.** $(e^2 - 1)$ sq units

45. $y = -\frac{1}{2}x + \frac{1}{2} + \frac{1}{2}\ln 2$ **47.** $(e^3 + \frac{1}{2})$ ft ≈ 20.586 ft   **49.** $(-9.17$ lb/ft$^2)$ per sec

51. 0.006   **53.** \$10,000; \$33,834 hundred $\approx$ \$3,383,382   **55. (b)** 2.7181459; 2.7184177; 2.7182818

61. See accompanying figure. **(a–b)** $f(1) = e^{-1}$ is a relative maximum; **(c)** $(-\infty, 1]$; **(d)** $[1, +\infty)$; **(e)** $\{x \mid x > 2\}$; **(f)** $\{x \mid x < 2\}$;
   (g) The slope of the line tangent to f at $x = 2$ is $-e^{-2}$

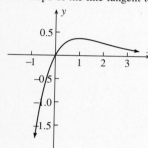

EXERCISES 5.5   (page 476)

1. $5\ln 3 \cdot 3^{5x}$ **3.** $4^{3t^2} \cdot \ln 4 \cdot 6t$ **5.** $4^{\sin 2x} \cdot 2\ln 4 \cdot \cos 2x$ **7.** $2^{5x}3^{4x^2}(5\ln 2 + 8x\ln 3)$ **9.** $\dfrac{1}{x^2}\log_{10}\dfrac{e}{x}$ **11.** $\dfrac{\log_a e}{2x\sqrt{\log_a x}}$

13. $3^{t^2}\sec 3^{t^2}\tan 3^{t^2} \cdot 2t\ln 3$ **15.** $x^{\sqrt{x}-(1/2)}(1 + \frac{1}{2}\ln x)$ **17.** $z^{\cos z - 1}(\cos z - z\ln z\sin z)$

19. $(\sin x)^{\tan x}[1 + \ln(\sin x)\cdot \sec^2 x]$ **21.** $\dfrac{3^{2x}}{2\ln 3} + C$ **23.** $\dfrac{a^t e^t}{1 + \ln a} + C$ **25.** $\dfrac{10^{x^3}}{3\ln 10} + C$

27. $\dfrac{6^{e^y}}{\ln 6} + C$ **29.** $\dfrac{(\ln|x|)^2}{\ln 2} + C$ **31. (a)** 0.62133; **(b)** 1.7712   **33. (a)** 3.3219; **(b)** 0.43429   **35.** 2.999

45. (a) 61 sales per day; **(b)** 2.26 sales per day   **49. (a)** $y = 200 \cdot 2^{t/10}$; **(b)** \$12,800; **(c)** \$877 per year

51. (a)   **(b)**

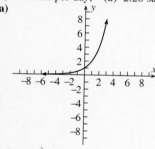

53. $\left(\dfrac{4}{\ln 5} - 1\right)$ sq units   **55.** $\pi\left(\dfrac{12}{\ln 5} - 1\right)$ cu units   **57.** 0.73306 sq units

59. (a)   **(b)** $f(1) = 1$ is a relative minimum;
   (c) $[1, +\infty)$; **(d)** $(0, 1]$;
   (e) The graph is concave upward on its
      entire domain: $(0, +\infty)$;
   (f) none

67. domain: $(0, 1) \cup (1, +\infty)$; endpoint at $f(0) = 0$; unbounded at $x = 1$; decreasing on all intervals in domain; point of inflection at $(e^{-2}, -\frac{1}{2} \ln 5)$; concave upward on $[0, e^{-2}]$ and $(1, +\infty)$; concave downward on $[e^{-2}, 1)$

EXERCISES 5.6 *(page 489)*

1. (a) $y = 40{,}000(1.5)^{t/40}$; **(b)** 64,000; **(c)** 2023   **3. (a)** $i = 40(0.375)^{100t}$; **(b)** 5.625 amperes   **5.** 506   **7.** 10.6
9. 123,456   **11.** 29.15 years   **13. (a)** \$5256.355; **(b)** \$5256.337; **(c)** 5.127%   **15.** 15.8 years   **17.** 43.9 g
19. 11.6 kg   **21.** 6600 years ago   **23.** 70   **25. (a)** 1 min 42 sec; **(b)** 42.1°
27. (a) $y = 60 - 60(0.75)^{t/20}$; **(c)** 35; **(d)** 55   **29.** 0.34134   **31.** 0.84270   **33.** $\ln\left|\ln\dfrac{a}{y}\right| + kt = C$

EXERCISES 5.7 *(page 505)*

1. (a) $\frac{1}{6}\pi$; **(b)** $-\frac{1}{6}\pi$; **(c)** $\frac{1}{3}\pi$; **(d)** $\frac{2}{3}\pi$ **3. (a)** $\frac{1}{6}\pi$; **(b)** $-\frac{1}{3}\pi$; **(c)** $\frac{1}{6}\pi$; **(d)** $\frac{7}{6}\pi$
5. (a) $\frac{1}{2}\pi$; **(b)** $-\frac{1}{2}\pi$; **(c)** $\frac{1}{2}\pi$; **(d)** $-\frac{1}{2}\pi$; **(e)** 0   **7. (a)** $\frac{2}{3}\sqrt{2}$; **(b)** $\frac{1}{4}\sqrt{2}$; **(c)** $2\sqrt{2}$; **(d)** $\frac{3}{4}\sqrt{2}$; **(e)** 3
9. (a) $\frac{2}{3}\sqrt{2}$; **(b)** $-\frac{1}{4}\sqrt{2}$; **(c)** $-2\sqrt{2}$; **(d)** $\frac{3}{4}\sqrt{2}$; **(e)** -3
11. (a) $-\frac{2}{3}\sqrt{5}$; **(b)** $\frac{1}{5}\sqrt{5}$; **(c)** $-\frac{1}{2}$; **(d)** $\sqrt{5}$; **(e)** $-\frac{1}{2}\sqrt{5}$
13. $\frac{1}{6}\pi$; **(b)** $-\frac{1}{6}\pi$; **(c)** $\frac{1}{6}\pi$; **(d)** $-\frac{1}{6}\pi$ **15. (a)** $\frac{1}{3}\pi$; **(b)** $\frac{1}{3}\pi$; **(c)** $\frac{2}{3}\pi$; **(d)** $\frac{2}{3}\pi$
17. (a) $\frac{1}{6}\pi$; **(b)** $-\frac{1}{3}\pi$; **(c)** $\frac{1}{6}\pi$; **(d)** $-\frac{1}{3}\pi$ **19. (a)** $\frac{1}{3}\pi$; **(b)** $\frac{1}{3}\pi$; **(c)** $\frac{4}{3}\pi$; **(d)** $\frac{4}{3}\pi$
21. (a) $\sqrt{3}$; **(b)** $\frac{1}{7}\sqrt{21}$ **23. (a)** $\frac{1}{2}\sqrt{3}$; **(b)** $\frac{1}{2}\sqrt{3}$

25.

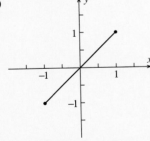

27.

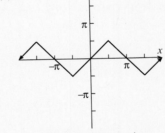

29.

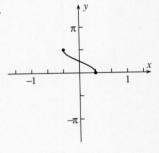

31. (a)

domain: $[-1, 1]$;

range: $[-1, 1]$

(b)

domain: $(-\infty, +\infty)$;

range: $\left[-\dfrac{\pi}{2}, \dfrac{\pi}{2}\right]$

33. (a) $\dfrac{1}{\sqrt{4 - x^2}}$; **(b)** $\dfrac{2}{1 + 4x^2}$ **35. (a)** $-\dfrac{1}{\sqrt{x - x^2}}$; **(b)** 0   **37. (a)** $-\dfrac{x}{|x|\sqrt{1 - x^2}}$; **(b)** $\dfrac{2}{4 + x^2}$

39. (a) $-\dfrac{\cos x}{|\cos x|}$; **(b)** $2\sqrt{4 - x^2}$ **41. (a)** $\tan^{-1} x$; **(b)** $\dfrac{3}{\sqrt{4e^{6x} - 1}}$

43. (a) $t = -\dfrac{1}{4\pi}\sin^{-1}\dfrac{y}{2} + \dfrac{1}{8} + \dfrac{n}{2}$, for any integer $n \geq 0$ or $t = \dfrac{1}{4\pi}\sin^{-1}\dfrac{y}{2} - \dfrac{1}{8} + \dfrac{k}{2}$, for any integer $k \geq 1$; **(b)** $\frac{1}{12}, \frac{5}{12}, \frac{7}{12}$

45. tangent line: $y = \dfrac{\sqrt{3}x}{3} - \dfrac{\sqrt{3}}{6} + \dfrac{\pi}{3}$; normal line: $y = -\sqrt{3}x + \dfrac{\sqrt{3}}{2} + \dfrac{\pi}{3}$

47. $\sqrt{10}$ ft ≈ 3.16 ft   **49.** $\frac{1264}{16{,}241}$ rad/sec ≈ 0.078 rad/sec   **51.** $\frac{52}{3}\pi$ km/min   **53.** 8 ft/sec   **55.** $\dfrac{6}{x\sqrt{x^2 - 64}}$

EXERCISES 5.8 (page 511)

1. $\frac{1}{2}\sin^{-1} 2x + C$ **3.** $\frac{1}{12}\tan^{-1}\frac{3}{4}x + C$ **5.** $\frac{1}{16}\sec^{-1}\frac{1}{4}x + C$ **7.** $\frac{1}{6}\sin^{-1}\frac{3}{4}r^2 + C$ **9.** $\frac{1}{\sqrt{7}}\tan^{-1}\frac{e^x}{\sqrt{7}} + C$

11. $2\tan^{-1}\sqrt{x} + C$ **13.** $\frac{2}{\sqrt{7}}\tan^{-1}\frac{2x-1}{\sqrt{7}} + C$ **15.** $\sin^{-1}\frac{x-1}{4} + C$ **17.** $\frac{1}{4}\pi + \frac{1}{2}\ln 2$

19. $\frac{1}{3}\pi$ **21.** $\tan^{-1} e - \frac{1}{4}\pi$ **23.** $\frac{1}{4}\pi$ **25.** $-\sqrt{5} - \sin^{-1}\frac{2}{3} + 3 \approx 0.0342044$

27. $\frac{21}{2} + \frac{5}{4}\ln 3 + \frac{1}{2}\sqrt{2}(\tan^{-1}\sqrt{2} - \pi) \approx 10.3273$ **29.** π sq units   **31.** $\frac{1}{3}\pi$ sq units

EXERCISES 5.9 (page 524)

1. (a) 0; **(b)** 1; **(c)** $\frac{1}{2}(e - e^{-1}) \approx 1.175$; **(d)** $\frac{1}{2}(e^{-1} - e) \approx -1.175$

3. (a) $\frac{e^2 - e^{-2}}{e^2 + e^{-2}} \approx 0.9640$; **(b)** $\frac{e^{-2} - e^2}{e^{-2} + e^2} \approx -0.9640$; **(c)** $\frac{5}{4}$; **(d)** $\frac{5}{4}$

5. (a) $\frac{2}{e^2 + e^{-2}} \approx 0.2658$; **(b)** $\frac{2}{e^{-2} + e^2} \approx 0.2658$; **(c)** $\frac{e^{-1} + e}{e^{-1} - e} \approx -1.313$; **(d)** $\frac{12}{5}$

13. (a) $2x\cosh x^2$; **(b)** $-8\,\text{sech}^2\,4w\tanh 4w$ **15. (a)** $\frac{1}{x^2}\,\text{csch}^2\frac{1}{x}$; $\frac{1}{\sinh x\cosh x} = 2\,\text{csch}\,2x; \ x > 0$

17. (a) $2\,\text{sech}\,2x$; **(b)** $(\cosh x)^x[\ln(\cosh x) + x\tanh x]$ **19.** $\frac{1}{5}\sinh^5 x + C$ **21.** $-\frac{1}{3}\coth x^3 + C$

23. $\frac{1}{4}\ln^2(\cosh 2x) + C$ **27.** $\frac{4}{5} = 0.8$ **29.** $2(\cosh 2 - \cosh 1) \approx 4.438$ **31.** $\frac{1}{6}(\tanh^6 3 - \tanh^6 2) \approx 0.02800$

33. (a) 0; **(b)** $\frac{1}{2}\ln 3$ **35. (a)** $\ln(\frac{1}{2} + \frac{1}{2}\sqrt{5})$; **(b)** $\frac{1}{2}\ln\frac{1}{3} = -\frac{1}{2}\ln 3$

41. (a) $\frac{4}{\sqrt{16x^2 + 1}}$; **(b)** $\frac{2x}{1 - x^4}, |x| > 1$ **43. (a)** $\frac{\sec^2 x}{\sqrt{\tan^2 x - 1}}, \tan x > 1$; **(b)** $-\csc x$

45. (a) $\frac{6z(\coth^{-1} z^2)^2}{1 - z^4}$; **(b)** $\frac{e^x}{\cos e^x}$ **47.** $\sinh^{-1} x$ **49.** $\sinh^{-1}\frac{x}{2} + C = \ln\frac{x + \sqrt{x^2 + 4}}{2} + C$

51. $\frac{1}{2}\cosh^{-1} x^2 + C = \frac{1}{2}\ln(x^2 + \sqrt{x^4 - 1}) + C$

53. $\frac{1}{4}\ln\left|\frac{2 + e^t}{2 - e^t}\right| + C = \begin{cases}\frac{1}{2}\tanh^{-1}(\frac{1}{2}e^t) + C, & \text{if } e^t < 2 \\ \frac{1}{2}\coth^{-1}(\frac{1}{2}e^t) + C, & \text{if } e^t > 2\end{cases}$

55. $\cosh^{-1}\frac{5}{2} - \cosh^{-1}\frac{3}{2} \approx 0.6044$ **57.** $\tanh^{-1}\frac{1}{2} - \tanh^{-1}(-\frac{1}{2}) \approx 1.099$ **59.** $\frac{1}{3}(\cosh^{-1}\frac{7}{3} - \cosh^{-1}\frac{4}{3}) \approx 0.2319$

63. 105 sq units   **65. (a)** $v = e^{-t/2}(\frac{5}{2}\sinh t + \cosh t); a = e^{-t/2}(2\cosh t - \frac{1}{4}\sinh t)$ **69.** $4000(31 - 20\sinh 1) \approx 29{,}983$

MISCELLANEOUS EXERCISES FOR CHAPTER 5 (page 528)

1. $f^{-1}(x) = \sqrt[3]{x} + 4$, domain: $(-\infty, +\infty)$, range: $(-\infty, +\infty)$ **3.** no inverse

5. $f^{-1}(x) = \frac{4}{3 - x}$, domain: $\{x \mid x \ne 3\}$, range: $\{y \mid y \ne 0\}$ **7.** $f^{-1}(x) = x^3 - 1$ **9.** $\frac{1}{4}$ **11.** $\frac{1}{12}$

13. (a) $-3\tan 3x, \cos 3x > 0$; **(b)** $\frac{4x}{x^2 + 1}$ **15. (a)** $4e^{4t}\cos e^{4t}$; **(b)** $2^{\tan t} \cdot \ln 2 \cdot \sec^2 t$

17. (a) $\frac{e^x}{1 + e^{2x}}$; **(b)** $\frac{-e^{\cot^{-1} x}}{1 + x^2}$ **19. (a)** $6\sinh^2(2w)\cosh(2w)$; **(b)** $\sinh(2w^3)6w^2$

21. (a) $-\text{sech}(\tan x)\tanh(\tan x)\sec^2 x$; **(b)** $\text{sech}^2(\sec x)\tan x\sec x$ **23.** $\frac{4}{(1 - x^2)\ln 10}$ **25.** $(\sin t)^{2t}(2\ln(\sin t) + 2t\cot t)$

27. $\frac{1}{2\sqrt{x}\sqrt{x - 1}}$ **29.** $-2\,\text{sech}(2x)$ **31.** $x^2(x^2 + 1)(x - 1)^3(11x^3 - 7x^2 + 7x - 3)$ **33. (a)** 4.7288; **(b)** 8.8250

35. $\frac{3}{2}\ln(1 + e^{2x}) + C$ **37.** $\frac{1}{3}\left(e^{3x} + \frac{2^{3x}}{\ln 2}\right) + C$ **39.** $\frac{2e^x}{\ln 2} + C$ **41.** $2\sin^{-1} x^2 + C$ **43.** $\frac{1}{3}\tan^{-1}\frac{x + 1}{3} + C$

45. $\frac{1}{4}\sqrt{2}\sin^{-1} 2\sqrt{2}e^{-x} + C$ **47.** $w - \frac{\tanh 3w}{3} + C$ **49.** $\frac{1}{3}(e^8 - 1)$ **51.** $\frac{3}{2}\ln 2$ **53.** $1 + 5\ln\frac{3}{4}$ **55.** $\frac{2}{3}\pi + \sqrt{3} - 2$

57. $\frac{1}{2}(e + e^{-1}) - 1$ **59.** $\frac{-ye^x - e^y - 1}{e^x + xe^y + 1}$ **61. (a)** $\ln(2 + \sqrt{3})$; **(b)** $\frac{1}{2}\ln\frac{5}{3}$ **63.** $y = (2\ln 2 + 1)x - 4\ln 2$

65. $v = e^t - e^{-t} + 1; s = e^t + e^{-t} + t$ **67.** $\frac{1}{2}\pi(1 - e^{-2b}); \frac{1}{2}\pi$ **69.** $g(x) = -e^x$, domain: $(-\infty, +\infty)$

73. (a) $y = 65(0.5)^{t/30}$; **(b)** 81 years from now   **75. (a)** $y = 50 - 50(0.6)^{t/30}$; **(c)** 32; **(d)** 3 hours, 50 minutes

77. 8.66 years   **79.** 187,500   **81.** 8212 years   **83.** 8.63 min   **85.** 73.7°   **87. (a)** $t = \frac{n}{60} + \frac{1}{120\pi}\cos^{-1}\frac{E}{20}$, for any

integer $n \ge 0$ or $t = \frac{k}{60} - \frac{1}{120\pi}\cos^{-1}\frac{E}{20}$, for any integer $k \ge 1$; **(b)** $\frac{1}{360}$; **(c)** 0.0035; **(d)** $\frac{1}{180}$; **(e)** 0.0048

89. $9\sin^{-1}(\frac{2}{3}\sqrt{2})$ sq units   **91. (a)** 120 rad/hr; **(b)** 60 rad/hr   **93.** 0.007 rad/sec   **95.** $\frac{1}{10}\pi$ hr; he walks all the way

103. $(\text{sgn}\,t)(1 - e^{-|t|})$

EXERCISES 6.1   (page 540)
1. $\sqrt{10}$ **3.** $\sqrt{97}$ **5.** $\frac{14}{3}$ **7.** $\frac{33}{16}$ **9.** $\frac{1}{27}(97^{3/2} - 125)$ **11.** 12   **13.** $\frac{22}{3}$ **15.** $\frac{9}{8}$
17. $\dfrac{8a^3 - (a^2 + 3b^2)^{3/2}}{8(a^2 - b^2)}$ if $b \neq a$; $\frac{9}{8}a$ if $b = a$ **19.** $2\sqrt{3} - \frac{4}{3}$ **21.** $\ln(\sqrt{2} + 1)$ **23.** 2   **25.** 4.647   **27.** 3.820
29. 1.089   **31.** 8.815   **33.** 2.422   **35.** 400 sinh $\frac{3}{4}$ ft $\approx$ 328.9 ft

EXERCISES 6.2   (page 547)
1. 250 lb   **3.** 4000 dynes   **5.** $\frac{3}{2}$ m/sec^2 **7.** $\frac{8}{3}$ slugs   **9.** 4   **11.** 6   **13.** 54 kg; $\frac{11}{3}$ m from the given end
15. 171 slugs; 5.92 in. from the given end   **17.** 42 g; $\frac{44}{7}$ cm from the left end   **19.** $\frac{63}{2}$ kg; $\frac{18}{7}$ m from the end farthest from the external point   **21.** 16 slugs; $\frac{16}{5}$ ft from the given end   **23.** $\frac{6}{5}$ m from the end farthest from the external point
25. 8 ln 2 g; $\left(\dfrac{15}{4 \ln 2} - 1\right)$ cm from the given end   **27.** 12 kg/m

EXERCISES 6.3   (page 556)
1. $(2, \frac{1}{3})$ **3.** $\frac{29}{7}$ **5.** $(\frac{2}{3}, 1)$ **7.** $(0, \frac{8}{5})$ **9.** $(0, \frac{12}{5})$ **11.** $(\frac{16}{15}, \frac{64}{21})$ **13.** $(\frac{1}{2}, -\frac{3}{2})$ **15.** $(2, 0)$ **17.** $(0, -0.4762)$
19. $(0, -0.1020)$ **21.** $(0.5126, 1.970)$ **23.** $(0.4910, -1.083)$ **25.** $(1.048, 0.7793)$ **27.** $(1.504, 2.375)$
29. $(0.4183, 0.5792)$ **31.** $(0.5300, 1.590)$ **33.** $\frac{5}{3}p$ **35.** The centroid is on the radius bisecting the region, at a distance from the diameter of $\dfrac{4}{3\pi}$ times the length of the radius.   **37.** $(\frac{1}{2}\pi + \frac{2}{3})r^3$

EXERCISES 6.4   (page 562)
1. $\frac{158}{3}$ ft-lb   **3.** $\frac{1076}{15}$ joules   **5.** $\frac{1}{2}(3 + \sqrt{393})$ **7.** 180 in.-lb   **9.** 8 joules   **11.** 1350 ergs   **13.** 409,500 ft-lb
15. 50,185 ft-lb   **17.** 100,000 ft-lb   **19.** 5500 ft-lb   **21.** 2.9×10^7 joules   **23.** 3.20×10^6 joules   **25.** 163.4 sec
27. $2\sqrt{3}$ ft   **29.** $31.2\pi(e^{-2} - e^{-8})$ ft-lb $\approx$ 13.2 ft-lb   **31.** 3000 ln $\frac{3}{2}$ in.-lb $\approx$ 1216 in.-lb

EXERCISES 6.5   (page 568)
1. 19,968 lb   **3.** 3993.6 lb   **5.** 140.4 lb   **7.** 942,000 N   **9.** 4.09×10^6 N   **11.** 2.54   **15.** 874,000 lb
17. 6.24×10^6 ft-lb   **19.** 756 lb   **21.** 3.15×10^5 lb   **23.** 1.22×10^6 lb

MISCELLANEOUS EXERCISES FOR CHAPTER 6   (page 570)
1. $\frac{16}{3}\sqrt{3}$ **3.** $\frac{1}{53,208}[\frac{1}{2}(10,999)^{3/2} - (2251)^{3/2}] \approx 7.03$ **5.** $\frac{2}{13}$ **7.** $(\frac{3}{2}, 2)$ **9.** $\frac{104}{3}$ slugs; $\frac{298}{65}$ in. from the left end   **11.** $(\frac{9}{8}, \frac{18}{5})$
13. $(\frac{9}{20}, \frac{9}{20})$ **15.** $\frac{256}{3}\pi$ m^3 **17.** $(0, 0)$ **19.** $(0.3597, 0.5357)$ **21.** 3.214   **23.** 1.876   **25.** $\frac{7}{12}$ **27.** 6000 ergs
29. 400 ft-lb   **31.** 44,145,000 joules   **33.** 57,262 ft-lb   **35.** 22.6 lb   **37.** $\frac{5120}{3}$ lb   **39.** 888,694 lb

EXERCISES 7.1   (page 582)
1. $\frac{1}{3}xe^{3x} - \frac{1}{9}e^{3x} + C$ **3.** $x \sec x - \ln|\sec x + \tan x| + C$ **5.** $x \ln 5x - x + C$ **7.** $\frac{1}{3}(\ln t)^3 + C$
9. $\frac{1}{2}(x^2 + 1)\tan^{-1} x - \frac{1}{2}x + C$ **11.** $\dfrac{e^x}{x + 1} + C$ **13.** $\frac{1}{2}y \sin(\ln y) - \frac{1}{2}y \cos(\ln y) + C$ **15.** $\frac{1}{2}e^x(\cos x + \sin x) + C$
17. $-x^2\sqrt{1 - x^2} - \frac{2}{3}(1 - x^2)^{3/2} + C$ **19.** $x^2 \cosh x - 2x \sinh x + 2 \cosh x + C$ **21.** $2\sqrt{z} \cot^{-1}\sqrt{z} + \ln(1 + z) + C$
23. $2\sqrt{x} \sin\sqrt{x} + 2 \cos\sqrt{x} + C$ **25.** $\dfrac{36}{\ln 3} - \dfrac{36}{(\ln 3)^2} + \dfrac{16}{(\ln 3)^3} \approx 15.008$ **27.** $\frac{9}{16} = 0.5625$ **29.** $\frac{32}{3}\ln 2 - \frac{28}{9} \approx 4.2825$
31. $\frac{5}{6}\pi - \sqrt{3} + 1 \approx 1.8859$ **33.** $12e^3 + 2e \approx 246.463$ **35.** $(e^2 + 1)$ sq units   **37.** $\frac{1}{2}\pi(3e^4 + 1)$ cu units
39. $(8 - 24e^{-2})$ sq units   **41.** $2(1 - e^{-6})$ kg; $\dfrac{e^6 - 7}{e^6 - 1}$ m from one end   **43.** $(0.267, 0.604)$ **45.** 48.86 ft-lb
47. $C(x) = x \ln x - x + 6$ **51.** $\frac{3}{25}e^{4\pi/3} - \frac{4}{25}e^{2\pi/3}$ **55.** $50(6e^{-1} - \frac{13}{4}e^{-2} - \frac{7}{4})$

EXERCISES 7.2   (page 592)
1. (a) $\frac{1}{5}\sin^5 x + C$;   (b) $-\frac{1}{16}\cos^4 4x + C$ **3.** (a) $\frac{1}{3}\cos^3 x - \cos x + C$;   (b) $\frac{1}{2}\sin x + C$
5. (a) $\frac{1}{3}\sin^3 x - \frac{1}{5}\sin^5 x + C$;   (b) $\frac{2}{7}\cos^{7/2} z - \frac{2}{3}\cos^{3/2} z + C$ **7.** $\frac{1}{14}\sin 7x + \frac{1}{2}\sin x + C$ **9.** $-\frac{1}{16}\cos 8y + \frac{1}{4}\cos 2y + C$
11. $\frac{1}{5}\tan 5x - x + C$ **13.** $-\frac{1}{4}\cot 2x^2 - \frac{1}{2}x^2 + C$ **15.** $-\frac{1}{2}\cot^2 t - \ln|\sin t| + C$

17. $\frac{1}{15}\tan^5 3x - \frac{1}{9}\tan^3 3x + \frac{1}{3}\tan 3x - x + C$ **21.** $\frac{1}{3}\tan^3 e^x - \tan e^x + e^x + C$ **23.** $\frac{1}{9}\tan^9 x + \frac{1}{7}\tan^7 x + C$

25. $-\frac{1}{15}\cot^5 3x - \frac{1}{9}\cot^3 3x + C$ **27.** $\frac{1}{2}(\tan 2x - \cot 2x) + C$ **29.** $2\sec w - \tan w + C$

31. $-2\cot 2x + C$ **33.** $-\frac{1}{3}\csc^3 x + C$ **35.** $\frac{2}{3}$ **37.** $\frac{3}{8}$ **39.** $\frac{1}{8}$ **41.** $\frac{1}{8}(\sqrt{2}-1)$ **43.** $\frac{1}{4} - \frac{1}{8}\ln 2$ **45.** $\frac{56}{15}$ **47.** $\frac{1}{5}$

49. $\frac{1}{2}\pi$ sq units   **51.** $\frac{3}{8}\pi^2$ cu units   **53.** $\frac{5}{8}\pi^2$ cu units   **55.** $\left(\dfrac{\frac{1}{2}\pi - \cos 1 - \sin 1}{1 - \sin 1}, \dfrac{\frac{1}{8}\pi - \frac{1}{8}\sin 2 - \frac{1}{4}}{1 - \sin 1}\right)$

57. $(1 - \frac{1}{4}\pi)$ sq units   **59.** $\frac{4}{3}\pi$ cu units   **65. (b)** $\frac{1}{4}\sec^3 x \tan x + \frac{3}{8}\sec x \tan x + \frac{3}{8}\ln|\sec x + \tan x| + C$

67. (b) $-\frac{1}{5}\sin^4 x \cos x - \frac{4}{15}\sin^2 x \cos x - \frac{8}{15}\cos x + C$ **69. (b)** $\dfrac{1}{n}\sec^n x + C$

EXERCISES 7.3   (page 600)

1. $-\dfrac{\sqrt{4-x^2}}{4x} + C$ **3.** $\dfrac{1}{2}\ln\left|\dfrac{\sqrt{x^2+4}-2}{x}\right| + C$ **5.** $\sqrt{x^2-25} + C$ **7.** $-\dfrac{x}{9\sqrt{4x^2-9}} + C$

9. $\dfrac{\tan x}{4\sqrt{4-\tan^2 x}} + C$ **11.** $\frac{1}{3}\sqrt{\ln^2 w - 4}(8 + \ln^2 w) + C$ **13.** $-\frac{1}{5}\ln(10 - 4\sqrt{6}) \approx 0.3199$

15. $\dfrac{1}{5}\ln\dfrac{4(\sqrt{106}-5)}{9(\sqrt{41}-5)} \approx 0.10345$ **17.** $\ln(3 + 2\sqrt{2}) - \ln(2 + \sqrt{3}) \approx 0.4458$ **19.** $\frac{128}{3} - 24\sqrt{3} \approx 1.097$

21. $\frac{2}{45}\sqrt{5} \approx 0.09938$ **23.** $\frac{1}{27}(6 - 2\sqrt{3}) \approx 0.09392$ **25.** $\frac{1}{2}\cos^{-1}\frac{1}{3} - \frac{1}{6}\pi \approx 0.17808$

27. $\frac{625}{16}\pi \approx 122.72$ **29.** $\frac{5}{36} - \frac{2}{27}\sqrt{3} \approx 0.010588$ **31.** $\sec^{-1}\frac{2}{3}x + C$ **33.** $\sqrt{4-x^2} + \ln\dfrac{2 - \sqrt{4-x^2}}{2 + \sqrt{4-x^2}} + C$

35. $\ln\left(\dfrac{\sqrt{10}-1}{3\sqrt{2}-3}\right) + \sqrt{10} - \sqrt{2}$ **37.** $\frac{81}{16}\pi^2$ cu units   **39.** $\dfrac{392}{60 + 27\ln 3}$ cm from the left end

41. $\left(\dfrac{20 - 15\cos^{-1}\frac{3}{5}}{5\ln 3 - 4}, \dfrac{26}{225(5\ln 3 - 4)}\right)$ **43.** $(\frac{8}{3}\pi + 3\sqrt{3})(62.4)$ lb ≈ 847 lb

45. $(\frac{512}{3}\pi + 192\sqrt{3})(0.39)$ oz ≈ 338.8 oz   **47. (a)** $15\ln 2 \approx 10.40$;   **(b)** $\dfrac{30e^{4/3}}{e^{8/3}+1} \approx 7.39$ **49. (a)** $\frac{1}{4}\ln\frac{3}{5}$

EXERCISES 7.4   (page 611)

1. $\dfrac{1}{4}\ln\left|\dfrac{x-2}{x+2}\right| + C$ **3.** $\ln\left|\dfrac{C(w+4)^3}{2w-1}\right|$ **5.** $x + \dfrac{1}{5}\ln\left|\dfrac{C(x-2)^4}{(x+3)^9}\right|$ **7.** $\dfrac{1}{t+2} + \ln\left|\dfrac{C(t+1)}{t+2}\right|$

9. $\dfrac{1}{9}\ln\left|\dfrac{x+3}{x}\right| - \dfrac{1}{3x} + C$ **11.** $\dfrac{1}{4}\ln\left|\dfrac{Cx^4(2x+1)^3}{2x-1}\right|$ **13.** $\dfrac{1}{2}\tan^{-1}\dfrac{x}{2} + \dfrac{1}{2}\ln\dfrac{x^2}{x^2+4} + C$

15. $\dfrac{1}{8}\ln\left|\dfrac{2x-1}{2x+1}\right| - \dfrac{1}{4}\tan^{-1}2x + C$ **17.** $\ln|x-1| + \tan^{-1}x + C$ **19.** $\ln|\tan x + 1| + \dfrac{2}{\sqrt{3}}\tan^{-1}\left(\dfrac{2\tan x - 1}{\sqrt{3}}\right) + C$

21. $4\ln\frac{4}{3} - \frac{3}{2}$ **23.** $\ln\frac{27}{4} - 2$ **25.** $6\ln 2$ **27.** $13\ln 2 - 4\ln 5$ **29.** $\frac{3}{4}\ln 2 + \frac{5}{8}\pi$ **31.** $\frac{3}{8}\ln\frac{9}{5}$ **33.** $\ln 4.5$ sq units

35. $2\pi(2 + 6\ln 3 - 2\ln 2)$ cu units   **37.** $\left(\dfrac{6\ln 3 - 2\ln 2 + 2}{2\ln 3 - \ln 2}, \dfrac{48\ln 2 - 48\ln 3 + 35}{24(2\ln 3 - \ln 2)}\right)$ **39.** $\frac{1}{16}$ sq units

41. $(\frac{2}{9}\sqrt{3}\pi^2 - \frac{2}{3}\pi\ln 3)$ cu units   **43. (a)** $\frac{1}{3}\ln|C(x^3 - 6x^2 + 18x)|$;   **(b)** $\dfrac{9x+8}{6(x+2)^3} + C$

45. (a) $f(t) = \dfrac{5000}{1 + 4999e^{-0.5t}}$;   **(b)** 1328;   **(c)** 4075;   **(d)** 5000   **47. (a)** $y(t) = \dfrac{5000}{1 + 249e^{-9t/98}}$;   **(b)** $y(10) = 50$;

  (c) $y(20) = 123$;   **(d)** $y(30) = 297$;   **(e)** $y(60) = 2491$;   **(f)** $y(180) = 4999.9 \approx 5000$ **(g)** $y(t) = 2500$ when $t = 60.0$

49. 10 A.M.   **51.** $\frac{31}{19}$ **53.** 7.4 lb   **55.** $\dfrac{3}{50}\ln\dfrac{(t_1+2)^2}{4(t_1{}^2+1)} - \dfrac{7}{5(t_1+2)} - \dfrac{4}{25}\tan^{-1}t_1 + \dfrac{7}{10}$

EXERCISES 7.5 (page 619)

1. $\frac{2}{3}x^{3/2} - 3x + 18\sqrt{x} - 54\ln(3 + \sqrt{x}) + C$ **3.** $\ln\left|\dfrac{\sqrt{1 + 4x} - 1}{\sqrt{1 + 4x} + 1}\right| + C$ **5.** $\frac{1}{9}\sqrt{1 + 2x^3}\,(2x^3 + 7) + C$

5. $-2\sqrt{1 + x} + \sqrt{2}\ln\left|\dfrac{\sqrt{1 + x} + \sqrt{2}}{\sqrt{1 + x} - \sqrt{2}}\right| + C$ **7.** $\sqrt{2}\ln\left|\dfrac{\tan x + \sqrt{2}}{\tan x - \sqrt{2}}\right| + C$ **9.** $\dfrac{6}{\sqrt{15}}\tan^{-1}\left(\dfrac{1}{\sqrt{15}}\tan\dfrac{x}{2}\right) + C, |x| < \pi$

11. $\dfrac{1}{5}\ln\left|\dfrac{\tan\frac{1}{2}x - \frac{1}{3}}{\tan\frac{1}{2}x + 3}\right| + C$ **13.** $4 - 2\ln 3 \approx 1.80278$ **15.** $\ln\frac{11}{10} \approx 0.0953102$ **17.** $\frac{1}{4}\ln 3 \approx 0.274653$

19. $\frac{1}{2}\sqrt{3}\ln(1 + \frac{1}{2}\sqrt{3}) \approx 0.540236$ **21.** $2\sqrt{3}\ln(1 + \sqrt{3}) \approx 3.481604$ **23.** $\frac{3}{2}\pi - \frac{152}{35} \approx 0.369532$

25. $x + \dfrac{36}{6 - x} + 12\ln|6 - x| + C$ **27.** $\frac{1}{30}(3x - 1)(1 + 2x)^{3/2} + C$ **29.** $\dfrac{1}{4}\ln\left|\dfrac{x + 2}{x - 2}\right| + C$

31. $\ln|x + 3 + \sqrt{x^2 + 6x}| + C$ **33.** $\sqrt{9 - 4x^2} - 3\ln\left|\dfrac{3 + \sqrt{9 - 4x^2}}{2x}\right| + C$

35. $\dfrac{1}{3}(x^2 - x - 6)\sqrt{4x - x^2} + 4\cos^{-1}\left(\dfrac{2 - x}{2}\right) + C$ **37.** $-\frac{1}{5}\sin^4 x\cos x - \frac{4}{15}\sin^2 x\cos x - \frac{8}{15}\cos x + C$

39. $t^4\sin t + 4t^3\cos t - 12t^2\sin t - 24t\cos t + 24\sin t + C$ **41.** $x\sec^{-1}3x - \frac{1}{3}\ln|3x + \sqrt{9x^2 - 1}| + C$

43. $\dfrac{e^{4x}}{32}(8x^2 - 4x + 1) + C$ **45.** $\dfrac{x^4}{16}(4\ln 3x - 1) + C$ **47.** $\frac{3}{5}y\cosh 5y - \frac{3}{25}\sinh 5y + C$ **49.** $\frac{1}{60} + \frac{1}{25}\ln\frac{8}{3}$

51. $\frac{15}{2} - 8\ln 2$ **53.** $\frac{32}{5}\ln 2 - \frac{31}{25}$ **55.** $\frac{15}{2} - 8\ln 2$ **57.** $\frac{1}{3}\pi + \frac{1}{2}\sqrt{3}$ **59.** $\frac{1}{4} - \frac{1}{8}\sqrt{2}$ **61.** 0 **63.** $\frac{1}{8}(e^2 + 3)$

61. $2\ln|\sqrt{x} - 1| + C$ **71.** $\tan\frac{1}{2}x + C$

EXERCISES 7.6 (page 632)

1. (a) 4.250; (b) 4   **3.** (a) 0; (b) 0   **5.** (a) 0.696; (b) 0.693   **7.** (a) 0.880; (b) 0.881   **9.** 0.248

11. 3.689   **13.** $-0.5 \le \epsilon_T \le 0$ **15.** $-0.161 \le \epsilon_T \le 0.161$ **17.** $-0.007 \le \epsilon_T \le -0.001$ **19.** 4.000

21. (a) 0.6932; (b) 0.6931   **23.** (a) 0.6045; (b) 0.6046   **25.** 0   **27.** $-0.0005 \le \epsilon_S \le 0$ **29.** 0.2375

31. 1.5690   **33.** 1.4022   **35.** 3.090   **37.** (a) 0.3401; (b) 0.3414   **39.** 3.8203   **41.** (a) 15.95; (b) 16.03

43. 26.6 sq units   **45.** 5.9 mi   **47.** 8.218 sq units   **49.** 3.06 m/sec   **51.** 56   **53.** 222

EXERCISES 7.7 (page 642)

1. 1   **3.** $-\pi$ **5.** $\ln 2 - \ln 3 \approx -0.4055$ **7.** 1   **9.** 1.5   **11.** 1.5   **13.** 2

15. $-\frac{1}{8}$ **17.** 0   **19.** $\frac{1}{3}$ **21.** $\frac{1}{2}$ **23.** $\frac{3}{5}$ **25.** 2   **27.** -1 **29.** $\frac{4}{3}$ **31.** $\frac{1}{2}\pi$ **33.** $\dfrac{2}{\sqrt{\ln 3}}$

35. $\ln\frac{1}{2}(e^2 + 1)$ **37.** $\dfrac{Et}{L}$ **39.** $-\frac{1}{2}$ **43.** $a = -3, b = \frac{9}{2}$

EXERCISES 7.8 (page 649)

1. 0   **3.** 0   **5.** $\frac{1}{2}$ **7.** 1   **9.** 0   **11.** 1   **13.** $\frac{1}{2}$ **15.** e^3 **17.** 0   **19.** $\overset{\cdot}{e}^2$ **21.** 1   **23.** 0   **25.** e^2

27. $e^{-1/3}$ **29.** $\frac{1}{2}$ **31.** 0   **33.** 1   **35.** (a) $+\infty$; (b) 0   **39.** 1   **41.** $\dfrac{1}{\ln 3}$

47. $f(e) = e^{1/e}$, rel. max.; $y = 1$ is an asymptote   **49.** 1   **51.** (a) 0; (b) 0; no

EXERCISES 7.9 (page 657)

1. 3   **3.** $-\dfrac{1}{2\ln 5}$ **5.** $\dfrac{1}{(\ln 2)^2}$ **7.** divergent   **9.** divergent   **11.** $\frac{1}{3}\pi$ **13.** 2   **15.** 1   **17.** divergent

19. (a) divergent; (b) 0   **21.** (a) 0   **23.** π **25.** $\frac{1}{2}\pi$ **27.** (a) 0.565; (b) 0.287   **29.** (a) 0.203; (b) 0.188

31. 6.95 mi/sec   **33.** $\dfrac{1000}{0.08 + \ln 2}$ dollars $\approx \$1293.41$ **39.** $n > 1$ **41.** $\frac{1}{3}; \frac{1}{9}\ln\frac{32}{27}$

EXERCISES 7.10 (page 664)

1. 2   **3.** -4 **5.** $\frac{1}{3}\pi$ **7.** divergent   **9.** divergent   **11.** divergent   **13.** $\frac{1}{4}\pi$ **15.** divergent   **17.** 0

19. divergent   **21.** 0   **23.** $\frac{1}{3}\pi$ **25.** divergent   **27.** $n > -1$; $\dfrac{1}{n+1}$ **29.** $n > -1$; $\dfrac{2}{(n+1)^3}$ **31.** yes; 6π

MISCELLANEOUS EXERCISES FOR CHAPTER 7   (page 666)

1. $\frac{1}{8}x - \frac{1}{128}\sin 16x + C$ **3.** $-2\sqrt{4-e^x} + C$ **5.** $(x+1)\tan^{-1}\sqrt{x} - \sqrt{x} + C$ **7.** $\frac{1}{2}x + \frac{3}{4}\sin\frac{2}{3}x + C$

9. $\ln|x-1| - 2(x-1)^{-1} - (x-1)^{-2} + C$ **11.** $\frac{1}{4}\sin 2x - \frac{1}{8}\sin 4x + C$ **13.** $3\ln\left|\dfrac{x^{1/3}}{1+x^{1/3}}\right| + C$

15. $\frac{1}{3}\tan 3x - \frac{1}{3}\cot 3x + \frac{2}{3}\ln|\tan 3x| + C$ **17.** $2t + \ln\dfrac{t^2}{(t+2)^{10}} - \dfrac{15}{t+2} + C$ **19.** $x - \tan^{-1}x + \frac{1}{2}\ln\left|\dfrac{x-1}{x+1}\right| + C$

21. $\frac{1}{16}x - \frac{1}{192}\sin 12x - \frac{1}{144}\sin^3 6x + C$ **23.** $\sin^{-1}\left(\dfrac{r+2}{\sqrt 7}\right) + C$ **25.** $\frac{1}{2}x^2\sin x^2 + \frac{1}{2}\cos x^2 + C$

27. $\frac{2}{17}e^{t/2}(4\sin 2t + \cos 2t) + C$ **29.** $\frac{1}{4}\tan^{-1}(\frac{1}{2}\sin^2 x) + C$ **31.** $-\tan^{-1}(\cos x) + C$

33. $2\sin^{-1}\left(\dfrac{t-2}{2}\right) + \frac{1}{2}(t-2)\sqrt{4t-t^2} + C$ **35.** $\frac{1}{2}\ln|x-1| + \frac{1}{2}\ln|x+1| - \ln|x| + C$ **37.** $\frac{1}{3}\sin^{-1}(\frac{3}{2}e^x) + C$

39. $-\frac{1}{15}\cot^5 3x - \frac{1}{9}\cot^3 3x + C$ **41.** $\frac{1}{3}x^3\sin^{-1}x + \frac{1}{9}(x^2+2)\sqrt{1-x^2} + C$ **43.** $\tan^{-1}(\cos x) + C$

45. $\frac{2}{3}\sec^{-1}(2\sin 3t) + C$ **47.** $\sqrt{2t} - \sqrt{1-2t}\sin^{-1}\sqrt{2t} + C$ **49.** $\dfrac{4}{15}\ln\left|\dfrac{\tan\frac{1}{2}x - 3}{\tan\frac{1}{2}x + 3}\right| + \dfrac{x}{5} + C$

51. $\begin{cases}\frac{1}{n}(-\cos nx + \frac{2}{3}\cos^3 nx - \frac{1}{5}\cos^5 nx) + C & \text{if } n \neq 0 \\ C & \text{if } n = 0\end{cases}$ **53.** $\begin{cases}\dfrac{x^{n+1}\ln x}{n+1} - \dfrac{x^{n+1}}{(n+1)^2} + C & \text{if } n \neq -1 \\ \frac{1}{2}\ln^2 x + C & \text{if } n = -1\end{cases}$

55. 4   **57.** $\frac{1}{2} + 2\ln\frac{6}{5}$ **59.** $\frac{16}{3} - \frac{8}{3}\sqrt{2}$ **61.** $\frac{4}{3}\sqrt{3} - \frac{1}{2}\pi$ **63.** $\frac{4}{3}$ **65.** $\frac{1}{2} - \frac{1}{4}\ln 2$ **67.** $\sqrt{3} - \frac{1}{2}\ln(2+\sqrt{3})$

69. $\frac{1}{2}\ln\frac{9}{2} - \frac{1}{6}\pi$ **71.** 5   **73.** $\frac{1}{6} + \ln\frac{3}{2}$ **75.** $\frac{4}{3}$ **77.** $1 - \frac{1}{2}\ln 3$ **79.** $\frac{1}{24}\pi$ **81.** $\frac{1}{5}\ln\frac{3}{2}$ **83.** $\frac{256}{15}$

85. 2.977   **87.** 2.958   **89.** (a) 1.624; (b) 1.563   **91.** 1   **93.** 1.5   **95.** -0.5 **97.** 1

99. -1 **101.** 0   **103.** 1   **105.** $+\infty$ **107.** $\frac{1}{3}$ **109.** $+\infty$ **111.** e^{12} **113.** 0   **115.** 1   **117.** e **119.** divergent

121. $\frac{1}{2}$ **123.** divergent   **125.** $\dfrac{32}{\ln 2}$ **127.** divergent   **129.** $\frac{1}{4}\pi$ **131.** divergent   **133.** $n > 1$; $\dfrac{1}{(1-n)^2}$

135. $\frac{1}{3}k(1 - e^{-9})$ kg; $\dfrac{e^9 - 10}{3(e^9 - 1)}$ m from one end   **137.** $9\sqrt{2} - 3\sqrt{5} + \frac{3}{2}\ln\left(\dfrac{3+2\sqrt{2}}{\sqrt{5}+2}\right)$ **139.** $\frac{1}{8}\pi$ sq units

141. $\pi(e^2\ln 2 + \frac{1}{2}e^2 + \frac{1}{8})$ cu units   **143.** (a) $x = 300\left(\dfrac{18^t - 17^t}{3 \cdot 18^t - 2 \cdot 17^t}\right)$; (b) 35.94 lb   **145.** $\left(0, \dfrac{32}{15\pi}\right)$ **147.** $(\frac{1}{2}\pi - 1, \frac{1}{2})$

149. 187.2 lb   **151.** (a) t days from today $P(t) = \dfrac{12{,}000}{1 + 11(11/29)^{t/5}}$; (c) 1193; (d) $-5\dfrac{\ln 11}{\ln(11/29)} \approx 12.37$

153. $\frac{64}{3}$ **155.** 1   **157.** \$152,500   **159.** (a) $-\infty$; (b) 0

EXERCISES 8.1 (page 680)

1. $P_4(x) = -\frac{1}{2} - \frac{1}{4}x - \frac{1}{8}x^2 - \frac{1}{16}x^3 - \frac{1}{32}x^4$; $R_4(x) = \dfrac{x^5}{(z-2)^6}$, z between 0 and x

3. $P_5(x) = 1 - x + \dfrac{x^2}{2!} - \dfrac{x^3}{3!} + \dfrac{x^4}{4!} - \dfrac{x^5}{5!}$; $R_5(x) = \dfrac{e^{-z}}{6!}x^6$, z between 0 and x

5. $P_6(x) = 1 - \dfrac{x^2}{2!} + \dfrac{x^4}{4!} - \dfrac{x^6}{6!}$; $R_6(x) = \dfrac{\sin z}{7!}x^7$, z between 0 and x

7. $P_4(x) = x + \frac{1}{6}x^3$; $R_4(x) = \frac{1}{120}(\cosh z)x^5$, z between 0 and x

9. $P_3(x) = 1 + \frac{3}{2}x + \frac{3}{8}x^2 - \frac{1}{16}x^3$; $R_3(x) = \frac{3}{128}(1+z)^{-5/2}x^4$, z between 0 and x

11. $P_3(x) = 8 + 3(x-4) + \frac{3}{16}(x-4)^2 - \frac{1}{128}(x-4)^3$; $R_3(x) = \dfrac{3(x-4)^4}{128z^{5/2}}$, z between 4 and x

13. $P_3(x) = \frac{1}{2} + \frac{1}{2}\sqrt{3}(x - \frac{1}{6}\pi) - \frac{1}{4}(x - \frac{1}{6}\pi)^2 - \frac{1}{12}\sqrt{3}(x - \frac{1}{6}\pi)^3$; $R_3(x) = \frac{1}{24}\sin z(x - \frac{1}{6}\pi)^4$, z between $\frac{1}{6}\pi$ and x

15. $P_5(x) = x - 1 - \frac{1}{2}(x-1)^2 + \frac{1}{3}(x-1)^3 - \frac{1}{4}(x-1)^4 + \frac{1}{5}(x-1)^5$; $R_5(x) = -\frac{1}{6}z^{-6}(x-1)^6$; z between 1 and x

17. $P_3(x) = -\ln 2 - \sqrt{3}(x - \frac{1}{3}\pi) - 2(x - \frac{1}{3}\pi)^2 - \frac{4}{3}\sqrt{3}(x - \frac{1}{3}\pi)^3$; $R_3(x) = -\frac{1}{12}(3\sec^4 z - 2\sec^2 z)(x - \frac{1}{3}\pi)^4$, z between $\frac{1}{3}\pi$ and x

19. 2.71828   **21.** 0.515   **23.** $|\text{error}| < \dfrac{(0.1)^4}{24} < 0.000005$ **25.** $|\text{error}| < \dfrac{(0.01)^2}{8} = 0.0000125$

27. $|\text{error}| < \dfrac{e^{0.01}}{6}(0.01)^2 = 0.00000017$ **29.** 0.1823   **31.** $\dfrac{55\sqrt{2}}{672}$, $|\text{error}| < \dfrac{1}{7680}\sqrt{2}$

35. $x \approx \dfrac{\pi}{2(1 + m)}$ **37.** $2(x - 1) + 5(x - 1)^2 + 3(x - 1)^3 + (x - 1)^4$

39. (a) same; **(b)** 1; **(c)** same

EXERCISES 8.2   (page 692)

1. $\frac{1}{2}$ **3.** divergent   **5.** -2 **7.** 0   **9.** 1   **11.** divergent   **13.** divergent   **15.** $e^{1/3}$ **17.** 1   **19.** 0
21. (a) 0; **(b)** 4   **23. (a)** $\frac{1}{2}$; **(b)** 1   **27.** increasing   **29.** decreasing   **31.** not monotonic   **33.** not monotonic
35. decreasing   **37.** increasing after the first two terms   **39.** increasing   **41.** decreasing   **43.** not bounded

55. $\left\{\dfrac{(-1)^{n+1}}{n}\right\}$ **57.** converges to $\dfrac{a}{b}$

EXERCISES 8.3   (page 706)

1. $s_n = \dfrac{n}{2n + 1}; \dfrac{1}{2}$ **3.** $s_n = \dfrac{5n}{3n + 1}; \dfrac{5}{3}$ **5.** $s_n = -\ln(n + 1)$; divergent   **7.** $s_n = \dfrac{5}{2}\left(1 - \dfrac{1}{5^n}\right); \dfrac{5}{2}$

9. $\displaystyle\sum_{n=1}^{\infty} \dfrac{2}{(3n - 2)(3n + 1)}; \dfrac{2}{3}$ **11.** $\dfrac{1}{3} - \displaystyle\sum_{n=2}^{\infty} \dfrac{2}{3^n}; 0$ **13.** $\displaystyle\sum_{n=1}^{\infty} \ln\left(\dfrac{2n + 1}{2n - 1}\right)$; divergent   **15.** divergent

17. 2   **19.** divergent   **21.** 1   **23.** $\dfrac{1}{e - 1}$ **25.** divergent   **27.** divergent   **29.** 3   **31.** $\frac{10}{3}$

33. $\dfrac{63 \cdot 2^{10} + 1}{2^{16}}$ **35.** divergent   **37.** $\frac{3}{2}$ **39.** divergent   **41.** divergent   **43.** 2

45. $\frac{3}{11}$ **47.** $\frac{137}{111}$ **49.** 8 m   **51.** 84 ft   **53. (b)** $(6 + \frac{7}{2}\sqrt{3})$sec   **55.** 24 units

57. (a) 3.8160; **(b)** 4.4992; **(c)** 4.9014; **(d)** 5.1874   **59.** 12,367

EXERCISES 8.4   (page 719)

1. convergent   **3.** convergent   **5.** divergent   **7.** convergent   **9.** divergent   **11.** convergent   **13.** divergent
15. convergent   **17.** divergent   **19.** convergent   **21.** divergent   **23.** convergent   **25.** divergent   **27.** convergent
29. convergent   **31.** convergent   **33.** divergent   **35.** convergent   **37.** convergent   **39.** convergent   **41.** convergent

43. convergent   **45.** divergent   **53.** $0.7032 < \displaystyle\sum_{m=50}^{100} \dfrac{1}{m} < 0.7134$

EXERCISES 8.5   (page 731)

1. convergent   **3.** convergent   **5.** convergent   **7.** convergent   **9.** convergent   **11.** divergent   **13.** convergent

15. $|R_4| < \frac{1}{5}$ **17.** $|R_4| < \frac{1}{81}$ **19.** $|R_4| < \frac{1}{25}$ **21.** $|R_4| < \dfrac{1}{6 \ln 6}$ **23.** 0.333   **25.** 0.632   **27.** 0.113

29. absolutely convergent   **31.** absolutely convergent   **33.** absolutely convergent   **35.** divergent
37. absolutely convergent   **39.** absolutely convergent   **41.** absolutely convergent
43. absolutely convergent   **45.** absolutely convergent   **47.** divergent   **49. (b)** convergent

EXERCISES 8.6   (page 734)

1. $\frac{3}{16}, \frac{15}{64}, \frac{63}{256}, \frac{255}{1024}; s_n = \dfrac{4^n - 1}{4^{n+1}}; \frac{1}{4}$ **3.** convergent; 3   **5.** divergent   **7.** convergent; $4 + 2\sqrt{3}$

9. convergent; $\frac{1}{6}$ **11.** convergent; $\frac{649}{729}$ **13.** convergent   **15.** divergent   **17.** convergent
19. divergent   **21.** convergent   **23.** divergent   **25.** divergent   **27.** convergent   **29.** convergent
31. absolutely convergent   **33.** conditionally convergent   **35.** divergent   **37.** absolutely convergent
39. absolutely convergent   **41.** $\frac{437}{330}$ **43.** $\left(\frac{15}{4}\sqrt{2} + 3\sqrt{3}\right)$ sec

EXERCISES 8.7 (page 743)

1. (b) $\sum\limits_{n=0}^{+\infty} (-2x)^n$ **3. (b)** $\sum\limits_{n=0}^{+\infty} (-9x^2)^n$ **5.** $[-1, 1)$ **7.** $[-1, 1]$ **9.** $\left[-\frac{1}{2}, \frac{1}{2}\right]$ **11.** $(-3, 3)$ **13.** $(-\infty, +\infty)$

15. $(-5, -1)$ **17.** $(-9, 9)$ **19.** $(0, 2]$ **21.** $\left(-\dfrac{1}{e^2}, \dfrac{1}{e^2}\right)$ **23.** $[-1, 1]$ **25.** $(-4, 6)$ **27.** $[4, 6)$ **29.** $[-1, 1]$

31. $(-e, e)$ **35.** $+\infty$

EXERCISES 8.8 (page 753)

1. (a) $R = 1, [-1, 1]$;   **(b)** $\sum\limits_{n=1}^{+\infty} \dfrac{x^{n-1}}{n}, R = 1$;   **(c)** $[-1, 1)$ **3.** $R = 1, [-1, 1)$;   **(b)** $\sum\limits_{n=1}^{+\infty} \sqrt{n}\, x^{n-1}, R = 1$;   **(c)** $(-1, 1)$

5. (a) $R = +\infty, (-\infty, +\infty)$;   **(b)** $\sum\limits_{n=1}^{+\infty} (-1)^{n-1} \dfrac{x^{2n-2}}{(2n-2)!}, R = \infty$;   **(c)** $(-\infty, +\infty)$ **7. (a)** $R = \frac{1}{3}, (0, \frac{2}{3})$;

(b) $\sum\limits_{n=1}^{+\infty} 3n(n+1)(3x-1)^n, R = \frac{1}{3}$;   **(c)** $(0, \frac{2}{3})$ **9. (a)** $R=3, [-2, 4)$;   **(b)** $\sum\limits_{n=1}^{+\infty} \dfrac{(x-1)^{n-1}}{3^n}, R = 3$;   **(c)** $(-2, 4)$

11. $\frac{1}{2} \sum\limits_{n=2}^{+\infty} n(n-1)x^{n-2}$ **13.** $\sum\limits_{n=0}^{+\infty} (-1)^n(n+1)x^n$ **15.** $\sum\limits_{n=0}^{+\infty} \dfrac{x^{2n+1}}{(2n+2)!}$ **17. (a)** $\sum\limits_{n=0}^{+\infty} \dfrac{x^{2n}}{n!}$;   **(b)** $\sum\limits_{n=0}^{+\infty} \dfrac{x^{2n+1}}{n!}$ **19.** 0.60653

21. (a) $\sum\limits_{n=0}^{+\infty} \dfrac{x^{2n+1}}{(2n+1)!}$;   **(b)** $\sum\limits_{n=0}^{+\infty} \dfrac{x^{2n}}{(2n)!}$ **29.** $\sum\limits_{n=0}^{+\infty} \dfrac{x^{n+1}}{(n+1)!}; R = +\infty$ **31.** $\sum\limits_{n=1}^{+\infty} \dfrac{(x-2)^n}{n\, 2^n}; R = 2$ **33.** 1.718   **35.** 0.693

37. (b) $\sum\limits_{n=1}^{+\infty} \dfrac{x^n}{n(n!)}; R = +\infty$ **39.** 1.318   **41.** 0.485   **43.** 0.0413   **45.** 0.450   **47.** 0.2450   **49.** 0.24

51. (a) $\sum\limits_{n=0}^{+\infty} (-1)^n \dfrac{x^{n+2}}{n!}$ **55.** $\sum\limits_{n=0}^{+\infty} \dfrac{x^n}{n!}$

EXERCISES 8.9 (page 763)

1. $\sum\limits_{n=0}^{+\infty} \dfrac{(-1)^n x^{2n}}{(2n)!}$ **3.** $\sum\limits_{n=0}^{+\infty} \dfrac{x^{2n}}{(2n)!}$ **5.** $\sum\limits_{n=0}^{+\infty} \dfrac{x^{2n+1}}{(2n+1)!}$ **7.** $e^3 \sum\limits_{n=0}^{+\infty} \dfrac{(x-3)^n}{n!}$ **9.** $\sum\limits_{n=1}^{+\infty} \dfrac{(-1)^{n+1}(x-1)^n}{n}$

11. $2 + 2\sum\limits_{n=1}^{+\infty} \dfrac{1(-2)(-5)\ldots(4-3n)}{24^n n!}(x-8)^n; R = 8$

13. $\frac{1}{2} - \frac{1}{2}\sqrt{3}(x - \frac{1}{3}\pi) - \frac{1}{4}(x - \frac{1}{3}\pi)^2 + \frac{1}{12}\sqrt{3}(x - \frac{1}{3}\pi)^3 + \frac{1}{48}(x - \frac{1}{3}\pi)^4 - \ldots; R = +\infty$ **15.** $\frac{1}{2} \sum\limits_{n=1}^{+\infty} \dfrac{(-1)^{n-1}(2x)^{2n}}{(2n)!}$

17. $x + \frac{1}{3}x^3 + \frac{2}{25}x^5$ **19.** $1 + x^2 + \frac{2}{3}x^4$ **21.** $\frac{1}{2}x^2 + \frac{1}{12}x^4 + \frac{1}{45}x^6$ **23.** 0.5299   **25.** 1.97435

27. -0.2231 **29.** 2.7182818   **31.** 0.0415   **33.** 0.0048   **35. (a)** $\sum\limits_{n=1}^{+\infty} \dfrac{(-1)^{n+1}x^{2n}}{2n(2n)!}$;   **(b)** 0.2398

37. $a_4 = 3; a_3 = -5; a_2 = 2; a_1 = -1; a_0 = 6$

EXERCISES 8.10 (page 771)

1. 1.0986   **3.** 0.3365   **5.** $\ln a + \sum\limits_{n=1}^{+\infty} \dfrac{(-1)^{n-1}(x-a)^n}{na^n}$ **7.** $\ln 2 + \sum\limits_{n=1}^{+\infty} (-1)^{n-1} \dfrac{(x-2)^n}{n\, 2^n}$

9. $1 + \dfrac{x}{2} + \sum\limits_{n=2}^{+\infty} \dfrac{(-1)^{n+1} \cdot 1 \cdot 3 \cdot \ldots \cdot (2n-3)}{2^n n!}x^n; R = 1$ **11.** $\dfrac{1}{2} + \dfrac{1}{2}\sum\limits_{n=1}^{+\infty} \dfrac{(-1)^n \cdot 1 \cdot 3 \cdot 5 \cdot \ldots \cdot (2n-1)x^n}{8^n n!}; R = 4$

13. $1 + \sum\limits_{n=1}^{+\infty} -\dfrac{2 \cdot 5 \cdot 8 \cdot \ldots \cdot (3n-4)}{3^n n!}x^{3n}; R = 1$ **15.** $\dfrac{1}{3} + \dfrac{1}{3}\sum\limits_{n=1}^{+\infty} \dfrac{(-1)^n \cdot 1 \cdot 3 \cdot 5 \cdot \ldots \cdot (2n-1)x^{4n}}{18^n n!}; R = \sqrt{3}$

17. $x^2 + \sum\limits_{n=1}^{+\infty} \dfrac{(-1)^n \cdot 1 \cdot 3 \cdot 5 \cdot \ldots \cdot (2n-1)x^{n+2}}{2^n n!}; R = 1$

19. (a) $1 + \dfrac{1}{4}x^2 + \sum\limits_{n=2}^{+\infty} \dfrac{(-1)^{n+1} \cdot 3 \cdot 7 \cdot 11 \cdot \ldots \cdot (4n-5)}{4^n n!}x^{2n}$;   **(b)** 0.510   **21.** 0.3349   **23.** 2.0271   **25.** 0.4970

27. **(b)** $\displaystyle\sum_{n=1}^{+\infty} \frac{(-1)^{n-1} x^n}{n^2}$; $R = 1$ **29.** 0.3090   **31.** $x + \displaystyle\sum_{n=1}^{\infty} \frac{(-1)^n \cdot 1 \cdot 3 \cdot 5 \cdot \ldots \cdot (2n-1) x^{2n+1}}{2^n n! \, (2n+1)}$; $R = 1$

33. 0.2424   **35.** -0.1494

MISCELLANEOUS EXERCISES FOR CHAPTER 8   *(page 774)*

1. $P_5(x) = x^2 - \dfrac{x^4}{3}$; $R_5(x) = \dfrac{2^5 \cos 2z}{6!} x^6$, z between 0 and x

3. $P_4(x) = \frac{1}{3} - \frac{1}{54}(x-9)^2 - \frac{5}{34,992}(x-9)^3 + \frac{35}{2,519,424}(x-9)^4$; $R_4(x) = -\frac{63}{256} z^{-11/2}(x-9)^5$, z between 9 and x

5. $P_6(x) = x + x^2 + \dfrac{x^3}{2!} + \dfrac{x^4}{3!} + \dfrac{x^5}{4!} + \dfrac{x^6}{5!}$; $R_6(x) = \dfrac{(z+7)e^z}{7!} x^7$, z between 0 and x **7.** 0.0873   **9.** $\frac{1}{12}$ **11.** $1, \frac{3}{2}, \frac{9}{5}, 2; 3$

13. $0, \frac{3}{5}, \frac{4}{5}, \frac{15}{17}; 1$ **15.** $1, 3, 1, 3$; no limit   **17.** $4, \frac{81}{16}, \frac{4096}{729}, \frac{390,625}{65,536}; e^2$ **19.** 0   **21.** -2 **25.** $[-1, 1)$

27. $[-3, 3]$ **29.** $x = 3$ **31.** $(-7, 5)$ **33.** $(-1, 3]$ **35.** $(-1, 1)$ **37.** **(a)** $R = 1, [-1, 1]$;   **(b)** $\displaystyle\sum_{n=1}^{+\infty} (-1)^n x^{2n-1}$, $R = 1$;

(c) $(-1, 1)$ **39.** **(a)** $R = +\infty, (-\infty, +\infty)$;   **(b)** $\displaystyle\sum_{n=1}^{+\infty} \frac{nx^{n-1}}{(n!)^2}$, $R = +\infty$;   **(c)** $(-\infty, +\infty)$ **41.** $\displaystyle\sum_{n=0}^{+\infty} \frac{(-1)^n x^{2n+1}}{2^{4n+4}(2n+1)}$; $R = 4$

43. 0.161   **45.** 0.493   **47.** **(d)** 0.261   **49.** 0.0124   **51.** 1.2840   **53.** 0.1947

55. 0.9986   **57.** 1.6094   **59.** 3.1416   **61.** 0.5773   **63.** $1 + \dfrac{x}{2} + \displaystyle\sum_{n=2}^{+\infty} (-1)^{n+1} \frac{1 \cdot 3 \cdot 5 \cdot \ldots \cdot (2n-3)x^n}{2^n n!}$; $(-1, 1)$

65. $\displaystyle\sum_{n=0}^{\infty} \frac{(\ln a)^n x^n}{n!}$; $(-\infty, +\infty)$ **67.** $\displaystyle\sum_{n=1}^{\infty} \frac{(-1)^n (3x + \pi)^{2n-1}}{(2n-1)!}$ **69.** $\displaystyle\sum_{n=1}^{\infty} -\frac{(x+1)^n}{n}$ **71.** 0   **73.** $1 + \displaystyle\sum_{n=1}^{+\infty} \frac{(-1)^n 2^{2n-1} x^{2n}}{(2n)!}$

EXERCISES 9.1   *(page 784)*

1. $x^2 + y^2 = 16$ **3.** $x^2 + y^2 = 16, x \geq 0$ **5.** $(x/4)^2 + (y/25)^2 = 1$

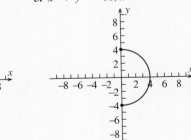
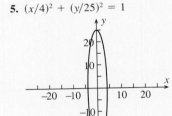

7. $(x/4)^2 - (y/9)^2 = 1, x \geq 0$ **9.** $x + 2y = 11$ **11.** $\frac{4}{3}t; \frac{4}{9}$

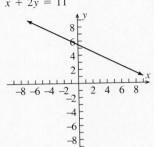

13. $\dfrac{1 + \ln t}{te^t(2 + t)}$; $\dfrac{(2 + t) - (1 + \ln t)(2 + 4t + t^2)}{t^3 e^{2t}(2 + t)^3}$ **15.** $-\dfrac{b}{a} \cot t; -\dfrac{b}{a^2} \csc^3 t$

17. (a) horizontal tangent: $y = 1$;
vertical tangent: $x = -1$;
(b) concave upward: $t > \frac{1}{2}$;
concave downward: $t < \frac{1}{2}$

19. (a) no horizontal tangent;
vertical tangent: $x = 0$;
(b) concave downward for all t

21. (a) horizontal tangent: $y = 0$, $y = 2^{2/3}$;
vertical tangent: $x = 0$, $x = 2^{2/3}$;
(b) concave upward: $t < -1$, $-1 < t < 2^{-1/3}$;
concave downward: $t > 2^{-1/3}$

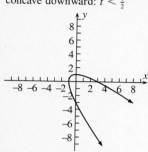
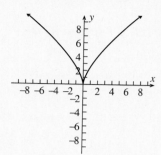
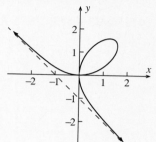

23. $x^3 + y^3 = 3xy$ **25.** $5\sqrt{3}x + 2y = 20$ **27.** $\dfrac{dy}{dx} = 0$; $\dfrac{d^2y}{dx^2} = -\dfrac{1}{4a}$; $\dfrac{d^3y}{dx^3} = 0$ **29.** $3\pi a^2$ sq units

31. (b) is solid,   **(c)** is dashed   **33. (a)** 3 cusps;   **(b)** 6 cusps   **35. (b)** is solid,   **(c)** is dashed

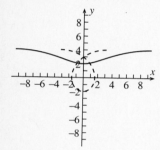
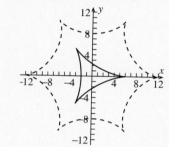
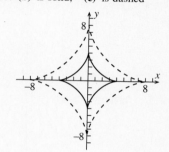

EXERCISES 9.2 *(page 789)*

1. $1 + \frac{1}{2}\sqrt{2}\ln(1 + \sqrt{2})$ **3.** $2\sqrt{10} + \sqrt{2}\ln(2 + \sqrt{5})$ **5.** $\frac{2}{27}[(40)^{3/2} - (13)^{3/2}]$ **7.** 120 **9.** $\sqrt{2}(e - 1)$
11. $\ln(1 + \sqrt{2})$ **13.** 8π **15.** 39.19 **17.** 3.966 **19.** 8.462 **21.** 55.31 **23.** $6a$ **25.** $a[\ln(\cosh 2) - \ln(\cosh 1)]$

EXERCISES 9.3 *(page 803)*

5. (a) $(-3, 0)$;   **(b)** $(-1, -1)$;   **(c)** $(2, -2\sqrt{3})$;   **(d)** $(\frac{1}{2}\sqrt{3}, -\frac{1}{2})$
7. (a) $(\sqrt{2}, \frac{7}{4}\pi)$;   **(b)** $(2, \frac{5}{6}\pi)$;   **(c)** $(2\sqrt{2}, \frac{1}{4}\pi)$;   **(d)** $(5, \pi)$ **9. (a)** $(x^2 + y^2)^2 = 4xy$;   **(b)** $(x^2 + y^2)^3 = x^2$
11. (a) $x = -1$;   **(b)** $4x^2 - 5y^2 - 36y - 36 = 0$
13. (a) line through the pole with slope $\sqrt{3}$;   **(b)** circle with center at the pole and radius $\frac{1}{3}\pi$
15. (a) line through the pole with slope $\tan^{-1} 2$;   **(b)** circle with center at the pole and radius 2
17. (a) line parallel to the $\frac{1}{2}\pi$ axis and 4 units to the right of it;   **(b)** circle tangent to the $\frac{1}{2}\pi$ axis with center on the polar axis and radius 2
19. (a) line parallel to the polar axis and 4 units below it;   **(b)** circle tangent to the polar axis with center on the extension of the $\frac{1}{2}\pi$ axis and radius 2
21. cardioid; symmetric with respect to polar axis; points to left
23. cardioid; symmetric with respect to $\frac{1}{2}\pi$ axis; points upward
25. limaçon with a loop; symmetric with respect to $\frac{1}{2}\pi$ axis; points downward

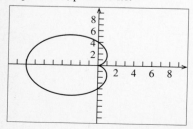
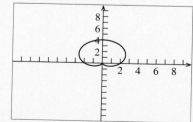
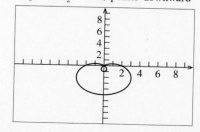

27. limaçon with a dent;
symmetric with respect to
polar axis; points to the left

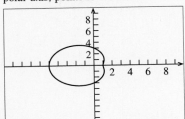

29. convex limaçon; symmetric
with respect to $\frac{1}{2}\pi$ axis;
points upward

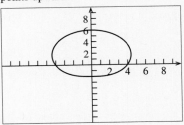

31. 3-leafed rose

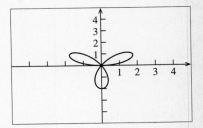

33. 8-leafed rose

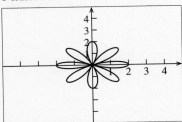

35. 4-leafed rose

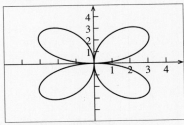

37. logarithmic spiral, some of whose points (r, θ) are given in the following table:

r	1	$e^{\pi/2} \approx 5$	$e^{\pi} \approx 23$	$e^{3\pi/2} \approx 111$	$e^{2\pi} \approx 535$	$e^{5\pi/2} \approx 2576$	$e^{3\pi} \approx 12,392$
θ	0	$\frac{1}{2}\pi$	π	$\frac{3}{2}\pi$	2π	$\frac{5}{2}\pi$	3π

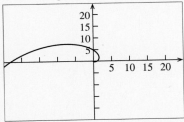

39. reciprocal spiral, some of whose points (r, θ) are given in the following table:

r	$\frac{6}{\pi} \approx 1.9$	$\frac{3}{\pi} \approx 0.95$	$\frac{2}{\pi} \approx 0.63$	$\frac{1}{\pi} \approx 0.32$	$\frac{1}{2\pi} \approx 0.16$	$\frac{1}{3\pi} \approx 0.12$	$\frac{1}{4\pi} \approx 0.08$	$\frac{1}{6\pi} \approx 0.05$
θ	$\frac{1}{6}\pi$	$\frac{1}{3}\pi$	$\frac{1}{2}\pi$	π	2π	3π	4π	6π

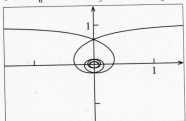

41.

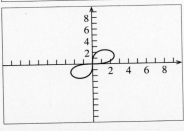

43.

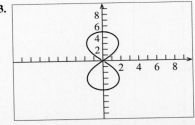

45.

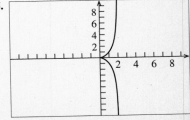

47.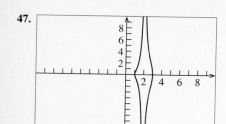

49. 4-leafed rose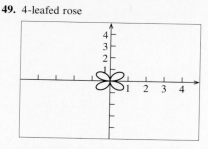

51.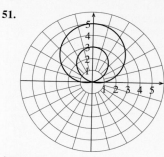

53. horizontal tangent lines at $(7, \frac{1}{2}\pi)$, $(1, \frac{3}{2}\pi)$, $(2, 3.87)$; vertical tangent lines at $(5.34, 0.46)$, $(5.34, 2.68)$

55. horizontal tangent lines at $(4.73, 1.95)$, $(4.73, 4.34)$; vertical tangent lines at $(2, 0)$, $(6, \pi)$

57. horizontal tangent lines at $(-1, \frac{1}{2}\pi)$, $(-1, \frac{3}{2}\pi)$, $(\frac{2}{3}, 0.42)$, $(\frac{2}{3}, 2.72)$, $(\frac{2}{3}, 5.86)$; vertical tangent lines at $(0, 1)$, $(1, \pi)$, $(-\frac{2}{3}, 1.99)$, $(-\frac{2}{3}, 4.29)$, $(-\frac{2}{3}, 5.13)$

59. horizontal tangent lines at $(0, 0)$, $(\sqrt[4]{12}, \frac{1}{3}\pi)$, $(-\sqrt[4]{12}, \frac{1}{3}\pi)$; vertical tangent lines at $(0, \frac{1}{2}\pi)$, $(\sqrt{2}, \frac{1}{6}\pi)$, $(-\sqrt{2}, \frac{1}{6}\pi)$

61. $(1.5, 2.60)$; $(1.5, -2.60)$ **63.** $(0, 0)$; $(1.73, 1)$; $(-1.73, 1)$ **65.** $(3, \frac{1}{3}\pi)$; $(3, -\frac{1}{3}\pi)$ **67.** the pole; $(2, \frac{1}{6}\pi)$; $(2, -\frac{5}{6}\pi)$

EXERCISES 9.4 *(page 812)*

1. 5π **3.** $2\pi a$ **5.** 32 **7.** 12 **9.** $\frac{1}{2}\sqrt{5}(e^8 - 1)$ **11.** 6π **13.** 19.38 **15.** 2.505 **17.** 4.455

19. 26.22 **21.** $\frac{9}{4}\pi$ sq units **23.** 4π sq units **25.** 4 sq units **27.** $\frac{9}{16}\pi^3$ sq units **29.** $\frac{9}{8}\pi$ sq units

31. $(\frac{11}{4}\pi - \frac{11}{2}\sin^{-1}\frac{1}{3} - 3\sqrt{2})$ sq units **33.** $(\frac{19}{3}\pi - \frac{11}{2}\sqrt{3})$ sq units **35.** $(\frac{9}{2}\pi - 9)$ sq units

37. $(18 - \frac{9}{4}\pi)$ sq units **39.** $\frac{1}{2}(\pi + 1)$ sq units **41.** (a) $(1, \pm\frac{1}{2}\pi)$; $(-1, \pm\frac{2}{3}\pi)$; (b) $(\frac{8}{3}\pi - 2\sqrt{3})$ sq units

43. (a) $(2, \pm\frac{1}{6}\pi)$; $(2, \pm\frac{7}{6}\pi)$; $(-2, \pm\frac{1}{3}\pi)$; $(-2, \pm\frac{4}{3}\pi)$; (b) $(\frac{8}{3}\pi + 4\sqrt{3})$ sq units

45. 4 sq units **47.** $8\pi^3 a^2$ sq units **49.** $\frac{1}{2}\pi a^2$ sq units

EXERCISES 9.5 *(page 821)*

1. (a) $e = \frac{1}{3}\sqrt{5}$;
foci: $(\pm\sqrt{5}, 0)$;
directrices: $x = \pm\frac{9}{5}\sqrt{5}$
(b)

3. (a) $e = \frac{1}{5}\sqrt{21}$;
foci: $(0, \pm\sqrt{21})$;
directrices: $y = \pm\frac{25}{21}\sqrt{21}$;
(b)

5. (a) $e = \frac{1}{5}\sqrt{29}$;
foci: $(\pm\sqrt{29}, 0)$;
directrices: $x = \pm\frac{25}{29}\sqrt{29}$;
(b)

7. (a) $e = \frac{5}{3}$;
foci: $(\pm 5, 0)$;
directrices: $x = \pm\frac{9}{5}$;
(b)

9. (a) parabola; (b) hyperbola; (c) ellipse; (d) circle

11. (a) 1; (b) parabola;
(c) $r\cos\theta = -2$;
(d)

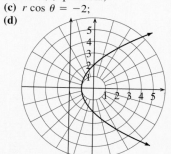

13. (a) $\frac{1}{2}$; (b) ellipse;
(c) $r\sin\theta = 5$;
(d)

15. (a) $\frac{2}{3}$; **(b)** ellipse;
(c) $r\cos\theta = -3$;
(d)
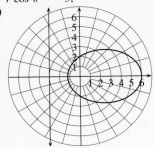

17. (a) $\frac{6}{5}$; **(b)** hyperbola;
(c) $r\sin\theta = -\frac{3}{2}$;
(d)
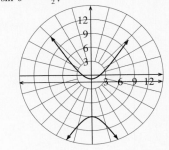

19. (a) $\frac{2}{7}$; **(b)** ellipse;
(c) $r\sin\theta = -5$;
(d)
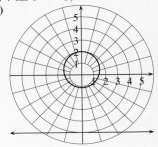

21. (a) $\frac{5}{4}$; **(b)** hyperbola;
(c) $r\cos\theta = 2$;
(d)
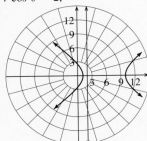

23. $r = \dfrac{8}{1-\sin\theta}$ **25.** $r = \dfrac{36}{3+4\cos\theta}$ **27.** $r = \dfrac{3}{2-\cos\theta}$

29. (a) $r = \dfrac{5}{1-3\cos\theta}$; **(b)** $r\cos\theta = -\dfrac{5}{3}$ **31.** $\frac{16}{3}\sqrt{3}\pi$ sq units

37. (a) $r = \dfrac{40{,}000{,}000}{1-\cos\theta}$; **(b)** 20,000,000 miles   **39.** 4600 miles

MISCELLANEOUS EXERCISES FOR CHAPTER 9   (page 823)

1. (a)
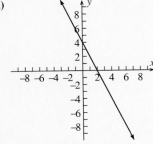

3. (a)
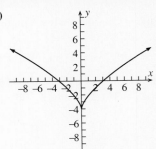

5. $\dfrac{dy}{dx} = \dfrac{1}{6t}$; $\dfrac{d^2y}{dx^2} = -\dfrac{1}{108t^3}$

7. $x = 12$; $y = 16$; $y = -16$
9. (a) $(2, \frac{11}{4}\pi)$, $(-2, \frac{7}{4}\pi)$; **(b)** $(-3, -\frac{5}{6}\pi)$, $(3, \frac{1}{6}\pi)$ **11. (a)** $(0, 1)$; **(b)** $(1, -\sqrt{3})$; **(c)** $(-2\sqrt{2}, -2\sqrt{2})$, $(-\frac{3}{2}\sqrt{3}, -\frac{3}{2})$
13. (a) $(4\sqrt{2}, \frac{3}{4}\pi)$; **(b)** $(2, \frac{5}{3}\pi)$; **(c)** $(6, \frac{1}{2}\pi)$; **(d)** $(4, \frac{7}{6}\pi)$ **15.** $r^2(4\cos^2\theta - 9\sin^2\theta) = 36$
17. $r = 9\cos\theta - 8\sin\theta$ **19.** $xy = 2$ **21.** $x^4 + 2x^2y^2 + y^4 - y^2 = 0$
23. (a) line through the pole with slope 1; **(b)** circle with center at the pole and radius 4
25. (a) line perpendicular to polar axis through the point $(3, 0)$; **(b)** circle with center at $(\frac{3}{2}, 0)$ and tangent to the $\frac{1}{2}\pi$ axis at the pole
27. limaçon with a dent; symmetric with respect to polar axis; points to right   **29.** cardioid, symmetric with respect to polar axis, points to left   **31.** limaçon with a loop; symmetric with respect to $\frac{1}{2}\pi$ axis; points downward

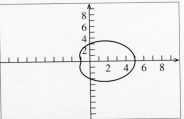
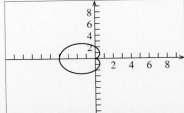
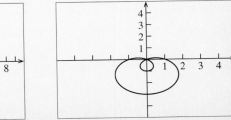

33. 4-leafed rose

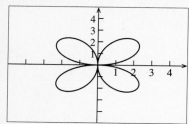

35.

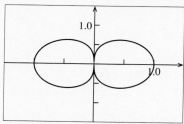

37. lemniscate

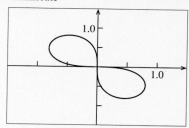

39. (a)

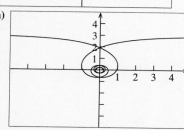

(b)

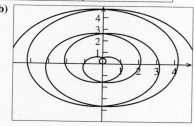

41. $\frac{3}{2}\sqrt{37} + \frac{1}{4}\ln(6 + \sqrt{37})$ **43.** 32   **45. (a)** $(16\pi - 24\sqrt{3})$ sq units;   **(b)** $(32\pi + 24\sqrt{3})$ sq units

47. $a^2(\frac{1}{3}\pi + \frac{1}{2}\sqrt{3})$ sq units   **49.** $\dfrac{e^{4k\pi} - 1}{4k}$ sq units   **51.** $r^2 - 2r_0 r \cos(\theta - \theta_0) + r_0{}^2 = a^2$

53. (a) $e = \frac{1}{2}$;   **(b)** ellipse;   **(c)** $r \sin \theta = -2$ **55. (a)** $e = \frac{3}{2}$;   **(b)** hyperbola;   **(c)** $3r \cos \theta = 4$

57. $r = \dfrac{8}{1 - 3 \cos \theta}$ **59.** $r = \dfrac{6}{1 - \sin \theta}$ **61.** 38.014   **63.** 26.73   **65. (a)** 28.6 million miles;   **(b)** 43.4 million miles

EXERCISES 10.1   (page 836)

1. (b) 5   **3. (b)** $\frac{1}{2}\sqrt{1 + 4e^2}$ **5. (a)** $\frac{7}{4}\pi$;   **(b)** π;   **(c)** $\tan^{-1} 0.4 \approx 0.38$ **7.** $\langle 2, -3 \rangle$ **9.** $\langle 5, 6 \rangle$
11. $(-4, 3)$ **13.** $(12, -5)$ **15. (a)** $\langle -1, 9 \rangle$;   **(b)** $\langle 1, -5 \rangle$ **17. (a)** $\langle -9, -4 \rangle$;   **(b)** $\langle 4, -e \rangle$
19. (a) $\langle 6, 1 \rangle$;   **(b)** $\sqrt{74}$;   **(c)** $\sqrt{1061}$ **21. (a)** $10\mathbf{i} + 15\mathbf{j}$;   **(b)** $-24\mathbf{i} + 6\mathbf{j}$;   **(c)** $6\mathbf{i} + 2\mathbf{j}$;   **(d)** $2\sqrt{10}$
23. (a) $\sqrt{13} + \sqrt{17}$;   **(b)** $-14\mathbf{i} + 21\mathbf{j}$;   **(c)** $7\sqrt{13}$;   **(d)** $5\sqrt{13} - 6\sqrt{17}$ **25. (a)** $-28\mathbf{i} + 6\mathbf{j}$;   **(b)** $2\sqrt{205}$
27. $\dfrac{11}{\sqrt{137}}\mathbf{i} + \dfrac{4}{\sqrt{137}}\mathbf{j}$;   **29. (a)** $5(\frac{3}{5}\mathbf{i} - \frac{4}{5}\mathbf{j}), \frac{3}{5}\mathbf{i} - \frac{4}{5}\mathbf{j}$;   **(b)** $2\sqrt{2}(\cos\frac{1}{4}\pi\mathbf{i} + \sin\frac{1}{4}\pi\mathbf{j}), \frac{1}{2}\sqrt{2}\mathbf{i} + \frac{1}{2}\sqrt{2}\mathbf{j}$
31. (a) $8(\cos\frac{2}{3}\pi\mathbf{i} + \sin\frac{2}{3}\pi\mathbf{j}), -\frac{1}{2}\mathbf{i} + \frac{1}{2}\sqrt{3}\mathbf{j}$;   **(b)** $16(\cos \pi\mathbf{i} + \sin \pi\mathbf{j}), -\mathbf{i}$ **33.** $h = 2, k = 3$
37. (a) 135 lb;   **(b)** 17°   **39.** 29.0°   **41. (a)** 364.1°;   **(b)** 243 mi/hr   **43. (a)** 28.1°;   **(b)** 1.7 mi/hr;   **(c)** 0.53 mi
51. (a) $\langle 1, -2 \rangle$;   **(b)** $\langle 1, -2 \rangle$

EXERCISES 10.2   (page 848)

1. (b) $(7, 2, 0), (0, 0, 3), (0, 2, 0), (0, 2, 3), (7, 0, 3) (7, 0, 0)$;   **(c)** $\sqrt{62}$
3. (b) $(2, 1, 2), (-1, 3, 2), (-1, 1, 5), (2, 3, 2), (-1, 3, 5), (2, 1, 5)$;   **(c)** $\sqrt{22}$
5. (b) $(3, -1, 0), (3, 3, 0), (1, 3, 0), (1, 3, 5), (1, -1, 5), (3, -1, 5)$;   **(c)** $3\sqrt{5}$ **7. (a)** 3;   **(b)** $(2, 5, \frac{5}{2})$
9. (a) $\frac{13}{2}$;   **(b)** $(\frac{5}{4}, -1, 2)$ **11. (a)** $7\sqrt{2}$;   **(b)** $(-1, \frac{9}{2}, -\frac{1}{2})$ **13.** $(\pm 4\sqrt{6}, 4, 2)$
17. (a) $|\overline{AB}| = 9\sqrt{2}; |\overline{AC}| = 2\sqrt{62}; |\overline{BC}| = \sqrt{62}$;   **(b)** midpoint of AB: $(\frac{1}{2}, 1, \frac{3}{2})$; midpoint of AC: $(-1, 2, 5)$;
midpoint of BC: $(-\frac{5}{2}, 8, \frac{7}{2})$ **21.** sphere with center at $(4, -2, -1)$ and $r = 5$ **23.** the point $(0, 0, 3)$
25. the empty set   **27.** $x^2 + (y - 1)^2 + (z + 4)^2 = 9$ **29. (a)** $\langle 21, -13, -2 \rangle$;   **(b)** $\langle -25, -26, 5 \rangle$;
(c) $7\sqrt{59} - 5\sqrt{41}$;   **(d)** $\sqrt{1326}$ **31. (a)** $\langle -19, -16, -1 \rangle$;   **(b)** $\langle -6\sqrt{91}, -8\sqrt{91}, -2\sqrt{91} \rangle$ **33.** $a = 0, b = 0$
35. $\dfrac{4}{\sqrt{89}}; \dfrac{3}{\sqrt{89}}; \dfrac{8}{\sqrt{89}}$ **37.** $-\dfrac{6}{\sqrt{86}}; -\dfrac{1}{\sqrt{86}}; -\dfrac{7}{\sqrt{86}}$ **39.** $(\frac{13}{3}, 0, -\frac{4}{3})$ **41.** $(\frac{17}{3}, \frac{4}{3}, -6)$
43. (a) $7(-\frac{6}{7}\mathbf{i} + \frac{2}{7}\mathbf{j} + \frac{3}{7}\mathbf{k})$;   **(b)** $\sqrt{14}\left(-\dfrac{2}{\sqrt{14}}\mathbf{i} + \dfrac{1}{\sqrt{14}}\mathbf{j} - \dfrac{3}{\sqrt{14}}\mathbf{k}\right)$ **45. (a)** $\langle \frac{1}{9}, \frac{8}{9}, \frac{4}{9} \rangle$;   **(b)** $\left\langle -\dfrac{1}{\sqrt{3}}, \dfrac{1}{\sqrt{3}}, \dfrac{1}{\sqrt{3}} \right\rangle$

EXERCISES 10.3 (page 858)

1. (a) 10; **(b)** -1 **3. (a)** $-\frac{2}{5}$; **(b)** 9   **15. (a)** 0; **(b)** no k **17. (a)** $-\dfrac{80}{\sqrt{85}}$; **(b)** $\dfrac{-112}{17}\mathbf{i} + \dfrac{96}{17}\mathbf{j}$

19. $\frac{29}{50}\sqrt{50}$ **21. (a)** -44; **(b)** -468; **(c)** -31; **(d)** $\langle -84, 198, 124\rangle$ **23. (a)** $-\frac{1}{5}\sqrt{5}$; **(b)** -3; **(c)** $\langle 2, 1, -2\rangle$

25. (a) $-\frac{13}{9}\sqrt{6}$; **(b)** $\langle -\frac{26}{27}, -\frac{91}{27}, \frac{13}{27}\rangle$ **27.** $\frac{1}{11}\sqrt{4422}$ **31.** $\frac{7}{2}\sqrt{3}$ sq units   **33.** $\langle \frac{1}{17}\sqrt{17}, \frac{4}{17}\sqrt{17}\rangle$; $\langle -\frac{1}{17}\sqrt{17}, -\frac{4}{17}\sqrt{17}\rangle$

35. $-\frac{46}{57}\sqrt{19}$ **37. (a)** 24 ft-lb; **(b)** $24\sqrt{3}$ ft-lb   **39.** $(18 - 9\sqrt{3})$ ft-lb   **41.** 25 ft-lb   **43.** $\frac{5}{3}\sqrt{6}$ ft-lb   **45.** $\frac{2}{5}$

59. $\mathbf{E_1} = \dfrac{\mathbf{E} \cdot \mathbf{H}}{\mathbf{H} \cdot \mathbf{H}}\mathbf{H}$; $\mathbf{E_2} = \mathbf{E} - \dfrac{\mathbf{E} \cdot \mathbf{H}}{\mathbf{H} \cdot \mathbf{H}}\mathbf{H}$

EXERCISES 10.4 (page 871)

1. $x + 2y - 3z + 1 = 0$ **3.** $y - z + 3 = 0$ **5.** $x - 3y - 4z - 3 = 0$ **7.** $3x + 2y + 6z = 23$

9. $\langle \frac{2}{3}, -\frac{1}{3}, \frac{2}{3}\rangle$; $\langle -\frac{2}{3}, \frac{1}{3}, -\frac{2}{3}\rangle$ **11.** $\langle \frac{4}{13}, \frac{3}{13}, -\frac{12}{13}\rangle$; $\langle -\frac{4}{13}, -\frac{3}{13}, \frac{12}{13}\rangle$ **13.** $\left\langle \dfrac{3}{\sqrt{13}}, 0, \dfrac{2}{\sqrt{13}}\right\rangle$; $\left\langle -\dfrac{3}{\sqrt{13}}, 0, -\dfrac{2}{\sqrt{13}}\right\rangle$

15. $5x - 3y + 7z + 14 = 0$ **17.** $2x - y - z + 1 = 0$ **19.** $4y - 3z - 1 = 0$ and $z = 1$

21. $67.6°$ **23.** $69.2°$ **25.** $\frac{16}{15}\sqrt{6}$ **27.** $\frac{3}{2}$ **29.** $x = 1 + 4t, y = 2 - 3t, z = 1$; $\dfrac{x-1}{4} = \dfrac{y-2}{-3}, z = 1$

31. $x = 13t, y = -12t, z = -8t$; $\dfrac{x}{13} = \dfrac{y}{-12} = \dfrac{z}{-8}$ **33.** $x = 2t - 2, y = -16t; z = 13t + 3$; $\dfrac{x+2}{2} = \dfrac{y}{-16} = \dfrac{z-3}{13}$

35. $x = 4 + t, y = -5 + 3t, z = 20 - 6t$; $\dfrac{x-4}{1} = \dfrac{y+5}{3} = \dfrac{z-20}{-6}$ **37.** $\dfrac{x - \frac{1}{7}}{2} = \dfrac{y}{7} = \dfrac{z - \frac{10}{7}}{13}$

41. $8x - y - 66 = 0; 13x - 5z - 102 = 0; 13y - 40z + 42 = 0$

43. $4x + y + 3 = 0; 3x - z + 4 = 0; 3y + 4z - 7 = 0$ **45.** $\frac{5}{18}\sqrt{6}$ **47.** $4x + 7y - 3z + 7 = 0$

49. $4x + 2y - 3z + 5 = 0$ **51.** $(\frac{5}{3}, -\frac{17}{6}, \frac{5}{12})$ **53.** $\dfrac{x-3}{1} = \dfrac{y-6}{2} = \dfrac{z-4}{1}$ **55.** $\frac{2}{5}\sqrt{70}$ **61.** $x = x_0, y = y_0$

EXERCISES 10.5 (page 884)

1. $\langle 7, 13, -11\rangle$ **3.** -490 **11.** $\langle 9, -1, -23\rangle$ **15.** $\frac{2}{3}\sqrt{2}$ **17.** $\sqrt{89}$ sq units   **19.** $9\sqrt{29}$ sq units

21. $5x - 2y + 7z = 0$ **23.** $x + 2y + z - 2 = 0$ **25.** $\pm\dfrac{1}{\sqrt{3}}(\mathbf{i} + \mathbf{j} - \mathbf{k})$ **27.** $\pm\dfrac{1}{\sqrt{6}}(\mathbf{i} + 2\mathbf{j} + \mathbf{k})$ **29.** 20 cu units

31. $\dfrac{38}{3\sqrt{78}}$ **33.** 187.9 in-lb

EXERCISES 10.6 (page 900)

13. $x^2 + z^2 = 4y$ **15.** $x^2 + 4y^2 + 4z^2 = 16$ **17.** $y^2 = 9x^2 + 9z^2$ **19.** $y^2 + z^2 = \sin^2 x$ **21.** $x^2 + z^2 = 16$; x axis or y axis; or $x^2 + z^2 = 16$, x axis or z axis; or $y^2 + z^2 = 16$, y axis or z axis   **23.** $x^2 - z^2 = 4$, z axis; or $y^2 - z^2 = 4$, z axis

25. $x^2 = |y|$, y axis; or $z^2 = |y|$, y axis   **27.** $y^2 = 9x^2$, y axis; or $y^2 = 9z^2$, y axis   **29. (i)** (d): elliptic paraboloid; **(ii)** (e): ellipsoid; **(iii)** (b): hyperbolic paraboloid; **(iv)** (f): hyperboloid of 2 sheets; **(v)** (a): hyperboloid of 1 sheet; **(vi)** (c): elliptic cone   **31.** ellipsoid   **33.** hyperboloid of 1 sheet   **35.** elliptic cone   **37.** elliptic paraboloid   **39.** hyperbolic paraboloid   **41.** elliptic hyperboloid of two sheets   **43. (a)** $1 < |k| < \sqrt{2}$; **(b)** $|k| < 1$ **45.** vertex: $(1, -\frac{1}{3}, 0)$; focus $(1, 0, 0)$ **49.** 8π cu units   **51.** $\dfrac{abh^2}{2c}\pi$ cu units

MISCELLANEOUS EXERCISES FOR CHAPTER 10 (page 904)

1. $-25\mathbf{i} + 63\mathbf{j}$ **3.** $\sqrt{4594}$ **5.** $15\sqrt{2} - 14\sqrt{13}$ **7.** 92   **9.** $\dfrac{9}{\sqrt{106}}\mathbf{i} - \dfrac{5}{\sqrt{106}}\mathbf{j}$ **11.** $h = -\frac{1}{2}; k = \frac{1}{2}$

13. $-\frac{19}{5}\sqrt{2}$ **15.** $-\frac{19}{25}\mathbf{i} - \frac{133}{25}\mathbf{j}$ **17.** $-\frac{19}{13}\sqrt{13}$ **19.** $\frac{1}{13}(80 \pm 58\sqrt{3})$ **21.** $\mathbf{i} + 26\mathbf{j} - 16\mathbf{k}$ **23.** -3 **25.** $7\sqrt{1270}$

27. $-\frac{1}{3}\sqrt{21}$ **29.** $\frac{1}{9}(\mathbf{i} + 2\mathbf{j} - 2\mathbf{k})$ **31.** $\langle 60, -40, 80\rangle$ **33.** 16   **35.** 295   **37.** a point on the x axis in R, a line parallel to the y axis in R^2, a plane parallel to the yz plane in R^3 **39.** the x axis   **41.** the circle in the xz plane with center at the origin and radius 2   **43.** the plane perpendicular to the xy plane and intersecting the xy plane in the line $y = x$ **45.** the paraboloid of revolution generated by revolving $y^2 = 9z$ about the z axis   **47.** the right circular cone generated by revolving $y = x$ about the x axis

49. (a) 104.4 lb; **(b)** 35.5°   **51.** 127.28 ft-lb   **53.** $(-3, \sqrt{167}, 1), (-3, -\sqrt{167}, 1)$

55. $(x + 2)^2 + (y + 1)^2 + (z - 3)^2 = 17$ **57.** $z^2 = e^{4y}$ or $x^2 = e^{4y}$; the y axis   **59.** 3

61. (a) $\cos \alpha = -\dfrac{7}{\sqrt{78}}$, $\cos \beta = -\dfrac{5}{\sqrt{78}}$, $\cos \gamma = -\dfrac{2}{\sqrt{78}}$;   **(b)** $-\dfrac{7}{\sqrt{78}}\mathbf{i} - \dfrac{5}{\sqrt{78}}\mathbf{j} - \dfrac{2}{\sqrt{78}}\mathbf{k}$

63. (a) $-\frac{4}{5}\sqrt{3}$;   **(b)** $-\frac{28}{25}\mathbf{i} + \frac{4}{25}\mathbf{j} - \frac{4}{5}\mathbf{k}$ **65.** $x - 6y - 10z + 23 = 0$ **67.** $\frac{47}{10}\sqrt{2}$ **69.** 3   **71.** $\frac{1}{3}\sqrt{3}$

73. $\dfrac{x}{4} = \dfrac{y}{-3} = \dfrac{z}{1}$, $x = 4t$, $y = -3t$, $z = t$ **77.** $\frac{54}{25}\pi$ sq units   **79.** 24 cu units

EXERCISES 11.1 (page 913)

1. $(-\infty, 0) \cup (0, 4]$ **3.** $(-1, 1]$ **5.** $[-2, 0) \cup (0, \pi) \cup (\pi, 4]$ **7.** $(-4, -\pi) \cup (-\pi, 0) \cup (0, \pi) \cup (\pi, 4]$

9. (a) $2t\mathbf{i} + t^2\mathbf{j} + 2t\mathbf{k}$;   **(b)** $2\mathbf{i} + (t^2 - 2)\mathbf{j} - 2\mathbf{k}$;   **(c)** $3t^2 - 3$;   **(d)** $(t^3 + t^2 - 2t)\mathbf{i} - 4t\mathbf{j} + (2t - t^3 + t^2)\mathbf{k}$

11. (a) $(\cos t + \sin t)\mathbf{i} + (\cos t - \sin t)\mathbf{j}$;   **(b)** $(\cos t - \sin t)\mathbf{i} - (\cos t + \sin t)\mathbf{j} + 2t\mathbf{k}$;
 (c) $-t^2$; **(d)** $t(\sin t - \cos t)\mathbf{i} + t(\sin t + \cos t)\mathbf{j} + \mathbf{k}$

13. (a) $(t^2 - 1)\mathbf{i} + (t^3 - t^2 - t + 1)\mathbf{j} + (t^2 - 2t + 1)\mathbf{k}$;   **(b)** $(t^2 - 2t + 1)\mathbf{i} + (t - 1)\mathbf{j} + (t^2 - 1)\mathbf{k}$;
 (c) $(2 + t)\mathbf{i} + (t^2 + 2t)\mathbf{j} + t\mathbf{k}$;   **(d)** $t\mathbf{i} + \mathbf{j} + (t + 2)\mathbf{k}$

15. (a) $\sin t \cos t\mathbf{i} - \sin^2 t\mathbf{j} + t \sin t\mathbf{k}$;   **(b)** $\sin^2 t\mathbf{i} + \sin t \cos t\mathbf{j} - t \sin t\mathbf{k}$;   **(c)** $\sqrt{1 - t^2}\,\mathbf{i} - t\mathbf{j} + \sin^{-1} t\mathbf{k}$;
 (d) $t\mathbf{i} + \sqrt{1 - t^2}\,\mathbf{j} - \sin^{-1} t\mathbf{k}$

17. $4\mathbf{j} + 2\mathbf{k}$ **19.** $\mathbf{j} + \mathbf{k}$ **21.** $-\mathbf{i} - \frac{1}{2}\pi\mathbf{j} + \pi\mathbf{k}$ **23.** $e(\mathbf{i} + \mathbf{j} + \mathbf{k})$ **25.** $(1, 2) \cup (2, +\infty)$

27. all real numbers except $(k + \frac{1}{2})\pi$, where k is any integer   **29.** all real numbers

31.

33.

35.

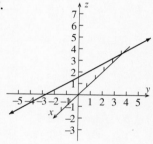

37.

39.

41.

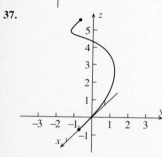

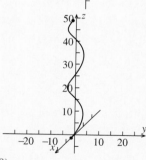

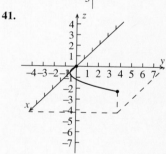

43. (a) $(0, 8, 0)$;   **(b)** $(4, 8, 4)$;   **(c)** $(0, 0, 8)$

45. (a) $(0, 0, 10)$;   **(b)** $(-10, 0, 0)$;   **(c)** $(10, 0, 0)$

EXERCISES 11.2 (page 923)

1. $\mathbf{R}'(t) = \mathbf{i} - t^{-2}\mathbf{j}$; $\mathbf{R}''(t) = 2t^{-3}\mathbf{j}$ **3.** $\mathbf{R}'(t) = 2(t + 1)^{-2}\mathbf{i} + 2t^{-2}\mathbf{j}$; $\mathbf{R}''(t) = -4(t + 1)^{-3}\mathbf{i} - 4t^{-3}\mathbf{j}$

5. $\mathbf{R}' = 2e^{2t}\mathbf{i} + t^{-1}\mathbf{j} + 2t\mathbf{k}$; $\mathbf{R}''(t) = 4e^{2t}\mathbf{i} - t^{-2}\mathbf{j} + 2\mathbf{k}$

7. $\mathbf{R}'(t) = \dfrac{1}{1 + t^2}\mathbf{i} + \dfrac{1}{\sqrt{1 - t^2}}\mathbf{j} - \dfrac{1}{\sqrt{1 - t^2}}\mathbf{k}$; $\mathbf{R}''(t) = -\dfrac{2t}{(1 + t^2)^2}\mathbf{i} + \dfrac{t}{(1 - t^2)^{3/2}}\mathbf{j} - \dfrac{t}{(1 - t^2)^{3/2}}\mathbf{k}$

9. $\mathbf{R}'(t) = 10 \cos 2t\mathbf{i} - 4 \sec 4t \tan 4t\mathbf{j} - 8 \sin 2t\mathbf{k}$; $\mathbf{R}''(t) = -20 \sin 2t\mathbf{i} + (16 \sec 4t - 32 \sec^3 4t)\mathbf{j} - 16 \cos 2t\mathbf{k}$

11. $(2t - 3)(2t^2 - 6t + 5)^{-1/2}$ **13.** $\dfrac{12e^{6t}}{\sqrt{1 + 4e^{6t}}}$ **33.** $\ln|\sec t|\mathbf{i} - \ln|t|\mathbf{j} + \mathbf{C}$

35. $(t \ln t - t)\mathbf{i} + \frac{1}{3}t^3\mathbf{j} + \mathbf{C}$ **37.** $\frac{1}{3}e^{3t}\mathbf{i} - \frac{1}{3}e^{-3t}\mathbf{j} + (\frac{1}{9}e^{3t} - \frac{1}{3}te^{3t})\mathbf{k} + \mathbf{C}$ **39.** $\ln|\sec t|\,\mathbf{i} + \ln|\sec t + \tan t|\,\mathbf{j} + \ln|t|\,\mathbf{k} + \mathbf{C}$

41. $(\frac{1}{3}t^3 - 7)\mathbf{i} + (\ln|t - 2| - 5)\mathbf{j}$ **43.** $\left[\frac{1}{2}e^t(\sin t - \cos t) + \frac{3}{2}\right]\mathbf{i} + (\sin t - 1)\mathbf{j} + (2 - e^t)\mathbf{k}$ **45.** $x^2 + y^2 = 1$; 0   **47.** 0

49. $\sqrt{21} + \frac{3}{2} + \frac{5}{4}\ln(4 + \sqrt{21})$ **51.** 13   **53.** 9.571   **55.** 3.096

EXERCISES 11.3   (page 931)

1. $\mathbf{T}(t) = -\sin t\mathbf{i} + \cos t\mathbf{j}$; $\mathbf{T}(\frac{1}{2}\pi) = -\mathbf{i}$; $\mathbf{N}(t) = -\cos t\mathbf{i} - \sin t\mathbf{j}$; $\mathbf{N}(\frac{1}{2}\pi) = -\mathbf{j}$

3. $\mathbf{T}(t) = \cos t\mathbf{i} + \sin t\mathbf{j}$; $\mathbf{T}(\frac{1}{2}\pi) = \mathbf{j}$; $\mathbf{N}(t) = -\sin t\mathbf{i} + \cos t\mathbf{j}$; $\mathbf{N}(\frac{1}{2}\pi) = -\mathbf{i}$

5. $\mathbf{T}(t) = \dfrac{t^2 - 1}{t^2 + 1}\mathbf{i} + \dfrac{2t}{t^2 + 1}\mathbf{j}$; $\mathbf{T}(2) = \frac{3}{5}\mathbf{i} + \frac{4}{5}\mathbf{j}$; $\mathbf{N}(t) = \dfrac{2t}{t^2 + 1}\mathbf{i} + \dfrac{1 - t^2}{t^2 + 1}\mathbf{j}$; $\mathbf{N}(2) = \frac{4}{5}\mathbf{i} - \frac{3}{5}\mathbf{j}$

7. $\mathbf{T}(t) = \sin t\mathbf{i} + \cos t\mathbf{j}$; $\mathbf{N}(t) = \cos t\mathbf{i} - \sin t\mathbf{j}$ **9.** $\mathbf{T}(t) = \dfrac{\mathbf{j} + t\mathbf{k}}{\sqrt{1 + t^2}}$; $\mathbf{N}(t) = \dfrac{-t\mathbf{j} + \mathbf{k}}{\sqrt{1 + t^2}}$

11. $\mathbf{T}(\frac{1}{2}\pi) = \mathbf{i}$; $\mathbf{N}(\frac{1}{2}\pi) = -\mathbf{j}$; $\mathbf{B}(\frac{1}{2}\pi) = -\mathbf{k}$ **13.** $\mathbf{T}(1) = \frac{1}{2}\sqrt{2}(\mathbf{j} + \mathbf{k})$; $\mathbf{N}(1) = \frac{1}{2}\sqrt{2}(-\mathbf{j} + \mathbf{k})$; $\mathbf{B}(1) = \mathbf{k}$

15. $\mathbf{T}(t) = -\cos t\mathbf{i} + \sin t\mathbf{j}$; $\mathbf{N}(t) = \sin t\mathbf{i} + \cos t\mathbf{j}$; $\mathbf{B}(t) = -\mathbf{k}$ **17.** osculating: $z = 2$; rectifying: $y = \frac{1}{2}\pi$; normal: $x = 1$

19. osculating: $x = 1$; rectifying: $-(y - \frac{1}{2}) + (z - \frac{1}{3}) = 0$; normal: $(y - \frac{1}{2}) + (z - \frac{1}{3}) = 0$

21. osculating: $z = 2$; rectifying: $(x - \frac{1}{4}\sqrt{2}) + (y - \frac{1}{4}\sqrt{2}) = 0$; normal: $-(x - \frac{1}{4}\sqrt{2}) + (y - \frac{1}{4}\sqrt{2}) = 0$

23. $\mathbf{T}(\frac{1}{2}\pi) = \frac{1}{5}\sqrt{5}(-2\mathbf{i} + \mathbf{k})$; $\mathbf{N}(\frac{1}{2}\pi) = -\mathbf{j}$; $\mathbf{B}(\frac{1}{2}\pi) = \frac{1}{5}\sqrt{5}(\mathbf{i} + 2\mathbf{k})$; osculating: $x + 2z - 4 = 0$; rectifying: $y = 1$; normal: $2x - z + 2 = 0$

25. $\frac{3}{91}\sqrt{273}$ **27.** $\frac{1}{4}\pi$ **29.** $s = \frac{1}{27}[(4 + 9t)^{3/2} - 8]$

31. $\mathbf{R}(s) = (\sin\sqrt{2s} - \sqrt{2s}\cos\sqrt{2s})\mathbf{i} + (\cos\sqrt{2s} + \sqrt{2s}\sin\sqrt{2s})\mathbf{j} + 2\mathbf{k}$

33. $\mathbf{R}(s) = \mathbf{i} + \frac{1}{2}[(3s + 1)^{2/3} - 1]\mathbf{j} + \frac{1}{3}[(3s + 1)^{2/3} - 1]^{3/2}\mathbf{k}$ **35.** $\mathbf{R}(s) = (1 - \frac{2}{3}s)^{3/2}\mathbf{i} + (\frac{2}{3}s)^{3/2}\mathbf{j} + 2\mathbf{k}$

EXERCISES 11.4   (page 939)

1. $K = \frac{1}{3}$; $\rho = 3$ **3.** $K = 1$; $\rho = 1$ **5.** $K = \frac{2}{25}$; $\rho = \frac{25}{2}$ **7.** $\dfrac{1}{|t|}$ **9.** $\dfrac{1}{t(1 + t^2)^{3/2}}$ **15.** 2

17. $K(t) = \dfrac{\sqrt{2}|1 - t^2|^3}{(1 + 6t^2 + t^4)^{3/2}}$; $K(0) = \sqrt{2}$; $\rho(0) = \frac{1}{2}\sqrt{2}$ **19.** $K = \frac{1}{2}$; $\rho = 2$ **21.** $K = \frac{1}{4}\sqrt{2}$; $\rho = 2\sqrt{2}$

23. $K = \frac{4}{49}\sqrt{7}$; $\rho = \frac{7}{4}\sqrt{7}$ **25.** $K = \frac{2}{289}\sqrt{17}$; $\rho = \frac{17}{2}\sqrt{17}$ **27.** $\dfrac{(2 - x^2)^{3/2}}{|x|}$ **29.** $\frac{1}{576}(16x^2 + 81y^2)^{3/2}$

31. $\dfrac{2(x + y)^{3/2}}{a^{1/2}}$ **33.** $4|a \sin\frac{1}{2}t|$ **35.** $(-\frac{1}{2}\ln 2, \frac{1}{2}\sqrt{2})$ **37.** $(-3, -1)$ **41.** $K = 2$; $\rho = \frac{1}{2}$; $(0, -\frac{1}{2})$

43. $\left(3x + 2p, -\dfrac{y^3}{4p^2}\right)$ **45.** $\left(\dfrac{a^2 - b^2}{a}\cos^3 t, \dfrac{b^2 - a^2}{b}\sin^3 t\right)$ **47.** $C = (\frac{2}{9}, \frac{37}{12})$, $\rho = \frac{125}{36}$ **49.** $(x + 2)^2 + (y - 3)^2 = 8$

51. $K = \frac{23}{98}\sqrt{7}$; $\rho = \frac{14}{23}\sqrt{7}$ **53.** $K = \dfrac{1}{16|a|}$; $\rho = 16|a|$ **59.** $\dfrac{1}{2b}$

EXERCISES 11.5   (page 950)

1. (a) $\mathbf{V}(t) = 2t\mathbf{i} + \mathbf{j}$; $\mathbf{A}(t) = 2\mathbf{i}$; $\|\mathbf{V}(t)\| = \sqrt{4t^2 + 1}$; $\|\mathbf{A}(t)\| = 2$;   (b) $\mathbf{V}(3) = 6\mathbf{i} + \mathbf{j}$; $\mathbf{A}(3) = 2\mathbf{i}$

3. (a) $\mathbf{V}(t) = -10\sin 2t\mathbf{i} + 6\cos 2t\mathbf{j}$; $\mathbf{A}(t) = -20\cos 2t\mathbf{i} - 12\sin 2t\mathbf{j}$; $\|\mathbf{V}(t)\| = 2\sqrt{25\sin^2 2t + 9\cos^2 2t}$; $\|\mathbf{A}(t)\| = 4\sqrt{25\cos^2 t + 9\sin^2 2t}$;   (b) $\mathbf{V}(\frac{1}{4}\pi) = -10\mathbf{i}$; $\mathbf{A}(\frac{1}{4}\pi) = -12\mathbf{j}$

5. (a) $\mathbf{V}(t) = e^t\mathbf{i} + 2e^{2t}\mathbf{j}$; $\mathbf{A}(t) = e^t\mathbf{i} + 4e^{2t}\mathbf{j}$; $\|\mathbf{V}(t)\| = e^t\sqrt{1 + 4e^{2t}}$; $\|\mathbf{A}(t)\| = e^t\sqrt{1 + 16e^{2t}}$;   (b) $\mathbf{V}(\ln 2) = 2\mathbf{i} + 8\mathbf{j}$; $\mathbf{A}(\ln 2) = 2\mathbf{i} + 16\mathbf{j}$

7. (a) $\mathbf{V}(t) = \mathbf{i} + \tan t\mathbf{j}$; $\mathbf{A}(t) = \sec^2 t\mathbf{j}$; $\|\mathbf{V}(t)\| = |\sec t|$; $\|\mathbf{A}(t)\| = \sec^2 t$;   (b) $\mathbf{V}(\frac{1}{4}\pi) = \mathbf{i} + \mathbf{j}$; $\mathbf{A}(\frac{1}{4}\pi) = 2\mathbf{j}$

9. (a) $\mathbf{V}(t) = (2t + 3)\mathbf{i} - 6t\mathbf{j}$; $\mathbf{A}(t) = 2\mathbf{i} - 6\mathbf{j}$; $\|\mathbf{V}(t)\| = \sqrt{40t^2 + 12t + 9}$; $\|\mathbf{A}(t)\| = 2\sqrt{10}$;   (b) $\mathbf{V}(\frac{1}{2}) = 4\mathbf{i} - 3\mathbf{j}$; $\mathbf{A}(\frac{1}{2}) = 2\mathbf{i} - 6\mathbf{j}$ **11.** $\mathbf{V}(\frac{1}{2}\pi) = -2\mathbf{i} + \mathbf{k}$; $\mathbf{A}(\frac{1}{2}\pi) = -2\mathbf{j}$; $\|\mathbf{V}(\frac{1}{2}\pi)\| = \sqrt{5}$ **13.** $\mathbf{V}(2) = \mathbf{i} + 2\mathbf{j} + 2\mathbf{k}$; $\mathbf{A}(2) = 2\mathbf{j}$; $\|\mathbf{V}(2)\| = 3$

15. $\mathbf{V}(0) = \mathbf{i} + \mathbf{j} + \mathbf{k}$; $\mathbf{A}(0) = 2\mathbf{j} + \mathbf{k}$; $\|\mathbf{V}(0)\| = \sqrt{3}$ **17.** $(4 - \frac{1}{t + 1})\mathbf{i} + (\frac{1}{2}t^2 + t + 2)\mathbf{j}$

19. $(e^{-t} + 3t - 1)\mathbf{i} + (\frac{2}{9}e^{3t} + \frac{1}{3}t + \frac{25}{9})\mathbf{j}$ **21.** $(t + 1)\mathbf{i} + (t + 2)\mathbf{j} - 16t^2\mathbf{k}$ **23.** $(t^3 + 2t)\mathbf{i} + (t^4 + 3t)\mathbf{j} + (\frac{1}{2}t^2 + 4)\mathbf{k}$

25. $\mathbf{V}(t) = 2\mathbf{i} + 2t\mathbf{j}$; $\mathbf{A}(t) = 2\mathbf{j}$; $\mathbf{T}(t) = \dfrac{1}{\sqrt{1 + t^2}}\mathbf{i} + \dfrac{t}{\sqrt{1 + t^2}}\mathbf{j}$; $\mathbf{N}(t) = \dfrac{-t}{\sqrt{1 + t^2}}\mathbf{i} + \dfrac{1}{\sqrt{1 + t^2}}\mathbf{j}$; $\|\mathbf{V}(t)\| = 2\sqrt{1 + t^2}$;

$A_T(t) = \dfrac{2t}{\sqrt{1 + t^2}}$; $A_N(t) = \dfrac{2}{\sqrt{1 + t^2}}$; $K(t) = \dfrac{1}{2(1 + t^2)^{3/2}}$; $\mathbf{V}(2) = 2\mathbf{i} + 4\mathbf{j}$; $\mathbf{T}(2) = \dfrac{1}{\sqrt{5}}\mathbf{i} + \dfrac{2}{\sqrt{5}}\mathbf{j}$; $\mathbf{A}(2) = 2\mathbf{j}$;

$\mathbf{N}(2) = \dfrac{-2}{\sqrt{5}}\mathbf{i} + \dfrac{1}{\sqrt{5}}\mathbf{j}$, $\|\mathbf{V}(2)\| = 2\sqrt{5}$; $A_N(2) + \dfrac{2}{\sqrt{5}}$; $K(2) = \dfrac{1}{10\sqrt{5}}$

27. $\mathbf{V}(t) = -15\sin 3t\mathbf{i} + 15\cos 3t\mathbf{j}$; $\mathbf{A}(t) = -45\cos 3t\mathbf{i} - 45\sin 3t\mathbf{j}$; $\mathbf{T}(t) = -\sin 3t\mathbf{i} + \cos 3t\mathbf{j}$; $\mathbf{N}(t) = -\cos 3t\mathbf{i} - \sin 3t\mathbf{j}$; $\|\mathbf{V}(t)\| = 15$; $A_T(t) = 0$; $A_N(t) = 45$; $K(t) = \frac{1}{5}$; $\mathbf{V}(\frac{1}{3}\pi) = -15\mathbf{j}$; $\mathbf{A}(\frac{1}{3}\pi) = 45\mathbf{i}$; $\mathbf{T}(\frac{1}{3}\pi) = -\mathbf{j}$; $\mathbf{N}(\frac{1}{3}\pi) = \mathbf{i}$; $\|\mathbf{V}(\frac{1}{3}\pi)\| = 15$

29. $\mathbf{V}(t) = e^t\mathbf{i} - e^{-t}\mathbf{j}$; $\mathbf{A}(t) = e^t\mathbf{i} + e^{-t}\mathbf{j}$; $\mathbf{T}(t) = \dfrac{e^{2t}}{\sqrt{e^{4t}+1}}\mathbf{i} - \dfrac{1}{\sqrt{e^{4t}+1}}\mathbf{j}$; $\mathbf{N}(t) = \dfrac{1}{\sqrt{e^{4t}+1}}\mathbf{i} + \dfrac{e^{2t}}{e^{4t}+1}\mathbf{j}$; $\|\mathbf{V}(t)\| = \dfrac{\sqrt{e^{4t}+1}}{e^t}$;

$A_T(t) = \dfrac{e^{4t}-1}{e^t\sqrt{e^{4t}+1}}$; $A_N(t) = \dfrac{2e^t}{\sqrt{e^{4t}+1}}$; $K(t) = \dfrac{2e^{3t}}{(e^{4t}+1)^{3/2}}$; $\mathbf{V}(0) = \mathbf{i} - \mathbf{j}$; $\mathbf{A}(0) = \mathbf{i} + \mathbf{j}$; $\mathbf{T}(0) = \dfrac{1}{\sqrt{2}}\mathbf{i} - \dfrac{1}{\sqrt{2}}\mathbf{j}$;

$\mathbf{N}(0) = \dfrac{1}{\sqrt{2}}\mathbf{i} + \dfrac{1}{\sqrt{2}}\mathbf{j}$; $\|\mathbf{V}(0)\| = \sqrt{2}$; $A_T(0) = 0$; $A_N(0) = \sqrt{2}$; $K(0) = \dfrac{1}{\sqrt{2}}$

31. $\dfrac{4t}{\sqrt{4t^2+2}}\mathbf{T}(t) + \dfrac{2\sqrt{2}}{\sqrt{4t^2+2}}\mathbf{N}(t)$ **33.** $1\mathbf{T}(t) + t\mathbf{N}(t)$ **35.** $2\sqrt{2}t\,\mathbf{T}(t) + 2\mathbf{N}(t)$ **39.** $3(x-1) - 3(y-1) + (z-1)0$

41. (a) $160\sqrt{2}\mathbf{i} + 160\sqrt{2}\mathbf{j}$; (b) $x(t)\mathbf{i} + y(t)\mathbf{j} = 160\sqrt{2}t\mathbf{i} + (160\sqrt{2}t - 16t^2)\mathbf{j}$; (c) $10\sqrt{2}$ sec; (d) 3200 ft;
(e) 800 ft; (f) $160\sqrt{2}\mathbf{i} - 160\sqrt{2}\mathbf{j}$; 320 ft/sec;
(g) $\mathbf{R}(6) = 960\sqrt{2}\mathbf{i} + (960\sqrt{2} - 576)\mathbf{j}$; $\mathbf{V}(6) = 160\sqrt{2}\mathbf{i} + (160\sqrt{2} - 192)\mathbf{j}$; $64\sqrt{34 - 15\sqrt{2}} \approx 229$ ft/sec;
(h) $y = x - \dfrac{x^2}{3200}$ **45.** $(25 + \sqrt{631})$ sec; $(20{,}000\sqrt{3} + 800\sqrt{1893})$ ft   **47.** 283 m/sec

49. lands in water 24.3 ft from ship   **51.** 40°8′   **53.** clears the tree by 5 ft and lands 25 ft short of the pin
55. (c) $\mathbf{T}(t) = -\sin \omega t\,\mathbf{i} + \cos \omega t\,\mathbf{j}$; $\mathbf{N}(t) = -\cos \omega t\,\mathbf{i} - \sin \omega t\,\mathbf{j}$; $A_T(t) = 0$; $A_N(t) = r\omega^2$; (d) quadrupled

MISCELLANEOUS EXERCISES FOR CHAPTER 11 (page 954)

1. $[0, 3) \cup (3, +\infty)$ **3.** $[-2, -\frac{1}{2}\pi) \cup (-\frac{1}{2}\pi, -\frac{1}{2}] \cup [\frac{1}{2}, \frac{1}{2}\pi) \cup (\frac{1}{2}\pi, 2]$ **5.** $\frac{1}{2}\mathbf{i} + \frac{1}{2}\mathbf{j}$
7. $\mathbf{k}$ **9.** $(0, 4)$ **11.** all real numbers   **13.**   **15.**

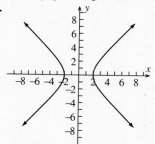
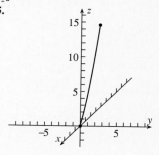

17. $\mathbf{R}'(t) = \dfrac{-2t}{(t^2+9)^2}\mathbf{i} - \dfrac{1}{t^2}\mathbf{j} - \dfrac{1}{t}\mathbf{k}$; $\mathbf{R}''(t) = 6\dfrac{t^2-3}{(t^2+9)^3}\mathbf{i} + \dfrac{2}{t^3}\mathbf{j} + \dfrac{1}{t^2}\mathbf{k}$

19. $D_t\|\mathbf{R}(t)\| = \dfrac{9e^{2t}}{\sqrt{9e^{2t}+8}}$; $\|D_t\mathbf{R}(t)\| = 3e^t$ **21.** $[\ln(t+2) - \ln 2]\mathbf{i} + (\tan^{-1}t + 1)\mathbf{j}$

23. $(4e^{t/2} - 2e)\mathbf{i} + (4e^{-t/2} - 6e^{-1})\mathbf{j} + (4\sinh\frac{1}{2}t - 4\sinh 1 + 1)\mathbf{k}$ **25.** $\frac{1}{8}\pi\sqrt{8+\pi^2} + \sinh^{-1}\frac{1}{4}\sqrt{2}\pi$ **27.** 0.9950

29. $\mathbf{T}(t) = \dfrac{e^{2t}\mathbf{i} + \mathbf{j}}{\sqrt{e^{4t}+1}}$; $\mathbf{N}(t) = \dfrac{\mathbf{i} - e^{2t}\mathbf{j}}{\sqrt{e^{4t}+1}}$; $\mathbf{T}(\ln 2) = \dfrac{4\mathbf{i} + \mathbf{j}}{\sqrt{17}}$; $\mathbf{N}(\ln 2) = \dfrac{\mathbf{i} - 4\mathbf{j}}{\sqrt{17}}$

31 and 35. $\mathbf{T}(t) = \dfrac{t^2\mathbf{i} + 2t\mathbf{j} + 2\mathbf{k}}{t^2+2}$; $\mathbf{N}(t) = \dfrac{2t\mathbf{i} + (2-t^2)\mathbf{j} - 2t\mathbf{k}}{t^2+2}$; $\mathbf{B}(t) = \dfrac{-2\mathbf{i} + 2t\mathbf{j} - t^2\mathbf{k}}{t^2+2}$;
osculating: $-2(x - \frac{1}{3}) + 2(y-1) - (z-2) = 0$; rectifying: $2(x - \frac{1}{3}) + (y-1) - 2(z-2) = 0$;
normal: $(x - \frac{1}{3}) + 2(y-1) + 2(z-2) = 0$

33 and 37. $\mathbf{T}(t) = \dfrac{1}{\sqrt{13}}(3\cos 2t\mathbf{i} + 2\mathbf{j} - 3\sin 2t\mathbf{k})$; $\mathbf{N}(t) = -\sin 2t\mathbf{i} - \cos 2t\mathbf{k}$; $\mathbf{B}(t) = \dfrac{1}{\sqrt{13}}(-2\cos 2t\mathbf{i} + 3\mathbf{j} + 2\sin 2t\mathbf{k})$;
osculating: $-2x + 3y = 0$; rectifying: $z = 3$; normal: $3x + 2y = 0$ **39.** $\frac{1}{3}t^3 + 2t$
41. $\mathbf{R}(s) = [2(3s + 17^{3/2})^{2/3} - 34]\mathbf{i} + \frac{1}{3}[(3s + 17^{3/2})^{2/3} - 16]^{3/2}\mathbf{j}$ **43.** $\mathbf{R}(s) = 3\sin(s/\sqrt{13})\mathbf{i} + 2s/\sqrt{13}\mathbf{j} + 3\cos(s/\sqrt{13})\mathbf{k}$

45. $K = \dfrac{8}{17^{3/2}}$; $\rho = \dfrac{17^{3/2}}{8}$ **47.** $K = \dfrac{2}{(t^2+2)^2}$ **49.** $K = \frac{3}{13}$

53. $K = \frac{2}{75}$; $\rho = \frac{75}{2}$ **55.** $(-\frac{21}{2}, 32)$
57. (a) $\mathbf{V}(t) = 3\mathbf{i} + (4 - 2t)\mathbf{j}$; $\mathbf{A}(t) = -2\mathbf{j}$; $\|\mathbf{V}(t)\| = \sqrt{4t^2 - 16t + 25}$; $\|\mathbf{A}(t)\| = 2$; (b) $\mathbf{V}(1) = 3\mathbf{i} + 2\mathbf{j}$; $\mathbf{A}(1) = -2\mathbf{j}$
59. $\mathbf{V}(\frac{1}{2}\pi) = -\frac{1}{2}\pi\mathbf{i} + \mathbf{j} + \mathbf{k}$; $\mathbf{A}(\frac{1}{2}\pi) = -2\mathbf{i} - \frac{1}{2}\pi\mathbf{j}$; speed: $\sqrt{\frac{1}{4}\pi^2 + 2}$ **61.** $\mathbf{R}(t) = (\frac{1}{2}e^{2t} + \frac{3}{2})\mathbf{i} - e^{-t}\mathbf{j}$
63. $\mathbf{R}(t) = 2\cos t\mathbf{i} + (2\sin t + 2)\mathbf{j} + t\mathbf{k}$ **65.** $(t+1)\mathbf{i} + (\frac{3}{2}t^2 - 3t + \frac{11}{2})\mathbf{j} + (3t - t^2 - 2)\mathbf{k}$

67. $\mathbf{V}(t) = 3\mathbf{i} + (4 - 2t)\mathbf{j}$; $\mathbf{A}(t) = -2\mathbf{j}$; $\mathbf{T}(t) = \dfrac{3\mathbf{i} + (4 - 2t)\mathbf{j}}{\sqrt{4t^2 - 16t + 25}}$; $\mathbf{N}(t) = \dfrac{(4 - 2t)\mathbf{i} - 3\mathbf{j}}{\sqrt{4t^2 - 16t + 25}}$; $\|\mathbf{V}(t)\| = \sqrt{4t^2 - 16t + 25}$;

$A_T(t) = \dfrac{4t - 8}{\sqrt{4t^2 - 16t + 25}}$; $A_N(t) = \dfrac{6}{\sqrt{4t^2 - 16t + 25}}$; $K(t) = \dfrac{6}{(4t^2 - 16t + 25)^{3/2}}$; $\mathbf{V}(1) = 3\mathbf{i} + 2\mathbf{j}$; $\mathbf{A}(1) = -2\mathbf{j}$;

$\mathbf{T}(1) = \dfrac{1}{\sqrt{13}}(3\mathbf{i} + 2\mathbf{j})$; $\mathbf{N}(1) = \dfrac{1}{\sqrt{13}}(2\mathbf{i} - 3\mathbf{j})$; $\|\mathbf{V}(1)\| = \sqrt{13}$. $A_T(1) = \dfrac{-4}{\sqrt{13}}$; $A_N(1) = \dfrac{6}{\sqrt{13}}$. $K(1) = \dfrac{6}{13^{3/2}}$

69. $\mathbf{A}(t) = \dfrac{e^{2t} - e^{-2t}}{\sqrt{4 + e^{2t} + e^{-2t}}} \mathbf{T}(t) + \sqrt{\dfrac{4 + 4e^{2t} + 4e^{-2t}}{4 + e^{2t} + e^{-2t}}} \mathbf{N}(t)$

71. (a) $\mathbf{V}(t) = 2 \sinh 2t\mathbf{i} + 2 \cosh 2t\mathbf{j}$; $\mathbf{A}(t) = 4 \cosh 2t\mathbf{i} + 4 \sinh 2t\mathbf{j}$;

  (b) $\| \mathbf{V}(t) \| = 2\sqrt{\cosh 4t}$; **(c)** $A_T(t) = \dfrac{4 \sinh 4t}{\sqrt{\cosh 4t}}$; $A_N(t) = \dfrac{4}{\sqrt{\cosh 4t}}$

73. (a) $75\sqrt{3}t\mathbf{i} + (75t - 16t^2)\mathbf{j}$; **(b)** $\frac{5625}{16}\sqrt{3}$ ft; **(c)** $\frac{5625}{64}$ ft; **(d)** 150 ft/sec   **75.** 98.73 ft/sec
77. (a) 0.85 sec; **(b)** 18.38 ft

EXERCISES 12.1 (page 967)

1. (a) $-\frac{1}{7}$; **(b)** 5; **(c)** $\dfrac{x + y}{x - y + 2}$; **(d)** 0 **3. (a)** 1; **(b)** $\frac{1}{2}\sqrt{2}$; **(c)** $\frac{1}{2}\sqrt{16 - x^2 - y^2 - z^2}$; **(d)** $4x + 4y + 8$

5. $\{(x, y) \mid x^2 + y^2 \neq 1\}$ **7.** $\{(x, y) \mid x^2 + y^2 \leq 1\}$ **9.** $\{(x, y) \mid x^2 - y^2 \geq 1\}$ **11.** $\{(x, y) \mid x^2 + y^2 \geq 1\}$
13. $\{(x, y) \mid x^2 + y^2 < 1\}$ **15.** $\{(x, y) \mid y \neq \pm x\}$ **17.** $\{(x, y) \mid -1 \leq x - y \leq 1\}$ **19.** $\{(x, y) \mid xy > 1\}$
21. $\{(x, y, z) \mid x - y - z \neq 0\}$ **23.** $\{(x, y, z) \mid x^2 + 4y^2 + z^2 \leq 16\}$ **25.** $\{(x, y, z) \mid |x| \leq 1, |y| \leq 1, |z| \leq 1\}$
27. $\{(x, y, z) \mid x^2 + y^2 < 4\}$ **29.** $\{(x, y) \mid x^2 + y^2 \leq 16\}$ **31.** R^2 **33.** R^2 **35.** R^2

37. circles centered at origin of radius $\sqrt{16 - k^2}$, $k = 0, 1, 2, 3, 4$
39. circles centered at origin of radius $\sqrt{16 - k}$, $k = 16, 12, 7, 0, -9, -20$
41. hyperbolas $x^2 - y^2 = k$, $k = 16, 9, 4, 0^*, -4, -9, -16$ (* the lines $y = \pm x$)   **43.** circles of radius $\sqrt{2k}$, $k = 8, 6, 4, 2, 0$
45. hyperbolas $xy = k$, $k = 0^*$, ln 2, 1, ln 4, ln $\frac{1}{2}$, -1, ln $\frac{1}{4}$ (* the x and y axes)
47. (a) 2; **(b)** 6; **(c)** $\sqrt{x - y^2}$; **(d)** $|x - y|$; **(e)** $|x - y|$
49. $h(x, y) = \sin^{-1} \sqrt{1 - x^2 - y^2}$; domain: $\{(x, y) \mid x^2 + y^2 \leq 1\}$ **51. (b)** (iii)   **53. (a)** (iv)

55. (a) x ft is width, y ft is height, $C is cost. $C(x, y) = .32\left[xy + \dfrac{12}{x} + \dfrac{18}{y} \right]$, $x > 0, y > 0$; **(b)** \$5.92

57. (a) $V = \frac{1}{2}xy(6 - x - 3y)$, $x \geq 0, y \geq 0, x + 3y \leq 6$; **(b)** 0.78125 cubic units
59. circles centered at the origin of radius $\sqrt{9 - 16/V^2}$, $V = 16, 12, 8, 4$
61. branch in first quadrant of hyperbolas $xy = f, f = 5, 4, 3, 2, 1$
63. spheres centered at the origin of radius $\sqrt{\ln(4/P)}$, $P = 4, 2, 1, \frac{1}{2}$

EXERCISES 12.2 (page 984)

1. 0 **3.** -4 **5.** 0 **7.** $\delta = \frac{1}{7}\epsilon$
21. limit exists and is 0; take $\delta = \sqrt{\epsilon}$ **23.** limit does not exist **25.** $\frac{1}{4}\pi$ **27.** $\frac{1}{2}$
29. continuous at every point (x, y) in R^2 that is not on the line $y = 1$
31. continuous at every point (x, y) in R^2 that is not on the y axis
33. continuous at every point (x, y) in R^2 that is not on the line $y = 2x$
35. continuous at every point (x, y) in R^2 that is interior to the circle $x^2 + y^2 = 25$ **37.** continuous at every point in R^2
39. continuous at every point $(x, y) \neq (0, 0)$ in R^2 **41.** continuous at every point in R^2
43. all points (x, y) in R^2 that are interior to the circle $x^2 + y^2 = 16$
45. all points (x, y) in R^2 that are exterior to the ellipse $4x^2 + 9y^2 = 36$ **47.** all points (x, y) in R^2 for which $|xy| > 1$
49. all points (x, y) in R^2 in the first and third quadrants for which $|x + y| < 1$ **51.** all points in R^2
53. essential   **55.** removable; $f(0, 0) = 0$ **57.** essential   **59.** removable; $f(0, 0) = 0$
67. 0   **69.** continuous at every point (x, y, z) in R^3 that is exterior to the sphere $x^2 + y^2 + z^2 = 1$
71. continuous at all points in R^3

EXERCISES 12.3 (page 997)

1. 6   **3.** $3x - 2y$ **5.** $\dfrac{x}{\sqrt{x^2 + y^2}}$ **7.** $x^2 - 6xy + 2z$ **9.** $xy + yt + zt$ **11.** 4   **13.** $\dfrac{x}{x^2 + y^2}$

15. $-2 \sin 3\theta \sin 2\phi$ **17.** $\dfrac{e^{y/x}}{xy}\left(y \ln \dfrac{x^2}{y} - x \right)$ **19.** $\dfrac{-z}{(x^2 + y^2 + z^2)^{3/2}}$ **21.** $4xy + \dfrac{1}{z}$ **23.** $xze^{xyz} + \dfrac{exz^2}{z^4 + 9x^2y^2}$

25. (a) -1; **(b)** 12   **27.** $-\ln \sin x$; ln $\sin y$ **29. (a)** $\dfrac{2}{y} - \dfrac{6y}{x^4}$; **(b)** $\dfrac{2x^2}{y^3}$ **31. (a)** $4e^{2x} \sin y$; **(b)** $-e^{2x} \sin y$

33. (a) $2 \tan^{-1}\dfrac{y}{x} - \dfrac{2xy}{x^2 + y^2}$; **(b)** $2 \tan^{-1}\dfrac{y}{x} + \dfrac{2xy}{x^2 + y^2}$ **35. (a)** $3y \cosh x$; **(b)** $4x \sinh y$

37. (a) $e^x \cos y - \dfrac{2x \ln y}{(1 + x^2)^2}$; **(b)** $-e^x \cos y - \dfrac{\tan^{-1} x}{y^2}$ **39. (a)** $12x + 20y$; **(b)** $12x + 20y$ **41. (a)** 0; **(b)** e^y

43. (a) $-2e^z \sin e^z$;   **(b)** $-2we^z(\sin e^z + e^z \cos e^z)$ **45. (a)** $\dfrac{-320rst}{(r^2 + 4s^2 - 5t^2)^3}$;   **(b)** $\dfrac{16r(5t^2 + 12s^2 - r^2)}{(r^2 + 4s^2 - 5t^2)^3}$ **55.** 4

57. -4 deg/cm; -8 deg/cm   **59. (a)** $\dfrac{100}{i^2}\left[\dfrac{9i+1}{(1+i)^9} - 1\right]$;   **(b)** $\dfrac{1}{0.0036}\left[\dfrac{1.54}{(1.06)^9} - 1\right] \approx -24.4$;   **(c)** $\dfrac{5000 \ln 1.06}{3(1.06)^t}$;

(d) $-\dfrac{5000 \ln 1.06}{3(1.06)^8} \approx -61$ **61. (a)** 1;   **(b)** 1   **63. (a)** -2;   **(b)** 0   **65.** neither exists

67. $f_{12}(0, 0) = -1; f_{21}(0, 0) = 1$ **69.** 0.0943 m²/kg; 6.42 m²/m

EXERCISES 12.4 (page 1009)

1. (a) $3(\Delta x)^2 + 2(\Delta x)(\Delta y) - (\Delta y)^2 + 14\,\Delta x - 6\,\Delta y$;   **(b)** 0.5411;   **(c)** $14\,\Delta x - 6\,\Delta y$;   **(d)** 0.54
3. (a) $(2 + \Delta x)(-4 + \Delta y)e^{(2+\Delta x)(-4+\Delta y)} + 8e^{-8}$;   **(b)** -0.0026;   **(c)** $28e^{-8}\,\Delta x - 14e^{-8}\,\Delta y$;   **(d)** -0.0019
5. (a) $\Delta x + 4\,\Delta y + (\Delta x)(\Delta y) + \ln(5 + \Delta z) - \ln 5$;   **(b)** 0.2141;   **(c)** $\Delta x + 5\,\Delta y + \frac{1}{5}\,\Delta z$;   **(d)** 0.214
7. $(12x^2 - y^2)\,dx + (3 - 2xy)\,dy$ **9.** $(\cos y - y \cos x)\,dx + (-x \sin y - \sin x)\,dy$

11. $\dfrac{2x\,dx + 2y\,dy + 2z\,dz}{x^2 + y^2 + z^2}$ **13.** $\tan^{-1} z\,dx - \dfrac{2y}{z^2}\,dy + \left(\dfrac{x}{1+z^2} + \dfrac{y^2}{z^2}\right)dz$

15. (a) $2(x_0 y_0 - y_0)\,\Delta x + (x_0{}^2 - 2x_0)\,\Delta y + (y_0\,\Delta x + \Delta x\,\Delta y)\,\Delta x + 2(x_0\,\Delta x - \Delta x)\,\Delta y$;
    (b) $\epsilon_1 = y_0\,\Delta x + \Delta x\,\Delta y$; $\epsilon_2 = 2(x_0\,\Delta x - \Delta x)$

17. (a) $\dfrac{2x_0 y_0\,\Delta x + y_0(\Delta x)^2 - x_0{}^2\,\Delta y}{y_0{}^2 + y_0\,\Delta y}$;   **(b)** $\epsilon_1 = \dfrac{y_0{}^2\,\Delta x - 2x_0 y_0\,\Delta y}{y_0{}^3 + y_0{}^2\,\Delta y}$; $\epsilon_2 = \dfrac{x_0{}^3\,\Delta y}{y_0{}^3 + y_0{}^2\,\Delta y}$

31. (a) $(y_0 - z_0)\,\Delta x + x_0\,\Delta y + (2z_0 - x_0)\,\Delta z - (\Delta z)(\Delta x) + \Delta x\,\Delta y + (\Delta z)(\Delta z)$;   **(b)** $\epsilon_1 = -\Delta z$, $\epsilon_2 = \Delta x$, $\epsilon_3 = \Delta z$

35. 7.36 m³   **37.** 0.14 cm; 1.4 percent   **39.** $\dfrac{13}{1600}$; 0.325 percent   **41.** \$7200

43. $D_1 f(x, y) = \begin{cases} 2x \sin \dfrac{1}{\sqrt{x^2 + y^2}} - \dfrac{x}{\sqrt{x^2 + y^2}} \cos \dfrac{1}{\sqrt{x^2 + y^2}} & \text{if } (x, y) \ne (0, 0) \\ 0 & \text{if } (x, y) = (0, 0); \end{cases}$

$D_2 f(x, y) = \begin{cases} 2y \sin \dfrac{1}{\sqrt{x^2 + y^2}} - \dfrac{y}{\sqrt{x^2 + y^2}} \cos \dfrac{1}{\sqrt{x^2 + y^2}} & \text{if } (x, y) \ne (0, 0) \\ 0 & \text{if } (x, y) = (0, 0) \end{cases}$

EXERCISES 12.5 (page 1019)

1. $\dfrac{\partial u}{\partial r}$:   **(a)** $6x - 2y$;   **(b)** $16r - 10s$; $\dfrac{\partial u}{\partial s}$:   **(a)** $-2x - 4y$;   **(b)** $-10r - 6s$

3. $\dfrac{\partial u}{\partial r}$:   **(a)** $13x - 2y + 5$;   **(b)** $24r - 41s + 5$; $\dfrac{\partial u}{\partial s}$:   **(a)** $-17x - 7y - 10$;   **(b)** $-41r + 44s - 10$

5. $\dfrac{\partial u}{\partial r}$:   **(a)** $\dfrac{2e^{y/x}}{x^2}(2x \sin t - y \cos t)$;   **(b)** 0; $\dfrac{\partial u}{\partial t}$:   **(a)** $\dfrac{2re^{y/x}}{x^2}(y \sin t + 2x \cos t)$;   **(b)** $2e^{2\tan t}\sec^2 t$

7. $\dfrac{\partial u}{\partial r} = 2r(x + y) + 3x$; $\dfrac{\partial u}{\partial s} = 2s(x + y) - 2x$ **9.** $\dfrac{\partial u}{\partial r} = \dfrac{6re^s + s \cos rs}{\sqrt{1 - (3x + y)^2}}$; $\dfrac{\partial u}{\partial s} = \dfrac{3e^2 e^s + r \cos rs}{\sqrt{1 - (3x + y)^2}}$

11. $\dfrac{\partial u}{\partial r} = \dfrac{6s}{x^2} \sinh \dfrac{y}{x}(xe^r - ry)$; $\dfrac{\partial u}{\partial s} = \dfrac{3}{x^2} \sinh \dfrac{y}{x}(2xe^r - yr^2) = 0$

13. $\dfrac{\partial u}{\partial r} = 2x \sin \phi \cos \theta + 2y \sin \phi \sin \theta + 2z \cos \phi$; $\dfrac{\partial u}{\partial \phi} = 2xr \cos \phi \cos \theta + 2yr \cos \phi \sin \theta - 2zr \sin \phi$;

$\dfrac{\partial u}{\partial \theta} = -2xr \sin \phi \sin \theta + 2yr \sin \phi \cos \theta$

15. (a) $e^x(\cos t - y \sin t) + e^y(x \cos t - \sin t)$;   **(b)** $e^{\cos t}(\cos t - \sin^2 t) + e^{\sin t}(\cos^2 t - \sin t)$

17. (a) $\dfrac{x \sec^2 t - y \sin t + z \cos t}{\sqrt{x^2 + y^2 + z^2}}$;   **(b)** $\tan t \sec t$ **19.** $\dfrac{txe^t - y}{t(x^2 + y^2)}, t > 0$ **21.** $\dfrac{x + y + 2t + ty - tx}{t(y + t)^2}, t > 0$

23. $-\dfrac{3x^2 - 8y}{3y^2 - 8x}$ **25.** $-\dfrac{\sin y - y \cos x}{x \cos y + \cos x}$ **27.** $\dfrac{\partial z}{\partial x} = \dfrac{3y - 6x - 4z}{2z + 4x}$; $\dfrac{\partial z}{\partial y} = \dfrac{3x - 2y}{2z + 4x}$ **29.** $\dfrac{\partial z}{\partial x} = -\dfrac{z}{x}$; $\dfrac{\partial z}{\partial y} = \dfrac{xyz + 1}{3xy \tan 3xz - xy^2}$

35. $6se^{r-s}(2 + r) - 8e^{-2s}$ **37.** $10 \cos^2 \theta + 8$ **39.** $-10r \sin 2\theta$ **43.** decreasing at a rate of $\frac{8}{61}$ rad/min
45. increasing at a rate of 3840π cm³/min   **47.** increasing at a rate of 1.6 liters/min

EXERCISES 12.6 (page 1029)

1. $2\sqrt{2}x + 5\sqrt{2}y$ **3.** $3x + \sqrt{2}y + 4z$ **5.** $\dfrac{17}{13(x-y)^2}$ **7.** $(8x - 3y)\mathbf{i} + (2y - 3x)\mathbf{j}$ **9.** $\dfrac{x}{x^2 + y^2}\mathbf{i} + \dfrac{y}{x^2 + y^2}\mathbf{j}$

11. $\dfrac{y+z}{(x+z)^2}\mathbf{i} + \dfrac{1}{x+z}\mathbf{j} - \dfrac{x-y}{(x+z)^2}\mathbf{k}$ **13.** $e^{-2y}\sec z(\mathbf{i} - 2x\mathbf{j} + x\tan z\,\mathbf{k})$ **15.** 6   **17.** -42 **19.** -2

21. $-3e^{\pi/4}\cos\frac{1}{12}\pi$ **23. (a)** $\langle -4, -4\rangle$; **(b)** $-2 - 2\sqrt{3}$ **25. (a)** $\langle -12, 2, 14\rangle$; **(b)** $\frac{6}{7}$ **29.** $\frac{3}{20}\pi + \frac{2}{5}$; $\frac{1}{4}\sqrt{\pi^2 + 4}$

31. $-\frac{29}{11}$; $\sqrt{2}$ **33.** $\theta = \tan^{-1}\dfrac{3}{3\pi + 1}$ and $\theta = \tan^{-1}\dfrac{3}{3\pi + 1} - \pi$

35. (a) $6\sqrt{2}$ degrees per meter; **(b)** direction of the vector $\dfrac{1}{\sqrt{2}}\mathbf{i} + \dfrac{1}{\sqrt{2}}\mathbf{j}$

37. (a) -1 volts per foot; **(b)** direction of the vector $-\mathbf{j}$ and magnitude 2 volts per foot

EXERCISES 12.7 (page 1035)

1. $2x - 2y + 3z = 17$; $\dfrac{x-2}{2} = \dfrac{y+2}{-2} = \dfrac{z-3}{3}$ **3.** $4x + 8y + 3z + 22 = 0$; $\dfrac{x+2}{4} = \dfrac{y+4}{8} = \dfrac{z-6}{3}$

5. $ex - y = 0$; $\dfrac{x-1}{-e} = \dfrac{y-e}{1}$, $z = 0$ **7.** $x - y - 3 = 0$; $\dfrac{x-6}{1} = \dfrac{y-3}{-1}$, $z = 3$

9. $x + 2y + 2z - 8 = 0$; $\dfrac{x-4}{1} = \dfrac{y-1}{2} = \dfrac{z-1}{2}$ **11.** $3x - 2y - 6z - 84 = 0$; $\dfrac{x-8}{-3} = \dfrac{y-27}{2} = \dfrac{z-1}{6}$

13. $\dfrac{x-2}{4} = \dfrac{y+2}{-1} = \dfrac{z}{20}$ **15.** $x = 4$, $y = 16$ **17.** $\dfrac{x}{1 - 8\pi} = \dfrac{y-2}{-2\pi} = \dfrac{z-1}{-1}$ **19.** surfaces are tangent

21. $9x - 4y - 1 = 0$ **23.** $4x - 5y + 6 = 0$

EXERCISES 12.8 (page 1048)

1. $f(0, 0) = 4$, abs. max.   **3.** $f(2, 4) = -4$, abs. min.   **5.** $f(1, 0) = 9$, abs. max.
7. $f(4, -\frac{1}{2}) = -\frac{133}{4}$, rel. min.; $f(0, -\frac{1}{2}) = -\frac{5}{4}$, saddle point   **9.** $f(1, 2) = 0$, saddle point   **11.** $f(-\frac{1}{4}, 16) = -12$, rel. max.
13. $f(0, \pm\frac{1}{2}) = 0$, saddle points   **15.** $f(1, 1) = 5$, rel. min.; $f(-1, -3) = 31$, rel. max.; $f(1, -3) = 27$, $f(-1, 1) = -1$, saddle
points   **17.** $f(0, 0) = 1$, saddle point   **19.** $f(2, 4) = -4$, abs. min.; $f(0, 0) = f(2, 0) = 16$, abs. max.
21. $f(-\frac{2}{3}, 4) = -\frac{4}{3}$, abs. min.; $f(2, 4) = 20$, abs. max.   **23.** $f(0, 1) = -2$, abs. min.; $f(0, 2) = 2$, abs. max.   **25.** 8, 8, 8
27. $(\frac{41}{14}, -\frac{5}{7}, \frac{33}{14})$; $\frac{9}{14}\sqrt{14}$ **29.** $\left(0, \dfrac{1}{\sqrt{17}}, -\dfrac{4}{\sqrt{17}}\right)$ and $\left(0, \dfrac{1}{\sqrt{17}}, \dfrac{4}{\sqrt{17}}\right)$; 1   **31.** $\frac{1}{3}c$ mg of drug A and $\frac{1}{2}c$ mg of drug B
33. $\frac{16}{3}\sqrt{3}$ cu units   **35.** length of the base is $2\frac{2}{3}$ ft; width of the base is 2 ft; depth is 3 ft   **37.** 3 machine-hours and 9 person-hours
39. \$25,400   **41. (a)** 3120; **(b)** 9   **43. (a)** $y = 534.7 - 0.423x$ **(b)** 390.6 milliliters per minute per kilogram
45. (a) $y = 0.8329x - 25.13$; **(b)** \$62,320   **47.** 12 of type 1; 10 of type 2; total profit \$1064   **49.** l: w: h = 1: 1: $\frac{1}{2}$

EXERCISES 12.9 (page 1060)

1. $(0, 0)$ and $(0, 4)$ **3.** $(\frac{6}{7}, -\frac{4}{7}, \frac{2}{7})$ **5.** $f(\pm\frac{1}{2}\sqrt{35}, \frac{1}{2}) = \frac{37}{4}$, rel. max.; $f(0, 3) = 3$, rel. min.; $f(0, -3) = -3$, rel. min.
7. $f(-\frac{2}{3}\sqrt{3}, -\frac{1}{3}\sqrt{6}, -\frac{1}{3}\sqrt{3}) = f(-\frac{2}{3}\sqrt{3}, \frac{1}{3}\sqrt{6}, \frac{1}{3}\sqrt{3}) = f(\frac{2}{3}\sqrt{3}, -\frac{1}{3}\sqrt{6}, \frac{1}{3}\sqrt{3}) = f(\frac{2}{3}\sqrt{3}, \frac{1}{3}\sqrt{6}, -\frac{1}{3}\sqrt{3}) = -\frac{2}{9}\sqrt{6}$, rel. min.;
$f(\frac{2}{3}\sqrt{3}, \frac{1}{3}\sqrt{6}, \frac{1}{3}\sqrt{3}) = f(-\frac{2}{3}\sqrt{3}, -\frac{1}{3}\sqrt{6}, \frac{1}{3}\sqrt{3}) = f(-\frac{2}{3}\sqrt{3}, \frac{1}{3}\sqrt{6}, -\frac{1}{3}\sqrt{3}) = f(\frac{2}{3}\sqrt{3}, -\frac{1}{3}\sqrt{6}, -\frac{1}{3}\sqrt{3}) = \frac{2}{9}\sqrt{6}$, rel. max.
9. $f(\pm\frac{1}{2}\sqrt{35}, \frac{1}{2}) = \frac{37}{4}$, abs. max.; $f(0, -3) = -3$, abs. min.   **11.** extrema of Ex. 7 are all absolute
13. 3   **15.** $3\sqrt{3}$ **17. (a)** 12; **(b)** 4; **(c)** 1   **19.** $\frac{4}{3}\sqrt{26}$ **21.** 2, 6   **23.** $\frac{37}{13}$ **25.** $\frac{7}{32}$ **37.** 22.5, 7.5, 3.625
39. $T(\pm\frac{1}{2}\sqrt{3}, -\frac{1}{2}) = \frac{9}{4}$; $T(0, \frac{1}{2}) = -\frac{1}{4}$ **41.** 15, 10, 7.5, 30, 6

MISCELLANEOUS EXERCISES FOR CHAPTER 12 (page 1062)

1. $\{(x, y) \mid x^2 + 4y^2 \geq 16\}$ **3.** $\{(x, y) \mid y > x^2\}$
5. $\{(x, y, z) \mid y \neq \pm z\}$; the set of all points in R^3 except those on the planes $y = \pm z$
7. $\{(x, y) \mid 4x^2 + 9y^2 \leq 36\}$; the upper half of the ellipsoid $\dfrac{x^2}{9} + \dfrac{y^2}{4} + \dfrac{z^2}{36} = 1$ **9.** $y = \dfrac{k}{4x^{1/2}}$, $k = 16, 8, 4, 2$
11. (a) $4xy - 3y^2 + 4$; **(b)** $2x^2 - 6xy - 2$; **(c)** $4y$; **(d)** $-6x$; **(e)** $4x - 6y$; **(f)** $4x - 6y$

13. (a) $\dfrac{2x}{3y^2}$; (b) $\dfrac{y - 2x^2}{3y^3}$; (c) $-\dfrac{4x}{3y^3}$; (d) $-\dfrac{4x}{3y^3}$

15. (a) $t^2 \cos st^2 + te^s$; (b) $2st \cos st^2 + e^s$; (c) $2t(\cos st^2 - st^2 \sin st^2) + e^s$; (d) $2t(\cos st^2 - st^2 \sin st^2) + e^s$

17. (a) $\dfrac{1}{y}e^{x/y} + \dfrac{1}{x}$; (b) $-\dfrac{x}{y^2}e^{x/y} - \dfrac{1}{y}$; (c) $\dfrac{1}{y^2}e^{x/y} - \dfrac{1}{x^2}$; (d) $\dfrac{2x}{y^3}e^{x/y} + \dfrac{x^2}{y^4}e^{x/y} + \dfrac{1}{y^2}$

19. (a) $\dfrac{y^2 + z^2 - x^2}{(x^2 + y^2 + z^2)^2}$; (b) $\dfrac{-2xy}{(x^2 + y^2 + z^2)^2}$; (c) $\dfrac{-2xz}{(x^2 + y^2 + z^2)^2}$

21. (a) $\dfrac{-320uvw}{(u^2 + 4v^2 - 5w^2)^3}$; (b) $\dfrac{16u(12v^2 + 5w^2 - u^2)}{(u^2 + 4v^2 - 5w^2)^3}$ **23.** (a) $\dfrac{1}{rt^2}$; (b) $\dfrac{-2}{rt^3}$; (c) $\dfrac{2}{r^2t^3}$

27. (a) $\dfrac{\partial u}{\partial t} = \dfrac{6y(x + y)}{x^2 + y^2} + 3 \ln(x^2 + y^2)$; $\dfrac{\partial u}{\partial s} = \dfrac{4y(x - y)}{x^2 + y^2} - 2 \ln(x^2 + y^2)$;

  (b) $\dfrac{\partial u}{\partial t} = (3t - 2s)\dfrac{18t}{4s^2 + 9t^2} + 3 \ln(8s^2 + 18t^2)$; $\dfrac{\partial u}{\partial s} = (3t - 2s)\dfrac{8s}{4s^2 + 9t^2} - 2 \ln(8s^2 + 18t^2)$

29. (a) $18xyse^{3rs} + 6yse^{3rs} + 9x^2r^2s^2 + 6xr^2s^2 - 9zr^2s^2$; (b) $[9(1 + 2rs)e^{6rs} + 6(1 + rs)e^{3rs} - 9 \ln 4]r^2s^2$

31. (a) $3x \cos t - 4(y + 2x) \sin t$; (b) $12 \cos 2t - 16 \sin 2t$; $\left.\dfrac{du}{dt}\right|_{t=\pi/4} = -16$

33. (a) $3(-1 + \Delta x)(3 + \Delta y)^2 - 5(-1 + \Delta x)(2 + \Delta z)^2 - 2(-1 + \Delta x)(3 + \Delta y)(2 + \Delta z) - 5$; (b) -0.48;
  (c) $-5\Delta x - 14\Delta y + 26\Delta z$; (d) -0.48 **35.** 2   **37.** $\frac{1}{6}\pi$ **39.** $\delta = \min(1, \frac{1}{35}\epsilon)$

41. limit exists and is 0; take $\delta = \sqrt[4]{\epsilon}$ **43.** limit does not exist
45. continuous at all points (x, y) in R^2 not on the lines $x = \pm 2y$ **47.** continuous at all points in R^2
49. 14   **51.** $-\frac{5}{2}\sqrt{2}$ **53.** $-\frac{3}{8}$ **55.** (a) $\frac{1}{2}\mathbf{i} + \frac{1}{2}\mathbf{j}$; (b) $\frac{1}{4}(1 + \sqrt{3})$ **59.** $f(-1, 1) = 1$, rel. max.
63. 39¢   **65.** -3200π cm³/min   **67.** decreasing at the rate of 0.44 atm/min
69. $4x + 2y + z - 12 = 0$; $\dfrac{x - 2}{4} = \dfrac{y - 1}{2} = \dfrac{z - 2}{1}$ **71.** $\dfrac{x - 1}{17} = \dfrac{y + 2}{20} = \dfrac{z - 11}{-4}$
73. (a) the direction of the vector $-12\mathbf{i} - 150\mathbf{j}$; (b) ascending;
  (c) the direction of either of the vectors: $\dfrac{25}{\sqrt{629}}\mathbf{i} - \dfrac{2}{\sqrt{629}}\mathbf{j}$ or $-\dfrac{25}{\sqrt{629}}\mathbf{i} + \dfrac{2}{\sqrt{629}}\mathbf{j}$
75. $f(\pm\sqrt{5}, 0) = 10$, rel. min.   **77.** $f(9, 11, 15) = -362$, rel. max.   **79.** $\frac{7}{6}\sqrt{6}$
81. $\frac{100}{3}, \frac{100}{3}, \frac{100}{3}$ **83.** $2\sqrt{3}$ by $\frac{2}{3}\sqrt{3}$ by $2\sqrt{3}$
85. (a) $-\dfrac{3\sqrt{3} + 2}{11}$ degrees per cm; (b) $\frac{2}{11}\sqrt{13}$ degrees per cm in the direction of the vector $-\dfrac{3}{\sqrt{13}}\mathbf{i} - \dfrac{2}{\sqrt{13}}\mathbf{j}$
87. 18 ft by 18 ft by 18 ft   **89.** square base and a depth that is one-half the length of a side of the base
91. (a) $y = 0.285x - 0.951$; (b) 11 days   **93.** (a) $y = 9.628x - 1488.2$; (b) 2740 kilograms per hectare
95. (a) 12; (b) -3

EXERCISES 13.1 (page 1073)

1. (a) $(0, 3, 5)$; (b) $(-\frac{7}{2}, \frac{7}{2}\sqrt{3}, -4)$; (c) $(\cos 1, \sin 1, 1)$ **3.** (a) $(\sqrt{6}, \sqrt{2}, 2\sqrt{2})$; (b) $(0, 2\sqrt{3}, 2)$; (c) $(\frac{1}{2}\sqrt{3}, \frac{3}{2}, -\sqrt{3})$
5. (a) $(2, \frac{2}{3}\pi, -2\sqrt{3})$; (b) $(0, \frac{3}{4}\pi, -\sqrt{2})$; (c) $(\sqrt{6}, \frac{1}{3}\pi, \sqrt{6})$ **7.** ellipsoid; $r^2 + 4z^2 = 16$ **9.** elliptic paraboloid; $r^2 = 3z$
11. elliptic cone; $r^2 \cos 2\theta = 3z^2$ **13.** sphere; $\rho = 9 \cos \phi$ **15.** right circular cylinder; $\rho \sin \phi = 3$
17. sphere; $\rho = 8 \sin \phi \cos \theta$ **19.** (a) right circular cylinder; $x^2 + y^2 = 16$; (b) plane through z axis; $y = x$
21. $x^2 - y^2 = z^3$ **23.** (a) sphere; $x^2 + y^2 + z^2 = 81$; (b) half-plane through z axis; $x = y$ where x and y are non-negative;
  (c) half of a cone with vertex at origin; $z = \sqrt{x^2 + y^2}$ **25.** right circular cylinder; $x^2 + y^2 = 36$
27. $x\sqrt{x^2 + y^2 + z^2} = 2y$ **29.** (a) (iii); (b) (vi); (c) (viii)   **31.** (a) (ix); (b) (v)   **35.** (b) $2\pi\sqrt{a^2 + 1}$

EXERCISES 13.2 (page 1087)

1. 45   **3.** 50   **5.** 1368   **7.** 704   **9.** 50.75   **11.** 1376   **13.** 68.6   **15.** 38.2   **17.** $[0, 24]$ **19.** $[1, e]$
21. 42   **23.** $\frac{98}{3}$ **25.** $-\frac{49}{5}$ **27.** $\frac{1}{3}$ **29.** $\frac{1}{3}$ **31.** 45   **33.** $\frac{152}{3}$ **35.** $\frac{3}{2}\pi$ **37.** $\frac{864}{5}$ **39.** $\frac{512}{3}$ cu units
41. $\frac{16}{3}$ cu units   **43.** $\dfrac{15\pi - 32}{120}$ cu units   **45.** $\frac{1}{12}$ sq units   **47.** 72 sq units

49. $2c \displaystyle\int_{-a}^{a}\int_{-b\sqrt{1-(x/a)^2}}^{b\sqrt{1-(x/a)^2}} \sqrt{1 - \dfrac{x^2}{a^2} - \dfrac{y^2}{b^2}}\, dy\, dx$ **51.** $\frac{337}{30}$ cu units   **53.** (a) $\frac{2}{3}\displaystyle\int_{0}^{a}\int_{0}^{\sqrt{a^2-y^2}} (2x + y)\, dx\, dy$ **55.** 0

EXERCISES 13.3   (page 1100)

1. 12 kg; $(2, \frac{3}{2})$ **3.** $\frac{27}{2}$ kg; $(\frac{6}{5}, \frac{9}{5})$ **5.** $\frac{176}{5} k$ kg; $(\frac{35}{22}, \frac{102}{77})$ **7.** $\frac{2}{3} ka^3$ kg; $(\frac{3}{32}a(2 + \pi), \frac{3}{32}a(2 + \pi))$ **9.** $\frac{1}{4} k\pi$ kg; $\left(\dfrac{\pi}{2}, \dfrac{16}{9\pi}\right)$

11. $\frac{4}{3}$ kg; $(\frac{6}{5}, \frac{6}{5})$ **13.** $9k$ kg-m^2 **15.** $\frac{1}{2}\pi ka^4$ kg-m^2 **17.** $\frac{96}{35}k$ kg-m^2 **19.** (a) $\frac{144}{5}$ kg-m^2;   (b) 54 kg-m^2;   (c) $\frac{2}{5}\sqrt{15}$ m;

   (d) $\frac{414}{5}$ kg-m^2 **21.** (a) $\frac{3}{32}\pi k$ kg-m^2;   (b) $\frac{1}{24}\pi(2\pi^2 - 3)k$ kg-m^2;   (c) $\frac{1}{4}\sqrt{6}$ m;   (d) $(\frac{1}{12}\pi^3 - \frac{1}{32}\pi)k$ kg-m^2

23. $\dfrac{19{,}904}{315}k$ kg-m^2 **25.** $\sqrt{6}$ sq units   **27.** $2\sqrt{1633}$ sq units   **29.** 9 sq units   **31.** $\frac{1}{12}(135\sqrt{10} - 13\sqrt{26})$ sq units

33. 32 sq units   **35.** $9\sqrt{2}$ sq units   **37.** $\pi b\sqrt{a^2 + b^2}$ sq units   **39.** $2\pi a^2(1 - e^{-1})$ sq units   **41.** 12π sq units
43. $\frac{1}{12}b\sqrt{6}$ ft

EXERCISES 13.4   (page 1109)

1. 6π sq units   **3.** $\frac{1}{4}a^2(8 + \pi)$ sq units   **5.** $(4\pi + 12\sqrt{3})$ sq units   **7.** 4π cu units   **9.** $\frac{128}{9}(3\pi - 4)$ cu units

11. $\frac{7}{3}\pi$ cu units   **13.** $\frac{40}{3}\pi k$ kg; $(0, \frac{21}{10})$ **15.** $\frac{22}{3}k\pi$ kg; $(-\frac{57}{44}, 0)$ **17.** $\frac{20}{3}k$ kg; $(\frac{23}{25}, \frac{531}{1280}\pi)$

19. $\frac{8}{9}(27\sqrt{3} - 14\pi)k$ kg; $\left(0, \dfrac{3}{10}\cdot\dfrac{297\sqrt{3} - 160\pi}{27\sqrt{3} - 14\pi}\right)$ **21.** $\frac{5}{64}k\pi$ kg-m^2 **23.** $\frac{11}{16}k\pi a^4$ kg-m^2 **25.** $\frac{1}{4}\sqrt{2\pi}$ m

27. $\pi e(e^8 - 1)$ **29.** 8π sq units   **31.** 12π sq units   **33.** $\frac{1}{6}\pi(2\sqrt{2} - 1)a^2$

EXERCISES 13.5   (page 1115)

1. $\frac{1}{10}$ **3.** $\frac{7}{8}$ **5.** $-e(\ln 2)^2$ **7.** $\frac{1}{2}\pi - 1$ **9.** $\frac{15}{2}$ **11.** $\frac{1}{24}$ **13.** 36   **15.** $\frac{243}{2}\pi$ **17.** $\frac{648}{5}$ **19.** $\frac{1}{4}$ cu units
21. $\frac{3}{2}\pi$ cu units   **23.** 4π cu units   **25.** $\frac{4}{3}\pi abc$ cu units   **27.** $\frac{80}{3}k$ kg   **29.** $\frac{1}{28}k$ kg   **31.** $\frac{2}{5}(2\sqrt{2} - 1)$ kg

EXERCISES 13.6   (page 1123)

1. $\frac{1}{3}a^3$ **3.** $6\pi(e - 1)$ **5.** πa^3 **7.** $\frac{4}{3}a^3$ **9.** $\frac{1}{3}$ **11.** 8π **13.** $\frac{4}{5}a^5\pi k$ kg   **15.** $1250\pi k$ slug-ft^2 **17.** $\frac{4}{3}a^5\pi k$ kg
19. 8π **21.** $\frac{512}{75}k$ kg-m^2 **23.** $8k\pi$ kg   **25.** $\frac{56}{9}\pi a^3 k$ slug-ft^2 **27.** $(0, 0, \frac{1}{2})$ **29.** 18π **31.** $\frac{1}{15}\pi(2\sqrt{2} - 1)$

MISCELLANEOUS EXERCISES FOR CHAPTER 13   (page 1125)

1. $(\frac{3}{2}\sqrt{3}, \pi, \frac{3}{2})$ **3.** (a) $z = r^2(1 + \sin 2\theta) + 1$;   (b) $r^2(25\cos^2\theta + 4\sin^2\theta) = 100$ **5.** $\frac{1}{40}$ **7.** $\frac{1}{8}\pi$
9. $\frac{1}{8}e^4 - \frac{3}{4}e^2 + e - \frac{3}{8}$ **11.** $\frac{3}{4}\pi$ **13.** $\frac{1}{8}$ **15.** $\frac{1}{3}$ **17.** $\frac{1}{2}\pi\ln 2$ **19.** $\frac{1}{2}(1 - \cos 1)$ **21.** $\frac{4}{15}$ sq units   **23.** 9π
25. $\frac{8}{3}$ sq units   **27.** $\frac{8}{3}$ sq units   **29.** $\frac{1}{2}$ cu units   **31.** $\frac{1}{2}$ cu units   **33.** $\frac{1104}{35}$ cu units   **35.** 18 sq units   **37.** $(\frac{1}{2}\pi - \frac{2}{3})$ sq units
39. $(2, \frac{3}{2})$ **41.** $\frac{1}{108}(3\pi - 7)$ kg   **43.** $6\pi a^4$ cu units   **45.** $\frac{5}{3}\pi$ cu units   **47.** $\frac{1}{64}(7e^8 + 1)$ kg-m^2 **49.** $k(\pi + \frac{8}{3})$ kg-m^2
51. $2k\pi$ kg-m^2; $\frac{1}{2}\sqrt{2\pi}$ m   **53.** $65k\pi$ kg   **55.** $\frac{32}{5}k\pi$ kg-m^2

EXERCISES 14.1   (page 1140)

7. $6x\mathbf{i} + 6y^2\mathbf{j}$ **9.** $\dfrac{2xy}{1 + x^4y^2}\mathbf{i} + \dfrac{x^2}{1 + x^4y^2}\mathbf{j}$ **11.** $(6x^2 - 6xy + y^2)\mathbf{i} + (-3x^2 + 2xy - 12y^2)\mathbf{j}$

13. $2xye^{-4z}\mathbf{i} + e^{-4z}\mathbf{j} - 4x^2ye^{-4z}\mathbf{k}$ **15.** conservative   **17.** not conservative   **19.** conservative

21. $\phi(x, y) = xy + C$ **23.** $\phi(x, y) = e^x \sin y + C$ **25.** $\phi(x, y) = x^2 y^2 - xy^3 + 2y + C$
27. $\phi(x, y, z) = \frac{1}{3}x^3 + \frac{1}{2}z^2 - xy + C$ **29.** $\phi(x, y, z) = ze^x + xe^y - ye^z + C$
31. $\phi(x, y, z) = x^2 \cos y - yz^2 - 3x + 2z + C$ **33.** $0; 5$ **35.** $2e^x \sin y \mathbf{k}; 2e^x \cos y$ **37.** $0; 2x + 2y + 2z$

39. $\sin z \mathbf{i} + \sin x \mathbf{j} + \sin y \mathbf{k}; 0$ **41.** $\dfrac{x - y}{\sqrt{x^2 + y^2 + 1}} \mathbf{k}; \dfrac{x + y}{\sqrt{x^2 + y^2 + 1}} + 2z$

EXERCISES 14.2 (page 1149)

1. 1 **3.** $\pi - \frac{8}{3}$ **5.** 8π **7.** 1 **9.** $\frac{16}{3}$ **11.** $\frac{4}{3}$ **13.** $-\frac{5}{12}$ **15.** $\frac{1477}{2}$ **17.** $\frac{35}{2}$ **19.** $\pi(a^2 + 2a)$ **21.** 8
23. $\frac{4}{3}$ joules   **25.** $20\frac{3}{4}$ joules   **27.** $27\frac{3}{4}$ joules   **29.** $(\frac{1}{16}\pi a^4 + a^2)$ joules   **31.** 3 joules   **33.** $(e^2 + e^4 + e^8 - 3)$ joules
35. $2\frac{1}{2}$ joules

EXERCISES 14.3 (page 1160)

1. 2 **3.** e^2 **5.** -4 **7.** 15 **9.** $-4e$ **11.** -14 **13.** 18 **15.** $2e^2 - 3e^3 + e^4$ **17.** $\frac{3}{4}$ **19.** 11 **21.** $\frac{13}{2}$
23. 4 **25.** 0 **27.** 3 **29.** 4 **31.** -13 **33.** 216 joules   **35.** $32,766$ joules   **37.** $\frac{2}{15}k$ joules

EXERCISES 14.4 (page 1173)

1. -1 **3.** $-\frac{5}{12}$ **5.** $-\frac{1}{2}\pi$ **7.** $-\frac{32}{15}$ **9.** $-\frac{3}{7}$ **11.** $\frac{1}{5}$ **13.** $\frac{1}{24}(5 - 4\sqrt{2})\pi$ **15.** 0 **17.** -10π **19.** $\frac{41}{70}$
21. $\frac{9}{2}$ sq units   **23.** $\frac{1}{3}$ sq units   **25.** $\frac{3}{8}\pi a^2$ sq units   **31.** 24π joules   **33.** 0 **35.** 8π cm²/sec   **37.** $\frac{3}{2}\pi$ cm²/sec
39. 15; (i)   **41.** 0; (iii)

EXERCISES 14.5 (page 1181)

1. 8π **3.** $\frac{8}{3}\sqrt{3}$ **5.** $\frac{9}{5}\sqrt{14}$ **7.** $\frac{1}{6}(5\sqrt{5} - 1)$ **9.** $\frac{15}{2}\sqrt{2}\pi$ **11.** $\frac{7}{3}\sqrt{61}$ **13.** 0 **15.** $8k\pi$ kg   **17.** 9π kg
19. $\frac{665}{6}\sqrt{2}\pi$ kg   **21.** 18 **23.** 45π **25.** $\frac{7}{2}$

EXERCISES 14.6 (page 1188)

1. $\frac{8}{3}\pi$ **3.** 1 **5.** 18 **7.** $\frac{7}{2}$ **9.** 27 **11.** 32π **13.** 144π **15.** $\frac{11}{12}$ **17.** 0 **19.** π **21.** 54π **23.** -1
25. 8π **27.** -2

MISCELLANEOUS EXERCISES FOR CHAPTER 14 (page 1190)

1. $f(x, y) = e^{x^2} \ln y + C$ **3.** $f(x, y, z) = \dfrac{y}{x + z} - \dfrac{1}{x} - \dfrac{2}{z} + C$

5. (a) $(4xy + 3y^3)\mathbf{i} + (2x^2 + 9xy^2)\mathbf{j}$; (b) $e^y\mathbf{i} + (xe^y - yze^y - ze^y)\mathbf{j} - ye^y\mathbf{k}$ **7.** $\phi(x, y) = \tan^{-1} 2xy^2 + C$

9. $\phi(x, y, z) = z^2 \tan x + y^2 e^{3z} + C$ **11.** $x(e^{xy} - e^{xz})\mathbf{i} + y(e^{xz} - e^{yz})\mathbf{k}; 0$ **13.** $\dfrac{1 - 2y}{y^2}\mathbf{k}; \dfrac{2x}{y^2}$

15. $-\frac{4}{3}$ **17.** $\frac{44}{3} - 3\pi$ **19.** $\frac{27}{10}$ **21.** $\frac{19}{4}$ **23.** $9e^2 - 1$ **25.** π **27.** 13 **29.** 4
31. 12π **33.** 0 **35.** $\frac{9}{2}$ sq units   **37.** $\frac{1568}{15}$ joules   **39.** $\frac{23}{6}$ joules   **43.** 0 **45.** 54 cm²/sec   **47.** $\frac{1}{2}\pi$
49. $\frac{3}{2}\sqrt{14}$ **51.** $\frac{1}{6}(37\sqrt{37} - 1)$ **53.** $\frac{8}{3}k\pi$ kg   **55.** $108\sqrt{2}\pi$ kg   **57.** 56π **59.** 160π **63.** 0

EXERCISES A.1 (page A-12)

1. $\{-10, -7, -\sqrt{5}, -2, -\frac{7}{4}, -\frac{5}{3}, -1, 0, \frac{2}{3}, \frac{3}{4}, \sqrt{2}, 3, 5, 21\}$ **3.** (a) $\{x \mid -9 < x < 8\}$; (b) $\{y \mid -12 < y < -3\}$;
  (c) $\{z \mid 4z - 5 < 0\}$ **5.** (a) $\{x \mid 2x + 4 \geq 0\}$; (b) $\{r \mid 2 \leq r < 8\}$; (c) $\{a \mid -5 < a - 2 \leq 7\}$
7. (a) $(2, +\infty)$; (b) $(-4, 4]$ **9.** (a) $(2, 12)$; (b) $(-\infty, -4] \cup (4, +\infty)$ **11.** (a) $(2, 12)$; (b) $(-\infty, -4] \cup (4, +\infty)$
13. (a) $(-4, 0]$; (b) $(-\infty, 7]$ **15.** (a) $\{x \mid 2 < x < 7\}$; (b) $\{x \mid -3 \leq x \leq 6\}$; (c) $\{x \mid -5 < x \leq 4\}$;
  (d) $\{x \mid -10 \leq x < -2\}$ **17.** (a) $\{x \mid x \geq 3\}$; (b) $\{x \mid x < 0\}$; (c) $\{x \mid x > -4\}$; (d) the set R of real numbers
19. (a) 7; (b) $\frac{3}{4}$; (c) $3 - \sqrt{3}$; (d) $3 - \sqrt{3}$ **21.** (a) 6; (b) 10; (c) 10; (d) 6 **23.** (a) t; (b) $-t$

EXERCISES A.2   (page A-21)

1. (a) first quadrant;   **(b)** third quadrant;   **(c)** fourth quadrant;   **(d)** second quadrant   **3. (a)** $(1, 2)$;   **(b)** $(-1, -2)$;
(c) $(-1, 2)$;   **(d)** $(-2, 1)$ **5. (a)** $(2, -2)$;   **(b)** $(-2, 2)$;   **(c)** $(-2, -2)$;   **(d)** does not apply
7. (a) $(-1, 3)$;   **(b)** $(1, -3)$;   **(c)** $(1, 3)$;   **(d)** $(-3, -1)$ **9. (a)** $(-\frac{3}{2}, 2)$ **11.** $|\overline{AB}| = 10$; $|\overline{BC}| = \sqrt{17}$; $|\overline{CA}| = 13$
13. $\sqrt{26}; \frac{1}{2}\sqrt{89}; \frac{1}{2}\sqrt{53}$ **15.** $|\overline{AB}| = \sqrt{41}$, $|\overline{AC}| = \sqrt{41}$, $|\overline{BC}| = \sqrt{82}$, and $|\overline{AB}|^2 + |\overline{AC}|^2 = |\overline{BC}|^2$ **21.** $17\sqrt{2}$
23. -2 or 8
In Exercises 25–31, the graph of (i) is shown. The solid part is the graph of (ii); the dashed part is that of (iii).
25. symmetric with respect to x axis   **27.** symmetric with respect to x axis

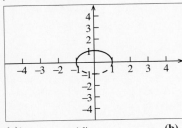   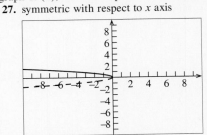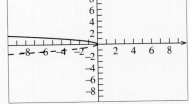

29. symmetric with respect to x axis,   **31.** symmetric with respect to x axis,
  y axis, and origin y axis, and origin

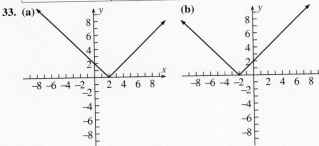   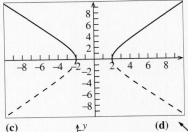

33. (a) **(b)** **(c)** **(d)**

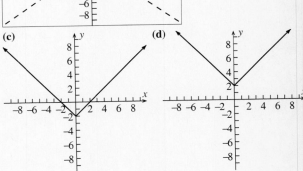

35. All are symmetric with respect to the origin   **37.** All are symmetric with respect to the y axis

EXERCISES A.3   (page A-30)

1. (a) slope is $\frac{1}{5}$ **(b)** slope is -1

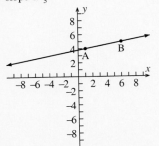   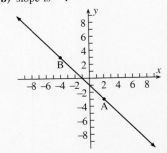

3. (a) slope is $-\frac{3}{4}$

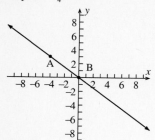

5. (a) slope is 0

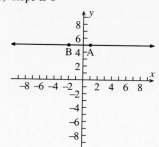

7. (a)

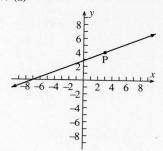

(b) slope is $-\frac{1}{7}$

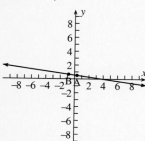

(b) slope is $\frac{1}{4}$

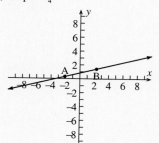

(b)

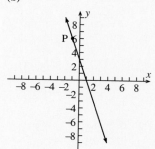

9. (a) $4x - y - 11 = 0$; **(b)** $11x - 4y - 9 = 0$ **11. (a)** $2x + 3y - 3 = 0$; **(b)** $6x - 3y + 8 = 0$ **13. (a)** $y = -7$;
(b) $x = 2$ **15. (a)** $4x - 3y + 12 = 0$; **(b)** $x - y = 0$ **17.** $2x - y + 7 = 0$ **19.** $5x + y - 14 = 0$
21. (a) slope is $-\frac{1}{3}$, y intercept is 2

(b) slope is 0, y intercept is $\frac{9}{4}$

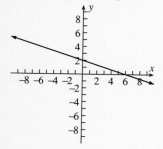

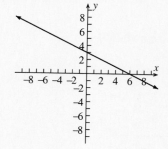

23. (a) slope is $\frac{7}{8}$, y intercept is 0

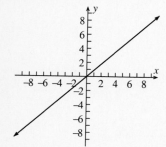

(b) slope is $-\frac{1}{2}$, y intercept is

25. $y = -5x + 8$

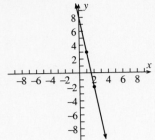

27. slope of each line is $-\frac{3}{5}$

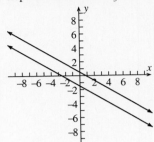

29. slopes of lines are $\frac{2}{3}$ and $-\frac{3}{2}$

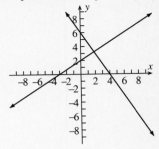

31. $\pm\frac{2}{3}$ **33. (a)** collinear; **(b)** not collinear   **35. (a)** not collinear; **(b)** collinear
37. slopes of two sides are $-\frac{1}{2}$; slopes of other two sides are $\frac{3}{5}$ **39.** area is 5 square units
41. (a) $y = 25x + 3000$ **43. (a)** \$600; **(b)** $y = 30x + 600$ **45.** 8
49. from $(3, -2)$: $y = -\frac{9}{5}(x - 3) - 2$; from $(2, 4)$: $y = \frac{9}{2}(x - 2) + 4$; from $(-1, 1)$: $y = 1$

EXERCISES A.4 (page A-36)

1. (a) $(0, 0)$; **(b)** $x = 0$;
  (c) $(0, 1)$; **(d)** $y = -1$;
  (e) $(-2, 1), (2, 1)$

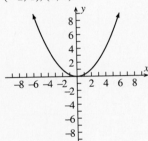

3. (a) $(0, 0)$; **(b)** $x = 0$;
  (c) $(0, -4)$; **(d)** $y = 4$;
  (e) $(-8, -4), (8, -4)$

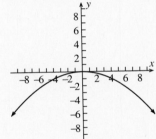

5. (a) $(0, 0)$; **(b)** $x = 0$;
  (c) $(0, \frac{1}{4})$; **(d)** $y = -\frac{1}{4}$;
  (e) $(-\frac{1}{2}, \frac{1}{4}), (\frac{1}{2}, \frac{1}{4})$

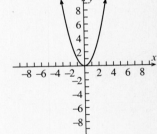

7. (a) $(0, 0)$; **(b)** $y = 0$;
  (c) $(3, 0)$; **(d)** $x = -3$;
  (e) $(3, -6), (3, 6)$

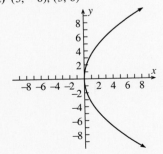

9. (a) $(0, 0)$; **(b)** $y = 0$;
  (c) $(-2, 0)$; **(d)** $x = 2$;
  (e) $(-2, -4), (-2, 4)$

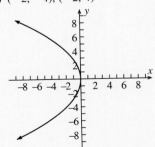

11. (a) $(0, 0)$; **(b)** $y = 0$;
  (c) $(\frac{5}{4}, 0)$; **(d)** $x = -\frac{5}{4}$;
  (e) $(\frac{5}{4}, -\frac{5}{2}), (\frac{5}{4}, \frac{5}{2})$

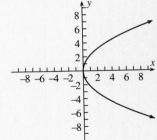

13. (a) $(0, 0)$;   **(b)** $x = 0$;
   (c) $(0, -\frac{2}{3})$;   **(d)** $y = \frac{2}{3}$;
   (e) $(-\frac{4}{3}, -\frac{2}{3}), (\frac{4}{3}, -\frac{2}{3})$

15. (a) $(0, 0)$;   **(b)** $y = 0$;
   (c) $(\frac{9}{8}, 0)$;   **(d)** $x = -\frac{9}{8}$;
   (e) $(\frac{9}{8}, -\frac{9}{4}), (\frac{9}{8}, \frac{9}{4})$

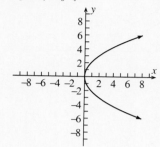

23. $x^2 = 16y$

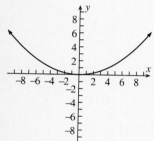

25. $x^2 = -20y$

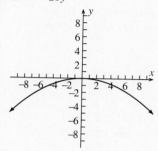

27. $y^2 = 8x$

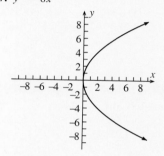

29. $3y^2 = -20x$

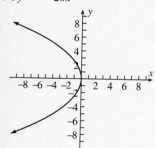

31. $x^2 = 12y$

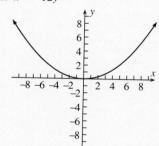

33. $3y^2 = -8x$

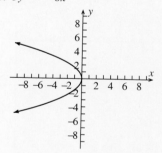

35. $x^2 = y$

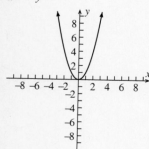

37. $\frac{32}{45}$ in.
39. 16.6 m
43. (a) $-\frac{5}{2}$;   **(b)** $x^2 = -10y$

EXERCISES A.5 (page A-41)

1. The graph of (c) is shown. The solid part is the graph of (a); the dashed part is that of (b).

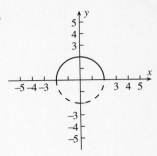

3. 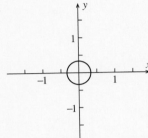   **5.** 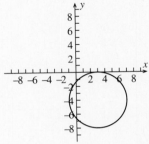   **7.**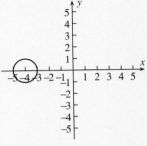

15. $(x - 4)^2 + (y + 3)^2 = 25$; $x^2 + y^2 - 8x + 6y = 0$ **17.** $(x + 5)^2 + (y + 12)^2 = 9$; $x^2 + y^2 + 10x + 24y + 160 = 0$
19. $x^2 + (y - 7)^2 = 1$; $x^2 + y^2 - 14y + 48 = 0$ **21.** $(x - 1)^2 + (y - 2)^2 = 13$ **23.** $(x - 5)^2 + (y + 1)^2 = 13$
25. $(3, 4)$; 4   **27.** $(-1, -5)$; $2\sqrt{2}$ **29.** $(0, -\frac{2}{3})$; $\frac{5}{3}$ **33.** circle   **35.** the empty set   **37.** point $(\frac{1}{2}, -\frac{3}{2})$
39. $y = \frac{4}{3}(x + 4) + 3$ **41.** $y = -\frac{3}{4}(x - 5) + 1$ **45.** $D^2 + E^2 > 4F$
49. If O is the unit circle centered at the origin and P is the circle of radius 2 centered at the origin, then the set consists of the points
which are: **(a)** inside or on circle O; **(b)** outside circle O and inside or on circle P; **(c)** outside circle P.

EXERCISES A.6 (page A-47)

1. $x'^2 + y'^2 = 13$; $x' = x + 3, y' = y + 2$

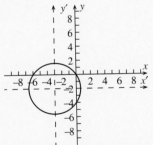

3. $x'^2 + y'^2 = \frac{1}{4}$; $x' = x + \frac{1}{2}, y' = y - 1$

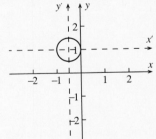

5. $x'^2 = 8y'$; $x' = x - 2, y' = y + 4$

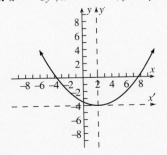

7. $y'^2 = -6x'$; $x' = x + 5, y' = y + 3$

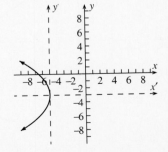

9. (a) $(0, -4)$; **(b)** $x = 0$;
(c) $(0, -\frac{15}{4})$; **(d)** $y = -\frac{17}{4}$;
(e) $(\frac{1}{2}, -\frac{15}{4})$, $(-\frac{1}{2}, -\frac{15}{4})$;
(f)

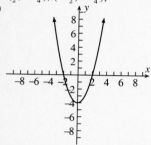

11. (a) $(2, -1)$; **(b)** $x = 2$;
(c) $(2, -\frac{5}{4})$; **(d)** $y = -\frac{3}{4}$;
(e) $(\frac{5}{2}, -\frac{5}{4})$, $(-\frac{3}{2}, -\frac{5}{4})$;
(f)

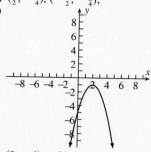

13. (a) $(-9, 3)$; **(b)** $y = 3$;
(c) $(-\frac{35}{4}, 3)$; **(d)** $x = -\frac{37}{4}$;
(e) $(-\frac{35}{4}, \frac{7}{2})$, $(-\frac{35}{4}, \frac{5}{2})$;
(f)

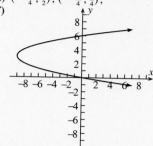

15. (a) $(3, 1)$; **(b)** $x = 3$;
(c) $(3, 2)$; **(d)** $y = 0$;
(e) $(5, 2)$, $(1, 2)$;
(f)

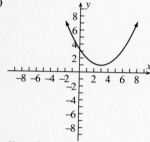

17. (a) $(9, -6)$; **(b)** $y = -6$;
(c) $(8, -6)$; **(d)** $x = 10$;
(e) $(8, -4)$, $(8, -8)$;
(f)

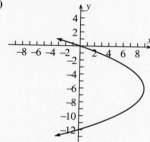

19. (a) $(4, 3)$; **(b)** $x = 4$;
(c) $(4, \frac{5}{2})$; **(d)** $y = \frac{7}{2}$;
(e) $(5, \frac{5}{2})$, $(3, \frac{5}{2})$;
(f)

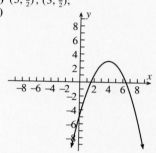

21. (a) $(2, -2)$; **(b)** $x = 2$;
(c) $(2, 0)$; **(d)** $y = -4$;
(e) $(6, 0)$, $(-2, 0)$;
(f)

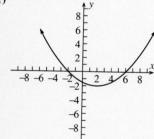

23. (a) $(3, -2)$; **(b)** $y = -2$;
(c) $(\frac{23}{8}, -2)$; **(d)** $x = \frac{25}{8}$;
(e) $(\frac{23}{8}, -\frac{7}{4})$, $(\frac{23}{8}, -\frac{9}{4})$;
(f)

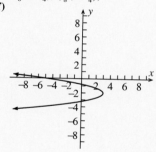

In Exercises 29–45, the graph of the first equation is dashed; that of the second is solid.

29.

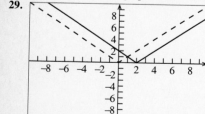

31.

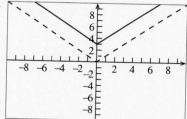

33.

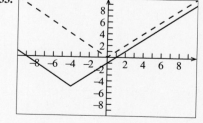

35.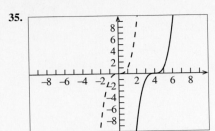

37.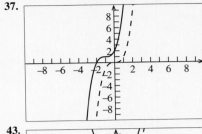

39.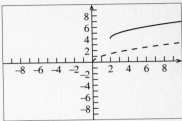

41.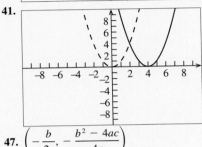

43.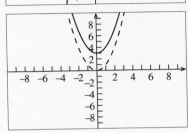

45.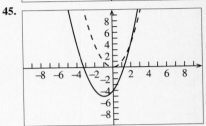

47. $\left(-\dfrac{b}{2a}, -\dfrac{b^2 - 4ac}{4a}\right)$

EXERCISES A.7 (page A-56)

1. (a) $(0, 0)$; **(b)** x axis;
(c) $(-5, 0), (5, 0)$;
(d) $(0, -3), (0, 3)$;
(e) $(-4, 0), (4, 0)$;
(f)
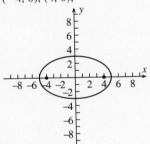

3. (a) $(0, 0)$; **(b)** y axis;
(c) $(0, -4), (0, 4)$;
(d) $(-2, 0), (2, 0)$
(e) $(0, -2\sqrt{3}), (0, 2\sqrt{3})$;
(f)
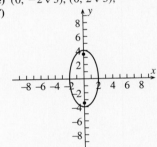

5. (a) $(0, 0)$; **(b)** x axis;
(c) $(-10, 0), (10, 0)$;
(d) $(0, -6), (0, 6)$;
(e) $(-8, 0), (8, 0)$;
(f)
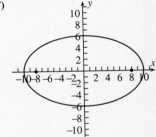

7. (a) $(0, 0)$; **(b)** y axis;
(c) $(0, -3), (0, 3)$
(d) $(-1, 0), (1, 0)$;
(e) $(0, -2\sqrt{2}), (0, 2\sqrt{2})$;
(f)
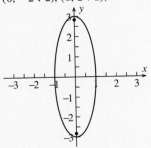

9. (a) $(2, 1)$; **(b)** $y = 1$;
(c) $(-1, 1), (5, 1)$;
(d) $(2, -1), (2, 3)$
(e) $(2 - \sqrt{5}, 1), (2 + \sqrt{5}, 1)$;
(f)
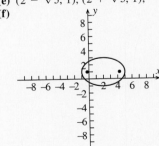

11. (a) $(-1, 2)$; **(b)** $x = -1$;
(c) $(-1, -8), (-1, 12)$;
(d) $(-6, 2), (4, 2)$;
(e) $(-1, 2 - 5\sqrt{3}), (-1, 2 + 5\sqrt{3})$;
(f)
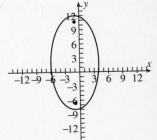

13. point $\left(-\frac{5}{2}, 4\right)$

15. **(a)** $(2, 0)$; **(b)** x axis;
(c) $(2 - 3\sqrt{3}, 0)$, $(2 + 3\sqrt{3}, 0)$;
(d) $(2, -3)$, $(2, 3)$;
(e) $(2 - 3\sqrt{2}, 0)$, $(2 + 3\sqrt{2}, 0)$;
(f)

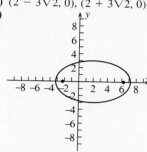

17. point $(1, -1)$

19. $16x^2 + 25y^2 = 100$

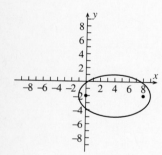

21. $3x^2 + 2y^2 = 54$

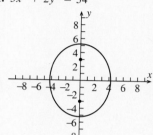

23. $x^2 + 4y^2 = 4$

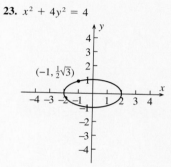

$\left(-1, \frac{1}{2}\sqrt{3}\right)$

25. $\dfrac{(x - 4)^2}{25} + \dfrac{(y + 2)^2}{9} = 1$

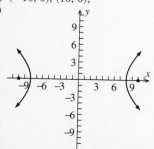

27. $\dfrac{(x + 1)^2}{48} + \dfrac{(y - 3)^2}{64} = 1$

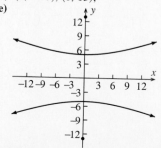

29. 8.4 m
31. $9x^2 + 25y^2 = 562{,}500$, where the unit is 1 million miles?

EXERCISES A.8 *(page A-66)*

1. **(a)** $(0, 0)$; **(b)** x axis;
(c) $(-8, 0)$, $(8, 0)$;
(d) $(-10, 0)$, $(10, 0)$;
(e)

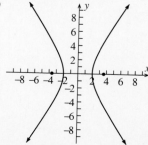

3. **(a)** $(0, 0)$; **(b)** y axis;
(c) $(0, -5)$, $(0, 5)$;
(d) $(0, -13)$, $(0, 13)$;
(e)

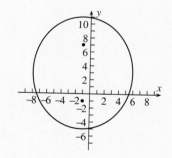

5. **(a)** $(0, 0)$; **(b)** x axis;
(c) $(-2, 0)$, $(2, 0)$;
(d) $(-\sqrt{13}, 0)$, $(\sqrt{13}, 0)$;
(e)

7. (a) $(0, 0)$;   **(b)** x axis;
(c) $(-5, 0)$, $(5, 0)$;
(d)

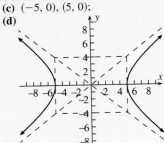

9. (a) $(0, 0)$;   **(b)** y axis;
(c) $(0, -2)$, $(0, 2)$;
(d)

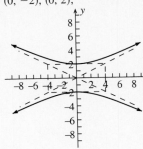

11. (a) $(0, 0)$;   **(b)** y axis;
(c) $(0, -6)$, $(0, 6)$;
(d)

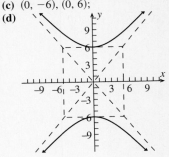

13. (a) $(-3, -2)$;   **(b)** $y = -2$;
(c) $(-6, -2)$, $(0, -2)$;
(d)

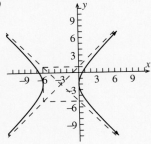

15. (a) $(-3, -1)$;   **(b)** $y = -1$;
(c) $(-7, -1)$, $(1, -1)$;
(d)

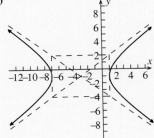

17. (a) $(-1, 4)$;   **(b)** $x = -1$;
(c) $(-1, 4 - 2\sqrt{7})$,
     $(-1, 4 + 2\sqrt{7})$;
(d)

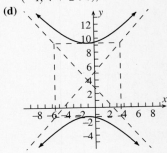

19. (a) $(1, -2)$;   **(b)** $x = 1$;
(c) $(1, -5)$, $(1, 1)$;
(d)

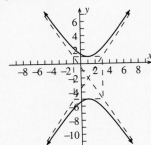

21. $y = -\frac{4}{5}x$, $y = \frac{4}{5}x$
23. $y = -x + 5$, $y = x + 1$
25. $y = -\frac{3}{2}x - \frac{1}{2}$, $y = \frac{3}{2}x - \frac{7}{2}$

27. $\dfrac{x^2}{4} - \dfrac{y^2}{9} = 1$

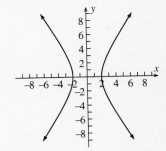

29. $32y^2 - 33x^2 = 380$

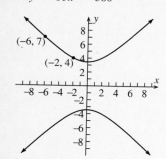

$(-6, 7)$
$(-2, 4)$

31. $\dfrac{x^2}{576} - \dfrac{y^2}{100} = 1$

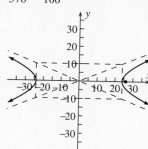

33. $\dfrac{(y + 1)^2}{144} - \dfrac{(x + 2)^3}{81} = 1$

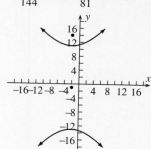

35. $72(x - 3)^2 - 9(y - 4)^2 = 128$

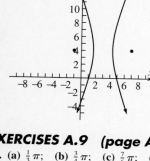

37. **(a)** $\dfrac{(x + 2)^2}{1} - \dfrac{(y + 1)^2}{4} = 1$; **(b)** $y = 2x + 3, \ y = -2x - 5$

39. $\dfrac{x^2}{4} - \dfrac{y^2}{7} = 1$ **41.** the right branch of the hyperbola $\dfrac{x^2}{900} - \dfrac{y^2}{1600} = 1$

EXERCISES A.9 (page A-74)

1. (a) $\frac{1}{3}\pi$; **(b)** $\frac{3}{4}\pi$; **(c)** $\frac{7}{6}\pi$; **(d)** $-\frac{5}{6}\pi$; **(e)** $\frac{1}{9}\pi$; **(f)** $\frac{5}{2}\pi$ **(g)** $-\frac{5}{12}\pi$; **(h)** $\frac{5}{9}\pi$
3. (a) $45°$; **(b)** $120°$; **(c)** $330°$; **(d)** $-90°$; **(e)** $28°39'$; **(f)** $540°$; **(g)** $-114°36'$; **(h)** $15°$
5. (a) $\frac{1}{2}$; **(b)** $\frac{1}{2}\sqrt{2}$; **(c)** 1; **(d)** $\frac{1}{2}$ **7. (a)** $-\frac{1}{2}\sqrt{3}$; **(b)** $\frac{1}{2}\sqrt{2}$; **(c)** -1; **(d)** 0 **9. (a)** $\sqrt{3}$; **(b)** 1; **(c)** -1; **(d)** 1
11. (a) $\frac{2}{3}\sqrt{3}$; **(b)** $\sqrt{2}$; **(c)** $-\frac{1}{3}\sqrt{3}$; **(d)** 1 **13. (a)** $\frac{1}{2}\sqrt{2}$; **(b)** $\frac{1}{2}\sqrt{2}$; **(c)** $\sqrt{2}$; **(d)** $\sqrt{2}$
15. (a) $-\frac{1}{2}\sqrt{3}$; **(b)** $-\frac{1}{2}$; **(c)** -2; **(d)** $-\frac{2}{3}\sqrt{3}$ **17. (a)** 0; **(b)** 1; **(c)** -1; **(d)** undefined
19. (a) 1; **(b)** 0; **(c)** undefined; **(d)** 1 **21. (a)** -1; **(b)** -1; **(c)** $\frac{1}{3}\sqrt{3}$; **(d)** $\sqrt{3}$
23. (a) $-\sqrt{3}$; **(b)** $-\frac{1}{3}\sqrt{3}$; **(c)** 0; **(d)** 0 **25. (a)** $\frac{1}{2}\pi$; **(b)** π; **(c)** $\frac{1}{4}\pi, \frac{5}{4}\pi$; **(d)** 0
27. (a) $0, \pi$; **(b)** $\frac{1}{2}\pi, \frac{3}{2}\pi$; **(c)** $0, \pi$; **(d)** $\frac{1}{2}\pi, \frac{3}{2}\pi$ **29. (a)** $\frac{7}{6}\pi, \frac{11}{6}\pi$; **(b)** $\frac{1}{3}\pi, \frac{5}{3}\pi$; **(c)** $\frac{3}{4}\pi, \frac{7}{4}\pi$; **(d)** $\frac{1}{6}\pi, \frac{5}{6}\pi$
31. (a) $\frac{1}{2}\pi, \frac{3}{2}\pi$; **(b)** $0, \pi$ **33. (a)** π; **(b)** $\frac{3}{2}\pi$ **35.** $x = 5\cos t, \ y = 3\sin t$ **37.** $x = 2\cos t, \ y = 4\sin t$
39. $x = 3\cos t + 2, \ y = 2\sin t + 1$ **41.** $x = 5\cos t - 1, \ y = 10\sin t + 2$ **45.** $x = 8\sec t = 8/\cos t, \ y = 6\tan t$
47. $x = 12\tan t, \ y = 5\sec t = 5/\cos t$ **49.** $x = 3\sec t - 3 = 3/\cos t - 3, \ y = 3\tan t - 2$
51. $x = \sqrt{21}\tan t - 1, \ y = 2\sqrt{7}\sec t + 4 = 2\sqrt{7}/\cos t + 4$

EXERCISES A.10 (page A-83)

1. (a) hyperbola; **(b)** ellipse; **(c)** parabola; **(d)** two intersecting lines   **3. (a)** point; **(b)** hyperbola; **(c)** parabola; **(d)** empty set

5. (a) hyperbola;
(b) $\bar{x}^2 - \bar{y}^2 = 16$;
(c)

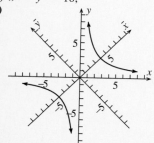

7. (a) hyperbola;
(b) $\bar{x}\,\bar{y} = -4$;
(c)

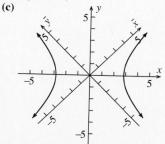

In Exercises 9–25, the $\overline{x}\overline{y}$ axes have been rotated through an angle of measure α.

9. (a) hyperbola;
  (b) $\alpha \approx 36.9°$,
    $16\overline{y}^2 - 9\overline{x}^2 = 36$;
(c)

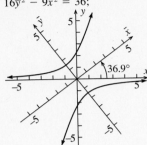

11. (a) parabola;
  (b) $\alpha = \frac{1}{4}\pi$,
    $\overline{x}^2 + 4\sqrt{2}\,\overline{y} = 0$;
(c)

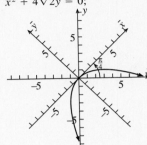

13. (a) hyperbola;
  (b) $\alpha = \frac{1}{4}\pi$,
    $\overline{y}^2 - \overline{x}^2 = 32$;
(c)

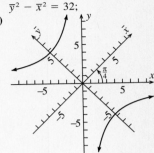

15. (a) ellipse;   **(b)** $\alpha = \frac{1}{6}\pi$, $\dfrac{\overline{x}^2}{4} + \dfrac{\overline{y}^2}{9} = 1$ **(c)**

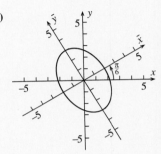

In Exercises 17–25, the $x'y'$ axes have also been translated such that $x' = \overline{x} - h$, $y' = \overline{y} - k$.

17. (a) ellipse;   **(b)** $\alpha = \frac{1}{4}\pi$,
  $h = \frac{1}{2}\sqrt{2}$, $k = \frac{3}{2}\sqrt{2}$, $\dfrac{x'^2}{6} + \dfrac{y'^2}{18} = 1$;
(c)

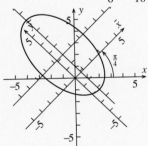

19. (a) ellipse;   **(b)** $\alpha \approx 63.4°$,
  $h = \dfrac{2}{\sqrt{5}}$, $k = -\dfrac{4}{\sqrt{5}}$, $\dfrac{x'^2}{16} + \dfrac{y'^2}{4} = 1$;
(c)

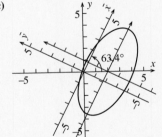

21. (a) parabola;   **(b)** $\alpha = \frac{1}{4}\pi$,
  $h = 0$, $k = -2\sqrt{2}$, $\sqrt{2}\,x'^2 = y'$;
(c)

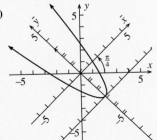

23. (a) hyperbola;   **(a)** $\alpha \approx 53.1°$,
  $h = 5$, $k = 0$, $\dfrac{x'^2}{16} - \dfrac{y'^2}{4} = 1$;
(c)

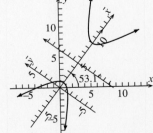

25. (a) parabola;   **(b)** $\alpha \approx 26.6°$,
$\sqrt{5}\,\bar{x}^2 + 6 = 0$;

(c)

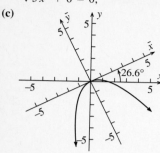

27. cf. Exercise 9(c)
29. cf. Exercise 11(c)
31. cf. Exercise 17(c)
33. cf. Exercise 21(c)

EXERCISES A.11   (page A-89)

1. $\dfrac{3}{x-2} - \dfrac{3}{x+2}$

3. $-\dfrac{1}{x} + \dfrac{2}{x+1}$

5. $\dfrac{4}{x-3} - \dfrac{3}{x-1}$

7. $\dfrac{-5}{3x+1} + \dfrac{2}{x-2}$

9. $\dfrac{2}{x} - \dfrac{3}{3x-2} - \dfrac{1}{2x+3}$

11. $2x + \dfrac{5}{x-2} + \dfrac{3}{x+2}$

13. $2x - 5 + \dfrac{3}{2x-3} + \dfrac{2}{x+2}$

15. $\dfrac{5}{x^2} - \dfrac{4}{x} + \dfrac{7}{x-2}$

17. $\dfrac{2}{x+2} - \dfrac{3}{(x-2)^2} - \dfrac{1}{x-2}$

19. $\dfrac{6}{(2x+1)^2} + \dfrac{\frac{14}{3}}{2x+1} + \dfrac{2}{(x-1)^2} - \dfrac{\frac{7}{3}}{x-1}$

21. $1 + \dfrac{16}{(x-2)^3} + \dfrac{18}{(x-2)^2} + \dfrac{6}{x-2}$

23. $\dfrac{4}{x} - \dfrac{x+5}{x^2+x+1}$

25. $\dfrac{1}{x-2} + \dfrac{2x+4}{x^2+2x+4}$

27. $-\dfrac{2}{x-1} + \dfrac{4x-3}{x^2+1}$

29. $\dfrac{4}{x+4} + \dfrac{3x-1}{2x^2+3}$

31. $\dfrac{x+2}{x^2+1} - \dfrac{x-2}{x^2-x-1}$

33. $\dfrac{2}{x^2} - \dfrac{1}{x} + \dfrac{x}{x^2+2x+3}$

35. $\dfrac{x-1}{x^2+1} - \dfrac{x-1}{(x^2+1)^2}$

37. $\dfrac{x-15}{(x^2+2)^2} + \dfrac{3x+4}{x^2+2} - \dfrac{2}{x-1}$

INDEX

44. $\displaystyle\int \frac{u^2\,du}{\sqrt{a^2-u^2}} = -\frac{u}{2}\sqrt{a^2-u^2} + \frac{a^2}{2}\sin^{-1}\frac{u}{a} + C$

45. $\displaystyle\int \frac{du}{u\sqrt{a^2-u^2}} = -\frac{1}{a}\ln\left|\frac{a+\sqrt{a^2-u^2}}{u}\right| + C$

$\displaystyle\qquad\qquad = -\frac{1}{a}\cosh^{-1}\frac{a}{u} + C$

46. $\displaystyle\int \frac{du}{u^2\sqrt{a^2-u^2}} = -\frac{\sqrt{a^2-u^2}}{a^2 u} + C$

47. $\displaystyle\int (a^2-u^2)^{3/2}\,du = -\frac{u}{8}(2u^2-5a^2)\sqrt{a^2-u^2}$

$\displaystyle\qquad\qquad + \frac{3a^4}{8}\sin^{-1}\frac{u}{a} + C$

48. $\displaystyle\int \frac{du}{(a^2-u^2)^{3/2}} = \frac{u}{a^2\sqrt{a^2-u^2}} + C$

Forms Containing $2au - u^2$

49. $\displaystyle\int \sqrt{2au-u^2}\,du = \frac{u-a}{2}\sqrt{2au-u^2} + \frac{a^2}{2}\cos^{-1}\left(1-\frac{u}{a}\right) + C$

50. $\displaystyle\int u\sqrt{2au-u^2}\,du = \frac{2u^2-au-3a^2}{6}\sqrt{2au-u^2}$

$\displaystyle\qquad\qquad + \frac{a^3}{2}\cos^{-1}\left(1-\frac{u}{a}\right) + C$

51. $\displaystyle\int \frac{\sqrt{2au-u^2}\,du}{u} = \sqrt{2au-u^2} + a\cos^{-1}\left(1-\frac{u}{a}\right) + C$

52. $\displaystyle\int \frac{\sqrt{2au-u^2}\,du}{u^2} = -\frac{2\sqrt{2au-u^2}}{u} - \cos^{-1}\left(1-\frac{u}{a}\right) + C$

53. $\displaystyle\int \frac{du}{\sqrt{2au-u^2}} = \cos^{-1}\left(1-\frac{u}{a}\right) + C$

54. $\displaystyle\int \frac{u\,du}{\sqrt{2au-u^2}} = -\sqrt{2au-u^2} + a\cos^{-1}\left(1-\frac{u}{a}\right) + C$

55. $\displaystyle\int \frac{u^2\,du}{\sqrt{2au-u^2}} = -\frac{(u+3a)}{2}\sqrt{2au-u^2}$

$\displaystyle\qquad\qquad + \frac{3a^2}{2}\cos^{-1}\left(1-\frac{u}{a}\right) + C$

56. $\displaystyle\int \frac{du}{u\sqrt{2au-u^2}} = -\frac{\sqrt{2au-u^2}}{au} + C$

57. $\displaystyle\int \frac{du}{(2au-u^2)^{3/2}} = \frac{u-a}{a^2\sqrt{2au-u^2}} + C$

58. $\displaystyle\int \frac{u\,du}{(2au-u^2)^{3/2}} = \frac{u}{a\sqrt{2au-u^2}} + C$

Forms Containing Trigonometric Functions

59. $\displaystyle\int \sin u\,du = -\cos u + C$

60. $\displaystyle\int \cos u\,du = \sin u + C$

61. $\displaystyle\int \tan u\,du = \ln|\sec u| + C$

62. $\displaystyle\int \cot u\,du = \ln|\sin u| + C$

63. $\displaystyle\int \sec u\,du = \ln|\sec u + \tan u| + C = \ln\left|\tan\left(\tfrac{1}{4}\pi + \tfrac{1}{2}u\right)\right| + C$

64. $\displaystyle\int \csc u\,du = \ln|\csc u - \cot u| + C = \ln\left|\tan\tfrac{1}{2}u\right| + C$

65. $\displaystyle\int \sec^2 u\,du = \tan u + C$

66. $\displaystyle\int \csc^2 u\,du = -\cot u + C$

67. $\displaystyle\int \sec u\tan u\,du = \sec u + C$

68. $\displaystyle\int \csc u\cot u\,du = -\csc u + C$

69. $\displaystyle\int \sin^2 u\,du = \tfrac{1}{2}u - \tfrac{1}{4}\sin 2u + C$

70. $\displaystyle\int \cos^2 u\,du = \tfrac{1}{2}u + \tfrac{1}{4}\sin 2u + C$

71. $\displaystyle\int \tan^2 u\,du = \tan u - u + C$

72. $\displaystyle\int \cot^2 u\,du = -\cot u - u + C$

73. $\displaystyle\int \sin^n u\,du = -\frac{1}{n}\sin^{n-1}u\cos u + \frac{n-1}{n}\int \sin^{n-2}u\,du$

74. $\displaystyle\int \cos^n u\,du = \frac{1}{n}\cos^{n-1}u\sin u + \frac{n-1}{n}\int \cos^{n-2}u\,du$

75. $\displaystyle\int \tan^n u\,du = \frac{1}{n-1}\tan^{n-1}u - \int \tan^{n-2}u\,du$

76. $\displaystyle\int \cot^n u\,du = -\frac{1}{n-1}\cot^{n-1}u - \int \cot^{n-2}u\,du$

77. $\displaystyle\int \sec^n u\,du = \frac{1}{n-1}\sec^{n-2}u\tan u + \frac{n-2}{n-1}\int \sec^{n-2}u\,du$

78. $\displaystyle\int \csc^n u\,du = -\frac{1}{n-1}\csc^{n-2}u\cot u + \frac{n-2}{n-1}\int \csc^{n-2}u\,du$

79. $\displaystyle\int \sin mu\sin nu\,du = -\frac{\sin(m+n)u}{2(m+n)} + \frac{\sin(m-n)u}{2(m-n)} + C$

80. $\displaystyle\int \cos mu\cos nu\,du = \frac{\sin(m+n)u}{2(m+n)} + \frac{\sin(m-n)u}{2(m-n)} + C$

81. $\displaystyle\int \sin mu\cos nu\,du = -\frac{\cos(m+n)u}{2(m+n)} - \frac{\cos(m-n)u}{2(m-n)} + C$

82. $\displaystyle\int u\sin u\,du = \sin u - u\cos u + C$

83. $\displaystyle\int u\cos u\,du = \cos u + u\sin u + C$

84. $\displaystyle\int u^2\sin u\,du = 2u\sin u + (2-u^2)\cos u + C$